BIOGENESIS OF
NATURAL COMPOUNDS

Biogenesis of
Natural Compounds

SECOND EDITION

Edited by

PETER BERNFELD

BIO-RESEARCH INSTITUTE
CAMBRIDGE, MASSACHUSETTS

THE QUEEN'S AWARD
TO INDUSTRY 1966

PERGAMON PRESS
OXFORD · LONDON · EDINBURGH · NEW YORK
TORONTO · SYDNEY · PARIS · BRAUNSCHWEIG

Pergamon Press Ltd., Headington Hill Hall, Oxford
4 & 5 Fitzroy Square, London W.1

Pergamon Press (Scotland) Ltd., 2 & 3 Teviot Place, Edinburgh 1

Pergamon Press Inc., 40–01 21st Street, Long Island City, New York 11101

Pergamon of Canada, Ltd., 6 Adelaide Street East, Toronto, Ontario

Pergamon Press (Aust.) Pty. Ltd., Rushcutters Bay, Sydney, New South Wales

Pergamon Press S.A.R.L., 24 rue des Écoles, Paris 5e

Vieweg & Sohn GmbH, Burgplatz 1, Braunschweig

First Edition 1963
Second (revised) edition 1967

Library of Congress Catalog Card No. 62–21549

Printed in Great Britain by
Page Bros. (Norwich) Ltd., Norwich
08 002925 6

CONTENTS

Chapter   *Page*

PREFACE   vii

PREFACE TO THE SECOND EDITION   viii

CONTRIBUTORS   ix

ABBREVIATIONS   xi

1   THE BIOSYNTHESIS OF AMINO ACIDS   1
     by James R. Mattoon

2   THE BIOGENESIS OF PURINE AND PYRIMIDINE NUCLEOTIDES   45
     by Armand J. Guarino

3   THE BIOGENESIS OF THE LIPIDS   103
     by K. P. Strickland

4   THE BIOSYNTHESIS OF STEROIDS   207
     by Ezra Staple

5   THE BIOGENESIS OF HEME, CHLOROPHYLLS, AND BILE PIGMENTS   247
     by Lawrence Bogorad and Robert F. Troxler

6   THE BIOGENESIS OF CARBOHYDRATES   315
     by Peter Bernfeld

7   THE BIOGENESIS OF PROTEINS   477
     by Theodore Peters

8   THE ENZYMIC SYNTHESIS OF NUCLEIC ACIDS   537
     by Roger Mantsavinos and Stephen Zamenhof

9   THE BIOGENESIS OF CONJUGATION AND DETOXICATION PRODUCTS   589
     by R. T. Williams

10   THE BIOSYNTHESIS OF CAROTENOIDS AND VITAMIN A   641
     by C. O. Chichester and T. O. M. Nakayama

11   THE BIOSYNTHESIS OF THE WATER-SOLUBLE VITAMINS   679
     by Vernon H. Cheldelin and Annette Baich

12   THE BIOSYNTHESIS OF PHENOLIC PLANT PRODUCTS   743
     by T. A. Geissman

13   THE BIOSYNTHESIS OF TANNINS   801
     by S. G. Humphries

14   THE BIOGENESIS OF TERPENES IN PLANTS   829
     by Harold J. Nicholas

15   THE BIOGENESIS OF LIGNINS   903
     by F. F. Nord and Walter J. Schubert

Chapter   *Page*
  16   RUBBER BIOGENESIS   941
            by James Bonner
  17   ALKALOID BIOGENESIS   953
            by Edward Leete
  18   THE BIOSYNTHESIS OF FUNGAL METABOLITES   1025
            by W. Basil Whalley
  19   FORMATION OF CARCINOGENIC POLYNUCLEAR HYDROCARBONS 1065
            by Eliahu Boger
        AUTHOR INDEX   1079
        SUBJECT INDEX   1139

CONTRIBUTORS

ANNETTE BAICH, Department of Chemistry, and Science Research Institute, Oregon State University, Corvallis, Oregon.

PETER BERNFELD, Bio-Research Institute, Cambridge, Massachusetts.

ELIAHU BOGER, Bio-Research Institute, Cambridge, Massachusetts.

LAWRENCE BOGORAD, Department of Botany, University of Chicago, Chicago, Illinois.

JAMES BONNER, Division of Biology, California Institute of Technology Pasadena, California.

VERNON H. CHELDELIN, Department of Chemistry, and Science Research Institute, Oregon State University, Corvallis, Oregon.†

C. O. CHICHESTER, Department of Food Science and Technology, University of California, Davis, California.

T. A. GEISSMAN, Department of Chemistry, University of California, Los Angeles, California.

ARMAND J. GUARINO, Department of Biochemistry, Woman's Medical College of Pennsylvania, Philadelphia, Pennsylvania.

S. G. HUMPHRIES, British Leather Manufacturers' Research Association, Milton Park, Egham, Surrey.

EDWARD LEETE, School of Chemistry, University of Minnesota, Minneapolis, Minnesota.

ROGER MANTSAVINOS, Department of Biochemical Pharmacology and Biochemistry, State University of New York at Buffalo, Buffalo, New York.†

JAMES R. MATTOON, Department of Physiological Chemistry, The Johns Hopkins University School of Medicine, Baltimore, Maryland.

T. O. M. NAKAYAMA, Department of Food Science, College of Agriculture, The University of Georgia, Athens, Georgia.

HAROLD J. NICHOLAS, Institute of Medical Education and Research, Max C. Starkloff Memorial Hospital, and Department of Biochemistry, St. Louis University School of Medicine, St. Louis, Missouri.

F. F. NORD, Laboratory of Organic Chemistry and Enzymology, Fordham University, Bronx, New York, 10458.

THEODORE PETERS, The Mary Imogene Bassett Hospital, Cooperstown, New York, and College of Physicians and Surgeons, Columbia University, New York, New York.

† Deceased.

WALTER J. SCHUBERT, Laboratory of Organic Chemistry and Enzymology, Fordham University, Bronx, New York, 10458.

EZRA STAPLE, Department of Biochemistry, School of Medicine, University of Pennsylvania, Philadelphia, Pennsylvania.

K. P. STRICKLAND, Department of Biochemistry, Faculty of Medicine, The University of Western Ontario, London, Canada.

ROBERT F. TROXLER, Department of Botany, University of Chicago, Chicago, Illinois.

W. BASIL WHALLEY, Department of Chemistry, School of Pharmacy, The University of London, London.

R. T. WILLIAMS, Department of Biochemistry, St. Mary's Hospital Medical School (University of London), London.

STEPHEN ZAMENHOF, Department of Medical Microbiology and Immunology, Department of Biological Chemistry, and Molecular Biology Institute, University of California, Los Angeles, California.

ABBREVIATIONS†

A	=	Adenosine
AAA	=	L-α-Aminoadipate
ACP	=	Acyl carrier protein
ADP	=	Adenosine-5′-diphosphate
ADR	=	Adenosine
AICAR	=	5-Amino-4-imidazolecarboxamide ribonucleotide = 5-amino-1-ribosyl-4-imidazolecarboxamide-5′-phosphate
ALA	=	Aminolevulinic acid
Ala or ala	=	Alanine
AMP	=	Adenosine-5′-monophosphate
APS	=	Adenosine-5′-phosphosulfate
ATP	=	Adenosine-5′-triphosphate
BMC	=	β-Methylcrotonyl residue = senecioyl residue
BOG	=	β-Methyl-β-hydroxyglutaryl residue
C	=	Cytidine
CDP	=	Cytidine-5′-diphosphate
CDR	=	Cytidine
CMP	=	Cytidine-5′-monophosphate
CMP-PC	=	Cytidine diphosphate choline
CMP-Pdig	=	Cytidine diphosphate diglyceride
CMP-PE	=	Cytidine diphosphate ethanolamine
CMP-PG	=	Cytidine diphosphate glycerol
CoA or HSCoA	=	Coenzyme A
CTP	=	Cytidine-5′-triphosphate
DAHP	=	3-Deoxy-D-*arabino*-heptulosonic acid-7-phosphate
dAMP	=	Deoxyadenosine-5′-monophosphate
DAP	=	α,ε-Diaminopimelic acid
dATP	=	Deoxyadenosine-5′-triphosphate
dCDP	=	Deoxycytidine-5′-diphosphate
dCMP	=	Deoxycytidine-5′-monophosphate
dCTP	=	Deoxycytidine-5′-triphosphate
dGMP	=	Deoxyguanosine-5′-phosphate
dGTP	=	Deoxyguanosine-5′-triphosphate
DHFA	=	Dihydrofolic acid

† See also Table 1, p. 479, Chapter 7, for abbreviations of amino acids, and footnote at the beginning of Chapter 8, p. 538, for some additional abbreviations used in that chapter.

xi

DNA	= Deoxyribonucleic acid
DNAase	= Deoxyribonuclease
DOPA	= 3, 4-Dihydroxyphenylalanine
DPI	= Diphosphoinositide
DPN or	
DPN+	= Diphosphopyridine nucleotide (oxidized)
DPNH	= Diphosphopyridine nucleotide (reduced)
dTDP	= Deoxythymidine-5'-diphosphate
dTMP	= Deoxythymidine-5'-phosphate
dTTP	= Deoxythimidine-5'-triphosphate
EDTA	= Ethylenediaminetetraacetic acid
FAD	= Flavin adenine dinucleotide
$FADH_2$	= Flavin adenine dinucleotide, reduced form
FMN	= Riboflavin phosphate
G	= Glucose or Guanosine
g	= Gravitational constant (also gram)
Gal	= Galactose
GDP	= Guanosine-5'-diphosphate
GDR	= Guanosine
Glu or glu	= Glutamic acid
GMP	= Guanosine-5'-monophosphate
GNAc	= N-Acetylglucosamine
GNAc-	
lactic	= N-Acetylmuramic acid
GP	= Glycerophosphate
GPC	= Glycerylphosphorylcholine
GPE	= Glycerylphosphorylethanolamine
GSH	= Glutathione
GTP	= Guanosine-5'-triphosphate
H^3	= Tritium
HDL	= High-density lipoproteins
I	= Inosine
IDP	= Inosine-5'-diphosphate
IGP	= Indole-3-glycerol phosphate
ImGP	= Imidazole glycerophosphate
IMP	= Inosine-5'-monophosphate
IpPP	= Δ^3-Isopentenyl pyrophosphate
ITP	= Inosine-5'-triphosphate
KDHP	= 2-Keto-3-deoxy-D-araboheptonic acid-7-phosphate
KDO	= 2-Keto-3-deoxyoctonate
LDF	= Low-density fractions of lipoproteins
LDL	= Low-density lipoproteins
L-α-GP	= L-α-glycerophosphate

LPS	= Lipopolysaccharide
Lys or lys	= Lysine
MPI	= Monophosphoinositide
mRNA or m-RNA	= Messenger RNA
MVA	= Mevalonic acid
N	= Nicotinamide
NAD or NAD$^+$	= DPN (DPN$^+$) = Nicotinamide adenine dinucleotide, oxidized form
NADH or NADH$_2$	= DPNH = Nicotinamide adenine dinucleotide, reduced form
NADP or NADP$^+$	= TPN (TPN$^+$) = Nicotinamide adenine dinucleotide phosphate, oxidized form
NADPH or NADPH$_2$	= TPNH = Nicotinamide adenine dinucleotide phosphate, reduced form
NâMN	= Nicotinic acid mononucleotide
NAN	= N-Acetylneuraminic acid
NGN	= N-Glycolylneuraminic acid
NMN or N$^+$MN	= Nicotinamide mononucleotide
NR or N$^+$R	= Nicotinamide riboside
NRP or N$^+$RP	= Nicotinamide riboside phosphate
NRPPRA	= DPN = Nicotinamide-riboside-phosphate-phosphate-ribosido-adenosine
NRPPRPA	= TPN = Triphosphopyridine nucleotide
p	= Phosphate in nucleotides in conjunction with a nucleotide base
P$_i$	= Inorganic orthophosphate
PA or Pa	= Pantothenic acid (pantothenate)
PABA	= p-Aminobenzoic acid
PAH	= Polycyclic aromatic hydrocarbons
PAP	= 3'-Phosphoadenosine-5'-phosphate
PAPS	= 3'-Phosphoadenosine-5'-phosphosulfate
PEP	= Phosphoenolpyruvate
PC	= Phosphoryl choline
PE	= Phosphoryl ethanolamine
PICE	= Protoporphyrin-iron chelating enzyme
poly A	= Polyadenylic acid
poly C	= Polycytidylic acid
poly dT	= Polydeoxythymidylic acid
poly G	= Polyguanylic acid

poly U	= Polyuridylic acid
PP_i	= Inorganic pyrophosphate
PRPP	= Phosphoribosyl pyrophosphate
PS	= Phosphoserine
RNA	= Ribonucleic acid
RNAase	= Ribonuclease
RPPRA	= Riboside-phosphate-phosphate-ribosido-adenosine
r-RNA	= Ribosomal RNA
— S or "S"	= Svedberg flotation rate
S_f	= Flotation rate according to Gofman
sRNA or s-RNA	= Adaptor RNA or soluble RNA
T	= Tritium or thymidine
TDR	= Thymidine
THFA	= Tetrahydrofolic acid
TPI	= Triphosphoinositide
TPN or TPN^+	= Triphosphopyridine nucleotide (oxidized)
TPNH	= Triphosphopyridine nucleotide (reduced)
TPP	= Thiamine pyrophosphate
t–RNA	= Transfer RNA
U	= Uridine
UDP	= Uridine-5'-diphosphate
UMP	= Uridine-5'-monophosphate
UTP	= Uridine-5'-triphosphate
$\Delta F'$	= Standard free energy change at pH7
ΔF_H	= Standard free energy of hydrolysis

CHAPTER 1

THE BIOSYNTHESIS OF AMINO ACIDS

JAMES R. MATTOON

Department of Physiological Chemistry, The Johns Hopkins University
School of Medicine, Baltimore, Maryland

CONTENTS

I.	INTRODUCTION	1
II.	GENERAL CONSIDERATIONS	2
	A. *Techniques used in studying amino acid biosynthesis*	2
	B. *Source of amino nitrogen*	4
	C. *General relationships between biosynthetic pathways*	4
III.	THE TRIOSE FAMILY	4
	A. *Serine*	4
	B. *Glycine*	6
	C. *Cysteine and cystine*	7
IV.	THE α-KETOGLUTARATE FAMILY	11
	A. *Proline and ornithine*	11
	B. *Arginine*	13
	C. *Hydroxyproline*	14
V.	THE PYRUVATE FAMILY	16
	A. *Threonine*	16
	B. *Methionine*	18
	C. *The branched-chain amino acids*	22
	D. *Lysine and diaminopimelic acid*	25
VI.	THE PENTOSE FAMILY	29
	A. *Histidine*	29
	B. *Phenylalanine and tyrosine*	32
	C. *Tryptophan*	34
	REFERENCES	37

I. INTRODUCTION

The wide variety of side-chain structures encountered in the common amino acids presents the living organism with an equally wide variety of synthetic problems to solve in producing the raw materials of protein synthesis. In many organisms, notably animals, the capacity for synthesizing many of these structures is totally or partially absent; hence such organisms must rely

1

on more "talented" organisms, such as plants and certain microorganisms, to do this synthetic work for them.

This chapter will be concerned only with those amino acids commonly found in proteins. The starting material for each biosynthetic path will be some product or intermediate in the well-known sequences of carbohydrate metabolism: the glycolytic path, the pentose phosphate pathway, and the citric acid cycle. Emphasis has been placed on those pathways of amino acid biosynthesis from carbohydrate which, in so far as it can be determined, are of the greatest "quantitative importance".

The primary aim of this discussion will be to present the known biosynthetic intermediates in appropriate sequences, and to list, whenever possible, the enzymes catalyzing the reactions. However, since the first edition of this book was undertaken, the emphasis in the study of amino acid biosynthesis has shifted markedly from the characterization of the intermediates and enzymes of the pathways to a study of the genetic and regulatory aspects of amino acid metabolism. Therefore a discussion of developments in these areas is included. It has been necessary to limit this review to a description of pathways without presenting a thorough discussion of the experimental evidence for these pathways. However, an effort has been made to document the text with important references so that the reader who so wishes may consult the original papers.

II. GENERAL CONSIDERATIONS

A. *Techniques Used in Studying Amino Acid Biosynthesis*

Two particularly valuable experimental tools are available for studying biosynthetic pathways: the microbial mutant, or auxotroph, and the isotopic tracer. A mutant organism, which is usually produced by irradiation or chemical treatment of a culture, followed by appropriate selection techniques, usually contains a single genetic lesion which manifests itself as a block in the metabolic pathway. Intermediates (preceding the block point), which normally have only a transient existence, may be accumulated by, and isolated from, mutant cultures.

Alternatively, intermediates located between the block and the amino acid in question may be identified by "feeding" the mutant with compounds thought to be on the pathway, and observing the growth response.

It is frequently possible to establish that a given enzyme is functioning in a given pathway by its susceptibility to regulation, either by endproduct inhibition of the enzyme or by the repression of its synthesis by an excess of the endproduct amino acid. Genetic mapping studies have also contributed to the elucidation of pathways, and frequently it has been possible to make deductions about subunit structure and even primary sequence of some of the enzymes. Knowledge of pathway sequences and enzymes, in turn, has contributed to greater understanding of the mechanisms by which genetic information is transcribed and translated into the final gene-products—the enzymes and metabolic regulators.

Tracer experiments are particularly valuable in "surveying" pathways. They frequently suggest possible intermediates which may be identified with mutants or classical enzymic studies.

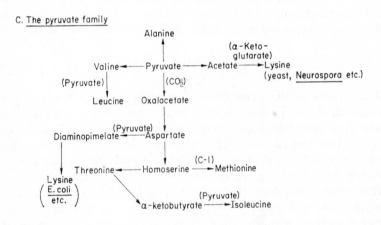

FIG. 1. Families of amino acids.

B. *Source of Amino Nitrogen*

The α-amino groups of the amino acids are introduced largely by means of transamination reactions involving glutamic acid, alanine, and aspartic acid as amino donors. The primary mechanism for entry of ammonia into the transamination system is by means of the enzyme glutamic dehydrogenase,[176] which catalyzes the reductive amination of α-ketoglutarate, with pyridine nucleotides serving as hydrogen carriers. No attempt will be made here to survey the extensive literature on transamination, since this has been reviewed elsewhere.[174, 175]

C. *General Relationships between Biosynthetic Pathways*

The relationships between amino acid biosynthetic pathways and the major paths of carbohydrate metabolism are summarized in Fig. 1. Since alanine, aspartic acid, and glutamic acid are derived directly by transamination (or reductive amination[176]) from intermediates of these pathways (pyruvic, oxalacetic, and α-ketoglutaric acids, respectively), the biosynthesis of these amino acids will not be considered further.

The amino acids may be conveniently divided into four families: the triose family (amino acids derived directly from glycolysis at the level of glyceric acid-3-phosphate), the α-ketoglutarate family, the pyruvate family, and the pentose family. In the aromatic amino acids, more than one family is involved. In some organisms lysine also involves two families.

III. THE TRIOSE FAMILY

A. *Serine*

The carbons of the serine molecule may be used effectively in the biosynthesis of the amino acids glycine, cysteine and cystine. The three carbons of the tryptophan side chain also arise from serine. Since the serine β-carbon is readily transformed into "active" C-1 units, serine plays an important role in the synthesis of the methionine methyl group and the ureide carbon of the histidine imidazole ring. A consideration of the genesis of serine from carbohydrate is therefore relevant to the origin of these related amino acids.

Serine is derived from carbohydrate at the level of phosphoglyceric acid, rather than from pyruvate, since glucose-1-C^{14} gives rise to serine labeled principally in the β-carbon,[17] while pyruvate-3-C^{14} gives rise to serine with nearly equal labeling in C-2 and C-3.[194] The results with labeled pyruvate show that pyruvate label is "randomized" (caused by pyruvate entry into symmetrical citric acid cycle intermediates) before entry into serine. Hence serine is not derived *directly* from pyruvate.

There is considerable evidence that two alternative pathways of serine biosynthesis occur in animal tissues.[118, 193, 34, 111, 233] Path A consists of reactions I, II and III, and path B of reactions V, VI and VII (Fig. 2). The relative contribution of these two routes is deduced from the relative activity ratios of the dehydrogenases catalyzing reactions I and VI and/or the trans-aminases catalyzing reactions II and VII.[323] The ratio of the dehydrogenases has been found to vary widely from one species of animal to another, e.g. path A is very active in the liver of birds and essentially inactive in rat liver, contrary to conclusions of earlier studies.[326] In calf liver the ratio of the two dehydrogenases is about unity. Relative distribution also varies from one organ to another within the same animal. The deduction of the relative quantitative physiological importance of the two paths in animals must be

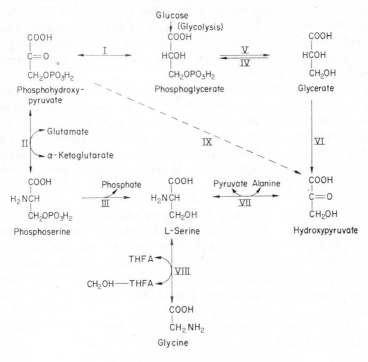

FIG. 2. Biosynthesis of serine and glycine.

interpreted with caution, since the various intermediates frequently may have multiple functions. The broad specificity of many phosphatases, which may contribute to reactions V and IX, further complicates the interpretation.

Enzymes catalyzing many of the reactions have been partially purified. D-3-Phosphoglycerate dehydrogenase (reaction I) has been purified from chicken liver.[323] Glutamate-phosphohydroxy-pyruvate transaminase (reaction II)[118] and a specific phosphoserine phosphatase (reaction III)[193, 34] have been studied. Alanine-hydroxypyruvate transaminase is found in liver and kidney of various animals.[111, 233] D-Glycerate dehydrogenase, which catalyzes the formation of hydroxypyruvate from D-glycerate, has been prepared from beef liver[323a] as well as from plants and microorganisms.[260,218] A *specific* phosphatase for phosphoglycerate has not been demonstrated. A glyceric acid kinase (reaction IV) has been purified from horse liver.[119] A third possible path for serine formation could occur by way of reactions I, IX and VII.

The existence in microorganisms of mutants requiring serine or glycine indicates that a single route of serine synthesis occurs. In *E. coli* and *Salmonella* this route is represented by path A, since mutants specifically deficient in the enzymes catalyzing reaction I or reaction III have been prepared.[294, 295] This path also appears to be of major importance in human tissue culture cell lines, where repression of the enzymes of the path by serine has been observed.[212] Regulation of the microbial path by endproduct inhibition[295] has also been observed.

The occurrence of L-alanine-hydroxypyruvate transaminase in plants[322] indicates the possible presence of pathway B. The serine-glycine biosynthetic picture in plants is further complicated by studies in short-term photosynthesis with labeled CO_2. This work suggests that rapidly-labeled phosphoglycerate is not the direct precursor of serine, but that a path involving the sequence glycolate $\rightarrow$ glyoxylate $\rightarrow$ glycine $\rightarrow$ serine is operating.[285a, 216]

B. *Glycine*

It has been well established that glycine and serine are readily interconverted. Therefore, the route from carbohydrate to serine serves also as a route to glycine.[19a] Serine transhydroxymethylase, which has been purified from beef liver[117] and from rabbit liver,[237] carries out the conversion of serine to glycine. In this reaction (VIII, Fig. 2) the hydroxymethyl group of serine is transferred to tetrahydrofolic acid (THFA) to form hydroxymethyl tetrahydrofolic acid (CH_2OH-THFA), which is sometimes referred to as "active formaldehyde". "Active formaldehyde" has been shown to be N^5, N^{10}-methylene THFA:

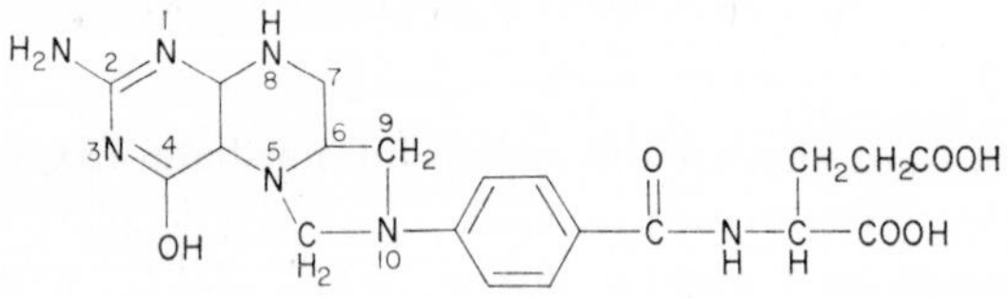

The participation of this compound serves to involve serine β-carbon in the large number of metabolic reactions in which C-1 derivatives of THFA participate, e.g. the reversible formation of methyl groups in various compounds such as methionine, choline and thymine; the synthesis of purines; and the formation and utilization of formate and formaldehyde.

Studies on highly purified enzyme from rabbit liver indicate that this enzyme contains four pyridoxal phosphate prosthetic groups per unit of 331,000 molecular weight.[237] The enzyme may also catalyze the conversion of D-alanine and pyridoxal phosphate to pyridoxamine phosphate and pyruvate.[236] This transamination appears to be a result of displacement of the *prosthetic* pyridoxal phosphate (bound to an ε-amino group of a lysyl residue in the enzyme) by D-alanine, followed by a re-formation of the holoenzyme with added pyridoxal phosphate.

The alternative path of glycine formation from glyoxylate (discussed above in Section A) may be important in plants. In microorganisms growing on acetate or other 2-carbon compounds as sole carbon sources, glyoxylate formed by the glyoxylate cycle may play an important precursor role in glycine synthesis.

C. *Cysteine and Cystine*

Since the carbon chain of cysteine may be derived entirely from serine, only the means whereby the serine hydroxyl is replaced by a thiol group to form cysteine requires further consideration.

Mammals and certain microorganisms use methionine as the source of thiol sulfur. Many microorganisms may use inorganic sulfur compounds or, in some cases, elemental sulfur in place of methionine sulfur.

Figure 3A summarizes the pathway by which methionine sulfur and serine are converted to cysteine in mammals. Enzymes catalyzing each of these reactions have been obtained in partially purified form. Reaction I is catalyzed by methionine transadenosylase, which has been found in animal tissues and in yeast.[44a, 188] The formation of S-adenosylmethionine represents an activating or "priming" reaction in which a relatively stable thioether (methionine) is converted into a labile sulfonium compound. The possible participation of sulfonium compounds of methionine in cysteine biosynthesis was suggested in 1940 by Toennies.[285] This suggestion was shown to be correct by the identification of "active methionine" as S-adenosylmethionine by Cantoni.[43] Sulfonium compounds are considered to be "energy rich" compounds[44] which lose an alkyl group in the presence of various acceptor molecules. The free energy change associated with the removal of the methyl group is believed to be similar to that associated with the hydrolysis of the terminal phosphate of ATP.[42] Indeed, ATP is required for the formation of the sulfonium compound and supplies both energy of formation and the adenosine moiety of the S-adenosylmethionine.

The removal of the "active" methyl group from S-adenosylmethionine (reaction II) may be carried out by any of several transmethylases (methylpherases). Certain groups on the acceptor molecules carry out a "nucleophilic attack" on the methyl carbon of the sulfonium compound with consequent transfer of the methyl group to the acceptor.[186]

Acceptors may be nitrogen, oxygen, sulfur, or carbon atoms. Several N-methylation reactions have been shown to involve S-adenosylmethionine as donor: nicotinamide methylation,[41] creatine formation from guanidinoacetic acid,[221] and N-methylation of purines.[45] A catechol-O-methyl transferase has been purified from rat liver;[23] the S-methylation of homocysteine,[243] and the introduction of the C-28 methyl into ergosterol (C-methylation)[198] have been demonstrated in yeast extracts; S-adenosylmethionine can act as methyl donor in all of these reactions. In fact, it appears that most, if not all, "ATP-dependent" transmethylations involve S-adenosylmethionine.

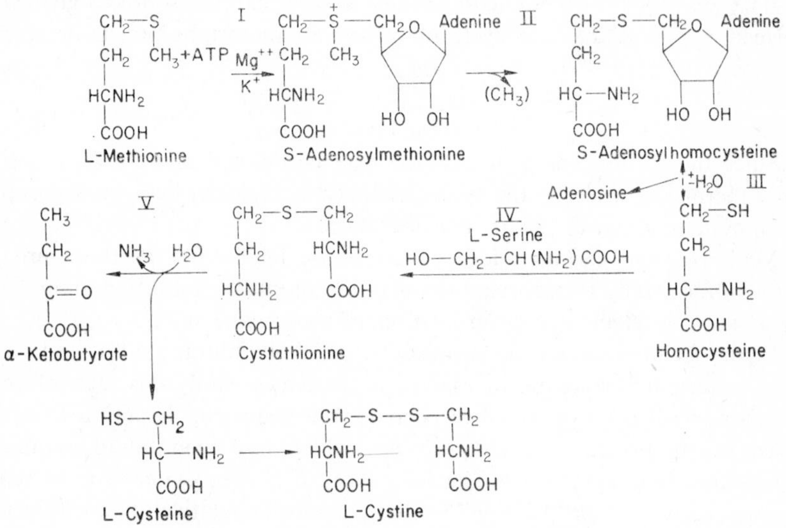

FIG. 3A. Biosynthesis of cysteine and cystine.

In certain cases, the 4-carbon alkyl group, instead of the methyl group of the sulfonium compound, undergoes nucleophilic attack. A yeast enzyme has been found which converts S-adenosylmethionine to α-aminobutyrolactone and 5'-methylthioadenosine.[186] In this reaction, the homocysteine carboxyl oxygen "attacks its own alkyl group" at the carbon adjacent to the sulfonium sulfur, yielding a lactone.[187] In spermidine biosynthesis, the homocysteine group (after decarboxylation) is removed by putrescine.[277]

Transethylation reactions involving ethionine have also been observed, but apparently do not take place under normal biological conditions.[199]

The formation of homocysteine from S-adenosylhomocysteine (reaction III) may be catalyzed by an enzyme obtained from rat liver.[60] However, since the reaction catalyzed by this enzyme greatly favors synthesis of S-adenosylhomocysteine from adenosine and homocysteine, its role in free homocysteine formation is open to question. It represents the only known route to homocysteine in mammals. Cleavage can be effected by removing homocysteine by enzymes.

The enzyme (cystathionine synthetase) which catalyzes the condensation of serine and homocysteine (reaction IV) has been purified from rat liver.[241, 242] Similar activity has been found in [Neurospora but not in bacteria.[61] (See also Section VB for additional discussion of cystathionine metabolism.) Cystathionine synthetase may also act as a potent serine deaminase. Since the enzyme contains bound pyridoxal phosphate, it is likely that an aldimine derivative of amino-acrylic acid is formed as an intermediate. The double bond of aminoacrylate may then react with the —SH of homocysteine to form cystathionine, or in the absence of homocysteine, hydrolysis will result in formation of pyruvate and ammonia. Since cysteine strongly inhibits the enzyme, it is likely that this is an expression of endproduct control of cysteine biosynthesis.

VI. serine + pyridoxal phosphate (R) → $O=\overset{O^-}{\underset{\underset{R}{\overset{\|}{N}}}{\overset{|}{C}}}-\overset{H}{\underset{|}{C}}-CH_2OH$

aldimine derivative of serine

VII. $O=\overset{O^-}{\underset{\underset{R}{\overset{\|}{N}}}{\overset{|}{C}}}-\overset{H}{\underset{|}{C}}-CH_2OH \xrightarrow{\ -H^+\ } O=\overset{O^-}{\underset{\underset{R}{\overset{|}{N}}}{\overset{|}{C}}}-\overset{}{\underset{\|}{C}}-CH_2OH$

VIII. $O=\overset{O^-}{\underset{\underset{R}{\overset{|}{N}}}{\overset{|}{C}}}-\overset{}{\underset{\|}{C}}-CH_2OH \xrightarrow{\ -OH^-\ } O=\overset{O^-}{\underset{\underset{R}{\overset{\|}{N}}}{\overset{|}{C}}}-\overset{}{\underset{}{C}}=CH_2$

Enzymes catalyzing reaction V have been prepared from liver[167, 168] and Neurospora,[78] but this activity has not been found in bacteria. Three types of activity are exhibited by this enzyme: cystathionase, homoserine dehydrase (deaminating) and cysteine desulfhydrase. It is now generally agreed that cysteine desulfhydrase activity in various biological materials is in fact due primarily, if not entirely, to cystathionase.[184, 992]

Although animals must obtain cysteine sulfur from methionine, it is interesting to note that the enzyme cysteine sulfhydrase, which converts serine and H_2S to cysteine has been purified from animal tissue as well as from various microorganisms and higher plants,[159, 238, 313, 38] and animals will incorporate sulfur from sulfide into cysteine. Incorporation from sulfate is very slow, and is probably a result of conversion of sulfate to sulfide by intestinal microorganisms.

Plants and microorganisms, unlike animals, readily utilize sulfate for cysteine biosynthesis, and certain bacteria appear to lack the pathway for incorporation of methionine sulfur into cysteine, as described above.[61] The detailed mechanism of sulfate reduction to sulfide has not been completely worked out, and appears to vary to some extent from one organism to another.[136, 311, 246, 247, 280] Figure 3B summarizes the reactions involved in sulfate reduction as they occur in yeast, *Neurospora* and certain enteric bacteria. The generality of this scheme is uncertain at this time, so it must be considered tentative, except for reactions I, II and VI.

The activation of sulfate occurs in all types of organisms[102, 336, 70, 72] and involves two enzymes, ATP-sulfurylase (reaction I) and APS-kinase (reaction II). The product of reaction II, PAPS, may then be utilized either

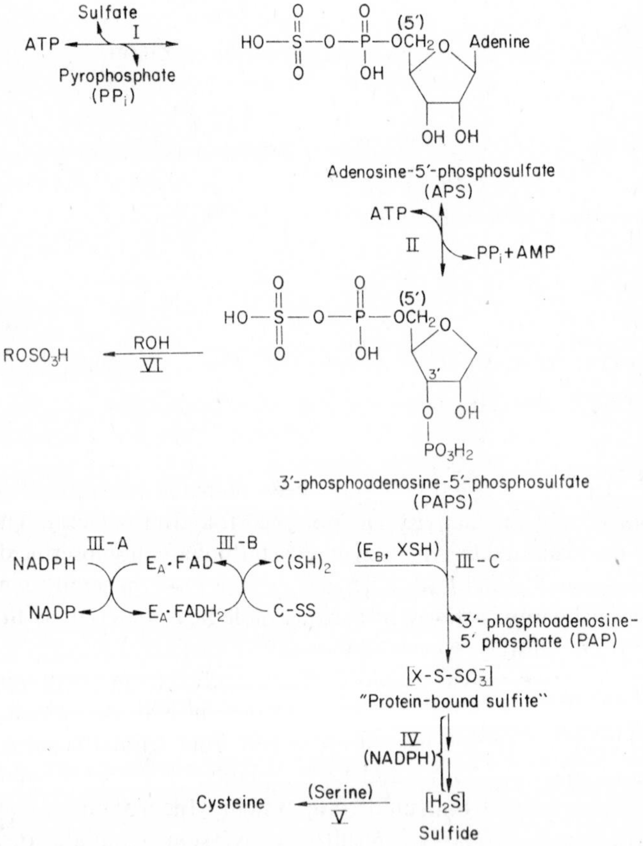

FIG. 3B. Reduction of sulfate to sulfide.

for formation of various organic sulfates such as chondroitin sulfates, found in connective tissue, and other sulfopolysaccharides (reaction VI), or for further reduction to sulfide. Organic sulfate formation occurs in higher animals, but sulfate reduction is confined to plants and microorganisms.

In most organisms PAPS is reduced to the level of sulfite. This process is not completely understood, but in yeast (and presumably in many microorganisms) there appears to be a transport of electrons from NADPH to PAPS involving at least three proteins: a "diaphorase" (E_A) which probably contains FAD; a protein (C-SS) containing a dithiol–disulfide system undergoing alternate oxidation and reduction; and a third enzyme (E_B) which may also contain participating —SH group(s) (reactions III-A, B and C).[286, 29] The products of this complex reaction are 3'-phosphoadenosine-5'-phosphate (PAP), and a protein-bound sulfite, designated $X—S—SO_3^-$, where X is one of the three proteins listed above. Whether *free* sulfite subsequently forms *in vivo* is uncertain. The similarity between this system and that required in reduction of methionine sulfoxide, as well as relevant information derived from studies of lipoyl dehydrogenase (Straub diaphorase) and of glutathione reductase has been pointed out.[29]

The reduction of sulfite to sulfide by NADPH (reaction IV) is the most controversial reaction in the scheme. Whether the apparently conflicting results from various laboratories represent widely different mechanisms in different organisms is not certain.[136, 71, 311, 246, 247, 280] It is possible that a particulate electron transport system is involved in some organisms; perhaps this possibility and the demonstration of "protein-bound sulfite" will prove to be unifying principles. It may be added that nitrite and hydroxylamine are also reduced by several sulfite-reducing systems.

Neither cysteine sulfinic acid nor inorganic thiosulfate appear to be intermediates in the sulfate–sulfide reactions of yeast, bacteria or *Neurospora*,[151] but a system in *Aspergillus nidulans* involving inorganic thiosulfate and S-sulfocysteine has been described.[190]

The final reaction, the incorporation of sulfide into serine, is catalyzed by cysteine sulfhydrase, as discussed above.

IV. THE α-KETOGLUTARATE FAMILY

A. *Proline and Ornithine*

The routes for synthesis of proline and ornithine are illustrated in Fig. 4. In yeast[59, 26] and bacteria[302a, 302b, 302] the conversion of glutamate to ornithine involves N^α-acetylated intermediates instead of the free amino compounds as shown in the figure. In mammals, the mechanism of reduction of glutamate to glutamic-γ-semialdehyde (reactions I and II) remains to be clarified. In some bacteria and yeast, glutamate is first acetylated, either by direct acetylation (enteric bacteria)[306] or by transacetylation (yeast and

Micrococcus glutamicus).[59, 306] The reduction process in *E. coli* involves formation of an intermediate, probably N-acetyl-γ-glutamyl phosphate,[25] which then is reduced by NADPH to give N-acetyl-glutamic-γ-semialdehyde. Free semialdehyde, which cyclizes readily, may arise from the acetylated intermediate, possibly by direct reduction of glutamate, or from ornithine under certain conditions (see below).

The enzyme, Δ¹-pyrroline-5-carboxylate reductase, which catalyzes the reduction of the cyclized semialdehyde (reaction V), has been partially

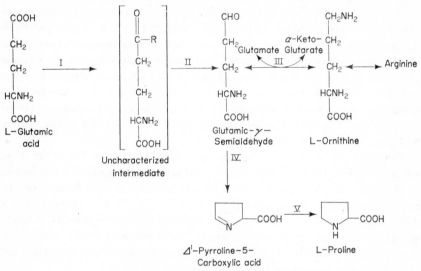

FIG. 4. Proline and ornithine biosynthesis.

purified from *Neurospora*[338] and animal tissues.[250, 204, 178, 179] This reaction, which utilizes NADH (or NADPH), appears to be essentially irreversible; consequently the conversion of proline to glutamate involves an independent pathway.[204, 272, 273] In animal tissues this conversion to glutamate is a mitochondrial process.[122]

A factor which has rendered interpretation of proline–ornithine interrelationships difficult is the presence of the enzyme ornithine-δ-transaminase in animals, higher plants, fungi, and in gram positive bacteria.[235] This enzyme in *Neurospora* serves to convert *exogenous* ornithine to glutamic semialdehyde for use in proline synthesis. However, *endogenous* ornithine, an intermediate in arginine synthesis, apparently cannot be converted to proline by this enzyme. This lack of participation of endogenous ornithine in proline synthesis has led to a proposal[303, 304, 305] that the ornithine and proline synthesis pathways are physically separated in the cell, so that interchange of intermediates cannot occur. However, the possibility that this "channeling" has a chemical explanation has not been disproved.

The formation of ornithine from glutamic semialdehyde (reaction III) may be catalyzed by ornithine-δ-transaminase.[75, 173] The physiological importance of this reaction has been questioned, since the equilibrium favors semialdehyde formation.[274] It may be mentioned in this connection that this enzyme is induced in rat liver by forced feeding of protein-depleted rats.[210, 205] Perhaps a clue to this problem is the recent discovery in kidney of a pathway dependent on glutamate or aspartate for converting proline to ornithine, which does not depend on the δ-transaminase.[248]

While the pathway of conversion of glutamate to ornithine is still somewhat obscure in animals and *Neurospora*, it is clear that the sequence of reactions in *E. coli* is as follows: glutamate, N-acetylglutamate, N-acetyl-(γ-glutamyl phosphate), N-acetylglutamic semialdehyde, Nα-acetylornithine, ornithine. Since all of the enzymes of this pathway are repressed by arginine in *E. coli* strains, this is probably the physiological biosynthetic route from glutamate to arginine in this organism.[306, 97, 160]

B. *Arginine*

The conversion of ornithine to arginine by reactions of the "ornithine cycle" is so well known that only a summary will be given here (see Fig. 5). The "ornithine cycle" may occur in both animals and microorganisms.[253a] Urea is excreted as such in mammals, while the enzyme urease converts urea to carbon dioxide and ammonia in *Neurospora*.

It is important to point out some additional facts about arginine biosynthesis. First, the formation of carbamyl phosphate from CO_2 and NH_3

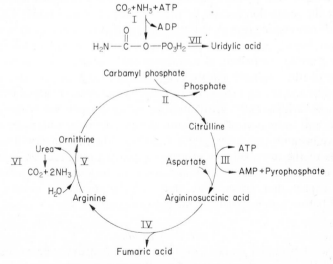

FIG. 5. Ornithine-arginine interconversion.

(reaction I) may take place by two mechanisms.[97] In microorganisms and plants the enzyme carbamate kinase catalyzes the reaction of one mole of carbamic acid, formed non-enzymatically from NH_4^+ and HCO_3^-, with one mole of ATP to form a mole of carbamyl phosphate. In ureotelic animals the enzyme carbamyl phosphate synthetase catalyzes the reaction of NH_4^+ and HCO_3^- with *two* moles of ATP to form carbamyl phosphate. In this reaction N-acetylglutamate plays a catalytic role. It is required for binding the second ATP molecule to the enzyme.[160] Carbamyl phosphate formation is a part of both the arginine path and the pathway for uridylic acid biosynthesis (reaction VII). The last three steps of arginine biosynthesis (reactions II, III and IV) from ornithine are catalyzed respectively by the enzymes ornithine transcarbamylase, argininosuccinate synthetase, and argininosuccinase.

Studies of the regulation of the enzymes of arginine biosynthesis from glutamate in microorganisms, particularly in *E. coli*, have led to important findings concerning the action of regulator genes. Endproduct (feedback) inhibition of acetyl glutamate synthetase in *E. coli* has been observed,[306] and a parallel repression of synthesis of all the enzymes of the arginine pathway of *E. coli* has been found.[306, 160, 97, 302] The mechanism by which repression occurs is complex. Unlike the system for histidine biosynthesis, the structural genes regulating synthesis of the various arginine biosynthetic enzymes are scattered throughout the bacterial chromosome, as determined by mapping studies. In spite of this non-contiguous arrangement of genes in an "operon" or cluster, *all* of the enzymes of the pathway are repressed by arginine; perhaps several sites of arginine repression (operator regions) are responsible for this parallel control.[96] Additional complications are also added to the regulation picture by the presence in some strains of *E. coli* of a second repression system. In this strain the enzyme levels are under repression control by a glucose catabolite but not by arginine. Other findings of interest are the formation of non-repressible mutants, the *induction* of the enzymes of the arginine pathway by the first member of the pathway (glutamate), and the repression of arginine biosynthesis by uracil (which can give rise to uridylate).[96] Also multiple enzymes with the same catalytic function, and induction of a biosynthetic enzyme in a mutant by arginine itself have been observed.[220, 127, 302] In view of the multiplicity of metabolic functions of the intermediates of arginine biosynthesis, such as proline formation, uridylate formation, urea and ammonia production, it seems reasonable to expect that much more study of the regulation system will be required before a well-correlated picture can emerge.

C. *Hydroxyproline*

The use of bacterial mutants in the study of hydroxyproline biosynthesis appears to be out of the question since this amino acid does not appear to occur in bacterial protein.[4] In animals, hydroxyproline is found primarily in connective tissue materials such as collagen. Although a very small metabolic pool of free hydroxyproline has been shown to exist in animals,[326] practically all of the tissue hydroxyproline is derived from proline after an "activation" or "binding" of the proline.[326, 262, 223] Consequently, most of the hydroxyproline does not exist as *free* hydroxyproline which would be expected to mingle with a metabolic pool. There is now a considerable body of evidence which shows that collagen hydroxyproline can arise by specific hydroxylation of some of the proline residues already incorporated into collagen precursor peptide.[158, 98, 214, 208] Pre-collagen peptides, containing proline but no hydroxyproline, may be formed in preparations from chick embryos under anaerobic conditions. These peptides may serve as substrates for a microsomal hydroxylase which incorporates atmospheric oxygen into the 4-position of some of the proline residues in the peptide. Hydroxylation can take place on the protein either while bound to the microsome or after release by various treatments. Although several reports of isolation of a soluble RNA-hydroxyproline have appeared,[163, 53, 120] the incorporation of hydroxy-proline into collagen from this material has not been demonstrated.[208]

There is considerable circumstantial evidence which suggests that ascorbic acid is a cofactor in the hydroxylation reaction. Not only is collagen synthesis reduced in scorbutic animals, but ascorbic acid stimulates hydroxylation of proline markedly in *in vitro* systems.[222, 208] Whether or not it is a *physiological* hydrogen donor in the hydroxylation reaction remains uncertain, since *in vitro* other reducing agents can be used.

Collagen contains both 4-hydroxy-L-proline and 3-hydroxy-L-proline. In chick embryo the ratio of the 4-hydroxy- to the 3-hydroxy- material is about 70 to 1.[195, 130] The 3-hydroxyproline also arises from proline, but its biosynthesis in the available *in vitro* systems is difficult to study because of the low content in collagen.[130]

Hydroxyproline has also been found in plant cell wall protein. Here again it arises from proline. It has been suggested that the hydroxyl group plays a key role in controlling plant cell differentiation by providing a network of crosslinks with cellulose, thereby controlling cell plasticity.[146]

Both 4-hydroxyproline and 4-ketoproline are formed by *Streptomyces antibioticus*, but unlike the animal system, *free* hydroxyproline is incorporated into actinomycin polypeptides produced by this organism.[134] Proline may act as a precursor of these two derivatives, but the detailed biosynthetic reactions have not been studied.

Since hydroxyproline in animals is confined to collagen, assay for this amino acid is useful in studying the *in vitro* biosynthesis of the protein. This assay has been utilized in measuring the half-life of messenger RNA[27] and in the study of polysomes.[143]

V. THE PYRUVATE FAMILY

A. *Threonine*

Threonine, like methionine, arises from aspartic acid through the common intermediate, homoserine. The sequence of reactions is given in Fig. 6. The enzymes catalyzing reactions I, II and III have been partially purified by Black and Wright.[30, 31, 32] Reaction I is catalyzed by β-aspartokinase[30] which has been prepared from yeast. Equilibrium studies show that ATP formation is greatly favored. The second reaction involves aspartic semialdehyde dehydrogenase.[31] Here reduced NADP is consumed and inorganic phosphate appears. Since the formation of the semialdehyde is greatly favored (K = about 3×10^6), the unfavorable equilibrium in reaction I is counteracted. The next reduction (reaction III) requires homoserine dehydrogenase,[32] an enzyme which uses NADH (or NADPH at a lower rate) as hydrogen carrier.

The last two reactions in this scheme are peculiar to threonine biosynthesis. Homoserine kinase,[314] which has been purified from yeast extracts, causes formation of O-phosphohomoserine. Mg^{++} ion is required. The utilization of ATP in this step seems to be a device for channeling homoserine toward threonine by means of an exergonic reaction. The final reaction, catalyzed by phosphohomoserine mutaphosphatase[315, 79] (threonine synthetase), requires pyridoxal phosphate. The following mechanism has been proposed for this reaction.[79] R represents pyridoxal phosphate linked to the amino acid through the aldehyde group of the coenzyme.

$$
\begin{array}{l}
\overset{-H^+}{CH_2-CH_2-CH-COOH\longrightarrow} \\
\quad | \qquad\quad | \\
\quad O \qquad\quad N \\
\quad | \qquad\quad \| \\
\quad PO_3H_2 \quad R
\end{array}
$$

$$
\begin{array}{l}
\overset{-H_3PO_4}{CH_2CH_2-C-COOH\longrightarrow CH_2=CH-C-COOH}\overset{+H^+}{\longrightarrow} \\
\quad | \qquad\quad \| \qquad\qquad\qquad\qquad \| \\
\quad O \qquad\quad N \qquad\qquad\qquad\qquad N \\
\quad | \qquad\quad | \qquad\qquad\qquad\qquad | \\
\quad PO_3H_2 \quad R \qquad\qquad\qquad\qquad R
\end{array}
$$

$$
\begin{array}{l}
\overset{+H_2O}{CH_3-CH=C-COOH\longrightarrow CH_3-CH(OH)-CH-COOH\longrightarrow THREONINE} \\
\qquad\qquad | \qquad\qquad\qquad\qquad\qquad\qquad\quad | \\
\qquad\qquad N \qquad\qquad\qquad\qquad\qquad\qquad\quad N \\
\qquad\qquad \| \qquad\qquad\qquad\qquad\qquad\qquad\quad \| \\
\qquad\qquad R \qquad\qquad\qquad\qquad\qquad\qquad\quad R
\end{array}
$$

The enzyme threonine aldolase purified from sheep liver,[131] which affects the reversible condensation of acetaldehyde and glycine, provides a possible alternative pathway for threonine synthesis. The lack of appreciable acetaldehyde formation in animals would appear to limit the importance of this pathway.

The reactions illustrated in Fig. 6 have been of considerable interest in the study of the control mechanisms of biosynthetic pathways. Several of the intermediates in this scheme, as well as threonine itself, are utilized as starting materials for the biosynthesis of other amino acids. In bacteria, but not in *yeast* or *Neurospora*, part of the lysine carbon chain is derived from aspartic-β-semialdehyde (reaction VI). Homoserine plays a similar role in methionine biosynthesis (reaction VII) and part of the isoleucine molecule is derived from threonine (reaction VIII).

Repression or inhibition of aspartokinase by one of the amino acids utilizing reaction I in its biosynthesis might be expected to interfere with the synthesis of the other amino acids utilizing the same reaction. However, this interference does not occur because multiple aspartokinases, differing in susceptibility to both inhibition and repression by different endproducts, exist in bacteria such as *E. coli*.[258, 259, 257] In this organism two asparto-kinases, one inhibited or repressed selectively by lysine, and another inhibited or repressed selectively by threonine have been separated. Some evidence for

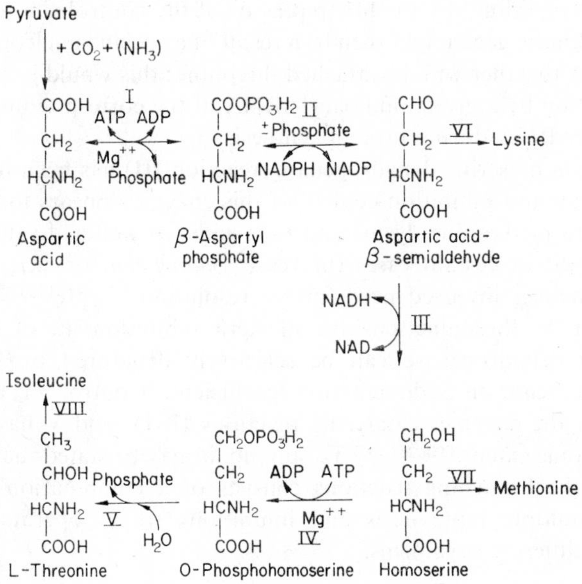

FIG. 6. Threonine biosynthesis.

a third enzyme susceptible to inhibition by homoserine, but not methionine, has been obtained. The existence of multiple enzymes with the same catalytic function, but bearing different allosteric sites, therefore avoids a potential complication in control and shows that separate physical "compartments" are not necessary for independent functioning of metabolic pathways prior to their points of divergence, provided additional controls are imposed later in the respective sequences.[257]

In different *E. coli* strains, the relative susceptibility of the lysine-sensitive and threonine-sensitive aspartokinases may vary.[257] In yeast, where lysine arises from glutamate, there is present a repressible kinase,[63] although no functional role for this repression can be assigned at present. In yeast also, the relative sensitivity of the kinase activity to methionine, lysine, and threonine inhibition and repression is different from that of *E. coli*, and can be varied by growth conditions. Still another variation in control of this reaction is seen in *Bacillus polymyxa* in which "multivalent" endproduct inhibition is observed.[203] In this case both threonine and lysine are required for detectable inhibition, indicating the presence of two separate allosteric sites on the enzyme. There is an indication that isoleucine may also affect the control of bacterial aspartokinase activity, since the lysine-insensitive portion of the activity requires not only threonine but also isoleucine for repression.[84] This example of "multivalent repression" (see also Section VD) suggests the possibility that threonine-sRNA might be the "holorepressor" of the enzyme. Specific "recognition" by the holorepressor of the control site (operator) on the aspartokinase gene might then be a result of a specific nucleotide sequence in the sRNA together with its attached threonine; this would be analogous to the recognition by a given aminoacyl-sRNA of the corresponding code word in messenger RNA during protein synthesis.

Only one homoserine dehydrogenase (reaction III) has been found. Again the repression and inhibition control of this enzyme appears to be complex. Sensitivity to methionine, lysine and isoleucine, as well as to threonine, has been observed in certain cases (in yeast, *Salmonella*, or *E. coli*), but the general principles involved need further resolution.[257, 84, 132, 64, 51] It is of interest that the threonine-sensitive allosteric inhibition site of *E. coli* K-12 homoserine dehydrogenase can be selectively denatured by heat with a resultant decrease in sedimentation coefficient. Control of activity and synthesis of the enzymes catalyzing reactions II, IV and V have also been studied to some extent.[328, 64, 84] To sum up, it may be stated that differential control of the branching reactions consists of a combination of multiple enzymes, multiple repressions and inhibitions which operate in various patterns in different organisms.

B. *Methionine*

In discussing methionine biosynthesis, it is convenient to consider this amino acid as the thioether, S-methyl homocysteine, and to discuss the origin of the two alkyl groups separately. Since both threonine and methionine arise from homoserine,[283] the first reaction peculiar to methionine biosynthesis is the formation of cystathionine from cysteine and homoserine[81] or a related 4-carbon compound. The enzyme presumably catalyzing this reaction (reaction I-A, Fig. 7) has been purified from *Neurospora* extracts.[76, 80] The donor of the 4-carbon moiety (designated as homoserine in the figure) has not been identified with certainty for fungi,[80, 78] but in bacteria, homoserine is first converted to O-succinylhomoserine, in the presence of ATP and CoA.[227, 77] Neither the O-succinyl derivative nor phosphohomoserine are active in the *Neurospora* system. Cleavage of cystathionine to yield cysteine (see section on cysteine biosynthesis, above) and α-ketobutyrate (reaction I-B, Fig. 7) is catalyzed by enzymes from liver and *Neurospora*;[80, 78, 168] the *Neurospora* enzyme appears to be concerned physiologically with incorporation of homocysteine sulfur into cysteine rather than in reaction I-A. Reaction I-B does not appear to occur in bacteria, while reaction I-A is absent in animals.[80]

The conversion of cystathionine to homocysteine, pyruvate and NH_3 (reaction II-A) occurs in *Neurospora* and bacteria.[80, 61] In addition, reaction II-B (which is not the reverse of II-A) occurs in animals and *Neurospora*.[61, 242] In summary then, animals, fungi and bacteria differ in the biosynthesis of the sulfur amino acids as follows: (1) animals utilize methionine sulfur for cysteine biosynthesis, but cannot utilize cysteine sulfur for methionine formation. (2) Bacteria such as *Salmonella* can form methionine utilizing cysteine sulfur, but apparently cannot reverse this process. They therefore must obtain cysteine sulfur from inorganic sulfur compounds. (3) *Neurospora* has the enzymatic equipment for reversible interchange of sulfur between methionine and cysteine, and may also utilize inorganic sulfur compounds. This interchange involves at least four enzymes (reactions I-A, I-B, II-A, II-B) and probably more, since the genetic control of reaction I-A in *Neurospora* is complex.[80]

The mechanism by which the methyl group of methionine is synthesized is not yet fully understood. While this group may arise from various C-1 sources, such as formaldehyde and formate, it appears likely that the β-carbon (hydroxymethyl group) of serine is the primary physiological source.[90, 19] Studies of this problem have been made with both animal and microbial systems.

In liver preparations, it has been shown that C-1 units may give rise to the methyl groups of methionine[263] and of choline[299] under conditions where transmethylation between methionine and choline does not occur. Methyl groups of thymidylic acid may also be formed from C-1 units in animal[100] and microbial[310] systems. In these conversions of C-1 units to methyl groups, folic acid derivatives play key roles.[90, 191]

Synthesis of thymidylate[310, 100, 86] and probably choline[209] methyl groups involve a pathway which involves THFA as a reducing agent and formation of dihydrofolate.[86, 121] Methionine methyl, on the other hand, is formed *de novo* from N^5, N^{10}-methylene-THFA by a route involving (1) reduction to N^5-methyl-THFA, catalyzed by an FAD enzyme[110, 66, 109,

[147, 148, 135] and (2) methyl transfer from methyl-THFA to homocysteine.[108, 110, 147, 109, 279, 138, 278, 82, 104]

The enzyme catalyzing the reduction reaction (reaction V, Fig. 7) has been purified, both from animal tissue[66] and from certain microorgan-

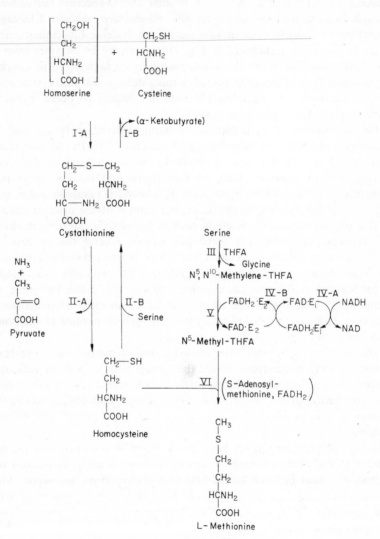

FIG. 7. Methionine biosynthesis.

isms.[66, 148, 135] Enzyme prepared from liver or *E. coli* will utilize either mono- or trigultamate forms of the tetrahydropterolyl coenzyme to form the corresponding methylated derivatives.[148] Studies with the *E. coli* reductase

(E_2) indicate that NADH cannot react directly, but requires a "diaphorase", FAD reductase (E_1), as an electron-transferring agent catalyzing reactions IV A and IV-B. The status of this reductase as a "physiological" diaphorase remains to be established, perhaps by repression experiments. Methionine has been shown to repress E_2 synthesis in *E. coli*,[135] thereby regulating the biosynthetic pathway. It appears unlikely that either the animal or the microbial enzyme functions as a methyl-THFA oxidase, although menadione can be used to drive reaction V in reverse.[66, 135]

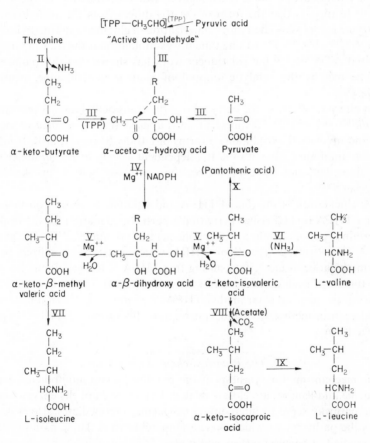

FIG. 8. Biosynthesis of branched-chain amino acids. TPP = thiamine pyrophosphate; R = H or CH_3.

The final step in methionine synthesis, the transfer of methyl from N^5-methyl-THFA to homocysteine (reaction VI) is catalyzed by an enzyme containing a derivative of vitamin B_{12}.[15, 99, 112, 139] The transmethylases purified from mammalian liver [155] and *E.coli* [148, 225] are very similar.

This enzyme exhibits properties which have stimulated much interest in the mechanism of its action. The specificity of the transmethylase is not exacting, since methyl derivatives of tetrahydropteroyltriglutamate or monoglutamate, or even S-adenosylmethionine can serve as donors, while homocysteine or mercaptoethanol can act as methyl acceptors.[155] The reasons for the requirements for catalytic amounts of S-adenosylmethionine and for a reducing agent such as $FADH_2$[155] are uncertain, but recent studies on activation of the apoenzyme with alkylated vitamin B_{12} derivatives indicate that a cobalt-carbon bond is associated with the reduction of the B_{12}.[37, 320, 121] It appears that the form of the B_{12} differs from the adenylcobamide coenzyme forms associated with isomerization of glutamate and methylmalonyl CoA.[279, 138, 319, 261, 121] At one time it was thought that the transmethylation required ATP,[162, 224] but subsequent work has shown that this requirement may be met by the catalytic amount of S-adenosylmethionine mentioned above.

An alternative means for carrying out the transmethylation is available in *E. coli*.[121, 103, 104, 276] This mechanism is apparently independent of vitamin B_{12}, and involves the triglutamate forms of tetrahydropteroic acid. It may be present simultaneously with the B_{12}-dependent system in *E. coli* under some conditions,[155] and appears to be the exclusive system in *Aerobacter aerogenes*.[320]

The elucidation of the role of THFA and vitamin B_{12} in the conversion of methyl-THFA to THFA has permitted a partial explanation for the response of certain types of anemia to either folic acid or vitamin B_{12}.[135] The methyl-THFA is a "storage form" of THFA which must be mobilized by the transmethylation route. The resulting free THFA is then available for other vital functions such as nucleotide synthesis. Needed THFA can arise from dietary folic acid, or from methyl-THFA, if vitamin B_{12} is administered to stimulate transmethylation and concomitant liberation of THFA from its storage form.

C. *The Branched-chain Amino Acids*

The mechanisms for synthesis of the branched-chain amino acids, valine, isoleucine and leucine, are closely related. In fact, most of the enzymes of the valine pathway serve to interconvert isoleucine intermediates also. Figure 8 shows the pathways by which these amino acids arise. These pathways have been studied in bacteria, yeasts and molds. It is noteworthy that the general outline of this scheme, first proposed on the basis of labeling experiments,[270] has been confirmed by studies with mutant organisms and cell-free systems.

The first reaction involves decarboxylation of pyruvate to form an "active acetaldehyde" which consists of a two-carbon unit bound to thiamine pyrophosphate to form hydroxyethylthiamine pyrophosphate:[180, 46]

$$\text{CH}_3-\underset{\underset{\displaystyle \text{thiazolium ring}}{}}{\overset{\displaystyle \text{OH}}{\text{CH}}}$$

(chemical structure: thiamine-derived "active" aldehyde, with pyrimidine ring H_3C, N, N, NH_3^+, CH_2-N^+, thiazole ring with S, CH_3, $CH_2CH_2O-\overset{O}{\underset{O^-}{P}}-O-PO_3^=$)

Presumably, this "active" aldehyde is bound to the enzyme, and in the presence of a suitable acceptor carbonyl (pyruvate or α-ketobutyrate) forms an acyloin: acetolactate[106] or α-aceto-α-hydroxybutyrate.[308, 217, 150] Reactions I and III are catalyzed by a single enzyme,[217] which may be called acetohydroxyacid synthetase. While pyruvic acid is readily available from glycolysis, α-ketobutyric acid[290] arises primarily from threonine[5] by the action of a threonine deaminase (threonine dehydrase).[291] Although a second L-threonine deaminase is known which is involved in anaerobic catabolism of threonine, it is not under repression control, and presumably is not concerned with the biosynthetic pathway.[114]

Reaction IV, which requires NADH, consists of an isomerization (migration of a methyl or ethyl group) and a reduction. A single enzyme, which has been partially purified from *Salmonella*,[13] is involved.[309, 218, 293, 269, 14] This enzyme, α-hydroxy-β-ketoacid reductoisomerase, can be converted to an altered form which will no longer carry out the isomerization but will catalyze the reduction of the α-keto-β-hydroxy acids. To some extent this conversion may be reversed, and appears to involve thiol groups. Possibly α-keto-β-hydroxy-isovaleric and α-keto-β-hydroxy-β-methylvaleric acids are formed as intermediates on the native enzyme surface before reduction occurs. The resulting dihydroxy acids[181] are converted to the α-keto analogues of valine and isoleucine by a dihydroxy-acid dehydrase which has been purified from *E. coli*[189] and higher plants.[129] The cofactor requirement varies somewhat depending upon the source of the enzyme: *E. coli* enzyme requires Fe^{++} and cysteine, while yeast and spinach enzymes require Mg^{++}.[325, 129] Reactions VI and VII are normally carried out by transamination with glutamate, but in mutants lacking this enzyme, a less active transamination with alanine occurs.[307]

Tracer studies have also been of major importance in determining the pathway of leucine biosynthesis. Labeling patterns in the "isobutyryl" portion of the leucine and valine molecules are very much alike in yeasts, *Neurospora*, and bacteria[1, 268, 33, 219] grown in the presence of tracers such as acetate, lactate, and glucose labeled in various carbon atoms. It has also been shown that *Ruminococcus flavefaciens*, which requires isovalerate or isobutyrate for growth, incorporates these acids effectively into leucine.[6] The results of tracer experiments led to the postulation of a leucine synthesis pathway similar to the conversion of acetate and oxalacetate to glutamate by the citric acid cycle.[268] Recent studies with mutants and cell-free extracts have demonstrated the essential correctness of the postulated pathway:

VIII-A.   α-keto-isovalerate + acetyl-CoA ⟶

$$\text{OH}$$
$$|$$
$$(CH_3)_2CH—C(COOH)—CH_2—COOH$$
β-hydroxy, β-carboxy-isocaproate

VIII-B.   β-hydroxy, β-carboxy-isocaproate ⟶
$$(CH_3)_2CH—CH(COOH)—CH(OH)—COOH$$
α-hydroxy, β-carboxy-isocaproate

VIII-C.   α-hydroxy, β-carboxy-isocaproate + NAD $\xrightarrow{\text{Mg}^{++}}$
α-ketoisocaproate + CO_2 + NADH

The condensing enzyme catalyzing reaction VIII-A has been studied in bacterial and yeast extracts.[127, 128, 126, 264] Reaction VIII-B, the isomerization reaction, has been studied with the aid of a partially purified *Neurospora* enzyme. With the purified enzyme there is some formation of the unsaturated compound, dimethylcitraconate, but this is not considered to be a normal intermediate.[101]

An analogous situation is found with aconitase,[253] although aconitase requires Fe^{++}, while the isomerase of leucine biosynthesis exhibits no metal requirement. The absolute configuration of the product of reaction VIII-B has been determined, and the name *threo*-D_s-α-hydroxy-β-carboxyisocaproic acid assigned.[40] The dehydrogenation of this compound (reaction VIII-C) has been studied in extracts of *Salmonella* and *Neurospora*,[102, 126] and a purified preparation of the enzyme from the former organism has been studied.[39] Both monovalent and divalent cations are required for activity. The final transamination apparently does not require the presence of the same transaminase normally involved in isoleucine and valine biosynthesis.[101]

The problems of endproduct inhibition and repression are of particular interest in the case of the branched chain amino acids because of the dual role played by several of the enzymes, plus the fact that α-ketoisovaleric acid is a common intermediate in the biosynthesis of valine, leucine and pantothenic acid.[10, 85] The genes for enzymes of the valine–isoleucine pathway on the one hand, and the genes for enzymes of the leucine "branch" on the other, are organized into clusters (operons) in *Salmonella* and *E. coli*.[10] Isoleucine exerts feedback control by virtue of its strong inhibitory effect on threonine deaminase, which catalyzes the first reaction peculiar to isoleucine biosynthesis.[292] In order to *repress* the enzymes of the isoleucine–valine pathway, all three branched chain amino acids are required (and probably pantothenate also, for a full effect).[10, 85] This phenomenon has been termed "multivalent repression" and represents an alternative means for meeting control problems when more than one endproduct comes from a common precursor; the other solution being multiple enzymes forming the same compound (see Section VA). Leucine alone is required to repress the enzymes catalyzing reactions VIII-A, -B and -C, as expected.

E. coli strain K-12 exhibits an unusual "abnormality" in its control system. Growth is inhibited by valine as a result of a very high sensitivity of the condensing enzyme (reaction III) to valine (which is relieved by isoleucine), an effect which is lacking in other strains of E. coli and in Salmonella. Resistance to this effect may be achieved by mutation to a strain having a more resistant enzyme, or to a strain which permits derepression of this enzyme along with the other enzymes of the pathway when valine is added—the "normal" situation.[289, 284]

D. Lysine and Diaminopimelic Acid

The amino acid a,ϵ-diaminopimelic acid (DAP) appears to be confined to bacterial cells and blue-green algae.[327] DAP is an important constituent of some bacterial cell walls.[116] Of particular interest is the observation that lysine is formed from DAP by simple decarboxylation, and that this reaction is on the main pathway of lysine production in bacteria.[65, 57] The DAP-lysine pathway is summarized in Fig. 9. Most of the work in the study of this pathway has been carried out with E. coli, but a survey of a large variety of organisms has indicated its presence in a variety of bacteria, algae, some lower fungi and various plants.[301, 177]

Although in this pathway the first three intermediates are the same as those in the pathways to threonine, isoleucine (derived from threonine), and methionine, an aspartokinase, specifically inhibited and repressed by lysine, catalyzes reaction I.[258, 259, 257] (See Section VA also.) This enzyme appears to supply the "lysine-diaminopimelate quota" of β-aspartylphosphate to a common pool of this intermediate. Apparently a single enzyme,[92] aspartic semialdehyde dehydrogenase,[31] catalyzes reaction II. Reaction III, the condensation of pyruvate and aspartic semialdehyde to form a 7-carbon intermediate,[337] is the branching reaction which separates DAP and lysine biosynthesis from the biosynthesis of homoserine (reaction XI) and those amino acids derived from it (threonine, isoleucine and methionine). The condensing enzyme for this step is specifically inhibited by L-lysine.[94] Therefore it appears that this inhibition may serve as a "secondary" control permitting the channeling of the aspartic semialdehyde pool (which will be reduced as a result of inhibition and repression by lysine of the lysine-sensitive aspartokinase) to homoserine.

In reaction IV, dihydrodipicolinic acid[95] is reduced to Δ^1-piperideine-2,6-dicarboxylate, the cyclized (dehydrated) form of 2-amino-6-ketopimelate. The NADP-specific reductase catalyzing this reaction has been partially purified.[74] It is possible also that dihydrodipicolinic acid is converted to dipicolinic acid, a component of bacterial spores[206, 213, 24] (reaction X). The demonstration that succinylation (reaction V) occurs after condensation and reduction was unexpected, since it appeared reasonable to assume that

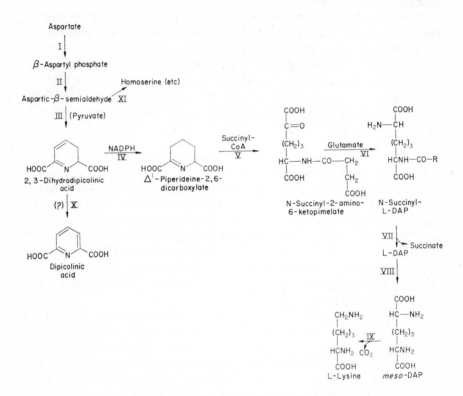

FIG. 9. Lysine and diaminopimelic acid biosynthesis.

the function of acylation of the amino group was prevention of cyclization reactions. Perhaps this endergonic succinylation reaction represents a means of controlling sporulation in many bacteria, since DAP is essential for cell-wall formation, while dipicolinic acid is found in spores. It is well known that sporulation occurs when conditions are unfavorable for growth, e.g. depletion of an energy source.

Subsequent reactions transform N-succinyl-2-amino-6-ketopimelate[93] into N-succinyl-L-DAP, L-DAP, *meso*-DAP, and finally lysine. A specific glutamic-DAP transaminase,[207] and a Co++-activated deacylase[137] have been purified. Conversion of L-DAP to the *meso* form by DAP racemase follows, since DAP decarboxylase will not act on L-DAP.[12] Lysine, the final product, has also been shown to regulate its own synthesis by repressing DAP decarboxylase formation.[202] This regulation presumably permits channeling of DAP into cell walls without concomitant production of unneeded lysine.

There is a marked difference between the above mode of lysine biosynthesis and that found in another group of organisms comprising certain lower fungi, higher fungi, such as the ascomycetes and basidiomycetes, and the euglenids.[301, 177] This pathway, in which L-α-aminoadipate (AAA) is the best-documented intermediate, has been studied most extensively in yeast and *Neurospora*.[170, 171, 182, 324] Although there are a number of puzzling observations yet to be clarified, the bulk of the experimental information indicates that the pathway is essentially that given in Fig. 10.

Reactions I–IV, originally proposed on the basis of tracer studies,[271] have been demonstrated in cell-free yeast extracts.[316, 265, 267] Preliminary data indicate that homoaconitate may also be formed in these reactions,[266] but it may well be that this is a side product formed in the homoaconitase reaction.

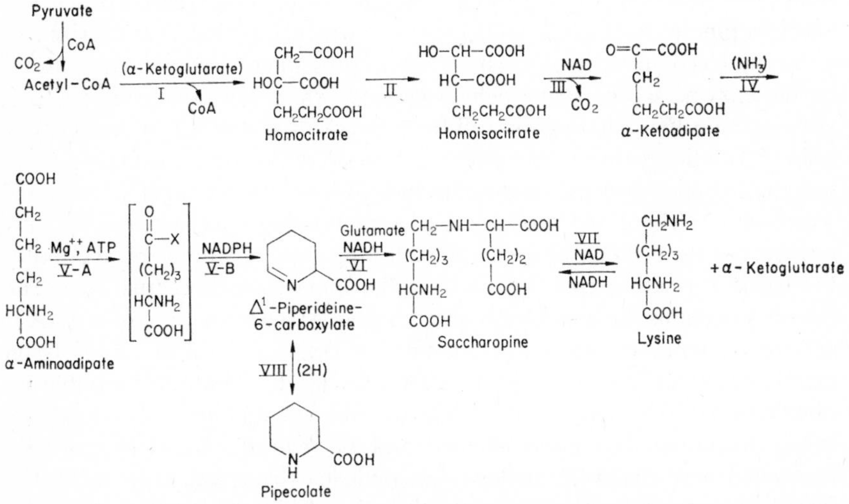

FIG. 10. Lysine synthesis by the α-aminoadipate pathway.

Analogous side product formation is observed with aconitase[253] and a related enzyme involved in leucine biosynthesis[101] (see Section Vc). Other data which support this pathway are the efficient utilization of glutamate carbon in lysine synthesis in yeast[316] and the observation that labeled α-ketoglutarate is an effective precursor of the D-α-aminoadipyl residue in the antibiotic cephalosporin C.[287]

An alternative to this pathway has been suggested in which a "direct" utilization of acetate to form AAA occurs.[298, 169] It is possible that a pathway involving glutarylcoenzyme A is involved in *Penicillium citreo-viride*, a mold having the unusual capacity to produce large quantities of dipicolinic acid. This compound was thought to be confined to spore-forming bacteria,[281, 197] and may arise as a result of branching of the lysine pathway at α-ketoadipate. In this connection the accumulation of glutarate by a lysine-less yeast mutant[169] may be relevant. However, it is important to take into account the relative contribution of the glyoxylate cycle in interpreting these experiments.

The reduction of α-aminoadipate to the semialdehyde "level" (reactions V-A and V-B) has been studied in cell-free preparations.[228, 229, 36, 231, 149] As in the formation of aspartic and glutamic semialdehyde discussed above, an activation step appears to precede reduction.[229, 171, 231] It has been suggested that this activating group is AMP.[229, 231] The formation of piperidone carboxylate by yeast[171, 144, 145] may reflect this activation reaction. Whether the *free* semialdehyde is involved is uncertain.[20, 229, 230, 231, 149]

The conversion of synthetic AAA-semialdehyde and glutamate to saccharopine (reaction VI) has been observed in cell-free yeast extracts.[125] Saccharopine (ε-N-(L-glutaryl-2)-L-lysine), which was first characterized as a "normal" component of yeast,[56, 140] is subsequently converted to lysine by the enzyme saccharopine dehydrogenase, which has been purified from yeast extracts.[234] Although in cell-free extracts it is difficult to demonstrate lysine formation with this enzyme, it is considered to be the catalyst for the terminal reaction because of the existence of lysineless mutants of yeast and *Neurospora* lacking the enzyme and accumulating saccharopine.[234] The enzyme has the peculiar property of exhibiting markedly different pH optima for lysine formation (pH 10) and saccharopine formation (pH 7·0). This property explains the difficulty in observing net lysine formation from AAA in cell-free systems, but does not account for the high level of "free" lysine extractable with hot water from yeast cells (J. R. Mattoon, unpublished observations). The enzyme is widely distributed, and in those organisms tested, including *Aspergillus nidulans* and *Euglena gracilis*, it is invariably associated with the AAA pathway, as indicated by tracer experiments.[297, 301, 177] These observations indicate that the efficient utilization of labeled pipecolate in lysine formation by the latter organism[226] may result from conversion of this material to Δ^1-piperideine-6-carboxylate prior to saccharopine formation. A similar explanation for the accumulation of pipecolate (derived from AAA) in mutants of *A. nidulans*[22] can be made by assuming the existence of reaction VIII. The function of pipecolate in these organisms remains to be explained.

A number of observations remain to be explained in the study of the AAA pathway. Among these is the question of the role of D-AAA which occurs in the related antibiotics penicillin N and cephalosporin C.[18, 16, 288, 252] These compounds, which are structurally related to glutathione, may indicate the existence of a possible cofactor containing AAA. The relationship of the activation of the δ-carboxyl of AAA in semialdehyde formation to formation of the amide bond in the antibiotics is also of interest. The accumulation of a peptide-like material by lysineless yeast mutants may also be related to this.[142] Another puzzling observation has been made on aconitateless yeast mutants. One class of mutants is respiratory sufficient and shows no lysine requirement, while a second class appears to lose respiratory sufficiency (cytochromes a and b), glutamate formation and lysine formation simultaneously.[196]

There are indications that lysine represses and/or inhibits its own synthesis (M. P. Thornton and J. R. Mattoon, unpublished experiments). In this connection the inhibition of pipecolate accumulation by lysine noted above, and the inhibition of penicillin synthesis by lysine (reversed by AAA)[252] may be cited.

Hydroxylysine, found in collagen, appears to be formed in a manner similar to hydroxyproline (see Section IVB).

VI. THE PENTOSE FAMILY

A. *Histidine*

The study of the origin of the imidazole of histidine has led to the discovery of an interesting cyclic pathway. In this pathway, a 1-carbon unit (supplied by way of formyl tetrahydrofolic acid from an appropriate 1-carbon source), and two nitrogen atoms (one supplied by aspartate and one by glutamine) combine with 5-phosphoribosyl-1-pyrophosphate (PRPP) to produce imidazole glycerol phosphate (ImGP).[185, 161, 11, 245, 244] Purine nucleotides, derivatives of adenine nucleotides, 5-amino-1-ribosyl-4-imidazole-carbox-amide-5′-phosphate (AICAR), and an uncharacterized compound serve as catalytic intermediates in a cycle analogous to the citric acid cycle. The reactions of this "ATP-Imidazole" cycle are given in Fig. 11.

Reactions I-V and IX are part of the path for the biosynthesis of purine nucleotides (discussed in Chapter 2 of this book). ATP "loans" a carbon atom and a nitrogen atom,[192] PRPP (derived from the pentose phosphate pathway) provides the "backbone", and glutamine donates a nitrogen atom to complete the formation of the imidazole ring of ImGP (reactions VI–VIII). The other product of the reactions, AICAR, then accepts a C-1 fragment from formyl tetrahydrofolic acid (reaction II), and the amino group of AMP is regained from aspartic acid (reactions III and IV). The "loan" of the two ATP ring atoms is thus repaid.

The detailed pathway for the conversion of ATP and PRPP to histidine is given in Fig. 12.[141, 157, 321, 249] Only one intermediate, designated (Y) in the figure, remains to be characterized. Enzymes catalyzing the various steps have been obtained from various microbial sources.[2, 3, 7, 8, 9, 157, 321, 156, 166] Of

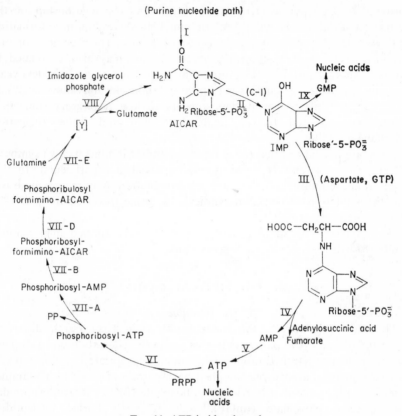

Fig. 11. ATP-imidazole cycle.

particular interest is the work of Martin, Ames, Hartman and their associates with the enzymes of *Salmonella typhimurium*.[157, 321, 10] By utilizing sucrose density gradient centrifugation they have been able to estimate the molecular weights of all of the enzymes required for the pathway (Fig. 12), even though impure preparations were employed. This information, together with a detailed genetic map[157] of the cluster of genes (operon) determining the enzymes of histidine biosynthesis, has permitted a comparison of the number of cistrons or complementation units and molecular weight. Their work has also contributed experimental support for the operon hypothesis[10] and the coding ratio of three nucleotides per amino acid.[321] Table 1 lists the enzymes, their approximate molecular weights, and the number of complementation units found by crossing mutants.

Several of the enzymes are controlled by genes with more than one complementation unit, while others, controlled by a single cistron, exhibit multiple subunits. It appears likely that three types of enzymes are involved in histidine biosynthesis: (1) enzymes with a single polypeptide chain, (2) enzymes with multiple, identical subunits, (3) enzymes with dissimilar subunits which may or may not be multiple. Two of the enzymes exhibit rather unusual behavior. The enzyme catalyzing reaction X (shown as two reactions in Fig. 12) has been highly purified from *Salmonella*[156] and appears to be homogenous by several criteria. While both genetic and chemical evidence indicate that it has subunit structure, a distinction between repeating monomer or mixed dimer structure has not been made. Furthermore, no mutant enzyme acting

TABLE 1.   ENZYMES OF HISTIDINE BIOSYNTHESIS IN *Salmonella typhimurium*[141]

Reaction no. (Fig. 12)	Enzyme	Approximate molecular weight	Number of complementation units	Number of subunits demonstrated
I	ATP-PRPP pyrophosphorylase	200,000	1	4
II	Phosphoribosyl-ATP pyrophosphohydrolase	43,000	2	
III	Hydrolase	48,000	2	
IV	Isomerase	27,000	1	
V	Amidotransferase	44,000	1	
VI	Cyclase	41,000	1	
VII	ImGP dehydrase	145,000	4	
VIII	IAP transaminase	68,000	1	2
IX	HP phosphatase	(this activity and that of reaction VII reside on the same protein)		
X	Histidinol dehydrogenase	75,000	2	

on either histidinol or histidinal has been found among thirty mutants tested. Apparently, both subunits are needed for both activities. On the other hand, the enzyme which catalyzes both reactions VII and IX does display properties indicating that one subunit (or multiple) carries the site for reaction VII and another the site for reaction IX. Although the protein displaying both activities acts as a unit immunologically and is not resolved by various purification treatments, it is possible to obtain proteins with a *single* activity from certain mutants. Apparently the two (or more) subunit polypeptides are so closely associated that they are not readily resolved. In *Neurospora*, however, separate enzymes catalyzing the two reactions have been purified.[7, 8]

The pyrophosphorylase which carries out the initial step in histidine biosynthesis (reaction I, Fig. 12) is susceptible to endproduct control by histidine or the histidine analogue, 2-thiazole alanine. This feedback inhibition is noncompetitive, can be selectively lost by mutation or aging, and consists of two steps, histidine binding, followed by a conformational change which is required for the inhibition.[157]

All of the genes concerned with histidine biosynthesis are located together in a cluster (operon) on the *Salmonella* chromosome. The synthesis of all the

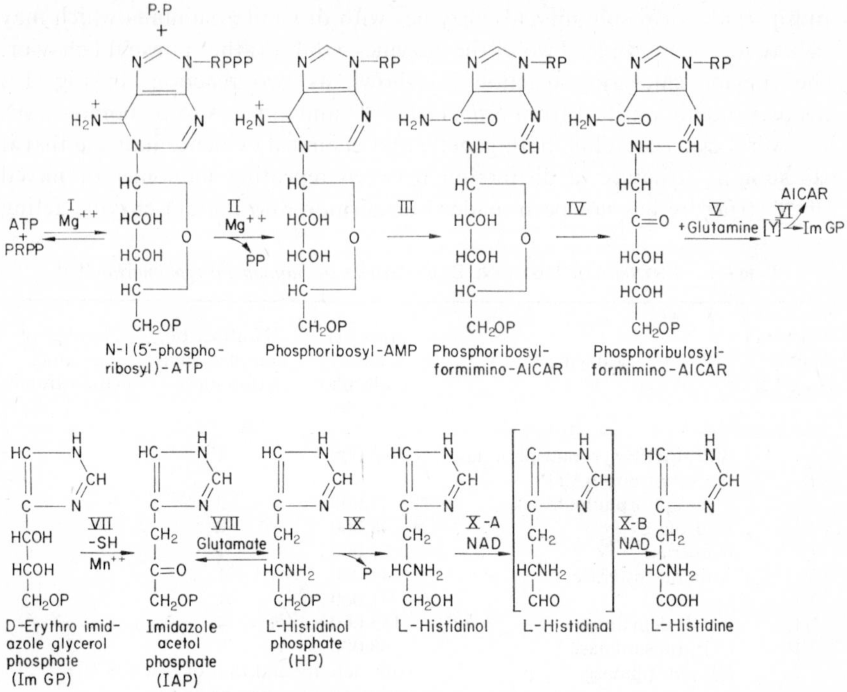

FIG. 12. Biosynthesis of histidine.

enzymes is regulated by an "operator" gene located at one end of the operon, so that the ratio of any enzyme to any other enzyme in the cluster is constant regardless of the degree of repression (coordinate repression).[10] Presumably then, the agent carrying the genetic information from the operon to the site of protein synthesis is polycistronic messenger RNA.

B. *Phenylalanine and Tyrosine*

The existence of mutant strains of *E. coli*, *A. aerogenes*, and other bacteria with multiple requirements for certain aromatic compounds indicates that there is a common pathway for the synthesis of the aromatic ring of amino acids and some other aromatic compounds such as *p*-aminobenzoic acid. The compounds representing the branch-points of the three pathways are of considerable interest, and recent work has indicated that two compounds previously thought to represent these positions, shikimate-5-phosphate[153, 318] and prephenic acid[58, 133, 317] actually are precursors of the "branch" compounds.[89, 88, 52]

Figure 13 summarizes the present knowledge of the pathways leading from glucose to phenylalanine and tyrosine. The building blocks for the aromatic ring are phosphoenolpyruvate and erythrose-4-phosphate, which are formed from glucose through the glycolytic and pentose phosphate pathways respectively. The condensation of these two compounds to form 3-deoxy-D-*arabino*-heptulosonic acid-7-phosphate (DAHP) and inorganic phosphate (reaction I, Fig. 13) is catalyzed by DAHP synthetase, which has been purified from *E. coli* extracts.[256] Reaction II, the cyclization of DAHP, is catalyzed by a single enzyme, 5-dehydroquinate synthetase, which has an unusual cofactor requirement for NAD and CO^{++}. A possible mechanism for this

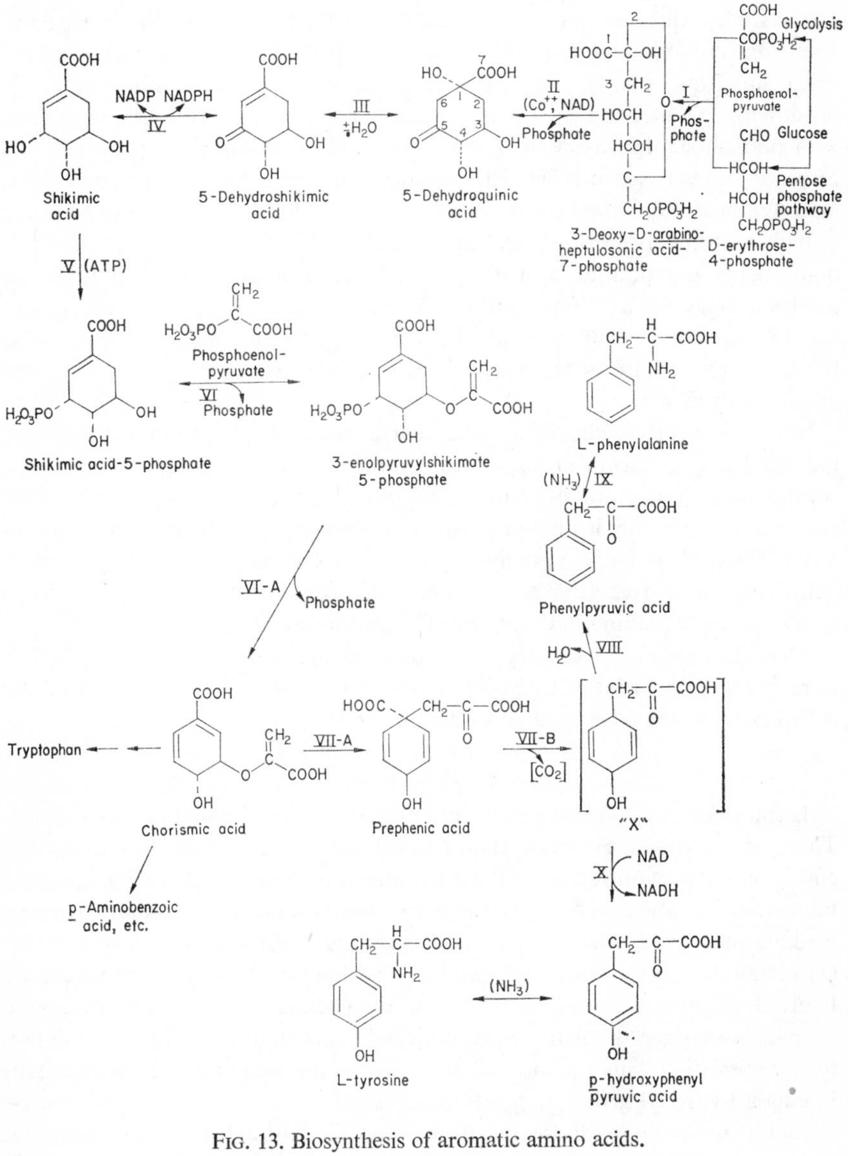

FIG. 13. Biosynthesis of aromatic amino acids.

C

reaction involves the formation of a δ-diketone intermediate which would be expected to cyclize readily.[88, 254] Carbons 1, 2 and 3 of phosphoenolpyruvate form the first three carbons of DAHP, then appear as carbons 7, 1 and 2, respectively, of 5-dehydroquinate. The remaining carbons of the ring are derived from the tetrose.

The dehydration of dehydroquinate to form 5-dehydroshikimate (reaction III) is catalyzed by 5-dehydroquinase, which has been prepared from *E. coli* extracts.[183] Shikimic acid is formed by action of an NADP-specific 5-dehydroshikimic reductase[329] which has been found in various microorganisms and plants, but not in animals. Shikimate-5-phosphate,[318] presumably formed by means of a kinase reaction (reaction V), combines with phosphoenolpyruvate to form 3-enolpyruvyl shikimate-5-phosphate in *E. coli* extracts (reaction VI). This reaction, catalyzed by 3-enolpyruvylshikimate synthetase (purified from *E. coli*)[154] is readily reversible in the presence of high concentrations of phosphate, indicating that the enolpyruvyl ether is a high energy compound. A mechanism involving a diphospho-intermediate has been suggested for this reaction. The 3-enolpyruvylshikimate-5-phosphate is then converted to chorismic acid ("separating" acid), which appears to be the last intermediate in the pathway which is common to all the aromatic amino acids.[89, 88]

In reaction VII-A chorismic acid rearranges to form prephenic acid. As indicated above, recent studies with *Neurospora*[52] mutants indicate that a compound of uncertain structure ("X" in the figure) is the actual "branch" compound from which phenyl pyruvate is formed by dehydration (reaction VIII),[317] and *p*-hydroxyphenyl pyruvate is formed by an NAD-linked dehydrogenation (reaction X).[240] The ketoacids are then converted respectively to phenylalanine and tyrosine by appropriate transaminases.

All of the reactions necessary for synthesis of the three aromatic amino acids have been demonstrated to occur in microbial extracts, but several of the enzymes have not been studied in detail.

C. *Tryptophan*

Tryptophan, like phenylalanine and tyrosine, arises from chorismate.[89, 67] There is no direct evidence that the formation of anthranilic acid from chorismate (reaction I, Fig. 14) and the amide nitrogen of glutamine involves more than a single step,[89, 88] but two observations suggest that an intermediate may exist, whose possible structure is given in brackets in Fig. 14: (1) certain *E. coli* mutants accumulate *O*-dihydric phenols[211, 89] which are likely breakdown products of labile intermediates. (2) The compound *trans*-2,3-dihydro-3-hydroxy-anthranilic acid is accumulated by *Streptomyces aureofaciens*.[172] This compound differs from the suggested intermediate by having a hydroxyl group at position 3.[154]

In the next phase of the sequence, the formation of the pyrrole ring, phosphoribosyl pyrophosphate (PRPP) provides the two necessary carbon atoms, while the carboxyl carbon of anthranilic acid is lost.[330] The immediate product of the interaction of PRPP and anthranilate (reaction II) is the labile compound anthranilic ribonucleotide (N-*o*-carboxyphenyl-D-ribosylamine-5-phosphate,[69, 67] which appears to undergo an Amadori rearrangement[115] to form anthranilic-1-deoxy-ribulonucleotide[1-(*o*-carboxyphenylamino)-1-deoxyribulose-5-phosphate].[68, 251] An alternative intermediate in yeast, an N-fructosyl anthranilic acid, has been suggested.[200] Ring closure, with accompanying production of CO_2 and H_2O (reaction IV), gives rise to indole-3-glycerol phosphate.[331] The partially purified *E. coli* enzyme catalyzing this step exhibits the unusual property of sensitivity to inhibition by anthranilic acid, an *earlier* intermediate in the pathway.[91] A recent report[62] comparing *E. coli*, *Saccharomyces cerevisiae*, and *Neurospora* has indicated that a number of the enzymes occurring as discrete proteins in *E. coli* are combined in yeast and *Neurospora*. In yeast, reactions I and IV appear to involve a single protein, while in *Neurospora*, reactions I, III and IV may be catalyzed by one complex.

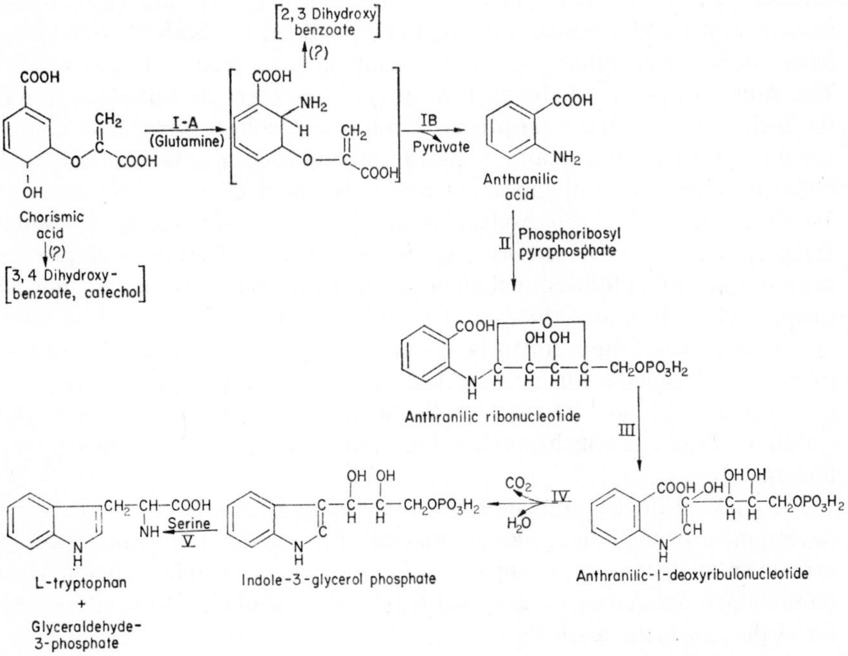

FIG. 14. Biosynthesis of tryptophan.

The last reaction in the sequence (V) has been of outstanding importance in the development of biochemical genetics.[333, 28, 62, 331] The enzyme catalyzing this reaction has been studied in great detail, particularly for *E. coli* and

Neurospora. In *E. coli* the enzyme consists of two separable components, A and B,[333] which cooperatively catalyze reaction V. Either of these components can be modified separately by mutation. In *Bacillus subtilis*, tryptophan synthetase also has the form A + B ⇌ AB, but the degree of "cooperation" between the two components required is less than in *E. coli*, where *full* activity is realized only in complex. Since in yeast and *Neurospora*, a "single" protein (consisting of tightly-bound subunits) represents the activity, there appears to be an evolutionary order evident.[239]

Another feature of the enzyme, which requires pyridoxal phosphate for activity,[296] is its ability to catalyze several different reactions. Three of these reactions have been recognized for some time: (1) reaction V, (2) indole + serine → tryptophan, and (3) indole-3-glycerolphosphate $\underset{(3R)}{\overset{(3F)}{\rightleftarrows}}$ indole + glyceraldehyde-3-phosphate.[239, 49] While indole will support growth of some tryptophan auxotrophs[282] and is produced by others, it is unlikely that *free* indole is involved as an intermediate in tryptophan synthesis.[332, 275, 55, 335] Recent studies[54, 87] have indicated that a variety of other reactions may be catalyzed by tryptophan synthetase from *E. coli* or *Neurospora*, e.g. the deamination and desulfhydration of cysteine and the synthesis of tryptophan from cysteine and indole-3-glycerol phosphate have been demonstrated.[54] The A-chain protein of the *E. coli* enzyme has been crystallized,[113] and the B-chain protein has been prepared in homogeneous form.[54] The *Neurospora* enzyme (which has both A and B functions) has also been prepared in highly purified form, and appears to consist of 2 pairs of subunits of approximately equal size. *E. coli* A-chain catalyzes reaction (3) readily,[107] while B-chain is an effective catalyst for reaction (2).[54] The B-chain protein possesses several activities, including serine dehydrase. In some, but not all cases, A-chain increases the rate of these different catalytic activities. Such "multiple activity" appears to be a common feature of enzymes requiring pyridoxal phosphate for activity (see also cystathionine synthetase and cystathionase, Section III c). This should not be surprising in view of the variety of reactions which pyridoxal phosphate-*activated* intermediates may undergo.[35]

The study of the tryptophan synthetase reactions played a vital role in the development of the "one gene-one enzyme" hypothesis, since it provided an experimental system with which it was possible to establish that a gene mutation, recognized as a nutritional requirement, could in fact be accounted for at the enzymatic level.[333, 28]

This work has been extended, and with pure A-protein from wild type, and genetically altered A-proteins, recognized by immunological reactions, it has been possible to construct a fine-structure genetic map of the A-gene and to correlate this map with the primary structure of the A-protein (the A-gene product). This "marriage" of genetic mapping and analysis of primary protein structure has contributed a wealth of valuable information confirming and extending many of the concepts of molecular biology: (1) colinearity of A-gene structure and A-protein structure has been demonstrated.[47, 105] (2) *Single* amino acid substitutions result from mutations and reversions.[107, 47] (3) Support for code degeneracy has been obtained.[105] (4) Important information on the mechanism of suppressor mutations has been obtained. [333, 28] (5) Information on primary structure of wild type A-protein can be obtained by use of peptides from mutant A-proteins, thus facilitating determination of amino acid sequence.[105] (6) The primary structure within the catalytic site of the enzyme is accessible to analysis.[107]

In addition to these contributions, two recent developments in the study of tryptophan synthetase show great promise. First, by studying many amino acid replacements at a single position in the A-chain, induced either by primary mutation or reversion, information has been obtained which can probably eventually lead to ordering of bases in a triplet code word. Finally, cell-free systems capable of producing the enzyme *in vitro* have been prepared. Both DNA-dependent and DNA-independent systems have been found.[312, 165] These systems should be extremely valuable tools for the further elucidation of the mechanism of translation of genetic information into enzyme structure, especially when they are correlated with mapping and primary structure studies.

REFERENCES

1. ABELSON, P. H. and VOGEL, H. J. *J. Biol. Chem.* **213**, 355 (1955).
2. ADAMS, E. *J. Biol. Chem.* **209**, 829 (1954).
3. ADAMS, E. *J. Biol. Chem.* **217**, 325 (1955).
4. ADAMS, E. *J. Biol. Chem.* **234**, 2073 (1959).
5. ADELBERG, E. A., COUGHLIN, C. A., and BARRATT, R. W. *J. Biol. Chem.* **216**, 425 (1955).
6. ALLISON, M. J., BRYANT, M. P., and DOETCH, R. N. *Arch. Biochem. Biophys.* **84**, 245 (1959).
7. AMES, B. N. *J. Biol. Chem.* **226**, 583 (1957).
8. AMES, B. N. *J. Biol. Chem.* **228**, 131 (1957).
9. AMES, B. N. and HORECKER, B. L. *J. Biol. Chem.* **220**, 113 (1956).
10. AMES, B. N. and MARTIN, R. G. *Ann. Rev. Biochem.* **33**, 235 (1964).
11. AMES, B. N., MARTIN, R. G., and GARRY, B. J. *J. Biol. Chem.* **236**, 2019 (1961).
12. ANITA, M., HOARE, D. S., and WORK, E. *Biochem. J.* **65**, 448 (1957).
13. ARMSTRONG, F. B. and WAGNER, R. P. *J. Biol. Chem.* **236**, 2027 (1961).
14. ARMSTRONG, F. B. and WAGNER, R. P. *J. Biol. Chem.* **236**, 3252 (1961).
15. ARNSTEIN, H. R. V. *Biochem. J.* **73**, 23P (1959).
16. ARNSTEIN, H. R. V., ARTMAN, M., MORRIS, D. and TOMS, E. J. *Biochem. J.* **76**, 353 (1960).
17. ARNSTEIN, H. R. V. and KEGLEVIC, D. *Biochem. J.* **62**, 199 (1956).
18. ARNSTEIN, H. R. V. and MORRIS, D. *Biochem. J.* **76**, 357 (1960).
19. ARNSTEIN, H. R. V. and NEUBERGER, A. *Biochem. J.* **55**, 259 (1953).
19a ARNSTEIN, H. R. V. and NEUBERGER, A. *Biochem. J.* **55**, 271 (1953).
20. ASPEN, A. J. and MEISTER, A. *Abstracts 138th Meeting, Am. Chem. Soc.*, 1960, p. 81C.
21. ASPEN, A. J. and MEISTER, A. *Abstracts 135th Meeting, Am. Chem. Soc.*, 1959, p. 62C.
22. ASPEN, A. J. and MEISTER, A. *Biochemistry* **1**, 606 (1962).
23. AXELROD, J. and TOMCHICK, R. *J. Biol. Chem.* **233**, 702 (1958).

24. BACH, M. and GILVARG, C. *Federation Proc.* **23**, 313 (1964).
25. BAICH, A. and VOGEL, H. J. *Biochem. Biophys. Res. Commun.* **7**, 491 (1962).
26. BECHET, J., WIAME, J. M. and GRENSON, M. *Arch. Intern. Physiol. Biochim.* **73**, 136 (1965).
27. BEKHOR, I. J. and BAVETTA, L. A. *Proc. Natl. Acad. Sci., U.S.* **53**, 613 (1965).
28. BENNETT, C. J. and DREYER, W. J. *Ann. Rev. Biochem.* **33**, 205 (1964).
29. BLACK, S. *Ann. Rev. Biochem.* **32**, 399 (1963).
30. BLACK, S. and WRIGHT, N. G. *J. Biol. Chem.* **213**, 27 (1955).
31. BLACK, S. and WRIGHT, N. G. *J. Biol. Chem.* **213**, 39 (1955).
32. BLACK, S. and WRIGHT, N. G. *J. Biol. Chem.* **213**, 51 (1955).
33. BLOCH, K. and REISS, O. *J. Biol. Chem.* **216**, 703 (1955).
34. BORKENHAGEN, F. L. and KENNEDY, E. P. *J. Biol. Chem.* **234**, 849 (1959)
35. BRAUNSTEIN, A. E. In *The Enzymes*, 2nd ed., vol. 2, p. 113, edited by P. D. Boyer, H. Lardy and K. Myrback. Academic Press, New York, 1960.
36. BROQUIST, H. P., LARSON, R. L., and SANDINE, W. E. *Federation Proc.* **20**, 9 (1961).
37. BROT, N. and WEISSBACH, H. *Federation Proc.* **24**, 420 (1965).
38. BRÜGGEMANN, J., SCHLOSSMANN, K., MERKENSCHLAGER, M. and WALDSCHMITT, M. *Biochem. Z.* **335**, 392 (1962).
39. BURNS, R. O., UMBARGER, H. E. and GROSS, S. R., *Biochemistry* **2**, 1053 (1963).
40. CALVO, J. M., STEVENS, C. M., KALYANPUR, M. G. and UMBARGER, H. E. *Biochemistry* **3**, 2024 (1964).
41. CANTONI, G. L. *J. Biol. Chem.* **189**, 745 (1951).
42. CANTONI, G. L. In *Phosphorus Metabolism*, vol. 2, p. 129, edited by W. D. McElroy and B. Glass. The Johns Hopkins Press, Baltimore, 1952.
43. CANTONI, G. L. *J. Am. Chem. Soc.* **74**, 2942 (1952).
44. CANTONI, G. L. In *Comparative Biochemistry*, Vol. I, p. 181, edited by M. Florkin and H. S. Mason, Academic Press, New York (1960).
44a CANTONI, G. L. and DURELL, J. *J. Biol. Chem.* **225**, 1033 (1957).
45. CANTONI, G. L. and VIGROS, P. J., JR. *J. Biol. Chem.* **209**, 647 (1954).
46. CARLSON, G. L. and BROWN, G. M., *J. Biol. Chem.* **236**, 2099 (1961).
47. CARLTON, B. and YANOFSKY, C. *J. Biol. Chem.* **240**, 690 (1965).
48. CARSIOTIS, M., APELLA, E., PROVOST, P., GEMERSHAUSEN, J. and SUSKIND, S. R. *Biochem. Biophys. Res. Commun.* **18**, 877 (1965).
49. CARSIOTIS, M. and SUSKIND, S. R. *J. Biol. Chem.* **239**, 4227 (1964).
50. COHEN, P. P. In *The Enzymes*, Vol. VI, p. 477, edited by P. D. Boyer, H. Lardy and K. Myrbàck, Academic Press, New York (1962).
51. COHEN, G. N. and PATTE, J. C. *Cold Spring Harbor Symp. Quant. Biol.* **28**, 513 (1963).
52. COLBURN, R. W. and TATUM, E. L. *Biochim. Biophys. Acta* **97**, 442 (1965).
53. CORONADO, A., MARDONES, E. and ALLENDE, J. E. *Biochem. Biophys. Res. Commun.* **13**, 75 (1963).
54. CRAWFORD, I. P. and ITO, J. *Proc. Natl. Acad. Sci., U.S.* **51**, 390 (1964).
55. CRAWFORD, I. P. and YANOFSKY, C. *Proc. Natl. Acad. Sci. U.S.* **44**, 1161 (1958).
56. DARLING, S. and LARSEN, P. O. *Acta Chem. Scand.* **15**, 743 (1961).
57. DAVIS, B. D. *Nature* **169**, 534 (1952).
58. DAVIS, B. D. *Science* **118**, 251 (1953).
59. DEDEKEN, R. H. *Biochem. Biophys. Res. Commun.* **8**, 462 (1962).
60. DE LA HABA, G. and CANTONI, G. L. *J. Biol. Chem.* **234**, 603 (1959).
61. DELAVIER-KLUTCHKO, C. *Federation Proc.* **22**, 234 (1963).
62. DEMOSS, J. A. *Biochem. Biophys. Res. Commun.* **18**, 850 (1965).
63. DEROBICHON-SZULMAJSTER, H. and CORRIVAUX, D. *Biochim. Biophys. Acta* **73**, 248 (1963).
64. DEROBICHON-SZULMAJSTER, H. and CORRIVAUX, D. *Biochim. Biophys. Acta* **92**, 1 (1964).
65. DEWEY, D. L. and WORK, E. *Nature* **169**, 533 (1952).
66. DONALDSON, K. O. and KERESZTESY, J. C. *J. Biol. Chem.* **237**, 1298 (1962).
67. DOY, C. H. *Biochim. Biophys. Acta* **90**, 180 (1964).
68. DOY, C. H. and GIBSON, F. *Biochem. J.* **72**, 586 (1959).

69. DOY, C. H., RIVERA, A., and SRINIVASAN, P. R. *Biochem. Biophys. Research Commun.* **4**, 83 (1961).
70. DREYFUSS, J. and MONTY, K. J. *Federation Proc.* **22**, 234 (1963).
71. DREYFUSS, J. and MONTY, K. J. *J. Biol. Chem.* **238**, 1019 (1963).
72. DREYFUSS, J. and MONTY, K. J. *J. Biol. Chem.* **238**, 3781 (1963).
73. FAHIEN, L. A. and COHEN, P. P. *J. Biol. Chem.* **239**, 1925 (1964).
74. FARKAS, W. *Federation Prooc.* **21**, 9 (1962).
75. FINCHAM, J. R. S. *Biochem. J.* **53**, 313 (1953).
76. FISCHER, G. A. *Biochim. Biophys. Acta* **25**, 50 (1957).
77. FLAVIN, M., DELAVIER-KLUTCHKO, C. and SLAUGHTER, C. *Science* **143**, 50 (1964).
78. FLAVIN, M. and SEGAL, A. *J. Biol. Chem.* **239**, 2220 (1964).
79. FLAVIN, M. and SLAUGHTER, C. *J. Biol. Chem.* **235**, 1112 (1960).
80. FLAVIN, M. and SLAUGHTER, C. *J. Biol. Chem.* **239**, 2212 (1964).
81. FLING, M. and HOROWITZ, N. H. *J. Biol. Chem.* **190**, 277 (1951).
82. FOSTER, M. A., TEJERINA, G., and WOODS, D. D. *Biochem. J.* **81**, P1 (1961).
83. FOWDEN, L. *Ann. Rev. Biochem.* **33**, 173 (1964).
84. FREUNDLICH, M. *Biochem. Biophys. Res. Commun.* **10**, 277 (1963).
85. FREUNDLICH, M., BURNS, R. O. and UMBARGER, H. E. *Proc. Natl. Acad. Sci., U.S.* **48**, 1804 (1962).
86. FRIEDKIN, M. *Ann. Rev. Biochem.* **32**, 185 (1963).
87. GARRICK, M. O., ELBERFELD, H. and SUSKIND, S. R. *Science* **145**, 491 (1964).
88. GIBSON, F. *Biochem. J.* **90**, 256 (1964).
89. GIBSON, M. I. and GIBSON, F. *Biochem. J.* **90**, 248 (1964).
90. GIBSON, F. and WOODS, D. D. *Biochem. J.* **74**, 160 (1960).
91. GIBSON, F. and YANOFSKY, C. *Biochim. Biophys. Acta* **43**, 489 (1960).
92. GILVARG, C. *J. Biol. Chem.* **237**, 482 (1962).
93. GILVARG, C. *J. Biol. Chem.* **236**, 1429 (1961).
94. GILVARG, C. and YUGARI, Y. *Biochem. Biophys. Acta* **62**, 612 (1962).
95. GILVARG, C. *Abstr. 143rd Meeting Am. Chem. Soc.*, 1963, p. 46a.
96. GORINI, L. *Bacteriol. Rev.* **27**, 182 (1963).
97. GORINI, L., GUNDERSON, W. and BURGER, M. *Cold Spring Harbor Symp. Quant. Biol.* **26**, 173 (1961).
98. GOTTLIEB, A. and UDENFRIEND, S. *Federation Proc.* **24**, 358 (1965).
99. GREGORY, J. D. and ROBBINS, P. W. *Ann. Rev. Biochem.* **29**, 347 (1960).
99a GREENBERG, D. M. *Ann. Rev. Biochem.* **33**, 633 (1964).
100. GREENBERG, D. M., NATH, R., and HUMPHREYS, G. K. *J. Biol. Chem.* **236**, 2271 (1961).
101. GROSS, S. R., BURNS, R. O. and UMBARGER, H. E. *Biochemistry* **2**, 1046 (1963).
102. GROSS, S. R., JUNGWIRTH, C., and UMBARGER, E. *Biochem. Biophys. Research Commun.* **7**, 5 (1962).
103. GUEST, J. R. and JONES, K. M. *Biochem. J.* **75**, 12P (1960).
104. GUEST, J. R. and WOODS, D. D. *Biochem. J.* **82**, 26 (1962).
105. GUEST, J. R. and YANOFSKY, C. *J. Biol. Chem.* **240**, 679 (1965).
106. HALPERN, Y. S. and UMBARGER, H. E. *J. Biol. Chem.* **234**, 3067 (1959).
107. HARDMAN, J. K. and YANOFSKY, C. *J. Biol. Chem.* **240**, 725 (1965).
108. HATCH, F. T., CATHOU, R. E., and LARRABEE, A. R. *Federation Proc.* **19**, 417 (1960).
109. HATCH, F. T., LARRABEE, A. R., CATHOU, R. E., and BUCHANAN, J. M. *J. Biol. Chem.* **236**, 1095 (1961).
110. HATCH, F. T., TAKEYAMA, S., CATHOU, R. E., LARRABEE, A. R., and BUCHANAN, J. M. *J. Am. Chem. Soc.* **81**, 6525 (1959).
111. HEDRICK, J. L. and SALLACH, H. J. *Biochim. Biophys. Acta* **41**, 531 (1960).
112. HELLEINER, C. W. and WOODS, D. D. *Biochem. J.* **63**, 26P (1956).
113. HENNING, U., HELINSKI, D. R., CHAO, F. C. and YANOFSKY, C. *J. Biol. Chem.* **237**, 1523 (1962).
114. HIRATA, M., TOKUSHIGE, M., INAGAKI, A. and HAYAISHI, O. *J. Biol. Chem.* **240**, 1711 (1965).
115. HODGE, J. E. In *Advances in Carbohydrate Chem.* **10**, 169 (1955).
116. HOLDSWORTH, E. S. *Biochim. Biophys. Acta* **9**, 19 (1952).

117. HUENNEKENS, F. M., HATEFI, Y., and KAY, L. D. *J. Biol. Chem.* **224**, 435 (1957).
118. ICHIHARA, A. and GREENBERG, D. M. *J. Biol. Chem.* **224**, 331 (1957).
119. ICHIHARA, A. and GREENBERG, D. M. *J. Biol. Chem.* **225**, 949 (1957).
120. JACKSON, D. S., WATKINS, D. and WINKLER, A. *Biochim. Biophys. Acta* **87**, 152 (1964).
121. JAENICKE, L. *Ann. Rev. Biochem.* **33**, 287 (1964).
122. JOHNSON, A. B. and STRECKER, H. J. *J. Biol. Chem.* **237**, 1876 (1962).
124. JONES, E. E., ORTIGOZA-FERADO, J. A. and VOGEL, H. J. *Federation Proc.* **24**, 416 (1965).
125. JONES, E. E. and SAUNDERS, P. P. *Federation Proc.* **22**, 243 (1963).
126. JUNGWIRTH, C., GROSS, S. R., MARGOLIN, P. and UMBARGER, H. E. *Biochemistry* **2**, 1 (1963).
127. JUNGWIRTH, C., MARGOLIN, P., UMBARGER, E., and GROSS, S. R. *Biochem. Biophys. Research Commun.* **5**, 435 (1961).
128 JUNGWIRTH, C. and UMBARGER, H. E. *Federation Proc.* **21**, 10 (1962).
129. KANAMORI, M. and WIXOM, R. L. *J. Biol. Chem.* **238**, 998 (1963).
130. KAPLAN, A., WITKOP, B. and UDENFRIEND, S. *J. Biol. Chem.* **239**, 2559 (1964).
131. KARASEK, M. A. and GREENBERG, D. M. *J. Biol. Chem.* **227**, 191 (1957).
132. KARASSEVITCH, Y. and DeROBICHON-SZULMAJSTER, H. *Biochim. Biophys. Acta* **73**, 414 (1963).
133. KATAGIRI, M. and SATO, R. *Science* **118**, 250 (1953).
134. KATZ, E., PROCKOP, D. J. and UDENFRIEND, S. *J. Biol. Chem.* **237**, 1585 (1962).
135. KATZEN, H. M. and BUCHANAN, J. M. *J. Biol. Chem.* **240**, 825 (1965).
136. KEMP, J. D., ATKINSON, D. E., EHRET, A. and LAZZARINI, R. A. *J. Biol. Chem.* **238**, 3466 (1963).
137. KINDLER, S. H. and GILVARG, C. *J. Biol. Chem.* **235**, 3532 (1960).
138. KISLIUK, R. L. *Federation Proc.* **19**, 416 (1960).
139. KISLIUK, R. L. and WOODS, D. D. *Biochem. J.* **75**, 467 (1960).
140. KJAER, A. and LARSEN, P. O. *Acta Chem. Scand.* **15**, 750 (1961).
141. KLOPTOWSKI, T., LUZZATI, M., and SLONIMSKI, P. P. *Biochem. Biophys. Research Commun.* **3**, 150 (1960).
142. KREISER, T. H., *Ph.D. Thesis, University of Nebraska* (1964).
143. KRETSINGER, R. H., MANNER, G., GOULD, B. S. and RICH, A. *Nature* **202**, 438 (1965).
144. KUO, M. M., SAUNDERS, P. P., and BROQUIST, H. P. *Federation Proc.* **21**, 9 (1962).
145. KUO, M. H., SAUNDERS, P. P., and BROQUIST, H. P. *J. Biol. Chem.* **239**, 508 (1964).
146. LAMPORT, D. T. A. *J. Biol. Chem.* **238**, 1438 (1963).
147. LARRABEE, A. R., ROSENTHAL, S., CATHOU, R. E., and BUCHANAN, J. M. *J. Am. Chem. Soc.* **83**, 4094 (1961).
148. LARRABEE, A. R., ROSENTHAL, S., CATHOU, R. E. and BUCHANAN, J. M. *J. Biol. Chem.* **238**, 1025 (1963).
149. LARSON, R. L., SANDINE, W. D. and BROQUIST, H. P. *J. Biol. Chem.* **238**, 275 (1963).
150. LEAVITT, R. I. and UMBARGER, H. E. *J. Biol. Chem.* **236**, 2486 (1961).
151. LEINWEBER, F. and MONTY, K. J. *J. Biol. Chem.* **238**, 3775 (1963).
152. LEINWEBER, F. and MONTY, K. J. *J. Biol. Chem.* **240**, 782 (1965).
153. LEVIN, J. G., and SPRINSON, D. B. *Biochem. Biophys. Research Commun.* **3**, 157 (1960).
154. LEVIN, J. G. and SPRINSON, D. B. *J. Biol. Chem.* **239**, 1142 (1964).
155. LOUGHLIN, R. E., ELFORD, H. L. and BUCHANAN, J. M. *J. Biol. Chem.* **239**, 2888 (1964).
156. LOPER, J. C. and ADAMS, E. *J. Biol. Chem.* **240**, 788 (1965).
157. LOPER, J. C., GRABNAR, M., STAHL, R. C., HARTMAN, Z. and HARTMAN, P. E. *Brookhaven Symposia in Biology*, vol. 17, p. 15, Brookhaven National Laboratory, Upton, New York (1964).
158. LUKENS, L. N. *J. Biol. Chem.* **240**, 1661 (1965).
159. LYNEN, F. and SCHLOSSMANN, K. *Angew. Chem.* **69**, 179 (1957).
160. MAAS, W. K. *Cold Spring Harbor Symp. Quant. Biol.* **26**, 183 (1961).
161. MAGASANIK, B. and KARIBIAN, D. *J. Biol. Chem.* **235**, 2672 (1960).
162. MANGUM, J. H. and SCRIMGEOUR, K. G. *Federation Proc.* **21**, 242 (1962).
163. MANNER, G. and GOULD, B. S. *Biochim. Biophys. Acta* **72**, 243 (1963).
164. MARSHALL, M., METZENBERG, R. L. and COHEN, P. P. *J. Biol. Chem.* **233**, 102 (1958).
165. MARUSHIGE, K., YURA, T. and IMAI, M. *Biochim. Biophys. Acta* **87**, 90 (1964).

166. MARTIN, R. G. *J. Biol. Chem.* **238**, 257 (1963).
167. MATSUO, Y. and GREENBERG, D. M. *J. Biol. Chem.* **234**, 507 (1959).
168. MATSUO, Y. and GREENBERG, D. M. *J. Biol. Chem.* **234**, 516 (1959).
169. MATTOON, J. R. and HAIGHT, R. D. *J. Biol. Chem.* **237**, 3486 (1962).
170. MATTOON, J. R. and MOSHIER, T. A. *Federation Proc.* **20**, 10 (1961).
171. MATTOON, J. R., MOSHIER, T. A. and KREISER, T. H. *Biochim. Biophys. Acta* **51**, 615 (1961).
172. McCORMICK, J. R. D., REICHENTHAL, J., HIRSCH, U. and SJOLANDER, N. O. *J. Am. Chem. Soc.* **84**, 3711 (1962).
173. MEISTER, A. *J. Biol. Chem.* **206**, 587 (1954).
174. MEISTER, A. In *Advances in Enzymol.* **16**, 185 (1955).
175. MEISTER, A., *Biochemistry of the Amino Acids*, 2nd edition, p. 338, Academic Press, New York (1965).
176. Op. cit., p. 340.
177. Op. cit., p. 934.
178. MEISTER, A. and BUCKLEY, S. D. *Biochim. Biophys. Acta* **23**, 202 (1957).
179. MEISTER, A., RADHAKRISHNAN, A. N., and BUCKLEY, S. D. *J. Biol. Chem.* **229**, 789 (1957).
180. METZLER, D. E. In *The Enzymes*, 2nd ed., vol. 2, p. 334, edited by F. D. Boyer, H. Lardy, and K. Myrback. Academic Press, New York, 1960.
181. MEYERS, J. W. and ADELBERG, E. A. *Proc. Natl. Acad. Sci. U.S.* **40**, 493 (1954).
182. MITCHELL, H. K. and HOULAHAN, M. B. *J. Biol. Chem.* **174**, 883 (1948).
183. MITSUHASHI, S. and DAVIS, B. D. *Biochim. Biophys. Acta* **15**, 54 (1954).
184. MONDOVI, B., SCIOSCIA-SANTORO, A. and CAVALLINI, D. *Arch. Biochem. Biophys.* **101**, 363 (1963).
185. MOYED, H. S. and MAGASANIK, B. *J. Biol. Chem.* **235**, 149 (1960).
186. MUDD, S. H. *J. Biol. Chem.* **234**, 87 (1959).
187. MUDD, S. H. *J. Biol. Chem.* **234**, 1784 (1959).
188. MUDD, S. H. and CANTONI, G. L. *J. Biol. Chem.* **231**, 481 (1958).
189. MYERS, J. W. *J. Biol. Chem.* **236**, 1414 (1961).
190. NAKAMURA, T. and SATO, R. *Biochem. J.* **86**, 328 (1963).
191. NAKAO, A. and GREENBERG, D. M. *J. Biol. Chem.* **230**, 603 (1958).
192. NEIDLE, A. and WAELSCH, H. *J. Biol. Chem.* **234**, 586 (1959).
193. NEUHAUS, F. C. and BYRNE, W. L. *J. Biol. Chem.* **234**, 113 (1959).
194. NYC, J., and ZABIN, F. *J. Biol. Chem.* **215**, 35 (1955).
195. OGLE, J. D., ARLINGHAUS, R. B. and LOGAN, M. A. *J. Biol. Chem.* **237**, 3667 (1962).
196. OGUR, M., ROSHANMANESH, A. and OGUR, S. *Science* **147**, 1590 (1965).
197. OOYAMA, J. *Rept. Ferment. Inst.* **20**, 95 (1961).
198. PARKS, L. W. *J. Am. Chem. Soc.* **80**, 2023 (1958).
199. PARKS, L. W. *J. Biol. Chem.* **232**, 169 (1958).
200. PARKS, L. W. and DOUGLAS, H. C. *Biochim. Biophys. Acta* **23**, 207 (1957).
201. PATTE, J. C., LEBRAS, G., LOVINY, T. and COHEN, G. N. *Biochim. Biophys. Acta* **67**, 16 (1963).
202. PATTE, J., LOVINY, T., and COHEN, G. N. *Biochim. Biophys. Acta* **58**, 359 (1962).
203. PAULUS, H. and GRAY, E. *J. Biol. Chem.* **239**, PC 4008 (1964).
204. PEISACH, J. and STRECKER, H. J. *J. Biol. Chem.* **237**, 2255 (1962).
205. PERAINO, C. and PITOT, H. C. *J. Biol. Chem.* **239**, 4308 (1964).
206. PERRY, J. J. and FOSTER, J. W. *J. Bacteriol.* **69**, 337 (1955).
207. PETERKOFSKY, B. and GILVARG, C. *J. Biol. Chem.* **236**, 1432 (1961).
208. PETERKOFSKY, B. and UDENFRIEND, B. *Proc. Natl. Acad. Sci., U.S.* **53**, 335 (1965).
209. PETERS, J. M. and GREENBERG, D. M. *J. Am. Chem. Soc.* **80**, 6679 (1958).
210. PITOT, H. C. and PERAINO, C. *J. Biol. Chem.* **239**, 1783 (1964).
211. PITTARD, A. J., GIBSON, F. and DOY, C. H. *Biochim. Biophys. Acta* **57**, 290 (1962).
212. PIZER, L. I. *J. Biol. Chem.* **239**, 4219 (1964).
213. POWELL, J. F. and STRANGE, R. E. *Nature* **184**, 878 (1959).
214. PROCKOP, D. J. and JUVA, K. *Proc. Natl. Acad. Sci., U.S.* **53**, 661 (1965).
215. PROCKOP, D., KAPLAN, A. and UDENFRIEND, S. *Biochem. Biophys. Res. Commun.* **9**, 162 (1962).

216. RABSON, R., TOLBERT, N. E. and KEARNEY, P. C. *Arch. Biochem. Biophys.* **98**, 154 (1962).
217. RADHAKRISHNAN, A. N. and SNELL, E. E. *J. Biol. Chem.* **235**, 2316 (1960).
218. RADHAKRISHNAN, A. N., WAGNER, R. P., and SNELL, E. E. *J. Biol. Chem.* **235**, 2322 (1960).
219. RAFELSON, M. E., JR. *Arch. Biochem. Biophys.* **72**, 376 (1957).
220. RAMOS, F., STALON, V., PIERARD, A. and WIAME, J. M. *Arch. Intern. Physiol. Biochem.* **73**, 155 (1965).
221. REMY, C. N. *J. Biol. Chem.* **234**, 1485 (1959).
222. ROBERTSON, W. and HEWITT, J. *Biochim. Biophys. Acta* **49**, 404 (1961).
223. ROBERTSON, W., HEWITT, J., and HERMAN, C. *J. Biol. Chem.* **234**, 105 (1959).
224. ROSENTHAL, S. and BUCHANAN, J. M. *Federation Proc.* **21**, 470 (1962).
225. ROSENTHAL, S., SMITH, L. C. and BUCHANAN, J. M. *J. Biol. Chem.* **240**, 836 (1965).
226. ROTHSTEIN, M. and SAFFRAN, E. M. *Arch. Biochem. Biophys.* **101**, 373 (1963).
227. ROWBURY, R. J. *J. Gen. Microbiol.* **28**, V (1962).
228. SAGISAKA, S. and SHIMURA, K. *Nature* **184**, 1709 (1959).
229. SAGISAKA, S. and SHIMURA, K. *Nature* **188**, 1189 (1961).
230. SAGISAKA, S. and SHIMURA, K. *J. Biochem.* (*Tokyo*) **51**, 27 (1962).
231. SAGISAKA, S. and SHIMURA, K. *J. Biochem.* (*Tokyo*) **52**, 155 (1962).
232. SAKAMI, W. and HARRINGTON, H. *Ann. Rev. Biochem.* **32**, 355 (1963).
233. SALLACH, H. J. In *Amino Acid Metabolism*, p. 182, edited by W. D. McElroy and B. Glass, The Johns Hopkins Press, Baltimore, 1955.
234. SAUNDERS, P. P., JONES, E. E. and BROQUIST, H. P. *Federation Proc.* **23**, 313 (1964).
235. SCHER, W. I. and VOGEL, H. J. *Proc. Natl. Acad. Sci. U.S.* **43**, 796 (1957).
236. SCHIRCH, L. V. and JENKINS, T. W. *J. Biol. Chem.* **239**, 3797 (1964).
237. SCHIRCH, L. G. and MASON, M. *J. Biol. Chem.* **238**, 1032 (1963).
238. SCHLOSSMAN, K., BRÜGGEMANN, J. and LYNEN, F. *Biochem. Z.* **336**, 258 (1962).
239. SCHWARTZ, A. K. and BONNER, D. M. *Biochim. Biophys. Acta* **89**, 337 (1964).
240. SCHWINK, I. and ADAMS, E. *Biochim. Biophys. Acta* **36**, 102 (1959).
241. SELIM, A. S. M. and GREENBERG, D. M. *J. Biol. Chem.* **234**, 1474 (1959).
242. SELIM, A. S. M. and GREENBERG, D. M. *Biochim. Biophys. Acta* **42**, 211 (1960).
243. SHAPIRO, S. K. *Biochim. Biophys. Acta* **29**, 405 (1958).
244. SHEDLOVSKY, A. E. and MAGASANIK, B. *J. Biol. Chem.* **237**, 3731 (1962).
245. SHEDLOVSKY, A. E. and MAGASANIK, B. *J. Biol. Chem.* **237**, 3725 (1962).
246. SIEGEL, L. M., CLICK, E. M. and MONTY, K. J. *Biochem. Biophys. Res. Commun.* **17**, 125 (1964).
247. SIEGEL, L. M. and MONTY, K. J. *Biochem. Biophys. Res. Commun.* **17**, 201 (1964).
248. SMITH, A. D. and STRECKER, H. J. *Federation Proc.* **23**, 313 (1964).
249. SMITH, D. W. E. and AMES, B. N. *J. Biol. Chem.* **239**, 1848 (1964).
250. SMITH, M. E. and GREENBERG, D. M. *J. Biol. Chem.* **226**, 317 (1957).
251. SMITH, O. H. and YANOFSKY, C. *J. Biol. Chem.* **235**, 2051 (1960).
252. SOMERSON, N. L., DEMAIN, A. L. and NUNHEIMER, T. D., *Arch. Biochem. Biophys.* **93**, 238 (1961).
253. SPEYER, J. F. and DICKMAN, S. R. *J. Biol. Chem.* **220**, 193 (1956).
253a SRB, A. M. and HOROWITZ, N. H. *J. Biol. Chem.* **154**, 129 (1944).
254. SRINIVASAN, P. R., KATAGIRI, M., and SPRINSON, D. B. *J. Biol. Chem.* **234**, 713 (1959).
255. SRINIVASAN, P. R., ROTHSCHILD, J. and SPRINSON, D. B. *J. Biol. Chem.* **238**, 3176 (1963).
256. SRINIVASAN, P. R. and SPRINSON, D. B. *J. Biol. Chem.* **234**, 761 (1959).
257. STADTMAN, E. R. *Bacteriol. Rev.* **27**, 170 (1963).
258. STADTMAN, E. R., COHEN, G. N., LEBRAS, G., and DE ROBICHON-SZULMAJSTER, H. *J. Biol. Chem.* **236**, 2033 (1961).
259. STADTMAN, E. R., COHEN, G. N., LEBRAS, G. and DEROBICHON-SZULMAJSTER, H. *Cold Spring Harbor Symp. Quant. Biol.* **26**, 319 (1961).
260. STAFFORD, H. A., MAGALDI, A., and VENNESLAND, B. *J. Biol. Chem.* **207**, 621 (1954).
261. STERN, J. R. and FRIEDMAN, D. L. *Biochem. Biophys. Research Commun.* **2**, 82 (1960).
262. STETTEN, M. R. *J. Biol. Chem.* **181**, 31 (1949).
263. STEVENS, A. and SAKAMI, W. *J. Biol. Chem.* **234**, 2063 (1959).

264. STRASSMAN, M. and CECI, L. N. *Federation Proc.* **21**, 10 (1962).
265. STRASSMAN, M. and CECI, L. *Biochem. Biophys. Res. Commun.* **14**, 262 (1964).
266. STRASSMAN, M., CECI, L. N. and MARAGOUDAKIS, M. E. *Federation Proc.* **24**, 228 (1965).
267. STRASSMAN, M., CECI, L. N. and SILVERMAN, B. E. *Biochem. Biophys. Res. Commun.* **14**, 268 (1964).
268. STRASSMAN, M., LOCKE, L. A., THOMAS, A. J., and WEINHOUSE, S. *J. Am. Chem. Soc.* **78**, 1599 (1956).
269. STRASSMAN, M., SHATTON, J. B., and WEINHOUSE, S. *J. Biol. Chem.* **235**, 700 (1960).
270. STRASSMAN, M., THOMAS, A. J., and WEINHOUSE, S. *J. Am. Chem. Soc.* **75**, 5135 (1953).
271. STRASSMAN, M. and WEINHOUSE, S. *J. Am. Chem. Soc.* **75**, 1680 (1953).
272. STRECKER, H. J. *J. Biol. Chem.* **235**, 2045 (1960).
273. STRECKER, H. J. *J. Biol. Chem.* **235**, 3218 (1960).
274. STRECKER, H. J. *J. Biol. Chem.* **240**, 1225 (1965).
275. SUSKIND, S. R. and JORDON, E. *Science* **129**, 1614 (1959).
276. SZULMAJSTER, J. and WOODS, D. D. *Biochem. J.* **75**, 3 (1960).
277. TABOR, H., ROSENTHAL, S. M., and TABOR, C. W. *J. Biol. Chem.* **233**, 907 (1958).
278. TAKEYAMA, S., HATCH, F. T., and BUCHANAN, J. M. *J. Biol. Chem.* **236**, 1102 (1961).
279. TAKEYAMA, S. and BUCHANAN, J. M. *Federation Proc.* **19**, 417 (1960).
280. TAMURA, G. *J. Biochem.* (*Tokyo*) **57**, 207 (1965).
281. TANENBAUM, S. W. and KANEKO, K. *Biochemistry* **3**, 1314 (1964).
282. TATUM, E. L. and BONNER, J. *Proc. Natl. Acad. Sci. U.S.* **30**, 30 (1944).
283. TEAS, H. J., HOROWITZ, N. H., and FLING, M. *J. Biol. Chem.* **172**, 651 (1948).
284. TEMPLE, R. J., UMBARGER, H. E. and MAGASANIK, B. *J. Biol. Chem.* **240**, 1219 (1965).
285. TOENNIES, G. *J. Biol. Chem.* **132**, 455 (1940).
285a TOLBERT, N. E. and COHAN, M. S. *J. Biol. Chem.* **204**, 649 (1953).
286. TORII, K. and BANDURSKI, R. S. *Biochem. Biophys. Res. Commun.* **14**, 537 (1964).
287. TROWN, P. W., SHARP, M. and ABRAHAM, E. P. *Biochem. J.* **86**, 280 (1963).
288. TROWN, P. W., SMITH, B. and ABRAHAM, E. P. *Biochem. J.* **86**, 284 (1963).
289. UMBARGER, H. E. *Biochem. Biophys. Res. Commun.* **18**, 889 (1965).
290. UMBARGER, H. E. and ADELBERG, E. A. *J. Biol. Chem.* **192**, 883 (1951).
291. UMBARGER, H. E. and BROWN, B. *J. Bacteriol.* **73**, 105 (1957).
292. UMBARGER, H. E. and BROWN, B. *J. Biol. Chem.* **233**, 415 (1957).
293. UMBARGER, H. E., BROWN, B., and EYRING, E. J. *J. Biol. Chem.* **235**, 1425 (1960).
294. UMBARGER, H. E. and UMBARGER, M. A. *Biochim. Biophys. Acta.* **62**, 193 (1962).
295. UMBARGER, H. E., UMBARGER, M. A. and SIU, P. M. L. *J. Bacteriol.* **85**, 1431 (1963).
296. UMBREIT, W. W., WOOD, W. A., and GUNSALUS, I. C., *J. Biol. Chem.* **165**, 731 (1946).
297. VAUGHAN, S. T. and BROQUIST, H. P. *Federation Proc.* **24**, 218 (1965).
298. VAVRA, J. J. and JOHNSON, M. J. *J. Biol. Chem.* **220**, 33 (1956).
299. VENKATARAMAN, R. and GREENBERG, D. M. *J. Am. Chem. Soc.* **80**, 2025 (1958).
300. VOGEL, H. J. *Proc. Natl. Acad. Sci. U.S.* **39**, 578 (1953).
301. VOGEL, H. J. *Proc. 5th Intern. Congr. Biochem., Moscow*, Vol. 3, p. 341 (1963).
302. VOGEL, H. J., BACON, D. F. and BAICH, A. In *Informational Macromolecules*, p. 293, edited by H. J. Vogel, V. Bryson and J. O. Lampen, Academic Press, New York (1963).
302a VOGEL, H. J., ABELSON, P. H., and BOLTON, E. T. *Biochim. Biophys. Acta* **11**, 584 (1954).
302b VOGEL, H. J. and ALBRECHT, A. M. *Federation Proc.* **19**, 2 (1960).
303. VOGEL, H. J. and BONNER, D. M. *Proc. Natl. Acad. Sci. U.S.* **40**, 688 (1954).
304. VOGEL, R. H. and KOPAC, M. J. *Biochim. Biophys. Acta* **36**, 505 (1959).
305. VOGEL, R. H. and KOPAC, M. J. *Biochim. Biophys. Acta* **37**, 539 (1960).
306. VYAS, S. and MAAS, W. K. *Arch. Biochem. Biophys.* **100**, 542 (1963).
307. WAGNER, R. P. and BERGQUIST, A. *Genetics* **45**, 1375 (1960).
308. WAGNER, R. P., BERGQUIST, A., and FORREST, H. S. *J. Biol. Chem.* **234**, 99 (1959).
309. WAGNER, R. P., RADHAKRISHNAN, A. N., and SNELL, E. E. *Proc. Natl. Acad. Sci. U.S.* **44**, 1047 (1958).
310. WAHBA, A. J. and FRIEDKIN, M. *J. Biol. Chem.* **236**, PC11 (1961).
311. WAINWRIGHT, T. *Biochem. J.* **83**, 39 P (1962).

312. WAINWRIGHT, S. D. and CHAN, E. *Biochem. Biophys. Res. Commun.* **18**, 775 (1965).
313. WALDSCHMITT, M. *Biochem. Z.* **335**, 400 (1962).
314. WATANABE, Y., KONISHI, S., and SHIMURA, K. *J. Biochem.* (*Tokyo*) **44**, 299 (1957).
315. WATANABE, Y. and SHIMURA, K. *J. Biochem.* (*Tokyo*) **47**, 226 (1960).
316. WEBER, M. A., HOAGLAND, A. N., KLEIN, J. and LEWIS, K. *Arch. Biochem. Biophys.* **104**, 257 (1964).
317. WEISS, U. and GILVARG, C. *Science* **119**, 774 (1954).
318. WEISS, U. and MINGIOLI, E. S. *J. Am. Chem. Soc.* **78**, 2894 (1956).
319. WEISSBACH, H., LADD, J. N., VOLCANI, B. E., SMYTH, R. D., and BARKER, H. A. *J. Biol. Chem.* **235**, 1462 (1960).
320. WEISSBACH, H., REDFIELD, B., DICKERMAN, H. and BROT, N. *J. Biol. Chem.* **240**, 856 (1965).
321. WHITFIELD, H. J., JR., SMITH, D. W. E. and MARTIN, R. G. *J. Biol. Chem.* **239**, 3288 (1964).
322. WILLIS, J. E. and SALLACH, H. J. *Phytochemistry* **2**, 23 (1963).
323. WILLIS, J. E. and SALLACH, H. J. *Biochim. Biophys. Acta* **81**, 39 (1964).
323a WILLIS, J. E. and SALLACH, H. J. *J. Biol. Chem.* **237**, 910 (1962).
324. WINDSOR, E. *J. Biol. Chem.* **192**, 607 (1951).
325. WIXOM, R. L., SHATTON, J. B., and STRASSMAN, M. *J. Biol. Chem.* **235**, 128 (1960).
326. WOLF, G. and BERGER, C. R. A. *J. Biol. Chem.* **230**, 231 (1958).
327. WORK, E. and DEWEY, D. L. *J. Gen. Microbiol.* **9**, 394 (1953).
328. WORMSER, E. H. and PARDEE, A. B. *Arch. Biochem.* **78**, 416 (1958).
329. YANIV, H. and GILVARG, C. *J. Biol. Chem.* **213**, 787 (1955).
330. YANOFSKY, C. *Biochim. Biophys. Acta* **16**, 594 (1955).
331. YANOFSKY, C. *Biochim. Biophys. Acta* **20**, 438 (1956).
332. YANOFSKY, C. *Biochim. Biophys. Acta* **31**, 408 (1959).
333. YANOFSKY, C. *Bacteriol. Revs.* **24**, 221 (1960).
334. YANOFSKY, C. *Biochem. Biophys. Res. Commun.* **18**, 898 (1965).
335. YANOFSKY, C. and RACHMELER, M. *Biochim. Biophys. Acta* **28**, 640 (1958).
336. YOSHIDA, H. and EGAMI, F. *J. Biochem.* (*Tokyo*) **57**, 215 (1965).
337. YUGARI, Y. *Federation Proc.* **21**, 10 (1962).
338. YURA, T. and VOGEL, H. J. *Biochim. Biophys. Acta* **17**, 582 (1955).

CHAPTER 2

THE BIOGENESIS OF PURINE AND PYRIMIDINE NUCLEOTIDES

ARMAND J. GUARINO

Department of Biochemistry, Woman's Medical College of Pennsylvania,
Philadelphia, Pa.

CONTENTS

I. INTRODUCTION   45
II. BIOGENESIS OF NUCLEOTIDE SUGARS   51
   A. *Ribose phosphate*   51
   B. *D-2-Deoxyribose phosphate*   56
III. BIOGENESIS OF PURINE NUCLEOSIDE MONOPHOSPHATES   59
   A. De novo *pathway to inosinic acid*   59
   B. *Biogenesis of adenylic acid from inosinic acid*   66
   C. *Biogenesis of guanylic acid from inosinic acid*   67
   D. *Utilization of preformed purines*   68
   E. *Biogenesis of purine deoxyribonucleotides*   70
IV. BIOGENESIS OF PYRIMIDINE NUCLEOSIDE MONOPHOSPHATES   71
   A. De novo *synthesis to uridylic acid*   71
   B. *Amination of uridylic acid to cytidylic acid*   75
   C. *Other pathways of pyrimidine synthesis*   76
   D. *Utilization of preformed pyrimidines*   76
   E. *Biogenesis of pyrimidine deoxyribonucleotides*   77
V. SYNTHESIS OF DI- AND TRIPHOSPHATE DERIVATIVES OF
   NUCLEOSIDES   78
VI. BIOGENESIS OF OTHER NUCLEOTIDES   80
   SUMMARY   96
   REFERENCES   96

I. INTRODUCTION

The importance of purine and pyrimidine nucleotides as components and structural units of the nucleic acids has been recognized for many years. One of the important chemical properties of these high molecular weight compounds, the biosynthesis of which is discussed in Chapter 8 of this book, is their precipitability or insolubility in acidic solution. Free nucleotides of low molecular weight also exist in tissues and cells in a form termed the "acid-soluble fraction". This chapter will deal, for the most part, with the biogenesis of those nucleotides which are solubilized by extraction of tissues with reagents such as cold trichloroacetic acid or 70 per cent ethanol. This will include the biological precursors to the nucleic acids such as AMP, GMP, UMP, and CMP, their di- and triphosphate derivatives as well as the corresponding deoxyribonucleotides.

It is recognized that the nucleotides do not only assume importance with regard to their participation in nucleic acid structure, but that they have more diversified roles, in some instances as coenzymes in enzyme catalyzed reactions, and in other instances as portions of complex substrate molecules. Therefore the second major part of this chapter will deal with the biogenesis of those nucleotides which have functions other than that of precursors to nucleic acids.

In a discussion of nucleotide biogenesis, we must be concerned with the pathways of reactions by which pentose phosphate is formed, as well as with the mechanisms by which the synthesis of the two heterocyclic ring systems, pyrimidine and purine, is achieved. The nucleotides we are going to discuss have the typical structure outlined below.

Purine nucleotide   Pyrimidine nucleotide

In most instances, the purine is either adenine or guanine, although purine nucleotides containing xanthine or hypoxanthine also assume importance in the biosynthetic reactions leading to the *de novo* formation of adenine and guanine. In addition other purines have been obtained from natural sources such as methylated purines, free purine, as well as higher oxidized forms of the purine ring such as uric acid. The biogenesis of these latter few compounds will not be discussed here. The purines, in almost every instance, are linked to the sugar at position 9 of the purine ring and through a β-N-glycosidic bond.

In the case of the pyrimidines, cytosine, uracil, and thymine are perhaps the most important ones. Cytosine and uracil are the pyrimidine constituents of RNA while cytosine and thymine are the major constituents of DNA. Although these are not the only pyrimidine compounds found in nature, they

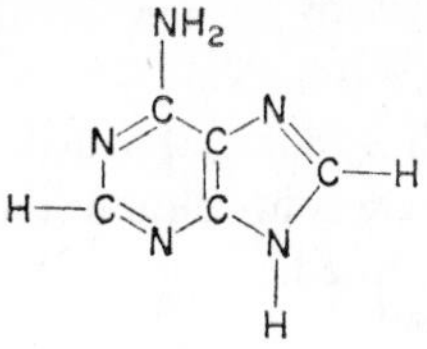

Adenine

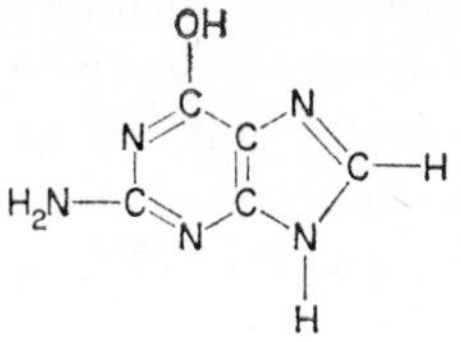

Guanine

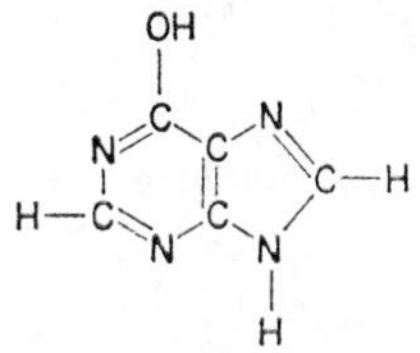

Hypoxanthine

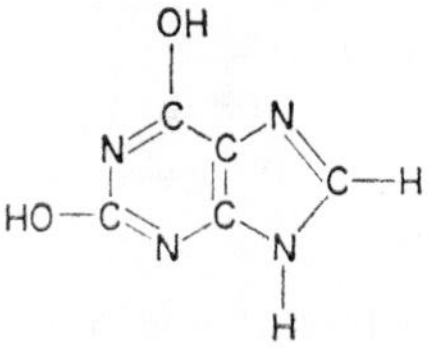

Xanthine

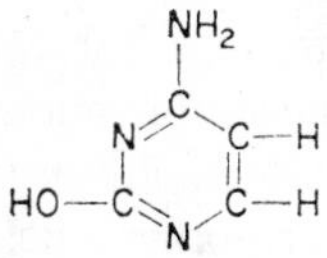

Cytosine

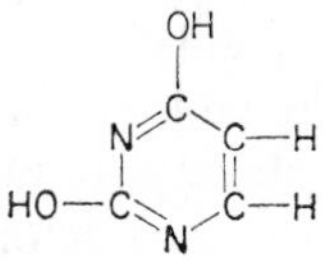

Uracil

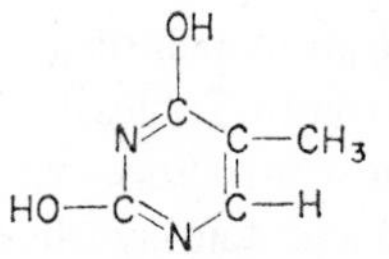

Thymine

are the major ones with which we shall be concerned. Others, such as hydroxy-methyl cytosine, a constituent of certain types of DNA, and orotic acid, an intermediate in pyrimidine biogenesis, will also be discussed. The sugar moiety is attached at position 1 of the pyrimidine ring through a β-N-glyco-sidic linkage.

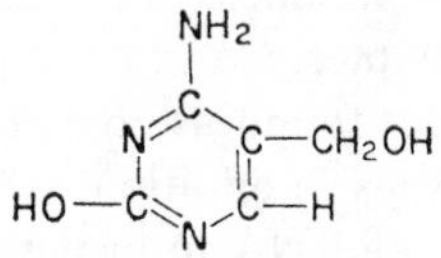

Hydroxymethyl
cytosine

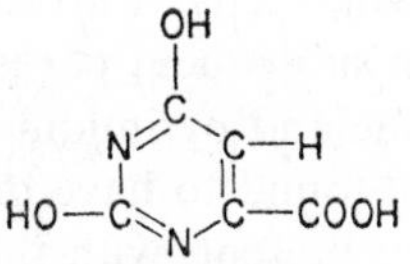

Orotic acid

The sugars present in the nucleotides to be discussed are D-ribose and D-2-deoxyribose. In the typical nucleotide, the sugar is linked to the purine or pyrimidine ring through the anomeric carbon atom, and, in almost every instance, is of the β-configuration.

The position of the phosphate ester on the sugar moiety of the nucleotide depends on the mode of isolation of the latter. In the acid-soluble fraction of tissues, the phosphate is usually at the 5 position. Nucleotides isolated from alkaline hydrolyzates of RNA have the phosphate esterified to the 2 or 3 position of the sugar. In addition, 2′, 3′ cyclic phosphodiesters of the ribonucleotides have also been isolated and identified.

D – ribose   D – 2 – deoxyribose

In the case of D-2-deoxyribose, only the 3 and 5 positions are available for ester formation. The deoxyribonucleotides in the acid-soluble fraction from tissues have the phosphate esterified to the 5 position of the sugar. Specific phosphodiesterases, however, will hydrolyze DNA to mononucleotides containing the phosphate esterified to the 3′-position.

The nomenclature of the nucleotides and their customary abbreviations are given in Tables 1 and 2. These tables include only the simple nucleotides, i.e. those structures which, at some stage of their metabolism, are precursors to nucleic acid synthesis. As mentioned before, there are other nucleotides which serve important roles in metabolism and which are of a highly diversified chemical composition. Combinations between nucleotides and certain vitamins, for instance, are known to be of utmost importance.

In fact, it may be taken as a generalization that the major role certain vitamins assume in metabolism, is their participation in enzyme-catalyzed reactions where they are part of coenzymes. Many nucleotides contain, in addition to their basic nucleotide structure, another sugar and, as we shall see below, these substances play a role in sugar interconversions and transfers within living cells. Further diversity in nucleotide structure will be brought out in subsequent pages of this chapter.

All the purine and pyrimidine nucleotides found as constituents of RNA have also been found to have other functions in addition. Although we are preoccupied, at present, with the function of RNA in protein synthesis, we should perhaps consider another of its not less important functions, i.e. its possible role as a storehouse for nucleotides required for synthesis of other nucleotides.[238] When the need arises for a given nucleotide, RNA could be broken down through phosphorolysis to provide the required compound. Since nucleotides play such an important part in enzyme-catalyzed reactions, the availability of nucleotides could be a means of controlling metabolic reactions. The release of these nucleotides from RNA might be important in this regard.

TABLE 1. RIBONUCLEOSIDE AND RIBONUCLEOTIDE NOMENCLATURE

| | | | Abbreviations | | |
| | | | Nucleotide | | |
Name of base	Name of nucleoside	Name of nucleotide	Mono-phosphate	Di-phosphate	Tri-phosphate
PURINES					
Adenine	Adenosine	Adenylic acid or Adenosine-5'-phosphate	AMP	ADP	ATP
Guanine	Guanosine	Guanylic acid or Guanosine-5'-phosphate	GMP	GDP	GTP
Hypoxanthine	Inosine	Inosinic acid or Inosine-5'-phosphate	IMP	IDP	ITP
Xanthine	Xanthosine	Xanthylic acid or Xanthosine-5'-phosphate	XMP	—	—
PYRIMIDINES					
Cytosine	Cytidine	Cytidylic acid or Cytidine-5'-phosphate	CMP	CDP	CTP
Uracil	Uridine	Uridylic acid or Uridine-5'-phosphate	UMP	UDP	UTP
Orotic Acid	Orotidine	Orotidylic acid or Orotidine-5'-phosphate	—	—	—

TABLE 2. DEOXYRIBONUCLEOSIDE AND DEOXYRIBONUCLEOTIDE NOMENCLATURE

Name of base	Name of nucleoside	Name of nucleotide	Abbreviations		
			Nucleotide		
			Mono-phosphate	Di-phosphate	Tri-phosphate
PURINES					
Adenine	Deoxyadenosine	Deoxyadenylic acid or Deoxyadenosine-5′-phosphate	dAMP	dADP	dATP
Guanine	Deoxyguanosine	Deoxyguanylic acid or Deoxyguanosine-5′-phosphate	dGMP	dGDP	dGTP
PYRIMIDINES					
Cytosine	Deoxycytidine	Deoxycytidylic acid or Deoxycytidine-5′-phosphate	dCMP	dCDP	dCTP
Thymine	Thymidine	Thymidylic acid or Thymidine-5′-phosphate	TMP	TDP	TTP
Uracil	Deoxyuridine	Deoxyuridylic acid or Deoxyuridine-5′-phosphate	dUMP	dUDP	dUTP

II. BIOGENESIS OF NUCLEOTIDE SUGARS

We know of several pathways of carbohydrate metabolism that can adequately account for the biogenesis of D-ribose or D-2-deoxyribose through which they will become available for nucleotide or nucleic acid synthesis. It is the purpose of this section to summarize what appears to be the most important of these pathways at the present time. For the most part, the ones we shall discuss are well understood in that the enzymes catalyzing individual reactions in the pathways have been purified and, in some cases, crystallized. There are certainly other pathways which are not so well defined and, indeed, there are probably others still waiting to be discovered.

The main question, largely unanswered today, is: Assuming we know of several pathways available for the synthesis of pentose phosphates, how do we evaluate their relative contributions to the synthesis of pentoses present in nucleic acids and nucleotides? As we shall see below, efforts are being made to answer this question, but are hindered by the complexity and interaction of the various routes.

Pathways available for the synthesis of deoxyribose or its phosphate derivatives are in much less satisfactory state of knowledge than those for ribose synthesis. Therefore, we shall begin our discussion of sugar biosynthesis with the biogenesis of D-ribose.

A. *Ribose Phosphate*

1. *Oxidative Pentose Phosphate Pathway*

Although the occurrence of carbohydrate as a constituent of RNA has been known since 1891, its actual identification as D-ribose was not made until some 20 years later. [127, 128] In the middle 1930's, indications for the existence of a pathway of carbohydrate metabolism of an oxidative nature began to evolve. Work of Warburg *et al.* [259–261] and Lipmann [135] perhaps laid the groundwork for this pathway. It was discovered that glucose-6-phosphate was oxidized to 6-phosphogluconate, [261] and that this substance could be further oxidized, with the evolution of carbon dioxide, to form a substance giving a test for pentose. [135, 259] Similar results were reported by Dickens [45] who postulated that ribose phosphate was the pentose produced in the further oxidation of 6-phosphogluconate. The more recent developments involving other pentose phosphate intermediates in this pathway have been made by Horecker, Racker, and Cohen. [67, 88, 195] This pathway has been variously called the "hexosemonophosphate shunt", the "Lipmann–Warburg–Dickens Pathway", "the oxidative pathway", "the pentose cycle", and numerous other names. For our purposes, we shall consider it as the oxidative pentose phosphate pathway which, in light of our present knowledge, is believed to proceed according to reactions (1–4). In reaction 1, glucose-6-phosphate is oxidized in the presence of a TPN-linked dehydrogenase to

$$
\begin{array}{ccc}
\text{H}\diagdown_{\text{C}}\diagup\text{OH} & & \text{C}\diagup^{\text{O}} \\
\text{H---C---OH} & \xrightarrow[\text{TPN}^{+}\quad\text{TPNH}]{} & \text{H---C---OH} \\
\text{HO---C---H}\quad\text{O} & & \text{HO---C---H}\quad\text{O} \\
\text{H---C---OH} & & \text{H---C---OH} \\
\text{H---C} & & \text{H---C} \\
\text{CH}_2\text{OPO}_3^{=} & & \text{CH}_2\text{OPO}_3^{=}
\end{array}
\tag{1}
$$

Glucose–6–phosphate　　　6–phosphogluconolactone

6-phosphogluconolactone. The enzyme catalyzing the reaction is called glucose-6-phosphate dehydrogenase. The lactone, in the presence of a lactonase, is hydrolyzed to the free acid. It is interesting to note here that the hydrolysis of the lactone is known to take place spontaneously to the free acid, but

$$
\begin{array}{l}
\text{6-phosphogluconolactone} \longrightarrow \\
\quad\quad\quad\overset{+}{\text{H}_2\text{O}}
\end{array}
\quad
\begin{array}{c}
\text{COO}^{-} \\
\text{H---C---OH} \\
\text{HO---C---H} \\
\text{H---C---OH} \\
\text{H---C---OH} \\
\text{CH}_2\text{OPO}_3^{=} \\
\text{6-phosphogluconate}
\end{array}
\tag{2}
$$

careful investigation showed the presence of an enzyme which facilitated the reaction. [40]

6-Phosphogluconate is further oxidized, again by a TPN-linked enzyme, with the loss of carbon atom 1 to a pentose phosphate (reaction 3). The enzyme catalyzing the reaction is called 6-phosphogluconic dehydrogenase. The pentose, ribulose-5-phosphate, has several potential metabolic fates. It can be epimerized to xylulose-5-phosphate (reaction 8 below), a reaction which links this oxidative pentose pathway to the non-oxidative pentose

$$
\text{6 - phosphogluconate} \xrightarrow[\text{CO}_2]{\text{TPN}^{+}\quad\text{TPNH}}
\begin{array}{c}
\text{CH}_2\text{OH} \\
\text{C}=\text{O} \\
\text{H---C---OH} \\
\text{H---C---OH} \\
\text{CH}_2\text{OPO}_3^{=}
\end{array}
\tag{3}
$$

Ribulose – 5 – phosphate

phosphate pathway, as will be shown below; it can be phosphorylated to form ribulose-diphosphate which is an intermediate in the photosynthetic process; or it can be isomerized to ribose-5-phosphate (reaction 4). It is this

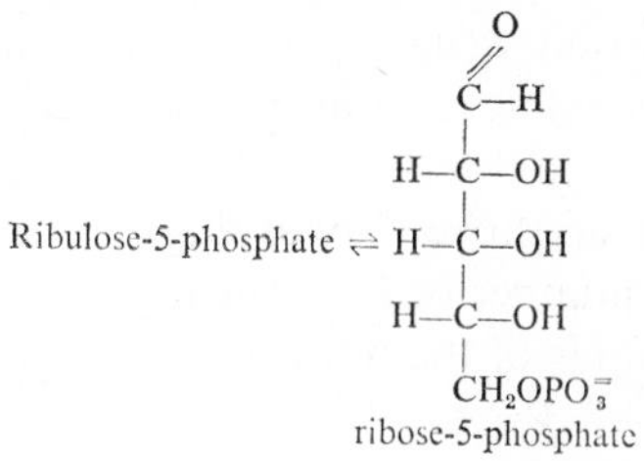

$$
\text{Ribulose-5-phosphate} \rightleftharpoons
\begin{array}{c}
\overset{O}{\underset{\parallel}{}} \\
C\text{—}H \\
|\\
H\text{—}C\text{—}OH \\
|\\
H\text{—}C\text{—}OH \\
|\\
H\text{—}C\text{—}OH \\
|\\
CH_2OPO_3^= \\
\text{ribose-5-phosphate}
\end{array}
\tag{4}
$$

isomerization reaction which completes the synthesis of ribose-5-phosphate from hexose phosphate through the oxidative pentose phosphate pathway. This reaction catalyzed by the enzyme, pentose phosphate isomerase, proceeds equally well in either direction.

Thus the presence of four enzymes, glucose-6-phosphate dehydrogenase, 6-phosphogluconolactonase, 6-phosphogluconic dehydrogenase, and pentose phosphate isomerase, accounts for the net synthesis of ribose-5-phosphate from hexose phosphate. In the overall conversion, one mole of carbon dioxide is lost and 2 moles of TPN become reduced. It should be pointed out that certain organisms can utilize DPN in these reactions, but usually the enzyme has been found to be TPN specific. The enzymes of this pathway have been found in yeast, bacteria, plants, and animal tissues. The operation of the pathway *in vivo* may depend to a large extent on the availability of oxidized TPN.

2. *Non-oxidative Pentose Phosphate Pathway*

Another pathway for the synthesis of ribose-5-phosphate from hexose phosphate has been demonstrated in a variety of organisms, and is non-oxidative in nature. It involves the utilization of three enzymes: transketolase, transaldolase, and phosphoketopentose epimerase. Starting with hexose

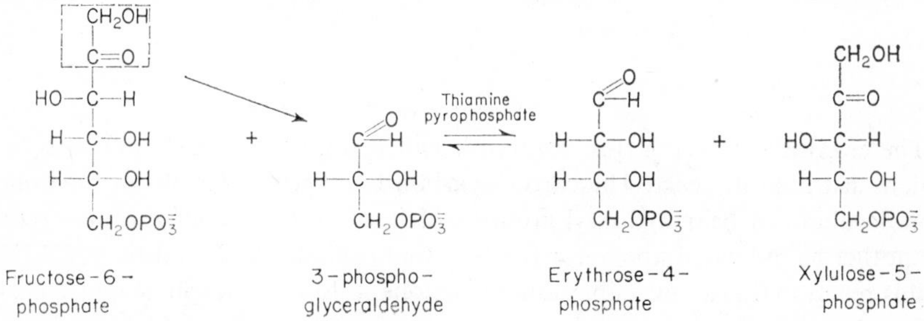

(5)

phosphate and triose phosphate, two intermediates in the glycolytic sequence, it is possible to achieve a net synthesis of ribose-5-phosphate utilizing reactions (4–8).

Transketolase [89, 197] is a transferring enzyme in which two carbon atoms are transferred from one donor sugar molecule to an acceptor as illustrated in reaction (5). This is a reversible reaction and requires thiamine pyrophosphate as a cofactor. In the reverse direction, xylulose-5-phosphate would serve as the "ketol" donor and erythrose-4-phosphate as the "ketol" acceptor. It should be noted that a number of keto sugars can serve as the substrate as long as the "ketol" group is of the following configuration.

```
        CH₂OH
         |
        C=O
         |
   HO—C—H
         |
```

A variety of aldehydes can serve as acceptor molecules. The erythrose-4-phosphate formed in this reaction can then undergo a reaction with another molecule of fructose-6-phosphate in a manner illustrated in reaction (6). This is a group transfer in which the top three carbons of the hexose phosphate are transferred to the tetrose phosphate to form a seven carbon sugar and a triose.

```
   CH₂OH                                                                    CH₂OH
    |                                                                        |
   C=O                                                                      C=O
    |                  O                          O                  HO—C—H
  HO—C—H            C—H                       C—H                    H—C—OH
    |          +    H—C—OH       ⇌           H—C—OH        +        H—C—OH
  H—C—OH           H—C—OH                    H—C—OH                 H—C—OH
    |               |                         |                      |
  H—C—OH          CH₂OPO₃⁻                  CH₂OPO₃⁻                CH₂OPO₃⁻
    |
  CH₂OPO₃⁻
```

Fructose – 6 –   Erythrose – 4 –   3 – phospho –   Sedoheptulose – 7 –
phosphate   phosphate   glyceraldehyde   phosphate

(6)

The enzyme catalyzing this reaction is called transaldolase, [90] and was first demonstrated in yeast. The carbon–carbon bond which is split in the donor molecule must bear hydroxyl groups which are in trans-configuration to one another as indicated above for fructose-6-phosphate. It should be noted that this reaction is also reversible, and the sedoheptulose-7-phosphate molecule, in donating its top three carbon atoms to 3-phosphoglyceraldehyde in the reverse direction, has the same configuration as that noted in fructose-6-phosphate.

A third reaction, again involving transketolase, takes place between sedoheptulose-7-phosphate and 3-phosphoglyceraldehyde giving two pentose phosphates as products. One of these pentoses is D-ribose-5-phosphate,

$$
\begin{array}{ccccc}
CH_2OH \\
| \\
C=O \\
| \\
HO-C-H & & O & C-H \\
| & & \| & | & CH_2OH \\
H-C-OH & & C-H & H-C-OH & | \\
| & O & | & | & C=O \\
H-C-OH & + & C-H & \rightleftharpoons H-C-OH & + HO-C-H \\
| & \| & | & | & | \\
H-C-OH & C-H & H-C-OH & H-C-OH & H-C-OH \\
| & | & | & | & | \\
CH_2OPO_3^= & CH_2OPO_3^= & CH_2OPO_3^= & CH_2OPO_3^= \\
\text{sedoheptulose-7-} & \text{3-phospho-} & \text{D-ribose-5-} & \text{xylulose-5-} \\
\text{phosphate} & \text{glyceraldehyde} & \text{phosphate} & \text{phosphate}
\end{array}
\qquad (7)
$$

the other is xylulose-5-phosphate. The latter compound formed as a product of both transketolase reactions, can be epimerized (reaction 8) to ribulose-5-phosphate and then isomerized (reaction 4) to D-ribose-5-phosphate

$$
\begin{array}{ccc}
 & & O \\
 & & \| \\
CH_2OH & CH_2OH & C-H \\
| & | & | \\
C=O & C=O & H-C-OH \\
| & (8) \quad | & (4) \quad | \\
HO-C-H & \rightleftharpoons H-C-OH & \rightleftharpoons H-C-OH \\
| & | & | \\
H-C-OH & H-C-OH & H-C-OH \\
| & | & | \\
CH_2OPO_3^= & CH_2OPO_3^= & CH_2OPO_3^= \\
\text{xylulose-5-} & \text{ribulose-5-} & \text{D-ribose-5-} \\
\text{phosphate} & \text{phosphate} & \text{phosphate}
\end{array}
$$

The net result of these reactions, starting with two hexose phosphates and one triose phosphate, will be as follows:

Hexose-P + Triose-P	$\longrightarrow$	Tetrose-P + Xylulose-P	(5)
Hexose-P + Tetrose-P	$\longrightarrow$	Heptulose-P + Triose-P	(6)
Heptulose-P + Triose-P	$\longrightarrow$	Xylulose-P + Ribose-P	(7)
2 Xylulose-P	$\longrightarrow$	2 Ribulose-P	(8)
2 Ribulose-P	$\longrightarrow$	2 Ribose-P	(4)

2 Hexose-P + Triose-P	$\longrightarrow$	3-Ribose-P	Net

The enzyme catalyzing reaction (8) is phosphoketopentose epimerase. The reaction is reversible and, in fact, might be considered to tie the oxidative pentose phosphate pathway and the non-oxidative pentose phosphate pathway together. Starting with hexose phosphate and proceeding through the oxidative pathway to ribulose-5-phosphate, through the "epimerase" reaction to xylulose-5-phosphate, and a reversal of the non-oxidative pathway, it would be possible to account for the complete oxidation of glucose-6-phosphate to carbon dioxide and water.

As was mentioned above, the relative contributions of these pathways *in vivo* to ribose phosphate synthesis remains one of the major problems. Attempts to get at an answer have utilized for the most part an isotope approach. In the oxidative pentose phosphate pathway, carbon 1 of glucose is lost in the 6-phosphogluconic dehydrogenase reaction. Experiments have been carried out *in vivo* in which the utilization of glucose-1-C^{14} for pentose phosphate synthesis has been compared with that of glucose-6-C^{14}. If the oxidative pathway were responsible for pentose formation, the use of glucose-6-C^{14} as starting material would yield acid-soluble nucleotides or nucleic acids with highly labeled pentose, whereas glucose-1-C^{14} would cause incorporation of only small amounts of C^{14} into the nucleotides.

Experiments by Bernstein [20] utilizing this approach have shown that this pathway could indeed be providing the ribose necessary for nucleic acid synthesis in *E. coli*. This does not appear to be true for all organisms investigated, in fact not even for *E. coli* under all conditions of growth. Using other isotopic approaches, it seems likely that, in the rat, this pathway is not the sole mechanism by which ribose can be made. It has been estimated that ribose formation from hexose in the rat occurs to the extent of 30 to 50 per cent by the oxidative route, and the remainder by the non-oxidative pentose phosphate pathway. [86]

The difficulty with experiments of this type lies in the fact that both the oxidative and non-oxidative pentose phosphate pathways, the glycolytic sequence, as well as possibly other not yet discovered pathways are all operating at the same time. This results in such randomization of isotope as to make assessment of pathways by isotopic methods quite difficult.

B. *D-2-Deoxyribose Phosphate*

1. *Aldolase Pathway*

As was mentioned above, the biogenesis of D-2-deoxyribose is in a less satisfactory state of knowledge than the synthesis of D-ribose. An enzyme has been discovered in *E. coli* and rat liver which is capable of catalyzing the condensation of acetaldehyde with D-glyceraldehyde-3-phosphate according to reaction (9).

The relative importance of this route as a means of synthesis of deoxyribose-5-phosphate has been questioned on the grounds of the low affinity of the enzyme for acetaldehyde. In addition, there are essentially no tracer data

$$
\begin{array}{c}
\overset{O}{\underset{|}{\overset{\|}{C}-H}} \\
CH_3 \\
\text{acetaldehyde} \\
+ \\
\overset{O}{\overset{\|}{C}-H} \\
\overset{|}{H-C-OH} \\
CH_2OPO_3^= \\
\text{3-phospho-} \\
\text{glyceraldehyde}
\end{array}
\rightleftharpoons
\begin{array}{c}
\overset{O}{\overset{\|}{C}-H} \\
CH_2 \\
H-C-OH \\
H-C-OH \\
CH_2OPO_3^= \\
\text{D-2-deoxyribose-5-} \\
\text{phosphate}
\end{array}
\tag{9}
$$

strongly favoring this mechanism. It is possible that this enzyme is responsible for the breakdown of deoxyribose rather than its synthesis. The reaction is reversible and the enzyme is called DR-aldolase. [196]

2. Synthesis of Deoxyribose from Ribonucleosides or Ribonucleotides

At the time 5-phosphoribosylpyrophosphate (Section III of this chapter) was discovered and found to play a predominant role in ribonucleotide synthesis, it was thought that deoxyribose incorporation into deoxyribonucleotides might occur by a similar route. To date, no enzyme system has been found, however, capable of catalyzing the reaction of ATP with deoxyribose-5-phosphate to form 5-phosphodeoxyribosylpyrophosphate. In addition, evidence accumulates indicating that the biogenesis of the deoxy-sugar of deoxyribonucleotides occurs from either ribonucleosides or ribonucleotides. First indications of this came from the work of Rose and Schweigert [208] in which cytidine uniformly labeled with C^{14} was administered to rats, and the nucleosides of both the RNA and DNA isolated and examined for radioactivity. The ratio of specific activities of the deoxyribose to bases in the isolated deoxyribonucleosides was the same as the corresponding ratio in the ribonucleosides. This indicates that a conversion of the ribonucleoside to the deoxyribonucleoside has taken place without breaking the N-glycosidic bond. Similar data have also been found for nucleotides. [207]

Experiments in cell-free systems have been described recently which indicate that the conversion occurs at the nucleotide level. Enzymes which catalyze the conversion of CMP to dCMP have been obtained from bacterial extracts [201] and with such preparations dCDP appeared to be one of the first products formed. Other evidence indicating the conversion occurred at the nucleotide level has been found in mammalian systems as well. [3, 92] Much of this early work was done with the cytidine nucleotides.

Evidence is accumulating which indicates that other purine or pyrimidine containing nucleotides are converted to their corresponding deoxyribonucleo-tides. For instance, the conversion of GMP to dGMP has been reported in a mammalian system. [199] Conversion of uracil containing nucleosides or nucleotides to the corresponding deoxyribose derivatives has been reported in bacterial systems. [76, 22]

The mechanism of the reductive step continues to remain elusive. Purifi-cation of the enzyme system responsible for the conversion of the cytidine nucleotides to deoxycytidine nucleotides [22] indicated that CDP rather than CMP or CTP was the preferred substrate. The reaction required ATP, Mg^{++}, and reduced lipoic acid as a reductant. More recent evidence seems to indicate that reduced lipoic acid is not the immediate reductant. [200] A protein preparation was obtained from *E. coli B* which, in the presence of NADPH, replaced reduced lipoate as the hydrogen donor in the reduction of CDP to dCDP. The name thioredoxin was proposed for this substance. Combined evidence indicates that thioredoxin is a low molecular weight protein (12,300–12,600) consisting of a single polypeptide chain with one disulfide bond. This disulfide apparently is reduced in the presence of NADPH and a specific reductase, and it was proposed that the immediate hydrogen donor in the reduction of ribonucleotides to deoxyribonucleotides is reduced thioredoxin.

The relationship existing between the cytidine nucleotides and their deoxyribonucleotide derivatives may be summed up as indicated in reaction (10), with the reduction occurring at the dinucleotide level:

(10)

Whether this same relationship exists for other pyrimidine and purine nucleotides remains to be seen.

Since 1948 vitamin B_{12} has been implicated in this reductive process largely from the observation that deoxyribonucleosides are able to replace the vitamin B_{12} requirement for growth of a variety of species of *Lactobacillus*. [220, 234, 268] In the early 1960's, we went through a period where it was felt that B_{12} probably was not involved. In 1964, Blakely and Barker [23] were able to demonstrate an absolute requirement for 5,6-dimethylbenzimidazole coba-mide coenzymes in a cell-free system which catalyzed the conversion of CMP to a deoxyribose derivative. More recently, Abrams and Duraiswami, [2] using soluble extracts obtained from *L. leichmanii*, were able to confirm this observation and, in addition, showed that the conversion took place without a cleavage of the glycosidic bond. In their system ATP, Mg^{++}, dihydrolipoate, and a cobamide were required. Exactly where vitamin B_{12} fits into the scheme shown in reaction (10) is not known at the present time.

Further support for a rather direct conversion of ribose derivatives to deoxyribose derivatives comes from isotope experiments utilizing labeled glucose. [12, 13, 21] In essence, these studies showed that the carbons of the deoxyribose of DNA had the same relative radioactivities as the corresponding carbons of the RNA ribose when C^{14}-labeled glucose was used as the precursor. These results would indicate that either deoxyribose synthesis occurred through ribose or that the synthesis of both pentoses originate in relatively common precursors.

Purine and pyrimidine biogenesis probably proceeds, through intermediate ribose derivations, as described below in Sections III and IV. Once the ribonucleotides are formed, these can be utilized for RNA or nucleotide synthesis or they can be reduced, probably at the nucleotide level, to deoxyribonucleotides which may then be used for DNA synthesis. The mechanism of this reductive reaction is not known.

III. BIOGENESIS OF PURINE NUCLEOSIDE MONOPHOSPHATES

The speculative participation of urea, histidine, pyrimidine, or arginine as possible precursors of purine ring synthesis is indicated in Fig. 1. These compounds have actually been tested as possible precursors for purine ring synthesis on the basis of the structural similarity of part of their molecules to a portion of the purine ring system. In almost every instance, they were shown to be unimportant in this respect. Observations of this sort indicate that biological systems do not always utilize what appears to be the obvious approach to the biogenesis of complex molecules.

A. De Novo *Pathway to Inosinic Acid*

Perhaps the most fundamental work with regard to purine ring biogenesis began with the experiments of Buchanan [26, 27, 236, 237] in which C^{13}-labeled substances of simple structure were administered to pigeons and the uric acid of the excreta systematically examined for the isotope distribution. Among the compounds tested in this series of experiments were C^{13}-labeled carbon dioxide, glycine, formate, and lactate. N^{15}-labeled compounds such as glycine, ammonia, aspartate, glutamate, and glutamine were also tested for their possible contribution as nitrogen donors to the ring. In essence, studies of this sort resulted in the conclusion that uric acid was formed from low molecular weight precursors as indicated in Fig. 2. Subsequent degradative studies of the purines obtained from the nucleic acids of animals fed these or similar compounds yielded analogous results. This supports the view that not only are small molecules important precursors of the chief excretory form of nitrogen in the pigeon, but that they are important as well in the biogenesis of biologically active purine compounds like the nucleic acids.

Studies of this kind were indicative of the types of molecules that participate in the biogenesis of the purine ring, but gave little information on how the molecule is put together. In 1948, Greenberg[71] reported the synthesis

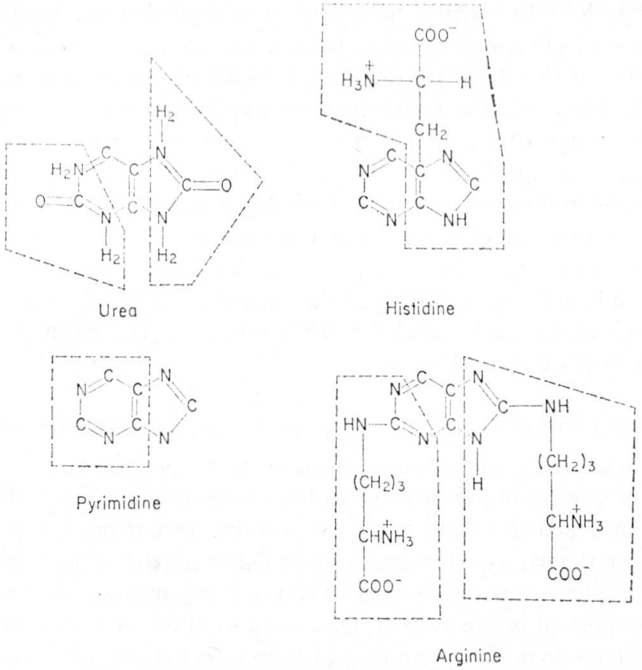

Urea   Histidine

Pyrimidine   Arginine

Fig. 1. Seeming precursors of the purine ring.

of the purine, hypoxanthine, in homogenates of pigeon liver and, with this discovery, launched the study of purine biogenesis in cell-free systems. In the ten years that followed, the pathway of *de novo* purine ring synthesis was practically resolved, the rapid advance in large measure being due to the

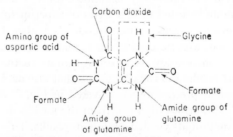

Fig. 2. Precursors of uric acid in the pigeon.

ready availability of the enzymes concerned in a soluble form from extracts of bird liver.

Simultaneously with these classical experiments of Buchanan and Greenberg, a completely different approach to this problem demonstrated the accumulation of a diazotizable amine in *E. coli* grown in the presence of sulfonamides. [239] This substance was identified as 4-amino-5-imidazolecarboxamide, [219] and was postulated to be involved in the biogenesis of purines. We now know that the pentose phosphate derivative of this compound is an intermediate in purine ring biosynthesis, and that it needs the

4 – amino – 5 – imidazolecarboxamide
("carboxamide")

addition of only one more carbon atom to complete the ring system. The fact that "carboxamide" (as the free base) is not on the path of purine ring synthesis, was demonstrated both by Greenberg [74] and Buchanan [216] in experiments in which C^{14}-labeled formate or glycine was incubated together with an excess of labeled "carboxamide" in the presence of cell-free extracts of avian liver. At the end of the experiment, the "carboxamide" was isolated and found to contain no label. In addition, the presence of excess "carboxamide" in the medium had no effect on the incorporation of label from formate or glycine into hypoxanthine in the same system. The observation was also made that ribose-phosphate stimulated the synthesis of hypoxanthine from C^{14}-formate, [72, 73] and this was perhaps the first indication that the nucleotide, inosinic acid, and not the free base, hypoxanthine, is the primary product formed from the precursor molecules. [72] This then led to the suggestion that the ribose phosphate derivative of "carboxamide" is a true intermediate in purine ring synthesis, and it further indicated that the ribose and phosphate parts of the molecule must be added at some stage prior to completion of the ring. In fact, as we know it today, the pentose phosphate is added in the first step of the synthesis. A key compound in this regard is 5-phosphoribosyl-1-pyrophosphate (PRPP) first described by Kornberg *et al.* [112] which was shown to be synthesized according to reaction (11). The two terminal phosphates of ATP are transferred to ribose-5-phosphate in the presence of the enzyme 5-phosphoribose pyrophosphokinase.

5-Phosphoribosyl-1-pyrophosphate can react with a number of free heterocyclic bases (Section IIID of this chapter) or with acyclic precursors to form nucleotides or pentose phosphate derivatives of precursors, respectively.

$$\text{Ribose-5-phosphate} \quad\quad \text{5-phosphoribosyl-1-pyrophosphate (PRPP)} \tag{11}$$

Reactions of this sort are catalyzed by "pyrophosphorylases", they liberate inorganic pyrophosphate in the direction of nucleotide synthesis and, in many instances, are readily reversible.

$$\text{(12)}$$

An important reaction in the *de novo* synthesis of purines is that of PRPP with the amide nitrogen of glutamine to form 5-phosphoribosylamine.[68, 80] Although this compound is believed to be the product of the reaction, it has never been isolated because of its extreme lability. Even though several steps appear to be involved in this synthesis, the enzyme catalyzing the reaction, 5-phosphoribosyl pyrophosphate amidotransferase, has not been resolved into multiple components. Therefore reaction (12) is thought to be catalyzed by a single enzyme, it is believed to be essentially irreversible, and does not appear to proceed through N-(5-phosphoribosyl) glutamine, a conceivable intermediate. It is interesting to note that the carbon-1 atom of the ribose in PRPP has the α-configuration and that a β-configuration presumably results during the reaction of PRPP with glutamine to form 5-phosphoribosylamine. The nitrogen attached to the ribose during this reaction later assumes position 9 of the completed purine ring.

A molecule of glycine is then added to 5-phosphoribosylamine according to reaction (13) to provide carbon atoms 4 and 5 of the ring, as well as nitrogen atom 7.[68, 81] The resulting compound is called glycinamide ribonucleotide, and the reaction catalyzing its synthesis is known to require the participation of ATP as a source of energy. This reaction is reversible, and has been shown

$$\text{(13)}$$

Glycinamide ribonucleotide

to proceed in a reverse direction only when ADP and inorganic ortho-phosphate or arsenate are present. The enzyme catalyzing this reaction is called glycinamide ribonucleotide kinosynthase.

Carbon 8 of the purine ring is added next through the participation of folic acid as a coenzyme to form formylglycinamide ribonucleotide. [69, 264] The enzyme catalyzing this reaction (14), glycinamide ribonucleotide trans-formylase, has been purified from avian liver. As we shall see later, there is

$$\text{(14)}$$

formylglycinamide
ribonucleotide

another transformylase reaction (20) which catalyzes the incorporation of carbon 2 into the purine ring. These two similar reactions are catalyzed by different enzymes.

Nitrogen 3 of the ring is then added. The donor, in this case, is again the amide nitrogen of glutamine. [126] This reaction (15) has been shown to require ATP, and to yield ADP and inorganic orthophosphate as by-products. As in the case of reaction (12), it has been impossible to demonstrate the reversi-bility of reaction (15). An interesting phenomenon related to the biosynthesis

$$\text{(15)}$$

formylglycinamidine
ribonucleotide

of formylglycinamidine ribonucleotide is the finding that azaserine and 6-diazo-5-oxonorleucine which are antitumor agents, have a pronounced inhibitory effect on this reaction. They work apparently by competing with the natural substrate, glutamine, for the enzyme site.

$$\overset{-}{N}=\overset{+}{N}=CH-CO-O-CH_2-CH\overset{+}{N}H_3-COO^-$$
azaserine

$$\overset{-}{N}=\overset{+}{N}=CH-CO-CH_2-CH_2-CH\overset{+}{N}H_3-COO^-$$
6-diazo-5-oxonorleucine

The next step in purine synthesis is the completion of its imidazole ring. This reaction again requires the participation of ATP which, in the course of the reaction, is broken down to ADP and inorganic orthophosphate. [126] The enzyme catalyzing this reaction (16) has also been partially purified from avian liver, and has been found to be relatively unstable. The reaction is irreversible.

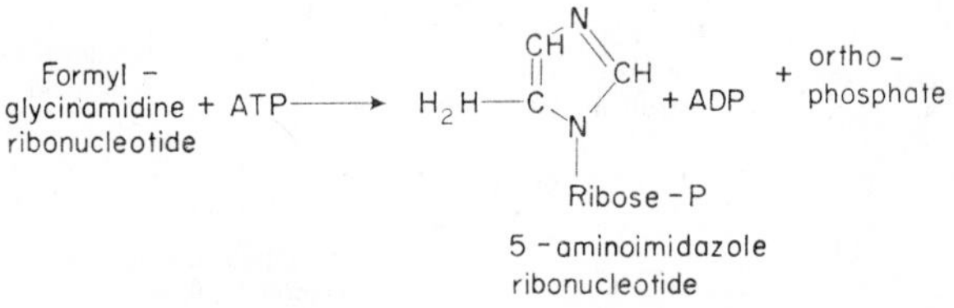

$$\text{(16)}$$

Formyl-glycinamidine + ATP $\longrightarrow$ 5-aminoimidazole ribonucleotide + ADP + orthophosphate

In the next reaction, a molecule of carbon dioxide is fixed to the imidazole ring, to form 5-amino-4-imidazole carboxylic acid ribonucleotide. [136] The enzyme catalyzing this reaction (17), 5-aminoimidazole ribonucleotide carboxylase, has been purified about forty-fold, and is active in either direction.

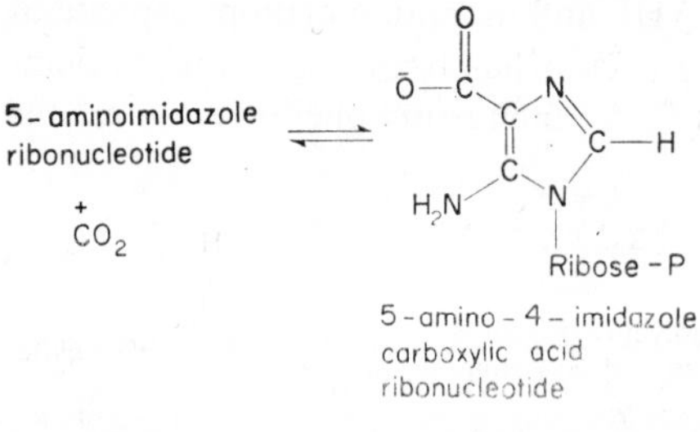

$$\text{(17)}$$

5-aminoimidazole ribonucleotide + CO_2 $\rightleftharpoons$ 5-amino-4-imidazole carboxylic acid ribonucleotide

As has been mentioned above, nitrogen atom 1 of the purine ring is provided by the amino nitrogen of aspartic acid. While this nitrogen is added to

5-amino-4-imidazole carboxylic acid ribonucleotide, the whole molecule of aspartic acid is attached as indicated in reaction 18, and this requires the participation of ATP as a source of energy.[136] The reaction is reversible and requires the presence of ADP and inorganic orthophosphate when it proceeds in the direction from right to left in reaction (18).

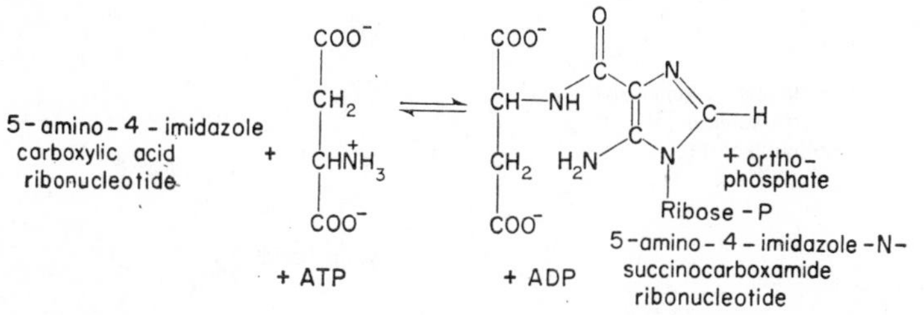

(18)

A molecule of fumarate is lost subsequently and 5-amino-4-imidazole-carboxamide ribonucleotide is produced.[154] The enzyme catalyzing the latter reaction (19) is probably the same as the one involved in the cleavage of adenylosuccinate which serves as an intermediate in adenylic acid synthesis from inosinic acid (reaction 23). Reaction (19) is reversible. Its product of synthesis is found to accumulate as the free base or the ribosyl derivative

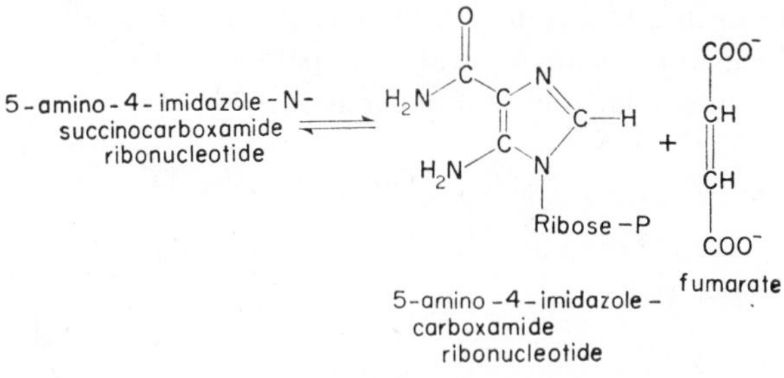

(19)

in *E. coli* grown in the presence of sulfonamides. As mentioned earlier, the free base or nucleoside does not constitute an intermediate in purine biogenesis.

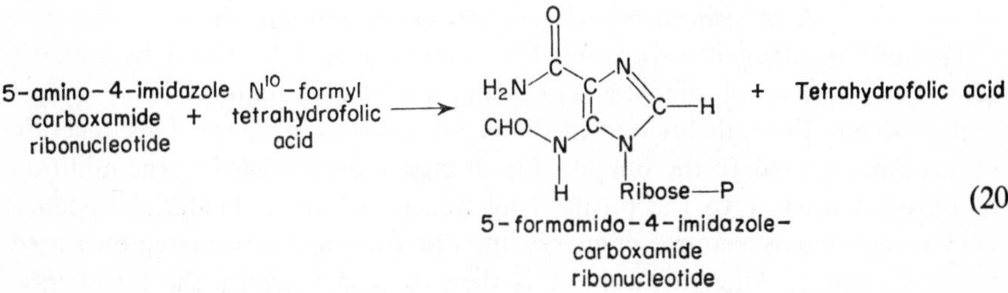

(20)

D

A formyl group is then added to give 5-formamido-4-imidazolecarboxa-mide ribonucleotide (reaction 20) and, as in reaction (14), the participation of folic acid is required. [50, 75] A transformylase catalyzes this reaction, but so far it has proved difficult to separate this enzyme from inosinicase, the enzyme which catalyzes the last step in inosinic acid biogenesis (reaction 21).

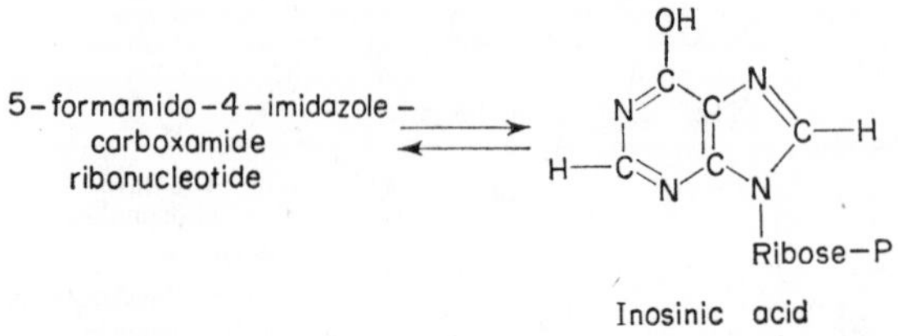

$$
\begin{array}{c}
\text{5 - formamido - 4 - imidazole -} \\
\text{carboxamide} \\
\text{ribonucleotide}
\end{array}
\quad \rightleftharpoons \quad
\text{[Inosinic acid structure]}
\quad (21)
$$

Inosinicase will not act on the free carboxamide or its ribonucleoside, but is specific for the phosphoribosyl derivative. The equilibrium of this reaction is highly in favor of inosinic acid.

Thus, inosinic acid was the first purine to be completely synthesized by the *de novo* pathway. It is not a constituent of nucleic acids, nor has it been shown to occur in important coenzymes. Replacement of the hydroxyl group at position 6 of the ring with an amino group is necessary for the formation of the important nucleotide, adenylic acid. Addition of an amino group to position 2 of inosinic acid results in the formation of the other major purine containing nucleotide, guanylic acid. The pathways describing these trans-formations are now relatively well understood.

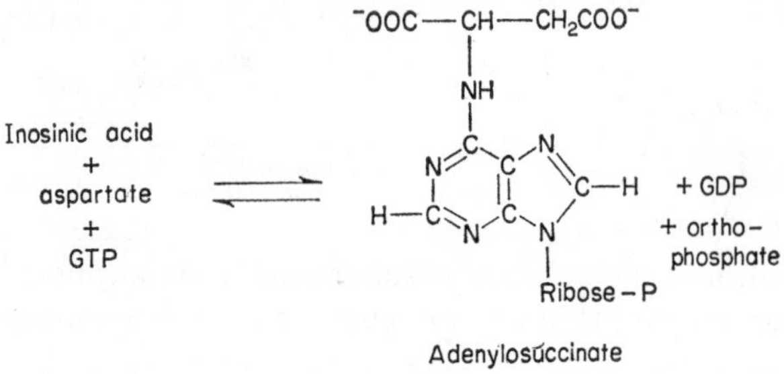

$$
\begin{array}{c}
\text{Inosinic acid} \\
+ \\
\text{aspartate} \\
+ \\
\text{GTP}
\end{array}
\quad \rightleftharpoons \quad
\text{[Adenylosuccinate structure]}
\quad
\begin{array}{c}
+ \text{GDP} \\
+ \text{ortho-} \\
\text{phosphate}
\end{array}
\quad (22)
$$

Adenylosúccinate

B. *Biogenesis of Adenylic Acid from Inosinic Acid*

The amino nitrogen in position 6 of the adenine is provided by aspartic acid. The synthesis of adenylic acid from inosinic acid requires two enzymes and proceeds through an intermediate, adenylosuccinate. [35] This reaction (22) is quite similar to the one already discussed with regard to the addition of nitrogen atom 1 to the purine ring (reaction 18). In bacterial systems, GTP is required as a source of energy and the reaction has been demonstrated to be reversible. Adenylosuccinate is then cleaved whereby the nitrogen is left with the ring and fumarate becomes the other product. As was mentioned above, the enzyme catalyzing this reaction (23), adenylosuccinase, is probably the same one which catalyzes the cleavage of 5-amino-4-imidazolecarboxamide ribonucleotide (reaction 19).

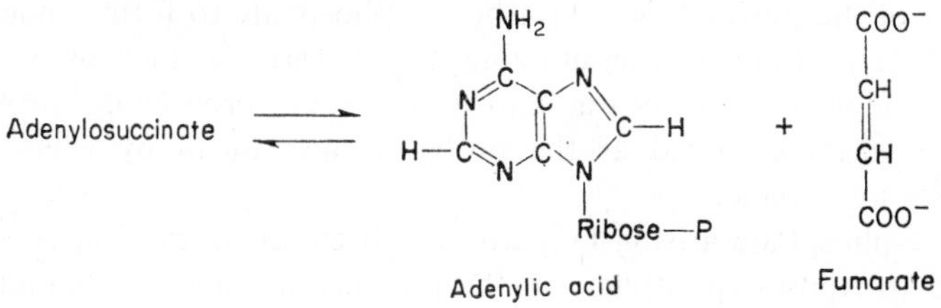

Adenylic acid   Fumarate

C. Biogenesis of Guanylic Acid from Inosinic Acid

The first step in the synthesis of guanylic acid from inosinic acid involves the oxidation of the latter compound to xanthylic acid. The enzyme catalyzing this reaction (24) is called inosinic dehydrogenase and requires DPN as a coenzyme. [121, 138] The reaction as written is irreversible. The donor of the

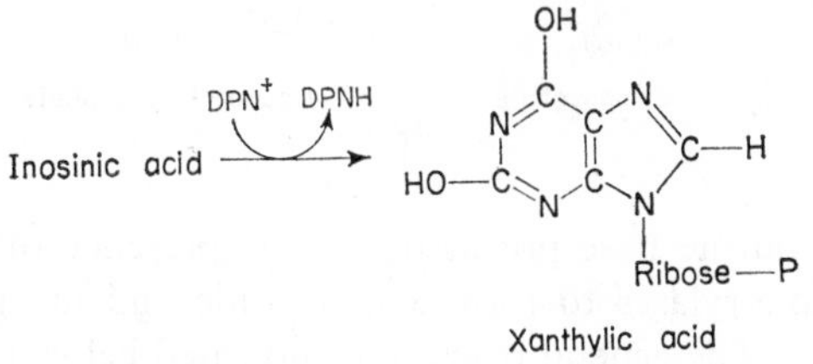

Xanthylic acid

amino group on the 2 position of guanine apparently depends upon the organism. In avian and mammalian systems, glutamine is the preferred donor, [1, 122] while in bacterial systems, it appears to be ammonia. [159] ATP provides this energy necessary for the reaction, but it is broken down to AMP and inorganic pyrophosphate rather than ADP and inorganic orthophosphate. The reaction (25) is essentially irreversible.

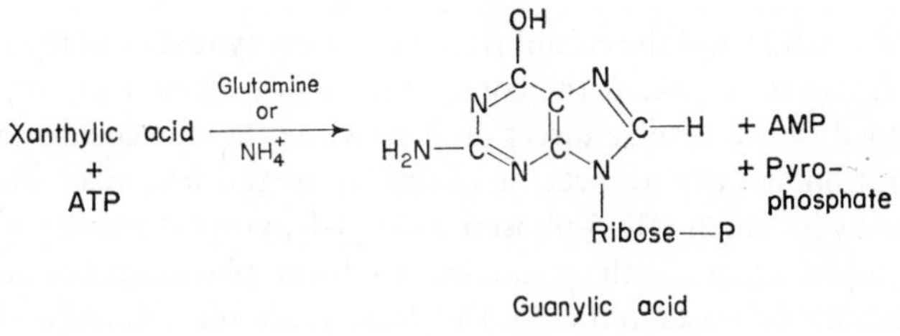

Guanylic acid

D. *Utilization of Preformed Purines*

The *de novo* pathway discussed above for purine nucleotide formation is presently considered to be the major one by which purine nucleotides originate for nucleic acid or coenzyme synthesis. There are, however, other routes which lead to the nucleotide structure. They involve, for the most part, a reaction of the purine base with ribose-1-phosphate to form a nucleoside, followed by a phosphorylation utilizing ATP to form the nucleotide. Indeed, before the *de novo* pathway was known, the route proceeding through the nucleoside was considered as the probable mechanism by which purine nucleotides were made.

Ribose-5-phosphate arising by pathways discussed in Section IIA, can be converted to ribose-1-phosphate in the presence of phosphoribomutase according to reaction (26). [77] Ribose-1-phosphate can react with a number of

$$(26)$$

purine bases or purine base precursors in the presence of enzymes termed nucleoside phosphorylases to form a nucleoside and inorganic orthophosphate as products. The general reaction is indicated below (27). The reaction

$$(27)$$

is readily reversible and the equilibrium favors the synthesis of the nucleoside. It is interesting to note that the configuration of carbon 1 of ribose-1-phosphate formed in the reverse direction is α, while the nucleoside contains the β-configuration. In this respect, it is similar to the first reaction in the *de novo* pathway in which α-D-5-phosphoribosyl-1-pyrophosphate which has the α-configuration reacts with glutamine to form phosphoribosylamine (12) which presumably exists in the β-form. Nucleoside phosphorylase of rat liver was first reported by Kalckar, [102] and was shown to work with either guanine or hypoxanthine to form guanosine or inosine respectively. Since that time, a number of other purine or purine precursors have been shown to undergo a similar reaction to form nucleosides.

The nucleosides formed by this reaction or the nucleosides present in cells, can be phosphorylated by ATP to the corresponding nucleotide derivatives as indicated in reaction (28). Such "kinase" reactions have been described for a number of nucleosides, and they transfer the terminal phosphate of ATP to the 5′-position of the nucleoside to form the 5′-nucleotide.

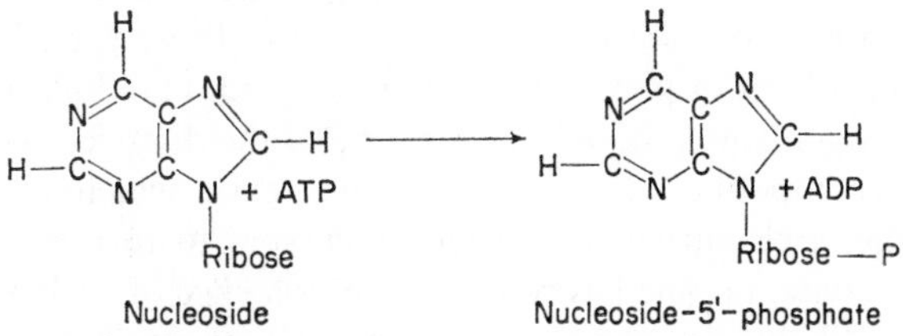

$$(28)$$

Nucleoside   Nucleoside-5′-phosphate

Enzymes have been described which can catalyze the condensation of a free purine or purine precursor with 5-phosphoribosyl-1-pyrophosphate to form nucleotides directly without going through the level of the nucleoside. This is indicated in reaction (29) for adenine. Similar reactions have been demonstrated for guanine, hypoxanthine, xanthine, and 5-aminoimidazolecarboxamide. The other product in the reaction is inorganic pyrophosphate. The reaction is reversible and is catalyzed by a group of enzymes which have been termed nucleotide pyrophosphorylases.

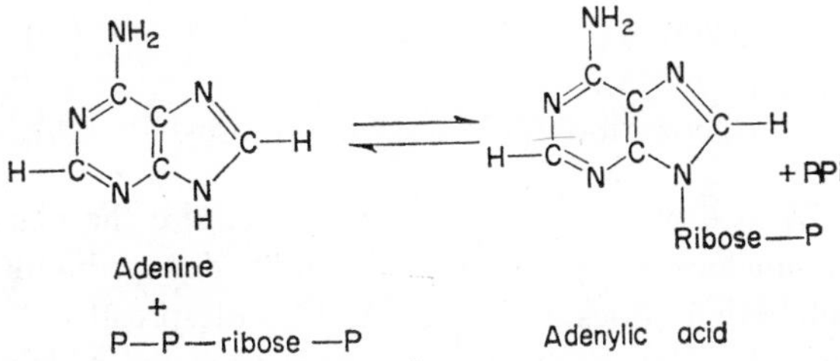

$$(29)$$

Adenine
+
P—P—ribose —P   Adenylic acid

The widespread distribution of enzymes of the *de novo* pathway, the rather poor utilization of intact purines into the nucleic acids of higher animals, and the ready incorporation of smaller precursors into purines all tend to support the hypothesis that the major portion of the purine nucleotides for nucleic acid and coenzyme synthesis are made by the *de novo* pathway.

The nucleoside phosphorylases and the nucleoside kinases participate in a pathway by which free purines can be re-used for synthetic reactions. The same may be said of the nucleotide pyrophosphorylase reaction. It is also possible that these latter two sequences, in part, account for the reactions by which coenzymes or nucleotides derived from nucleic acids are broken down. This would leave their pentose phosphate moiety re-usable for various other metabolic reactions. Such a mechanism has been postulated to prevail in erythrocytes.

E. *Biogenesis of Purine Deoxyribonucleotides*

As mentioned in Section IIB, the pathways known for deoxyribose synthesis are in a less satisfactory state of knowledge than those for ribose. Consequently, the biogenesis of purine deoxyribonucleotides are likewise in a poor state of knowledge. It was thought at the time of the discovery of PRPP that an analogous compound, deoxyPRPP, might exist which could likewise react with either free purines or purine precursors to form the deoxyribonucleotides. To date, no one has reported the existence of such a compound. It seems more likely that the *de novo* synthesis of purines occurs as the ribonucleotide derivative as discussed above in Section IIIA, and that the corresponding deoxyribonucleotides are formed by a reduction of the ribonucleotide (Section IIB).

Reactions involving nucleoside phosphorylases work with free bases and deoxyribose-1-phosphate to form deoxyribonucleosides according to reaction

$$\text{Purine} + \text{Deoxyribose-1-P} \rightleftharpoons \begin{array}{c} \text{Purine deoxyribonucleoside} \\ + \\ \text{orthophosphate} \end{array} \tag{30}$$

(30). Deoxyribose-5-phosphate can be a source of deoxyribose-1-phosphate through a 'mutase' reaction (31). However, to synthesize the deoxyribonucleo-

$$\text{Deoxyribose-5-P} \rightleftharpoons \text{Deoxyribose-1-P} \tag{31}$$

tides by this sequence of reactions would then require the phosphorylation of the deoxyribonucleoside by ATP to form the 5'-deoxyribonucleotide. The presence of such activity does not appear to be widespread.

Trans-N-deoxyribosylases [210] have also been reported which catalyze the interchange of bases of deoxyribonucleosides without proceeding through free deoxyribose-1-phosphate. However, as in the case of the nucleoside phosphorylase reaction, this would not result in the synthesis of the deoxyribonucleotide, but would yield only the deoxyribonucleoside.

The acid-soluble extracts of tissues contain deoxyribonucleotides as the mono-, di-, and triphosphates. These compounds are precursors to DNA.

IV. BIOGENESIS OF PYRIMIDINE NUCLEOSIDE MONOPHOSPHATES

A. De Novo *Synthesis to Uridylic Acid*

In the *de novo* biogenesis of purines, pentose phosphate is added prior to ultimate closure of the ring. *De novo* synthesis of pyrimidine, in contrast to this, consists in the formation of a completed ring before the pentose phosphate becomes attached. The sole pathway of *de novo* pyrimidine synthesis, known at the present time, leads first to orotic acid which fulfils the role of a parent compound for all other pyrimidines.

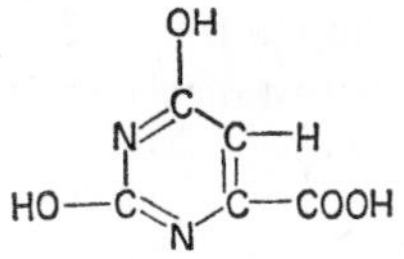

Orotic acid

It was known that small molecules participate in the biogenesis of pyrimidines. This was shown by experiments in which precursors were fed to animals, and the incorporation of these substances into the pyrimidine rings of nucleic acid was determined. For instance, in this way it was shown that N^{15}-labeled ammonium citrate could lead to labeling of the pyrimidines of polynucleotides of birds and mammals. [16] The N-3 position of the pyrimidine ring was shown to be derived from ammonia, [120] while carbon dioxide was demonstrated to contribute to the C-2 position. [85] The remainder of the molecule has been shown to be derived from aspartic acid. [123, 203] The connection between these precursors and the structure of the pyrimidine ring is shown in Fig. 3.

Orotic acid and carbamyl aspartate were demonstrated to be incorporated

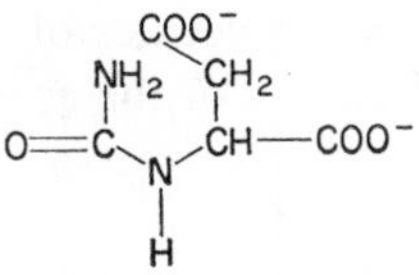

Carbamyl aspartate

into the polynucleotides of *Lactobacillus bulgaricus*. [267] The incorporation of orotic acid into the acid-soluble pyrimidine nucleotides as well as into the pyrimidines of polynucleotides of a wide variety of organisms has since been shown, and this fact certainly confirms the importance of these substances as intermediates in pyrimidine biogenesis. From these early observations involving studies in intact organisms work on pyrimidine ring biogenesis then proceeded through levels of tissue slice experiments and eventually arrived at

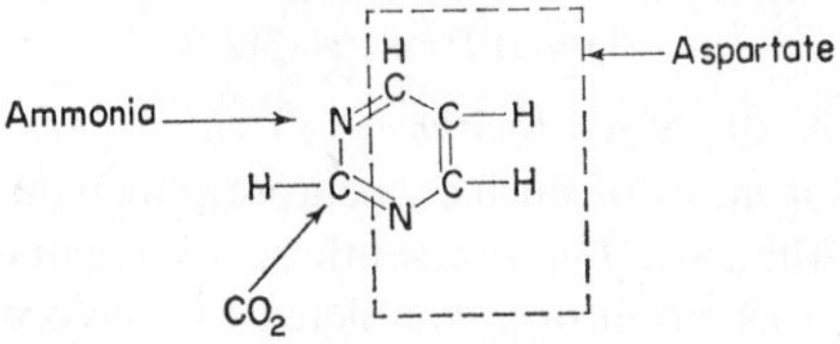

FIG. 3. Precursors of the pyrimidine ring.

studies in cell-free systems. As a result of such studies, we now have a rather complete picture of the mechanism of *de novo* synthesis of pyrimidines.

We might consider the first step in pyrimidine biogenesis to be the synthesis of carbamyl phosphate. This substance can be synthesized through several pathways.

carbamyl phosphate

One of these is the *de novo* synthesis (reaction 32) from ammonia, carbon dioxide and ATP first reported by Jones et al. [100] in extracts of *Streptococcus faecalis*.

$$CO_2 + NH_3 + ATP \rightleftharpoons H_2N-\overset{O}{\overset{\|}{C}}-O-\overset{O}{\overset{\|}{P}}-O^- + ADP \qquad (32)$$
$$\underset{O^-}{|}$$

In the bacterial system, the reaction has been shown to be reversible, and appears to be relatively simple. In mammalian systems (reaction 33), it is more complex, and requires two molecules of ATP, as well as the presence of acetylglutamate. [153] The function of the acetylglutamate is not known.

$$CO_2 + NH_3 + 2\,ATP \xrightarrow[glutamate]{acetyl} H_2N-\overset{O}{\overset{\|}{C}}-O-\overset{O}{\overset{\|}{P}}-O^- + 2\,ADP \qquad (33)$$
$$\underset{O^-}{|}$$

Not only is carbamyl phosphate an intermediate in pyrimidine biogenesis, but it also plays a dominant role in citrulline synthesis from ornithine (reaction 34), one of a series of reactions leading to the overall synthesis of urea in higher organisms. Since reaction (34) is reversible, the carbamyl group of citrulline (outlined by dotted lines) can also be a source of carbamyl phosphate for pyrimidine biogenesis.

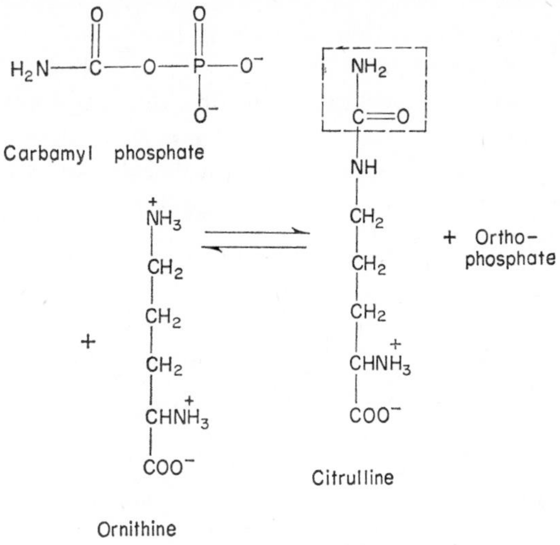

Carbamyl phosphate

Ornithine

Citrulline

$$(34)$$

In addition to this, carbamyl phosphate may also originate from a reaction involving citrulline, ATP, and acetylglutamate (reaction 35).[205, 233] This reaction has been shown to have an absolute dependence on citrulline and ATP and, in addition, is stimulated greatly by acetylglutamate.

$$\text{citrulline} + \text{ATP} \xrightarrow[\text{glutamate}]{\text{acetyl-}} \text{carbamyl phosphate} + \text{ornithine} + \text{ADP} \quad (35)$$

In essence, then, carbamyl phosphate for pyrimidine synthesis can be made available in three ways. The first by *de novo* synthesis from ammonia, carbon dioxide, and ATP; the other two from citrulline. At present, it appears that the *de novo* source is the most important one.

The actual participation of carbamyl phosphate in pyrimidine biogenesis was confirmed by Reichard and Hanshoff.[202] Carbamyl phosphate undergoes a reaction with aspartate in the presence of the enzyme aspartic carbamyl transferase to form carbamyl aspartate, an important intermediate in pyrimidine biogenesis (reaction 36).

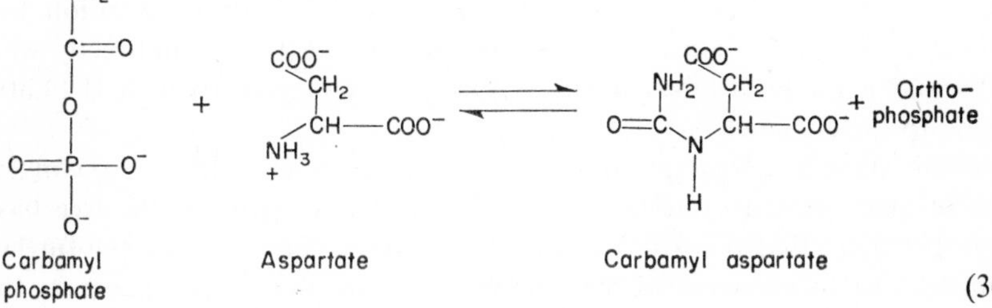

Carbamyl phosphate

Aspartate

Carbamyl aspartate

$$(36)$$

The reaction has been shown to be reversible, but the equilibrium is in favor of carbamyl aspartate. The enzyme appears to have a wide distribution, and has been found in mammalian and avian tissues, as well as in bacteria.

The next step involves a cyclization to form dihydroorotate through the elimination of a water molecule. This reaction (37) is catalyzed by dihydroorotase and is reversible. Its activity was first detected in extracts of microorganisms obtained from soil.[132] The same activity has been found in mammalian systems as well.

$$\text{(37)}$$

Carbamyl aspartate   Dihydroorotate

A dehydrogenation of dihydroorotate then takes place to form orotate (reaction 38). The enzyme catalyzing this reaction is dihydroorotic dehydrogenase which utilizes DPN or TPN as the hydrogen acceptor, depending on the organism.

$$\text{(38)}$$

Dihydroorotate   Orotate

This activity was also found in the same bacteria containing dihydroorotase activity.[131] The equilibrium of the reaction with DPN as the hydrogen acceptor is in favor of dihydroorotate. Through oxidation of the reduced coenzyme by one means or another a net synthesis of orotate from dihydroorotate can be easily achieved.

After purification of this enzyme, preparations were obtained that did not appear to be stimulated by the addition of DPN. This observation has ultimately led to the conclusion that the enzyme reacts only indirectly with DPN and actually requires flavin as the prosthetic group which is tightly bound to the enzyme.

At this stage, the basic pyrimidine ring structure is completed. No conversion of orotic acid to nucleic acid pyrimidines takes place at the free base level. It is here that the pentose phosphate moiety is added, and the further steps leading to nucleic acid pyrimidines from this point take place as the pentose phosphate derivatives. Again, the key substance in this regard is PRPP which reacts with orotic acid to form orotidine-5'-phosphate [133] according to reaction (39).

Orotate   Orotidine − 5' − phosphate

$$\text{Orotate} + P\!-\!P\!-\!\text{Ribose}\!-\!P \rightleftharpoons \text{Orotidine-5'-phosphate} + PPi \qquad (39)$$

The enzyme catalyzing this reaction is called orotidine-5'-phosphate pyrophosphorylase. The activity is apparently specific for orotic acid, since none of the precursors to orotic acid synthesis appear to act as a substrate. The reaction has been demonstrated to be reversible.

The next step involves the loss of carbon dioxide to form uridine-5'-phosphate as a product (reaction 40).

Uridine − 5' − phosphate

$$\text{Orotidine-5'-phosphate} \xrightarrow{-CO_2} \text{Uridine-5'-phosphate} \qquad (40)$$

This reaction is not reversible, and is catalyzed by an enzyme called orotidine-5'-phosphate decarboxylase. [133] Both orotidine-5'-phosphate pyrophosphorylase and decarboxylase have been found in a wide variety of tissues and organisms, and this fact supports the view that UMP formation *de novo* proceeds probably through the outlined pathway. It also implicates uridine-5'-phosphate as an intermediate in the biogenesis of other pyrimidines contained in nucleic acids and nucleotides.

B. *Amination of Uridylic Acid to Cytidylic Acid*

The replacement of the hydroxyl group at position 4 of uridylic acid with an amino group results in the formation of cytidylic acid. This amination reaction takes place at the nucleotide level as the triphosphate derivative of uridine, as indicated in reaction (41). [129, 130] In bacterial systems, ammonia was found to be the amino donor and the reaction was found to require ATP. No reaction took place with glutamine. In mammalian systems, glutamine serves as the source of the amino group. The amination of uridylic acid parallels the amination of xanthylic acid discussed in section IIIc, in that bacterial systems utilize ammonia as the amino donor while mammalian systems utilize glutamine. [214]

(41)

Uridine triphosphate   Cytidine triphosphate

C. *Other Pathways of Pyrimidine Synthesis*

The pathway described above has been found to occur widely in bacteria, yeasts, fungi, and mammals, and is believed to account for the *de novo* synthesis of pyrimidines. However, the possibility of the existence of other pathways should not be excluded. Evidence has already accumulated indicating that the pathway through orotic acid may not be the only one. [158] In this respect, it has been postulated that carbamyl-β-alanine ribonucleotide may be an intermediate in another pathway of pyrimidine ring biogenesis. If this is true, then it is interesting to note that, here too, the pentose-phosphate moiety has been added prior to ring closure.

Carbamyl-β-alanine
ribonucleotide

The relative importance of a pathway passing through this compound remains to be evaluated.

D. *Utilization of Preformed Pyrimidines*

Free pyrimidine bases are utilized rather poorly for RNA synthesis. [185] Yet under certain conditions, notably in cancerous tissues, the free bases are utilized quite well. [84, 212] However, it has also been demonstrated that uracil at higher extracellular concentrations does result in significant incorporation into nucleic acids of normal rat tissues. [31] Studies of this sort indicate that there are pathways by which free pyrimidines can be incorporated into a nucleotide form. These pathways, in essence, are the same as those observed for free purines. The nucleotide can be formed by one of two mechanisms:

first, through reaction with nucleoside phosphorylase and ribose-1-phosphate to form the nucleoside and inorganic phosphate. The nucleoside so formed is then phosphorylated to form the nucleotide in the presence of a "kinase" and ATP. The second pathway involves a reversal of the nucleotide pyrophosphorylase reaction. It might be mentioned, however, that there is a notable lack of knowledge concerning enzymatic activities of this type, with regard to cytosine. For the most part, the activities of both the phosphorylase and pyrophosphorylase have been found and described for uracil. Perhaps a deamination has to occur before significant reutilization of cytosine or cytosine compounds occurs.

A uridine phosphorylase, catalyzing reaction (42), has been reported in extracts of Ehrlich ascites tumor cells, [204] as well as a kinase which catalyzes the phosphorylation of the nucleoside (reaction 43). In extracts of the same cells, a mild activity of uridine-5'-phosphate pyrophosphorylase was also reported. This same activity has not been detectable in rat liver preparations.

The reaction catalyzed by this enzyme is indicated below (reaction 44).

E. Biogenesis of Pyrimidine Deoxyribonucleotides

1. Thymidine-5'-phosphate

The available evidence at the present time seems to favor the view that the synthesis of thymidylic acid occurs from uridylic acid, although deamination of methyldeoxycytidylic acid is a possibility and has been demonstrated.

Thymidylic acid synthesis from uridine-5′-phosphate requires two fundamental transformations, the methylation of the ring, and the reduction of the
sugar. The reduction takes place first, and is followed by the methylation.
Evidence for this came from experiments in which 5-methyldeoxyuridine
and 5-methyluridine were tested as precursors of RNA and DNA pyrimidines
of the rat. [198] The results indicated that deoxyuridine was the preferred
precursor. As mentioned in Section IIB, this reduction probably takes place
at the nucleotide level as the di- or triphosphate derivative.

The methylation reaction requires tetrahydrofolic acid and a one-carbon
source. Cell-free extracts of *E. coli* were shown to be able to convert deoxyuridylic acid to thymidylic acid in the presence of serine, tetrahydrofolic
acid, ATP, and Mg^{++}. At one time, it was doubtful whether the methylation
occurred at the nucleoside or nucleotide level, but it appears quite likely now
that the deoxyribonucleotide is involved. [91] The sequence of reactions involved in the overall conversion of uridylic acid to thymidylic acid is indicated in sequence (45).

Uridylic acid   Deoxyuridylic acid   Thymidylic acid

$$(45)$$

2. Biogenesis of Deoxycytidylic Acid

Deoxycytidylic acid synthesis occurs by reduction of cytidylic acid, the
latter compound being synthesized by the pathway outlined in Section IVB.
It has been reported recently that cell-free extracts of *E. coli* were able to carry
out this reduction at the diphosphate level by a mechanism described in
Section IIB.

V. SYNTHESIS OF DI- AND TRIPHOSPHATE DERIVATIVES OF NUCLEOSIDES

The monophosphate derivatives of the nucleotides appear to be rather
inactive in biological systems with regard to their conversion into nucleoproteins or coenzymes. Pathways exist for the further phosphorylation of
these compounds to their di- and triphosphate derivatives, which in this more
reactive form participate in such syntheses. These pathways consist of transphosphorylation reactions between the triphosphate of one nucleotide and
the mono- or diphosphate derivative of another. The first such reaction was
demonstrated in 1943, [37] and involved the phosphorylation of AMP by

ATP to form ADP. The enzyme which was called myokinase catalyzes the equilibrium indicated in reaction (46).

$$ATP + AMP \rightleftharpoons 2\,ADP \qquad (46)$$

We know through the technique of ion exchange chromatography that the di- and triphosphate derivatives of all the ribonucleotides exist in the acid-soluble extracts of tissues. [94]

The most common type of transphosphorylation reactions observed are those in which ATP serves as the donor molecule and a single phosphate is transferred to a monophosphate derivative with the formation of two nucleoside diphosphates. Reactions (47) to (49) have been reported in addition to reaction (46).

$$ATP + UMP \rightleftharpoons ADP + UDP \qquad (47)$$
$$ATP + CMP \rightleftharpoons ADP + CDP \qquad (48)$$
$$ATP + GMP \rightleftharpoons ADP + GDP \qquad (49)$$

It is not yet established whether there is a specific kinase for each substrate but some separation of activities for UMP, CMP, GMP, and AMP has been reported.

A second series of reactions is known whereby ATP can transfer its terminal phosphate to a nucleoside diphosphate to form a nucleotide triphosphate and ADP according to reactions (50) to (52). Again, the enzymes catalyzing these

$$ATP + UDP \rightleftharpoons ADP + UTP \qquad (50)$$
$$ATP + CDP \rightleftharpoons ADP + CTP \qquad (51)$$
$$ATP + GDP \rightleftharpoons ADP + GTP \qquad (52)$$

reactions have not been separated from one another, although an enzyme has been reported which catalyzes rather specific transphosphorylation between ATP and GDP in extracts of avian liver [118] and hog kidney. [55]

A third type of reaction is known in which various triphosphates can serve as phosphoryl donors to AMP as indicated in equation (53). Reactions of this type have also been reported with CTP, ATP, GTP, and ITP.

$$UTP + AMP \rightleftharpoons UDP + ADP \qquad (53)$$

As has been mentioned for the other kinase reactions above, these reactions are reversible and, in the reverse direction, can account for the utilization of ADP as a phosphoryl donor in triphosphate synthesis.

Reactions of the type in which a nucleoside triphosphate other than ATP serves as the primary phosphoryl donor and the acceptor molecule is a non-adenine containing nucleotide, are rather difficult to establish. For instance, the reaction of GTP and UMP to form GDP and UDP according to equation (54) might be explained

$$GTP + UMP \rightleftharpoons GDP + UDP \tag{54}$$

by the sum of the reactions represented by equations (46), (47), and (55).

$$GTP + AMP \rightleftharpoons ADP + GDP \tag{55}$$

$$2\,ADP \rightleftharpoons AMP + ATP \tag{46}$$

$$UMP + ATP \rightleftharpoons ADP + UDP \tag{47}$$

$$GTP + UMP \rightleftharpoons GDP + UDP \tag{54}$$

In this sequence only a catalytic amount of an adenine nucleotide would be required to keep the reaction going, and the net of the reaction would make it appear as though there had been a direct phosphoryl transfer from GTP to UMP.

A reaction has been reported in which 2 molecules of UDP dismutate to UTP and UMP[134] according to equation (56).

$$2\,UDP \rightleftharpoons UTP + UMP \tag{56}$$

Phosphoryl transfers in all reactions mentioned in this discussion involve only a single phosphate group. Reactions in which the two terminal phosphate groups of a nucleoside triphosphate are transferred simultaneously to an acceptor nucleotide have not been established.

At the present time, it seems that adenine nucleotides play a dominant role in these transphosphorylation reactions. More work has to be done to obtain information on the specificity of the kinases involved, as well as to establish the existence of transphosphorylation between non-adenine containing nucleotides.

VI. BIOGENESIS OF OTHER NUCLEOTIDES

As mentioned earlier in this discussion, many nucleotides of the acid-soluble class serve as coenzymes in enzyme-catalyzed reactions. In many instances, the nucleotide contains only the heterocyclic base, the pentose and phosphate. In others, another substituent is also present in the molecule such as another sugar, a vitamin, or other nitrogenous constituents. It is beyond the scope of this chapter to include the biosynthesis of coenzyme constituents which are chemically unrelated to nucleotides. These will be mostly treated in Chapter 11. Rather, what follows will outline some of the known schemes by which these substances are eventually combined with the nucleotide to form the coenzyme.

Many enzymes require adenylic acid-containing compounds as cofactors. AMP, ADP, and ATP, as such, participate in enzyme-catalyzed reactions, and their biogenesis has been discussed. The number of known coenzymes containing adenylic acid as part of their molecule is becoming quite numerous. The biogenesis of the more important ones is discussed below.

1. Pyridine Nucleotides

Diphosphopyridine Nucleotide (*DPN*). Two of the most important adenylic acid containing coenzymes are DPN and TPN-coenzymes concerned in oxidation reactions in biological systems. In addition to adenylic acid, both of these cofactors contain another ribose, extra phosphate, and a molecule of nicotinamide.

The ability of nicotinamide to be incorporated into a nucleotide structure was demonstrated in 1951. [124] ATP and hexose diphosphate were required for the synthesis. It was later established that PRPP and nicotinamide reacted in the presence of red blood cell hemolysates to form nicotinamide mononucleotide (NMN) according to reaction (57). [192]

$$(57)$$

However, the enzyme had such a low affinity for the substrate, nicotinamide, that the relative importance of this reaction in DPN synthesis was questioned. Nicotinic acid was shown to be able to condense with PRPP in this system to form nicotinic acid mononucleotide (desamido NMN) instead of NMN according to equation (58). [193, 194]

The enzyme catalyzing this reaction is apparently different from the one catalyzing the synthesis of NMN. The affinity of the enzyme for nicotinic acid is about 300 times that for nicotinamide which makes it more likely that nicotinic acid is the true intermediate in DPN synthesis. Two routes seem possible from this point to complete the synthesis of DPN. First, the

$$\text{Nicotinic acid} + P\text{—}P\text{—ribose—}P \longrightarrow \text{Nicotinic acid mononucleotide (desamido NMN)} + P\text{—}P \qquad (58)$$

amination of desamido NMN to form NMN which would then react with ATP to form DPN; or secondly, the reaction of desamido NMN with ATP to form desamido DPN which would then be aminated as the last step in the synthesis. The second alternative seems to be the preferred one in the biological system.

It had been demonstrated in 1950 that NMN and ATP in the presence of a yeast or liver enzyme forms DPN. [110] The enzyme catalyzing this reaction was called DPN pyrophosphorylase. More recently, it has been demonstrated that this enzyme is also capable of catalyzing a reaction between desamido NMN and ATP to form desamido DPN [194] (reaction 59).

$$\text{Desamido NMN} + \text{ATP} \longrightarrow \text{Desamido DPN} + \text{PPi} \qquad (59)$$

Another enzyme which has been found in yeast and rat liver is capable of catalyzing the conversion of desamido DPN to DPN (reaction 60). The enzyme has been called DPN synthetase and requires ATP, Mg^{++}, and either

$$\text{Desamido DPN} + \text{ATP} + \text{glutamine or } NH_3 \longrightarrow DPN^+ \qquad (60)$$

glutamine or ammonia as the source of nitrogen. Again, ammonia is the donor in the yeast system, while glutamine is the donor in mammalian systems. Further support for the existence of desamido DPN as an intermediate in the synthesis of DPN comes from a report of the presence of desamido DPN in *Penicillium chrysogenum*. [217]

It would appear, at the present time, that free nicotinamide does not play a role in DPN synthesis. Instead, the synthesis probably involves free nicotinic acid which is converted to nicotinic acid mononucleotide which, in turn, goes to desamido DPN, and, as a last step in the synthesis, the conversion leads to the amide. More recently another pathway has been postulated, [169] which is outlined in reaction (60a).

(60a)   Quinolinic acid   Quinolinic acid   Desamido NMN
                                        Ribonucleotide

The basic difference between this pathway and that outlined in reactions (58–60) is that the pentose phosphate moiety is added at an earlier stage in the synthesis, namely to quinolinic acid, which in turn is formed from tryptophan. Once the desamido NMN is formed, the further synthesis then proceeds to DPN$^+$ as outlined in reactions (59) and (60).

Alternative pathway for DPN synthesis. Nicotinamide and ribose-1-phosphate react in the presence of a nucleoside phosphorylase to form nicotinamide ribonucleoside. This product can then be further acted on by a kinase and ATP to form nicotinamide mononucleotide. Both of these activities have been demonstrated in liver. [211] This sequence of reactions is identical to that by which free purines or pyrimidines may be utilized for nucleotide synthesis as described in Sections IIID and IVD. The relative importance of these reactions in DPN synthesis has again been questioned on the grounds of the unphysiological level of nicotinamide required for the nucleoside phosphorylase reaction.

Triphosphopyridine Nucleotide (TPN). The biosynthesis of TPN consists in the introduction of another phosphate residue into position 2′ of the adenylic acid portion of DPN. Enzymes catalyzing reaction 61 have been reported in extracts of avian liver [258] and yeast. [111] Although reaction 61 is shown for the oxidized form of the coenzyme, the yeast enzyme has the ability to catalyze the phosphorylation of the reduced coenzyme as well.

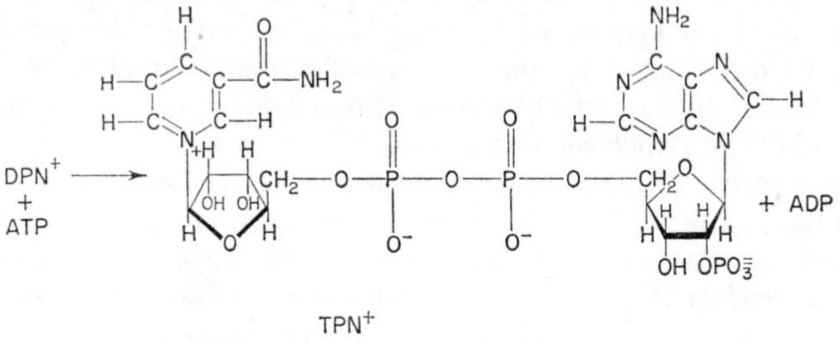

$$(61)$$

TPN⁺

2. Flavin Adenine Dinucleotide

It is not the purpose of this section to outline the steps of riboflavin synthesis. In fact, the pathway of riboflavin synthesis is not known with certainty. The structure of riboflavin is indicated in Fig. 4. It should be noted that the side chain attached to the heterocyclic ring is not the sugar D-ribose, but rather ribityl alcohol, the reduced form of the sugar. In essence, rings B and C have been shown to be derived from purine precursors, [137, 182] while ring A is probably formed from 2 carbon fragments. [183] The 5 carbon side chain is attached to nitrogen 9 of the ring. The pathway which leads to this

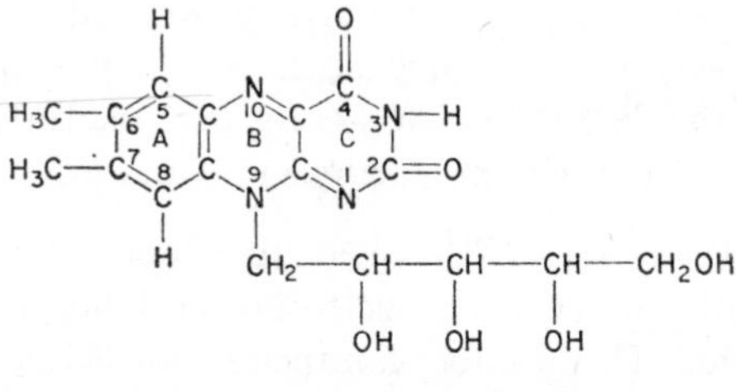

FIG. 4. Structure of riboflavin.

substance is not known except that the oxidative and non-oxidative pentose phosphate pathways have been implicated, as evidenced largely through labeling experiments. [184] An interesting question arises concerning the stage at which the ribityl group is added. Two possibilities present themselves; first, the ribityl group or ribose is added to the precursor before completion of the ring system as seen in the case of purine synthesis, or secondly, the ring system is first completed and the ribityl group added last. Unfortunately we cannot answer this question at the present time. There is some evidence [152] that the nucleosides and nucleotides are not more efficient than the free bases for the stimulation of riboflavin synthesis in E. ashbyii, but this certainly does not eliminate the possibility that the nucleosides or nucleotides may not be intermediates.

Flavin mononucleotide and flavin adenine dinucleotide have been shown to be important in reactions involving oxidations and reductions. The synthesis of these nucleotides from the vitamin is quite similar to that described for the pyridine nucleotide coenzymes.

A "kinase" which catalyzes the phosphorylation of riboflavin by ATP has been reported in yeast. Like other kinase reactions, Mg^{++} was found necessary for the reaction. The reaction proceeds according to equation (62).

Flavin mononucleotide (FMN)

$$(62)$$

The synthesis of flavin adenine dinucleotide from FMN involves a reaction with ATP. The product of the reaction as indicated in reaction (63) is FAD and pyrophosphate.

Flavin adenine dinucleotide (FAD)

$$(63)$$

The reaction is reversible and the enzyme has been purified from yeast. [215]

3. Coenzyme A

The structure of coenzyme A (CoASH) is indicated in Fig. 5. In essence, it is composed of one molecule of adenylic acid, one molecule of pantothenic acid, and one molecule of β-mercaptoethanol amine. There are two other molecules of phosphate present, one joining the adenylic acid portion to pantothenic acid, and the other esterified to the 3 position of the ribose. The biogenesis of adenylic acid has been discussed.

It was demonstrated in 1941 that yeast macerates could synthesize pantothenic acid from pantoic acid and β-alanine. [265]

The β-mercaptoethanolamine portion of the coenzyme has been shown to be derived from cysteine. [24, 181] Pantothenic acid is converted to pantetheine in a phosphorylated form. Two more enzymatic reactions complete the synthesis of the coenzyme. The first involves the addition of the adenylic

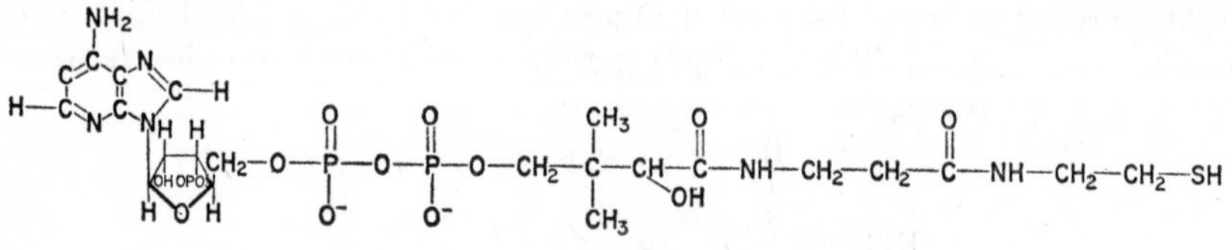

FIG. 5. Structure of coenzyme A (CoASH).

acid (reaction 64), the second, the addition of the extra phosphate group on the 3 position of ribose (reaction 65). The enzyme which converts 4'-phospho-pantetheine to dephospho coenzyme A is called dephospho CoA pyro-phosphorylase, while the second, which adds the additional phosphate group to the sugar has been named dephospho CoA kinase. [87]

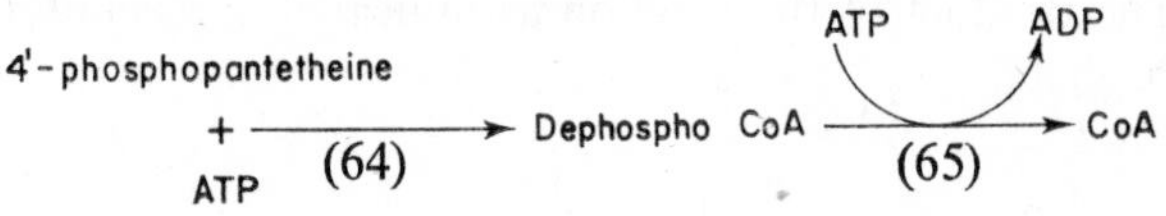

$$4'\text{-phosphopantetheine} + \text{ATP} \xrightarrow{(64)} \text{Dephospho CoA} \xrightarrow[(65)]{\text{ATP} \quad \text{ADP}} \text{CoA}$$

4. Amino Acid Adenylates

The activation of amino acids involves the formation of amino acyl adenylates, and these compounds, as a class, are believed to be important intermediates in protein biogenesis. The amino acid-activating enzymes catalyze a reaction of the general type indicated in reaction (66).

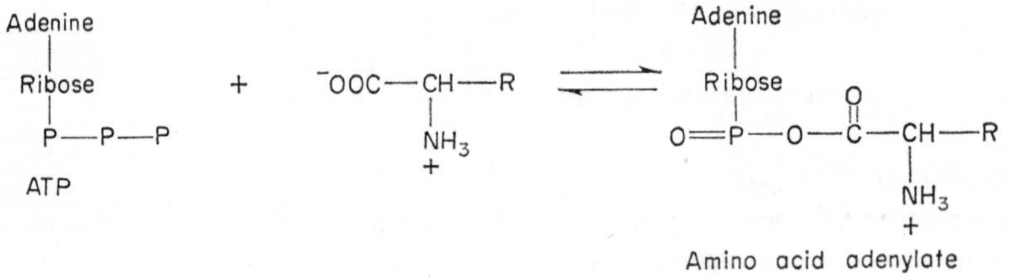

Amino acid adenylate

Enzymatic activity of this type from a variety of sources has been demonstrated for many amino acids. Although the reaction is reversible whereby a pyrophosphorolysis of the adenylate can take place, the equilibrium appears to be in favor of the synthesis. The products of this reaction are mixed anhydrides of adenylic acid and the amino acid concerned. As such, the amino acid is "activated" and is of a sufficient energy level to be transferred to a low molecular weight soluble RNA, the next step in protein synthesis.

5. Mixed Anhydrides of Sulfuric and Adenylic Acids

There are two important compounds of adenylic acid and sulfuric acid. One of these is adenosine-5'-phosphosulfate (APS) (Fig. 6a). This compound was first characterized in 1958, [206] and occurs as an important intermediate in the activation and transfer of sulfate. Its synthesis involves a reaction with ATP and sulfate to form sulfuryl adenylate according to reaction (67.) The

$$ATP + Sulfate \rightleftharpoons APS + PP_i \qquad (67)$$

enzyme catalyzing this reaction is called ATP-sulfurylase and is highly specific for ATP. The equilibrium is far to the left.

Another mixed anhydride of adenylic and sulfuric acids exists in which another mole of phosphate is present in the 3'-position of APS. The product of this reaction is phosphoadenosine-5'-phosphosulfate (PAPS), the structure of which is given in Fig. 6b. It is this latter compound that serves as the

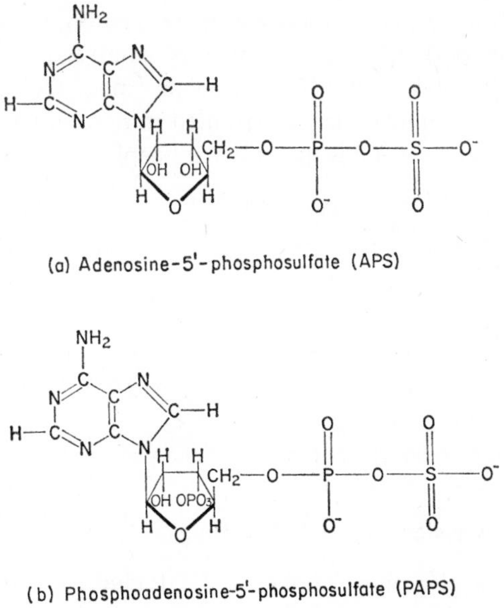

(a) Adenosine-5'-phosphosulfate (APS)

(b) Phosphoadenosine-5'-phosphosulfate (PAPS)

FIG. 6. Mixed anhydrides of sulfuric and adenylic acid.

primary sulfate donor in reactions involving a transfer of this group. Its synthesis is illustrated in equation (68).

$$ATP + APS \rightleftharpoons PAPS + ADP \qquad (68)$$

The equilibrium is to the right. The enzyme catalyzing the reaction is called APS-sulfokinase. It is not sure at the present time whether ATP must be the phosphoryl donor in this reaction, or whether other triphosphates can work as well. Although the sulfurylase reaction has an unfavorable equilibrium with regard to synthesis of APS, the sulfokinase reaction succeeds in pulling the former with a net formation of "active" sulfate from ATP and sulfate.

Both enzymes catalyzing these two reactions have been purified and shown to be distinct. They apparently have a wide distribution in nature and have been found in mammalian tissues as well as in yeast.

In addition to these adenylic acid-containing coenzymes, adenosine diphosphate glucose has also been found, as indicated in Table 3 (see p. 90).

The first demonstration of a specific function of cytidine nucleotides other than that of being a constituent of nucleic acids was made in 1955[106, 107] when it was found that traces of CTP stimulated the enzymatic incorporation of phosphorylcholine into lecithin. This led to the discovery of CDP-choline and CDP-ethanolamine which are essential intermediates in phospholipid biogenesis (see also Chapter 3).

6. *Cytidine Diphosphate Choline*

CDP-choline (Fig. 7) is synthesized in a reaction in which CTP and phosphorylcholine participate and which is catalyzed by a cytoplasmic bound enzyme (reaction 69). This enzyme, phosphorylcholine cytidyl transferase, has been found widely distributed in nature, i.e. in yeast, plants, and mammalian systems. CTP is the only triphosphate compound acceptable

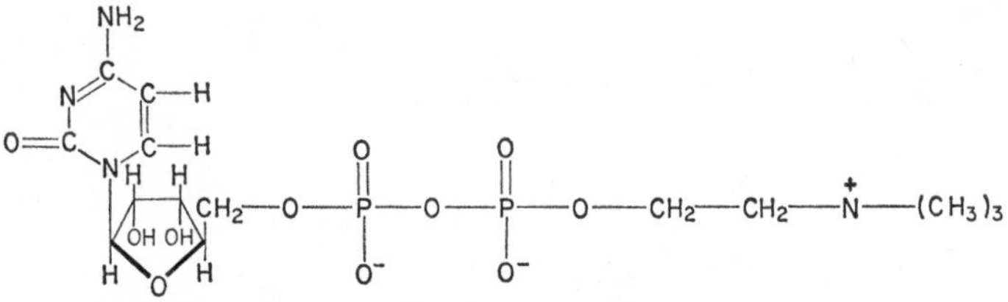

FIG. 7. Structure of cytidine diphosphate choline.

as a substrate in this system. The CDP-choline thus formed is then transferred

$$CTP + phosphorylcholine \rightleftharpoons CDP\text{-}choline + PP_i \qquad (69)$$

to an α, β-diglyceride to form lecithin and CMP as products.

7. *Cytidine Diphosphate Ethanolamine*

The biosynthesis of this compound from CTP and phosphorylethanolamine (equation 70) is analogous to that of CDP-choline. The enzyme, phosphorylethanolamine-cytidyl transferase which catalyzes this reaction, appears to be

different from the enzyme catalyzing the synthesis of CDP-choline. [105] Like
the latter, it is also specific for CTP. Cytidine diphosphate ethanolamine,

$$CTP + phosphorylethanolamine \rightleftharpoons CDP\text{-}ethanolamine + PP_i \quad (70)$$

like CDP-choline, serves as the donor of the phosphorylethanolamine group
to the α, β-diglyceride to form phosphatidylethanolamine.

8. Cytidine Diphosphate Glycerol

The isolation of CDP-glycerol from *Lactobacillus arabinosus* was first
reported in 1956. [9] A complex molecule has also been isolated from this
organism, and has been found to contain glycerolphosphate as part of its
structure. [10] Chiefly on the basis of isotope exchange data, it has been speculated that CDP-glycerol is synthesized in a reaction from CTP and glycerolphosphate according to equation (71). The CDP-glycerol so formed would then
serve as the phosphoryl-glycerol donor in the synthesis of the polymeric
molecule isolated from *Lactobacillus*.

$$CTP + glycerolphosphate \rightleftharpoons CDP\text{-}glycerol + PP_i \quad (71)$$

9. Cytidine Diphosphate Diglyceride

The structure of this compound is indicated in Fig. 8.

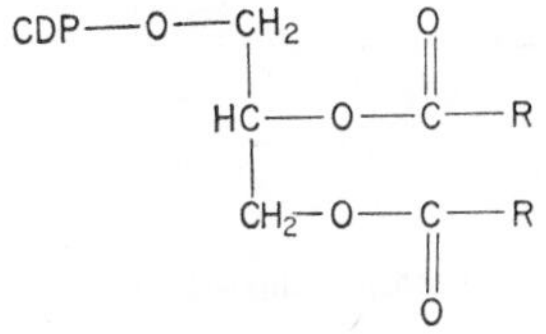

Fig. 8.

The proposed mechanism of synthesis [4] is indicated in reaction (72).

$$CDP\text{-}choline + L\text{-}phosphatidic\ acid \longrightarrow$$
$$CDP\text{-}\alpha,\beta\text{-}diglyceride + P\text{-}choline \quad (72)$$

10. Deoxycytidine Diphosphate Derivatives

Deoxycytidine diphosphate choline was first isolated from sea urchin
eggs. [252] Deoxycytidine diphosphate ethanolamine was obtained and
identified from calf thymus. [189, 190] A second compound from calf thymus,
originally designated as deoxyCDP-X, is believed to be deoxyCDP-choline.
The biosynthesis of these compounds proceeds probably by reactions

analogous to those discussed for CDP-choline and CDP-ethanolamine, involving deoxyCTP instead of CTP. The metabolic function of these compounds is not known.

In addition to the cytidine nucleotides indicated above, which for the most part are concerned with phospholipid synthesis, there are other cytidine nucleotides which are associated with a variety of sugars, and these are outlined in Tables 4 and 5.

Within the past few years, a host of nucleotide sugars have been discovered in which several nucleotides are involved, as well as a wide variety of sugars or sugar derivatives. The major functions of these nucleotide sugars in metabolism appear to be as glycosyl donors for the synthesis of more complex polysaccharides. In addition, these nucleotides serve as the "active form" in which many sugar interconversions take place.

This chapter will not attempt to delve into the synthesis of these nucleotide sugars, except to indicate the general nature of the reactions which may be

TABLE 3. ADENOSINE-DIPHOSPHATE DERIVATIVES OF SUGARS

Sugar or sugar derivative	Source of nucleotide	Type of enzyme	Source of enzyme
D-Glucose	Chlorella[103a]	Pyrophosphorylase	Higher plants[47a]

TABLE 4. CYTIDINE-DIPHOSPHATE DERIVATIVES OF SUGARS

Sugar or sugar derivative	Source of nucleotide	Type of enzymes	Source of enzymes
3,6-Dideoxy-D-arabino-hexose ("tyvelose")	Salmonella enteritidis[168]		
3,6-Dideoxy-D-xylo-hexose ("abequose")	Salmonella typhimurium[168]		
D-Glucose		Pyrophosphorylase	Salmonella paratyphi[62]
Glycerol	Lactobacillus[11]	Pyrophosphorylase	Bacteria, Chlorella, yeast[218]
Ribitol	Lactobacillus,[7, 8, 96] Staphylococcus aureus[241]	Pyrophosphorylase	Bacteria, Chlorella, yeast[218]

TABLE 5. CYTIDINE MONOPHOSPHATE DERIVATIVES OF SUGARS

Sugar or sugar derivative	Source of nucleotide	Types of enzyme	Source of enzyme
N-Acetyl-neuraminic acid	*Escherichia coli*[39]	Pyrophosphorylase	Submaxillary gland,[209] *Neisseria meningitidis*[262, 263]
3-Deoxyoctulosonic acid		Pyrophosphorylase	*Escherichia coli*[54]
N-Glycolyl-neuraminic acid		Pyrophosphorylase	*Escherichia coli*[54]

TABLE 6. URIDINE-DIPHOSPHATE DERIVATIVES OF SUGARS

Sugar or sugar derivative	Source of nucleotide	Type of enzyme	Source of enzyme
2-Acetamido-2-deoxy-D-glucose 6-(D-galacto-pyranosyl phosphate)	Hen oviduct[52, 253]		
2-Acetamido-2-deoxy-D-galactose	Liver,[186] hen oviduct,[242, 243, 249] milk,[42] insect hemolymph,[33] higher plant[70]	Epimerase	*Bacillus subtilis*,[64] liver[140]
2-Acetamido-2-deoxy-D-glucose-6-sulfate	Hen oviduct[242, 243]		
2-Acetamido-2-deoxy-D-glucose	Yeast,[30] bacteria,[36, 230] fungi,[14, 19, 232] higher plants,[17, 18, 235] liver,[79, 93, 225] mammary gland[43, 143] milk,[42] aorta,[104] lens,[108, 142] hen oviduct,[242, 243] insect hemolymph[33]	Pyrophosphorylase	Yeast,[65] *Staphylococcus aureus*,[250] liver[139, 156, 231, 250]
N-Acetylmuramic acid-peptides	*Staphylococcus aureus* inhibited by penicillin and other drugs[177, 244]	Transfer of amino acids to UDP-N acetylmuramic acid	*Staphylococcus aureus*[38, 97, 244]
N-Acetylneuraminic acid→D-galacto-pyranosyl-(1→4)-2-acetamido-2-deoxy-D-glucose; and (1→6) isomer of above	Colostrum[101]		

TABLE 6—(cont.)

Sugar or sugar derivative	Source of nucleotide	Type of enzyme	Source of enzyme
2-Amino-2-deoxy-D-galactose		Epimerase	Liver[140]
2-Amino-2-deoxy-D-glucose		Pyrophosphorylase	Liver,[141] mast-cell tumor[221]
L-Arabinose	Seedlings[63]	Pyrophosphorylase Epimerase	Higher plants[165] Higher plants[49, 165]
Colominic acid	Escherichia coli[171]		
1,3-Dihydroxy-2-propanone ("dihydroxyacetone")	Pneumococcus[222]		
D-Fructose	Higher plants[70]		
L-Fucosyl-(1→?)-D-galactopyranosyl-(1→4)-2-acetamido-2-deoxy-D-glucose	Milk and colostrum [109]		
D-Galactose	Yeast,[157] bacteria,[167, 266] algae,[25, 251] Penicillium,[14] seedlings,[63] liver,[79] mammary gland,[43] milk,[42] aorta,[104] lens,[108, 142] insect hemolymph[33]	Pyrophosphorylase Transferase Epimerase	Yeast,[103] higher plants,[165] liver[95] Yeast,[103, 125] bacteria,[116, 119] higher plants,[179] mammary gland,[224] liver[117, 150] Yeast,[125, 148, 149] bacteria,[78] higher plants,[165] liver[147]
D-Galacturonic acid	Pneumococcus,[229] seedlings[164]	Pyrophosphorylase Epimerase	Seedlings[48] Pneumococcus,[228] higher plants[49]
D-Glucose	Yeast,[32, 187] algae,[25, 251] bacteria,[36, 230] fungi,[14, 19, 232] higher plants,[17, 18, 63] liver,[79, 93, 213, 225] mammary gland,[43, 143, 226] milk,[42] lens,[108, 142] aorta,[104] insect hemolymph[33]	Pyrophosphorylase	Yeast,[161, 162] bacteria,[116, 230] higher plants,[28, 53, 57, 165, 255] liver,[176, 156, 231] muscle,[256] mammary gland[224]
D-Glucuronic acid	Bacteria,[36, 230] seedlings,[235] red alga,[251] milk,[42] liver[46, 47, 79, 93, 225, 240]	Dehydrogenase	Bacteria,[145, 227] seedlings,[246] liver,[151, 245, 247] skin[99]
L-Iduronic acid		Pyrophosphorylase Epimerase	Seedlings[48] Skin[98]
L-Rhamnose	Pneumococcus[223]	Reduction of UDP-glucose	Leaves[15]
D-Xylose	Seedlings[63]	Pyrophosphorylase Decarboxylase	Higher plants[165] Higher plants[49]

TABLE 7. GUANOSINE-DIPHOSPHATE DERIVATIVES OF SUGARS

Sugar or sugar derivative	Source of nucleotide	Type of enzyme	Source of enzyme
?-Arabinose	Colostrum,[44] mammary gland[44]		
6-Deoxy-D-mannose and 6-deoxy-D-talose		Reduction of GDP-mannose	Bacteria[144]
3,6-Dideoxy-L-xylo-hexose ("colitose")	Escherichia coli[82]	Reduction of GDP-mannose	Escherichia coli[83]
D-Fructose	Streptomyces griseus[188]		
L-Fucose	Aerobacter aerogenes,[60] mammary gland,[43, 44] milk[41, 42, 44]	Reduction of GDP-mannose	Aerobacter aerogenes,[58, 59] rabbit tissues[51]
L-Galactose	Red alga[251]		
?-Galactose	Aorta,[104] mammary gland,[44] milk[44]		
D-Glucose	Streptomyces griseus,[188] mammary gland,[34, 44] milk[44]	Pyrophosphorylase	Mammary gland[34]
D-Glycero-D-mannoheptose	Yeast[61]	Pyrophosphorylase	Yeast[170]
Lactose and un-identified oligosaccharides	Milk[44]		
D-Mannose	Yeast,[29] red alga,[251] molds,[14, 188] mammary gland,[34, 43, 44] milk,[42, 44] hen oviduct,[242, 243] aorta,[104] animals[155]	Pyrophosphorylase	Yeast,[160] mammary gland,[34] bacteria[191]
D-Mannuronic acid		Dehydrogenase	Arthrobactet

TABLE 8. THYMIDINE-DIPHOSPHATE DERIVATIVES OF SUGARS

Sugar or sugar derivatives	Source of nucleotide	Type of enzyme	Source of enzyme
2-Acetamido-2-deoxy-D-galactose		Epimerase	Pseudomonas aeruginosa[113, 114]
2-Acetamido-2-deoxy-D-glucose		TDP-2-amino-2-deoxy-D-glucose	Pseudomonas aeruginosa[113, 114]

TABLE 8—*(cont.)*

Sugar or sugar derivatives	Source of nucleotide	Type of enzyme	Source of enzyme
Acetamidodideoxy sugars	*Escherichia coli*[175]	Reduction and amination of dTDP-glucose	*Escherichia coli* [146, 257]
2-Amino-2-deoxy-D-glucose		Pyrophosphorylase	*Pseudomonas aeruginosa*[113, 114]
D-Galactose		Pyrophosphorylase	Bacteria,[178] seedlings[163]
		Epimerase	Bacteria,[178, 254] seedlings[163]
D-Glucose		Pyrophosphorylase	Bacteria,[115, 180] seedlings[180]
D-Mannose	*Streptomyces griseus*[5]	Epimerase	*Streptomyces griseus*[6]
L-Rhamnose and related 6-deoxy-hexoses	Bacteria,[172, 173, 248] *Streptomyces griseus*[5]	Reduction of dTDP-glucose	Bacteria,[66, 174, 180] *Streptomyces griseus*[6]
D-Ribose	*Streptomyces griseus*[5]		

nvolved. Tables 3–8 list most of the currently known nucleotide sugars. The source of the material is also indicated in these tables and an attempt is made to indicate the nature of the enzymatic reaction involved in the synthesis. These data are drawn from two excellent reviews on this subject, and the reader is referred to the papers by Neufeld and Hassid [166] and Ginsburg. [56]

The most common pathway available for the synthesis of nucleotide sugars involves a reaction with the triphosphate derivative of the nucleotides and the sugar phosphate, as indicated in reaction (73). The enzyme catalyzing the reaction is termed a pyrophosphorylase.

$$\text{UTP} + \text{glucose-1-P} \rightleftharpoons \text{UDP-glucose} + \text{PP}_i \qquad (73)$$

In like manner pyrophosphorylase reactions in which GTP, TTP, ATP and CTP serve as substrates with a variety of other sugars have been described.

A second type of reaction which can introduce a sugar to a nucleotide derivative involves a transfer of a sugar as the "sugar phosphate" to a nucleotide-bound sugar as indicated in reaction (74) for UDP-glucose and galactase-1-phosphate. The enzymes involved in this type of reaction are classified as transferases.

$$\text{UDP-glucose} + \text{galactose-1-phosphate} \rightleftharpoons$$
$$\text{UDP-galactose} + \text{glucose-1-phosphate} \qquad (74)$$

Again, the diversity of nucleotide diphosphate sugars as well as the sugar-1-phosphates involved in this type of reaction is indicated in Tables 3–8.

The previous two reactions, namely those catalyzed by pyrophosphorylases and transferases, constitute the two major ways by which a sugar can be brought to the "nucleotide level". In most instances these result in formation of the diphosphate derivative of the nucleotide, but one exception appears to be the formation of a class of CMP-derivatives in which a pyrophosphorylase reaction is involved. These compounds are cited in Table 5.

Once the nucleotide sugar is formed, it can then undergo a variety of transformations while still bound to the nucleotide. These may be classified as follows:

(A) *Epimerization reactions.* In this transformation on epimerization of one of the carbons of the sugar takes place. In some instances more than one carbon atom may be eventually epimerized. An example of this is given in reaction (75).

$$\text{UDP-glucose} \rightleftharpoons \text{UDP-galactose} \tag{75}$$

Epimerase reactions of this type are known for a number of sugars and are cited in Tables 3–8. The mechanism of the epimerization has not yet been elucidated. Most appear to involve the hydroxyl in carbon 4 of the sugar, but others have been reported for carbon atoms 2 and 5.

(B) *Oxidation of the primary alcohol group.* Many sugars are apparently oxidized to their uronic acid derivatives while bound to a nucleotide as illustrated in reaction (75) for UDP-glucose.

$$\text{UDP-glucose} \rightarrow \text{UDP-glucuronic acid} \tag{75}$$

The enzyme catalyzing this reaction may be called a dehydrogenase.

(C) *Decarboxylation reactions.* Once a uronic acid derivative is formed (as indicated in reaction 75) it may then undergo a decarboxylation to form a nucleotide-pentose derivative as indicated in reaction (76) for the conversion of UDP-glucuronic acid to UDP-xylose.

$$\text{UDP-glucuronic acid} \rightarrow \text{UDP-xylose} \tag{76}$$

The enzyme catalyzing such a reaction is termed a decarboxylase.

(D) *Formation of deoxyhexoses.* The transformation of a primary alcohol group of a sugar to a deoxy derivative involves a complex sequence of reactions in which the sugar being transformed still remains nucleotide bound. Oftentimes in this conversion the configuration of several carbon atoms are involved. An example of this transformation is given in reaction (77) for the transformation of GDP-D-mannose to GDP-L-fucose.

$$\text{GDP-D-Mannose} \rightarrow \text{GDP-L-fucose} \tag{77}$$

In this transformation epimerization at carbons 3 and 5 as well as reduction at carbon atom 6 are involved.

It should become obvious from Tables 3–8 that the nature of these inter-conversions is quite diverse, and that the reactions as a whole are spread rather widely throughout the plant and animal kingdom.

SUMMARY

The heterocyclic rings, purine and pyrimidine, are made *de novo* from small precursor molecules. Pathways also exist for the transformation of preformed purines and pyrimidines into nucleotides, but these reactions are believed to play minor roles in nucleotide biogenesis.

Several routes are available for the synthesis of the sugar moieties of the nucleotides, but an actual assessment at the present time of the contribution of these routes *in vivo* is difficult. It would appear, however, that the non-oxidative and oxidative pentose phosphate pathways are both involved. Deoxyribose is either derived directly from ribose, or both sugars are synthesized through very closely related pathways. The reduction may occur at the nucleotide level, since evidence has been found for the transformation of ribonucleotides to deoxyribonucleotides in cell-free systems. The mechanism of the reductive step is not known, however.

In the case of purine nucleotide biogenesis, the sugar phosphate is added prior to completion of the ring, while in pyrimidine biogenesis the heterocyclic ring system is completed first, and the pentose phosphate added subsequently.

A number of other nucleotides are now known which contain uridylic, guanylic, adenylic, and cytidylic acids as part of their structure. Since these nucleotides are all present in RNA, one of its functions may be that of a storehouse of nucleotides which are necessary for other functions.

REFERENCES

1. ABRAMS, R. and BENTLEY, M. *Arch. Biochem. Biophys.* **79**, 91 (1959).
2. ABRAMS, R. and DURAISWAMI, D. *Biochem. Biophys. Res. Commun.* **18**, 409 (1965).
3. ABRAMS, R., LIBENSON, L. and EDMONDS, M. *Biochem. Biophys. Res. Commun.* **3**, 272 (1960).
4. AGRANOFF, B. W., BRADLEY, R. M. and BRADY, R. O. *J. Biol. Chem.* **233**, 1077 (1958).
5. BADDILEY, J. and BLUMSON, N. L. *Biochim. Biophys. Acta* **39**, 376 (1960).
6. BADDILEY, J., BLUMSON, N. L., DIGIROLOMO, A. and DIGIROLOMO, M. *Biochim. Biophys. Acta* **50**, 391 (1961).
7. BADDILEY, J., BUCHANAN, J. G. and CARSS, B. *J. Chem. Soc.* 1869 (1957).
8. BADDILEY, J., BUCHANAN, J. G., CARSS, B. and MATHIAS, A. P. *J. Chem. Soc.* 4583 (1956).
9. BADDILEY, J. BUCHANAN, J. G., CARSS, B., MATHIAS, A. P. and SANDERSON, A. R. *Biochem. J.* **64**, 599 (1956).
10. BADDILEY, J., BUCHANAN, J. G. and GREENBERG, G. R. *Biochem. J.* **66**, 51P (1957).
11. BADDILEY, J., BUCHANAN, J. G., MATHIAS, A. P. and SANDERSON, A. R. *J. Chem. Soc.* 4186 (1956).
12. BAGATELL, F. K., WRIGHT, E. W. and SABLE, H. Z. *Biochim. Biophys. Acta* **28**, 216 (1958).
13. BAGATELL, F. K., WRIGHT, E. W. and SABLE, H. Z. *J. Biol. Chem.* **234**, 1369 (1959).
14. BALLIO, A., CASINOVI, C. and SERLUPPI-CRESCENZI, G. *Biochim. Biophys. Acta* **20**, 414 (1956).

15. BARBER, G. *Biochem. Biophys. Res. Commun.* **8**, 204 (1962).
16. BARNES, F. W. and SCHOENHEIMER, R. *J. Biol. Chem.* **151**, 123 (1943).
17. BERGKVIST, R. *Acta Chem. Scand.* **10**, 1303 (1956).
18. BERGKVIST, R. *Acta Chem. Scand.* **11**, 1457 (1957).
19. BERGKVIST, R. *Acta Chem. Scand.* **12**, 1549, 1554 (1958).
20. BERNSTEIN, I. A. *J. Biol. Chem.* **221**, 873 (1956).
21. BERNSTEIN, I. A. and SWEET, D. *J. Biol. Chem.* **233**, 1194 (1958).
22. BERTANI, L. E., HÄGGMARK, A. and REICHARD, P. *J. Biol. Chem.* **236**, PC67 (1961).
23. BLAKLEY, R. L. and BARKER, H. A. *Biochem. Biophys. Res. Commun.* **16**, 391 (1964).
24. BROWN, G. M. and SNELL, E. E. *J. Am. Chem. Soc.* **75**, 2782 (1953).
25. BUCHANAN, J. G., BASSHAM, J. A., BENSON, A. A., BRADLEY, D. F., CALVIN, M. DAUS, L. L., GOODMAN, M., HAYES, P. M., LYNCH, V. H., NORRIS, L. T. and WILSON, A. T. *Johns Hopkins Univ. McCollum-Pratt Inst. Contrib.* **36**, 440 (1962).
26. BUCHANAN, J. M. and SONNE, J. C. *J. Biol. Chem.* **166**, 781 (1946).
27. BUCHANAN, J. M., SONNE, J. C. and DELLUVA, A. M. *J. Biol. Chem.* **173**, 81 (1948).
28. BURMA, D. P. and MORTIMER, D. C. *Arch. Biochem. Biophys.* **62**, 16 (1956).
29. CABIB, E. and LELOIR, L. F. *J. Biol. Chem.* **206**, 779 (1954).
30. CABIB, C. E., LELOIR, L. F. and CARDINI, C. E. *J. Biol. Chem.* **203**, 1055 (1953).
31. CANELLAKIS, E. S. *J. Biol. Chem.* **227**, 701 (1957).
32. CAPUTTO, R., LELOIR, L. F., CARDINI, C. E. and PALADINI, A. C. *J. Biol. Chem.* **184**, 333 (1950).
33. CAREY, F. G. and WYATT, G. R. *Biochim. Biophys. Acta* **41**, 178 (1960).
34. CARLSON, D. M. and HANSEN, R. G. *J. Biol. Chem.* **237**, 1260 (1962).
35. CARTER, C. E. and COHEN, L. H. *J. Biol. Chem.* **222**, 17 (1960).
36. CIFONELLI, J. A. and DORFMAN, A. *J. Biol. Chem.* **228**, 547 (1957).
37. COLOWICK, S. P. and KALCKAR, H. M. *J. Biol. Chem.* **148**, 117 (1943).
38. COMB, D. G. *J. Biol. Chem.* **237**, 1601 (1962).
39. COMB, D. G., SHIMIZU, F. and ROSEMAN, S. *J. Am. Chem. Soc.* **81**, 5513 (1959).
40. CORI, O. and LIPMANN, F. *J. Biol. Chem.* **194**, 417 (1952).
41. DENAMUR, R., FAUCONNEAU, G. and GUNTZ, G. *Compt. Rend.* **246**, 2820 (1958).
42. DENAMUR, R., FAUCONNEAU, G. and GUNTZ, G. *Compt. Rend.* **246**, 492, 652 (1958).
43. DENAMUR, R., FAUCONNEAU, G. and GUNTZ, G. *Compt. Rend.* **248**, 2531 (1959).
44. DENAMUR, R., FAUCONNEAU, G. and JARRIGE-GUNTZ, G. *Ann. Biol. Animale Biochim. Biophys.* **1**, 74 (1961).
45. DICKENS, F. *Biochem. J.* **32**, 1626 (1938).
46. DUTTON, G. J. *Biochem. J.* **71**, 141 (1959).
47. DUTTON, G. J. and STOREY, I. D. E. *Biochem. J.* **57**, 275 (1954).
47a ESPADA, J. *J. Biol. Chem.* **237**, 3577 (1962).
48. FEINGOLD, D. S., NEUFELD, E. F. and HASSID, W. *Arch. Biochem. Biophys.* **78**, 401 (1958).
49. FEINGOLD, D. S., NEUFELD, E. F. and HASSID, W. Z. *J. Biol. Chem.* **235**, 910 (1960).
50. FLAKS, J. G., ERWIN, M. J. and BUCHANAN, J. M. *J. Biol. Chem.* **229**, 603 (1957).
51. FOSTER, D. W. and GINSBURG, V. *Biochem. Biophys. Acta* **54**, 376 (1961).
52. GABRIEL, O. and ASHWELL, G. *J. Biol. Chem.* **237**, 1400 (1962).
53. GANGULI, N. C. *J. Biol. Chem.* **232**, 337 (1958).
54. GHALAMBOR, M. A. and HEATH, E. C. *Biochem. Biophys. Res. Commun.* **10**, 346 (1963).
55. GIBSON, D. M., AYENGAR, P. and SANADI, D. R. *Biochim. Biophys. Acta.* **21**, 86 (1956).
56. GINSBURG, V. *Advances in Enzymology* **26**, 35 (1964).
57. GINSBURG, V. *J. Biol. Chem.* **232**, 55 (1958).
58. GINSBURG, V. *J. Biol. Chem.* **235**, 2196 (1960).
59. GINSBURG, V. *J. Biol. Chem.* **236**, 2389 (1961).
60. GINSBURG, V. and KIRKMAN, H. N. *J. Am. Chem. Soc.* **80**, 3481 (1958).
61. GINSBURG, V., O'BRIEN, P. J. and HALL, C. W. *J. Biol. Chem.* **237**, 497 (1962).
62. GINSBURG, V., O'BRIEN, P. J. and HALL, C. W. *Biochem. Biophys. Res. Commun.* **7**, 1 (1962).
63. GINSBURG, V., STUMPF, P. K. and HASSID, W. Z. *J. Biol. Chem.* **223**, 977 (1956).
64. GLASER, L. *Biochim. Biophys. Acta* **31**, 575 (1959).

65. GLASER, L. and BROWN, D. H. *Proc. Natl. Acad. Sci. U.S.* **41**, 253 (1955).
66. GLASER, L. and KORNFELD, S. *J. Biol. Chem.* **236**, 1795 (1961).
67. GLOCK, G. E. *The Nucleic Acids*, vol. 2, p. 248, ed. by E. Chargaff and J. N. Davidson. Academic Press, New York, 1955.
68. GOLDTHWAIT, D. A. *J. Biol. Chem.* **222**, 1051 (1956).
69. GOLDTHWAIT, D. A., PEABODY, R. A. and GREENBERG, G. R. *J. Biol. Chem.* **221**, 569 (1956).
70. GONZALES, N. S. and PONTIS, H. G. *Biochim. Biophys. Acta* **69**, 179 (1963).
71. GREENBERG, G. R. *Arch. Biochem.* **19**, 337 (1948).
72. GREENBERG, G. R. *Federation Proc.* **9**, 179 (1950).
73. GREENBERG, G. R. *Federation Proc.* **10**, 192 (1951).
74. GREENBERG, G. R. *J. Biol. Chem.* **190**, 611 (1951).
75. GREENBERG, G. R., JAENICKE, L. and SILVERMAN, M. *Biochim. Biophys. Acta* **17**, 589 (1955).
76. GROSSMAN, L. and HAWKINS, G. R. *Biochim. Biophys. Acta* **26**, 657 (1957).
77. GUARINO, A. J. and SABLE, H. Z. *Biochim. Biophys. Acta* **20**, 201 (1956).
78. HANSEN, R. G. and CRAINE, E. M. *J. Biol. Chem.* **208**, 293 (1954).
79. HANSEN, R. G., FREEDLAND, R. A. and SCOTT, H. M. *J. Biol. Chem.* **219**, 391 (1956).
80. HARTMAN, S. C. and BUCHANAN, J. M. *J. Biol. Chem.* **233**, 451 (1958).
81. HARTMAN, S. C. and BUCHANAN, J. M. *J. Biol. Chem.* **233**, 456 (1958).
82. HEATH, E. C. *Biochim. Biophys. Acta* **39**, 377 (1960).
83. HEATH, E. C. and ELBEIN, A. D. *Proc. Natl. Acad. Sci. U.S.* **48**, 1209 (1962).
84. HEIDELBERGER, C., LIEBMAN, K. C. HARBERS, E. and BHARGAVA, P. M. *Cancer Research* **17**, 399 (1957).
85. HEINRICH, M. R. and WILSON, D. W. *J. Biol. Chem.* **186**, 447 (1950).
86. HIATT, H. H. and LAREAU, J. *J. Biol. Chem.* **233**, 1023 (1958).
87. HOAGLAND, M. B. and NOVELLI, G. D. *J. Biol. Chem.* **207**, 767 (1954).
88. HORECKER, B. L. and MEHLER, A. H. *Ann. Rev. Biochem.* **24**, 207 (1955).
89. HORECKER, B. L. and SMYRNIOTIS, P. Z. *J. Am. Chem. Soc.* **75**, 1009 (1953).
90. HORECKER, B. L. and SMYRNIOTIS, P. Z. *J. Biol. Chem.* **212**, 811 (1955).
91. HUMPHREYS, G. K. and GREENBERG, D. M. *Arch. Biochem. Biophys.* **78**, 275 (1958).
92. HURLBERT, R. B. and MOORE, E. C. *Biochim. Biophys. Acta* **55**, 651 (1962).
93. HURLBERT, R. B. and POTTER, V. R. *J. Biol. Chem.* **209**, 1 (1954).
94. HURLBERT, R. B., SCHMITZ, H., BRUMM, A. F. and POTTER, V. R. *J. Biol. Chem.* **209**, 1, 23, 41 (1954).
95. ISSELBACHER, K. J. *Science*, **126**, 652 (1957).
96. ITO, E. and SATO, M. *Seikagaku* **34**, 403 (1962).
97. ITO, E. and STROMINGER, J. L. *J. Biol. Chem.* **237**, 2689, 2696 (1962).
98. JACOBSON, B. and DAVIDSON, E. A. *J. Biol. Chem.* **237**, 638 (1962).
99. JACOBSON, B. and DAVIDSON, E. A. *J. Biol. Chem.* **237**, 635 (1962).
100. JONES, M. E., SPECTOR, L. and LIPMANN, F. *J. Am. Chem. Soc.* **77**, 819 (1955).
101. JOURDIAN, G. W., SHIMIZU, F. and ROSEMAN, S. *Federation Proc.* **20**, 161 (1961).
102. KALCKAR, H. M. *J. Biol. Chem.* **167**, 477 (1947).
103. KALCKAR, H. M., BRAGANCA, B. and MUNCH-PETERSEN A. *Nature* **172**, 1038 (1953).
103a KANO, H. and KANDLER, O. *Z. Naturforsch* **17b**, 858 (1962).
104. KEMPF, E. and MANDEL, P. *Compt. Rend.* **253**, 2155 (1961).
105. KENNEDY, E. P. *The Enzymes*, vol. 2, p. 72, edited by P. D. Boyer, H. Lardy and K. Myrbäck. Academic Press, New York and London, 1960.
106. KENNEDY, E. P. and WEISS, S. B. *J. Am. Chem. Soc.* **77**, 250 (1955).
107. KENNEDY, E. P. and WEISS, S. B. *J. Biol. Chem.* **222**, 193 (1956).
108. KLETHI, J. and MANDEL, P. *Biochim. Biophys. Acta* **57**, 359 (1962).
109. KOBATA, A. *Biochem. Biophys. Res. Commun.* **7**, 346 (1962).
110. KORNBERG, A. *J. Biol. Chem.* **182**, 779 (1950).
111. KORNBERG, A. *J. Biol. Chem.* **182**, 805 (1950).
112. KORNBERG, A., LIEBERMAN, I. and SIMMS, E. S. *J. Biol. Chem.* **215**, 389 (1955).
113. KORNFELD, S. and GLASER, L. *J. Biol. Chem.* **237**, 3052 (1962).
114. KORNFELD, S. and GLASER, L. *Biochim. Biophys. Acta* **56**, 184 (1962).

115. KORNFELD, S. and GLASER, L. *J. Biol. Chem.* **236**, 1791 (1961).
116. KURAHASHI, K. *Science* **125**, 115 (1957).
117. KURAHASHI, K. and ANDERSON, E. P. *Biochim. Biophys. Acta* **29**, 498 (1958).
118. KURAHASHI, K., PENNINGTON, R. J. and UTTER, M. F. *J. Biol. Chem.* **226**, 1059 (1957).
119. KURAHASHI, K. and SUGIMURA, A. *J. Biol. Chem.* **235**, 940 (1960).
120. LAGERKVIST, U. *Arkiv. Kemi* **5**, 569 (1953).
121. LAGERKVIST, U. *J. Biol. Chem.* **233**, 138 (1958).
122. LAGERKVIST, U. *J. Biol. Chem.* **233**, 143 (1958).
123. LAGERKVIST, U., REICHARD, P. and EHRENSVARD, G. *Acta Chem. Scand.* **5**, 1212 (1951).
124. LEDER, I. G. and HANDLER, P. In *Phosphorus Metabolism*, vol 1, p. 421, edited by W. D. McElroy and B. Glass. Johns Hopkins Press, Baltimore, 1951.
125. LELOIR, L. F. *Arch. Biochem.* **33**, 186 (1951).
126. LEVENBERG, B. and BUCHANAN, J. M. *J. Biol. Chem.* **224**, 1019 (1957).
127. LEVENE, P. A. and JACOBS, W. A. *Ber.* **42**, 1198 (1909).
128. LEVENE, P. A. and JACOBS, W. A. *Ber.* **44**, 746 (1911).
129. LIEBERMAN, I. *J. Am. Chem. Soc.* **77**, 2661 (1955).
130. LIEBERMAN, I. *J. Biol. Chem.* **222**, 765 (1956).
131. LIEBERMAN, I. and KORNBERG, A. *Biochim. Biophys. Acta* **12**, 223 (1953).
132. LIEBERMAN, I. and KORNBERG, A. *J. Biol. Chem.* **207**, 911 (1954).
133. LIEBERMAN, I., KORNBERG, A. and SIMMS, E. S. *J. Biol. Chem.* **215**, 403 (1955).
134. LIEBERMAN, I., KORNBERG, A. and SIMMS, E. S. *J. Biol. Chem.* **215**, 429 (1955).
135. LIPMANN, F. *Nature* **138**, 588 (1936).
136. LUKENS, L. N. and BUCHANAN, J. M. *J. Am. Chem. Soc.* **79**, 1511 (1957).
137. MacLAREN, J. A. *J. Bact.* **63**, 233 (1952).
138. MAGASANIK, B., MOYED, H. S. and GEHRING, L. B. *J. Biol. Chem.* **226**, 339 (1957).
139. MALEY, F. and LARDY, H. A. *Science* **124**, 1297 (1956).
140. MALEY, F. and MALEY, G. F. *Biochim. Biophys. Acta* **31**, 577 (1959).
141. MALEY, F., MALEY, G. F. and LARDY, H. A. *J. Am. Chem. Soc.* **78**, 5303 (1956).
142. MANDEL, P. and KLETHI, J. *Biochim. Biophys. Acta* **28**, 199 (1958).
143. MANSON, W. *Biochim. Biophys. Acta* **19**, 398 (1956).
144. MARKOVITZ, A. *Biochem. Biophys. Res. Commun.* **6**, 250 (1961).
145. MARKOVITZ, A., CIFONELLI, J. A. and DORFMAN, A. *J. Biol. Chem.* **234**, 2343 (1959).
146. MATSUHASHI, M. *Federation Proc.* **22**, 465 (1963).
147. MAXWELL, E. S. *J. Biol. Chem.* **229**, 139 (1957).
148. MAXWELL, E. S. and deROBICHON-SZULMAJSTER, H. *J. Biol. Chem.* **235**, 308 (1960).
149. MAXWELL, E. S., deROBICHON-SZULMAJSTER and KALCKAR, H. M. *Arch. Biochem. Biophys.* **78**, 407 (1958).
150. MAXWELL, E. S., KALCKAR, H. M. and BURTON, R. M. *Biochim. Biophys. Acta* **18**, 444 (1955).
151. MAXWELL, E. S., KALCKAR, H. M. and STROMINGER, J. L. *Arch. Biochem. Biophys.* **65**, 2 (1956).
152. McNUTT, W. S. *J. Biol. Chem.* **210**, 511 (1954).
153. METZENBERG, R. L., HALL, L. M., MARSHALL, M. and COHEN, P. P. *J. Biol. Chem.* **229**, 1019 (1957).
154. MILLER, R. W., LUKENS, L. N. and BUCHANAN, J. M. *J. Am. Chem. Soc.* **79**, 1513 (1957).
155. MILLS, G. C. and JONES, C. A. *Texas Rept. Biol. Med.* **21**, 57 (1963).
156. MILLS, G. T., ONDARZA, R. and SMITH, E. E. B. *Biochim. Biophys. Acta* **14**, 159 (1954).
157. MILLS, G. T., SMITH, E. E. B. and LOCHHEAD, A. C. *Biochim. Biophys. Acta* **25**, 521 (1957).
158. MOKRASCH, L. C. and GRISOLIA, S. *Biochim. Biophys. Acta* **27**, 226 (1958).
159. MOYED, H. S. and MAGASANIK, B. *J. Biol. Chem.* **226**, 351 (1957).
160. MUNCH-PETERSEN, A. *Acta Chem. Scand.* **10**, 298 (1956).
161. MUNCH-PETERSEN, A. *Acta Chem. Scand.* **9**, 1523 (1955).
162. MUNCH-PETERSEN, A., KALCKAR, H. M., CUTOLO, E. and SMITH, E. E. B. *Nature* **172**, 1037 (1953).

163. NEUFELD, E. F. *Biochem. Biophys. Res. Commun.* 7, 461 (1962).
164. NEUFELD, E. F. and FEINGOLD, D. S. *Biochim. Biophys. Acta* 53, 589 (1961).
165. NEUFELD, E. F., GINSBURG, V., PUTMAN, E. W., FANSHIER, D. and HASSID, W. Z. *Arch. Biochem. Biophys.* 69, 602 (1957).
166. NEUFELD, E. F. and HASSID, W. Z. *Advances in Carbohydrate Chemistry* 18, 309 (1963).
167. NIKAIDO, H. *Biochim. Biophys. Acta* 48, 460 (1962).
168. NIKAIDO, A. and JOKURA, K. *Biochem. Biophys. Res. Commun.* 6, 304 (1961).
169. NISHIZUKA, Y. and HAYAISHI, O. *J. Biol. Chem.* 238, 3369 (1963).
170. O'BRIEN, P. J. and GINSBURG, V. *Federation Proc.* 21, 155 (1962).
171. O'BRIEN, P. J. and ZILLIKEN, F. *Biochim. Biophys. Acta* 31, 543 (1959).
172. OKAZAKI, R. *Biochim. Biophys. Acta* 44, 478 (1960).
173. OKAZAKI, R., OKAZAKI, T. and KURIKI, Y. *Biochim. Biophys. Acta* 38, 384 (1960).
174. OKAZAKI, R., OKAZAKI, T., STROMINGER, J. L. and MICHELSON, A. M. *J. Biol. Chem.* 237, 3014 (1962).
175. OKAZAKI, R., OKAZAKI, T., STROMINGER, J. L. and SUZUKI, S. *Biochem. Biophys. Res. Commun.* 7, 300 (1962).
176. OLIVER, I. T. *Biochim. Biophys. Acta* 52, 75 (1961).
177. PARK, J. T. *J. Biol. Chem.* 194, 877, 885, 897 (1952).
178. PAZUR, J. H., KLEPPE, K. and CEPURE, A. *Biochem. Biophys. Res. Commun.* 7, 157 (1962).
179. PAZUR, J. H. and SHADAKSHARASWAMY, M. *Biochem. Biophys. Res. Commun.* 5, 130 (1961).
180. PAZUR, J. H. and SHUEY, E. W. *J. Biol. Chem.* 236, 1780 (1961).
181. PIERPONT, W. S. and HUGHES, D. E. *II Congr. Internatl. Biochem. Abstr.* p. 91 (1952).
182. PLAUT, G. W. E. *J. Biol. Chem.* 208, 513 (1954).
183. PLAUT, G. W. E. *J. Biol. Chem.* 211, 111 (1954).
184. PLAUT, G. W. E. and BROBERG, P. L. *J. Biol. Chem.* 219, 131 (1956).
185. PLENTL, A. A. and SCHOENHEIMER, R. *J. Biol. Chem.* 153, 203 (1944).
186. PONTIS, H. G. *J. Biol. Chem.* 216, 195 (1955).
187. PONTIS, H. G., CABIB, E. and LELOIR, L. F. *Biochim. Biophys. Acta* 26, 146 (1957).
188. PONTIS, H. G., JAMES, A. L. and BADDILEY, J. *Biochem. J.* 75, 428 (1960).
189. POTTER, R. L. and BUETTNER-JANUSCH, V. *Federation Proc.* 16, 234 (1957).
190. POTTER, R. L. SCHLESINGER, S., BUETTNER-JANUSCH, V. and THOMPSON, L. *J. Biol. Chem.* 226, 381 (1957).
191. PREISS, J. *Biochem. Biophys. Res. Commun.* 9, 235 (1962).
192. PREISS, J. and HANDLER, P *J. Biol. Chem.* 225, 759 (1957).
193. PREISS, J. and HANDLER, P. *J. Biol. Chem.* 233, 488 (1959).
194. PREISS, J. and HANDLER, P. *J. Biol. Chem.* 233, 493 (1959).
195. RACKER, E. *Advances in Enzymology* 15, 141 (1954).
196. RACKER, E. *J. Biol. Chem.* 196, 347 (1952).
197. RACKER, E., DE LA HABA, G. and LEDER, I. G. *J. Am. Chem. Soc.* 75, 1010 (1953).
198. REICHARD, P. *Acta Chem. Scand.* 9, 1275 (1955).
199. REICHARD, P. *J. Biol. Chem.* 236, 2511 (1961).
200. REICHARD, P. *Biochem. J.* 92, 28P (1964).
201. REICHARD, P., BALDESTEN, A. and RUTBERG, L. *J. Biol. Chem.* 236, 1150 (1961).
202. REICHARD, P. and HANSHOFF, G. *Acta Chem. Scand.* 10, 548 (1956).
203. REICHARD, P. and LAGERKVIST, U. *Acta Chem. Scand.* 7, 1207 (1953).
204. REICHARD, P. and SKÖLD, O. *Acta Chem. Scand.* 11, 17 (1957).
205. REICHARD, P., SMITH, L. H., JR. and HANSHOFF, G. *Acta Chem. Scand.* 9, 1010 (1955).
206. ROBBINS, P. W. and LIPMANN, F. *J. Biol. Chem.* 233, 681, 686 (1958).
207. ROLL, P. M., WEINFELD, H. and CARROLL, E. *J. Biol. Chem.* 220, 455 (1956).
208. ROSE, I. A. and SCHWEIGERT, B. S. *J. Biol. Chem.* 202, 635 (1953).
209. ROSEMAN, S. *Proc. Natl. Acad. Sci. U.S.* 48, 437 (1962).
210. ROUSH, A. H. and BETZ, R. F. *J. Biol. Chem.* 233, 261 (1958).
211. ROWEN, J. W. and KORNBERG, A. *J. Biol. Chem.* 193, 497 (1951).
212. RUTMAN, R. J., CANTAROW, A. and PASCHKIS, K. E. *Cancer Research* 14, 119 (1954).
213. RUTTER, W. J. and HANSEN, R. G. *J. Biol. Chem.* 202, 323 (1953).

214. SALZMAN, N. P., EAGLE, H. and SEBRING, E. E. *J. Biol. Chem.* **230**, 1001 (1958).
215. SCHRECKER, A. W. and KORNBERG, A. *J. Biol. Chem.* **182**, 795 (1950).
216. SCHULMAN, M. P. and BUCHANAN, J. M. *J. Biol. Chem.* **196**, 513 (1952).
217. SERLUPI-CRESCENZI, G. and BALLIO, A. *Nature, London* **180**, 1203 (1957).
218. SHAW, D. R. D. *Biochem. J.* **82**, 297 (1962).
219. SHIVE, W., ACKERMAN, W. W., GORDON, M., GETZENDANER, M. E. and EAKIN, R. E. *J. Am. Chem. Soc.* **69**, 725 (1947).
220. SHIVE, W., RAVEL, J. M. and EAKIN, R. E. *J. Am. Chem. Soc.* **70**, 2614 (1948).
221. SILBERT, J. E. and BROWN, D. H. *Biochim. Biophys. Acta* **54**, 590 (1961).
222. SMITH, E. E. B., GALLOWAY, B. and MILLS, G. T. *Biochem. Biophys. Res. Commun.* **5**, 148 (1961).
223. SMITH, E. E. B., GALLOWAY, B. and MILLS, G. T. *Biochim. Biophys. Acta* **33**, 276 (1959)
224. SMITH, E. E. B. and MILLS, G. T. *Biochim. Biophys. Acta* **18**, 152 (1955).
225. SMITH, E. E. B. and MILLS, G. T. *Biochim. Biophys. Acta* **13**, 386 (1954).
226. SMITH, E. E. B. and MILLS, G. T. *Biochim. Biophys. Acta* **13**, 587 (1954).
227. SMITH, E. E. B., MILLS, G. T., BERNHEIMER, H. P. and AUSTRIAN, R. *J. Gen. Microbiol.* **20**, 654 (1959).
228. SMITH, E. E. B., MILLS, G. T., BERNHEIMER, H. P. and AUSTRIAN, R. *Biochim. Biophys. Acta* **29**, 640 (1958).
229. SMITH, E. E. B., MILLS, G. T. and HARPER, E. M. *Biochim. Biophys. Acta* **23**, 662 (1957).
230. SMITH, E. E. B., MILLS, G. T. and HARPER, E. M. *J. Gen. Microbiol.* **16**, 426 (1957).
231. SMITH, E. E. B., MUNCH-PETERSEN, A. and MILLS, G. T. *Nature* **172**, 1038 (1953).
232. SMITH, E. J. and WHEAT, R. W. *Arch. Biochem. Biophys.* **86**, 267 (1960).
233. SMITH, L. H., JR. and REICHARD, P. *Acta Chem. Scand.* **10**, 1024 (1956).
234. SNELL, E. E., KITAY, E. and MacNUTT, W. S. *J. Biol. Chem.* **175**, 473 (1948).
235. SOLMS, J. and HASSID, W. Z. *J. Biol. Chem.* **228**, 357 (1957).
236. SONNE, J. C., BUCHANAN, J. M. and DELLUVA, A. M. *J. Biol. Chem.* **166**, 395 (1946)
237. SONNE, J. C., BUCHANAN, J. M. and DELLUVA, A. M. *J. Biol. Chem.* **173**, 69 (1948).
238. SOODAK, M. *J. Cell. and Comp. Physiol.* **47**, 103 (1956).
239. STETTEN, M. R. and FOX, C. L. *J. Biol. Chem.* **161**, 333 (1945).
240. STOREY, I. D. E. and DUTTON, G. J. *Biochem. J.* **59**, 279 (1955).
241. STROMINGER, J. L. *J. Biol. Chem.* **234**, 1520 (1959).
242. STROMINGER, J. L. *J. Biol. Chem.* **237**, 1388 (1962).
243. STROMINGER, J. L. *Biochim. Biophys. Acta* **17**, 283 (1955).
244. STROMINGER, J. L. *Federation Proc.* **21**, 134 (1962).
245. STROMINGER, J. L., KALCKAR, H. M., AXELROD, J. and MAXWELL, E. S. *J. Am. Chem. Soc.* **76**, 6411 (1954).
246. STROMINGER, J. L. and MAPSON, L. W. *Biochem. J.* **66**, 567 (1957).
247. STROMINGER, J. L., MAXWELL, E. S., AXELROD, J. and KALCKAR, H. M. *J. Biol. Chem.* **224**, 79 (1957).
248. STROMINGER, J. L. and SCOTT, S. S. *Biochim. Biophys. Acta* **35**, 552 (1959).
249. STROMINGER, J. L. and SMITH, M. S. *J. Biol. Chem.* **234**, 1828 (1959).
250. STROMINGER, J. L. and SMITH, M. S. *J. Biol. Chem.* **234**, 1822 (1959).
251. SU, J. C. and HASSID, W. Z. *Biochemistry* **1**, 474 (1962).
252. SUGINO, Y. *J. Am. Chem. Soc.* **79**, 5074 (1957).
253. SUZUKI, S. *J. Biol. Chem.* **237**, 1393 (1962).
254. TINELLI, R., OKAZAKI, R., OKAZAKI, T. and STROMINGER, J. L. *Proc. Intern. Congr. Microbiol., Montreal*, 1962, p. A1.10.
255. TURNER, D. H. and TURNER, J. F. *Biochem. J.* **69**, 448 (1958).
256. VILLAR-PALASI, C. and LARNER, J. *Arch. Biochem. Biophys.* **86**, 61 (1960).
257. VOLK, W. A. and ASHWELL, G. *Biochem. Biophys. Res. Commun.* **12**, 116 (1963).
258. WANG, T. P. and KAPLAN, N. O. *J. Biol. Chem.* **206**, 311 (1954).
259. WARBURG, O. and CHRISTIAN, W. *Biochem. Z.* **287**, 440 (1936).
260. WARBURG, O. and CHRISTIAN, W. *Biochem. Z.* **292**, 287 (1937).
261. WARBURG, O., CHRISTIAN, W. and GRIESE, A. *Biochem. Z.* **282**, 157 (1935).
262. WARREN, L. and BLACKLOW, S. *Biochem. Biophys. Res. Commun.* **7**, 433 (1962).

263. WARREN, L. and BLACKLOW, S. *J. Biol. Chem.* **237**, 3527 (1962).
264. WARREN, L. and BUCHANAN, J. M. *J. Biol. Chem.* **229**, 613 (1957).
265. WIELAND, T. and MÖLLER, E. F. *Z. Physiol. Chem.* **269**, 227 (1941).
266. WIESMEERY, H. and JORDAN, E. *Anal. Biochem.* **2**, 281 (1961).
267. WRIGHT, L. D., MILLER, S. C., SKEGGS, H. R., HUFF, J. W., WEED, L. L. and WILSON, D. W. *J. Am. Chem. Soc.* **73**, 1898 (1951).
268. WRIGHT, L. D., SKEGGS, H. R. and HUFF, J. W. *J. Biol. Chem.* **175**, 475 (1948).

CHAPTER 3

THE BIOGENESIS OF THE LIPIDS

K. P. STRICKLAND

Department of Biochemistry, University of Western Ontario, London, Canada

CONTENTS

INTRODUCTION
A. SIMPLE LIPIDS   104
  (a) *Glycerol esters (mono-, di- and triglycerides)*   106
    (1) Fatty acid   106
      Fatty acid synthesis in the soluble portion of the cell   109
      Fatty acid synthesis associated with particulate fractions   116
    (2) Glycerol moiety   122
    (3) Formation of phosphatidic acid and its role in triglyceride
      synthesis   124
    (4) Carbohydrate-containing glycerides   130
  (b) *Cholesterol esters*   131
  (c) *Higher alcohol esters, glyceryl ethers and hydrocarbons*   133
B. PHOSPHOGLYCERIDES (GLYCEROPHOSPHATIDES)   133
  Biosynthesis of Phosphoglycerides   139
  Origin of the individual moieties   139
  (a) *Phosphate monoester lipid (phosphatidic acid)*   142
  (b) *Phosphate diester lipids*   142
    (i) Choline-containing   142
      Lecithin   142
      Choline plasmalogen   152
    (ii) Ethanolamine-containing   153
      Phosphatidyl ethanolamine   153
      Ethanolamine plasmalogen   155
      Glyceryl ether phospholipids (Kephalin B)   155
    (iii) Serine-containing   156
      Phosphatidyl serine and serine plasmalogen   156
    (iv) Glycerol-containing   158

(v) Inositol-containing		159
Phosphatidyl inositol (monophosphoinositide)		159
Diphosphoinositide and triphosphoinositide		162
(c) *Phosphate triester lipids*		164
C. SPHINGOLIPIDS		165
Biosynthesis of Sphingosine		166
(a) *Sphingomyelin*		168
(b) *Cerebroside*		170
(c) *Sulfatide*		172
(d) *Gangliosides (mucolipids, strandin)*		173
D. DERIVED LIPIDS		177
E. COMPLEX LIPIDS		177
(a) *Lipoproteins*		178
(b) *Proteolipids*		182
(c) *Phosphatidopeptides*		182
SUMMARY AND CONCLUSIONS		185
REFERENCES		188

INTRODUCTION

During the past decade considerable progress has been made toward the elucidation of the pathways whereby the various lipids are synthesized in nature. This progress undoubtedly owes much to the availability of some of the modern techniques of biochemistry. The labeling of precursors with isotopes or other tracers, the more refined techniques of lipid fractionation by chemical and chromatographic methods and the development of convenient methods for tissue fractionation and enzyme purification have made it possible to study many of the individual reactions concerned in the biosynthesis of the different lipids. The term "lipid" includes a wide variety of naturally occurring substances. Hanahan[287] quite reasonably restricted the term "lipid" to "esters of long-chain fatty acids and alcohols, or closely related derivatives". No detailed classification of lipids is available which is universally acceptable and, until such a system becomes available, it seems best to utilize the brief and broad scheme shown in Table 1 which is based, in part, on classifications reported in the literature.[69, 187, 345, 287] In order to exclude the water-soluble products from the Derived Lipids it is necessary to impose the added restriction of Bloor[69] that lipids must, with few exceptions, be soluble in the "so-called" fat solvents (e.g. ether, chloroform, benzene, etc.).

With the exception of cholesterol and the generically related fat-soluble vitamins, some consideration will be given to the biosynthesis of each of the lipids listed in Table 1. Where it seems advisable, the biological formation of certain of the constituents (e.g. fatty acids, nitrogenous bases, sphingosine, etc.) will be discussed. The derived lipids, in general, will be considered under the lipid of origin. In the space available it will not be possible to present a detailed discussion of the chemical composition and structure of lipids, but structural formulae will be given where known and brief discussion of recent contributions on structure will be included wherever it appears necessary.

TABLE 1. SIMPLE CLASSIFICATION OF LIPIDS

A. Simple lipids (mainly esters of fatty acid and alcohol).
    (a) glycerol esters (mono-, di- and triglycerides)
    (b) cholesterol esters
    (c) higher alcohol esters
    (d) glycerol ethers
    (e) hydrocarbons

B. Phosphoglycerides (esters of phosphate and the free α-hydroxyl of α,β-diglyceride or α-(vinyl alkane ether), β-monoglyceride)
    (a) phosphate-monoester (phosphatidic acid)
    (b) phosphate-diesters containing:
        (i) choline (lysolecithin, lecithin, choline plasmalogen)
        (ii) ethanolamine (phosphatidyl ethanolamine, ethanolamine plasmalogen, kephalin B)
        (iii) serine (phosphatidyl serine, serine plasmalogen)
        (iv) glycerol (phosphatidyl glycerol, cardiolipin)
        (v) inositol (phosphatidyl inositol, di- and tri-phosphoinositides)
    (c) phosphate-triesters (complexes of phosphatidyl ethanolamine and phosphatidyl serine)
C. Sphingolipids (sphingosine containing N-fatty acyl group)
    (a) sphingomyelin
    (b) cerebrosides
    (c) sulfatides
    (d) gangliosides, (mucolipids and strandin)

D. Derived lipids
    (a) fatty acids
    (b) cholesterol
    (c) higher alcohols
    (d) sphingosine

E. Complex lipids
    (a) lipoproteins
    (b) proteolipids
    (c) phosphatidopeptides

There are a number of treatises which are concerned with the chemistry and metabolism (which include biogenesis) of lipids. [69, 187, 188, 189, 314, 315, 450, 287, 66, 15, 178] Reviews relating to specific lipids or groups of lipids (e.g. simple lipids, phosphoglycerides, etc.) will be referred to in the appropriate sections.

A. SIMPLE LIPIDS

(a) *Glycerol Esters* (*Mono-, Di- and Triglycerides*)

Esterification of glycerol by fatty acids gives rise to monoglyceride (Ia), diglyceride (Ib) and triglyceride (Ic). The aliphatic chains represented by R-

$$
\begin{array}{ccc}
CH_2OCOR & CH_2OCOR & CH_2OCOR \\
| & | & | \\
HOCH & R'COOCH & R'COOCH \\
| & | & | \\
CH_2OH & CH_2OH & CH_2OCOR'' \\
\alpha\text{-monoglyceride} & D\text{-}\alpha,\ \beta\text{-diglyceride} & Triglyceride \\
Ia & Ib & Ic
\end{array}
$$

may be the same or different. In general, the fatty acids esterified to glycerol are usually even-numbered C_{14}–C_{18} fatty acids which may be either saturated or unsaturated. Considerable work has been done on the distribution of the fatty acids occurring in natural triglycerides (neutral fat), and this information is summarized in a number of more detailed reviews. [187, 314, 315, 450, 273, 287, 138] From distribution data calculations of the abundance of various types (e.g. with the R groups all the same, all different or two different and whether saturated or unsaturated) of triglycerides have been made. The exact location of these fatty acids has been difficult to establish with good chemical and biochemical data. However, information has become available through studies such as those reported by Hanahan *et al.* [289] in which it was shown that rat and beef liver triglycerides contain a relatively large amount of unsaturated fatty acid in the β-position.

From the structure of triglycerides it is evident that two main components (glycerol and fatty acid) are present. Prior to any consideration of the biogenesis of triglycerides from glycerol and fatty acid, a brief discussion of the biological formation of these constituent parts will be presented.

(1) *Fatty Acid*

As noted in other reviews [308, 267] some of the earliest suggestions on fatty acid synthesis included the possibility that chains were built up by the condensation of two-carbon units. Experiments with isotopically labeled acetate have supported this contention. Thus Rittenberg and Bloch, [564] Wood *et al.* [723] and Barker *et al.* [38] demonstrated that the rat and certain micro-organisms are capable of forming fatty acid from C^{13} (Carbon-13) and deuterium-labeled acetate. Zabin [728] and Anker [11] showed that the elongation of palmitate or myristate involved the condensation of a two-carbon unit to the carboxyl end. Bloch [63, 64, 65] has reviewed these experiments with labeled acetate and outlined the evidence suggesting that fatty acid was built up uniformly by a "head to tail" condensation of acetate units. Further support for acetate as a precursor was provided by *in vitro* and *in vivo* experiments with lactating mammary gland (reviewed by Popják[541] and Hele).[308] More recent literature on the incorporation of C^{14}-acetate into the lipids of various tissues has been summarized by Stumpf.[650]

Suggestions of a mechanism for synthesis and detailed studies of the steps involved in synthesis were not forthcoming until after the mechanism of fatty acid oxidation had been elucidated (for references on fat oxidation see Lynen and Ochoa;[460] Green[262, 263, 267] and Lynen.[451, 452, 453, 456, 457] Attempts were then directed to assessing whether synthesis occurred by a reversal of the four reactions (i.e. through action of β-ketothiolase, β-hydroxylacyl dehydrogenase, enoyl hydrase and acyl dehydrogenase) of the fatty acid spiral (in one turn of the spiral the above four reactions were shown to be responsible for the removal of two-carbon atoms as acetyl CoA by a process of β-oxidation) which appeared to occur mainly in the mitochondria. Stansly and Bienert[625] working with purified enzymes were able to obtain small amounts of butyryl CoA from two molecules of acetyl CoA in the presence of the dye, benzyl viologen. The relatively negative oxidation-reduction potential of this dye permitted it to reduce the flavin adenine dinucleotide prosthetic group of the acyl dehydrogenase. Efficient removal of acetoacetyl CoA was necessary in order to reverse the β-ketothiolase catalyzed reaction since the equilibrium normally very much favors the formation of acetyl CoA from acetoacetyl CoA.[267, 454]

Enzymes capable of the synthesis of butyrate from ethanol were demonstrated in *Clostridium kluyveri* by Stadtman and Barker.[618, 619, 620, 621, 622, 623] The evidence (summarized by Barker[36, 37]) suggested that synthesis occurred by a pathway which first involved the oxidation of ethanol to acetaldehyde and then to acetyl CoA in the presence of two moles of DPN and CoA. Two moles of acetyl CoA were then condensed to form acetoacetyl CoA and the latter was converted to butyryl CoA by what essentially amounted to reversal of the steps in the β-oxidation of fatty acids with the reduction in each case utilizing DPNH.

Particularly rewarding results in systems from higher animals were obtained using "high-speed supernatant" fractions (supernatant left after centrifugation at 100,000 g for 30 min). Brady and Gurin[86] first described a system from pigeon-liver which was capable of the synthesis of long-chain fatty acids from C^{14}-labeled acetate. The optimal system consisted of "high-speed supernatant" reinforced with a water-soluble extract of acetone-dried mitochondria, Mg^{++}, DPN, ATP and CoA. The addition of citrate greatly stimulated synthesis. The synthesizing activity was shown to be confined to the supernatant fraction obtained on high speed centrifugation.[88]

Popják and co-workers[542, 543] achieved the synthesis of short-chain fatty acids from C^{14}-acetate using a "high-speed supernatant" from lactating rat mammary gland. The addition of mitochondria was slightly inhibitory, while microsomes had a variable effect. Oxalacetate and α-ketoglutarate caused a slight stimulation but particularly noteworthy was the large stimulation produced by malonate; ATP, DPN and CoA were also required. Further purification yielded a system which not only synthesized short-chain fatty acids but accumulated the corresponding β-keto and β-hydroxy acids [309, 310] apparently as their CoA derivatives. [684] ATP, CoA, Mg⁺⁺, cysteine and DPNH were necessary co-factors. These experiments suggested that the products of synthesis were similar to those of oxidation.

The earlier difficulty of reversing the reaction catalyzed by the flavoprotein enzyme, acyl dehydrogenase, appeared to be circumvented by the discovery of another enzyme system (enoyl reductase) in the cytoplasm of rat liver which was capable of reducing α,β-unsaturated acyl CoA in the presence of reduced TPN. [424, 425] Langdon was able to demonstrate that a "high-speed super-natant" isolated from rat liver was capable of forming fatty acids from acetate-1-C¹⁴ in the presence of ATP, Mg⁺⁺ and sources of reduced DPN and TPN. Both short and long-chain fatty acids were formed. The enzymes, β-hydroxyacyl dehydrogenase, enoyl hydrase (crotonase) and the TPNH-requiring enoyl reductase were shown to be present in the soluble fraction. On the basis of this evidence it was suggested that fatty acid synthesis was achieved by reversal of the last three reactions of fatty acid oxidation and reduction of the α,β-unsaturated acyl CoA formed by action of enoyl reductase in the presence of TPNH. Some support for this pathway was provided by the experiments of Seubert et al. [604] using purified enzymes of fat oxidation and a particulate fraction of pig liver which contained enoyl reductase activity. In the presence of acetyl CoA and accessory systems for the generation of DPNH and TPNH, the combined enzyme preparations formed short-chain fatty aids, but not the more natural long-chain fatty acids. Subsequently it was demonstrated that butyrate is formed from crotonyl CoA by the addition of rat liver microsomes and a source of TPNH to a crotonyl CoA synthesizing system obtained from lactating rabbit mammary gland. [418]

The evidence outlined, thus far, has indicated that enzymes of fatty acid synthesis are mainly confined to the soluble portion of the cell. Although as noted, it was possible to achieve synthesis of short-chain fatty acids by the coupling of purified enzymes of fat oxidation from mitochondria with a suitable dye or enoyl reductase, little or no support was available to indicate that this was a significant pathway for the synthesis of long-chain fatty acids in tissues other than the mammary gland. In the latter system the preponderance of short-chain fatty acids may be due to the equilibrium of the β-keto-thiolase reaction greatly favoring the cleavage reaction rather than the condensation reaction.

As will be shown the main pathway for the synthesis of saturated fatty acids is found in the soluble portion of the cell. Research on this system has been very active with the result that several highly purified preparations referred to as fatty acid synthetases have been obtained. The continued active work on fatty acid synthesis has also revealed that there are additional synthesizing systems associated with the particulate fractions of the cell (see Wakil[689a, 690, 691] and Vagelos[676] for reviews). The latter systems seem to be particularly important in the elongation and desaturation of fatty acids. It is now more appropriate to discuss fatty acid synthesis in relation to the various pathways demonstrated, i.e. (1) *fatty acid synthesis in the soluble portion of the cell* and (2) *fatty acid synthesis associated with particulate fractions*.

Fatty acid synthesis in the soluble portion of the cell. Attempts were made to purify the fatty acid synthesizing system which had been demonstrated in the "high-speed supernatant". Wakil and his colleagues in a series of investigations succeeded in fractionating avian liver "supernatant" into two main protein fractions (R_{1gc} and R_{2gc}) which on recombination synthesized long-chain fatty acid from acetyl CoA in the presence of ATP, Mn^{++}, HCO_3^- and TPNH.[696, 546, 242, 243] The principal free fatty acid produced by this system was palmitic.[545] The purified enzyme system was relatively free of the enzymes of fatty acid oxidation, enoyl reductase and acetic thiokinase (the latter had to be added for incorporation of acetate). The labeled bicarbonate was not incorporated into fatty acid. These experiments were the first to demonstrate an absolute requirement for bicarbonate but not the first to suggest the implication of bicarbonate. A number of reports had previously indicated that in liver slices bicarbonate stimulated the synthesis of long chain fatty acids from octanoate.[650] Furthermore, Klein[386] observed that the presence of CO_2 caused a four- to eightfold increase in the incorporation of acetate into fatty acid in yeast extracts. In this system labeled bicarbonate was not incorporated into fatty acid. Aqueous extracts of acetone-dried particulates from avocado fruit also demonstrated a bicarbonate requirement for the synthesis of long-chain fatty acid (mainly oleic) from acetate-1-C^{14} in the presence of TPN, ATP and Mn^{++}.[614]

Biotin was shown to be concentrated in the R_1 fraction and to persist with this fraction during purification.[698] Biotin was implicated further by the observation that avidin (an antagonist of biotin), added in low concentrations, caused an inhibition of fatty acid synthesis. This inhibition was overcome by the addition of catalytic amounts of biotin.[698] A similar inhibition of fatty acid synthesis was observed in the avocado system.[613, 42]

During 1958, evidence appeared from at least two laboratories which strongly suggested that malonyl CoA was an intermediate of fatty acid synthesis.[692, 80] Using a partially purified pigeon liver system, Brady[80] demonstrated the synthesis of long-chain fatty acids from acetaldehyde and malonyl CoA in the presence of TPNH and Mn^{++} ions. It was suggested that malonyl CoA may be formed from acetyl CoA, ATP and CO_2 by a reaction similar to the carboxylation of propionyl CoA to form methylmalonyl CoA.[213] Wakil[692] independently demonstrated that the biotin-rich R_{1gc}

fraction, in the presence of Mn^{++}, ATP and HCO_3^-, accumulated a product possessing the properties of a malonyl derivative. Wakil and Ganguly[693, 694] presented evidence that the first step in fatty acid synthesis was the carboxylation of acetyl CoA to malonyl CoA by the biotin-rich R_{1gc} fraction in the presence of ATP and Mn^{++}. The malonyl CoA was then converted to palmitate by the R_{2gc} fraction and TPNH. Acetyl CoA increased the synthesis of palmitate. The CoA derivatives of C^{14}-acetate, -butyrate and -octanoate were all incorporated. Acetaldehyde did not dilute the labeling from C^{14}-acetyl CoA and therefore did not appear to be an intermediate. None of the substituted intermediates of β-oxidation could replace the fatty acyl CoA esters.

Waite and Wakil[688, 689] have extensively purified the enzyme in chicken liver that is responsible for malonyl CoA synthesis. The enzyme, acetyl carboxylase, contains biotin as a prosthetic group, and in forming malonyl CoA it catalyzes the carboxylation of acetyl CoA. ATP, HCO_3^- and Mn^{++} are required. Propionyl CoA and butyryl CoA are 60 per cent and 10 per cent as active as acetyl CoA. UTP can replace ATP. The carboxylation reaction is strongly inhibited by avidin. Hydrolysis with papain shows that the biotin is in amide linkage with acetyl CoA carboxylase. Waite and Wakil have obtained evidence in experiments with $HC^{14}O_3^-$ which suggests involvement of the ureido C in the transfer of CO_2 to acetyl CoA. The latter is at variance with the evidence obtained for other biotin-containing carboxylases (see Vagelos.[676]) where evidence supports the view that the CO_2 of the CO_2-enzyme complex is bound to the 1-N of biotin.

The reaction catalyzed by acetyl CoA carboxylase may be depicted as a two-step reaction:

$$\text{ATP} + CO_2 + \text{biotin-enzyme} \overset{Mn^{++}}{\rightleftharpoons} CO_2\text{-biotin-enzyme} + \text{ADP} + P_i \qquad (1)$$

$$CO_2\text{-biotin-enzyme} + CH_3COSCoA \rightleftharpoons HOOCCH_2COSCoA + \text{biotin-enzyme} \qquad (2)$$

Current evidence supports the view that the acetyl-CoA carboxylase step is the rate-limiting one in fatty acid synthesis. Considerable investigation has been carried out attempting to show that physiological control of fatty acid synthesis may be regulated by stimulation or inhibition of this enzyme. Vagelos[676] has summarized recent studies on this subject. A number of investigations have shown that citrate, in particular, and other intermediates of the tricarboxylic acid cycle cause activation of acetyl CoA carboxylase. Feedback inhibition of acetyl CoA carboxylase by long-chain acyl CoA derivatives has been observed. It appears that this type of control may be concerned in the following conditions where acetyl CoA carboxylase activity is decreased: (1) starvation, (2) diabetes and (3) after excessive fat feeding.

The second step in the synthesis of C_{16} palmitic acid involves condensation of malonyl CoA with acetyl CoA in the presence of TPNH and the fatty acid-synthesizing enzyme system (fatty acid synthetase). Several systems have been independently studied with each making contribution to our overall understanding of fatty acid synthesis.

Brady *et al.* [84] purified by 580 times a fatty acid-synthesizing enzyme system from rat liver. Using this system evidence was obtained which indicated that palmitate is formed from 1 mole of acetyl CoA and 7 moles of malonyl CoA. Tritium from $TPNH^3$ was shown to be directly transferred to alternate carbon atoms of palmitate beginning with the β carbon. A similar preparation from developing brain yielded a system free of malonyl CoA decarboxylase, an enzyme normally contaminating other purified systems. [81] With the brain system it was shown that decarboxylation of malonyl CoA was dependent upon the addition of either acetyl CoA or butyryl CoA. The reaction was particularly sensitive to arsenite thus suggesting involvement of sulfhydryl groups. Experiments on the binding of substrate to enzyme suggested that both acetyl CoA and malonyl CoA were bound by the enzyme. It was suggested by Brady that independent binding results in the formation of acetyl-S-enzyme and malonyl-S-enzyme, and that the latter two condense, with simultaneous decarboxylation, to form a product which on reduction by 2 moles of TPNH yields a butyryl radical on the enzyme. It was further postulated that the butyryl radical is displaced by malonyl CoA to the sulfhydryl originally containing the acetyl moiety and that the butyryl-S-enzyme arising undergoes condensation with the newly formed malonyl-S-enzyme.

This scheme is at slight variance with that originally proposed by Lynen [454, 456] for a partially purified preparation from yeast. Synthesis of long-chain fatty acids by this yeast preparation was shown to be dependent on bicarbonate but the latter was not incorporated into fatty acid. Evidence was obtained that the intermediate malonyl CoA was formed through fixation of CO_2 to acetyl CoA by a mechanism in which biotin-enzyme reacts with ATP and CO_2 to form "active CO_2" (CO_2 was considered to be bound to one of ureido N atoms) which was capable of acylating the carbanion form of acetyl CoA. [454] In an investigation of the condensation reaction between $1\text{-}C^{14}$-acetyl CoA and malonyl CoA it was concluded that $3\text{-}C^{14}$-acetoacetyl-enzyme was formed. [456] Mild alkaline hydrolysis of the acetoacetyl-enzyme complex produced labeled acetate whereas direct reduction of the precipitated protein with KBH_4 yielded $3\text{-}C^{14}\text{-}\beta$-hydroxy-butyric acid. These experiments indicated that malonyl CoA is formed initially and that condensation of the latter with acetyl CoA must then occur by a nucleophilic attack on the methylene carbon of malonyl CoA with simultaneous decarboxylation. This step is followed by the reduction of acetoacetyl-enzyme to butyryl-enzyme by steps requiring 2 moles of TPNH.

There is now general agreement (as first suggested by Vagelos [677]) that during the condensation reaction there is simultaneous release of the CO_2

that is fixed in the formation of malonyl CoA. If as proposed originally by Wakil and Ganguly,[694] the carboxyl group is retained during reduction of the condensation product, then complete randomization of the hydrogen atoms derived from the α-carbon of acetate except for the terminal CH_3-group should occur. The early experiments of Rittenberg and Bloch[564] on the incorporation of deuterium-labeled acetate into fatty acid do not support the view of complete randomization of these hydrogens since the deuterium in fatty acid was present in much higher abundance than in body water. Furthermore, the experiments of Brady et al.[84] with $TPNH^3$ indicated that in fatty acid synthesis the hydrogen atoms of alternate carbons (beginning with the β-carbon) arose by direct hydrogen transfer without any significant randomization on the α-carbon. Also, the release of the unesterified carboxyl of malonyl-1,3-C^{14}-CoA as $C^{14}O_2$ in the presence of acetyl or butyryl CoA, in the absence of added TPNH, supports the view that CO_2 is released during the condensation reaction. Confirmation of this has been provided by Bressler and Wakil[96] in a study using tritiated malonyl CoA and a highly purified enzyme system (R_{2a}) prepared from the R_{2gc} protein fraction isolated from pigeon liver.

In recent years, numerous fatty acid synthetase systems have been prepared. These include a number from animal sources (avian liver;[96, 97] rat liver;[84] rat brain;[81] adipose tissue[483] and mammary gland;[483, 193]) and from insects (the moth *Prodenia eridenia*[734]) in which the principal saturated fatty acid synthesized is C_{16} palmitic. The systems isolated from plants and microorganisms (avocado mescocarp;[40] carrot;[626] yeast;[458] *Clostridium kluyveri*[5, 252] and *Escherichia coli*[5, 252]) seem to show a greater tendency to yield C_{18} fatty acids. Studies with these various synthetases have firmly established that the stoichiometric relationship existing for the synthesis of palmitic acid is:

$$CH_3COSCoA + 7\,HOOCCH_2COSCoA + 14\,TPNH \longrightarrow CH_3(CH_2)\,COOH \\ + 7\,CO_2 + 8\,HSCoA + 14\,TPN^+ + 6\,H_2O \qquad (3)$$

For C_{18} fatty acids an additional C_2 unit is provided by malonyl CoA. Acetyl CoA in each substance provides the two carbons at the methyl end. Present evidence indicates that the synthetases are complexes of several enzymes. However, attempts to separate out the various enzymatic entities have met with mixed success. Little resolution of animal and yeast synthetase complexes has been accomplished. Considerable success is now being achieved with systems from bacterial preparations with contributions coming from several laboratories (see Vagelos et al.,[6, 466, 467, 468] Bloch et al.[440, 516] and Wakil et al.[697, 671]). Combining the information provided from studies on the various synthetases it is possible to make a number of conclusions concerning the nature of the synthetic process.

Lynen *et al.*[458, 459] have obtained a highly purified synthetase from yeast which electrophoretically or by electron microscopy appears to be a homogeneous particle with a molecular weight of $2\cdot3 \times 10^6$. The synthetase forms stearyl CoA from 1 mole of acetyl CoA and 8 moles of malonyl CoA in the presence of reduced TPN. Seven different enzymatic activities are associated with the synthetase (six were demonstrated using model substrates[458]). This is supported by terminal group analysis which shows seven different polypeptides units to be present (three each per particle). Treatment with deoxycholate splits the complex into subunits with loss of activity. Acetyl-enzyme, malonyl-enzyme, acetoacetyl-enzyme and D(-)-β-hydroxybutyryl-enzyme were isolated. Binding was shown to occur with different types of sulfhydryl groups. Acetyl and the higher acyl groups are bound to one type referred to as "peripheral sulfhydryl groups" (these are cystein residues which react rapidly with iodoacetamide and N-ethyl maleimide). The second type are referred to as "central sulfhydryl groups" (relatively resistant to SH inhibitors) to which malonyl-, β-ketoacyl-, β-hydroxyacyl-, α,β-unsaturated and saturated acyl groups are bound. The mechanism suggested is one in which malonyl CoA reacts with a central SH group and condensation with decarboxylation occurs using acyl groups (C_2 acetyl first, then C_4 butyryl ..., C_{16} palmityl) associated with the peripheral SH group. The β-ketoacyl-enzyme undergoes reduction, dehydration and reduction to form saturated acyl-enzyme which transfers to peripheral SH. When C_{16} or C_{18} acyl-enzyme is formed the saturated acyl group is transferred to CoA.

Using their highly purified enzyme fractions from pigeon liver, Wakil and co-workers[97, 691] have further studied the nature of fatty acid synthesis. They have shown, based on observed stimulations by sulfhydryl agents and inhibitions by sulfhydryl-binding agents and arsenite, that the synthetase has an essential requirement for intact SH groups. Acetyl CoA protects against inhibition by sulfhydryl agents with propionyl CoA and butyryl CoA having lesser effects. The mechanism proposed for fatty acid synthesis is one in which both acetyl CoA and malonyl CoA are bound to enzymes in the synthetase through SH groups. The enzyme-bound acyl groups formed are then considered to participate in a condensation reaction involving simultaneous decarboxylation which is followed by reduction, dehydration and reduction to form first a C_4 saturated acyl-enzyme. The latter is considered to participate in a second series of reactions to yield a C_6 saturated acyl-enzyme. Five more repetitions of this type are believed to occur yielding a C_{16} saturated acyl-enzyme which appears to undergo deacylation to form palmitic acid. No intermediate of these steps could be readily demonstrated. In contrast to this, Robinson *et al.*[569] have shown that their partially purified preparation from rat brain is capable of utilizing β-keto-, β-hydroxy- and α,β-unsaturated CoA derivatives in the presence of reduced TPN. Acetoacetyl CoA, β-hydroxybutyryl CoA and crotonyl CoA all served as precursors of long-chain fatty acids; all three derivatives were shown to undergo reduction first before condensation with malonyl CoA.

Relatively greater success has been achieved by Vagelos and his associates in regard to the separation of different enzymatic activities from the fatty acid synthetase of *E. coli* (in particular) and *C. kluyveri*. In a study of the nature of the condensation reaction in fatty acid synthesis catalyzed by bacterial preparations, the above workers were able to resolve the synthetase into two protein fractions, Enzyme I and Enzyme II.[467] Enzyme I was heat-labile and possessed a sulfhydryl site that is very sensitive to alkylating agents. Partial protection against this type of inhibition was provided by acyl derivatives of CoA. Enzyme II was relatively stable to boiling in dilute acid and possessed an SH group which had to be first reduced before becoming sensitive to alkylating agents. As found for the other synthetases, acetyl CoA, malonyl CoA and reduced TPN are the precursors utilized.[6] The synthetase from *C. kluyveri* formed C_{16}–C_{20} saturated fatty acids while that from *E. coli* formed *cis*-vaccenic acid (11,12-octadecenoic acid, established by Lennarz *et al.*[440]) mainly with lesser amounts of palmitate and stearate. With the *E. coli* system it was shown that in the condensation reaction the acetoacetate formed is bound to the heat-stable Enzyme II through a thioester linkage.[253] The acetoacetyl-S-enzyme was sufficiently stable to be isolated and used as an intermediate in fatty acid synthesis.

Subsequent investigation has shown Enzyme II to be a unique acyl carrier protein (ACP),[467] with all acyl compounds involved in fatty acid synthesis being bound through thioester linkage to an SH group of ACP. ACP has been isolated and shown to contain one SH group. This protein has been purified to the point of homogeneity as judged by column chromatography, starch gel electrophoresis and sedimentation and has been found to have a molecular weight of 9500. The stability of the intermediates have permitted isolation of acetyl-ACP, malonyl-ACP, acetoacetyl-ACP and butyryl-ACP.[467, 251] Alberts *et al.*[6] have partially purified out several enzymatic activities from *E. coli* fatty acid synthetase. Two activities, acetyl transacylase and malonyl transacylase catalyse the transfer of acetyl and malonyl groups from CoA to ACP. An enzyme responsible for the condensation-decarboxylation reaction accompanies malonyl transacylase during purification. Acetoacetyl-ACP is reduced to the D(-)β-hydroxy derivative by a β-ketoacyl-ACP reductase utilizing reduced TPN. An enoyl hydrase specific for acyl-ACP thioesters (either the β-hydroxy or α,β-unsaturated derivative) has been partially purified.[466]

Workers from the laboratories of Bloch[440, 516] and Wakil[697, 671] have also achieved partial fractionation of the *E. coli* synthetase. Their observations compliment and support the findings already described. Thus, independent enzymes have been demonstrated for each of the steps in fatty acid synthesis which appear in summary form in Fig. 1.

This scheme for the synthesis of a C_{16} or C_{18} saturated fatty acid may prove to be generally applicable to all synthetases utilizing acetyl CoA, malonyl CoA and reduced TPN as precursors. Thus, for example, Lynen[459] has been able to demonstrate the existence of seven polypeptides units in the yeast synthetase and, furthermore, he has been able to split the complex into subunits bearing different acyl groups. The correspondence to the *E. coli*

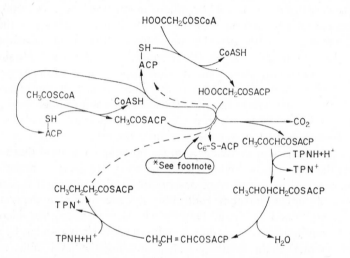

FIG. 1. Scheme showing steps considered to occur in the synthesis of a C_{16} saturated fatty acid (based on studies by Vagelos,[6, 466, 467, 468] Wakil[671, 697] and Bloch[440, 516] on fatty acid synthetase of *E. coli*).
* Repetition of steps in cycle six (or seven) times and deacylation from ACP will yield C_{16} palmitic acid (or C_{18} stearic acid). Reactions for formation of C_6-S-ACP are indicated in broken lines.

system is very close with the exception that the isolated acyl-enzyme subunits isolated from yeast are no longer active. Overath and Stump[525] have been able to obtain a heat-stable protein (Fraction IIav) from heat-labile protein (Fraction Iav) from the soluble fatty acid synthetase of avocado mesocarp. Also Brady[569] has shown that brain synthetase possesses some ability to utilize predicted intermediates in the synthesis of fatty acid. However, what perhaps is the most convincing evidence is the ability shown by certain animal fatty acid synthetases (in rat liver, adipose tissue) to be able to utilize acyl-S-ACP isolated from *E. coli* systems,[6] and Fraction IIav of the avocado system can replace Enzyme II_{EC} (ACP) in the *E. coli* system.[525] It is also of interest to note that quite recently the nature of the SH group in ACP has been investigated and shown to be due to the presence of 4′-phospho-pantetheine as a prosthetic group which is bound in phosphodiester linkage to a serine hydroxyl.[468] If this is true for yeast fatty acid synthetase, it is now not surprising that Lynen[458] was able to use acetyl- and malonyl-pantetheine as model substrates and pantetheine as an acceptor of a malonyl group from malonyl-S-enzyme.

There is every indication that this pathway for fatty acid synthesis involving malonyl CoA is a major pathway for the C_{16} saturated fatty acid, palmitic. Synthetases from widely differing sources (references cited earlier) tend to support this view. Even in the case of mammary gland where considerable evidence supported the view that synthesis might occur by a reversal of three of the steps of β oxidation plus the action of enoyl reductase, the more recent evidence favors the view that an avidin sensitive malonyl CoA pathway is the most important one.[193, 344] It would seem that on a physiological basis the pathway involving malonyl CoA which appears to exist primarily in the soluble portion of the cell is the more important since the site of synthesis is removed from the site of active oxidation (mitochondria). Also the generation of TPNH (which is required in fatty acid synthesis) seems to be mainly confined to the soluble portion of the cell.

Although there is much evidence to support the contention that the fatty acid synthetases for the malonyl CoA pathway are located in the soluble portion of the cell, there are some observations which indicate that particulate fractions may either exert some controlling influence or contain the synthetase. Lorch et al.[449] and Smith and Dils[609] have demonstrated that microsomes affect the synthesis of fatty acid by mammary gland, in particular, by extending the average chain length and by increasing the level of acetyl CoA carboxylation. Hülsmann and colleagues[129, 344] have obtained evidence which suggests that the enzyme system for the malonyl CoA pathway of fatty acid syntheses may be ultimately derived from mitochondria in the case of rabbit heart muscle, pigeon liver and rat mammary gland. Harland and Wakil[291, 292] have demonstrated than an avidin-sensitive pathway exists in mitochondria of rat liver. Further support for this view is provided by the observations that the fatty acid synthetase from avocado mesocarp is prepared in soluble form from mitochondria.[504, 40] Also, fatty acid synthesis in the leaf (spinach, lettuce) appears to be confined to the chloroplast.[503, 648] Since evidence for a CO_2 and ATP requirement was obtained, it seems likely that the malonyl CoA pathway is, in part, if not entirely, responsible for fatty acid syntheses in the chloroplast. It would seem that sufficient evidence is available from a wide enough variety of sources to warrant careful reassessment of the possibility that mitochondria or particle preparations may be main sources of fatty acid synthetases.

Fatty acid synthesis associated with particulate fractions. There is good evidence for the existence of other pathways and other reactions concerned in the synthesis of fatty acids. These appear to be most important in the elongation of existing fatty acids and in the formation of monoenoic and polyenoic acids. The enzymes concerned are most generally found to be associated with particulate fractions of the cell. Some of these systems are now described (for recent reviews see Mead, [494] Wakil [691] and Vagelos [676]).

The possibility that an elongation mechanism for fatty acids existed was suggested by observations such as those of Zabin [728] and of Radin and his group. [282, 283] Zabin observed that C^{14}-stearic acid isolated from rats injected with acetate-1-C^{14} had significantly more activity in the carboxyl carbon than would be observed for an even distribution throughout the chain. Hajra and Radin [282, 283] have noted a similar observation for lignoceric acid. Wakil and his colleagues [689a, 691, 291, 292] have successfully demonstrated that enzymes for the elongation of fatty acids exist in mitochondria. The system requires the acyl CoA to be elongated (i.e. palmityl CoA for stearyl CoA, stearyl CoA for arachidyl CoA, and behenyl CoA for lignoceryl CoA}, TPNH and DPNH. Bicarbonate is not required and the system is insensitive to avidin. It seems most likely that the elongation involves an enoyl reductase and enzymes of the β-oxidation pathway.

Breusch [98] and Mead [495] have summarized the early evidence which suggested that the mammalian organism (the liver particularly) could form monounsaturated fatty acids. From the various observations made it was concluded that myristoleic and palmitoleic acids were formed from their corresponding saturated fatty acids while oleic acid seemed to arise mainly from a chain lengthening process and not from stearic acid. It, therefore, appeared that an enzyme system existed that was capable of catalyzing dehydrogenation between carbons 9 and 10 of long-chain fatty acids.

In determining the nature of the desaturation reaction, support has not been obtained for the soluble system from rat liver described by Jacob. [350] However, following the discovery by Bloomfield and Bloch [67, 68] of an oxygen-dependent system in yeast for the desaturation of palmitic and stearic acids, several laboratories [54, 328, 481, 691] have demonstrated that rat liver preparations can desaturate palmitic acid to palmitoleic acid and stearic acid to oleic acid. The system for desaturation is associated with the microsomal fraction and requires ATP, CoA, O_2 and TPNH. Palmityl-CoA and stearyl CoA could replace the requirements for ATP, CoA and fatty acid. Marsh and James [481] obtained evidence which supported the view that the 9- or 10-hydroxyl derivatives were involved as intermediates. This suggested that the mechanism of desaturation for rat liver microsomes was similar to that for the yeast system. Wakil [691] has studied the desaturation reaction noting that it is inhibited by cyanide and other inhibitors. No intermediates could be demonstrated in the desaturation of stearyl CoA. It is evident that there are several aspects of the mechanism of this reaction which remain to be elucidated.

This type of desaturation process involving O_2 apparently occurs quite widely. Plants may be a notable exception since direct desaturation of palmitate and stearate is not readily demonstrable. [204] Besides liver, epididymal fat pads have been shown to convert stearic acid to oleic acid. [370]

Also, Bloch and his associates [204, 231] have shown the presence of this system in protozoa, primitive algae and certain bacteria. It appears that the system is also associated with a particulate fraction since Fulco and Bloch [231] found the activity in *M. phlei* to be in the fraction sedimenting at 100,000 g. CoA derivatives of palmitic and stearic acids, O_2, Fe^{2+} and FAD or FMN were specifically required.

With the demonstration of the wide occurrence of *cis*-vaccenic acid in nature, [691] it is of interest to comment briefly on the systems capable of synthesizing this C_{18} fatty acid with a double bond at the 11, 12 position in *cis* configuration. Holloway and Wakil, [329] besides demonstrating that *cis*-vaccenic acid is a normal constituent of animal tissues, have shown *in vivo* that palmitate-1-C^{14} and not stearate-1-C^{14} are converted to *cis*-vaccenic acid. This observation suggested that palmitic acid is first desaturated to palmitoleic acid followed by elongation to form *cis*-vaccenic acid. Such a pathway was confirmed with the observation that rat liver mitochondria were capable of synthesizing labeled *cis*-vaccenic acid from palmitoleyl CoA and 1-C^{14} acetyl CoA in the presence of DPNH and TPNH.

Considerable information is available on the synthesis of *cis*-vaccenic acid by soluble extracts of *E. coli* and other bacteria. For some time, Bloch and his colleagues have been studying the anaerobic pathway whereby certain bacteria produce monoenoic acids, the most notable being *cis*-vaccenic acid. [204] Lennarz et al. [440] were able to show that soluble extracts of *E. coli* formed this acid from acetyl CoA and TPNH and that O_2 was not required for formation of the double bond. Following fractionation of the *E. coli* system into heat-stable and heat-labile protein fractions it was observed that the latter fraction catalysed the dehydration of β-hydroxydecanoyl CoA to α,β and β,γ unsaturated homologues. Accordingly, it was suggested that a β-hydroxydecanoyl derivative (probably as an acyl-S-enzyme) might first undergo partial β,γ unsaturation and that this derivative would undergo chain extension to eventually yield C_{18} *cis*-vaccenic acid. Confirmation of this is provided by the experiments of Wakil et al. [697] who have fractionated the heat-labile fraction into four fractions. It was necessary to combine E_{IV} fraction with the other three (E_I, E_{II} and E_{III}) and the heat-stable protein in order to form *cis*-vaccenic acid. Recently Norris et al. [516] have extended the study of Lennarz et al. to the point of separating out from *E. coli* synthetase a β-hydroxydecanoyl CoA dehydrase capable of transforming β-hydroxy-decanoyl thioesters to a mixture of α,β- and β,γ decenoates.

As commented on by Bloch [62, 204] it seems that monounsaturated fatty acids are synthesized in biological systems by at least two independent mechanisms, one that is aerobic and the other anaerobic. Organisms employ one or the other but not both mechanisms. In the aerobic pathway, long-chain fatty acyl esters of CoA undergo desaturation at the 9, 10 position by enzymes which are particle-bound and require O_2. This pathway as already noted occurs widely. The anaerobic pathway, as typified by *E. coli*, appears to be associated with a soluble fatty acid synthetase with monoenoic acids arising by β,γ-dehydration of medium-chain β-hydroxy acyl thioesters and subsequent chain elongation of the 3-enoates.[597] Depending on the medium-chain β-hydroxy acid involved in β,γ-dehydration and the subsequent chain elongation, a variety of monounsaturated fatty acids are possible (see Scheuerbrandt and Bloch[597]). This pathway is relatively rare occurring only in certain bacteria. It seems likely that a third type of pathway exists in higher plants, green algae and certain phytoflagellates since neither of the above pathways can be demonstrated in these sources. However, the existence of this third pathway remains circumstantial particularly in view of the evidence from two laboratories (summarized by Vagelos[676]) that oleate synthesis by castor bean (*Ricinus communis*) is associated with a particulate fraction and that the mechanism involves O_2. Neither stearyl CoA nor stearate could act as precursors of oleate.

Mechanisms for the synthesis of polyunsaturated fatty acids are less well understood. It appears that most organisms except bacteria possess some ability to continue the desaturation of oleic acid. Bloch[66, 204] and others[494, 691, 676] have reviewed the current status of this problem. The evidence available suggests that desaturation of oleate proceeds in two directions. In the one referred to as "the α-linolenate or plant pathway", oleate undergoes progressive desaturation towards the methyl end of the molecule producing linoleic and α-linolenic acids. In the second referred to as "the γ-linolenate or animal pathway", linoleate is also formed but desaturation occurs thereafter in divinyl methane relationship to the double bond (beginning with carbons 9, 10) nearest the carboxyl group. The latter is supported by the *in vitro* and *in vivo* studies of Klenk,[394, 398, 400] Mead,[493, 495] and Leupold and Kremer[441] using C^{14}-labeled acetate, oleate, linoleate and linolenate. Following the desaturation steps, elongation may occur followed by desaturation to yield C_{20} arachidonate. This series arising from oleate contains what are called the "essential fatty acids". Klenk[389, 402, 388] has extended this work considerably with studies on the fatty acids of the liver of rats fed a fat-free diet. Three groups of unsaturated fatty acids were found to exist, the palmitoleic acid type (Δ^9-hexadecenoic, palmitoleic, Δ^{11}-octadecenoic, $\Delta^{8,11}$-octadecadienoic, Δ^{13}-eicosenoic, $\Delta^{7,10,13}$-eicosatrienoic and $\Delta^{4,7,10,13}$-eicosatetraenoic), the oleic acid type (Δ^9-octadecenoic, or oleic acid, and $\Delta^{5,8,11}$-eicosatrienoic acid) and the linoleic acid type ($\Delta^{9,12}$-octadecadienoic, or linoleic, and $\Delta^{5,8,11,14}$-eicosatetraenoic, or arachidonic). Feeding of 8-C^{14} *cis* Δ^9-octadecenoic acid actively labeled $\Delta^{5,8,11}$-eicosatrienoic acid and in one experiment stearic acid appeared to be converted to this trienoic acid via oleic acid.

Concerning the mechanism of desaturation for polyunsaturated fatty acids, Yuan and Bloch[726] first reported that *Torulopsis utilis* required oxygen for the conversion of oleic to linoleic acid thus suggesting an aerobic mechanism. Mead's proposed pathway for polyunsaturated fatty acid synthesis in animal tissues has gained only partial support from the work of Stoffel. [636, 637] He has shown that linoleyl CoA may be extended to the corresponding C_{20} acid ($\Delta^{11,14}$-eicosadienoic acid) by a soluble fraction from rat liver involving malonyl CoA. The CoA esters of both the $C_{20:2}$ acid ($\Delta^{11,14}$-eicosadienoic) and the $C_{20:3}$ acid ($\Delta^{8,11,14}$-eicosatrienoic) are converted to arachidonic acid by liver microsomes in the presence of oxygen and reduced pyridine nucleotides. No evidence was obtained for the conversion of linoleic acid to linolenic acid but rather elongation appeared to occur before desaturation. These results appear to differ from the conclusions reached by Mead [493] with C^{14}-labeled linoleic and linolenic acids. His findings were consistent with the view that mammals can convert linoleic acid to γ-linolenic acid and the latter, after chain elongation, to arachidonic acid. Also, studies by Nugteren [517] indicate that rat liver can desaturate linoleic to γ-linolenic acid. The evidence suggested that the desaturation system is present in microsomes and that it requires O_2, TPNH and the CoA ester of linoleate. It may be that two pathways exist in the rat for arachidonate formation, one in which linoleate is desaturated before elongation and the other in which elongation occurs before desaturation. More recently, Wakil and his colleagues [328, 691] have reported that oleyl CoA may be converted to 6,9-octadecadienoyl-CoA by rat liver microsomes in the presence of oxygen and TPNH. No linoleic acid (C_{18-2} $\Delta^{9,12}$) was formed thereby confirming the evidence obtained from nutritional studies that mammals do not synthesize linoleic acid, possibly because of lack of the necessary enzymes.

Brief reference should be made to other studies on polyunsaturated fatty acid formation. Bloch et al. [343, 204] have obtained evidence with *Euglena gracilis* that, when this organism is grown in light, it reflects a lipid pattern characteristic of plants with α-linolenic acid being the principal product, and when adapted for growth in the dark it reflects a pattern characteristic of animals where arachidonic acid predominates. This work suggests a close correlation between the "α-linolenic pathway" and photosynthesis. Studies on plants would confirm this general conclusion. Thus James et al. [351, 294] have obtained evidence that oleic acid is converted to linoleic acid by chloroplast preparations, and Stumpf and McMahon [649] have reported that plastids from developing safflower seeds efficiently converted oleyl CoA to linoleic acid. Oxygen and TPNH were required. In flax, soybean and safflower plants there is good evidence, based on the appearance of label from sucrose or $C^{14}O_2$, that oleic acid is formed first, followed by linoleic acid and then by linolenic acid. [197, 649] It seems fair to presume that the conversion from linoleic to linolenic acids involves desaturation by a system similar to that for the oleic to linoleic conversion.

Korn and his associates have recently carried out extensive studies on the biosynthesis of unsaturated fatty acids in the soil amoeba, *Acanthamoeba sp.*,[408] the slime mold, *Dictyostelium discoideum*,[161] and guinea-pig liver.[162] By growing amoebas in the presence of a variety of radioactive fatty acids, evidence was obtained which suggested the following sequence:

acetate $\longrightarrow$ stearate $\longrightarrow$ oleate $\longrightarrow$ linoleate $\longrightarrow$ $\Delta^{11,14}$-eicosadienoate $\longrightarrow$ $\Delta^{8,11,14}$-eicosatrienoate $\longrightarrow$ $\Delta^{5,8,11,14}$-eicosatetraenoate (arachidonate).

This type of pathway is similar to that shown by Stoffel[636, 637] for the conversion of linoleic acid to arachidonic acid by rat liver. The study with the slime mold, *D. discoideum* gave results consistent with the view that palmitate is a common intermediate in the biosynthesis of all long-chain unsaturated fatty acids. Direct desaturation yielded Δ^9 (palmitoleic) and $\Delta^{5,9}$-acids; elongation of palmitoleic acid yielded *cis*-vaccenic (C_{18} Δ^{11}) which on further desaturation gave a C_{18}-dienoic acid ($\Delta^{5,11}$), and direct elongation of palmitate to stearate followed by stepwise desaturation yielded oleate (Δ^9) and a $\Delta^{5,9}$-dienoic acid. C_{17} Margaric acid was found to undergo desaturation to Δ^9- and $\Delta^{5,9}$-acids. Recently, Davidoff and Korn[162, 163] have extended their work on slime mold with the demonstration that enzymes are present in particulate fractions which can cause the formation and accumulation of α,β-unsaturated, β,γ-unsaturated and β-hydroxy derivatives of long-chain fatty acyl CoA. The steps involved appeared to be a reversible dehydration of the β-hydroxy acid to the α,β-unsaturated acid and reversible isomerization of the α,β-unsaturated acid to the β,γ-unsaturated acid. Similar enzymes have been demonstrated in guinea-pig liver mitochondria. Guinea-pig liver microsomes appear to possess hydrase activity toward α,β-hexadecenyl CoA but no significant α,β- $\rightleftharpoons$ β,γ-isomerase activity. The significance of these types of interconversions is unknown, but it is possible that with their demonstration the products formed may prove to be interesting intermediates in relation to both fatty acid synthesis and possibly more complex lipid synthesis.

This treatment on fatty acid synthesis has included very little on odd-numbered fatty acids, branched-chain fatty acids, cyclic fatty acids or some of the more complex acids found in certain bacterial species. Only a brief summary is presented here (for reviews on some aspects see Asselineau and Lederer,[25] Lederer,[434, 435] and Asselineau and Bennet[24]).

Following the demonstration of the malonyl CoA pathway for the synthesis of fatty acids, Horning *et al.*[332] showed that a partially purified enzyme from rat adipose tissue is capable of forming odd-numbered and branched-chain fatty acids from malonyl CoA and CoA derivatives of propionic, isobutyric, isocaproic, isovaleric and α-methyl butyric acids. Long-chain fatty acids of C_{13} to C_{18} were formed with malonyl CoA supplying all the carbon atoms in addition to those from one molecule of the starting acyl-CoA derivative. Bressler and Wakil[96] have shown that their R_{2a} fraction will incorporate propionyl CoA into the C_{17} saturated fatty acid, heptadeconic acid.

The group led by Hofmann has demonstrated that in *Lactobacillus*, lactobacillic acid (a cyclic acid) is formed by the addition of a methylene bridge across the double bond of *cis*-vaccenic acid. [315a] The methylene carbon may arise from formate or methionine and the *cis*-vaccenic in the manner already described. The more recent evidence indicates that the methyl group from S-adenosyl methionine is added to an olefinic fatty acid derivative. [446, 733, 130] Zalkin *et al.* found extracts of *Serratia marcescens* and *Clostridium butyricum* to be capable of forming cyclopropane fatty acids from S-adenosyl methionine and endogenous and exogenous substrates, respectively. In both instances the substrates appeared to be the fatty acids of phosphatidyl ethanolamine. Chung and Law [130] have obtained a partially purified preparation of the cyclopropane fatty acid synthetase. This enzyme catalyzes the transfer of the methyl group of S-adenosylmethionine to an unsaturated fatty acid of phosphatidyl ethanolamine. The synthetase is inhibited by the S-adenosylhomocysteine arising from the reaction unless prevented by a second protein fraction capable of hydrolysing S-adenosyl-homocysteine. Both cyclopropane and cyclopropene acids (C_{19}, sterculic and C_{18} malvalic) are produced by the plant family, *malvaceae*, from acetate and methionine. [608, 330] It is suggested that the methyl group of methionine reacts with an unsaturated fatty acid to form a cyclopropane acid and that the latter is desaturated in the ring to yield a cyclopropene acid.

As noted by Asselineau and Bennet, [24] every species of the genus *Myco-bacterium* studied so far contains characteristic branched-chain fatty acids which are not found in any other species of living organisms. Three main types of branched-chain fatty acids are found: (1) acids of the tuberculo-stearic group containing one methyl branch in the middle of a chain which derive from oleic acid and methionine; (2) acids containing three or four methyl branches located near the carboxyl end of the molecule (these include the phthienoic and mycocerosic acid group which seem to arise by addition of propionate groups possibly through condensation at the α-carbon to normal long-chain fatty acids) [241, 25] and (3) acids containing several long branches and one or two oxygenated functions (the mycolic acid group which contain up to 88 carbons and appear to derive from two molecules of stearic (palmitic) and 2 molecules of C_{26} hexacosanoic acid). It is remarkable that these more complex and, in the case of the mycolic acids, much larger fatty acids appear to be synthesized by *mycobacteria* from the more normal fatty acids which in turn arise via the malonyl CoA pathway.

(2) *Glycerol Moiety*

There is good evidence that for one of the pathways of triglyceride synthesis the glycerol moiety utilized arises mainly from the specific L-isomer of α-glycerophosphate (L-α-GP). [704, 107, 705] The L-α-GP may be formed either from the glycolysis intermediate, dihydroxyacetone phosphate, by the action of L-α-GP dehydrogenase (reaction 4) or by the phosphorylation of the glycerol in the presence of ATP and the enzyme, glycerokinase (reaction 5):

$$\text{dihydroxyacetone phosphate} + DPNH + H^+ \rightleftharpoons L\text{-}\alpha\text{-}GP + DPN^+ \qquad (4)$$

$$\text{glycerol} + ATP \longrightarrow L\text{-}\alpha\text{-}GP + ADP \qquad (5)$$

Whether L-α-GP arises from dihydroxyacetone phosphate or free glycerol, probably depends greatly on the distribution of the two enzyme systems in nature. Two specific L-α-GP dehydrogenases are known, one, present in brain and yeast, which is particulate in nature and is not DPN-linked; [261, 674, 562, 563] a second, found in muscle, is soluble and requires DPN. [683] The dehydrogenase from muscle has been crystallized. [35, 727] Similar enzymes are also present in insects. [125, 205] The particulate enzyme is now more generally referred to as mitochondrial α-GP oxidase. Recent work has established that the presence of these enzymes in the cytoplasm and mitochondria of insect muscle permits the oxidation of DPNH by way of the glycerophosphate cycle. [106, 593] The experiments of Buell and Reiser [107]

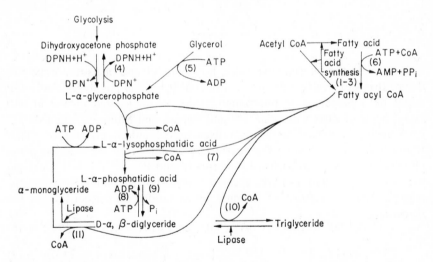

FIG. 2. Scheme showing the biological formation of phosphatidic acid and triglyceride. Numbers in parentheses refer to reactions described in the text.

provide evidence that in the intestinal mucosa L-α-GP is mainly derived from glycolysis. In developing a method for the biological preparation of L-α-GP it was possible to demonstrate the presence of small amounts of this enzyme in a soluble extract of yeast. [635]

Bublitz and Kennedy [105] were the first to obtain a partially purified kinase enzyme (glycerokinase) which catalyzed the direct phosphorylation of glycerol by the transfer of phosphate from ATP. Earlier evidence suggested that the latter reaction could be carried on by kidney extracts [357] and certain bacteria (*Propionibacterium pentosaceum*). [39] Glycerokinase has been prepared in crystalline form by Wieland and Suyter. [711] Initial surveys showed that only kidney and liver contained glycerokinase. Subsequently, studies on the utilization of free glycerol by intestinal mucosa [596] prompted studies to reinvestigate the possibility that intestinal mucosa does contain glycerokinase. The presence of this enzyme has now been demonstrated in the intestinal mucosa of the hamster [276] and the cat. [134]

The reactions (reaction (4) catalyzed by L-α-GP dehydrogenase and reaction (5) catalyzed by glycerokinase) concerned with the formation of L-α-GP are shown as part of the scheme presented in Fig. 2.

(3) *Formation of Phosphatidic Acid and its Role in Triglyceride Synthesis*

Discussion of phosphatidic acid (II) formation could quite justifiably be

$$
\begin{array}{l}
CH_2OCOR \\
| \\
R'COOCH \qquad O \\
| \qquad\qquad \| \\
CH_2\!-\!O\!-\!P\!-\!OH \\
\qquad\qquad | \\
\qquad\qquad O_-
\end{array}
$$

L-α-phosphatidic acid
II

included with the phosphoglycerides, however, because of its importance in the synthesis of triglycerides it is considered here. The possibility that α-GP might be a precursor of phosphoglycerides was suggested by the *in vivo* experiments of Zilversmit *et al.* [736] and Popják and Muir. [542] Kennedy [371] confirmed this suggestion using a liver mitochondrial preparation. That L-α-GP was a precursor of phosphatidic acid (one of the simplest phosphoglycerides) was established by Kornberg and Pricer. [410, 412, 413] Starting with fatty acids and L-α-GP, these workers showed that a liver enzyme preparation was capable of forming phosphatidic acid according to the reactions:

$$\text{fatty acid} + \text{ATP} + \text{CoA} \rightleftharpoons \text{fatty acyl CoA} + \text{AMP} + \text{PP}_i \qquad (6)$$

$$2 \text{ fatty acyl CoA} + \text{L-}\alpha\text{-GP} \longrightarrow \text{L-}\alpha\text{-phosphatidic acid} + 2 \text{ CoA} \qquad (7)$$

The enzyme system showed greatest activity for fatty acyl CoA of C_{14}–C_{18} in length.

The enzyme (fatty acyl CoA synthetase) catalysing reaction (6) has been demonstrated in a number of sources which include in addition to liver, brain, [353] intestinal mucosa, [602, 3] adipose tissue [629] and *Bacillus megaterium*. [484] Except for *B. megaterium* where localization is in the cytoplasmic portion, the enzyme appears to be localized in the microsomal [602, 3, 156] or the nuclear fraction. [156]

Some uncertainty still exists as to the mechanism of reaction (6). Berg[51] has provided convincing evidence that the activation of acetate involved two reactions; in the first, acetate and ATP react to form acetyl adenylate and PP_i, and in the second, the acetyl adenylate reacts to yield acetyl CoA and AMP. Findings consistent with this mechanism have been obtained for an enzyme preparation from hog liver particles which specifically catalyzed the activation of fatty acids with 4 to 12 carbon atoms.[352] Results also supporting the involvement of an acyl adenylate intermediate are reported for the activation of butyrate[658, 437] and palmitate.[601, 602] Although synthetic acyl adenylates could participate in the activation reaction it was not possible to demonstrate any accumulation of these intermediates after the addition of fatty acids, Mg^{++} and ATP to the activating system. This failure to demonstrate accumulation of acyl adenylate and the finding that radioactivity derived from acetate-C^{14} during activation is associated with a protein fraction caused Whitehouse et al.[708] to suggest that acyl adenylate is normally firmly bound to enzyme. It was suggested that added acyl adenylate may acetylate CoA without the formation of the intermediate acyl adenylate-enzyme complex.

An alternative interpretation of the activation reaction has been made by Ingraham and Green[348] (see also Green and Wakil[267]). They have assumed that Mg^{++} bound to the enzyme forms a chelate with both ATP and CoA. Then reaction between acetate and Mg-bound ATP yields Mg-bound acetyl adenylate and PP_i. The acetyl group is transferred to Mg-bound CoA to form Mg-bound acetyl CoA, and the enzyme on dissociation gives rise to acetyl CoA, AMP and Mg-bound enzyme. Cornforth[154] suggests an interesting alternative mechanism which in some respects reconciles the proposals already described. By analogy to methods for the chemical synthesis of thioesters it is postulated that the reaction catalyzed by acetic thiokinase may be base-catalyzed. It is then suggested that the active centre contains a basic group (e.g. tertiary amine) surrounded by receptors for Mg^{++}, adenylate, acetate and CoA. The sites for adenylate and acetate are assumed to act in concert as a receptor of acetyl adenylate while those for acetate and CoA act as a receptor of acetyl CoA. The site for Mg^{++} is a receptor for pyrophosphate or ATP. In the mechanism it is suggested that Mg^{++} and ATP become attached first and that attack by acetate follows, with pyrophosphate and a dissociated base-complex of acetyl adenylate being formed. Attack by CoA and dissociation of products from the enzyme yield acetyl CoA and AMP.

Some modification of the mechanism of activation of fatty acid (reaction 6) may be necessary in view of the work of Campagnari and Webster.[112] These workers have succeeded in realizing conditions for both acetyl CoA- and butyryl CoA-synthetases from beef heart mitochondria which permit the accumulation of acetyl-C^{14} and butyryl-C^{14} adenylates from ATP and the corresponding C^{14} acid in the presence of added Mg^{++}. The most critical factor in the system accumulating acyl adenylates seemed to be the amount of synthetase, with large amounts being required for significant synthesis of the adenylate. As Compagnari and Webster [112] note it is likely that additional information on mechanism (particularly in relation to binding on the enzyme) can only come once more highly purified preparations of acyl CoA synthetases become available.

A number of findings have supported the view that L-α-phosphatidic acid is formed by reactions (6) and (7). Stansly [624] observed phosphatidic acid synthesis in a system similar to that of Kornberg and Pricer. [413] It has also been observed that the incorporation of α-GP^{32} [410, 371, 492, 607] and C^{14}-labeled α-GP [587, 643] into phosphatidic acid and C^{14}-palmitate into the glycerophosphatides [353] were greatly increased by CoA. Optimal incorporation required metabolic energy (presumably as ATP). C^{14}-Glycerol could not replace the L-α-GP.

The order of esterification still remains in doubt, but the work of Pieringer and Hokin [536] and Lands and Hart [422] indicate that microsomes of brain and liver can actively acylate lysophosphatidic acid (α'-acyl GP). This acylation is more rapid than the acylation of α-GP thus suggesting a stepwise acylation.

There is good evidence that an alternative pathway exists for the formation of phosphatidic acid. Strickland [641] found that the incorporation of P_i^{32} into phosphatidic acid of glycolyzing brain homogenates or respiring brain mitochondria was greatly stimulated by the addition of a number of diglyceride preparations (α,β-diglycerides from egg and spinal cord lecithin and synthetic D-α,β-dimyristin). The omission of Mg^{++} ions or the addition of fluoride or iodoacetate to the homogenate system prevented this stimulation, suggesting that the phosphorylation was dependent upon active metabolism by the tissue preparations. The phosphorylation appeared to be stereospecific since synthetic D-α,β-diolein caused a seven-fold increase in the labeling from P^{32} compared to a negligible increase caused by synthetic L-α,β-diolein. [642] Hokin and Hokin [317, 326] have demonstrated the presence of a diglyceride kinase in deoxycholate-treated microsomes from brain. This enzyme catalyzed the reaction:

$$D\text{-}\alpha,\beta\text{-diglyceride} + ATP \longrightarrow \text{phosphatidic acid} + ADP \qquad (8)$$

The most effective substrate was diglyceride prepared from cabbage phosphatidic acid. Diglycerides prepared from brain lecithin and α-palmityl-β-oleyl diglyceride were less effective. The formation of lysophosphatidic acid had been demonstrated using a somewhat similar enzyme system. [324, 535] Pieringer and Hokin [536] have further demonstrated that the lysophosphatidic acid formed is readily acylated to form phosphatidic acid by cytoplasmci particulate preparations from guinea-pig brain or liver. Mitochondria from pea cotyledons have been shown to catalyze the direct phosphorylation of both α- and α,β-diglycerides from ATP[32]. [79]

The possible implication of diglyceride kinase in Na,K-transport [320, 325] has promoted great interest in the occurrence of this enzyme. Brain microsomes, [326] erythrocyte ghosts [319] and the salt gland of the gull [327] are particularly rich sources.

The relative importance of the two pathways for the synthesis of phosphatidic acid remains uncertain. However, the implication of phosphatidic acid in the synthesis of several different lipids (triglycerides, phosphoglycerides, etc.) leads to the speculation that the different pathways may be necessary for the multiplicity of roles played by this phosphatide in lipid biosynthesis. It is possible that the two pathways exist to meet differences in precursor pools (e.g. L-α-GP and fatty acyl CoA or α,β-diglyceride and ATP) which may arise from tissue to tissue or even from one intracellular site to another. Other aspects of the interesting role played by phosphatidic acid thereby stressing the need for different pathways of formation will become evident in discussions on both triglyceride and glycerophosphatide biosynthesis.

An important role for phosphatidic acid in lipid synthesis was suggested by the discovery that liver contains an enzyme, phosphatidic acid phosphatase, which removes phosphate (P_i) from phosphatidic acid to form D-α,β-diglyceride (reaction 9): [610]

$$\text{L-α-phosphatidic acid} \longrightarrow \text{D-α,β-diglyceride} + P_i \qquad (9)$$

The D-α,β-diglyceride derived from this reaction was shown to be a precursor of triglyceride [704] and the phosphoglycerides, phosphatidyl choline (III) and phosphatidyl ethanolamine (IV). [380] Dephosphorylation of phos-

L-α-lecithin
(L-α-phosphatidyl choline)
III

L-α-phosphatidyl ethanolamine
IV

phatidic acid has also been demonstrated in homogenates of brain. [587] Reaction (9) was found to be strongly inhibited by Mg^{++}. It seems likely that this inhibition has been responsible for the accumulation of phosphatidic acid, [413, 371, 169, 492] or a "phosphatidic acid-like" substance [473, 474] which has been observed for various tissue preparations. Normally almost negligible amounts of phosphatidic acid are present in tissues *in vivo* [171, 478, 479, 464] and it is only with difficulty that it has been possible to demonstrate the existence of phosphatidic acid in fresh tissue.[321, 335, 336]

Phosphatidic acid phosphatase has been more extensively studied by Coleman and Hübscher.[139] The distribution of activity in several species of animal (rabbit, rat, guinea pig, ox and pig) was determined revealing the pattern that kidney and intestine possessed the greatest activity followed by brain and liver. Most of the activity resides in the microsomal fraction. The enzyme after partial purification (4–5 times) showed extreme specificity for phosphatidic acid and its phosphoric ester. Hokin and Hokin,[320] because of the role of this enzyme in the "phosphatidic acid cycle" (which has been implicated in Na^+ transport), have also surveyed the occurrence of this enzyme obtaining a similar result to Coleman and Hübscher with the notable addition that salt glands possess activities comparable to kidney.

Although there is good evidence that glycerol–fatty acid ester bonds can be formed by reversal of lipase action (see, for example, Borgström;[71] Bergström and Borgström[53]), it seems unlikely that conditions exist *in vivo* for the esterification of free glycerol by this mechanism. Tietz and Shapiro[669] provided evidence for an alternative pathway in liver homogenate. ATP and a heat-stable factor were found to be necessary for incorporation of labeled fatty acid (palmitic) into neutral fat. Weiss *et al.*,[704, 705] after establishing the importance of phosphatidic acid as a source for α,β-diglycerides in the synthesis of phosphoglycerides, then investigated the possibility that these diglycerides may also function in triglyceride synthesis. This hypothesis was substantiated by the demonstration that net synthesis of triglyceride could be achieved by a particulate enzyme from chicken liver in the presence of added palmityl CoA and α,β-diglyceride. The evidence strongly suggested that triglyceride is formed according to the reaction:

$$\alpha,\beta\text{-diglyceride} + \text{fatty acyl CoA} \longrightarrow \text{triglyceride} + \text{CoA} \qquad (10)$$

The enzyme system was about twice as active towards D-α,β-diolein as to L-α,β-diolein, thus suggesting some stereospecifity. The scheme for phosphatidic acid and triglyceride synthesis is shown in Fig. 2.

Support for this pathway of triglyceride synthesis has been provided by a number of reports from Shapiro *et al.*[669, 627, 628] In this work two enzyme systems of rat liver, one microsomal and the other predominantly mitochondrial, have been obtained which catalyze the incorporation of C^{14}-palmitic acid into triglyceride. The microsomal system required the addition of α-GP, CoA and ATP for maximal activity while the mitochondrial system did not require α-GP but rather a thermostable factor in the supernatant and a small amount of native supernatant. More recently, Shapiro[607] has indicated that α-GP is present in the thermostable fraction and that it can stimulate the esterification. This evidence is consistent with the synthesis of triglyceride occurring according to the above scheme in both microsomes and mitochondria.

Several investigations have indicated that triglycerides are synthesized in the intestinal mucosa by a pathway similar to that described. Buell and Reiser [107] have shown that glyceride-glycerol for triglyceride synthesis arises mainly from fructose-1,6-diphosphate by way of dihydroxyacetone phosphate and L-α-GP. It has also been established that fatty acid activation can be carried on by homogenates of human brain or rat intestinal mucosa, providing CoA, ATP and Mg^{++} are added. [602] The participation of phosphatidic acid is strongly suggested by the observation that there is an increase in incorporation of labeled phosphate or palmitic acid into phosphatidic acid during the triglyceride synthesis associated with active fat absorption by *in vitro* preparations of small intestine. [356] Also, the optimal incorporation of C^{14}-palmitic acid into triglyceride by mitochondrial preparations of intestinal mucosa from the rat or rabbit required α-GP, ATP, CoA, GSH and Mg^{++}. [336] The latter workers have obtained evidence that phosphatidic acid is dephosphorylated [139] and that the diglyceride formed is utilized for triglyceride synthesis. [131]

In an investigation of glyceride synthesis by mitochondria of rabbit intestinal mucosa, Clark and Hübscher [132, 133] observed that both α-GP and α-monoglyceride stimulated the incorporation of C^{14}-palmitate into glycerides in the presence of ATP, CoA and other cofactors. The effect of each appeared to be additive. Their results suggested the existence of an alternative pathway for triglyceride synthesis with monoglyceride as the starting precursor. Confirmation of the existence of this pathway comes from several laboratories. Thus, Senior and Isselbacher [603] have shown that the microsomal fraction of rat or rabbit gut mucosa contains an active acylase capable of forming diglyceride from α-monoglycerides and palmityl CoA. More recently, convincing evidence has been obtained showing that intestinal mucosal preparations contain an active monoglyceride transacylase and an active diglyceride transacylase. Brown and Johnston [103] have observed that doubly labeled-α-monopalmitin is incorporated intact into triglyceride by way of an intermediate α,α'-diglyceride. These same workers [104] have also studied the specificity of the monoglyceride transacylase towards α- and β-monoglycerides. Both isomers are utilized by the enzyme but a preference is shown towards the β-monoglyceride. Ailhaud *et al.* [4] have confirmed this finding and have further shown that diglyceride transacylase preferentially utilizes α,β-diglycerides rather than α,α'-diglycerides.

It can be concluded on the basis of the available evidence that triglyceride may be formed from monoglyceride by enzymes catalyzing reaction (11) and

$$\beta\text{-monoglyceride} + \text{fatty acyl-CoA} \longrightarrow \alpha,\beta\text{-diglyceride} + \text{CoA} \quad (11)$$

F

reaction (10) (see Fig. 2 for summary). Several recent reviews [334, 337, 355, 601] on glyceride biosynthesis outline the evidence for, and the importance of, the above two pathways much more fully. However, it would seem reasonable to conclude that the monoglyceride pathway is particularly important in triglyceride synthesis that follows the absorption of micelles of fat which are relatively high in β-monoglyceride. [104, 4] On the other hand, if lipolysis has yielded predominantly free fatty acids then the pathway via α-GP and phosphatidic acid becomes of major importance.

(4) *Carbohydrate-containing Glycerides*

Relative large amounts of lipids containing galactose or galactose and sulfur have been found in chloroplasts of higher plants (see Benson [46]). Structural studies by Benson *et al.*, [50, 48] Carter *et al.* [118] and Sastry and Kates [595] indicate that these lipids are α,β-diglycerides with one or two D-galactosyl residues attached to the remaining hydroxyl group of the diglyceride. Formulae V and VI show the structures of these lipids.

α-galactosyl diglyceride
V

α-(6-sulfogalactosyl) diglyceride
VI

Neufeld and Hall [513] have observed that isolated spinach chloroplasts catalyze the transfer of galactose from UDP-galactose (see section on cerebrosides for formation of this intermediate) to an endogenous acceptor which is presumably diglyceride in nature. This pathway of formation would require diglyceride to be formed and then reaction with UDP-galactose would yield the α-galactosyl diglyceride. This reaction, if proven, is somewhat analogous to that for lecithin or phosphatidyl ethanolamine formation (see Section B (b) (i), reaction (17) of this chapter) where phosphorylated base is provided via a cytosine-containing nucleotide.

Benson [46] has summarized evidence which suggests that the sulfur-containing galactosyl diglyceride may be formed similarly with the exception that a nucleoside diphosphosulfoquinovose substitutes for UDP-galactose. If this type of reaction occurs then the sulfur group must be transferred to the sugar while it is free or in combination with a nucleotide. Benson, [46] in summarizing, is careful to note that only very limited evidence supports this pathway. Much additional work is needed to clearly define the pathways of formation of the galactosyl-containing glycerides.

(b) *Cholesterol Esters*

The biosynthesis of cholesterol is considered in Chapter 4 of this volume and, therefore, only a brief description of the esterification process need be included here. Cholesterol esterases from the pancreas have been reported to have the required specificity and activity to catalyze the synthesis and hydrolysis of esters of long-chain fatty acids and cholesterol. [725, 657, 415] The cholesterol esterase of hog pancreas has been purified 400-fold by ammonium sulfate and ethanol fractionation in the cold and by chromatography on cellulose. [311] During purification it was noted that the hydrolytic and synthetic activities paralleled each other, suggesting that a single enzyme catalyzed the reaction: [12]

$$\text{fatty acid} + \text{cholesterol} \rightleftharpoons \text{cholesterol ester} \qquad (12)$$

More recently, Murthy and Ganguly [506] have obtained evidence, on the basis of differences in optimal pH, sensitivity or response to inhibitors and separation of activities during purification, that the hydrolytic and synthetic activities are separable. The presence of bile salts was found to be essential to the point of assigning to them a possible coenzyme role.

Studies on the specificity of purified [311] and crude [415, 414] cholesterol esterase preparations towards cholesterol have demonstrated that for esterification (a) the α-configuration of the hydroxyl group on carbon 3 is essential, (b) the double bond between carbon atoms 5 and 6 is not essential, (c) saturation at carbon 7 is necessary and (d) certain modifications of the side chain are permissible.

Some uncertainty exists with regard to the specificity shown by cholesterol esterases towards fatty acids when functioning in a synthetic capacity. Earlier work [311] and even up until fairly recently, most reports [507, 362] have indicated that the esterification process shows some degree of preference towards fatty acids that are unsaturated. The general order favored seems to be oleic > linoleic > linolenic > C_{18}-C_{14} saturated fatty acids > shorter chain saturated fatty acids. Recently, interest has centered around the importance of adequate micellar solubilization of cholesterol and fatty acid. Vahouny et al. [679] observed that the use of micellar preparations of substrates gave hydrolytic rates that were higher, but for esterification these preparations did not provide adequate substrate for optimal activity. It is possible that the deficiency arose because cholesterol and fatty acid were not equally available to the enzyme. The very recent *in vitro* work of Shah et al. [606] helps to clarify the problem. Using pancreatic juice and intestinal mucosal preparations they have shown that bile acid is necessary and that no exogenous source is required for ATP, CoA or Mg^{++} as cofactors for esterification. When single fatty acids are provided as substrate the preference fits perfectly to the pattern cited earlier. However, if saturated fatty acids and unsaturated fatty acids are provided as a mixture then enhancement of esterification of saturated fatty acids occurs. This observation has led to the suggestion "that any difference in esterification of cholesterol with saturated fatty acids and esterification with unsaturated fatty acids, as well as the enhancement of the esterification with saturated fatty acids by the addition of an unsaturated fatty acid, is accounted for by micellar solubilization of cholesterol and of saturated fatty acid in the presence of an unsaturated fatty acid and bile salts". [606]

Several investigators have also reported a cholesterol-esterifying system in liver. [387, 611, 515, 111, 225] Swell et al. [655] have suggested that the liver activity is due to an esterase which acts only on short-chain fatty acids. More recently Mukherjee et al. [505] have studied a system in rat liver which can synthesize cholesterol esters from cholesterol and the long-chain fatty acid, palmitic. The esterification was shown to require ATP and CoA. On the basis of this evidence it was proposed that the esterification mechanism involves acylation of the cholesterol by fatty acyl CoA (reaction 13):

$$\text{fatty acyl CoA} + \text{cholesterol} \longrightarrow \text{cholesterol acylate} + \text{CoA} \quad (13)$$

The fatty acyl CoA for reaction (13) would presumably be readily supplied by the fatty acid activation system described in relation to reaction (6).

Goodman et al. [249] have recently further investigated the nature of the enzyme system in rat liver which catalyzes cholesterol ester formation. Proof for the involvement of a fatty acyl CoA intermediate was provided with the observation that oleyl-CoA could completely replace ATP and CoA in the optimal system. The enzymes are particulate with mitochondria and microsomes possessing about equal activity. Concerning fatty acid specificity in the esterification of free cholesterol the order observed at the CoA ester level was oleyl CoA > palmityl CoA > stearyl CoA > linoleyl CoA. It was concluded that the enzyme involved is a fatty acyl coenzyme A-cholesterol acyltransferase.

Cholesterol esters appear to be formed by a third mechanism which may or may not involve one of the previous enzyme systems. Swell et al. [656] in an in vivo study of the role of liver in the metabolism of cholesterol esters obtained results suggesting that a portion of the cholesterol esters taken up by liver participate in a series of transferase reactions with fatty acid donors. However, Bennet [45] was unable to demonstrate the existence in rat liver mitochondria or microsomes of any pathway other than that requiring ATP and CoA. This finding is in contrast to that of Glomset et al. [245] and Shah et al. [605] who have observed that rat plasma possesses a fatty acid transferase capable of catalyzing a transesterification between the β-fatty acid of lecithin and free cholesterol. Triglycerides were very much less effective as donors.

Two pathways (reactions 13 and 14), and possibly a third, exist for the formation of cholesterol esters. More evidence is required to establish whether one reaction is more important than the other *in vivo* or whether each plays an important role in its respective tissue site.

(c) *Higher Alcohol Esters, Glyceryl Ethers and Hydrocarbons*

These lipids are considered here collectively mainly because little is known about their particular pathways of synthesis. A wide variety of lipids which fall into each of the above groups have been found to occur naturally. These lipids are listed in some detail in treatises by Deuel, [187, 189] Lovern [450] and Hanahan. [287] It seems reasonable to speculate that the higher alcohol esters (true wax esters) which form the major components of many waxes are formed from smaller fatty acid units (C_2 or larger) in a manner similar to that described for fatty acid synthesis. The glyceryl ethers, consisting of one of the three fatty alcohols, i.e. palmityl, stearyl and oleyl in ether linkage at the α-position of glycerol (either with or without the remaining hydroxyls esterified) might arise by the partial reduction or hydration of the α,β-unsaturated side chain which exists in ether linkage in "plasmalogenic" diglyceride, a possible precursor of plasmalogens (see later section on plasmalogens). The α,β-unsaturated side chain is known to be derived from acetate or palmitate. The more completely saturated hydrocarbons may arise by partial reduction of squalene or any of its precursors. The mechanism of formation of these highly unsaturated hydrocarbons from acetate is described in the chapter on cholesterol.

B. PHOSPHOGLYCERIDES (GLYCEROPHOSPHATIDES)

This group of lipids consists of glycerol with phosphate or one of a number of phosphomonoesters esterified at the α-position and fatty acid esterified at the β-position. The α'-position either is esterified with a second fatty acid (phosphatidyl compound) or is in ether linkage with an α,β-unsaturated aliphatic chain (plasmalogen). The esterification of orthophosphate at the free hydroxyl of α,β-diglyceride gives rise to the phosphate-monoester lipid, phosphatidic acid (II), which has already received some discussion. A variety of phosphate-diester lipids are known which differ in the second grouping esterified to phosphate or in the type of groupings attached to the β- and

a'-position of glycerol. Each of the phosphate-esters of the nitrogenous bases, choline, ethanolamine and serine on esterification with the free a-position (1) of a- or β-monoglyceride yields the corresponding lysophosphatide (VII), (2) of a,β-diglycerides yields lecithin (phosphatidyl choline, (III), phosphatidyl ethanolamine (IV) and phosphatidyl serine (VIII), respectively,

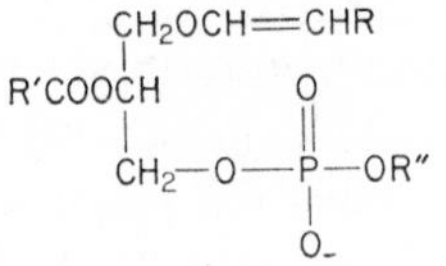

$$CH_2OCH{=}CHR$$
$$R'COOCH$$
$$CH_2-O-\overset{O}{\underset{O_-}{\overset{\|}{P}}}-OR''$$

Plasmalogens (phosphatidal compounds)

IX

$$\left[\begin{array}{l} R=\text{aliphatic chain} \\ R'=\text{fatty acid} \\ R''=\text{choline, ethanolamine or serine} \end{array}\right]$$

and (3) of $a(a,\beta$-unsaturated aliphatic ether), β-monoglyceride gives rise to the corresponding plasmalogen or phosphatidal compounds (IX). Recently, quite good proof has been provided for the existence of an a'-aliphatic ether (kephalin B) which is thought to be similar in structure to ethanolamine plasmalogen except for the vinyl ether linkage. [581] L-a-Glycerophosphate and inositol-1-phosphate when esterified through the phosphate group to the free hydroxyl position of D-a,β-diglyceride yield phosphatidyl glycerol and phosphatidyl inositol (monophosphoinositide) (XI). Evidence has also been

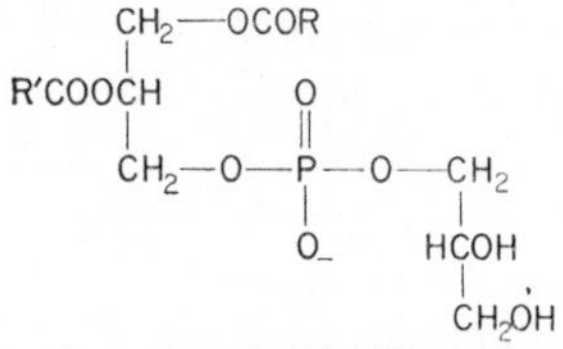

$$CH_2-OCOR$$
$$R'COOCH$$
$$CH_2-O-\overset{O}{\underset{O_-}{\overset{\|}{P}}}-O-CH_2$$
$$HCOH$$
$$CH_2OH$$

L-a-phosphatidyl glycerol

X

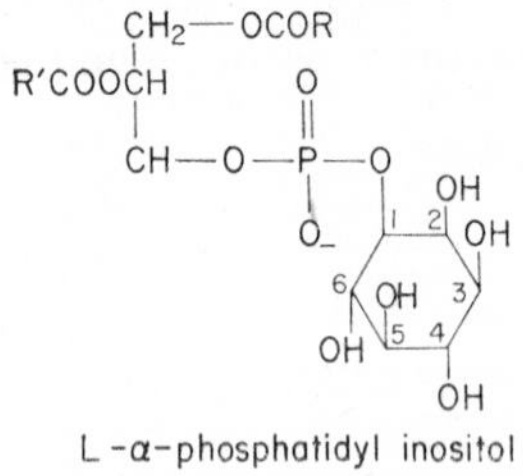

$$CH_2-OCOR$$
$$R'COOCH$$
$$CH-O-\overset{O}{\underset{O_-}{\overset{\|}{P}}}-O$$

L-a-phosphatidyl inositol

XI

described which suggests the existence of phosphate-triesters of phosphatidyl ethanolamine and phosphatidyl serine (XII).

Before consideration of the biosynthesis of each of these glycerophosphatides, brief discussion of some of the more recent contributions towards the structure of certain of these phosphatides is included. Other details on structure have been described in numerous reviews by Deuel, [187] Wittcoff, [718] Baer, [28] Folch and LeBaron, [218] Hanahan, [287] Hawthorne [304, 305] and Ansell and Hawthorne. [15]

$$
\begin{array}{c}
CH_2OCOR \\
| \\
R'COOCH \quad\quad O \\
| \quad\quad\quad\quad || \\
CH—O—P—O—R'' \\
| \\
O \\
| \\
CH_2CH_2\overset{+}{N}H_3
\end{array}
$$

Phosphate triester complexes
XII

⎡ Where R and R' are fatty acids and R''=
⎢ lysolecithin, cardiolipin or sphingomyelin
⎨ linked through the free hydroxyl or alter-
⎢ natively the primary hydroxyls of glycerol
⎢ may provide a bridge between two phospho-
⎣ lipid molecules by phosphate triester bonds ⎦

Although the fully acylated phosphoglycerides may have both fatty acids either saturated or unsaturated, it seems that in most cases the fatty acids are a mixture. Studies of the hydrolysis of phosphoglycerides by phosphatidase A suggested that the mixture of saturated and unsaturated fatty acids liberated, fitted a certain pattern. Thus, with lecithin from liver [285] and egg [286, 559, 309] and phosphatidyl ethanolamine from egg, [558] it was shown that the α'-position contained unsaturated fatty acid and the β-position the saturated fatty acid. This conclusion depended on the finding that phosphatidase A acted specifically at the α'-position. [284, 448, 260] On the basis of phosphatidase A action the acyl group in the plasmalogens was also assigned to the α'-position. [555, 557, 260] The position of attack of phosphatidase A was questioned by Marinetti et al. [472, 476] who presented evidence that the β-position was attacked to an appreciable extent. Debuch [181] found that reduction of ethanolamine plasmalogens yielded batyl and chimyl alcohols (glyceryl ethers) which consumed periodate equivalent to that expected for glyceryl ethers with an aliphatic side chain at the α'-position. The latter could only be derived from plasmalogen in which the ether linkage was at the α'-position. This work not only removed doubt as to the position of the "aldehydogenic" group but also substantiated the reports [555, 556, 557, 260, 181] of an α,β-unsaturated ether structure rather than the hemiacetal form suggested earlier by Klenk and Debuch. [392, 393] Finally, re-evaluation of the action of phosphatidase A by Tattrie [659] and Hanahan et al. [289] has provided conclusive evidence that this enzyme specifically attacks the β-position of lecithin. In the study it was also demonstrated that unsaturated fatty acids are preferentially located at the β-position. A much more detailed presentation of the action of phosphatidase A by Van Deenen [678] has appeared recently.

Phosphatidyl glycerol has been identified and shown to be present in appreciable quantities in *Scenedesmus* and higher plants. [47] Using phosphatidases C and D, Van Deenen [678] has recently established that phosphatidyl glycerol purified from bacteria and green leaves has the structure of L-α-phosphatidyl-D-glycerol. It is uncertain whether "cardiolipin" which was originally isolated from ox heart by Pangborn [529, 530] should be considered as a complex of phosphatidic acid. Macfarlane and Wheeldon [463] have presented evidence which suggests that "cardiolipin" consists of three molecules of glycerol linked through two phosphoric acids and that the two hydroxyls on the terminal glycerol units are esterified with fatty acid while the hydroxyl on the central glycerol is unesterified. The data are consistent with the structure (XIII) that is formed on condensation of the phosphate of a

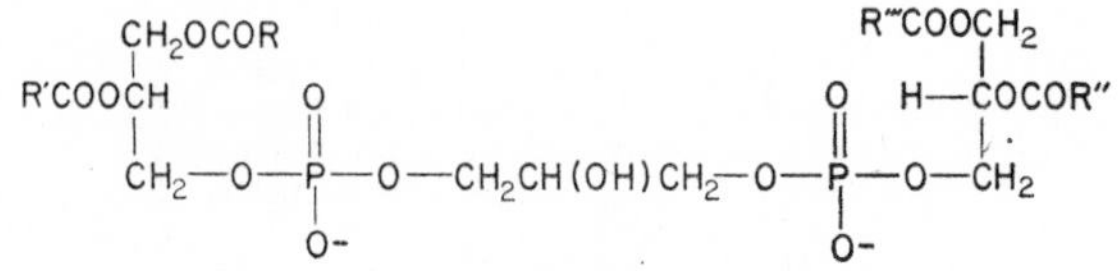

Cardiolipin
XIII

phosphatidic acid molecule with the free α-hydroxyl of a phosphatidyl glycerol molecule. There is evidence for the existence of a similar substance in liver, [488, 174, 176, 461] skeletal muscle, kidney, brain and lung. [176] Diphosphatidyl glycerol which is identical in structure to animal cardiolipin (XIII) has been identified in chlorella, *Rhodospirillum rubrum* and higher plants. [49] Additional information on the identification, isolation and chemistry of the phosphatidyl glycerols is contained in a review by Macfarlane. [462] Ballou [31] has recently established that cardiolipin from beef heart and *Mycobaterium phlei* does in fact have the 1,3-diphosphatidyl glycerol structure shown in formula XIII.

Recent publications on the inositol phosphatides have helped to clarify some of the problems which have existed in relation to these lipids since their presence was demonstrated in a number of different sources (see Folch and LeBaron [218] for references). The main problems have been related to the establishment of structure and what relationship, if any, exists between "monophosphoinositides" (phosphatidyl inositol), "diphosphoinositides" and other preparations such as "lipositol".

Some of the evidence is consistent with the view that monophosphoinositides may represent portions of a more complex structure. Phosphatidyl inositol has been isolated from a wide variety of sources, liver, [487, 208, 290] heart [206, 260] and several plant sources. [499, 686, 443] The inositol phosphatide of plants may be derived from a more complex structure by enzymic degradation. [685, 470] There is evidence that a substance possessing the properties of phosphatidyl inositol exists in guinea pig kidney, [2] pancreas and brain, [322, 323] rat brain [645, 664] and beef brain. [331, 194]

Pizer and Ballou [538] have presented good evidence that the inositol monophosphate derived by alkaline hydrolysis of phytin is myo-inositol-2-phosphate whereas that derived from the monophosphoinositides of soybean, wheat germ, beef heart and liver is principally the optically active myo-inositol-1-phosphate. In the latter case, since a small amount of the 2-phosphate ester is formed, it is suggested that the hydrolysis produces an intermediate 1,2-cyclic diester which in the presence of base yields predominantly the 1-phosphate ester. Brockerhoff and Hanahan [102] obtained evidence consistent with this structure and also noted that the glycerol moiety is linked to the phosphate through the α-position. On the basis of these reports and others (summarized by Hanahan, [287] and Hawthorne [304, 305] and Law [427]) phosphatidyl inositol or monophosphoinositide should be assigned the structure given in (X) and be designated 1-phosphatidyl-L-myo-inositol. [32, 33] A separate study of the structure of liver phosphatidyl inositol yielded results which supported structure (X). [303, 306]

In 1946, Folch [214] first reported the existence of "diphosphoinositide" in beef brain. The ratio of myo-inositol to P to glycerol to fatty acid was 1:2:1:1. On acid hydrolysis this lipid yielded a product which responded to periodate oxidation in a manner similar to that expected for inositol metadiphosphate. [215] On the basis of these findings it was suggested that "diphosphoinositide" consists of an inositol metadiphosphate structure containing a monoglyceride group esterified to phosphate and that the other phosphate may be involved in the linkage of one "diphosphoinositide" monomer unit to another. [218] Hawthorne [302] at first suggested that "diphosphoinositide" may have a cyclic structure with a β-monoglyceride bridge between the two phosphates of inositol metadiphosphate, but on the basis of more recent work he indicates that the latter structure is no longer tenable. [304]

Independent work in two laboratories [194, 257, 258] revealed the existence of "triphosphoinositides" in the inositol phosphatide fraction of beef brain. Dittmer and Dawson [194] obtained two "triphosphoinositide" fractions A and B which were tightly bound to protein. "Triphosphoinositide A" yielded glycerol to inositol to phosphorus to acyl ester ratios of 1:1:3:2 which are consistent with a phosphatidyl inositol diphosphate structure. "Triphosphoinositide B" seemed to be more complex, possessing the following simplest composition: (fatty acid)$_6$ (phosphate)$_6$ (glycerol)$_3$ (inositol)$_2$. A subsequent preliminary report [177] suggested that in the structure of "Triphosphoinositide B" there are three phosphates esterified to each inositol ring with each glycerol esterified with two fatty acids and the free hydroxyl esterified with a phosphate group on inositol. Further investigation [177a, 195] has revealed that "Triphosphoinositide B" was complexed with neutral lipid and that

"Triphosphoinositide A" represents the true triphosphoinositide which according to hydrolytic studies is a phosphatidylinositol diphosphate (diacylglycerylphosphorylinositol diphosphate). Grado and Ballou[257, 258] have investigated the *myo*-inositol phosphates that are derived from beef brain phosphoinositide on base hydrolysis. It was found that a mixture of inositol phosphates (one inositol monophosphate, two inositol diphosphates and two inositol triphosphates) were obtained from the phosphoinositide fraction prepared according to Folch.[215] Periodate oxidation followed by reduction of the dialdehyde and dephosphorylation of the polyol phosphate yielded *D*-iditol. This suggested that the inositol triphosphate must have a configuration in which phosphates are attached at positions 1, 4 and either 5 or 6. The major monophosphate proved to be inositol-4-phosphate. Subsequent studies[670, 99] have established that inositol triphosphate has the configuration shown in structure (XIV) in which phosphates are attached at

$$H_2O_3PO$$

Inositol triphosphate
XIV

In phosphatidyl
inositol diphosphate
$R = \alpha, \beta$-diglyceride

positions 1, 4 and 5. Brockerhoff and Ballou[99] have concluded that brain contains mono-, di- and triphosphoinositides in which the triphosphates are esterified to α,β-diglyceride through the phosphate in the L-1-position. These three phosphoinositides are, therefore, correctly designated as 1-phosphatidyl-L-myo-inositol, 1-phosphatidyl-L-myo-inositol-4-phosphate and 1-phosphatidyl-L-myo-inositol-4,5-diphosphate.

Recently Ballou and his colleagues[29, 30, 34] have extended their very fine work on structure of inositol containing phospholipids to the phosphatidyl myo-inositol mannosides of *Mycobacteria*. These organisms have been found to contain a family of glyco-phospholipids each having different numbers of mannose units attached to inositol, but all having the phosphatidyl grouped on the L-1-position. In the monomannoside D-mannose is in α-glycosidic linkage with the 2-position on inositol, the dimannoside has an additional mannose in a similar linkage at the 6 position. Tri-, tetra- and pentamanno-sides have additional mannose units attached in 1,6- or 1,2-linkage with the mannose units already attached. The general formula XV illustrates these structures.

There are a number of reviews which consider structural aspects of the phosphoglycerides in more detail.[718, 187, 218, 287, 304, 305] Klenk and

Debuch [394] have reviewed this topic in relation to the phosphoglycerides of brain. Ansell and Hawthorne's [15] recent treatise also covers a number of aspects relating to structure.

M = mannose
In dimannoside, x and y = 1
In pentamannoside, x and y = 5
R = α, β-diglyceride

Phosphatidyl myoinositol mannosides
XV

Biosynthesis of Phosphoglycerides

It has been well established that, when isotopically labeled compounds which form a component part of these lipids are administered *in vivo* or are incubated in suitable *in vitro* systems, label appears in the respective components of the phosphoglycerides (see Rossiter and Strickland [588]). For example, this pattern has been observed in experiments carried out with inorganic P labeled with P^{32}, fatty acid labeled with deuterium, C^{14} or I^{131}, glycerol (or glucose) labeled with C^{14}, the nitrogen-containing bases (choline, ethanolamine and serine) labeled with C^{14} or N^{15} and inositol labeled with C^{14} or tritium. These experiments provided good evidence that these lipids, in general, are continually being renewed. There are many reviews which consider this evidence in detail. [120, 312, 313, 121, 718, 189, 173, 534, 582]

It is only in recent years that progress has been made towards the elucidation of the metabolic pathways concerned in the biosynthesis of the phosphoglycerides. This has been initiated to a large extent by the notable contributions of Kennedy (see reviews [373, 375, 376, 377, 377a]) who was able to establish pathways of synthesis for the two phosphoglycerides, lecithin and phosphatidyl ethanolamine using partially purified preparations from liver. Support for these pathways has been provided by experiments with other tissues (brain [584, 585] and seminal vesicles [713]). More recent work has revealed considerable information regarding the pathways of some of the other phosphoglycerides (e.g. inositol-containing) and also suggested the existence of alternative pathways for the above phosphatides. Each of the reviews by Kennedy, [373, 375, 376, 377, 377a] Dawson, [173] Paysant-Diament, [534] Trusov, [672] Rossiter and Strickland, [587, 588] Klenk and Debuch, [394] Rossiter, [581] Hawthorne [304, 305] and Ansell and Hawthorne [15] summarizes certain aspects of the biological formation of the phosphoglycerides.

Origin of the Individual Moieties

In the discussion of the formation of phosphatidic acid, the origin of the fatty acids, glycerol and glycerophosphate was described. As will be shown, these precursors through the involvement of phosphatidic acid are also necessary for the other phosphoglycerides. In addition to sources of phosphate, the nitrogenous bases (choline, ethanolamine and serine) and inositol are required for the complete synthesis of these phosphatides.

The phosphate appearing in certain of the phosphoglycerides is not that arising from phosphatidic acid, although it is probable that both have their origin in the "energy-rich" phosphate compounds such as ATP which are ultimately supplied by metabolism. Many experiments with tissue slices and cell-free preparations have demonstrated that the labeling of phosphatides from P_i^{32} is dependent on metabolic energy.[229, 371, 168, 640, 491, 490, 55] McMurray et al.[492] showed that label from ATP^{32} was more readily incorporated into the phosphatides than inorganic P^{32}.

The nitrogenous bases may, in the intact animal, be supplied by the diet or, as seems probable for a portion of the bases, by *de novo* synthesis (reviewed by Artom,[21] Deuel,[189] Paysant-Diament,[534] Rossiter and Strickland[588] and Ansell and Hawthorne[15]). Both choline and ethanolamine are derived, in part, from serine which in turn may arise from glycine. The N^{15} label from the latter two amino acids has been shown to appear in ethanolamine[633, 634] probably by the decarboxylation of serine.[707, 442, 19] Ethanolamine can give rise to choline by methylation.[633, 198, 537] Experiments with both deuterium and C^{14}-labeled serine, glycine and formate showed that, in the rat, the α- and β-carbons of serine appear in ethanolamine, that glycine and formate form serine prior to incorporation into ethanolamine and that all three compounds are precursors of the methyl groups of choline.[202]

In the conversion of ethanolamine to choline there has been doubt as to the origin of the methyl groups. Stekol and colleagues[630, 631, 632] in *in vivo* and *in vitro* studies using folic acid-deficient rats provided evidence that the first two methyl groups were derived from a folic acid derivative and that the third came from methionine by the intermediate S-adenosyl-L-methionine. Some support for this pathway was provided by Venkatoraman and Greenberg[680] but this work was later retracted.[269] Wilson et al.[715] have reinvestigated the origin of the methyl groups and report evidence that in rat liver slices the methyl groups arise from various "C_1" sources by way of methionine. This conclusion was based on the observation that inactive methionine depressed the incorporation of C^{14}-formate and C^{14}-formaldehyde into the choline of phospholipids and that all of the incorporation into choline from C^{14}-formate could be explained on the basis of prior incorporation into methionine. This interpretation is also supported by the earlier observations that methionine stimulated by 19 times the incorporation of ethanolamine-1,2-C^{14} into the phosphatidyl choline of rat liver slices.[537] Evidence from recent *in vivo* experiments with C^{14}- and deuterium labeled formaldehyde indicate that one hydrogen is lost to give a formyl type of intermediate which can be utilized for methyl group formation in methionine and choline.[550]

There is general agreement that serine undergoes conversion to ethanolamine, but some doubt remains as to whether this occurs with free serine or as seems most likely with serine in ester linkage with P. Nemer and Elwyn [509] studied the conversion of L-serine-3-C^{14} to ethanolamine in the rat both *in vivo* and *in vitro* and found results which suggested that phosphoethanolamine was the first product formed from serine. However, the conversion was quite slow. Wilson *et al.*, [716] on the other hand, observed that slices of rat liver and brain caused the C^{14} from L-serine to appear in the ethanolamine of phospholipid much earlier than its appearance in ethanolamine or phosphoethanolamine. The observations that rat brain slices [549] and washed rat liver mitochondria [338] convert serine-C^{14} to phosphatidyl ethanolamine are not inconsistent with the suggestion that interconversion may occur on the intact lipid. It has also been suggested that choline, as phosphatidyl choline, arises by the methylation of phosphatidyl ethanolamine and that the latter results from decarboxylation of phosphatidyl serine. [92, 93, 94, 95] Kaneshiro and Law [358] have recently partially purified a phosphatidyl ethanolamine N-methyltransferase from *Agrobacterium tumefaciens* that catalyzes the conversion of phosphatidyl ethanolamine to the N-methyl derivative: enzymes are present in the small particle fraction which catalyze the stepwise methylation of the N-methyl derivative to phosphatidyl choline. These types of conversions at the intact lipid level will be discussed in more detail later in the appropriate sections on phosphoglycerides.

The conversion of serine to ethanolamine does not appear to be reversible and it seems likely that serine must by synthesized by other pathways. One pathway involves the formation of serine from glycine and an active "C_1" unit in the form of hydroxymethyltetrahydrofolic acid [341] or methylenetetrahydrofolic acid. [57] This reaction is catalyzed by serine hydroxymethylase. An alternative route seems to be one in which the carbons arise from carbohydrate. Arnstein and Keglević [19] observed that a deficiency of folic acid in the rat did not reduce the labeling of serine from glucose-C^{14} thus suggesting that the labeling occurred by a pathway not involving glycine. The authors suggested that serine arose from a C_3 glycolytic intermediate. This view was substantiated by several investigations. Koeppe *et al.* [403] observed lack of randomization in the labeling of serine from glycerol-1,3-C^{14} when the latter was administered to rats intraperitoneally. It was shown by Sallach [594] that serine could arise from hydroxypyruvate by transamination with alanine. Finally, Ichihara and Greenberg [346] were able to show, with a crude preparation from rat liver, that serine arose from carbohydrate by way of phosphoglyceric acid. Evidence was obtained which was consistent with the formation proceeding by way of the intermediate, phosphohydroxypyruvic acid and O-phosphoserine. The latter compound, which is formed by transamination from glutamic acid, may then undergo hydrolysis to yield serine and P_i. A specific O-phosphoserine phosphatase which not only catalyzes hydrolysis of O-phosphoserine but also exchange of the serine moiety has been demonstrated and partially purified in a number of tissues. [76, 77, 510, 511, 514, 600]

This pathway for serine formation seems to be of major importance in *E. coli*, [675, 539] *Salmonella typhimurium* and cultured human cells. [540] Evidence also exists for a pathway of serine formation involving the non-phosphorylated intermediates, glycerate and hydroxypyruvate. [714]

Similar pathways of synthesis for the nitrogenous bases probably exist in microorganisms [271, 720, 721] and plants (etiolated wheat seedlings, [158] beet [185]) but details of the mechanism remain to be elucidated. For example, work with a choline-deficient strain of *Neurospora crassa* has demonstrated that not only do monomethyl- and dimethyl-ethanolamine accumulate but so do the phosphate esters of these amines. [720, 721] It is uncertain whether choline derives from the free amine, the phosphate ester, or even phospholipids containing monomethyl-and dimethyl-ethanolamine which are known to be formed. [278]

(a) *Phosphate Monoester Lipid* (*Phosphatidic Acid*)

The pathway of biological synthesis of phosphatidic acid has been described under triglycerides and requires no further comment.

(b) *Phosphate Diester Lipids*

(i) *Choline-containing*

Lecithin. Kornberg and Pricer [411] first demonstrated that phosphoryl choline (PC), doubly-labeled with C^{14} and P^{32}, is incorporated as a unit into the phosphatides of rat liver preparations. Previous to this the results of the *in vivo* experiments of Riley [561] suggested that PC was not a precursor of choline phosphatides. It has since been shown that $PC-C^{14}$ and $P^{32}C$ are incorporated into the lecithin of liver [372, 572] and brain. [587, 492] Kennedy [372] originally reported that choline-C^{14} was more readily incorporated into lecithin than $PC-C^{14}$, however subsequent work has established that free choline is incorporated into some choline-containing lipid other than lecithin. [380]

Further support for PC as a precursor of the choline-containing phosphoglycerides was provided by the studies of Dawson [171, 172] on possible precursor-product relationships between PC and lecithin and glycerylphosphorylcholine (GPC) and lecithin. After the injection of P_i^{32} into rats it was found that the specific activity of PC exceeded that of lecithin [172] while that of GPC was less than that of lecithin initially. [171] The results tended, on the basis of the immediate precursor-product relationship established mathematically by Zilversmit *et al.*, [737] to suggest that lecithin was the precursor of GPC and that PC was probably a precursor of lecithin.

It would seem that PC is formed in most tissues by phosphorylation of choline in the presence of ATP and the enzyme, choline phosphokinase [719] (reaction 14):

$$\text{choline} + \text{ATP} \longrightarrow \text{PC} + \text{ADP} \tag{14}$$

Wittenberg and Kornberg [719] have partially purified a yeast enzyme which catalyzes reaction (14). The enzyme preparation also catalyzed the phosphorylation of dimethylaminoethanol, monomethylaminoethanol and aminoethanol at 70, 20 and 7 per cent, respectively, of the rate for choline. Rapeseed [554] and brain and nerve tissue [56] contain enzymes capable of catalyzing this reaction.

It was not until the brilliant discovery of the participation of cytidine nucleotides by Kennedy and Weiss [379, 380] that a real "break-through" was made in the elucidation of the mechanism of phosphoglycerides. It was found that ATP contained an impurity, cytidine triphosphate (CTP), that was essential for the incorporation of $P^{32}C$ into lecithin. None of a number of other nucleoside-5'-triphosphates was active in the liver preparation. [380] A similar requirement for CTP has been shown for brain. [492] The actual participation of CTP was established when Kennedy and Weiss [380] demonstrated the formation of the intermediate, cytidine diphosphate choline (CMP-PC) (XVI) according to reaction (15):

$$\text{PC} + \text{CTP} \rightleftharpoons \text{CMP-PC} + \text{PP}_i \tag{15}$$

Cylidine diphosphate choline (CMP-PC)
XVI.

The intermediate (CMP-PC) has been characterized and its synthesis achieved by condensation of cytidine monophosphate (CMP) and PC using the condensing agent, dicyclohexylcarbodiimide. [374] CMP-PC is reported to occur in a number of animal tissues [380, 75, 15] and in yeast. [52, 75] There is little or no change in the CMP-PC content of the liver of rats deficient in choline. [712] The deoxy derivative, deoxycytidine diphosphate choline, has been demonstrated in sea urchin eggs [651] and in Novikoff hepatoma. [598] Deoxycytidine diphosphate choline, if present in liver, occurs in very low concentration. [378] The deoxy derivative, however, does function as well as CMP-PC in the synthesis of lecithin by liver enzymes. [378]

The enzyme, PC-cytidyl transferase, which catalyzes reaction (15) is known to be present in most mammalian tissues, avian liver, several strains of yeast and carrot root. [75] PC-cytidyl transferase has been partially purified from guinea pig liver by Borkenhagen and Kennedy [75] and properties of the preparation have been studied. Either of the two divalent cations, Mg^{++} or Mn^{++}, is required to give optimal activity. The enzyme readily catalyzes the reverse reaction with CMP-PC undergoing pyrophosphorolysis by PP_i to form PC and CTP. The requirement of CTP for the "activation" of PC explains the necessity of a coupled source of energy for the incorporation of labeled PC into lecithin. [572, 380, 492] The coupled energy source probably is required by the synthesizing system to maintain the concentration of CTP by phosphorylation of CMP. This phosphorylation could be achieved by transphosphorylase enzymes capable of catalyzing reaction (16) (see, for example, Herbert and Potter, [307] Strominger et al. [647]):

$$CMP + ATP \rightleftharpoons CTP + AMP \qquad (16)$$

The intermediate, CMP-PC, has been shown by Kennedy and Weiss [380] to undergo reaction with the "lipid acceptor" D-α,β-diglyceride (II) to form lecithin and CMP (reaction 17):

$$CMP\text{-}PC + D\text{-}\alpha,\beta\text{-diglyceride} \rightleftharpoons L\text{-}\alpha\text{-lecithin} + CMP \qquad (17)$$

It was possible to obtain a 10–12-fold stimulation of lecithin synthesis from CMP-PC by the addition of mixed D-α,β-diglycerides only in the presence of the surface active agent "Tween 20". [380]

Partial purification of the enzyme, PC-glyceride transferase, which catalyzes reaction (17) has been achieved from particle preparations of chicken and rat liver. [706] When CMP-PC was added to this enzyme preparation containing mixed D-α,β-diglyceride (derived from egg lecithin by the action of phosphatidase D from *Clostridium perfringens*) emulsified with Tween 20, net synthesis of lecithin was obtained. The enzyme appeared to require no additional cofactors. In the presence of lecithin, CMP^{32} and purified enzyme, radioactivity was observed in CMP-PC thus demonstrating the reversibility of reaction (17). Chojnacki and Korzybski [127] have recently studied the specificity of the reaction with analogues of CMP-PC. It was observed that activity was lost when the C-6 amino group was removed or replaced by a monomethyl amino group. Replacement of choline by 2-monomethyl- or 2-dimethyl-aminoethanol had little effect on precursor activity. The enzyme catalyzing reaction (17) was found in several tissues of the rat (liver, kidney, heart and brain). Weiss et al. [705] have found that a β-unsaturated diglyceride with the D-configuration is required to obtain significant synthesis of lecithin. Diunsaturated D-α,β-diolein was, however, the most active of a number of synthetic diglycerides. It cannot be stated with certainty whether the apparent specificity shown is real or not since the difficulty of solubilizing diglycerides increases with the degree of saturation of the fatty acids.

Support for the above pathway of lecithin synthesis (shown in Fig. 3) has been provided by independent studies using preparations of brain, [584, 492, 585, 587, 588, 590, 645] seminal vesicle, [713] intestinal mucosa [340] and Ehrlich

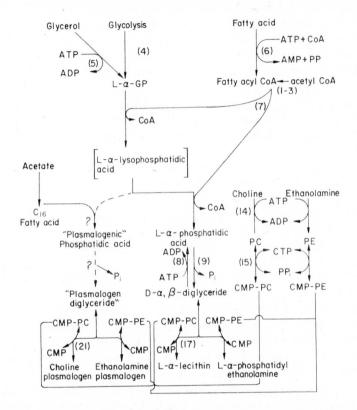

FIG. 3. Scheme showing the pathways for the formation of choline- and ethanolamine-containing phosphoglycerides. Numbers in parentheses refer to reactions in the text.

ascites tumour cells. [583, 196] The latter studies provide evidence that these tissues contain the PC-cytidyl and PC-glyceride transferase enzymes necessary for reactions (15) and (17), respectively.

It is probable that the D-α,β-diglycerides required for reaction (17) are derived by the dephosphorylation of phosphatidic acid (reaction 9). Even though the steady state concentration of phosphatidic acid is apparently low, since only trace amounts occur in vivo, [321] it is entirely possible that the D-α,β-diglyceride for lecithin synthesis may arise this way. The demonstration in vitro that the phosphatidic phosphatase enzyme is sufficiently active even in the presence of strongly inhibitory concentrations of Mg^{++} to release diglyceride for lecithin synthesis would favor the participation of reaction (9). [610, 587, 645] Additional support is provided by the observations of Strickland and Rossiter [643] which show that rat liver particles are capable of incorporating C^{14} α-GP into lecithin and that the addition of inactive CMP-PC causes a diversion of labeling from triglyceride to lecithin.

As already noted, α,β-diglycerides may also arise from triglycerides by the action of lipases. [186, 486, 72, 73, 485, 53] It is, however, uncertain whether lipase action is an important source of diglyceride for lecithin synthesis since the product arising from lipase action [364, 365] appears to lack the necessary D-stereospecificity required for lecithin synthesis. [705]

The positional asymmetry already commented on for lecithin must be reflected in the diglyceride utilized in its synthesis. It would seem essential that the β-position should be esterified with an unsaturated fatty acid and the α-position with a saturated fatty acid in view of the findings of Hanahan et al. [289] on phosphatidase A action. The earlier evidence of Hanahan and Blomstrand, [288] if interpreted on the basis that phosphatidase A cleaves the β-position, would suggest the asymmetry exists at the metabolic level since it was found that saturated C^{14}-labeled fatty acids administered to rats exchanged with the fatty acids esterified at the α-position and unsaturated fatty acids exchanged largely with the β-position. [285, 289] This same asymmetry has been noted for the fatty acids of egg lecithin. [286, 558, 559, 301] The observation by Weiss et al. [705] that an unsaturated fatty acid on the β-position is necessary for lecithin synthesis is consistent with these views. Although it would seem likely that the asymmetry described might arise during the esterification of L-α-GP the work of Lands and Hart [421] does not support this contention. In a study of the esterification of α-GP they observed that linoleate and stearate were incorporated at both the α'- and β-positions. There was only a slight preponderance of linoleate at the β-position which seemed to be more closely related to the rate of fatty acid activation rather than to differences in specificities of the acyl transferases. The first acylation of α-GP was found to be much slower than the second acylation suggesting that two different enzymes catalyze these reactions with the first enzyme being present in lower concentration in the liver microsome preparations studied. Proof of the existence of two different acyl transferases has recently been obtained on the basis of the greater sensitivity to SH-binding reagents of the enzyme catalyzing the first acylation. [421] Lands and Hart [421] suggest that the final fatty acid pattern observed for the phospholipids (including lecithin) may be the result of redistribution after the nitrogenous bases are attached.

Some evidence of both chemical and metabolic heterogeneity has been obtained for rat liver lecithin. [143, 293] Thus, for example, Harris et al. [293] obtained two fractions of lecithin (A and B) on silicic acid chromatography of the phospholipids from the livers of rats injected with $P_i{}^{32}$. Fraction B contained a higher percentage of mono- and polyunsaturated fatty acids than fraction A. The latter fraction contained stearic as the main saturated fatty acid and arachidonic as the main unsaturated fatty acid, whereas fraction B contained palmitic and linoleic respectively. The radioactivity incorporated from P_i^{32} was predominantly located in fraction B thereby suggesting the existence of metabolic differences in addition to the chemical differences noted. More recent extension of this work by Collins [145, 148] indicates that an even greater heterogeneity exists for lecithin. Collins has calculated that specific activities for P^{32} incorporation into the lecithins, stearoyl arachidonyl lecithin, palmitoyl arachidonyl lecithin, the other stearoyl lecithins and the other palmitoyl lecithins are respectively 20, 80, 160 and 1000. This degree of chemical and metabolic heterogeneity, if true, stresses the need for devising methods to separate the various lecithins and even other lipids since the existence of a similar heterogeneity amongst other phospholipids [591a] and triglycerides [478a] has been observed.

More recently, evidence has been reported which suggests the existence of alternative pathways for lecithin synthesis. Marinetti *et al.* [477] noted that a soluble enzyme preparation from rat liver was capable of the net conversion of added P^{32}-labeled lysolecithin to lecithin in a period of 90 min. In an investigation of the biological synthesis of lecithin in lung tissues using C^{14}-fatty acid and C^{14}-glycerol, Lands [419] observed a higher fatty acid activity to glycerol activity in lecithin than in triglyceride. One explanation suggested was that there might be a greater turnover of the fatty acid portion of lecithin. Subsequent work by Lands [420] has revealed the existence in rat liver microsomes of an enzyme system capable of the acylation of lysolecithin (reaction 18):

$$\text{lysolecithin} + \text{fatty acyl CoA} \longrightarrow \text{lecithin} + \text{CoA} \qquad (18)$$

The lysolecithin was prepared by the action of snake venom (containing phosphatidase A) on purified lecithin and, on the basis of the recent findings discussed earlier, would be α'-acyl lysolecithin. The microsomal preparation catalyzed the acylation of this lysolecithin in the presence of either ATP, CoA and oleic acid or the CoA thiol ester of this acid. It is noteworthy that the only fatty acyl CoA tried in these experiments was the monounsaturated oleyl CoA which presumably acylated at the β-position where an unsaturated fatty acid is normally located. More recently, Lands [423, 421] has observed that acyl transfereases of guinea pig liver microsomes function to acylate both the β- and α'-positions of α'-acyl GPC or β-acyl GPC. The β-OH is preferentially acylated with unsaturated fatty acids while the α'-OH is primarily acylated with saturated fatty acids. The importance of this pathway remains to be established, but it does provide a means for the exchange of fatty acids as long as some deacylation mechanism exists for the formation of lysolecithin or as long as the latter is formed *de novo*. This specificity of the acyl transferase enzyme fits well with the fatty acid pattern observed in lecithin and, hence, it seems likely that much of the asymmetry in the fatty acid pattern is due to the actions of these acyl transferases.

Quite a lot of circumstantial evidence supports the view that the redistribution of fatty acids on lecithin could occur by the combined actions of phosphatidase A and of a β-acyl transferease. *In vitro* studies with red blood cells suggest that there is a selective incorporation of fatty acids into the phospholipids.[505a] The demonstration of both phosphatidase A activity in various tissues[565, 237] and acyl transferease activity in red blood cells,[518] liver[423] and brain[700] are consistent with the possibility that the above cycle is of importance in establishing the distribution pattern of fatty acids seen in lecithin.

A second alternative pathway has arisen from a number of experiments on the biosynthesis of choline[92, 93, 94] and a series of studies on dimethylethanolamine incorporation.[159, 20, 22] Greenberg and colleagues[92, 93, 94] in a study of the biosynthesis of choline in the intact rat showed that label from serine-3-C^{14}, ethanolamine-1,2-C^{14} and methyl-C^{14} methionine, appeared in the choline of lecithin and that labeled choline did not accumulate. There was no evidence that this labeling occurred by way of intermediates such as the phosphorylated bases or their cytidine derivatives. A time study with methyl-labeled methionine indicated that monomethyl and dimethylethanolamine had higher turnover rates than choline and that choline of lecithin was labeled slightly more rapidly than cytidine diphosphate choline. *In vitro* experiments with rat liver microsomes showed that the label of methyl labeled *S*-adenosyl methionine appeared in the choline of lecithin. In the experiments with serine-3-C^{14} it was found that label appeared in both the hydroxyethyl- and the methyl-groups of choline phospholipid as well as in the ethanolamine of phosphatidyl ethanolamine. Time studies indicated that the label appears most rapidly in phosphatidyl serine followed very closely by label in the methyl portion of the choline of lecithin. The appearance of label in the hydroxyethyl portion of choline was much slower and paralleled that in the ethanolamine phospholipid. This pattern of labeling also resulted when methyl-labeled methionine was the precursor. Bremer and Greenberg[95] have further studied the methyl transferring enzyme system present in liver microsomes which catalyzes the stepwise methylation of phosphatidyl ethanolamine from S-adenosyl methionine. It was concluded that the transfer system required an intact SH-group and that the first methylation was the rate limiting step. In fact, no stimulation of choline formation was observed when dipalmitoyl-α-cephalin was added. S-Adenosyl ethionine competitively inhibited the system. The above and comparable experiments carried out by Gibson *et al.*[244] suggest that serine undergoes decarboxylation to form phosphatidyl ethanolamine and that the latter phosphatide is methylated by transmethylation from S-adenosyl-methionine to form lecithin as summarized in reaction (19):

Phosphatidyl ethanolamine + 3 S-adenosyl methionine ⟶ lecithin
+ 3 S-adenosyl homocysteine   (19)

Independent experiments by Artom[20, 22] offered some support for this pathway. In experiments with rat liver slices, homogenates and particles, it was found that C^{14}-labeled dimethylethanolamine gave rise to labeled phosphoglycerides. The mitochondrial and microsomal fractions formed phosphatidyl dimethylethanolamine. The incorporation of label into this lipid was increased by the cytidine nucleotides (CMP, CDP or CTP) and strongly inhibited by choline. In experiments with slices, lecithin was found to be readily labeled from C^{14}-dimethylethanolamine. It appeared that this labeling occurred by the direct methylation of phosphatidyl ethanolamine since incubation of the latter lipid (labeled with C^{14}) in a microsomal system containing S-adenosyl methionine yielded lecithin with C^{14}-activity. It would seem that synthesis of phosphatidyl dimethylethanolamine might be achieved by a pathway requiring cytidine nucleotides and that the lipid is methylated to form phosphatidyl choline (lecithin). In this regard Ansell and Chojnacki[13] have observed that in both liver and brain homogenates the formation of phospholipids containing monomethyl- and dimethylaminoethanol can occur by the transfer of the phosphorylated base from its cytidine diphosphate ester to an acceptor which is presumably diglyceride. Chojnacki and Korzybski[127] have extended this work by showing that the phospholipids formed from P^{32}-CDP-N,N-dimethylaminoethanol and P^{32}-CDP-N-monomethylaminoethanol in homogenates of rat liver are converted into lecithins upon the addition of S-adenosylmethionine. Corresponding cephalins obtained from CDP-ethanolamine did not undergo methylation upon the addition of S-adenosyl methionine. This latter observation again points to the very slow or perhaps non-existent rate of the first methylation step. In a detailed study of phospholipid synthesis in Ehrlich ascites tumor, Rossiter and Donisch[583, 196] have obtained evidence that a portion of the lecithin may be formed by way of the stepwise methylation of phosphatidylethanolamine.

A series of studies[279, 280, 157] on both wild type and mutants of *Neurospora crassa* indicates that both pathways for lecithin formation probably occur. Two lecithin-deficient strains were shown to possess deficiencies at either the first methylation step (strain 34486) or the second and third methylation steps (strain 47904). Both of these strains were observed to independently incorporate supplements of either monomethylethanolamine or choline into phospholipids. It was concluded that these results could only be interpreted on the basis that both pathways are present with the relative contribution of each being influenced by mutations and culture supplementation. In regard to methylation of intact lipids it should be noted that *Agrobacterium tumefaciens*[358] contains the necessary enzyme systems for the conversion of phosphatidyl ethanolamine to lecithin utilizing S-adenosylmethionine as methyl donor. The enzyme catalyzing the first methylation, phosphatidyl-ethanolamine N-methyltransferase was purified forty-fold and shows no cofactor requirement but is inhibited strongly by S-adenosyl homocysteine. A similar enzyme probably exists in *Clostridium butyricum* since this organism forms N-methylethanolamine phospholipids (but no dimethylethanolamine or choline phospholipids) such that the ethanolamine phospholipids behave as precursors for the N-methyl ethanolamine phospholipids.[43]

A third alternative pathway merits brief comment. Dils and Hübscher[190, 191, 192] have shown that choline is incorporated into the lecithin of rat liver mitochondria. The incorporation was stimulated to a greater extent by CMP than by CTP. Similar results, to be commented on later, were obtained for C^{14}-serine.[335, 338] In this work Dils and Hübscher[191, 192] observed that the labeling from both C^{14}-precursors (choline and serine) is stimulated by Ca^{++} ions and that the optimal pH was 9·0 compared to 7·4–7·8 for the *de novo* synthesis of lecithin via the cytidine nucleotide pathway. Serine competitively inhibited the incorporation of choline. Both authors[191, 192] and Haw-thorne[304] have offered the tempting suggestion that some of these observations could be accounted for by the reversible reaction (20), catalyzed by an enzyme with phosphatidase C-like activity:

$$\text{Phosphatidyl choline} \longrightarrow \text{choline} + \text{phosphatidic acid} \qquad (20)$$

This reaction does not account for the stimulation by CMP. It would seem that much more evidence is required before the existence and biological importance of reaction (20) can be established.

The various pathways for lecithin synthesis are shown schematically in Fig. 4. Little can be said concerning the relative importance of each pathway. The latter two pathways have the virtue of permitting interconversion at the phosphoglyceride level. The *de novo* synthesis of what might be termed the "parent" phosphoglyceride must, however, depend on some other pathway such as that involving the cytidine nucleotides. The acylation of lysolecithin can only become an important pathway for the net synthesis of lecithin if the lyso-compound is supplied in adequate amounts biologically. It is entirely possible that lysolecithin is formed enzymatically by reactions analogous to, or different from, those described earlier for lecithin. However, until experi-mental work is available to support the latter possibility, it cannot be regarded as a significant pathway for *de novo* synthesis of lecithin. Marinetti *et al.*[475] in a time course study of the variables affecting the incorporation of C^{14}-glycerol into phosphatidic acid, lecithin, phosphatidyl choline, diglycerides and triglycerides of rat liver homogenates obtained evidence which, in part, confirms the pathways involving cytidine diphosphate derivatives. However, cofactors such as ATP, Mg^{++} and CTP, depending on their concentrations seem to exert varying regulatory roles. In fact, CTP at 10^{-3} M and 10^{-2} M caused increases in the labeling of diglyceride and triglyceride but not of lecithin or phosphatidyl ethanolamine.

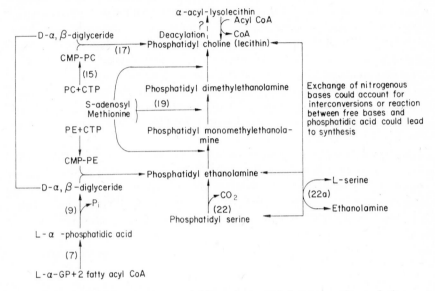

Fig. 4. Alternative pathways of biosynthesis and interconversions of the phosphatidyl compounds containing nitrogenous bases. Numbers in parentheses refer to reactions in the text.

The final assessment of the relative importance of the various pathways for lecithin synthesis will depend on careful, well-designed and unequivocal data from experiments with the intact organism. Recently, two interesting attempts have been made. [254, 717] Gøransson [254] has studied the pattern of labeling of triglyceride and phospholipids in liver following injection of H^3-palmitic acid and C^{14}-oleic acid either alone or in combination. The pattern observed was consistent with diglyceride being a precursor of both triglyceride and phospholipid thus pointing to the relatively greater importance of the Kennedy pathway. Support for this conclusion is provided by the study of Wise and Elwyn. [717] Following measurement of the incorporation of L-serine-C^{14} into various phosphorylated bases and phospholipids, they have calculated, by use of appropriate models, the rates of a number of reactions concerned in phospholipid biosynthesis *in vivo*. It was concluded that phosphatidyl choline synthesis in rat liver went 30 times faster via the CMP-PC pathway than via the methylation of phosphatidyl ethanolamine.

Choline plasmalogen. Although information on the biosynthesis of the plasmalogens [588, 581] is limited, the evidence available does suggest that the pathway involves the cytosine nucleotides in a manner analogous to that for lecithin synthesis. [383, 384] Korey and Orchen [406] have found that C^{14}-label in the α,β-unsaturated side chains of the plasmalogens in the developing brain of rats can be derived from 1-C^{14}-acetate or palmitate. These precursors also readily label the fatty acids of the lipids. With either precursor it is necessary to achieve reduction of the carboxyl to the aldehyde level before the enol ether structure is attained. Whether this is done on the intact phosphatide, or before, is not known. Gambal and Monty [240] have reported that a supernatant fraction of rat brain containing microsomes is capable of catalyzing the incorporation of palmitate-1-C^{14} into the enol ether chain of plasmalogen in the presence of CoA, ATP, Mg^{++}, DPNH and α-GP. Further stimulation was achieved with CTP and ethanolamine. There was no indication that choline was tried.

CMP-PC has been implicated in the biosynthesis of choline plasmalogen by the work of Kiyasu and Kennedy. [382, 383] A particle preparation from rat liver has been shown to catalyze the formation of choline-containing plasmalogen from C^{14}-labeled CMP-PC and "plasmalogenic diglyceride", i.e. α-(α,β-unsaturated aliphatic ether), β-monoglyceride (reaction 21):

$$\text{"plasmalogenic diglyceride"} + \text{CMP-PC} \longrightarrow \text{choline plasmalogen} + \text{CMP} \qquad (21)$$

The "plasmalogenic diglyceride" was formed by prolonged action of phosphatidase D from *Clostridium perfringens* on beef heart plasmalogen. The enzyme catalyzing reaction (21) is believed to be similar to the transferase enzyme catalyzing lecithin formation in reaction (17). In fact, as the authors note, it is possible the synthesis is the result of a lack of specificity toward the conventional diglycerides by the transferase in lecithin synthesis. Reaction (21) has been demonstrated to occur in homogenates of developing rat brain by McMurray [489] and in Ehrlich's ascites tumor cells by Donisch and Rossiter. [196]

There is ample evidence that choline plasmalogen is readily formed, once a "plasmalogenic diglyceride" is formed. However, there is no definite evidence on how "plasmalogenic diglyceride" is formed if, indeed, it is formed biologically. Thus, there still remains the main problem of how a vinyl ether glyceryl derivative is formed and whether its formation occurs on a glycerol unit that is phosphorylated either by orthophosphate or by a monophosphate ester such as PC (or phosphoethanolamine which undergoes subsequent methylation to give a choline derivative as suggested by the evidence of Donisch and Rossiter [196]). The earlier work of Korey and Orchen [406] shows that acetate and palmitate can act as precursors of the

a,β-unsaturated chain. Attempts to prove that aldehydes rather than fatty acids may act as precursors of this chain have generally met with failure. [113, 295] Apart from the observation of Keenan et al. [368] that stearyl alcohol is a better precursor of the end ether group in plasmalogens of a heart–lung preparation, most studies point to long-chain fatty acids as the precursors for these groups. This view is well illustrated by the observation that the branched-chain fatty acid, isobutyrate and the straight-chain fatty acid, valerate are, following chain lengthening, both incorporated into the plasmalogens of *Bacteroides succinogens*. [702] Hartree [295] has recently speculated on the precursors and possible mechanisms whereby vinyl ether side chains may be formed. Whether this can occur on an intact, preformed phospholipid (e.g. a β-acyl lysophosphatide) is uncertain. Results from P^{32}-labeling studies show a pattern for the phospholipids of *Clostridium butyricum* which would be consistent with the diacylglycerophosphatides acting as precursors of the corresponding plasmalogens. This pattern contrasts with that observed for the incorporation of the C^{14}-bases (choline or ethanolamine) into the plasmalogens of Ehrlich's ascites tumor. [583]

It may be concluded that many unanswered questions remain in regard to the biosynthesis of choline plasmalogen (and plasmalogens generally). Answers to these questions are likely to come from "more thorough and systematic investigation" as proposed by Thompson. [661] This author concluded from a study of the incorporation of glucose-6-C^{14}, palmitate-1-C^{14} and chimyl alcohol-H^3 into total phospholipids and both neutral and phospholipid glyceryl ethers (saturated and vinyl type) of the slug *Arion ater* that glycerol (as for the diacylglycerophosphatides) arises from carbohydrate (possibly via a-GP) and that there is no evidence to indicate interconversions between the three classes of phospholipids, diacylglycerophosphatides, the glyceryl ether phospholipids (e.g. Kephalin B) and the vinyl glyceryl ether phospholipids (the plasmalogens). Plasmalogens were labeled least readily of these phospholipids with the other two types being about equally labeled. Thompson suggests that the glyceryl ether and vinyl glyceryl ether phospholipids may derive from a common precursor.

(ii) *Ethanolamine-containing*

Phosphatidyl ethanolamine. Almost without exception the experiments on lecithin formation have been repeated for phosphatidyl ethanolamine and have provided results which suggest a pathway similar to that for lecithin (see Fig. 4). Early *in vivo* studies with phosphoryl ethanolamine (PE) suggested that this compound was not involved in the synthesis of phosphatidyl ethanolamine. [124] Later, the work of Dawson [171] using P_i^{32} showed a relation for glycerylphosphoryl ethanolamine (GPE) and phosphatidyl ethanolamine that was similar to that existing for GPC and lecithin. That is, phosphatidyl ethanolamine appeared to be the precursor of GPE. By analogy to the relation for lecithin [172] it seems likely that PE might be the precursor of phosphatidyl ethanolamine.

The demonstration that PC was concerned in lecithin synthesis also suggested that PE might be a precursor of phosphatidyl ethanolamine. Kennedy and Weiss [380] found that the liver (chicken, rat) contains an enzyme capable of forming this phosphoglyceride from PE in the presence of added CTP. The mechanism of synthesis was shown to involve the formation of cytidine diphosphate ethanolamine (CMP-PE) as an intermediate. CMP-PE, which is readily synthesized in most tissues, then undergoes reaction with D-α,β-diglyceride in a manner analogous to that described in reaction (17) to form phosphatidyl ethanolamine. Similar reactions appear to occur in brain [587, 489, 13] and Ehrlich ascites cells. [196]

As just noted, there are close similarities between the pathways for the synthesis of lecithin and phosphatidyl ethanolamine. A number of the precursors (CTP and α,β-diglyceride) are common and must be competed for in both syntheses. The earlier discussion on the origin of the D-α,β-diglyceride also applies to the formation of phosphatidyl ethanolamine. There is, as already cited, evidence that CMP-PE is formed in most tissues. Free PE, as well as PC, has been shown to be present in a number of mammalian tissues [173, 544] and *in vivo* experiments with P^{32} indicate that the phosphorus moiety is readily labeled. [14] The *in vivo* labeling of PE is reduced under conditions of insulin hypoglycemia which also reduces the labeling of phosphatidyl ethanolamine. [17] It seems probable that the PE arises by phosphorylation of ethanolamine. Ansell and Dawson [14] have shown that actively metabolizing rat brain mince catalyzes the formation of labeled PE from P_i^{32} and added ethanolamine. The phosphokinase described by Wittenberg and Kornberg [719] can phosphorylate ethanolamine, but at a slower rate than choline or the intervening monomethyl- and dimethyl-derivatives. Nemer and Elwyn [509] have obtained evidence that labeled serine is converted to ethanolamine by way of phosphoethanolamine.

Merkl and Lands [496] have discovered an acyl transferase system in rat liver microsomes which is capable of acylating lysophosphatidylethanolamine to form the diacyl compound. This enzyme system is similar in action to that already described for the acylation of lysolecithin (reaction 18). Fatty acyl CoA is necessary for the reaction. Unsaturated acyl CoA preferentially acylated at the 2-position while saturated acyl CoA acylated the 1-position in accordance with the distribution of fatty acids. [496, 421]

The work of Bremer *et al.*, [94] referred to previously, would suggest that some phosphatidyl ethanolamine may be formed by decarboxylation of phosphatidyl serine. Wilson *et al.*, [716] in studies on the conversion of L-serine-C^{14} to ethanolamine by slices of liver and brain and homogenates of liver from rats, noted that C^{14}-activity first appeared in the ethanolamine of phospholipid. The activity is mainly confined to the microsomes. The evidence from these experiments is consistent with the view that ethanolamine may be derived from phosphatidyl serine (see Fig. 4). More recently Kennedy and colleagues have described a cell-free extract of liver [78] and a crude extract of E. coli [360] that are capable of catalyzing the decarboxylation of phosphatidyl serine to phosphatidyl ethanolamine, according to reaction (22a):

$$\text{phosphatidyl serine} \longrightarrow \text{phosphatidyl ethanolamine} + CO_2 \qquad (22a)$$

Of the pathways outlined for the synthesis of phosphatidyl ethanolamine, that involving CMP-PE as intermediate is the only one which permits *de novo* synthesis of a phospholipid molecule. However, if other pathways can provide *de novo* either lysophosphatidyl ethanolamine or phosphatidyl serine, then accumulation of phosphatidyl ethanolamine could occur from these precursors by the alternate pathways described.

Ethanolamine plasmalogen. The previous discussion on the origin of the α,β-unsaturated ether chain and the "plasmalogen diglyceride" is applicable here since Kiyasu and Kennedy [383] have also been able to demonstrate the formation of ethanolamine plasmalogen from CMP-PE and "plasmalogen diglyceride". The reaction is similar to reaction (21) for the formation of choline plasmalogen and may be catalyzed by the same transferase.

Glyceryl ether phospholipids (Kephalin B). In 1949 Brante [91] reported the presence in brain of a phospholipid (which he designated Kephalin B) different from sphingomyelin but which was resistant to both mild alkaline and acid hydrolysis. The presence in nature of this type of lipid has been reported by several laboratories. Svennerholm and Thorn [654] isolated a similar lipid from calf and human brain and showed that this lipid had a structure similar to that of a lipid isolated by Carter *et al.* [119] from egg yolk. The latter lipid was a phosphoryl ethanolamine derivative of the glyceryl ethers batyl or chimyl alcohol. It appears that Kephalin B may be assigned the structure (XVII) which is glycerol-1-alkoxyl-2-acyl-3-phosphorylethano-

$$
\begin{array}{l}
CH_2OCH_2R \\
| \\
R'COOCH \qquad\quad O \\
| \qquad\qquad\qquad || \\
CH_2\!-\!O\!-\!\overset{\;}{P}\!-\!OCH_2CH_2\overset{+}{N}H_3 \\
\qquad\qquad | \\
\qquad\qquad O_-
\end{array}
$$

Glycerol-1-alkoxyl-2-acyl-3-
phosphoryl ethanolamine (kephalin B)

XVII

lamine. Hanahan and Watts [290a] have isolated a similar lipid from ox erythrocytes. McMurray [489] and Ansell and Spanner [17] have obtained supportive evidence for the existence of long-chain ether analogues of phosphatidyl ethanolamine in brain. In general, most of the recent studies on phospholipids support the view that this type of lipid occurs in small amounts in many species throughout nature.

Details of the pathway of biosynthesis of this glyceryl ether analogue of phosphatidyl ethanolamine are by no means well established. McMurray[489] has shown that label from CMP-PE-C^{14} is readily incorporated into the glyceryl ether phospholipid. The specific radioactivity of the latter greatly exceeded that of either phosphatidyl ethanolamine or ethanolamine plasmalogen. Plasmalogenic diglyceride did not stimulate this labeling. These findings are consistent with the glyceryl ether phospholipid being formed by transfer of phosphorylethanolamine from CMP-PE to some unknown acceptor.

By analogy with the pathway for phosphatidyl ethanolamine it might be predicted that the acceptor is a diether analogue of a diglyceride. However, attempts to prove this for the developing brain system were unsuccessful. [489] Karnovsky and co-workers[363, 200] have established that both alkyl and alkenyl ethers of glycerol occur in the hepato-pancreas of starfish. Label from acetate-C^{14} is incorporated into the alkyl and alkenyl groups of both neutral and phospholipid ethers but were generally less active than fatty acids. The neutral alkenyl ethers reached values much higher than the alkyl ethers suggesting a possible precursor–product relationship. Frosolono et al.[230] have studied incorporation of palmitate-1-C^{14} into alkenyl ether groups. A very rapid synthesis of the alkenyloxy linkage in neutral and phospholipid plasmalogens occurred with evidence pointing to the conversion occurring in the neutral lipid fraction. Both Thompson[661] and Belfrage[44] have obtained evidence that glyceryl ethers become incorporated into ether lipids of the slug *A. ater* and rat epididymal adipose tissue respectively. It is evident that much more experimental evidence is required to establish the true nature of the acceptor, or for that matter, to establish that the main pathway of glyceryl ether phospholipid formation involves a cytosine nucleotide intermediate as suggested by the experiments of McMurray. [489]

(iii) *Serine-containing*

Phosphatidyl serine and serine plasmalogen. Metabolic pathways for the synthesis of these lipids appear to differ from those for the choline and ethanolamine-containing phospholipids. Experiments in which C^{14}-labeled acetate, glycerol and serine are incubated with brain or liver slices indicate that these precursors label the expected moiety of phosphatidyl serine (see, for example, Rossiter;[582] Majno and Karnovsky;[469] Pritchard[549]). It might be expected that phosphatidyl serine would be formed by a pathway analogous to those described for phosphatidyl choline and phosphatidyl ethanolamine but all attempts to establish this pathway have been unsuccessful. Serine is not readily phosphorylated by plant[554] or animal tissues. [346, 508, 511, 512, 77] There is, however, evidence that phosphoserine (PS) may be formed in liver from 3-phosphoglyceric acid by way of 3-phosphohydroxypyruvic acid. [346] The importance of phosphoserine in the synthesis of phosphatidyl serine is very uncertain since the incubation of C^{14}-phosphoserine with rat liver mitochondria [338] or rat brain homogenates or mitochondria (Strickland, unpublished experiments) does not result in any labeling of phospholipid. Furthermore, CTP has no effect.

An active phosphoserine phosphatase [76, 77, 510, 511, 514, 600, 644] adds to the problem of establishing the role, if any, of phosphoserine in the formation of phosphatidyl serine. This enzyme not only catalyzes the hydrolysis of phosphoserine but will catalyze exchange of D- or L-serine with phosphoserine. For some time there was no indication that a similar exchange could occur on larger molecules such as the phosphoglycerides, but more recently Borkenhagen et al. [78] have shown that cell-free extracts of liver are capable of catalyzing the exchange:

$$\text{phosphatidyl ethanolamine} + \text{L-serine} \rightleftharpoons \text{phosphatidyl serine} + \text{ethanolamine} \qquad (22b)$$

With the demonstration of reaction (22b) it now becomes possible for phosphatidyl serine to be synthesized at the expense of other phosphoglycerides (see Fig. 4). This view does not disagree with the evidence available. In the experiments reported above it has been found that, if labeled phosphoserine is replaced by L-serine-C^{14}, good labeling of phosphatidyl serine is obtained in rat liver mitochondria supplemented with CMP, ATP, CoA, glutathione, glycerophosphate and Mg^{++}. CTP was less effective than CMP. [335, 338] Hübscher [333] has observed that the amount of L-serine incorporated into phosphatidyl serine by microsomes of rat liver depends very much on Ca^{++} ion and that this increase is energy-independent. As commented on, this is only one of several similar reactions involving exchange of nitrogenous bases (e.g. choline, ethanolamine) and inositol. Whether exchange of phosphatidyl groups from one base to another can occur or not remains to be established (see Fig. 4).

The systems described above do not permit de novo synthesis of a phosphoglyceride, although they can provide any amount of phosphatidyl serine, providing phosphatidyl ethanolamine is supplied. An alternative pathway leading to de novo synthesis has been demonstrated by Kanfer and Kennedy. [360, 361] These workers have partially isolated a phosphatidyl serine synthetase system (L-serine-CMP phosphatidyltransferase) from E. coli. The synthetase catalyzes formation of phosphatidyl serine from cytidine diphosphate diglyceride (CMP-Pdig)* and L-serine (reaction 23):

$$\text{CMP-Pdig} + \text{L-serine} \longrightarrow \text{phosphatidyl serine} + \text{CMP} \qquad (23)$$

There is no evidence to indicate that this pathway occurs in animal systems.

* Structure analogous to that of CMP-PC (XVI) only α,β-diglyceride replaces -PC portion.

However, numerous experiments cited earlier have implicated cytosine nucleotides, particularly CMP. Recently, two reports provide evidence which again suggest the possibility of CMP participation. Artom and Wainer [23] observed that for a mitochondrial plus supernatant fraction CMP or CTP stimulated serine-3-C^{14} incorporation. Miras et al. [497] have noted a slight effect of CMP on serine-3-C^{14} incorporation into microsomal phospholipids of human leucocytes. The greatest dependence was on ATP thus pointing to a definite energy requirement.

There appears to be little, or no, information available on the synthesis of serine plasmalogen. This fraction because of its relatively lower concentration is more difficult to study. It is possible that it may be formed by a pathway similar to that for phosphatidyl serine. However, information on this suggestion can only be assessed, once the status for phosphatidyl serine is clearly known.

(iv) Glycerol-containing

As already noted, these lipids contain glycerol esterified to a free hydroxyl on the phosphate of phosphatidic acids, i.e. they are phosphatidyl glycerols. Marinetti et al. [473, 474] have shown that an unidentified phosphatide with properties similar to a polyglycerophosphatide is actively labeled from P_i^{32} in rat liver homogenates and mitochondria. Benson and Maruo [47] in their description of phosphatidyl glycerol in plants suggested that the pathway of synthesis might be analogous to that for lecithin with cytidine diphosphate glycerol (CMP-PG) as the cytidine intermediate. The occurrence of CMP-PG has been described by Baddiley et al. [26, 27] However, the evidence available indicates that CMP-Pdig rather than CMP-PG is the cytidine intermediate that is involved. [384, 385] On the basis of studies with C^{14}-L-α-GP and L-α-GP^{32}, CMP-Pdig was found to react with L-α-GP to form phosphatidyl glycerophosphate according to the reaction:

$$\text{CMP-Pdig} + \text{L-α-GP} \longrightarrow \text{phosphatidyl glycerophosphate} + \text{CMP} \quad (24)$$

It was further observed that the phosphatidyl glycerophosphate was dephosphorylated to form phosphatidyl glycerol according to reaction (25):

$$\text{phosphatidyl glycerophosphate} \longrightarrow \text{phosphatidyl glycerol} + P_i \quad (26)$$

Kiyasu et al. [385] indicate that phosphatidyl glycerol-synthesizing enzymes are found widely distributed in nature with activity being found in rat heart, kidney and liver, chicken liver and heart and in Micrococcus lysodeikticus and E. coli. The system in E. coil has been studied more fully by Kanfer and Kennedy. [361] Possmayer and Strickland [547] have obtained evidence for the existence in rat brain of the reactions (24) and (25) leading to the formation of phosphatidyl glycerol. This pathway for phosphatidyl glycerol formation is summarized in Fig. 5.

As yet there is little information on the biosynthesis of other lipids closely related to phosphatidyl glycerol. These include cardiolipin which is diphosphatidylglycerol (XII) and one of the recently described lipoamino acids [462] which has an amino acid in O-ester linkage with phosphatidyl glycerol.

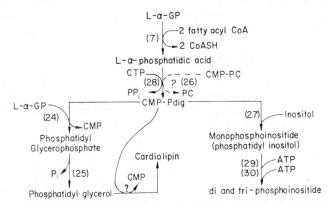

FIG. 5. Scheme showing the pathways for the formation of mono-phosphoinositide and phosphatidyl glycerol (after Paulus and Kennedy [531, 532, 533]). Numbers in parentheses refer to reactions in the text.

Kiyasu *et al.* have suggested that cardiolipin may be formed from phosphatidyl glycerol and CMP-Pdig according to reaction (26a):

$$\text{phosphatidyl glycerol} + \text{CMP-Pdig} \longrightarrow \text{cardiolipin} + \text{CMP} \qquad (26a)$$

Direct evidence for this reaction has not been reported. As noted by Macfarlane [462] there is little evidence available on the biosynthesis of the lipoamino esters of phosphatidyl glycerol.

(v) *Inositol-containing*

Phosphatidyl inositol. Studies on the *in vivo* or *in vitro* incorporation of P_i^{32} into the phospholipids of a variety of tissues (reviewed by Rossiter [582] and Hawthorne [304]) indicated that inositol phosphatide was actively labeled. It was observed that α-GP^{32} also readily labeled the inositol phospholipid of cell-free preparations of brain. [492] CTP stimulated the labeling from P_i^{32}, but apparently not from α-GP^{32}.

Because of a possible analogy in the synthetic pathways of the phosphoglycerides, a number of unsuccessful attempts were made to demonstrate an inositol phosphokinase (see Hawthorne [304] and Paulus and Kennedy [533] for evidence). More recently, some evidence has been obtained which suggests that a weakly active inositol phosphokinase does exist in rat liver [238] and salmon liver. [673] The initial experiments with labeled inositol indicated that free inositol was incorporated into inositol phospholipid. [2, 531, 589, 665] There is good evidence available that plants readily form inositol with CO_2 as the carbon source.[500, 560, 664] It is possible that glucose is an intermediate in this assimilation. In mammalian organisms the status of inositol is less certain, since there is some evidence that inositol is a vitamin and as such is required in the diet (see Lardy[426]). However, it is generally believed that most mammals carry out significant synthesis of inositol. In the intact rat it has been shown that C^{14}-labeled glucose can yield small amounts of labeled inositol.[160, 281] A similar observation has been made for yeast.[122] Charalampous,[122] on the basis of degradation studies on the C^{14}-inositol formed, indicated that inositol was not formed by a direct cyclization of glucose, but rather from C_2 and C_4 fragments derived from glucose.

More recent studies have confirmed the fact that in rat tissues[228, 297, 299, 347] labeled glucose is converted to inositol. Houser and Finelli[297] have observed with tissue slices of the rat that in the conversion of glucose to inositol carbon atom 6 was less readily utilized than carbon atoms 1 and 2. These observations seemed to be at variance with the findings for the intact animal,[228, 347] for rat testis *in vitro*[199] and for plants[447, 381] which suggested that conversion occurred without fragmentation of glucose and that C-6 of glucose became C-1 of inositol. It is noteworthy that in a number of these studies[297, 299] the labeled inositol formed appeared in the lipid fraction. Chen and Charalampous,[126] realizing that in the conversion of glucose to inositol by intact yeast cells considerable randomization of carbons may occur, have used purified enzymes from yeast to study the conversion. They have described a soluble enzyme from yeast which catalyzes the biosynthesis of inositol from glucose and glucose-6-phosphate. The apparent requirements for both DPN and DPNH suggest that an oxidation step and a reduction step must occur in the conversion. A requirement for Mg^{++} and inhibition by phosphate possibly indicate that a phosphorylated intermediate undergoes dephosphorylation prior to its conversion to inositol (see also Chapter 11, Section IX).

Arganoff et al.[1, 2] were the first to report a possible pathway for the synthesis of inositol phosphatide. These workers observed that the addition of CMP-PC or CMP greatly stimulated the incorporation of tritium-labeled myo-inositol into what was shown to be mainly the monophosphoinositide or phosphatidyl inositol of a particulate preparation of guinea-pig kidney. CTP and CDP were less effective. Phosphatidic acid, but not D-α,β-diglyceride, also greatly stimulated the incorporation of inositol. The findings suggested that monophosphoinositide was formed according to the following reactions which involve the formation of CMP-Pdig as an intermediate:

$$\text{CMP-PC} + \text{L-}\alpha\text{-phosphatidic acid} \longrightarrow \text{CMP-Pdig} + \text{PC} \qquad (26b)$$

$$\text{CMP-Pdig} + \text{inositol} \longrightarrow \text{monophosphoinositide} + \text{CMP} \qquad (27)$$

The CMP-Pdig formed in reaction (26b) was considered to react with one of the hydroxyls (e.g. OH at C_1) of myo-inositol in a manner analogous to that for the formation of lecithin from CMP-PC and D-α,β-diglyceride (reaction 17). CMP was believed to exert its effect through formation of CMP-PC by reversal of the latter reaction (17).

Preliminary reports by Thompson *et al.*[589, 665] indicate that the incorporation of C^{14}- and tritium-labeled inositol into the inositol phosphatide of brain homogenates was stimulated greatest by CTP and least by CMP and CMP-PC. A stimulatory effect by phosphatidic acid was consistent with the view that CMP-Pdig is involved, but suggested that it might be formed by a different reaction (28):

$$CTP + \text{L-}\alpha\text{-phosphatidic acid} \longrightarrow CMP\text{-Pdig} + PP_i \qquad (28)$$

Paulus and Kennedy[531] observed that H^3-inositol was readily incorporated into the monophosphoinositide of chicken or rat liver homogenates. In Tris (trishydroxylmethylaminomethane) buffer, optimal incorporation was achieved by the addition of Mn^{++} and it was only in phosphate buffer that a cytidine nucleotide effect could be shown. It was suggested that much of the labeling from H^3-inositol might simply reflect an exchange which is only stimulated by cytidine nucleotide (CMP in particular) when there is a limiting concentration of Mn^{++}. Whether this type of exchange is catalyzed by the enzyme system (phosphatidic acid–inositol transferase) that catalyzes the final reaction (27) in the formation of monophosphoinositide or by a phosphatidase C-like action analogous to the systems described by Hübscher [333] for serine and choline is not certain.

Paulus and Kennedy[531, 532, 533] obtained evidence that the *de novo* synthesis of labeled monophosphoinositide could be carried out by a dialyzed homogenate of guinea-pig liver in the presence of L-α-GP^{32}, inositol, CTP, ATP, oleic aid, CoA and a divalent cation (Mn^{++} or Mg^{++}). P^{32}-labeled phosphatidic acid yielded labeled inositol phosphatide in the presence of added inositol and CTP. It was shown that CMP-Pdig was formed enzymatically from α-GP, CTP and a suitable acylating system. The CMP-Pdig, formed biologically, or that prepared chemically by the condensation of CMP and dipalmitin by dicyclohexylcarbodiimide, was converted to monophosphoinositide in the presence of inositol. Myo-inosose-2 and DL-epiinosose-2 could replace inositol to a significant extent. These results strongly suggested that inositol phosphatide was formed by a combination of the reactions concerned in the synthesis of phosphatidic acid (reactions 4–7, and reactions 28 and 27). These reactions are included in Fig. 5.

More recent findings with homogenate preparations of rat brain have supported the existence of reactions (27) and (28) and in addition, provided evidence that was suggestive of an alternative pathway.[646, 666, 664, 547] It

G

was observed that CTP stimulated the labeling of inositol monophospho-inositide from C^{14}-phosphatidic acid (prepared by the enzymatic degradation of lecithin biologically labeled with C^{14} in the glycerol moiety) as expected on the basis of the pathway already outlined. Further support for the pathway was provided by the observation that synthetic CMP-Pdig (di-palmitin derivative) greatly increased the incorporation of inositol-H^3 into lipid catalyzed by a solubilized enzyme preparation obtained by treating rat brain microsomes with the detergent "cutscum".[664] However, in experiments with C^{14}- and P^{32}-labeled L-α-GP it was found that CMP-PC caused a much larger increase than CTP in the labeling of inositol monophospho-inositide in the brain homogenate system supplemented with ATP, CoA and Mg^{++}. Both cytosine nucleotides strongly suppressed the labeling of phosphatidic acid. These results suggested that in brain L-α-GP becomes incorporated into inositol phosphatide by a pathway involving CMP-PC, but possibly not phosphatidic acid. Possmayer and Strickland[547, 548] have continued to investigate the actions of cytosine-nucleotides on monophospho-inositide synthesis. Their recent findings suggest that even in the presence of CMP-PC, labeled α-GP is incorporated by way of phosphatidic acid and CMP-Pdig. The reason for the greater stimulation by CMP-PC compared to CTP has not been fully elucidated. One explanation that may be offered is that CTP or a product of it such as CDP or CMP may be inhibiting phosphatidic acid formation.

An enzyme system analogous to that described by Lands for the formation of phosphatidyl choline and ethanolamine from their corresponding lyso-derivatives has been described by Keenan and Hokin[369] for phosphatidyl inositol. They have observed that homogenates of pigeon pancreas and guinea-pig brain are able to acylate lysophosphatidyl inositol to phosphatidyl inositol in the presence of oleic acid, CoA and ATP.

Diphosphoinositide and triphosphoinositide. As summarized earlier, these two types of inositol-containing phospholipids, referred to collectively as polyphosphoinositides have only recently been fully characterized. There was every indication, even prior to the elucidation of the structures of these lipids, that P_i^{32} was rapidly incorporated into fractions now known to contain portions of these lipids (see, for example, Strickland;[641, 209] Dawson[170]).

However, once the nature of the polyphosphoinositides was established active work on the synthesis of these lipids was undertaken in several laboratories (recently summarized by Hawthorne[304, 305]). The *in vivo* experiments of Wagner et al.[687] and Ellis and Hawthorne[201] showed that P_i^{32} was more actively incorporated into the polyphosphoinositides than into phosphatidyl inositol (MPI). Activities of fractions tentatively identified as triphosphoinositide (TPI) and disphosphoinositide (DPI) were in the order TPI > DPI > MPI.

Brockerhoff and Ballou[100, 101] have carried out a series of studies *in vitro* using rabbit brain slices. Labeling of the three phosphoinositides with inositol-H^3, glycerol-2-C^{14} and P_i^{32} was measured. The activity from P_i^{32} incorporated into the 4- and 5-phosphates of the di- and triphosphoinositides was determined following removal of the phosphates by monophospho-esterase action. The latter study showed that the 4- and 5-phosphates were both actively and about equally labeled. Studies on the diester phosphate and with other precursors showed a similar pattern with the order of molar radioactivities being MPI > DPI > TPI. The higher but similar activities of the 4- and 5-phosphates suggested that the phosphorus is supplied via a highly active donor such as ATP. It is also noteworthy that homogenate preparations of rabbit brain incorporated P_i^{32} only into MPI. DPI and TPI could not be detected no doubt because of the presence of degrading enzymes such as those described by Thompson and Dawson. [662, 663, 179]

In this laboratory, Palmer and Rossiter [526, 527, 528, 586] have carried out extensive *in vivo* and *in vitro* studies on the biosynthesis of the polyphospho-inositides of brain and also of Ehrlich's ascites tumor cells. The results from the *in vivo* experiments indicated for the precursors inositol-H^3, glycerol-1-C^{14} and P_i^{32} that the pattern of labeling was similar to the results of Brockerhoff and Ballou. [100, 101] However, *in vitro* experiments with cat brain slices or Ehrlich's ascites tumor cells gave results which differed and showed instead a pattern with the molar radioactivities of DPI > MPI > TPI. These authors (private communication) suggest that this pattern may be indicative either of a small pool of MPI which is rapidly turned over and is a precursor of DPI or of an alternative pathway where DPI is formed independently of MPI. Further evidence is needed to determine whether either possibility applies or an alternative explanation is required.

A number of the studies already cited and others to be mentioned point to the likelihood that the polyphosphoinositides are formed by the stepwise phosphorylation of MPI as shown in reactions (29) and (30):

$$\text{monophosphoinositide} + \text{ATP} \longrightarrow \text{diphosphoinositide} + \text{ADP} \quad (29)$$

$$\text{diphosphoinositide} + \text{ATP} \longrightarrow \text{triphosphoinositide} + \text{ADP} \quad (30)$$

The recent work of Hawthorne's group [305, 239] provides strong evidence for the view that the rapidly labeled inositol-containing lipid described by Garbus *et al.* [240a] in rat liver and kidney mitochondria is diphosphoinositide. The 4-phosphate of DPI was found to be actively labeled from P_i^{32}. The inhibition of label by inhibitors of phosphorylation and a strong inhibition by ATP suggest that DPI is probably formed in mitochondria (rat liver, kidney and brain) via reaction (29). Colodzin and Kennedy [150] in a preliminary communication have described an enzyme associated with the microsomes of brain which catalyzes the phosphorylation of MPI to DPI in the presence of added ATP. Hokin and Hokin [318] have shown that erythrocyte ghosts have enzymes capable of transferring the γ-P of γ-P^{32} ATP into DPI, TPI, phosphatidic acid and another unidentified lipid. Most of this radioactivity was associated with monoesterified P. The addition of exogenous MPI increased the label in DPI but inhibited that in TPI. Thus, apart from the findings of Palmer and Rossiter referred to above there is considerable evidence supporting the view that DPI and TPI are formed via reactions (29) and (30). A summary of the reactions concerned in poly-phosphoinositide biosynthesis is given in Fig. 5.

Recent work on the "phosphatidopeptide" fraction to be discussed later indicates that this fraction should more properly be called a "phospho-inositide" complex.[7, 8] Investigation of the deacylated products of this complex indicate that both DPI and TPI may be present in the complex. Measurement of incorporation from P_i^{32} showed that both DPI and TPI were actively labeled and that the pattern of labeling was consistent with that described for MPI $\rightarrow$ DPI $\rightarrow$ TPI.

(c) *Phosphate Triester Lipids*

Collins[140, 141, 142, 144] in a series of investigations on the phospholipids of rat liver and sheep brain obtained evidence for the existence of complexes of phospholipids. On subjection of the phospholipids (after dinitropheny-lation and methylation) to counter current distribution, three unknown amino-phospholipid fractions were obtained which were distinguished by their partition coefficients (k) in carbon tetrachloride–methanol–water. Two of these lipids with k of 2·5 and 8·0 and ratios of dinitrophenyl groups/P of 0·5 and 0·67, respectively, were found in liver. Sheep brain contained complexes having k equal to 1·0 (predominant fraction equal to 28 per cent of total phospholipids) and 8·0 and corresponding dinitrophenyl groups/P equal to 0·5 and 0·67. The complex with a k of 1·0 was found to contain small amounts of choline, but no inositol. The molecular weight was slightly more than twice that of the average phosphoglyceride. Mild treatment of the unknown lipid with triethylamine, tetramethyl ammonium hydroxide, acetic acid or silicic acid yielded phosphatidyl ethanolamine as the main product. Very small amounts of phosphatidyl serine were found. The results seemed to support the existence of a complex of at least two phosphoglyceride molecules. Collins[144] has suggested that the properties of these complexes are consistent with those expected for compounds arising by phosphate triester bonding. Two types of compound were suggested as possibilities (see Formula XII). One in which a phosphate triester exists between the phosphate of phosphatidyl ethanolamine and the free hydroxyl of other phospholipids, such as lysolecithin, sphingomyelin or cardiolipin. The other, in which phosphatidyl ethanolamine is linked through a polyhydroxy compound such as glycerol to either a second molecule of phosphatidyl ethanolamine or some other phospholipid by phosphate triester bonds. Collins and Shotlander[146,

[147] have extended this study to other tissues of the rat and to other species. Complex phospholipids of the type described were shown to be present in rat tissues, egg yolk and allantonic membrane, influenza virus, human plasma and brain, cabbage leaf, yeast and freshwater crustacea. The mitochondrial lipids appear to lack a component of the complex amino phospholipids which is present in microsomes. In a more recent report Collins[149] has observed that these complex lipids produce counter-current distributions which were interpreted as resulting from the association of two components (a situation fulfilled by components of the phosphate triester complex).

Some support for the existence of a distinct fraction such as that described above was provided by a study using P_i^{32}.[144] It was found that the specific activity of the free phosphatidyl ethanolamine fraction was 30–50 per cent higher than that of the complex fraction from rat liver 90 min after the injection of P_i^{32}. This difference in specific activity suggests the complex is a distinct fraction which is metabolically different. Until a time study is carried out, it is not possible to say whether free phosphatidyl ethanolamine is a precursor of the complex which contains phosphatidyl ethanolamine in phosphate triester linkage. However, the higher specific activity of the free phospholipid is not inconsistent with a precursor–product relationship.

Much more work is required to firmly establish the nature and, indeed, the unequivocal existence of phosphate triester lipids. DeKoning[183] has questioned the structures proposed by Collins for these complex lipids on the basis that phosphate triesters are normally quite stable. As an alternative it was suggested that the evidence supports the presence of a pyrophosphate linkage which on mild hydrolysis would yield two phosphatidyl compounds. Very recently Galanos and Kapoulas[234, 235, 236] have carried out extensive studies on milk and tissue glycophospholipids and have obtained results which they interpret as supporting the view that these lipids are phosphate triester derivatives. Examples of these are galactophosphatidyl ethanolamine, galactophosphatidyl serine, galactophosphatidyl choline, galacto- and glucomanno-sphingomyelins. The further suggestion is made that these lipids occur in proteolipids and that they are possibly precursors of the commonly known phospholipids. At present it can only be concluded that there is considerable evidence accumulating which is suggestive of the existence of certain types of phosphate triester lipids. Only with more extensive investigation will the true nature of these lipids become evident and their biosynthetic pathways established.

C. SPHINGOLIPIDS

This group of lipids has sphingosine (in some instances, dihydro-sphingosine or phytosphingosine) as a common constituent. Excellent reviews by Carter et al.,[115, 116] Zabin[730] and Ansell and Hawthorne[15] describe the methods whereby the structure and stereochemistry of sphingosine were determined. The structure of natural sphingosine (XVIII) has been established as D-*erythro*-1,3-dihydroxy-2-amino-4-*trans*-octadecene. Four sub-groups (sphingomyelin, cerebrosides, sulfatides and gangliosides) of sphingosine-containing lipids are known which differ mainly in the substituents attached to the primary hydroxyl group (for reviews see LeBaron and Folch[430] and

$$H^3C\,(OH)\,CH{=}CH\,(CH_2)_{12}CH_3$$
$$H_2N^2CH$$
$$^1CH_2OH$$

Sphingosine
XVIII

Klenk and Debuch[394]). The latter three groups of sphingolipids are also often classified as glycolipids along with other carbohydrate-containing glyceride compounds (for a recent review on the biosynthesis of these lipids see Brady[83]). Each sphingolipid has a N-acyl group in which the fatty acid or α-hydroxy fatty acid is predominently C_{24} in length. The structures of the various sphingolipids are shown in the appropriate sections on biogenesis that follow.

Biosynthesis of Sphingosine

From *in vivo* experiments with both acetate-1-C^{14} and L-serine-3-C^{14}, it was established that carbons 3–18 arose from acetate (presumably by synthesis of a C_{16} unit from acetyl CoA) and that carbons 1 and 2 and the amino group were provided by carbons 2 and 3 and the amino group of serine.[731, 732, 612] Zabin[729] later described a rat brain system that was capable of forming ceramide (N-acyl sphingosine) from serine and palmityl CoA in the presence of added TPN, Mg^{++} ions and pyridoxal phosphate. Brady and Koval[87] also found that a preparation of young rat brain catalyzed the formation of sphingosine from serine and palmityl CoA in the presence of similar cofactors. Palmityl CoA was shown to undergo reduction by TPNH before incorporation into the carbon chain of sphingosine.

The mechanism of synthesis of sphingosine was more completely elucidated by the work of Brady *et al.*[85] who provided evidence that, in the reduction of palmityl CoA by the rat brain system, palmitic aldehyde is formed (reaction 31):

$$\text{palmityl CoA} + \text{TPNH} \longrightarrow \text{palmitic aldehyde} + \text{CoA} + \text{TPN}^+ \quad (31)$$

Activation of the methylene carbon of serine was believed to occur in the presence of pyridoxal phosphate, Mn^{++} and the enzyme system, with the result that palmitic aldehyde adds to the activated C_2 position of serine to form dihydrosphingosine and CO_2 (from C_1 of serine) according to the

$$\text{palmitic aldehyde} + \text{serine} \longrightarrow \text{dihydrosphingosine} + \text{CO}_2 \quad (32)$$

It was suggested that activation results from the formation of a resonating Schiff base-metal complex which on loss of a proton from the α-carbon of serine yields a resonance-stabilized carbanion that participates in a carbon to carbon addition with palmitic aldehyde.

Reaction (32), which is somewhat analogous to an aldol condensation of the Knoevenagel type, gives rise to fully reduced sphingosine. The finding that the presence of either Safranin T [87] or phenazine methosulfate [85] was necessary for the oxidation or dehydrogenation of dihydrosphingosine suggested that a flavin enzyme was involved. Accordingly sphingosine may arise by the flavoenzyme catalyzed reaction (33):

$$\text{dihydrosphingosine} + \text{flavin} \longrightarrow \text{sphingosine} + \text{flavin-2H} \qquad (33)$$

More recently Weiss, [703] using serine-2,3-H^3 and serine-2-C^{14}, has studied the biosynthesis of sphingosine in young rats undergoing myelination. The very close agreement between the (C-1):(C-2) ratio of tritium in the isolated sphingosine and the β:α ratio of tritium in the administered serine-2,3-H^3 strongly indicated that the α-hydrogen of serine is retained during the biosynthesis of sphingosine. This observation does not confirm the above mechanism proposed by Brady et al. [85] Rather, the conclusion reached is that in the condensation of serine with a C_{16} unit (supplied either as palmitaldehyde or palmityl CoA + TPNH), CO_2 is split out without loss of configuration at C-2. Weiss has expressed the opinion that a number of unanswered problems exist in regard to the sequence of steps in sphingosine biosynthesis. He states it is unknown (1) whether serine is decarboxylated before or simultaneously with condensation of a long chain aldehyde, (2) whether or not the Schiff-base or the free base is involved in the oxidation of dehydrosphingosine to sphingosine and (3) whether the free aldehyde or an activated form participates directly in the reaction since palmitoyl CoA and TPNH fulfil the requirement. Further investigation will be required to clarify these points and establish whether or not reactions (31–33) adequately describe the sequence for sphingosine synthesis.

The sphingosine that is formed may then undergo acylation at the free amino group to form ceramide according to reaction (34), or undergo substitution at position 1 as described later:

$$\text{sphingosine} + \text{acyl CoA} \longrightarrow \text{ceramide} + \text{CoA} \qquad (34)$$

Sribney [615] described the presence of an enzyme in chicken liver and rat brain which catalyzes a reaction between free sphingosine and palmitoyl CoA. The product formed was, on the basis of chromatographic separations, shown to be identical with the ceramide formed by phosphatidase D action on natural sphingomyelin. In regard to ceramide formation it is of interest to note that Gatt[241a] has described a soluble enzyme preparation from brain which catalyzes both the hydrolysis of ceramide to sphingosine and fatty acid and its synthesis from these components. Recently, Kopaczyk and Radin[404] have obtained evidence suggesting that in rat brain ceramide may be formed from cerebroside by galactosidase action. The reactions concerned in sphingosine formation appear as part of Fig. 6.

(a) *Sphingomyelin*

Sphingomyelin consists of N-acyl sphingosine or ceramide in combination with phosphorus and choline. Although earlier evidence was very suggestive that choline was attached through a phosphate diester linkage to the primary hydroxyl of sphingosine, it remained for conclusive proof to be provided by the work of Stotz and co-workers.[591, 471] The latter workers through periodate oxidation studies on sphingosine sulfate (which yielded glycol-aldehyde phosphate) and performic hydroxylation, periodate and perman-ganate oxidation of sphingomyelin showed that PC was attached at C_1 as shown in structure XIX.

$$
\begin{array}{l}
\text{HC(OH) CH=CH (CH}_2\text{)}_{12}\text{CH}_3 \\
\text{RCOHNCH} \qquad \text{O} \\
\qquad\quad | \qquad\qquad \| \\
\qquad\ \ \text{CH}_2\text{O—P—O—CH}_2\text{CH}_2\overset{+}{\text{N}}\text{(CH}_3\text{)}_3 \\
\qquad\qquad\quad | \\
\qquad\qquad\ \ \text{O}_-
\end{array}
$$

Sphingomyelin
XIX

What might be described as the final reaction in the synthesis of sphingo-myelin was established by Sribney and Kennedy.[616] They demonstrated the presence in chicken liver of an active enzyme system capable of catalyzing the transfer of PC from CMP-PC to ceramide (N-acyl sphingosine) with the formation of sphingomyelin (reaction 35):

$$CMP\text{-}PC + ceramide \longrightarrow sphingomyelin + CMP \qquad (35)$$

The enzyme was given the name PC-ceramide transferase. The type of reaction catalyzed is similar to that for lecithin (reaction 17) and choline plasmalogen (reaction 21) formation. The report of Rossiter *et al.*[584, 585] that some of the radioactivity of CMP-P^{32}C was incorporated into an alkali-resistant phosphatide fraction of rat brain suggested that this pathway may be operative in brain. This interpretation has been confirmed more recently by *in vitro* studies in which CMP-PC-C^{14} was incubated with cell-free preparations of developing brain.[489]

Sribney and Kennedy[617] in a more detailed report of the above work indicate that the enzyme, PC-ceramide transferase, occurs widely in mammalian tissues and that it demonstrates a definite specificity toward both CMP-PC and the type of ceramide. The specific ceramide must contain sphingosine which has a *trans*-configuration at the double bond and a *threo* relationship for the hydroxyl at carbon 3 relative to carbon 2. The active sphingosine may, therefore, be designated as *threo*-1,3-dihydroxy-2-amino-4-*trans*-octadecene. The sphingosine in the sphingomyelin produced by reaction (35) also consisted of the *threo-trans*-configuration, rather than of the natural-occurring *erythro-trans*-configuration.[114, 617, 730] Sribney and Kennedy[617] suggest that *in vivo* a second enzyme system may be involved which catalyzes the conversion of *threo*-sphingomyelin to *erythro*-sphingomyelin. It is uncertain, however, whether this explanation is sufficient since the work of Sribney[615] would suggest that the natural *erythro* form of sphingosine is necessary for ceramide formation via reaction (34). In addition, Groom and Sribney[272] have established that the ceramides isolated from beef brain and chicken liver have a sphingosine moiety possessing the *erythro* configuration.

The pathway for sphingomyelin synthesis is summarized in Fig. 6.

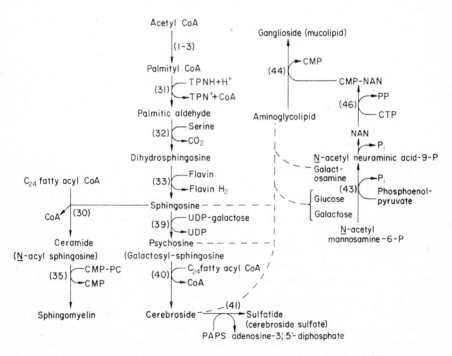

Fig. 6. Pathways of biosynthesis of the sphingosine-containing lipids.

(b) *Cerebroside*

These sphingolipids contain the nitrogenous base, sphingosine (or di-hydrosphingosine), a long-chain fatty acid and a sugar which is usually galactose but may be glucose or even a disaccharide. Classically, four cerebrosides (phrenosine or cerebron, kerasin, nervon and oxynervon) have been described which differ in their C_{24} fatty acid. Phrenosine contains saturated C_{24} cerebronic acid, kerasin contains the α-hydroxy C_{24} acid, lignoceric, nervon contains $\Delta 15$ C_{24} nervonic acid and oxynervon contains $\Delta 15$-α-hydroxy C_{24} oxynervonic acid. The fatty acid is linked to the amino group of sphingosine. Carter and Greenwood [117] have established that galactose is attached to carbon 1 of sphingosine. Earlier observations had indicated no aldehyde function and thus suggested that galactose was in galactoside linkage. It has not been firmly established whether the galactosidic link is α- or β- in nature (for details see Carter *et al.*, [115] Zabin [730]). Cerebroside may, therefore, be depicted by the formula XX.

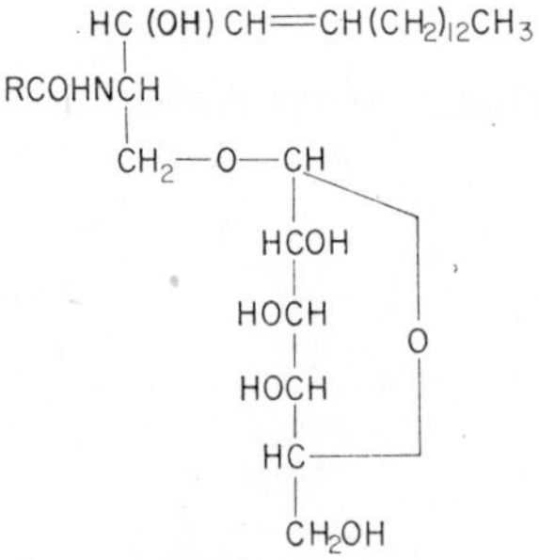

Cerebroside

XX

Studies in which C^{14}-labeled hexoses have been administered to the rat or mouse have revealed that C^{14} is incorporated into the glycolipids of brain. [533, 501, 110] Burton *et al.* [110] in extending these observations noted that in the rat the greatest incorporation of glucose and galactose into neutral glyco-lipids occurred between 10 and 20 days following birth. *In vitro* studies by these same workers showed that the microsomal fraction of young rat brain contains the enzymes necessary for the incorporation of the above hexoses into the neutral glycolipids. Uridine diphosphate galactose (UDP-gal (see Chapter 6, Section VIIA) was found to be the primary precursor for the addition of hexose to an endogenous "lipid acceptor" which was presumed to be sphingosine or N-acyl sphingosine. It was possible to replace UDP-gal by two combinations, (a) galactose, ATP and UDP-glucose and (b) galactose-1-phosphate and UDP-glucose, each of which is capable of forming UDP-gal in the brain microsome system. [109, 110] Chromatographic and infra-red spectral studies suggested that the glycolipid formed *in vitro* was a cerebroside and probably equivalent to N-cerebronyl-O'-galactosyl sphingosine. These results suggested that cerebroside may be formed according to reaction (36):

$$\text{UDP-gal} + \text{``lipid acceptor''} \longrightarrow \text{cerebroside} + \text{UDP} \qquad (36)$$

Labeled glucose was believed to be incorporated into cerebroside through its conversion to galactose in the reaction (37) catalyzed by UDP-galactose-4-epimerase. [109, 110]

$$\text{UDP-glucose} \longrightarrow \text{UDP-galactose} \qquad (37)$$

The UDP-glucose is known to be formed enzymatically by reaction between glucose-1-phosphate, a product of glycolysis, and uridine triphosphate (UTP). A direct pathway for labeled galactose was thought to involve phosphorylation of galactose to galactose-1-phosphate which was then converted to UDP-gal by reaction (38) catalyzed by galactose-1-phosphate uridyl transferase:

$$\text{galactose-1-phosphate} + \text{UDP-gluc} \longrightarrow \text{glucose-1-phosphate} \\ + \text{UDP-gal} \qquad (38)$$

Evidence obtained from the *in vivo* experiments of Moser and Karnovsky [502] indicated that C^{14} glucose was more readily incorporated into the cerebrosides of mouse brain than C^{14}-galactose thus suggesting that the glucose pathway described above might be more important.

Information on the possible nature of the "lipid acceptor" has been obtained by Cleland and Kennedy. [135, 136] They have demonstrated that a microsome preparation from brain of young guinea pigs and rats is capable of catalyzing the formation of psychosine (galactosyl sphingosine) from sphingosine and UDP-gal (reaction 39):

$$\text{sphingosine} + \text{UDP-gal} \longrightarrow \text{psychosine} + \text{UDP} \qquad (39)$$

The two naturally-occurring sphingosines, the *erythro-trans* and *erythro*-dihydro compounds, were found to be the most active acceptors of galactose. The enzyme was highly specific for UDP-gal. Cleland and Kennedy [136] indicate that preliminary experiments, in which unlabeled acyl CoA thioesters were added to the psychosine-synthesizing system, offer some support for the reaction:

$$\text{psychosine} + \text{acyl CoA} \longrightarrow \text{cerebroside} + \text{CoA} \qquad (40)$$

Ceramides were found to be essentially inactive in reaction (39) thus suggesting that this alternative pathway of cerebroside synthesis may be relatively unimportant compared to that by way of reaction (40).

Brady [82, 83] has extensively studied the requirements for cerebroside formation using washed rat brain microsomes. Total synthesis was achieved from sphingosine, stearoyl-CoA and UDP-galactose or UDP-glucose. Added ceramide was ineffective in this system. Psychosine proved to be a very effective acceptor of stearoyl CoA. UDP-galactose was a much more effective donor of the carbohydrate than UDP-glucose. All of these findings confirmed that cerebroside is formed according to reactions (39) and (40).

Some of the reactions involved in the enzymatic synthesis of cerebroside have been summarized in Fig. 6.

(c) Sulfatide

The structure of this sphingolipid, which was first isolated by Blix [58] in 1933, was established by Thannhauser and co-workers [660] as a cerebroside with sulfate esterified to carbon 6 of galactose. Recent reassessment of the structure of sulfatide by exhaustive methylation studies by Yamakawa et al. [724a] and Stoffyn and Stoffyn [638] have established that the sulfate is esterified to carbon 3 of galactose. The structure of this lipid may, therefore, be presented as shown in formula XXI. Through the simplified technique

Sulfatide. (cerebroside sulfate)
XXI

described by Lees et al. [436] for the isolation of brain cerebroside sulfate, it has been possible to demonstrate the existence of this lipid in a variety of rat tissues (kidney, spleen, liver, brain, possibly heart and a mast cell tumor [268]). Fractionation of brain, kidney and liver demonstrated that cerebroside sulfate (sulfatide) sedimented with the mitochondria in brain, with the microsomes in liver and remained in the soluble portion in liver.

There is only limited evidence available on the biosynthesis of this sphingolipid (see Goldberg [248] and Brady [83]). Turnover studies with S^{35} indicated that cerebroside sulfate turned over relatively rapidly in mast cells and organs such as liver, spleen and kidney as compared to the turnover in brain. [268] In in vitro studies Goldberg [246, 247, 248] has observed that a rat liver supernatant is capable of catalyzing the sulfurylation of lipid by S^{35}-labeled 3'-phosphoadenosine-5'-phosphosulfate (PAPS) and that the transfer of sulfate is increased by the addition of a crude mixture of the stereoisomers of N-acetyl sphingosine. If it is assumed that cerebroside is formed or present under these conditions, then it is possible to postulate that sulfatide or cerebroside sulfate is formed according to reaction (41):

$$\text{cerebroside} + \text{PAPS} \longrightarrow \text{sulfatide} + \text{PAP} \qquad (41)$$
$$\text{(cerebroside sulfate)}$$

This pathway for sulfatide formation is also included in Fig. 6.

This pathway of formation depends upon cerebroside as a precursor. Hauser[298] has recently examined this problem and concluded on the basis of his own studies on glucose-C^{14} incorporation into the brain of young rats and existing data in the literature that cerebrosides are likely to be precursors of sulfatides. However, Radin and co-workers[404] whose earlier studies supported the conclusions reached by Hauser have not been able to demonstrate any conversion of injected C^{14}-labeled cerebroside into sulfatide by rat brain. It must be concluded that the biosynthetic pathway for sulfatide remains uncertain and requires much additional detailed work to clarify its nature.

(d) Gangliosides (Mucolipids, Strandin)

This group of sphingolipids includes a number of complex materials having in common, besides sphingosine, the presence of sialic acids among their constituents. Because sialic acids are found in mucins and mucoproteins it has been suggested by Rosenberg et al.[580, 578, 579] that these lipids should be called mucolipids. Sialic acid was originally isolated in crystalline form from submaxillary mucin by Blix.[59] This substance and one in brain[60] were observed to give the same deep red color on heating with Bial's reagent (orcinol and hydrochloric acid). Later, Klenk[390] isolated a crystalline acid from a brain lipid preparation which exhibited comparable color reactions and which he called neuraminic acid. The exact relationship between sialic and neuraminic acid has been resolved by Blix, Gottschalk and Klenk[61] so that sialic acid is reserved for the group of N-acylated neuraminic acids and neuraminic acid refers to the free base compound. The structure and metabolism of sialic acids have been reviewed by Cornforth et al.[155] Gottschalk[255] and Roseman.[574, 573] The main sialic acid obtained normally from the mucolipids is N-acetyl neuraminic acid (NAN). Its exact structure has been established,[255, 151, 152, 577] (see also Chapter 6, Section VIIID, 26).

As Gottschalk[255] has noted chemical synthesis of NAN can be achieved starting with either N-acetyl glucosamine and oxaloacetic acid or N-acetyl-mannosamine and oxaloacetic acid. The studies of Comb and Roseman[151, 577, 152, 574] provide good evidence that biological degradation and synthesis may be achieved by the action of an aldolase type enzyme (NAN aldolase) which catalyzes the reversible reaction (42):

N-acetylmannosamine + pyruvate ⟶ N-acetylneuraminic acid (NANA)
$$(42)$$

The enzyme has been purified over 100-fold from *Clostridium perfringens* and 20-fold from *Escherichi coli K*-235. Since N-acetyl glucosamine did not act as a substrate it was suggested that the configuration at the amino-substituted carbon of the product is the same as that of N-acetylmannosamine.

Although NAN-aldolase is widely distributed in nature the enzyme could not be detected in tissues producing mucins containing sialic acid. [574] This observation suggests that reaction (42) may be involved in the degradation rather than the biosynthesis of sialic acid. Warren and Felsenfeld [699] have discovered an alternative pathway for the synthesis of NAN. Using rat liver extracts free of NAN-aldolase these workers obtained two protein fractions which on incubation with N-acetyl-mannosamine, phosphoenolpyruvate, ATP and Mg^{++} ions produced NAN in high yield. Roseman [574, 575] found that submaxillary extracts contained an enzyme that catalyzed reaction (43):

$$\text{N-acyl-D-mannosamine-6-P + phosphoenolpyruvate} \xrightarrow{Mg^{++}}$$
$$\text{N-acyl neuraminic acid-9-P} + P_i \qquad (43)$$

The acyl groups may be acetyl or glycolyl in nature, thereby producing either N-acetyl- or N-glycolyl neuraminic acid-9-P. A phosphatase seems to be responsible for the final conversion to N-acyl neuraminic acid.

Two preparations of mucolipid have received particular attention. The first is a preparation obtained from brain by Klenk in 1941 [390] (see Klenk and Debuch [394, 395]). Repeated purification yielded a crystalline material which was called "ganglioside" because of its apparent concentration in ganglion cells. The preparation contained neuraminic acid (21%), sphingo-sine or related substances (13%) fatty acids (mainly stearic, 20%) and sugars (mainly galactose, with small amounts of glucose and galactosamine, 43%). Folch and co-workers [217] in 1951 isolated, under milder conditions, a high molecular weight (250,000) substance that was water-soluble. It was called strandin because it was obtained in the form of birefringent strands (see LeBaron and Folch, [430] Zabin [730] for details). Highly purified homogeneous preparations were obtained which contained sialic acid (30%), galactose and glucose (in approximately 2:1 ratio, 25%), galactosamine (11%) and fatty acids and sphingosine or related compounds (30–35%). [223, 578, 579] Treatment of strandin with hot glacial acetic acid caused removal of sialic acid and the production of a product more nearly approaching ganglioside. Most of the evidence (summarized by LeBaron and Folch, [430] Klenk and Debuch [394, 395] and Zabin [730]) now suggests that strandin is a type of polyganglioside.

This problem has been clarified further by the independent discovery in several laboratories (reviewed by Svennerholm [653]) that calf and human brain gangliosides are a complex mixture of different gangliosides, each varying in either the hexose content or the sialic acid content. Kühn *et al.* [416] found one monosialoganglioside, two disialogangliosides and one trisialoganglioside. Besides Svennerholm's group [653] a number of other workers have confirmed the presence of these different gangliosides [354, 722] in human brain. Although gangliosides are characteristic components of nerve cells they have been isolated from spleen and erythrocyte stroma. Svennerholm [653] has attempted to clarify the matter of nomenclature with the result that he recommends retaining the term ganglioside and dropping the names strandin and mucolipid.

The complexity of brain gangliosides has been responsible for the many difficulties encountered in establishing the structure(s) of these lipids. Svennerholm [653] has very ably summarized the more recent studies carried out on the determination of the structure of gangliosides. The tentative structures proposed by Klenk and Gielen [397] and presented in the earlier edition of this book have had to undergo some modification. Kühn and Wiegandt [417] have provided conclusive evidence that the major or "parent" brain ganglioside has the structure shown in formula XXII. This structure

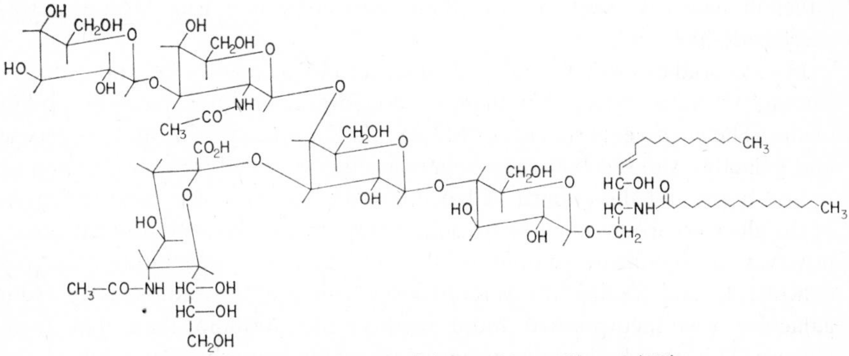

Structure of ganglioside G_{MI} (G_I) From Kuhn and Wiegandt (417)
XXII

is closely related to that suggested by Klenk and Gielen [396] for their Ganglioside B. The composition and linkages may be represented as follows:

Acylsphingosine (1 ⟵ 1) glucose (4 ⟵ 1) galactose (4 ⟵ 1) N-acetyl galactosamine (3 ⟵ 1) galactose $\begin{pmatrix} 3 \\ \uparrow \\ 2 \end{pmatrix}$

N-acetylneuraminic acid

Since trisialoganglioside can be converted to the disialogangliosides which in turn can be converted to monosialoganglioside, [653] it may be concluded that di- and trisialogangliosides have the same basic structure but with additional sialic acid groups attached. Svennerholm [653] has suggested that in the disialo-compounds the second sialic acid is attached at either C_3 or C_6 of the terminal galactose and that in trisialoganglioside, sialic acid is attached to both C_3 and C_6 of this galactose. The abnormal ganglioside accumulating in brain from patients with Tay–Sachs disease is short one galactose unit. [399] It is also noteworthy that the ganglioside from horse erythrocytes has only two hexose (glucose and galactose) units, no hexosamine and N-glycolyl-neuraminic acid instead of NAN. [401]

Since sufficient information to assign a structure for gangliosides has become available only very recently, it follows that little is known concerning the biosynthetic pathways. With the basic structure containing N-acyl sphingosine linked to a tetrasaccharide unit to which one, two or three NAN molecules are attached, it seems likely that both N-acyl sphingosine (or sphingosine) and NAN may arise as already described and that these are brought together by enzymatic systems capable of catalyzing the formation of glycosidic linkages. Very probably, uridine derivatives of the hexoses may be involved. One possible pathway might involve the formation first of a gluco-cerebroside, which then is linked to galactose, galactosamine and NAN, either in successive steps or after their prior combination to form a "tetra-saccharide-like" unit.

In vivo studies with C^{14}-labeled glucose and galactose [502] and galacto-samine [108] have shown that these carbohydrates are precursors of gangli-osides. The *in vivo* experiments of Moser and Karnovsky [502] with C^{14}-glucose and galactose showed that these sugars are incorporated into the strandin of mouse brain and the pattern of labeling indicated that little randomization of the glucose carbons occurred during incorporation. With labeled galactose, however, a significant amount of the activity in C_1 was randomized. In contrast to the finding for cerebroside formation the radioactivity from galactose was incorporated more readily into strandin than that from glucose. This observation might suggest that a gluco-cerebroside is not on the pathway of synthesis of ganglioside. A much more tenable explanation is that the two or more additional hexoses arise from galactose. Then, if it is assumed that galactose is incorporated at a rate which ranges from about 50 to 100 per cent of that for glucose, a higher incorporation of galactose would be expected. Klenk [391] has observed that part of the acetate-1-C^{14} incorporated into rat brain following injection into the subdural space appeared in the stearic acid of ganglioside.

Recently some success has been achieved with *in vitro* systems. Thus, Korey *et al.* [405] showed that slices of biopsy samples from human brain could incorporate C^{14}-glucose into gangliosides. Suzuki [652] has extended this work to the point of obtaining a cell-free system (microsomes plus supernatant) from rat brain that is capable of incorporating C^{14}-glucose into mono-, di- and trisialogangliosides. It is probable that this system will be of considerable use for further studies. Kanfer et al.[359] have succeeded in obtaining an enzyme preparation that is capable of incorporating labeled NAN into gangliosides. It was also shown that CMP-NAN-C^{14} was an effective donor for some of the NAN molecules of gangliosides. Aminoglycolipid (ceramide-glucose-galactose-N-acetylgalactosamine) in the presence of a surface active agent ("cutscum") stimulated the incorporation from CMP-NAN-C^{14} three-fold, thus pointing to the possibility of the following series of reactions (reactions 44 and 45) for ganglioside formation in which Tay–Sachs ganglioside is an intermediate:

$$\text{aminoglycolipid} + \text{CMP-NAN} \longrightarrow$$

$$\underset{\underset{\text{(Tay–Sachs ganglioside)}}{\overset{|}{\text{NAN}}}}{\text{ceramide–glucose–galactose–N–acetylgalactosamine}} + \text{CMP} \qquad (44)$$

$$\text{Tays–Sachs ganglioside} + \text{UDP-gal} \longrightarrow \text{monosialoganglioside} + \text{UDP} \quad (45)$$

Although not established subsequent reaction with CMP-NAN might be expected to produce the di- and trisialo derivatives. This scheme leaves unanswered the problem of how the aminoglycolipid is formed. Roseman[574, 576] has partially purified enzyme systems from bacteria and submaxillary gland which catalyze the formation of CMP-NAN (or the CMP-N-glycolyl derivative) according to the reaction:

$$\text{CTP} + \text{NAN} \longrightarrow \text{CMP-NAN} + \text{PP}_i \qquad (46)$$

Mg^{++} ion is required for this reaction. It seems reasonable that this enzyme functions to provide CMP-NAN for ganglioside formation by brain.

The reactions outlined above for ganglioside formation are included in Fig. 6.

D. DERIVED LIPIDS

The biosynthesis of each of the derived lipids with the exception of cholesterol (which may or may not be rightly classified as a derived lipid) has been described in relation to the parent lipid. The biogenesis of cholesterol is described in Chapter 4 of this volume.

E. COMPLEX LIPIDS

While complexes have been described for both the phosphoglycerides and the gangliosides, the classification described in this review has been more restrictive and the term "complex lipid" reserved for combinations between lipid and non-lipid substances such as proteins. At present it is possible to describe three types of complex lipids, (a) lipoproteins, (b) proteolipids and (c) phosphatidopeptides, which are not well defined structurally.

(a) *Lipoproteins*

Since the isolation from horse serum of what must now be regarded as a High-Density Lipoprotein (HDL) by Macheboeuf in 1929 (see Macheboeuf[465]), numerous preparations of lipoproteins have been described. It is appropriate to divide the lipoproteins into those derived from tissues and those derived from plasma. Relatively little information is available on the tissue lipoproteins although recent evidence suggests that they form integral parts of all membranous portions of the cell (cellular, mitochondrial, endoplasmic reticular and nuclear membranes).[137, 274] As components of the metabolically active regions of the cell, they appear to be of considerable importance in certain metabolic processes (see, for example, Green[264, 265, 266]). Proteins in combination with lipids are believed to be responsible for the lamellar structure of the myelin sheath of nerve fibers.[207, 208, 210, 212] Lipoproteins possessing thromboplastic activity have been obtained from tissues such as brain and lung.[123, 137] Lipovitellin and lipovitellenin are two lipoproteins which have been isolated from egg yolk[137] and have recently been studied in some detail.[153] The plasma lipoproteins have been studied rather extensively. Except for a few brief comments little will be said regarding the isolation, estimation, composition, physical properties and structure of the plasma lipoproteins. However, this information is available in reviews by Anfinsen,[9, 10] Oncley,[519, 520, 521, 522, 523] Frederickson and Gordon,[226] Lindgren et al.,[444, 445] Gurd[274] and Olson and Vester.[524]

The plasma lipoproteins are generally classified according to their centrifugal flotation rates (S_f) in a medium of fixed density (e.g. NaCl of density, 1·063). This technique was introduced by Gofman (for details see deLalla and Gofman[184]) and has gained wide acceptance. Centrifugation at densities of 1·063 or less yields a series of chylomicrons (S_f, 10^4–10^5) and Low-Density Fractions (LDF$_1$, $S_f = 20$–400; LDF$_2$, $S_f = 12$–20; LDF$_3$, $S_f = 0$–12). The HDL fractions (HDL$_2$, $-S = 4$–20 and HDL$_3$, $-S = 0$–4) are obtained by centrifugation at density 1·21 and are expressed in Svedberg flotation units ($-S$). The more classical α- and β-lipoprotein fractions obtained by electrophoresis correspond, respectively, to the HDL and LDF fractions. Olson and Vester[524] have summarized evidence on the chemical composition of the plasma of lipoproteins. The chylomicrons contain relatively small amounts of phospholipid (8%), cholesterol ester (3%), cholesterol (1%) and protein (1% or less) compared to its major triglyceride (87%) component. In the LDF$_1$ (S_f 20–400) the triglyceride content is decreased (52%) and the amounts of the other components are increased (phospholipid, 19%; cholesterol ester, 14%; cholesterol, 7% and protein, 7%). Throughout the low-density lipoproteins the triglyceride content reduces parallel with the flotation rate to the extent that in the LDF_3 (S_f 0–4) triglyceride comprises only about 10 per cent of the fraction and the remainder consists of phospholipid (22 %); cholesterol ester (49 %); cholesterol (8 %) and protein (21 %). The triglyceride content of 10 per cent remains at approximately this value for both HDL fractions. HDL_2 contained, in addition to the small amount of triglyceride (11 %); phospholipid (28 %); cholesterol ester (21 %); cholesterol (7 %); and protein (33 %). The protein in HDL_3 is increased to 57 per cent at the expense of each of the lipids (phospholipid, 20 %; cholesterol ester, 12 %; cholesterol, 3 %; and triglyceride, 6 %). In more recent studies on composition, the availability of excellent gas chromatographic techniques for fatty acid analysis has permitted measurement of the fatty acid composition of the plasma lipoproteins (see, for example, Wood et al. [724] and Goodman and Shiratori [250]). Except for small amounts bound to the LDL and HDL fractions, all of the unesterified fatty acid is thought to be bound to albumin in a lipoprotein complex which is composed principally of protein (99 %). No definite structure can be assigned to the lipoproteins, but generally it is suggested that a central lipid core is surrounded by the more polar protein component and possibly by some phospholipid. Relatively stable lipoprotein particles result which range in size from 5000 Å for chylomicrons to about 100 Å for HDL. Recently a method has been developed for the fractionation of very low-density lipoproteins by angle-head preparative ultra-centrifugation [275] which may be of use in further studies on lipoproteins.

The formation of plasma lipoproteins of necessity must be discussed in relation to their role in lipid transport. A number of reviews consider the latter topic. [226, 445, 524, 521] Study with isotopically labeled lipids indicate that practically all lipids following their absorption enter the circulation by way of the lymph. The lipids are transported in the form of chylomicrons which appear to arise from the intestinal mucosa. Studies on the human chylomicron protein indicate that it is similar to that of plasma HDL on the basis of N-terminal amino acids (N-terminal aspartic acid for protein A and N-terminal serine for protein B), paper electrophoretic mobilities and "fingerprint patterns", [570] but experiments with C^{14}-labeled amino acids do not support the view that the protein of chylomicrons is derived from the HDL of plasma. Rodbell et al. [571] observed that, in the dog, labeled amino acid appeared more rapidly in the proteins (A and B) of the chylomicrons and HDL of lymph than in the HDL of plasma. After the chylomicrons entered the plasma, protein A rapidly equilibrated with the HDL of plasma while protein B seemed to disappear parallel with the chylomicrons and then reappear in a small pool of soluble lipoprotein. The triglycerides of chylomicrons probably arise in the intestinal mucosa either by absorption of the intact lipid or by synthesis as described in Part A. The evidence favors the view that much of the triglyceride is normally hydrolyzed to a mixture of free fatty acids, mono- and diglycerides before absorption, and that the active synthetic systems in the intestinal mucosa utilize these absorbed products as precursors for triglyceride synthesis. While it is possible that the other lipids (cholesterol and phospholipid) are derived from exogenous sources, there is good evidence that both cholesterol [256] and phospholipid [588] may be synthesized in significant amounts in the intestinal mucosa.

The more recent evidence has confirmed the view that the protein for chylomicrons is formed in the intestinal mucosa. Thus, it may be concluded that synthesis of all components of the chylomicron may go on within the epithelial cell of the intestinal mucosa (for a recent review on all aspects of the intestinal absorption of fats including chylomicron formation see Senior [601]). In two independent *in vitro* studies [349, 296] using intact cell preparations from the intestinal mucosa of rats previously fed olive oil, it has been shown that C^{14}-leucine is incorporated into the protein of chylomicrons isolated from these preparations and that the inhibitor of protein synthesis, puromycin will prevent this incorporation. Sabesin *et al.* [592] have investigated the effect of *in vivo* administration of puromycin on intestinal fat absorption. These workers observed that puromycin caused accumulation of fat in the jejunal cells with little appearing in the lymphatics. Compared to an untreated animal the serum triglyceride levels were reduced to one-tenth of normal. All these observations are consistent with the interpretation that active synthesis of chylomicron protein must go on in the intestinal mucosa and that the elaboration of this protein is vital to the formation and release of chylomicrons into the lymphatics.

Concerning the lipids present in chylomicrons, mention should be made of the recent detailed *in vivo* studies on fatty acid esterification and chylomicron formation carried on by Goodman's groups. [362, 710, 709] It is rather striking that the general pattern of fatty acid esterification for the lipids in chylomicrons fits the specificity pattern already noted for the esterification steps described in earlier sections on the biosynthesis of the individual lipids. Thus, chylomicron cholesterol ester formation showed marked specificity towards oleic acid, chylomicron triglyceride ester formation showed almost complete randomization towards fatty acids and lecithin ester formation showed definite specificity with saturated fatty acid going into the α'-position and unsaturated fatty acid to the β-position. It is also significant that, in each instance, appreciable quantities of fatty acids arose from endogenous sources.

The origin of the HDL fraction (α-lipoproteins) is briefly considered now because of the possible close relationship between its protein moiety and that of the chylomicron. In fact, it has been noted that after the chylomicrons reach the plasma, the protein moiety can readily interchange with the protein portion of HDL. On this basis it seems that some of the HDL of plasma may arise from that of the lymph which is derived mainly from the intestinal mucosa. In addition, there is good evidence that HDL may be formed in the liver. Radding *et al.* [551, 552] observed the incorporation of labeled amino acids into the lipoproteins (including HDL) of serum that had been incubated with slices of rat liver. Marsh and Whereat [482] indicated that preliminary experiments with an antiserum against HDL suggested that the liver could synthesize the protein of HDL. Several later reports have now provided convincing evidence that HDL is formed by liver. Thus, Haft et al. [277] demonstrated amino acid incorporation into both high- and low-density lysoproteins of perfused liver. Marsh [480] has succeeded in obtaining cell-free preparations from rat liver which are capable of forming both types of lipoproteins. As might be expected microsomes were most active, but it is noteworthy that mitochondria possessed a weak capacity for forming lipoproteins. The lipoproteins formed were shown to be those of plasma and not of tissue on the basis of specific antisera and a modified "fingerprint" study. Robinson and Seakins [568] have provided very convincing evidence of the vital role played by liver. They observed that the administration of puromycin to rats caused a reduction of plasma lipids and the occurrence of a fatty liver. Slices from livers of puromycin-treated animals showed reduced incorporation of C^{14} leucine into high- and low-density lipoproteins.

Although there may be some uncertainty as to whether interconversions occur between the HDL (α-) and the LDF (β-), most of the evidence [226, 524] favors little interconversion. This finding fits well with the observation that the protein component of HDL (with N-terminal aspartic acid and C-terminal threonine) differs from that of the LDF (predominantly N-terminal glutamic acid at low S_f but at higher flotation rates, the amounts of N-terminal serine, threonine and aspartic acid increase). As noted by Oncley [523, 521] and Frederickson et al. [226, 227] the lipid moieties do exchange or interconvert among the lipoproteins more readily than the protein portion. However, most rapid interconversion appears to be from the chylomicrons to HDL where interconversion of protein also occurs. It has been suggested that HDL functions only in the transport of lipid from the intestine to the liver. [524]

The low-density lipoproteins or β-lipoproteins represent a more heterogeneous group in which some differences in the terminal groups of the protein moiety are noted, but the whole group appears to be immunochemically indistinguishable. The latter characteristic has formed the basis of demonstrating net synthesis of low-density lipoproteins by rat liver slices. [482] Goat antiserum against the low-density lipoproteins isolated from rat plasma was used to precipitate the low-density lipoproteins produced by the liver slices. It was found that 70 μg of lipoprotein-protein and 20 μg of lipoprotein-cholesterol could be synthesized per gram of tissue per hour. In perfusion experiments 125 μg of low-density lipoprotein was formed per gram per hour. Olson et al. [524] has also reported evidence to support the view that the low density or β-lipoproteins are formed in the liver. Convincing support also comes from studies cited earlier for high-density lipoproteins. Evidence cited by Olson and Vester [524] indicates that the low-density lipoproteins with higher flotation rates (S_f 15–400) give rise to the fractions with lower flotation rates (S_f 3–15). The half-life for these different fractions (8–12 hr for S_f 15–400 and 3–4 days for S_f 3–9) suggested that the β-lipoprotein does not recycle or exchange with newly formed peptide in the liver. This observation contrasts with that for the lipid moieties which seem to exchange readily. There are many experiments which indicate that plasma cholesterol and phospholipid may be derived by synthesis in the liver. [735] On the basis of turnover of the individual lipids it has been suggested that low-density lipoproteins retain their phospholipid, cholesterol and cholesterol ester in the transport of other lipids such as triglyceride from the liver to the storage depots. [524]

Brief mention should be made of the enzyme system referred to as lipoprotein lipase by Korn [407, 409] and extensively reviewed by Robinson. [566] This enzyme is believed to be responsible for the hydrolysis of triglyceride contained in the chylomicrons and low-density lipoproteins. [567, 409, 226, 89, 74] The fatty acids, derived by action of this enzyme both in plasma and in adipose tissue, are thought to be bound to albumin until their removal for utilization by tissues. Bragdon and Gordon [90] have reported that radioactivity readily appears in tissues following the intravenous injection of either C^{14}-labeled unesterified fatty acids bound to albumin or C^{14}-labeled chylomicrons. A later report by Havel et al. [300] summarizes some of the evidence indicating that there is a rapid turnover of free fatty acids and provides data showing that free fatty acids in the post absorptive state are the major fuel for muscle. Exercise increases the turnover and utilization of free fatty acids.

(b) Proteolipids and (c) Phosphatidopeptides

Folch and his colleagues have achieved the isolation of these two distinct complexes of protein and lipid. In 1951, Folch and Lees [221] described the extraction by chloroform-methanol (2:1) of fractions containing peptide and lipid which were referred to as *proteolipids* because of their insolubility in water. The proteolipids were found to occur in both white and grey matter, heart muscle, kidney, liver, lung, skeletal and smooth muscle. None are apparently present in blood and only very little in the myelin of peripheral nerve. [211, 222, 219] This latter observation has posed a difficulty in classifying proteolipids as part of the "myelin lipids". Folch-Pi [219] has commented on this problem and, using data of Amaducci, has indicated that the best correlation appears to exist between proteolipid content and the sum total of axon circumferences.

The crude proteolipid fraction, which is obtained as a fluffy white layer at the interphase created by the layering of chloroform–methanol extract below water, has been fractionated to yield three proteolipids, A, B and C. [221] These were obtained from the fluffy layer essentially by cold temperature precipitation following the addition of methanol (proteolipid A), acetone (proteolipid B) and precipitation by ethanol from a chloroform solution of the residue (proteolipid C). Proteolipid A consists of 20 per cent protein 65–75 per cent cerebrosides and 5–15 per cent phosphatides; proteolipid B, consists of 50 per cent protein, 20 per cent cerebrosides and 30 per cent phosphatides; proteolipid C consists of 70–75 per cent protein and the balance mainly phosphatides. It seems likely that these proteolipids are to some extent contaminated with free lipids since it has been possible more recently to obtain by an emulsion centrifugation procedure a preparation of concentrated proteolipid that contains little free lipid and yet accounts almost quantitatively for the proteolipids of brain white matter. [224, 219] Preparations obtained by this procedure are quite reproducible and appear to contain a minimum of 65 per cent protein with the remaining 35 per cent consisting of lipids containing phosphorus and carbohydrate. Lees et al. [436] have prepared a similar preparation of proteolipid from bovine brain white matter proteo-lipids by dialysis in organic solvents. The lipid moiety consists mainly of phospholipids with varying amounts of cerebrosides. The phospholipids consist of about one-half phosphatidyl serine, one-third phosphoinositides and small amounts of phosphatidyl ethanolamine and sphingomyelin. Only trace amounts of plasmalogen cholesterol and lecithin are present. [219] Webster and Folch [701] have observed that proteolipids are split readily by pH > 7.5 and by increasing ionic strengths. Folch-Pi [219] has used this evidence to suggest that proteolipids consist of a protein core covered by an outer layer of lipid molecules bound to each other and to the protein by noncovalent bonds.

The second lipid–protein complex, referred to as *phosphatidopeptide*, was obtained as a result of an investigation on the classical neurokeratin fraction. [216] The complex was originally obtained by extracting a beef brain trypsin-resistant protein residue, previously freed of all other lipids, with chloroform–methanol containing HCl (at least 0.03N). Sphingosine (or a sphingosine-like substance) inositol, phosphorus and nitrogen (2.4% as α-NH$_2$-nitrogen after acid hydrolysis) were all reported to be present. Inositol diphosphate was shown to account for much of the inositol and phosphorus. LeBaron and Rothleder [433] have described a modified procedure for the preparation of phosphatidopeptides which does not require trypsin digestion. In the procedure, the water-soluble materials and the lipids and proteolipids soluble in chloroform–methanol are exhaustively removed before extraction of the phosphatidopeptides by chloroform–methanol (2:1) containing HCl (0.04N). The presence of phosphatidopeptides has been demonstrated in a wide variety of tissues. [342, 233]

LeBaron and his colleagues [431, 429] have extensively studied the protein-bound phosphoinositides (including those in phosphatidopeptide and those in proteolipid). The major lipid involved appears to be triphosphoinositide.

It was found that practically all phosphoinositide could be dissociated from protein by using a sufficiently non-polar acidified solvent for the extraction. LeBaron[429] suggests that the data obtained are consistent with the view that phosphoinositide-protein complexes exist *in situ* and that the principal bonding is electrostatic. This arrangement might mean that it would be possible for lipid and protein components to be synthesized separately before being brought together to form the above complexes.

Andrade and Huggins [7, 8] have extended the work on the "phosphatido–peptide fraction" originally obtained using the extraction method of Le Baron and Folch. Andrade and Huggins on the basis of a series of chemical studies conclude that this fraction should more properly be called a phosphoinositide complex. Evidence was also obtained that the phosphoinositide portion was a mixture of mono-, di- and triphosphoinositides.

Little is known concerning the details of formation of proteolipids or phosphatidopeptides. It seems probable that the constituent lipids and proteins are synthesized by the normal pathways and that they combine in some unknown manner to form a lipid–protein complex. Most studies on the formation of these lipid–protein complexes have given results consistent with this suggestion.

A number of reports have appeared on the incorporation into proteolipid of either a labeled amino acid or a labeled precursor of some part of the lipid component. Studies by Giatonde [232, 233] on the incorporation of S^{35}-labeled methionine and cysteine and by Davison [164] on the incorporation of glycine-1-C^{14} into the proteolipids of the brain of young rats show that there is active incorporation at this stage, but the degree of incorporation is much less than into either protein generally or into phosphatidopeptide. Davison has found that glycine-1-C^{14} is much more slowly incorporated into adult brain thus suggesting its relative metabolic inertness. The latter is a pattern that Davison has observed for myelin lipids. Gaitonde [233] has noted a similar pattern for labeling from P_i^{32}. This observation seems to be at variance with LeBaron et al. [431] who have observed both active and approximately equal *in vivo* incorporation of P_i^{32} into the proteolipids and phosphatidopeptides. The incorporation of P_i^{32} into these fractions is greater than into the total lipid fraction and fits with the view that the P_i^{32} is being incorporated into di- and triphosphoinositides by way of ATP^{32} as described in reactions 29 and 30.

Mokrasch and Manner [498] have recently investigated proteolipid biosynthesis using brain slices from young 30-day-old rats. They provide evidence that these slices were capable of genuine incorporation of C^{14}-amino acids into the protein portion and C^{14}-palmitate into the lipid portion of proteolipid. Support for this contention was provided by the observed inhibitions caused by inhibitors of protein synthesis in the case of C^{14}-amino acid incorporation and by stimulation of incorporation of C^{14} palmitate caused by cofactors known to be involved in lipid synthesis. Both of these observations lend support to the earlier suggestion that the protein and lipid components may be formed first before complexing.

Gaitonde, [233] coincident with his later studies on amino acid incorporation into proteolipid, has measured the incorporation of S^{35}-labeled methionine and cysteine into the peptide portion of phosphatidopeptide. The incorporation has, in general, been comparable in amount to that incorporated into the protein residue. Based on Gaitonde's evidence all components of the phosphatidopeptide fraction appear to be metabolically quite active. A number of earlier studies on the incorporation of P_i^{32} into the phosphorus compounds of brain, [639, 170, 209, 316] summarized by Folch-Pi and Le-Baron, [218] have suggested that the phosphate moiety of phosphatidopeptide is labeled rapidly. Huggins and Cohn [342] have isolated a phosphatidopeptide (containing inositol, glycerol, phosphate, fatty acids, sphingosine or sphingosine-like material and amino acids) from kidney cortex which has been shown to be actively labeled by P_i^{32}. Also, LeBaron et al. [432, 431] have reported that in vivo the rat more readily incorporates P_i^{32} into the phosphatidopeptide phosphorus than the phospholipid phosphorus. It was found that much of this label was present in an inositol phosphate which appeared to be more highly phosphorylated than inositol monophosphate. Confirmation of the fact that phosphatidopeptide contains metabolically active di- and triphosphoinositides is provided by Andrade and Huggins [7, 8] in their work on the phosphoinositide complex of kidney. In unpublished results, Thompson has observed that the labeling from P_i^{32} of a fraction similar to that of phosphatidopeptide in homogenates of adult rat brain requires the addition of ATP. The labeling of this fraction relative to the labeling of the inositol phosphatide fraction isolated with the total lipids was appreciably greater from P_i^{32} than from α-GP^{32}. The much lower relative labeling from α-GP^{32} and the observations that tritium-inositol only weakly labels the phosphatidopeptide fraction in rats by the time they are 20 days old [1] suggest that a portion of the lipid consisting of one phosphorus, glycerol and inositol may be relatively inert metabolically and that a second portion may exist in which the phosphorus is actively labeled through exchange or net synthesis.

SUMMARY AND CONCLUSIONS

The various lipids discussed are found to occur widely in nature. There is increasing evidence that the lipids play important roles in the overall maintenance and integrity of cells. The triglycerides are important storage forms for fuel; the waxes (higher alcohol esters) form necessary outer protective coatings for a variety of plants and animal organisms. As summarized by Rossiter and Strickland [588] the phosphoglycerides are now implicated in a variety of functions. This group of phosphatides may be involved in important functions of the cell such as protein synthesis and secretion. Certain of the phosphoglycerides appear to be concerned in some way with fat absorption, fat transport and normal blood coagulation. There is much evidence indicating the importance of the phosphoglycerides, sphingolipids and complex lipids in cellular structure (e.g. membranes, myelin sheath, etc.). As important constituents of the membranes of cells and their intracellular components (mitochondrion, endoplasmic reticulum, nucleus) these lipids play essential roles in relation to the metabolic processes carried on by cellular structures. These processes include anabolic and catabolic pathways, oxidation and reduction multienzyme systems and ion transport mechanisms. The importance of the plasma lipoproteins in fat transport is now well established.

For a full understanding of the biological importance of these lipids it is, of course, essential to know as much as possible about the metabolism of these compounds. That is, we should know the pathways whereby lipids are degraded and synthesized within cells. Much information is available on the degradation of lipids and has been summarized in recent reviews by Borgström, [74] Kates [366] and Van Deenen. [678] The pathways of biosynthesis for the lipids are described in this chapter. In order to establish the dynamic state of the lipids in nature both the catabolic and anabolic aspects of metabolism are important and, therefore, it is essential to keep in mind the counterpart of each aspect when it is considered in a separate treatise.

With the availability of recent techniques (tracer, chromatography) it has become possible to obtain a considerable amount of information with regard to the biosynthesis of a number of the individual lipids. Both *in vivo* and *in vitro* studies with constituent parts bearing isotopic label reveal that these appear in the appropriate portion of the lipid. Extension of these studies, using a variety of precursors ranging in complexity from the simple constituent parts up to but not including the complete lipid, has resulted in the elucidation of pathways of synthesis for the triglycerides, and a number of the phosphoglycerides and sphingolipids.

Pathways of synthesis of some of the constituent parts have been described. It is well established that fatty acids, in most instances, are formed by a pathway not involving the reversal of fatty acid oxidation. The synthetic pathway involves the formation of malonyl CoA from acetyl CoA and CO_2. The malonyl CoA then participates in reaction with acyl groups (C_2 to C_{14} in length) attached to a special carrier protein to form an acyl carrier protein two carbon atoms longer. Acyl groups of C_{16} or C_{18} in length are then released as free acids. Both glycerol and inositol seem to be mainly derived from a carbohydrate source such as glucose. The nitrogenous bases arise from the amino acids of protein or, as in the case of serine, the carbon atoms may come from carbohydrate by way of 3-phosphoglyceric acid. There is evidence that choline arises by the methylation of ethanolamine and that the latter is formed by decarboxylation of serine.

It has been found that phosphatidic acid, which is synthesized from

L-α-glycerophosphate by esterification of the free hydroxyls with fatty acyl CoA, is an essential precursor for the formation of D-α,β-diglycerides. The latter are either acylated by a third fatty acyl CoA to form triglyceride or undergo reaction with cytidine diphosphate choline and cytidine diphosphate ethanolamine to form the two phosphoglycerides, phosphatidyl choline (lecithin) and phosphatidyl ethanolamine. The novel cytidine compounds are formed by reaction of cytidine triphosphate with phosphoryl choline and phosphoryl ethanolamine. The plasmalogens of choline and ethanolamine seem to be formed by pathways analogous to those for the phosphatidyl compounds. In these instances, "plasmalogenic" diglycerides react with cytidine diphosphate choline and cytidine diphosphate ethanolamine. There are a number of experiments which strongly suggest that some synthesis of phosphoglyceride may occur in which the nitrogenous bases are either exchanged or synthesized on the intact lipid.

Further involvement of both phosphatidic acid and the cytidine nucleotides has been shown in the synthesis of phosphatidyl glycerol and phosphatidyl inositol (monophosphoinositide). The evidence suggests that phosphatidic acid and cytidine triphosphate react to form cytidine diphosphate diglyceride. This latter compound on further reaction with α-glycerophosphate and subsequent dephosphorylation yields phosphatidyl glycerol. Alternatively, cytidine diphosphate diglyceride may enter into reaction with inositol to form phosphatidyl inositol. It seems likely that the phosphatidyl glycerol and phosphatidyl inositol might be utilized in the formation of more complex structures such as cardiolipin and di- and tri-phosphoinositide, respectively.

The pathways of biological synthesis of the sphingolipids are not as well worked out as those for the triglycerides and the phosphoglycerides. Considerable information is known about the synthesis of sphingomyelin. Sphingosine is formed from palmitic aldehyde and serine. Acylation by the appropriate fatty acyl CoA derivative can yield ceramide (N-acyl sphingosine) which is known to react with cytidine diphosphate choline, to form sphingomyelin. Alternatively sphingosine may combine with uridine diphosphate galactose to form psychosine (galactosylsphingosine) which can react with a suitable fatty acyl CoA to form cerebroside. Sulfatide (cerebroside sulfate) may arise by sulfurylation from "active" sulfate (3'-phospho-adenosine-5'-phosphosulfate). It is possible that the more complex gangliosides are formed from cerebroside (or its constituents) and uridine nucleotide derivatives of galactose and possibly galactosamine with N-acetyl neuraminic acid, a characteristic component of these lipids, being provided via its CMP-derivative. There is evidence that N-acetyl neuraminic acid is synthesized by reaction between N-acetyl mannosamine-6-phosphate and phosphoenol-pyruvate and subsequent dephosphorylation of the 9-phosphate that is formed.

Little detailed information is known about the formation of the complex lipids (lipoproteins, proteolipids and phosphatidopeptides) of tissues. A portion of the phosphate (thought to be associated with an inositol di- or tri-phosphate) of phosphatidopeptides has been found to be readily labeled from P_i^{32} in actively metabolizing systems. Precursors of phosphatidyl inositol (e.g. L-α-glycerophosphate and inositol) seem to be more slowly incorporated. Some information is available on the origin of the plasma lipoproteins. It is believed that the constituents of the chylomicrons are synthesized in the intestinal mucosa. Some of the high density or α-lipoproteins may arise from chylomicrons and the remainder from the liver. The low density or β-lipoproteins appear to be formed by the liver.

There is evidence that a wide variety of organisms can carry on the synthesis of lipids. Thus, microorganisms carry on the synthesis of a variety of lipids peculiar to them; plants seem to be capable of forming most of the classical lipids, but here again the lipids may show certain characteristics peculiar to the source. This has been proven more and more by the constant appearance in the literature of new types of lipids which in some instances are briefly referred to in the text or have not been considered at all because little or nothing is known concerning their biosynthesis. A good example of the latter situation is the diether analogue of phosphatidyl glycerophosphate found by Kates et al. [367] to be peculiar to *Halobacterium cutirubrum*. Kates has speculated that a diether analogue of CDP-diglyceride may be involved in the biosynthetic pathway. Most of the cells of animals are capable of synthesizing triglycerides, phosphoglycerides, sphingolipids and protein lipid complexes. In some instances the synthesis may become very slow after the initial synthesis occurs. This seems to be especially true for the lipid-forming permanent structures within the cell and is perhaps best illustrated by experiments on the labeling of the phospholipid components of myelin from C^{14}-serine, C^{14}-glycerol or P_i^{32} where the results suggest that the constituent phospholipids become almost metabolically inert after their initial synthesis during myelin formation. [165, 166, 167] If these observations are confirmed for other tissues, it would seem that the original dynamic concept of Schoenheimer [599] will need to be modified to the view that within a class of compounds such as the lipids (or the proteins and carbohydrates) there may be certain ones which are almost inert metabolically after their initial formation during growth. It is likely that these inert compounds would be confined to the more permanent structural parts of cells of organs.

REFERENCES

1. AGRANOFF, B. W. In *The Neurochemistry of Nucleotides and Amino Acids*, edited by R. O. Brady and D. B. Tower, John Wiley, New York, 1960, p. 38.
2. AGRANOFF, B. W., BRADLEY, R. M. and BRADY, R. O. *J. Biol. Chem.* **233**, 1077 (1958).
3. AILHAUD, G., SAMUEL, D. and DESNUELLE, P. *Biochim. Biophys. Acta*, **67**, 150 (1963).
4. AILHAUD, G., SAMUEL, D., LAZDUNSKI, M. and DESNUELLE, P. *Biochim. Biophys. Acta* **84**, 643 (1964).
5. ALBERTS, A. W., GOLDMAN, P. and VAGELOS, P. R. *J. Biol. Chem.* **238**, 557 (1963).

6. ALBERTS, A. W., MAJERUS, P. W., TALAMO, B. and VAGELOS, P. R. *Biochemsitry* **3**, 1563 (1964).
7. ANDRADE, F. and HUGGINS, C. G. *Biochim. Biophys. Acta* **84**, 98 (1964).
8. ANDRADE, F. and HUGGINS, C. G. *Biochim. Biophys. Acta* **84**, 681 (1964).
9. ANFINSEN, C. B. In *Fat Metabolism*, edited by V. A. Najjar. The Johns Hopkins Press, Baltimore, 1954, p. 93.
10. ANFINSEN, C. B., JR., *Federation Proc.* **15**, 894 (1956).
11. ANKER, H. S. *J. Biol. Chem.* **194**, 177 (1952).
12. ANSELL, G. B. and BAYLISS, B. J. *Biochem. J.* **78**, 209 (1961).
13. ANSELL, G. B. and CHOJNACKI, T. *Nature* **196**, 545 (1962).
14. ANSELL, G. B. and DAWSON, R. M. C. *Biochem. J.* **50**, 241 (1952).
15. ANSELL, G. B. and HAWTHORNE, J. N. *Phospholipids*, Elsevier Publishing Co., Amsterdam, 1964.
16. ANSELL, G. B. and SPANNER, S. *J. Neurochem.* **4**, 325 (1959).
17. ANSELL, G. B. and SPANNER, S. *Biochem. J.* **88**, 56 (1963).
18. ARNSTEIN, H. R. V. *Biochem. J.* **48**, 27 (1951).
19. ARNSTEIN, H. R. V. and KEGLEVIĆ, D. *Biochem. J.* **62**, 199 (1956).
20. ARTOM, C. *Federation Proc.* **19**, 233 (1960).
21. ARTOM, C. In *Phosphorus Metabolism*, edited by W. D. McElroy and B. Glass. Johns Hopkins Press, Baltimore, 1952, vol. 2, p. 203.
22. ARTOM, C. and LOFLAND, H. B. *Biochem. Biophys. Res. Communs.* **3**, 244 (1960).
23. ARTOM, C. and WAINER, A. *Fed. Proc.* **22**, 415 (1963).
24. ASSELINEAU, J. and BENNET, P. In *Metabolism and Physiological Significance of Lipids*, edited by R. M. C. Dawson and D. N. Rhodes. John Wiley, London, New York and Sydney, 1964, p. 111.
25. ASSELINEAU, J. and LEDERER, E. In *Lipide Metabolism*, edited by K. Bloch. John Wiley, New York, 1960, p. 337.
26. BADDILEY, J., BUCHANAN, J. G., CARSS, B. and MATHIAS, A. P. *Biochim. Biophys. Acta* **21**, 191 (1956).
27. BADDILEY, J., BUCHANAN, J. G. CARSS, B., MATHIAS, A. P. and SANDERSON, A. R. *Biochem. J.* **64**, 599 (1956).
28. BAER, E. *Can. J. Biochem. and Physiol.* **34**, 288 (1956).
29. BALLOU, C. E. Abstracts *Sixth International Congress of Biochemistry*, New York, 1964, p. 547.
30. BALLOU, C. E. *Biochemistry* **3**, 682 (1964).
31. BALLOU, C. E. *Biochemistry* **3**, 976 (1964).
32. BALLOU, C. E. and PIZER, L. I. *J. Am. Chem. Soc.* **81**, 4745 (1959).
33. BALLOU, C. E. and PIZER, L. I. *J. Am. Chem. Soc.* **82**, 3333 (1960).
34. BALLOU, C. E., VILKAS, E. and LEDERER, E. *J. Biol. Chem.* **238**, 69 (1963).
35. BARANOWSKI, T. *J. Biol. Chem.* **180**, 535 (1949).
36. BARKER, H. A. In *Phosphorus Metabolism*, edited by W. D. McElroy and B. Glass. Johns Hopkins Press, Baltimore, 1951, vol. 1, p. 204.
37. BARKER, H. A. *Bacterial Fermentations*, John Wiley, New York, 1956, p. 28.
38. BARKER, H. A., KAMEN, M. D. and BORNSTEIN, B. T. *Proc. Natl. Acad. Sci. U.S.* **31**, 373 (1945).
39. BARKER, H. A. and LIPMANN, F. *J. Biol. Chem.* **179**, 247 (1949).
40. BARRON, E. J., SQUIRES, C. and STUMPF, P. K. *J. Biol. Chem.* **236**, 2610 (1961).
41. BAR-TANA, J. and SHAPIRO, B. *Biochem. J.* **93**, 533 (1964).
42. BARRON, E. J., SQUIRES, C. and STUMPF, P. K. *J. Biol. Chem.* **236**, 2610 (1961).
43. BAUMAN, N. A., HAGEN, P. O. and GOLDFINE, H. *J. Biol. Chem.* **240**, 43 (1965).
44. BELFRAGE, P. *Biochem. J.* **92**, 41P (1964).
45. BENNET, J. R. *Biochim. Biophys. Acta* **70**, 465 (1963).
46. BENSON, A. A. In *Advances in Lipid Research*, edited by R. Paoletti and D. Kritchevsky. Academic Press, New York and London, 1963, vol. 1, p. 387.
47. BENSON, A. A. and MARUO, B. *Biochim. Biophys. Acta* **27**, 189 (1958).
48. BENSON, A. A., DANIEL, H. and WISER, R. *Proc. Natl. Acad. Sci. U.S.* **45**, 1582 (1959).
49. BENSON, A. A. and STRICKLAND, E. H. *Biochim. Biophys. Acta* **41**, 328 (1960).

50. BENSON, A. A., WISER, R., FERRARI, R. A. and MILLER, J. A. *J. Am. Chem. Soc.* **80**, 4740 (1948).
51. BERG, P. *J. Biol. Chem.* **222**, 991 (1956).
52. BERGER, L. and GIMENEZ, W. T. *Science*, **124**, 81 (1956).
53. BERGSTRÖM, S. and BORGSTRÖM, B. In *Progress in the Chemistry of Fats and other Lipids*, edited by R. T. Holman, W. O. Lunberg and T. Malkin. Pergamon Press, London and New York, 1955, vol. 3, p. 351.
54. BERNHARD, K., VONBULOW-KOSTER, J. and WAGNER, H. *Helv. Chim. Acta* **42**, 152 (1959).
55. BERRY, J. F. and MCMURRAY, W. C., *Can. J. Biochem. and Physiol.* **35**, 799 (1957).
56. BERRY, J. F., MCPHERSON, C. and ROSSITER, R. J. *J. Neurochem.* **3**, 65 (1958).
57. BLAKLEY, R. L. *Biochem. J.* **77**, 459 (1960).
58. BLIX, G. *Z. physiol. Chem.*, Hoppe-Seyler's, **219**, 82 (1933).
59. BLIX, G. *Z. physiol. Chem.*, Hoppe-Seyler's, **240**, 43 (1936).
60. BLIX, G. *Skand. Arch. Physiol.* **80**, 46 (1938).
61. BLIX, G., GOTTSCHALK, A. and KLENK, E. *Nature (London)* **179**, 1088 (1957).
62. BLOCH, K. In *The Control of Lipid Metabolism*, edited by J. K. Grant. Academic Press, London and New York, 1963, p. 1.
63. BLOCH, K. *Physiol. Revs.* **27**, 574 (1947).
64. BLOCH, K. *Cold Spr. Harb. Symp. Quant. Biol.* **13**, 29 (1948).
65. BLOCH, K. *Ann. Rev. Biochem.* **21**, 273 (1952).
66. BLOCH, K. *Lipide Metabolism*, John Wiley, New York and London, 1960.
67. BLOOMFIELD, D. K. and BLOCH, K. *Biochim. Biophys. Acta* **30**, 220 (1958).
68. BLOOMFIELD, D. K. and BLOCH, K. *J. Biol. Chem.* **235**, 337 (1960).
69. BLOOR, W. R. *Biochemistry of the Fatty Acids and Their Compounds, The Lipids*. Reinhold Publishing Corp., New York (1943).
70. BOGOCH, S. *Biochem. J.* **68**, 319 (1958).
71. BORGSTRÖM, B. *Acta Physiol. Scand.* **25**, 328 (1952).
72. BORGSTRÖM, B. *Acta Chem. Scand.* **7**, 557 (1953).
73. BORGSTRÖM, B. *Acta Physiol. Scand.* **30**, 231 (1954).
74. BORGSTRÖM, B. In *Lipide Metabolism*, edited by K. Bloch. John Wiley, New York, 1960, p. 128.
75. BORKENHAGEN, L. F. and KENNEDY, E. P. *J. Biol. Chem.* **227**, 951 (1957).
76. BORKENHAGEN, L. F. and KENNEDY, E. P. *Biochim. Biophys. Acta* **28**, 222 (1958).
77. BORKENHAGEN, L. F. and KENNEDY, E. P. *J. Biol. Chem.* **234**, 849 (1959).
78. BORKENHAGEN, L. F., KENNEDY, E. P. and FIELDING, L. *J. Biol. Chem.* **236**, PC28 (1961).
79. BRADBEER, C. and STUMPF, P. K. *J. Lipid Res.* **1**, 214 (1960).
80. BRADY, R. O. *Proc. Natl. Acad. Sci. U.S.* **44**, 993 (1958).
81. BRADY, R. O. *J. Biol. Chem.* **235**, 3099 (1960).
82. BRADY, R. O. *J. Biol. Chem.* **237**, PC2416 (1961).
83. BRADY, R. O. In *Metabolism and Physiological Significance of Lipids*, edited by R. M. C. Dawson and D. N. Rhodes. John Wiley, London and New York, 1964, p. 95
84. BRADY, R. O., BRADLEY, R. M. and TRAMS, E. G. *J. Biol. Chem.* **235**, 3093 (1960).
85. BRADY, R. O., FORMICA, J. V. and KOVAL, G. J. *J. Biol. Chem.* **233**, 1072 (1958).
86. BRADY, R. O. and GURIN, S. *J. Biol. Chem.* **199**, 421 (1952).
87. BRADY, R. O. and KOVAL, G. J. *J. Biol. Chem.* **233**, 26 (1958).
88. BRADY, R. O., MAMOON, A. M. and STADTMAN, E. R. *J. Biol. Chem.* **222**, 795 (1956).
89. BRAGDON, J. H. In *The Lipoproteins Methods and Clinical Significance*, edited by F. Hamburger and P. Bernfeld, S. Karger, Baseland, New York, 1958, p. 37.
90. BRAGDON, J. H. and GORDON, R. S., JR. *J. Clin. Invest.* **37**, 574 (1958).
91. BRANTE, G. *Acta Physiol. Scand.* **18**, Suppl. 63, 14 (1949).
92. BREMER, J., FIGARD, P. H. and GREENBERG, D. M. *Biochim. Biophys. Acta* **43**, 477 (1960).
93. BREMER, J. and GREENBERG, D. M. *Biochim. Biophys. Acta* **35**, 287 (1959).
94. BREMER, J. and GREENBERG, D. M. *Biochim. Biophys. Acta* **37**, 173 (1960).
95. BREMER, J. and GREENBERG, D. M. *Biochim. Biophys. Acta* **46**, 205 (1961).

96. BRESSLER, R. and WAKIL, S. J. *J. Biol. Chem.* **236**, 1643 (1961).
97. BRESSLER, R. and WAKIL, S. J. *J. Biol. Chem.* **237**, 1441 (1962).
98. BREUSCH, F. L. *Advances in Enzymol.* **8**, 343 (1948).
99. BROCKERHOFF, H. and BALLOU, C. E. *J. Biol. Chem.* **236**, 1907 (1961).
100. BROCKERHOFF, H. and BALLOU, C. E. *J. Biol. Chem.* **237**, 49 (1962).
101. BROCKERHOFF, H. and BALLOU, C. E. *J. Biol. Chem.* **237**, 1764 (1962).
102. BROCKERHOFF, H. and HANAHAN, D. J. *J. Am. Chem. Soc.* **81**, 2591 (1959).
103. BROWN, J. and JOHNSTON, J. M. *Biochim. Biophys. Acta* **84**, 264 (1964).
104. BROWN, J. and JOHNSTON, J. M. *Biochim. Biophys. Acta* **84**, 448 (1964).
105. BUBLITZ, C. and KENNEDY, E. P. *J. Biol. Chem.* **211**, 951 (1954).
106. BÜCHER, T. *Abstracts Sixth International Congress of Biochemistry*, New York, p. 491, 1964.
107. BUELL, G. C. and REISER, R. *J. Biol. Chem.* **234**, 217 (1959).
108. BURTON, R. M., GARCIA-BUNUEL, L., GOLDEN, M. and BALFOUR, Y. M. *Biochemistry* **2**, 580 (1963).
109. BURTON, R. M. In *The Neurochemistry of Nucleotides and Amino Acids*, edited by R. O. Brady and D. B. Tower. John Wiley, New York, 1960, p. 51.
110. BURTON, R. M., SODD, M. A. and BRADY, R. O. *J. Biol. Chem.* **233**, 1053 (1958).
111. BYRON, J. E., WOOD, W. A. and TREADWELL, C. R. *J. Biol. Chem.* **205**, 483 (1953).
112. CAMPAGNARI, F. and WEBSTER, L. T., JR. *J. Biol. Chem.* **238**, 1628 (1963); and *J. Biol. Chem.* **237**, 1050 (1962).
113. CARR, H. G., HAERLE, H. and EILER, J. J. *Biochim. Biophys. Acta* **70**, 205 (1963).
114. CARTER, H. E. and FUJINO, Y. *J. Biol. Chem.* **221**, 879 (1956).
115. CARTER, H. E., GALANOS, D. S. and FUJINO, Y. *Can. J. Biochem. Physiol.* **34**, 320 (1956).
116. CARTER, H. E., GALANOS, D. S., GIGG, R. H., LAW, J. H., NAKAYAWA, T., SMITH, D. B. and WEBER, E. J. *Federation Proc.* **16**, 817 (1957).
117. CARTER, H. E. and GREENWOOD, F. L. *J. Biol. Chem.* **199**, 283 (1952).
118. CARTER, H. E., HENDRY, R. A. and STANACEV, N. Z. *J. Lipid Res.* **2**, 223 (1961).
119. CARTER, H. E., SMITH, D. B. and JONES, O. N. *J. Biol. Chem.* **232**, 681 (1958).
120. CHAIKOFF, I. L. *Physiol. Revs.* **22**, 291 (1942).
121. CHAIKOFF, I. L. and ZILVERSMIT, D. B. *Advances in Biol. and Med. Phys.* **1**, 321 (1948).
122. CHARALAMPOUS, F. C. *J. Biol. Chem.* **225**, 595 (1957).
123. CHARGAFF, E. *Advances in Protein Chemistry* **1**, 1 (1944).
124. CHARGAFF, E. and KESTON, A. S. *J. Biol. Chem.* **134**, 515 (1940).
125. CHEFURKA, W. *Biochim. Biophys. Acta* **28**, 660 (1958).
126. CHEN, I-W. and CHARALAMPOUS, F. C. *J. Biol. Chem.* **239**, 1905 (1964).
127. CHOJNACKI, T. and KORZYBSKI, T. *Abstracts Sixth International Congress of Biochemistry*, New York, p. 568, 1964.
128. CHOJNACKI, T. and KORZYBSKI, T. *Acta Biochim. Polon.* **11**, 341 (1964).
129. CHRIST, E. J. and HÜLSMANN, W. C. *Biochim. Biophys. Acta* **60**, 72 (1962).
130. CHUNG, A. E. and LAW, J. H. *Biochemistry* **3**, 967 (1963).
131. CLARK, B. and HÜBSCHER, G. *Biochim. Biophys. Acta* **46**, 479 (1961).
132. CLARK, B. and HÜBSCHER, G. *Biophys. Acta* **70**, 43 (1963).
133. CLARK, B. and HÜBSCHER, G. *Nature*, **185**, 35 (1960).
134. CLARK, B. and HÜBSCHER, G. *Nature*, **195**, 599 (1962).
135. CLELAND, W. W. and KENNEDY, E. P. *Federation Proc.* **17**, 202 (1958).
136. CLELAND, W. W. and KENNEDY, E. P. *J. Biol. Chem.* **235**, 45 (1960).
137. COHEN, P. P. In *Chemistry of Lipides as related to Atherosclerosis*, edited by I. H. Page. C. Thomas (Publishers), Springfield, Ill., 1958, p. 95.
138. COLEMAN, M. H. In *Advances in Lipid Research*, vol. I, p. 2, edited by R. Paoletti and D. Kritchevsky. Academic Press, New York and London, 1963.
139. COLEMAN, R. and HÜBSCHER, G. *Biochim. Biophys. Acta* **56**, 479 (1962).
140. COLLINS, F. D. *Nature* **182**, 865 (1958).
141. COLLINS, F. D. *Biochem. J.* **72**, 281 (1959).
142. COLLINS, F. D. *Biochem. J.* **72**, 532 (1959).
143. COLLINS, F. D. *Nature*, **186**, 366 (1960).
144. COLLINS, F. D. *Nature*, **188**, 297 (1960).

145. Collins, F. D. *Biochem. Biophys. Res. Communs.* **9**, 289 (1962).
146. Collins, F. D. and Shotlander, V. L. *Biochem. J.* **79**, 316 (1961).
147. Collins, F. D. and Shotlander, V. L. *Biochem. J.* **79**, 321 (1961).
148. Collins, F. D. *Biochem. J.* **88**, 319 (1963).
149. Collins, F. D. *Biochem. J.* **89**, 177 (1963).
150. Colodzin, M. and Kennedy, E. P. *Fed. Proc.* **23**, 229 (1964).
151. Comb, D. G. and Roseman, S. *J. Am. Chem. Soc.* **80**, 497 (1958).
152. Comb, D. G. and Roseman, S. *J. Biol. Chem.* **235**, 2529 (1960).
153. Cook, W. H. and Martin, W. G. *Canad. J. Biochem. and Physiol.* **40**, 1273 (1962).
154. Cornforth, J. W. *J. Lipid Res.* **1**, 3 (1959).
155. Cornforth, J. W., Firth, M. E. and Gottschalk, A. *Biochem. J.* **68**, 57 (1958).
156. Creasey, W. A. *Biochim. Biophys. Acta* **64**, 559 (1962).
157. Crocken, B. J. and Nyc, J. F. *J. Biol. Chem.* **239**, 1727 (1964).
158. Cromwell, B. T. and Rennie, S. D. *Biochem. J.* **58**, 322 (1954).
159. Crowder, M. and Artom, C. *Federation Proc.* **11**, 199 (1952).
160. Daughaday, W. H., Larner, J. and Hartnett, C. *J. Biol. Chem.* **212**, 869 (1955).
161. Davidoff, D. and Korn, E. D. *J. Biol. Chem.* **238**, 3210 (1963).
162. Davidoff, F. F. and Korn, E. D. *Abstracts Sixth International Congress of Biochemistry, New York*, p. 570 (1964).
163. Davidoff, F. and Korn, E. D. *J. Biol. Chem.* **239**, 2496 (1964).
164. Davison, A. N. *Biochem. J.* **78**, 272 (1961).
165. Davison, A. N. and Dobbing, J. *Biochem. J.* **75**, 565 (1960).
166. Davison, A. N. and Dobbing, J. *Biochem. J.* **75**, 571 (1960).
167. Davison, A. N., Morgan, R. S., Wajda, M. and Payling Wright, G. *J. Neurochem.* **4**, 360 (1959).
168. Dawson, R. M. C. *Biochem. J.* **55**, 507 (1963).
169. Dawson, R. M. C. *Biochim. Biophys. Acta* **14**, 374 (1954).
170. Dawson, R. M. C. *Biochem. J.* **57**, 237 (1954).
171. Dawson, R. M. C. *Biochem. J.* **59**, 5 (1955).
172. Dawson, R. M. C. *Biochem. J.* **62**, 693 (1956).
173. Dawson, R. M. C. *Biol. Revs. Cambridge Phil. Soc.* **32**, 188 (1957).
174. Dawson, R. M. C. *Biochem. J.* **68**, 352 (1958).
175. Dawson, R. M. C. *Biochem. J.* **60**, 325 (1959).
176. Dawson, R. M. C. *Biochem. J.* **75**, 45 (1960).
177. Dawson, R. M. C. and Dittmer, J. C. *Biochem. J.* **76**, 42P (1960).
177a. Dawson, R. M. C. and Dittmer, J. C. *Biochem. J.* **81**, 540 (1961).
178. Dawson, R. M. C. and Rhodes, D. N. *Metabolism and Physiological Significance of Lipids*. John Wiley, London, New York and Sydney, 1964.
179. Dawson, R. M. C. and Thompson, W. *Biochem. J.* **91**, 244 (1964).
180. Debuch, H., *J. Neurochem.* **2**, 243 (1958).
181. Debuch, H. *Z. Physiol. Chem.*, Hoppe-Seyler's, **314**, 49 (1959).
182. DeHaas, G. H., Mulder, L. and VanDeenen, L. L. M. *Biochem. Biophys. Res. Communs.* **3**, 287 (1960).
183. DeKoning, A. J. *Nature*, **200**, 1211 (1963).
184. DeLalla, O. F. and Gofman, J. W. In *Methods of Biochemical Analysis*, edited by D. Glick. Interscience Publishers Inc., New York, 1954, vol. 1, p. 459.
185. Delwiche, C. C. and Bregoff, H. M. *J. Biol. Chem.* **233**, 430 (1958).
186. Desnuelle, P. and Constantin, J. M. *Biochim. Biophys. Acta* **9**, 531 (1952).
187. Deuel, H. J., Jr. *The Lipids*, Vol. 1, *Chemistry.* Interscience Publishers Inc., New York, 1951.
188. Deuel, H. J., Jr. *The Lipids, Their Chemistry and Biochemistry*, vol. 2, *Biochemistry, Digestion, Absorption, Transport and Storage.* Interscience Publishers, Inc. New York, 1955.
189. Deuel, H. J., Jr. *The Lipids, Their Chemistry and Biochemistry*, vol. 3, *Biosynthesis, Oxidation, Metabolism and Nutritional Value.* Interscience Publishers, New York, 1957.
190. Dils, R. R. and Hübscher, G. *Biochim. Biophys. Acta* **32**, 293 (1959).

191. DILS, R. R. and HÜBSCHER, G. *Biochem. J.* **73**, 26P (1959).
192. DILS, R. R. and HÜBSCHER, G. *Biochim. Biophys. Acta* **46**, 505 (1961).
193. DILS, R. and POPJÁK, G. *Biochem. J.* **83**, 41 (1962).
194. DITTMER, J. C. and DAWSON, R. M. C. *Biochim. Biophys. Acta* **40**, 379 (1960).
195. DITTMER, J. C. and DAWSON, R. M. C. *Biochem. J.* **81**, 535 (1961).
196. DONISCH, V. and ROSSITER, R. J. *Proc. Can. Fed. Biol. Soc.* **8**, 56 (1965).
197. DUTTON, H. J. and MOUNTS. T. L. *Abstracts Sixth International Congress of Biochemistry*, New York, p. 571, 1964.
198. DUVIGNEAUD, V., CHANDLER, J. P., SIMMONDS, S., MOYER, A. W. and COHN, M. *J. Biol. Chem.* **164**, 603 (1946).
199. EISENBERG, F., JR., BOLDEN, A. H. and LOEWUS, F. A. *Biochem. Biophys. Res. Communs.* **14**, 419 (1964).
200. ELLINGBOE, J. and KARNOVSKY, M. L. *Fed. Proc.* **24**, 477 (1965).
201. ELLIS, R. B. and HAWTHORNE, J. N. *Biochem. J.* **84**, 19P (1962).
202. ELWYN, D. A., WEISSBACH, A., HENRY, S. S. and SPRINSON, D. B. *J. Biol. Chem.* **213**, 281 (1955).
203. ERWIN, J. and BLOCH, K. In *Metabolism and Physiological Significance of Lipids*, p. 29, edited by R. M. C. Dawson and D. N. Rhodes. John Wiley, London, New York and Sydney, 1964.
204. ERWIN, J. and BLOCH, K. *Science* **143**, 1006 (1964).
205. ESTABROOK, R. W. and SACKTOR, B. *J. Biol. Chem.* **233**, 1014 (1958).
206. FAURE, M. and MORELEC-COULON, M. J. *Compt. rend.* **238**, 411 (1954).
207. FERNÁNDEZ-MORAN, H. In *Metabolism of the Nervous System*, edited by D. Richter. Pergamon Press, London (1957), p. 1.
208. FERNÁNDEZ-MORAN, H. and FINEAN, J. B. *J. Biophys. Biochem. Cytol.* **3**, 725 (1958).
209. FINDLAY, M., STRICKLAND, K. P. and ROSSITER, R. J. *Can. J. Biochem. and Physiol.* **32**, 504 (1954).
210. FINEAN, J. B. *Exptl. Cell Research, Suppl.* **5**, 18 (1958).
211. FINEAN, J. B., HAWTHORNE, J. N. and PATTERSON, J. D. E. *J. Neurochem.* **1**, 256 (1957).
212. FINEAN, J. B. and ROBERTSON, J. D. *British Med. Bull.* **14**, 267 (1958).
213. FLAVIN, M. and OCHOA, S. *J. Biol. Chem.* **229**, 965 (1957).
214. FOLCH, J. *Federation Proc.* **5**, 134 (1946).
215. FOLCH, J. *J. Biol. Chem.* **177**, 505 (1949).
216. FOLCH, J. In *Phosphorus Metabolism*, edited by W. D. McElroy and B. Glass. The Johns Hopkins Press, Baltimore, 1952, vol. 2, p. 186.
217. FOLCH, J., ARSOVE, S. and MEATH, J. A. *J. Biol. Chem.* **191**, 819 (1951).
218. FOLCH, J. and LeBARON, F. N. *Can. J. Biochem. and Physiol.* **34**, 305 (1956).
219. FOLCH-PI, J. In *Brain Lipids and Lipoproteins and the Leucodystrophies*, p. 18, edited by J. Folch-Pi and H. Bauer. Elsevier Publishing, Amsterdam, London and New York, 1963.
220. FOLCH-PI, J. and LeBARON, F. N. In *Fourth Intern. Cong. Biochem. Biochemistry of the Central Nervous System*, edited by J. Brücke. Pergamon Press, London, 1959, vol. 3, p. 157.
221. FOLCH, J. and LEES, M. *J. Biol. Chem.* **191**, 807 (1951).
222. FOLCH, J., LEES, M. and CARR, S. *Exptl. Cell Research, Suppl.* **5**, 58 (1958).
223. FOLCH, J., MEATH, J. A. and BOGOCH, S. *Federation Proc.* **15**, 254 (1956).
224. FOLCH, J., WEBSTER, G. R. and LEES, M. *Federation Proc.* **18**, 228 (1959).
225. FREDERICKSON, D. S. *J. Biol. Chem.* **222**, 109 (1956).
226. FREDERICKSON, D. S. and GORDON, R. S., JR. *Physiol. Revs.* **38**, 585 (1958).
227. FREDERICKSON, D. S., McCOLLESTER, D. L., HAVEL, R. J. and ONO, K. In *Chemistry of Lipides as related to Atherosclerosis*, edited by I. H. Page. Charles C. Thomas (Publisher), Springfield, Ill., 1958, p. 205.
228. FREINKEL, N. and DAWSON, R. M. C. *Biochem. J.* **81**, 250 (1961).
229. FRIEDKIN, M. and LEHNINGER, A. L. *J. Biol. Chem.* **177**, 775 (1949).
230. FROSOLONO, M. F., ANDERSON, C. E. and PIANTADOSI, C. *Fed. Proc.* **24**, 497 (1965).
231. FULCO, A. J. and BLOCH, K. *J. Biol. Chem.* **239**, 993 (1964).
232. GAITONDE, M. K. *Biochem. J.* **80**, 277 (1961).

H

194 K. P. STRICKLAND

233. GAITONDE, M. K. In *Comparative Neurochemistry*, p. 117, edited by D. Richter. Pergamon Press, Oxford, 1964, p. 117.
234. GALANOUS, D. S. and KOUPALAS, V. M. *Biochim. Biophys. Acta* **98**, 252 (1965).
235. GALANOUS, D. S. and KOUPALAS, V. M. *Biochim. Biophys. Acta* **98**, 278 (1965).
236. GALANOUS, D. S. and KOUPALAS, V. M. *Biochim. Biophys. Acta* **98**, 293 (1965).
237. GALLAI-HATCHARD, J., MAGEE, W. L., THOMPSON, R. H. S. and WEBSTER, G. R. *J. Neurochem.* **9**, 545 (1962).
238. GALLIARD, T. and HAWTHORNE, J. N. *Biochem. J.* **88**, 38P (1963).
239. GALLIARD, T. and HAWTHORNE, J. N. *Biochim. Biophys. Acta* **70**, 479 (1963).
240. GAMBAL. D. and MONTY, K. *Federation Proc.* **18**, 232 (1959).
240a. GARBUS, J., DELUCA, H. F., LOOMANS, M. E. and STRONG, F. M. *J. Biol. Chem.* **238**, 59 (1963).
241. GASTAMBIDE-ODIER, M., DELAUMENY, J.-M. and LEDERER, E. *Biochim. Biophys. Acta* **70**, 670 (1963).
241a. GATT, S. *J. Biol. Chem.* **238**, PC3131 (1963).
242. GIBSON, D. M., TITCHENER, E. B. and WAKIL, S. J. *J. Amer. Chem. Soc.* **80**, 2908 (1958).
243. GIBSON, D. M., TITCHENER, E. B. and WAKIL, S. J. *Biochim. Biophys. Acta* **30**, 376 (1958).
244. GIBSON, K. D., WILSON, J. D. and UDENFRIEND, S. *J. Biol. Chem.* **236**, 673 (1961).
245. GLOMSET, J. A., PARKER, F., TJADEN, M. and WILLIAMS, R. H. *Biochim. Biophys. Acta* **58**, 398 (1962).
246. GOLDBERG, I. H. and DELBRÜCK, A. *Federation Proc.* **18**, 235 (1959).
247. GOLDBERG, I. H. *Federation Proc.* **19**, 220 (1960).
248. GOLDBERG, I. H. *J. Lipid Res.* **2**, 103 (1961).
249. GOODMAN, DEW. S., DEYKIN, D. and SHIRATORI, T. *J. Biol. Chem.* **239**, 1335 (1964).
250. GOODMAN, DEW. S. and SHIRATORI, T. *J. Lipid Res.* **5**, 307 (1964).
251. GOLDMAN, P. *J. Biol. Chem.* **239**, 3663 (1964).
252. GOLDMAN, P., ALBERTS, A. W. and VAGELOS, P. R. *J. Biol. Chem.* **238**, 1255 (1963).
253. GOLDMAN, P., ALBERTS, A. W. and VAGELOS, P. R. *J. Biol. Chem.* **238**, 3579 (1963).
254. GØRANSSON, G. *Biochem. J.* **92**, 41P (1964).
255. GOTTSCHALK, A. *The Chemistry and Biology of Sialic Acids and Related Substances*, Cambridge University Press, Cambridge, 1960.
256. GOULD, R. G. In *Cholesterol Chemistry, Biochemistry and Pathology*, edited by R. P. Cook. Academic Press Inc., New York, 1958, p. 209.
257. GRADO, C. and BALLOU, C. E. *J. Biol. Chem.* **235**, PC23 (1960).
258. GRADO, C. and BALLOU, C. E. *J. Biol. Chem.* **236**, 54 (1961).
259. GRAY, G. M. *Biochem. J.* **70**, 425 (1958).
260. GRAY, G. M. and MACFARLANE, M. G. *Biochem. J.* **70**, 409 (1958).
261. GREEN, D. E. *Biochem. J.* **30**, 629 (1936).
262. GREEN, D. E. *Biol. Revs. Cambridge Phil. Soc.* **29**, 330 (1954).
263. GREEN, D. E. In *Biochemical Problems of Lipids*, edited by G. Popják and E. Le Breton. Butterworth Scientific Publications, London, 1956, p. 233.
264. GREEN, D. E. *Advances in Enzymol.* **21**, 73 (1959).
265. GREEN, D. E. and FLEISCHER, S. *Biochim. Biophys. Acta* **70**, 554 (1963).
266. GREEN, D. E. and FLEISCHER, S. In *Metabolism and Physiological Significance of Lipids*, p. 581, edited by R. M. C. Dawson and D. N. Rhodes. John Wiley, London, New York and Sydney, 1964.
267. GREEN, D. E. and WAKIL, S. J. In *Lipide Metabolism*, edited by K. Bloch. John Wiley, New York, London, 1960, p. 1.
268. GREEN, J. P. and ROBINSON, J. D., JR., *J. Biol. Chem.* **235**, 1621 (1960).
269. GREENBERG, D. M. and FIGARD, P. *J. Am. Chem. Soc.* **81**, 3158 (1959).
270. GREVILLE, G. D. and STEWART, H. B. *Ann. Rep. Chem. Soc.* **50**, 301 (1954).
271. GRIFFITH, W. H. and NYC, J. F. In *The Vitamins, Chemistry, Physiology, Pathology*, edited by W. H. SEBRELL, JR., and R. S. HARRIS. Academic Press Inc., New York, 1954, vol. 2, p. 49.
272. GROOM, V. and SRIBNEY, M. *J. Lipid Res.* **6**, 220 (1965).

273. GUNSTONE, F. D. *An Introduction to the Chemistry of Fats and Fatty Acids*, John Wiley, 1958.
274. GURD, F. R. N. In *Lipide Chemistry*, edited by D. J. Hanahan. John Wiley, New York, 1960, p. 260.
275. GUSTAFSON, A., ALAUPOVIC, P. and FURMAN, R. H. *Biochemistry* **4**, 596 (1965).
276. HAESSLER, H. A. and ISSELBACHER, K. J. *Am. J. Diseases Children* **104**, 543 (1962).
277. HAFT, D. E., ROHEIM, P. S., WHITE, A. and EDER, H. A. *J. Clin. Invest.* **41**, 842 (1962).
278. HALL, M. O. and NYC, J. F. *J. Am. Chem. Soc.* **81**, 2275 (1959).
279. HALL, M. O. and NYC, J. F. *J. Lipid Res.* **2**, 321 (1961).
280. HALL, M. O. and NYC, J. F. *Biochim. Biophys. Acta* **56**, 370 (1962).
281. HALLIDAY, J. W. and Anderson, L. *J. Biol. Chem.* **217**, 797 (1955).
282. HAJRA, A. K. and RADIN, N. S. *Biochim. Biophys. Acta* **70**, 97 (1963).
283. HAJRA, A. K. and RADIN, N. S. *J. Lipid Res.* **4**, 270 (1963).
284. HANAHAN, D. J. *J. Biol. Chem.* **207**, 879 (1954).
285. HANAHAN, D. J. *J. Biol. Chem.* **211**, 313 (1954).
286. HANAHAN, D. J. *J. Biol. Chem.* **211**, 321 (1954).
287. HANAHAN, D. J. *Lipide Chemistry*, John Wiley, New York, London, 1960.
288. HANAHAN, D. J. and BLOMSTRAND, R. *J. Biol. Chem.* **222**, 677 (1956).
289. HANAHAN, D. J., BROCKERHOFF, H. and BARRON, E. J. *J. Biol. Chem.* **235**, 1917 (1960).
290. HANAHAN, D. J. and OLLEY, J. N. *J. Biol. Chem.* **231**, 813 (1958).
290a. HANAHAN, D. J. and WATTS, R. *J. Biol. Chem.* **236**, PC 59 (1961).
291. HARLAN, W. R., JR. and WAKIL, S. J. *Biochem. Biophys. Res. Communs*, **8**, 131 (1962).
292. HARLAN, W. R., JR. and WAKIL, S. J. *J. Biol. Chem.* **238**, 3216 (1963).
293. HARRIS, P. M., ROBINSON, D. S. and GETZ, G. *Nature* **188**, 742 (1960).
294. HARRIS, R. V., WOOD, B. J. B. and JAMES, A. T. *Biochem. J.* **94**, 22P (1965).
295. HARTREE, E. F. In *Metabolism and Physiological Significance of Lipids*, p. 205, edited by R. M. C. Dawson and D. N. Rhodes. John Wiley, London, New York and Sydney, 1964.
296. HATCH, F. T., HAGOPIN, L. M., RUBENSTEIN, J. J. and CANELLOS, G. P. *Circulation* **28**, 659 (1963).
297. HAUSER, G. *Biochim. Biophys. Acta* **70**, 278 (1963).
298. HAUSER, G. *Biochim. Biophys. Acta* **84**, 212 (1964).
299. HAUSER, G. and FINELLI, V. N. *J. Biol. Chem.* **238**, 3224 (1963).
300. HAVEL, R. J., NAIMARK, A. and BORCHGREVINK, C. F. *J. Clin. Invest.* **42**, 1054 (1962).
301. HAWKE, J. C. *Biochem. J.* **71**, 588 (1959).
302. HAWTHORNE, J. N. *Biochim. Biophys. Acta* **18**, 389 (1955).
303. HAWTHORNE, J. N. *Biochem. J.* **75**, 495 (1960).
304. HAWTHORNE, J. N. *J. Lipid Res.* **1**, 255 (1960).
305. HAWTHORNE, J. N. and KEMP, P. In *Advances of Lipid Research*, vol. 2, p. 127, edited by R. Paoletti and D. Kritchevsky. Academic Press, New York and London, 1964.
306. HAWTHORNE, J. N., KEMP, P. and ELLIS, R. B. *Biochem. J.* **75**, 501 (1960).
307. HERBERT, E. and POTTER, V. R. *J. Biol. Chem.* **222**, 453 (1956).
308. HELE, P. *British Med. Bull.* **14**, 201 (1958).
309. HELE, P. and POPJÁK, G. In *Biochemical Problems of Lipids*, edited by G. Popják and E. LeBreton, Butterworth Scientific Publications, 1956, p. 135.
310. HELE, P., POPJÁK, G. and LAURYSSENS, M. *Biochem. J.* **65**, 348 (1957).
311. HERNANDEZ, H. H. and CHAIKOFF, I. L. *J. Biol. Chem.* **228**, 447 (1957).
312. HEVESY, G. *Advances in Enzymol.* **7**, 111 (1947).
313. HEVESY, G. *Radioactive Indicators*, Interscience Publishers Inc., New York and London, 1948.
314. HILDITCH, T. P. *The Chemical Constitution of Natural Fats*, 3rd edition revised, John Wiley, New York, 1956.
315. HILDITCH, T. P. and WILLIAMS, P. N. *The Chemical Constitution of Natural Fats*, 4th ed., Chapman & Hall, London, 1964.
315a. HOFMANN, K. and LIU, T-Y. *Biochim. Biophys. Acta* **37**, 364 (1960).
316. HOKIN, L. E. and HOKIN, M. R. *Biochim. Biophys. Acta* **18**, 102 (1955).

317. HOKIN, L. E. and HOKIN, M. R. *Biochim. Biophys. Acta* **31**, 285 (1958).
318. HOKIN, L. E. and HOKIN, M. R. *Biochim. Biophys. Acta* **84**, 563, (1964).
319. HOKIN, L. E. and HOKIN, M. R. *Biochim. Biophys. Acta* **67**, 470 (1963).
320. HOKIN, L. E. and HOKIN, M. R. *Fed. Proc.* **22**, 8 (1963).
321. HOKIN, L. E. and HOKIN, M. R. *J. Biol. Chem.* **233**, 800 (1958).
322. HOKIN, L. E. and HOKIN, M. R. *J. Biol. Chem.* **233**, 805 (1958).
323. HOKIN, L. E. and HOKIN, M. R. *J. Biol. Chem.* **233**, 818 (1958).
324. HOKIN, L. E. and HOKIN, M. R. *Biochim. Biophys. Acta* **37**, 176 (1960).
325. HOKIN, M. R. and HOKIN, L. E. In *Metabolism and Physiological Significance of Lipids*, p. 423, edited by R. M. C. Dawson and D. N. Rhodes. John Wiley, London, New York and Sydney, 1964.
326. HOKIN, M. R. and HOKIN, L. E. *J. Biol. Chem.* **234**, 1381 (1959).
327. HOKIN, M. R. and HOKIN, L. E. *J. Biol. Chem.* **239**, 2116 (1964).
328. HOLLOWAY, P. W., PELUFFO, R. O. and WAKIL, S. J. *Biochem. Biophys. Res. Communs.* **12**, 300 (1963).
329. HOLLOWAY, P. W. and WAKIL, S. J. *J. Biol. Chem.* **239**, 2489 (1964).
330. HOOPER, N. K. and LAW, J. H. *Biochem. Biophys. Res. Communs.* **18**, 426 (1965).
331. HÖRHAMMER, L., WAGNER, H. and RICHTER, G. *Biochem. Z.* **331**, 155 (1959).
332. HORNING, M. G., MARTIN, D. B., KARMEN, A. and VAGELOS, P. R. *Biochem. Biophys. Res. Communs.* **3**, 101 (1960).
333. HÜBSCHER, G. *Biochim. Biophys. Acta* **57**, 555 (1962).
334. HÜBSCHER, G. In *Biosynthesis of Lipids*, vol. VII, p. 139, Fifth International Congress of Biochemistry, edited by G. Popják. Pergamon Press, Oxford, London, New York, Paris, 1963.
335. HÜBSCHER, G. and CLARK, B. *Biochem. J.* **72**, 7P (1959).
336. HÜBSCHER, G. and CLARK, B. *Biochim. Biophys, Acta* **41**, 45 (1960).
337. HÜBSCHER, G., CLARK, B., WEBB, M. E. and SHERRATT, H. S. A. In *Biochemical Problems of Lipids*, p. 201, edited by A. C. Frazer. Elsevier Publishing. Amsterdam, London and New York, 1963.
338. HÜBSCHER, G., DILS, R. R. and POVER, W. F. R. *Biochim. Biophys. Acta* **36**, 518 (1959).
339. HÜBSCHER, G. and HAWTHORNE, J. N. *Biochem. J.* **67**, 523 (1957).
340. HÜBSCHER, G., SMITH, M. E. and GURR, M. I. In *Metabolism and Physiological Significance of Lipids*, p. 229, edited by R. M. C. Dawson and D. N. Rhodes. John Wiley, London, New York and Sydney, 1964.
341. HUENNEKENS, F. M., HATEFI, Y. and KAY, L. D. *J. Biol. Chem.* **224**, 435 (1957).
342. HUGGINS, C. G. and COHN, D. V., *J. Biol. Chem.* **234**, 257 (1959).
343. HULANICKA, D., ERWIN, J. and BLOCH, K. *J. Biol. Chem.* **239**, 2778 (1964).
344. HÜLSMANN, W. C. and DOW, D. S. *Biochim. Biophys. Acta* **84**, 486 (1964).
345. HUTT, H. H. *Nature (London)* **175**, 303 (1955).
346. ICHIHARA, A. and GREENBERG, D. M. *J. Biol. Chem.* **224**, 331 (1957).
347. IMAI, Y. *Biochem. (Tokyo)* **53**, 50 (1963).
348. INGRAHAM, L. L. and GREEN, D. E. *Science* **128**, 310 (1958).
349. ISSELBACHER, K. J. and BUDZ, D. M. *Nature* **200**, 364 (1963).
350. JACOB, A. *Compt. rend. Acad. Sci.* **242**, 2180 (1956).
351. JAMES, A. T. In *The Control of Lipid Metabolism*, p. 17, edited by J. K. Grant. Academic Press, London and New York, 1963.
352. JENCKS, W. P. and Lipmann, F. *J. Biol. Chem.* **225**, 207 (1957).
353. JEDEIKIN, L. A. and WEINHOUSE, S. *Arch. Biochem. Biophys.* **50**, 134 (1954).
354. JOHNSON, G. A. and McCLUER, R. H. *Biochim. Biophys. Acta* **70**, 487 (1963).
355. JOHNSTON, J. M. In *Advances in Lipid Research*, vol. 1, p. 105, edited by R. Paoletti and D. Kritchevsky. Academic Press, New York and London, 1963.
356. JOHNSON, J. M. and BEARDEN, J. H. *Arch. Biochem. Biophys.* **90**, 57 (1960).
357. KALCKAR, H. *Biochem. J.* **33**, 631 (1939).
358. KANESHIRO, T. and LAW, J. N. *J. Biol. Chem.* **239**, 1705 (1964).
359. KANFER, J., BLACKLOW, R. S., WARREN, L. and BRADY, R. O. *Biochem. Biophys. Res. Communs.* **14**, 287 (1964).
360. KANFER, J. N. and KENNEDY, E. P. *J. Biol. Chem.* **237**, PC270 (1962).

361. KANFER, J. and KENNEDY, E. P. *J. Biol. Chem.* **239**, 1720 (1964).
362. KARMEN, A., WHYTE, M. and GOODMAN, DEW. S. *J. Lipid Res.* **4**, 312 (1963).
363. KARNOVSKY, M. L. and BRUMM, A. F. *J. Biol. Chem.* **216**, 689 (1955).
364. KARNOVSKY, M. L. and WOLFF, D. *Proc. Intern. Congr. Biochem.* 4th Congr., Vienna, 1958, p. 208.
365. KARNOVSKY, M. L. and WOLFF, D. In *Biochemistry of Lipids*, edited by G. Popják. Pergamon Press, London (1960), p. 53.
366. KATES, M. In *Lipide Metabolism*, p. 165, edited by K. Bloch. John Wiley, New York and London, 1960.
367. KATES, M., YENGOYAN, L. S. and SASTRY, P. S. *Biochim. Biophys. Acta* **98**, 252 (1965).
368. KEENAN, R. W., BROWN, J. B. and MARKS, B. H. *Biochim. Biophys. Acta* **51** 226 (1961).
369. KEENAN, R. W. and HOKIN, L. E. *Biochim. Biophys. Acta* **60**, 428 (1962).
370. KELLERMAN, G. M. and JOLLOW, D. J. *Biochem. Biophys. Acta* **84**, 478 (1964).
371. KENNEDY, E. P. *J. Biol. Chem.* **201**, 399 (1953).
372. KENNEDY, E. P. *J. Biol. Chem.* **209**, 525 (1954).
373. KENNEDY, E. P. *Can. J. Biochem. and Physiol.* **34**, 334 (1956).
374. KENNEDY, E. P. *J. Biol. Chem.* **222**, 185 (1956).
375. KENNEDY, E. P. *Ann. Rev. Biochem.* **26**, 119 (1957).
376. KENNEDY, E. P. *Federation Proc.* **16**, 847 (1957).
377. KENNEDY, E. P. *Federation Proc.* **20**, 934 (1961).
377a KENNEDY, E. P. In *Biosynthesis of Lipids*, Fifth International Congress of Biochemistry, edited by G. Popják. Pergamon Press, Oxford, London, New York and Paris, 1963, vol. VII, p. 113.
378. KENNEDY, E. P., BORKENHAGEN, L. F. and SMITH, S. W. *J. Biol. Chem.* **234**, 1998 (1959).
379. KENNEDY, E. P. and WEISS, S. B. *J. Am. Chem. Soc.* **77**, 250 (1955).
380. KENNEDY, E. P. and WEISS, S. B. *J. Biol. Chem.* **222**, 193 (1956).
381. KINDL, H. and HOFFMAN-OSTENHOF, O. *Biochem. Z.* **339**, 374 (1964).
382. KIYASU, J. Y. *Federation Proc.* **17**, 255 (1958).
383. KIYASU, J. Y. and KENNEDY, E. P. *J. Biol. Chem.* **235**, 2590 (1960).
384. KIYASU, J., PAULUS, H. and KENNEDY, E. P. *Federation Proc.* **19**, 233 (1960).
385. KIYASU, J. Y., PIERINGER, R. A., PAULUS, H. and KENNEDY, E. P. *J. Biol. Chem.* **238**, 2293 (1963).
386. KLEIN, H. P. *J. Bacteriol.* **73**, 530 (1957).
387. KLEIN, W. *Z. Physiol. Chem.*, Hoppe-Seyler's **254**, 1 (1938).
388. KLENK, E. *Abstracts Sixth International Congress of Biochemistry*, New York, p. 537 (1964).
389. KLENK, E. *Z. Physiol. Chem.* Hoppe-Seyler's, **331**, 50 (1963).
390. KLENK, E. *Z. Physiol. Chem.*, Hoppe-Seyler's **268**, 50 (1941).
391. KLENK, E. In Fourth Intern. Congr. Biochem. *Biochemistry of the Central Nervous System*, edited by F. Brücke, Pergamon Press, London, vol. 3, p. 146, 1959.
392. KLENK, E. and DEBUCH, H. *Z. Physiol. Chem.*, Hoppe-Seyler's **296**, 179 (1954).
393. KLENK, E. and DEBUCH, H. *Z. Physiol. Chem.*, Hoppe-Seyler's **299**, 66 (1955).
394. KLENK, E. and DEBUCH, H. *Ann. Rev. Biochem.* **28**, 39 (1959).
395. KLENK, E. and DEBUCH, H. In *Modern Scientific Aspects of Neurology*, edited by J. N. Cummings. Edward Arnold (Publishers) Ltd., London, p. 255, 1960.
396. KLENK, E. and GIELEN, W. *Z. Physiol. Chem.*, Hoppe-Seyler's **330**, 218 (1963).
397. KLENK, E. and GIELEN, W. *Z. Physiol. Chem.* Hoppe-Seyler's **319**, 283 (1960).
398. KLENK, E. and KREMER, G. *Z. Physiol. Chem.* Hoppe-Seyler's **320**, 111 (1960).
399. KLENK, E., LIEDTKE, U. and GIELEN, W. *Z. Physiol. Chem.*, Hoppe-Seyler's **334**, 186 (1963).
400. KLENK, E. and MOHRHAUER, H. *Z. Physiol. Chem.*, Hoppe-Seyler's **320**, 218 (1960).
401. KLENK, E. and PADBERG, G. *Z. Physiol. Chem.*, Hoppe-Seyler's **327**, 249 (1962).
402. KLENK, E. and PFLÜGER, H. *Physiol. Chem.*, Hoppe-Seyler's **335**, 53 (1963).
403. KOEPPE, R. E., MINTHORN, M. L., JR. and HILL, R. J. *J. Arch Biochem. Biophys.* **68**, 355 (1957).
404. KOPACZYK, K. C. and RADIN, N. S. *J. Lipid Res.* **6**, 140 (1965).

405. KOREY, S. R., GONATAS, J. and STEIN, A. *J. Neuropath & Exp. Neurol. XXII*, 56 (1963).
406. KOREY, S. R. and ORCHEN, M. *Arch. Biochem. Biophys.* **83**, 381 (1959).
407. KORN, E. D. *J. Biol. Chem.* **215**, 1 (1955).
408. KORN, E. D. *J. Biol. Chem.* **239**, 396 (1964).
409. KORN, E. D. In *Chemistry of Lipides as related to Atherosclerosis*, edited by I. H. Page. Charles C. Thomas (Publisher), Springfield, Ill., 1958, p. 169.
410. KORNBERG, A. and PRICER, W. E., JR. *J. Am. Chem. Soc.* **74**, 1617 (1952).
411. KORNBERG, A. and PRICER, W. E., JR. *Federation Proc.* **11**, 242 (1952).
412. KORNBERG, A. and PRICER, W. E., JR. *J. Biol. Chem.* **204**, 329 (1953).
413. KORNBERG, A. and PRICER, W. E., JR. *J. Biol. Chem.* **204**, 345 (1953).
414. KORZENOVSKY, M., DILLER, E. R., MARSHALL, A. C. and AUDA, B. M. *Biochem. J.* **76**, 238 (1960).
415. KORZENOVSKY, M., RUST, A. C. and DILLER, E. R. *Federation Proc.* **14**, 239 (1955).
416. KUHN, R., WIEGANDT, H. and EGGE, H. *Angew. Chem.* **73**, 580 (1961).
417. KUHN, R. and WIEGANDT, H. *Chem. Ber.* **96**, 866 (1963).
418. LACHANCE, J. P., POPJÁK, G. and WAARD, A. DE. *Biochem. J.* **68**, 7P (1958).
419. LANDS, W. E. M. *J. Biol. Chem.* **231**, 883 (1958).
420. LANDS, W. E. M. *J. Biol. Chem.* **235**, 2233 (1960).
421. LANDS, W. E. M. and HART, P. *J. Biol. Chem.* **240**, 1905 (1965).
422. LANDS, W. E. M. and HART, P. *J. Lipid Res.* **5**, 81 (1964).
423. LANDS, W. E. M. and MERKL, I. *J. Biol. Chem.* **238**, 898 (1963).
424. LANGDON, R. G. *J. Amer. Chem. Soc.* **77**, 5190 (1955).
425. LANGDON, R. G. *J. Biol. Chem.* **226**, 615 (1957).
426. LARDY, H. A. In *The Vitamins, Chemistry, Physiology, Pathology*, edited by W. H. Sebrell Jr. and R. S. Harris. Academic Press, Inc., New York, vol. 2, 342 (1954).
427. LAW, J. H. *Ann. Rev. Biochem.* **29**, 131 (1960).
428. LAW, J. H., ZALKIN, H. and KANESHIRO, T. *Biochim. Biophys. Acta* **70**, 143 (1963).
429. LEBARON, F. N. *Biochim. Biophys. Acta* **70**, 658 (1963).
430. LEBARON, F. N. and FOLCH, J. *Physiol. Revs.* **37**, 539 (1957).
431. LEBARON, F. N., HAUSER, G. and RUIZ, E. E. *Biochim. Biophys. Acta* **60**, 338 (1962).
432. LEBARON, F. N., KISTLER, J. P. and HAUSER, G. *Biochim. Biophys. Acta* **44**, 170 (1960).
433. LEBARON, F. N. and ROTHLEDER, E. E. In *Biochemistry of Lipids*, edited by G. Popják. Pergamon Press, London, 1960, p. 1.
434. LEDERER, E. *Angewandte Chem.* **3**, 393 (1964).
435. LEDERER, E. *Biochem. J.* **93**, 449 (1964).
436. LEES, M. B., CARR, S. and FOLCH, J. *Biochim. Biophys. Acta* **84**, 464 (1964).
437. LEE PENG, C. H. *Biochim. Biophys. Acta* **22**, 42 (1956).
438. LEES, M., FOLCH, J., SLOANE STANLEY, G. H. and CARR, S., *J. Neurochem.* **4**, 9 (1959).
439. LENNARZ, W. J. and BLOCH, K. *J. Biol. Chem.* **235**, PC26 (1960).
440. LENNARZ, W. J., LIGHT, R. J. and BLOCH, K. *Proc. Natl. Acad. Sci. U.S.* **48**, 840 (1962).
441. LEUPOLD, F. and KREMER, G. *Z. physiol. Chem.* Hoppe-Seyler's **318**, 251 (1960).
442. LEVINE, M. and TARVER, H. *J. Biol. Chem.* **184**, 427 (1950).
443. LEWIN, L. M. and WAGENKNECHT, A. C. *Nature* **188**, 146 (1960).
444. LINDGREN, F. T., NICHOLS, A. V., HAYES, T. L., FREEMAN, N. K. and GOFMAN, J. W. *Ann. N.Y. Acad. Sci.* **72**, 826 (1959).
445. LINDGREN, F. T. and NICHOLS, A. V. In *The Plasma Proteins*, vol. 2. *Biosynthesis, Metabolism, Alterations in Disease*, edited by F. W. Putnam. Academic Press, New York and London, 1960, p. 2.
446. LIU, T.-Y. and HOFMANN, K. *Biochemistry* **1**, 189 (1962).
447. LOEWUS, F. A. and KELLY, S. *Biochem. Biophys. Res. Communs.* **7**, 204 (1962).
448. LONG, C. and PENNY, I. F. *Biochem. J.* **65**, 382 (1957).
449. LORCH, E., ABRAHAM, S. and CHAIKOFF, I. L. *Biochim. Biophys. Acta* **70**, 627 (1963).
450. LOVERN, J. A. *The Chemistry of Lipids of Biochemical Significance*, Methuen & Co., Ltd., London, 1957.
451. LYNEN, F. *Federation Proc.* **12**, 683 (1953).
452. LYNEN, F. *Harvey Lectures, Ser.* **48** (1952–3), 210 (1954).
453. LYNEN, F. *Ann. Rev. Biochem.* **24**, 653 (1955).

454. LYNEN, F. *J. Cell. Comp. Physiol.* **54**, Suppl., 33 (1959).
456. LYNEN, F. In *Drugs Affecting Lipid Metabolism*, edited by S. Garattini and R. Paoletti. Elsevier Publishing Co., Amsterdam, 1961, p. 3.
457. LYNEN, F., DECKER, K., WIELAND, O. and REINWEIN, D. In *Biochemical Problems of Lipids*, edited by G. Popják and E. LeBreton. Butterworth Scientific Publications, London, 1956, p. 142.
458. LYNEN, F. *Federation Proc.* **20**, 941 (1961).
459. LYNEN, F., HOPPER, I., LORCH, E., KIRSCHNER, K., HAGEN, A. and SCHWEIZER, E. *Abstracts Sixth International Congress of Biochemistry*, New York, p. 535.
460. LYNEN, F. and OCHOA, S. *Biochim. Biophys. Acta* **12**, 299 (1953).
461. MACFARLANE, M. G. *Biochem. J.* **78**, 44 (1961).
462. MACFARLANE, M. G. In *Advances in Lipid Research*, vol. 2, p. 91, edited by R. Paoletti and D. Kritchevsky. Academic Press, New York and London, 1964.
463. MACFARLANE, M. G. and WHEELDON, L. W. *Nature* (London) **183**, 1808 (1959).
464. MACFARLANE, M. G., GRAY, G. M. and WHEELDON, L. W. *Biochem. J.* **77**, 626 (1960).
465. MACHEBOEUF, M. In *Blood Cells and Plasma Proteins*, edited by J. L. Tulis. Academic Press, Inc., New York, 1953, p. 358.
466. MAJERUS, P. W., ALBERTS, A. W. and VAGELOS, P. R. *J. Biol. Chem.* **240**, 618 (1965).
467. MAJERUS, P. W., ALBERTS, A. W. and VAGELOS, P. R. *Proc. Nat. Acad. Sci. U.S.* **51**, 1231 (1964).
468. MAJERUS, P. W., ALBERTS, A. W. and VAGELOS, P. R. *Proc. Nat. Acad. Sci.* **53**, 410 (1965).
469. MAJNO, G. and KARNOVSKY, M. L. *J. Exptl. Med.* **107**, 475 (1958).
470. MALKIN, T. and POOLE, A. G. *J. Chem. Soc.* **3470** (1953).
471. MARINETTI, G., BERRY, J. F., ROUSER, G. and STOTZ, E. *J. Am. Chem. Soc.* **75**, 313 (1953).
472. MARINETTI, G. V., ERBLAND, J. and STOTZ, E. *Biochim. Biophys. Acta* **33**, 403 (1959).
473. MARINETTI, G. V., ERBLAND, J., ALBRECHT, M. and STOTZ, E. *Biochim. Biophys. Acta* **25**, 585 (1957).
474. MARINETTI, G. V., ERBLAND, J., ALBRECHT, M. and STOTZ, E. *Biochim. Biophys. Acta* **26**, 130 (1957).
475. MARINETTI, G. V., ERBLAND, J. and BROSSARD, M. In *Metabolism and Physiological Significance of Lipids*, edited by R. M. C. Dawson and D. N. Rhodes. John Wiley, London, New York and Sydney, 1964, p. 71.
476. MARINETTI, G. V., ERBLAND, J., TEMPLE, K. and STOTZ, E. *Biochim. Biophys. Acta* **38**, 524 (1960).
477. MARINETTI, G. V., ERBLAND, J., WITTER, R. F., PETIX, J. and STOTZ, E. *Biochim. Biophys. Acta* **30**, 223 (1958).
478. MARINETTI, G. V., KOCHEN, J., ERBLAND, J. and STOTZ, E. *J. Biol. Chem.* **229**, 1027 (1957).
478a MARINETTI, G. V., GRIFFITH, M. and SMITH, T. *Biochim. Biophys. Acta* **57**, 543 (1962).
479. MARINETTI, G. V. and STOTZ, E. *Biochim. Biophys. Acta* **21**, 168 (1956).
480. MARSH, J. B. *J. Biol. Chem.* **238**, 1752 (1963).
481. MARSH, J. B. and JAMES, A. T. *Biochim. Biophys. Acta* **60**, 320 (1962).
482. MARSH, J. B. and WHEREAT, A. F. *J. Biol. Chem.* **234**, 3196 (1959).
483. MARTIN, D. B., HORNING, M. G. and VAGELOS, P. R. *J. Biol. Chem.* **236**, 663 (1961).
484. MASSARO, E. J. and LENNARZ, W. J. *Biochemistry* **4**, 85 (1965).
485. MATTSON, F. H. and BECK, L. W. *J. Biol. Chem.* **214**, 115 (1955).
486. MATTSON, F. H., BENEDICT, J. H., MARTIN, J. B. and BECK, L. W. *J. Nutrition* **48**, 335 (1952).
487. MCKIBBIN, J. M. *J. Biol. Chem.* **220**, 537 (1956).
488. MCKIBBON, J. M. and TAYLOR, W. E. *J. Biol. Chem.* **196**, 427 (1952).
489. MCMURRAY, W. C. *J. Neurochem.* **11**, 315 (1964).
490. MCMURRAY, W. C., BERRY, J. F. and ROSSITER, R. J. *Biochem. J.* **66**, 629 (1957).

200 K. P. STRICKLAND

491. McMurray, W. C., Strickland, K. P., Berry, J. F. and Rossiter, R. J. *Biochem. J.* **66**, 621 (1957).
492. McMurray, W. C., Strickland, K. P., Berry, J. F. and Rossiter, R. J. *Biochem. J.* **66**, 634 (1957).
493. Mead, J. F. *Federation Proc.* **20**, 952 (1961).
494. Mead, J. F. *Ann. Rev. Biochem.* **32**, 241 (1963).
495. Mead, J. F. In *Lipide Metabolism*, edited by K. Bloch. John Wiley, New York and London, 1960, p. 41.
496. Merkl, I. and Lands, W. E. M. *J. Biol. Chem.* **238**, 905 (1963).
497. Miras, C. J., Mantzos, J. and Levis, G. *Biochim. Biophys. Acta* **84**, 101 (1964).
498. Mokrasch, L. C. and Manner, P. *J. Neurochem.* **10**, 541 (1963).
499. Morelec-Coulon, M. J. and Faure, M. *Bull. Soc. Chim. Biol.* **39**, 947 (1957).
500. Moscatelli, E. A. and Larner, J. *Federation Proc.* **16**, 223 (1957).
501. Moser, H. and Karnovsky, M. L. *Neurology* **8** (Suppl. 1) 81 (1958).
502. Moser, H. W. and Karnovsky, M. L. *J. Biol. Chem.* **234**, 1990 (1959).
503. Mudd, J. B. and McManus, T. T. *J. Biol. Chem.* **237**, 2057 (1962).
504. Mudd, J. B. and Stumpf, P. K. *J. Biol. Chem.* **236**, 2692 (1961).
505. Mukherjee, S., Kunitake, G. and Alfin-Slater, R. B. *J. Biol. Chem.* **230**, 91 (1958).
505a Mulder, E., DeGier, J. and Van Deenen, L. L. M. *Biochim. Biophys. Acta* **70**, 94 (1963).
506. Murthy, S. K. and Ganguly, J. *Biochem. J.* **83**, 460 (1962).
507. Murthy, S. K., Mahadevan, S., Seshadri Sastry, P. and Ganguly, J. *Nature* **189**, 482 (1961).
508. Nemer, M. and Elwyn, D. *J. Am. Chem. Soc.* **79**, 6564 (1957).
509. Nemer, M. J. and Elwyn, D. *J. Biol. Chem.* **235**, 2070 (1960).
510. Neuhaus, F. C. and Byrne, W. L. *Biochim. Biophys. Acta* **28**, 224 (1958).
511. Neuhaus, F. C. and Byrne, W. L. *J. Biol. Chem.* **234**, 109 (1959).
512. Neuhaus, F. C. and Byrne, W. L. *J. Biol. Chem.* **234**, 113 (1959).
513. Neufeld, E. F. and Hall, C. W. *Biochem. Biophys. Res. Communs.* **14**, 503 (1964).
514. Neuhaus, F. C. and Byrne, W. L. *J. Biol. Chem.* **235**, 2019 (1960).
515. Nieft, M. L. and Deuel, H. J., Jr. *J. Biol. Chem.* **177**, 143 (1949).
516. Norris, A. T., Matsumura, S. and Bloch, K. *J. Biol. Chem.* **239**, 3653 (1964).
517. Nugteren, D. H. *Biochim. Biophys. Acta* **60**, 656 (1962).
518. Oliveira, M. M. and Vaughan, M. *Fed. Proc.* **21**, 296 (1962).
519. Oncley, J. L. *Harvey Lectures*, Ser. **50** (1954–5), 71 (1956).
520. Oncley, J. L. In *Brain Lipids and Lipoproteins and the Leucodystrophies*, edited by J. Folch-Pi and H. Bauer. Elsevier Publishing, Amsterdam, London and New York, 1963, p. 1.
521. Oncley, J. L. In *Lipid Transport*, edited by H. C. Meng, J. G. Coniglio, V. S. Lequire, G. V. Mann and J. M. Mernill. Charles C. Thomas, Springfield, 1964, p. 70.
522. Oncley, J. L. In *The Lipoproteins Methods and Clinical Significance*, edited by F. Homburger and P. Bernfeld, S. Karger, Basel and New York, 1958, p. 14.
523. Oncley, J. L. In *Chemistry of Lipides as related to Athersclerosis*, edited by I. H. Page, Charles C. Thomas, Springfield, Ill., 1958, p. 114.
524. Olson, R. E. and Vester, J. W. *Physiol. Revs.* **40**, 677 (1960).
525. Overath, P. and Stumpf, P. K. *J. Biol. Chem.* **239**, 4103 (1964).
526. Palmer, F. B. *Proc. Can. Fed. Biol. Soc.* **8**, 85 (1965).
527. Palmer, F. B. and Rossiter, R. J. *Can. J. Biochem.* **43**, 671 (1965).
528. Palmer, F. B. and Rossiter, R. J. *Fed. Proc.* **23**, 229 (1964).
529. Pangborn, M. C. *J. Biol. Chem.* **143**, 247 (1942).
530. Pangborn, M. C. *J. Biol. Chem.* **168**, 351 (1947).
531. Paulus, H. and Kennedy, E. P. *J. Am. Chem. Soc.* **80**, 6689 (1958).
532. Paulus, H. and Kennedy, E. P. *J. Am. Chem. Soc.* **81**, 4436 (1959).
533. Paulus, H. and Kennedy, E. P. *J. Biol. Chem.* **235**, 1303 (1960).
534. Paysant-Diament, M. *Ann. nutrition et aliment* **11**, 125 (1957).
535. Pieringer, R. A. and Hokin, L. E. *J. Biol. Chem.* **237**, 653 (1962).
536. Pieringer, R. A. and Hokin, L. E. *J. Biol. Chem.* **237**, 659 (1962).

537. PILGERAM, L. O., GAL, E. M., SASSENRATH, E. N. and GREENBERG, D. M. *J. Biol. Chem* **204**, 367 (1953).
538. PIZER, F. L. and BALLOU, C. E. *J. Am. Chem. Soc.* **81**, 915 (1959).
539. PIZER, L. I. *J. Biol. Chem.* **238**, 3934 (1963).
540. PIZER, L. I. *J. Biol. Chem.* **239**, 4219 (1964).
541. POPJÁK, G. *Symp. Biochem. Soc.* **9**, 37 (1952).
542. POPJÁK, G. and MUIR, H. *Biochem. J.* **46**, 103 (1950).
543. POPJÁK, G. and TIETZ, A. *Biochem. J.* **60**, 147 (1955).
544. PORCELLATI, G. *J. Neurochem.* **2**, 128 (1958).
545. PORTER, J. N. and TIETZ, A. *Biochim. Biophys. Acta*, **25**, 41 (1957).
546. PORTER, J. W., WAKIL, S. J., TIETZ, A., JACOB, M. I. and GIBSON, D. M. *Biochim. Biophys. Acta*, **25**, 35 (1957).
547. POSSMAYER, F. and STRICKLAND, K. P. *Can. Fed. Biol. Soc.* **7**, 33 (1964).
548. POSSMAYER, F. and STRICKLAND, K. P. *Proc. Can. Fed. Biol. Soc.* **8**, 85 (1965).
549. PRITCHARD, E. T. *Can. J. Biochem. and Physiol.* **36**, 1211 (1958).
550. RACHELE, J. R., WHITE, A. M. and GRÜNEWALD, H. *J. Biol. Chem.* **239**, 353 (1964).
551. RADDING, C. M., BRAGDON, J. H. and STEINBERG, D. *Biochim. Biophys. Acta*, **30**, 443 (1958).
552. RADDING, C. M. and STEINBERG, D. *J. Clin. Invest.* **39**, 1560 (1960).
553. RADIN, N. S., MARTIN, F. B. and BROWN, J. R. *J. Biol. Chem.* **224**, 499 (1957).
554. RAMASARMA, T. and WETTER, L. R. *Can. J. Biochem. Physiol.* **35**, 853 (1957).
555. RAPPORT, M. M. and FRANZL, R. E. *J. Neurochem.* **1**, 303 (1957).
556. RAPPORT, M. M. and FRANZL, R. E. *J. Biol. Chem.* **225**, 851 (1957).
557. RAPPORT, M. M., LERNER, B., ALONZO, N. and FRANZL, R. E. *J. Biol. Chem.* **225**, 859 (1957).
558. RHODES, D. N. *Biochem. J.* **68**, 380 (1958).
559. RHODES, D. N. and LEA, C. H. *Nature (London)* **177**, 1129 (1956).
560. RICHARDSON, K. E. and AXELROD, B. *Fed. Proc.* **17**, 296 (1958).
561. RILEY, R. F. *J. Biol. Chem.* **153**, 535 (1944).
562. RINGLER, R. L. and SINGER, T. P. *Biochem. Biophys. Acta* **29**, 661 (1958).
563. RINGLER, R. L. and SINGER, T. P. *J. Biol. Chem.* **234**, 2211 (1959).
564. RITTENBERG, D. and BLOCH, K. *J. Biol. Chem.* **160**, 417 (1945).
565. ROBERTSON, A. F. and LANDS, W. E. M. *Biochemistry*, **1**, 804 (1962).
566. ROBINSON, D. S. In *Advances in Lipid Research* vol. 1, edited by R. Paoletti and D. Kritchevsky. Academic Press, New York and London, 1963, p. 133.
567. ROBINSON, D. S. and FRENCH, J. E. *Quart. J. Expt. Physiol.* **42**, 151 (1957).
568. ROBINSON, D. S. and SEAKINS, A. *Biochim. Biophys. Acta* **62**, 163 (1962).
569. ROBINSON, J. D., BRADLEY, R. M. and BRADY, R. O. *J. Biol. Chem.* **238**, 528 (1963).
570. RODBELL, M. and FREDERICKSON, D. S. *J. Biol. Chem.* **234**, 562 (1959).
571. RODBELL, M., FREDERICKSON, D. S. and ONO, K. *J. Biol. Chem.* **234**, 567 (1959).
572. RODBELL, M. and HANAHAN, D. J. *J. Biol. Chem.* **214**, 607 (1955).
573. ROSEMAN, S. *Abstracts Sixth International Congress of Biochemistry*, New York, p. 467, (1964).
574. ROSEMAN, S. *Fed. Proc.* **21**, 1075 (1962).
575. ROSEMAN, S., JOURDIAN, G. W., WATSON, D. and ROOD, R. *Proc. Natl. Acad. Sci. U.S.* **47**, 958 (1961).
576. ROSEMAN, S. *Proc. Natl. Acad. Sci. U.S.* **48**, 437 (1962).
577. ROSEMAN, S. and COMB, D. G. *J. Am. Chem. Soc.* **80**, 3166 (1958).
578. ROSENBERG, A. and CHARGAFF, E. *Biochim. Biophys. Acta* **21**, 588 (1956).
579. ROSENBERG, A. and CHARGAFF, E. *J. Biol. Chem.* **232**, 1031 (1958).
580. ROSENBERG, A., HOWE, C. and CHARGAFF, E. *Nature (London)* **177**, 284 (1956).
581. ROSSITER, R. J. In *Metabolism and Physiological Significance of Lipids*, edited by R. M. C. Dawson and D. N. Rhodes. John Wiley, London and New York, 1964, p. 511.
582. ROSSITER, R. J. In *Metabolism of the Nervous System*, edited by D. Richter. Pergamon Press, London, 1957, p. 355.
583. ROSSITER, R. J. and DONISCH, V. *Proc. Can. Fed. Biol. Soc.* **7**, 6 (1964).

584. Rossiter, R. J., McLead, I. M. and Strickland, K. P. *Can. J. Biochem. and Physiol.* **35**, 945 (1957).
585. Rossiter, R. J., McMurray, W. C. and Strickland, K. P. *Fed. Proc.* **16**, 853 (1957).
586. Rossiter, R. J. and Palmer, F. B. *Biochem. Z.* In press.
587. Rossiter, R. J. and Strickland, K. P. *Ann. N.Y. Acad. Sci.* **72**, 790 (1959).
588. Rossiter, R. J. and Strickland, K. P. In *Lipide Metabolism*, edited by K. Bloch. John Wiley, New York and London, 1960, p. 69.
589. Rossiter, R. J., Thompson, W. and Strickland, K. P. *Can. Fed. Biol. Sci.* **1**, 43 (1958).
590. Rossiter, R. J., Thompson, W. and Strickland, K. P. In *The Neurochemistry of Nucleotides and Amino Acids*, edited by R. O. Brady and D. B. Tower. John Wiley, New York and London, 1960, p. 28.
591. Rouser, G., Berry, J. F., Marinetti, G. and Stotz, E. *J. Am. Chem. Soc.* **75**, 310 (1953).
591a Rowe, C. E. *Biochem. J.* **73**, 438 (1960).
592. Sabesin, S. M., Drummey, G. D., Budz, D. M. and Isselbacher, K. J. *Clin. Invest.* **43**, 1281 (1964).
593. Sacktor, B. *Abstracts Sixth International Congress of Biochemistry*, p. 493, New York, 1964.
594. Sallach, H. J. *J. Biol. Chem.* **223**, 1101 (1956).
595. Sastry, P. S. and Kates, M. *Biochim. Biophys. Acta* **70**, 214 (1963).
596. Saunders, D. R. and Dawson, A. M. *Biochem. J.* **82**, 477 (1962).
597. Scheuerbrandt, G. and Bloch, K. *J. Biol. Chem.* **237**, 2064 (1962).
598. Schneider, W. C. and Rotherham, J. *J. Biol. Chem.* **233**, 948 (1958).
599. Schoenheimer, R. *The Dynamic State of Body Constituents*, Harvard University Press, Cambridge, Mass. (1946).
600. Schramm, M. *J. Biol. Chem.* **233**, 1169 (1958).
601. Senior, J. R. *J. Lipid Res.* **5**, 495 (1964).
602. Senior, J. R. and Isselbacher, K. J. *Biochim. Biophys. Acta* **44**, 399 (1960).
603. Senior, J. R. and Isselbacher, K. J. *J. Biol. Chem.* **237**, 1454 (1962).
604. Seubert, W., Greull, G. and Lynen, F. *Angew. Chem.* **69**, 359 (1957).
605. Shah, S. N., Lossow, W. J. and Chaikoff, I. L. *Biochim. Biophys. Acta* **84**, 176 (1964).
606. Shah, S. N., Lossow, W. J. and Chaikoff, I. L. *J. Lipid Res.* **6**, 228 (1965).
607. Shapiro, B. In *Metabolism and Physiological Significance of Lipids*, edited by R. M. C. Dawson and D. N. Rhodes. John Wiley, London, New York and Sydney, 1964, p. 33.
608. Smith, G. N. and Bulock, J. D. *Biochem. Biophys. Res. Communs.* **17**, 433 (1964).
609. Smith, S. and Dils, R. *Biochim. Biophys. Acta* **84**, 776 (1964).
610. Smith, S. W., Weiss, S. B. and Kennedy, E. P. *J. Biol. Chem.* **228**, 915 (1957).
611. Sperry, W. M. and Brand, F. C. *J. Biol. Chem.* **137**, 377 (1941).
612. Sprinson, D. B. and Coulon, A. *J. Biol. Chem.* **207**, 585 (1954).
613. Squires, C. and Stumpf, P. K. *Fed. Proc.* **18**, 329 (1958).
614. Squires, C. C., Stumpf, P. K. and Schmid, C. *Plant Physiol.* **33**, 365 (1958).
615. Sribney, M. *Fed. Proc.* **21**, 280 (1962).
616. Sribney, M. and Kennedy, E. P. *J. Am. Chem. Soc.* **79**, 5325 (1957).
617. Sribney, M. and Kennedy, E. P. *J. Biol. Chem.* **233**, 1315 (1958).
618. Stadtman, E. R. and Barker, H. A. *J. Biol. Chem.* **180**, 1085 (1949).
619. Stadtman, E. R. and Barker, H. A. *J. Biol. Chem.* **180**, 1095 (1949).
620. Stadtman, E. R. and Barker, H. A. *J. Biol. Chem.* **180**, 1117 (1949).
621. Stadtman, E. R. and Barker, H. A. *J. Biol. Chem.* **180**, 1169 (1949).
622. Stadtman, E. R. and Barker, H. A. *J. Biol. Chem.* **181**, 221 (1949).
623. Stadtman, E. R. and Barker, H. A. *J. Biol. Chem.* **184**, 769 (1950).
624. Stansly, P. G. *Biochim. Biophys. Acta*, **18**, 411 (1955).
625. Stansly, P. G. and Beinert, H. *Biochim. Biophys. Acta* **11**, 600 (1953).
626. Steberl, E. A., Wasson, G. W. and Porter, J. W. *Biochem. Biophys. Res. Commun.* **2**, 174 (1960).
627. Stein, Y. and Shapiro, B. *Biochim. Biophys. Acta* **24**, 197 (1957).
628. Stein, Y., Tietz, A. and Shapiro, B. *Biochim. Biophys. Acta* **26**, 286 (1957).

629. STEINBERG, D., VAUGHAN, M., MARGOLIS, M. and KAMEN, A. *Fed. Proc.* **19**, 227 (1960).
630. STEKOL, J. A., ANDERSON, E. I. and WEISS, S. *J. Biol. Chem.* **233**, 425 (1958).
631. STEKOL, J. A., WEISS, A. and ANDERSON, E. I. *J. Am. Chem. Soc.* **77**, 5192 (1955).
632. STEKOL, J. A., WEISS, S., ANDERSON, E. I. and WATJEN, A. *Fed. Proc.* **15**, 362 (1956).
633. STETTEN, D., JR. *J. Biol. Chem.* **140**, 143 (1941).
634. STETTEN, D., JR. *J. Biol. Chem.* **144**, 501 (1942).
635. STEWART, H. B. and STRICKLAND, K. P. *Can. J. Biochem. Physiol.* **39**, 1133 (1961).
636. STOFFEL, W. *Biochem. Biophys. Res. Communs.* **6**, 270 (1961).
637. STOFFEL, W. *Z. Physiol. Chem.*, Hoppe-Seyler's, **333**, 71 (1963).
638. STOFFYN, P. and STOFFYN, A. *Biochim. Biophys. Acta* **70**, 218 (1963).
639. STRICKLAND, K. P. *Can. J. Med. Sci.* **30**, 484 (1952).
640. STRICKLAND, K. P. *Can. J. Biochem. Physiol.* **32**, 50 (1954).
641. STRICKLAND, K. P. *Chem. in Can.* **9**, 74 (1957).
642. STRICKLAND, K. P. *Can. J. Biochem. and Physiol.* **40**, 247 (1962).
643. STRICKLAND, K. P. and ROSSITER, R. J. *Can. J. Biochem. Physiol.* **40**, 1051 (1962).
644. STRICKLAND, K. P. and SUBRAHMANYAM, D. *Can. Fed. Biol. Soc.* **3**, 49 (1960).
645. STRICKLAND, K. P., SUBRAHMANYAM, D., PRITCHARD, E. T., THOMPSON, W. and ROSSITER, R. J. *Biochem. J.* **87**, 128 (1963).
646. STRICKLAND, K. P., THOMPSON, W., SUBRAHMANYAM, D. and ROSSITER, R. J. *Biochem. J.* **76**, 41P (1960).
647. STROMINGER, J. L., HEPPEL, L. A. and MAXWELL, E. S. *Biochim. Biophys. Acta* **32**, 412 (1959).
648. STUMPF, P. K. and JAMES, A. T. *Biochim. Biophys. Acta* **70**, 20 (1963).
649. STUMPF, P. K. and MCMAHON, V. *Biochim. Biophys. Acta* **84**, 359 (1964).
650. STUMPF, P. K. *Ann. Rev. Biochem.* **29**, 261 (1960).
651. SUGINO, Y. *J. Am. Chem. Soc.* **79**, 5074 (1957).
652. SUZUKI, K. *Biochem. Biophys. Res. Communs.* **16**, 88 (1964).
653. SVENNERHOLM, L. *J. Lipid Res.* **5**, 145 (1964).
654. SVENNERHOLM, L. and THORIN, H. *Biochim. Biophys. Acta* **41**, 371 (1960).
655. SWELL, L., BOITER, T. A., FIELD, H., JR. and TREADWELL, C. R. *Am. J. Physiol.* **181**, 193 (1955).
656. SWELL, L., LAW, M. D. and TREADWELL, C. R. *Arch. Biochem. Biophys.* **105**, 541 (1964).
657. SWELL, L. and TREADWELL, C. R. *J. Biol. Chem.* **182**, 479 (1950).
658. TALBERT, P. T. and HUENNEKENS, F. M. *J. Am. Chem. Soc.* **78**, 4671 (1956).
659. TATTRIE, N. H. *J. Lipid Res.* **1**, 60 (1959).
660. THANNHAUSER, S. J., FELLIG, J. and SCHMID, G. *J. Biol. Chem.* **215**, 211 (1955).
661. THOMPSON, G. A., JR. *J. Biol. Chem.* **240**, 1912 (1965).
662. THOMPSON, W. and DAWSON, R. M. C. *Biochem. J.* **91**, 233 (1964).
663. THOMPSON, W. and DAWSON, R. M. C. *Biochem. J.* **91**, 237 (1964).
664. THOMPSON, W., STRICKLAND, K. P. and ROSSITER, R. J. *Biochem. J.* **87**, 136 (1963).
665. THOMPSON, W., STRICKLAND, K. P. and ROSSITER, R. J. *Fed. Proc.* **18**, 338 (1959).
666. THOMPSON, W., SUBRAHMANYAM, D. and STRICKLAND, K. P. *Fed. Proc.* **19**, 234 (1960).
667. TIETZ, A. *Biochim. Biophys. Acta* **25**, 303 (1957).
668. TIETZ, A. and POPJÁK, G. *Biochem. J.* **60**, 155 (1955).
669. TIETZ, A. and SHAPIRO, B. *Biochim. Biophys. Acta* **19**, 374 (1956).
670. TOMLINSON, R. and BALLOU, C. E. *J. Biol. Chem.* **236**, 1902 (1961).
671. TOOMEY, R. E., WAITE, M., WILLIAMSON, I. P. and WAKIL, S. J. *Fed. Proc.* **24**, 888 (1965).
672. TRUSOV, V. I. *Uspekhi Sovremennoï Biol.* **45**, 28 (1958).
673. TSUYUKI, H. and IDLER, D. R. *Can. J. Biochem.* **39**, 1037 (1961).
674. TUNG, T-C., ANDERSON, L. and LARDY, H. A. *Arch. Biochem. Biophys.* **40**, 194 (1952).
675. UMBARGER, H. E. and UMBARGER, M. A. *Biochim. Biophys. Acta* **62**, 193 (1962).
676. VAGELOS, P. R. *Ann. Rev. Biochem.* **33**, 139 (1964).
677. VAGELOS, P. R. *J. Amer. Chem. Soc.* **81**, 4119 (1959).

678. VanDeenen, L. L. M. In *Metabolism and Physiological Significance of Lipids*, edited by R. M. C. Dawson and D. N. Rhodes. John Wiley, London, New York and Sydney, 1964, p. 155.

679. Vanhouny, G. V., Weersing, S. and Treadwell, C. R. *Arch. Biochem. Biophys.* 107, 7 (1964).

680. Venkataraman, R. and Greenberg, D. M. *J. Am. Chem. Soc.* 80, 2025 (1958).

681. Vignais, P. M., Gallagher, C. H. and Zabin, I. *J. Neurochem.* 2, 283 (1958).

682. Vignais, P. V. and Zabin, I. *Biochim. Biophys. Acta* 29, 263 (1958).

683. VonEuler, H., Adler, E. and Günther, G. *Z. Physiol. Chem.* Hoppe-Seyler's, 249, 1 (1937).

684. Waard, A. de and Popják, G. *Biochem. J.* 68, 6P (1958).

685. Wagenknecht, A. C. and Lewin, L. M. *Fed. Proc.* 17, 329 (1958).

686. Wagenknecht, A. C., Lewin, L. M. and Carter, H. E. *J. Biol. Chem.* 234, 2265 (1954).

687. Wagner, H., Lissau, A., Holl, J. and Hörhammer, L. *J. Lipid Res.* 3, 177 (1962).

688. Waite, M. and Wakil, S. J. *J. Biol. Chem.* 237, 2750 (1962).

689. Waite, M. and Wakil, S. J. *J. Biol. Chem.* 238, 81 (1963).

689a Wakil, S. J. *J. Lipid Res.* 2, 1 (1961).

690. Wakil, S. J. *Ann. Rev. Biochem.* 31, 369 (1962).

691. Wakil, S. J. In *Metabolism and Physiological Significance of Lipids*, edited by R. M. C. Dawson and D. N. Rhodes. John Wiley, London, New York and Sydney, 1964, p. 3.

692. Wakil, S. J. *J. Amer. Chem. Soc.* 80, 6465 (1958).

693. Wakil, S. J. and Ganguly, J. *Fed. Proc.* 18, 346 (1959).

694. Wakil, S. J. and Ganguly, J. *J. Amer. Chem. Soc.* 81, 2597 (1959).

695. Wakil, S. J., McLain, L. W. and Warshaw, J. B. *J. Biol. Chem.* 235, PC31 (1960).

696. Wakil, S. J., Porter, J. W. and Gibson, D. M. *Biochim. Biophys. Acta* 24, 453 (1957).

697. Wakil, S. J., Pugh, E. L. and Sauer, F. *Proc. Natl. Acad. Sci.* 52, 106 (1964).

698. Wakil, S. J., Titchener, E. B. and Gibson, D. M. *Biochim. Biophys. Acta* 29, 225 (1958).

699. Warren, L. and Felsenfeld, H. *Biochem. Biophys. Res. Communs.* 4, 232 (1961).

700. Webster, G. R. and Alpern, R. *J. Biochem. J.* 90, 35 (1964).

701. Webster, G. R. and Folch, J. *Biochim. Biophys. Acta* 49, 399 (1961).

702. Wegner, G. H. and Foster, E. M. *J. Bacteriol.* 85, 53 (1963).

703. Weiss, B. *J. Biol. Chem.* 238, 1953 (1963).

704. Weiss, S. B. and Kennedy, E. P. *J. Am. Chem. Soc.* 78, 3550 (1956).

705. Weiss, S. B., Kennedy, E. P. and Kiyasu, J. Y. *J. Biol. Chem.* 235, 40 (1960).

706. Weiss, S. B., Smith, S. W. and Kennedy, E. P. *J. Biol. Chem.* 231, 53 (1958).

707. Weissbach, A., Elwyn, D. and Sprinson, D. B. *J. Am. Chem Soc.* 72, 3316 (1950).

708. Whitehouse, M., Moeksi, H. and Gurin, S. *J. Biol. Chem.* 226, 813 (1959).

709. Whyte, M., Goodman, De W. S. and Karmen, A. *J. Lipid Res.* 6, 233 (1965).

710. Whyte, M., Karmen, A. and Goodman, De W. S. *J. Lipid Res.* 4, 322 (1963).

711. Wieland, O. and Suyter, M. *Biochem. Z.* 329, 320 (1957).

712. Wilgram, G. F., Holloway, C. F. and Kennedy, E. P. *J. Biol. Chem.* 235, 37 (1960).

713. Williams-Ashman, H. G. and Banks, J. *J. Biol. Chem.* 223, 509 (1956).

714. Willis, J. E. and Sallach, H. J. *J. Biol. Chem.* 237, 910 (1962).

715. Wilson, J. D., Gibson, K. D. and Udenfriend, S. *J. Biol. Chem.* 235, 3213 (1960).

716. Wilson, J. D., Gibson, K. D. and Udenfriend, S. *J. Biol. Chem.* 235, 3539 (1960).

717. Wise, E. M., Jr. and Elwyn, D. *J. Biol. Chem.* 240, 1537 (1965).

718. Wittcoff, H. *The Phosphatides*, Reinhold Publishing Corp., New York (1951).

719. Wittenberg, J. and Kornberg, A. *J. Biol. Chem.* 202, 431 (1953).

720. Wolf, B. and Nyc, J. F. *Biochim. Biophys. Acta* 31, 208 (1959).

721. Wolf, B. and Nyc, J. F. *J. Biol. Chem.* 234, 1068 (1959).

722. Wolfe, L. S. and Lowden, J. A. *Can. J. Biochem.* 42, 1041 (1964).

723. Wood, H. G., Brown, R. W. and Werkman, C. H. *Arch. Biochem.* 6, 243 (1945).

724. Wood, P., Imaichi, K., Knowles, J., Michaels, G. and Kinsell, L. *J. Lipid Res.* 5, 225 (1964).

724a Yamakawa, T., Kiso, N., Handa, S., Makita, A. and Yokoyama, S. *J. Biochem.* (*Tokyo*) 52, 468 (1962).

725. YAMANOTO, R. S., GOLDSTEIN, N. P. and TREADWELL, C. R. *J. Biol. Chem.* **180**, 615 (1949).
726. YUAN, C. and BLOCH, K. *J. Biol. Chem.* **236**, 1277 (1961).
727. YOUNG, H. L. and PACE, N. *Arch. Biochem. Biophys.* **75**, 125 (1958).
728. ZABIN, I. *J. Biol. Chem.* **189**, 355 (1951).
729. ZABIN, I. *J. Am. Chem. Soc.* **79**, 5834 (1957).
730. ZABIN, I. In *Lipide Chemistry*, edited by D. J. Hanahan. John Wiley, New York and London, 1960, p. 134.
731. ZABIN, I. and MEAD, J. F. *J. Biol. Chem.* **205**, 271 (1953).
732. ZABIN, I. and MEAD, J. F. *J. Biol. Chem.* **211**, 87 (1954).
733. ZALKIN, H., LAW, J. H. and GOLDFINE, H. *J. Biol. Chem.* **238**, 1242 (1963).
734. ZEBE, E. C. and McSHAN, W. H. *Biochim. Biophys. Acta* **31**, 513 (1959).
735. ZILVERSMIT, D. B. *Amer. J. Med.* **23**, 120 (1957).
736. ZILVERSMIT, D. B., CHAIKOFF, I. L. and ENTENMAN, C. *J. Biol. Chem.* **172**, 637 (1948).
737. ZILVERSMIT, D. B., ENTENMAN, C. and FISHLER, M. C. *J. Gen. Physiol.* **26**, 325 (1943).

CHAPTER 4

THE BIOSYNTHESIS OF STEROIDS

EZRA STAPLE

Department of Biochemistry, School of Medicine,
University of Pennsylvania, Philadelphia 4, Pennsylvania

CONTENTS

I. CHOLESTEROL   207
II. OTHER STEROLS   218
    A. *Ergosterol*   219
    B. *Zymosterol*   219
    C. *Lanosterol*   220
    D. *Dihydrolanosterol*   220
    E. *Agnosterol*   221
    F. *Methostenol and 4 α methyl-Δ8-cholestenol*   221
    G. *Desmosterol*   222
    H. *Lathosterol*   222
    I. *7-Dehydrocholesterol*   223
    J. *Eburicoic acid*   223
    K. *Coprostanol*   224
    L. *Cholestanol*   224
    M. *Phytosterols*   225
III. ADRENOCORTICAL AND SEX STEROID HORMONES   226
    A. *Adrenocortical steroid hormones*   226
    B. *Sex hormones*   230
IV. BILE ACIDS   233
V. VITAMIN D   239
    REFERENCES   241

OF ALL the work on the biosynthesis of steroids, the most exhaustive and thorough is that which has been done on cholesterol. Because of the importance of the problem itself, because knowledge of this centrally important precursor of other steroids is vital and because its mechanism illustrates a "general" mechanism for sterol formation, we shall begin our discussion with it.

I. CHOLESTEROL

The work on the biosynthesis of cholesterol may be considered in retrospect to have started with the work of Dezani and Cattoretti[1] who first observed the synthesis of cholesterol in animals on a cholesterol-free diet. Since that time there have been other studies which have confirmed this observation. [2, 3, 4] However, the first work which demonstrates the chemical nature of this biosynthesis begins with the studies of Sonderhoff and Thomas.[5] These authors found in 1937 that on incubation of yeast with deuterium-labeled acetate, they were able to isolate a heavily labeled unsaponifiable fraction which, although it was not analyzed by them, consisted of a large proportion of sterol. In extending this work, Bloch and Rittenberg [6, 7] found that similarly labeled deuterio-acetate when fed to rats and mice led to an amount of deuterium labeling in the cholesterol which was manifold in excess of that which would result if the deuterium-labeled acetate was converted to water and the new sterol formed in its presence. They also concluded that the higher fatty acids were not involved, as intermediates, in the biosynthesis of cholesterol. By a chemical degradation of the labeled cholesteryl chloride, thus obtained, into isooctane and isooctene representing the side chain, and the hydrocarbon $C_{19}H_{30}$, first obtained by Bergmann and Bergmann, [8] which represents the nucleus, it was found that both contained deuterium. The side chain was found to contain a higher concentration. Several explanations of this apparent discrepancy were possible including the fact that the amount of methyl groups of acetic acid was greater in the side chain that in the nucleus or that there was migration or greater dilution of the hydrogen atoms in forming the nucleus. The complete resolution of this isotope distribution problem had to await the later work of Bloch and Cornforth using carbon-14 labeled cholesterol derived from acetate, and will be discussed later.

Of course, besides acetate, many other low-molecular weight compounds were tested for their ability to be incorporated into cholesterol. Acetoacetate, [9, 10] acetaldehyde, [9] acetamide, [11] pyruvate, [12] acetone, [9, 13-15] ethanol, [16] as well as butyrate, [16, 17] valerate, [16] hexanoate, [17] octanoate [17] and palmitate [16] were found to be incorporated to some extent. It appeared that the efficiency of many of the suggested precursors was proportional to their ability to yield the two-carbon atom fragment, acetate. Leucine and isovalerate also were observed to be incorporated to some extent. [18, 41]

Rabinowitz and Gurin [19] and Rudney [20] showed that hydroxymethylglutarate was synthesized by rat liver and that this could be incorporated into cholesterol. Rudney [21] further observed that hydroxymethylglutaryl CoA is synthesized from acetoacetyl CoA and acetyl CoA in yeast. The observations of Bloch, Clark and Harary [22] that dimethylacrylate, hydroxyisovalerate and trans-β-methylglutaconate, all of which have been observed to arise from acetate, could be similarly incorporated into cholesterol raised the possibility that hydroxymethylglutarate, which could be considered to be related to these compounds, might be a key intermediate. A schematic possible relationship according to Gurin [23] is shown below (Fig. 1).

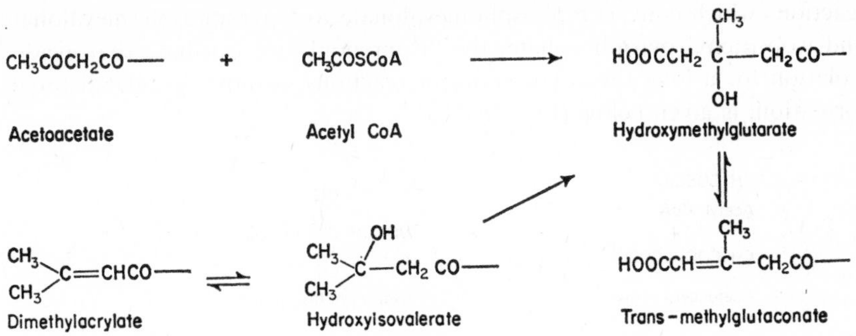

$$CH_3COCH_2CO— \quad + \quad CH_3COSCoA \quad \longrightarrow \quad HOOCCH_2 \overset{CH_3}{\underset{OH}{\underset{|}{\overset{|}{C}}}}—CH_2CO—$$

Acetoacetate   Acetyl CoA   Hydroxymethylglutarate

$$\underset{CH_3}{\overset{CH_3}{>}}C{=}CHCO— \quad \rightleftarrows \quad \underset{CH_3}{\overset{CH_3}{>}}\overset{OH}{\underset{|}{C}}—CH_2CO— \qquad HOOCCH{=}\overset{CH_3}{\underset{|}{C}}—CH_2CO—$$

Dimethylacrylate   Hydroxyisovalerate   Trans–methylglutaconate

FIG. 1.

The most dramatic breakthrough in the problem of cholesterol precursors came when Tavormina, Gibbs and Huff[24] reported that mevalonic acid (β,δ-dihydroxy-β-methylvaleric acid), an acetate-replacing factor for bacteria first found in brewers' solubles, was capable of being incorporated into cholesterol in very high yield. Further work with this compound has indicated that the radioactivity of mevalonic acid-1-C^{14} was not incorporated, while mevalonic acid-2-C^{14} yielded radioactive cholesterol.[25] This indicated that decarboxylation occurred early in the sequence of reactions, apparently at the six-carbon atom level, to give a five-carbon atom active intermediate. Furthermore, Ferguson, Durr and Rudney[26] have established that an enzyme exists in yeast which is capable of converting hydroxymethylglutaryl CoA to mevalonic acid, establishing its pathway of biosynthesis from acetoacetate and acetate. Knauss, Porter and Wasson[27] have demonstrated the formation of mevalonic acid from acetate in liver tissue, so that an excellent case for its intermediacy has now been made. Further, Lynen and Grassl[28] have shown that the ($+$) isomer of mevalonic acid is the only one that has biological activity.

Dituri, Rabinowitz and Gurin,[29] and Cornforth, Cornforth, Popják and Gore[30] investigated the pattern of labeling in squalene which derived from mevalonic acid-2-C^{14}. They found there was evidence that only one of the methyl groups in the five-carbon atom units forming squalene was still radioactive. This would indicate that there is little or no rearrangement of mevalonate before or during incorporation and that there is no completely "free" five-carbon atom intermediate (since both methyl groups would then be indistinguishable) before squalene formation.

Tchen[31] working with mevalonic acid in yeast preparations found a mevalonic kinase which transforms the acid to 5-phosphomevalonic acid. In addition he found that ATP was necessary to transform the 5-phosphomevalonate to squalene. The enzyme has also been characterized further by others in liver tissue as well as yeast.[32] Lynen, Eggerer, Henning and Kessel,[33] and Chaykin, Law, Phillips, Tchen and Bloch[37] have described the further reactions which convert 5-phosphomevalonate to 5-pyrophosphomevalonate and isopentenyl pyrophosphate, the "isoprenoid" intermediate that evaded isolation for a long time. The series of reactions, as now postulated for its formation, is given below (Fig. 2).

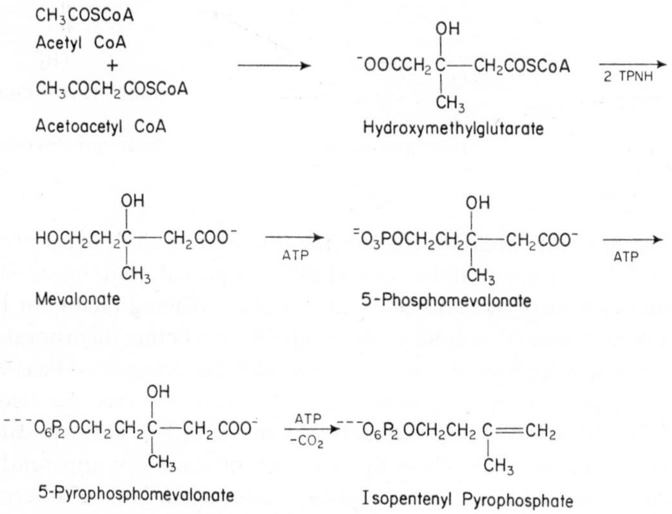

CH₃COSCoA
Acetyl CoA
+
CH₃COCH₂COSCoA
Acetoacetyl CoA

$$CH_3COSCoA + CH_3COCH_2COSCoA \longrightarrow {}^-OOCCH_2\underset{CH_3}{\overset{OH}{C}}\!\!-\!\!CH_2COSCoA \xrightarrow{\text{2 TPNH}}$$

Hydroxymethylglutarate

$$HOCH_2CH_2\underset{CH_3}{\overset{OH}{C}}\!\!-\!\!CH_2COO^- \xrightarrow{\text{ATP}} {}^=O_3POCH_2CH_2\underset{CH_3}{\overset{OH}{C}}\!\!-\!\!CH_2COO^- \xrightarrow{\text{ATP}}$$

Mevalonate   5-Phosphomevalonate

$$\ ^{---}O_6P_2OCH_2CH_2\underset{CH_3}{\overset{OH}{C}}\!\!-\!\!CH_2COO^- \xrightarrow[-CO_2]{\text{ATP}} \ ^{---}O_6P_2OCH_2CH_2\underset{CH_3}{\overset{}{C}}\!\!=\!\!CH_2$$

5-Pyrophosphomevalonate   Isopentenyl Pyrophosphate

FIG. 2.

The condensation of dimethylallyl pyrophosphate, an isomerization product of isopentenyl pyrophosphate, and isopentyl pyrophosphate has been reported by Lynen, Agranoff, Eggerer, Henning and Moslein [35] to result in the formation of geranyl pyrophosphate. This compound can then condense with an additional molecule of isopentenyl pyrophosphate to yield farnesyl pyrophosphate. The reductive dimerization of two molecules of farnesyl pyrophosphate, tail to tail, to yield squalene [33, 35] has been demonstrated in liver and yeast by these same workers (Fig. 3).

More recently Popják [36] and also Popják and Goodman [37] have observed the enzymic formation of nerolidol from mevalonate with rat liver preparations, and Cornforth and Popják [38] have proposed a modification in the biosynthetic pathway for formation of squalene as shown in Fig. 4. This new pathway involves the enzymic isomeric formation of a molecule of nerolidyl-X (possibly pyrophosphate) which may condense with a molecule of farnesyl pyrophosphate much as isopentenyl pyrophosphate with dimethylallyl pyrophosphate in Fig. 3. They picture a cationic intermediate which is stabilized by the successive loss of a proton, anion X⁻, and another proton successively to yield dehydrosqualene. A reductive step possibly involving TPNH is pictured as yielding squalene. This scheme would explain the isotopic

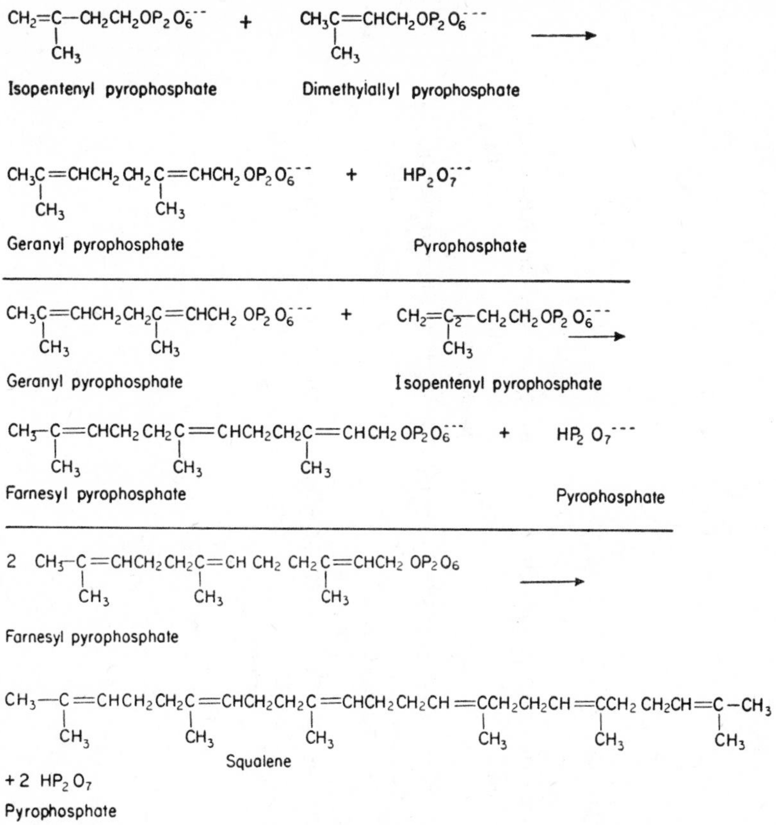

$$CH_2=\underset{\underset{CH_3}{|}}{C}-CH_2CH_2OP_2O_6^{---} \quad + \quad CH_3\underset{\underset{CH_3}{|}}{C}=CHCH_2OP_2O_6^{---} \quad \longrightarrow$$

Isopentenyl pyrophosphate   Dimethylallyl pyrophosphate

$$CH_3\underset{\underset{CH_3}{|}}{C}=CHCH_2CH_2\underset{\underset{CH_3}{|}}{C}=CHCH_2OP_2O_6^{---} \quad + \quad HP_2O_7^{---}$$

Geranyl pyrophosphate   Pyrophosphate

$$CH_3\underset{\underset{CH_3}{|}}{C}=CHCH_2CH_2\underset{\underset{CH_3}{|}}{C}=CHCH_2OP_2O_6^{---} \quad + \quad CH_2=\underset{\underset{CH_3}{|}}{C_2}-CH_2CH_2OP_2O_6^{---} \quad \longrightarrow$$

Geranyl pyrophosphate   Isopentenyl pyrophosphate

$$CH_3-\underset{\underset{CH_3}{|}}{C}=CHCH_2CH_2\underset{\underset{CH_3}{|}}{C}=CHCH_2CH_2\underset{\underset{CH_3}{|}}{C}=CHCH_2OP_2O_6^{---} \quad + \quad HP_2O_7^{---}$$

Farnesyl pyrophosphate   Pyrophosphate

$$2 \quad CH_3-\underset{\underset{CH_3}{|}}{C}=CHCH_2CH_2\underset{\underset{CH_3}{|}}{C}=CH\,CH_2\,CH_2\underset{\underset{CH_3}{|}}{C}=CHCH_2\,OP_2O_6 \quad \longrightarrow$$

Farnesyl pyrophosphate

$$CH_3-\underset{\underset{CH_3}{|}}{C}=CHCH_2CH_2\underset{\underset{CH_3}{|}}{C}=CHCH_2CH_2\underset{\underset{CH_3}{|}}{C}=CHCH_2CH_2CH=\underset{\underset{CH_3}{|}}{C}CH_2CH_2CH=\underset{\underset{CH_3}{|}}{C}CH_2CH_2CH=\underset{\underset{CH_3}{|}}{C}-CH_3$$

Squalene

$$+\,2\ HP_2O_7$$

Pyrophosphate

FIG. 3.

hydrogen data found by Rilling and Bloch [39] and would also be consistent with the other data on the formation of squalene.

As early as 1926, Channon [40, 41] had investigated the possibility that squalene was a possible intermediate in cholesterol biosynthesis, after the suggestion of Heilbron, Kamm and Owens [42] and later of Robinson. [43] He concluded erroneously that it was not true, but his experiments did indicate some involvement of squalene in cholesterol biosynthesis. However, it was not until 1953 that Bloch and his collaborators reinvestigated the matter using isotopes. The initial experiments in which they used synthetic C^{14} labeled squalene failed. They persisted, however, in their investigation of the problem, first demonstrating that squalene is indeed synthesized by rats. [44] With the use of this naturally labeled squalene, Langdon and Bloch [45] were able to demonstrate that squalene is indeed converted into cholesterol. The failure of these first experiments with synthetic squalene has now been explained [46] on the basis of an isomerization that occurs on forming the

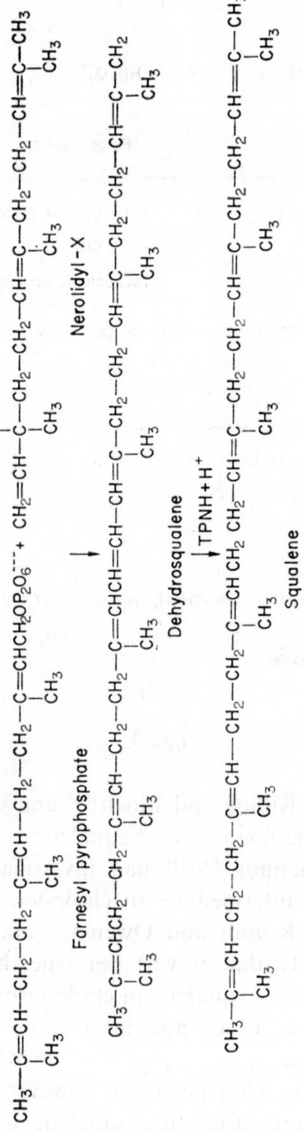

$CH_3-C=CH-CH-CH_2-CH_2-C=CH-CH_2-CH_2-C=CHCH_2OP_2O_6^{---}$ + $CH_2=CH-C-CH_2-CH_2-CH_2-CH=C-CH_3$

$X^{(-)}$

Farnesyl pyrophosphate

Nerolidyl-X

$CH_3-C=CH-CH-CH_2-CH_2-C=CH-CH_2-CH_2-C=CHCH=CH-CH_2-CH_2-CH_2-CH=C-CH_2$

Dehydrosqualene

TPNH+H⁺

$CH_3-C=CH-CH_2-CH_2-CH_2-C=CH-CH_2-CH_2-CH=C-CH_2CH_2-CH_2-CH_2-CH_2-CH_2-CH=C-CH_3$

Squalene

Fig. 4.

hexahydrochloride, a step in the purification of the synthetic material. It has been found that all-*trans* squalene[47] is the natural isomer required for the cyclization to cholesterol and that very little or none of this isomer survives the synthetic purification.

Earlier suggestions by Robinson[43] and a more detailed mechanism by Ruzicka, Eschenmoser and Heusser[48] indicated how squalene might be cyclized to yield cholesterol. Woodward and Bloch[49] in their latest suggested mechanism have made a proposal that is consistent with all of the isotope distribution data and enzymological evidence that has been obtained so far. Unlike the earlier suggestion of Robinson, that squalene cyclizes according to Fig. 5, Woodward and Bloch now propose the following type of cyclization that is consistent with all of the present data (see Fig. 6). This type of folding of squalene differs from the earlier suggestion in labeling at carbon atoms 7,

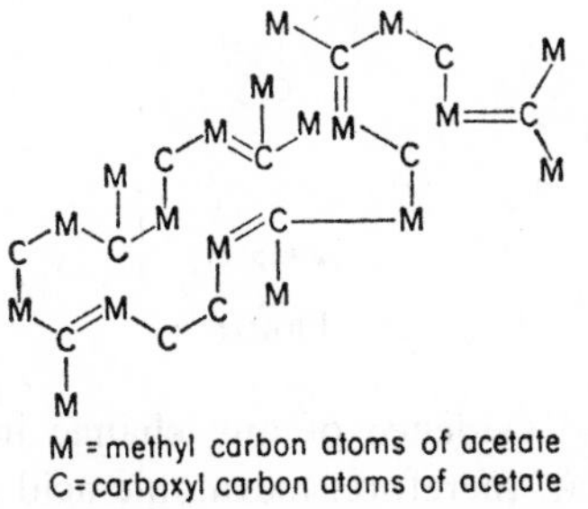

M = methyl carbon atoms of acetate
C = carboxyl carbon atoms of acetate

FIG. 5. Robinson's scheme for folding of squalene.

8, 12 and 13 of cholesterol, when synthesized biologically from acetate. The pattern predicted by this mechanism has in fact been found in epiandrosterone derived from cholesterol biosynthesized from acetate-C^{14}.

Very interestingly, the formation of squalene from its precursors has been demonstrated by Bucher and McGarrahan[50] not to require oxygen. The cyclization of squalene to lanosterol and cholesterol does require oxygen.

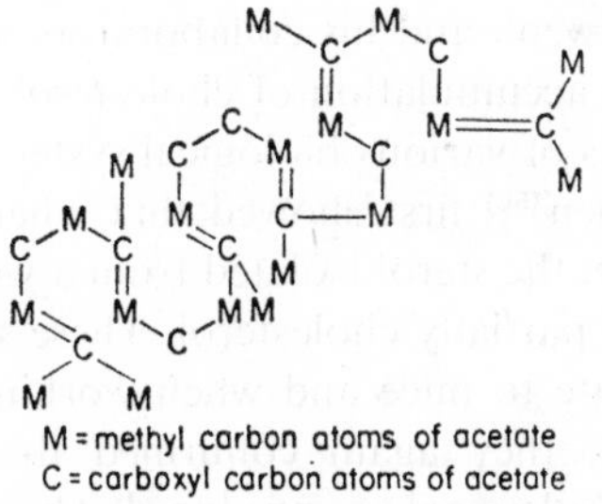

M = methyl carbon atoms of acetate
C = carboxyl carbon atoms of acetate

FIG. 6. Woodward-Bloch's scheme for folding of squalene.

Tchen and Bloch [51] looking farther into this cyclization mechanism, have utilized oxygen-18 and deuterium labeled water. On the basis of the pattern of labeling obtained in these experiments they were able to conclude that during the cyclization of squalene to lanosterol (an intermediate on the way to cholesterol), no proton or hydroxyl ion from the medium is incorporated into the sterol, while molecular oxygen is. They have ruled out an isoeuphol type of intermediate (Fig. 7), and also the mechanism proposed earlier by Ruzicka, Eschenmoser and Heusser. [48] Amdur, Rilling and Bloch [52] found that in experiments in which 2-C^{14}, 5-di-H^3-mevalonic acid was transformed to

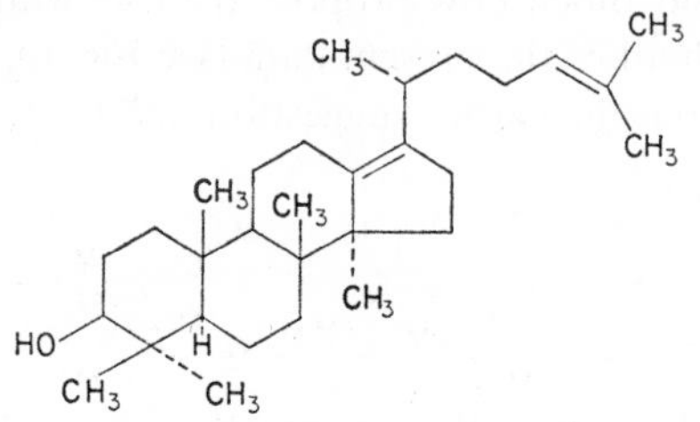

Isoeuphol

FIG. 7.

squalene, there was no evidence of any change in the oxidation level of mevalonic acid and that, therefore, mevalonic acid itself or some derivative at the same oxidation level was involved in the condensations. This, of course, ruled out mevaldic acid or oxidation of the primary hydroxyl group of mevalonic acid.

Several investigators have examined the mechanism of the cyclization of squalene to cholesterol, especially with respect to the problem of migration of a methyl group to carbon atom 13 from carbon atom 8 of the intermediate sterol. This may involve a 1:3 shift or a double 1:2 shift as outlined by Eschenmoser. [53] Cornforth [54] using steric isotope labeling found that a 1:2 shift was the biologically preferred mechanism. Maudgal, Tchen and Bloch [55] also arrived at the same conclusion.

Already in 1952, Schwenk and his collaborators were beginning to gather strong evidence for the accumulation of cholesterol intermediates, especially in short-term treatments of various biological systems with sterol precursors. Schwenk and Werthessen [56] first showed that when pig liver was perfused with radioactive acetate, the sterol isolated from a work-up of the liver tissue and perfusate was only partially cholesterol. These same authors [57] administered radioactive acetate to mice and when working up the sterols formed during a short period, they again confirmed that digitonin precipitable substances other than cholesterol are produced. These constitute the so-called "high counting companions" of cholesterol. Further work-up of this fraction by Schwenk and his group and also by others has indicated the presence of lanosterol, agnosterol and zymosterol.

From the work of Schwenk and his collaborators it had thus become clear that some of the precursors between squalene and cholesterol may accumulate in incubations or perfusions of liver tissue, especially if the time of treatment was quite short. Bloch and his collaborators have in fact tested a number of these possible intermediate compounds for their convertibility to cholesterol. Johnston and Bloch[58] have shown that zymosterol-C^{14} prepared by incubation of yeast with labeled acetate could be readily converted to cholesterol by rat liver enzymes. Alexander and Schwenk[59] have demonstrated this same conversion in the intact animal. Clayton and Bloch[60] prepared biosynthetically labeled lanosterol and demonstrated that this compound is also readily converted to cholesterol. Evidence was also accumulated that there existed an unknown intermediate in the conversion of lanosterol to cholesterol. This was identified by Gautschi and Bloch[61] as $\Delta^{8, 24}$ 4,4-dimethylcholestadiene-3β-ol. Olson, Lindberg and Bloch[62] have evidence that the three methyl groups at carbon atoms 4 and 14 of lanosterol are lost as carbon

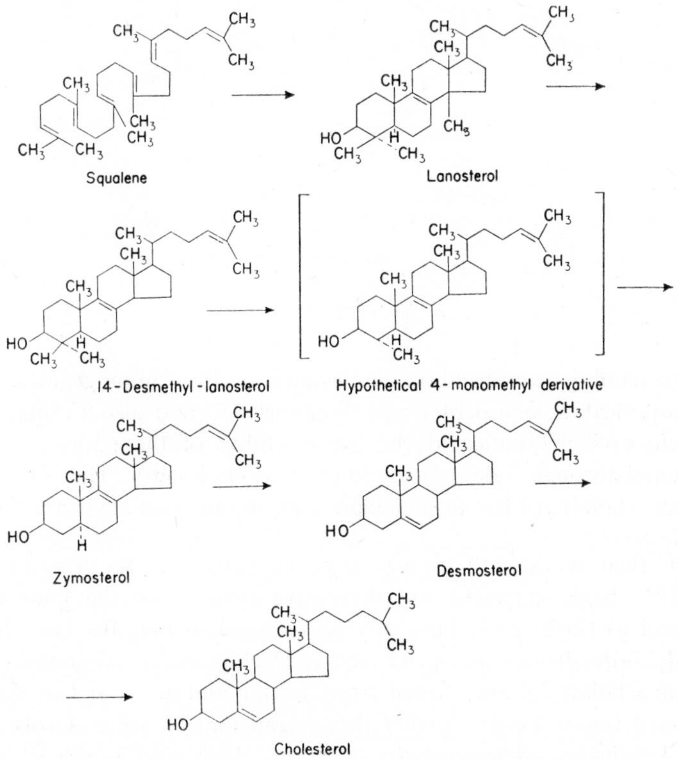

FIG. 8. First scheme for formation of cholesterol from squalene.

dioxide in the final formation of cholesterol. There is added weight for the existence of a 4-monomethyl intermediate compound in Fig. 8 from the isolation of 4α-methyl-Δ⁷-cholestenol (see below, Fig. 18) from plant and animal sources. Additionally 4α-methyl-Δ⁸-cholestenol has been isolated from certain tumor tissue and prepared as an intermediate in cholesterol biosynthesis by Kandutsch and Russell[63] as will be described below.

Interestingly Djerassi, Knight and Wilkinson[64] report the isolation of macdougallin, 14α-methyl-Δ⁸-cholesten-3β-6α diol (Fig. 9), from cactus and have made the suggestion that in cactus at least, removal of the 4-methyl groups may precede the demethylations at carbon 14. In addition, the suggestion is made that this may also be true in mammalian system.

The conversion of desmosterol to cholesterol has been shown in the intact rat by Stokes, Hickey and Fish. [65] Thus one scheme based on this and related observations may be postulated for the conversion of squalene to cholesterol (Fig. 8).

Frantz, Davidson, Dulit and Mobberley[66] first showed in 1959 that

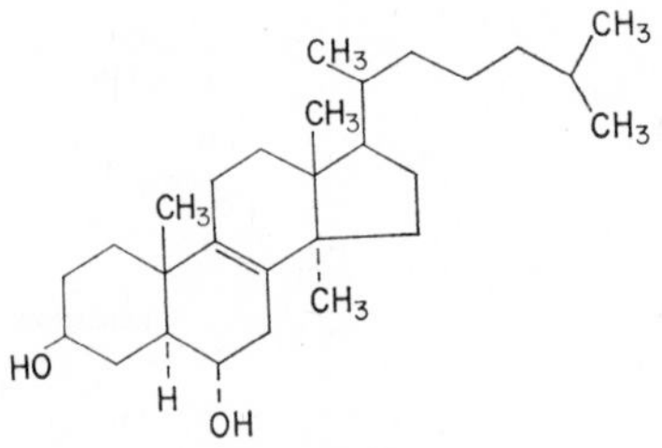

Macdougallin

FIG. 9.

Δ⁷-cholestenol is converted to cholesterol in liver homogenates. Further Dempsey, Seaton, Schroepfer and Trockman[67] and also Frantz, Sanghvi and Schroepfer[68] indicated the irreversibility of the pathway from Δ⁷-cholestenol through 7-dehydrocholesterol to cholesterol. They showed that 7-dehydrocholesterol has to be included as an intermediate in the formation of cholesterol.

From their work with mouse preputial gland tumors, Kandutsch and Russell[69] have suggested an alternative system for the conversion of lanosterol to cholesterol. This may be outlined in Fig. 10. They found[70] that 24,25-dihydrolanosterol, 4α-methyl-Δ⁸-cholestenol, Δ⁷-cholestenol and 7-dehydrocholesterol are formed from acetate and are found in the above-mentioned tumor tissue. Further they found that all these sterols are converted readily to cholesterol. In addition, Wells and Lorah[71] obtained cholesterol from 4α-methyl-Δ⁷-cholestenol (methostenol) and found that

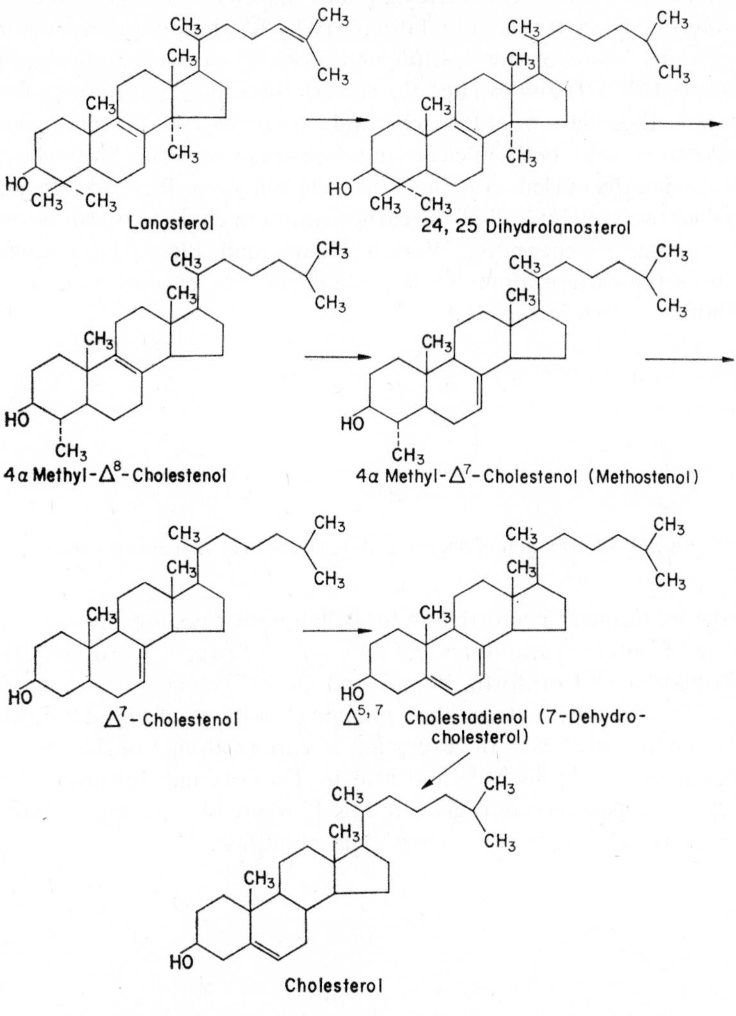

FIG. 10. Second scheme for formation of cholesterol from lanosterol.

acetate is converted to methostenol in the rat. Additional weight is lent to this scheme by Avigan, Goodman and Steinberg[72] who showed that liver homogenates readily convert lanosterol to 24,25-dihydrolanosterol. Thus there is convincing evidence for the existence of the alternate scheme shown in Fig. 10. Whether the schemes shown in Figs. 8 and 10 both operate at the same time in the same tissue or in different tissues cannot be settled at this time.

The incorporation of the two-carbon-atom fragment from acetate into cholesterol has been a very interesting and challenging problem of consider-able importance. After the initial discovery by Bloch that acetate was indeed incorporated into cholesterol, Little and Bloch [73] carried out an experiment with $C^{14}H_3C^{13}OOH$ and isolated the cholesterol resulting from this substrate. By suitable degradations of the sterol and measurement of the relative isotope incorporation into both nuclear and side-chain moieties they concluded correctly that the nucleus contains fifteen carbon atoms from acetate, and the side chain twelve. Thus, all of the carbon atoms in cholesterol can be derived from acetate. Furthermore, Wursch Huang and Bloch [74] succeeded in degrading the carbon atoms of the side chain, one by one, and found the distribution shown in Fig. 11.

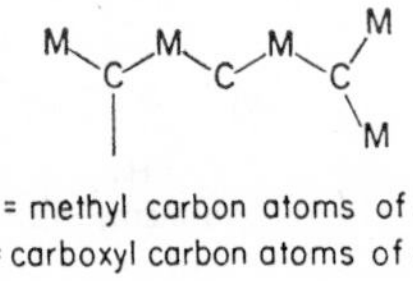

M = methyl carbon atoms of acetate
C = carboxyl carbon atoms of acetate

FIG. 11. Distribution of acetate carbon atoms in cholesterol side chain.

In the meantime, Cornforth and his collaborators became interested in the problem of isotope distribution and, in a series of papers, Cornforth, Hunter and Popják [75, 76] Cornforth, Popják and Gore [77] and Cornforth, Gore and Popják [78] were able to trace the remaining positions of the acetate carbon atoms in cholesterol with the exception of carbon atom 7 of the sterol. This latter was done by Bloch [79] and also by Dauben and Takemura. [80] The final and complete picture is given in Fig. 12 where M = methyl carbon atom of acetate and C = carboxyl carbon atom of acetate.

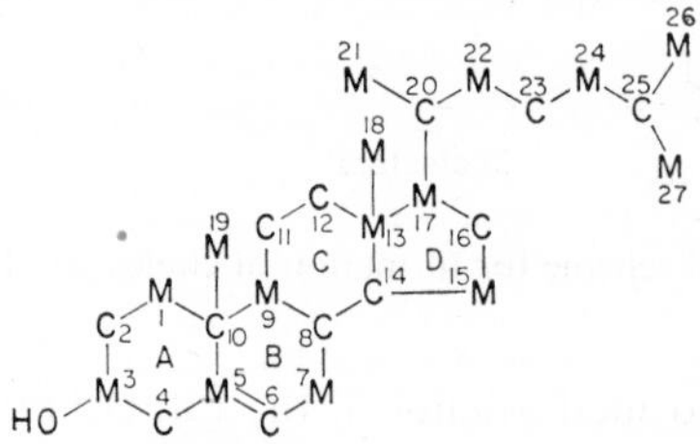

FIG. 12. Distribution of acetate carbon in cholesterol.

II. OTHER STEROLS

While the main detailed work on the biosynthesis of sterols has largely been involved with cholesterol, other sterols have been investigated both as part of this mainstream and also for their own sake. It should be noted that present indications are that the cyclization of squalene forms a part of the biosynthesis of each of the following sterols.

A. *Ergosterol* (Fig. 13)

The biogenesis of this sterol was the first studied with isotopic tracers and antedates any similar work on cholesterol. The first isotopic experiment in this field was done with deuterium-labeled acetate by Sonderhoff and Thomas [5] who incubated this labeled acetate with *Saccharomyces cerevisiae* and isolated the labeled sterol fraction. Further work with carbon-14 was done by

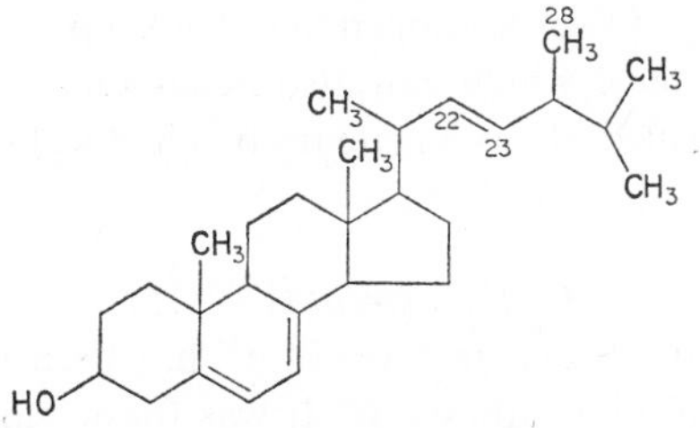

Ergosterol

FIG. 13.

Hanahan and Wakil [81] and Schwenk and co-workers. [82] It was found that twenty-seven of the twenty-eight carbon atoms of the ergosterol skeleton apparently arise from the cyclization of squalene (viz. cholesterol), but that the twenty-eight carbon atom (at carbon atom 24) arises by an independent route. Dauben, Fonken and Boswell [83] found that formate may serve as a source of this twenty-eighth carbon atom, and Alexander, Schwenk and Gold [84] have subsequently observed that methionine is an even better source of this carbon atom. There is also some evidence for the direct donation of a methyl group to the carbon skeleton. Dauben and Hutton [85] have obtained evidence from the labeling of carbon atoms 11 and 12 of ergosterol by carboxyl-labeled acetate that is consistent with the origin of the carbon skeleton of ergosterol from squalene.

B. *Zymosterol* (Fig. 14)

This sterol, also synthesized by yeast, was first isolated in radioactive form by Schwenk and his group [82] from *Saccharomyces cerevisiae* which had been previously incubated with carbon-14 carboxyl-labeled acetate. The origin of this sterol from the cyclization of squalene has been postulated by Bloch. [86] The further metabolism of zymosterol to cholesterol in rat liver homogenates has been observed by Johnston and Bloch [87] and it has been postulated as an intermediate in the biosynthesis of cholesterol from acetate. The process from zymosterol to cholesterol is aerobic and requires both particulate and

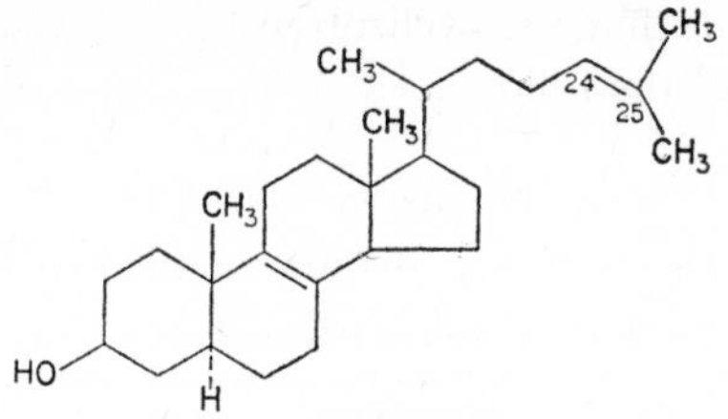

Zymosterol

Fig. 14.

supernatant fractions of liver homogenates. The conversion of 24,25-dihydro-zymosterol to cholesterol which can also occur under the same conditions, has apparently been ruled out as a primary biochemical reaction in cholesterol biosynthesis.

C. *Lanosterol* (Fig. 15)

This sterol originally found in "wool fat" has been indicated as an intermediate in cholesterol biosynthesis. [86] It was found that it could be synthesized from radioactive acetate by the addition to liver homogenates of a

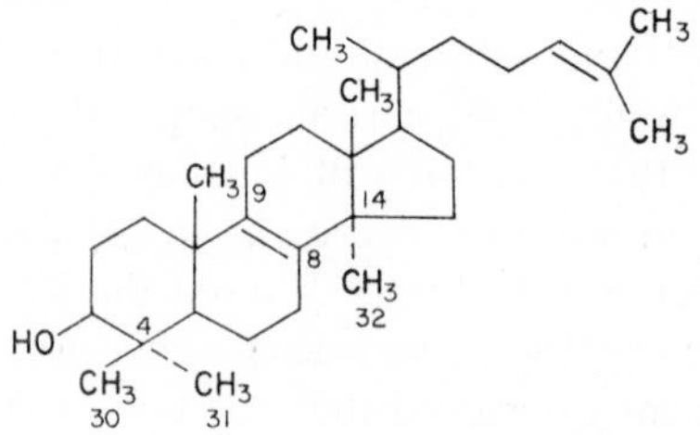

Lanosterol

Fig. 15.

lanosterol-containing fraction as trapping agent. [88] Clayton and Bloch [89] subsequently demonstrated its ready conversion to cholesterol in rat liver homogenates.

D. *Dihydrolanosterol* (Fig. 16)

The formation of 24,25-dihydrolanosterol from acetate has been reported in mouse preputial gland tumors by Kandutsch and Russell. [90] It has been implicated, as already mentioned, as an intermediate in the formation of cholesterol. Further, as has already been mentioned, [72] it has been found that rat liver homogenates convert lanosterol to 24,25-dihydrolanosterol, and that TPNH appears to be required for this process.

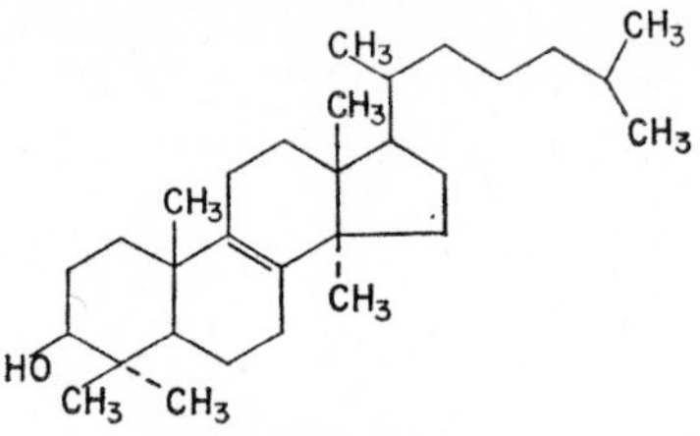

Dihydrolanosterol

FIG. 16.

E. *Agnosterol* (Fig. 17)

This sterol originally found in "wool fat" has been indicated as an intermediate in cholesterol biosynthesis. [86] It was found that it could be synthesized from radioactive acetate by the addition to liver homogenates of a

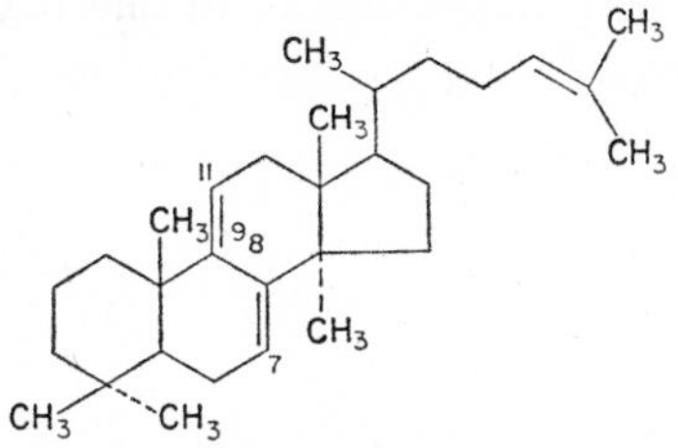

Agnosterol

FIG. 17.

lanosterol-containing fraction as trapping agent. [88] Clayton and Bloch [89] subsequently demonstrated its ready conversion to cholesterol in rat liver homogenates.

F. *Methostenol and 4α-Methyl-Δ8-cholestenol* (Fig. 18)

These two isomers, i.e. 4α-methyl-Δ^7 and 4α-methyl-Δ^8-cholestenol, have been found to be formed from acetate in various tissues.

The Δ^7-isomer, methostenol, was shown by Frantz, Ener and Mobberley [91] and also by Wells and Lorah [71] to be formed from acetate in the rat. Its possible implication as an intermediate in cholesterol formation from acetate was suggested by its ready conversion to cholesterol.

The formation of the Δ^8-isomer from acetate was reported in mouse preputial gland tumors by Kandutsch and Russell. [90] Its production from acetate indicated it too might be an intermediate when compared with cholesterol and several other sterols formed at the same time. These authors

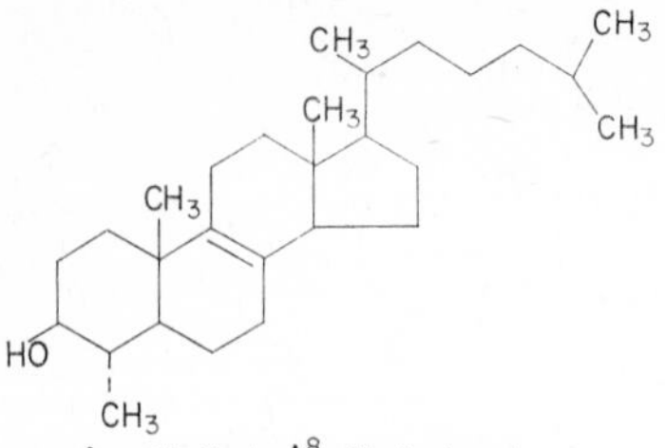

4 α - Methyl - Δ^8 - Cholestenol 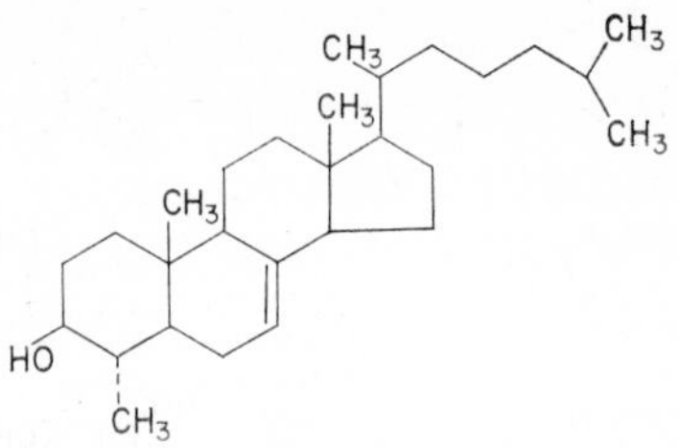   Methostenol

FIG. 18.

have proposed a scheme, already cited (Fig. 8), which implicates this compound as an intermediate in the conversion of lanosterol to cholesterol.

G. *Desmosterol* (Fig. 19)

Stokes, Fish and Hickey[92] first isolated this compound from chick embryos. It has since been implicated as an intermediate in the biogenesis of cholesterol.[65] In fact, its appearance in animals that have been treated

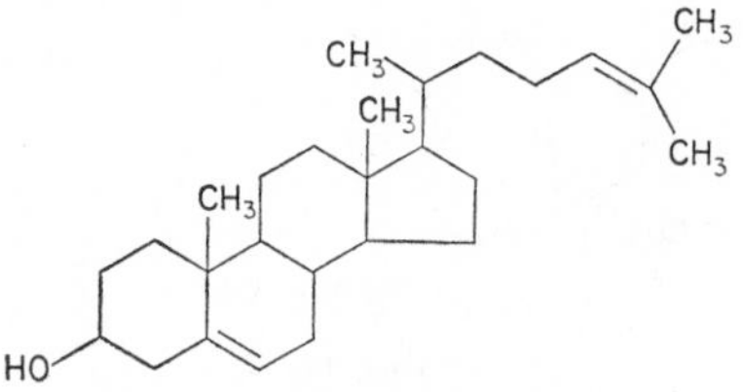

Desmosterol

FIG. 19.

with "MER-29"† has been attributed by Avigan, Steinberg, Thompson and Mosettig[93] to interference by this drug in the last step of cholesterol biosynthesis. It has also been found in developing rat brain by Kritchevsky and Holmes.[94]

H. *Lathosterol* (Fig. 20)

Lathosterol (Δ^7-cholestenol) was first found to be formed from cholesterol in rabbits by Biggs, Lemmon and Pierce.[95] Its biosynthesis from cholesterol was subsequently reported in rat liver homogenates and also the supernatant fraction of such homogenates by Davidson, Dulit and Frantz.[96] Its specific

† "MER-29"; "TRIPARANOL"; 1-*p*-(β-diethylaminoethoxyl) phenyl-1-(*p*-tolyl)-2-(*p*-chlorophenyl) ethanol; manufactured by William S. Merrell Co., Cincinnati, Ohio.

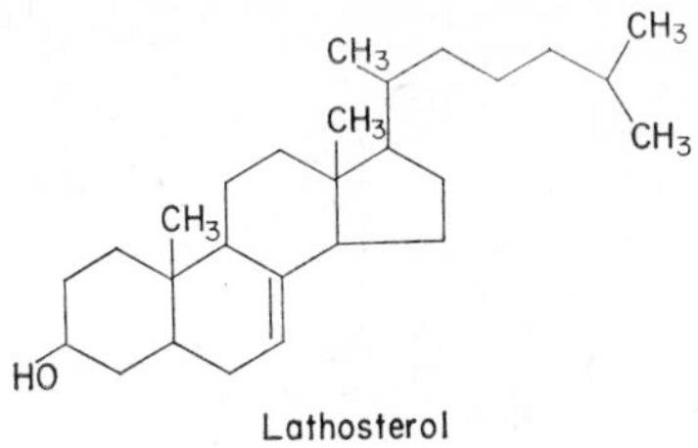

Lathosterol

FIG. 20.

activity, when formed from acetate, relative to cholesterol and other sterols formed under the same conditions, indicated that it might be an intermediate in cholesterol biosynthesis.

I. 7-*Dehydrocholesterol* (Fig. 21)

7-Dehydrocholesterol ($\Delta^{5, 7}$-cholestadienol) and its actual relationships to cholesterol has been a matter of conjecture for some time. This dehydro sterol has been implicated early as a precursor of Vitamin D_3 (q.v.). However,

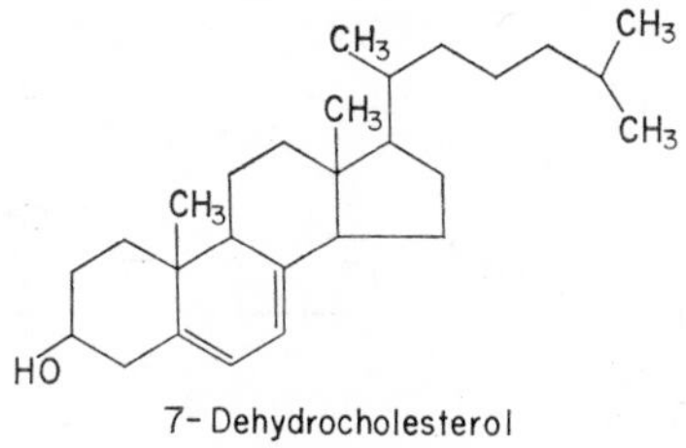

7-Dehydrocholesterol

FIG. 21.

whether it was formed from cholesterol or whether cholesterol was formed from it was not resolved until the work of Dempsey, Seaton, Schroepfer and Trockman[67] and Frantz, Sanghvi and Schroepfer[68] definitely established that it is irreversibly converted to cholesterol.

J. *Eburicoic Acid* (Fig. 22)

Dauben, Ban and Richards[97] have demonstrated the biosynthesis of eburicoic acid from methyl-labeled acetate in *P. sulfureus*, a fungus. Degradation of this triterpenoid acid has shown that the carboxyl carbon atom at position 21 and the two methyl groups, carbon atoms 30 and 31, of the *gem*-dimethyl group of ring A are derived from the methyl carbon atoms of acetate. This distribution is consistent with the squalene hypothesis "universal" biosynthetic mechanism leading to all triterpenes and sterols. The extra carbon atom, 28, which is attached to the side-chain at position 24 is not derived from acetate.

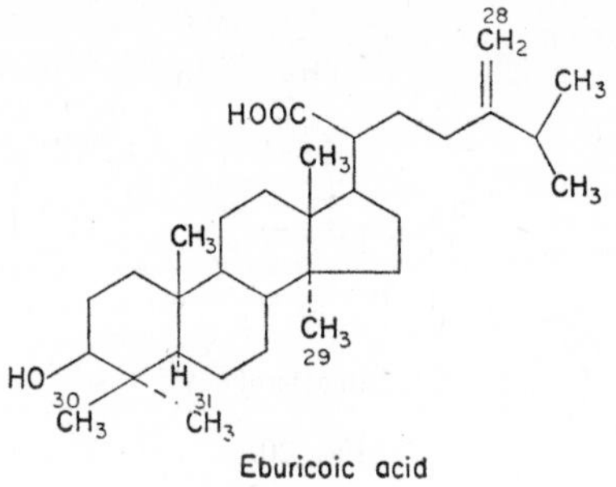

Eburicoic acid

FIG. 22.

K. *Coprostanol* (Fig. 23)

This sterol, which is found in the feces of animals, has been demonstrated definitely to arise from cholesterol by Rosenfeld, Fukushima, Hellman and Gallagher.[98] The conversion of cholesterol by intestinal microorganisms has also been shown. Quite surprisingly, the earlier proposal of Schönheimer, Rittenberg and Graff[99] that postulated the conversion of cholesterol to coprostanol via the 3-ketone has been negated by the work of Rosenfeld,

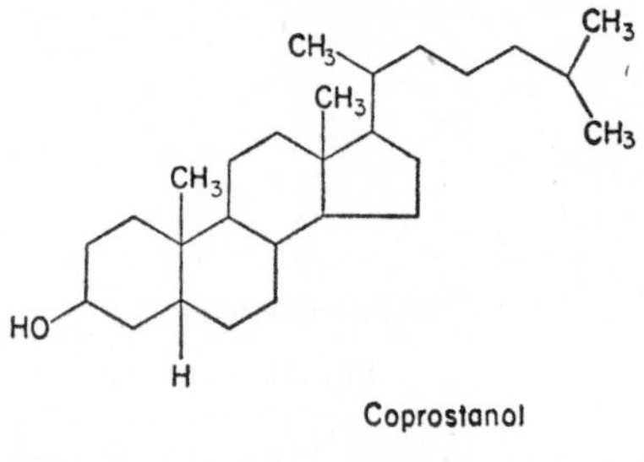

Coprostanol

FIG. 23.

Hellman and Gallagher.[100] They have shown, using appropriate deuterium labeling at position 3, that retention of the deuterium in the resultant coprostanol indicates that reduction of the double bond may take place without prior oxidation to the ketone. Recent additional work by Rosenfeld and Gallagher[101] has not resolved this problem.

L. *Cholestanol* (Fig. 24)

Cholestanol (dihydrocholesterol) was first found to be formed in the rat by Anker and Bloch.[102] It has been found in various mammalian tissues and Werbin, Chaikoff and Phillips[103] reported its formation from cholesterol in the guinea pig. Shefer, Milch and Mosbach[104] studied its biosynthesis in the rabbit and guinea pig from various precursors such as acetate, mevalonate, desmosterol, cholestenone and cholesterol. They found a considerable variation in the possible precursor with the animal and with various tissues. Werbin *et al.*, cited above, have proposed a mechanism based on oxidation of cholesterol to cholestenone and a two-step reduction to

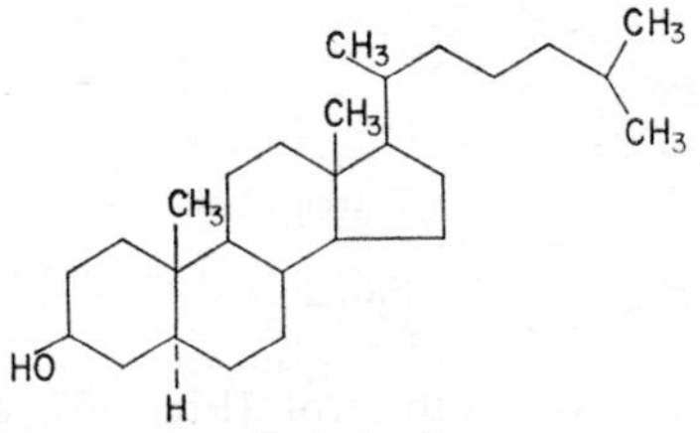

Cholestanol

FIG. 24.

cholestanol. Kandutsch [105] has suggested another mechanism involving 7-dehydrocholesterol as precursor. Which of these pathways is important or if both are operative, remains to be proved.

M. *Phytosterols*†

This group of sterols which includes β-sitosterol, stigmasterol (Figs. 25, 26) and many other important sterols has, up to this time, not been very thoroughly investigated. Owing to the inherent difficulty of administering substrates to plants and their slow rates of metabolism, the work has proceeded very slowly. The preliminary reviews of Sandermann, [106] Arigoni [107] and

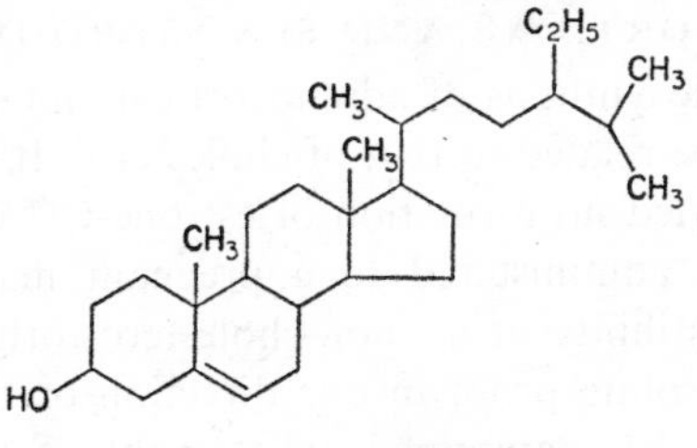

"β" Sitosterol

FIG. 25.

Heftmann [108] on this subject may be cited. It appears intuitively as if the main features of the squalene hypothesis will also hold good here, but it remains for further work to substantiate this. There have been some preliminary investigations on the biosynthesis of phytosterols undertaken recently.

Baisted, Capstak and Nes [109] working with germinating seeds of *Pisum sativum* and Nicholas [110] investigating *Salvia officinalis* have shown that

† See also Chapter 14.

I

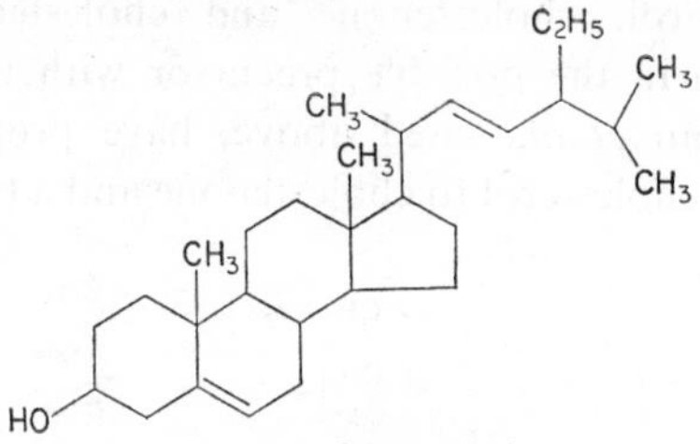

Stigmasterol

FIG. 26.

mevalonate is converted to β-sitosterol (Fig. 25). Johnson, Wright and Heftmann [111] in experiments with *Dictyostelium discoideum* found that mevalonate was converted to stigmasterol (Fig. 26). In another study Johnson, Heftmann and Houghland [112] have also reported the formation of both β-sitosterol and stigmasterol from mevalonate in *Solanum tuberosum*. The incorporation of mevalonate into the sterol sapogenins of *Dioscorea speculiflora* has likewise been reported by Bennet, Heftmann, Preston and Haun. [113] The sapogenin compounds which they isolated, derived from mevalonate, were: diosgenin (25α-Δ^5-spirosten-3β-ol), yamogenin (25β-Δ^5 spirosten-3β-ol), gentrogenin (25α-Δ^5-spirosten-3β-ol-12-one) and correllogenin (25β-Δ^5-spirosten-3β-ol-12-one).

There appears to be an increasing interest in the biogenesis of plant steroids and the field is on the threshold of what may lead to an important understanding of sterol biosynthesis in general.

III. ADRENOCORTICAL AND SEX STEROID HORMONES

The work on the biosynthesis of adrenocortical and sex steroid hormones may also, of course, be related to that of cholesterol. It should be noted that Heard *et al.* [114] reported no formation of estrone-C^{14} when a large dose of cholesterol-4-C^{14} was administered to a pregnant mare, and Hechter [115] has suggested the possibility of a non-cholesterol origin of some of these compounds. Until absolute proof in one direction or the other is supplied, this reservation must be maintained. The doubt of the obligatory intermediacy of cholesterol rests in part on relative specific activity data of steroid hormones and cholesterol when originating in the same tissue from the same precursors. Other factors may come into play here and making a final judgment on the basis of such data is not warranted. The very large weight of factual evidence tends to confirm that cholesterol is, indeed, the actual precursor of adrenocortical and sex hormones.

A. *Adrenocortical Steroid Hormones*

Early work on the structures of the various adrenocortical steroids and cholesterol had indicated their chemical similarity, especially with respect to their common cyclopentanoperhydrophenanthrene nucleus. There was, thus, a very strong indication that this sterol could serve as a precursor of adrenocortical steroid hormones. The first experiments by Bloch [116] with isotopically labeled cholesterol showed that it is converted to pregnanediol, a known metabolite of progesterone, in the human and helped to confirm the early suspicion. More recently, Hechter et al., [117] Saba, Hechter and Stone, [118] and Solomon, Lang, Vande Weile and Lieberman [119] have established by experiments with carbon-14 labeled cholesterol that this sterol serves as a source, *in vivo* and *in vitro*, of the adrenocortical precursor compounds, pregnenolone and progesterone. Staple, Lynn and Gurin [120] have further established that this reaction occurs by a split of a six-carbon compound from the side chain of cholesterol, first obtained as isocaproic acid. The steroid product of this cleavage is pregnenolone. The reaction is shown in Fig. 27. Constantopoulos and Tchen [121] investigating this reaction further, have

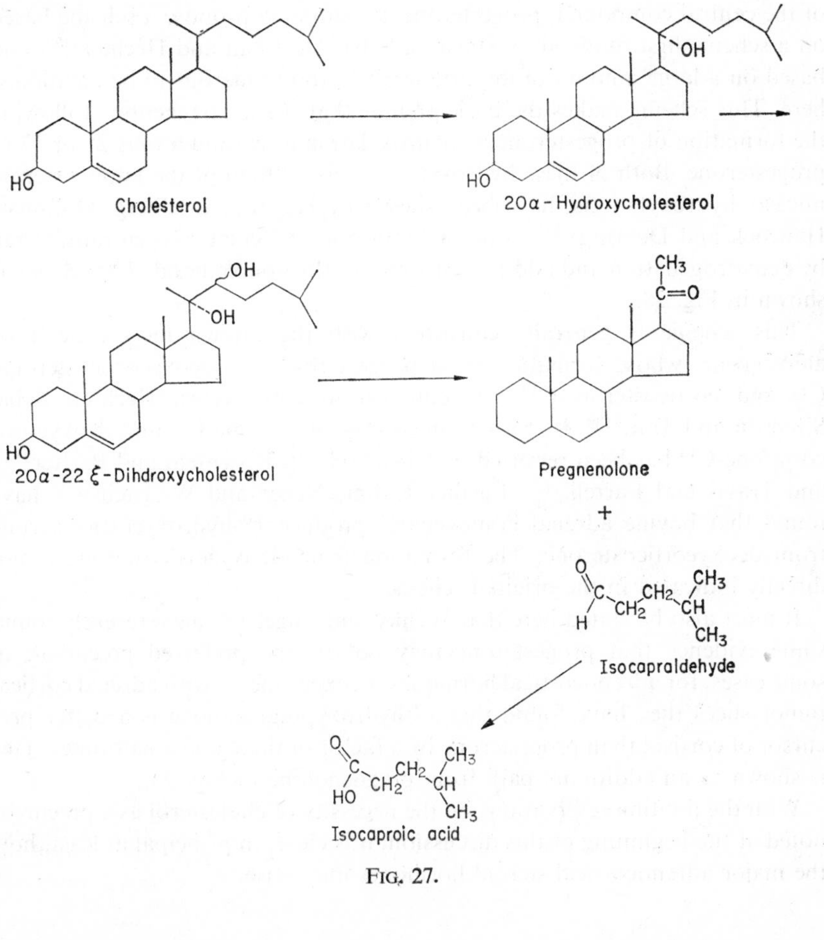

Cholesterol

20α – Hydroxycholesterol

20α-22 ξ-Dihdroxycholesterol

Pregnenolone

+

Isocapraldehyde

Isocaproic acid

FIG. 27.

established a primary requirement for TPN and have also found that the primary cleavage product is isocapraldehyde. Halkerston, Eichhorn and Hechter [122, 123] and also Constantopoulos, Satoh and Tchen [124] have investigated possible intermediates of the oxygen-substituted cholesterol (carbon atoms 20 and 22) type. However, Shimizu, Dorfman and Gut [125] and Shizizu, Hayano, Gut and Dorfman [126] have now established that 20α-hydroxycholesterol is an intermediate in the reaction. Further Shimizu, Gut and Dorfman [127] have demonstrated that 20α-22ξ-dihydroxycholesterol is formed and is apparently the compound which is cleaved to yield pregnenolone and isocapraldehyde. Although 22ξ-hydroxycholesterol is converted to pregnenolone enzymatically, Chaudhuri, Harada, Shimizu, Gut and Dorfman [128] do not believe that it is in fact a normal intermediate in this process. The complete reaction is shown in Fig. 27.

The enzymatic 3β-hydroxydehydrogenase system, which yields progesterone from pregnenolone, has now been well established. [129] With the biogenesis of the central compound, progesterone, we can now propose a scheme based on a scheme first outlined by Hayano, Saba, Dorfman and Hechter [130] and based on a large amount of important work, too numerous to be mentioned here. This scheme makes the basic premise that the next reaction, following the formation of progesterone, is hydroxylation at carbon atoms 21 or 17 of progesterone. Both of these hydroxylations, as with all of the known steroid nuclear hydroxylations, have been shown by Hayano, Lindberg, Dofmnar, Hancock and Doering [131] to occur by use of molecular oxygen rather than by dehydrogenation and addition of water to the double bond. The scheme is shown in Fig. 28.

This scheme is generally consistent with the known facts concerning aldosterone, whose formation from progesterone-C^{14}, deoxycorticosterone-C^{14} and corticosterone-C^{14} was demonstrated by Ayres, Hechter, Saba, Simpson and Tait. [132] Its formation from progesterone-C^{14} and deoxycorticosterone-C^{14} has been reported by Chen, Schedl, Rosenfeld and Bartter [133] and Travis and Farrell. [134] Further Kahnt, Neher and Wettstein [135] have found that bovine adrenal homogenates produce 18-hydroxycorticosterone from deoxycorticosterone. The formation from deoxycorticosterone is not directly indicated in the original scheme.

It must also be stated here that Weliky and Engel [136] have recently found some evidence that progesterone may not be the preferred precursor, in some cases, for adrenocortical hormones. In experiments with adrenal cortical tumor slices they have found that 17-hydroxypregnenolone is a better precursor of cortisol than progesterone by a factor of three and a half times. This is shown as an additional path from pregnenolone in Fig. 28.

With the limiting reservations on the necessity of cholesterol as a precursor noted at the beginning of this discussion, it is clear, in principal at least, how the major adrenocortical steroid hormones may arise.

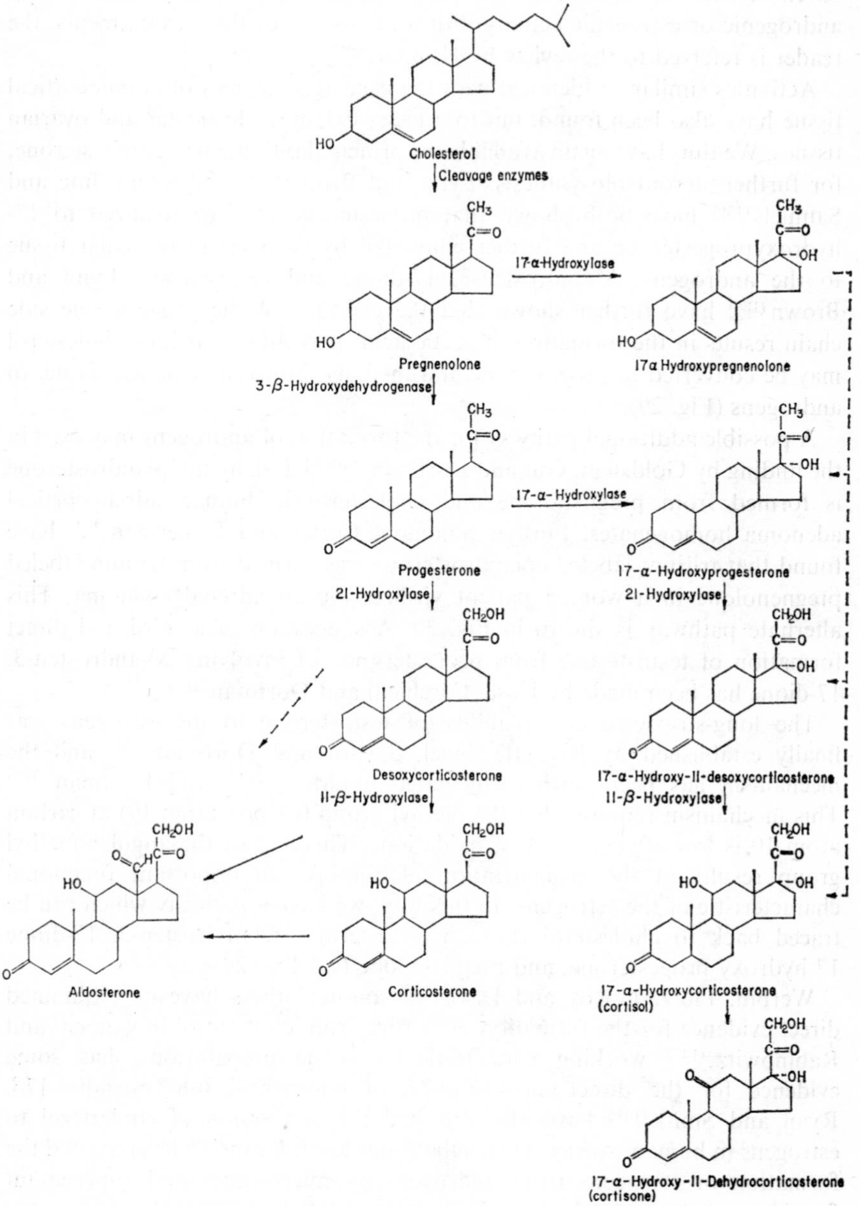

FIG. 28. Pathway of adrenocortical steroids based on the scheme of Hayano *et al.*

B. *Sex Hormones*

There have been numerous preliminary demonstrations of the conversion of cholesterol or its metabolite, progesterone, to steroid hormones with androgenic or estrogenic activity. For a discussion of these experiments, the reader is referred to the review by Hechter. [137]

Activities similar or identical with the cleavage enzymes of adrenocortical tissue have also been found, but to a lesser extent, in testicular and ovarian tissues. We thus have again available the principal intermediate, progesterone, for further steroid biosynthesis. Lynn and Brown [138] and Slaunwhite and Samuels [139] have both shown that progesterone may be oxidized to 17-hydroxyprogesterone and further converted by cleavage in testicular tissue to the androgens, Δ^4-androsten-3, 17-dione and testosterone. Lynn and Brown [138] have further shown that the cleavage of the progesterone side chain results in the formation of acetic acid. It is thus clear how cholesterol may be converted to progesterone and then, as shown in testicular tissue, to androgens (Fig. 29).

A possible additional pathway for the formation of androgens may exist in the finding by Goldstein, Gut and Dorfman [140] that dehydroepiandrosterone is formed from pregnenolone and cholesterol in human adrenocortical adenoma homogenates. Further Solomon, Carter and Lieberman [141] have found that tritium labeled epiandrosterone was formed from tritium labeled pregnenolone in a woman patient virilized by an adrenal adenoma. This alternate pathway is shown in Fig. 30. A suggestion of a third and direct formation of testosterone from progesterone not involving Δ^4-androsten-3, 17-dione has been made by Kase, Forchielli and Dorfman. [142]

The long-suspected convertibility of testosterone to the estrogens was finally established by Baggett, Engel, Savard and Dorfman, [143] and the mechanism has been further elucidated by Meyer [144] and Dorfman. [145] This mechanism requires that the methyl group (carbon atom 19) at carbon atom 10 is lost after a series of oxidations. This loss of the angular methyl group results in the aromatization of ring A, an important functional characteristic of the estrogens. In this way, we have a pathway which can be traced back to cholesterol through testosterone, Δ^4-androsten-3, 17-dione 17-hydroxy progesterone, and pregnenolone (see Fig. 29).

Werbin, Plotz, LeRoy and Davis [146] among others have now obtained direct evidence for the formation of estrone from cholesterol in women, and Rabinowitz, [147] working with testicular tissue preparations, has some evidence for the direct incorporation of cholesterol into estradiol-17β. Ryan and Smith [148] have also reported the conversion of cholesterol to estrogens in human ovaries. On a subcellular level, Ryan [149] has reported the formation of estrogens from androgens by microsomes and supernatant fractions of human placenta homogenates. This conversion apparently requires TPN. It would appear that the experiments of Heard *et al.*, previously referred to, must be explained in some other way.

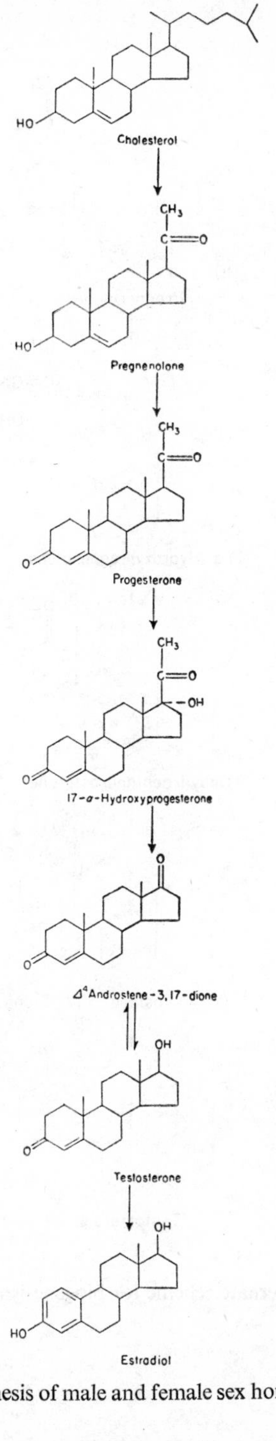

FIG. 29. Scheme for biogenesis of male and female sex hormones from cholesterol.

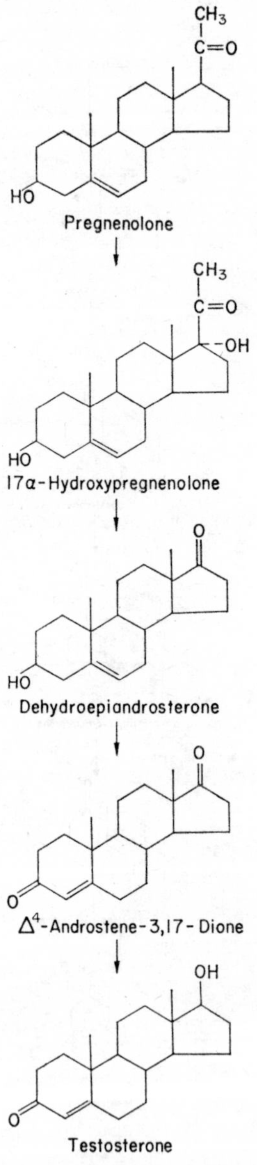

FIG. 30. Alternate scheme for biogenesis of testosterone.

The loss of carbon atom 19, referred to above, which is, of course, critical to the conversion of androgens to estrogens has now been studied in some detail. Meyer [144] had originally implicated 19-hydroxy androstenedione in the conversion of androstenedione to estrogens and this has been confirmed by Longchampt, Gual, Ehrenstein and Dorfman. [150] Morato, Hayano, Dorfman and Axelrod [151] have shown that 19-oxoandrostenedione was more rapidly converted to estrone than the corresponding 19-hydroxy compound. Further, androstenedione-19-oic acid and 19-norandrostenedione were poorly converted to estrone. It therefore appears that neither of these latter compounds are intermediates in the process.

Breuer and Grill [152] using microsomes from human placental tissue have found that incubation of androstenedione, testosterone and 19-hydroxyandrostenedione yielded formaldehyde and estrogen. Dorfman, Gual, Morato, Hayano and Gut [153] have found that formic acid as well as formaldehyde is formed from C-19 of 19-hydroxyandrostenedione and that 19-oxoandrostenedione yields principally formic acid from this carbon atom. Various postulations have been made on the mechanism of aromatization of Ring A of estrogens but there has been no final proof. A possible scheme for this is presented in Fig. 31.

IV. BILE ACIDS

The conversion of cholesterol to cholic acid, or other bile acids, and the mechanisms of this reaction have been the object of many studies. Here again the early work on the structures of the steroid compounds [154] has indicated that the sterols and bile acids might be related biologically. There are a number of suggestions in the literature, one of the oldest by Lifschütz, [155] that cholesterol may serve as a source of bile acids in the living organism. Once again Bloch and his collaborators, Berg and Rittenberg, [156] found in 1943 that deuterium labeled cholesterol which was administered to a dog, was converted to labeled cholic acid in the bile. This work was later repeated by Bergström [157] and Siperstein, Jayko, Chaikoff and Dauben [158] in the rat using cholesterol-C^{14}, and the conversion was confirmed.

Again the problem of obligatory intermediacy of cholesterol arises and cannot be resolved with the present knowledge. Zabin and Barker [159] and Staple and Gurin [160] have carried out decompositions of cholic acid obtained biosynthetically from labeled acetate. From their data on the isotope distribution, they concluded that the distribution of isotope was the same in cholic acid as in cholesterol. Thus the problem, if it exists, must await more refined techniques obtained from a knowledge of the developing enzymology of the biosynthesis of cholesterol and formation of bile acids before an absolute conclusion in regard to this point can be made.

In the *in vivo* conversion of cholesterol to bile acids, Berström and his collaborators have done a monumental piece of work which he has

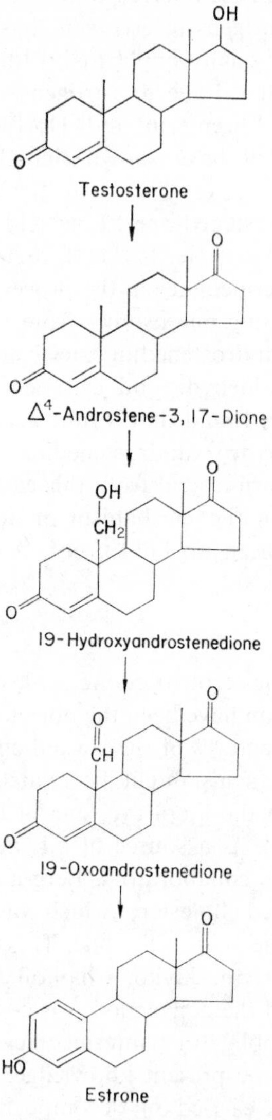

FIG. 31. Scheme for biosynthesis of estrogens.

reviewed. [161, 162] After the aforementioned demonstration of the conversion of cholesterol-C^{14} to C^{14}-labeled bile acids, a number of suspected labeled precursors were administered to intact animals and the products in the bile were worked up to identify them. Using this sort of method, Bergström [159] and Harold, Jayko and Chaikoff [163] found that Δ^4-cholesten-3-one, Δ^5-cholesten-3-one, Δ^5-3β-hydroxycholenic acid (the cleavage product of cholesterol), 3β-hydroxycoprostane and cholesten-3β-ol are not converted in the animal into the normal bile acid, cholic acid. 25-Hydroxycholesterol and 26-hydroxycholesterol found in the incubation of liver preparations with cholesterol by Fredrickson and Ono[164] are also not converted to cholic acid. In each case the steroid compound was oxidized to acidic products, but in no instance were they able to isolate the normal bile acids of the rat. Only with cholesterol and a few compounds which will be mentioned later, did they find the usual bile acids *in vivo*. Since the above mentioned 25- and 26-hydroxycholesterols gave no normal bile acids and since also Δ⁵-3β-hydroxy-cholenic acid, corresponding to the direct cleavage of cholesterol, could not be found in the *in vivo* bile products or an *in vitro* product, Bergström and his group were led to try compounds having the completely converted, or almost completely converted, bile acid nucleus, but the isooctyl side chain of cholesterol. They[165] found in fact that such a compound 3α,7α,12α-trihydroxy-coprostane, could be converted readily, *in vivo*, to cholic acid. Thus, they had confirming evidence that nuclear configuration and the processes which bring about these changes may have a controlling effect on the cleavage reaction. Bergström and Lindstedt[166] have also done some work with 3α,7α-dihydroxycoprostane and have demonstrated that it is readily converted *in vivo* to chenodesoxycholic acid and cholic acids. Chenodesoxycholic acid is, however, not convertible to cholic acid in any of the animals studied. This indicates that chenodesoxycholic acid may be a primary cleavage product as is cholic acid. If, however, 3α,12α-dihydroxycoprostanic acid is administered to the animal, no cholic acid appears from this compound. It thus appears that hydroxylation at position 7 may be a critical step in cholic and bile acid formation. The following scheme (Fig. 32) may summarize the work on bile acid formation *in vivo* to date.

The inability of *in vivo* work, furnishing important and interesting results as it has, to yield a detailed picture of the bile acid formation mechanism must be recognized.

Chaikoff *et al.*[167] observed originally that when cholesterol-26-C^{14} and cholesterol-4-C^{14} were administered to intact rats, the nuclear labeled compound gave little or no respiratory carbon dioxide-C^{14} but the side-chain labeled cholesterol yielded large amounts of radioactive carbon dioxide in a short time. This observation is in accord with the general observation that the steroid nucleus is a relatively stable moiety and that the side chain of cholesterol is extensively cleaved during its metabolism, Carrying this observation farther, Anfinsen and Horning[168] found that homogenates of mouse liver were also able to carry out the oxidation of cholesterol-26-C^{14} to yield radioactive carbon dioxide. These authors with Fredrickson[169] as well as Fredrickson[170] continued the study of this system and were able to determine that a heat stable cofactor present in the supernatant fraction of their homogenates was necessary for the formation of carbon dioxide from the side

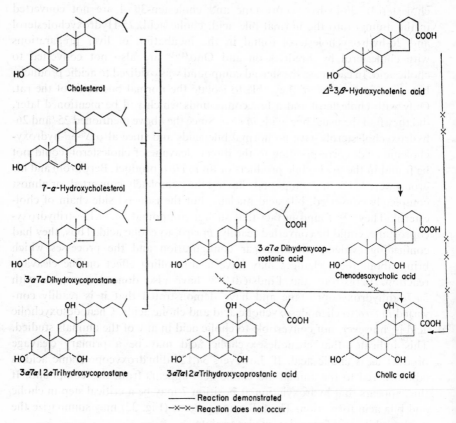

— Reaction demonstrated
—×—×— Reaction does not occur

FIG. 32. Some metabolic reactions in bile acid biogenesis in the rat according to Bergstrom.

chain. They were also able to examine the system and determine some additional optimal factors for this oxidation. Fredrickson and Ono [164] have made a careful study of the products of these incubations but could find no cholic acid or normal bile acids in the products, although they were able to find several acids of the cholanic variety. Whitehouse, Staple and Gurin [171, 172] who were also investigating this reaction, were able to confirm Anfinsen and Horning's work using rats. They, in similar fashion, also found that the presence of a heat-stable cofactor in the supernatant fraction was necessary for the formation of radioactive carbon dioxide from the side chain in the rat. They were also able to establish a number of other factors which affected this reaction. In addition they carried out studies with mitochondria from a few non-hepatic tissues. They found that, while these non-hepatic mitochondria were able to oxidize cholesterol only feebly, the largest oxidation rate occurred in preparations from liver tissue. Whitehouse, Cottrell,

Briggs and Staple [173] have also observed that bird and mammalian livers carried out this cleavage, while there was little reaction in preparations from turtle, alligator and frog livers. This seems to be consistent with the observation that the latter species have twenty-seven or twenty-eight carbon atom bile acids and steroids in their bile.

However, the carrying out of this oxidative reaction with mitochondria, so that the cleavage product yielded carbon dioxide ultimately, was still unsatisfactory from the standpoint of yielding much detailed mechanistic information. From the previously mentioned observations of Bergström that 3α,7α,12α-trihydroxycoprostane is converted smoothly to cholic acid *in vivo*, Shimizu, Fujioki, Otogaki and Yamasaki [174] studied the formation in rats of cholic acid from 3α,7α,12α-trihydroxycoprostane, the 24-keto trihydroxycoprostane, and 3α,7α,12α,24-tetrahydroxycoprostane. They concluded that 3α,7α,12α-trihydroxycoprostane was converted to cholic acid much more effectively than the other two derivatives. At the same time Whitehouse, Staple and Gurin [175] undertook the study of these compounds, labeled at position 26 with carbon-14, in *in vitro* liver preparations. Using mitochondrial fractions, they observed that 3α,7α,12α-trihydroxycoprostane and 3α,7α,12α-trihydroxy-24-oxo-coprostane were actively metabolized by such liver preparations. Furthermore, their evidence suggested that, of these compounds, 3α,7α,12α-trihydroxycoprostane might be an intermediate. Briggs, Whitehouse and Staple [176] demonstrated that cholesterol is in fact converted to trihydroxycoprostanic acid in the alligator, and when appropriately 26-labeled cholesterol is used, terminally labeled trihydroxycoprostanic acid is formed. This acid, when incubated with rat liver mitochondria, yielded radioactive carbon dioxide. [177] In addition, 4-labeled 3α, 7α, 12α-trihydroxycoprostanic acid derived from the similarly labeled cholesterol is also readily converted to cholic acid by these same mammalian

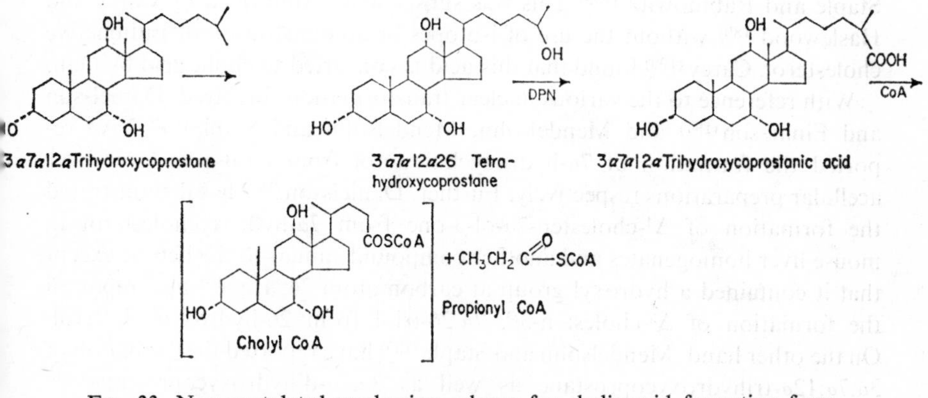

FIG. 33. New postulated mechanism scheme for cholic acid formation from trihydroxycoprostane.

mitochondrial preparations. Additional evidence is provided to support the theory of possible intermediacy of 3a,7a,12a-trihydroxycoprostane by the work of Danielsson [178] who isolated 3a,7a,12a-trihydroxycoprostanic acid and 3a,7a,12a,26-tetrahydroxycoprostane from the incubation of mouse liver mitochondria with 3a,7a,12a-trihydroxycoprostane. Suld, Staple and Gurin [179] have reported that 3a,7a 12a-trihydroxycoprostanic acid and 3a,7a,12a,26-tetrahydroxycoprostane are formed in rat liver mitochondrial preparations and that in the absence of DPN the tetrahydroxycoprostane is formed from the trihydroxycoprostane but it is not converted to acid. In extension of these results Herman and Staple [180] have recently reported the isolation, solubilization and partial purification of a dehydrogenase system from rat liver for the conversion of 3a,7a,12a,26-tetrahydroxycoprostane to 3a,7a,12a-trihydroxycoprostanic acid. This system also appears to require DPN only as hydrogen acceptor. Further, Suld, Staple and Gurin [179] have reported that, using a microsomal fraction of liver, propionic acid, probably as propionyl CoA, is split off when 3a,7a,12a-trihydroxycoprostanic acid is cleaved and that the cleavage mechanism may be a thiolytic one (Fig. 33). This would be consistent with the known requirement for cholyl CoA in the conjugation of this bile acid by the amino acid, glycine as reported by Bremer [181] and also in the formation of taurocholic acid by Siperstein [182] and Elliott. [183] This mechanism of three carbon atoms being split at once is a variance with an early speculative hypothesis of Lynn, Staple and Gurin [184] and also differs from a cleavage of the terminal three carbon atoms as acetone which was found to occur to a small extent in rat liver by Whitehouse, Rabinowitz, Staple and Gurin. [185] Reference should be made to reviews by Bergstrom, Danielsson and Samuelsson [186] and Danielsson [187] for additional ideas on the mechanism of formation of bile acids.

Mention should be made here of the finding of 3a,7a,12a-trihydroxycoprostanic acid formed from radioactive cholesterol in human bile by Staple and Rabinowitz. [188] This was subsequently confirmed by Carey and Haslewood [189] without the use of isotopes or administration of radioactive cholesterol. Carey [190] found that this acid is converted to cholic acid by man.

With reference to the various nuclear transformations involved, Danielsson and Einarsson [191] and Mendelsohn, Mendelsohn and Staple [192] have reported the formation of 7a-hydroxycholesterol from mouse and rat liver acellular preparations respectively. Further, Danielsson [193] has demonstrated the formation of Δ^4-cholesten-7a-ol-3-one from 7a-hydroxycholesterol in mouse liver homogenates and another compound similar to the ketone except that it contained a hydroxyl group at carbon atom 26. He [194] also reported the formation of Δ^5-cholesten-3β, 7a,26-triol from 26-hydroxycholesterol. On the other hand, Mendelsohn and Staple [195] have reported the formation of 3a,7a,12a-trihydroxycoprostane as well as 3a,7a-dihydroxycoprostane [196] but no 3a,12a-dihydroxycoprostane in a rat liver preparation consisting principally of a supernatant fraction and microsomes. The exact sequence and importance of the various nuclear reactions in the formation of bile acids is unknown at the present time.

It is interesting to note the fact that certain important interconversions of bile acids are brought about by microorganisms. This work has been done in large part in Bergström s laboratory. [197] Lindstedt and Sjövall [198] first established that deoxycholic acid is formed from cholic acid by microorganisms in the gut of the rabbit. Bergström, Lindstedt and Samuelsson [199] and Lindstedt and Samuelsson [200] prepared 7β-H^3, 24-C^{14}-cholic acid and studied its conversion to deoxycholic acid *in vivo*. They found that tritium was retained in the 7α-position on conversion to deoxycholic acid and the 7-keto compound was not an intermediate in this process. More recently, Samuelsson [201] has obtained evidence, from the study of the conversion of $6\alpha,6\beta,8\beta$-H^3, 24-C^{14}-cholic acid to deoxycholic acid that a *trans* elimination of water occurs followed by a stereospecific reduction of the resultant olefinic compound. Matkovics and Samuelsson [202] in subsequent work with 24-C^{14}-3α, 12-dihydroxy-Δ^6-cholenic acid found that this postulated intermediate acid is in fact converted to labeled deoxycholic acid by the microorganisms in the intestine.

In addition to demonstrations that bile acids of various mammalian species can be formed from cholesterol, the conversion of cholesterol to the characteristic bile acids in the following non-mammalian species has been shown: *Cyprinus carpio*, Haslewood; [203] *Alligator mississippiensis*, Briggs, Whitehouse, and Staple; [204] *Boidae* family, Bergström, Danielsson and Kazuno; [205] domestic chicken, Briggs; [206] *Bufo vulgaris japonicus*, Kazuno and Okada; [207] *Rana catesbiana*, Masui. [208] An excellent review of the various bile salts in a large number of species has been reported by Haslewood. [209]

V. VITAMIN D

The vitamins of this class may be considered to arise naturally by irradiation of $\Delta^{5,\ 7}$ sterols, the most common natural sources being ergosterol and 7-dehydrocholesterol, which possess these structures. The first, ergosterol, is found principally in yeasts while the second, 7-dehydrocholesterol, is found in the skins of many animals and the feathers of birds. Other $\Delta^{5,7}$ sterols such as $\Delta^{5,7,20}$-cholestatriene-3β-ol which is found in certain mussels, may serve as a source of vitamin D activity. The effect of the type and length of side chain on vitamin D activity is quite pronounced. Substitution of an ethyl group at carbon atom 24 as in 7-dehydrostigmasterol and 7-dehydro-"β"-sitosterol, for instance, leads on photolysis to compounds of low vitamin D activity.

There has been a great deal of work done on the conversion of $\Delta^{5,7}$ diols and similar compounds to vitamins D. Lythgoe [210] has written an excellent

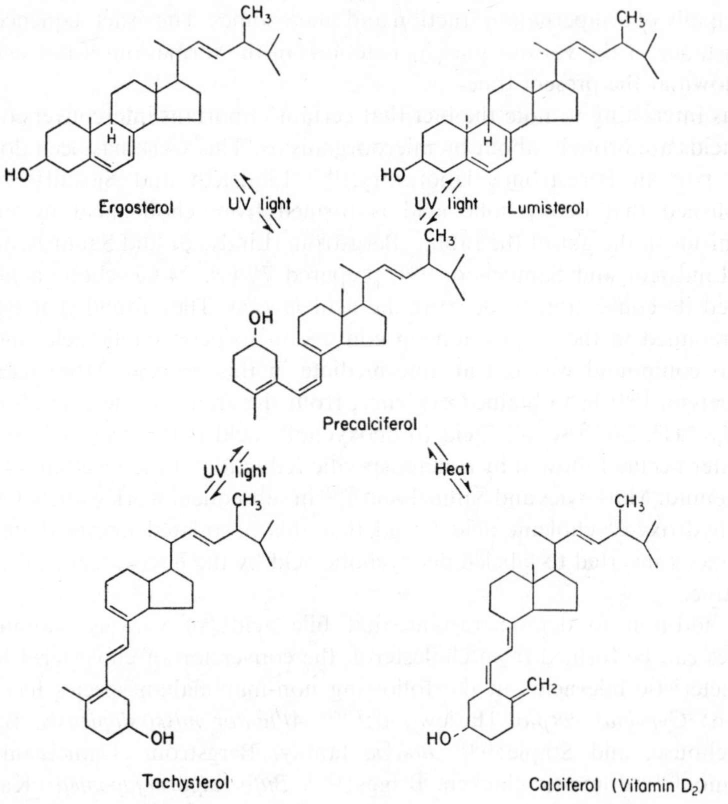

FIG. 34. Simplified scheme for formation of vitamin D_2 from ergosterol according
to Velluz *et al.*

review of the chemistry of this field. The photochemical transformations are
complex but a simple scheme for vitamin D_2, according to Velluz, Amiard
and Goffinet, [211] may be outlined as follows (see Fig. 34).

The biosyntheses of the important vitamins D may therefore be said to be
directly related to those of ergosterol and 7-dehydrocholesterol. Ergosterol
has been previously discussed and its origin from acetate and all of the known
cholesterogenic intermediates, including squalene, has been established. The
conversion of cholesterol to 7-dehydrocholesterol has been shown by Glover,
Glover and Morton [212] and by Festenstein and Morgan. [213] The origin of
7-dehydrocholesterol by a route independent of cholesterol itself must be
left open at this time, but appears to be highly likely in view of the work of
Frantz, Sanghrai and Schroepfer. [68] It is clear, in principle however, how
vitamin D_3 may arise from cholesterol.

Recently, Blondin, Kulkarni and Nes [214] have reported the formation
of vitamin D_3 from 7-dehydrocholesterol in fish. Interestingly, this conversion

takes place enzymatically in the absence of light. These authors believe that it proceeds through an intermediate 5,8-peroxide of 7-dehydrocholesterol. They further hypothesize the formation of Δ^7-3β, 5α-diol by reduction of the peroxide. Certain aspects of these reactions are, they believe, comparable to some known biologic reactions.

REFERENCES

1. DEZANI, S. and CATTORETTI, E. *Arch. Farm. Sper.* **17**, 4 (1913).
2. BEUMER, H. and LEHMANN, F. *Z. Ges. Exptl. Med.* **37**, 274 (1923).
3. GAMBLE, J. L. and BLACKFAN, K. D. *Z. J. Biol. Chem.* **42**, 401 (1920).
4. SCHÖNHEIMER, R. and BREUSCH, F. *J. Biol. Chem.* **103**, 439 (1933).
5. SONDERHOFF, R. and THOMAS, H. *Ann.* **530**, 195 (1937).
6. BLOCH, K. and RITTENBERG, D. *J. Biol. Chem.* **143**, 297 (1946).
7. BLOCH, K. and RITTENBERG, D. *J. Biol. Chem.* **145**, 625 (1942).
8. BERGMANN, E. and BERGMANN, F. *J. Chem. Soc.* **1934**, 1019.
9. BRADY, R. O. and GURIN, S. *J. Biol. Chem.* **189**, 371 (1951).
10. CURRAN, G. L. *J. Biol. Chem.* **191**, 775 (1951).
11. ANKER, H. S. and RAPER, R. *J. Biol. Chem.* **176**, 1353 (1948).
12. ANKER, H. S. *J. Biol. Chem.* **176**, 1337 (1948).
13. BOREK, E. and RITTENBERG, D. *J. Biol. Chem.* **179**, 843 (1949).
14. ZABIN, I. and BLOCH, K. *J. Biol. Chem.* **185**, 117 (1950).
15. PRICE, T. D. and RITTENBERG, D. *J. Biol. Chem.* **185**, 449 (1950).
16. BLOCH, K. and RITTENBERG, D. *J. Biol. Chem.* **155**, 243 (1944).
17. BRADY, R. O. and GURIN, S. *J. Biol. Chem.* **186**, 461 (1950).
18. COON, M. J. and GURIN, S. *J. Biol. Chem.* **180**, 1159 (1949).
19. RABINOWITZ, J. L. and GURIN, S. *J. Biol. Chem.* **208**, 307 (1954).
20. RUDNEY, H. *J. Am. Chem. Soc.* **76**, 2595 (1954).
21. RUDNEY, H. *Federation Proc.* **15**, 342 (1956).
22. BLOCH, K., CLARK, L. C. and HARARY, I. *J. Biol. Chem.* **211**, 687 (1954).
23. GURIN, S. In *Lipids Related to Atherosclerosis*, ed. Irvine H. Page. Charles C. Thomas, Springfield, Illinois, 1958.
24. TAVORIMINA, P. A., GIBBS, M. H. and HUFF, J. W. *J. Am. Chem. Soc.* **78**, 4498 (1956).
25. TAVORIMINA, P. A. and GIBBS, M. H. *J. Am. Chem. Soc.* **78**, 6210 (1956).
26. FERGUSON, J. J., DURR, I. F. and RUDNEY, H. *Proc. Natl. Acad. Sci. U.S.* **45**, 499 (1959).
27. KNAUSS, H. J., PORTER, J. W. and WASSON, G. *J. Biol. Chem.* **234**, 2835 (1959).
28. LYNEN, F. and GRASSL, M. *Z. Physiol. Chemie* **313**, 291 (1958).
29. DITURI, F., GURIN, S. and RABINOWITZ, J. L. *J. Am. Chem. Soc.* **79**, 2650 (1957).
30. CORNFORTH, J. W., CORNFORTH, R. H., POPJÁK, G. and GORE, I. Y. *Biochem. J.* **69**, 146 (1958).
31. TCHEN, T. T. *J. Biol. Chem.* **233**, 1100 (1958).
32. POPJÁK G. In *Biosynthesis of Terpenes and Sterols*, p. 148. A Ciba Foundation Symposium. Little, Brown & Co., Boston, 1959.
33. LYNEN, F., EGGERER, H., HENNING, U. and KESSEL, I. *Angew. Chem.* **70**, 738 (1958).
34. CHAYKIN, S., LAW, J., PHILLIPS, A. H., TCHEN, T. T. and BLOCH, K. *Proc. Natl. Acad. Sci. U.S.* **44**, 998 (1958).
35. LYNEN, F., AGRANOFF, B. W., EGGERER, H., HENNING, U. and MOSLEIN, E. M. *Angew. Chem.* **71**, 657 (1959).
36. POPJÁK, G. *Tetrahedron Letters* **19**, 19 (1959).
37. GOODMAN, D. W. and POPJÁK, G. *J. Lipid Res.* **1**, 286 (1960).
38. CORNFORTH, J. W. and POPJÁK, G. *Tetrahedron Letters* **19**, 29 (1959).
39. RILLING, H. C. and BLOCH, K. *J. Biol. Chem.* **234**, 1424 (1959).
40. CHANNON, H. J. *Biochem. J.* **20**, 400 (1926).
41. CHANNON, H. J. and TRISTRAM, G. R. *Biochem. J.* **31**, 738 (1937).
42. HEIBRON, I. M., KAMM, E. D. and OWENS, W. M. *J. Chem. Soc.* **1926**, 1630.

43. ROBINSON, R. *J. Soc. Chem. Ind.* (*London*) **53**, 1062 (1934).
44. LANGDON, R. G. and BLOCH, K. *J. Biol. Chem.* **200**, 129 (1953).
45. LANGDON, R. G. and BLOCH, K. *J. Biol. Chem.* **200**, 135 (1953).
46. TOMKINS, G., DAUBEN, W. G., SHEPPARD, H. and CHAIKOFF, I. L. *J. Biol. Chem.* **202**, 487 (1953).
47. NICOLAIDES, N. and LAVES, F. *J. Am. Chem. Soc.* **76**, 2596 (1954).
48. RUZICKA, L., ESCHENMOSER, A. and HEUSSER. *Experientia* **9**, 357 (1953).
49. WOODWARD, R. B. and BLOCH, K. *J. Am. Chem. Soc.* **75**, 2023 (1953).
50. BUCHER, N. L. R. and McGARRAHAN, K. *J. Biol. Chem.* **222**, 1 (1956).
51. TCHEN, T. T. and BLOCH, K. *J. Biol. Chem.* **226**, 931 (1957).
52. AMDUR, B. H., RILLING, H. and BLOCH, K. *J. Am. Chem. Soc.* **79**, 2646 (1957).
53. ESCHENMOSER, A., RUZICKA, L., JEGER, O. and ARIGONI, D. *Helv. Chim. Acta* **38**, 1890 (1955).
54. CORNFORTH, J. W., CORNFORTH, R. H., HORNING, M. G., PELTER, A. and POPJÁK, G. In *Biosynthesis of Terpenes and Sterols*, p. 119. A Ciba Foundation Symposium. Little, Brown & Co., Boston, 1959.
55. MAUDGAL, R. K., TCHEN, T. T. and BLOCH, K. *J. Am. Chem. Soc.* **80**, 2589 (1958).
56. SCHWENK, E. and WERTHESSEN, N. T. *Arch. Biochem. Biophys.* **40**, 334 (1952).
57. SCHWENK, E. and WERTHESSEN, N. T. *Arch. Biochem. Biophys.* **42**, 91 (1953).
58. JOHNSTON, J. D. and BLOCH, K. *J. Am. Chem. Soc.* **79**, 1145 (1957).
59. ALEXANDER, G. J. and SCHWENK, E. *Arch. Biochem. Biophys.* **66**, 381 (1957).
60. CLAYTON, R. B. and BLOCH, K. *J. Biol. Chem.* **218**, 305 (1956).
61. GAUTSCHI, F. and BLOCH, K. *J. Biol. Chem.* **233**, 1343 (1958).
62. OLSON, J. A., LINDBERG, M. and BLOCH, K. *J. Biol. Chem.* **226**, 941 (1957).
63. KANDUTSCH, A. A. and RUSSEL, A. E. *J. Biol. Chem.* **235**, 2253 (1960).
64. DJERASSI, C., KNIGHT, J. C. and WILKINSON, D. I. *J. Am. Chem. Soc.* **85**, 835 (1963).
65. STOKES, W. M., HICKEY, F. C. and FISH, W. A. *J. Biol. Chem.* **232**, 347 (1958).
66. FRANTZ, I. D., JR., DAVIDSON, A. G., DULIT, E. and MOBBERLEY, M. L. *J. Biol. Chem.* **234**, 2290 (1959).
67. DEMPSEY, M. E., SEATON, J. D., SCHROEPFER, G. J., JR. and TROCKMAN, R. W. *J. Biol. Chem.* **239**, 1381 (1964).
68. FRANTZ, I. D. JR., SANGHVI, A. T. and SCHROEPFER, G. J., JR. *J. Biol. Chem.* **239**, 1007 (1964).
69. KANDUTSCH, A. A. and RUSSELL, A. E. *Federation Proc.* **19**, 237 (1960).
70. KANDUTSCH, A. A. and RUSSELL, A. E. *J. Biol. Chem.* **235**, 2256 (1960).
71. WELLS, W. W. and LORAH, C. L. *J. Biol. Chem.* **235**, 978 (1960).
72. AVIGAN, J., GOODMAN, D. S. and STEINBERG, D. *J. Biol. Chem.* **238**, 1283 (1963).
73. LITTLE, H. N. and BLOCH, K. *J. Biol. Chem.* **183**, 33 (1950).
74. WURSCH, J., HUANG, R. L. and BLOCH, K. *J. Biol. Chem.* **195**, 439 (1952).
75. CORNFORTH, J. W., HUNTER, G. D. and POPJÁK, G. *Biochem. J.* **54**, 590 (1953).
76. CORNFORTH, J. W., HUNTER, G. D. and POPJÁK, G. *Biochem. J.* **54**, 597 (1953).
77. CORNFORTH, J. W., POPJÁK, G. and GORE, I. Y. In *Biochemical Problems of Lipids*, Proceedings of the 2nd Intl. Conference on Biochemical Problems of Lipids, Ghent, 1955, pp. 216–23. Butterworth's Scientific Publications, London, England, 1956.
78. CORNFORTH, J. W., GORE, I. Y. and POPJÁK, G. *Biochem. J.* **65**, 94 (1957).
79. BLOCH, K. *Helv. Chim. Acta* **36**, 1611 (1953).
80. DAUBEN, W. G. and TAKEMURA, K. H. *J. Am. Chem. Soc.* **75**, 6302 (1953).
81. HANAHAN, D. J. and WAKIL, S. *J. Am. Chem. Soc.* **75**, 273 (1953).
82. SCHWENK, E., ALEXANDER, G., STOUDT, T. H. and FISH, C. A. *Arch. Biochem. Biophys.* **55**, 274 (1955).
83. DAUBEN, W. G., FONKEN, G. J. and BOSWELL, G. A. *J. Am. Chem. Soc.* **79**, 1000 (1957).
84. ALEXANDER, G. J., GOLD, A. M. and SCHWENK, E. *J. Am. Chem. Soc.* **79**, 2967 (1957).
85. DAUBEN, W. G. and HUTTON, T. W. *J. Am. Chem. Soc.* **78**, 2647 (1956).
86. BLOCH, K. *Vitamins and Hormones*, **15**, 121 (1957).
87. JOHNSTON, J. D. and BLOCH, K. *J. Am. Chem. Soc.* **79**, 1145 (1957).
88. CLAYTON, R. B. and BLOCH, K. *J. Biol. Chem.* **218**, 305 (1956).

89. CLAYTON, R. B. and BLOCH, K. *J. Biol. Chem.* **218**, 319 (1956).
90. KANDUTSCH, A. A. and RUSSELL, A. E. *J. Biol. Chem.* **235**, 2253 (1960).
91. FRANTZ, I. D., JR., ENER, M. and MOBBERLEY, M. L. *Federation Proc.* **19**, 240 (1960).
92. STOKES, W. M., FISH, W. A. and HICKEY, F. C. *J. Biol. Chem.* **220**, 415 (1956).
93. AVIGAN, J., STEINBERG, D., THOMPSON, M. J. and MOSETTIG, E. *Biochem. Biophys. Res. Communs.* **2**, 63 (1960).
94. KRITCHEVSKY, D. and HOLMES, W. L. *Biochem. Biophys. Res. Communs.* **7**, 128 (1962).
95. BIGGS, M. W., LEMMON, R. M. and PIERCE, F. T., JR. *Arch. Biochem. Biophys.* **51**, 155 (1954).
96. DAVIDSON, A. G., DULIT, E. G. and FRANTZ, I. D., JR. *Federation Proc.* **16**, 169 (1957).
97. DAUBEN, W. G., BAN, Y. and RICHARDS, J. H. *J. Am. Chem. Soc.* **79**, 968 (1957).
98. ROSENFELD, R. S., FUKUSHIMA, D. K., HELLMAN, L. and GALLAGHER, T. F. *J. Biol. Chem.* **211**, 301 (1951).
99. SCHÖNHEIMER, R., RITTENBERG, D. and GRAFF, M. *J. Biol. Chem.* **111**, 183 (1935).
100. ROSENFELD, R. S., HELLMAN, L. and GALLAGHER, T. F. *J. Biol. Chem.* **222**, 321 (1956).
101. ROSENFELD, R. S. and GALLAGHER, T. F. *Steroids* **4**, 515 (1964).
102. ANKER, H. S. and BLOCH, K. *J. Biol. Chem.* **178**, 971 (1949).
103. WERBIN, H., CHAIKOFF, I. L. and PHILLIPS, B. P. *Biochemistry* **3**, 1558 (1964).
104. SHEFER, S., MILCH, S. and MOSBACH, E. H. *J. Biol. Chem.* **239**, 1731 (1964).
105. KANDUTSCH, A. A. *J. Lipid Res.* **4**, 179 (1963).
106. SANDERMANN, W. In *Proceedings of the Fourth International Congress of Biochemistry*, Vienna, 1958, vol. 2. Pergamon Press, London, 1959.
107. ARIGONI, D. In *Biosynthesis of Terpenes and Steroids*. A Ciba Foundation Symposium, p. 231. Little, Brown & Co., Boston, 1959.
108. HEFTMANN, E., *Ann. Rev. Plant Physiol.* **14**, 225 (1963).
109. BAISTED, D. J., CAPSTACK, E., JR. and NES, W. R. *Biochemistry* **1**, 537 (1962).
110. NICHOLAS, H. J. *J. Biol. Chem.* **237**, 1476 (1962).
111. JOHNSON, D. F., WRIGHT, B. E. and HEFTMANN, E. *Arch. Biochem. Biophys.* **97**, 232 (1962).
112. JOHNSON, D. F., HEFTMANN, E. and HOUGHLAND, G. V. C. *Arch. Biochem. Biophys.* **104**, 102 (1964).
113. BENNETT, R. D., HEFTMANN, E., PRESTON, W. H., JR. and HAUN, J. R. *Arch. Biochem. Biophys.* **103**, 74 (1963).
114. HEARD, R. D. H., BLIGH, E. G., CANN, M. C., JELLINEK, P. H., O'DONNELL, V. J., RAO, B. G. and WEBB, J. L. *Recent Progress in Hormone Research* **9**, 383 (1954).
115. HECHTER, O. In *Cholesterol*, ed. R. P. Cook, p. 337. Academic Press Inc., New York, 1958.
116. BLOCH, K. *J. Biol. Chem.* **157**, 661 (1945).
117. HECHTER, O., ZAFFARONI, A., JACOBSEN, R. P., LEVY, H., JEANLOZ, R. W., SCHENKER, V. and PINCUS, G. *Recent Progress in Hormone Research* **6**, 215 (1951).
118. SABA, N., HECHTER, O. and STONE, D. *J. Am. Chem. Soc.* **76**, 3862 (1954).
119. SOLOMON, S., LANG, A. L., VANDE WEILE, R. and LIEBERMAN, S. *Abstracts American Chemical Society Meeting*, p. 29C. New York, 1955.
120. STAPLE, E., LYNN, W. S., JR. and GURIN, S. *J. Biol. Chem.* **219**, 845 (1956).
121. CONSTANTOPOULOS, G. and TCHEN, T. T. *J. Biol. Chem.* **236**, 65 (1961).
122. HALKERSTON, I. D. K., EICHHORN, J. and HECHTER, O. *Arch. Biochem. Biophys.* **85**, 287 (1959).
123. HALKERSTON, I. D. K., EICHHORN, J. and HECHTER, O. *J. Biol. Chem.* **236**, 347, (1961)
124. CONSTANTOPOULOS, G., SATOH, P. S. and TCHEN, T. T. *Biochem. Biophys. Res. Communs.* **8**, 50 (1962).
125. SHIMIZU, K., DORFMAN, R. I. and GUT, M. *J. Biol. Chem.* **235**, PC 25 (1960).
126. SHIMIZU, K., HAYANO, M., GUT, M. and DORFMAN, R. I. *J. Biol. Chem.* **236**, 695 (1961).
127. SHIMIZU, K., GUT, M. and DORFMAN, R. I. *J. Biol. Chem.* **237**, 699 (1962).
128. CHAUDHURI, A. C., HARODA, Y., SHIMIZU, K., GUT, M. and DORFMAN, R. I. *J. Biol. Chem.* **237**, 703 (1962).
129. BEYER, K. F. and SAMUELS, L. T. *J. Biol. Chem.* **219**, 69 (1965).

130. HAYANO, M., SABA, N., DORFMAN, R. I. and HECHTER, O. *Recent Progress In Hormone Research* **12**, 79 (1956).
131. HAYANO, M., LINDBERG, M. C., DORFMAN, R. I., HANCOCK, J. E. H. and DOERING, W. VON E. *Arch. Biochem. Biophys.* **59**, 529 (1955).
132. AYRES, P. J. HECHTER, O., SABA, N., SIMPSON, S. A. and TAIT, J. F. *Biochem. J.* **65**, 22P (1957).
133. CHEN, P. S., SCHEDL, H. P., ROSENFELD, G. and BARTTER, F. C. *Proc. Soc. Exptl. Biol. Med.* **97**, 683 (1958).
134. TRAVIS, R. H. and FARRELL, G. L. *Federation Proc.* **17**, 324 (1958).
135. KAHNT, F. W., NEHER, R. and WETTSTEIN, A. *Experientia* **11**, 446 (1955).
136. WELIKY, I. and ENGEL, L. L. *J. Biol. Chem.* **238**, 1302 (1963).
137. HECHTER, O. In *Cholesterol* P. 332, ed. R. P. Cook. Academic Press Inc., New York, 1958.
138. LYNN, W. S., JR. and BROWN, R. *Biochim. Biophys. Acta* **21**, 403 (1956).
139. SLAUNWHITE, W. R., JR. and SAMUELS, L. T. *J. Biol. Chem.* **220**, 341 (1956).
140. GOLDSTEIN, M., GUT, M. and DORFMAN, R. I. *Biochim. Biophys. Acta* **38**, 190 (1960).
141. SOLOMON, S., CARTER, A. C. and LIEBERMAN, S. *J. Biol. Chem.* **235**, 351 (1960).
142. KASE, N., FORCHIELLI, E. and DORFMAN, R. I. *Acta Endocrinol.* **37**, 19 (1961).
143. BAGGETT, B., ENGEL, L. L., SAVARD, K. and DORFMAN, R. I. *Federation Proc.* **14**, 175 (1955); *J. Biol. Chem.* **221**, 931 (1956).
144. MEYER, A. S. *Biochim. Biophys. Acta* **17**, 441 (1955); *Experientia* **11**, 99 (1955).
145. DORFMAN, R. I. *Am. J. Med.* **21**, 679 (1956).
146. WERBIN, H., PLOTZ, LEROY, G. V. and DAVIS, E. M. *J. Am. Chem. Soc.* **79**, 1012 (1957).
147. RABINOWITZ, J. L. *Atompraxis* **5**, 1 (1959).
148. RYAN, K. J. and SMITH, O. W. *J. Biol. Chem.* **236**, 2204 (1961).
149. RYAN, K. J. *J. Biol. Chem.* **234**, 268 (1959).
150. LONGCHAMPT, J. E., GUAL, C., EHRENSTEIN, M. and DORFMAN, R. I. *Endocrinology* **66**, 416 (1960).
151. MORATO, T., HAYANO, M., DORFMAN, R. I. and AXELROD, L. R. *Biochem. Biophys. Res. Commun.* **6**, 334 (1961).
152. BREUER, H. and GRILL, P. *Z. Physiol. Chem.* **324**, 254 (1961).
153. DORFMAN, R. I., GUAL, C., MORATO, T., HAYANO, M. and GUT, M. *Abstracts, International Congress on Hormonal Steroids*, p. 270, Milan, Italy, 1962.
154. FIESER, L. F. and FIESER, M. *Steroids*, Reinhold Publishing Corp., New York, 1959.
155. LIFSCHÜTZ, J. *Z. Physiol. Chem.* **91**, 309 (1914).
156. BLOCH, K., BERG, B. N. and RITTENBERG, D. *J. Biol. Chem.* **149**, 511 (1943).
157. BERGSTRÖM, S. *Kgl. Fysiograf. Sallskap. Lund. Forh.* **22**, (16) 1 (1952).
158. SIPERSTEIN, M. D., JAYKO, M. E., CHAIKOFF, I. L. and DAUBEN, W. G. *Proc. Soc. Exptl. Biol. Med.* **81**, 720 (1952).
159. ZABIN, I. and BARKER, W. F. *J. Biol. Chem.* **205**, 633 (1953).
160. STAPLE, E. and GURIN, S. *Biochim. Biophys. Acta* **15**, 372 (1954).
161. BERGSTRÖM, S. *Record Chem. Progr.* (Kresge-Hooker Sci. Lib.) **16**, 63 (1955).
162. BERGSTRÖM, S. In *Biosynthesis of Terpenes and Sterols*, A Ciba Foundation Symposium. Little, Brown & Co., Boston, 1959.
163. HAROLD, F. M., JAYKO, M. E. and CHAIKOFF, I. L. *J. Biol. Chem.* **216**, 439 (1955).
164. FREDRICKSON, D. S. and ONO, K. *Biochim. Biophys. Acta* **22**, 183 (1956).
165. BERGSTRÖM, S., PAABO, K. and RUMPF, J. A. *Acta Chem. Scand.* **8**, 1109 (1954).
166. BERGSTRÖM, S. and LINDSTEDT, S. *Biochim. Biophys. Acta* **19**, 556 (1956).
167. CHAIKOFF, I. L., SIPERSTEIN, M. D., DAUBEN, W. G., BRADLOW, H. L., EASTHAM, J. F., TOMKINS, G. M., MEIER, J. R., CHEN, R. W., HOTTA, S. and SRERE, P. A. *J. Biol. Chem.* **194**, 413 (1952).
168. ANFINSEN, C. B., JR. and HORNING, M. G. *J. Am. Chem. Soc.* **75**, 1511 (1953).
169. HORNING, M. G., FREDRICKSON, D. S. and ANFINSEN, C. B. *Arch. Biochem. Biophys.* **71**, 266 (1957).
170. FREDRICKSON, D. S. *J. Biol. Chem.* **222**, 109 (1956).
171. WHITEHOUSE, M. W., STAPLE, E. and GURIN, S. *J. Biol. Chem.* **234**, 276 (1959).

172. WHITEHOUSE, M. W., STAPLE, E. and GURIN, S. *J. Biol. Chem.* **236**, 68 (1961).
173. WHITEHOUSE, M. W., COTTRELL, M., BRIGGS, T. and STAPLE, E. *Arch. Biochem. Biophys.* **98**, 305 (1962).
174. SHIMIZU, K., FUJIOKI, T., OTAGAKI, M. and YAMASAKI, K. YONAGO. *Acta Medica* **3**, 158 (1959).
175. WHITEHOUSE, M. W., STAPLE, E. and GURIN, S. *J. Biol. Chem.* **236**, 73 (1961); *Federation Proc.* **16**, 254 (1957).
176. BRIGGS, T., WHITEHOUSE, M. W. and STAPLE, E. *Arch. Biochem. Biophys.* **85**, 275 (1959).
177. BRIGGS, T., WHITEHOUSE, M. W. and STAPLE, E. *J. Biol. Chem.* **236**, 688 (1961).
178. DANIELSSON, H. *Acta Chem. Scand.* **14**, 348 (1960).
179. SULD, H. M., STAPLE, E. and GURIN, S. *Federation Proc.* **20**, 284 (1961); *J. Biol. Chem.* **237**, 338 (1962).
180. HERMAN, R. and STAPLE, E. *Federation Proc.* **24**, 661 (1965).
181. BREMER, J. *Acta Chem. Scand.* **9**, 268, 683 (1955).
182. SIPERSTEIN, M. D. *Federation Proc.* **14**, 282 (1955).
183. ELLIOTT, W. H. *Biochem. J.* **62**, 433 (1956).
184. LYNN, W. S. JR., STAPLE, E. and GURIN, S. *Federation Proc.* **14**, 783 (1955).
185. WHITEHOUSE, M. W., RABINOWITZ, J. L., STAPLE, E. and GURIN, S. *Biochim. Biophys. Acta* **37**, 382 (1960).
186. BERGSTRÖM, S., DANIELSSON, H. and SAMUELSSON, B. In *Lipid Metabolism*, ed. K. Bloch. Wiley, New York, 1960.
187. DANIELSSON, H. In *Advances in Lipid Research*, eds. D. Kritchevsky and R. Paoletti, Academic Press, New York, 1963.
188. STAPLE, E. and RABINOWITZ, J. L. *Biochim. Biophys. Acta* **59**, 735 (1962).
189. CAREY, J. B., JR. and HASLEWOOD, G. A. D. *J. Biol. Chem.* **238**, PC 855 (1963).
190. CAREY, J. B., JR. *J. Clin. Invest.* **43**, 1443 (1964).
191. DANIELSSON, H. and EINARSSON, K. *Acta Chim. Scand.* **18**, 831 (1964).
192. MENDELSOHN, D., MENDELSOHN, L. and STAPLE, E. *Biochim. Biophys. Acta* **97**, 379 (1965).
193. DANIELSSON, H. *Arkiv. Kemi.* **17**, 363 (1961).
194. DANIELSSON, H. *Arkiv. Kemi.* **17**, 373 (1961).
195. MENDELSOHN, D. and STAPLE, E. *Biochemistry* **2**, 577 (1963).
196. MENDELSOHN, D., MENDELSOHN, L. and STAPLE, E. *Biochemistry* **4**, 441 (1965).
197. BERGSTRÖM, S. In *Biosynthesis of Terpenes and Sterols*, Little, Brown & Co., Boston, 1959.
198. LINDSTEDT and SJÖVALL, *Acta. Chem. Scand.* **11**, 421 (1957).
199. BERGSTRÖM, S., LINDSTEDT, S. and SAMUELSSON, B. *J. Biol. Chem.* **234**, 2022 (1959).
200. LINDSTEDT, S. and SAMUELSSON, B. *J. Biol. Chem.* **234**, 2026 (1959).
201. SAMUELSSON, B. *J. Biol. Chem.* **235**, 361 (1960).
202. MATKOVICS, B. and SAMUELSSON, B. *Acta Chem. Scand.* **16**, 683 (1962).
203. HASLEWOOD, G. A. D. In *Biosynthesis of Terpenes and Sterols*, Little, Brown & Co., Boston, 1959.
204. BRIGGS, T., WHITEHOUSE, M. W. and STAPLE, E. *Arch. Biochem. Biophys.* **85**, 275 (1959).
205. BERGSTRÖM, S., DANIELSSON, H. and KAZUNO, T. *J. Biol. Chem.* **235**, 983 (1960).
206. BRIGGS, T. Ph.D. Dissertation, Univ. of Pennsylvania 1960.
207. KAZUNO, T. and OKUDA, K. *J. Biochem. (Japan)* **50**, 352 (1961).
208. MASUI, T. *J. Biochem. (Japan)* **49**, 211 (1961).
209. HASLEWOOD, G. A. D. *Biological Rev.* **39**, 537 (1964).
210. LYTHGOE, B. *Proceedings of the Chemical Society* **1959**, 141.
211. VELLUZ, L., AMIARD, G. and GOFFINET, B. *Compt. Rend.* **240**, 2576 (1955); *Bull Soc. Chim. France* **1955**, 1341.
212. GLOVER, M., GLOVER, J. and MORTON, R. A. *Biochem. J.* **51**, 1 (1952).
213. FESTENSTEIN, G. N. and MORTON, R. A. *Biochem. J.* **60**, 22 (1955).
214. BLONDIN, G. A., KULKARNI, B. D. and NES, W. R. *J. Am. Chem. Soc.* **86**, 2528 (1964).

CHAPTER 5

THE BIOGENESIS OF HEME, CHLOROPHYLLS, AND BILE PIGMENTS

LAWRENCE BOGORAD† and ROBERT F. TROXLER
Department of Botany, University of Chicago, Chicago, Illinois

CONTENTS

I. INTRODUCTION   248
II. PORPHYRINS   249
   A. *Structural relationships among porphyrins. Distribution in nature*   249
   B. *The biogenesis of porphyrins*   252
     1. The biosynthesis of δ-aminolevulinic acid   254
     2. The biosynthesis of porphobilinogen   257
     3. Uroporphyrinogens   257
     4. Coproporphyrinogens   261
     5. Protoporphyrin IX   264
     6. Heme   264
     7. Magnesium protoporphyrin IX   266
     8. The formation of chlorophyll *a* from magnesium protoporphyrin IX   266
     9. Chlorophylls *b*, *c*, *d*, and *e*   270
    10. Bacterial chlorophylls   270
    11. Porphyrins with hydroxyl and carbonyl substituents 270
    12. The control of porphyrin biosynthesis   272
III. BILE PIGMENTS   274
   A. *Structural relationships*   274
   B. *The biogenesis of bile pigments*   276
     1. The biogenesis of biliverdin   277
     2. The biogenesis of "urobilin"   287
IV. BILIPROTEINS   289
   A. *Distribution and composition*   289

† Research Career Awardee of the National Institute of General Medical Sciences, United States Public Health Service.

247

  B. *The biogenesis of phyco biliproteins*   292
    1. Experiments and observations   292
    2. Speculations on biliprotein biogenesis   295
  V. VITAMIN B$_{12}$ 299
    A. *The structural relationship of vitamin B$_{12}$ corrin to
       porphyrins*   299
    B. *Possible mechanisms for the formation of the corrin ring*   299
    1. Origin from Uroporphyrinogen isomer III   301
    2. Origin from Uroporphyrin III—metal complexes   301
  VI. PRODIGIOSIN   303
  VII. SUMMARY   305
    REFERENCES   306

I. INTRODUCTION

The most abundant porphyrin in photosynthetic plants is chlorophyll *a*. It is normally accompanied by smaller amounts of one or another additional chlorophylls in all but algae of the phyla *Xanthophyta* and *Cyanophyta*. [24] Hemoglobin, containing iron-protoporphyrin IX prosthetic groups, is the most prominent mammalian porphyrin-protein. On the other hand, cytochromes, catalase, and peroxidases, all iron-porphyrin-protein complexes, are found in the largest number of different organisms.

The biological capture of solar energy and its conversion to chemical bond energy for subsequent use is mediated by chlorophylls and cytochromes. Cytochromes are also vital agents for the transfer of electrons through potential gradients coupled to the formation of immediately usable high energy bonds, such as high energy phosphate bonds. In addition, hemoproteins serve as activators of molecular oxygen in aerobic metabolism.

Besides the chlorophylls, cytochromes, hemoglobins, and heme enzymes like peroxidases and catalase, a number of porphyrins of undetermined function, if any, have been found in a wide variety of organisms.

Many functional porphyrin-proteins are localized in specialized cells—e.g. hemoglobin in erythrocytes—or in subcellular particles—e.g. chlorophylls in plastids or chromatophores of photosynthetic organisms, and cytochromes in mitochondria and plastids. Furthermore, within mitochondria and plastids, chlorophylls and cytochromes are incorporated into the lamellar structure. Consequently, the metabolism of these porphyrins is intimately associated with the production, development, and destruction of the structures and cells in which they are located and in which, at least in part, they may be synthesized and degraded. These important interrelationships are omitted from the present discussion.

Biochemical aspects of the formation and degradation of porphyrins in biological systems are discussed in this chapter. Enough facts are available to permit the presentation of a detailed and probably fairly accurate account of porphyrin biogenesis. Less information is at hand concerning some of the other areas examined here; in these cases current knowledge is systematized, in part, by pointing out possible biosynthetic mechanisms and pathways. As usual, the amount of speculation indulged in is inversely proportional to the mass of the body of relevant facts.

II. PORPHYRINS

A. Structural Relationships among Porphyrins. Distribution in Nature

The heterocyclic pyrrole ring (I) is the fundamental unit of a porphyrin. Each pyrrole has four substitutable carbon atoms. The two bound to the nitrogen atom are designated "α" and "α'"; the other two carbon atoms as "β" and "β'". The pyrroles are colorless in solution. The precise locations of their absorption maxima in the ultraviolet region is influenced by the nature and position of the substituents on the ring. [57]

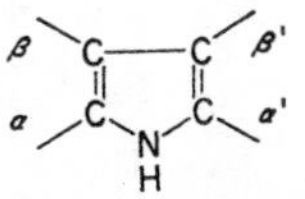

Pyrrole skeleton

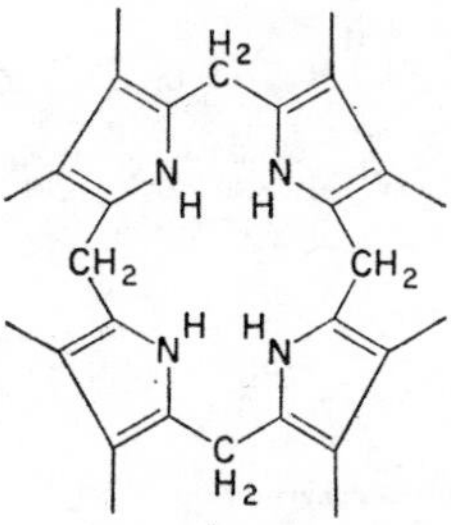

Porphyrinogen skeleton
II

FIG. 1.

A colorless *porphyrinogen* (II, Fig. 1) is formed when four pyrroles are joined into a large ring by saturated carbon (methane) bridges linking the α-carbon atoms. Porphyrinogens are readily oxidized to colored, planar porphyrins (e.g. Fig. 2) by O_2 or iodine; porphyrins can be reduced to porphyrinogens by sodium amalgam or other relatively mild reducing agents at room temperature. The carbon bridges between pyrrole residues of porphyrins are *unsaturated* (methene bridges). Unstable orange intermediates, semiporphyrinogens, which absorb strongly at about 500 mμ are formed when only one or two pairs of pyrroles are in resonance, i.e. when one carbon bridge or two opposite pairs of bridges are oxidized. [17, 19, 190]

Variations in physical and biological properties among porphyrins depend largely upon differences in the nature and arrangement of the substituents

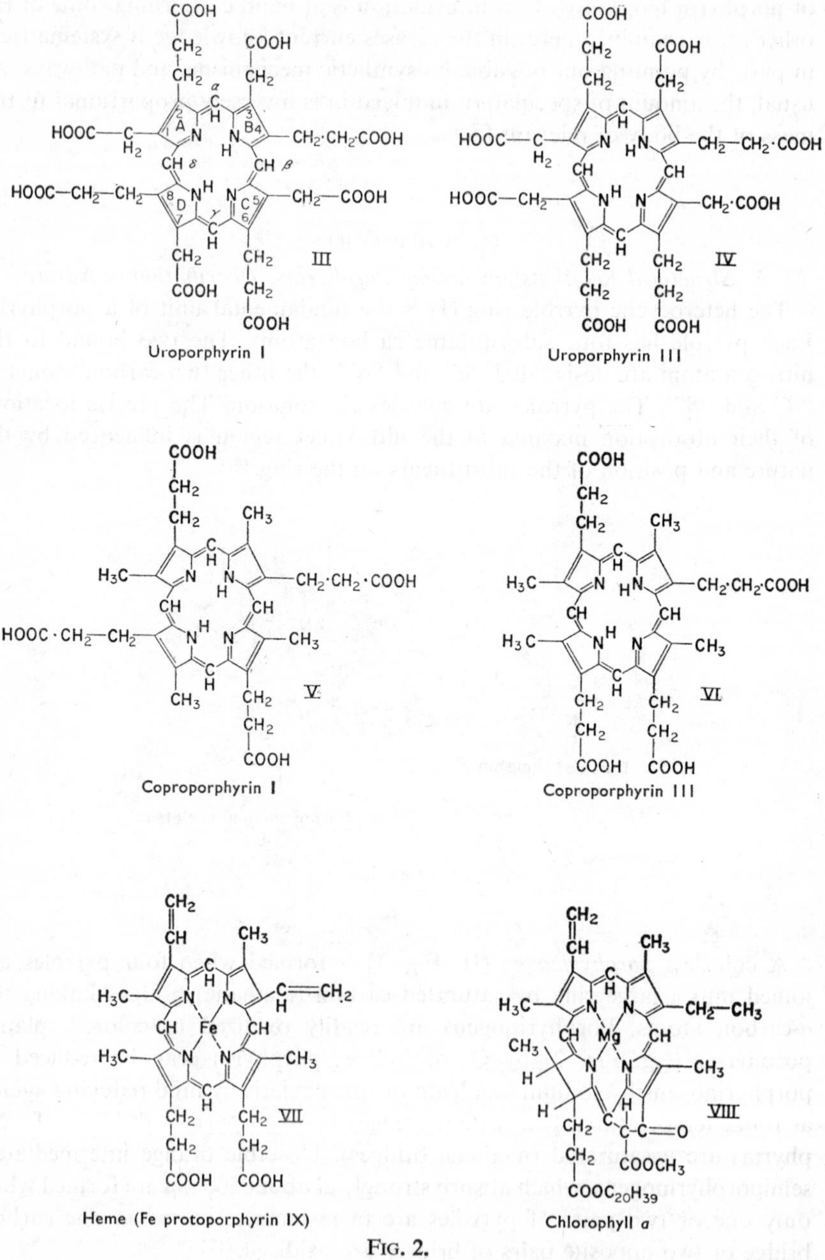

FIG. 2.

on the eight substitutable β-carbons of the pyrrole moieties and upon the kind of metal, if any, which is present. Uroporphyrin III (IV), coproporphyrin III (VI), and iron protoporphyrin IX (VII) are shown in Fig. 2.

A further detail of porphyrin structure and classification which is of paramount importance biologically is the *arrangement* of a given set of side chains. For example, fifteen isomers of protoporphyrin, each with two pyrrole rings bearing vinyl and acetic acid groups and two substituted with propionic and acetic acid residues, can be visualized but only one, that designated "IX" by Fischer, [59] has been recovered from biological material. Similarly, although four isomers of uroporphyrin and four of coproporphyrin have been prepared, only the I and III isomers have been identified in animals or plants. The hallmark of normal biological activity of porphyrins, as opposed merely to occurrence, is the position of the propionic acid residue on ring D. This can be seen by comparing the structures of uroporphyrins I and III (formulae III and IV), coproporphyrin I and III (formulae V and VI), chlorophyll a (VIII), and heme (VII) in Fig. 2. The propionic acid residue on ring D of coproporphyrin III, chlorophyll a, and heme is the substitutent of β-carbon atom 7. On the other hand, porphyrins of the biologically occurring isomer I series, e.g. coproporphyrin I, have an alternating arrangement of propionic and acetic acid residues; the propionic acid residue on ring D is bound to β-carbon atom 8. Mammals with certain diseases produce and excrete coproporphyrin I and uroporphyrin I; isomers of this series are not known to play any role in normal metabolism although they do also accumulate naturally under non-pathological conditions, for example in the shell of the pearl oyster, *Pinctada vulgaris* (uroporphyrin I) [44] and in planarian, *Dugesia dorotocephala* (uroporphyrin I; E. K. MacRae, unpublished data).

Differences between heme (VII, Fig. 2) and chlorophyll a (VIII, Fig. 2) provide additional examples of variations among porphyrins of biological origin with regard to (a) the nature of the side chains; e.g. the ethyl group on carbon 2 of chlorophyll a, as against the vinyl group on the same position of heme; (b) the metal with which the porphyrin is complexed; Mg in chlorophyll and Fe in heme: (c) the formation of an additional ring; as in the case of the cyclopentanone ring of chlorophyll produced by the cyclization of the modified propionic acid substituent on carbon 6 with bridge carbon γ; and (d) the partial reduction of one or more of the pyrrole residues; chlorophyll, in which the D ring is partially reduced, is a chlorin; bacteriochlorophyll is a dihydrochlorin, i.e. rings B and D are equally reduced.

Biological activity depends upon the structure of the porphyrin and the protein to which it is attached, as well as, in some cases, upon the appropriate incorporation of the complex into functional subcellular units such as chloroplasts or mitochondria.

The absorption spectrum of hematoporphyrin dimethyl ester in pyridine solution is shown in Fig. 3; the precise location of the absorption maxima and the relative intensities of the absorption bands are affected by the nature and arrangement of the substituents on the β-positions of the pyrrole residues. Porphyrins in acid solution and metalloporphyrins show characteristic two-banded spectra in the visual region.

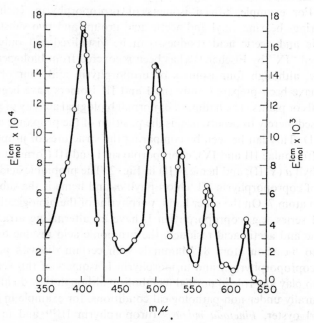

FIG. 3. Absorption spectrum of hematoporphyrin dimethyl ester in pyridine.[93]
(*Reproduced by courtesy of the American Society of Biological Chemists.*)

B. *The Biogenesis of Porphyrins*

Investigations of the synthesis of heme in avian erythrocytes *in vitro* and *in vivo* showed that glycine, of all the amino acids tested, was the most direct source of nitrogen atoms for all four pyrrole residues. [196, 254, 305] During the late 1940's and 1950's, isotopic tracer techniques were employed masterfully in a number of laboratories to establish the metabolic origins of the carbon atoms of heme. One α-carbon in each pyrrole residue and each of the four bridge carbons was found to arise from the methyl carbon of glycine. [197, 306] (The carboxyl carbon of glycine is not incorporated into heme. [103, 182]) All the remaining carbon atoms of this porphyrin are derived from acetate [234] (Fig. 4). From the pattern of labeling found in heme which was synthesized by avian red cells supplied with carboxyl or methyl C^{14}-labeled acetate, Shemin and Wittenberg [258] deduced that the carbon atoms of acetate passed through the Krebs cycle and probably were incorporated into porphyrin as succinate or via a succinyl derivative. Shemin and Kumin[140] subsequently showed that succinate was incorporated into heme without rearrangement. Succinyl-CoA was postulated to be an intermediate.

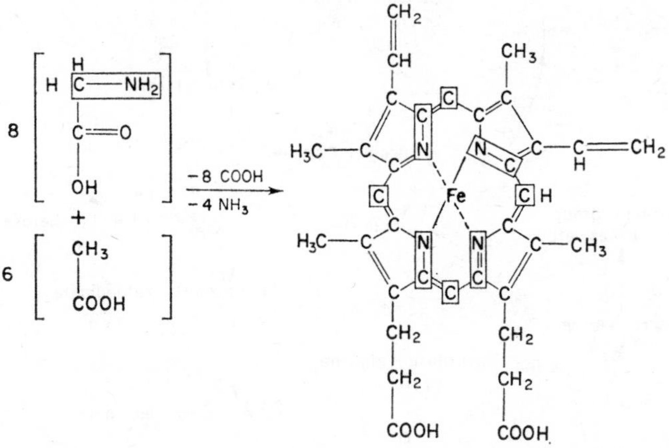

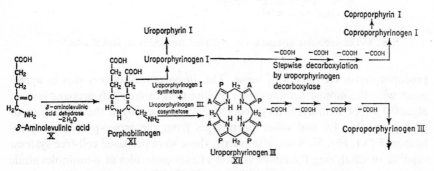

FIG. 4. Location of α-carbon and nitrogen atoms of glycine utilized for the biosynthesis of heme. Atoms of heme derived from glycine are marked: □ The carboxyl carbon atom of glycine is not used. All unmarked carbon atoms of heme are derived from acetate.

FIG. 5. Scheme for the biosynthesis of uroporphyrinogen III from δ-aminolevulinic acid.

Proceeding from the knowledge that the methyl carbon and nitrogen atoms of glycine, but not the carboxyl carbon atom of this amino acid, coupled with a succinyl derivative could be visualized as the source of all the carbon and nitrogen atoms of heme, Shemin et al.[256, 257] prepared C^{14}-δ-amino-levulinic acid (X, Fig. 5), supplied it to suspensions of avian erythrocytes in vitro, and demonstrated that it could serve as the sole precursor of the

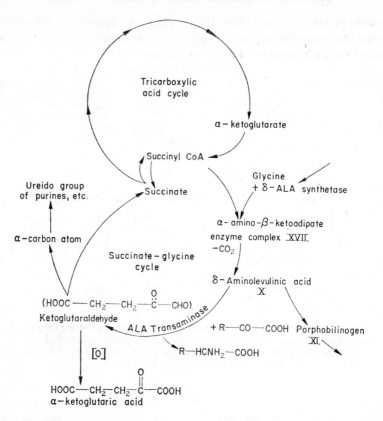

Fig. 6. The succinate-glycine cycle. Adapted from Shemin and Russel.[256]

protoporphyrin IX moiety of heme. This important discovery was in agreement with the almost simultaneous finding that broken cell preparations of algae [30] or of hemolyzed erythrocytes [52] could catalyze the formation of protoporphyrin IX and other porphyrins from the mono-pyrrole porphobilinogen (XI, Fig. 5). Soon afterwards, there were prepared cell-free systems capable of catalyzing the condensation of two molecules of δ-aminolevulinic acid to produce one of porphobilinogen. [78, 87, 249]

A scheme for the biosynthesis of porphobilinogen from glycine and acetate, via the cycle proposed by Shemin, [256] is shown in Fig. 6, and the pathways leading to porphyrins from porphobilinogen are presented in Figs. 5 to 10. Each of the steps shown will be discussed in greater detail.

1. The Biosynthesis of δ-Aminolevulinic Acid

Shemin's suggestion that succinate might be used for porphyrin biosynthesis via a CoA derivative was supported by Lascelles observation [155] that a strain of *Tetrahymena vorax* which normally accumulated protoporphyrin, barely did so when cultured on suboptimal levels of pyridoxal but with adequate glycine for growth. She found, however, that normal amounts of protoporphyrin were produced under these conditions if δ-aminolevulinic acid was supplied. Thus, pyridoxal and pantothenate were apparently required for the formation of δ-aminolevulinic acid but not for other steps in protoporphyrin formation. Similar observations were made by Schulman and Richert[250] in studies on the formation of heme from glycine and succinate or from δ-aminolevulinic acid by red cells of vitamin B_6 or pantothenate-deficient ducklings.

δ-Aminolevulinic acid synthetase, which catalyzes the synthesis of δ-aminolevulinic acid (X) from glycine and succinyl-CoA, with pyridoxal phosphate serving as a cofactor, has been prepared as freeze-dried particles from chicken erythrocytes[76] and a soluble enzyme has been purified from extracts of *Rhodospirillum rubrum* and *Rodopseudomonas spheroides*.[143, 39] The bacterial enzyme is inhibited by hemin.[39]

The expected product of the condensation of glycine and succinate, α-amino-β-ketoadipic acid, has been sought but not identified in reaction mixtures of glycine, succinyl-CoA, pyridoxal phosphate, and δ-aminolevulinic acid synthetase. However, Laver *et al.*[158, 159] have shown that the α-keto acid decarboxylates rapidly and spontaneously to δ-aminolevulinic acid; the half-life of α-amino-β-ketoadipic acid is estimated to be less than one minute in aqueous solution at pH 7. Neuberger's suggestions regarding the mechanism of formation of δ-aminolevulinic acid may provide another explanation for the failure to detect α-amino-β-ketoadipic acid as an intermediate.[203]

In discussing possible mechanisms for the formation of δ-aminolevulinic acid from glycine and succinyl-CoA, Neuberger[203] points out that aminoketone synthetase systems are relatively unspecific with respect to the acyl group of the acyl-CoA derivative used, but that glycine is the only amino acid active with the enzyme. Because of this specificity for glycine, he proposes that the amino acid is, in part, bound to the enzyme protein and that the initial step in the sequence of reactions is the binding of glycine to a pyridoxal phosphate-enzyme complex (XIII, Fig. 7). In the succeeding step succinate is added to form an α-amino-β-ketoadipate-pyridoxal phosphate-enzyme complex (XVII, Fig. 7). Neuberger points out that the structure which he has postulated for the pyridoxal phosphate-enzyme-glycine complex (XV) is identical to a proposed intermediate in the enzymatic decarboxylation of many amino acids not containing a β-carbonyl function. Thus, the glycine-pyridoxal phosphate-enzyme complex (XV) might itself constitute an enzyme for the decarboxylation of the α-amino-β-ketoadipate complex (XVII). Alternative "A" (Fig. 7) is simply that a spontaneous decarboxylation may follow quickly and non-enzymatically after the liberation of α-amino-β-

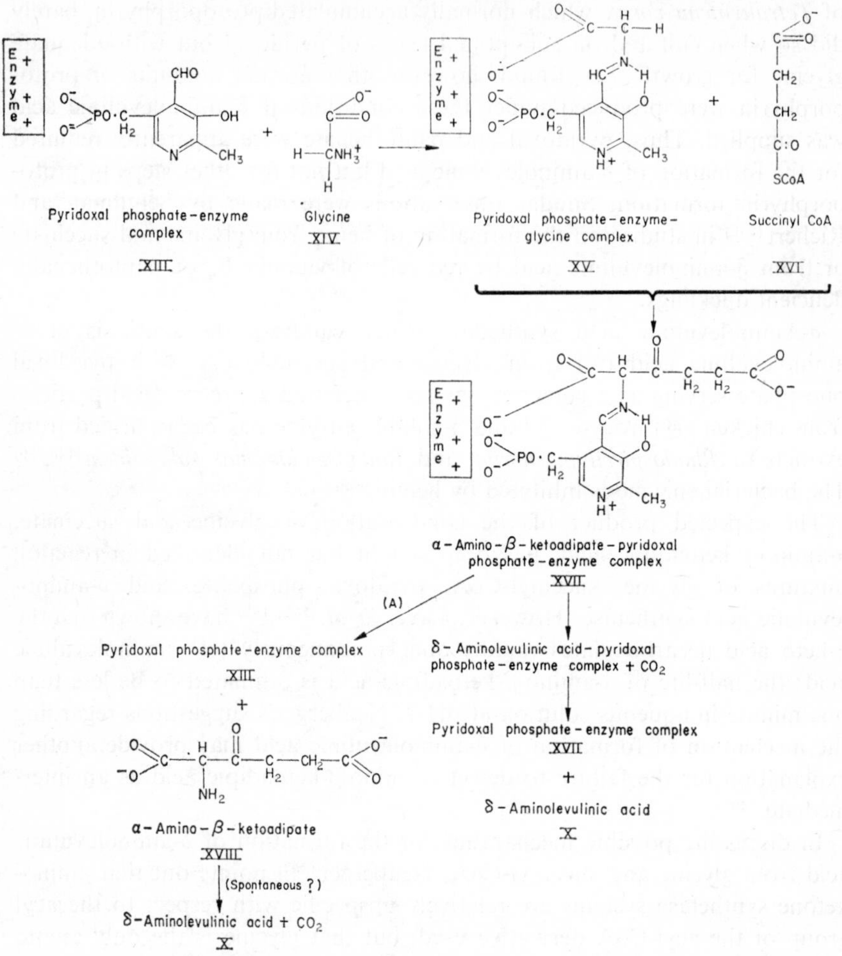

FIG. 7. Hypothetical scheme for steps in the formation of δ-aminolevulinic acid from glycine and succinyl-CoA. Adapted from Neuberger.[203]

ketoadipate (XVIII) from its complex with the enzyme as is suggested by the rapid decay of the compound *in vitro*.

Studies by Urata and Granick [291] suggest, however, that there may be several α-aminoketone synthetases and that these may vary in their specificity for acyl-CoA substrates. Mitochondria from livers of porphyric guinea pigs readily formed δ-aminolevulinic acid from succinyl-CoA but frozen and thawed liver mitochondria from normal animals formed aminoacetone from glycine and acetyl-CoA or malonyl-CoA and an α-aminoketone from glycine and propionyl-CoA but not from butyryl-CoA or succinyl-CoA.

Nemeth *et al.* [202] found that the δ-carbon atom of δ-aminolevulinic acid administered to pigeons or rats appears as formate and in the uriedo group of guanine, just as does the δ-carbon of glycine, while succinate is generated from the succinyl moiety. These observations support the scheme shown in Fig. 6.

δ-Aminolevulinic acid transaminase has been demonstrated to occur in mammalian tissues, [145, 146] *Corynebacterium diptheriae*, [7] *Rhodopseudomonas spheroides*, [205, 77] and *Chlorella vulgaris* (M. Gassman, J. Pluscec and L. Bogorad, unpublished). The mammalian enzyme from most tissues favors α-oxoglutarate over pyruvate as an amino group acceptor. The equilibrium for the reaction catalyzed by the enzyme from *R. spheroides* is toward the formation of δ-aminolevulinic acid; L-alanine appears to be the preferred amino group donor. It is not known whether, in any organism, this enzyme plays a significant role in the formation of δ-aminolevulinate or the regulation of the amount of this compound available for use in porphyrin production by diversion of the product of the δ-aminolevulinic acid synthetase reaction.

2. The Biosynthesis of Porphobilinogen

Freshly passed urine of individuals with the hereditary disease, acute porphyria, generally looks fairly normal but on standing at room temperature, particularly in the light, it comes to resemble heavy port wine in color. The wine color is partly that of uroporphyrin but is mainly attributable to porphobilin, a compound which has not been characterized but which is probably a long pyrrole polymer. Another characteristic of acute porphyria urine is that, when fresh, it gives a strong red color with Ehrlich's reagent, *p*-dimethylaminobenzaldehyde in acid solution. This reaction is characteristic of some pyrroles and polypyrroles with at least one unsubstituted α-position. Reddened porphyria urine, on the other hand, gives a weak or negative Ehrlich reaction. Thus, the increase is in uroporphyrin and porphobilin is accompanied by a decrease in Ehrlich reactivity. The Ehrlich-reacting material, first observed by Sachs, [241] was named porphobilinogen. In 1952 porphobilinogen was crystallized by Westall [299] and its structure (XI, Fig. 5) was established. [45, 92]

δ-Aminolevulinic acid dehydrase, the enzyme which catalyzes the condensation of two molecules of δ-aminolevulinic acid to one of porphobilinogen, has been partially purified from avian erythrocytes, [87, 249] rabbit reticulocytes, [88] *R. spheroides*, [39] and liver of various animals. [78, 129] This enzyme is activated by sulfhydryl groups, is inhibited by various metals, as well as by ethylene-diaminetetraacetic acid, has a pH optimum at 6·3–6·7, and the K_m is reported to range from 1·4 to 5×10^{-4} depending upon the source.

3. Uroporphyrinogens

Uroporphyrinogens are the cyclic tetrapyrroles formed from porpho-

K

bilinogen. As already pointed out, only the I and III isomers of uroporphyrin, the porphyrin formed by the removal of six hydrogen atoms from uroporphyrinogen, are found in nature. *In vitro* uroporphyrinogens I or III (XII), or a mixture of the two, can be produced from porphobilinogen with the appropriate enzymes. Porphobilinogen also condenses moderately rapidly in a spontaneous reaction (see discussion on porphyria urine). In neutral or alkaline solution the yield of porphyrin is 40 to 55 per cent; in acid solution the yield may reach 78 per cent. [189] The relative amounts of the isomers formed also depend upon the pH of the solution.

In early studies on the enzymatic synthesis of porphyrins from porphobilinogen it was found that preparations of broken *Chlorella* cells capable of catalyzing the formation of uroporphyrinogen III (XII) and porphyrins related to this isomer, e.g. coproporphyrin III (VI, Fig. 2) and protoporphyrin IX (XXXII, Fig. 14), synthesized only uroporphyrinogen I if they had been heated at 55°C prior to incubation with substrate. [30] The rate of consumption of porphobilinogen was found to be approximately the same in heated and unheated preparations. These observations were confirmed in systems of hemolyzed avian and human erythrocytes. [33, 237]

On the basis of these observations, it was suggested that a single, relatively stable, enzyme sufficed for synthesis of the I isomer but that at least two enzymes were required for the formation of the III isomer; a very heat-labile one together with the stable enzyme which, alone, catalyzes the formation of uroporphyrinogen I. [30]

(a) *Uroporphyrinogen I synthetase.* Uroporphyrinogen I synthetase (porphobilinogen deaminase) catalyzes the consumption of porphobilinogen and the formation of uroporphyrinogen I. It has been identified in a number of organisms and partially purified from aqueous extracts of spinach leaf tissue, [17, 19] and from *Rhodopseudomonas spheroides.* [119, 124]

The enzyme from spinach leaf tissue is relatively heat stable. It is only slightly affected by heating at 70°C at pH 8·2 but is inactivated at 100°, and at lower temperatures at other pH values.

The product, uroporphyrinogen I, is completely symmetrical and can be visualized as being formed by the linear condensation of four porphobilinogen molecules, with the liberation of one molecule of ammonia per pair of pyrroles linked, followed by cyclization of the open chain tetrapyrrole. Since the enzyme can form uroporphyrinogen I from porphobilinogen and a dipyrrylmethane equivalent to that which would be produced by condensing two molecules of porphobilinogen, but not from dipyrrylmethane molecules alone, it appears that uroporphyrinogen I synthetase catalyzes the sequential addition of porphobilinogen molecules (J. Pluscec, L. Bogorad and S. F. MacDonald, unpublished).

The uroporphyrinogen I formed during anaerobic incubation of porphobilinogen with uroporphyrinogen I synthetase accounts for close to 100 per cent of the mono-pyrrole consumed (uroporphyrinogen is oxidized to uroporphyrin which is measured in the spectrophotometer; porphobilinogen is measured quantitatively as the colored complex with p-dimethylamino-benzaldehyde). However, the rate of porphobilinogen utilization is essentially unaffected, but yields as low as about 30 per cent are obtained if ammonium ions or hydroxylamine are included in the reaction mixture. Under these conditions compounds which react with p-dimethylaminobenzaldehyde (Ehrlich's reagent), but differ from porphobilinogen, accumulate. The low yields are only "temporary" for, upon prolonged incubation, the "new Ehrlich-positive" compounds disappear and additional uroporphyrinogen I forms at their expense. The final yield of porphyrinogen again approaches 100 per cent. Thus, the "new-Ehrlich-positive" compounds formed from porphobilinogen are intermediates in the synthesis of uroporphyrinogen I; ammonium ions and hydroxylamine appear to decrease the rate of their utilization for porphyrinogen production without appreciably affecting the rate of the enzymatic consumption of porphobilinogen for their formation. Little is known about these intermediates except that, from the absorption maximum at about 498 mμ of the oxidized form and the character of the reaction with Ehrlich's reagent, the likelihood appears great that they include polypyrrylmethanes with free α-positions—perhaps di-, tri-, and tetrapyrroles. [25] It is not clear whether preparations of uroporphyrinogen synthetase contain an enzyme for the condensation of the intermediates or if the presence of such an enzyme is required, since the rate of spontaneous condensation of the ends of open chain tetrapyrrylmethanes formed from porphobilinogen would be expected to be very high.

p-Chloromercuribenzoate, unlike ammonium ions or hydroxylamine, inhibits porphobilinogen consumption; this inhibition is reversed by cysteine. Opsopyrrole dicarboxylic acid is a competitive inhibitor of porphobilinogen utilization. [18, 40] With neither of these agents, at concentrations below those which cause complete inhibition, have intermediates in uroporphyrinogen formation been detected. Isoporphobilinogen, an isomer of porphobilinogen in which the aminomethyl substituent is on the "same side" of the pyrrole ring as the propionic acid residue, is also a competitive inhibitor of uroporphyrinogen I synthetase [41].

(b) *Uroporpyrinogen III cosynthetase.* As described in the preceding section, uroporphyrinogen I is produced in incubation mixtures of porphobilinogen and uroporphyrinogen I synthetase. However, if an appropriate concentration of uroporphyrinogen III cosynthetase is included during incubation only uroporphyrinogen III (XII, Fig. 5) is accumulated. [20]

Uroporphyrinogen III cosynthetase from wheat germ is relatively easily inactivated by heating and is presumably the enzyme required for isomer III synthesis which is destroyed when *Chlorella* preparations or red cell hemolysates are heated.

It is simple to visualize the formation of uroporphyrinogen I from porphobilinogen, as we have already done. The mechanism of the enzymatic synthesis of uroporphyrinogen III presents more difficulty. To review the differences between the two isomers: Isomer I is completely symmetrical, the porphobilinogen residues are neatly laid out head to tail, the acetic and propionic acid substituents alternate completely around the porphyrin molecule. The substituents on rings A, B, and C of the III isomer are also alternately acetic acid and propionic acid residues but the side-chains on ring D are different in isomers I and III. (See Fig. 2, structures III and IV.) It is as though the porphobilinogen molecule which was used for ring D was inserted "backwards" into isomer III after the carbon of the amino methyl side chain had been transferred from one to the other α-position of the pyrrole.

The two enzymes which participate in the synthesis of uroporphyrinogen III appear to act either in concert or, more likely, uroporphyrinogen III cosynthetase acts after uroporphyrinogen I synthetase. Only uroporphyrinogen I is detected in experiments of the following types: (a) uroporphyrinogen III cosynthetase is first incubated with porphobilinogen, then the enzyme is inactivated by mild heating, finally uroporphyrinogen I synthetase is added and the mixture is incubated. (b) porphobilinogen and uroporphyrinogen I synthetase are incubated until all of the substrate has been consumed—the solution now contains uroporphyrinogen I—and then uroporphyrinogen III cosynthetase is added and the incubation is continued.

Experiment "(a)" demonstrates that uroporphyrinogen III cosynthetase is completely inactive in the absence of products of uroporphyrinogen I synthetase. The second experiment shows that uroporphyrinogen III cosynthetase does not utilize uroporphyrinogen I as a substrate. These observations, taken together with the fact that uroporphyrinogen III *is* formed when the two enzymes are incubated with porphobilinogen simultaneously, suggest that uroporphyrinogen III cosynthetase is active only in the presence of some product of the action of uroporphyrinogen I synthetase on porphobilinogen and that this product is not uroporphyrinogen I but must be some compound, such as a di-, tri-, or tetrapyrrole, which can also be utilized for the formation of uroporphyrinogen I if uroporphyrinogen III cosynthetase is absent.

The rate of porphobilinogen consumption is mainly regulated by the concentration of uroporphyrinogen I synthetase but V_{max} for reaction mixtures containing both enzymes is higher than when uroporphyrinogen I synthetase is present alone with porphobilinogen. Uroporphyrinogen III cosynthetase alone, at a concentration adequate to bring about the synthesis of uroporphyrinogen III when included with uroporphyrinogen I synthetase, produces no measurable change in porphobilinogen concentration. The difference in V_{max} suggests that uroporphyrinogen III cosynthetase catalyzes the consumption of porphobilinogen when uroporphyrinogen I synthetase is present and active. Altogether, it can be argued that these are the substrates for later step(s) in isomer III formation: a linear polypyrrole and porphobilinogen. The nature of the polypyrrole is undetermined.

The occurrence of type I porphyrin in nature, as in certain porphyrias, [324] may be an accident of an excess of uroporphyrinogen I synthetase activity which results in the production of linear tetrapyrrylmethanes—e.g. as a consequence of abnormally high rates of porphobilinogen production and/or too low uroporphyrinogen III cosynthetase activity to consume some shorter polymers before they accumulate—coupled with the high probability of cyclization of the tetrapyrrole.

A number of mechanisms for the formation of isomer III have been advanced. A few hypotheses [46, 130, 257] are no longer tenable because of experimental evidence which contradicts them; [20, 31, 40, 53] serious but not conclusive arguments can be lodged against others. [30] several have not been tested. [22, 38, 188, 240, 304] Most of the hypotheses have been considered and compared; [23] space does not permit a detailed re-examination here. Two hypotheses [30, 188] are shown in Figs. 8 and 9 to illustrate some ways in which this problem has been considered.

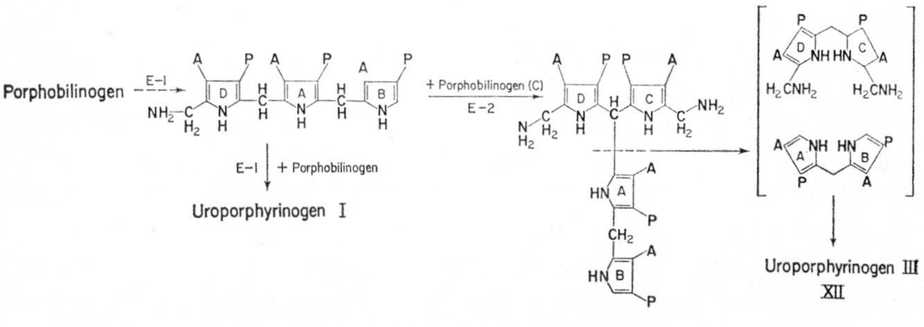

FIG. 8. A hypothetical scheme for the formation of uroporphyrinogen isomers I and III from porphobilinogen adapted from Bogorad and Granick. [30] A = CH_2—COOH; P = —CH_2—CH_2—COOH. E-1 = uroporphyrinogen I synthetase; E-2 = uroporphyrinogen III cosynthetase. Porphobilinogen "C" is substituted for one of the hydrogen atoms of the carbon bridge between rings A and D of the tripyrrole. After the postulated break of A–B from C–D the pair of dipyrroles [ ] may or may not exist free in solution.

4. Coproporphyrinogens

Uroporphyrinogen III (XII), but not its oxidation product, uroporphyrin III (IV), is used for the enzymatic synthesis of protoporphyrin IX and heme. [21, 29, 206] The first step is the decarboxylation of uroporphyrinogen III

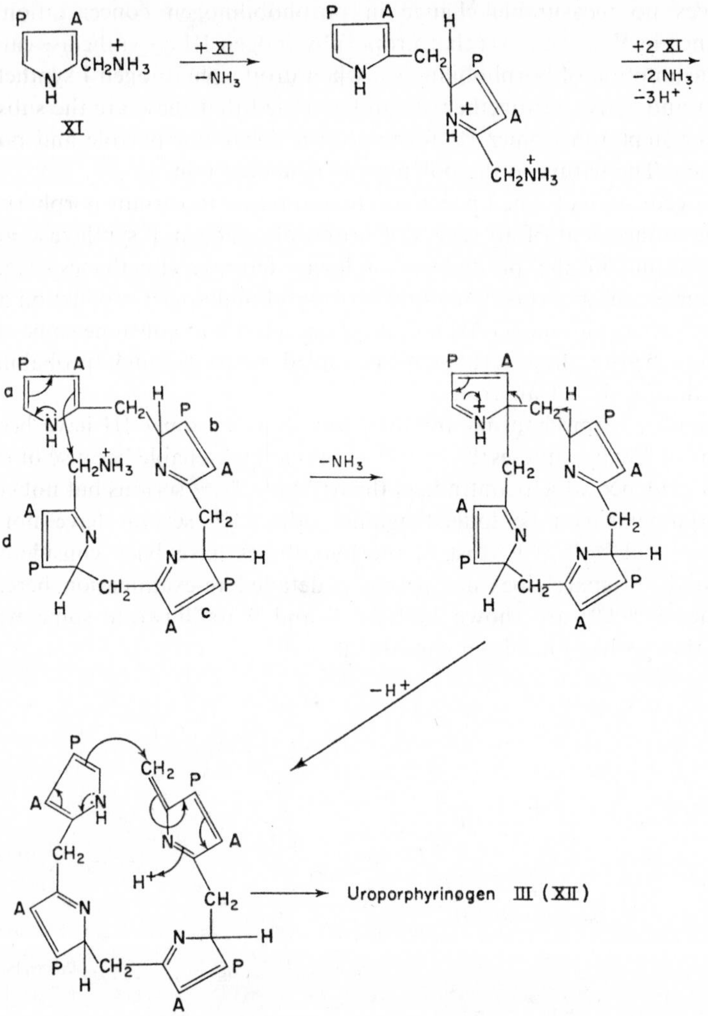

FIG. 9. A hypothetical scheme for the formation of uroporphyrinogen isomers
I and III from porphobilinogen (Mathewson and Corwin[188]). *Reproduced by
courtesy of the American Chemical Society.*

(XII, Fig. 5) to the coproporphyrinogen (XIX, Fig. 10) by the removal of
the —COOH groups of the acetic acid side chains at positions 1, 3, 5 and 8.
All four decarboxylations appear to be catalyzed by a single enzyme, uroporphyrinogen decarboxylase. [190] Intermediates between uroporphyrinogen
and coproporphyrinogen, porphyrinogens with four propionic acid residues
plus three, two, or one acetic acid groups still unaltered, have been detected
in enzymatic reaction mixtures. Corresponding porphyrins have been found

in urine of porphyriacs [192, 238] and in the culture medium of an algal mutant. [29]

The decarboxylase catalyzes the decarboxylation of all four uroporphyrinogen isomers, but the reaction rates vary with the substrate in the following order: uroporphyrinogen III > IV > II > I.

Uroporphyrinogen decarboxylase prepared from avian red cells by Mauzerall and Granick [190] is inhibited by Hg^{++}, Cu^{++}, Mn^{++}, iodoacetate, and p-chloromercuribenzoate. Inhibition by these agents is reversed by glutathione. The enzyme from *Rhodopseudomonas spheroides* is reported to be unstable in the absence of sulfhydryl compounds. [124]

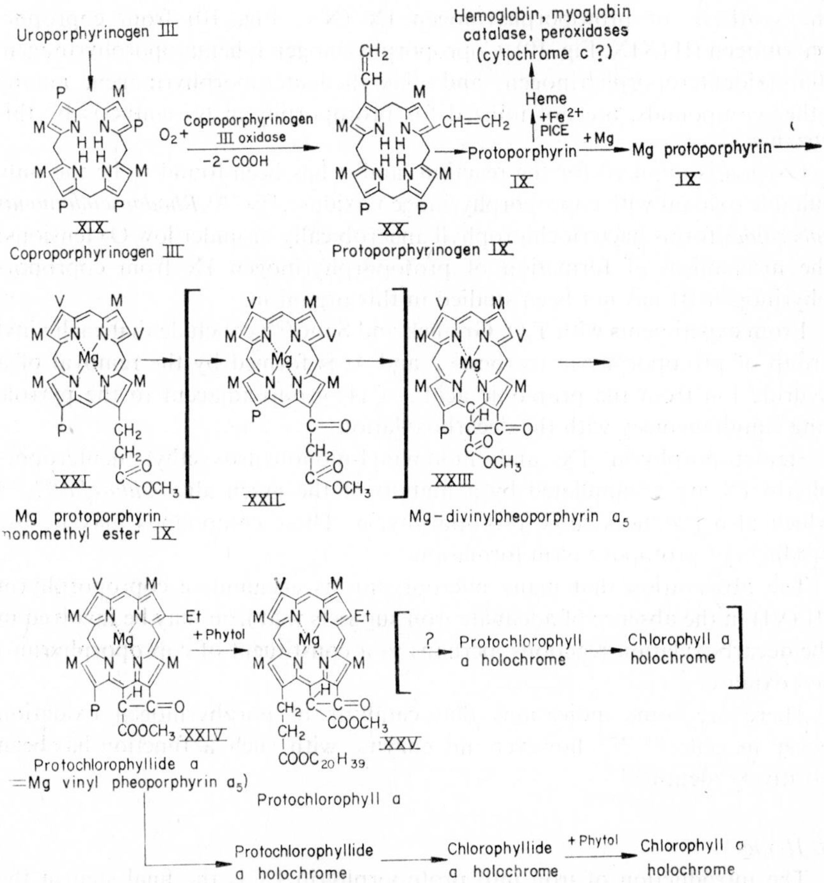

FIG. 10. Scheme for the biosynthesis of porphyrins including heme and chlorophyll a. Compounds whose structure is uncertain or which are postulated but not demonstrated intermediates are enclosed in brackets. A = CH_2—COOH; P = —CH_2—CH_2—COOH; M = CH_3; V = —CH=CH_2; Et = —CH_2—CH_3. Earlier steps in porphyrin formation are summarized in Fig. 5.

A stable cofactor for coproporphyrinogen formation has been observed in *Rhodopseudomonas spheroides* by Heath and Hoare. [119]

Coproporphyrin III (VI, Fig. 2) is accumulated in cultures of *Mycobacterium tub. avium* in which heme synthesis is inhibited by traces of Co or Zn [228] and by the following microorganisms when they are grown on low levels of iron: *Bacillus cereus*; [244] *Rhodopseudomonas spheroides*; [154] *Corynebacterium diptheriae*; [99, 225] and *Micrococcus lysodeikticus*. [235]

5. *Protoporphyrin IX*

Sano and Granick [242] and Porra and Falk [228, 229] have partially purified coproporphyrinogen oxidase from liver mitochondria. This enzyme catalyzes the synthesis of protoporphyrinogen IX (XX, Fig. 10) from coproporphyrinogen III (XIX, Fig. 10). Coproporphyrinogen I, hematoporphyrinogen, diacetyldeuteroporphyrinogen, and diacrylicdeuteroporphyrinogen, among other compounds, are not utilized for protoporphyrin biosynthesis by this enzyme.

Oxygen is required for the reaction, and it has been found to be the only suitable oxidant with coproporphyrinogen oxidase. [57, 242] *Rhodopseudomonas spheroides* forms bacteriochlorophyll anaerobically or under low O_2 tensions; the mechanism of formation of protoporphyrinogen IX from coproporphyrinogen III has not been studied in this organism.

From experiments with T_2O, Granick and Sano [95] conclude that each vinyl group of protoporphyrin (carbons 2 and 4) is formed by the removal of a hydride ion from the propionic acid —CH_2 group adjacent to the pyrrole ring simultaneously with the decarboxylation.

Hematoporphyrin IX and monovinyl-monohydroxyethyl deuteroporphyrin IX are accumulated by a mutant of the green alga *Chlorella* [29, 93] which also produces some protoporphyrin. These compounds may be by-products of protoporphyrin formation.

The observation that many microorganisms accumulate coproporphyrin III (VI) in the absence of adequate iron suggests that iron may be involved in the decarboxylation reactions, perhaps as a constituent of coproporphyrinogen oxidase.

There are some indications that catalysts of porphyrinogen oxidation occur in cells; [19, 242] however, no enzyme with such a function has been positively identified.

6. *Heme*

The introduction of iron into protoporphyrin IX is the final step in the biosynthesis of heme (VII). Labbe and co-workers [148, 150, 151, 210] have described some properties of a soluble protoporphyrin-iron chelating enzyme (PICE) prepared from rat liver mitochondria. Either ferrous or cobalt ions are inserted into protoporphyrin IX (XXXII, Fig. 14) by this enzyme. Ferric and stannous ions are not incorporated. Ions of Mg, Ca, Ni, Cd, Pb, Cu, Mn, Zn, and Hg inhibit the utilization of ferrous ions. In addition to being active towards protoporphyrin IX, the enzyme can catalyze the chelation of iron by deuteroporphyrin, hematoporphyrin, mesoporphyrin (XXXI, Fig. 14), and 2,4-dibromodeuteroporphyrin but not by uroporphyrin (IV), coproporphyrin (VI), 2,4-diacetyldeuteroporphyrin or 2,4-bis (2-carboxycyclopropyl) deutero-porphyrin. An enzyme with similar properties, but isolated from pig liver, fails to act upon porphyrin a or porphyrin c, the porphyrin moieties of cytochromes a and c respectively. [231] Inactive porphyrins do not inhibit the utilization of usable porphyrins such as protoporphyrin. Labbe and Hubbard[150] conclude from these studies on substrate specificity that rat liver PICE has two binding sites: one for the metal, another for the porphyrin.

PICE has also been prepared from duck [224] and chicken erythrocytes, [251] pig liver mitochondria, baker's yeast, *Escherichia coli*, *Thiobacillus* X and *Chromatium* strain D. [230, 231] PICE preparations from chicken erythrocytes have been separated into two heat-labile, non-dializable components. [251] Porra and Jones [230, 231] observed that the porphyrin specificity of PICE prepared from fresh broken cells of *Thiobacillus* X differed from that of PICE from stored cells; fresh pig liver enzyme preparations compared with aged ones differed similarly. This, together with asymmetry in the pH-activity curve, led them to suggest that more than one ferrochelatase may occur in a single organism. The pig liver extract was active only under anaerobic conditions.

An enzyme which catalyzes the incorporation of zinc into protoporphyrin has been detected in chromatophore preparations from *Rhodopseudomonas spheroides* [204] and extracts of barley leaves. [177] Incorporation of zinc by the bacterial enzyme is inhibited competitively by ferrous ions but iron is incorporated if ascorbate is included in the reaction mixture. Ascorbate, cysteine or homocysteine, glutathione, and DPN were shown to stimulate the activity of PICE prepared from rat liver mitochondria by Labbe and Hubbard; [150] the enzyme is inhibited by sulfhydryl group inhibitors such as p-chloro-mercuribenzoate, iodoacetamide and iodoacetic acid as well as by metal binding agents [150] and is competitively inhibited by bilirubin. [152] It is not clear whether the *R. spheroides* preparations contain two chelatases or if this is a single enzyme whose normal function is the catalysis of iron incorporation into protoporphyrin.

Crude extracts of *Clostridium tetanomorphum* contain an enzyme which stimulates the incorporation of Co^{2+} into meso-, deutero-, and protoporphyrins but not into tetra- or octacarboxylic porphyrins. [232] Fe^{2+} ions are incorporated into some porphyrins by the enzyme but at a much slower rate than Co^{2+} ions. The behavior of the *R. spheroides* preparations encourage a cautious attitude regarding interpretations of function.

7. Magnesium Protoporphyrin IX

The isolation of one *Chlorella* mutant which accumulates protoporphyrin IX and another which produces Mg-protoporphyrin IX led Granick [83, 84] to suggest that protoporphyrin is the last common member of the biosynthetic chains of heme and chlorophyll. Insertion of iron commits the porphyrin for use in cytochromes, hemoglobin, or other hemoproteins; insertion of magnesium to use for chlorophyll formation. This picture has been complicated by the discovery of a *Chlorella* mutant which produces protoporphyrin monomethyl ester. [90] However, evidence is provided below which shows Mg protoporphyrin to be the preferred substrate for the next enzymatic step —the esterification of the propionic acid residue at position 6.

Smith [269] described an ether-soluble magnesium fraction whose concentration declines concommittantly with the accumulation of chlorophyll during short periods of illumination of dark grown barley leaves. Information on enzymatic incorporation of magnesium into protoporphyrin IX, comparable to that for iron incorporation, has not been acquired. As pointed out above, magnesium inhibits chelation of iron by protoporphyrin catalyzed by rat liver mitochondrial PICE; apparently another enzyme must be sought. An enzyme has been found in barley leaf tissue which catalyzes the incorporation of zinc but not magnesium into protoporphyrin. [177]

8. The Formation of Chlorophyll a from Magnesium Protoporphyrin IX

Magnesium protoporphyrin IX esterified with a low molecular weight alcohol which may be methanol (XXI, Fig. 10) has been isolated from a *Chlorella* mutant and from etiolated barley seedlings supplied with δ-amino- levulinic acid and α,α'-dipyridyl, while in darkness. [89, 90] It has also been found in the medium of *Rhodopseudomonas spheroides* cultures. [131] Assuming that it is the carboxyl group on ring C which is esterified, this intermediate esterification step would prevent the decarboxylation of the propionic acid residue during or after oxidation to the carbonyl level of the carbon adjacent to the pyrrole ring. After the formation of the carbonyl group, the central carbon atom of the side chain (XXII, Fig. 10) would become more reactive than before and be more likely to form a bond with the γ-bridge carbon atom to complete the cyclopentanone ring (XXIII, Fig. 10).

The occurrence of protoporphyrin monomethyl ester, as well as Mg protoporphyrin and Mg protoporphyrin monoester in plants [90] introduces some uncertainty as to the normal sequence of the esterification and incorporation of magnesium. It is possible that Mg protoporphyrin mono(methyl) ester can be formed by either of two routes. However, Tait and Gibson [283] have shown that magnesium protoporphyrin is esterified fifteen times more rapidly than protoporphyrin in enzymatic reaction mixtures containing the porphyrin, S-adenosylmethionine, and chromatophores isolated from *Rhodopseudomonas spheroides*. Protoporphyrinogen is ineffective as a substrate.

In 1950 Granick isolated a mutant of *Chlorella* which produces Mg-vinyl pheoporphyrin a_5. [86] This porphyrin, which is protochlorophyll *a* lacking the phytol group, or protochlorophyllide *a*(XXIV, Fig. 10), was subsequently identified in seedlings of etiolated barley by Loeffler. [178]

The formation of protochlorophyllide *a* from magnesium protoporphyrin IX monomethyl ester requires the following modifications of the latter:

(a) The reduction of the vinyl group on ring B to an ethyl group.

(b) The cyclization of the propionic acid group on ring C to form the cyclopentanone ring.

(c) The esterification of the carboxyl group of the propionic acid residue on ring C.

Magnesium 2,4-divinylpheoporphyrin a_5 (XXIII) has been recovered from the medium of *Rhodopseudomonas spheroides* grown in the presence of 8-hydroxyquinoline under conditions normally conducive to bacterio-chlorophyll formation. [132] This suggests that enroute to the formation of bacteriochlorophyll—and presumably chlorophyll *a*—the cyclopentanone ring is formed before the vinyl group at position 4 is reduced. The divinyl-pheoporphyrin has many properties in common with a porphyrin isolated from a tan mutant of *R. spheroides* by Stanier and Smith; [283] the two compounds may be identical.

A possible intermediate between magnesium protoporphyrin monomethyl ester (XXI) and magnesium 2,4-divinylpheoporphyrin a_5 (XXIII) is shown in Fig. 10.

Many plants, including conifer seedlings and some algae, can form chloro-phylls in darkness but only traces of these pigments have been detected in dark-grown (etiolated) angiosperms. [79, 82] Leaves of etiolated angiosperm, contain relatively small amounts of protochlorophyllide *a* (XXIV, Fig. 10) and its phytol ester, protochlorophyll *a* (XXV); the former is converted to chlorophyllide *a* upon illumination. [270, 293, 307] The fate of the protochloro-phyll is not known. Etiolated bean leaves contain three to four times more protochlorophyllide than protochlorophyll. [307] The chlorophyll content of fully greened leaves per gram fresh weight is of the order of 300 times the protochlorophyllide in etiolated ones of the same species.

In vivo, protochlorophyllide *a* (no other type has been identified) normally shows an absorption maximum at 650 mμ; it is difficult to ascertain the absorption maximum in the blue region of the spectrum because of the carotenoids which are present. The action spectrum for the photoconversion of protochlorophyllide to chlorophyllide *a* corresponds to the absorption spectrum of the former *in vivo*, i.e. protochlorophyllide *a* absorbs light for its own photoreduction. As chlorophyllide *a* is formed the absorption band of protochlorophyllide *a* disappears and a new band with a maximum at 684 mμ develops. After about 10 min the maximal absorption in the red region of the spectrum shifts to about 673 mμ; finally, after an additional two hours the maximum is at 677 mμ. Light is required for the first spectral shift (650 → 684 mμ) only—the subsequent changes can also proceed in darkness.[259] Smith and Coomber[274] speculate that the spectral shifts might be caused by rearrangement of the pigment on the protein with which it is associated, or a transfer of the pigment from one carrier to another. The final shift could result from the realignment of pigment molecules on protein interfaces as a consequence of esterification of the chlorophyllide with phytol.

The production of chlorophyll (more probably chlorophyllide) in dried or frozen dark-grown leaves was observed by Liro[176] in 1909. Monteverde and Lubimenko[195] confirmed these observations in 1911. Lubimenko,[184] using a micro-spectroscope, observed spectral shifts in intact living and dried etiolated leaves upon illumination—the displacements he reported seeing were not in the same direction as those described above. Madsen[185] has confirmed that the photoconversion of protochlorophyllide to chlorophyllide can occur in dried leaves.

The photoconversion of protochlorophyllide to chlorophyllide also occurs *in vitro* in homogenates or aqueous extracts of leaves[176, 271] but only if the protochlorophyllide is a member of a specific protein complex. Smith[271] termed this complex the "protochlorophyll holochrome" but in view of present knowledge it is more appropriately termed the "protochlorophyllide holochrome". Thus, strictly speaking, protochlorophyllide holochrome is converted to chlorophyllide holochrome by light *in vitro*, and presumably *in vivo*. As to be expected from observations on dried and frozen leaves, isolated protochlorophyllide holochrome is also converted in the dry[276] or frozen[16, 272, 273] state, Partial purification of protochlorophyllide holochrome from etiolated bean leaves has been achieved.[147, 15, 16, 272]

There are a few disagreements about some physical properties of the protochlorophyllide holochrome.[15, 16, 147, 272] Boardman[16, 15] reports that the molecular weight of the complex per protochlorophyllide is $0.6 \pm 0.05 \times 10^6$, the density is 1·37, the sedimentation coefficient is 18, and that it is a sphere whose diameter is 100–110 Å. Smith[275] reports that the molecular weight is 0·5 to 1.4×10^6 and the density 1·16. The quantum efficiency for the photoreduction of protochlorophyllide is 0·60 per hydrogen (or electron) transferred.[272] The photoconversion may involve restricted collisions within the holochrome.[16] Smith and Coomber[274] suggest that perhaps 30 per cent of the protochlorophyll is bound to the protein through the phenolic group of tyrosine and the remainder through either the sulfhydryl group of cysteine, the ϵ-amino group of lysine, or both.

The enzyme chlorophyllase probably catalyzes the esterification of the propionic acid side chain at position 7 of chlorophyllide with phytol ($C_{20}H_{39}OH$) to form chlorophyll *a*.[26, 126, 260, 275, 302] This enzyme, which is active in 40 per cent and stronger aqueous acetone, reversibly catalyzes the hydrolysis of chlorophylls, bacteriochlorophyll, *Chlorobium* chorophyll

"650", and their Mg-free derivatives (pheophytins); it is reported to not hydrolyze protochlorophyll (Fig. 10, XXV).(191, 59, 281) How the protochlorophyll which is present in etiolated plants is formed is not known.

Only one chemical form of chlorophyll *a* is known, but several spectral varieties have been detected *in vivo*: e.g. chlorophylls *a* with absorption maxima at 673, 683, and 694 mμ respectively. Two or more of these occur together in all plants which have been examined.(64) The physical bases for the spectral differences are not known.

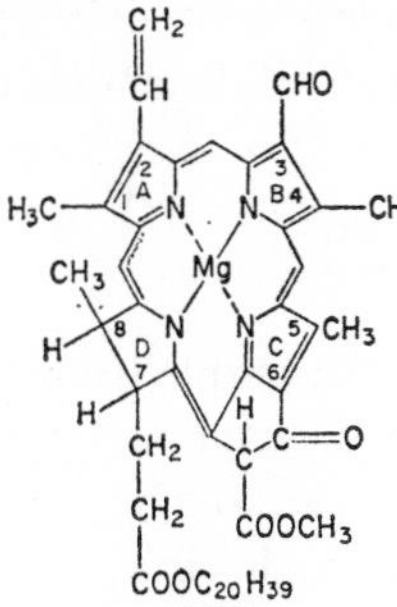

XXVI
Chlorophyll *b*

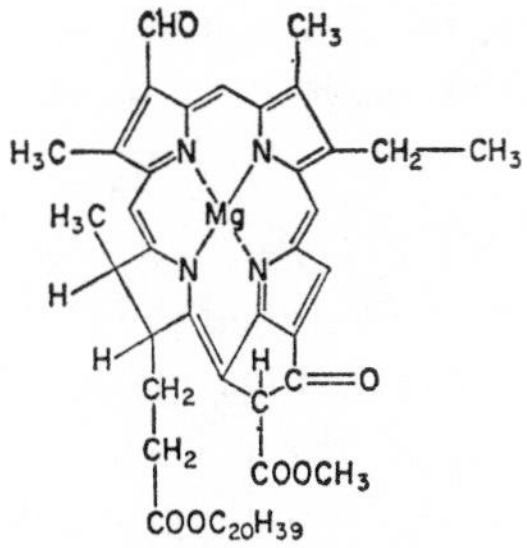

XXVII
2 Desvinyl, 2 formyl chlorophyll *a* = chlorophyll *d*

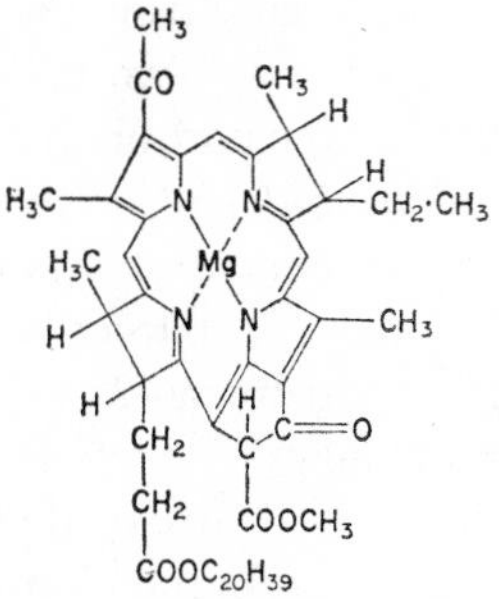

XXVIII
Bacteriochlorophyll.

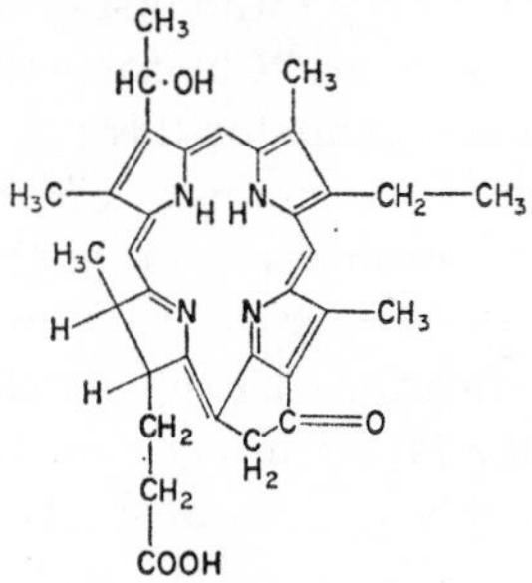

XXIX
2 Desvinyl, 2 *a*—hydroxyethyl pyrropheophorbide *a*.

FIG. 11.

9. *Chlorophylls* b, c, d *and* e

Chlorophyll *b* (XXVI, Fig. 11) is 3-desmethyl, 3-formyl chlorophyll *a*; it is present together with chlorophyll *a* in all higher green plants and the following groups of algae: *Charophyta, Chlorophyta* and *Englenophyta.* There is no evidence for protochlorophyll or protochlorophyllide *b*. It seems at present that the two most likely immediate precursors of chlorophyll *b* are: (1) chlorophyll *a*, or (2) a common precursor of chlorophylls *a* and *b*. The evidence bearing on this question is voluminous but not conclusive (see discussions by Shlyk *et al.*,(261) Smith and French(275) and Bogorad(26)). Two spectral forms of chlorophyll *b* may be present in the alga *Ulva.*(64)

Chlorophyll c is not esterified with phytol and pyrrole ring D is not reduced; thus it resembles protochlorophyllide. Granick [85] has suggested that chlorophyll c may be modified magnesium pheoporphyrin derived from protochlorophyllide. Chlorophyll c occurs in members of the following groups of algae: *Bacillariophyta*, *Phaeophyta* (brown algae), *Pyrrophyta* and *Cryptophyta*.

Chlorophyll d (XXVII), Fig. 11) is reported to be 2-desvinyl, 2-formyl chlorophyll a. [127a] Its immediate antecedents are undetermined; it is found in some red algae and perhaps in some *Chrysophytes*.

The structure of chlorophyll e is not known; it has been observed only in *Tribonema bombycinum*.

10. Bacterial Chlorophylls

Fischer *et al.* [58] identified the chlorophyll of the purple bacteria, bacteriochlorophyll (XXVIII, Fig. 11), as 2-desvinyl, 2-acetyl, 3,4-dihydrochlorophyll a. It occurs *in vivo* in several spectral forms although, as in the case of chlorophyll a in algae and higher plants, only a single chemical and spectral form can be isolated.

The chlorophyll of the green bacteria is different. It was named "bacterio-verdin" by Metzner [193] who first observed its difference from the chlorophyll of the purple bacteria. "Chlorobium chlorophyll" has been introduced as a more appropriate name for this pigment. [153] Two chlorobium chlorophylls, one from each of two strains of *Chlorobium thiosulfatophilum*, have now been isolated. [280] Chlorobium chlorophyll 660 has its main absorption maxima at 432 and 660 $m\mu$ in ether solution and at 460 and 747 $m\mu$ *in vivo*; the corresponding maxima for Chlorobium chlorophyll 650 are at 425 and 650 $m\mu$ in ether and 450 and 725 $m\mu$ *in vivo*. Holt and Hughes [127b] report that the 650 form is probably a derivative of 2-desvinyl, 2-α-hydroxyethylpyrropheophorbide a (XXIX, Fig. 11) and that the chlorobium chlorophylls are closely related to one another in that: "(1) each possesses an α-hydroxyalkyl substituent; (2) each yields methyl-n-propylmaleimide upon oxidative degradation; (3) each yields an alcohol upon hydrolysis; by paper chromatography these appear to be identical with each other but to differ from phytol; and (4) each gives a negative Molisch phase test."

11. Porphyrins with Hydroxyl and Carbonyl Substituents

Chlorophyll b (XXVI) has a formyl substituent on β-pyrrolic carbon atom 3; heme a, the prosthetic group of cytochromes a, a_1, and a_3, has a formyl group joined to carbon atom 8; its structural formula was suggested by Clezy and Barrett [42] (XXX, Fig. 12). In both of these porphyrins, using chlorophyll a (VIII) or protoporphyrin IX (XXXII) as the reference compounds, a methyl group has been oxidized to a formyl group. The mechanism has not been determined; the possibility of replacement of the methyl group by —CHO is not excluded.

The variations in the substituent at β-pyrrolic carbon atom 2 among naturally occurring porphyrins are summarized in Table 1. "Chlorophyll-types" are porphyrins with cyclopentanone rings and with at least one partially reduced pyrrole ring. "Protoporphyrin-types" include porphyrins whose substitution pattern, in general, resembles that of protoporphyrin IX. Hematoporphyrin, 2:4-desvinyl, 2:4-hydroxyethyl protoporphyrin IX, has been recovered from cultures of a *Chlorella* mutant. [29, 93]

Two possible metabolic pathways for the production of the hydroxyl-alkyl, acetyl, and formyl side chains of these porphyrins are outlined in Fig. 13. In case "A", the precursor is assumed to be a 2-vinyl porphyrin such as protoporphyrin or protochlorophyllide *a*. In "B" a 2-propionyl porphyrin, such

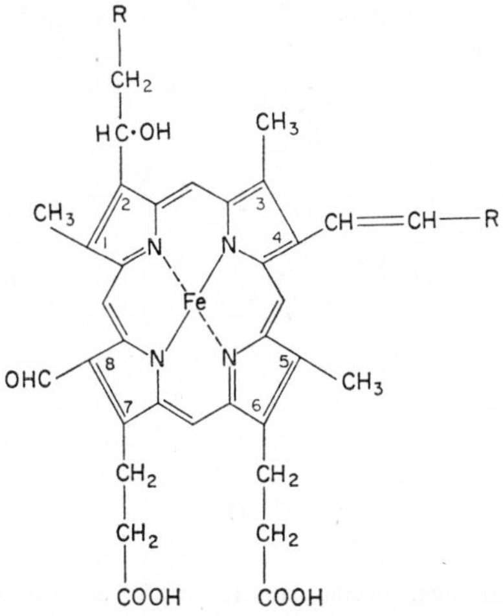

XXX

FIG. 12. Structure of heme *a* suggested by Clezy and Barrett.[42]

TABLE 1. SUBSTITUENTS OF β-PYRROLIC CARBON ATOM 2 OF SOME PORPHYRINS

Hematoporphyrin IX	—CHOH—CH$_3$
"Chlorophyll-types":	
Chlorobium chlorophylls	—CHOH—CH$_3$
Bacteriochlorophyll	—CO—CH$_3$
Chlorophyll *d*	—CHO
"Protoporphyrin IX-types":	
Heme *a*	—CHOH—CH$_2$—R
Spirographis porphyrin†	—CHO

† 2-desvinyl, 2-formyl protoporphyrin IX, *Spirographis* heme is the prosthetic group of chlorocruorin, a hemoglobin found in several species of the order *Polychaeta*, e.g. *Spirographis*, a marine worm.

as coproporphyrin or some tricarboxylic intermediate between coproporphyrin and protoporphyrin, is taken as the substrate.

The vinyl side chains of intermediates at oxidation levels between photoporphyrinogen and protoporphyrin IX seem extraordinarily reactive with sulfhydryl groups. Porphyrin-c (the porphyrin moiety of cytochrome c) is formed if protoporphyrinogen IX is photooxidized in an acid solution containing cysteine. [242] Such a compound would be hydrolyzed to hematoporphyrin IX. The enzyme or enzymes for the oxidation of the substituent at position 2 may work in some such manner.

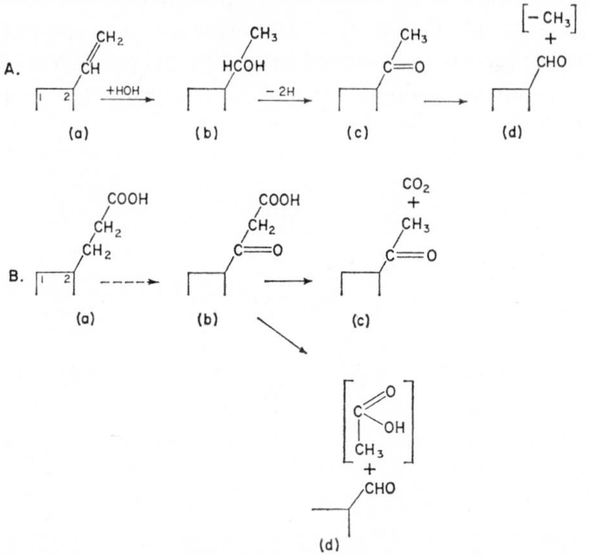

FIG. 13. Two hypothetical mechanisms for the formation of side-chains containing hydroxyl or carbonyl groups at β-pyrrolic carbon atom 2 of some porphyrins (see Table 1).

12. *The Control of Porphyrin Biosynthesis*

Higher green plants grown in darkness contain small amounts of protochlorophyllide and protochlorophyll but no other precursors of chlorophyll can be detected. If leaves of etiolated plants are not illuminated but are supplied δ-aminolevulinic acid they form additional protochlorophyllide—about ten times more than they contain normally. [89, 90] Thus, all the enzymes required for the synthesis of protochlorophyllide from δ-aminolevulinic acid are present and active—the synthesis of δ-aminolevulinate is, however, not going on. Upon illumination of normal etiolated plants, i.e. those not supplied δ-aminolevulinate, the protochlorophyllide is converted to chlorophyllide, as described, and additional protochlorophyllide forms. If etiolated barley or wheat leaves are illuminated with a bright flash for 1/1000 sec and returned to darkness, after a short lag (max. ∼5 min) they begin to form additional protochlorophyllide; within about 12 to 19 min after the flash they contain as much photoconvertible pigment as they had originally and by 60 min, when the rate of pigment formation approaches zero, their protochlorophyllide content is about twice the original one. [186] The capacity to form pigment, presumably by production of the δ-aminolevulinate generating system, is thus fairly rapidly developed and somewhat more slowly, halted. If rapidly greening bean leaves are returned to darkness, the rate of pigment formation drops very quickly and falls to zero within a few hours; administration of chloramphenicol, puromycin, or actinomycin D (i.e. inhibitors of protein or ribonucleic acid synthesis) arrests pigment formation very rapidly even when illumination of the plants is continued. [72, 28] One interpretation of these observations is that protein (enzyme or enzymes for the production of ALA or a cofactor required for its action) and ribonucleic acids, perhaps in the plastids, must be produced constantly to maintain protochlorophyllide synthesis—these materials may decay very rapidly. If this interpretation is correct, light must promote the production of general or specific ribonucleic acids and proteins in cells or their plastids. The production of the photosynthetic cytochrome f is also controlled by light in some algae.

Rhodopseudomonoas spheroides produces maximal amounts of bacteriochlorophyll when grown anaerobically in the light. Upon vigorous aeration pigment formation quickly ceases. [43] Lascelles [156] has shown a close correlation between this phenomenon and a decrease in the activity of δ-aminolevulinic acid synthetase. Inhibitors of ribonucleic acid and protein synthesis arrest bacteriochlorophyll production.

A number of compounds including Sedormid [248, 80, 1] (allylisopropylacetylcarbamide), allylisopropylacetimide, [80, 101, 149, 194] hexachlorobenzene [214, 48] and 3,5-dicarbethoxy-1,4-dihydrocollidine [106, 96, 278, 279] can stimulate the production and excretion of porphobilinogen, δ-aminolevulinic acid and porphyrins by many animals. These responses resemble symptoms of acute porphyria. Granick and Urata [96] have shown that δ-aminolevulinic acid synthetase activity of liver parenchyma cells is elevated more than forty times above normal in guinea pigs poisoned with 3,5-dicarbethoxy-1,4-dihydrocollidine. Similarly Miyakoshi and Kikuchi [194] found δ-aminolevulinic acid synthesis by liver mitochondria from rats treated with allylisopropylacetimide to be about twenty-five times greater than normal. Using isolated liver cells Granick [91] has shown that stimulation of porphyrin production by allylisoprophylacetimide—presumably by raising δ-aminolevulinic acid synthetase activity—is blocked by the administration of inhibitors of protein and ribonucleic acid formation. Thus, allylisopropylacetimide, and presumably the other compounds mentioned which also promote δ-aminolevulinic acid synthetase activity, act as inducers or derepressors.

It has been shown recently that globin and hemoglobin synthesis may be controlled by δ-aminolevulinic acid[175] and by hemin.[108, 37] If these observations are correct, the control of globin formation would be regulated by activity in the biosynthetic chain of porphyrins and heme.

III. BILE PIGMENTS

A. *Structural Relationships*

All bile pigments known to occur naturally can be visualized as derivatives of protoporphyrin IX (XXXII, Fig. 14) or mesoporphyrin IX (XXXI) although they are not formed directly from either free acid. A comparison of the structures of biliverdin (XXXIII, Fig. 14) and protoporphyrin illustrates the relationships between bile pigments and porphyrins. The nature and sequence of the substituents on the β-positions of the pyrrole residues of biliverdin and protoporphyrin IX are the same, but the bile pigment lacks the α-methane bridge carbon of the porphyrin. The bile pigments are thus open-chained tetrapyrroles. Except for substance XXXIII in Fig. 14, the bile pigments will be written in linear form for convenience although, because of steric restrictions imposed when two or more pyrroles are in conjugation, most of them should be shown in "curved" forms.

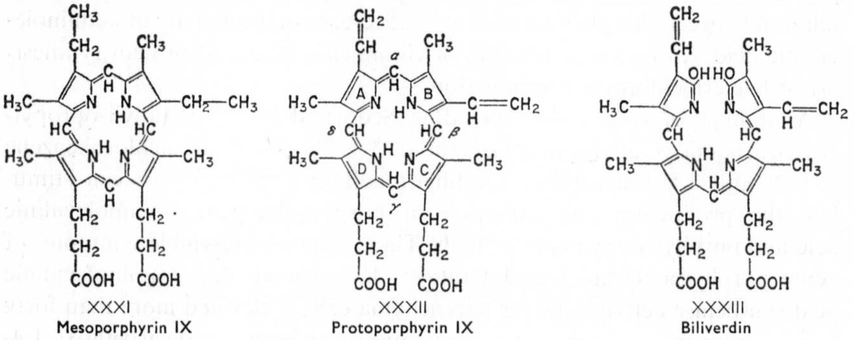

FIG. 14. Structural relationships between biliverdin and protoporphyrin IX. Mesoporphyrin side-chain types of bile pigments (Fig. 15) bear similar relationships to mesoporphyrin IX.

The structural formulae of some bile pigments are shown in Fig. 15. There are three principal kinds of differences among the naturally occurring bile pigments:

(a) The nature of the substituents on the β-carbon atoms of the pyrrole residues may vary. (Compare proto- and mesoporphyrin side chain types of bile pigments, Fig. 15.)

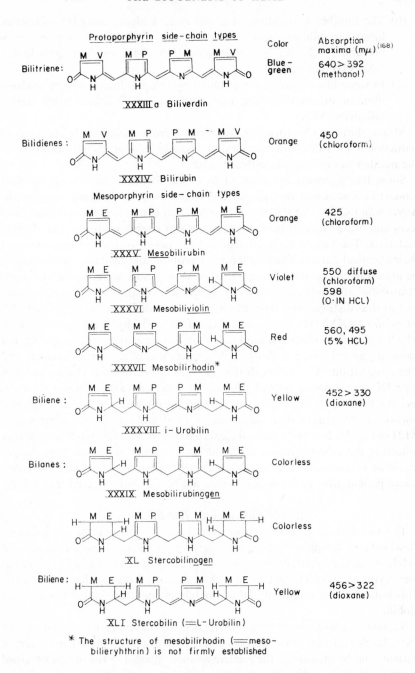

FIG. 15. Structural relationships among bile pigments.
$M = -CH_3$; $V = -CH_2$; $E = -CH_2 - CH_3$; $P = -CH_2 - CH_2 - COOH$

(b) The number of oxidized, i.e. methane, bridges (compare bilitrienes, bilidienes, bilienes, and bilanes) and their position (compare mesobilirubin, XXXV; mesobiliviolin, XXXVI; and mesobilirhodin, XXXVII) may vary.

(c) In some bile pigments the terminal pyrrole residues are more oxidized than in others (compare mesobilirubinogen, XXXIX, with stercobilinogen, XL).

Minor shifts in absorption maxima result from variations in the level of reduction of the side chains; major differences in color are due to variations in the number of conjugated double bonds.

Some bile pigments are referred to in the literature by several different names; in other cases very similar names are used for different compounds: *Stercobilin* (XLI) = *urobilin* = *l-urobilin*. This compound was isolated from feces and urine at about the same time but was later described as two distinct materials. The names assigned reflected the origin of the tetrapyrroles, not their chemical nature. The two terms, stercobilin and urobilin, have come to be used interchangeably. However, some writers now prefer to use the name "l-urobilin" to emphasize the strong levorotatory character of this compound and to thus distinguish it from other, chemically different "urobilins". [97, 168] *i-Urobilin* (XXXVIII) = *urobilin IXa*: This optically inactive compound, which also differs from stercobilin in that its terminal pyrrole rings are not reduced, can be formed *in vitro* by dehydrogenation of mesobilirubinogen. [375] The designation "IX" refers to the arrangement of the side chains, i.e. as in type IX proto- or mesoporphyrin, and "α" to the carbon bridge which is lacking, i.e. the α-bridge carbon atom of the porphyrins. *d-Urobilin*: Gray and Nicholson [100] report that the structure of d-urobilin is that of substance XLII in Fig. 16. It is not a normal fecal constituent but is excreted temporarily following the administration of broad spectrum antibiotics such as Aureomycin or Terramycin. Gray and Nicholson [100] have reported finding a thalessemia patient who had not been given antibiotics but excreted d-urobilin.

B. *The Biogenesis of Bile Pigments*

The metabolism of bile pigments has been studied mainly in mammals. Hawkins and Whipple [117] found a close correspondence between the amount of bile pigment excreted by dogs and the quantity of hemoglobin from circulating erythrocytes calculated to have been destroyed during the same period. This indicates that essentially all of the bile pigment originated from hemoglobin.

Shemin and Rittenberg [254] demonstrated the incorporation of isotopically (N^{15}) labeled glycine into the prosthetic group of hemoglobin in a human patient, and by measuring the relative amount of label in the hemin obtained from circulating erythrocytes at intervals following the initial feeding and ingestion of isotope, estimated the life span of red blood cells to be 120 days. [255]

London *et al.* [179, 181, 182] studied the origin of bile pigments in humans by administering N^{15}-glycine intravenously or orally and then, by following the levels of labeling in circulating erythrocytes and in stercobilin which was excreted, confirmed and extended the observations of Hawkins and Whipple. [114] They concluded that in normal humans at least 11 per cent, in pernicious anemia at least 40 per cent, and in congenital porphyria patients at least 31 per cent of the bile pigment excreted did not come from hemoglobin of mature erythrocytes. [179, 181, 182] The origin of these fractions is obscure and, at least in part, appears to be unrelated to hemoglobin formation in red cells; myoglobin appears to be ruled out as a major source. Catalase and peroxidase can give rise to bile pigment *in vitro* [141] but these also appear unlikely sources of such large quantities of open-chain tetrapyrroles. The normal daily excretion of bile pigments, mostly stercobilin and bilirubin, by adult humans is 250–300 mg per day.

1. The Biogenesis of Biliverdin

Biliverdin (XXXIIIa), the first open-chained tetrapyrrolic intermediate between hemoproteins with Fe-protoporphyrin IX prosthetic groups and urobilins, are some of the principal bile pigments excreted in the urine and feces of normal humans. The rupture of the porphyrin ring system is thought to occur via a series of oxidative attacks on the α-bridge culminating in the substitution of an oxygen atom for the α-bridge carbon atom; the latter is released in carbon monoxide. Finally, biliverdin is formed after the oxygen bridge between pyrroles A and B is opened and the now terminal α-positions of these pyrrole residues are substituted with hydroxyl groups, which rearrange to become carbonyls.

The evidence and speculations upon which these conclusions are based are derived from non-enzymatic "model systems" *in vitro*. Whether these systems are indeed models for bile pigment formation *in vivo*, will be discussed below.

A number of compounds—none of which has been completely purified and characterized—have been suggested as intermediates in the oxidation of heme to biliverdin. Confusing trivial names have been assigned to these intermediates. In the interest of simplifying the ensuing discussion systematic names will be used. These designations are based on the structures suggested by their discoverers. The evidence for composition and structure, in almost every case, is marginal at best. Association of systematic names with hypothetical structure is dangerous but seems worthwhile only because many of the trivial names are redundant and easily confused with one another, e.g. oxyheme, oxypseudoheme, pseudoheme. The numbering system used is shown in Fig. 16.

The synonyms are:

Pseudoheme [164] is assumed to be: α, 5-dihydroxy heme.

Oxyheme [162, 166, 167] is assumed to be: α-OH heme

Oxypseudoheme [63] is assumed to be: α-keto, 5-OH heme.

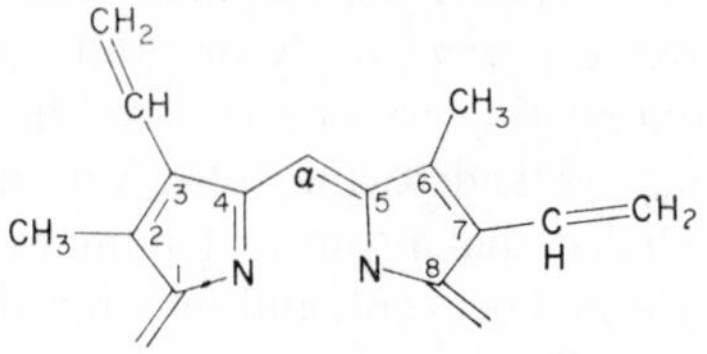

FIG. 16. Numbering system used in discussion of bile pigment formation.

(a) *Observations on "model systems".* Biliverdin is produced non-enzymatically *in vitro* during the incubation of hemoglobin, myoglobin, or certain other hemoproteins with ascorbic acid in air at 37°C. Other reducing agents such as hydrazine are also effective as partners in the coupled oxidation of the α-bridge of the porphyrin ring. The addition of hydrogen peroxide to the reaction mixture generally accelerates the process.

(i) *The nature of the primary substrate.*—(a) An obvious possibility is that first the protoporphyrin might become dissociated from the iron and the protein; then oxidative rupture of the porphyrin ring would follow. However, no bile pigment is formed if protoporphyrin IX (XXXII) is incubated under conditions which result in the production of biliverdin from hemoglobin *in vitro.* If the assumption that these conditions are quasi-biological is valid, protoporphyrin is excluded as the natural substrate for bile pigment synthesis.

(b) Heme, itself (VII) could become available for bile pigment synthesis upon the dissociation of iron protoporphyrin from globin. Under O_2 in the presence of ascorbic acid, hematin can be converted to biliverdin almost as readily as can ferrihemoglobin. [140, 141] However, *in vitro,* the production of biliverdin from hemoglobin is better under 2 per cent O_2 than in air. [166] Under these conditions the rate of biliverdin production from hematin is very slow. Lemberg [164] has argued from this that heme is not the natural precursor of bile pigments.

(c) In contrast to the behavior of protoporphyrin and of heme, biliverdin is produced more readily from the pyridine hemochromogen of protoheme (XLIV, Fig. 18) than from hemoglobin in the presence of ascorbic acid and air at 37°C. [166, 167]

Lemberg [168] considered it significant that the heme iron is bound to nitrogenous bases in both pyridine hemochromogen and hemoglobin; these observations on *in vitro* reactions led him to suggest that biliverdin formation *in vivo* proceeds by a direct attack on the heme *in situ,* i.e. while still a component of the hemoprotein. Furthermore, it was postulated that the tetrapyrrole remains associated with the protein through all the modifications of the molecule until biliverdin is formed, and only after this do the iron, the open-chain tetrapyrrole, and the protein separate from one another.

(ii) *Choleglobin and pseudoheme.* Assuming the validity of Lemberg's hypothesis that hemoproteins are the "primary substrates" for bile pigment formation, what are the intermediates between hemoprotein and biliverdin?

Essentially nothing is known about the biochemistry of bile pigment formation from investigations *in vivo*, although some recent enzymological investigations have been made by Nakajima *et al.* Some details of the observations made during the incubation of hemoglobin or myoglobin with ascorbic acid in "model systems" are:

(a) The absorption maxima of hemoglobin decline and vanish; a new absorption band with a maximum at about 630 mμ appears. The material responsible for the new band has been named "choleglobin". The 630 mμ absorbing form is probably the ferrous compound. [170]

Choleglobin has been defined by Lemberg [164] as ". . . the specific mixture, obtained by coupled oxidation (of hemoglobin) with ascorbic acid, which is rich in . . . compounds with a C_{19} ring (i.e. compounds lacking the α-bridge carbon atom) *and* the physiological intermediate in bile pigment formation".

Choleglobin appears to be a mixture of variously oxidized tetrapyrroles associated with globin. Biliverdin can be obtained from these solutions but a major tetrapyrrolic constituent of choleglobin is pseudoheme, i.e. $\alpha,5$-dihydroxyheme, whose assumed structure is shown in Fig. 17 (XLIII). [164] The term choleglobin will be used in the ensuing discussion to designate the complex of $\alpha,5$-dihydroxyheme and globin.

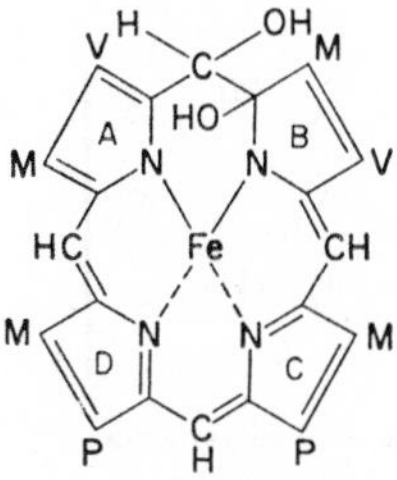

XLIII

FIG. 17. Pseudoheme. [164] ($\alpha,5$-dihydroxyheme) Abbreviations as in Fig. 15.

$\alpha,5$-dihydroxyheme is prepared by treatment of dicyano-ferroprotoporphyrin with hydrogen peroxide followed by removal of the cyanide by dialysis. [63] The complex which can be formed between $\alpha,5$-dihydroxyheme and native globin has, after reduction with dithionite, an absorption maximum at 630 mμ, as does ferrous choleglobin. [63]

Identification of the heme of choleglobin (choleheme) as pseudoheme is also supported by the observation that the pyridine hemochromogens of these two substances both display absorption maxima at 618 mμ. [170, 63]

Evidence for the structure assigned to pseudoheme (i.e. asα, 5-dihydroxy-heme) and further support for the chemical identity of this compound and the major tetrapyrrole of choleglobin, comes from the observation that both compounds can be reconverted to protoheme.

Cholehemochromogen and dicyano-ferropseudoheme are both partially reconverted to protoheme derivatives when boiled in NaOH in the presence of dithionite. This supports the hypothetical structure for α,5-dihydroxy heme shown above, by demonstrating that the α-bridge carbon atom of heme is still in place in this compound. Furthermore, Sjöstrand[266] discovered that the α-bridge carbon atom of heme is liberated as carbon monoxide during bile pigment formation. He also found[267, 268] that CO liberation from horse hemoglobin–ascorbic acid mixtures continued even after the choleglobin component had reached a maximum concentration and had begun to decline, thus indicating that the loss of the α-bridge carbon atom occurs sometimes after the formation of choleglobin.

Finally, biliverdin can be recovered from "choleglobin mixtures" upon treatment with 66 per cent acetic acid.

(iii) *α-Hydroxyheme and verdoheme.* Evidence on the nature of inter-mediates between choleglobin (α,5-dihydroxyheme + globin) and biliverdin come not from investigations of the reactions during the coupled oxidation of hemoglobin and ascorbic acid but primarily from studies on the formation of open-chain tetrapyrrole from iron protoporphyrin pyridine hemochromogen treated with hydrazine or ascorbic acid, in the presence of O_2 or H_2O_2.[162, 166, 167] The sequence in which the presumed intermediates in these reactions may occur is shown in Fig. 18.

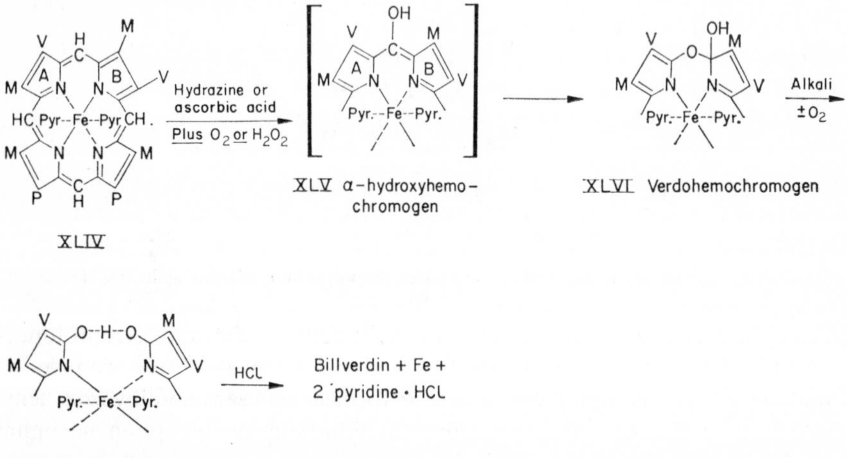

FIG. 18. Intermediates in the conversion of pyridine hemochromogen to bili-verdin. Only pyrrole rings A and B are shown, except for pyridine hemo-chromogen. The structure shown for oxyhemochromogen is hypothetical.[63,164 (Abbreviations as in Fig. 15.)

α-Hydroxyhemochromogen (XLV) is known only as a spectral pheno-menon; its structure is hypothetical, and is based on the ability to regenerate pyridine protohemochromogen by treatment with dithionite.

Verdohemochromogen (XLVI) has been isolated, but knowledge of its structure is based on indirect evidence. The most pertinent structural feature of verdoheme, as an intermediate in bile pigment synthesis, is the oxygen, rather than carbon, link between pyrrole residues A and B. The nature of the bridging atom is deduced from the following observations: (i) Monoaza-hemochromogen is obtained upon treatment of verdohemochromogen with ammonia, i.e. the atom bridging pyrrole residues A and B is easily replaced by nitrogen. [163] (ii) Verdohemochromogen, unlike some other presumed intermediates, cannot be reconverted to protohemochromogen by dithionite in alkaline solution. [63] (iii) Relatively mild non-oxidative conditions suffice for the formation of biliverdin from verdohemochromogen. [63]

(iv) *Additional postulated intermediates.* In the preceeding discussion, two courses of biliverdin production have been reviewed:
(1) Hemoglobin $\to$ α,5-dihydroxyheme-globin $\to$ $\to$ biliverdin + Fe + globin.
(2) Pyridine protohemochromogen $\to$ pyridine α-hydroxy hemochromogen $\to$ $\to$ pyridine verdohemochromogen (with the loss of CO) $\to$ biliverdin + Fe. This series is summarized in Fig. 18. (Kaziro and Kikuchi [134, 136] have reported that pyridine α,5-dihydroxyhemochromogen, rather than the α-hydroxyhemochromogen, may be an intermediate in this reaction sequence. [2] This would seem to rationalize the two postulated se-quences. Lemberg, [169] however, declares that there is weighty evidence against this identification.)

Studies on the oxidation of nitrogenous complexes of α,5-dihydroxyheme provide some evidence which has been taken to indicate that:

(a) α-Keto,5-hydroxyheme is an intermediate in the formation of biliverdin from α,5-dihydroxyheme. A compound with an absorption maximum at 660–670 mμ, which is *believed* to be α-keto, 5-hydroxyheme (XXIX, Fig. 19), is produced upon the treatment of dicyanoferric α,5-dihydroxyheme (XLVIII) sequentially with hydrogen peroxide and dithionite. [63]

(b) Verdoheme is an intermediate in the production of biliverdin in reaction (1) as well as (2). When incubated with hydrogen peroxide and ascorbate, dicyano α,5-dihydroxyheme is oxidized to dicyanoverdoheme, presumably via dicyano α-keto, 5-hydroxyheme. (Furthermore, Kaziro *et al.* [135] have observed an absorption band at 760–70 mμ during the later stages of the formation of "choleglobin mixture" from hemoglobin or myoglobin. A complex with similar spectral properties was prepared by adding pyridine or globin to alkaline solutions of verdoheme. This observation would appear to establish verdoglobin as an intermediate in the production of biliverdin from hemoglobin *in vitro*. Unfortunately, the complex of biliverdin-Fe with

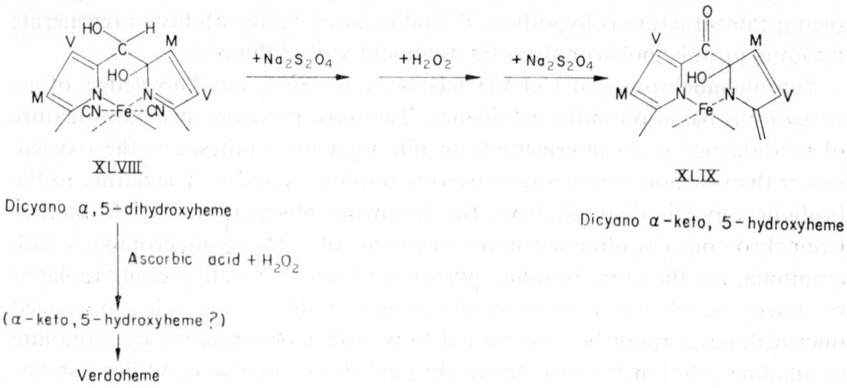

FIG. 19. Conversion of dicyano α,5-dihydroxyheme (pseudohome) to dicyano α-keto, 5-hydroxyheme (oxypseudoheme).

globin would also absorb in the same region, and the identification of the 760–70 mμ absorbing material from the "choleglobin mixture" cannot be considered positive. [(164)]

(v) *Summary of observations on non-enzymatic model systems.* These conclusions are incorporated into the summary hypothetical scheme shown in Fig. 20. The enzymatic synthesis of biliverdin may be similar. The place of α-hydroxyheme is even more uncertain than that of the other postulated intermediates. The facts are: during the incubation of hemoglobin or various protochemochromogens (e.g. dipyridine or dicyanide hemochromogens) with oxidizing agents, a number of changes in the absorption spectrum of the solutions can be detected. Structural formulae have been postulated for each presumed spectral species. At some stages the oxidation process seems to be reversible by the addition of dithionite, a reducing agent. Later, during incubation, such reversal cannot be accomplished—the compound alleged to be present at this point is verdoheme, in which the carbon atom of the α-bridge has been replaced by oxygen.

The non-enzymatic synthesis of biliverdin is concluded by the oxidation of verdoheme. It is believed that the tetrapyrrole, iron and the nitrogenous bases (e.g. globin, cyanide, pyridine) remain associated until after the formation of biliverdin (see biliverdin–Fe–globin, Fig. 20). It should be kept in mind that the structures of most of the intermediates are hypothetical; that very heavy reliance has been placed on spectroscopic observations alone in speculations on individual steps; and that two very crucial assumptions have been made: first, that *in vitro* non-enzymatic conversion of hemoglobin to biliverdin resembles the biological process, and second, that choleheme

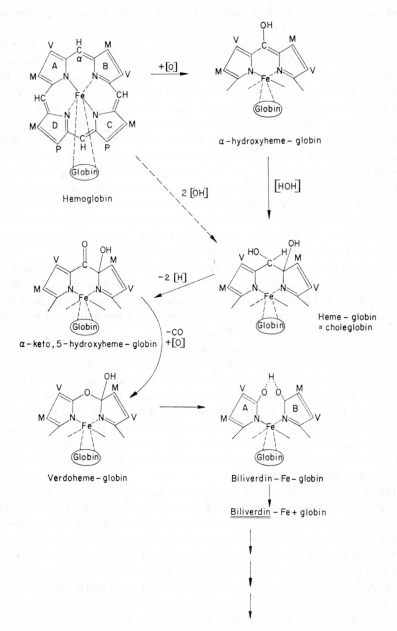

Fig. 20. Summary hypothetical scheme for the formation of biliverdin *in vivo*, based on observations of non-enzymatic reactions in "model systems" *in vitro*.

and pseudoheme (α,5-dihydroxyheme) are identical, although the structure of neither is known with much certainty.

(a) *The mechanism of choleglobin formation.* The ferryl (FeO^{2+}) complex of myoglobin is produced when metmyoglobin is incubated with hydrogen peroxide, alkyl peroxides, or strong oxidizing agents like potassium molybdicyanide. Between pH 8 and 9, with hydrogen peroxide as the oxidizing agent, 90–100 per cent of the metmyoglobin used can be recovered with mild reducing agents. Above pH 9 incubation of metmyoglobin with hydrogen peroxide results in the production of cholemyoglobin. Methyl- or ethyl-peroxides bring about the formation of the ferryl complex without cholemyoglobin formation even above pH 9. [73, 74, 75] It follows that the ferryl complex, which is itself a good oxidizing agent, cannot alone oxidize other myoglobin molecules to cholemyoglobin and that the conversion of myoglobin to the ferryl complex does not *per se* lead to cholemyoglobin formation. The oxidation of the heme to the ferryl level *and* the presence of hydroxyl radicals may both be required for cholemyoglobin formation.

Anan and Mason [5] studied the production of biliverdin from hemoglobin in the presence of ascorbate and O_2.[5] They concluded from analyses of the bile pigment that two or more atoms of molecular oxygen might have been incorporated during the oxidation and suggested a mechanism of biliverdin formation involving hydroxyl radicals.

An autocatalytic lag phase has been noted during early stages of the conversion of hemoglobin to "choleglobin mixture" but not of myoglobin to cholemyoglobin by Kaziro *et al.* [135] Kikuchi and Tomimura [142] and Kaziro *et al.* [137] have shown the importance of denatured hemoglobin in the initiation of the reactions. It has been suggested that perturbed, that is, reversibly altered, hemoglobin is formed during the lag phase. The perturbed hemoglobin would be expected to be a more active oxidase than hemoglobin itself, and thus contribute to the accelerated degradation of hemoglobin which occurs after the lag phase.

(b) *Biliverdin biogenesis. Enzymological investigations.* The problem of biliverdin formation has been attacked in a different manner by Nakajima and co-workers. They have partially purified an enzyme from aqueous extracts of beef liver acetone powder which catalyzes the formation of verdohemochrome from heme complexes. [200] TPNH and ferrous ions are cofactors for this oxygenase. [200] Ferric ions, ethylenediaminetetraacetate (EDTA), α,α'-dipyridyl, iodoacetate, and *p*-chloromercuribenzoate inhibit the enzymatic reaction. [200]

Nakajima *et al.* have used pyridine protohemichromogen (i.e., the Fe^{+++} proto-pyridine complex) as the substrate in their routine assay procedure but studies of substrate specificity have been very revealing. During two-hour incubation periods, the following yields of biliverdin were obtained: [200]

Substrate		Biliverdin (μmoles)
Pyridine protohemichromogen	2·00 μmoles	1·20
Alkaline hematin	2·00 μmoles	0·00
Protoporphyrin IX	2·00 μmoles	0·00
Hemoglobin	2·00 μmoles	0·10
Methemoglobin	2·00 μmoles	0·16
Hemoglobin–haptoglobin	2·00 μmoles	0·98

Myoglobin also serves as a substrate. [201]

Biliverdin was obtained from the reaction mixture by the addition of acetic acid which converts verdohemochromogen to the bile pigment. The yields of biliverdin are strikingly high compared with those obtained in non-enzymatic "model reactions". The data on hematin and protoporphyrin IX support Lemberg's deductions but the discovery of the effect of complexing hemoglobin with haptoglobin could not have been predicted from the "model experiments". Yamaguchi et al.[308] found that haptoglobin alone of the serum components promoted the enzymatic degradation of hemoglobin; it is not known whether any other body protein can have a similar effect. Data on the susceptibility to enzymatic degradation of hemichromogens other than those of the proto-type have not yet been reported.

It is especially interesting that the addition of catalase to the reaction mixture has no effect upon bile pigment formation.[116b] Thus, hydrogen peroxide appears not to be a reactant in the enzymatic formation of biliverdin.

A series of complex spectral changes occur during the enzymatic degradation of pyridine protohemichromogen.[200] The substrate has absorption maxima at 408, 530, and 558 mμ. Spectral changes which occur during the first two minutes of the reaction suggest that the hemochromogen (i.e., Fe^{++}) may be an intermediate. During this same interval an absorption band appears at 630 mμ (probably attributable to a choleheme–pseudoheme type of compound). At a later stage, as verdohemochromogen (?) accumulates, an absorption band with a maximum at 656 mμ develops. At the termination of the reaction, absorption maxima at 395, 498, 530, and 656 mμ are prominent—indicating that intermediates, and perhaps by-products, are present together with the end product. These changes were observed by Nakajima et al. only when the mixture was incubated in air, never when oxygen was excluded. This, together with the observation that H_2O_2 is not involved, supports their contention that the enzyme is an oxygenase. (The enzyme is unstable in air. For example, at 0°C in solution at pH 7·4, the pH of maximum stability of the enzyme, about 40 per cent of the activity was lost in 24 hours. However, under the same conditions of pH and temperature but in an atmosphere of nitrogen a loss of only 3 per cent was incurred. [200])

Nakajima [199] has isolated in crystalline form a compound which resembles, but is not identical with, the verdoheme of Lemberg. Nakajima's compound dissolved in chloroform shows absorption maxima at 397, 495, 530 and 657 $m\mu$; forms a 2,4-dinitrophenyl hydrazone and exhibits a positive Schiff reaction and other aldehyde reactions; and is easily convertible to biliverdin with the concomitant liberation of iron and formaldehyde. The structure suggested by Nakajima for this compound is shown in Fig. 21.

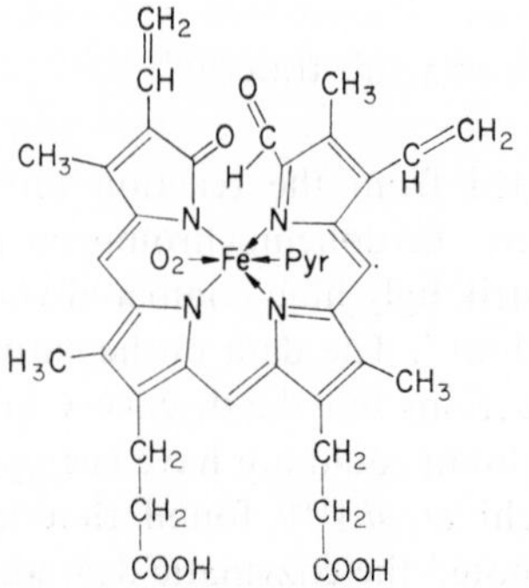

FIG. 21. "Verdohemochrome" according to Nakajima. [199]

Drabkin and Wise [51] reported that an enzyme from the hemophagous organ of dogs was capable of making essentially a single isomer of biliverdin. (Pure biliverdin, then called "uteroverdin", was first isolated from canine placentas. [161]) Maximum synthesis of biliverdin-C^{14} was observed in a reaction mixture containing hemin-C^{14} or hemoglobin-C^{14}, enzyme, ATP, DPN, TPN, NAD and boiled cell sap. Ascorbate substituted for the latter component. The enzyme was associated with the light mitochondria, oxygen was required, and $C^{14}O$ was produced during the reaction. [303] When subjected to thin layer chromatography, 88 per cent of the biliverdin label was associated with a single reference compound, thought to be the IXa isomer of biliverdin. Neither a detailed description of the reaction mixture, nor the spectral properties of the enzymatically produced biliverdin has been published.

The determination by Drabkin and Wise [51] that the principal product of their reaction was probably the IXa isomer of biliverdin is of crucial significance. For, although theoretically, bile pigments could arise by the oxidative removal of any bridge carbon atom, in biological systems, there seems to be something special about the bridge carbon between pyrrole rings A and B of protoporphyrin in that rupture of the ring is thought to always occur at this position. The specificity of the position for ring opening is widely quoted, but the evidence for the biological reality of this process is limited. It is based largely on the observation that the monopyrrolic products which result from chemical degradation of naturally occurring bilirubin, d-urobilin, and stereocobilin (after conversion to mesobiliverdin) could arise only from IXa-type isomers of the respective bile pigments (Gray *et al.*). [102]

Lemberg [168] deduced the preferential attack at the α-bridge in "model reactions" because the biliverdin diethyl ester (m.p. 208) produced from pyridine protohemochromogen during its coupled oxidation with hydrazine hydrate, was not able to effect a melting point depression of biliverdin diethyl ester prepared from naturally occurring bilirubin. Also mesobiliverdin diethyl ester prepared from mesobiliverdin by coupled oxidations as above, did not alter the melting point of the ester of natural mesobiliverdin. It is possible that other mesobiliverdin isomers may have been present in the mother liquor of the chemically prepared mesobiliverdin. It has subsequently been shown that in the reaction of pyridine protohemochromogen with hydrazine sulfate under oxygen, a mixture of biliverdin isomers is produced. [307]

These observations raise some doubts about the probable identity of biliverdin production in non-enzymatic "model systems" and *in vivo*. However, regardless of which bridge carbon atom is attacked, the sequence of intermediates (whatever they are) may be the same in both situations.

The principal factors which complicate investigations on the formation of bile pigments (e.g. biliverdin) from their precursors enzymatically *in vitro* are: (a) non-enzymatic synthesis of biliverdin (i.e. in "model systems") ordinarily occurs under near-physiological conditions in the presence of ascorbate or other substances many of which are commonly found in crude tissue homogenates; (b) cells of the reticulo-endothelial system, in which the catabolism of hemoglobin is thought to occur, are not localized in one specific organ, but are found throughout the body; consequently it is difficult to predict which tissue or organ will be rich in the sought-after enzyme or enzymes, and (c) despite the conclusions drawn by Lemberg on the basis of the "model systems", the nature of the "primary substrate" for enzymatic biliverdin formation is not entirely resolved.

2. *The Biogenesis of "Urobilin"*

The probable sequence of intermediates between biliverdin and the urobilinoid pigments is: biliverdin → bilirubin → bilirubin-glucuronide → dihydrobilirubin → mesobilirubin → dihydromesobilirubin → mesobilirubinogen → "urobilinogens" → "urobilins".

The enzymatic synthesis of bilirubin from biliverdin was described by Lemberg and Wyndam. [173] The enzyme from the liver of rats which catalyzed this reduction (the insertion of two hydrogen atoms at the central methene bridge position of biliverdin (XXXIII)—the γ-bridge based on porphyrin designations—see Fig. 15) was partially purified. It was found as well in tissues of the liver, kidney, brain, and spleen, but not in the lung, muscle or heart.

Singleton and Laster [265] partially purified an enzyme which they named "biliverdin reductase". This enzyme was present in the soluble fraction from guinea-pig liver breis, it was inactivated by short-term exposure to heat, required the cofactor DPN but not TPN, and the reaction rates were estimated by the loss of optical density of substrate at 670 mμ. [265]

The conversion of biliverdin-C^{14} to bilirubin-C^{14} by rats *in vivo* has been described by Goldstein and Lester. [81] Following infusion of radiochemically pure biliverdin-C^{14} into rats prepared with an external biliary fistula, about 80 per cent of the isotope was recoverd in the bile as bilirubin after 20 hours.

Studies with isotopically labeled bilirubin indicate that this pigment is bound solely to albumin during its transfer from sites of formation to the liver where it is removed from the plasma and excreted into the bile. [223] The complex appears to consist of two molecules of tetrapyrrole to one molecule of albumin. [246]

The transfer of bilirubin from plasma to the bile is undoubtedly a complex process, and there is little direct evidence of the mechanisms involved. [174, 98]

There are several reports describing the enzymatic synthesis of bilirubin-glucuronide from glucuronic acid and the orange pigment. [157, 104, 247, 6] This enzyme was found in the liver, was associated with the microsome fraction, [157, 104, 247, 6] and requires cofactors, its operation *in vivo* would require the presence of a uridine diphosphoglucuronic acid generating system. The reaction has been summarized as follows:

$$\text{Glucose-1-P} + \text{UTP} \xrightarrow{\text{UDP-glucose pyrophosphorylase}} \text{UDP-glucose} + \text{pyrophosphate}$$

$$\text{UDP-glucose} + 2\text{DPN}^+ \xrightarrow{\text{dehydrogenase}} \text{UDP-glucuronic acid} + 2\text{DPNH} + \text{H}^+$$

$$\text{UDP-glucuronic acid} + \text{bilirubin} \xrightarrow{\text{transferase}} \text{bilirubin glucuronide} + \text{UDP}$$

The product of the enzymatic reaction (i.e. bilirubin-glucuronide) has not been isolated in pure form, probably because of its instability; the existence of the complex in reaction mixtures after incubation with the liver enzymes is based on: (a) its "direct" reacting behavior in the van den Bergh reaction [157, 104, 6, 247] (free bilirubin gives an "indirect" reaction with diazotized sulfanilic acid), (b) its hydrolysis with β-glucuronidase, [104, 247] (c) the chromatographic behavior of its azo derivatives, [104, 247, 6] and (d) the release of glucuronic acid during non-enzymatic hydrolysis of its azo derivative. [104, 247, 6]

Once in the gut, bilirubin-glucuronide probably remains intact until it reaches the terminal ileum and the large bowel where it is transformed into a number of colorless chromogens by the bacteria in the mixed fecal flora. [98, 144]

Mesobilirubinogen (XXXIX) is formed by the saturation of the vinyl side chains and methene bridges of bilirubin (XXXIV); mesobilirubin (XXXV), in which the vinyl groups but not the bridges are saturated, may be an intermediate. Still in the gut, the terminal pyrrole residues of mesobilirubinogen are reduced and stercobilinogen (XL) is formed. Finally, stercobilin (XLI) is produced by oxidation of the central carbon bridge of stercobilinogen. By a similar oxidation, *i*-urobilin (XXXVIII) may arise from mesobilirubinogen.

Gustafson and Lanke [105] found that urobilinogen was not detectable in the intestines of germ-free rats, but was produced in these animals after the introduction of a *Clostridium* species (cultured from the feces of normal rats) into the gut. The presence of *E. coli* was found to enhance urobilinogen production. Watson *et al.* [297] found that bilirubin and bilirubin-glucuronide were converted to colorless urobilinogens during incubations with mixed fecal flora cultures from humans. In these studies, the bacteria were capable of making *l*-, *d*-, and *i*-urobilinogens. Lowry *et al.* [183] had previously shown that the *l*-stercobilinogen and stercobilin isomers are produced from mesobilirubinogen by bacteria in the fecal flora of humans.

Baumgartel [8] has suggested that bilirubin is converted only to *l*-stercobilin by the intestinal flora. Stercobilin formation was related to a cystine–cysteine redox system, and a dehydrogenase from different bacterial species.

Further studies on the enzymes and reaction mechanisms must be made before the synthesis of other bile pigments from bilirubin is completely understood. Except for the reduction of the terminal pyrrole residues to form the stercobilin types of pigments, the chemistry of bile pigment interconversion seems to be straightforward and the transformation of biliverdin through to other urobilins can be performed rationally *in vitro*.

IV. BILIPROTEINS

A. *Distribution and Composition*

The most thoroughly studied, as well as the most abundant, bile pigment-protein complexes are the water-soluble, easily crystallizable phycoerythrins, phycocyanins, and allophycocyanins, the red and blue biliproteins of the blue-green and red algae and the *Cryptomonads*. These phycobiliproteins are localized in the photosynthetic apparatus and participate in photosynthesis, at least as accessory absorbing pigments [55, 65, 115] and probably more directly. [28] The concentration of phycobiliproteins is frequently very high. *Anacystis nidulans* has been reported to contain 40 per cent of its soluble protein as phycocyanin when cultured under some conditions. [198] Chromoproteins which appear to be related to phycobiliproteins have been recovered from the integument of *Mantis religiosa* and other *Orthoptera*, [222] from secretions of certain glands of the sea snail *Aplysia*, [49, 62, 160] and from the Mediterranean fish *Crenilabus*. [64] Other biliproteins have been isolated from butterflies. [61] Phytochrome, a chromoprotein which is the photo-receptive pigment controlling numerous developmental processes in plants [122] is remarkably similar to allophycocyanin in its absorption spectrum. [264]

The nomenclature used for phycobiliproteins and their prosthetic groups

L

is inadequate and confused. [218] Phycocyanins and phycoerythrins were originally assigned the prefix C- or R-, which referred to their origin from either *Rhodophycean* or *Cyanophycean* species. [282] The R- and C-phycocyanins and phycoerythrins are spectrally distinct. However, recent studies have revealed the existence of allophycocyanin and B-phycoerythrin; each differs spectrally from previously studied phycobiliproteins. [2, 116] The biliproteins from cryptomonads fall into yet another spectral "class". [4, 116, 221, 212] Variations in the absorption of phycoerythrins, phycocyanins, and allophycocyanins, are shown in Table 2 along with some estimates of molecular weight. Absorption at the maxima in the region beyond 500 mμ is generally three to six times that at maxima in the region 300 to 400 mμ.

TABLE 2. SOME PHYSICAL PROPERTIES† OF PHYCOBILIPROTEINS; DATA ASSEMBLED BY O'HEOCHA [217]

Biliprotein	Molecular weight and pH of determination	Absorption λ_{max} (mμ)					Fluorescence λ_{max} (mμ)
C-phycoerythrin	226,000 (7·2–8·3)	275	305~370			562	575
Cryptomonad phycoerythrin (type ii)	—	275	310			556	580
B-phycoerythrin	290,000 (5)	278	307~370		546	565	578
R-phycoerythrin	291,000 (3–10)	278	307~370	498	540	568	578
C-phycocyanin	138,000 (7·2–8·3)	278~350				615	647
Allophycocyanin	134,000 (7·2–8·3)	278~350				(610) 650	660
Cryptomonad (HV-) phycocyanin	—	270~350	583			(625) 643	660
R-phycocyanin	273,000 (2·5–6·0)	278~355	553			615	565 637

† Sources of data are: Ericksson-Quensel, [56] Airth and Blinks, [2] Hattori and Fujita, [110] Ó'hEocha and Ó'Carra, [219] Ó'Carra, [211] Ó'hEocha et al. [220]

Phycobilins, the bile pigment prosthetic groups of phycobiliproteins, are tightly bound to their respective apoproteins. The separation of phycobilins from phycocyanin and phycoerythrin was reported to occur during long incubation with concentrated HCl. [165] O'hEocha [216] and Ó'Carra *et al.* [213] have reinvestigated this problem, and have described the isolation of pure phycobilins, free from protein, under somewhat milder conditions. The association of phycobilins with their apoproteins can be broken by refluxing these pigments in 90 per cent methanol containing ascorbic acid (personal communication from C. O'hEocha and H. W. Siegelman).

The native prosthetic group of phycocyanin is phycocyanobilin. [165] At the present time a structure cannot be confidently assigned to this phycobilin but recently O'hEocha [216] has shown that phycocyanobilin is probably a monobasic, bilidiene bile pigment with spectral properties intermediate between those of violins and verdins, and which undergoes isomerization to a mesobiliviolin-like tetrapyrrole when subjected to strong acid for long periods. It is estimated that the number of phycobilin residues in one molecule of C- and R-phycocyanin may be as high as 22 and 30, respectively. [211]

Phycoerythrobilin, the chromophore of phycoerythrin, as redefined by O'Carra et al.[213] is a violin-type bilidiene bile pigment which can be isomerized to a urobilin (bilene) in strong acid, or transformed into a verdin by dehydrogenation with acid ferric chloride. Phycourobilin, another non-cyclic tetrapyrrole reported to occur in R-phycoerythrin[219] appears to be a bilene with spectral properties similar to i- or d-urobilin. [292] It is estimated that the C-phycoerythrin protein is associated with as many as twenty-five phycoerythrobilin residues; the R-phycoerythrin molecule is thought to contain twelve phycourobilin chromophores as well. [211]

Phycoerythrin is stable and homogenous in the ultracentrifuge. In the pH range 3–10, $S_{20,w}$ values of 12 and 10·3 have been reported from different laboratories. Between pH 10·5 and 11·6, the sedimentation co-efficient is reported to be about 2. [56, 110] In view of the dissociation at this pH it has been suggested that the subunits of phycoerythrin may be joined to one another by tyrosine–carboxyl linkages. [215]

Phycocyanin shows a more complicated behavior with change in pH. In the pH range from 2·5–6, $S_{20·w}$ values of 10·9 [110] and 11·4 [56] have been reported but unlike phycoerythrin or allophycocyanin, in the pH range 7–8·5 reversible dissociation occurs and particles of $S_{20·w}$ of 6·2 are observed in the ultracentrifuge. [56, 110] The $S_{20·w}$ values at pH 4·7 and 7·2 for phycocyanin purified from *Plectonema calothricoides* grown in D_2O or water varied depending on the ionic strength of the buffer and on the concentrations of pigment used in the sedimentation studies. [12, 113] Phycocyanin undergoes irreversible dissociations at pH 11·6, and particles with a sedimentation coefficient of 2·4, are found. [110]

Sedimentation coefficients of 6·3, 5·9, and 1·7 have been observed for allophycocyanin at pH values 5·2, 7·2–8·3, and 11·6, respectively; the dissociation to lower molecular weight units is irreversible. [110]

Studies on the immunochemical behavior of phycobiliproteins may prove to be valuable for understanding evolutionary relationships among certain of the algae, and more hopefully, in view of the effects of hydrogen ion concentration on the structural integrity of these pigments, for understanding some of the chemical and physical properties of their proteins. Immunological techniques have been applied to the study of *C. caldarium* phycocyanin. [294, 27] Crystalline phycocyanin from this alga proved to be an effective antibody when administered to rabbits. Serum from animals receiving the antigen contained antibodies which could react with *C. caldarium* phycocyanin but not allophycocyanin of the same species or *Porphyra laciniata* phycoerythrin, in agar double diffusion plates at pH 5·5, 7·4 and 8·3. At these pH values phycocyanins from five other algal species were capable of reacting with the serum from rabbits injected with *C. caldarium* phycocyanin, although the shapes and intensities of the precipitin lines in the gel suggested that there were differences in the respective algal proteins. That two dissimilar precipitation arcs were observed in the reaction of phycocyanin from *Nostoc muscorum* with the antiserum to "Cyanidium" phycocyanin at pH 8·3 (e.g. under conditions favoring dissociation of the biliprotein molecule into subunits) is of particular interest. The behavior of phycocyanin from the two algae was measurably different at pH 5·5 and 7·4, but at pH 8·3, one of the *N. muscorum* precipitin bands coincided with the one produced by *C. caldarium* phycocyanin; this suggests the possibility that identical subunits are present in the two pigments.

In another investigation the immunological properties of phycocyanin from *Plectonema calothricoides* grown in water, and deuterium, were studied. [11] Phycocyanins ("deuterio"- and "protio"-phycocyanin) obtained from algal cells grown in D_2O and H_2O, when administered to rabbits, were capable of stimulating the production of antibodies. Serum from rabbits injected with "protio"-phycocyanin reacted (in agar on double diffusion plates) with both "protio"- and "deuterio"-phycocyanin. The antiserum to "deuterio"-phycocyanin, when allowed to diffuse against "D" phycocyanin produced a single preciptin line, and an additional preciptin line was observed in the reaction "H" phycocyanin. Antisera resulting from injection with the deuterated and protonated *P. calothricoides* phycocyanins was immuno-chemically reactive with "protio" *Synechococcus lividus* phycocyanin and "deuterio" *P. luridum* phycocyanin, although the shapes of the red fluorescing precipitin lines differed.

In immunochemical studies the physical condition of the antigen (e.g. possible dissociation of the phycocyanin due to the hydrogen ion concentration) at the antibody-forming sites or the possible involvement of the phycocyanin prosthetic groups in the immune response is not known.

A number of investigators have studied the amino acid content of biliproteins. [71, 133, 144, 12, 235] O'hEocha [217, 218] has summarized these results along with the other information regarding the physical and chemical properties of phycocyanins and phycoerythrins.

B. *The Biogenesis of Phycobiliproteins*

1. *Experiments and Observations*

As of this writing, there are no reports in the literature on the biosynthesis of biliproteins *in vitro*, although numerous investigations have been made of the effects of light on their formation. For instance, certain blue-green algae accumulate more biliproteins when grown at lower than at higher intensities of light. [107] In another study, Brody and Emerson [36] reported that the red alga, *Porphyridium cruentum*, produced more phycoerythrin in blue (436 mμ) than in green (546 mμ) light of high intensity.

The blue-green alga *Tolypothrix tenuis* contains phycocyanin, phycoery-thrin, and allophycocyanin in addition to chlorophyll *a* and carotenoids. The relative concentration of phycocyanin and phycoerythrin and the total phycobiliprotein is influenced by the quality of light in which the cells are grown. Phycocyanin-rich cells are produced by cells grown in incandescent light, phycoerythrin-rich cells, with a higher total concentration of biliprotein, are obtained from fluorescent light illuminated cultures. [68, 70, 109, 112]

Cells of this alga are bleached with high intensity fluorescent light (20,000 lux for 24 hours) in a medium lacking inorganic nitrogen. They subsequently produce phycobiliproteins when a source of nitrogen is provided: (a) phy-coerythrin is produced in darkness or in 400 or 550 mμ light; (b) phycocyanin and allophycocyanin are produced only if cells are irradiated with light of wavelengths 600 to 700 mμ. [109, 112, 68, 70] Thus, red light promotes phyco-cyanin production and potential phycoerythrin-producing cells can be converted to phycocyanin production by red irradiation. Furthermore, cells illuminated with red light *before* nitrate is provided—and thus are poised for phycocyanin production—can be reconverted to the phycoerythrin synthe-sizing state by irradiation with 550 mμ light (Fig. 22). The total amount of biliprotein produced is independent of these manipulations. After bleaching, biliprotein biosynthesis by *T. tennis* does not occur in the absence of a nitrogen source and is blocked by chloramphenicol (6×10^{-5}M), an inhibitor of protein synthesis. [67]

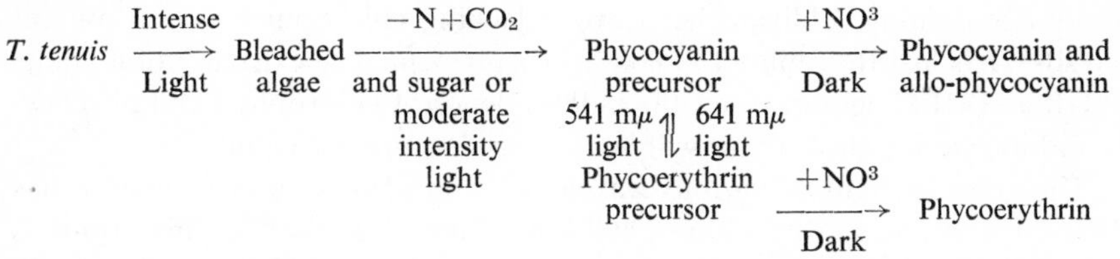

FIG. 22. Summary of the experiments of Fujita and Hattori. [68, 70, 109, 112]

Despite the feeling by Fujita and Hattori [67] that chromatic illumination with the appropriate colors of light effects the interconversion of *pre-existing* phycocyanin and phycoerythrin precursors, it seems more likely that light is acting on a photoreceptive pigment which is responsible for controlling the subsequent synthesis of the biliprotein prosthetic group, of the apoprotein, or, more probably, of both, because: (a) phycobilins are not detectable in sufficient quantity in the "bleached" cells to serve as a metabolic pool for subsequent biliprotein formation, (b) the apoproteins of phycocyanin and phycoerythrin differ sufficiently with respect to amino acid content, molecular weight, and immunochemical behavior, that the possibility of their coming from a common precursor is unlikely, and (c) inhibition of biliprotein synthesis by withholding nitrogen or administering chloramphenicol demonstrate that the apoproteins of these pigments are not present during irradiations which qualitatively alter the biliprotein synthesizing capacity of the cells.

In view of the above, it seems likely that synthesis of the pyrrolic, and of the proteinaceous parts of the biliprotein molecule may go on concurrently.

Light can affect biliprotein formation by *T. tenuis* quantitatively as well as qualitatively. For example, cells which are actively forming phycoerythrin, or are about to do so, produce reduced amounts of biliprotein upon illumination with red light (i.e. phycocyanin-promoting wavelengths). The reciprocal —reduction of total phycobiliprotein synthesis by irradiation of phycocyanin-producing cells with 550 mμ light—is also observed. [69, 70]

Cells of the wild-type *Cyanidium caldarium*, an acidophilic single-celled alga, contain chlorophyll *a*, phycocyanin, allophycocyanin and carotenoids when grown in the light. Photosynthetic pigments are not produced during heterotrophic growth of cells in darkness. Nichols and Bogorad [208] have partially characterized a number of variously pigmented *C. caldarium* mutants produced by irradiation of the wild-type with ultra-violet light (Table 3).

Mutant III-D-2 is capable of making chlorophyll *a*, phycocyanin and allophycocyanin when cultured in the light, but it makes more pigment per cell and grows more rapidly than does the wild-type. Mutant III-C produces chlorophyll *a* but not phycocyanin in the light. Mutant GGB is a phycocyanin-containing, obligate heterotroph-lacking chlorophyll *a*, and mutant GGB-Y has lost the ability to make either pigment. The existence of mutants GGB and III-C demonstrates the independence of chlorophyll and phycocyanin biogenesis. This matter will be discussed in greater detail later.

The effect of light of various wavelengths on phycocyanin formation has been studied using the chlorophyll-less mutant GGB. [209] This strain is especially favorable for this purpose because it contains no chlorophyll, which, if present, might act as a light-absorbing filter at certain critical wavelengths and thus make the results difficult·to interpret. The heterotrophic character of this mutant also eliminates the confusion which might arise from the effects of light on growth, superimposed upon those on phycocyanin formation, *per se*.

The spectral response curve for phycocyanin formation by cultures of mutant GGB grown in darkness for 7 days prior to illumination shows a sharp maximum at 420 mμ and a region of lower effectiveness at 550–595 mμ. Cells of mutant GGB from 15- and 22-day-old cultures which were first illuminated with 420 mμ light produced more phycocyanin when exposed to 595 mμ light than cells receiving equal doses of light at the latter wavelength alone. The synergystic effect of the two wavelengths of light suggests the possible involvement of two photoreceptive pigments. [209]

Phycocyanin formation by mutant GGB in response to various wavelengths of light resembles the absorption spectrum of a hemoprotein. In view of the probable origin of the prosthetic group of phycocyanin from a porphyrin, a metalloporphyrin (heme), or a metalloporphyrin-protein complex (hemoprotein), it is tempting to try to correlate the action spectrum for phycocyanin formation with the absorption spectrum of a hypothetical hemoprotein precursor of phycocyanin which might be photooxidized to a biliprotein. However, *C. caldarium* forms a blue bile pigment in darkness when incubated with δ-aminolevulinic acid. [287, 288] Consequently the photoreceptive pigment(s)—which may be hemoprotein in nature—may play a role in controlling the formation of: (a) δ-aminolevulinic acid or its precursors, (b) an essential amino acid necessary for making the phycocyanin protein, (c) coenzymes, or, (d) of the photosynthetic apparatus. It is noteworthy that similar action spectra to that obtained for phycocyanin formation in mutant GGB have been described for other processes in plants such as inhibition of root elongation in wheat, [14] vesicle dispersion in proplastids of etiolated beans, [121] and inhibition of cell division in the alga *Prototheca*. [9]

2. Speculations on Biliprotein Biogenesis

The course of formation of bile pigments from hemoproteins, e.g. hemoglobin, postulated in an earlier section, can provide a basis for some speculation on the biogenesis of at least the prosthetic group, and possibly of the entire biliprotein. The non-enzymatic conversion of hematin and of heme-proteins but not of protoporphyrin IX into biliverdin *in vitro*, [141] the excretion of bilirubin-C^{14} in the bile of cannaliculized rats following intravenous injections of hematin-C^{14} in serum or bound to albumin, [277] and the enzymatic synthesis of biliverdin precursors from hemoglobin-haptoglobin, pyridine hemochromogen [200] or myoglobin [201] suggests the possibility that biliprotein prosthetic groups may also be produced from the complex of a protein with one or more molecules of type IX protoporphyrin or heme, rather than either free acid. Starting again with a hemoprotein, by mechanisms already discussed, one could visualize the rupture of the porphyrin (or heme) ring by removal of the α-bridge carbon while the tetrapyrrole is still complexed with the protein. Then, either of two courses might be suggested (Fig. 23).

(A) The newly formed bile pigment molecules (biliverdin–protein complex Fig. 23) might fail to separate from the protein because of covalent bonding between the two (there is indirect evidence suggesting the involvement of ester and thioether linkages between phycobilins and their respective proteins). Reduction of the chromophores, according to this hypothesis, would occur while the biliverdin is attached to the protein; the product would be "phycobilin–protein complex" (Fig. 23). The tendency of biliproteins to

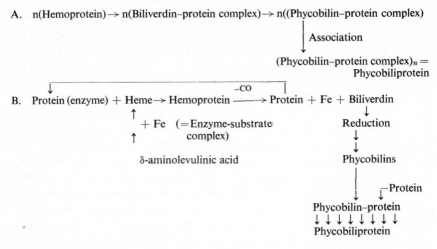

FIG. 23. Two possible metabolic pathways for the production of biliproteins.

dissociate depending upon the hydrogen ion concentration suggests that the unit of synthesis may be a phycobilin–protein complex of relatively low molecular weight. To account for the high molecular weight of some phycobiliproteins (*ca.* 275,000) and the large number of phycobilins which are contained in each molecule of native protein (e.g. some phycocyanins are thought to have thirty prosthetic groups), one could visualize the terminal step in formation by this route as consisting of an aggregation of smaller molecular weight phycobilin-containing protein units; the minimum size to be expected for such subunits containing three phycobilins would be approximately 27,500. (C-phycocyanin was calculated to have a minimum molecular weight of about 30,000 under some conditions on the basis of its sedimentation properties in the ultracentrifuge [13].)

If scheme (A) outlined above operated, one would expect a hemoprotein to be produced in large amounts for this specific purpose. From the standpoint of evolution, it is tempting to speculate on such a hemoprotein as an enzyme previously involved in a primitive biological reaction. There may have been a selection for the phylogenetic ancestors of certain algae which were capable of utilizing the breakdown products of these hemoproteins as accessory pigments for efficient photosynthesis.

(B) The prosthetic groups of hemoproteins might be degraded to bile pigment *in situ* followed by the separation of protein, bile pigment and iron. The protein could then be re-utilized for forming additional hemoproteins. After release from the protein the biliverdin-like bile pigments could be enzymatically transformed into, e.g., phycocyanobilins and then one or more of these could become covalently associated with subunit apoprotein.

Aggregation of bile pigment-protein complexes would then complete the synthesis of the native biliprotein.

Schemes (A) and (B) differ fundamentally in the nature of the substrate for phycobiliprotein formation. In (A) the entire hemoprotein is the sole substrate, and both the pyrrolic and protein segments are postulated to ultimately become part of the finished chromoprotein. According to (B), the initial hemoprotein is, in fact, an enzyme-substrate complex; this protein is an enzyme for phycobilin formation; synthesis of the tetrapyrrolic and high molecular weight protein portions of the native pigment occur separately, the association of these two kinds of molecules would constitute the terminal step in chromoprotein formation.

Recent observations on the synthesis of free phycobilins by wild-type and mutant *C. caldarium* strains favor scheme (B). Dark-grown or previously illuminated cells were incubated with δ-aminolevulinic acid (7×10^{-3}M) in darkness (Table 3). During 24-hour incubations with substrate, the algal

TABLE 3. PORPHYRINS AND PHYCOBILIN IN THE SUSPENDING MEDIUM OF WILD-TYPE AND MUTANT *C. caldarium* CELLS AFTER INCUBATION FOR 24 HR WITH ALA ($7\cdot0 \times 10^{-3}$M) [287, 288]

Cell type	Normal Pigmentation		Total porphyrins† (μmoles/ml $\times 10^3$)		Phycobilin (μmoles/ml $\times 10^3$)	
	Chl.†	P.C.†	dark-grown cells	pre-illuminated cells	dark-grown cells	pre-illuminated cells
1. III-D-2	+	+	3·62	18.88	8.54	37·20
2. Wild-type	+	+	6·28	14·72	10·85	17·80
3. III-C	+	−	5·96	15·00	9·39	19·70
4. GGB	−	+	5·12	14·48	9·10	26·40
5. GGB-Y	−	−	4·00	14·72	8·15	23·20

† Chl. = chlorophyll *a*; P.C. = phycocyanin.

cells excreted porphobilinogen, porphyrins, and a blue phycobilin (Table 3) into the suspending medium. [287, 288] The spectral properties of the blue phycobilin were intermediate between those of verdins (bilitrienes) and violins (bilidienes). The red-fluorescing zinc complex of the blue pigment in methanol suggested its similarity to biliviolins, and its behavior in the Gmelin reaction was characteristic of biliverdins. [289] The phycobilin produced by the δ-aminolevulinate-treated *C. caldarium* cells resembled the phycobilin obtained from native phycocyanin by refluxing the latter in 90 per cent methanol. This suggests that the phycobilin produced by the cells incubated with δ-aminolevulinate may be phycocyanobilin. [288, 289] δ-Aminolevulinate utilization for bile pigment production does not occur in *C. caldarium* cells—incubated with substrate and chloromycetin (10^{-2} to 10^{-5} M) or ethionine (10^{-3} M), and in cells incubated with substrate in suspending medium lacking nitrogen. [287] The failure of cells to utilize δ-aminolevulinic acid under these conditions suggests that the biosynthesis of phycobilins, and of their pyrrolic precursors, may depend upon the ability of the cells to make proteins but clearly the protein of *Cyanidium*, phycocyanin is not one of them. The production of porphyrins and bile pigments from exogenous δ-aminolevulinic acid is enhanced by previous exposure of the cells to light (Table 3). [288, 289]

One possible biosynthetic relationship between the production of chlorophyll and of bile pigments by an alga such as *C. caldarium* is:

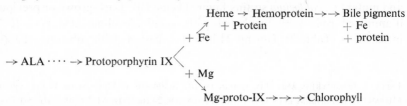

A mutant which produces phycocyanin but not chlorophyll (*C. caldarium* GGB) would appear to have a lesion in the magnesium branch of the biosynthetic chain, e.g. lacks the magnesium incorporating enzyme. The sub-strain GGB–Y, which forms neither chlorophyll *a* nor biliproteins and which does not accumulate tetrapyrrolic precursors of these compounds, would appear to have lost the capacity to produce ALA; this possibility is supported by the observations summarized in Table 3. On the other hand, a strain which forms chlorophyll *a* but not phycobiliproteins, such as III C, could be visualized to lack an enzyme early in the bile pigment branch, e.g. PICE if heme is indeed an intermediate. Such a simple explanation for strain III C seems to be precluded by the fact that such algae make bile pigment when supplied with ALA (Table III C). This forces the conclusion that either (i) the mutation really affects the rate of ALA synthesis and that the activity of the enzyme which diverts protoporphyrin into the chlorophyll branch is so much greater than that which directs the tetrapyrrole toward bile pigment synthesis that only when large amounts of substrate are available can both branches operate, or (ii) separate sets of enzymes, perhaps in multienzyme complexes, exist within the *C. caldarium* chloroplast—one set for the production of bile pigment from ALA precursors and another for the formation of chlorophyll from the same materials. The observations that GGB grown in the light without exogenous ALA produces no more phycocyanin than wild-type cells which also make chlorophyll and that III C normally makes less chlorophyll than wild-type cells which also form biliproteins could be taken to support either proposal. On the other hand, it is curious that ALA-fed cells of, for example, wild-type, III D-2, or III C, do not build up protochlorophyllide or chlorophyll—this might reflect some photocontrol over an enzyme early in the bile pigment branch or a complete or relative inaccessibility to exogenous ALA of the chlorophyll-forming multienzyme system postulated above.

V. VITAMIN B_{12}

A. *The Structural Relationship of Vitamin B_{12} Corrin to Porphyrins*

The porphyrin-like, corrin moiety (L) of vitamin B_{12} (LI, Fig. 24) consists of a large ring which is made up of four partially reduced pyrrole (pyrroline and pyrrolidine) rings. [31, 125] Unlike porphyrins, the four heterocyclic rings of the corrin are joined by only three carbon bridges; rings A and D are joined directly. The B_{12} corrin is heavily substituted with methyl groups but other side chains at positions 2, 3, 7, 8, 13, 17, 18 (these groups are designated a, b, c, d, e, f, and g respectively in B_{12}) are amides of acetic or propionic acid. The resemblance to uroporphyrin III in the nature and arrangement of side chains is striking.

Corcoran and Shemin [47] have demonstrated that δ-aminolevulinic acid is incorporated into vitamin B_{12}, probably without rearrangement, by cultures of an *Actinomycete* strain; this links the synthesis of vitamin B_{12} directly to that of uroporphyrin III and other porphyrins. This conclusion is also supported by the observation by Schwartz *et al.* [252] that porphobilinogen is incorporated into vitamin B_{12}.

When synthesized in the presence of C^{14}-methyl-labeled methionine radioactivity appears in the methyl groups of vitamin B_{12}. [34, 35] However, one of the methyl substituents at position 12 (ring C) appears to arise from carbon 3 of δ-aminolevulinic acid and the methyl substituent on position 1 of the B_{12} ring may be derived from the δ-carbon atom of δ-aminolevulinic acid—i.e. it and the three methene bridge carbon atoms may have a common origin. [35] When the actinomycete is grown in the presence of 5-C^{14}-δ-aminolevulinic acid radiocarbon appears among the methyl groups of vitamin B_{12}. The only methyl group which could be derived directly from the δ-carbon of δ-aminolevulinic acid appears to be the one at position 1. It is, of course, possible that some of this radioactivity comes indirectly via the one-carbon pool [202] but Bray and Shemin [35] feel that the dilution of radioactivity would have been much greater than they observed if it entered by such an indirect route.

B. *Possible Mechanisms for the Formation of the Corrin Ring*

Several mechanisms which have been proposed to explain the formation of uroporphyrinogen III from porphobilinogen have also sought to include features which would provide a path for corrin biogenesis. [32, 38, 23] In these hypotheses, some polypyrrolic precursor, common to uroporphyrinogen III and vitamin B_{12}, has been postulated. Thus, it is suggested, there might be

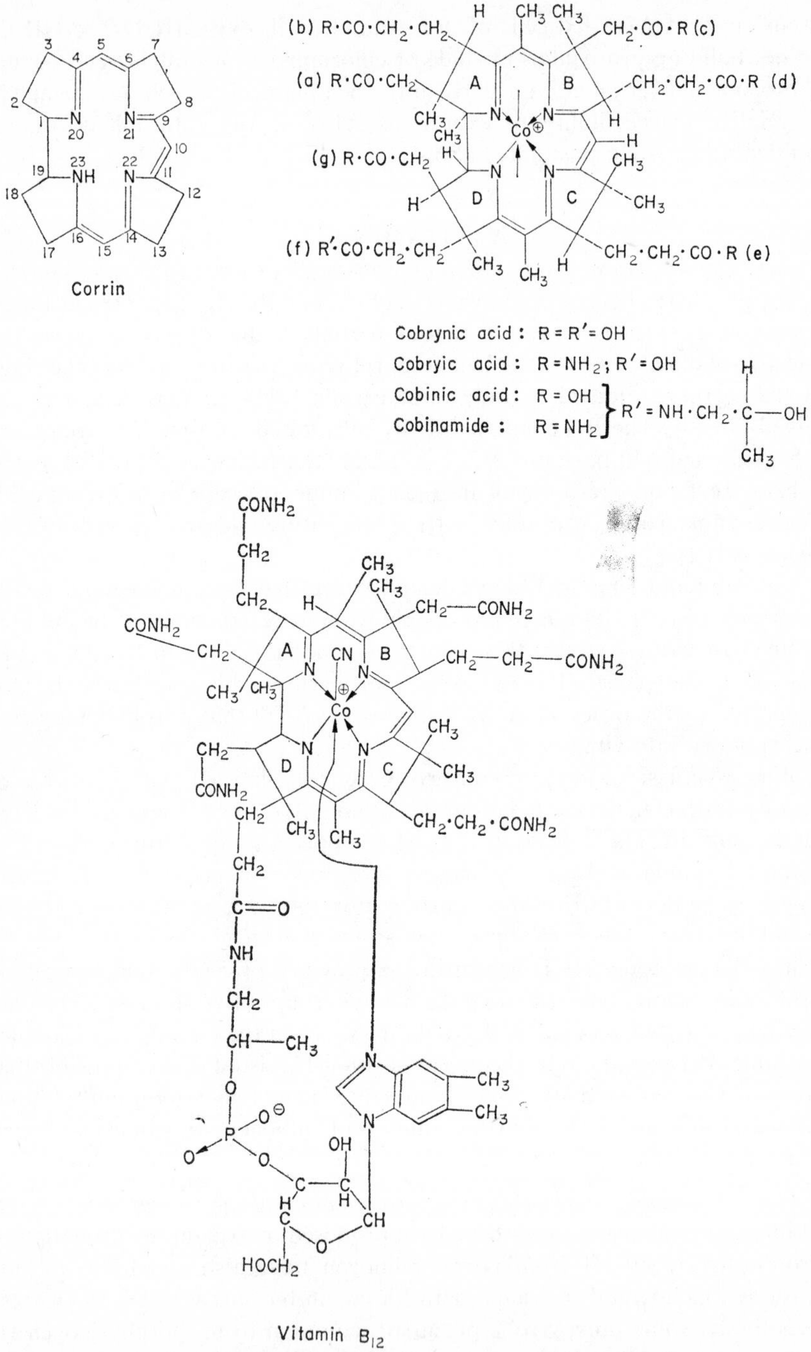

Corrin

Cobrynic acid : R = R' = OH
Cobryic acid : R = NH₂; R' = OH
Cobinic acid : R = OH
Cobinamide : R = NH₂

$R' = NH \cdot CH_2 \cdot \overset{H}{\underset{CH_3}{C}} \!\!-\!\! OH$

Vitamin B₁₂

FIG. 24. The structure of corrinoid compounds.

two enzyme-catalyzed modes of closure of a tetrapyrrole ring formed from porphobilinogen. Bonnet et al. [32] have suggested that one possible sequence leading from the hypothetical polypyrrole to vitamin B_{12}, might be: (1) methylation (in the course of which the pyrrole rings would become partially reduced); (2) the formation of a direct bond between the α-carbon atoms of rings A and D by dehydrogenation in the presence of cobalt; and (3) the introduction of the amide groups and the nucleotide portion as well as the necessary decarboxylation of the acetic acid side chain at position 12. The only fact available to judge this proposal by comes from the experiments of Friedrich. [66] He has shown that amidation can follow methylation of the Co-corrin; cobrynic acid is amidated enzymatically. On the other hand, the recent isolation of a Co-free corrinoid compound (reported to be corrin–aminopropanol–phospho–ribose) from the photosynthetic green sulfur bacteria Chromatium [285] raises some question as to the time of insertion of Co into the corrin ring—although it is possible that the removal of Co from the corrin complex might be secondary.

A number of additional possibilities exist, particularly in the absence of experimental data.

1. Origin from Uroporphyrinogen Isomer III

Uroporphyrinogens are known to isomerize readily in acid solution and to incorporate formaldehyde even in near neutral solutions upon heating. [31, 10] Opening and reclosing of the tetrapyrrole ring together with exchange or displacement of methane bridge carbon atoms must undoubtedly occur. It is clear that processes of this sort are not involved in the enzymatic formation of uroporphyrinogen III but it is quite conceivable that they might be involved in corrin formation. This possibility is included in the diagram shown in Fig. 25 and described as "ring contraction."

2. Origin from Uroporphyrin III—Metal Complexes

These possibilities are derived from considerations of the probable sequence of events in bile pigment formation. Co- or Fe-uroporphyrin might serve as the substrate. The events might be: Fe-uroporphyrin partially oxidized at the δ-bridge followed by ring contraction or even ring-opening and reclosure. Ring contraction of Co-uroporphyrin is yet another possibility.

Conjectures on the biogenesis of the corrin moiety are summarized in Fig. 25. The formation of the entire vitamin B_{12} molecule, including the corrin ring, has been discussed recently by Bernhauer et al. [10] and the proceedings of a symposium on vitamin B_{12} have been published. [120]

VI. PRODIGIOSIN

The formation of prodigiosin (LII, Fig. 26) [236, 295] has been studied primarily in wild-type and mutant strains of Serratia marcescens. Hubbard

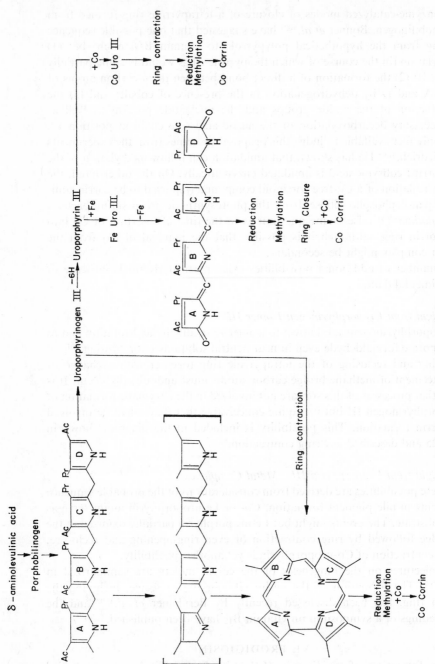

FIG. 25. Some hypothetical mechanisms for corrin ring formation.

and Rimington [128] determined that the nitrogen and methylene carbon atoms of glycine are utilized in the biosynthesis of prodigiosin but the carboxyl carbon atom is not. They also found that both carbon atoms of acetate are incorporated into the pigment. In 1950, when this work was done, exactly the

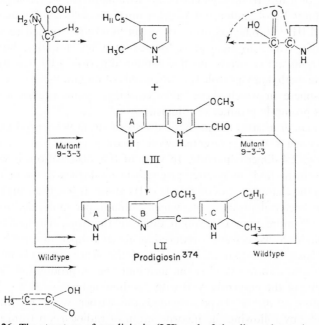

FIG. 26. The structure of prodigiosin (LII) and of the dipyrrole produced by mutant 9—3—3 of *S. marcescens* (LIII).[295] Carbon and nitrogen atoms from glycine, proline, and acetate are used for the synthesis of LII and LIII as shown by solid lines; dashed lines show the presumed utilization of these carbon atoms for the formation of methylamylpyrrole. Carbon atom 2 of proline is incorporated into methylamylpyrrole but not appreciably into LIII. Norprodigiosin, in which a hydroxyl group replaces the methoxal substituent of ring B, has been isolated from an orange mutant of *S. marcescens.*[118]

same information was available about porphyrin biosynthesis and it was concluded that porphyrins and prodigiosin were synthesized from glycine and acetate by the same pathway. In 1960 Marks and Bogorad [187] confirmed that the methylene carbon atom of glycine is incorporated into prodigiosin by *S. marcescens* but found that the bacteria produced only unlabeled pigment when supplied with δ-aminolevulinic acid-5-C^{14}. Furthermore, L-proline was found to be about 2·5 times more efficient a precursor of prodigiosin than glycine. Thus, the formation of prodigiosin provides an example of pyrrole biogenesis not involving δ-aminolevulinic acid or porphobilinogen. Radio-active prodigiosin is also produced from DL-ornithine-2-C[14] but not from DL-glutamic acid-2-C[14] or DL-hydroxyproline-2-C[14].

Santer and Vogel, [322] Wasserman et al., [374] and Rizki [318] have contributed to the discovery that the final step in the formation of prodigiosin is the con-densation of a dipyrrolic segment (LIII) with methylamylpyrrole. S. marces-cens mutant 9-3-3 of Santer and Vogel is normally colorless but accumulates dipyrrole LIII. [158] When cultures of strain 9-3-3 are exposed to vapors of methylamylpyrrole, prodigiosin is formed in a few minutes. Some other mutant strains are colorless, do not contain dipyrrole LIII, but apparently accumulate methylamylpyrrole for, when cells of mutant 9-3-3 are exposed to the atmosphere in which these other colorless strains are growing, 9-3-3 organisms promptly produce prodigiosin.

Wasserman et al. also found that cultures of strain 9-3-3 produced prodi-giosin analogues when presented with pyrroles other than methylamyl-pyrrole, e.g. 2,4-dimethylpyrrole. In view of this observation, it would not be surprising to find, in nature, prodigiosin analogues different from one another in the characteristics of ring C (LII) alone. It has been suggested [158] that some bacterial prodigiosins, which contain, per molecule, five carbon atoms [25, 119] more than LII, might differ in this way. The production of prodigiosin by S. marcescens is reduced at higher temperatures. [301] Williams et al. [300] have found that at least one of the synthetic reactions affected by temperatures above 35°C is the terminal one in prodigiosin formation, the coupling of the bipyrrole A–B with 2,4-dimethylpyrrole. [300]

Shrimpton et al. [262] have extended the earlier work of Marks and Bogorad [187] by following the incorporation of radiocarbon from glycine-2-C[14], proline-1-C[14], and proline-2-C[14] into dipyrrole LIII and into prodigiosin by cultures of mutant 9-3-3 and wild-type S. marcescens, respectively. The following data indicate that the methylamylpyrrolic and "9-3-3 dipyrrolic" segments of prodigiosin are formed via distinct, but not completely inde-pendent, pathways:

(1) The methylene carbon atom of glycine is used about equally in the formation of both parts of the pigment.
(2) The carboxyl carbon atom of proline is also used in the synthesis of both moieties.
(3) Carbon atom 2 of proline, however, is incorporated into the methyl-amylpyrrolic segment, but not appreciably into other portions of the prodigiosin molecule. It is not certain whether the heterocyclic ring of proline is utilized intact, or whether the ring is opened and individual carbon atoms are used for the biogenesis of methylamylpyrrole.

The utilization of the carboxyl, but not the number 2 carbon atom of pro-line, for the formation of the "9-3-3 dipyrrole" suggests that the carboxyl carbon atom may be removed from the amino acid and transferred to some precursor of the dipyrrole.

Investigations of prodigiosin formation may provide information on the metabolism of glycine, proline, and some pyrrolic compounds different from porphobilinogen, but the bearing on porphyrin biosynthesis is not clear, if at all related. It is conceivable, however, that some as yet uncharacterized porphyrins might be formed in part from porphobilinogen and in part from pyrroles synthesized in other ways.

VII. SUMMARY

Facts and speculations on the biogenesis of pyrrolic compounds are summarized in Figs. 5–10, 13, 18–20, 23, 25, and 26.

Many of the enzymes which catalyze reactions between glycine plus succinyl-CoA and heme and chlorophyl a (Figs. 5, 6, and 10) have been identified and partially purified: δ-aminolevulinic synthetase; δ-aminolevulinic acid dehydrase, which catalyzes the formation of porphobilinogen by the condensation of two molecules of δ-aminolevulinic acid; uroporphyrinogen I synthetase, which catalyzes the synthesis of uroporphyrinogen I from porphobilinogen; uroporphyrinogen III cosynthetase, a cocatalyst with uroporphyrinogen I synthetase for the formation of uroporphyrinogen III; uroporphyrinogen decarboxylase, the enzyme responsible for the decarboxylation of uroporphyrinogens to coproporphyrinogens; coproporphyrinogen oxidase, the catalyst for the formation of protoporphyrinogen IX from coproporphyrinogen; and protoporphyrin-iron chelating enzyme (PICE), responsible for the formation of heme from ferrous iron and protoporphyrin IX. However, the mechanism of action of most of these enzymes remains to be determined. In some other areas of porphyrin biogenesis, the nature of the intermediates appears reasonably clear, but direct demonstrations of interconversions have not been made; this is particularly true of steps between protoporphyrin IX and protochlorophyllide a. Finally, the origins of some porphyrins, e.g. bacterial chlorophylls, heme a, can only be speculated on.

In vitro, biliverdin, the open-chained tetrapyrrolic derivative of protoporphyrin IX, is produced during the coupled oxidation of compounds, such as ascorbic acid or hydrazine, and the heme of an intact hemoprotein such as hemoglobin. The α-bridge of the heme (i.e. the methene carbon bridge joining pyrrole residues A and B) is thought to be attacked oxidatively or peroxidatively; intermediates between heme and biliverdin are postulated to be partially oxidized forms such as chole- and oxyheme-globins, which still contain the bridging carbon atom, and verdohemoglobin in which the carbon atom of the α-bridge had been replaced by oxygen. Verdohemoglobin still contains the iron originally present in the hemoprotein. Of the intermediates advanced on the basis of observations of reactions *in vitro* (Fig. 20), only choleglobin has been reported to occur *in vivo*. Hemes of catalase and peroxidases, but not of cytochrome c, have been shown to be degraded to biliverdin *in vitro* under the same conditions as hemoglobin. The mode of breakdown of cytochrome c and some other hemoproteins cannot be guessed at from *in vitro* reactions. Except for some studies on chlorophyllase, which catalyzes the hydrolysis of the phytol from the propionic residue at position 7, nothing is known about the catabolism of chlorophylls.

In mammals, biliverdin is converted to bilirubin in tissues; slices and macerates of organs, such as liver, can catalyze the reaction *in vitro*. A few experiments have now been performed on the production of biliverdin from heme complexes by enzyme preparations *in vitro*. Other transformations, oxidations and reductions at various positions, take place in the gut by bacterial action. Variations in the intestinal flora, as occur upon ingestion of antibiotics, can affect the nature of the bile pigments excreted.

Some plants, notably the blue-green and red algae, and the Cryptomonads, contain functional bile pigments as bile pigment–protein complexes, the phycobiliproteins. These participate in photosynthesis. Some require light for the formation of phycobiliprotein. Two hypothetical biogenetic pathways for plant bile pigment–protein complexes are outlined in Fig. 23.

Vitamin B_{12} contains a tetrapyrrole-like moiety, corrin, related to uroporphyrin III in the character and arrangement of some of the side chains. However, two of the heterocyclic rings of the corrin are joined directly rather than by a carbon bridge as in the porphyrins (Fig. 24). Some of the heterocyclic rings are more reduced than pyrroles. It has been demonstrated that δ-aminolevulinic acid is a precursor of corrin but the intervening steps are unknown. It has been suggested that the corrin of vitamin B_{12} might be derived from a tetrapyrrolic intermediate, formed directly from porphobilinogen, common to both vitamin B_{12} and uroporphyrinogen III. This and other possibilities, e.g. the formation of corrin via a uroporphyrin-type of bile pigment, are summarized in Fig. 25.

Finally, the tripyrrolic microbial pigment, prodigiosin, provides an example of the biogenesis of pyrrolic compounds from substances other than δ-aminolevulinic acid. Proline, or at least some of its carbon atoms, have been shown to be used for prodigiosin biosynthesis by *Serratia marcescens*; δ-aminolevulinic acid is not utilized.

ACKNOWLEDGEMENTS

The preparation of this chapter was supported in part by research grants from the National Institute of Arthritis and Metabolic Diseases, United States Public Health Service, and from the National Science Foundation.

REFERENCES

1. ABBOT, L. D., JR. and RUDOLPH, S. G. *Federation Proc.* **20**, 376 (1961).
2. AIRTH, R. L. and BLINKS, L. R. *Biol. Bull.* **111**, 321 (1956).
3. ALLEN, M. B. *Arch. Mikrobiol.* **32**, 270 (1959).
4. ALLEN, M. B., DOUGHERTY, E. C. and McLAUGHLIN, J. J. A. *Nature* **184**, 1047 (1959).

5. ANAN, F. K. and MANSON, H. S. *J. Biochem.* (*Tokyo*) **49**, 765 (1961).
6. ARIAS, I. M. and LONDON, I. M. *Science* **126**, 563 (1957).
7. BAGDASARIAN, M. *Nature* **181**, 1399 (1958).
8. BAUMGARTEL, J. *Physiologie und Pathologie des Bilirubin Stoffwechsels als Grundlagen der Ikterusforschung.* Georg Thieme Verlag, Stuttgart, 1950.
9. BERNARD, E. and KRAUSS, R. W. *Plant Physiol.* **40**, xliii (1965).
10. BERNHAUER, K., MULLER, O. and WAGNER, F. *Advances Enzymol.* **26**, 233 (1965).
11. BERNS, D. S. *J. Am. Chem. Soc.* **85**, 1676 (1963).
12. BERNS, D. S., CRESPI, H. L. and KATZ, J. J. *J. Am. Chem. Soc.* **85**, 8 (1963).
13. BERNS, D. S., SCOTT, E. and O'REILLY, K. T. *Science* **145**, 1054 (1964).
14. BJÖRN, L. O., SUZUBEI, Y. and NILSSON, J. *Physiol. Plantarum* **16**, 132 (1963).
15. BOARDMAN, N. K. *Biochim. Biophys. Acta* **62**, 63 (1962).
16. BOARDMAN, N. K. *Biochim. Biophys. Acta* **64**, 279 (1962).
17. BOGORAD, L. *Science* **121**, 878 (1955).
18. BOGORAD, L. *Pl. Physiol.* **32**, xl (1957).
19. BOGORAD, L. *J. Biol. Chem.* **233**, 501 (1958).
20. BOGORAD, L. *J. Biol. Chem.* **233**, 510 (1958).
21. BOGORAD, L. *J. Biol. Chem.* **233**, 516 (1958).
22. BOGORAD, L. In *Conference on Hemoglobin*, Natl. Acad. Sci., Natl. Research Council (U.S.) Publ. 557, p. 74 (1958).
23. BOGORAD, L. In *Comparative Biochemistry of Photoreactive Systems*, p. 437, ed. M. B. Allen. Academic Press, N.Y., 1960.
24. BOGORAD, L. In *Physiology and Biochemistry of Algae*, p. 385, ed. R. A. Lewin. Academic Press, N.Y., 1962.
25. BOGORAD, L. *Ann. New York Acad. Sci.* **104**, 676 (1963).
26. BOGORAD, L. In *The Biochemistry of Plant Pigments* (T. W. Goodwin, Ed.). Academic Press, New York, 1965.
27. BOGORAD, L. *Record Chem. Progress* **26**, 1 (1965).
28. BOGORAD, L. In *Subcellular Structure and Function* (J. M. Allen, Ed.). In press.
29. BOGORAD, L. and GRANICK, S. *J. Biol. Chem.* **202**, 793 (1953).
30. BOGORAD, L. and GRANICK, S. *Proc. Natl. Acad. Sci. U.S.* **39**, 1176 (1953).
31. BOGORAD, L. and MARKS, G. S. *J. Biol. Chem.* **235**, 2127 (1960).
32. BONNETT, R., CANNON, J. R., JOHNSON, A. W., SUTHERLAND, I., TODD, A. R. and SMITH, E. L. *Nature* **176**, 328 (1955).
33. BOOIJ, H. L. and RIMINGTON, C. *Biochem. J.* **65**, 4pp. (1957).
34. BRAY, R. and SHEMIN, D. *Biochim. Biophys. Acta* **30**, 647 (1958).
35. BRAY, R. C. and SHEMIN, D. *J. Biol. Chem.* **238**, 1501 (1963).
36. BRODY, M. and EMERSON, R. *Am. J. Bot.* **46**, 433 (1959).
37. BRUNS, G. P. and LONDON, I. M. *Biochem. Biophys. Res. Commun.* **18**, 236 (1965).
38. BULLOCK, E., JOHNSON, A. W., MARKHAM, E. and SHAW, K. B. *J. Chem. Soc.* **287**, 1430 (1958).
39. BURNHAM, B. F. and LASCELLES, J. *Biochem. J.* **87**, 462 (1963).
40. CARPENTER, A. T. and SCOTT, J. J. *Biochem. J.* **71**, 325 (1959).
41. CARPENTER, A. T. and SCOTT, J. J. *Biochem. Biophys. Acta* **52**, 195 (1961).
42. CLEZY, P. S. and BARRETT, J. *Biochem. J.* **78**, 798 (1961).
43. COHEN-BAZIRE, G., SISTROM, W. R. and STANIER, R. *J. Cell. Comp. Physiol.* **49**, 25 (1957).
44. COMFORT, A. *Science* **112**, 279 (1950).
45. COOKSON, G. H. and RIMINGTON, C. *Nature* **171**, 875 (1953).
46. COOKSON, G. H. and RIMINGTON, C. *Biochem. J.* **57**, 476 (1954).
47. CORCORAN, J. W. and SHEMIN, D. *Biochem. Biophys. Acta* **25**, 661 (1957).
48. DE MATTEIS, F., PRIOR, B. E. and RIMINGTON, C. *Nature* **191**, 363 (1961).
49. DERRIEN, E. and TURCHINI, J. *Comp. Rend. Soc. Biol.* **92**, 1030 (1925).
50. DIETZEL, E. *Z. Physiol. Chem.* **284**, 262 (1949).
51. DRABKIN, D. L. and WISE, C. D. *Federation Proc.* (1965).
52. DRESEL, E. I. B. and FALK, J. E. *Nature* **172**, 1185 (1953).
53. DRESEL, E. I. B. and FALK, J. E. *Biochem. J.* **63**, 388 (1956).

54. EMERSON, R. *Ann. Rev. Plant Physiol.* **9**, 1 (1958).
55. EMERSON, R. and LEWIS, C. M. *J. Gen. Physiol.* **25**, 579 (1942).
56. ERIKSSON-QUENSEL, I. B. *Biochem. J.* **32**, 585 (1938).
57. FALK, J. E., DRESEL, E. I. B. and RIMINGTON, C. *Nature* **172**, 292 (1953).
58. FISCHER, H., LAMBRECHT, R. and MITTENZWEI, H. *Z. Physiol. Chem.* **253**, 1 (1938).
59. FISCHER, H. and ORTH, H., *Die Chemie des Pyrroles*. Akademische Verlag, Leipzig. Vol. II. 1, p. 764, 1937; Vol. II. 2 (with A. Stern), p. 478, 1940.
60. FONTAINE, M. *Compt. Rend. Soc. Biol.* **117**, 420 (1934).
61. FONTAINE, M. *Bull. Inst. Oceanog.* Nos. 792, 793 (1941).
62. FONTAINE, M. and RAFFY, A. *Bull. Soc. Zool. France* **61**, 49 (1936).
63. FOULKES, E. C., LEMBERG, R. and PURDOM, P. *Proc. Roy. Soc.* B**138**, 386 (1951).
64. FRENCH, C. S., BROWN, J. S., ALLEN, M. B. and ELLIOTT, R. F. *Carnegie Inst. of Wash. Year Book* **58**, 327 (1959).
65. FRENCH, C. S. and YOUNG, V. K. *J. Gen. Physiol.* **35**, 873 (1952).
66. FRIEDRICH, W. *Biochem. Z.* **342**, 143 (1965).
67. FUJITA, Y. and HATTORI, A. *Plant and Cell Physiol.* **1**, 281 (1960).
68. FUJITA, Y. and HATTORI, A. *Plant and Cell Physiol.* **1**, 293 (1960).
69. FUJITA, Y. and HATTORI, A. *Plant and Cell Physiol.* **3**, 209 (1962).
70. FUJITA, Y. and HATTORI, A. In *Studies on Microalgae and Photosynthetic Bacteria*, p. 431, ed. Japanese Soc. Plant Physiol. (1963).
71. FUJIWARA, T. *J. Biochem.* (*Tokyo*) **43**, 195 (1956).
72. GASSMAN, M. and BOGORAD, L. *Plant Physiol.* **40**, lii (1965).
73. GEORGE, P. and IRVINE, D. H. *Biochem. J.* **52**, 511 (1952).
74. GEORGE, P. and IRVINE, D. H. *Biochem. J.* **55**, 230 (1953).
75. GEORGE, P. and IRVINE, D. H. *Biochem. J.* **58**, 188 (1954).
76. GIBSON, K. D., LAVER, W. G. and NEUBERGER, A. *Biochem. J.* **70**, 71 (1958).
77. GIBSON, K. D., MATTHEW, M., NEUBERGER, A. and TAIT, G. H. *Nature* **192**, 204 (1961).
78. GIBSON, K. D., NEUBERGER, A. and SCOTT, J. J. *Biochem. J.* **61**, 618 (1955).
79. GODNER, T. N., SHLYK, A. A. and ROTFARB, R. M. *Fiziol. Rastenii* **6**, 36 (1959).
80. GOLDBERG, A., RIMINGTON, C. and FENTON, J. L. B. *Proc. Roy. Soc. London*, Ser. B, **143**, 257 (1953).
81. GOLDSTEIN, G. W. and LESTER, R. *Soc. for Exp. Biol. and Med.* **117**, 681 (1964).
82. GOODWIN, R. H. and OWENS, O. H. *Pl. Physiol.* **22**, 197 (1947).
83. GRANICK, S. *J. Biol. Chem.* **172**, 717 (1948).
84. GRANICK, S. *J. Biol. Chem.* **175**, 333 (1948).
85. GRANICK, S. *J. Biol. Chem.* **179**, 505 (1949).
86. GRANICK, S. *J. Biol. Chem.* **183**, 713 (1950).
87. GRANICK, S. *Science* **120**, 1105 (1954).
88. GRANICK, S. *J. Biol. Chem.* **232**, 1101 (1958).
89. GRANICK, S. *Plant Physiol.* **34**, xviii (1959).
90. GRANICK, S. *J. Biol. Chem.* **236**, 1168 (1961).
91. GRANICK, S. *J. Biol. Chem.* **238**, PC2248 (1963).
92. GRANICK, S. and BOGORAD, L. *J. Am. Chem. Soc.* **75**, 3610 (1953).
93. GRANICK, S., BOGORAD, L. and JAFFE, H. *J. Biol. Chem.* **202**, 801 (1953).
94. GRANICK, S. and GILDER, H. *Advances in Enzymol.* **7**, 305 (1947).
95. GRANICK, S. and SANO, S. *Federation Proc.* **20**, 376 (1961).
96. GRANICK, S. and URATA, G. *J. Biol. Chem.* **238**, 821 (1963).
97. GRAY, C. H. *The Bile Pigments*, 142 pp. Methuen, London, 1953.
98. GRAY, C. H. *Bile Pigments in Health and Disease*. Charles C. Thomas, Springfield, Ill. (1961).
99. GRAY, C. H. and HOLT, L. B. *J. Biol. Chem.* **169**, 235 (1947).
100. GRAY, C. H. and NICHOLSON, D. C. *Nature* **180**, 336 (1957).
101. GRAY, C. H., KELLY, M. and MOSES, V. *Nature* **190**, 1014 (1961).
102. GRAY, C. H., NICHOLSON, D. C. and NICOLAUS, R. A. *Nature* **181**, 183 (1958).
103. GRINSTEIN, M., KAMEN, M. D., and MOORE, C. U. *J. Biol. Chem.* **174**, 767 (1948).
104. GRODSKY, G. M. and CARBONNE, J. U. *J. Biol. Chem.* **226**, 449 (1957).
105. GUSTAFSON, B. E. and LANKE, L. S. *J. Exptl. Med.* **112**, 975 (1960).

106. HAEGER-ARONSON, B. *Acta Pharmacol. et Toxicol.* **18**, 1965 (1961).
107. HALLDAL, P. *Physiol. Plantarum* **11**, 401 (1958).
108. HAMMEL, C. L. and BESSMAN, S. P. *Arch. Biochem. Biophys.* **110**, 622 (1965).
109. HATTORI, A. and FUJITA, Y. *J. Biochem. (Tokyo)* **46**, 521 (1959).
110. HATTORI, A. and FUJITA, Y. *J. Biochem. (Tokyo)* **46**, 633 (1959).
111. HATTORI, A. and FUJITA, Y. *J. Biochem. (Tokyo)* **46**, 903 (1959).
112. HATTON, A. and FUJITA, Y. *J. Biochem. (Tokyo)* **49**, 1259 (1959).
113. HATTON, A. CRESPI, H. L. and KATZ, J. *J. Biochem.* **4**, 1255 (1965).
114. HAWKINS, W. B. and WHIPPLE, G. H. *Am. J. Physiol.* **122**, 418 (1938).
115. HAXO, F. T. and BLINKS, L. R. *J. Gen. Physiol.* **33**, 389 (1950).
116. HAXO, F. T. and FORK, D. C. *Nature* **184**, 1051 (1959).
117. HAXO, F. T., Ó'HEOCHA, C. and NORRIS, P. *Arch. Biochem. Biophys.* **54**, 162 (1955).
118. HEARN, W. R., WORTHINGTON, R. E., BURGUS, R. C. and WILLIAMS, R. P. *Biochem. Biophys. Res. Commun.* **17**, 517 (1964).
119. HEATH, H. and HOARE, D. S. *Biochem. J.* **72**, 14 (1959).
120. HEINRICH, H. E. (Ed.) "*Vitamin* B12 *and Intrinsic Factor*, 2nd European Symposium". 798 pp. Ferdinand Enke Verlag, Stuttgart, 1962.
121. HEMMINGSEN, D. In *Physiology and Biochemistry of Plastids* (T. W. Goodwin, Ed.). Academic Press, London. In Press.
122. HENDRICKS, S. B. and BORTHWICK, H. A. In *Biochemistry of Plant Pigments*, pp. 519, ed. T. W. Goodwin, Pergamon Press, London (1964).
123. HIGUCHI, M., GOTO, K., FUJIMOTO, M., NAMIKO, O. and KIKUCHI, G. *Biochem. Biophys. Acta* **95**, 94 (1965).
124. HOARE, D. S. and HEATH, H. *Biochem. J.* **73**, 679 (1959).
125. HODGKIN, D. C., PICKWORTH, J., ROBERTSON, J. H., TRUEBLOOD, K. N., PROSEN, R. J. and WHITE, J. G. *Nature* **176**, 325 (1955).
126. HOLDEN, M. *Photochem. Photobiol.* **2**, 175 (1963).
127a. HOLT, A. S. In *The Biochemistry of Plant Pigments* (T. W. Goodwin, Ed.). Academic Press, New York, 1965.
127b. HOLT, A. S. and HUGHES, D. W. *J. Am. Chem. Soc.* **83**, 499 (1961).
128. HUBBARD, R. and RIMINGTON, C. *Biochem. J.* **46**, 220 (1950).
129. IODICE, A. A., RICHERT, D. A. and SCHULMAN, M. P. *Federation Proc.* **17**, 248 (1958).
130. JACKSON, A. H. and MACDONALD, S. F. *Can. J. Chem.* **35**, 715 (1957).
131. JONES, O. T. G. *Biochem. J.* **86**, 429 (1963).
132. JONES, O. T. G. *Biochem. J.* **89**, 182 (1963).
133. JONES, R. F. and BLINKS, L. R. *Biol. Bull.* **112**, 363 (1957).
134. KAZIRO, K. and KIKUCHI, G. *J. Biochem. (Tokyo)* **38**, 213 (1951).
135. KAZIRO, K., KIKUCHI, G. and HANAOKA, C. *J. Biochem. (Tokyo)* **42**, 423 (1955).
136. KAZIRO, K., TSUSHIMA, K. and UCHIMURA, F. *J. Biochem. (Tokyo)* **44**, 575 (1957).
137. KAZIRO, K., KIKUCHI, G., OGAWA, T. and YAMADA, M. *J. Biochem. (Tokyo)* **40**, 205 (1953).
138. KENCH, J. E. *Biochem. J.* **51**, 443 (1952).
139. KENCH, J. E. *Biochem. J.* **52**, xxvii (1952).
140. KENCH, J. E. *Biochem. J.* **56**, 669 (1954).
141. KENCH, J. E., GARDIKAS, C. and WILKINSON, J. F. *Biochem. J.* **47**, 129 (1950).
142. KIKUCHI, G. and TOMIMURA, T. *J. Biochem. (Tokyo)* **41**, 503 (1954).
143. KIKUCHI, G., KUMAR, A., TALMADGE, P. and SHEMIN, D. *J. Biol. Chem.* **233**, 1214 (1958).
144a. KIMMEL, J. R. and SMITH, E. L. *Bull. Soc. Chim. Biol.* **40**, 2049 (1958).
144b. KLATSKIN, G. *Ann. Rev. Med.* **12**, 211 (1961).
145. KOWALSKI, E., DANCEWICZ, A. M. and SZOT, Z. *Bull. Acad. Polon. Sci. Biol.* **5**, 223 (1957).
146. KOWALSKI, E., DANCEWICZ, A. M., SZOT, Z., LIPINSKI, B. and ROSIEK, O. *Acta Biochemica Polonica* **6**, 257 (1959).
147. KRASNOUSKY, A. A. and KOSOBUTSKAYA, L. M. *Dokl. Akad. Nauk, S.S.R.* **85**, 177 (1952).
148. LABBE, R. *Biochim. Biophys. Acta* **31**, 589 (1959).

149. LABBE, R. F. *Arch. Biochem. Biophys.* **92**, 373 (1961).
150. LABBE, R. and HUBBARD, N. *Biochim. Biophys. Acta* **41**, 185 (1960).
151. LABBE, R. and HUBBARD, N. *Federation Proc.* **20**, 376 (1961).
152. LABBE, R. F., ZASKE, M. R. and ALDRICH, R. A. *Science* **129**, 1741 (1959).
153. LARSEN, H. *Kgl. Norska Videnskab. Selskabs Skrifter* **1**, 1 (1953).
154. LASCELLES, J. *Biochem. J.* **62**, 78 (1956).
155. LASCELLES, J. *Biochem. J.* **66**, 65 (1957).
156. LASCELLES, J. *J. Gen. Microbiol.* **23**, 487 (1960).
157. LATHE, G. H. and WALKER, M. *Biochem. J.* **70**, 705 (1958).
158. LAVER, W. G., NEUBERGER, A. and SCOTT, J. J. *J. Chem. Soc.* 1474 (1959).
159. LAVER, W. G., NEUBERGER, A. and SCOTT, J. J. *J. Chem. Soc.* 1483 (1959).
160. LEDERER, E. and HUTTRER, C. *Trav. Membres Soc. Chim. Biol.* **24**, 1055 (1942).
161. LEMBERG, R. *Biochem. J.* **29**, 1322 (1932).
162. LEMBERG, R. *Biochem. J.* **29**, 1322 (1935).
163. LEMBERG, R. *Australian J. Exptl. Biol. Med. Sci.* **21**, 239 (1943).
164. LEMBERG, R. *Rev. Pure and Applied Chem.* **6**, 1 (1956).
165. LEMBERG, R. and BADER, G. *Liebigs Ann. Chem.* **505**, 151 (1933).
166. LEMBERG, R., CORTIS-JONES, B. and NORRIE, M. *Biochem. J.* **32**, 149 (1938).
167. LEMBERG, R., CORTIS-JONES, B. and NORRIE, M. *Biochem. J.* **32**, 171 (1938).
168. LEMBERG, R. and LEGGE, J. W. *Hematin Compounds and Bile Pigments*, p. 749. Interscience Publ., New York, 1949.
169. LEMBERG, R., LEGGE, J. W. and LOCKWOOD, W. H. *Nature* **142**, 148 (1938).
170. LEMBERG, R., LEGGE, J. W. and LOCKWOOD, W. H. *Biochem. J.* **35**, 328 (1941).
171. LEMBERG, R., LEGGE, J. W. and LOCKWOOD, W. H. *Biochem. J.* **35**, 339 (1941).
172. LEMBERG, R., LOCKWOOD, W. H. and LEGGE, J. W. *Biochem. J.* **35**, 363 (1941).
173. LEMBERG, R. and WYNDHAM, R. A. *Biochem. J.* **30**, 1147 (1936).
174. LESTER, R. and SCHMID, R. *New Engl. J. Med.* **270**, 779 (1964).
175. LEVERE, R. D. and GRANICK, S. *Proc. Natl. Acad. Sci. U.S.* **54**, 134 (1965).
176. LIRO, J. I. *Ann. Acad. Scient. Fenn. Ser. A*1 I:1 (1909).
177. LITTLE, H. N. and KELSEY, M. I. *Federation Proc.* **23**, 223 (1964).
178. LOEFFLER, J. E. *Carnegie Inst. of Wash. Year Book* **54**, 159 (1955).
179. LONDON, I. M. and WEST, R. *J. Biol. Chem.* **184**, 359 (1950).
180. LONDON, I. M., WEST, R., SHEMIN, D. and RITTENBERG, D. *Federation Proc.* **7**, 169 (1948).
181. LONDON, I. M., WEST, R., SHEMIN, D. and RITTENBERG, D. *J. Biol. Chem.* **184**, 351 (1950).
182. LONDON, I. M., WEST, R., SHEMIN, D. and RITTENBERG, D. *J. Biol. Chem.* **184**, 365 (1950).
183. LOWRY, P. T. ZEIGLER, N. R., CARDINAL, R. and WATSON, C. J. *J. Biol. Chem.* **208**, 543 (1954).
184. LUBIMENKO, M. V. *Revue Gén. de Botanique* **40**, 88 (1928).
185. MADSEN, A. *Physiol. Plantarum* **15**, 593 (1962).
186. MADSEN, A. *Physiol. Plantarum* **15**, 815 (1962).
187. MARKS, G. S. and BOGORAD, L. *Proc. Natl. Acad. Sci. U.S.* **46**, 25 (1960).
188. MATHEWSON, J. A. and CORWIN, A. H. *J. Am. Chem. Soc.* **83**, 135 (1961).
189. MAUZERALL, D. *J. Am. Chem. Soc.* **82**, 2605 (1960).
190. MAUZERALL, D. and GRANICK, S. *J. Biol. Chem.* **232**, 1141 (1958).
191. MAYER, H. *Planta* **11**, 294 (1930).
192. MCSWINNEY, R. R., NICHOLAS, R. E. H. and PRUNTY, F. T. G. *Biochem. J.* **46**, 147 (1950).
193. METZNER, P. *Ber. Deut. Botan. Ges.* **40**, 125 (1922).
194. MIYAKOSHI, T. and KIKUCHI, G. *Tohoku J. Exptl. Med.* **79**, 199 (1963).
195. MONTEVERDE, N. A. and LUBIMEUKO, W. *Biol. Centralblatt* **31**, 449 (1911).
196. MUIR, H. M. and NEUBERGER, A. *Biochem. J.* **45**, 163 (1949).
197. MUIR, H. M. and NEUBERGER, A. *Biochem. J.* **47**, 97 (1950).
198. MYERS, J. and KRATZ, W. A. *J. Gen. Physiol.* **39**, 11 (1955).
199. NAKAJIMA, H. *J. Biol. Chem.* **238**, 3797 (1963).

200. NAKAJIMA, H., TAKEMURA, T. and NAKAJIMA, O. *J. Biol. Chem.* **238**, 3784 (1963).
201. NAKAJIMA, O. *Proc. Japan Acad.* **40**, 576 (1964).
202. NEMETH, A. M., RUSSEL, C. S. and SHEMIN, D. *J. Biol. Chem.* **229**, 415 (1957).
203. NEUBERGER, A. *Biochem. J.* **78**, 1 (1961).
204. NEUBERGER, A. and TAIT, G. *Biochem. J.* **90**, 607 (1964).
205. NEUBERGER, A. and TURNER, J. M. *Biochem. Biophys. Acta* **67**, 345 (1963).
206. NEVE, R. A., LABBE, R. F. and ALDRICH, R. A. *J. Am. Chem. Soc.* **78**, 691 (1956).
207. NICHOLANS, R. A., NICOLLETTI, R. and ARCAMONE, F. *Ricera Sci.* **28**, 2314 (1958).
208. NICHOLS, K. E. and BOGORAD, L. *Nature* **188**, 870 (1960).
209. NICHOLS, K. and BOGORAD, L. *Bot. Gaz.* **124**, 85 (1962).
210. NISHIDO, G. and LABBE, R. *Biochim. Biophys. Acta* **31**, 519 (1959).
211. Ó'CARRA, P. Doctoral Thesis. The National University of Ireland (1962).
212. Ó'CARRA, P. and Ó'HEOCHA, C. *Phytochem.* **4**, 635 (1965).
213. Ó'CARRA, P., Ó'HEOCHA, C. and CARROLL, D. M. *Biochem.* **3**, 1343 (1964).
214. OCKNER, R. K. and SCHMID, R. *Nature* **189**, 499 (1961).
215. Ó'HEOCHA, C. In *Comparative Biochemistry of Photoreactive Systems*, 437 pp., ed. M. B. Allen. Academic Press, 1960.
216. Ó'HEOCHA, C. *Biochemistry* **2**, 375 (1963).
217. Ó'HEOCHA, C. In *Biochemistry of Plant Pigments*, ed. T. W. Goodwin, p. 175. Pergamon Press, London (1964).
218. Ó'HEOCHA, C. *Ann. Rev. Pl. Physiol.* **16**, 415 (1965).
219. Ó'HEOCHA, C. and Ó'CARRA, P. *J. Am. Chem. Soc.* **83**, 1091 (1961).
220. Ó'HEOCHA, C., Ó'CARRA, P. and MITCHELL, D. *Proc. Roy. Irish Acad.* **63** (B), 191 (1964).
221. Ó'HEOCHA, C. and RAFTERY, M. *Nature* **184**, 1049 (1959).
222. OKAY, S. *Nature* **155**, 635 (1944).
223. OSTROW, J. D. and SCHMID, R. *J. Clin. Invest.* **42**, 1286 (1962).
224. OYAMA, H., SUGITA, Y., YONEYAMA, Y. and YOSHIKAYA, H. *Biochim. Biophys. Acta* **47**, 413 (1961).
225. PAPPENHEIMER, A. M., JR. *J. Biol. Chem.* **167**, 251 (1947).
226. PATTERSON, D. S. P. *Biochem. J.* **76**, 189 (1960).
227. PETRYKA, Z., NICHOLSON, D. C. and GRAY, C. H. *Nature* **194**, 1047 (1962).
228. PORRA, R. J. and FALK, J. E. *Biochem. Biophys. Res. Comm.* **5**, 179 (1961).
229. PORRA, R. J. and FALK, J. E. *Biochem. J.* **90**, 69 (1964).
230. PORRA, R. J. and JONES, O. T. G. *Biochem. J.* **87**, 181 (1963).
231. PORRA, R. J. and JONES, O. T. G. *Biochem. J.* **87**, 186 (1963).
232. PORRA, R. J. and ROSS, B. D. *Biochem. J.* **94**, 557 (1965).
233. RADIN, N. S., RITTENBERG, D. and SHEMIN, D. *J. Biol. Chem.* **184**, 745 (1950).
234. RADIN, N. S., RITTENBERG, D. and SHEMIN, D. *J. Biol. Chem.* **184**, 755 (1950).
235. RAFTERY, M. A. and Ó'HEOCHA, C. *Biochem. J.* **94**, 166 (1965).
236. RAPOPORT, H. and HOLDEN, K. G. *J. Am. Chem. Soc.* **82**, 5510 (1960).
237. RIMINGTON, C. and BOOIJ, H. C. *Biochem. J.* **65**, 3p (1957).
238. RIMINGTON, C. and MILES, P. A. *Biochem. J.* **50**, 202 (1951).
239. RIZKI, M. T. M. *Proc. Natl. Acad. Sci. U.S.* **40**, 1057 (1954).
240. ROBINSON, R. *The Structural Relations of Natural Products.* Oxford Univ. Press, London and New York, 1955.
241. SACHS, P. *Klin. Wochschr.* **10**, 1123 (1931).
242. SANO, S. and GRANICK, S. *J. Biol. Chem.* **236**, 1173 (1961).
243. SANTER, U. V. and VOGEL, H. *J. Biochim. Biophys. Acta* **19**, 578 (1956).
244. SCHAEFFER, P. *Biochim. Biophys. Acta* **9**, 362 (1952).
245. SCHMID, R. (1960). In *The Metabolic Basis of Inherited Diseases* (J. B. Stanburg, Ed.), pp. 939–1012. McGraw-Hill, New York (1960).
246. SCHMID, R., DIAMOND, I., HAMMAKER, L. and GUNDENON, C. *Nature* **206**, 1041 (1965).
247. SCHMID, R., HAMMAKER, L. and AXELROD, J. *Arch. Biochem. Biophys.* **70**, 285 (1957).
248. SCHMID, R. and SCHWARTZ, S. *Proc. Soc. Exp. Biol. Med.* **81**, 685 (1952).
249. SCHMID, R. and SHEMIN, D. *J. Am. Chem. Soc.* **77**, 506 (1955).
250. SCHULMAN, M. P. and RICHERT, D. A. *J. Biol. Chem.* **226**, 181 (1957).

312   LAWRENCE BOGORAD AND ROBERT F. TROXLER

251. SCHWARTZ, H. C., HILL, R. C., CARTWRIGHT, G. E. and WINTROBE, M. M. *Federation Proc.* **18**, 545 (1959).
252. SCHWARTZ, S., IKEDA, K., MILLER, I. M. and WATSON, C. J. *Science* **129**, 40 (1959).
253. SHEMIN, D. and KUMIN, S. *J. Biol. Chem.* **198**, 827 (1952).
254. SHEMIN, D. and RITTENBERG, D. *J. Biol. Chem.* **166**, 621 (1946).
255. SHEMIN, D. and RITTENBERG, D. *J. Biol. Chem.* **166**, 627 (1946).
256. SHEMIN, D. and RUSSEL, C. S. *J. Am. Chem. Soc.* **76**, 4873 (1953).
257. SHEMIN, D., RUSSEL, C. S. and ABRAMSKY, T. *J. Biol. Chem.* **215**, 613 (1955).
258. SHEMIN, D. and WITTENBERG, J. *J. Biol. Chem.* **192**, 315 (1951).
259. SHIBATA, K. *J. Biochem. (Tokyo)* **44**, 147 (1957).
260. SHIMIZU, S. and TAMAKI, E. *Arch. Biochem. Biophys.* **102**, 152 (1963).
261. SHLYK, A. A., KALER, V. L., VLASENOK, L. I. and GAPONENKO, V. I. *Photochem. Photobiol.* **2**, 129 (1963).
262. SHRIMPTON, D. M., MARKS, G. S. and BOGORAD, L. *Biochim. Biophys. Acta* **71**, 408 (1963).
263. SIEGELMAN, H. W. and BUTLER, W. L. *Ann. Rev. Pl. Physiol.* **16**, 383 (1965).
264. SIEGELMAN, H. W. and HENDRICKS, S. B. *Federation Proc.* **24**, 863 (1965).
265. SINGLETON, J. W. and LASTER, L. *Federation Proc.* **20**, 247 (1961).
266. SJÖSTRAND, T. *Acta Physiol. Scand.* **24**, 314 (1951).
267. SJÖSTRAND, T. *Acta Physiol. Scand.* **26**, 328 (1952).
268. SJÖSTRAND, T. *Acta Physiol. Scand.* **26**, 334 (1952).
269. SMITH, J. H. C. *J. Am. Chem. Soc.* **69**, 1492 (1947).
270. SMITH, J. H. C. *Arch. Biochem. Biophys.* **19**, 449 (1948).
271. SMITH, J. H. C. *Carnegie Inst. Wash. Year Book* **51**, 151 (1952).
272. SMITH, J. H. C. In *Comparative Biochemistry of Photoreactive Systems*, 437 pp., ed. M. B. Allen. Academic Press, 1960.
273. SMITH, J. H. C. and BENITEZ, A. *Plant Physiol.* **29**, 135 (1954).
274. SMITH, J. H. C. and COOMBER, J. *Carnegie Inst. Wash. Year Book* **59**, 325 (1960).
275. SMITH, J. H. C. and FRENCH, C. S. *Ann Rev. Plant Physiol.* **14**, 181 (1963).
276. SMITH, J. H. C. and KUPKE, D. W. *Nature* **178**, 751 (1956).
277. SNYDER, A. L. and SCHMID, R. *J. Lab. Clin. Med.* **65**, 817 (1965).
278. SOLOMON, H. M. and FIGGE, F. H. *Proc. Soc. Exptl. Biol. Med.* **100**, 583 (1959).
279. SOLOMON, H. M. and FIGGE, F. H. *Proc. Soc. Exptl. Biol. Med.* **105**, 484 (1960).
280. STANIER, R. Y. and SMITH, J. H. C. *Biochim. Biophys. Acta* **41**, 478 (1960).
281. SUDYINA, E. G. *Photochem. Photobiol.* **2**, 181 (1963).
282. SVEDBERG, T. and KATSURAI, T. *J. Am. Chem. Soc.* **51**, 3573 (1929).
283. TAIT, G. H. and GIBSON, K. D. *Biochim. Biophys. Acta* **52**, 614 (1961).
284. TALMAN, E. L., LABBE, R. F. and ALDRICH, R. A. *Arch. Biochem. Biophys.* **66**, 289 (1957).
285. TOOHEY, J. I. *Proc. Natl. Acad. Sci. U.S.* **54**, 934 (1965).
286. TOWNSLEY, P. M. and NIELANDS, J. B. *J. Biol. Chem.* **224**, 695 (1957).
287. TROXLER, R. F. Ph.D. Thesis, University of Chicago (1965).
288. TROXLER, R. F. and BOGORAD, L. *Plant Physiol.* **41**, 491 (1966).
289. TROXLER, R. F. and BOGORAD, L. In *Physiology and Biochemistry of Plastids*, ed. T. W. Goodwin. Academic Press, London. In press.
290. TSUSHIMA, K., KIKUCHI, G., MAKITA, M., UCHIMURA, F. and KAZIRO, K. *J. Biochem. (Tokyo)* **44**, 525 (1957).
291. URATA, G. and GRANICK, S. (1963) *J. Biol. Chem.* **238**, 811.
292. VAUGHN, M. H. *Federation Proc.* **22**, 581 (1963).
293. VIRGIN, H. *Physiol. Plantarum* **13**, 155 (1960).
294. WALBRIDGE, C. T. M.S. Thesis, University of Chicago (1963).
295. WASSERMAN, H. H., McKEON, J. F. and SANTER, U. V. *Biochem. Biophys. Res. Comm.* **3**, 146 (1960).
296. WATSON, C. J. *J. Biol. Chem.* **200**, 691 (1953).
297. WATSON, C. J., CAMPBELL, M. and LOWRY, P. T. *Proc. Soc. Exptl. Biol.* **49**, 636 (1958).
98. WEILAND, H. and TARTTER, A. *Ann.* **545**, 197 (1940).

299. WESTALL, R. G. *Nature* **170**, 614 (1952).
300. WILLIAMS, R. P., GOLDSCHMIDT, M. E. and GOTT, C. L. *Biochem. Biophys. Res. Commun.* **19**, 177 (1965).
301. WILLIAMS, R. P. and GOTT, C. L. *VIII International Cong. Microbiol.* p. 24 (1962).
302. WILLSTÄTTER, R. and STALL, A. *Investigations on Chlorophyll*, 1913. English translation: by F. M. Schertz and G. R. Mertz, 385 pp. Science Press, Lancaster, Penna., 1928.
303. WISE, C. D. and DRABKIN, D. L. *Federation Proc.* **23**, 223 (1964).
304. WITTENBERG, J. *Nature* **184**, 876 (1959).
305. WITTENBERG, J. and SHEMIN, D. *J. Biol. Chem.* **178**, 47 (1949).
306. WITTENBERG, J. and SHEMIN, D. *J. Biol. Chem.* **185**, 103 (1950).
307. WOLFF, J. B. and PRICE, L. *Arch. Biochem. Biophys.* **72**, 293 (1957).
308. YAMAGUCHI, M., NAKAJIMA, H. and YAMAOKA, K. *Proc. Japan Acad.* **37**, 584 (1961).

CHAPTER 6

THE BIOGENESIS OF CARBOHYDRATES

PETER BERNFELD

Bio-Research Institute, Cambridge, Massachusetts

CONTENTS

I. INTRODUCTION 316
II. THE GENERAL PATTERNS OF CARBOHYDRATE BIOGENESIS 319
III. PHOTOSYNTHESIS 320
   A. *The photosynthesis cycle of carbon reduction* 321
   B. *Redistribution of carbon in photosynthetic carbohydrate* 326
   C. *The role of chlorophyll in photosynthesis* 327
   D. *The role of ferredoxin and other electron transfer substances in photosynthesis* 329
   E. *Factors governing photosynthesis* 331
   F. *Energy changes during photosynthesis* 333
   G. *Appearance of glycolic acid during photosynthesis* 335
   H. *Other pathways of CO_2 fixation* 336
IV. THE BIOGENESIS OF GLUCOSE-6-PHOSPHATE IN NONPHOTO-SYNTHETIC TISSUES 336
   A. *From the metabolic pool* 336
   B. *Formation of glucose-6-phosphate from glucose* 340
V. THE FORMATION OF "PRIMARY-HYDROXYL PHOSPHATES" OF OTHER SUGARS 343
   A. *Phosphorylation of monosaccharides other than glucose by ATP* 343
   B. *Intramolecular phosphate transfer* 345
   C. *Epimerization of sugar phosphates* 345
   D. *Ketose–aldose isomerization* 346
   E. *Decarboxylation of 6-phospho-aldohexonic acids* 347
   F. *Aldol condensation of sugar phosphates* 348
   G. *Other mechanisms* 350
   H. *Amination and N-acetylation of sugar phosphates* 351
VI. ALDOSE-1-PHOSPHATES 352
VII. NUCLEOSIDE DIPHOSPHATE SUGARS 355
   A. *Formation of UDP-sugars* 355
   B. *Sugar derivatives of other nucleoside diphosphates* 356
   C. *Epimerization of nucleoside diphosphate sugars* 358

D. *Dehydrogenation of nucleoside diphosphate sugars*   363
E. *Decarboxylation of nucleoside diphosphate sugars*   364
F. *Nucleoside diphosphates of dideoxyhexoses*   364
G. *Nucleoside diphosphates of other sugars*   366
VIII. THE FORMATION OF GLYCOSIDIC BONDS   368
A. *The glycosyl donor*   369
B. *The bond broken*   383
C. *The glycosyl acceptor and primer*   384
D. *The saccharide synthesized*   389
   Disaccharides: 1. Sucrose; 2. Trehalose; 3. Maltose; 4. Isomaltose; 5. Lactose; 6. Other disaccharides   389
   Trisaccharides: 7. Raffinose; 8. Melezitose; 9 Other trisaccharides   394
   Glucans: 10. Amylose, amylopectin and glycogen; 11. Dextran; 12. Cellulose; 13. Other glucans   397
   Other N-free polysaccharides: 14. Mannans and galactans; 15. Fructans; 16. Pentosans; 17. Methylpentose-containing polysaccharides; 18. Polyuronosides; 19. N-free heteropolysaccharides   416
   S-Free mucopolysaccharides: 20. Chitin; 21. Hyaluronic acid; 22. Bacterial cell wall polysaccharides   424
   Glycosides and other complex carbohydrates: 23. Glycosides; 24. Glucosiduronic acids; 25. Glycolipids; 26. Glycoproteins; 27. Nucleosides, nucleotides, nucleic acids   434
IX. THE FORMATION OF SULFOPOLYSACCHARIDES   439
X. THE REDUCING MONOSACCHARIDES   444
A. *Occurrence and formation*   444
B. *Transformations involving nonphosphorylated sugars*   445
XI. SUGAR ALCOHOLS   450
XII. SUMMARY AND CONCLUSIONS   453
REFERENCES   454

I. INTRODUCTION

The wide distribution of cellulose and starch throughout the vegetable kingdom makes glucose, the basic unit of these two polysaccharides, the most abundantly occurring organic compound in nature. Many other carbohydrates are known to exist in animal and plant tissues, as well as in fungal cells and in their exudates. They include a great variety of polysaccharides, ranging in molecular weight from a few thousands to many millions, large numbers of oligo-, di-, and monosaccharides and their derivatives, and complex carbohydrates, like glycosides, glycoproteins, bacterial cell wall substances, the nucleic acids, etc.

A classification of carbohydrates, with the specific purpose of its serving as a guide in the following discussion of the biogenetic aspects of carbohydrates, is presented in Table 1.

TABLE 1. CARBOHYDRATES OCCURRING IN NATURE†

I. SIMPLE CARBOHYDRATES
  A. *Monosaccharides*
      1. Hexoses: D-Glucose
                                           D-Mannose
                                           D-Fructose
      2. Pentoses: L-Arabinose
                                           L-Xylulose
      3. Heptoses: D-Sedoheptulose
                                           Mannoheptulose

  B. *Disaccharides*
      1. Nonreducing disaccharides: Sucrose
                                           Trehalose
      2. Reducing disaccharides: Maltose
                                           Isomaltose
                                           Lactose

  C. *Trisaccharides*
      1. Nonreducing trisaccharides: Raffinose
                                           Melezitose
                                           Glucosyl sucrose
                                           Galactosyl sucrose
                                           Fructosyl sucrose
      2. Reducing trisaccharides: Panose
                                           Isomaltotriose
                                           Galactosyl lactose

  D. *Polysaccharides containing no amino sugar*
      1. Glucans: Amylose
                                           Amylopectin
                                           Glycogen
                                           Dextrans
                                           Cellulose
                                           Laminaran
      2. Fructans: Inulin
                                           Phlean
                                           Levans
      3. Galactan
      4. Pentosans: Xylan
                                           Araban
                                           Hemicellulose constituents
      5. Polyuronides: Pectin
                                           Alginic acid
      6. Heteroglycans: Bacterial polysaccharides

  † No attempt is made to provide a complete list of all carbohydrates occurring in nature.
  A few synthetic carbohydrates are included in this table and in the present discussion, since they have been obtained through imitation *in vitro* of biosynthetic processes.

E. *Mucopolysaccharides*
   1. Neutral mucopolysaccharides: Chitin
   2. Simple acid mucopolysaccharides: Hyaluronic acid
                                     Bacterial polysaccharides
   3. Sulfomucopolysaccharides: Heparin
                                     Chondroitin sulfates
                                     Keratosulfate

II. COMPLEX CARBOHYDRATES
  A. *Glycosides*

  B. *Glycoproteins*

  C. *Glycolipids*

  D. *Nucleosides, Nucleotides, Nucleic Acids*

In all but the monosaccharides, glycosidic linkages are responsible for the connection between the monomeric sugar units, or between the carbohydrate and the noncarbohydrate moiety. This feature entails a considerable analogy in structure and properties among all carbohydrates and is reflected in marked analogies of their biological formation. The biogenesis of carbohydrates follows, therefore, certain general patterns common to that whole class of important organic compounds.

A vast number of scientists, including most of the great leaders in biochemistry, have participated in the assiduous and thorough study of the metabolism and biochemical behavior of carbohydrates which has produced, during the past few decades, considerable insight into the mechanisms underlying the biological synthesis of simple and complex saccharides. The biogenesis of all carbohydrates reverts originally to the process of photosynthesis, and is also intimately linked to those now classic sequences of reactions, known as the tricarboxylic acid cycle, the glycolytic cycle and others, that is the intracellular transformations of sugars and other foodstuffs under aerobic and anaerobic conditions. In addition, the thermodynamic concept of changes in free energy occurring during biological transformations has provided a valuable basis for the understanding of the principles governing the formation of natural compounds in general, and of carbohydrates in particular.

Considering the overall picture of carbohydrate biogenesis, one common feature may easily be recognized. In all cases so far investigated, the establishment of glycosidic bonds is preceded by the formation of the individual monomeric sugars. The latter are synthesized first and become available in the form of high-energy derivatives. Only the introduction of sulfate into sulfomucopolysaccharides may occur after the formation of the polysaccharide has already been completed. In the case of complex carbohydrates, the biosynthesis of the noncarbohydrate moiety (the aglycon) is also completed before it is coupled with the carbohydrate through glycosidic bonds. In contrast, the purine and to some extent the pyrimidine moieties of nucleotides are formed from fragments which already contain the sugar part.

Glucose-6-phosphate is well known to hold a key position in the biosynthesis of the high-energy carbohydrate precursors. Thus, Fig. 1 shows a generalized picture of carbohydrate biogenesis. At the present state of our knowledge, this overall scheme of carbohydrate formation has been well established in the case of a number of disaccharides, polysaccharides and

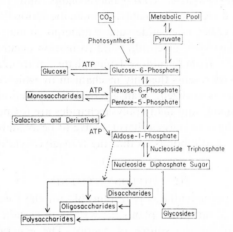

FIG. 1. General patterns of carbohydrate biogenesis.

glycosides. One can predict that much new information on biogenetic mechanisms of many other carbohydrates will become available during the coming years, and it appears likely that these mechanisms will more or less closely follow the general patterns outlined in Fig. 1.

II. THE GENERAL PATTERNS OF
CARBOHYDRATE BIOGENESIS

The simplified scheme of carbohydrate biogenesis in Fig. 1 consists of four distinct main steps. The first represents the formation of glucose-6-phosphate either through the photosynthetic pathway, or through phosphorylation of glucose, or through a reaction mechanism leading from the metabolic pool over pyruvate along a pathway which is essentially the reversal of glycolysis. The same step leads further to other hexose-6-phosphates, to N-acetylhexosamine-6-phosphates, or to pentose-5-phosphates. Glucose-6-phosphate has been represented as the key substance because it is the product of the photosynthetic process, although the direct phosphorylation of other monosaccharides by specific kinases is also known to occur.

The second step consists in the transformation of the sugar-6-phosphates (or pentose-5-phosphates) into the corresponding aldose-1-phosphates; the 1-phosphate esters of galactose, N-acetylgalactosamine and galacturonic acid may arise directly from the monosaccharides. The formation of aldose-1-phosphates is followed by the third step during which aldose-1-phosphate reacts with nucleotide triphosphate, e.g. UTP, to yield high-energy nucleotide diphospho-sugars, e.g. UDP-sugars. At this level, UDP-glucose acts as the parent compound for a number of other UDP-sugars (UDP-galactose, UDP-glucuronate, UDP-D-xylose, UDP-galacturonate, and UDP-L-arabinose) which are formed, directly or indirectly, through the action of various enzymes on UDP-glucose. Other nucleotide sugars undergo similar transformations.

Finally, in the last step, glycoside bond formation occurs either from the nucleotide-sugars, or from the aldose-1-phosphates, or from a combination of the two. This step represents the only mechanism by which *de novo* synthesis of glycoside bonds is realized. Transglycosylation reactions are known to occur in many systems, and many polysaccharides are formed in such a way. In this case, di-, oligo- or polysaccharides have to be available first, however, to provide the glycosidic bonds so that the transglycosylation may proceed.

III. PHOTOSYNTHESIS

The process of photosynthesis is responsible for the formation of carbohydrate from CO_2 in all green plants, as well as in certain purple bacteria; light serves thereby as the source of energy. The general photosynthetic reaction is represented by the equation:

$$nCO_2 + nH_2O + light \rightarrow (CH_2O)_n + nO_2 \qquad (1)$$

The sequence of chemical reactions leading to this overall equation is now well understood. The work of Calvin,[128, 129] Calvin et al.[65, 66, 590, 629] and of Weissbach, Horecker and Hurwitz[974] has demonstrated that D-ribulose-1, 5-diphosphate is the primary acceptor of CO_2. The mechanism of this first step of the assimilation of CO_2, studied in experiments with $C^{14}O_2$ and cell-free enzyme extracts from the unicellular green, freshwater alga, *Chlorella*, is shown in Fig. 2. It results in the formation of phosphoglyceric acid whereby

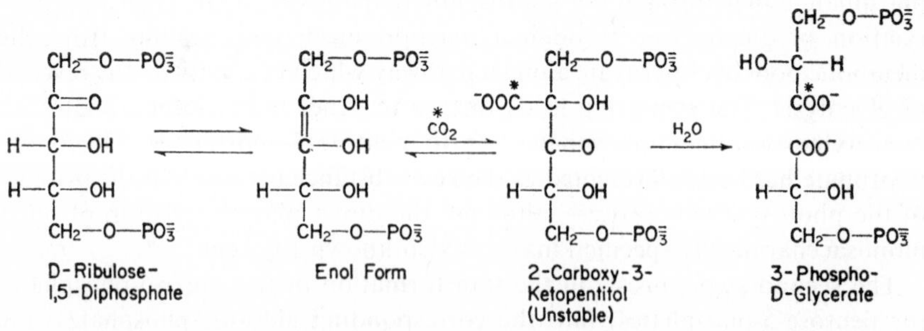

FIG. 2. Photosynthetic fixation of CO_2 by D-ribulose-1,5-diphosphate.

CO_2 condenses with the enol form of diphosphoribulose to give an unstable intermediate product, 2-carboxy-3-ketopentitol which, in turn, is split into two molecules of phosphoglycerate. Another intermediate, 2-carboxy-4-ketopentitol has also been encountered, [629] but its role is not yet understood. The enzyme, or the system of enzymes, catalyzing the reaction, shown in Fig. 2, is called *diphosphoribulose carboxylase* or *carboxydismutase*, and has been found in a large variety of photosynthetic tissues, [745, 975, 750, 446] where it is associated with the chloroplasts.

In *tetragonia expansa* an enzyme —Mg^{++}—CO_2 complex is formed just prior to the carboxylation of ribulose diphosphate, and the magnesium ion is considered the true or natural activator of the carboxydismutase system. [731] This enzyme —Mg^{++}—CO_2 complex reacts possibly with the ribulose diphosphate to form a second intermediate complex, enzyme —Mg^{++}—CO_2—ribulose diphosphate, which then yields two moles of phosphoglyceric acid, Mg^{++} and enzyme. [9]

In *chlorella pyrenoidosa* both triose phosphate and phosphoglyceric acid are formed by fixation of CO_2 on ribulose diphosphate, [68] but experiments with C^{14}-ribulose diphosphate and sonically ruptured spinach chloroplast showed that the product of the primary carboxylation reaction in this system in the presence of light is only phosphoglyceric acid. [694]

In addition to phosphoglyceric acid, a number of other phosphorylated sugars have been identified to occur during the earliest stages of photosynthesis by Calvin et al. [129, 66] and by Horecker et al., [422, 423] such as D-ribulose-5-phosphate, D-fructose-6-phosphate, D-glucose-6-phosphate, and D-sedoheptulose-7-phosphate. Most of these substances have subsequently been found to be intermediates in a series of enzymically catalyzed reactions which lead to the restoration of ribulose-diphosphate. The sequence of reactions through which triose phosphate is transformed to ribulose-1,5-diphosphate is known as the photosynthesis cycle, which is closely related to the pentose phosphate cycle.

A. *The Photosynthesis Cycle of Carbon Reduction*

At least ten different enzymes have been recognized to participate in the transformation of CO_2 to glucose-6-phosphate, with the simultaneous regeneration of ribulose-1,5-diphosphate. This cycle of reactions corresponds to the general equation:

$$6(CO_2) + 6(\text{ribulose-1,5-diphosphate}) \xrightarrow{\text{ATP}}$$
$$\text{glucose-6-phosphate} + 6(\text{ribulose-1,5-diphosphate}) \qquad (2)$$

and has been investigated in experiments in which either *Chlorella* or *Scenedesmus* algae, or green leaves, were exposed to bright incandescent light in the presence of labeled carbon dioxide, for short periods of time.

M

322   PETER BERNFELD

Examination of the radiocarbon distribution in the resulting reaction products has led to the carbon-reduction cycle, shown in Fig. 3. [129, 66, 67, 130, 872]

The formation of 3-phosphoglycerate from CO_2 and ribulose-1,5-diphosphate by the *carboxydismutase* system, according to the reactions shown in

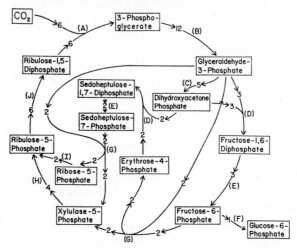

FIG. 3. Photosynthetic carbon reduction cycle. The arrows denote the directions in which the reactions proceed during the regeneration of ribulose-1,5-diphosphate in the photosynthesis cycle. They do not relate to equilibrium states. The numbers near the arrows indicate the moles of substrate undergoing transformation, or the moles of products being formed in each reaction; the letters refer to the enzymes which catalyze the reaction, i.e. A, carboxydismutase; B, D-glyceraldehyde-3-phosphate dehydrogenase; C, triose phosphate isomerase; D, aldolase; E, fructose-1,6-diphosphatase; F, phosphohexose isomerase; G, transketolase; H, phosphoketopentose epimerase; I, phosphoribose isomerase; J, D-ribulose-5-phosphate kinase.

Fig. 2, is followed by the reduction of phosphoglycerate to glyceraldehyde-3-phosphate by *D-glyceraldehyde-3-phosphate dehydrogenase* (Fig. 4). This step involves the same sequence of reactions known from the glycolytic cycle. It thus requires ATP, and 1,3-diphosphoglycerate is an intermediate product. While most glycolytic reactions require DPNH for this reduction,

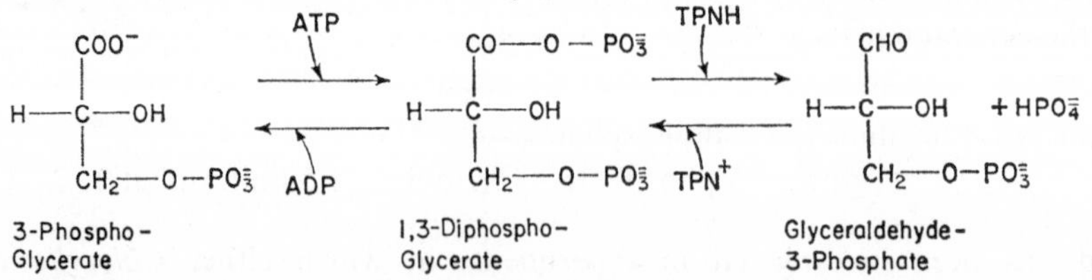

FIG. 4. Reaction catalyzed by D-glyceraldehyde-3-phosphate dehydrogenase (enzyme B in Fig. 3).

photosynthetic tissues generally contain TPNH. [24, 289] Hagerman and Ar-non [345] observed that the dehydrogenase from seeds and seedlings, germin-ated in the dark, require DPNH whereas a TPNH-requiring enzyme appears after the seedlings had been exposed to light.

The formation of dihydroxyacetone phosphate by *triose phosphate isomerase*, of fructose-1,6-diphosphate by *aldolase*, of fructose-6-phosphate by *fructose-1,6-diphosphatase*, and of glucose-6-phosphate by *phosphohexose isomerase*, according to the reactions shown in Fig. 5, is catalyzed by the

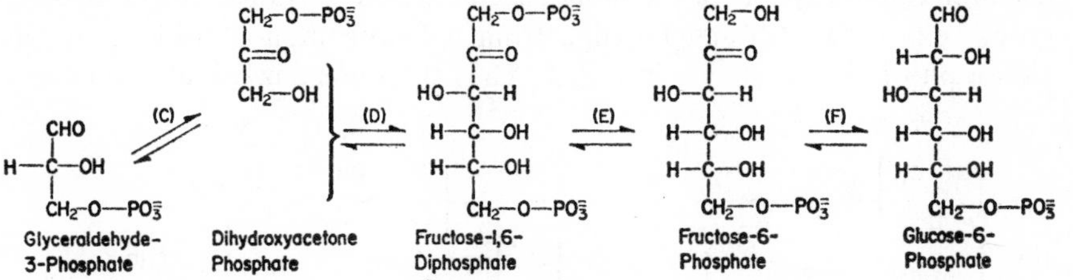

FIG. 5. Intermediate reactions common to photosynthetic and glycolytic cycles, although proceeding in inverse directions. The enzymes carry the same designa-tions as in Fig. 3.

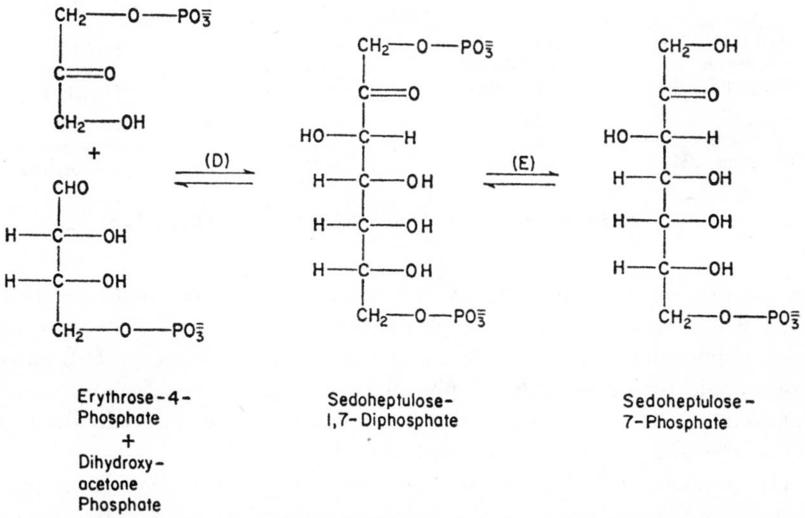

FIG. 6. Formation of sedoheptulose-7-phosphate from erythrose-4-phosphate and phosphodihydroxyacetone by aldolase (D) and fructose-1,6-diphosphatase (E).

same enzymes known to perform these transformations in the glycolytic cycle. Their presence in photosynthetic tissues has been demonstrated in many instances, i.e. triose phosphate isomerase in pea seeds, [912] aldolase in peas and various other plants, [888, 911] fructose-1,6-diphosphatase in spinach leaves[750] and phosphohexose isomerase in higher plants.[348, 859] Racker and Schroeder[755] described two different phosphatases from spinach; whereas each splits phosphate in fructose-1,6-diphosphate, one of the two has also been observed to attack the phosphate at carbon atom-1 in sedoheptulose-1,7-diphosphate, according to Fig. 6.

The enzyme *transketolase*, which catalyzes the condensation of fructose-6-phosphate with glyceraldehyde-3-phosphate to yield xylulose-5-phosphate and erythrose-4-phosphate, is not specific for this reaction alone. This enzyme has been found capable of the more general action of transferring a glycolyl group, e.g. carbon atoms 1 and 2 from a ketose monophosphate, to an aldose phosphate as shown in Fig. 7. Thus the same enzyme also catalyzes

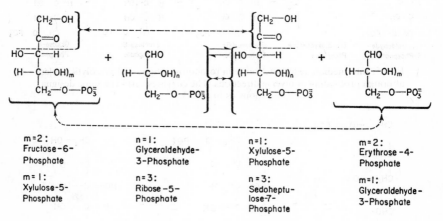

m = 2 :	n = 1 :	n = 1 :	m = 2 :
Fructose-6-Phosphate	Glyceraldehyde-3-Phosphate	Xylulose-5-Phosphate	Erythrose-4-Phosphate
m = 1 :	n = 3 :	n = 3 :	m = 1 :
Xylulose-5-Phosphate	Ribose-5-Phosphate	Sedoheptulose-7-Phosphate	Glyceraldehyde-3-Phosphate

FIG. 7. Reaction catalyzed by transketolase (enzyme G in Fig. 3).

the reaction of D-sedoheptulose-7-phosphate with glyceraldehyde-3-phosphate which yields two pentose phosphates, i.e. xylulose-5-phosphate and ribose-5-phosphate. A direct interconversion of two molecules of D-fructose-6-phosphate to sedoheptulose-7-phosphate and D-xylulose-5-phosphate by transketolase has also been reported.[97] Transketolase has been found in spinach[423] and has been crystallized from yeast.[752, 753]

The condensation of erythrose-4-phosphate with dihydroxyacetone phosphate to sedoheptulose-1,7-diphosphate is catalyzed by *aldolase* (see Fig. 6). This reaction is analogous to the condensation of two triose phosphates to fructose-1,6-diphosphate (Fig. 5).

The three pentose phosphates are in equilibrium with each other through the action of two enzymes, as shown in Fig. 8. *Phosphoketopentose epimerase* catalyzes the isomerization at carbon atom 3 in xylulose-5-phosphate and ribulose-5-phosphate, and *phosphoribose isomerase* is responsible for the interconversion between ribulose-5-phosphate and ribose-5-phosphate. The former enzyme is widely distributed in green plants, and the latter has been shown to exist in alfalfa [36] and spinach. [428]

The photosynthetic cycle of reactions is closed by the phosphorylation of D-ribulose-5-phosphate to ribulose-1,5-diphosphate through the action of the enzyme *D-ribulose-5-phosphate kinase*, which has been isolated [428] and

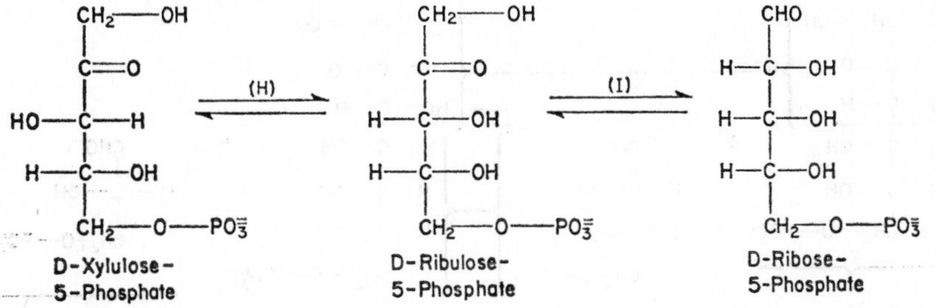

```
   CH2——OH              CH2———OH                   CHO
    |                     |                          |
    C==O                  C==O              H——C——OH
    |         (H)         |          (I)             |
HO——C——H   ————————   H——C——OH   ————————   H——C——OH
    |         ————         |          ————            |
 H——C——OH              H——C——OH              H——C——OH
    |                     |                          |
   CH2——O——PO3⁼          CH2———O———PO3⁼     CH2——O——PO3⁼

  D-Xylulose-            D-Ribulose-                D-Ribose-
  5-Phosphate           5-Phosphate                5-Phosphate
```

FIG. 8. Interconversion between pentose phosphates by the enzymes, H, phosphoketopentose epimerase, and I, phosphoribose isomerase.

crystallized [751] from spinach leaves. The phosphate donor for this reaction is ATP, as shown in Fig. 9.

An alternate pathway of carbon transformation during the regeneration of ribulose diphosphate, not included in the reaction cycle of Fig. 3, is the condensation of fructose-6-phosphate with erythrose-4-phosphate to sedo-heptulose-7-phosphate and glyceraldehyde-3-phosphate, [590] as shown in Fig. 10. In analogy to transketolase, *transaldolase* is a transferring enzyme.

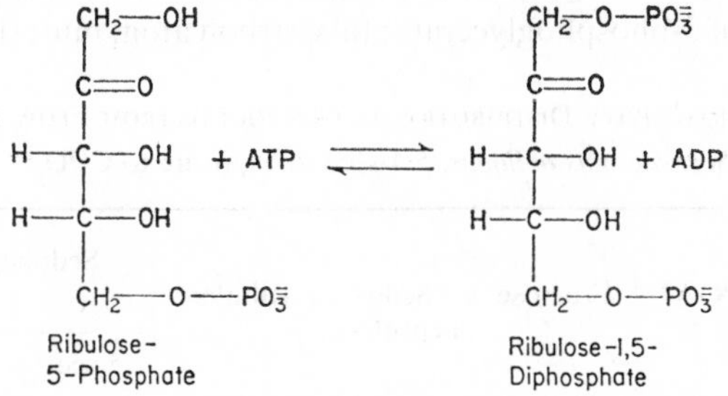

```
   CH2——OH                      CH2—O—PO3⁼
    |                            |
    C==O                         C==O
    |                            |
 H——C——OH  + ATP  ⇌  H——C——OH  + ADP
    |                            |
 H——C——OH                     H——C——OH
    |                            |
   CH2——O——PO3⁼                 CH2——O——PO3⁼

   Ribulose-                    Ribulose-1,5-
   5-Phosphate                  Diphosphate
```

FIG. 9. Reaction catalyzed by D-ribulose-5-phosphate kinase (enzyme J in Fig. 3).

D-Ribose-5-phosphate may replace D-erythrose-4-phosphate in this reaction, with the result of the formation of octulose-8-phosphate [754] which is not, however, a normal intermediate in the photosynthesis cycle. Transaldolase can also utilize L-sorbose-6-phosphate or erythrulose as the donor of the dihydroxyacetone moiety, and L-glyceraldehyde-3-phosphate or formalde-hyde as the acceptor aldehyde. [939]

The mechanism of action of transaldolase consists in the formation of an enzyme-dihydroxyacetone intermediate which subsequently reacts with erythrose-4-phosphate or another acceptor of dihydroxyacetone (e.g. ribose-5-phosphate) to yield sedoheptulose-7-phosphate (or octulose-8-phosphate). [421, 420]

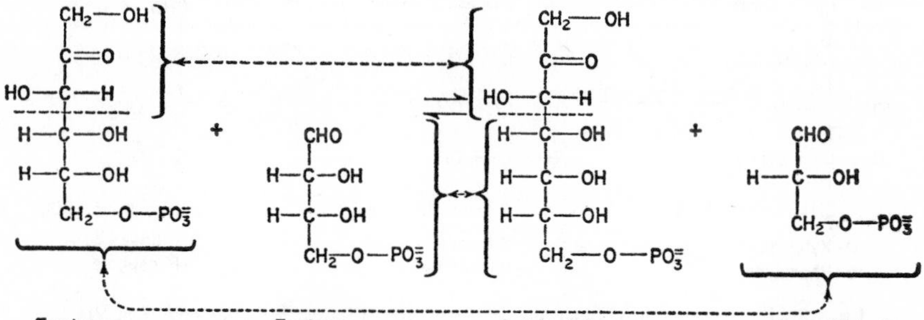

Fructose-6-Phosphate   Erythrose-4-Phosphate   Sedoheptulose-7-Phosphate   Glyceraldehyde-3-Phosphate

FIG. 10. Alternative pathway of sedoheptulose-7-phosphate formation by transaldolase, not included in Fig. 3.

Other phosphorylated carbohydrates were found to arise during photosynthesis, such as 2-keto-3,6-diphospho-L-gulonic acid which was isolated from *Chlorella pyrenoidosa*. [631]

B. *Redistribution of Carbon in Photosynthetic Carbohydrate*

It is apparent from Fig. 2 that the carbon from CO_2 will appear in the carboxyl group of 3-phosphoglycerate; this carbon atom must then be assumed

TABLE 2. RADIOACTIVITY DISTRIBUTION IN COMPOUNDS FROM FLOW EXPERIMENT
Scenedesmus obliquus, 5·4-second exposure to $C^{14}O_2$[†]

Carbon atom Sugar, PGA[‡]	PGA[‡]	Fructose	Sedo-heptulose	Ribulose	Sedoheptulose from soybean	
					5 sec	0·4 sec
1, carboxyl	82	3	2	11	2	assumed 0
2, alpha	6	3	2	10	4	assumed 0
3, beta	6	43	28	69	30	33
4,		42	24	5	29	8
5,		3	27	3	31	49
6,		3	2		4	assumed 0
7,					2	assumed 0

† According to Bassham and Calvin, [66] *The Path of Carbon in Photosynthesis*. © 1957. Prentice-Hall, Inc., by permission.
‡ Phosphoglyceraldehyde.

to get into position 1 of 3-phosphoglyceraldehyde (Fig. 4), and further in positions 3 and 4 of the hexose phosphates (Fig. 5). That this is actually the case has been demonstrated by experiments with $C^{14}O_2$, as seen from Table 2.[66] These results have been obtained with very short exposure times, where most of the reaction products were assumed to originate directly from $C^{14}O_2$ and unlabeled ribulose diphosphate previously existing in the plant tissue. Longer exposure times must necessarily result in the gradual increase of C^{14} in regenerated pentose phosphates, and hence also in the subsequently formed hexose phosphate. Thus, a triose phosphate with the radiocarbon distribution shown in Fig. 11 will result after a single full cycle,[66] logically leading to

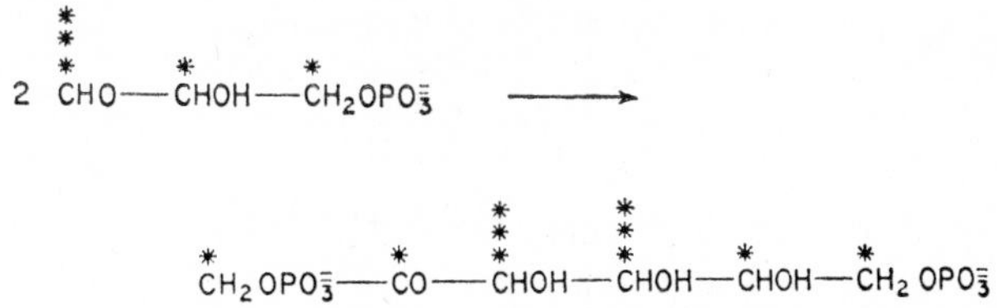

$$2 \quad \overset{*}{\underset{*}{\overset{*}{C}}}HO \!\!-\!\! \overset{*}{C}HOH \!\!-\!\! CH_2OPO_3^= \qquad \longrightarrow$$

$$CH_2OPO_3^= \!\!-\!\! \overset{*}{C}O \!\!-\!\! \overset{*}{\underset{*}{C}}HOH \!\!-\!\! \overset{*}{\underset{*}{C}}HOH \!\!-\!\! \overset{*}{C}HOH \!\!-\!\! \overset{*}{C}H_2 OPO_3^=$$

FIG. 11. Distribution of radiocarbon originating from $C^{14}O_2$ after one full photosynthesis cycle.

hexose phosphate containing higher amounts of C^{14} until, after many recycling periods, an even distribution of radiocarbon throughout the hexose molecule occurs.

C. *The Role of Chlorophyll in Photosynthesis*

The photosynthetic regeneration of TPNH from TPN^+, formed during the hydrogenation of 3-phosphoglycerate, has been considered to be accomplished through the action of α-lipoic acid, as represented in Fig. 12. This is

FIG. 12. Hydrogenation of α-lipoic acid in the presence of light.

the reaction which actually requires light quanta and which takes place in the presence of chlorophyll.

Green plants contain chlorophyll *a* and *b*; see Fig. 13. Chlorophyll *b* differs from chlorophyll *a* only in having a —CHO group on carbon 3 instead of the —CH$_3$ group. Purple bacteria, the *Thiorhodaceae* and *Athiorhodaceae* species contain a single bacteriochlorophyll[937] which differs from chlorophyll *a* by the structure of the pyrrole ring I, as shown in Fig. 14; in addition, bacteriochlorophyll contains two additional hydrogen atoms in the porphyrin structure, probably in ring II, i.e. it has one double bond less than chlorophyll *a* (see also Chapter 5).

Calvin [129] interprets the sequence of events in this way: the light quantum is absorbed by the chlorophyll, giving excited chlorophyll. The excited chlorophyll molecule then goes through some sort of energy transformation,

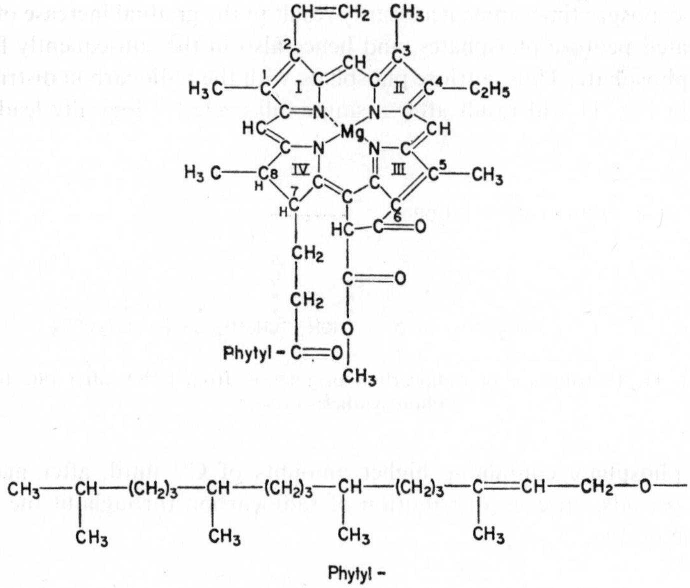

FIG. 13. Structure of chlorophyll *a*.

as yet unknown. This results in a situation which ultimately uses that energy to split the water molecule into a reducing agent, which can be used to reduce the glyceric acid, and some sort of oxidizing agent which eventually can rearrange itself and come out as oxygen gas.

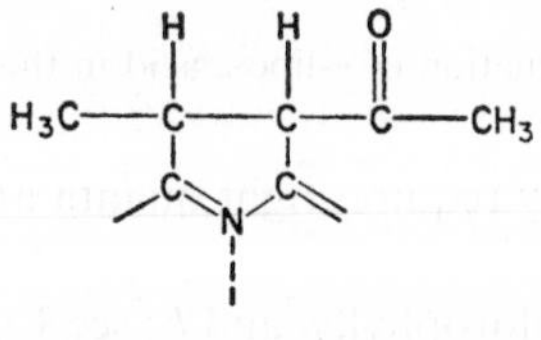

FIG. 14. Pyrrol ring I in chlorophyll of purple bacteria.

Taking into account the requirement of ATP and the regeneration of TPNH from TPN$^+$ with the ultimate liberation of oxygen, the photosynthetic process can now be represented by the scheme shown in Fig. 15.

When all the intermediate products, which are regenerated in cyclic reaction sequences, are left out, the reactions in Fig. 15 can be summarized by the equation:

$$6\ CO_2 + 23H_2O + 18\ ATP \xrightarrow{\text{light}} 1\ \text{(glucose-6-phosphate)} + 18\ ADP + 17\ P_i + 6\ O_2 \qquad (3)$$

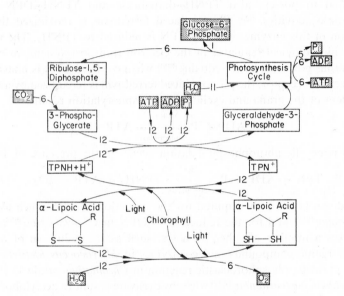

FIG. 15. The photosynthetic process. The shaded areas denote substances which, according to this scheme, are not recycled.

The regeneration of ATP from ADP is largely accomplished in the reactions associated with oxidations in the citric acid cycle.

Spinach chloroplasts contain two kinds of particles with different proportions of chlorophyll a and chlorophyll b.[95] They can be separated from one another because of their unlike solubilities in digitonin solutions. They have different roles in the light reactions of photosynthesis: the first type of particles has a chlorophyll a/b ratio of ~6; it is more soluble than the other type, causes the reduction of TPN and the oxidation of cytochrome. The less soluble particles have a chlorophyll a/b ratio of ~2; they are responsible for the reduction of cytochrome and the oxidation of water to oxygen.

D. *The Role of Ferredoxin and Other Electron Transfer Substances in Photosynthesis*

Ferredoxin, an iron-containing, nonheme protein, has been found in the chloroplasts of many photosynthetic tissues[899, 900, 26] and has been isolated from *Clostridium pasteurianum*.[627, 628, 935] Crystalline ferredoxin from

C. pasteurianum contains 7 moles of iron, mostly in the ferrous state, and 7 moles of inorganic sulfide per mole of protein; it has a molecular weight of 6000.[560] Ferredoxin is an electron transport factor in the reduction of TPN and is the most electronegative substance in the photosynthetic sequence.[976] It acts with the aid of a flavoprotein enzyme. This enzyme, ferredoxin-TPN reductase, has been crystallized from spinach chloroplasts and found to possess also $TPNH_2$-diaphorase and $TPNH_2$-DPN transhydrogenase activities.[826] Photoreduced ferredoxin is reoxidized through the action of this enzyme, whereby TPN is reduced to $TPNH_2$. The role of TPN as physiological regulator of the electron transport systems in chloroplasts is thus governed by ferredoxin:[900] when oxidized TPN is unavailable as an electron acceptor, the photoreduced ferredoxin is reoxidized by a bound component of the grana and cyclic photophosphorylation results,

$$ADP + P_i \xrightarrow[\text{chloroplasts}]{h\nu} ATP \qquad (4)$$

whereas noncyclic photophosphorylation occurs in the presence of TPN,

$$TPN + ADP + P_i \xrightarrow[\text{chloroplasts}]{h\nu} TPNH_2 + ATP + \tfrac{1}{2}O_2. \qquad (5)$$

Ferredoxin is not only required for the reduction of TPN, such as in *C. pasteurianum*[934] and for the reduction of DPN in *C. acidi-urici*,[933] but it also serves a number of other purposes, such as the reduction of organic acids, inorganic compounds and coenzymes in *Micrococcus lactilyticus*[984] and the pyruvate phosphoroclastic reaction in *Chromatium* strain D,[73] and in *Clostridium pasteurianum*,[627] whereby pyruvate is split to acetylphosphate, CO_2 and H_2.

A reaction scheme of the electron transport system of photosynthesis in green plants, involving ferredoxin, chlorophyll, cytochrome, and several other factors, has been derived from the analysis of short-term absorption changes measured by sensitive flash photometry,[993, 632] as seen in Fig. 16.

$\tfrac{1}{2}TPN + $ ferredoxin$^- \rightleftharpoons \tfrac{1}{2}TPNH_2 + $ ferredoxin

ferredoxin $+$ substance $Z^- \rightleftharpoons$ ferredoxin$^- +$ substance Z

substance Z $+$ chlorophyll $a_I \overset{h\nu_I}{\rightleftharpoons}$ substance $Z^- +$ chlorophyll a_I^+

chlorophyll $a_I^+ +$ cytochrome $\rightleftharpoons$ chlorophyll $a_I +$ cytochrome$^+$

cytochrome$^+ +$ substance E $\rightleftharpoons$ cytochrome $+$ substance E$^+$

substance E$^+ +$ plastoquinone II$^- +$ ADP $+$ P$_i \rightleftharpoons$ substance E $+$ plastoquinone II $+$ ATP

plastoquinone II $+$ substance Y $\overset{h\nu_{II}(\text{chlorophyll } a)}{=\!=\!=\!=\!=\!=\!=}$ plastoquinone II $+$ substance Y$^+$

substance Y$^+ + \tfrac{1}{2}H_2O \rightarrow$ substance Y $+ \tfrac{1}{4}O_2 + H^+$

FIG. 16. Reaction scheme of the electron-transport system of photosynthesis in green plants, derived from analysis by sensitive flash photometry.[993]

In addition to chlorophyll a_I, cytochrome and three unspecified substances, Z, E and Y, are involved in this scheme, as well as plastoquinone II. Evidence for the participation of chlorophyll b (chlorophyll a_{II}) in the electron transport during photosynthesis of green plants has also been obtained. [791]

A water-soluble, heat-stable factor, phosphodoxin which catalyzes photosynthetic phosphorylation by spinach chloroplasts or by bacterial chromatophores has been isolated from higher plants, algae, flagellate and bacteria. [89] Phosphodoxin may be identical with one of the factors of electron transport mentioned in Fig. 16.

Plastoquinone is either related to, or identical with, a quinone which has been found in spinach leaves and other green tissues. This quinone has coenzyme Q activity and is called coenzyme Q_{254}. [188] It is concentrated in the chloroplasts and chloroplast-containing tissues and is most likely to be involved in photosynthetic electron transport. The chemical structure of the quinone from alfalfa was established by Trenner et al. [922] (see Fig. 17) and was found to be very similar to that established simultaneously by Kofler et al. [493] for a quinone isolated from leaves of the horse chestnut, oak and ginkgo trees (see Fig. 18).

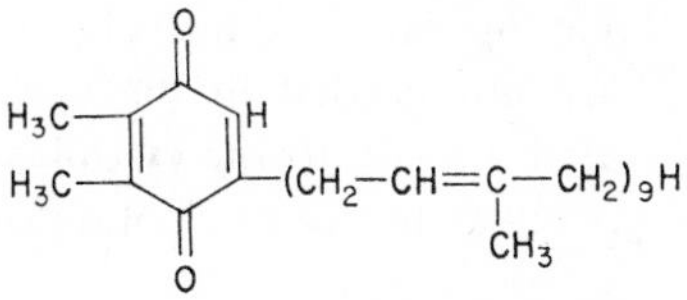

FIG. 17. Quinone isolated from alfalfa. [922]

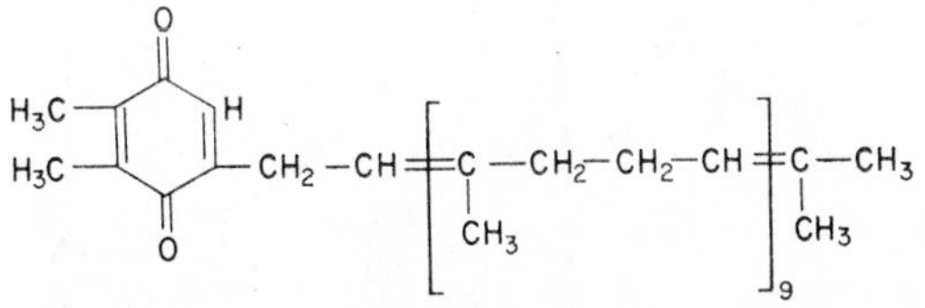

FIG. 18. Quinone isolated from leaves of the horse chestnut, oak, and ginkgo trees. [493]

E. Factors Governing Photosynthesis

Photosynthesis is influenced by various factors, such as light intensity, carbon dioxide pressure, and temperature.

While the respiration of photosynthetic tissue is independent of illumination and light intensity, the photosynthetic process is not. Consequently, the former process is in operation continuously, whereas the latter is governed entirely by, and changes with, the light intensity. Separation of these two processes into "dark" and "light" reactions of the photosynthesis, which normally overlap each other, has induced Warburg[955, 962] to postulate that the oxygen of carbon dioxide is loosened during the dark reaction; the carbonic acid derivative containing the loosened oxygen is probably a peroxide. A separation of the light and dark stages of photosynthesis showed that ADP, P_i and Mg^{++} are required during the latter step and the redox system during the former one, [407] and that the light reaction consists in the reduction of ferredoxin by the chloroplast pigment system, while the dark reaction represents the reduction of TPN by reduced ferredoxin, catalyzed by the TPN reductase in the chloroplasts. [976]

Variations in the light intensity produce differences in the response of photosynthetic processes by spinach chloroplasts, i.e. in the rate of CO_2 fixation, TPN reduction and ATP formation. [928]

The concentrations of intermediate compounds during photosynthesis are subject to considerable variations during light–dark changes. Phosphoglyceric acid and ribulose diphosphate are particularly affected, as can be seen from Fig. 19. It is evident from these results that the formation of phosphoglyceric acid in the photosynthesis cycle is a dark reaction which does not require light energy.

From experiments with spinach leaves it may be concluded that the photosynthetic carbon cycle operates exclusively in the chloroplasts. [375] Sugar phosphates which are not needed in the cyclic regeneration of the CO_2-acceptor are translocated directly to the cytoplasm where they undergo other transformations, e.g. conversion to nucleotide sugars.

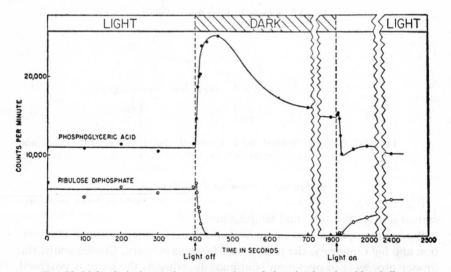

Fig. 19. Light–dark changes in concentrations of phosphoglyceric acid and ribulose diphosphate during photosynthesis, according to Bassham and Calvin, [66] *The Path of Carbon in Photosynthesis.* © 1957. Prentice-Hall, Inc., by permission.

F. Energy Changes During Photosynthesis

The energy expended in keeping the photosynthetic cycle running at a dynamic state has been calculated to be approximately − 120 (kcal) for the transformation of 6 CO_2 to glucose-6-phosphate. This result is obtained when the changes of free energy for each individual step are added up as shown in Table 3. [66]

The overall photosynthetic reduction of carbon dioxide to glucose

$$CO_2 + H_2O \xrightarrow{\text{light}} 1/6\ C_6H_{12}O_6 + O_2 \qquad (6)$$

involves storage of approximately 115 kcal per mole of oxygen; the values reported range from $\Delta F' = +$ 110 kcal to 118 kcal. According to the above calculations, 20 kcal ($\Delta F' = -$ 20 kcal: one-sixth of the 120 kcal computed in Table 3 for six moles of O_2) are expended in the cycle of reactions which involve the condensation of CO_2 with ribulose diphosphate and the regeneration of ribulose diphosphate. The total energy necessary for the photosynthesis of glucose ($-$ 20 $-$ 115 $= -$ 135 kcal) is supplied entirely by two reactions, namely by the oxidation of TPNH to TPN$^+$ furnishing 103 kcal, i.e. 76 per cent of the total energy, and by the hydrolysis of ATP to ADP ($\Delta F' = -$ 32 kcal, 24 per cent). The latter portion is assumed to be derived from respiratory processes not requiring light energy.

In contrast to Calvin who assumes the light-reactions of photosynthesis to be a photolysis of water, Warburg postulates the photolysis of CO_2 as a mechanism of the light stage. [960, 958, 959] He assumes that CO_2 is first activated by the energy of respiration (equation 7) such as phosphorylation. This phase results in a chlorophyll-bound activated CO_2 (equation 8) which can be split by light. Thus, activated CO_2 is reduced to carbohydrate, and O_2 is developed (equation 9).

$$\text{Dark:}\ \tfrac{2}{3}CH_2O\ \text{(carbohydrate)} + \tfrac{2}{3}O_2 = \tfrac{2}{3}H_2CO_3 + 77{,}000\ \text{cal.} \qquad (7)$$

$$\text{Dark:}\ H_2CO_3 + 77{,}000\ \text{cal.} = H_2CO_3^*\ \text{(activated)} \qquad (8)$$

$$\text{Light:}\ H_2CO_3^*\ \text{(activated)} + N_0h\nu = CH_2O\ \text{(carbohydrate)} + O_2 \qquad (9)$$

$$\text{Total:}\ \tfrac{1}{3}H_2CO_3 + N_0h\nu = \tfrac{1}{3}CH_2O\ \text{(carbohydrate)} + \tfrac{1}{3}O_2 \qquad (10)$$

The energy necessary for the oxidation of TPNH to TPN$^+$ by O_2 comes entirely or in part from light. In green plants, the chlorophylls absorb essentially that portion of the light having wave lengths between 660 and 700 mμ, while the remainder of white light is not used as energy source for photosynthesis. In some purple bacteria, however, wave lengths of as high as 900 mμ can be used. [526] At 660 mμ the energy of one light quantum is 43 kcal, and a total of 2·5 to 3 quanta should be necessary, therefore, for the production of one mole of oxygen. The experimental findings concerning the quantum yield of photosynthesis have been subject to considerable variations. Warburg and Burk [956] concluded that four quanta of light are absorbed by *Chlorella* suspensions for each mole of oxygen produced, later work of

TABLE 3. CHANGES IN FREE ENERGIES DURING THE PHOTOSYNTHESIS CYCLE [1]

Reaction shown in figure no. (a)	Product formed [2] (b)	No. of moles formed [3] (c)	$\Delta F'$ (kcal) Per reaction [4] (d)	$\Delta F'$ (kcal) Per complete cycle [5] (e)
2	3-Phosphoglycerate	12	− 8·9	− 53·4
4	Glyceraldehyde-3-phosphate	12	− 1·2	− 14·4
5	Dihydroxyacetone phosphate	5	− 1·3	− 6·5
5	Fructose-1,6-diphosphate	3	− 3·2	− 9·6
5	Fructose-6-phosphate	3	− 4·3	− 12·9
5	Glucose-6-phosphate	1	+ 0·1	+ 0·1
7	Xylulose-5-phosphate Erythrose-4-phosphate	2 [6]	+ 0·4	+ 0·8
6	Sedoheptulose-1,7-diphosphate	2	− 0·6	− 1·2
6	Sedoheptulose-7-phosphate	2	− 4·1	− 8·2
7	Xylulose-5-phosphate Ribose-5-phosphate	2 [6]	+ 1·0	+ 2·0
8	Ribulose-5-phosphate [7]	2	+ 0·4	+ 0·8
8	Ribulose-5-phosphate [8]	4	+ 0·5	+ 2·0
9	Ribulose-1,5-diphosphate	6	− 3·2	− 19·2
	Total [9]			− 119·7

(1) From data presented by Bassham and Calvin. [66]
(2) According to Fig. 3.
(3) During one complete cycle involving 6 moles of CO_2.
(4) Involving the number of moles specified in Figs. 2 to 9.
(5) Involving the transformation of 6 moles of CO_2 to glucose-6-phosphate. The values in column (e) are derived by multiplication of the figures in column (c) with those in column (d), with the exception of the case of 3-phosphoglycerate (first line), where two moles are formed according to Fig. 2, and where (d) is multiplied, therefore, by 6 instead of 12.
(6) Number of moles of each one of the two products formed.
(7) From ribose-5-phosphate.
(8) From xylulose-5-phosphate.
(9) Corresponding to the equation:

$$6 \, CO_2 + 12 \, TPNH + 18 \, ATP + 6 \, H_2O \rightarrow$$
$$\text{glucose-6-phosphate} + 12 \, TPN^+ + 18 \, ADP + 17 \, P_1 + 6 \, O_2$$

Warburg [955] yielded quantum requirements as low as three, and more recently a quantum yield of less than four was found in salad leaves. [961] In contrast, values from eight to ten have been obtained by many other investigators. [746, 280, 240, 90] Warburg explains the differences in quantum yields found by various groups of workers by dissimilarities of the partial CO_2 pressures during their experiments. [957] On the basis of Warburg's data, the efficiency of photosynthesis is, therefore, better than 90 per cent, but less than 30 per cent when one assumes a quantum requirement of eight to ten per mole of oxygen.

G. *Appearance of Glycolic Acid during Photosynthesis*

Glycolic acid accumulation during photosynthesis in barley seedlings [74] and in algae [987, 915] has long been recognized. Low concentrations of CO_2 are particularly conducive for glycolate formation. [914, 742, 985] *Chlorella* cells excrete glycolate if the CO_2 concentration is below 1·5 per cent and the oxygen concentration above 15 per cent. [610] The presence of isonicotinyl-hydrazide stimulated glycolate formation by *Chlorella pyrenoidosa* three-fold. [742] Tolbert [914] and Pritchard *et al.* [742] presume that ribulose diphosphate is the precursor of glycolate, but Bassham and Kirk [69] postulate a metabolic path of glycolic acid production which competes with the formation of ribulose diphosphate. The moiety of the alpha and beta carbons of phosphoglyceric acid may possibly be oxidized to phosphoglycolic acid at some early stage in the formation of phosphoglycerate from CO_2 and ribulose diphosphate.

Glycolate may also be consumed by *Chlorella* if the cells are previously exposed to glycolate in the growth medium or if they are pre-illuminated. [610] This substance is incorporated for the most part into normal intermediates of the carbon reduction cycle without being first converted to CO_2. [131]

In general, Mn^{++} is required for glycolate formation by *Chlorella*. [610] Tanner *et al.* [908] observed that the rate of oxygen development in manganese-deficient algae and aquatic plants was one-eighth of that in non-deficient controls. These authors suggested an alternate pathway for photosynthesis which would require both manganese and chloride. Carbon dioxide would be converted directly to glycolic acid passing through an undefined intermediate (CHO), while the role of manganese would be to liberate oxygen, the metal would thereby alternately exist in the bi- and the trivalent states. The following reaction sequence has been proposed:

$$ADP + P_i \rightarrow ATP + [H] + [OH] \tag{11}$$

$$2\,ADP + 2\,P_i + TPN^+ \rightarrow 2\,ATP + TPNH + H^+ + H_2O + \tfrac{1}{2}\,O_2 \tag{12}$$

$$TPNH + H^+ + HCO_3^- + MnCl^+ \rightarrow [CHO] + TPN^+ + MnCl(OH)_2 \tag{13}$$

$$H^+ + MnCl(OH)_2 \rightarrow MnCl^+ + 1\tfrac{1}{2}\,H_2O + \tfrac{1}{4}\,O_2 \tag{14}$$

$$2\,[CHO] \rightarrow [(CHO)_2] \tag{15}$$

$$[(CHO)_2] \rightarrow CH_2OHCOOH \tag{16}$$

where reaction 11 with suitable cofactors is "cyclic" photophosphorylation and reaction 12 is "non-cyclic" photophosphorylation. [25]

Thirty-one times more C^{14}-glycolate has been found in normal, Mn-containing cells of *Chlorella pyrenoidosa* after exposure to light in the presence of $C^{14}O_2$ than in Mn-deficient cells. [907] This is opposed to only a 2·1 fold increase of sucrose under the same conditions, or to a 1·7 fold increase of alanine, a 2·6 fold of glutamate, etc. While it thus appears that the alternative pathway in the presence of Mn favors the formation of glycolate which does accumulate, 1-C^{14} glycolate has been found on the other hand to be oxidized to glyoxalate:

$$4\,H^+ + 2\,Mn\,(OH)_3 + CH_2OHCOOH \rightarrow$$
$$CHOCOOH + 2\,Mn^{2+} + 6\,H_2O \qquad (17)$$

Although this reaction mechanism is hypothetical, it appears obvious that an alternative cycle does exist.

H. *Other Pathways of CO_2 Fixation*

A different pathway of CO_2 fixation was discovered in spinach and wheat germ. [47] These sources contain an enzyme, phosphopyruvate carboxylase, which catalyzes the reaction:

$$\text{phosphoenolpyruvate (PEP)} + CO_2 + H_2O \rightarrow \text{oxalacetate} + P_i \qquad (18)$$

A similar reaction has also been found to occur in germinating peanut cotyledons. [577] In this instance, the bicarbonate or carbonate ion, rather than CO_2, is the active substrate. Nucleophilic attack of either of these anions on the electrophilic phosphoryl in phosphoenolpyruvate is involved and leads to the formation of oxalacetate, according to equation 18.

Phosphoenolpyruvate can also act as an acceptor for CO_2 in *Propionibacterium shermanii*, although the mechanism of reaction is quite different from that occurring in higher plants. [840] In contrast to the latter reaction, the bacterial CO_2-fixing process requires inorganic phosphate, is reversible and leads to inorganic pyrophosphate as a product of reaction: [839]

$$\text{phosphoenolpyruvate (PEP)} + CO_2 + P_i \rightleftharpoons \text{oxalacetate} + PP_i \qquad (19)$$

Mg^{++} or Mn^{++} is also required. In this bacterial system the reaction catalyzed by phosphoenolpyruvate carboxytransphosphorylase represents the major CO_2-fixing mechanism. It is also the first example of inorganic pyrophosphate serving as a source of high energy phosphate (reverse direction of equation 19).

IV. THE BIOGENESIS OF GLUCOSE-6-PHOSPHATE IN NONPHOTOSYNTHETIC TISSUES

A. *From the Metabolic Pool*

The formation of glucose-6-phosphate in animal tissue and in most microorganisms may be considered to originate from pyruvate. Pyruvate assumes, indeed, a central position in the general metabolic pool of carbon-containing substances, including proteins and fatty acids, since it constitutes a direct link between the glycolytic and the tricarboxylic acid cycles. Thus, any substance which may be metabolized into pyruvate, acetate or an intermediate of the tricarboxylic acid cycle may, therefore, give rise to glucose-6-phosphate. The reactions describing the two cyclic pathways of utmost importance, and their interconversions, that is the tricarboxylic acid and the glycolytic cycles have recently been reviewed by Krebs and Lowenstein, [514] and by Axelrod, [34] respectively.

In liver and kidney, pyruvate is transformed into oxalacetate and phosphoenolpyruvate, via malate, as shown in Fig. 20A. [673, 930] The *"malic enzyme"* is widely distributed in animal tissues, [351, 936] in microorganisms, [761, 499, 942] as well as in roots and even in green leaves of plants, [672, 671, 946] where it might be responsible for the transformation back into carbohydrate of protein or fat, formed originally from photosynthetic carbohydrate. *"Oxalacetate-synthesizing enzyme"* has been found in liver and kidney, [456, 63, 64, 543] and its reaction has been studied by Utter and Kurahashi. [931, 932] This enzyme was observed to require inosine triphosphate (ITP) or guanosine triphosphate (GTP). [48, 518] The diphosphates of these nucleotides resulting during the action of oxalacetate-synthesizing enzyme, may be regenerated by ATP in a reaction catalyzed by the enzyme *nucleoside diphosphokinase*, [513, 76] according to the following equations:

$$IDP + ATP \rightleftharpoons ITP + ADP \tag{20}$$

$$GDP + ATP \rightleftharpoons GTP + ADP \tag{21}$$

Avian liver contains an enzyme, pyruvate carboxylase, which catalyzes the direct formation of oxalacetate from pyruvate, ATP and CO_2. [929] This reaction requires catalytic amounts of acetyl CoA or propionyl CoA and Mg^{++}:

$$\text{pyruvate} + ATP + CO_2 \overset{AcCoA,\ Mg^{++}}{\rightleftharpoons====} \text{oxalacetate} + ADP + P_i. \tag{22}$$

By combining the action of pyruvate carboxylase from rabbit liver or kidney (equation 22) with that of phosphoenolpyruvate carboxykinase (Fig. 20A, enzyme 5), also called oxalacetate synthesizing enzyme, [931] the synthesis *in vitro* of phosphoenolpyruvate was achieved, [471]

$$\text{pyruvate} + ATP + GTP \rightarrow$$
$$\text{phosphoenolpyruvate} + GDP + ADP + P_i \tag{23}$$

In contrast to the above sequence of reactions proceeding in liver and kidney, the phosphorylation of pyruvate in muscle is achieved directly by ATP and is catalyzed by *pyruvate kinase*. According to other reports, even in rat liver there is not a sufficient amount of malic enzyme to account for the four-carbon dicarboxylic acid formation during carbohydrate synthesis from pyruvate, and the direct phosphorylation of pyruvate by ATP prevails. [828] This reaction, seen in Fig. 20B, is well known from the glycolytic cycle where it proceeds, however, in the inverse direction. Direct phosphorylation of pyruvate in muscle by this enzyme was demonstrated by Hiatt et al. [402] These authors transformed pyruvate-2-C^{14} into glycogen by rat diaphragm and found that the glucose units of the glycogen thus formed were labeled in positions 2 and 5.

The transformation of phosphopyruvate into hexose phosphate follows the pathway shown in Fig. 21. This is the well-known reaction sequence of glycolysis, however, in inverse direction. For this reason, some individual reactions of this sequence are only schematically analogous with their glycolytic counterparts. Whereas the phosphorylation of fructose-6-phosphate to fructose-1,6-diphosphate is catalyzed in glycolysis by phosphohexokinase and requires ATP, the inverse reaction is more likely to be a hydrolytic process for which no phosphate acceptor like ADP is necessary, and which is

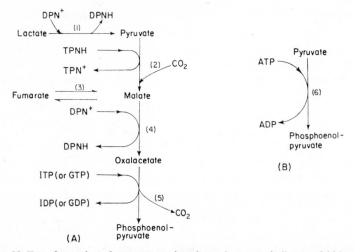

FIG. 20. Transformation of pyruvate to phosphoenolpyruvate in liver and kidney (20A), and in muscle (20B). The following enzymes are involved: (1) lactic dehydrogenase; (2) "malic enzyme"; (3) fumarase; (4) malic dehydrogenase; (5) oxalacetate synthesizing enzyme; (6) pyruvate kinase.

catalyzed by *fructose diphosphatase*. Similarly, the dehydrogenation of 1,3-diphospho-D-glycerate does not necessarily require a phosphate acceptor; this reaction may indeed proceed without ADP whereby inorganic phosphate is formed, as in the photosynthesis cycle.

In plant tissue, labeled pyruvate has been shown to be incorporated into carbohydrate [873, 652] and all three carbons of the pyruvate, in particular carbon atom 3, have been found to contribute to the sugar formation.

The conversion of any intermediate of the tricarboxylic acid cycle to carbohydrate can easily be explained by the formation of phosphoenolpyruvate

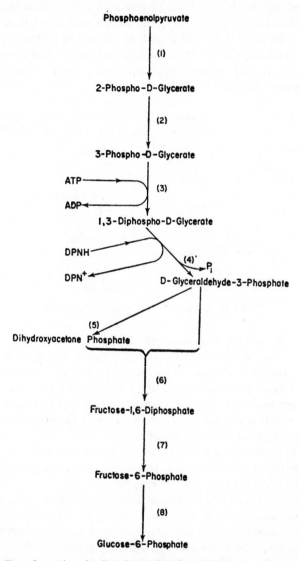

FIG. 21. Transformations leading from phosphoenolpyruvate to hexose phosphate. The enzymes involved are: (1) enolase; (2) phosphoglyceryl mutase; (3) phosphoglyceryl kinase; (4) glyceraldehyde phosphate dehydrogenase; (5) triosephosphate isomerase; (6) aldolase; (7) fructose diphosphatase; (8) phosphohexose isomerase.

from oxalacetate or malate. In certain organisms an enzyme is present which splits isocitrate into succinate and glyoxalate. The latter substance may then react with acetyl CoA to form L-malate, as an alternative route. [855, 497, 803] A "glyoxalate cycle" is frequently encountered in microorganisms [514, 346] and actually amounts to the synthesis of one molecule of succinate from two molecules of acetate as shown in Fig. 22. Such a mechanism is of importance in cases where acetate is the sole source of carbon. In particular, it provides an alternate pathway for the conversion of fatty acids into carbohydrate as seen in Fig. 23. In many plants, evidence for the existence of such a pathway has actually been found. [401, 102, 498]

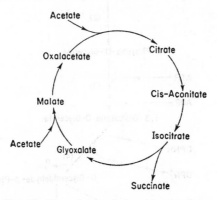

FIG. 22. Glyoxalate cycle in microorganisms.

B. *Formation of Glucose-6-Phosphate from Glucose*

In a great many instances, glucose or glucose-containing polysaccharides, in particular starch, contribute an essential part to the intake of carbon with food. This is true for a large number of animal families and species, and it also holds for a great number of microorganisms, like yeasts and all those bacteria and molds which emit starch-degrading enzymes or other polysaccharide-hydrolyzing enzymes into their culture media.

In order to be absorbed by the organism and to be capable of penetrating into the cells, the glucose-containing polysaccharides are at first broken down to glucose by a system of hydrolytic enzymes.

The digestion of starch in the human body, as well as in many animals and microorganisms, proceeds in two successive steps. The first is catalyzed by salivary and pancreatic α-*amylase*, and leads to a mixture of maltose, malto-triose, isomaltose, some branched tri-, tetra-, penta-, and hexasaccharides, and traces of glucose. [604, 979, 606, 80] Prolonged action of α-amylase yields some glucose in quantities never exceeding 16 to 19 per cent, however. The second step then completes the hydrolysis to glucose by the action of α-*glucosidases* or *maltase* from intestinal bacteria, [329] and α-1,6-*glucosidase* from intestinal mucosa. [523] In a few instances a single enzyme has been found capable of performing the degradation of starch to glucose in a single step, such as *glucamylase* from the mold *Rhizopus delemar.* [185, 726] The hydrolysis of cellulose in organisms feeding on this polysaccharide, such as

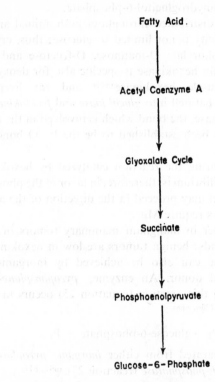

Fatty Acid

Acetyl Coenzyme A

Glyoxalate Cycle

Succinate

Phosphoenolpyruvate

Glucose-6-Phosphate

FIG. 23. Alternate pathway of transformation of fatty acids into carbohydrate in organisms where the glyoxalate cycle is operative.

in the intestinal tract of the Roman snail, in protozoa and in various bacteria, has been observed to follow a similar multi-step mechanism. At least two *cellulases* and a *β-glucosidase* appear to be involved, [767, 331] and this mode of degradation has been recently reviewed. [727, 81]

Phosphorylation of glucose is achieved by reaction with ATP through the catalytic action of *hexokinase* or glucokinase according to the general equation:

$$\text{glucose} + \text{ATP} \rightarrow \text{glucose-6-phosphate} + \text{ADP} \qquad (24)$$

Two glucose-phosphorylating enzymes coexist in rat liver and can be separated from one another. [945, 949] *Glucokinase* is the major part of the two enzymes. Its activity is decreased upon starvation and is very low in alloxan-induced diabetes; insulin restores glucokinase activity in alloxan-treated animals. *Hexokinase* is unaffected by either alloxan or insulin. Both enzymes behave differently with regard to inhibition by glucose-6-phosphates, N-acetyl-glucosamine and 1,5-anhydroglucitol-6-phosphate.

These enzymes are widely distributed throughout both animal and vegetable kingdoms. Their specificity is not limited to glucose; thus, crystalline yeast hexokinase may phosphorylate D-mannose, D-fructose and glucosamine as well;[77, 516, 107] brain hexokinase is specific also for deoxyglucose and mannose, whereas muscle hexokinase[844] and rat liver hexokinase[182, 863] may each be separated into *glucokinase* and *fructokinase*.

In the case of yeast hexokinase, the bond which is involved in the reaction catalyzed by this enzyme has been established to be the P—O bond rather than the C—O linkage.[157]

The free energy change during the reaction catalyzed by hexokinase is $\Delta F' = 3 \cdot 6$ kcal/mole. The equilibrium is, therefore, in favor of the phosphorylated product, and the reaction may proceed in the direction of the arrow in equation 24. Most hexokinases require Mg^{++}.

Hexokinase levels are higher in malignant mammary tumors of the rat than in normal, lactating glands; benign tumors are low in hexokinase.[821]

Phosphorylation of glucose can also be achieved by inorganic pyrophosphate as the phosphoryl donor. An enzyme, *pyrophosphate-glucose phosphotransferase*, catalyzing this reaction (equation 25) occurs in murine liver and kidney microsomes:[756, 868]

$$\text{glucose} + PP_i \rightarrow \text{glucose-6-phosphate} + P_i \tag{25}$$

This enzyme can not be separated from either *inorganic pyrophosphatase* (reaction 26) or from *glucose-6-phosphatase* (reaction 27).[667, 871]

$$PP_i + H_2O \rightarrow 2 P_i \tag{26}$$

$$\text{glucose-6-phosphate} + H_2O \rightarrow \text{glucose} + P_i \tag{27}$$

All three reactions (25, 26 and 27) are probably catalyzed by one and the same enzyme according to a mechanism which involves a phospho-enzyme intermediate (see Fig. 24).

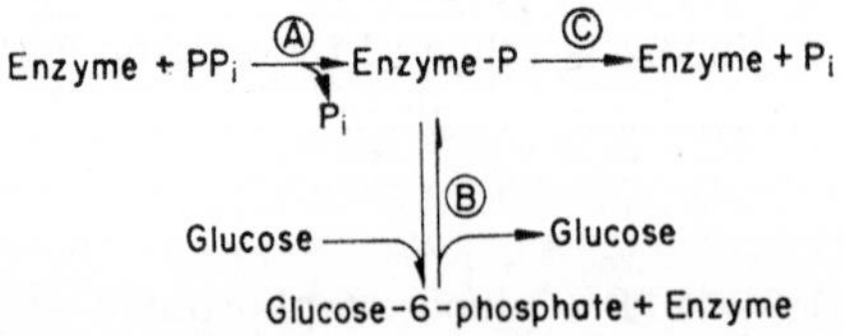

FIG. 24. Common identity of the enzymes, pyrophosphate-glucose phosphotransferase (A + B), inorganic pyrophosphatase (A + C), and glucose-6-phosphatase (B + C).[667]

The same triple enzyme has also been found in the liver and kidney of patients with type I glycogen storage disease. [432]

Some biogenetic significance must be attributed to the formation of glucose-6-phosphate from glucose-1-phosphate by the action of phosphoglucomutase. The acid-labile glucose-1-phosphate may originate from phosphorolytic degradation of polysaccharides, i.e. glycogen, amylopectin and amylose, or it may be formed from uridine diphosphate glucose which, in turn, is in an enzymically catalyzed equilibrium with uridine diphosphate derivatives of other sugars, such as in particular of galactose. It is obvious that these reactions are of prime biogenetic importance when they proceed in the inverse directions, i.e. in the direction of the polysaccharide formation, or of the conversion of glucose phosphates into phosphate esters of other sugars; they will be discussed in Section VI of this chapter.

V. THE FORMATION OF "PRIMARY-HYDROXYL PHOSPHATES" OF OTHER SUGARS

Various mechanisms are known for the formation of phosphate esters of sugars other than glucose, where the phosphate is bound to a primary hydroxyl group, such as in aldohexose-6-phosphates, in aldopentose-5-phosphates, in the corresponding ketose phosphates, etc. Many of these pathways or reactions are of general significance for the biosynthesis of the sugars; others may apply only to certain specific organisms. In some instances of the biogenesis of carbohydrates, these reactions are more likely to proceed in the inverse direction; they may then either be catalyzed by the same system of enzymes, or the inverse reaction may be due to the action of hydrolytic enzymes, in particular phosphatases, and will lead to the formation of monosaccharides.

A. Phosphorylation of Monosaccharides other than Glucose by ATP

This reaction is catalyzed by hexokinase and is characterized by the equation:

$$\text{Sugar} + \text{ATP} \rightleftharpoons \text{sugar phosphate} + \text{ADP} \tag{28}$$

Hexokinase, or rather the hexokinases are extremely widespread in nature. Some hexokinases are specific for a certain monosaccharide and will not act upon other sugars, such as fructokinase from rat liver. [863, 182] Other hexokinases, like the crystalline enzyme from yeast, are capable of phosphorylating several sugars, i.e. D-glucose, [77, 516] D-mannose, D-fructose and D-glucosamine, [107] but not D-galactose, D-xylose, L-rhamnose, nor di- and trisaccharides; brain hexokinase may transfer phosphate from ATP to glucose, deoxyglucose and mannose, as well as to sorbitol; [858] hexokinases from rat intestine, kidney or liver, were capable of using allose, talose or 2-deoxy-glucose as substrates;[519] the hepatic and intestinal enzymes could also phosphorylate glucosamine, whereas gulose was a substrate only for the rat liver enzyme; hexose-6-phosphates resulted in all cases from the action of the rat hexokinases, but N-acetylglucosamine or altrose were not phosphorylated by any of them;[519] N-acetyl-D-mannosamine was phosphorylated to the 6-phosphate by ATP and a kinase from mammalian tissues.[286] Reaction rates and affinity constants (Michaelis constants) vary from one substrate to another.

The phosphorylation of most aldohexoses, in particular of D-glucose and D-mannose, by ATP in the presence of hexokinase occurs at the primary hydroxyl group of the sugars, i.e. in the carbon-6 position.[539] Similarly, D-glucosamine,[352, 107, 534, 116] D-acetylglucosamine,[244, 540] and D-gluconate yield the carbon-6-phosphates.

Aldopentoses are converted to the corresponding pentose-5-phosphates, and ketoses (D-fructose, D-xylulose, and L-ribulose) yield the corresponding primary-hydroxyl phosphates in the 6 and 5 positions, respectively, i.e. D-fructose-6-phosphate, D-xylulose-5-phosphate and L-ribulose-5-phosphate. The formation of the latter substance has been observed only in *Lactobacillus* and *Aerobacter*.[119, 120, 836, 837, 18]

D-Ribulose is transformed into its 5-phosphate by D-ribulokinase from guinea-pig liver,[468] and L-fuculose yields L-fuculose-1-phosphate with an enzyme from *E. coli* or *E. freundii*.[371] L-Fucose is not phosphorylated by the latter enzyme. Phosphorylation of sedoheptulose-1-phosphate by ATP and an enzyme from *Streptococcus faecalis* leads to sedoheptulose-1,6-diphosphate.[856]

Fructose-1,6-diphosphate is the product of reaction of fructose-6-phosphate with ATP and is mediated by *phosphofructokinase*. This enzyme is inhibited by excess concentrations of ATP,[569, 760] whereas cyclic adenosine-3′,5′-phosphate, as well as AMP and ADP, abolish the inhibition and, thus, act as activators.[569, 697] In the cell, the enzyme occurs in the inhibited state. Its activity is regulated by changes in levels of activator nucleotides to meet physiological needs of the cell.[569, 760] The physiological role of AMP as activator of phosphofructokinase is further enhanced by the capacity of this nucleotide of inhibiting *fructose diphosphatase*;[906] AMP thus furthers the formation of fructose-1,6-diphosphate and simultaneously prevents its decomposition.

Galactose has been reported, however, to yield galactose-1-phosphate through the action of liver, brain or yeast hexokinase preparations;[925, 138] galactosamine[138] and N-acetyl-D-galactosamine[540] are also phosphorylated in the carbon-1 position. Other exceptions are D-fructose-1-phosphate which is obtained by the action of certain hexokinase preparations from muscle and from liver, and α-D-glucuronic acid-1-phosphate which results from the phosphorylation of D-glucuronic acid by ATP in the presence of an enzyme system from mung bean seedlings. [661]

D-Galacturonic acid yields α-D-galacturonic acid-1-phosphate with a kinase from germinating seeds of *Phaseolus aureus*, [662] and L-rhamnulo-kinase from *E. coli* forms L-rhamnulose-1-phosphate from L-rhamnulose and ATP. [151] The latter enzyme can also use UTP, CTP, GTP or dTTP instead of ATP, although at lower reaction rates.

An example of the phosphorylation by a phosphoryl donor other than ATP is the formation of mannose-6-phosphate from mannose and inorganic pyrophosphate. [667] The enzyme catalyzing this reaction is the same as that responsible for glucose-6-phosphate formation from pyrophosphate, and the reaction mechanisms of those two phosphoryl transfers are identical.

B. *Intramolecular Phosphate Transfer*

In analogy to the reaction catalyzed by phosphoglucomutase (see Section VI), an intramolecular transfer of the phosphate ester group from the primary hydroxyl group of the sugar to the carbon-1 position has been observed in the case of galactose-6-phosphate, [735] mannose-6-phosphate, [531] acetyl-glucos-amine-6-phosphate, [770] and ribose-5-phosphate. [487] The enzymes catalyzing these reactions are called *mutases*, and they have been found to require catalytic amounts of the corresponding sugar diphosphates in the same manner as phosphoglucomutase requires glucose-1,6-diphosphate. All reactions catalyzed by the mutases have been found to be reversible; the equilibrium is in most cases in favor of the primary-hydroxyl phosphate.

C. *Epimerization of Sugar Phosphates*

D-Xylulose-phosphate has been shown to undergo epimerization in two manners, i.e. to D-ribulose-5-phosphate, [208, 862, 427] involving an inversion of the hydroxyl group at carbon atom 3, and to L-ribulose-5-phosphate, [119, 120, 998, 999] whereby the hydroxyl group at carbon atom 4 is inverted. The *epimerases* which catalyze these reactions are widespread throughout plant and

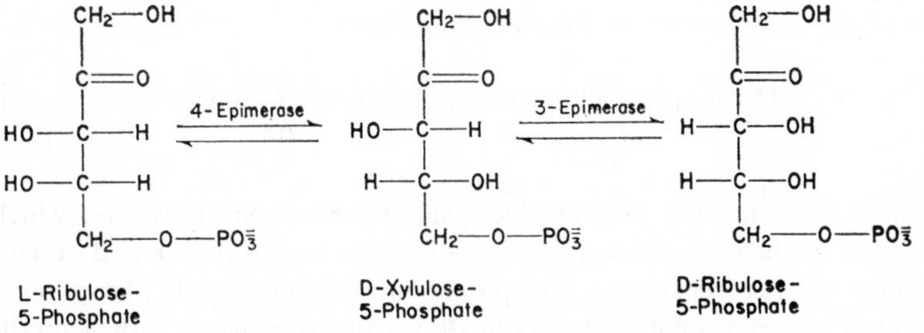

FIG. 25. Epimerization of ketopentose phosphates.

animal kingdoms. Two subsequent epimerization reactions of this kind may bring about the transformation of D-ribulose phosphate to the L-isomer, as seen in Fig. 25.

The formation of L-ribulose-5-phosphate has importance in the synthesis of L-arabinose. It is conceivable that L-ribulose-5-phosphate undergoes hydrolysis by phosphatase to L-ribulose, as seen in Fig. 26, which, in turn,

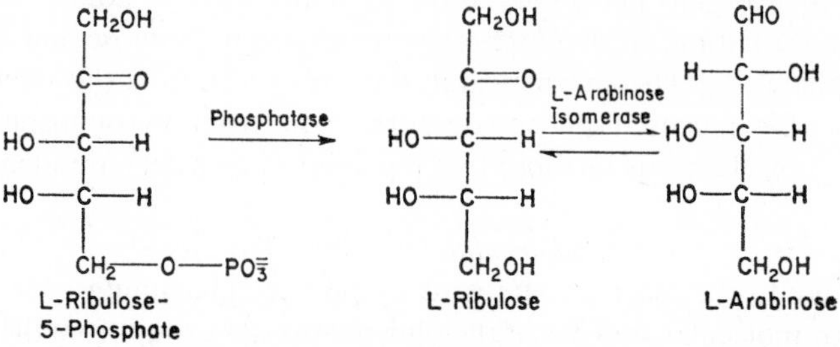

FIG. 26. Formation of L-arabinose from L-ribulose phosphate in *Lactobacillus plantarum.*

may yield L-arabinose by an *L-arabinose isomerase* known to exist in *Lactobacillus plantarum* and in *Lactobacillus pentosus.* [120, 373]

N-Acetyl-D-glucosamine-6-phosphate is transformed to N-acetyl-D-mannosamine-6-phosphate by an epimerase which has been found in *Aerobacter cloacae* [287] and in hog kidney. [288] ATP is required for the epimerization by the hog kidney enzyme. The resulting product is an immediate precursor of sialic acids (see Section VIII, 26, this chapter).

D. *Ketose–Aldose Isomerization*

D-mannose, which occurs in nature mainly in the form of mannosides or polysaccharides (mannan), is most likely to originate from D-mannose-6-phosphate. The latter substance may be formed from D-fructose-6-phosphate through the catalytic action of *phosphomannoisomerase* which has been found in yeast and in muscle. [842] This reaction is analogous to the isomerization of D-fructose-6-phosphate to glucose-6-phosphate,

$$\text{D-fructose-6-phosphate} \rightleftharpoons \text{D-glucose-6-phosphate} \qquad (29)$$
$$30\% \qquad\qquad\qquad 70\%$$

which is an important step in glycolysis and photosynthesis, and which is catalyzed by the enzyme *phosphoglucoisomerase*, widely distributed in nature.

That the two enzymes, phosphomannoisomerase and phosphoglucoisomerase, are not identical has been shown in experiments with deuterium-containing glucose-6-phosphate. [916] Consequently, the intermediates of the ketose-aldose isomerizations catalyzed by these two enzymes are believed to be different, i.e. to be *cis*-enediol and *trans*-enediol, respectively.

Based on this principle, glucose-6-phosphate may be transformed into mannose-6-phosphate by a two-step reaction involving both phosphogluco- and phosphomannoisomerases as seen in the following equation:

$$\text{D-glucose-6-phosphate} \underset{}{\overset{\text{phosphoglucoisomerase}}{\rightleftharpoons}}$$

$$\text{D-fructose-6-phosphate} \underset{}{\overset{\text{phosphomannoisomerase}}{\rightleftharpoons}} \text{D-mannose-6-phosphate} \qquad (30)$$

Another ketose–aldose isomerization is the transformation of D-ribulose-5-phosphate to D-ribose-5-phosphate, which is catalyzed by *phosphoriboisomerase* and which favors the formation of the aldose ester as follows:

$$\text{D-ribulose-5-phosphate} \rightleftharpoons \text{D-ribose-5-phosphate} \qquad (31)$$
$$(20\text{--}30\%) \qquad\qquad (70\text{--}80\%)$$

This reaction is of the utmost importance for the pathways of the photosynthesis cycle, where it proceeds in the direction from right to left in the above equation. In many tissues and organisms, ribulose-5-phosphate may also be formed from 6-phosphogluconate and may subsequently yield ribose-5-phosphate.

E. *Decarboxylation of 6-Phospho-aldohexonic Acids*

The formation of ribose-5-phosphate from glucose-6-phosphate is shown in Fig. 27.

The first step involves the dehydrogenation of glucose-6-phosphate by glucose-6-phosphate dehydrogenase which requires TPN. This enzyme, best known as "Zwischenferment", is most widely distributed and has been investigated in great detail. The primary oxidation product of glucose-6-phosphate has been found to be the δ-lactone of 6-phosphogluconate. [184] The latter may yield spontaneously 6-phosphogluconic acid without the intervention of enzymes. Under certain *in vivo* conditions, the reaction rate of this ring opening may be inadequate, however, and an enzyme, 6-*phosphogluconolactonase*, has actually been observed to exist; it is capable of increasing the rate of hydrolysis of the lactone. [184]

The subsequent oxidative decarboxylation has been studied by many workers; Horecker [419] has proposed a two-step reaction mechanism for it. The first step consists in the formation of 3-keto-6-phosphogluconate which has never been isolated, however. This reaction is catalyzed by 6-*phosphogluconate dehydrogenase* requiring TPN^+, and is followed by decarboxylation of the 3-keto intermediate to ribulose-5-phosphate. Then, D-ribose-5-phosphate is formed through the action of *phosphoriboisomerase*. The pentose will finally become available for nucleic acid synthesis after the latter substance has been transformed to ribose-1-phosphate by a mutase.

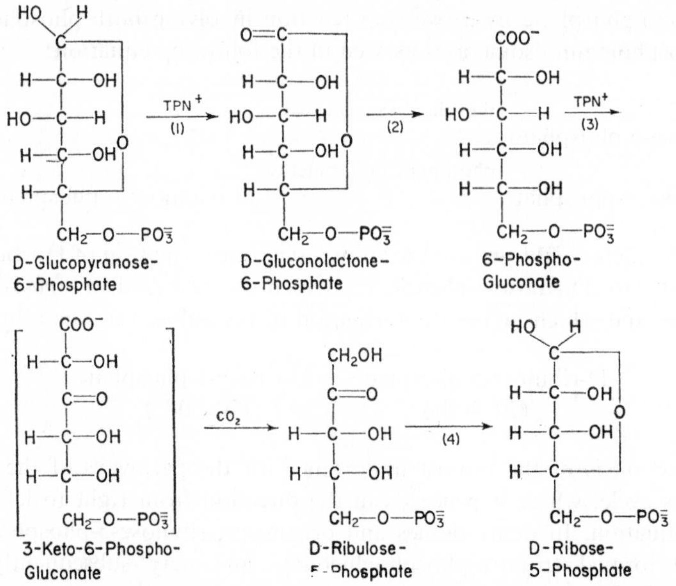

FIG. 27. Transformation of D-glucose-6-phosphate to D-ribose-5-phosphate. The following enzymes participate in this sequence of reactions: (1) glucose-6-phosphate dehydrogenase; (2) 6-phosphogluconolactonase; (3) 6-phosphogluconate dehydrogenase; (4) phosphoribose isomerase.

This sequence of reactions leading from glucose-6-phosphate to ribulose-5-phosphate has a counterpart of reactions resulting in the transformation of ribulose-5-phosphate back to glucose-6-phosphate. The latter series of reactions has been discussed previously in this chapter in connection with the photosynthesis cycle of carbon reduction. These reactions are an integral part of the photosynthesis cycle where they proceed, however, in the reverse direction, as seen in Fig. 3 (ribulose-1,5-diphosphate, CO_2, 3-glycerophosphate, and fructose-1,6-diphosphate do not participate in the present reaction sequence). The pathway leading from glucose-6-phosphate to ribulose-5-phosphate through phosphogluconate, and back to glucose-6-phosphate, via fructose-6-phosphate, xylulose-5-phosphate, erythrose-4-phosphate, the sedoheptulose phosphates and ribose-5-phosphates (see Fig. 3), is also known as the pentose phosphate cycle[35] which is active in many tissues and microorganisms.

F. Aldol Condensation of Sugar Phosphates
The most general form of an aldol condensation is represented in Fig. 28A.

In biological systems, one of the participating reactants is usually dihydroxy-acetone phosphate and the other is an aldehyde, most frequently an aldose, or a primary-hydroxyl phosphate ester of an aldose. The number of carbon atoms in the aldehyde may vary from one in formaldehyde to five in ribose-5-phosphate. The products of the biological aldol condensation, catalyzed by *aldolases*, are ketose-1-phosphates with numbers of carbon atoms depending on the structure of the participating aldose (see Fig. 28B). If the aldehyde contains a primary-hydroxyl phosphate group, the condensation product will be a diphosphate as in the case of the best-known aldolase-catalyzed

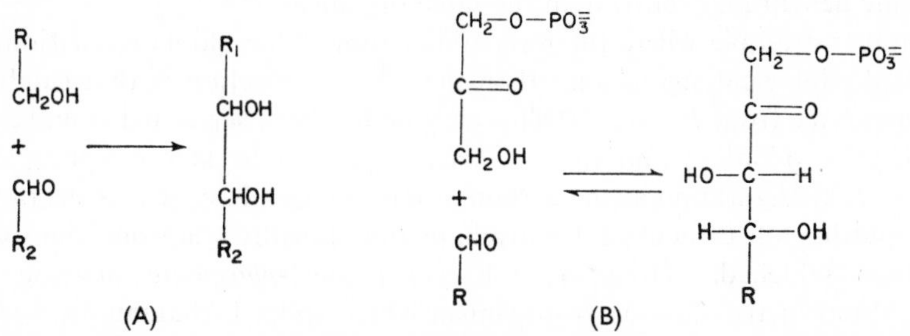

FIG. 28. Aldol condensations. A, general mechanism; B, reaction most frequently catalyzed by aldolases.

reaction, i.e. the condensation of dihydroxyacetone phosphate with glycer-aldehyde-3-phosphate to D-fructose-1,6-diphosphate. The condensation of dihydroxyacetone phosphate with glycolaldehyde phosphate, D-erythrose-4-phosphate, and D-ribose-5-phosphate yields D-xylulose-1,5-diphosphate, D-sedoheptulose-1,7-diphosphate, and D-octulose-1,8-diphosphate, respectively.

On the other hand, glycolaldehyde, D-glyceraldehyde, and D-erythrose produce the corresponding ketose-1-phosphates, i.e. D-xylulose-1-phosphate, D-fructose-1-phosphate, and D-sedoheptulose-1-phosphate.

Aldolase occurs widespread in nature, both in the animal and the vege-table kingdoms, including higher plants and microorganisms. Most of the above-named reactions have been observed with muscle aldolase. [609, 539] A 1-phosphofructoaldolase from muscle, liver and plants has also been described, and the aldol condensations yielding ketose-1-phosphates have been attributed to the action of this enzyme. [546, 393, 466] The question as to the difference between, or the identity of, 1-phosphofructoaldolase and aldolase proper, has not yet been solved, however. [547, 713]

A few biological aldol condensations, catalyzed by aldolase, have been noted in which dihydroxyacetone phosphate is replaced by other substances, and which yield important condensation products. The reaction of D-glyceraldehyde-3-phosphate with acetaldehyde has been reported by

Racker [749] to produce D-deoxyribose-5-phosphate through the action of aldolase preparations from *Escherichia coli* or from animal tissues. [749] On the other hand, Comb and Roseman [163] obtained N-acetyl neuraminic acid from N-acetyl-D-mannosamine and pyruvate, with an aldolase preparation from *Clostridium perfringens.*

An aldolase from *Pseudomonas fluorescens* catalyzes the cleavage of 2-keto-3-deoxy-gluconate-6-phosphate to pyruvate and glyceraldehyde-3-phosphate. [600] This reaction proceeds in the reverse direction of the equation shown in Fig. 28B, and its starting material, 2-keto-3-deoxy-gluconate-6-phosphate, is derived from gluconate-6-phosphate by the action of 6-phosphogluconic dehydrase occurring in the same organism. [599]

Another example where the reverse direction of the aldolase reaction has more physiological significance than the forward reaction is that catalyzed by an enzyme from *E. coli.* [283] This enzyme has been separated from hexose diphosphate aldolase and its specificity is limited to ketose-1-phosphates with a *cis* configuration at the carbon atoms 3 and 4. It catalyzes the reversible splitting of L-fuculose-1-phosphate into dihydroxyacetone phosphate and L-lactaldehyde. However, a *L-rhamnulose-1-phosphate aldolase* has been found in the same microorganism which splits L-rhamnulose-1-phosphate into dihydroxy-acetone phosphate and L-lactaldehyde; [802] the latter enzyme is, thus, capable of cleaving substrates with a *trans* configuration at carbon atoms 3 and 4. A similar enzyme was also detected in *Lactobacillus plantarum.* [214]

G. *Other Mechanisms*

A mechanism of condensation somewhat different from that catalyzed by the aldolases is found in the formation of sedoheptulose-7-phosphate by condensation of ribose-5-phosphate with enzymatically obtained *active glycolic aldehyde* in the presence of transketolase. [743] Active glycolic aldehyde is obtained by incubation of hydroxypyruvate with thiaminepyrophosphate and a pig heart enzyme. Its structure was established to be 2-(1,2-dihydroxyethyl)-thiaminepyrophosphate (see Fig. 29). [96] It is analogous to that of "active acetaldehyde" (see Chapter 1, pp. 22–23).

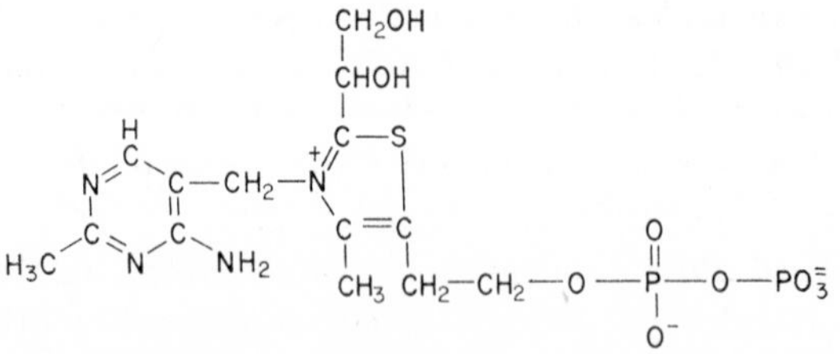

FIG. 29. Structure of "active glycolic aldehyde". [96]

In analogy to the hypothetical reverse direction of the above condensation of glycolic aldehyde with a sugar phosphate, phosphorolysis of xylulose-5-phosphate leads to acetyl phosphate and glyceraldehyde-3-phosphate. Similarly, fructose-6-phosphate undergoes phosphorolysis to acetyl phosphate and erythrose-4-phosphate. The enzyme phosphoketolase catalyzing these reactions was obtained and crystallized from *Leuconostoc mesenteroides*. These reactions proceed according to a two-step mechanism. [320] The first step consists in the nonphosphorolytic cleavage of the ketose phosphate into a two-carbon fragment, i.e. carbon atoms 1 and 2 of the ketose, and an aldose phosphate containing the remainder of the ketose phosphate (see Fig. 30). The two-carbon fragment, glycol aldehyde, forms an intermediate enzyme-glycolic-aldehyde product which is subsequently converted into acetyl phosphate and enzyme through phosphorolysis and isomerization. The same enzyme may also transform glycolic aldehyde into acetyl phosphate, according to the mechanism shown in Fig. 30.

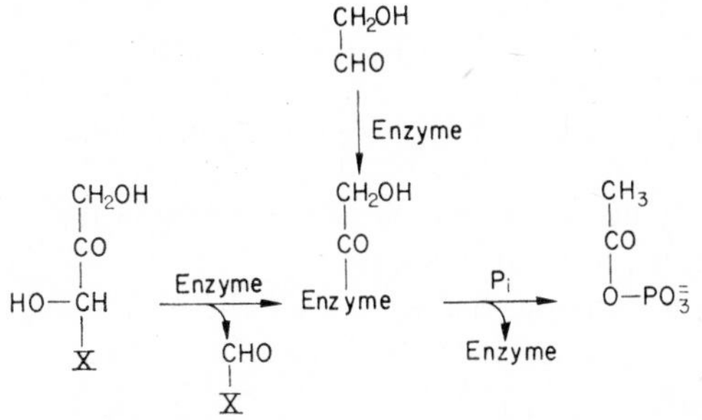

FIG. 30. Reactions catalyzed by phosphoketolase. When the group X is —CHOH · CH_2—O—$PO_3^=$, xylulose-5-phosphate is converted into glyceraldehyde-3-phosphate; when X is —CHOH · CHOH · CH_2—O—PO_3, fructose-6-phosphate yields erythrose-4-phosphate.

Erythronic acid-4-phosphate was isolated from an incubation mixture of hemolyzed human red blood cells with inosine. [436] It is assumed to arise from the metabolism of the ribose phosphate moiety of inosine by a branch pathway of the pentose phosphate cycle.

H. *Amination and N-Acetylation of Sugar Phosphates*

There are essentially two pathways for the formation of phosphate esters of amino sugars. The first consists in the phosphorylation of existing amino sugars by ATP, and is catalyzed by kinases. As pointed out before, glucosamine and its N-acetyl derivative yield the corresponding 6-phosphates, [352, 107, 534, 116, 244, 540] whereas galactosamine and N-acetyl galactosamine produce the 1-phosphates. [138, 540] Since amino sugars and their N-acetyl derivatives have not been found to occur in nature in the state of the free monosaccharides, and since their incorporation into polysaccharides is most likely to go through the phosphate esters, the phosphorylation of the free or N-acetylated amino sugars does not have much significance from the point of view of the biosynthesis of these substances.

The second pathway which involves the amination of sugar-6-phosphates, followed by N-acetylation, is more likely to be responsible for the formation of amino sugars in nature. Extracts from *Neurospora*[534, 92] and from liver[729, 730] have been found capable of activating the amination of hexose-6-phosphate by glutamine according to the following transamination reaction:

$$\text{fructose-6-phosphate} + \text{glutamine} \rightleftharpoons$$
$$\text{glucosamine-6-phosphate} + \text{glutamic acid} \qquad (32)$$

The aminotransferase from bovine aortic and pulmonary valves is markedly inhibited by sodium salicylate.[441]

A slightly different mechanism of introducing amino groups into sugar phosphates directly from free NH_4^+ has been observed to occur in a number of sources.[537, 994, 161, 164] This reaction, shown in the following equation:

$$\text{fructose-6-phosphate} + NH_3 \rightleftharpoons \text{glucosamine-6-phosphate} + H_2O \qquad (33)$$

has been originally noted to proceed in the direction from right to left, but has now been shown to be also reversible.

In a subsequent reaction, acetylation of the amino sugar phosphate by acetyl CoA will yield N-acetyl-D-glucosamine-6-phosphate, according to the following equation:

$$\text{glucosamine-6-phosphate} + \text{acetyl-CoA} \rightleftharpoons$$
$$\text{N-acetyl glucosamine-6-phosphate} + \text{CoA} \qquad (34)$$

The latter reaction is catalyzed by the enzyme *glucosamine-6-phosphate N-acetylase*, which has been detected in many microorganisms and in animal tissues.[534, 108, 200] In most cases, only the phosphate ester of the amino sugar will accept the acetyl group, but liver extracts may also acetylate free glucosamine.[200]

An enzyme from *Pseudomonas aeruginosa* is capable also of acetylating α-D-glucosamine-1-phosphate by acetyl-CoA to yield N-acetyl glucosamine-1-phosphate.[505]

VI. ALDOSE-1-PHOSPHATES

In 1936, glucose-1-phosphate was first isolated from frog muscle by Cori and Cori,[169] and was recognized to be the product of phosphorylation of glycogen. The transformation of this acid-labile phosphate ester into the acid-stable glucose-6-phosphate by an enzyme from various tissue extracts was soon discovered thereafter. [168, 173] The reaction catalyzed by this enzyme, *phosphoglucomutase*, was found to be reversible, and the equilibrium was shown to be markedly in favor of the 6-phosphate which makes up 95 per cent of the equilibrium mixture. [158] The enzyme has been crystallized by Najjar. [645]

The reaction catalyzed by phosphoglucomutase has been reported to be enhanced by the addition of hexose phosphates, [475, 445] and Cardini *et al.* [142] and Leloir [531] have established that α-D-glucose-1,6-diphosphate is the coenzyme of phosphoglucomutase. This coenzyme is active at extremely low concentrations. The mechanism of the intra-molecular phosphate transfer was studied by Najjar and Pullman, [646, 744, 647] who could find direct evidence for the existence of a phosphoenzyme form of phosphoglucomutase; phosphate transfer from the crystalline rabbit muscle enzyme to both glucose-1-phosphate and glucose-6-phosphate with a net synthesis of glucose-1,6-diphosphate was observed, and a two-step mechanism for this reaction was, therefore, suggested as shown in Fig. 31. The equilibrium constants of these two reactions have been determined separately. [830] The phosphorylated and dephosphorylated forms of phosphoglucomutase from rabbit muscle have been separated from one another by chromatography. [1007]

A new enzyme, *glucose-1-phosphate transferase*, was found in, and purified from *E. coli*, *Aerobacter aerogenes* and *Mycobacterium smegmatis*. [274] It

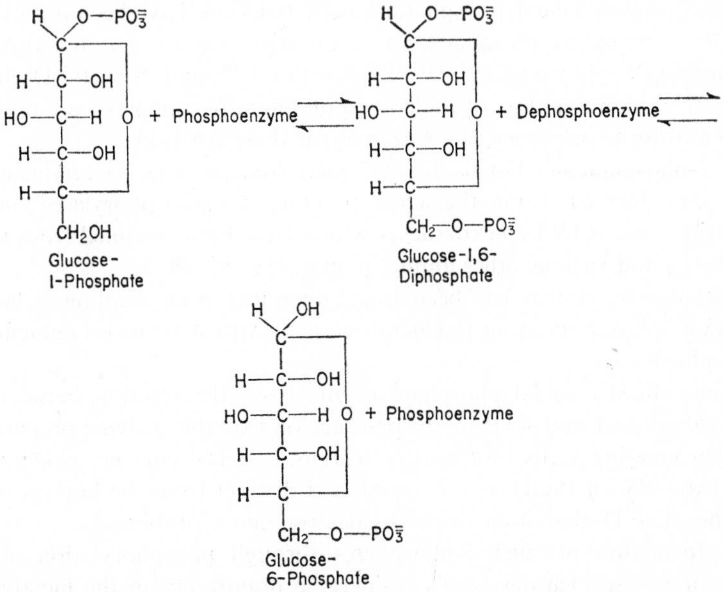

Fig. 31. Mechanism of the phosphoglucomutase reaction, according to Najjar and Pullman. [744, 647, 830]

catalyzes the formation of glucose-6-phosphate from glucose-1-phosphate and glucose. This enzyme differs from phosphoglucomutase by its substrate specificity and its lack of cofactor requirements. In the reaction catalyzed by this enzyme glucose-1-phosphate is the phosphoryl donor and free glucose is the acceptor (see equation 35):

$$\text{glucose-1-phosphate} + \text{glucose} \rightarrow \text{glucose-6-phosphate} + \text{glucose} \qquad (35)$$

Fructose-1-phosphate may also act as the donor according to reaction 36:

$$\text{fructose-1-phosphate} + \text{glucose} \rightarrow \text{glucose-6-phosphate} + \text{fructose} \qquad (36)$$

An analogous reaction of phosphoryl transfer has been described with an enzyme from the same organism, i.e. E. coli. [275] This enzyme, phosphoramidic hexose transphosphorylase, catalyzes the transfer of phosphate from monophosphoramidate, N-phosphorylglycine or monophosphorylhistidine to aldo- and ketohexoses or to sedoheptulose.

The biogenetic significance of glucose-1-phosphate and of the mutase which catalyzes its formation from glucose-6-phosphate lies in the potentiality to give rise to glucosidic bonds of di-, oligo-, or polysaccharides, either directly from the 1-phosphate or through an intermediate stage of the uridine diphosphate compound.

Similar intramolecular phosphate transfer reactions have been reported to occur for analogous phosphate esters of other sugars, e.g. for those of D-mannose, [479] D-ribose, [487, 342] D-galactose, [735] and N-acetyl-D-glucosamine. [770] Small amounts of the corresponding diphosphates were reported in all cases to be necessary as coenzymes for these reactions.

The 1-phosphates of D-galactose, D-galactosamine and N-acetylgalactosamine are formed from the corresponding nonphosphorylated monosaccharides and ATP by hexokinases which have been obtained from yeast, liver, brain and various other animal tissues. [925, 138, 540]

A hexokinase system has been found in mung bean seedlings which is capable of phosphorylating D-glucuronic acid with ATP to α-D-glucuronic acid-1-phosphate. [248]

D-Galacturonic acid-1-phosphate results from the reaction between D-galacturonic acid and ATP in the presence of a soluble enzyme preparation from germinating seeds of Phaseolus aureus. [662] The enzyme, galacturonic acid kinase, which catalyzes this reaction is distinct from the kinases which phosphorylate D-glucuronic acid, D-galactose and L-arabinose.

The formation of sugar-1-phosphates through phosphorylation of di-, oligo-, or polysaccharides is of considerable importance in the metabolism of complex saccharides. A continuous exchange between the sugar units in the polysaccharide and free sugar-1-phosphate has been observed with liver and muscle glycogen of the rat, [870] and a similar exchange must be assumed to exist also in the case of other complex saccharides. The importance of the formation of sugar-1-phosphates through phosphorolysis of polysaccharides, and the significance of this pathway in the biogenesis of complex saccharides must not be underestimated, therefore.

VII. NUCLEOSIDE DIPHOSPHATE SUGARS

A. *Formation of UDP-Sugars*

The isolation from biological material of uridine diphosphate glucose (UDP-glucose) by Caputto *et al.* [137] and by Leloir [530] (see Fig. 32), and the connection of this substance with certain transformation reactions of sugar phosphates [530, 464] has opened a new concept in our knowledge of the biological formation of saccharides. [532] The biosynthesis of UDP-glucose has been established by Kalckar [459] to proceed according to the equation:

$$\text{UTP} + \text{glucose-1-phosphate} \rightleftharpoons \text{UDP-glucose} + \text{PP}_i \qquad (37)$$

and to be catalyzed by the enzyme, *uridine diphosphoglucose pyrophosphorylase*. This enzyme has been further described by a number of investigators. [635, 293, 282, 926, 944, 710, 325]

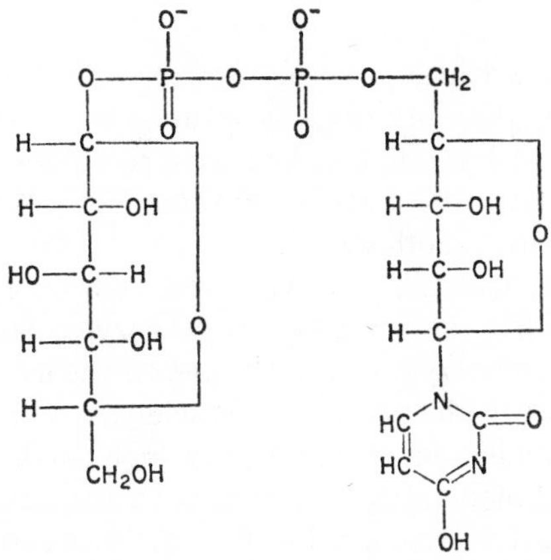

FIG. 32. Structure of uridine diphosphate glucose (UDP-glucose). [137]

Other uridine diphosphate glycosides have been isolated, e.g. the analogous derivatives of D-galactose, [530, 437] D-xylose, [301] L-arabinose, [301] L-rhamnose, [846, 470] D-glucuronic acid, [874, 248] D-galacturonic acid, [852, 248] N-acetyl-D-glucosamine, [127, 882] N-acetyl-D-glucosamine-6-phosphate, [879, 882]

N-acetyl-D-galactosamine, [732, 882] N-acetyl D-galactosamine sulfate, [879, 882] polyacetylneuraminic acid, [670] and muramic acid. [693] The biosynthesis of these UDP-glycosides was found to be analogous to that of UDP-glucose, namely:

$$UTP + aldose\text{-}1\text{-}phosphate \rightleftharpoons UDP\text{-}sugar + PP_i \qquad (38)$$

In order to enhance the synthesis of UDP-sugars by this reaction, *pyrophosphatase* is present in many tissues. This enzyme splits the pyrophosphate into inorganic phosphate and thus displaces the equilibrium of the above reaction in favor of the UDP-sugars. UDP-sugar-synthesizing enzymes have been reported to occur in numerous sources, and have been described for the formation of UDP-galactose, [464, 437, 710, 325] UDP-D-xylose, [298] UDP-L-arabinose, [298] UDP-glucuronic acid, [857, 248] UDP-galacturonic acid, [857, 248] and UDP-acetylglucosamine. [854, 565]

A second mechanism by which UDP-sugars may be formed is the incorporation of galactose-1-phosphate into uridine nucleotides, according to the equation described by Kalckar *et al.*: [462, 884, 463]

$$galactose\text{-}1\text{-}phosphate + UDP\text{-}glucose \rightleftharpoons$$
$$glucose\text{-}1\text{-}phosphate + UDP\text{-}galactose \qquad (39)$$

The enzyme catalyzing this reaction, *galactose-1-phosphate uridyl transferase* was found to occur in galactose-adapted yeast, [464] as well as in other sources, such as in germinating soy beans. [710, 708]

This transferase exchanges the hexose-1-phosphate moiety of uridine diphosphate for another hexose-1-phosphate. Its reaction is, therefore, distinct from that of uridine diphosphoglucose pyrophosphorylase (equation 37), in that it does not create a new UDP-sugar, but rather exchanges a preexisting UDP-sugar into another one.

A congenital human disease, galactosemia, is believed to be due to an inherited defect which consists in a lack of the enzyme galactose-1-phosphate uridyl transferase in the erythrocytes [438] and in the liver. [16] The disease is characterized by the inability of the individuals afflicted to metabolize galactose. [461] Accumulation of abnormally high amounts of galactose-1-phosphate in the red blood cells [814] and in the urine results, and is followed by mental and physical retardation. The disease, which commences in infancy, can be well controlled by a strictly galactose-free, that is milk-free, diet. [580] The metabolism of UDP-galactose and the enzyme reactions involved have been reviewed by Kalckar. [460]

B. Sugar Derivatives of Other Nucleoside Diphosphates

Uridine triphosphate and uridine diphosphate sugars were the first nucleosides discovered to play the outstanding role in the interconversions of carbohydrates and in the biogenesis of glycosidic bonds and complex saccharides, now well understood. [532] Subsequently, the important biolgocial implications of triphosphates and diphosphate sugar derivatives of other nucleosides were recognized.

The requirement of inosine triphosphate and guanosine triphosphate for the activity of the oxalacetate-synthesizing enzyme and their formation has been discussed earlier in this chapter (see Section IVA). Inosine diphosphate glucose and IDP-mannose were prepared from ITP and the corresponding hexose-1-phosphate with enzymes from lactating rat mammary gland, rat liver, or calf liver. [941]

GDP-Mannose was first isolated from yeast, [125] and later from the hen oviduct. [882] Its formation from GTP and mannose-1-phosphate by the enzyme GDP-*mannose pyrophosphorylase* [634] from yeast (reaction 40) was found to be analogous to that of UDP-glucose (reaction 37).

$$\text{GTP} + \text{mannose-1-phosphate} \rightleftharpoons \text{GDP-mannose} + \text{PP}_i \qquad (40)$$

An enzyme catalyzing reaction 40 was also found in, and purified from, *Arthrobacter sp. NRRL B 1973*. [741] Small quantities of GDP-glucose and GDP-fructose, in addition to GDP-mannose, were obtained from the mold, *Eremothecium ashbii*, [733] and the biosynthesis of GDP-glucose by this organism was shown to be analogous to that of GDP-mannose: [734]

$$\text{GTP} + \text{glucose-1-phosphate} \rightleftharpoons \text{GDP-glucose} + \text{PP}_i \qquad (41)$$

Enzymes which catalyze reaction 41 have also been found in higher plants, e.g. peas. [54] In addition to GDP-glucose, GDP-mannose, GDP-fructose, and GDP-fucose were found to be synthesized in lactating bovine mammary glands from GTP and the sugar-1-phosphates. [144]

Pazur and Shuey [711] demonstrated the biosynthesis of thymidine diphosphate glucose in *Streptococcus faecalis* to proceed with the use of dTTP, according to the equation:

$$\text{dTTP} + \text{glucose-1-phosphate} \rightleftharpoons \text{dTDP-glucose} + \text{PP}_i \qquad (42)$$

The same reaction is also operative with enzymes from *Pseudomonas aeruginosa ATCC-7700*, [503] from the yeast *Hansenula*, [467] and from *Salmonella*. [86] The enzymes from the two latter sources are distinct from the UDP-glucose pyrophosphorylases occurring in the same organisms. Moreover, dTDP-glucose pyrophosphorylase of *Salmonella* is inhibited competitively by UDP-glucose or by dTDP-rhamnose. [86, 598] This inhibition thus appears to provide a control mechanism for both the sugar and nucleoside utilization in this organism.

Streptococcus faecalis, grown on D-galactose, [707, 702] and mung beans [658, 272] contains *dTDP-galactose pyrophosphorylase* which catalyzes the formation of dTDP-galactose from d-TTP and α-D-galactose-1-phosphate in analogy to reaction 42. This enzyme differs from both dTDP-glucose pyrophosphorylase and UDP-galactose pyrophosphorylase.

Extracts of hog gastric mucosa were capable of forming dTDP-N-acetylglucosamine, [501] according to the generalized equation:

$$\text{nucleoside triphosphate} + \text{aldose-1-phosphate} \rightleftharpoons$$
$$\text{nucleoside diphosphate aldose} + \text{PP}_i \qquad (43)$$

In an analogous manner, sonic extracts of *Pseudomonas aeruginosa* catalyze the synthesis of dTDP-glucosamine from dTTP and α-D-glucosamine-1-phosphate, and the latter amino sugar derivative is subsequently acetylated by acetyl-CoA and an enzyme from the same organism to yield dTDP-N-acetylglucosamine. [504, 505]

ADP-glucose is synthesized from ATP and glucose-1-phosphate by a wheat enzyme [241] and by enzymes from calf liver and lactating rat mammary gland. [940] This reaction proceeds in accordance with equation 43. The isolation of ADP-glucose from alcoholic extracts of corn grains, [765] and from ripening rice grains [638] has been reported. In the latter source ADP-glucose is associated with about three times its quantity of UDP-glucose. *ADP-glucose pyrophosphorylase* from *E. coli* is activated by fructose diphosphate, glyceraldehyde-3-phosphate and phosphoenolpyruvate. [740] These phosphates stimulated the synthesis of ATP-glucose 20-fold and more.

Other ADP-hexoses, such as ADP-D-mannose, ADP-D-galactose and ADP-N-acetyl-D-glucosamine, were reported to arise with the aid of an enzyme from corn grains. Their biosynthesis follows the general reaction 43, [696] and they were isolated as minor components from corn grain extracts. [198] Formation of ADP-mannose was also shown to occur in calf, liver and the mammary gland of lactating rats. [940]

An enzyme from *Salmonella paratyphi* A catalyzes the formation of dCDP-D-glucose from dCTP and glucose-1-phosphate, [299] and dGDP-mannose was found to be synthesized by an enzyme from *Arthrobacter sp. NRRL B 1973*. [741] The latter enzyme, even after purification, appears to catalyze also the synthesis of GDP-mannose and IDP-mannose. [741] The synthesis of IDP-mannose in calf liver and rat mammary tissue is probably catalyzed by the enzymes responsible for the formation of ADP-mannose. [940]

C. *Epimerization of Nucleoside Diphosphate Sugars*

In addition to the important function of the nucleoside diphosphate sugars as potential precursors of glycosidic bond formation, a feature which will be discussed later in this chapter, another important property of this group of substances is their ability, under the influence of certain enzymes, to undergo epimerization at any of the carbon atoms, and hence, to originate nucleoside derivatives of different sugars. These transformations of one sugar into another in the form of their nucleoside diphosphate derivatives represent one of the most important pathways of biosynthesis for many hexoses, pentoses, and hexuronic acids, and are summarized in Fig. 33.

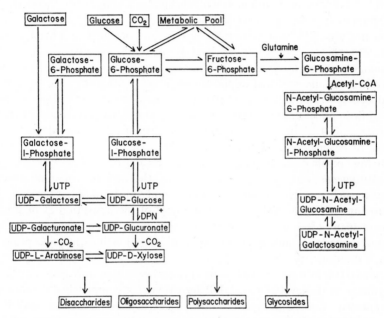

FIG. 33. The role of UDP-sugars in the formation of derivatives of different monosaccharides by epimerization, dehydrogenation, or decarboxylation reactions.

There are essentially two mechanisms by which the biological transformation of sugars into their epimers can be accomplished. In both cases, the nucleoside diphosphate sugars are involved.

The first mechanism is the transformation of UDP-glucose to UDP-galactose by the reaction represented in the above equation 39. Galactose-1-phosphate is necessary in this reaction to yield UDP-galactose.

The second mechanism consists in the inversion of a hydroxyl group of UDP-sugar, and is catalyzed by epimerases. The reversible epimerization:

$$\text{UDP-glucose} \rightleftharpoons \text{UDP-galactose} \qquad (44)$$

was first described by Leloir,[530] and was further investigated in several other laboratories.[793, 586, 462, 517, 589] The enzyme, *uridine diphospho-galactose-4-epimerase*, catalyzing this reaction, was found in various mammalian tissues, such as in liver[586] and mammary gland, in blood,[462] in germinating soy beans,[710] and further in protozoa,[325] in bacteria[793, 517] and yeast.[530, 588] The liver enzyme requires diphosphopyridine nucleotide as a coenzyme,[585] and the enzymes isolated from *E. coli*[988] and from yeast[589] contain protein-bound DPN which is essential for their activity. An epimerase from a bacterial source (*Lactobacillus bulgaricus*) may either not use DPN as a coenzyme, or may contain DPN in a firmly bound form.[508] The reaction catalyzed by UDP-galactose-4-epimerase from liver presumably passes through an oxidation-reduction process in which a UDP-4-ketohexose and reduced diphosphopyridine nucleotide are transitory products.[465] The application of tritiated glucose to the study of the mechanism of this epimerization reaction in *Saccharomyces fragilis* suggests that the H-atom at C-4 of the sugar is either stereospecifically removed or reintroduced, or never departs from the hexose.[88]

Highly purified UDP-galactose-4-epimerase from the yeast *Candida pseudotropicalis* was markedly activated by the addition of a number of cations, such as glycylglycine, ornithine and, most of all, spermine and spermidine.[199] This behavior is reminiscent of the activation at high dilutions of many other enzymes by polycations,[84, 85, 83] and suggests that the purified epimerase undergoes reversible dissociation into inactive products at high dilutions.[82]

The two reactions (39 and 44) which bring about the epimerization of sugar-phosphates at the level of their UDP derivatives are completely different from one another. Two pathways are known to exist, therefore, which lead from galactose-1-phosphate to glucose derivatives, and which are summarized by the following two sets of equations:

$$\text{galactose-1-P} + \text{UTP} \rightleftharpoons \text{UDP-galactose} + \text{PP}_i \tag{45}$$

$$\text{UDP-galactose} \rightleftharpoons \text{UDP-glucose} \tag{46}$$

$$\text{Total: galactose-1-P} + \text{UTP} \rightleftharpoons \text{UDP-glucose} + \text{PP}_i \tag{47}$$

$$\text{galactose-1-P} + \text{UDP-glucose} \rightleftharpoons \text{UDP-galactose} + \text{glucose-1-P} \tag{48}$$

$$\text{UDP-galactose} \rightleftharpoons \text{UDP-glucose} \tag{49}$$

$$\text{Total: galactose-1-P} \rightleftharpoons \text{glucose-1-P} \tag{50}$$

The difference between these two mechanisms is obvious. In the second one, the UDP-sugar does not accumulate and its role corresponds more to that of a coenzyme than of an intermediate product. The enzyme system involved in this latter reaction has formerly been referred to also as *galacto-waldenase*.

Analogous reactions of sugar transformations have been observed to occur with epimeric sugars of other nucleoside diphosphates and with other pairs of epimeric nucleoside diphosphate sugars. Thus, the galactose-glucose conversion was found to be accomplished also by an epimerase from *Streptococcus faecalis* which uses the thymidine diphosphate glycosides [707] according to the equation:

$$dTDP\text{-galactose} \rightleftharpoons dTDP\text{-glucose} \qquad (51)$$

and a similar enzyme has been described in higher plants, i.e. germinating seeds of *Phaseolus aureus*. [658]

Epimerization of 2-deoxy-D-galactose to 2-deoxy-D-glucose by enzymes from brewer's yeast [256] and higher plants [255] has been reported. UDP-Glucuronic acid is transformed into the corresponding galacturonic acid derivative by plant or bacterial enzymes [849, 660] and by an epimerase from rabbit skin. [444] The latter enzyme requires catalytic amounts of DPN for the reaction and is inhibited by DPNH. TPN is not active in this respect. A liver enzyme has been reported to epimerize UDP-acetylglucosamine to UDP-acetylmannosamine, [140, 162] and UDP-acetylglucosamine is converted to UDP-acetylgalactosamine by extracts from skin, [444] liver or bacteria. [305, 566] The enzyme in cell-free extracts of *Bacillus subtilis* catalyzing the latter reaction is distinct from galactose-4-epimerase from rat liver and rabbit skin in that it is fully active in the absence of added DPN. [306] Extracts of hog gastric mucosa [501] and of *Pseudomonas aeruginosa* [504, 505] catalyze the conversion of dTDP-N-acetylglucosamine to the corresponding galactosamine derivative. [733] The epimerization of UDP-D-xylose to UDP-L-arabinose by an enzyme from mung beans has been reported by Ginsburg et al. [298]

Guanosine diphosphate fucose was isolated by Ginsburg and Kirkman [297] from *Aerobacter aerogenes* which is known to produce an L-fucose containing polysaccharide. The parent substance of this fucose nucleotide was reported to be guanosine diphosphate mannose which is transformed in this microorganism into GDP-fucose by a TPNH requiring enzyme system according to the equation [292, 294]:

$$\text{GDP-D-mannose} \xrightarrow{\text{TPNH}} \text{GDP-L-fucose} \qquad (52)$$

This reaction appears to pass through guanosine-5'-diphosphate-4-keto-6-deoxy-D-mannose as an intermediate. [295]

A similar mechanism for L-fucose biosynthesis has been described in mammalian tissues, e.g. rabbit lung, where fucose is postulated to arise from glucose *via* glucose-6-phosphate, fructose-6-phosphate, mannose-6-phosphate, mannose-1-phosphate and GDP-mannose. [258] GDP-Mannose is also formed in bovine lactating mammary glands, together with GDP-fructose, GDP-fucose, and GDP-glucose. [144] The biosynthesis of the latter substance is catalyzed by an enzyme, *GTP: α-D-glucose-1-phosphate-guanylyl transferase*, according to the general mechanism of reaction 38, where UTP is replaced by GTP.

dTDP-Glucose is an important intermediate in the biosynthesis of the rhamnose nucleoside in *Streptococcus faecalis*. [711] The conversion requires TPNH [712] and proceeds according to the following equation:

$$\text{dTDP-glucose} \xrightarrow{\text{TPNH}} \text{dTDP-rhamnose} \tag{53}$$

An analogous reaction was demonstrated to occur in *Pseudomonas aeruginosa*. [502, 503] TPNH is also required in this case, and a 4-keto-6-deoxyhexose intermediate was reported to arise during the conversion of dTDP-glucose to the rhamnose nucleoside. [317, 307] The mechanism of L-rhamnose formation in *Streptomyces griseus* [93, 134] is discussed later in this chapter (see Fig. 37). Reaction 53 is also catalyzed by an enzyme system in sonic extracts of *E. coli* strain B. [680] In the absence of TPNH, or with extracts of certain other *E. coli* strains (Y 10), whether or not TPNH is added, the 4-keto-6-deoxy-D-glucose nucleoside is obtained. The enzyme catalyzing the latter reaction was purified. [219] Rhamnose formation from glucose appears to proceed in a manner analogous to the conversion of mannose to fucose, although different nucleotides are involved.

In contrast to the bacterial enzymes, which cannot use UDP-glucose as precursor of rhamnose, enzyme preparations from mung bean leaves [51] and from tobacco leaves [52] catalyze the reductive epimerization of UDP-D-glucose to UDP-L-rhamnose.

Crude extracts of a gram-negative bacterium (strain GS) isolated from soil converts GDP-D-mannose to GDP-D-rhamnose and GDP-talomethylose in the presence of TPNH: [572]

2 GDP-D-mannose + 2 TPNH + 2 H⁺ →
    GDP-D-rhamnose + GDP-talomethylose + 2 TPN + 2 H₂O   (54)

There are at least two enzymes involved in the above reaction. [573] The first, *GDP-mannose dehydrase*, yields GDP-4-keto-D-rhamnose and the other, requiring TPNH, catalyzes the reduction of this keto intermediate to either D-rhamnose or D-talomethylose nucleoside. The organism from which these enzyme extracts have been obtained is known to contain a polysaccharide composed of D-rhamnose and D-talomethylose.

Nonenzymatic epimerization of N-acetyl-D-galactosamine to N-acetyl-D-talosamine has been reported to occur in aqueous alkaline solutions. [273]

The formation of L-iduronic acid in rabbit skin originates from UDP-glucose either by way of epimerization of the latter to UDP-L-idose, in the presence of catalytic amounts of DPN, and subsequent dehydrogenation (see Section VIID of this chapter), or by epimerization, also in the presence of catalytic quantities of DPN, of UDP-D-glucuronic acid which is derived from dehydrogenation of UDP-glucose. [443]

The formation of deoxysugars in general, such as that of L-rhamnose, L-fucose, D-rhamnose, 6-deoxy-D-talose (D-talomethylose), etc., consists in the combination of the reduction and either epimerization or decarboxylation (see Section VIIE of this chapter) of the appropriate nucleotide, and was recently summarized by Glaser. [310] The biosynthesis of deoxyribose is treated in the chapter on nucleotides (Chapter 2).

D. *Dehydrogenation of Nucleoside Diphosphate Sugars*

The dehydrogenation of UDP-glucose by enzymes using DPN leads to UDP-glucuronate, according to Fig. 34. Neither an intermediate sugar

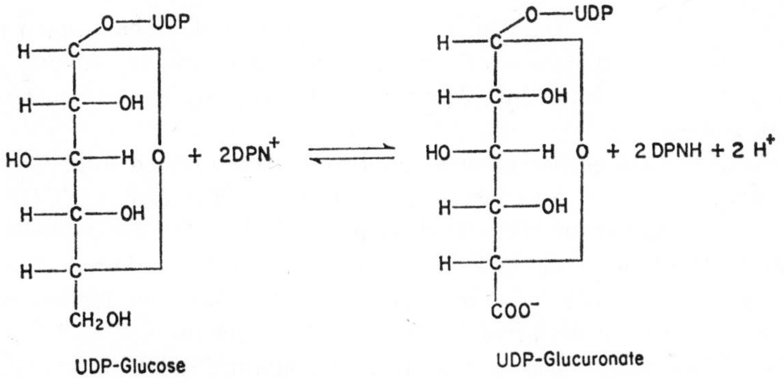

FIG. 34. Dehydrogenation of UDP-glucose to UDP-glucuronic acid.

dialdehyde nor its UDP derivative could be detected and, although it should be assumed that this dehydrogenation would actually proceed in two stages, it appears that only a single enzyme is necessary. [884] This enzyme, *UDP-glucose-dehydrogenase*, has been purified from rat liver, [587, 884] and has also been obtained from rabbit skin, [442] peas [883] and from *pneumococci*. [848]

UDP-Glucose dehydrogenase from calf liver is competitively inhibited *in vitro* by UDP-galactose and noncompetitively by UDP. [796] Barbital and chloretone enhance the activity *in vivo* of the guinea pig or rat liver dehydrogenase; this effect is prevented by hypophysectomy. [417]

The 5-fluorouracil and 6-azauracil analogues of UDP-glucose may serve as substrates of UDP-glucose dehydrogenase. [321]

UDP-Galacturonic acid was isolated from mung bean seedlings by Neufeld and Feingold. [659]

An extract of *Arthrobacter sp. NRRL B-1973* catalyzes the dehydrogenation of GDP-mannose to GDP-mannuronic acid in the presence of DPN. [738] The biosynthesis by this organism of an exocellular polysaccharide containing D-glucose, D-galactose and mannuronic acid may, thus, be explained. The same enzyme also catalyzes the analogous dehydrogenation of dGDP-mannose to dGDP-mannuronic acid. [739]

E. Decarboxylation of Nucleoside Diphosphate Sugars

A study of xylan from wheat plants, which had been treated with various labeled sugars, showed that the main carbon source for the biosynthesis of this pentosan was derived from D-glucose-1-C^{14} or from D-glucuronolactone-1-C^{14}. [654, 14, 655] Both monosaccharides had lost their carbon-6 atom during conversion to xylan, while D-xylose-1-C^{14} was incorporated into the pentosan only after extensive rearrangement of its carbon chain, such as would occur through hexose intermediates. The loss of the carbon-6 atom from D-glucuronic acid through decarboxylation has also been confirmed in corn coleoptiles. [841]

Similar results were obtained for the biosynthesis of araban which is a part of many pectic substances. Both the arabans from the boysenberry and from the strawberry were thus shown to originate from the carbon atoms 1 to 5 of glucose. [816, 817]

An enzyme, *UDP-glucuronic acid carboxylase*, was isolated from *Cryptococcus laurentii* which decarboxylates UDP-glucuronic acid to UDP-D-xylose in the presence of DPN. [21] It is probable that the decarboxylation occurs on a transient β-keto-acid intermediate formed by oxido-reduction at carbon atom 4. Extracts of mung-bean seedlings (*Phaseolus aureus*) were found to catalyze the decarboxylation of UDP-D-glucuronate to UDP-D-xylose. [660] The same reaction mixture also contained UDP-galacturonate and UDP-L-arabinose.

Thus, the pentose units in pentosans originate from glucose, D-xylose is the product of decarboxylation of D-glucuronate, and L-arabinose that of D-galacturonate. The presence in higher plants of UDP-D-xylose and of UDP-L-arabinose, as well as of the UDP derivatives of glucuronic and galacturonic acids [301, 248] makes it likely that the decarboxylation of the uronic acid occurs at the level of the UDP derivatives.

F. Nucleoside Diphosphates of Dideoxyhexoses

Several dideoxyhexose nucleotides were isolated from microorganisms, as summarized in Table 4. Their biosynthesis probably proceeds in two steps. The first one leads from a hexose nucleotide precursor to a 4-keto-6-deoxy intermediate, as shown in equation (55) for the biosynthesis of CDP-paratose, [582] CDP-tyvelose, [238] and CDP-ascarylose. [582]

$$\text{CDP-D-glucose} \xrightarrow{\text{DPN}} \text{CDP-4-keto-6-deoxy-D-glucose} \qquad (55)$$

This reaction requires DPN. [582] In the succeeding step, the intermediate keto-deoxysugar is converted into the dideoxyhexose nucleotide,[238, 584] probably with the aid of TPNH,[584] as seen in the example of CDP-tyvelose biosynthesis in Fig. 35.

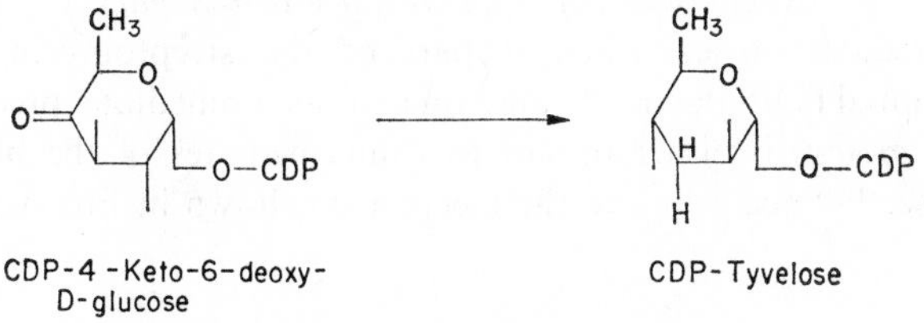

CDP-4-Keto-6-deoxy-
D-glucose

CDP-Tyvelose

FIG. 35. Formation of CDP-tyvelose.

Two unusual thymidine diphosphate-4-acetamido-dideoxyhexoses, termed TDP-X and TDP-X_2, were detected in *E. coli* strains.[679] They were identified as the corresponding D-galactose and D-glucose derivatives. Their biosynthesis originates from dTDP-D-glucose which is transformed into dTDP-4-keto-6-deoxy-D-glucose by an enzyme, *TDP-D-glucose oxidoreductase*. This enzyme is different from *CDP-D-glucose oxidoreductase*[582] and requires DPN.[291] Amination by L-glutamate in the presence of pyridoxal

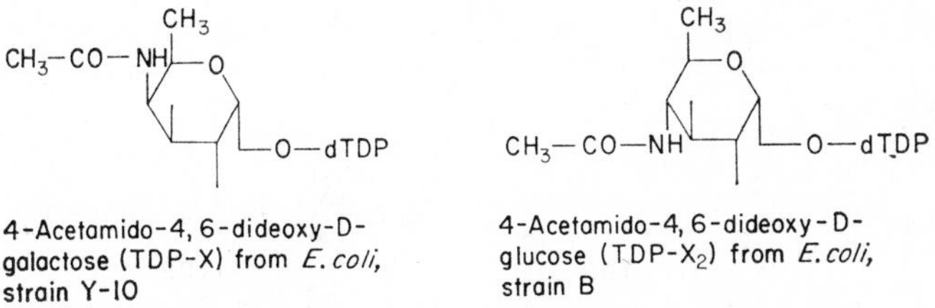

4-Acetamido-4,6-dideoxy-D-
galactose (TDP-X) from *E.coli*,
strain Y-10

4-Acetamido-4,6-dideoxy-D-
glucose (TDP-X_2) from *E.coli*,
strain B

FIG. 36. Structures of acetamide dideoxysugars in *E. coli* strains.

TABLE 4. ISOLATION OF DIDEOXYHEXOSE NUCLEOTIDES

Common name	Chemical name	Source	Reference
CDP-Paratose	CDP-3,6-Dideoxy-D-glucose	*Salmonella paratyphi* A	592
CDP-Abequose	CDP-3,6-Dideoxy-D-galactose	*Salmonella* mutants	665
GDP-Colitose	GDP-3,6-Dideoxy-L-galactose	*E. coli* 0111-B4	370
CDP-Tyvelose	CDP-3,6-Dideoxy-D-mannose	*Salmonella* mutants	665
CDP-Ascarylose	CDP-3,6-Dideoxy-L-mannose	*Pasteurella pseudo-tuberculosis*	584

phosphate yields the corresponding amino sugars, and subsequent acetylation by acetyl-CoA leads to the N-acetyl amino sugar nucleotides, [583] shown in Fig. 36.

G. Nucleoside Diphosphates of Other Sugars

The dialdose streptose, which is part of the streptomycin molecule, originates from dTDP-glucose,[93] and one of its immediate precursors in *Streptomyces griseus* is either one of two intermediates of the biosynthesis of L-rhamnose, [134] according to the mechanism shown in Fig. 37.

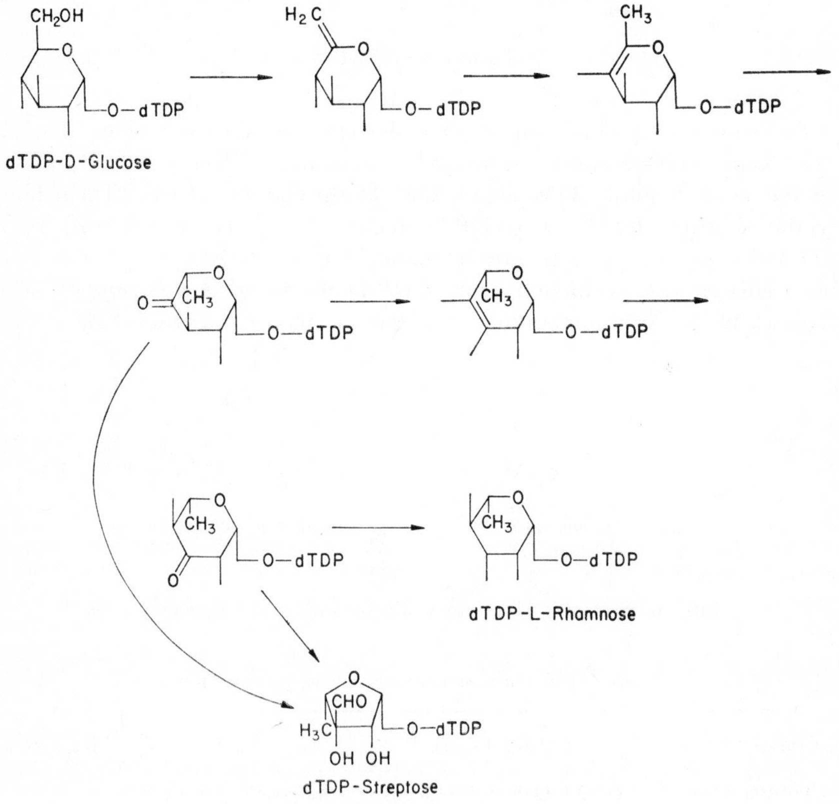

FIG. 37. Formation of dTDP-streptose and dTDP-L-rhamnose.

Apiose is a branched aldopentose which occurs, together with D-glucose, in the parsley glycoside apiin. Its biosynthesis from UDP-D-glucose, via UDP-D-glucuronic acid [339] is illustrated in Fig. 38.

Two novel CDP-sugars were found in *Azotobacter vinelandii*, strain O, and were characterized as a 2-O-methyl-deoxyaldose and its carboxylic acid, respectively. [681]

Dehydrogenation of UDP-glucosamine by UDP-glucose dehydrogenase from calf liver in the presence of DPN yielded UDP-glucosaminuronic acid. [835] This sugar has been found to be a constituent of two acidic poly-saccharides, one isolated from *Hemophilus influenzae*, type d, [986] and the other obtained from *Staphylococcus aureus* cells. [354]

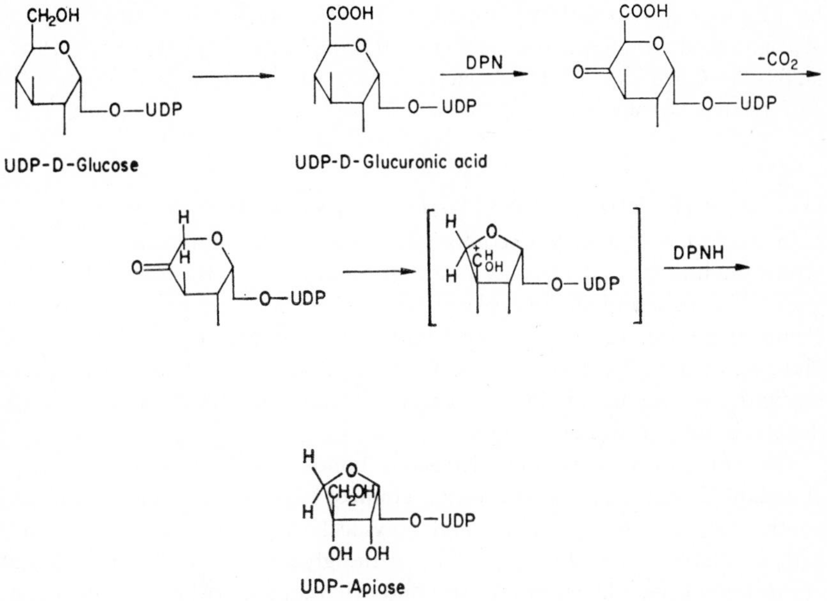

FIG. 38. Biosynthesis of apiose.

A heptose nucleotide, namely GDP-D-*glycero*-D-*manno*-heptose has been isolated from baker's yeast, [300] and its structure is shown in Fig. 39. A tentative pathway for its biosynthesis was proposed which leads from sedoheptulose-7-phosphate to D-glycero-O-mannoheptose-7-phosphate, then

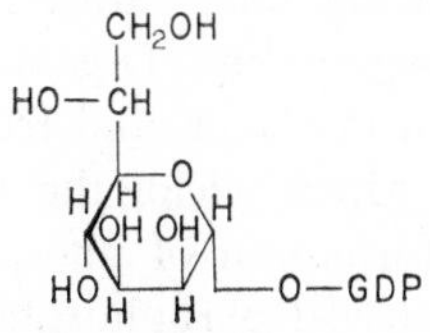

FIG. 39. Structure of GDP-D-*glycero*-D-*manno*-heptose.

to the corresponding 1-phosphate and finally to the nucleotide. [300] The bio-synthesis of D-*glycero*-D-*manno* heptose in *Azotobacter indicum* from hexose precursor was found to proceed along pathways involving the enzymes transaldolase, transketolase and aldolase. [451]

Several nucleoside diphosphate oligosaccharides have been described. These include UDP-N-acetyl glucosamine-6-fucose from the isthmus of hen oviduct; [905] UDP-N-acetyllactosamine and UDP-N-acetyllactosamine fucoside from human milk and colostrum; [490] an unusual sugar derivative from the isthmus of hen oviduct, i.e. the D-galactose-1-phosphate of UDP-N-acetylglucosamine in which galactose and N-acetylglucosamine are linked by an α-1,6-phosphodiester linkage; [894, 279] and finally some muramic acid-amino acid derivatives, such as UDP-AG-lactyl-Ala-Glu,† UDP-AG-lactyl-Ala-Glu-Lys, UDP-AG-lactyl-L-Ala-D-Glu-L-Lys-D-Ala-D-Ala, [885] and related substances. [567, 440, 881]

VIII. THE FORMATION OF GLYCOSIDIC BONDS

In accordance with the commonly accepted terminology by which a glycosidic linkage is defined as an acetal bond between the aldehyde or keto group of a sugar and any hydroxy group of a second compound of unspecified chemical nature, substances like uridine diphosphate sugars and aldose-1-phosphates are glycosides. These two substances are intermediates in the biosynthesis and metabolism of carbohydrates, and they occur in nature, therefore, only in trace amounts.

The commonly occurring glycosidic bonds which are infinitely more abundant in nature are those which connect two or more sugars with one another, such as in di-, oligo-, and polysaccharides, or which link a sugar with an alcohol or phenol (aglycon) in the glycosides. At the present state of our knowledge, the latter type of bond originates almost exclusively from a small number of high-energy phosphate derivatives of sugars, i.e. the aldose-1-phosphates or the nucleotide glycosides. The energy of the aldose-phosphate bond is thereby utilized to create the new glycosidic bond.

Consequently, only a few reactions of biological significance are known which lead to the *de novo* synthesis of glycosidic bonds, namely the intramolecular phosphate exchange catalyzed by the mutases, in particular by phosphoglucomutase, producing the aldose-1-phosphates, secondly, the phosphorylation of some sugars like D-galactose, D-galactosamine, N-acetylgalactosamine, D-glucuronic acid, and fructose-1-phosphate by ATP, catalyzed by hexokinases, which yield the corresponding 1-phosphate derivatives, and finally the formation of phosphoaldose-1-pyrophosphates, in particular of 5-phosphoribosyl-1-pyrophosphate from ribose-5-phosphate and ATP, as discovered by Kornberg *et al.* [496] The formation of disaccharides, oligosaccharides, or polysaccharides, as well as of aglycon-glycosides then follows through transglycosylation reactions where the glycosyl donor may be either an aldose-1-phosphate, a uridine diphosphate sugar, or a di-,

† AG-lactyl = acetylglucosamine lactyl = muramyl.

oligo-, or polysaccharide. These transglycosylations may be expressed by the general equation:

$$(glycosyl)—O—X \ + \ H—O—(acceptor) \rightleftharpoons$$
$$(glycosyl)—O—(acceptor) \ + \ H—O—X \qquad (56)$$

where (glycosyl)—O—X is the glycosyl donor; H—O—(acceptor) is a hydroxyl group-containing substance which may be either a saccharide (mono-, oligo-, or polysaccharide) or an aglycon, i.e. any other hydroxylated compound; (glycosyl)—O—(acceptor) is the synthesized glycoside, and H—O—X is the deglycosylated donor. The radical X may be one of three groupings, i.e. either a phosphate group, as in aldose-1-phosphates, or a nucleoside pyrophosphate as in nucleoside diphosphate glycosides, or a saccharide with one, two or any higher number of sugar units, like in sucrose, maltose, dextrins or polysaccharides. The enzymes which catalyze the glycosyl transfer from these three groups of donors are called phosphorylases, nucleoside diphosphate transglycosylases (sometimes also nucleoside diphosphate transferases), and transglycosylases proper (formerly transglucosidases), respectively. The principal reactions of these three groups of enzymes are summarized in Tables 5 to 8. The biosynthesis of saccharides from sugar nucleotides has been recently reviewed. [663, 296]

A. *The Glycosyl Donor*

The three main types of glycosyl donors, namely aldose-1-phosphates, nucleoside diphosphate glycosides, and di-, tri-, oligo-, or polysaccharides have a common feature in that they are capable of transferring the free energy of their glycoside bond to the newly formed saccharide and, hence, render the transglycosylation possible. Simultaneously, a deglycosylated product with a lower free energy is formed. The aldose-1-phosphates thus yield inorganic phosphate, the nucleoside diphosphate glycosides produce nucleoside diphosphate, disaccharides give monosaccharides, trisaccharides give disaccharides, and oligo-, or polysaccharides give rise to saccharides with a smaller number of glycosidic bonds, unless donor and acceptor are the same substances. In the latter case the reaction can be considered to be essentially an intramolecular transglycosylation, as for instance in the case of the reaction catalyzed by Branching enzyme.

When one compares the changes in free energy which accompany the formation of glycoside bonds (see Table 9), it becomes obvious that considerably more energy is expended when a uridine diphosphate glycoside serves as the glycosyl donor (line 12) than in the case of the formation of a saccharide from an aldose-1-phosphate (line 4). This difference becomes even more marked when the hydrolysis of pyrophosphate to inorganic phosphate

TABLE 5. PHOSPHORYLASE REACTIONS

Glycosyl donor (Glycosyl)-O-X + H-O-(acceptor)	Acceptor	Saccharide synthesized† (Glycosyl)-O-(acceptor)	Deglycosylated donor H-O-X	Name of enzyme	Source of enzyme	References
Aldose-1-phosphate	Primer = (monose)$_n$	Polysaccharide = (monose)$_{n+1}$	Inorg. phosphate	Phosphorylase		
α-D-Glucose-1-phosphate	Dextrin primer	Amylose (α)	Inorg. phosphate	Phosphorylase	Widespread	178, 481
α-D-Glucose-1-phosphate	D-Glucose	Cellobiose (β)	Inorg. phosphate	Cellobiose phosphorylase	Clostridium thermocellum	831
α-Glucose-1-phosphate	D-Glucose	Laminaribiose (β)	Inorg. phosphate	Specific phosphorylase	Euglenia gracilis, Astasia ocellata	570, 568
α-D-Glucose-1-phosphate	β-D-Fructose	Sucrose (α) (β)	Inorg. phosphate	Sucrose phosphorylase	Pseudomonas saccharophila, Pseudomonas putrifaciens, Leuconostoc mesenteroides, sugar cane	220, 360, 359, 829
α-D-Glucose-1-phosphate	Ketoses	Sucrose analogues (α) (β)	Inorg. phosphate	Sucrose phosphorylase	Pseudomonas saccharophila	218, 360, 359
β-D-Glucose-1-phosphate	D-Xylose	α-D-Glucosyl-D-xylose	Inorg. phosphate	Maltose phosphorylase	N. meningitidis	257
β-D-Glucose-1-phosphate	D-Glucose	Maltose (α), Maltose analogues (α)	Inorg. phosphate	Maltose phosphorylase	N. meningitidis	257, 626
α-D-Ribose-1-phosphate	Purine	Nucleoside (β)	Inorg. phosphate	Nucleoside phosphorylase	Rat liver	457

† The steric configuration of the synthesized glycoside bond is indicated in parentheses.

TABLE 6. NUCLEOSIDE DIPHOSPHATE GLYCOSIDE TRANSGLYCOSYLASES (INCLUDING NUCLEOSIDE MONOPHOSPHATE GLYCOSIDE TRANSGLYCOSYLASES)

Glycosyl donor (Glycosyl)-O-X	+	Acceptor H-O-(acceptor)	⇌	Saccharide synthesized† (Glycosyl)-O-(acceptor)	+	Deglycosylated donor H-O-X	Name of enzyme	Source of enzyme	References
UDP-Glucose		Dextrin primer = (Glucose)$_n$		Amylose (Glycogen) (α) = (Glucose)$_{n+1}$		UDP	UDPG-Glycogen transglucosylase	Mammalian liver, muscle, and diaphragm	538, 544, 943, 776
UDP-Glucose		Cellulose primer = (Glucose)$_n$		Cellulose (β) = (Glucose)$_{n+1}$		UDP		Acetobacter xylinum	303, 304
UDP-Glucose or GDP-Glucose				Cellulose (β)		UDP or GDP		Sarcina ventriculi, Lupinus albus, Phaseolus aureus	133, 113, 53
UDP-Glucose		‡		β-1,3-Glucan (Callose, Laminaran)		UDP		Mung bean, Euglena gracilis	249, 323, 571
UDP-Glucose				β-1,2-Glucan		UDP		Agrobacterium tumefaciens, Rhizobium japonicum	202
UDP-Glucose		β-D-Fructose		Sucrose (α) (β)		UDP		Wheat, corn, bean germs, potato sprouts, sugar cane leaf, rice grains, Jerusalem artichoke tubers, sugar beet roots	115, 535, 927, 141, 121, 648, 270, 32, 615, 638
ADP-Glucose		β-D-Fructose		Sucrose (α) (β)		ADP		Rice grains	638
UDP-Glucose		Monosaccharides		Disaccharides (α)		UDP		Pea	70

TABLE 6—(cont.)

Glycosyl donor (Glycosyl)-O-X	+	Acceptor H-O-(acceptor)	⇌	Saccharide synthesized† (Glycosyl)-O-(acceptor)	+	Deglycosylated donor H-O-X	Name of enzyme	Source of enzyme	References
UDP-Glucose		D-Fructose-6-phosphate		Sucrose phosphate (α) (β)		UDP		Wheat germ	536
UDP-Glucose		D-Glucose-6-phosphate		Trehalose phosphate (α) (α)		UDP		Yeast, Mycobacteria, silkmoth, locusts, insects, fish	533,126,135, 690, 324, 559, 641, 642, 153
UDP-D-Galactose and GDP-L-Galactose				DL-Galactan		UDP and GDP		*Porphyra perforata*	889
UDP-Galactose		D-Glucose		Lactose (β)		UDP		Bovine and guinea-pig mammary gland, bovine milk	350, 969, 38
UDP-Galactose		N-Acetyl-D-Glucosamine		N-Acetyl-lactose (β)		UDP		Bovine and guinea-pig mammary gland	969
UDP-Galactose		D-Glucose-1-phosphate		Lactose phosphate (β)		UDP		Bovine udder	281
GDP-Mannose UDP-Fructose UDP-Xylose		(D-Xylose)$_n$		Mannan (β) Fructosan (β) Xylan oligo-saccharides (β) = (D-xylose)$_{n+1}$		GDP UDP UDP		*Hansenula holstii* Dahlia tubers Asparagus extracts	12,103 327 250, 301
UDP-Arabinose		(L-Arabinose)$_n$		Araban (α) = (L-Arabinose)$_{n+1}$		UDP		Higher plants	301
GDP-L-Fucose and UDP-D-Galactose		D-Glucose		Fucosyl-lactose		GDP and UDP		Dog milk	340

Substrate		Product	Enzyme	Nucleotide	Organism	References
UDP-Galacturonate GDP-D-Mannuronic acid and DGP-L-Guluronic acid	++	Pectin (α) Alginic acid		UDP GDP	Higher plants *Fucus gardneri Silva*	817 549
GDP-Mannose + UDP-Glucuronic acid + UDP-Xylose		Extracellular polysaccharides		GDP and UDP	*Cryptococcus laurentii*	2
UDP-Acetylglucosamine	++	Chitin (β)	Chitin synthetase	UDP	*Neurospora crassa, Schistocerca gregaria, Prodenia eridania*	315, 314, 136, 447
UDP-Acetylglucosamine and UDP-Glucuronate	++	Hyaluronate		UDP	Rous Sarcoma, Hemolytic Streptococci, rat fetus	313, 574, 575, 808, 804
UDP-Glucuronic acid + UDP-N-Acetylglucosamine		Heparitin		UDP	Murine mast cell tumor	832, 833
UDP-Glucuronic acid + UDP-N-Acetylgalactosamine		Precursor of chondroitin sulfates A and C		UDP	Chick embryo epiphyses	723, 834
UDP-Glucose, or ADP-Glucose, or GDP-Glucose		Bacterial polysaccharides		UDP, ADP, or GDP	*Dictyostelium discoideum*	963
UDP-Galactose		Bacterial polysaccharides	Transferase	UDP	*Dictyostelium discoideum*	891
dTDP-L-Rhamnose		Bacterial cell wall polysaccharides		dTDP	*Streptococcus faecalis, Streptococcus pyogenes*	701, 1009

TABLE 6—(cont.)

Glycosyl donor (Glycosyl)-O-X	Acceptor + H-O-(acceptor)	⇌ Saccharide synthesized† (Glycosyl)-O-(acceptor)	Name of enzyme	+ Deglycosylated donor H-O-X	Source of enzyme	References
UDP-Glucose + UDP-Galactose + UDP-N-Acetylglucosamine	Lipid	Bacterial cell wall lipopolysaccharides		UDP	Salmonella typhimurum	684
UDP-N-Acetyl muramyl pentapeptide	Lipid	Lipid-P-muramyl pentapeptide (precursor of bacterial cell wall)		UDP	Staphylococcus aureus	887, 17
UDP-N-Acetylglucosamine UDP-N-Acetyl muramyl pentapeptide	++	Bacterial cell wall glycopeptide		UDP	Staphylococcus aureus	597, 146, 887
UDP-Glucose	Polyglycerophosphate	Teichoic acids		UDP	Bacillus subtilis	316
UDP-Acetylglucosamine	Polyribitolphosphate	Teichoic acids		UDP	Staphylococcus aureus	650, 651
dTDP-L-Rhamnose or UDP-L-Rhamnose	β-Hydroxydecanoyl-CoA	Rhamnolipids		dTDP or UDP	Pseudomonas aeruginosa	117, 52
UDP-Glycoside	Aglycon	Glycosides (β)		UDP	Higher plants	139, 143
dTDP-L-Rhamnose or UDP-L-Rhamnose	Quercitin-glucoside	Rutin (quercitin-rhamnosyl-(1 → 6)-glucoside)		dTDP or UDP	Mung bean	55, 52

UDP-D-Galactose	Inositol (*myo, scyllo, dextro,* or *levo*)	Galactosyl-inositol (*myo, scyllo, dextro,* or *levo*)	UDP	Unripe peas	271
ADP-Glucose, or UDP-Glucose, or CDP-Glucose, or dTDP-Glucose	Aglycon	Glucosides (β) (e.g. arbutin) or Gentiobiosides	ADP, UDP CDP, or dTDP	Wheat germ	924, 326
UDP-Glucuronate	Aglycon	Glucuronosides (β)	UDP	Mammalian liver and kidney	874, 223, 37, 224
CMP-NAN	Lactose	Sialyllactose	CMP	Rat mammary gland	453
CMP-NAN	Oligosaccharides	Sialyloligosaccharides	CMP	Rat mammary gland, *E. coli* K235	453, 787, 454
CMP-NAN		Sialic acid-containing glycoproteins	CMP		787, 454
CMP-NAN	‡	Colominic acid	CMP	*E. coli* K235	15
CMP-KDO		KDO-Lipopolysaccharides	CMP	*E. coli*	284, 233

† The steric configuration at the synthesized glycosidic bond is indicated in parentheses.

‡ The requirement of a primer has been observed only in a few instances. In the case of polysaccharide synthesis by UDP-glycosides, the formation of a glycoside bond represents a lengthening of the chain by one link, and the question as to the origin of the glycoside chain itself must be left open in many instances.

TABLE 7. TRANSGLYCOSYLASES (WITH DI- AND TRISACCHARIDES AS GLYCOSYL DONOR)

Glycosyl donor (Glycosyl)-O-X	Acceptor + H-O-(acceptor) ⇌	Saccharide synthesized (Glycosyl)-O-(acceptor)	Deglycosylated donor + H-O-X	Name of enzyme	Source of enzyme	References
Sucrose	Sucrose	Maltosyl-fructoside	D-Fructose	Invertase	Honey, aphids	982, 983 40,
Sucrose	Sucrose	Melezitose = Glucosyl-fructosyl-glucoside	D-Fructose	Invertase	Leaves of lime tree, aphids	40
Sucrose	Sucrose	Glucosyl-fructosyl fructosides	D-Glucose	Invertase	$A.\ niger$, leaves of sugar beets, yeast	13, 57, 39, 10
Sucrose	Sucrose	Fructosyl-glucosyl-fructoside	D-Glucose	Invertase	Leaves of sugar beets	13
Sucrose	L-Sorbose	D-Glucose-1-sorboside	D-Fructose	Transglucosylase activity of sucrose phosphorylase	$Pseudomonas$ $saccharophila$	217, 1000
Sucrose	$(Glucose)_n$	Amylodextrin = $(Glucose)_{n+1}$	D-Fructose	Amylosucrase	$Neisseria\ perflava$	380, 381, 384, 378
Sucrose	$(Glucose)_n$	Dextran $(Glucose)_{n+1}$	D-Fructose	Dextran sucrase	$Leuconostoc$ $mesenteroides$, $Leuconostoc$ $dextranicum$, $Betacoccus$ $arabinosus$, $Betabacterium$ $vermifore$, and others	376, 385, 377, 378

Substrate	Acceptor	Product	+ Sugar	Enzyme	Source	Reference
Sucrose	(Fructose)$_n$	Levan = (Fructose)$_{n+1}$	D-Glucose	Levansucrase	Aerobacter levanicum, Bacillus subtilis, Bacillus mesentericus, Leuconostoc mesenteroides, Pseudomonas prunicola	397, 396
Sucrose	Melibiose = Galactosyl-glucose	Raffinose = Galactosyl-sucrose	D-Glucose	Levansucrase	Aerobacter levanicum	398
Sucrose	Lactose	Galactosyl-glucosyl fructoside	D-Glucose	Levansucrase	Aerobacter levanicum	31
D-Glucose-1-xyloketoside	D-Fructose	Sucrose	D-Xylulose	Transglucosylase activity of sucrose phosphorylase	Pseudomonas saccharophila	360
Maltose	(Glucose)$_n$	Amylodextrin = (Glucose)$_{n+1}$	D-Glucose	Amylomaltase	E. Coli	620, 219
Maltose	Maltose	Panose = Glucosylmaltose	D-Glucose		Aspergillus niger	59, 996, 688
Maltose	Maltose	Isomaltotriose	D-Glucose	Transglucosylase	Aspergillus niger	59
Maltose	D-Glucose	Maltose	D-Glucose		Wheat germ	230
Maltose	Inorg. phosphate	β-D-Glucose-1-phosphate	D-Glucose	Maltose phosphorylase	Neisseria meningitidis	257
Cellobiose	D-Galactose	Glucopyranosyl-(1→6)-D-galactose	D-Glucose	Transglucosylase	Aspergillus niger	488
Lactose		Galactose containing di-, and trisaccharides			Yeast	700, 27, 1012
β,β-Trehalose, Laminaribiose, Cellobiose, or Gentiobiose		β-1,3- or β-1,6-di-, tri-, or tetrasaccharides		Extracellular laminarinases	Fungi	149

TABLE 7 —(cont.)

Glycosyl donor (Glycosyl)-O-X +	Acceptor H-O-(acceptor) ⇌	Saccharide synthesized (Glycosyl)-O-(acceptor)	Deglycosylated donor + H-O-X	Name of enzyme	Source of enzyme	References
Raffinose = galactosylsucrose	D-Xylose	Xylosucrose = Xylosyl fructoside	Galactosyl glucose (?)	Levansucrase	*Aerobacter levanicum*	33
Raffinose	D-Galactose	Galsucrose = Galactosyl fructoside	Galactosyl glucose (?)	Levansucrase	*Aerobacter levanicum*	246
Raffinose = Galactosyl-sucrose = Melibiosyl-fructoside	(Fructose)$_n$ = (Levan)	(Fructose)$_{n+1}$ = (Levan)	Melibiose = Galactosyl-glucose	Levansucrase	*Aerobacter levanicum*	397, 396, 399
Phenyl-α-glucoside	D-Mannose	Glucosyl-(1→3)-mannose; glucosyl-(1→6) mannose	Phenol	Cryst. taka-maltase	*Aspergillus oryzae*	890
o-Nitrophenyl-β-D-galactoside	D-Galactose	β-1,3-, or β-1,6-Galactosylgalactose	o-Nitrophenol	Transgalactosylase	Yeast	709
o-Nitrophenyl-β-D-galactoside	D-Arabinose	β-1,3-, or β-1,5-Galactosylarabinose	o-Nitrophenol	Transgalactosylase	Yeast	709

TABLE 8. TRANSGLYCOSYLASES (WITH OLIGO- AND POLYSACCHARIDES AS GLYCOSYL DONOR)

Glycosyl donor (Glycosyl)-O-X	+	Acceptor H-O-(acceptor)	⇌	Saccharide synthesized (Glycosyl)-O-(acceptor)	+	Deglycosylated donor H-O-X	Name of enzyme	Source of enzyme	References
Amylose=(Glucose)$_n$ unbranched		Amylose = (Glucose)$_n$ unbranched		Amylopectin = (Glucose)$_{n+x}$ branched‡		Amylose = (Glucose)$_{n-x}$ unbranched	Q-enzyme†	Potato, wrinkled pea, broad bean, Neisseria perflava, Polytomella coeca	368, 714, 668, 180, 290, 183, 411, 379, 72
Amylopectin or glycogen = (Glucose)$_n$ x branching points		Same as donor		Amylopectin or glycogen (glucose)$_n$; $(x+y)$ branching points‡		Same as saccharide synthesized	Branching enzyme†	Mammalian heart, brain, liver	176, 520
Amylodextrin (glucose)$_n$ unbranched; N* < 20		Same as donor		Amylodextrins (glucose)$_{n+x}$; unbranched§		Amylodextrin (glucose)$_{n-x}$ unbranched	D-enzyme	Potato	717, 951 715
Amylose, amylopectin, or linear dextrins = (Glucose)$_n$		Same as donor		Unbranched cyclic or straight dextrins (Schardinger dextrins) (Glucose)$_x$		(Glucose)$_{n-x}$	B. macerans enzyme, cyclodextrinase	Bacillus macerans	913, 990, 815, 262
α-1,4-Glucan oligosaccharides		Same as donor		α-1,4-Glucans		α-1,4-Glucans	Oligo-1,4→1,4-glucan transferase	Rabbit muscle, potato, Aspergillus niger, Streptococcus bovis, Bacillus macerans	111, 952, 718,703, 950, 977

TABLE 8—(cont.)

Glycosyl donor (Glycosyl)-O-X	+ H-O-(acceptor)	Acceptor H-O-(acceptor)	⇌	Saccharide synthesized (Glycosyl)-O-(acceptor)	+	Deglycosylated donor H-O-X	Name of enzyme	Source of enzyme	References
Amylodextrin, amyloheptaose (α-1,4 bonds) (Glucose)$_n$		Dextran (α-1,6-bonds) (Glucose)$_n$		Dextran (α-1,6 bonds) (Glucose)$_{n+1}$		Amylodextrin (α-1,4-bonds) (Glucose)$_{n-1}$	Dextrin dextranase	*Aerobacter capsulatum*	382, 261, 383
Inulin: (Fructose)$_n$		Sucrose		Fructosyl fructosyl glucoside		(Fructose)$_{n-1}$	Transfructosylase	Artichoke	809
Hyaluronic acid		Chondroitin sulfate		Hybrid oligosaccharides		Oligosaccharides	Hyaluronidase	Bovine testes	414

† Action not reversible, proceeds only in direction of equation from left to right.
‡ Formation of α-1,6-glucosidic bonds.
§ Formation of α-1,4-glucosidic bonds through disproportionation of chains.
* N = Chain length.

is taken into account which is most likely to occur (line 14). The reactions using nucleoside diphosphate glycosides as precursors of glycoside bonds in saccharides have equilibrium constants, therefore, which are more in favor of the saccharides to be synthesized than those using aldose-1-phosphates as glycosyl donors. The former reactions proceed, therefore, more to completion in the direction of the saccharide formation, and there can be no doubt that they constitute the preferred mechanism for the biosynthesis of most di-, oligo-, and polysaccharides. On the other hand, the reactions catalyzed by

TABLE 9. CHANGES IN FREE ENERGY DURING GLYCOSIDE BOND FORMATION [1]

A. With Aldose-1-phosphate as Glycosyl Donor [2]	$\Delta F'$ (cal/mole) [3]	Line no.
Glucose + ATP → Glucose-6-phosphate + ADP	− 4400	1
Glucose-6-phosphate → Glucose-1-phosphate	+ 1700	2
Glucose-1-phosphate [4] → Glucoside Bond + P_i	− 600	3
SUM: Glucose [4] + ATP → Glucoside Bond + ADP + P_i	− 3300	4
ADP + P_i → ATP	+ 7700	5
SUM: Glucose [4] → Glucoside Bond	+ 4400 [5]	6

B. With UDP-Sugar as Glycosyl Donor [2]	F' (cal/mole) [3]	
Glucose + ATP → Glucose-6-phosphate + ADP	− 4400	7
Glucose-6-phosphate → Glucose-1-phosphate	+ 1700	8
Glucose-1-phosphate + UTP → UDP-Glucose + PP_i	?	9
UDP-Glucose [4] → Glucoside Bond + UDP	?	10
UDP + ATP → UTP + ADP	?	11
SUM: Glucose [4] + 2 ATP → Glucoside Bond + 2 ADP + PP_i	− 4500 [6]	12
PP_i → 2 P_i	− 6500	13
SUM: Glucose [4] + 2 ATP → Glucoside Bond + 2 ADP + 2 P_i	− 11,000 [7]	14
2 ADP + 2 P_i → 2 ATP (2 × 7700)	+ 15,400	15
SUM: Glucose [4] → Glucoside Bond	+ 4400 [8]	16

(1) At pH 7 and 30°C.
(2) The direction of the arrows indicates the course in which the reactions proceed during the biosynthesis of glycoside bonds. It is understood that all reactions are actually reversible.
(3) The values for free-energy changes ($\Delta F'$) were taken from Atkinson and Morton. [30]
(4) In the presence of a primer.
(5) The figure is in good agreement with the numerical value for the energy of hydrolysis of glycogen, $\Delta F_H = - 4300$ cal. [123]
(6) Calculated as the difference between lines 14 and 13.
(7) Calculated as the difference between lines 16 and 15.
(8) Same as line 6.

phosphorylases may be considered to be involved in the biological breakdown of complex saccharides, as well as in their biosynthesis.

In both cases, glycoside synthesis is possible only when ATP is freely available. The energy for the regeneration of ATP from ADP (Table 9, lines 5 and 15) is furnished by photosynthetic, oxidative, or anaerobic processes such as for instance:

$$\text{succinyl-CoA} + \text{ADP} + \text{P}_i \rightleftharpoons \text{succinate} + \text{ATP} + \text{CoA} \tag{57}$$

$$2\text{ADP} \rightleftharpoons \text{ATP} + \text{AMP} \tag{58}$$

$$\text{1,3-diphosphoglycerate} + \text{ADP} \rightleftharpoons \text{3-phosphoglycerate} + \text{ATP} \tag{59}$$

$$\text{phosphoenolpyruvate} + \text{ADP} \rightleftharpoons \text{pyruvate} + \text{ATP} \tag{60}$$

Glycosyl donors of the saccharide type vary widely with regard to their free energy. The values for the standard free energy of hydrolysis of some of the most important representatives of this class are given in Table 10. Sucrose

TABLE 10. ENERGIES OF HYDROLYSIS OF GLYCOSYL DONORS AND OF SOME POLYSACCHARIDES

	Standard free energy of hydrolysis ΔF_{H} (cal/mole)	References
Glucose-1-phosphate	− 5000	30
UDP-glucose	− 7600†	539
Sucrose	− 6600	356
Maltose	− 3000	458
Lactose	− 3000	551
Glycogen	− 4300	123
Dextran	− 2000	458
Levan	− 4600	720

† Calculated by Leloir et al.[539] by adding to the standard free energy of hydrolysis of sucrose (− 6600 cal) the standard free energy change of sucrose synthesis (− 1000 cal).[141]

has the highest value which is only exceeded by a nucleotide glycosyl donor, e.g. UDP-glucose. Consequently, the reactions catalyzed by various transglycosylases in which sucrose is the glycosyl donor have generally equilibrium constants that are in favor of the synthesis of another saccharide (di-, oligo-, or polysaccharides); these reactions are frequently encountered in nature, and the corresponding transglycosylases are found in many tissues or organisms (see Table 7).

In spite of the relatively low energy of their glycosidic bonds, maltose and lactose have also been found to function as glycosyl donors. Reactions using these disaccharides as glycosyl donors have equilibrium constants which are usually not very much in favor of the synthesis of other glycosides, although the formation of an amylodextrin from maltose by the enzyme amylomaltase, [620, 219] and of trisaccharides from maltose or lactose have been clearly demonstrated (see Table 7).

The conditions of transglycosylation reactions using oligo- or polysaccharides as donors depend in many cases on the nature of the newly synthesized glycoside bond. The formation of α-1,6-glucosidic bonds from glucoside chains containing α-1,4-linkages has been recognized to represent an important mechanism for the biosynthesis of the former bonds in amylopectin and glycogen. There are strong indications that the free energy of hydrolysis of α-1,6-glucosidic bonds is markedly lower than that of the α-1,4-linkages, since dextran with mainly α-1,6-bonds (80 to 90 per cent) has a much lower ΔF_H value than glycogen which contains 90 per cent α-1,4-bonds (see Table 10). Accordingly, the synthesis of α-1,6-glucoside bonds from α-1,4 bonds is an exogonic process, and its equilibrium should be expected to allow the reaction to proceed in the direction of an accumulation of 1,6-linkages. That this is actually the case has been shown for the reactions catalyzed by Branching enzyme and by Q-enzyme. No evidence for a reversal of the action of Q-enzyme, i.e. for the cleavage of α-1,6-glucoside bonds in amylopectin by Q-enzyme, could indeed be found. [60]

B. *The Bond Broken*

The question as to whether a glycoside or a glycosyl group (see Fig. 40) is transferred during the formation of saccharides according to equation (56), has first been investigated by Cohn. [156] This author obtained evidence that the action of phosphorylases from muscle and from potato, as well as of

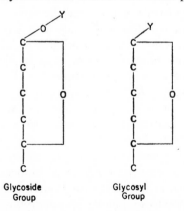

Glycoside
Group

Glycosyl
Group

FIG. 40. Difference between glycoside and glycosyl groups.

sucrose phosphorylase, actually splits the bond between the carbon-1 atom of glucose and oxygen, and not the one between oxygen and phosphorus. In complete analogy to these findings, the same mechanism of a transfer of glycosyl groups rather than of glycoside residues has been observed in a number of instances of saccharide synthesis,[378, 507] and it is for this reason that the terms of *glycosyl* donor and *transglycosylase* are used instead of glycoside donor or transglucosidase.

C. *The Glycosyl Acceptor and Primer*

Whereas the chemical nature of the glycosyl donor appears to be limited to a relatively small group of substances, the nature of the acceptor varies widely. If the acceptor is not a carbohydrate (i.e. if it is an aglycon) and contains at least one hydroxy group, the transglycosylation will yield what is commonly called a glycoside, e.g. methylglucoside, saligenin β-glucoside (salicin), etc.

In the biosynthesis of disaccharides the glycosyl acceptor is the corresponding monosaccharide. When the acceptor is a disaccharide, a trisaccharide will usually be synthesized. In general terms, the number of monosaccharide units (n) of the acceptor will be increased by one, and a saccharide with ($n + 1$) units will result from a single transglycosylation step, provided that the glycosyl donor is either an aldose-1-phosphate, a nucleoside diphosphate monosaccharide, or a disaccharide.

It is obvious that the mechanism of the biosynthesis of polysaccharides consists in a stepwise lengthening of existing saccharide chains whereby each saccharide molecule fulfills alternately the role of acceptor and of saccharide synthesized. It has been established in the case of a number of polysaccharides that such a lengthening of chains cannot begin with a monosaccharide, and that a certain chain length of the acceptor is required with which to start. For this reason, the acceptor in the biosynthesis of polysaccharides is usually an oligo- or a polysaccharide and is called the primer.

The effectiveness of the primer depends to a large degree on its chain length. While maltose is not capable of priming the synthesis of unbranched α-1,4-glucosidic chains (amylose) from glucose-1-phosphate, maltotriose has been found to be a fairly good primer for the reaction catalyzed by potato phosphorylase;[970, 45, 263, 978] maltotetraose and longer-chain unbranched dextrins are far more efficient, however. Muscle phosphorylase on the other hand, has been reported to require much larger primer molecules than maltotriose or maltotetraose.[183]

From unbranched primers arise unbranched polysaccharides, while branched primers lead to the formation of branched polysaccharides, as has been demonstrated in the synthesis of starch polysaccharides under the catalytic action of potato or muscle phosphorylases.[357] When branched primers initiate the reaction, the number of branching linkages does not increase, however, so that the relative portion of the branching bonds actually decreases, unless a second enzyme, like Q-enzyme or Branching enzyme, participates in the overall reaction. In accordance with the view that the primer is the glycosyl acceptor and that, in all instances of the synthesis of polysaccharides investigated so far, the nonreducing end-groups of the primer are the actual acceptor sites of new glycosyl groups, the efficiency of the primer is a function of the concentration of its end-groups rather than of its concentration in weight per volume or of its chain length, and a branched primer (amylopectin) has actually been observed to be more efficient on an equal weight basis than an unbranched primer (amylose). [357] An increase of end-groups of a primer through acid hydrolysis has also been shown to improve its priming efficiency, [403] until the molecular weight falls below certain limits.

It is interesting to note that the mechanism of polysaccharide formation through lengthening of the glycosidic chains of an acceptor is reflected in the fact that the equilibrium constant K of this reaction is independent of the primer concentration, provided no branching enzymes are present. This has been demonstrated in the case of the formation of amylose by muscle or potato phosphorylases. [348, 174, 175] The reaction is expressed by the equation

$$x(\text{glucose-1-phosphate}) + (\text{glucose})_n \rightleftharpoons$$
$$(\text{glucose})_{n+x} + x(\text{phosphate}) \qquad (61)$$

where $(\text{glucose})_n$ is the primer and $(\text{glucose})_{n+x}$ the amylose synthesized. From the mass-law equation of this reaction

$$\frac{[(\text{glucose})_{n+x}]\,[\text{phosphate}]^x}{[(\text{glucose})_n]\,[\text{glucose-1-phosphate}]^x} = K = \frac{[\text{phosphate}]^x}{[\text{glucose-1-phosphate}]^x} \qquad (62)$$

it follows that the concentrations of primer and of amylose synthesized are equal, because the concentrations of their nonreducing end-groups are equal, and these terms cancel out therefore.

The mechanism of polysaccharide synthesis, in the case of glycogen synthesis from glucose-1-phosphate, through stepwise lengthening of the nonreducing ends of the chains of an acceptor (primer) has originally been suggested by Cori et al., [183] and represents the now generally accepted view of the biogenesis of polysaccharides such as amylose, amylopectin, glycogen, dextran, cellulose, polyglucans of other structure, xylan, araban, levan, and others. The mechanism appears to be the same, independently of whether an aldose-1-phosphate, a nucleoside diphosphate sugar, sucrose, or maltose is the glycosyl donor.

It is in general not sufficiently recognized, however, that the above-described mechanism of polysaccharide synthesis does not make any provision for the formation of *new* polysaccharide molecules as was pointed out

o

earlier. [80] Independently of whether unbranched molecules are formed, or branched structures are obtained through the concurrent action of one or several additional enzymes, the number of polysaccharide molecules would always remain unchanged and equal to the original number of primer molecules, while only the molecular weight of the polysaccharide would increase (see Fig. 41). Obviously, the biosynthetic mechanism of polysaccharides must also be capable of creating new polysaccharide molecules, in addition to merely increasing the molecular weight of pre-existing primer

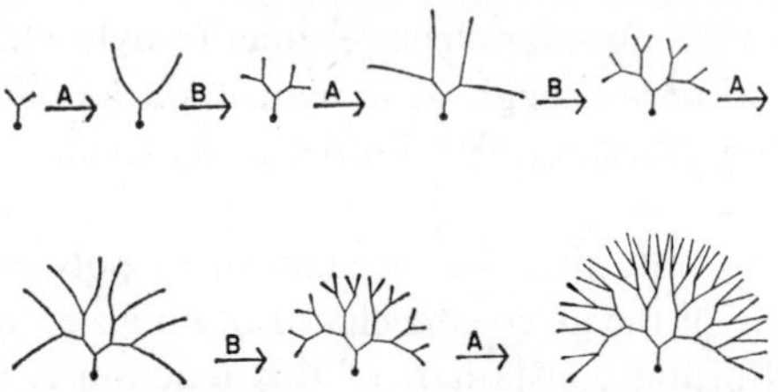

FIG. 41. Polysaccharide formation through lengthening of the chains of a primer molecule by transglycosylation from aldose-1-phosphate or from nucleoside diphosphate glycoside, and by the additional action of a branching enzyme. The molecular weight of the primer is increased, but no new polysaccharide molecules are obtained. The same phenomenon should occur during the formation of unbranched polysaccharides.

Each line represents a straight glycoside chain containing an unspecified number of monomeric sugar units. Each bifurcation of lines denotes the site of a branching point. The aldehydic end group of the molecule is marked by a dot.

The polysaccharide structure corresponds to the arrangement of glucose units in the bush-like model for amylopectin, advanced by Meyer and Bernfeld [603] which is now generally accepted for this polysaccharide. The arrangement of sugar units in other branched polysaccharides is likely to be analogous.

The reactions marked A are catalyzed by a phosphorylase or a nucleoside diphosphate glycoside transglycosylase. Those marked B are catalyzed by a branching enzyme.

molecules, and in addition it must replace the primer molecules used up during synthesis for future needs. These two tasks can be achieved only through the action of hydrolytic enzymes (see Fig. 42); the action patterns of these polysaccharidases should be such as to permit a random attack of their respective substrates, such as is the case for α-amylase, dextranase, [434, 426, 491, 767] c_x-cellulase, [767] and others.

It is understood that one of the functions of polysaccharide-hydrolyzing enzymes is their action of breaking down the high molecular-weight substances in food to smaller sizes for the purpose of permitting the material to pass across cell membranes and, hence, of making the carbohydrate available to further utilization in the cells. The requirement of polysaccharidases for the biosynthesis of their substrates represents no doubt an equally important function of this class of enzymes, and this hypothesis finds support in the observation that these enzymes frequently occur at the very same sites where their substrate is known to be synthesized. An excellent example of this circumstance is the existence of small amounts of an α-amylase in liver, as described by McGeachin, [596] where it may well participate in the production of glycogen primer molecules from glycogen. [792]

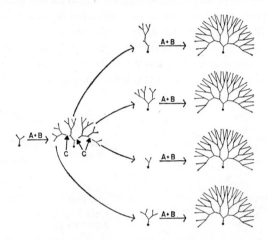

FIG. 42. Polysaccharide synthesis in the presence of small amounts of a poly-saccharide-hydrolyzing enzyme. The principle of synthesis is the same as the one shown in Fig. 41. The presence of a hydrolytic enzyme assures the formation of new polysaccharide molecules, controls the molecular weight of the carbo-hydrates synthesized, and secures the replacement of primer used up during the synthesis for future needs.

The reactions marked A are catalyzed by a phosphorylase or a nucleoside diphosphate glycoside transglycosylase. The reactions marked B are catalyzed by a branching enzyme, and those marked C by a hydrolytic enzyme.

Thus, the presence and the concentration of the polysaccharide-hydrolyzing enzyme during polysaccharide synthesis appears to be an important factor in establishing a certain molecular weight of the final product of biosynthesis. Very low concentrations of hydrolytic enzyme would permit the formation of very high molecular-weight carbohydrates and vice versa.

Illingworth et al. reported the biosynthesis of a polysaccharide in the absence of a primer, namely the formation of amylose from glucose-1-phosphate with highly purified phosphorylase a. [431] This reaction is extremely slow, however, [110] and it is not known whether it has physiological signifi-cance.

The reactions of glycosyl transfer from donors like aldose-1-phosphate, nucleoside diphosphate glycosides, or disaccharides have the common feature that single glycosyl units are transferred to the acceptor in a succession of steps. The majority of the reactions listed in Table 8 contrast with the former ones in that they represent the transfer of whole glycosidic chains containing more than a single sugar unit to an acceptor. In many cases, the acceptor is identical or analogous with the donor, and the glycosyl transfer may even be an intramolecular one.

Thus, the action of Branching enzyme and of Q-enzyme has been formulated by Larner[520] to proceed according to the general mechanism indicated in Fig. 43. Branching enzyme from liver requires for transglycosylation a chain-length of at least 11 glucose units in the outer branches of glycogen; Q-enzyme from potato causes branching in a polysaccharide containing 13 to 14 glucose units in the outer chains. In both cases, donor and acceptor are the same substances. While Branching enzyme is known to act on

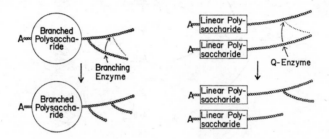

FIG. 43. Action of Branching enzyme and Q-enzyme. A, reducing end-group.

branched substrates only, Q-enzyme has been reported to use also amylose as donor and acceptor.[714]

The action mechanism of D-enzyme is probably somehow analogous to the ones of Q-enzyme and Branching enzyme (see Fig. 44). In contrast to the

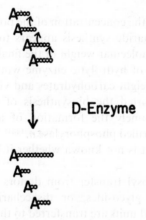

FIG. 44. Action of D-enzyme. A, reducing end-group.

latter enzymes, D-enzyme transfers its glycosyl bond, however, with the formation of a new α-1,4-glucoside bond. Because the energy of hydrolysis of the bond formed is similar, therefore, to that of the bond broken, the reaction of D-enzyme, unlike those of Q-enzyme and Branching enzyme is reversible. In addition, the substrate of D-enzyme must be of rather low molecular weight. [717]

The formation of cyclic dextrins from starch by the *B. macerans* enzyme [913, 990] presents an exception in that this is one of the rare cases where a transglycosylase actually produces a new molecule; no new aldehydic or nonreducing end-groups are formed, however, since the new molecule possesses a cyclic structure. In this case, amylose or amylopectin may be the donor and the nonreducing end-group of the chain split from the donor by the enzyme action then becomes the acceptor of the glycosyl group of the same chain segment. This reaction has been found to be reversible. [262, 644] In addition to the formation of cyclic dextrins, the enzyme from *B. macerans* is also capable of disproportioning chains of linear dextrins. [666] In this respect, the action of the *B. macerans* enzyme is similar to that of D-enzyme (see Fig. 44).

D. *The Saccharide Synthesized*

There exists no doubt that the biosynthesis of many saccharides may proceed through different pathways, depending on the choice of the glycosyl donor and, in some instances, also of that of the acceptor.

DISACCHARIDES

1. *Sucrose*

The biosynthesis of sucrose, or α-D-glucopyranosyl-β-D-fructofuranoside, in bacteria (*Pseudomonas*, etc.) [360, 359] and in sugar cane [829] was found to utilize α-D-glucose-1-phosphate as the donor. Later, a second mechanism for sucrose formation in many higher plants was discovered in which UDP-glucose serves as the donor. [115, 927, 141, 121]

In the first case, the standard free energy change (at pH 6·6 and 30°) is $\Delta F' = +1770$ cal [356] which indicates that the equilibrium of the reaction:

$$\text{glucose-1-phosphate} + \text{fructose} \rightleftharpoons \text{sucrose} + \text{phosphate} \qquad (63)$$

is more in favor of the phosphorolytic splitting than of the synthesis of sucrose.

The estimation by Cardini *et al.* [141] of the corresponding value of free energy change, $\Delta F' = -1000$ cal (at pH 7·4 and 37°), for the mechanism using UDP-glucose as the glycosyl donor:

$$\text{UDP-glucose} + \text{fructose} \rightleftharpoons \text{sucrose} + \text{UDP} \qquad (64)$$

makes it clear that this reaction is more suitable for the production of sucrose than the reaction catalyzed by phosphorylase, because the equilibrium of the UDP-glucose utilizing mechanism is much more in favor of the synthetic than of the reverse direction.

The enzyme, *UDP glucose: D-fructose-glucosyl transferase*, catalyzing reaction 64 was purified from sugar-beet roots. It cannot utilize dTDP as glucosyl acceptor in the reverse direction of the reaction. Ripening rice grains, however, contain an enzyme or enzymes which may catalyze reaction 64 with either UDP or ADP and, in the forward direction, with either UDP-glucose or ADP-glucose. [638]

In both cases, β-D-fructose is the glycosyl acceptor. This ketose is known to occur mainly in the pyranose form in the free monosaccharide, while sucrose contains β-D-fructofuranose. An equilibrium between the two forms:

$$\beta\text{-D-fructopyranose} \rightleftharpoons \beta\text{-D-fructofuranose} \tag{65}$$

is known to exist [435, 328] and to be established rapidly enough to provide sufficient amounts of the furanose as acceptor for reactions 63 and 64.

A third mechanism for sucrose synthesis has been described by Leloir and Cardini [536] in which fructose-6-phosphate replaces fructose as acceptor. In this substrate the fructose must exist in the furanose form; the saccharide synthesized will then be transformed into sucrose by the subsequent action of a phosphatase:

$$\text{UDP-glucose} + \text{fructose-6-phosphate} \rightleftharpoons$$
$$\text{sucrose phosphate} + \text{UDP} \tag{66}$$

$$\text{sucrose phosphate} \rightarrow \text{sucrose} + \text{phosphate} \tag{67}$$

The action of the hydrolytic enzyme is apt to further displace the equilibrium in the direction of sucrose synthesis.

The mechanism of action of sucrose phosphorylase from *Pseudomonas saccharophila* has been studied with the use of P^{32}-labeled inorganic phosphate [217] and with C^{14}-labeled fructose. [1000] As a result of these studies, it can be concluded that the enzyme acts alternately as an intermediate glycosyl acceptor and as glycosyl donor:

$$\text{glucose-1-phosphate} + \text{enzyme} \rightleftharpoons \text{glucosyl enzyme} + \text{phosphate} \tag{68}$$

$$\text{glucosyl enzyme} + \text{fructose} \rightleftharpoons \text{sucrose} + \text{enzyme} \tag{69}$$

This sequence of reactions makes it clear why fructose can be replaced by other ketoses as glycosyl acceptors whereby sucrose analogues are formed. [360, 359]

2. Trehalose

This nonreducing disaccharide has the following structure: O-α-D-glucopyranosyl-(1 → 1)-O-α-D-glucopyranoside; it has been found to occur in yeast and in certain fungi. Its biosynthesis is analogous to that of sucrose. Leloir and co-workers[533, 126] found a yeast enzyme which catalyzes the following reaction 70:

$$\text{UDP-glucose} + \text{glucose-6-phosphate} \rightleftharpoons$$
$$\text{trehalose phosphate} + \text{UDP} \qquad (70)$$

$$\text{trehalose phosphate} \rightarrow \text{trehalose} + \text{phosphate} \qquad (71)$$

A specific yeast phosphatase splits the phosphate group from the saccharide synthesized to form trehalose.[126] The latter reaction (equation 71) appears to be more rapid than the former one (equation 70), and Panek could not detect any accumulation of trehalose phosphate.[690] A similar mechanism for trehalose synthesis has been found in locusts[135] and in the fat body of the silkmoth.[641] The transglycosylase which catalyzes reaction (70) is also present in several strains of *Mycobacterium tuberculosis*,[324] but the avirulent strain H37Ra contains an inhibitor of this enzyme. The avirulent strain, thus, seems to possess low activity of this enzyme. Purification of the inhibitor yielded a low-molecular weight oligoribonucleotide containing adenine and guanine.[559]

Trehalose and glycogen are the principal storage carbohydrates in baker's yeast (*Saccharomyces cerevisiae*),[691] embryos of the brine shrimp, *Artemia salina*,[153] and in the fat body of the saturniid silkmoth, *Hyalophora cecropia*.[641, 642] Both carbohydrates are accumulated in resting yeast cells. Trehalose is rapidly consumed when these cells are reincubated into a growth medium and is broken down to CO_2 without giving rise to other storage carbohydrates, while the energy liberated is utilized for cell division.[691] In the brine shrimp, trehalose accumulation is much higher in the dormant than in the non-dormant embryos, while glycogen levels are about the same in both.[153] It therefore appears that storage of carbon in these organisms in the form of trehalose is of considerable physiological significance, and that the energy thus accumulated is more rapidly available than that from glycogen deposition.

3. Maltose

Although a mechanism for the reversible phosphorolysis of maltose in bacteria (*Neisseria meningitidis*) has been described,[257] the synthetic direction of this reaction is unlikely to be responsible for any production of maltose in nature. The glucose-1-phosphate which is formed during maltose phosphorolysis, and which would be required for maltose synthesis, has the β-configuration, and β-D-glucose-1-phosphate is not a normally available sugar derivative in nature. Even the phosphorolysis of cellobiose has been reported to yield α-D-glucose-1-phosphate. [831]

Maltose phosphorylase from *Neisseria meningitidis* is capable of synthesizing analogues of maltose when β-D-glucose-1-phosphate is allowed to react with 2-O-methyl-D-glucose, 6-O-methyl-D-glucose, 6-deoxy-6-fluoro-D-glucose, or D-xylose, instead of D-glucose. Also, 3-O-methyl-β-D-glucose-1-phosphate may replace β-D-glucose-1-phosphate. [626]

Maltose is formed in plants from amylose or amylopectin by the action of β-amylase, and constitutes the sole reducing sugar of the action of this enzyme. β-Amylase catalyzes a step-by-step splitting of the penultimate α-1,4-glucosidic linkages from the nonreducing chain ends of its substrate. [675, 676, 347, 799, 643] The maltose thus liberated appears in the downward mutarotating β-form because of a Walden inversion occurring simultaneously. The enzyme is widely distributed in higher plants and also occurs in certain microorganisms. [81]

The action of α-amylase on the same substrates causes a random hydrolysis of most α-1,4-glucosidic linkages and also yields maltose among the final products in addition to substantial amounts of trisaccharides and oligosaccharides of higher molecular weights. The action mechanism of this enzyme and its occurrence have been reviewed. [80, 81]

4. Isomaltose

The action of transglycosylases from some microorganisms (*A. niger*, *A. oryzae*) produces O-α-D-glucopyranosyl-(1 → 6)-D-glucopyranose, or isomaltose from maltose, in addition to tri- and tetrasaccharides. [59, 705]

5. Lactose

This reducing disaccharide of the structure O-β-D-galactopyranosyl-(1 → 4)-D-glucopyranose is formed in the mammary glands and occurs in milk to the extent of about 5 per cent.

The biogenesis of this important disaccharide has been studied by Gander *et al.* [281] These authors observed that homogenates of the bovine udder are capable of producing lactose phosphate from UDP-galactose and glucose-1-phosphate. In analogy to the biosynthesis of sucrose and of trehalose, lactose phosphate is split by a phosphatase to lactose and inorganic phosphate. A sequence of reactions thus leads from glucose and ATP to lactose:

$$2 \text{ (glucose)} + 2 \text{ ATP} \rightleftharpoons 2 \text{ (glucose-6-phosphate)} + 2 \text{ ADP} \quad (72)$$

$$2 \text{ (glucose-6-phosphate)} \rightleftharpoons 2 \text{ (glucose-1-phosphate)} \quad (73)$$

$$\text{glucose-1-phosphate} + \text{UTP} \rightleftharpoons \text{UDP-glucose} + \text{pyrophosphate} \quad (74)$$

$$\text{UDP-glucose} \rightleftharpoons \text{UDP-galactose} \quad (75)$$

UDP-galactose + glucose-1-phosphate $\rightleftharpoons$

$$\text{lactose-1-phosphate} + \text{UDP} \qquad (76)$$

$$\text{lactose-1-phosphate} + H_2O \rightarrow \text{lactose} + \text{phosphate} \qquad (77)$$

To complete this reaction sequence, one has to consider that pyrophosphate is hydrolyzed to inorganic phosphate, and that UTP is regenerated from UDP by ATP:

$$\text{pyrophosphate} + H_2O \rightarrow 2 \text{ (inorganic phosphate)} \qquad (78)$$

$$\text{UDP} + \text{ATP} \rightleftharpoons \text{UTP} + \text{ADP} \qquad (79)$$

The summation of equations (72)–(79) would then yield:

$$2 \text{ (glucose)} + 3 \text{ ATP} + 2H_2O \rightarrow$$
$$\text{lactose} + 3 \text{ ADP} + 3 \text{ (inorganic phosphate)} \qquad (80)$$

In contrast to the aforesaid, Hansen et al. found convincing evidence for a mechanism of lactose biosynthesis in bovine mammary glands by which UDP-galactose reacts with nonphosphorylated glucose to yield lactose directly without the formation of lactose-1-phosphate as an intermediate, [350] according to equation (81):

$$\text{UDP-galactose} + \text{D-glucose} \rightleftharpoons \text{lactose} + \text{UDP} \qquad (81)$$

This direct mechanism of lactose formation was confirmed by Watkins and Hassid with particulate enzyme preparations from lactating guinea-pig or cow mammary glands, [969] and with a soluble enzyme preparation from bovine milk. [38]

Wood et al. [1002, 1001] obtained evidence that the glucose moiety of lactose comes from blood glucose, while the pentose cycle must have been involved in the formation of the galactose part of lactose from glycerol.

An alternative mechanism for the formation of lactose from glucose-1-phosphate and starch by an enzyme system from guinea pig mammary gland has been reported. [484]

6. Other Disaccharides

Laminaribiose, 3-O-α-D-glucopyranosyl-D-glucose, is formed from α-D-glucose-1-phosphate and D-glucose by a specific phosphorylase from the protist, Euglenia gracilis, [570] or from Astasia ocellata. [568] Methyl-β-D glucoside or certain β-D-glucosyl residues-containing disaccharides and glucosides are better acceptors than D-glucose. [568]

N-Acetyl-D-glucosamine may substitute D-glucose in the reaction catalyzed by the lactose-synthesizing enzyme from mammary glands (equation 81) and the corresponding disaccharide, O-β-D-galactopyranosyl-(1 → 4)-D-N-acetyl-glucosamine, is formed. [969]

Aspergillus niger transglycosylase catalyzes the following reaction: [488]

cellobiose + D-galactose →

$$\text{O-}\beta\text{-D-glucopyranosyl-}(1 \rightarrow 6)\text{-D-galactose} + \text{D-glucose} \qquad (82)$$

and crystalline takamaltase acts on phenyl-α-glucoside in the presence of D-mannose to produce 3-O-α-D-glucosylmannose and 6-O-α-D-glucosyl-mannose. [890]

Yeast transgalactosylase uses *o*-nitrophenyl-β-D-galactoside as donor of galactosyl residues, while either D-galactose or D-arabinose may act as acceptors. [709] The resulting disaccharides are 6-β-D-galactopyranosyl-D-galactose, 3-β-D-galactopyranosyl-D-galactose, and 5-β-D-galactopyranosyl-D-arabinose, or 3-β-D-galactopyranosyl-D-arabinose.

TRISACCHARIDES

7. *Raffinose*

This nonreducing trisaccharide is found in nature in larger amounts than any other trisaccharide. It occurs in higher plants, in fungi, and especially in sugar beets. It can be obtained from sugar beet molasses, or from cotton seed meal which contains about 8 per cent of this sugar. According to Haworth *et al.* [366] the structure of raffinose is O-α-D-galactopyranosyl-(1 → 6)-O-α-D-glucopyranosyl-(1 → 2)-β-D-fructofuranoside, or galactosyl sucrose.

A reversible reaction was found to occur with a bacterial enzyme system from *Aerobacter levanicum*, better known as levansucrase, which produced melibiose and sucrose from raffinose and glucose. [398] This reaction consists in the transfer of the fructosyl group from raffinose to glucose and, in the reverse direction, from sucrose to melibiose:

galactosyl-glucosyl-fructoside (raffinose) + glucose ⇌ glucosyl-fructo-
    side (sucrose) + O-α-D-galactosyl-(1 → 6)-D-glucose (melibiose)   (83)

It is not known whether the biosynthesis of raffinose in higher plants is based on an analogous mechanism of transglycosylation from sucrose, or is due to the action of UDP-glycosyl transglycosylases or of phosphorylases. That the general principle of transglycosylation from sucrose to a disaccharide with the synthesis of a trisaccharide represents a mechanism used also by higher plants or by insects (aphids), had been shown in the biosynthesis of melezitose and other trisaccharides.

Raffinose and similar galactose-containing oligosaccharides act as soluble reserve carbohydrates in bean seeds (*Phaseolus vulgaris*) during dormancy; they disappear on germination and serve probably as an energy source. [330] Sucrose is also present, but prevails even during germination.

8. *Melezitose*

This trisaccharide occurs in the sap of the larch, scrub pine, and Douglas fir. It is nonreducing and has the following structure: O-α-D-glucopyranosyl-(1 → 3)-O-β-D-fructofuranosyl-(2 → 1)-α-D-glucopyranoside. Extracts of certain insects (*Eucallipterus tiliae* L.) have been found to contain an enzyme or an enzyme system which catalyzes the biosynthesis of melezitose from sucrose [40] according to the reaction shown in Fig. 45:

$$\text{G–F} \;+\; \text{G}\text{–F} \;\longrightarrow\; \text{G–F–G} \;+\; \text{F}$$

FIG. 45. Biosynthesis of melezitose (G-F-G) from sucrose (G-F) in insects. G stands for glucose, F for fructose and G-F for glucosyl fructoside (sucrose).

Assuming that sucrose biosynthesis in these insects proceeds according to the mechanism observed in many higher plants where UDP-glucose serves as the glucosyl donor, the following sequence of reactions may be surmised to lead to the trisaccharide, starting with the monosaccharides and ATP:

$$2\,(\text{glucose}) + 2\,\text{ATP} \rightleftharpoons 2\,(\text{glucose-6-phosphate}) + 2\,\text{ADP} \tag{84}$$

$$2\,(\text{glucose-6-phosphate}) \rightleftharpoons 2\,(\text{glucose-1-phosphate}) \tag{85}$$

$$2\,(\text{glucose-1-phosphate}) + 2\,\text{UTP} \rightleftharpoons \\ 2\,(\text{UDP-glucose}) + 2\,(\text{pyrophosphate}) \tag{86}$$

$$2\,\text{pyrophosphate} + 2\text{H}_2\text{O} \rightarrow 4\,(\text{inorganic phosphate}) \tag{87}$$

$$2\,(\text{UDP-glucose}) + 2\,\text{fructose} \rightleftharpoons 2\,(\text{sucrose}) + 2\,\text{UDP} \tag{88}$$

$$2\,\text{UDP} + 2\,\text{ATP} \rightleftharpoons 2\,\text{UTP} + 2\,\text{ADP} \tag{89}$$

$$2\,(\text{sucrose}) \rightleftharpoons \text{melezitose} + \text{fructose} \tag{90}$$

Sum: $2\,(\text{glucose}) + \text{fructose} + 4\,\text{ATP} + 2\text{H}_2\text{O} \rightarrow$
$$\text{melezitose} + 4\,\text{ADP} + 4\,(\text{inorganic phosphate}) \tag{91}$$

It appears, therefore, that the formation of each glycosidic bond in a compound oligosaccharide from the individual monosaccharides, requires, according to the above mechanism, the availability of at least two molecules of ATP. This is in agreement with the mechanism of glucoside bond formation utilizing UDP-glucose as glycosyl donor (line 12, Table 8).

Analogous transglycosylation reactions are responsible for the formation of many other trisaccharides.

9. *Other Trisaccharides*

The transglycosylase activity of invertases from various origins, such as from yeast, molds (*Aspergillus, Penicillium*), from flowers, honey, and from certain insects (aphids), as well as certain plant transfructosylases and bacterial transfructosylases (levansucrase) have been reported to be involved in the formation of trisaccharides and more complex saccharides. In most cases, the reactions consist in the transfer of β-fructofuranosyl residues which originate mainly from sucrose, and also from raffinose, but the transfer of glucosyl groups from sucrose or from maltose to an acceptor has also been observed.

The glucosyl transfer from sucrose to another sucrose molecule is catalyzed by honey invertase, and the trisaccharide, O-α-D-glucopyranosyl-(1 → 4)-O-α-D-glucopyranosyl-(1 → 2)-O-β-D-fructofuranoside (*maltosyl fructoside*, or *glucosyl sucrose*) is produced. [982, 983] The same trisaccharide is formed by extracts of aphids. [40]

Panose, O-α-D-glucopyranosyl-(1 → 6)-O-α-D-glucopyranosyl-(1 → 4)-D-glucopyranose, or glucosyl maltose, is formed from maltose by extracts of *Aspergillus niger*, [996, 688, 260] as well as by an enzyme from *Aspergillus oryzae*, [704, 705] which also synthesizes another trisaccharide, *isomaltotriose*.

The enzyme extract from *A. niger* synthesizes also O-α-D-glucopyranosyl-(1 → 2)-O-β-D-fructofuranosyl-(1 → 2)-β-D-fructofuranoside, or *fructosyl sucrose*. [57]

Another fructosyl sucrose, called *kestose*, O-α-D-glucopyranosyl-(1 → 2)-O-β-D-fructofuranosyl-(6 → 2)-β-D-fructofuranoside is obtained by the action of yeast invertase on sucrose. [10, 39]

The action of yeast invertase on lactose obviously transfers a galactosyl group to lactose and produces O-β-D-galactopyranosyl-(1 → 6)-O-β-D-galactopyranosyl-(1 → 4)-D-glucopyranose (*galactosyl lactose*), and another trisaccharide, O-D-galactosyl-(1 → 6)-O-D-galactosyl-(1 → 6)-D-glucose, as well as some disaccharides. [700]

Levansucrase from *Aerobacter levanicum* has been described to catalyze the transfer of fructosyl groups from sucrose to a suitable acceptor. The formation of raffinose with melibiose as acceptor has already been mentioned. The same enzyme system yields another nonreducing trisaccharide, O-β-D-galactopyranosyl-(1 → 4)-O-α-D-glucopyranosyl-(1 → 2)-β-D-fructofuranoside (*lactosyl fructoside* or *galactosyl sucrose*), when lactose is the acceptor. [31]

Transfructosylation reactions have also been observed in which higher-molecular-weight fructans like inulin serve as the donor. Through the catalytic action of an enzyme preparation from the tubers of the Jerusalem artichoke (*Helianthus tuberosus*), a trisaccharide and higher oligosaccharides are obtained with sucrose as acceptor. [229] Raffinose, melezitose, or fructose may also serve as acceptors, but not maltose, lactose, trehalose, or D-glucose.

Synthesis of O-α-L-fucopyranosyl-(1 → 2)-O-β-D-galactopyranosyl-(1 → 4)-D-glucose (fucosyl lactose) is accomplished in the milk of dogs from GDP-L-fucose, UDP-D-galactose and D-glucose.[340] The GDP-L fucose originates from D-fructose-6-phosphate, via D-mannose-6-phosphate (equation 30), D-mannose-1-phosphate and GDP-D-mannose (equation 52).

GLUCANS

10. Amylose, Amylopectin, and Glycogen

The structure, biosynthesis and the biological breakdown of these three polysaccharides have been studied in more detail than those of any other high-molecular-weight carbohydrate.

(a) *Structure.* That starch from most origins consists of two polysaccharides has been known for a long time,[798] because of the different physico-chemical properties of these two components and because of their different behavior toward hydrolytic enzymes. They both have been known to be made up of D-glucopyranose units, which are linked together by mostly α-1,4-glucosidic bonds. The presence of a few α-1,6-glucosidic bonds in starch had also been established. The methylation procedure by Haworth and co-workers[364] yielded one nonreducing end-group for each 25 to 30 glucose residues in starch and amylopectin. Comparative end-group determinations of amylose and amylopectin revealed the unbranched nature of the former with only 0·3 per cent end-groups.[607] Amylose was, thus, established to consist of unbranched, chain-like molecules and to contain only α-1,4-glucosidic bonds.

The existence of slightly branched amylose molecules, e.g. in potato, has been described.[485] The results of end-group determinations, in conjunction with enzymatic studies and with investigations of the macromolecular behavior of amylose and amylopectin led to the advancement of the bush-like structure for amylopectin[603] shown in Fig. 46 where the branching points are α-1,6-glucosidic bonds. A similar texture with a higher degree of branching has been suggested for glycogen[605] and has been confirmed by Cori's group,[433, 522] using amylo-1,6-glucosidase as a specific enzyme to break the branching points in glycogen and amylopectin, after exposing them to the action of phosphorylase or β-amylase.

The formation of the branched polysaccharides, amylopectin and glycogen, may be considered to proceed in two alternating steps. The first involves the synthesis of linear chain segments, which is followed by the formation of branchings whereby the average chain length of the linear segments is reduced. Then, linear chains are again lengthened, new branching points are created and so on, until a high molecular weight is reached (see Figs. 41 and 42).

The biosynthesis of the linear parts of the glucosidic chains in amylopectin and glycogen, and of amylose, has the interesting feature that it may be accomplished in not less than five possible ways, each using a different glycosyl donor, i.e. glucose-1-phosphate, nucleoside diphosphate glucose, sucrose, maltose, or dextrins.

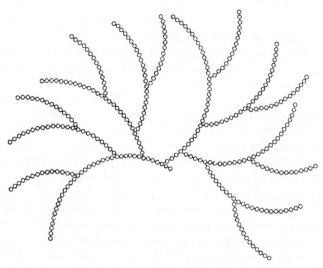

FIG. 46. Structure of amylopectin, according to Meyer and Bernfeld.[603, 80,] (*Reproduced by courtesy of John Wiley & Sons.*) Each circle represents a glucose unit.

(b) *The phosphorylase reaction.* The phosphorolytic breakdown of glycogen was first described by Parnas.[695] This finding was immediately followed by the classical work of the Coris, of Hanes, and of others [172, 174, 481, 348,175, 358, 183] on the synthetic direction of this reaction by which the concept of the formation of compound saccharides through glycosyl transfer from an energy-rich donor has been demonstrated for the first time. The reaction catalyzed by phosphorylase:

α-D-glucose-1-phosphate $+$ [-O-α-D-glucopyranosyl-$(1 \rightarrow 4)$-$]_n$ $\rightleftharpoons$
[-O-α-D-glucopyranosyl-$(1 \rightarrow 4)$-$]_{n + 1}$ (*amylose*) $+$ inorganic phosphate (92)

has been studied in detail. Its equilibrium constant varies greatly with pH.[170, 923] At pH 6·96, equilibrium is established when the total phosphorus is distributed between 24·4 per cent ester phosphate in glucose-1-phosphate and 75·6 per cent inorganic phosphate.[170] The equilibrium constant of this reaction is unaffected by the concentration of the primer. The influence of the chemical nature of the primer on its efficiency, as well as the general mechanism of the priming, has been discussed earlier in this chapter (Section VIIIc).

Highly purified phosphorylase a is also capable of forming amylose in the absence of a primer, however. [431] The initial *de novo* synthesis of the glycoside bond occurs extremely slowly with an absolute lag period without P_i formation or P_i^{32} exchange. Under optimal conditions, the rate of synthesis of amylose from glucose-1-phosphate by phosphorylase a in the absence of primer is one amylose chain per phosphorylase monomer in 6 hours. [110] The amylose chain thus formed does not have a phosphate group at its reducing end. [431]

In spite of these findings on the ability of phosphorylase to achieve *de novo* synthesis of polysaccharide, it is now generally accepted that the physiological role of the reaction catalyzed by phosphorylase in animal tissues is limited to the catabolism of glycogen, [943, 776, 525, 812, 539] whereas glycogen and starch synthesis is mediated by enzymes using nucleoside diphosphate glucose. Exceptions to this rule have been reported, however, such as the synthesis of glycogen in the uteri of ovariectomized rats which were found to be free of UDP-glucose: glycogen transglucosylase. [94]

Phosphorylase is widely distributed in nature, and its occurrence has been reviewed recently. [378, 539] Under certain pathological conditions, phosphorylase levels may drop considerably. It was less than 0·5 per cent of the normal concentration in the muscle homogenate of patients with progressive myopathy; [812] a muscle disorder characterized by rapid exhaustion of otherwise normal muscle, which can be prevented by intravenous administration of lactate, glucose or fructose, is due to the lack of phosphorylase and is combined with a considerable storage of glycogen. [619] The enzyme from normal rabbit muscle has been obtained in the crystalline form [335] and has been prepared in a state free from other enzymes. [394]

α-Glucan phosphorylase from rat liver microsomal fractions is associated with the "particulate" glycogen. After starvation of the animals, 80 per cent of the enzyme appears, however, in the soluble fraction and returns into the particulate material after refeeding. [909] The "particulate" glycogen from liver is a submicroscopic complex of glycogen containing about 1 per cent of protein which plays an important role in maintaining this complex. [529] The average molecular weight of "particulate" glycogen ranges from 50 to 20×10^6 in rabbit liver or *Ascaris* muscle. [683] It is possible that the association of phosphorylase with particulate glycogen is related to the formation of insoluble complexes resulting from the interaction of muscle phosphorylase with glycogen. [820]

Muscle and liver phosphorylases exist in two forms, a and b; [177] phosphorylase a is active in itself, whereas phosphorylase b is inactive and can be activated by the addition of adenosine-5'-phosphate. [388] Whereas the activity of phosphorylase a is not markedly influenced by this nucleotide at room temperature and at high substrate concentrations, i.e. under the experimental conditions most frequently used, muscle phosphorylase a may be stimulated as much as 40-fold by adenosine-5'-phosphate at 38°C and in the presence of low levels of either glycogen and P_i, or of glucose-1-phosphate. [561] AMP also has an influence on the kinetics of phosphorylase a. [794] Since the concentration of AMP in the tissues is usually low, measurable phosphorylase activity under physiological conditions must be due to the a form of this enzyme. [167]

The transformation of muscle phosphorylase a to b is catalyzed by another enzyme, called PR-enzyme (Prosthetic-group-Removing Enzyme) or phosphorylase phosphatase. [179] This process is accompanied by the decrease of the molecular weight of phosphorylase a to one-half, and by the loss of protein-bound phosphate: [474, 332]

$$\text{phosphorylose } a \rightarrow 2(\text{phosphorylase } b) + 4 \text{ P}_i \tag{93}$$

Phosphorylase phosphatase is inhibited by AMP, by combining with substrate, and by glucose-1-phosphate. [253] Glucose-1-phosphate and AMP, thus, contribute to a control mechanism of glycogen breakdown. Trypsin activates phosphorylase phosphatase. In solutions of high ionic strength or of low protein concentration, the tetrameric form of phosphorylase a dissociates into a dimeric species of higher catalytic activity, [954] and other variations in experimental conditions, such as pH and temperature, induce conformational changes of the multiple subunit structure of the enzyme. [389] The reactivation of phosphorylase b to a is accomplished by ATP in the presence of a specific kinase: [254, 509, 512]

$$2 \text{ (phosphorylase } b) + 4 \text{ ATP} \rightarrow \text{phosphorylase } a + 4 \text{ ADP} \tag{94}$$

The molecular weight of the enzyme is doubled during this process and four moles of phosphate are incorporated into one mole of phosphorylase a, where they are bound as serine phosphate. [252]

The enzyme catalyzing reaction 94, phosphorylase b-kinase, is activated by Ca^{++}. [608]

Liver phosphorylase behaves somewhat differently from the muscle enzyme. [893, 1005] Although the dog liver enzyme can be inactivated by a dephosphorylating enzyme, no decrease of the molecular weight could be observed to accompany the loss of enzyme activity and no reactivation by adenylic acid occurred. The reconstitution of active enzyme by phosphorylation with ATP in the presence of a kinase is similar, however, to that of the muscle enzyme. [759] Brain glycogen phosphorylase appears to be analogous to the muscle enzyme with respect to the a and b forms and their behavior toward AMP. [222]

Phosphorylase a has been found to contain a total of 8 moles of phosphate per mole of enzyme. [50] In addition to the four phosphate groups attached to seryl residues, four moles of pyridoxal phosphate have been shown to be contained in one mole of phosphorylase *a* from muscle, [50, 1008] and this prosthetic group has been demonstrated to be essential for enzyme activity. [171]

Crystalline muscle phosphorylase *b* has also been observed to contain bound pyridoxal phosphate, probably as a substituted pyridoxylamine derivative. [476] The amount of pyridoxal phosphate in human muscle phosphorylase *b* has been reported to be 2 moles per mole of enzyme. This indicates that on a weight-per-weight basis, the ratio of pyridoxal phosphate to protein remains constant during the dimerization of phosphorylase *b* to *a*, or during the splitting of phosphorylase *a* into *b*.

Evidence exists which shows that the reactions responsible for the transformation of phosphorylase *b* into *a* and back to *b* are of considerable importance in the regulation of carbohydrate metabolism (see Fig. 47).

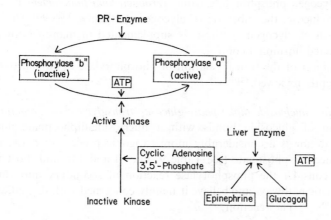

Fig. 47. Interconversion between phosphorylases *a* and *b*.

During rest, muscle phosphorylase is present almost entirely in the *b* form. It is rapidly converted to the *a* form during tetanic contraction through the action of phosphorylase *b* kinase. This latter enzyme thus exerts a regulatory control over muscle glycogenolysis while undergoing itself activation and deactivation during and following contraction. [196, 195]

It has been observed that the kinase may occur in an inactive state from which it can be activated by incubation with ATP in the presence of Mg ions, and that this activation is enhanced by the presence of added cyclic adenosine-3′,5′-phosphoric acid. [511, 682] This cyclic nucleotide is known to arise from ATP by the action of an enzyme in the particulate fraction of liver homogenate, [758, 757, 892] a reaction which may be stimulated by hormones such as epinephrine or glucagon. [34, 682] The increase of phosphorylase activity by epinephrine is indeed a well-known phenomenon, [181, 759] and the glycogenolytic action of this hormone thus finds an explanation.

Intraperitoneal injection of furomycin into rats and mice results in the depletion of hepatic glycogen. [413] The action of furomycin probably consists in an inhibition of the phosphodiesterase which cleaves cyclic adenosine-3′,5′-phosphate, thereby allowing this nucleotide to accumulate and to activate phosphorylase b kinase which, in turn, converts phosphorylase b to the active a form.

Like epinephrine, muscle stimulation by periodic electric shocks causes an increase of phosphorylase activity, but unlike epinephrine, it also activates phosphofructokinase. [469] Hence, lactate formation is proportional to the frequency of stimulation, while glucose-6-phosphate and P_i levels are hardly changed.

Anoxia also accelerates the rate of glycogenolysis. [624, 625]

The glycogen phosphorylase from *Agrobacterium tumefaciens* is inhibited by UDP-glucose, the substrate of glycogen synthetase. [562, 564] This control mechanism of glycogen synthesis is supplemented in mammals by a more sophisticated hormonal control.

The subject of the transformation of phosphorylase in animal tissues has been recently reviewed. [510]

(c) *The nucleoside-diphosphate-glucose transglycosylase reaction.* The formation of glucoside bonds with a nucleoside-diphosphate-glucose as glycosyl donor is a considerably more exogonic process than the reaction using glucose-1-phosphate (see Table 9, lines 4 and 14), and most workers actually consider the phosphorylase reaction of secondary importance for the synthetic pathways and believe it mainly concerned with degradation. [943, 776, 525, 812, 539] The reaction:

$$\text{UDP-glucose} + [\text{-O-}\alpha\text{-D-glucopyranosyl-}(1 \to 4)\text{-}]_n \,(primer) \rightleftharpoons$$
$$[\text{-O-}\alpha\text{-D-glucopyranosyl-}(1 \to 4)\text{-}]_{n+1} \,(amylose) + \text{UDP} \qquad (95)$$

was first described by Leloir and Cardini, [538] who used the soluble fraction of liver as enzyme. A similar enzyme has also been observed in skeletal muscle and diaphragm [943, 776] where it was found to be associated with UDP-glucose pyrophosphorylase (see this chapter, Section VIIA, equation 37). That the mechanism of this reaction consists in the lengthening of the outer chains of the glycogen primer was established by Leloir *et al.* [544] The activity of the enzyme catalyzing the glucoside bond formation was higher in muscle, heart and liver than in all other organs. [544] Glycogen synthesis in human leucocytes [611] and in Ehrlich's ascites tumor cells [480] proceeds according to equation 95. There is approximately 0·025 μmole of

UDP-glucose per ml of fresh tumor cell. [480] In the chick embryo it was found by histochemical techniques that heart, liver, brain and skeletal tissues contain the enzyme UDP-glucose: glycogen transglucosylase at an earlier stage during development than phosphorylase and that the former enzyme parallels the appearance of glycogen at these sites. [338]

Various names are being used for the enzyme catalyzing reaction 95, such as *glycogen* (or *α-glucan*, or *starch*) *synthetase*, or *UDP-glucose: glycogen* (or *α-glucan*, or *starch*)*transglucosidase* (or *transferase*).

Similar enzyme systems were also detected in higher plants, such as in the cotyledons and embryos of immature string beans (*Phaseolus vulgaris*) where UDP-glucose is utilized as glycosyl donor for starch synthesis. [781, 545] The use of UDP-glucose labeled with C^{14} in the glucose moiety yielded a starch fraction from which radioactive maltose could be obtained by β-amylolytic degradation. [781] This confirmed that the glucosylation must have occurred, at least in part, in the outer chains of the primer molecule. There is no agreement in the level of UDP-glucose transferase and the amylose content in starches. [44]

UDP-glucose: glycogen transglucosylase is also present in crustaceans, mollusks, fishes, and frogs, [953] as well as in certain bacteria. [563] Crustacean tissues contain a natural inhibitor of this enzyme. [953]

In 1961, Leloir and his group reported that the biosynthesis of starch may proceed from either UDP-glucose or ADP-glucose. [541, 766] The latter nucleotide was a better glucosyl donor for starch, and polymerization was ten times faster with it than with UDP-glucose. Starch synthesis from ADP-glucose is also more efficient than that from UDP-glucose in ripening rice grains, [637, 638, 639] in potato tubers, [266] and in photosynthetic tissues. [636, 211, 285] In spinach chloroplasts, the accumulation of phosphoglyceric acid stimulates the production of ADP-glucose from ATP and glucose-1-phosphate, and starch synthesis from ADP-glucose is, thus, controlled directly by the photosynthetic process. [285] Phytoglycogen in sweet corn is also formed from ATP-glucose or, to a lesser extent, from dATP-glucose. [267, 269]

In corn endosperm, sucrose is converted to starch in accordance with the scheme shown in Fig. 48. [251]

Waxy maize seeds, in contrast to most higher plants, appear to lack the ability to synthesize starch from UDP-glucose [656] or ADP-glucose. [657]

Glycogen formation in bacteria is even more dependent on ADP-glucose than is the α-glucan synthesis in animal tissues and in higher plants. [337] The ADP-glucose: glycogen transglucosylase from *Arthrobacter Sp. NRRL B 1973* is so specific for this nucleotide that it cannot use at all UDP-, CDP-, GDP-, IDP-, or dTDP-glucose as glucosyl donor. [824, 825]

Pseudouridine diphosphate glucose (ΨUDP-glucose), which is 5-ribosyl uridylic acid and has a carbon-to-carbon ribosyl linkage, may replace UDP-glucose as glycosyl donor for glycogen synthesis with the rat liver enzyme.

The rate of glucosyl transfer is, however, only 5 to 10 per cent of that from UDP-glucose, [748] the more common 1-ribosyl isomer which has a carbon-to-nitrogen ribosyl bond.

The general mechanism of polysaccharide synthesis through lengthening of the glycosidic chains of the primer molecule has been discussed earlier in this chapter (Section VIIIc). Starch, and maltodextrins with molecular weights

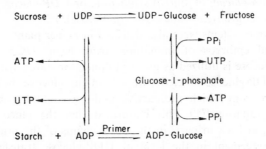

FIG. 48. Transformation of sucrose into starch in corn endosperm.

down to maltose behaved as potential glucosyl acceptors in the presence of an enzyme preparation from bean-starch granules, whereas sucrose, cellobiose, gentiobiose, glucose and fructose did not act as acceptors. [545] In addition to those substances, raffinose, melibiose, trehalose, mannose and even maltose did not prime the reaction catalyzed by an enzyme preparation from rat muscle. [544] Rat muscle UDP-glucose: glycogen transglucosylase was inactive without acceptor. [322] Maltose and maltotriose showed very little acceptor potency; the maltoside oligosaccharides with from four to eight glucose residues were hardly more active; even oligosaccharides of higher molecular weight were acceptors only at rather elevated concentrations, as compared to glycogen as primer. Brown et al. [112] reported that the same enzyme may use singly branched, low-molecular-weight oligosaccharides as acceptors, and that the transfer to such primers occurs almost exclusively to the main chain of these molecules. The enzyme acts principally by a multichain mechanism. With polysaccharides as acceptors, it extends some outer chains more than others.

The bean-starch UDP-glucose transglycosylase could not be extracted from the starch granules, [545] and high levels of this enzyme were associated with subcellular particles from the starch granules in potato tubers. [737]

On fractional centrifugation of liver homogenates, the enzyme remained associated with the sedimentation of glycogen, but could be separated from the polysaccharide by subsequent extraction of the glycogen precipitate. [542] Purification of the enzyme from rabbit skeletal muscle resulted in its separation from phosphorylase and it could, thus, be demonstrated that the UDP-glucose transglycosylase and phosphorylase are distinct enzymes. [361]

Soluble enzymes could also be obtained from plant sources, [268] and the soluble ADP-glucose: starch transglucosylase from glutinous rice grains was demonstrated to be adsorbed by amylose. [640, 8] After the rat liver enzyme is reversibly inactivated by heating to 37°C, it no longer binds glycogen; [864] it can again be transformed into the active enzyme through the addition of KF and glucose-6-phosphate. The reversible inactivation is probably due either to changes in the conformation of the enzyme molecule or to dissociation of enzyme protein into smaller, less active (or inactive) subunits, which do not effectively combine with glycogen. [867]

The polysaccharide-synthesizing reaction of UDP-glucose transglycosylase is generally reported to be activated by hexose-6-phosphates, [544, 866] in particular by glucose-6-phosphate, [921] and also by galactose-6-phosphate and glucosamine-6-phosphate. [542] The enzymes from both the toadfish and the frog require glucose-6-phosphate for activity, [782] and purified transglucosylase from rabbit muscle was stimulated by glucose-6-phosphate and Mg^{++}. [500] Cortisol injection into rats first induced formation of glucose-6-phosphate which then activated the glycogen synthetase. [406] An exception is the UDP-glucose : glycogen transglucosylase from the fat body of the American cockroach; this enzyme is stimulated by glucose-1-phosphate rather than by glucose-6-phosphate. [938]

The following scheme has been suggested for the mechanism by which glucose-6-phosphate activates glycogen synthetase: [601]

$$UDP^{2-} - glucose + glucose\text{-}6\text{-}phosphate \rightarrow$$
$$UDP^{3-} + disaccharide \ phosphate + H^+ \qquad (96)$$

$$disaccharide \ phosphate + (acceptor)_n \rightarrow$$
$$(acceptor)_{n+1} + glucose\text{-}6\text{-}phosphate \qquad (97)$$

$$UDP^{2-} - glucose + (acceptor)_n \rightarrow \quad UDP^{3-} + H^+ + (acceptor)_{n+1} \quad (98)$$

It was subsequently observed that the UDP-glucose: glycogen transglucosylases from rat skeletal muscle, [786] from rat liver, [409] and from yeast [11] each consist actually of two separate forms of the enzyme: one form is fully active without added hexose phosphate, and the other is activated by glucose-6-phosphate. Friedman and Larner have shown that the two forms of the enzyme from rat diaphragm are interconvertible by a mechanism of phosphorylation-dephosphorylation which requires ATP. These authors termed the phosphorylated form of the enzyme the glucose-6-phosphate-dependent or D-form, and the dephosphorylated enzyme, the independent or I-form. [264] The interconversion is of enzymic nature and involves the transfer of terminal phosphate from ATP to the enzyme by a Mg^{++}-requiring kinase: [265]

$$\text{transglucosylase I} + n\text{ATP} \xrightarrow[\text{Mg}^{++}]{\text{kinase}} \text{transglucosylase D} + n\text{ADP} \qquad (99)$$

The reverse reaction is catalyzed by a phosphatase:

$$\text{transglucosylase D} \xrightarrow{\text{phosphatase}} \text{transglucosylase I} + n\text{P}_i \qquad (100)$$

The two forms of UDP-glucose: α-glucan transglucosylase from rabbit skeletal muscle have been purified. [783] It is apparent that the mechanism of their interconversion is analogous to that involving the phosphorylases a and b, although in an opposite sense: [265, 22] Phosphorylation of transglucosylase I leads to the glucose-6-phosphate-dependent or less active form, whereas phosphorylation of phosphorylase b leads to the more active a form.

Dog skeletal muscle UDP-glucose: α-glucan transglucosylase is highly dependent on glucose-6-phosphate. This D-form can be converted to the I-form by incubating crude extracts of muscle in the presence of mercapto-ethanol. [784] The reverse reaction, i.e. the conversion of the I- to the D-form, occurs after incubation with ATP and Mg^{++} and is enhanced by cyclic adenosine-3′,5′-phosphate. The latter nucleotide is, thus, capable to inhibit glycogen synthesis and simultaneously to enhance glycogenolysis by converting phosphorylase b to the active a-form (see Fig. 47).

Glucose-6-phosphate was the most potent activator of the D-form of UDP-glucose:α-glucan transglucosylase from dog muscle. D-1,5-Sorbitan-6-phosphate exhibited 60 per cent of the potency of glucose-6-phosphate, D-galactose-6-phosphate (33%), D-glucosamine-6-phosphate (25%), D-sedoheptulose-7-phosphate (19%), D-allose-6-phosphate (18%), D-ribose-5-phosphate (18%), and all other sugar phosphates less than 10 per cent. [785]

In living muscle tissue, the variations in glycogen concentration are related to the changes in the levels of I- and D-forms of glycogen synthetase. [193] Glycogen, thus, controls its own synthesis by an as yet unidentified mechanism which effects the interconversion of the two forms of the glycogen-synthesizing enzyme; when tissue glycogen is low, the I-form prevails, and the D-form appears when tissue glycogen concentration is high.

A third form of transferase was found in liver and was inactive even in the presence of glucose-6-phosphate. [410] This form may be a normal intermediate in the interconversion of the D- to I-forms.

Cysteine or reduced glutathione slightly activated some enzyme preparations. [544] Glucose [545] or phlorizin [544] are inhibitors. Enzymatic activity was also markedly reduced by the addition of 2-deoxyglucose-6-phosphate which appears to compete with the hexose-6-phosphate activators. [866]

Like phosphorylase a, UDP-glucose:α-glucan transglucosylase is controlled by certain hormones. [866] Insulin and epinephrine act in an opposing manner. [524] Both the levels of the I- and D-forms of transglucosylase from intact rat diaphragm were decreased by incubation with epinephrine. [187] Insulin enhanced the I-form and decreased the D-form, whereas simultaneous incubation with both insulin and epinephrine produced no change at all. Epinephrine, like cyclic adenosine-3',5'-phosphate, thus has a regulatory role in glycogenesis, as well as in glycogenolysis. Insulin, which has no influence on phosphorylase activity, increases hepatic UDP-glucose:glycogen glucosyltransferase *in vivo*, e.g. in alloxan-diabetic rats. [865] This increase is accompanied by a rapid deposition of glycogen in the liver, while the concentration of glucose-6-phosphate in homogenates remains unchanged. [866] Insulin administration was suggested to accelerate the synthesis of the enzyme protein. [865] In insulinized rat diaphragm, the rate of glycogen formation *in vitro* is regulated by the interconversion of the D- and I-forms of glycogen synthetase. [194] Administration of glucagon to normal rats results in a small increase of synthetase activity. [866] Prednisolone increases hepatic glycogen without, however, affecting the activity of the synthetase in liver.

In wheat germ, a less sophisticated control mechanism of α-glucan synthesis exists in the form of the phosphorolysis of ADP-glucose by inorganic phosphate according to the reaction: [197]

$$\text{ADP—glucose} + P_i \rightarrow \text{ADP} + \text{glucose-1-phosphate} \qquad (101)$$

The enzyme catalyzing this reaction acts preferentially on ADP-glucose, and UDP-glucose is a less efficient glycosyl donor in this system.

(d) *The amylosucrase reaction.* The formation of a glycogen- or amylopectin-like polysaccharide from sucrose by cultures of *Neisseria perflava*, a Gram-negative coccus that can be obtained from the pharynx of healthy people, has been reported by Hehre and Hamilton. [380] The enzyme was found to be present in washed cells of this microorganism, and could be extracted therefrom; it was termed amylosucrase, and has been further investigated by Hehre and co-workers. [381, 384, 378, 377] It was assumed that a polysaccharide primer is necessary for this reaction which can be formulated as follows:

$$\text{glycosyl-fructoside } (sucrose) + [\text{-O-α-D-glucopyranosyl-}(1 \rightarrow 4)\text{-}]_n \ (primer)$$
$$\rightleftharpoons [\text{-O-α-D-glucopyranosyl-}(1 \rightarrow 4)\text{-}]_{n+1} + \text{fructose} \qquad (102)$$

The requirement for a primer would appear logical from the analogy of this reaction with those catalyzed by phosphorylase or nucleoside diphosphate glucose transglycosylase (reactions 92 and 95). Hassid [357] tried to justify the hypothesis that the amylosucrase reaction requires a primer by the fact that the polysaccharide synthesis by this reaction is inhibited by traces of salivary amylase. In the light of the priming mechanism, discussed in this chapter (Section VIIIc), the presence of α-amylase should produce more primer and, hence, increase the velocity of the reaction. The effect of salivary amylase on amylosucrase remains, therefore, unexplained.

It is believed that linear chains are first formed by amylosucrase according to reaction (102), and that a second enzyme, not as yet separated from amylosucrase, then introduces α-1,6-glucosidic bonds, thus producing the branched structure. In view of the fact that the bond energy of α-1,6-glucosidic bonds appears to be smaller than that of α-1,4 bonds (see this chapter, Section VIIIA, and Table 10), it is likely that, owing to the presence of a branching enzyme in amylosucrase preparations, the equilibrium of the reaction is shifted markedly towards polysaccharide synthesis and that for this reason the reversibility of reaction (102) has not yet been established.

(e) *The amylomaltase reaction.* A cell-free enzyme preparation has been isolated from *Escherichia coli* by Monod and Torriani [620] by means of which maltose is transformed into an amylose-like oligo- or polysaccharide. Although it has not been established whether or not a primer is necessary, maltose itself must be considered to be the glycosyl acceptor, and the reaction can be formulated as follows:

$$\text{glucosyl-glucose } (\textit{maltose}) + [\text{-O-}\alpha\text{-D-glucopyranosyl-}(1 \to 4)\text{-}]_n \rightleftharpoons$$
$$[\text{-O-}\alpha\text{-D-glucopyranosyl-}(1 \to 4)\text{-}]_{n+1} + \text{D-glucose} \qquad (103)$$

Assuming that no primer of a higher molecular weight is necessary for this reaction, the term n in equation (103) may be as low as 2 at the beginning of the reaction when only maltose is present.

The reversibility of this reaction has been ascertained, [917, 621] and an equilibrium is reached when approximately 65 per cent of the maltose has been used up. Accordingly, D-glucose is an inhibitor of the polysaccharide formation, whereas the removal of glucose during the reaction by D-glucose oxidase has been reported to shift the equilibrium toward the direction of polysaccharide synthesis. [917] The presence or absence of glucose during the reaction thus affects the chain length of the saccharide formed, as can be concluded from the iodine-staining properties of the reaction mixture; the removal of glucose intensifies the iodine-staining capacity of the polysaccharide synthesized and, hence, permits the accumulation of longer linear chains.

In the absence of added D-glucose oxidase, the chain length of the saccharide formed appears to be as low as five glucose units or less. [56] In the light of the possibility that maltose may itself serve as glycosyl acceptor, the low molecular weight of the saccharide synthesized would be due to the presence of very high concentrations of acceptor. The action of glucose oxidase would then not only displace the equilibrium toward saccharide synthesis, but would also permit the reaction to proceed until all maltose, i.e. all original acceptor as well as donor have been used up. At this point, the molecular weight or the chain length of the existing molecules may grow if one assumes that not only maltose but also maltodextrins of higher molecular weight may act as glycosyl donors. This would explain the appearance of polysaccharides which stain deep blue with iodine, when the reaction is permitted to proceed in the presence of glucose oxidase.

The assumption that maltose may be a glycosyl acceptor of the amylo-maltase-catalyzed reaction makes the transformations of the two disaccharides, sucrose and maltose, into amylodextrins analogous reactions. In each case, the glycosyl bond energy of the disaccharide is used for the formation of new saccharide bonds with the simultaneous liberation of a monosaccharide, i.e. D-fructose and D-glucose, respectively. One of the differences between these two reactions is the much higher value for the standard free energy of hydrolysis of sucrose than for that of maltose (see Table 10). Consequently one would expect the synthesis of polysaccharide from sucrose to proceed more toward completion than that from maltose. This is actually the case. As indicated, the latter reaction reaches an equilibrium when only 65 per cent of maltose is used up, whereas the amylosucrase reaction is known to proceed so far toward polysaccharide synthesis that its reversibility has not yet been demonstrated. The possibility that the seeming irreversibility of the amylo-sucrase reaction may also be due, at least in part, to the presence of branching enzymes has been mentioned before (Section VIIID, 10d).

A somewhat similar reaction was found to be catalyzed by an enzyme from rat liver and brain. [302] The formation of maltotetraose and maltotriose from maltose was noted with simultaneous liberation of D-glucose. The significance of this reaction may lie in the availability of a process permitting the *de novo* formation from maltose of low molecular maltodextrins as primers for the further synthesis of high-molecular-weight polysaccharides in liver from UDP–glucose. This enzyme catalyzing the formation of maltotetraose is different from the one found in *A. oryzae*, in that the former synthesizes only α-1,4 bonds while the latter produces a tetrasaccharide, a trisaccharide (panose) and a disaccharide (isomaltose) which all contain also α-1,6-bonds. [704, 705]

In analogy to the amylomaltase reaction (equation 103), a maltose-glucose transglucosylation reaction has been described to be catalyzed by an enzyme from wheat germ. [230] By the use of uniformly C^{14}-labeled glucose, the non-reducing glucosyl group of maltose was found to be replaced by free glucose, according to the equation:

$$\text{glucosyl-glucose } (\textit{maltose}) + C^{14}\text{-glucose} \rightarrow C^{14}\text{-glucosyl-glucose} + \text{glucose} \qquad (104)$$

(f) *The transglycosylation from dextrins.* The existence of an enzyme in liver was reported which is believed to catalyze the formation of oligo- and polysaccharides through transfer of glycosyl residues from maltotriose or from maltodextrins of longer chain lengths to a suitable acceptor. [724, 725] The nature of the bonds of the saccharide synthesized has not yet been established with certainty. Maltose or maltodextrins of higher molecular weight may serve as acceptors. There exists a considerable analogy between the action of this enzyme and that of amylomaltase. Unlike the latter, it cannot utilize maltose as a glycosyl donor, and it requires for this purpose homologous saccharides with longer chain lengths. Stetten, [869] however, isolated an enzyme from rat liver homogenates which could transfer the glycosyl group from maltose, and which had otherwise the same properties. The occurrence of such an enzyme in liver is interesting, since there are at least three other hepatic enzymes which are known to be involved in the formation of α-1,4-glucosidic bonds, i.e. phosphorylase, UDP-glucose transglycosylase, and the rat liver maltose transglycosylase.

Brown and Illingworth [109] found an *oligo*-1,4 → 1,4-*glucantransferase* in rabbit muscle as a contaminant of amylo-1,6-glucosidase. It acts by transferring preferentially maltotriosyl and, to a lesser extent, maltosyl residues from donor oligosaccharides, including glycogen, to linear or branched acceptor oligosaccharides. [111] It does not transfer single glucose units. This enzyme is presumably different from the transferase described by Abdullah and Whelan [1] which accomplishes the debranching of glycogen without requiring its prior phosphorolysis.

The absence of these or similar transglucosylases, which also cause maltose and glycogen breakdown to glucose, from the liver, heart and skeletal muscle is a characteristic feature in children with cardiomegalic glycogen-storage disease (Pompe's disease) and may be responsible for the glycogen accumulation in the tissues of these patients. [392]

A similar α-transglucosidase has been found in potatoes. [952, 718] It has been termed D-enzyme. Transglucosylases from barley malt possess also trans-α-glucosidase activities. [689] The principal oligosaccharides synthesized were isomaltose, panose, and maltotriose. [452] Fungal and bacterial transglucosylases have been reported in *Aspergillus niger*, [703] in *Streptococcus bovis*, [950] and in association with *cyclodextrin* transglucosylase from *Bacillus macerans*. [977]

(g) *The branching enzymes.* The enzymes discussed in the preceding paragraphs (Section VIIId, 10b to f) have the common feature of catalyzing the formation of α-1,4-glucosidic linkages only, and not that of α-1,6-glucoside bonds, although some of these enzymes have not yet been completely separated from enzymes which produce the latter type of bonds. The synthesis of α-1,6-bonds is brought about by enzymes which are different from those that form α-1,4-bonds, [521] and the action of the α-1,4-bonds synthetases must be assumed to precede that of the second group of enzymes which, once α-1,4-glucosidic chains of a certain length are available, cause the formation of α-1,6-bonds and, hence, transform the linear chains into branched structures (see Figs. 41 and 42). That amylopectin is formed in wheat kernels from amylose has been confirmed by the use of labeled precursors. [593]

An enzyme of this type was first described by Cori and Cori. [176] This transglycosylase was found in many animal tissues and organs such as the heart, the brain, and the liver and is usually referred to as the *Branching enzyme*. The combined action of Branching enzyme and of carefully purified, crystalline muscle phosphorylase yielded a highly branched polysaccharide. The two enzymes can be assumed to act alternately, as shown in Figs. 41 and 42. The mechanism of action of Branching enzyme has been carefully studied by Larner. [520] His results provided unequivocal evidence for the transfer of chain segments in the outer branches of glycogen. It is unlikely that this action consists in a step-by-step transfer of single glucosyl units, and should be considered more logically as a transfer of whole chain segments, several glucose units long, as indicated in Fig. 43. Amylose, amylopectin, or amylopectin-limit dextrin, obtained by exhaustive action of β-amylase, may serve as substrates for Branching enzyme from rat liver. [515] Simultaneous action of Branching enzyme with either crystallized phosphorylase [622] or UDP-glucose:α-glucan transglucosylase [112] has actually been shown to yield glycogen.

A similar enzyme was found in potato juice, [368] in other higher plants, [183, 411] and in microorganisms, [379, 72] and was called *Q-enzyme*. Q-enzyme from potato has been obtained in a crystalline form, [290] and that of the rice plant has been purified. [430] The action of this enzyme was found to be similar to that of Branching enzyme, but its main function appears to be the conversion of amylose into branched amylopectin. [714, 668, 180, 593] By choosing suitable conditions for the action of Q-enzyme on amylose, polysaccharide fractions could be obtained which were intermediate in their degree of branching between that of branched amylopectin and unbranched amylose. [669, 58] Amylose molecules of relatively small sizes (chain length up to 42 glucose units) are not utilized by Q-enzyme, and the amylose molecules have first to grow by the action of phosphorylase (or by other α-1,4-bonds synthesizing enzymes) until longer chains are available before the branching activity of Q-enzyme will become effective. [669, 716]

Sweet corn contains a polysaccharide, phytoglycogen, which is more extensively branched than amylopectin. Its biosynthesis is accomplished by the combined action of ADP-glucose:glucan transglucosylase and a branching enzyme, *α-1,4-glucan:α-1,4-glucan-6-glucosyl transferase*.† [527, 267] The latter enzyme which is responsible for the α-1,6-bonds in phytoglycogen (over 70%) is different from potato Q-enzyme, in that Q-enzyme cannot produce a more branched polysaccharide than amylopectin (2 to 4% α-1,6- bonds).

---

† Systematic name for the branching enzymes; the terms *amylose 1,4 → 1,6-transglucosidase* and *α-glucan branching glucosyl-transferase* have also been used.

Microorganisms, in contrast to most higher plants, produce glycogen, and branching enzymes have been described to occur in yeast [343, 486] and in bacteria. [1011]

The formation of α-1,6-glucosidic bonds in low-molecular-weight saccharides (isomaltose) by transglucosidation has also been demonstrated with extracts from barley malt (malt α-glucosidase), [452] and from *Aspergillus niger*. [703]

(h) *The formation of the starch granule.* The starch granule has a peculiar structure which consists of radially arranged, needle-like submicroscopic crystals. [602] Badenhuizen proposed that these granules are formed by abrupt crystallization of a mixture of amylose and amylopectin during the process of their biosynthesis. [43] The *in vitro* formation of polycrystalline granules, containing amylose and amylopectin, has actually been demonstrated. [213, 212] This phenomenon occurs as a result of phase separation of an amylopectin-amylose-water gel, and since the enzymes of amylose and amylopectin biosynthesis are apt to act in such a gel, starch precipitation as a granule may well occur in plastids in such a way. [212] The final ratio of amylopectin to amylose in the starch granule may be determined by a plastid protein. [44]

11. *Dextran*

The term dextran is used for those glucans which are produced by bacteria growing on sucrose-containing media. [980] These include most strains of *Leuconostoc*, e.g. *L. mesenteroides* and *L. dextranicum*, but also *Betabacterium vermiforme*. Natural dextrans have molecular weights which are well above 1,000,000, and most dextrans revert to water-insoluble precipitates. The study of their chemical structure has indicated that they contain exclusively D-glucose. The majority of the glucoside bonds are of the α-1,6 type. A variable amount of branching bonds of the α-1,4 type entails a more or less branched structure, depending on the bacterial strain and on other factors. Dextrans with considerable amounts of α-1,3-linkages at the branching points have also been isolated, and dextran-like substances from a number of other bacteria have been described which contain chiefly β-1,2-glucosidic or other bonds. [242, 448, 980] Linear dextrans containing only α-1,6-bonds are also known to exist. [46]

The biosynthesis of dextran has been described by Hehre. [376, 385, 377, 378] Cell-free enzyme extracts from *Leuconostoc* were found to catalyze the formation of this polysaccharide from sucrose, according to the following equation:

$$\text{glucosyl-fructoside } (\textit{sucrose}) + (\text{glucose})_n \, (\textit{primer}) \rightarrow$$
$$(\text{glucose})_{n+1} \, (\textit{dextran}) + \text{D-fructose} \qquad (105)$$

The enzyme responsible for dextran synthesis was called *dextran sucrase*.

Dextran sucrase can be induced in *Leuconostoc mesenteroides* by sucrose. [653] Enzymatically formed dextran was found to exhibit identical serological properties with the natural polysaccharides. The nature of the acceptor or primer (glucose)$_n$ has not yet been established, but can be assumed to consist of dextran-like oligo- or polysaccharides, in analogy to other transglycosylation reactions. It has been claimed that certain disaccharides, like maltose, isomaltose and melibiose, as well as some monosaccharides, i.e. D-glucose, D-galactose or D-fructose may act as glycosyl acceptors for dextran sucrase. [492] In the presence of these sugars, low molecular weight, dextran-like oligosaccharides result from the enzyme action instead of macromolecular dextrans. The low molecular weight may simply be a matter of the high initial concentration of primers, but it is interesting to note that a high specificity for the requirement of an acceptor does apparently not exist in the reaction catalyzed by dextran sucrase.

Dextran synthesis proceeds by binding of enzyme to the acceptor, followed by binding of sucrose and finally by lengthening of the chain. During the latter operation, the enzyme remains in contact with the lengthened dextran to continue the synthesis. [228]

Studies with O^{18}-labeled sucrose showed the mechanism of reaction to be a glucosyl, rather than a glucoside transfer, according to the equation: [237]

$$\underset{\text{sucrose}}{G\text{—}O^{18}\text{—}F} + \underset{\text{primer}}{G_n} \longrightarrow \underset{\text{dextran}}{G_{n+1}} + \underset{\text{fructose}}{O^{18}\text{—}F} \tag{106}$$

While a reversibility of dextran formation from sucrose has not yet been demonstrated, it must be assumed that, if reversibility of this reaction exists, its equilibrium should be markedly in favor of the polysaccharide synthesized. Failure to demonstrate reversibility may be due to the high degree of branching of dextran, or to the low standard free energy of hydrolysis of the α-1,6-glucosidic bonds in dextran, $\Delta F_H = 2000$ cal/mole (see Table 10). A second enzyme which would catalyze the formation of the branching points in dextran has not yet been described, but the existence of such an enzyme or such enzymes appears likely in analogy to our knowledge of the biosynthesis of amylopectin and glycogen.

The formation of linear dextrans which contain only α-1,6-glucosidic bonds has been described by Bailey. [46] The enzyme was derived from rumen strains of *Streptococcus bovis*.

A slightly different mechanism of dextran synthesis has been demonstrated in *Acetobacter viscosum*, and *Acetobacter capsulatum*. [382, 383] Those microorganisms, obtained from "ropy" beer, produce polysaccharides with serological properties identical with those of dextran; instead of using sucrose, however, they require starch dextrins as glycosyl donors. Whereas amylose, amylopectin, or glycogen cannot act as donors for this enzyme, called *dextran dextrinase*, amylose hydrolyzates, obtained by α-amylatic or acid treatment, as well as amyloheptaose have been found to be suitable substrates of this enzyme. [383] Schardinger dextrins, limit dextrins, or maltose have no effect.

It must be emphasized that the study by chemical means of the structure of the polysaccharides synthesized by these microorganisms has not yet been carried out, and that, in spite of the serological identity with dextrans, their chemical structure may be closer to the group of starch polysaccharides than to that of dextrans.

12. *Cellulose*

Cellulose is no doubt the most abundant carbohydrate in nature. It is composed of D-glucose units linked together by β-1,4-glucosidic bonds to linear chains. The most characteristic property of cellulose is the interaction between different chains, resulting in their orientation to fibrillar micelles and to fibers of very low water solubility. X-Ray diffraction diagrams of cellulose fibers show that a major portion of these fibers are in a crystalline arrangement. [602]

In *Acetobacter acetigenum*, cellulose, together with cellobiose, cellotriose, cellotetraose, glucose, fructose, xylose, ribulose and dihydroxy acetone, is produced when the organism is grown in a lactate-buffered glycerol medium. [762] Cellulose synthesis by succinate-grown cells of *Acetobacter xylinum* proceeds from pyruvate via phosphoenolpyruvate, phosphoglycerate, triosephosphate, and hexose. [75]

Although β-D-glucose-1-phosphate has been found to be formed from maltose by certain microorganisms, such as by *Neisseria meningitidis*: [257]

$$\text{glucosyl-glucose (} \textit{maltose} \text{)} + \text{inorganic phosphate} \rightleftharpoons$$
$$\beta\text{-D-glucose-1-phosphate} + \text{D-glucose} \qquad (107)$$

with the aid of an enzyme called *maltose phosphorylase*, no indications have been brought forward that β-D-glucose-1-phosphate can serve as a glycosyl donor for β-glucosidic polysaccharides.

Labeled D-glucose was found, however, to be incorporated into cellulose both in higher plants [14] and *Acetobacter xylinum*. [400, 616] Such incorporation must have occurred mainly without passing through intermediates other than derivatives of D-glucose itself, since the labeled carbon atoms were found in cellulose in the same positions in which they had been in D-glucose. Wolfrom *et al.* [997] observed, however, that part of the glucose incorporated into cotton cellulose must have first been broken down and then synthesized through the Embden-Meyerhof pathway.

Glaser [303, 304] could demonstrate that a particulate enzyme preparation from *Acetobacter xylinum* is capable of synthesizing cellulose from UDP-glucose in the presence of soluble dextrins as primer:

$$\text{UDP-glucose} + [\text{-O-}\beta\text{-D-glucopyranosyl-}(1 \to 4)\text{-}]_n \ (primer) \rightleftharpoons$$
$$[\text{-O-}\beta\text{-D-glucopyranosyl-}(1 \to 4)\text{-}]_{n+1} \ (cellulose) + \text{UDP} \qquad (108)$$

The bacterium *Sarcina ventriculi* contains an enzyme system by which UDP-glucose is formed from glucose-1-phosphate and UTP. It was assumed, therefore, that cellulose synthesis in this organism proceeds from UDP-glucose. [133]

In higher plants, the guanosine nucleotide appears to replace UDP-glucose for cellulose biosynthesis, such as in roots and hypocotyls of mung bean seedlings (*Phaseolus aureus*). [53] The enzyme from this source is specific for GDP-D-glucose, and does not react with the glucose derivatives of UDP, ADP, CDP or dTDP. [239] The plant, *Lupinus albus*, has been reported to produce cellulose from either UDP-glucose or GDP-glucose, but by the use of separate enzymes. [113] In either case, the biosynthesis of cellulose appears to proceed in a fashion analogous to amylose formation from UDP-glucose (see equation 95).

Reaction (108) is in agreement with the results of the incorporation of labeled glucose into cellulose.

A completely different pathway for cellulose synthesis was discovered by Khan and Colvin. [479] These authors isolated a precursor of cellulose from *A. xylinum* in the form of an ethanol soluble compound in which glucose is bound to a lipid. This compound is presumably synthesized within the cells from glucose taken up during incubation. It is transported across the cell wall, and is then capable of forming typical microfibrils of cellulose in an aqueous medium containing an extracellular enzyme. Although no necessity of a primer was noted, it appears that the transformation of soluble precursor into insoluble cellulose is accomplished by tip growth of the microfibrils. [160] An extracellular enzyme from pea or oat seedlings is also capable of producing microfibrils of cellulose from an ethanol-soluble precursor. [159] In *Acetobacter acetigenum*, the cell wall has been reported to be necessary for cellulose biosynthesis, although the final stage of cellulose formation must occur outside the cell. [106]

In glucose-containing cultures of this bacterium, chain initiators or primers are produced first, and glucose units are subsequently added to these primers. [105] The average growing time of the chain was less than 40 min, and no nonterminated chains were found at cell division. [105]

Studies with the electron microscope have shown that individual cellulose molecules are released at the cell surface of *Acetobacter xylinum*, from where they diffuse into the medium to enter finally into crystalline patterns. [674] The degree of polymerization of cellulose grown by this organism reaches a maximum of 6000 after 5 days and, thereafter, decreases again to about 2000, probably through the action of a cellulase.[429] Such a mechanism would create new primer molecules.

Kinetic investigations on the biosynthesis of cellulose in cotton show some analogy with the mechanism of cellulose formation in microorganisms. Primary-wall cellulose is first formed in a slow phase which is followed by a faster second phase during which secondary-wall cellulose arises. The latter phase yields 90 per cent of the total polysaccharide which has a rather even degree of polymerization with two maxima, i.e. 14,000 and 1000 to 2000; cellulose synthesis is, thus, assumed to involve a templet mechanism.[578, 579]

13. *Other Glucans*

Certain polysaccharides of β-1,3-glucosidic nature and of rather low molecular weight are known to occur in algae (*Laminaria*)[62] as well as in the phloem of higher plants; they are called laminaran and callose, respectively. The biosynthesis of a chemically similar glucan was accomplished from UDP-glucose by an enzyme obtained from mung bean seedlings (*Phaseolus aureus*) as well as from cabbage, parsley, spinach and zucchini.[249] The reaction for polysaccharide formation was reported to require an activator which is not incorporated into the product, however.

Paramylon, a water-insoluble β-1,3-glucan, has been shown to be formed from UDP-glucose by an enzyme of the photosynthetic protist, *Euglena gracilis*.[323, 571]

Certain extracellular fungal laminarinases possess transglucosylase activity, in addition to their hydrolytic action, and have been reported to produce di-, tri- and tetrasaccharides with β-1,3- and β-1,6-glucosidic linkages from β,β-trehalose, laminaribiose, cellobiose or gentiobiose.[149]

Another glucan, which possesses 80 per cent β-1,2 bonds and some β-1,3- and β-1,6-glucosidic bonds and occurs in *Agrobacterium tumefaciens* and in *Rhizobium japonicum*, is synthesized from UDP-glucose by an enzyme extract from the latter organism.[202]

OTHER N-FREE POLYSACCHARIDES

14. *Mannans and Galactans*

GDP-Mannose is the precursor of yeast mannan.[12] A phosphomannan from the yeast *Hansenula holstii* has been described by Jeanes and Watson.[449] It has 20 per cent (1 → phosphate → 6 bonds), 33 per cent (1 → 2), and 47 per cent (1 → 3) bonds, and it contains two diester phosphate groups for each ten mannose residues. Its biosynthesis from GDP-mannose was postulated.[103]

The marine red alga, *Porphyra perforata* contains a derivative of a D,L-galactan. While the D-galactose moiety of the polysaccharide arises from D-glucose-1-phosphate via UDP-D-glucose and UDP-D-galactose (see Section VIIc, equation (44) in this chapter), the L-galactose moiety is formed, according to Su and Hassid, [889] from D-mannose-1-phosphate via GDP-D-mannose and GDP-L-galactose by a transformation similar to the GDP-D-mannose to GDP-L- fucose conversion (see Section VIIc, equation (52) in this chapter). The D,L-galactan is further methylated (in C-6 position of the D-galactose), dehydrated in the L-galactose moiety to yield a 3,6 intramolecular ether, and is finally sulfated, probably in the C-6 positions of both D- and L-galactose.

15. *Fructans*

Many plants use water-soluble fructans as carbohydrate reserve in their tubers. These polysaccharides are, therefore, widely distributed throughout the vegetable kingdom. According to their chemical structure, plant fructans fall into two distinct groups, i.e. the inulin and the phlean group.

Inulin occurs in *Dahlia* and in the Jerusalem artichoke (*Helianthus tuberosus*). According to Haworth and Learner, [367] it consists of D-fructofuranose units linked through β-2,1-glycosidic bonds. Its molecular weight is rather small, but its solubility in water is low owing to the fact that this polysaccharide has a high tendency to form double-refractive spherocrystals which show a strong X-ray pattern. [980]

The tuber-like root *Phleum pratense* contains a different fructan, called *phlean*. It is made up of unbranched chains of D-fructofuranose attached to each other by β-2,6-glycosidic bonds. [365] Unlike inulin, phlean is water soluble.

Bacterial fructans are termed *levans*; they resemble phlean in that they consist of D-fructofuranose units joined by β-2,6-glycosidic links. Levans are highly water soluble. End-group determinations indicate that their chains consist of about 12 fructose residues. Since their molecular weight has been found to be very high, [247, 205] levans must be assumed to be highly branched. Like the bacterial dextrans, levans are synthesized by bacteria using sucrose or raffinose as substrates.

The biosynthesis of levans has been successfully studied by Hestrin *et al.* [397, 396] who were able to isolate an enzyme, *levan sucrase*, from autolyzed cells of *Acetobacter levanicum*. This enzyme was found to catalyze the following reaction:

$$\text{glucosyl-fructoside } (\textit{sucrose}) + [\text{-O-}\beta\text{-D-fructofuranosyl-}(2 \to 6)\text{-}]_n$$
$$(\textit{acceptor}) \rightleftharpoons [\text{-O-}\beta\text{-D-fructofuranosyl-}(2 \to 6)\text{-}]_{n+1} \ (\textit{levan}) +$$
$$\text{D-glucose} \qquad (109)$$

This reaction is analogous to the dextran formation from sucrose by dextransucrase (see reaction 105). In both cases, the glycoside-bond energy of sucrose is used for polysaccharide formation. While the D-glucopyranoside moiety of sucrose is incorporated into dextran with simultaneous liberation

P

of D-fructose, levan biosynthesis uses the fructofuranoside part of sucrose to build up polysaccharide and liberates D-glucose.

In the presence of low-molecular-weight levan, reaction (109) has been demonstrated to be reversible, [720] and the priming action of levan on this reaction was pointed out. [719]

Both natural fructans and *in vitro* synthesized levan oligosaccharides have been reported to contain a terminal glucose unit. [809, 204, 399, 245, 408] It appears likely, therefore, that this glucose residue originates from a sucrose molecule which may be assumed to have acted as the original acceptor of levan biosynthesis. That various disaccharides may be acceptors of the levan sucrase-catalyzed reaction, and that the corresponding trisaccharides become the products of such reactions, has been repeatedly observed. [398, 31] The first step of levan synthesis would then be the formation of a trisaccharide:

$$\text{sucrose } (donor) + \text{sucrose } (acceptor) \rightleftharpoons$$
$$\text{glucosyl-fructosido-fructoside} + \text{D-glucose} \qquad (110)$$

This trisaccharide would further grow by successive transfructosylation steps, whereby the terminal glucose unit remains attached to the polysaccharide being formed:

$$n \text{ (sucrose) } (donor) + \text{glucosyl-fructosido-fructoside } (acceptor) \rightleftharpoons$$
$$\text{glucosyl-(fructoside)}_{n+2} \text{ } (levan) + n \text{ (glucose)} \qquad (111)$$

Substitution of sucrose by raffinose (galactosyl glucosyl fructoside) also yields levan through the action of levan sucrase, but instead of D-glucose, the disaccharide melibiose (galactosyl glucose) is formed as the by-product. A number of other oligosaccharides which contain a terminal β-D-fructofuranosyl group linked to the C-1 position of a glycoside, have been reported to be capable of replacing sucrose in the levan synthesis, [399] with the exception of umbelliferose, [395] an isomer trisaccharide of raffinose. Umbelliferose has the structure: O-α-D-galactopyranosyl-(1 → 2)-O-α-D-glucopyranosyl-(1 → 2)-β-D-fructofuranoside, and is distinct from raffinose only in the position at which the galactosyl group is attached to the glucose moiety (C-6 in raffinose, C-2 in umbelliferose).

In analogy to the reaction catalyzed by dextran sucrase, which had been shown to consist of the transfer of a glucosyl, rather than a glucoside residue, from sucrose (see reaction 106), levan sucrase is responsible for the transfer of a fructosyl residue, [237] as was demonstrated with O^{18}:

$$\underset{\text{raffinose}}{\text{Gal} < \text{G} - \text{O}} \!-\!\! \text{F} + \underset{\text{glucose}}{\text{G} - 1 - \text{O}^{18}} \longrightarrow \underset{\text{melibiose}}{\text{Gal} < \text{G}} + \underset{\text{sucrose}}{\text{G} - \text{O}^{18}\text{F}} \qquad (112)$$

where Gal, G and F represent galactose, glucose and fructose, respectively, and the symbol $<$ signifies a glycosyl-glycoside linkage.

Levan sucrase has also been found in *B. subtilis*, and its action appears to be analogous to that of the enzyme from *Acetobacter levanicum*. [203, 763] The purified enzyme catalyzed also the ketosyl transfer from glucosyl-sorboside and glucosyl-xyluloside to D-xylose, L-arabinose, melibiose, and lactose, to yield the corresponding di-, or trisaccharides, according to the reaction: [764]

$$\text{glucosyl-}(1\rightarrow \leftarrow 2)\text{-ketoside} + \text{acceptor} \rightleftharpoons$$
$$\text{acceptor-}(1\rightarrow \leftarrow 2)\text{-ketoside} + \text{glucose} \quad (113)$$

Relatively little is known on the mechanism of biosynthesis of the plant fructans. Transfructosylation reactions are known to be catalyzed by enzymes of the Jerusalem artichoke: [539]

$$(\text{fructose})_n + \text{sucrose} \rightleftharpoons \text{glucosyl-fructosido-fructoside} + (\text{fructose})_{n-1} (114)$$

This reaction may account for the transformation of one fructan into another. A *de novo* synthesis of plant fructans may be possible by the reverse direction of reaction 114, possibly with substitution of the trisaccharide for sucrose or, as pointed out by Schlubach, [811, 810] by a mechanism similar to that of levan formation (see reaction 109). The *fructosyl sucrose: sucrose transfructo-sylase* activity from the same source is most likely due to the same enzyme and has been shown, by means of C^{14}-labeled sucrose, to catalyze inter-molecular fructosyl exchange according to the reaction: [231]

$$\text{G} < \text{F}\mathord{-}\mathord{\mid}\mathord{-}\text{F} + \text{G}^* < \text{F}^* \rightleftharpoons \text{G} < \text{F} + \text{G}^* < \text{F}^*\mathord{-}\text{F} \quad (115)$$

In addition to the mechanism of transfructosylation from saccharides discussed above, fructosan biosynthesis may also proceed through UDP-fructose. This nucleotide was indeed detected to occur in dahlia tubers, [327] and its existence at the site of fructosan formation strongly suggests its utilization in the biosynthesis.

16. *Pentosans*

Xylans and arabans are widely distributed throughout the vegetable kingdom.

Xylan has been found in practically all land plants and in some marine algae. It is abundant in corn cobs, corn stalks, grain hulls and stems, and accompanies cellulose in hardwoods and softwoods. Its structure appears to correspond to a polymer of D-xylopyranose units, joined together by β-1,4-glycosidic linkages, with the occurrence of an occasional β-1,3 cross linkage. Disregarding the rare branching points, this structure is obviously similar to that of cellulose, except that xylan lacks the $—CH_2OH$ groups of the position 6 in the D-glucose units of cellulose. It has often been postulated, therefore, that xylan may be formed by decarboxylation of the corresponding glucuronan which, in turn, might arise from cellulose by oxidation of the carbon atoms 6 in cellulose.

Such a hypothesis might seemingly find some support in the fact that both glucose and glucuronolactone have been found to be incorporated into xylan from wheat plants with loss of carbon 6, and without undergoing major rearrangements.[654, 14, 655] Xylan-like oligosaccharides have been synthesized, however, from UDP-xylose through the catalytic action of an enzyme preparation from asparagus shoots.[250] This reaction corresponds to the equation:

$$\text{UDP-xylose} + [\text{-O-}\beta\text{-D-xylopyranosyl-}(1 \to 4)\text{-}]_n \ (primer) \rightleftharpoons$$
$$[\text{-O-}\beta\text{-D-xylopyranosyl-}(1 \to 4)\text{-}]_{n+1} \ (xylan) + \text{UDP} \qquad (116)$$

and is thus analogous to that of cellulose or amylose formation (reactions 108 and 95).

That UDP-D-xylose may be formed either from D-xylose-1-phosphate and UTP (reaction 38),[301, 298] or, more likely, by decarboxylation of UDP-glucuronolactone[654, 14, 655] is now well known and has been discussed earlier in this chapter (Section VIIA and E). UDP-D-xylose and UDP-glucuronic acid have indeed been found in higher plants.[301, 248]

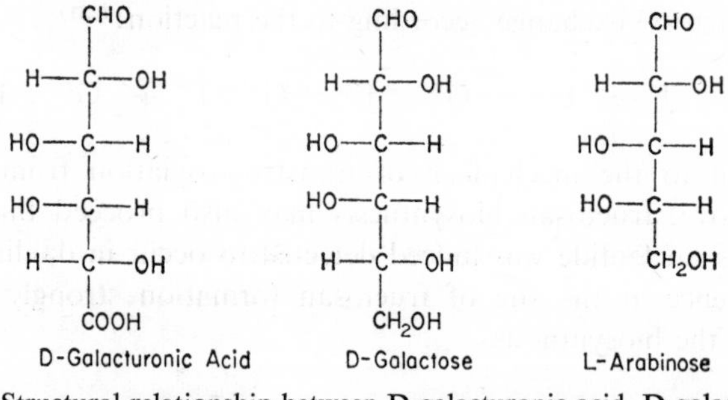

FIG. 49. Structural relationship between D-galacturonic acid, D-galactose, and L-arabinose, the three monosaccharides which make up the pectic substances: the *pectins* (methyl ester of α-1,4 linked D-galacturonopyranose units); *galactan* (β-1,4-linked D-galactopyranose units); and *araban* (α-1,5-linked L-arabo-furanose units, with α-1,3-cross linkages).

The biosynthesis of xylan from D-glucose can then be assumed to proceed along the following pathway:

$$\text{glucose} \xrightarrow{\text{ATP}} \text{glucose-6-phosphate} \longrightarrow \text{glucose-1-phosphate} \xrightarrow{\text{UTP}}$$
$$\text{UDP-glucose} \xrightarrow{\text{DPN}^+} \text{UDP-glucuronic acid} \xrightarrow{-\text{CO}_2} \text{UDP-xylose} \longrightarrow \text{xylan} \quad (117)$$

Araban is a polymer of L-arabinose, consisting of a main chain of arabo-furanose units linked through α-1,5-glycosidic bonds, with one-unit side chains joined through α-1,3 bonds. It is found in nature in association with pectic substances.

The structural relationship between L-arabinose and D-galacturonic acid (see Fig. 49) is analogous to that of the pair D-xylose and D-glucuronic acid. Since the UDP derivatives of L-arabinose and D-galacturonic acid have actually been found to occur in higher plants, [301, 248] and since studies with labeled glucose have shown that the arabans from the strawberry and from the boysenberry originate from the carbon atoms 1 to 5 of glucose, [814, 817] it appears likely that the biosynthesis of araban is analogous to that of xylan with the exception that it would include an additional step, i.e. either the transformation of UDP-glucose to UDP-galactose (reaction 44), or the epimerization

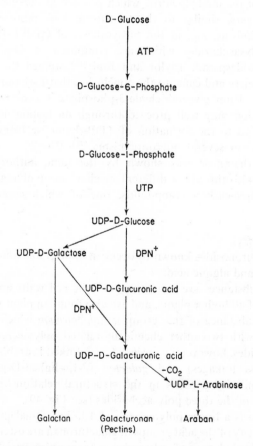

FIG. 50. Possible pathways for the biogenesis of pectic substances.

of UDP-glucuronic acid to UDP-galacturonic acid [849, 660] (see Figs. 33 and 50).

Hemicelluloses are extremely widespread in higher plants. A pathway leading to the biosynthesis of their pentosan components in the mung bean (*Phaseolus aureus*) was proposed by Kessler *et al.* [478] Both pentoses are formed as the UDP-derivatives from the corresponding uronic acid, according to the scheme in Figure 51. An analogous pathway for hemicellulose formation from *myo*-inositol was proposed in ripening strawberries. [558, 557]

17. *Methylpentose Containing Polysaccharides*

A polysaccharide containing D-glucose, D-galactose and L-fucose is synthesized in *Aerobacter cloacae*. The L-fucose was shown to arise directly from glucose or through fragments which are not interconvertible. [374] It appears likely that reduction and epimerization reactions are involved in the formation of the methylpentose which proceed at the level of nucleoside diphosphate sugars, similar to the transformations reported to occur in other microorganisms, e.g. in the biosynthesis of GDP-L-fucose. [292, 294]

Bacterial polysaccharides which are composed of D-glucose and L-rhamnose are widespread. Taylor and Juni [910] studied the origin of the deoxyhexose moiety and came to the conclusion that L-rhamnose originates, at least in part, from glyceraldehyde-3-phosphate via hexose phosphates. Such a conversion may well proceed through nucleotide derivatives, in a fashion analogous to the formation of TDP-rhamnose from TDP-glucose, known to occur in several microorganisms. [711, 712, 502]

However, L-rhamnose was shown by the same authors to originate simultaneously also through a different mechanism involving the condensation of two three-carbon compounds, one of which contains a methyl group. [910]

18. *Polyuronosides*

The two polyuronosides known to occur in appreciable amounts in nature are the pectins and alginic acid.

The pectic substances are constituents of the cell walls and of the intercellular layers of all higher plants, and are also found in plant juices and saps. The principal substance of this group is *galacturonan* which always occurs in association with two other chemically-related polysaccharides, that are not polyuronosides, however, i.e. *araban* (α-1,5-linked L-arabofuranose units, with α-1,3-cross linkages) and *galactan* (β-1,4-linked-D-galactopyranose units). The similarity consists in the structural relationship between the monomer units of the three polysaccharides (see Fig. 49).

Galacturonan is a linear polymer of α-1,4 linked D-galacturonopyranose units. The majority of the acid groups in galacturonan are esterified. Common names for the methyl ester of galacturonan (containing variable amounts of free carboxyl groups) are *pectinic acids* or *pectins*, depending on their ability to form colloidal or higher dispersed aqueous solutions, respectively.[980] Both pectinic acids and pectins are known to form gels with sugar and acid under suitable conditions.

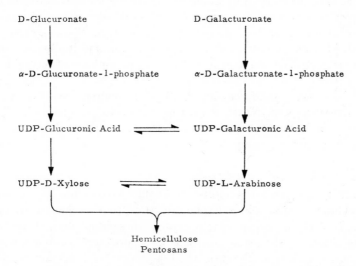

FIG. 51. Formation of hemicellulose pentosans in the mung bean according to Kessler *et al.*[478]

Incorporation of labeled hexose into strawberry pectins without essential rearrangement of the carbon skeleton,[817] in connection with the known facts on the formation of UDP-galacturonic acid in plant tissues,[857, 248] may be interpreted as indications for a pathway of pectin biosynthesis shown in Fig. 50.

The biosynthesis of pectin from *myo*-inositol in strawberry fruits or parsley leaves has been shown to proceed in a similar fashion.[558, 557] *Myo*-inositol, which may arise from glucose, is believed to be converted to L-bornesitol, a monomethyl ether of *myo*-inositol (see Fig. 52). This cyclitol is subsequently transformed to methyl-D-glucuronate, then to methyl-D-glucuronate nucleotide, which yields methyl-D-galacturonate nucleotide and finally pectin.[556]

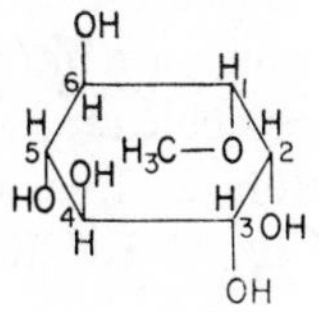

FIG. 52. Structure of L-bornesitol, a 1-O-methyl-*myo*-inositol.

Alginic acid is the polysaccharide of most brown algae and constitutes a linear polymer of D-mannuronic acid and L-guluronic acid units, linked through β-1,4 glycosidic bonds. Although its biosynthesis is not known, an attractive hypothesis of its formation from guanosine diphosphate mannose has been brought forward by Cabib and Leloir [125] who were able to isolate this potential intermediate from yeast. GPD-D-Mannuronic acid was subsequently found to occur in the marine brown alga, *Fucus gardneri Silva*, together with its 5-epimer, GDP-L-guluronic acid, and it appears probable that these nucleotides serve as precursors in the synthesis of the alginic acid polymer. [549]

The oxidation of GDP-mannose to GDP- mannuronic acid by an extract from *Arthrobacter sp. NRRL B 1973* has also been reported. [738, 739] Mannuronic acid had previously been detected to be a component of a polysaccharide from this organism. [489]

19. N-Free Heteropolysaccharides

The rhamnose in a L-rhamnose- and D-glucose-containing polysaccharide from a Gram-negative soil bacterium originates from succinate via fumarate, malate, oxalacetate, phosphoenolpyruvate, triosephosphate and hexose. [910]

In the leaves of the plum, glucose is incorporated into a polysaccharide, containing D-galactose, D-xylose and L-arabinose, without skeletal changes in the carbon chain, other than the loss of the terminal carbon atom in the synthesis of the pentoses. [19] Pathways such as shown in Figs. 50 and 51 are probably involved in the biosynthesis of this polysaccharide.

The extracellular polysaccharide of *Cryptococcus laurentii* is made up of D-mannose, D-glucuronic acid and D-xylose in the approximate ratio of 5 : 1 : 2. [2] It is formed from GDP-mannose, UDP-glucuronic acid and UDP-xylose. [154, 20] The carbohydrate moieties of all three nucleotides originate from glucose through pathways described earlier in this chapter. [20]

S-FREE MUCOPOLYSACCHARIDES

20. Chitin

Chitin is the most abundant of all mucopolysaccharides. It occurs as the structural carbohydrate of the shell of invertebrates, in crab and lobster shells, in insect cuticles, as well as in fungi. A remarkable analogy exists between the chemical structure of cellulose and chitin. Composed of N-acetyl-2-amino-2-deoxy-D-glucopyranose units which are linked together to linear chains by β-1,4-glycosidic bonds, a chitin molecule represents a cellulose chain in which the hydroxyl group at carbon atom 2 of each glucose residue has been exchanged for an acetylamino group, —$NHCOCH_3$. It is even less soluble and less reactive than cellulose.

Glaser and Brown [315] obtained a particulate, as well as a soluble enzyme preparation from *Neurospora crassa* both of which were capable of accomplishing the formation of insoluble chitin from UDP-N-acetylglucosamine. A soluble primer obtained by degradation of chitin appears to be required for this reaction:

$$\text{UDP-N-acetylglucosamine} + [\text{acetylglucosamine}]_n \ (primer) \rightleftharpoons$$
$$[\text{acetylglucosamine}]_{n+1} \ (chitin) + \text{UDP} \qquad (118)$$

but neither the monosaccharide, N-acetylglucosamine, nor a corresponding disaccharide served as acceptor of the reaction when catalyzed by the soluble enzyme preparation. The mechanism of chitin biosynthesis appears to be analogous to that of cellulose formation (reaction 108). In both cases, transglycosylation must proceed with the simultaneous inversion of an α-glycosidic bond in the UDP-sugar to a β-glycosidic linkage in the polysaccharide synthesized.

A similar mechanism of chitin formation is likely to exist in the wing of the desert locust, *Schistocerca gregaria*, where *UDP-N-acetylglucosamine pyrophosphorylase* has been detected.[136] *Chitin synthetase* has been found in cell-free extracts of the southern worm, *Prodenia eridania*.[447]

21. *Hyaluronic Acid*

This mucopolysaccharide consists of linear chains which contain alternating D-glucuronopyranose and N-acetyl-D-glucosamine units. The monomers are linked together through alternating β-1,3-glucosiduronic and β-1,4-hexosaminidic bonds. Hyaluronic acid occurs in vitreous humor, in umbilical cord, in mesenchymal tissues and tumors, in synovial fluid, and in hemolytic streptococci. It is water soluble and forms highly viscous solutions. The molecular weight of hyaluronic acid is subject to wide variations depending on its origin.

Glaser and Brown[313] observed the formation of hyaluronate-like oligosaccharides from cell-free homogenates of the Rous sarcoma, and postulated that UDP-D-glucuronic acid and UDP-N-acetylglucosamine are intermediates in this reaction. The biosynthesis of hyaluronic acid in cell-free extracts of group A hemolytic streptococci was studied with the use of tritium labeled UDP-sugars in Dorfman's laboratory,[574] and these workers arrived at a similar mechanism for the *in vivo* formation of that mucopolysaccharide, after they were able to isolate both UDP-N-acetylglucosamine and UDP-glucuronic acid from streptococci.[152]

Based upon results on the stimulation or inhibition of hyaluronate synthesis by acetylglucosamine-1-phosphate, UTP, or pyrophosphate, Dorfman[215] concluded that hyaluronic acid biosynthesis proceeds according to a mechanism shown in Fig. 53. Glycosidic bond formation would take place alternately from UDP-glucuronic acid and from UDP-N-acetylglucosamine.

An enzyme which catalyzed the polymerization of UDP-glucuronic acid and UDP-N-acetylglucosamine to yield hyaluronic acid was obtained from the protoplast membrane of group A streptococci. [575] This enzyme preparation was relatively free from nucleic acids and cell wall material. The reaction catalyzed by it required Mg^{++} and primer, but the primer represented less than 1 per cent of the polysaccharide formed. A similar enzyme was present in cell-free preparations of skin from rat fetuses, [808] and a soluble hyaluronic acid synthetase could be obtained therefrom after incubation with papain. [874]

A possible control mechanism for hyaluronic acid biosynthesis is mediated by an enzyme which is capable of splitting UDP-N-acetylglucosamine into UMP and N-acetylglucosamine-1-phosphate. [698] This enzyme was detected in sheep brain and was found to be inhibited by ATP, UTP, ADP and N-acetylglucosamine-1-phosphate. Inhibition of this decomposition of UDP-N-acetylglucosamine by any of the above substances results in the enhanced utilization of the amino sugar nucleotide for polysaccharide biosynthesis.

Glucosamine may be directly incorporated *in vivo* into connective tissue. [981] Vitamin A appears to be essential for hexosamine incorporation from glucose-6-phosphate into mucopolysaccharide by rat colon homogenates. [623]

The action of hyaluronidase, in addition to its hydrolytic mechanism, has been reported to cause some transglycosylidic rearrangements in the chains of hyaluronate and other mucopolysaccharides. [414] It is possible that such phenomena may also play a certain role in the biosynthesis of hyaluronate from primarily formed oligosaccharides.

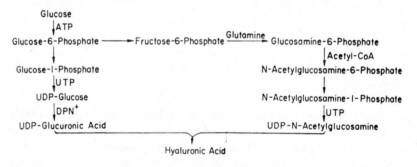

FIG. 53. Biosynthesis of hyaluronic acid.

22. *Bacterial Cell Wall Polysaccharides*

The composition of the bacterial cell wall changes from organism to organism. Among the principal carbohydrate components of the bacterial cell wall are D-glucose, D-galactose, D-mannose, L-rhamnose, D-glucuronic acid, D-galacturonic acid, N-acetyl-D-glucosamine, N-acetyl-D-galactosamine, L-fucosamine and N-acetylmuramic acid. The latter aminosugar was found to be 3-O-carboxyethyl-N-acetylglucosamine, or 3-O-D-lactic acid ether of N-acetylglucosamine, [876, 875] see Fig. 54. Muramic acid was shown to be linked in *S. aureus* to a polypeptide chain by its carboxylic group. [877] Other carbohydrate components of the bacterial cell wall include the following substances: a heptose, D-ribitol-5-phosphate, L-glycerol-3-phosphate,

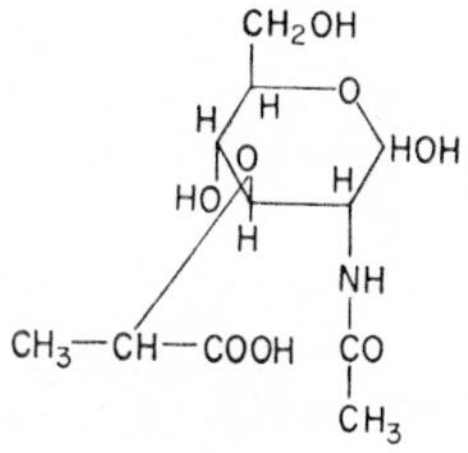

FIG. 54. Structure of muramic acid.

several dideoxyhexoses, namely tyvelose, colitose, and abequose, and finally the recently discovered sugar acid, 2-keto-3-deoxyoctonate (KDO). The component carbohydrates are combined in a very complex manner with protein or peptide which contains some amino acids of the unusual D-configuration, to make up the high molecular, multicross-linked, rigid framework of the bacterial cell wall.

A possible structure for the cell wall of a Gram-positive bacterium (*Staphylococcus aureus*) has been proposed by Strominger, [881] as seen in Fig. 55.

Acid hydrolysis cleaves off a linear polymer, called teichoic acid, which consists of a polyribitol phosphate chain (or in other cases polyglycerol phosphate) with N-acetylglucosamine and D-alanine residues attached as side chains. Teichoic acids are the antigenic components of the cell wall in Gram-positive bacteria.

Gram-negative organisms contain instead considerable amounts of lipo-polysaccharide, responsible for the antigenicity. The bacterial lipopolysaccharide consists of a backbone of polyheptose phosphate to which carbohydrate side chains are attached, as well as ketodeoxyoctonate (KDO), the latter carrying the lipid, according to Fig. 56. The carbohydrate side chains contain glucose, galactose, N-acetylglucosamine, mannose, rhamnose, colitose, or abequose. Gram-negative bacterial cell walls, in contrast to those of Gram-positive organisms, also contain a full range of amino acids as do glycoproteins. [722]

Reviews on the biosynthesis of bacterial cell wall polysaccharides have been published recently. [881, 42, 614, 797] In accordance with the complex structure of the cell wall, its several components have been investigated separately, and their biosynthesis proceeds along different, although analogous, pathways.

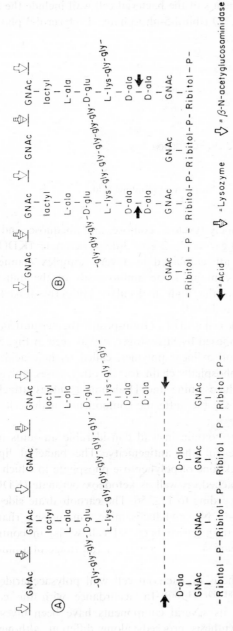

FIG. 55. Two possible structures of the cell wall of *S. aureus* (Copenhagen) (from Strominger[881]). In both structures the glycopeptide (polymer of N-acetylglucosamine and N-acetylglucosamine-lactyl-peptide) is shown cross-linked by a polyglycine component, linking the lysine of one peptide chain and the glutamic acid of another. In *structure A*, two species of peptides occur in the glycopeptide, and the means of attachment of the ribitol phosphate polymer (teichoic acid) to the rest of the wall is not specified. In *structure B*, the ribitol phosphate polymer is shown attached to the glycopeptide through the peptide. The antigenic component in the wall is an α-acetylglucosaminyl-ribitol grouping in the teichoic acid. These structures were derived from studies of fragments obtained after treatment with acid and with enzymes and from studies of the structure of the teichoic acid; points of cleavage are shown by *arrows*. Reproduced by courtesy of Federation of American Societies for Experimental Biology.

(a) *Muramic acid-containing mucopeptides.* The biosynthesis of the glyco-peptide moiety of the cell wall, i.e. the polymer of N-acetylglucosamine and N-acetylglucosamine-lactyl-peptide, starts with the formation of N-acetyl-muramic acid from N-acetylglucosamine. Phosphoenolpyruvate is the

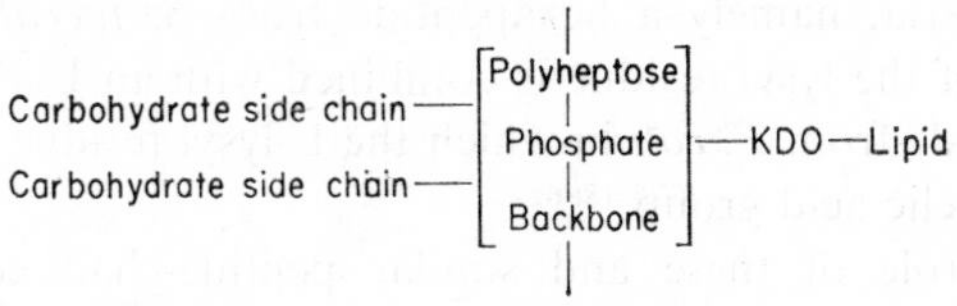

FIG. 56. Schematic structure of bacterial lipopolysaccharide.

most likely immediate precursor of the side chain of muramic acid during its biosynthesis in intact staphylococci (reaction 119). [771] Subsequent reduction of the pyruvate-containing intermediate is assumed to yield the N-acetyl-muramic acid nucleotide (reaction 120). [880, 881]

UDP-N-acetylglucosamine + phosphoenolpyruvate →

$$\text{UDP-N-acetylglucosamine-pyruvic acid} + P_i \quad (119)$$

UDP-N-acetylglucosamine-pyruvic acid →

$$\text{UDP-N-acetylmuramic acid} \quad (120)$$

The next step is the enzymatic addition of L-alanine, D-glutamic acid and L-lysine. Enzymes from *Staphylococcus aureus* that catalyze the sequential addition of these three amino acids to UDP-N-acetylmuramic acid have been described (reactions 121–123). [439]

$$\text{UDP-GNAc-lactic}^\dagger + \text{L-ala} \xrightarrow[\text{Mn}^{++}]{\text{ATP}} \text{UDP-GNAc-lactyl·L-ala} \quad (121)$$

$$\text{UDP-GNAc-lactyl·L-ala} + \text{D-glu} \xrightarrow[\text{Mn}^{++}]{\text{ATP}}$$
$$\text{UDP-GNAc-lactyl·L-ala·D-glu} \quad (122)$$

$$\text{UDP-GNAc-lactyl·L-ala·D-glu} + \text{L-lys,} \xrightarrow[\text{Mn}^{++}]{\text{ATP}}$$
$$\text{UDP-GNAc-lactyl·L-ala·D-glu·L-lys} \quad (123)$$

The addition of two D-alanyl groups by enzymes of *S. aureus* proceeds by a mechanism during which a dipeptide is formed first (reaction 124), followed by the lengthening of the peptide chain of the nucleotide tripeptide by this dipeptide as a unit (reaction 125). [440]

$$2 \text{ D-ala} \xrightarrow[\text{Mn}^{++}]{\text{ATP}} \text{D-ala·D-ala} \quad (124)$$

$$\text{UDP-GNAc-lactyl·L-ala·D-glu·L-lys} + \text{D-ala·D-ala} \xrightarrow[\text{Mn}^{++}]{\text{ATP}}$$

† GNAc = N-acetylglucosamine; GNAc-lactic = N-acetylmuramic acid.

$$\text{UDP-GNAc-lactyl·L-ala·D-glu·L-lys·L-ala·D-ala} \qquad (125)$$

All these reactions require ATP and Mn^{++}. The uridine-diphospho-acetylmuramyl pentapeptide was isolated from penicillin-treated *Staphylococcus aureus*. [885] Slightly different penta- or hexapeptides were obtained from other bacteria, namely a hexapeptide from *S. faecalis* in which the ϵ-amino group of the lysyl residue is combined with an L-alanyl group, [567] and a pentapeptide from *E. coli* in which the L-lysyl residue is replaced by a *meso*diaminopimelic acid group. [886]

The obvious role of these and similar peptide-chain-containing UDP derivatives of muramic acid in the biosynthesis of bacterial cell walls was pointed out. [692, 693] A particulate enzyme system from *S. aureus*, strain H, was found to catalyze the formation of a polymer from a mixture of UDP-N-acetylglucosamine and the UDP-N-acetylmuramyl pentapeptide, resulting from reaction 125. [597, 146] The polymer formed behaved like cell wall glyco-peptide in that it could be hydrolyzed by egg white lysozyme. [597] Evidence for the existence of an initial acceptor in the polymerization was obtained, [887] and was presumed to be a lipid. [17] This lipid would combine with the UDP-N-acetylmuramyl pentapeptide:

$$\text{UDP-GNAc-lactyl-pentapeptide} + \text{lipid} \rightarrow$$
$$\text{lipid-P-GNAc-lactyl-pentapeptide} + \text{UMP} \qquad (126)$$

to form lipid-muramyl pentapeptide. Alternate additions of N-acetylglucos-amine and N-acetylmuramyl pentapeptides from their UDP-derivatives would result in a linear glycopeptide from which the phospholipid would eventually be split off.

It is interesting to note that UDP-muramic acid derivatives accumulate particularly in bacteria inhibited by penicillin, vancomycin or bacitracin. These antibiotics interfere with the utilization of UDP-muramyl peptide in the polymerization reaction, [146] and this mode of action appears to consist, at least in part, in the inhibition of the glycoside bond transfer from the UDP-derivatives. [692, 693] Teichoic acid synthesis is inhibited in a similar manner.

(b) *Teichoic acids*. The chemical structure of teichoic acids has been described [41, 800] and reviewed. [42, 722] The polymer from *Staphylococcus aureus*, strain Copenhagen, is composed of 4-O-β-N-acetyl-D-glucosaminyl-D-ribitol units, linked by 1,5-phosphodiester linkages. [800] About 15 per cent of the units have α-configuration.

Its biosynthesis originates from ribulose-5-phosphate which is reduced to ribitol-5-phosphate: [308]

$$\text{ribulose-5-phosphate} + \text{TPNH} \rightleftharpoons \text{ribitol-5-phosphate} + \text{TPN} \qquad (127)$$

Next, CDP-ribitol is formed from ribitol-5-phosphate and CTP: [823]

$$\text{ribitol-5-phosphate} + \text{CTP} \rightleftharpoons \text{CDP-ribitol} + \text{PP}_i \qquad (128)$$

An enzyme preparation from *Lactobacillus plantarum* then catalyzes the incorporation of ribitol phosphate from CDP-ribitol into a polymer which is analogous to that formed as cell wall components of Gram-positive bacteria.[309] CMP is liberated during the polymerization reaction which requires Ca^{++} or Mg^{++} and an acceptor:[311]

$$n(\text{CDP-ribitol}) + \text{acceptor} \xrightarrow{Mg^{++}} \text{acceptor-(ribitol-phosphate)}_n + n(\text{CMP}) \quad (129)$$

Like the formation of the glycopeptide, this reaction is inhibited by some antibiotics, such as novobiocin and vancomycin. Finally, incorporation of the sugar moiety into the accomplished ribitol phosphate polymer occurs. It is mediated by a particulate enzyme from *S. aureus*, strain Copenhagen, with the use of UDP-N-acetylglucosamine:[650, 651]

$$\text{(ribitol phosphate)}_n + n(\text{UDP-acetylglucosamine}) \xrightarrow{Mg^{++}}$$
$$\underset{|}{\text{(ribitol-phosphate)}_n} + n(\text{UDP}) \quad (130)$$
$$\text{acetylglucosamine}$$

Teichoic acids from other bacteria consist of 1,3-glycerol phosphate polymers.[722, 42] Their biosynthesis is analogous to that of the ribitol phosphate polymers and utilizes CDP-glycerol for the polymerization:[823, 118, 312]

$$\text{L-}\alpha\text{-glycerophosphate} + \text{CTP} \rightleftharpoons \text{CDP-glycerol} + \text{PP}_i \quad (131)$$

$$n(\text{CDP-glycerol} + \text{acceptor} \xrightarrow{Mg^{++}}$$
$$\text{acceptor} - \text{(glycerophosphate)}_n + n(\text{CMP}) \quad (132)$$

A particulate enzyme which catalyzes reaction 132 has been found in *Bacillus licheniformis* and *B. subtilis*.[118] The enzyme requires Ca^{++} or Mg^{++} and is inhibited by vancomycin or novobiocin. In a subsequent reaction, glucose is added as a side chain to the polymer by an enzyme preparation of *B. subtilis*:[316]

$$\text{(glycerophosphate)}_n + n(\text{UDP-glucose}) \rightarrow$$
$$\underset{|}{\text{(glycerophosphate)}_n} + n(\text{UDP}) \quad (133)$$
$$\text{glucose}$$

(c) *Bacterial lipopolysaccharides.* In Gram-negative bacteria, the structure of the cell wall is even more complex than in Gram-positive organisms, and is less well understood. While teichoic acids are absent, the cell wall of this group of bacteria contains protein-lipopolysaccharide conjugates of high antigenicity.

A lipopolysaccharide (LPS) of a *Salmonella typhimurium* mutant consists of a highly branched complex polysaccharide. It has a backbone of polyheptose phosphate to which side chains are linked through galactose and glucose residues, and further has covalent bonds to a glucosamine-containing lipid. [259] Three nucleotide sugar-lipopolysaccharide transferase systems have been identified in the cell wall membranes to catalyze the incorporation of glucose and galactose into such a lipopolysaccharide (reactions 134–137): [684]

$$\text{UDP-glucose} + \text{LPS} \xrightarrow{\text{transferase I}} \text{glucose-LPS} + \text{UDP} \tag{134}$$

$$\text{UDP-galactose} + \text{glucose-LPS} \xrightarrow{\text{transferase II}}$$
$$\text{galactose-glucose-LPS} + \text{UDP} \tag{135}$$

$$\text{UDP-glucose} + \text{galactose-glucose-LPS} \xrightarrow{\text{transferase III}}$$
$$\text{glucose-galactose-glucose-LPS} + \text{UDP} \tag{136}$$

This sequence is followed by the addition of N-acetylglucosamine to the chain:

$$\text{UDP-N-acetylglucosamine} + \text{glucose-galactose-glucose-LPS} \rightarrow$$
$$\text{N-acetylglucosamine-glucose-galactose-glucose-LPS} + \text{UDP} \tag{137}$$

A mutant of *Salmonella typhimurium* is deficient in UDP-galactose-4-epimerase and, thus, produces abnormal cell wall lipopolysaccharides which lack galactose. [664] This block can be by-passed, however, by growing the organism in the presence of galactose, [685] and galactose may be transferred from UDP-galactose into galactose-deficient lipopolysaccharide. [790]

Escherichia coli K-12, another mutant strain, contains a cell wall lipopolysaccharide which possesses only minute amounts of glucose; this fact is due to a deficiency in this strain of the UDP-glucose synthetase system. [591]

The incorporation of rhamnose into cell wall polysaccharides from dTDP-L-rhamnose has been demonstrated in *Streptococcus faecalis* [701] and in *S. pyogenes*. [1009]

With the isolation of a trisaccharide, α-galactosyl-mannosyl-rhamnose, from a mutant strain of *Salmonella typhimurium*, evidence was provided that the incorporation of mannose, galactose and rhamnose into an acid-insoluble product pertains to the normal pathway of biosynthesis of the O-antigenic side chains. [1010]

Among the more unusual carbohydrate components of bacterial lipopolysaccharides are 3,6-dideoxy-D-mannose, or tyvelose, [238] and 3,6-dideoxy-L-galactose, or colitose, [233] as well as 2-keto-3-deoxyoctonate (KDO) which has been isolated from cell wall preparations of *Escherichia coli*. [372] The latter has the structure shown in Fig. 57. An enzyme from *E. coli* 0111-B4 catalyzes the formation of a KDO-nucleotide: [284]

$$\text{CTP} + \text{KDO} \xrightarrow{\text{Mg}^{++}} \text{CMP-KDO} + \text{PP}_i \tag{138}$$

The biosynthesis of KDO is assumed to originate with D-arabinose-5-phosphate, and to proceed according to equations 139 and 140: [284]

D-arabinose-5-phosphate + phosphoenolpyruvate →
$$\text{2-keto-3-deoxyoctonate-8-phosphate} + P_i \qquad (139)$$

$$\text{2-keto-3-deoxyoctonate-8-phosphate} → KDO + P_i \qquad (140)$$

Incorporation of KDO into lipopolysaccharide of *E. coli* occurs with CMP-KDO as the KDO-donor: [284, 233]

$$\text{CMP-KDO} + \text{LPS} → \text{KDO-LPS} + \text{CMP} \qquad (141)$$

(d) *Other bacterial polysaccharides.* The boisynthesis of capsular polysaccharides from *Pneumococcus*, Types I and III, has been investigated by Smith, Mills and co-workers. [852, 853, 613, 848-851, 847, 612] Type I polysaccharide

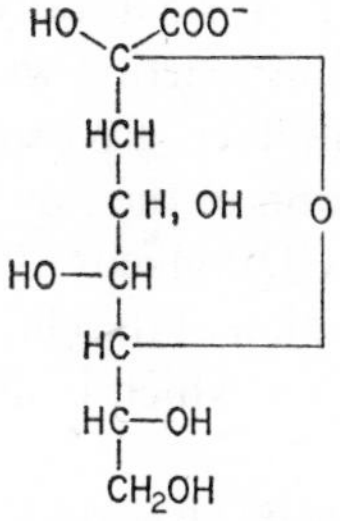

Fig. 57. Structure of 2-keto-3-deoxyoctonate (KDO) from *Escherichia coli*. [372]

contains 60 per cent galacturonate, 8 per cent of an aminosugar, fucose and another monosaccharide. The polysaccharide of Type III has the well-defined structure in which a disaccharide, [-O-β-D-glucuronosyl-(1 → 4)-O-D-β-glucosyl-(1 → 3)-]$_n$, is the repeating unit. [425, 768, 7] The metabolism of the uronic acids in *Pneumococcus* has been found very similar to that in other sites, and the synthesis of the polysaccharides from UDP-glucose, UDP-glucuronic acid, UDP-galacturonic acid, and other UDP-sugars has been ascertained.

The enzyme *UDP-galactose-polysaccharide transferase* is present in cell-free extracts of the cellular slime mold, *Dictyostelium discoideum*, but it appears only relatively late in the developmental sequence, i.e. shortly before the actual synthesis of a galactose-containing mucopolysaccharide takes place. [891] Labeled UDP-glucose has been identified as the glucose donor for the synthesis of cell wall material in this organism; ADP-glucose or GDP-glucose react only at much lower rates. [963]

GLYCOSIDES AND OTHER COMPLEX CARBOHYDRATES

23. *Glycosides*

A great many alcohols and phenols occur in nature as glycosides, and the vast majority of them possess a β-configuration. D-Glucose is a frequent constituent of glycosides, such as in arbutin (hydroquinone β-glucoside), the glycoside of the bearberry, further in salicin (o-hydroxybenzyl alcohol β-glucoside) which occurs in pine needles, also in phlorizine (phloretin β-glucoside), a component of rose bark, and in amygdalin (D-mandelonitrile β-gentiobioside; the disaccharide gentiobiose is β-D-glucopyranosyl-(1 → 6)-β-D-glucopyranose). Other sugars which have been found to be linked as mono-, di-, or oligosaccharide units to a great variety of aglycons are L-rhamnose, D-ribose, 2-deoxy-D-ribose, D-xylose, D-galactose, D-mannose,etc.

The biosynthesis of the aglycon and that of the monosaccharides are accomplished in separate mechanisms, and the glycosidic bond, or bonds, are then formed in a way analogous to the biosynthesis of glycosidic linkages in di-, tri-, or polysaccharides. Cardini and Leloir [139] demonstrated the formation of a glucoside, identical with naturally-occurring arbutin, from hydroquinone and UDP-glucose; this reaction was catalyzed by an enzyme extract from wheat germ. Later, another glycoside, hydroquinone gentiobioside, could be obtained by the action of the same enzyme extract on a mixture of hydroquinone glucoside and UDP-glucose. [143] The second reaction consists in the glycosylation of the 6-position of the glucose moiety in arbutin and may be due to the action of an enzyme which is different from that responsible for the formation of arbutin.

The biosynthesis of complex glycosides with more than one monosaccharide unit (e.g. amygdalin, digitonin, etc.) appears to be analogous, therefore, to the formation of di-, oligo-, and polysaccharides, whereby the aglycon may act as the original acceptor. After a first glycosyl unit has been transferred, the newly formed glycoside becomes the acceptor, and may be transformed into a new glycoside carrying two monosaccharide units; this procedure may repeat itself until the synthesis of the glycoside chain is completed.

An enzyme from unripe peas, *UDP-D-galactose: inositol galactosyl transferase*, catalyzes the transfer of galactosyl from UDP-D-galactose to *myo-inositol* to yield galactosylinositol. [271] The same enzyme also transfers galactose to other inositols, i.e. *scyllo-, dextro-* and *levo-inositols.*

In wheat germ, the synthesis of glucosides, e.g. arbutin, or gentiobiosides, is faster with ADP-glucose than with UDP-glucose; GDP-glucose and, to a lesser degree, CDP-glucose are also capable of acting as glucosyl donors. [924] dTDP-Glucose has likewise been shown, though at a lower efficiency than UDP-glucose, to participate in glucoside synthesis in wheat germ. [326]

The biosynthesis of rutin, i.e. 3-quercitin-(O-L-rhamnosyl-(1 → 6)-D-glucoside), proceeds in the mung bean by the transfer of a rhamnosyl residue from dTDP-L-rhamnose to 3-quercitin-D-glucoside. [55] UDP-L-Rhamnose, however, is a more efficient rhamnosyl donor than dTDP-L-rhamnose. [52]

24. Glucosiduronic Acids

The biosynthesis of glucosiduronic acids in the liver is known to proceed via UDP-glucuronic acid. [874, 223, 37] Many hydroxyl compounds may serve as acceptors in this reaction. An enzyme similar to the one which catalyzes the formation of this group of glycosides in liver has been found in kidney. [224] In both tissues, the enzyme activity is confined to the microsomes.

In contrast to UDP-glucuronic acid, pseudouridine-5'-glucuronic acid did *not* act as a glycosyl donor with an enzyme preparation from guinea-pig liver microsomes, even at ten times higher concentrations. [418]

25. Glycolipids

Brain tissues are known to contain glycolipids. Their biosynthesis has been studied by Burton *et al.* [124] with microsomal enzyme fractions of young rat brain. These authors arrived at the conclusion that neutral glycolipids are formed from UDP-galactose and a corresponding acceptor:

$$\text{UDP-galactose} + \text{acceptor} \rightleftharpoons \text{neutral glycolipid} + \text{UDP} \qquad (142)$$

Either glucose or galactose may be utilized to yield UDP-galactose necessary for this reaction, and the mechanism of formation of this UDP-sugar follows those previously discussed in this chapter (see also Chapter 3).

The biosynthesis of a rhamnolipid, i.e. L-rhamnosyl-$(1 \rightarrow 3)$-L-rhamnosyl-β-hydroxydecanoyl-β-hydroxydecanoic acid, was reported from dTDP-L-rhamnose and β-hydroxydecanoyl-CoA, with the aid of cell-free extracts of *Pseudomonas aeruginosa*. [117] dTDP-L-Rhamnose acts faster than UDP-L-rhamnose. [52] The rhamnose was shown to originate from glycerol without cleavage of its C-C bonds, probably through aldol condensation. [362, 363] Fructose-6-C^{14} was also converted to rhamnose-6-C^{14}. It may be speculated that TDP-L-rhamnose may be involved in the biosynthesis of this lipide. TDP-rhamnose has indeed been shown to originate from TDP-glucose in this microorganism [502, 503] and, thus, to be derived from three-carbon fragments or from fructose.

26. Glycoproteins

Inasmuch as the biosynthetic aspects of the carbohydrate moiety of glyco-proteins are closely related to the general mechanisms of carbohydrate and glycoside bond formation, this subject will be briefly treated here. Particular emphasis will be placed on the biosynthesis of a carbohydrate component most prominently occurring in glycoproteins, i.e. sialic acid.

(a) *General considerations.* From studies on the incorporation of labeled glucosamine into liver and plasma glycoproteins of the rat, it was concluded that glucosamine is transferred to the peptide chains of glycoproteins at some stage prior to the release of these proteins from the liver particulate fraction, [778] but after completion of the polypeptide chain. [838] Glucosamine incorporation into glycoproteins appears to depend, however, on polypeptide synthesis *de novo*, and inhibition of protein synthesis, e.g. by puromycin, also decreases glucosamine incorporation. [618] In any event, the liver is the sole site of biosynthesis of a_1-acid glycoprotein, at least in the dog, since no glucosamine incorporation into this serum protein could be detected in hepatectomized dogs. [29]

Glycoprotein biosynthesis in stroma is greatly elevated in thalassemia, a disorder characterized by low concentrations of hemoglobin A in erythropoietic cells. [243] It is believed that this phenomenon is due to a disturbance in membrane synthesis, at the point of association of glycoprotein with lipid and protein.

(b) *Sialic acid-containing substances.* Glycoproteins and mucins are composed of a protein backbone with relatively short carbohydrate side chains containing hexose, methylpentose, N-acetylhexosamine and, as an essential part, sialic acid. The latter component is responsible for the markedly acid nature of most glycoproteins and mucins. The term of sialic acid is the generic name for the various mono-, di-, or polyacylated neuraminic acids, see Fig. 58.

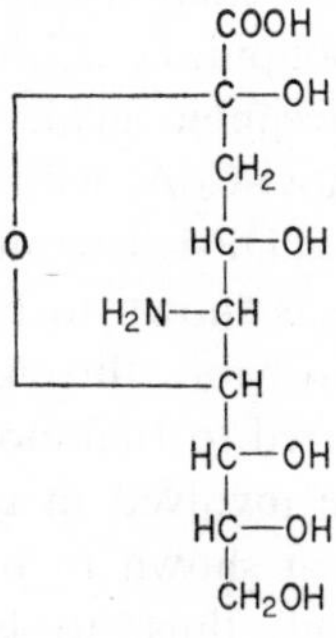

FIG. 58. Structure of neuraminic acid (2-keto-5-amino-3,5-dideoxynononic acid).

N-Acetylneuraminic acid was shown to be split into pyruvate and N-acetyl-D-mannosamine [165] by the enzyme *N-acetylneuraminic acid aldolase* from *Vibrio cholerae*, [386] as seen in equation (143):

$$\text{N-acetylneuraminic acid} \rightleftharpoons \text{pyruvate} + \text{N-acetyl-D-mannosamine} \quad (143)$$

The aldolase catalyzing reaction (143) has also been found in mammalian tissues and has been purified from hog kidney cortex. [114] The N-acyl group may be either acetyl or glycolyl. Although reaction 143 is reversible, its equilibrium favors breakdown and this pathway is, therefore, unlikely to play a role in the biosynthesis of neuraminic acid.

An enzyme system was found in rat liver and bovine submaxillary glands which catalyzes the synthesis of N-acetylneuraminic acid (NAN) from N-acetyl-D-mannosamine and phosphoenolpyruvate (PEP) in the presence of ATP, according to the sequence of reactions 144–147: [967, 968, 966, 286, 789]

N-acetyl-D-mannosamine + ATP →
$$\text{N-acetyl-D-mannosamine-6-phosphate} + \text{ADP} \qquad (144)$$

N-acetyl-D-mannosamine-6-phosphate + PEP + H_2O →
$$\text{NAN-9-phosphate} + P_i \qquad (145)$$

$$\text{NAN-9-phosphate} + H_2O \rightarrow \text{NAN} + P_i \qquad (146)$$

Sum: N-acetyl-D-mannosamine + ATP + PEP + $2H_2O$ →
$$\text{NAN} + \text{ADP} + 2P_i \qquad (147)$$

Reaction 145 requires Mg^{++} and glutathione (GSH). *Sialic acid-9-phosphatase*, which catalyzes reaction 146, has also been found in human erythrocytes. [455]

The formation of N-acetyl-D-mannosamine-6-phosphate by epimerization of N-acetyl-D-glucosamine-6-phosphate in the presence of an enzyme from *Aerobacter cloacae* [287] or from hog kidney [288] has been discussed earlier in this chapter (Section Vc).

In *Neisseria meningitidis*, PEP condenses directly with N-acetyl-D-mannosamine without preliminary phosphorylation. [91, 964]

N-Acetylneuraminic acid is incorporated into glycoproteins or other substances as an "activated" form. Activated sialic acid was first isolated from *Escherichia coli* K-235, [166] and its biosynthesis has been described by enzymes from *Neisseria meningitidis*, strain 1908, [964, 965] and from hog submaxillary gland, [788] as seen in reaction 148:

$$\text{CTP} + \text{NAN} \rightarrow \text{CMP-NAN} + PP_i \qquad (148)$$

Reaction 148 requires Mg^{++} ions and glutathione (GSH). The enzyme from hog submaxillary glands may also use N-glycolylneuraminic acid (NGN) as a substrate to produce CMP-NGN in an analogous manner. [788]

Reaction 148 is one of the few instances in which a *mono*-phosphonucleotide sugar is formed from a triphosphonucleotide for the subsequent transfer of the thus activated group Y (see general equation 149), in contrast to the frequent formation of diphosphonucleotide sugars (equation 150):

$$\text{XTP} + \text{Y} \rightarrow \text{XMP-Y} + PP_i \qquad (149)$$

$$\text{XTP} + \text{Y-phosphate} \rightarrow \text{XDP-Y} + PP_i \qquad (150)$$

where X is a nucleoside and Y a sugar. A second instance in which a *mono-phosphonucleotide* sugar fulfills the role of an activated glycoside is the formation of CMP-KDO and the subsequent incorporation of KDO into bacterial lipopolysaccharides (see Section VII, 22 and reactions 138 and 141 in this chapter).

Cytidine-5′-monophospho-N-acetylneuraminic acid (CMP-NAN) lends itself as a donor of N-acetylneuraminic acid. Thus, it reacts with lactose to form sialyl-lactose, or N-acetylneuraminyl-(2 → 3)-β-D-galactopyranosyl-(1 → 4)-D-glucose.[453] With other oligosaccharides it yields the corresponding sialyl oligosaccharides.[787, 454] In *E. coli* K-235, there is an enzyme system which is capable of polymerizing CMP-NAN to a polymer of sialic acid, colominic acid.[15] This substance has been found to occur in *E. coli* and has been shown to be a homopolymer of N-acetylneuraminic acid.[61] Incorporation of sialic acid from CMP-NAN into glycoproteins has been postulated.[787, 454]

The reactions involved in the formation of sialic acid and the incorporation of this amino sugar into substances in which it occurs in nature has been summarized by Jourdian and Roseman,[454] see Fig. 59.

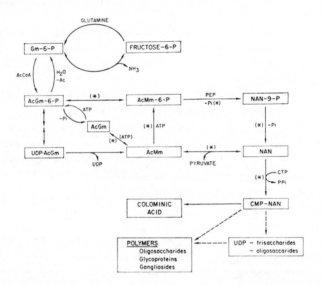

Fig. 59. Intermediary metabolism of N-acetylneuraminic and N-glycolylneuraminic acids (from Jourdian and Roseman[454]). Proposed steps are indicated by broken arrows. The abbreviations used are: Gm = glucosamine, P = phosphate ester, P_i = inorganic orthophosphate, PP_i = inorganic pyrophosphate, Mm = mannosamine, U = uridine, C = cytidine, NAN = *N*-acetylneuraminic acid, Ac = acetyl group. The reactions where the corresponding *N*-glycolyl derivative was shown to substitute for the N-acetyl compound are indicated by the symbol (*). Reproduced by courtesy of Federation of American Societies for Experimental Biology.

amounts of UDP-N-acetylgalactosamine-(4)-sulfate. However, no incorporation of this compound into mucopolysaccharides could be detected with extracts of the isthmus region of hen oviduct, [895, 896] and rats were found unable to utilize the sulfate of N-acetyl-D-galactosamine-6-O-[^{35}S]-sulfate in the synthesis of keratosulfate or chondroitin sulfate C of connective tissue. [554] It must be concluded, therefore, that the utilization of sulfated monomeric sugar derivatives for the synthesis of these sulfomucopolysaccharides is unlikely. No evidence has been obtained, however, that the formation of other sulfomucopolysaccharides and of chondroitin sulfate from other origins may not be formed from nucleoside diphosphate hexosamine sulfate precursors.

(2) That PAPS can transfer sulfate groups to high-molecular-weight polysaccharides was shown by D'Abramo and Lipmann. [191, 192] These authors observed the uptake of S^{35} by chondroitin sulfate from PAPS in the presence of cell-free enzyme preparations obtained from chicken embryo or beef cartilage. Similarly, Spolter and Marx [860] reported the direct incorporation of sulfate from PAPS into the full carbohydrate chain of heparin by homogenates of mouse mast cell tumor, while Korn [495] could demonstrate such an incorporation with particle-free extracts from the tumor.

It thus appears that the biosynthesis of sulfated polysaccharides proceeds by a mechanism in which the formation of the polysaccharide is first accomplished through any of the glycosidic bond-forming reactions, discussed in the preceding section of this chapter (Section VIII), and that the introduction of sulfate ester groups into the completed polysaccharide follows as a subsequent step. Evidence for the direct sulfation of polysaccharides has also been obtained for chondroitin, chondroitin sulfates A, B and C, and for a heparin-like oligosaccharide. [896] A cell-free enzyme from chick embryo epiphyses catalyzes the incorporation of sulfate into a polysaccharide, i.e. chondroitin, resulting in the formation of chondroitin sulfates A and C. [723] Sulfokinase from rabbit skin exhibited a much higher specificity for chondroitin B than for chondroitin A, or for the chondroitin sulfates A, B and C, as well as for keratosulfate and hyaluronic acid. [201] However, the sulfokinase from human chondrosarcoma, which contains chondroitin sulfate A, is specific only for the latter substrate. [353] Extracts of human breast carcinomas contain a sulfokinase which is specific for chondroitin sulfate B, [6] and the sulfokinase system of human serum was found to be specific for both chondroitin sulfates B and C, but not for the A-form which occurs only sparingly in serum. [5]

Bovine corneal mucopolysaccharides were shown to be sulfated by PAPS to yield sulfomucopolysaccharides similar to chondroitin sulfate. [1004]

(3) The possibility of the existence of a third mechanism for sulfopolysaccharide biosynthesis has been suggested by Suzuki and Strominger. [897, 898] These workers observed that oligosaccharides which are composed of alternate residues of glucuronic acid and N-acetylgalactosamine, possess an

unusually high efficiency as acceptors for the sulfotransferase system if the aminosugar is on the nonreducing end-group. It was concluded, therefore, that the esterification of carbohydrate with sulfate groups during the normal biosynthetic mechanism of sulfopolysaccharides occurs neither at the level of monomeric sugar derivatives, nor at the level of the completed poly-saccharides, but that sulfation takes place during the stepwise lengthening of glycosidic chains, every time immediately after an acetylgalactosamine residue has been added, and before another glucuronic acid group is attached. Such a mechanism would explain the relatively high degree of uniformity in the ratio of sulfate to hexosamine in most chondroitin sulfate preparations.

Mathews [581] suggested a combination of all three mechanisms and, thus, arrived at a hypothetical scheme for chondroitin sulfate A biosynthesis in frog cartilage in tyrosine-induced metamorphosis as seen in Fig. 61.

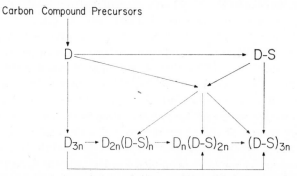

FIG. 61. Hypothetical scheme of biosynthesis of sulfopolysaccharides in frog cartilage, after Mathews and De C. Hinds. [581] D, glucuronido-acetyl-galactos-amine disaccharide repeating unit; D-S, sulfated disaccharide repeating unit, D_{3n}, a sulfur-free polymer, and $D_{2n}(D\text{-}S)_n$, $D_n(D\text{-}S)_{2n}$, $(D\text{-}S)_{3n}$ polymers with increasing degrees of sulfation.

It is also thought that a coexistence of sulfation mechanisms 2 and 3 might be apt to lead to sulfopolysaccharides containing more than one sulfate group per hexosamine residue, such as heparin and others. The introduction of a second sulfate group into N-acetylgalactosamine, and most likely also into mucopolysaccharides, proceeds more slowly than the esterification of the first group. [897, 898]

In the case of heparin, Korn has reported that an approximately equal distribution between ester sulfate and amide sulfate results from the incorpora-tion of S^{35} in tumor slices. [494] Only a minor portion, if any, of S^{35}-labeled heparin formation is accomplished through direct transfer of radioactive sulfate to a fully formed mucopolysaccharide molecule by an enzyme of the Furth mast-cell tumor. [861] It is suggested that there occurs an early incorpora-tion of sulfate into dialyzable molecules which are subsequently polymerized to form heparin.

The mechanism of formation of the glycosidic bonds in the chondroitin sulfates is analogous to that of hyaluronic acid. Incorporation of C^{14}-labeled glucose and acetate into the carbon chain and the acetate group, respectively, of chondroitin sulfate has been described.[100, 807, 806, 779] In chondroitin sulfate B, C^{14} was equally distributed between galactosamine and iduronic acid when the mucopolysaccharide was isolated from rat skin after administration of glucose-6-C^{14}, and the activity in both monosaccharides was so high that the uronic acid must have arisen from glucose without rearrangement of the carbon skeleton.[780] Adams[3, 4] suggested a priming or template mechanism for the biosynthesis of the chondroitin sulfates, since hyaluronic acid and chondroitin sulfates A and C stimulated chondroitin sulfate A formation. The C isomer was more active in stimulating $S^{35}O_4^=$ incorporation than the A isomer, whereas chondroitin sulfate B was ineffective. Insulin is believed to participate in the biosynthesis of acid mucopolysaccharides.[805]

An N-acetyl-containing polysaccharide, i.e. heparitin, is assumed to be a precursor of heparin in the mast-cell tumor of DBA mice. This was concluded because a cell-free fraction from that tumor was found to catalyze the incorporation of UDP-glucuronic acid and UDP-N-acetylglucosamine, but not that of UDP-glucosamine, into polysaccharide.[832, 833] A sulfate-free, high-molecular weight polysaccharide-precursor of chondroitin sulfates A and C was obtained from UDP-N-acetylgalactosamine and UDP-glucuronic acid with a cell-free enzyme from chick embryo epiphyses.[723, 834] This precursor was subsequently sulfated by the same enzyme mixture in the presence of PAPS.

A general scheme of the various pathways leading to the formation of sulfomucopolysaccharides and of some of the hormonal factors controlling these mechanisms was proposed by Dorfman,[216] see Fig. 62.

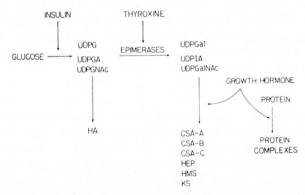

FIG. 62. Proposed pathways for the formation of connective tissue polysaccharides (from Dorfman[216]). Reproduced by courtesy of Federation of American Societies for Experimental Biology.

Hypothyroidism, induced by propylthiouracil, increases hyaluronic acid formation, i.e. blocks the epimerases. Thyroxine restores the formation of sulfomucopolysaccharides. In hypophysectomized rats, there is a drop in the chondroitin sulfates which can be overcome by growth hormone.

In embryonic chick cartilage, the site of formation of chondroitin sulfate lies within the cells. [216, 226, 132] Chondroitin sulfate, like heparin, occurs as a protein-sulfomucopolysaccharide complex, and both moieties are synthesized simultaneously within the cell. [132, 318] These two components are linked to each other by covalent bonds. In heparin, xylose and serine constitute the linkage between carbohydrate and protein. [550]

The material synthesized intracellularly in the chondrocytes may be packaged and the sac may then be pushed against the outer membranes of the cell. Formation of stoma at the point of contact may allow for extrusion of the products within the sac. [132, 318]

X. THE REDUCING MONOSACCHARIDES

A. Occurrence and Formation

The reservoir of reducing monosaccharides in living tissues and extracellular fluids is relatively small. [450] While at least 50 monosaccharides, including trioses, tetroses, pentoses, hexoses, heptoses, branched chain sugars, aldoses or ketoses, aminosugars, uronic acids, etc., are known to occur naturally in one form or another, i.e. as polysaccharides, oligosaccharides, disaccharides, phosphate esters, or other derivatives, there is only a small number that have been found to occur as free, non-phosphorylated monosaccharides.

It has been known for a long time that free *D-glucose* exists in plants, especially in sweet fruits, and in animal fluids such as blood, lymph and cerebrospinal fluid, as well as in the urine of diabetics. Orange peels and other plant sources (*Amorphophallus*) contain small amounts of free *D-mannose*. Free *D-fructose* is found in the fruits of many plants and in honey. The occasional occurrence of two free pentoses in urine is known as pentosuria. Each of these pentoses accumulates for a different reason: five-carbon sugars like *L-arabinose* are not utilized by the body in the sense that hexoses are; the ingestion of polysaccharides built up of arabinose, such as occur abundantly in cherries, grapes, prunes and plums, leads to the excretion of L-arabinose in the urine. In addition to this alimentary pentosuria, a chronic or pathologic pentosuria is known in which free *L-xylulose* passes into the urine. The appearance of this pentose in the urine is largely independent of food pentoses. Two free heptoses have been detected in plants, i.e. *D-sedoheptulose* in one of the *Crassulaceae* species (*Sedum spectabile*), and *mannoheptulose* in the avocado pear.

It must be assumed that the formation of most of these free monosaccharides is due to the action of hydrolytic enzymes, which liberate the sugars from poly-, oligo-, and disaccharides, or from phosphate derivatives. Thus, L-arabinose in the urine is no doubt derived from araban; fructose and, in some instances, glucose originate in higher plants from sucrose by the action of invertases; specific or unspecific phosphatases may form glucose, mannose and, in some cases, also fructose from the corresponding 6-phosphates. Such hydrolytic reactions are analogous to the liberation of sucrose, trehalose, or lactose from their corresponding phosphates (reactions 67, 71 and 77) and to the formation of maltose from starch and glycogen, etc.

The manifold possibilities of interconversion between various sugars (see Fig. 33) at the levels of their primary-hydroxyl phosphates (Section V), or of their nucleoside diphosphate derivatives (Section VII) would support the view that the majority of the free monosaccharides originate from a pool of sugar derivatives of higher energy content.

In many instances, transformations involving various nonphosphorylated sugars have been observed. Such enzyme-catalyzed reactions of the free monosaccharides occur frequently in microbial sources as well as in animal tissues and in higher plants. In bacteria these reactions are catalyzed mostly by adaptive enzymes, and these enzymes, as well as the monosaccharides involved, must be assumed to occur under normal conditions in not more than trace amounts. It is obvious, however, that carbohydrates must not necessarily be derived from the pool of sugar phosphates and of other sugar derivatives, or from complex saccharides, although there can be no doubt that all carbohydrates originate fundamentally from photosynthetic carbon skeletons.

B. *Transformations Involving Nonphosphorylated Sugars*

1. *Isomerizations*

Many microorganisms contain enzymes, called isomerases, capable of catalyzing the transformation of a free aldose into the corresponding ketose. Table 11 summarizes some of these reactions.[539] The transformation of aldouronic acids into the corresponding ketouronic acids, e.g. D-fructuronate and D-tagaturonate (reactions a and f, Fig. 63), and the formation of 2-keto-3-deoxygluconate from onic acids (D-mannonate and D-altronate) (reactions c and d, Fig. 63) are important steps in the pathway of uronic acid utilization by *E. coli*,[28, 974] and they lead eventually to 3-phosphoglyceraldehyde and pyruvate.

2. *Oxidations or Dehydrogenations*

The action of glucose oxidase or "Notatin" has been known for some time. Other aldose oxidases and dehydrogenases which act upon free sugars have been described (see Table 12). The oxidation of glucose by *Pseudomonas fragi* or by *P. fluorescens* is achieved by two groups of enzymes. One yields glucono δ-lactone, the other γ-lactone. The enzyme systems which produce the γ-lactone are particulate, those that form δ-lactone are soluble. [972]

An important step in the metabolism of free sugars, especially in pentosuria [919, 341, 918] is the dehydrogenation of L-gulonate to 3-ketogulonate which is an intermediate in the formation of L-xylulose [920, 355, 341] (see Fig. 64). Glucose is dehydrogenated to 5-ketogluconic acid by a particulate,

TABLE 11. TRANSFORMATIONS OF FREE ALDOSES INTO THE
CORRESPONDING KETOSES BY ISOMERASES [539]

Aldose	Ketose	Source	Reference
D-Glucose	D-Fructose	*Aerobacter aerogenes*	649
D-Mannose	D-Fructose	*Pseudomonas saccharophila*	686
L-Galactose	D-Tagatose	*Escherichia coli*	35
D-Altrose	D-Tagatose	*Escherichia coli*	35
L-Arabinose	L-Ribulose	*Lactobacillus pentosus, L. plantarum, Escherichia coli Pediococcus pentosaceus*	373, 336, 210, 209, 145
D-Arabinose	D-Ribulose	*Escherichia coli*	155
D-Xylose	D-Xylulose	bacterial	412, 617, 843, 210
D-Lyxose	D-Xylulose	*Pseudomonas saccharophila*	686
D-Rhamnose	D-Rhamnulose	*Pseudomonas saccharophila*	686
L-Rhamnose	L-Rhamnulose	*Escherichia coli*	989, 904
L-Fucose	L-Fuculose	*Escherichia coli*	336
D-Glucuronate	D-Fructuronate	*Serratia marescens, Escherichia coli*	699, 28, 947
D-Galacturonate	D-Tagaturonate	*Escherichia coli*	903, 28, 947
D-Mannonate	2-Keto-3-deoxygluconate	*Escherichia coli*	28, 947
D-Altronate	2-Keto-3-deoxygluconate	*Escherichia coli*	28, 947

DPN-specific enzyme preparation from *Acetobacter suboxidans*. [482] 5-Ketogluconic acid is accumulated in large amounts in the culture medium of this organism, and its formation appears to be due to the successive action of two soluble enzymes (see equation 155) which were separated from one another. [677]

$$\text{glucose} \xrightarrow{\text{glucose dehydrogenase}} \text{gluconic acid} \xrightarrow{\text{5-ketogluconate reductase}} \text{5-ketogluconic acid} \qquad (155)$$

The first enzyme, *glucose dehydrogenase*, is TPN-linked and thus contrasts with the DPN-dependent, particulate enzyme. [482] The other enzyme, 5-ketogluconate reductase, also requires TPN. [678] An analogous sequence of reactions converts 2-deoxy-D-glucose to 2-deoxy-3-ketogluconic acid by a DPN-requiring enzyme system from *Pseudomonas*. [234]

Another mechanism of oxidation of nonphosphorylated sugars is the formation of 3-ketoglycosides. Bacteria from river water, *Alcaligenes sp.* were found to convert lactose to 4-O-β-3-keto-D-galactosido-D-glucose, and lactobionate to 4-O-β-3-keto-D-galactosido-D-gluconate.[78] Corresponding 3-keto-glycosides were formed by *Alcaligenes faecalis* from lactose, maltose,

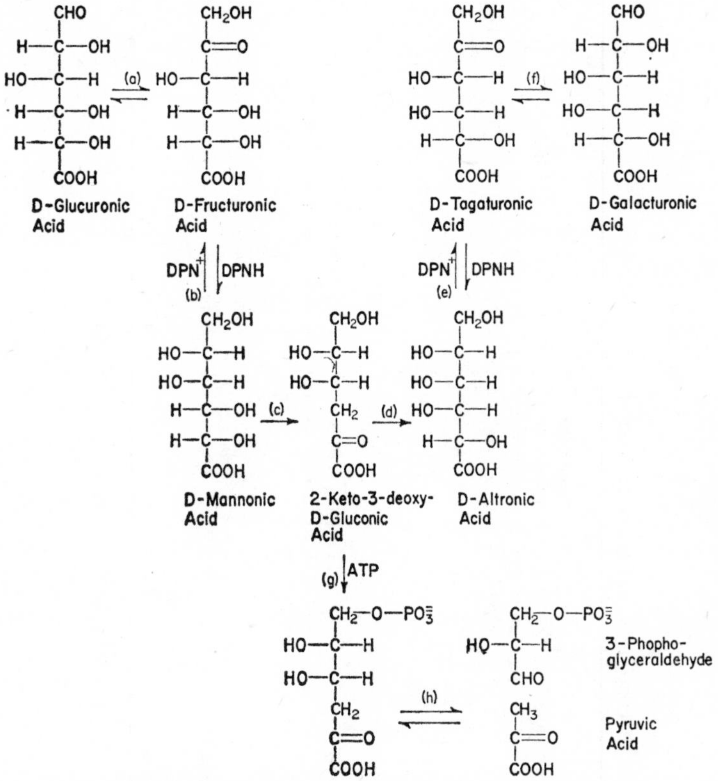

FIG. 63. Utilization of uronic acids by *Escherichia coli.*[28, 947]

lactobionate and maltobionate.[79] Analogous enzyme systems have been found in *Agrobacterium tumefaciens* and in *Micrococcus sp.* from soil which oxidize sucrose to "ketsucrose", i.e. β-D-fructofuranosyl-α-D-ribohexo-pyranosyl-3-ulose.[278, 333] D-Glucose, methyl-α-D-glucopyranoside, lactose, maltose, cellobiose, melibiose, trehalose, and raffinose yield the corresponding ketoglycosides.[277, 334] Ketosucrose formation is inhibited competitively by D-glucose.[276]

The enzyme from hog kidney catalyzing the conversion of L-gulonate to L-xylulose has been purified.[845] It was termed β-L-hydroacid dehydrogenase because of its broad specificity for all hexonic, pentonic or tetronic acids with a β-L-hydroxy configuration.

TABLE 12. OXIDATION OR DEHYDROGENATION OF FREE ALDOSES

Aldose	Oxidation products	Coenzyme requirements	Origin	References
β-D-Glucose	D-Gluconolactone H_2O_2	FAD	Penicillium notatum†, and other fungi	633, 777, 186, 472, 473
Aldohexoses D-Glucose, D-Galactose, or Disaccharides	Lactones		Aspergillus niger	706
	Corresponding lactones of onic acids H_2O_2	?	Algae (Iridophycus flaccidum)	71
D-Glucose	D-Gluconolactone	DPN or TPN	Beef or rat liver	878, 104
D-Glucose	D-Gluconolactone	Cytochrome system	Pseudomonas fluorescens	1003
D-Galactose	D-Galactono-γ-lactone	?	Pseudomonas saccharophila	206
D-Arabinose	D-Arabonolactone		Pseudomonas	390, 369, 687
L-Arabinose	L-Arabonolactone		Pseudomonas saccharophila	973
D-Xylose, D-Ribose	Corresponding pentonic acids	DPN	Fusarium	555, 369
Deoxy-D-glucose	Deoxy-D-gluconolactone		Aspergillus niger	706

† The enzyme is commonly called "Notatin".

3. Hydrogenations

The reduction of the aldehyde group in D-uronic acids, yielding L-onic acids, and the reduction of D-ketouronic acids to D-onic acids are frequently occurring reactions in microorganisms, and in animal tissues as well. They usually have a requirement for TPNH or DPNH and are reversible. The formation of L-gulonate from D-glucuronate is a step in the pathway of ascorbic acid synthesis. [355] A few of these reactions are indicated in Table 13.

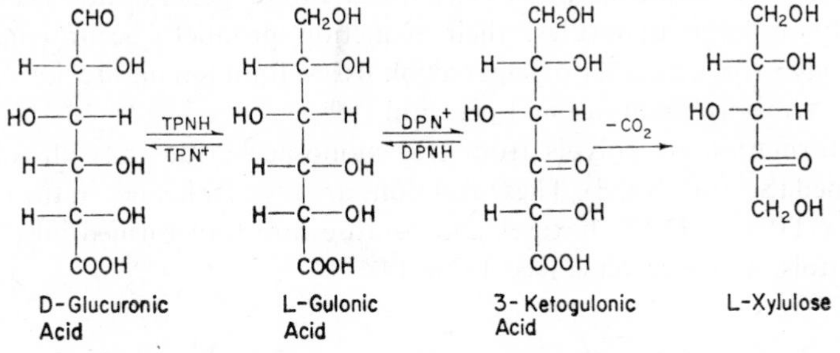

FIG. 64. Pathway of pentose formation from D-glucuronate in pathologic pentosuria.

The synthesis of sugar alcohols is a result of the hydrogenation of free monosaccharides (see Section XI). Thus, placenta and seminal vesicles contain an enzyme which reduces D-glucose to D-sorbitol and requires TPNH, [391] while D-xylitol is formed from D-xylose by a TPNH-depending enzyme from *Penicillium chrysogenum*. [150]

TABLE 13. HYDROGENATION OF URONIC ACIDS

Uronic acid	Product of hydrogenation	Source	References
D-Glucuronate	L-Gulonate	Mammalian tissues	920, 341
D-Fructuronate	D-Mannonate	*Escherichia coli*	28, 912
D-Tagaturonate	D-Altronate	*Escherichia coli*	28, 947

Certain strains of *Fusarium*, e.g. *sp.* 125, are capable of reducing 5-keto-D-gluconic acid to L-idonic acid which is an intermediate in L-ascorbic acid biosynthesis. [901] The enzyme, 5-*ketoglucono-idono-reductase*, requires TPN. [902]

4. Decarboxylations

In the same way as 6-phosphohexonic acids (Section VE) and UDP-hexuronic acids (Section VIID) can be decarboxylated by enzymes in animal, plant and microbial sources to the corresponding pentose derivatives, the

Q

formation of ketopentoses from free hexonic acids has been observed. Of particular interest is the decarboxylation of L-gulonolactone to L-xylulose in rat kidney[747, 122] where this reaction, together with others (see Fig. 64) is believed to be responsible for the formation of L-xylulose in pentosuria.[920, 919]

XI. SUGAR ALCOHOLS

Whereas the reducing monosaccharides do in general not accumulate naturally in large quantities, their reduction products occur commonly. Besides glycerol, a number of sugar alcohols are found in nature, i.e. erythrol, adonitol (ribitol), mannitol and perseitol.[450]

The formation of polyols from free monosaccharides has already been mentioned (Section XB, 3). These reactions are reversible and, in the presence of either TPN or DPN, hexoses and pentoses are transformed into hexitols or pentitols, and vice versa (see Table 14).

TABLE 14. OXIDATION-REDUCTION REACTIONS DESCRIBING REVERSIBLE TRANSFORMATIONS BETWEEN POLYOLS AND ALDOSES, OR KETOSES

Polyol	Aldose or Ketose	Coenzyme	Source	References
Sorbitol	Glucose	TPN	Seminal vesicles of sheep	391
Sorbitol	Fructose	DPN	Seminal vesicles of sheep, *Acetobacter suboxydans*, ram spermatozoa	391, 189, 190, 483
Sorbitol	Sorbose	TPN	*Acetobacter suboxydans*	190, 189
D-Mannitol	D-Fructose	DPN	*Aerobacter aerogenes*	548
D-Mannitol	D-Fructose	TPN	*Agaricus campestris*	232
L-Iditol	L-Sorbose	DPN	Rat liver	594
Dulcitol	Tagatose	DPN	*Pseudomonas*	822
Pentitols, heptitols	Reducing mono-saccharides	DPN	*Acetobacter suboxydans*, *Candida utilis*	23
Mannitol-1-phosphate	Fructose-6-phosphate	DPN	*Escherichia coli*, *Aerobacter aerogenes*, *Bacillus subtilis*	995, 387, 553, 424
Mannitol-6-phosphate	Fructose-6-phosphate	DPN	*Pneumococcus*, *Piricularia oryzae*	576, 1006
D-Sorbitol-6-phosphate	D-Fructose-6-phosphate	DPN	*Lactobacillus casei*, *Aerobacter aerogenes*	827, 553
Xylitol	D-Xylulose	DPN	Guinea-pig liver mito-chondria	415
Xylitol	L-Xylulose	TPN	Guinea-pig liver mito-chondria	415, 416
D-Arabitol	D-Ribulose	TPN	*Saccharomyces mellis*	971
D-Arabitol	D-Xylulose	DPN	*Aerobacter aerogenes*, *Acetobacter suboxydans*	548, 630
D-Arabitol	D-Xylulose		*Acetobacter*	349
D-Ribitol	D-Ribulose		Animal tissues	416, 595
D-Ribitol	L-Ribulose		*Acetobacter*	769, 630

In addition to animal sources (seminal vesicles of the sheep), there are a number of bacterial enzymes, frequently appearing through induction, which catalyze aldose-polyol reactions. The general reaction can be formulated as shown in Fig. 65. In some cases, the oxidation-reduction proceeds

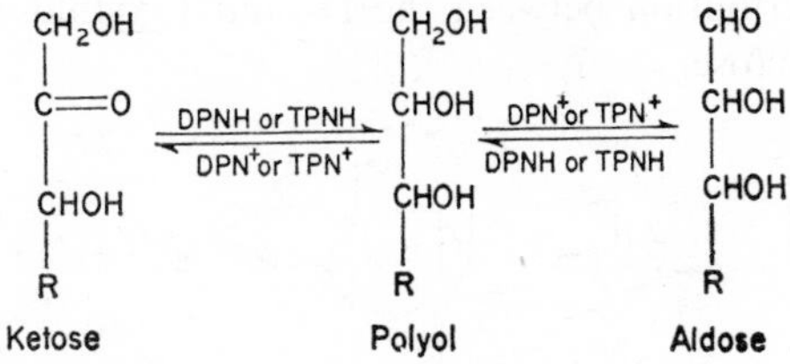

FIG. 65. Oxido-reductions by which polyols are transformed into aldoses or ketoses.

at the level of the hexose-6-phosphate, and the formation of fructose from sorbitol in human placenta is believed to proceed via intermediate phosphorylated derivatives. [344] By a suitable sequence of reactions of the phosphate derivatives, a hexitol may thus be converted into another hexitol. As an example, the reversible interconversion of D-mannitol-1-phosphate into D-sorbitol-6-phosphate proceeds through an intermediate ketose phosphate, namely D-fructose-6-phosphate. [553]

When these reactions are catalyzed by enzymes from *Acetobacter*, a *cis*-configuration of the hydroxyl groups in positions 2 and 3 of the polyol (arabitol and ribitol) is required. This is not necessary, however, for enzymes from other sources. It has been observed in two instances that the same enzyme system may use either DPN+ or TPN+, but that the product of dehydrogenation of the polyol depends on the nature of the pyridine nucleotide. Xylitol, because of the symmetrical structure of its molecule, may yield either D-xylulose or L-xylulose, depending on whether the reaction proceeds with the use of DPN+ or TPN+ (Fig. 66). In *Acetobacter* the oxidation of

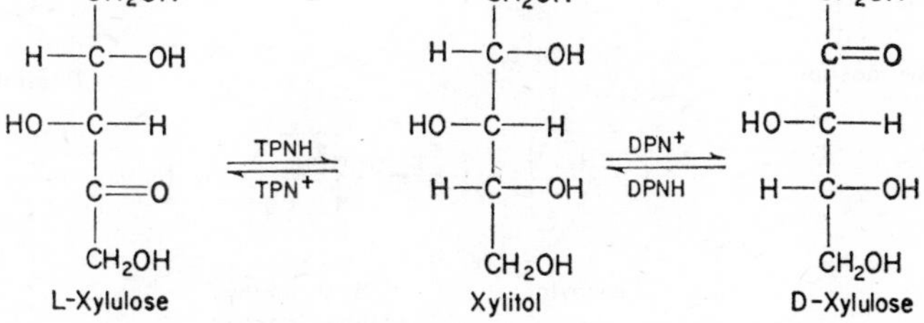

FIG. 66. Transformation of xylitol into D- or L-xylulose in liver, depending on the enzymes using DPN or TPN.

sorbitol leads to fructose and sorbose, respectively, and in seminal vesicles to
either fructose or glucose. These mechanisms provide a possibility for the
transformation of L-xylulose to D-xylulose, or of D-glucose to D-fructose
without passing through the phosphorylated derivatives, i.e. without requiring ATP. In addition, the ratio of DPN+ to TPN+ in such sources will
determine the distribution between the D- and L-xyluloses, or between D-
glucose and D-fructose.

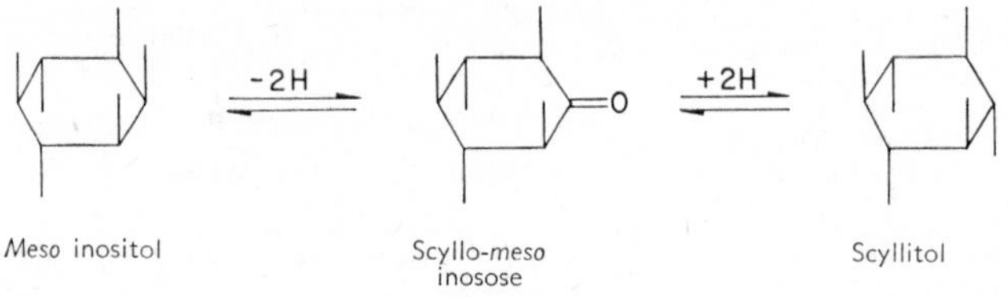

FIG. 67. Interconversion of *meso* inositol and scyllitol in the rat. [736]

Similar hydrogenations and dehydrogenations have been described to
occur in the interconversions of cyclitols. In the rat, like in yeast, *meso*-
inositol and scyllitol have a common precursor, i.e. scyllo-*meso*-inosose, as
seen in Fig. 67. [736]

In leaves of *Trifolium incarnatum*, *meso*-inositol is the precursor of D-
inositol and of cyclitol derivatives, namely sequoytol and D-pinitol. The
conversions proceed by a similar mechanism of alternate dehydrogenations
and hydrogenations, [813] see Fig. 68.

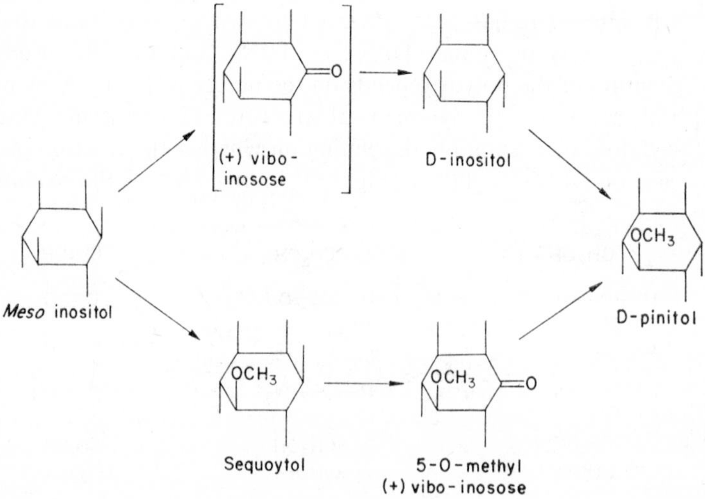

FIG. 68. Transformations of *meso* inositol into other cyclitols and cyclitol
derivatives in leaves. [813]

Glucose or glucose-6-phosphate is the precursor of inositol in yeast, [147, 148] and in rat testes. [235, 236]

XII. SUMMARY AND CONCLUSIONS

The majority of all naturally-occurring carbohydrates are compound saccharides, that is poly-, oligo-, and disaccharides, or glycosides in which the sugar moiety is combined with a noncarbohydrate component. More than 50 individual monosaccharides participate in the structure of these complex sugars, including tetroses, pentoses, hexoses, or heptoses, linear or branched-chain monosaccharides, aldoses or ketoses, aminosugars, uronic acids, or others.

A considerable analogy exists between all saccharides, i.e. among carbohydrates on the whole with the exception of monosaccharides or their derivatives, in that all members of this class contain glycosidic bonds which link the monosaccharide building blocks either to one another or to an aglycon. This structural analogy is paralleled by a marked similarity in the mechanism of the biosynthesis of all saccharides. The glycosidic bonds in most compound carbohydrates are only formed, once the biosynthesis of the monosaccharide building blocks, or more exactly that of certain high-energy derivatives of monosaccharides, has been completed. With the exceptions of the introduction of sulfate groups into the macromolecular structure of sulfomucopolysaccharides and the possible formation of deoxyribonucleotides from the corresponding ribonucleotides, there is no evidence for any alterations occurring in the chemical structure of monosaccharide units once they constitute an integral part of compound saccharides, especially of macromolecular nature. Such a mechanism has been encountered to operate universally, i.e. in animal and plant tissues, as well as in microbial sources, although there appears to exist no fundamental law prohibiting other pathways for the biosynthesis of complex saccharides.

Consequently, the number of possible high-energy monosaccharide precursors is as varied as the number of monosaccharides occurring in complex saccharides, and these precursors are, in effect, glycosides for themselves. The chemical nature of their high-energy providing moiety is limited, however, to a small number of combinations. The importance of aldose-1-phosphates for the biogenesis of saccharides, although it should not be underestimated, has now been recognized to be much smaller than it was originally believed. It has given way to the remarkable role of nucleoside diphosphate sugars, and new members of this group of compounds are reported in the literature in increasing numbers. First, this task was ascribed mainly to the glycosides of *uridine* diphosphate. The importance of diphosphate glycosides of the other principal nucleosides was soon recognized, however. It is now known that even certain monophosphate nucleoside glycosides may act as glycoside donors. In addition to the glycoside-bond formation from aldose-1-phosphates and from nucleoside diphosphate and monophosphate sugars, transglycosylations in which di- or oligosaccharides are the glycosyl donors, play also an important role.

Independently of the nature of the glycosyl donor, the transglycosylation reactions appear to proceed according to a uniform scheme: a high-energy derivative of the monosaccharide transfers its glycosyl group to an acceptor. When the acceptor is a mono-, di-, tri-, or a polysaccharide, the ensuing saccharide will have one glycoside unit more than the acceptor, and will be a di-, tri-, tetra-, or a polysaccharide, respectively. The acceptor may also be a material other than a carbohydrate, i.e. an aglycon, in which case a substance, commonly called a glycoside, results. In any case, the saccharide just synthesized may, in turn, become an acceptor and may, thus, give rise to another saccharide. Through continuous repetition of such a mechanism, a stepwise lengthening of the saccharide chains may result.

During the formation of polysaccharides, it has frequently been observed that the synthesizing enzyme system requires an oligosaccharide as the acceptor, and that the structure of this oligosaccharide must be analogous to that of the polysaccharide to be built up, and that its degree of polymerization, or the length of its linear chains, must be above a certain threshold. In this case, the acceptor is usually referred to as the primer of the reaction. Since polysaccharide synthesis in the presence of a primer consists essentially in the lengthening of pre-existing saccharide chains, no new saccharide molecules would be formed, unless an additional mechanism exists for this purpose. Simultaneously, all primer would eventually be used up, unless new primer molecules will become available. The replenishment of primer and the creation of new saccharide molecules may be accomplished in many instances by the concurrent action of hydrolytic enzymes, although other mechanisms may also exist.

There can be no doubt that all carbohydrate originally reverts to the process of photosynthesis. Tremendous amounts of carbohydrate produced in this way are stored in the form of starch, cellulose, or of other polysaccharides. A mechanism of interconversion between the various sugars at the level of their phosphate esters, of their nucleoside diphosphate derivatives or of the free monosaccharides is known to be in existence in animal and plant tissues, as well as in microorganisms, and to be responsible for the biosynthesis of carbohydrates from other carbohydrates, as well as from the metabolic pool.

REFERENCES

1. ABDULLAH, M. and WHELAN, W. J. *Nature* **197**, 979 (1963).
2. ABERCROMBIE, M. J., JONES, J. K. N., LOCK, M. V., PERRY, M. B. and STOODLEY, R. J. *Can. J. Chem.* **38**, 1617 (1960).
3. ADAMS, J. B. *Nature* **184**, Suppl. No. 5, 274 (1959).
4. ADAMS, J. B. *Biochem. J.* **76**, 520 (1960).

5. ADAMS, J. B. *Biochim. Biophys. Acta* **83**, 127 (1964).
6. ADAMS, J. B. and MEANEY, M. F. *Biochim. Biophys. Acta* **54**, 592 (1961).
7. ADAMS, M. H., REEVES, R. E. and GOEBEL, W. F. *J. Biol. Chem.* **140**, 653 (1941).
8. AKAZAWA, T. and MURATA, T. *Biochem. Biophys. Res. Commun.* **19**, 21 (1965).
9. AKOYUNOGLOV, G. and CALVIN, M. *Biochem. Z.* **338**, 20 (1963).
10. ALBON, N., BELL, D. J., BLANCHARD, P. H., GROSS, D. and RUNDELL, J. T. *J. Chem. Soc.* **1953**, 24.
11. ALGRANATI, I. D. and CABIB, E. *J. Biol. Chem.* **237**, 1007 (1962).
12. ALGRANATI, I. D., CARMINATTI, H. and CABIB, E. *Biochem. Biophys. Res. Commun.* **12**, 504 (1963).
13. ALLEN, P. J. and BACON, J. S. D. *Biochem. J.* **63**, 200 (1956).
14. ALTERMATT, H. A. and NEISH, A. C. *Can. J. Biochem. and Physiol.* **34**, 405 (1956).
15. AMINOFF, D., DODYK, F. and ROSEMAN, S. *J. Biol. Chem.* **238**, PC 1177 (1963).
16. ANDERSON, E. P., KALCKAR, H. M. and ISSELBACHER, K. J. *Science* **125**, 113 (1957).
17. ANDERSON, J. S., MATSUHASHI, M., HASKIN, M. A. and STROMINGER, J. L. *Proc. Natl. Acad. Sci., U.S.* **53**, 881 (1965).
18. ANDERSON, R. L. and WOOD, W. A. *J. Biol. Chem.* **237**, 1029 (1962).
19. ANDREWS, P., HOUGH, L. and PICKEN, J. M. *Biochem. J.* **94**, 75 (1965).
20. ANKEL, H., FARRELL, D. G. and FEINGOLD, D. S. *Biochim. Biophys. Acta* **90**, 397 (1964).
21. ANKEL, H. and FEINGOLD, D. S. *VIth Intern. Congr. Biochem., Abstracts* **1964**.
22. APPLEMAN, M. M., BELOCOPITOW, E. and TORRES, H. N. *Biochem. Biophys. Res. Commun.* **14**, 550 (1964).
23. ARCUS, A. C. and EDSON, N. L. *Biochem. J.* **64**, 385 (1956).
24. ARNON, D. I. *Science* **116**, 635 (1952).
25. ARNON, D. I. *Nature* **184**, 10 (1959).
26. ARNON, D. I., TSUJIMOTO, H. Y. and McSWAIN, B. D. *Proc. Natl. Acad. Sci. U.S.* **51**, 1274 (1964).
27. ARONSON, M. *Arch. Biochem. Biophys.* **39**, 370 (1952).
28. ASHWELL, G., WAHBA, A. J. and HICKMAN, J. *Biochim. Biophys. Acta* **30**, 186 (1958).
29. ATHINOES, E., KUKRAL, J. C. and WINZLER, R. J. *Arch. Biochem. Biophys.* **106**, 338 (1964).
30. ATKINSON, M. R. and MORTON, R. K. In *Comparative Biochemistry*, vol. II, p. 1, eds. M. Florkin and H. S. Mason. Academic Press, New York and London, 1960.
31. AVIGAD, G. *J. Biol. Chem.* **229**, 121 (1957).
32. AVIGAD, G. *J. Biol. Chem.* **239**, 3613 (1964).
33. AVIGAD, G., FEINGOLD, D. S. and HESTRIN, S. *Biochim. Biophys. Acta* **20**, 129 (1956)
34. AXELROD, B. In *Metabolic Pathways*, vol. 1, p. 97, ed. D. M. Greenberg, Academic Press, New York and London, 1960.
35. AXELROD, B. In *Metabolic Pathways*, vol. 1, p. 205, ed. D. M. Greenberg. Academic Press, New York and London, 1960.
36. AXELROD, B. and JANG, R. *J. Biol. Chem.* **209**, 847 (1954).
37. AXELROD, J., INSOCOE, J. K. and TOMKINS, G. M. *J. Biol. Chem.* **232**, 835 (1958).
38. BABAD, H. and HASSID, W. Z. *J. Biol. Chem.* **239**, PC 946 (1964).
39. BACON, J. S. D. *Biochem. J.* **57**, 320 (1954).
40. BACON, J. S. D. and DICKINSON, B. *Biochem. J.* **66**, 289 (1957).
41. BADDILEY, J. *Biochem. J.* **82**, 36P (1962).
42. BADDILEY, J. *Federation Proc.* **21**, 1084 (1962).
43. BADENHUIZEN, N. P. *Nature*, **197** 464 (1963).
44. BADENHUIZEN, N. P. and CHANDORKAR, K. R. *Cereal Chem.* **42**, 44 (1965).
45. BAILEY, J. M., WHELAN, W. J. and PEAT, S. *J. Chem. Soc.* **1950**, 3692.
46. BAILEY, R. W. *Biochem. J.* **71**, 23 (1959); **72**, 42 (1959).
47. BANDURSKI, R. S. and GREINER, C. M. *J. Biol. Chem.* **204**, 781 (1953).
48. BANDURSKI, R. S. and LIPMANN, F. *J. Biol. Chem.* **219**, 741 (1956).
49. BANDURSKI, R. S., WILSON, L. G. and SQUIRES, C. L. *J. Am. Chem. Soc.* **78**, 6408 (1956).
50. BARANOWSKI, T., ILLINGWORTH, B., BROWN, D. H. and CORI, C. F. *Biochim. Biophys. Acta* **25**, 16 (1957).
51. BARBER, G. A. *Biochem. Biophys. Res. Commun.* **8**, 204 (1962).

52 BARBER, G. A. *Arch. Biochem. Biophys.* **103**, 276 (1963).
53. BARBER, G. A., ELBEIN, A. D. and HASSID, W. Z. *J. Biol. Chem.* **239**, 4056 (1964).
54. BARBER, G. A. and HASSID, W. Z. *Biochim. Biophys. Acta* **86**, 397 (1964).
55. BARBER, G. A. and NEUFELD, E. F. *Biochem. Biophys. Res. Commun.* **6**, 44 (1961).
56. BARKER, S. A. and BOURNE, E. J. *J. Chem. Soc.* **1952**, 209.
57. BARKER, S. A., BOURNE, E. J. and CARRINGTON, T. R. *J. Chem. Soc.* **1954**, 2125.
58. BARKER, S. A., BOURNE, E. J. PEAT, S. and WILKINSON, I. A. *J. Chem. Soc.* **1950**, 3022.
59. BARKER, S. A., BOURNE, E. J. and STACEY, M. *J. Chem. Soc.* **1953**, 3084.
60. BARKER, S. A., BOURNE, E. J., WILKINSON, I. A. and PEAT, S. *J. Chem. Soc.* **1950**, 93.
61. BARRY, G. T. *J. Exptl. Med.* **107**, 507 (1958).
62. BARRY, V. C. *Nature* **152**, 537 (1943).
63. BARTLEY, W. *Biochem. J.* **54**, 677 (1953); **56**, 387 (1954).
64. BARTLEY, W. and AVI-DOR, Y. *Biochem. J.* **59**, 194 (1955).
65. BASSHAM, J. A., BENSON, A. A., KAY, L. D., HARRIS, A. Z., WILSON, A. T. and CALVIN, M. *J. Am. Chem. Soc.* **76**, 1760 (1954).
66. BASSHAM, J. A. and CALVIN, M. *The Path of Carbon in Photosynthesis*, pp. 39-66. Prentice-Hall, Englewood Cliffs, New Jersey, 1957.
67. BASSHAM, J. A. and CALVIN, M. *Comp. Biochem. and Physiol.* **4**, 187 (1962).
68. BASSHAM, J. A. and KIRK, M. *Biochim. Biophys. Acta* **43**, 447 (1960).
69. BASSHAM, J. A. and KIRK, M. *Biochem. Biophys. Res. Commun.* **9**, 376 (1962).
70. BEAN, R. C. and HASSID, W. Z. *J. Am. Chem. Soc.* **77**, 5737 (1955).
71. BEAN, R. C. and HASSID, W. Z. *J. Biol. Chem.* **218**, 425 (1956).
72. BEBBINGTON, A., BOURNE, E. J. and WILKINSON, I. A. *J. Chem. Soc.* **1952**, 246.
73. BENNETT, R. and FULLER, R. C. *Biochem. Biophys. Res. Commun.* **16**, 300 (1964).
74. BENSON, A. A. and CALVIN, M. *J. Exptl. Botany* **1**, 63 (1951).
75. BENZIMAN, M. and BURGER-RACHAMIMOV, H. *J. Bacteriol.* **84**, 625 (1962).
76. BERG, P. and JOKLIK, W. K. *Nature* **172**, 1081 (1953).
77. BERGER, L., SLEIN, M. W., COLOWICK, S. P. and CORI, C. F. *J. Gen. Physiol.* **29**, 379 (1946).
78. BERNAERTS, M. J. and DELEY, J. *Biochim. Biophys. Acta* **30**, 661 (1958).
79. BERNAERTS, M. J. and DELEY, J. *J. Gen. Microbiol.* **22**, 129 137 (1960).
80. BERNFELD, P. *Advances in Enzymol.* **12**, 379 (1951).
81. BERNFELD, P. In *Comparative Biochemistry.* vol. III, p. 355, eds. M. Florkin and H. S. Mason. Academic Press, New York and London, 1962.
82. BERNFELD, P. In *Metabolic Inhibitors*, vol. II, p. 437, eds. R. M. Hochster and J. H. Quastel. Academic Press, New York and London, 1963.
83. BERNFELD, P., BERKELEY, B. J. and BIEBER, R. E. *Arch. Biochem. Biophys.* **111**, 31 (1965).
84. BERNFELD, P., JACOBSON, S. and BERNFELD, H. C. *Arch. Biochem. Biophys.* **69**, 198 (1957).
85. BERNFELD, P., TUTTLE, L. P and HUBBARD, R. W. *Arch. Biochem. Biophys.* **92**, 232 (1961).
86. BERNSTEIN, R. L. and ROBBINS, P. W. *J. Biol. Chem.* **240**, 391 (1965).
87. BERNSTEIN, S. and MCGILVERY, R. W. *J. Biol. Chem.* **199**, 745 (1952).
88. BEVILL, R. D., NORDIN, J. H., SMITH, F. and KIRKWOOD, S. *Biochem. Biophys. Res. Commun.* **12**, 152 (1963).
89. BLACK, C. C., SAN PIETRO, A., LIMBACH, D. and NORRIS, G. *Proc. Natl. Acad. Sci., U.S.* **50**, 37 (1963).
90. BLACK, C. C., TURNER, J. F., GIBBS, M., KROGMANN, D. W. and GORDON, S. A. *J. Biol. Chem.* **237**, 580 (1962).
91. BLACKLOW, R. S. and WARREN, L. *J. Biol. Chem.* **237**, 3520 (1962).
92. BLUMENTHAL, H. J., HOROWITZ, S. T., HEMERLINE, A. and ROSEMAN, S. *Proc. Soc. Am. Bacteriologists* **1955**, 137.
93. BLUMSON, N. L. and BADDILEY, J. *Biochem. J.* **81**, 114 (1961).
94. BO, W. J. and SMITH, M. S. *Proc. Soc. Exptl. Biol. Med.* **113**, 812 (1963).
95. BOARDMAN, N. K. and ANDERSON, J. M. *Nature* **203**, 166 (1964).

96. BOCK, K. W., JAENICKE, L. and HOLZER, H. *Biochem. Biophys. Res. Commun.* **9**, 472 (1962).
97. BONSIGNORE, A., PONTREMOLI, S., MANGIAROTTI, G., DE FLORA, A. and MANGIAROTTI, M. *J. Biol. Chem.* **237**, 3597 (1962).
98. BOSTRÖM, H. *J. Biol. Chem.* **196**, 477 (1952).
99. BOSTRÖM, H. In *Polysaccharides in Biology*, p. 211, ed. G. F. Springer, Transact. of the 4th Conference, 1958, The Josiah Macy, Jr. Foundation, published 1959.
100. BOSTRÖM, H. and MÅNSSON, B. *Acta Chem. Scand.* **6**, 1559 (1952).
101. BOSTRÖM, H. and MÅNSSON, B. *J. Biol. Chem.* **196**, 483 (1952).
102. BRADBEER, C. *Nature* **182**, 1429 (1958).
103. BRETTHAUER, R. K., WILKEN, D. R. and HANSEN, R. G. *Biochim. Biophys. Acta* **78**, 420 (1963).
104. BRINK, N. G. *Acta Chem. Scand.* **7**, 1081 (1953).
105. BROWN, A. M. *J. Polymer Sci.* **59**, 155 (1962).
106. BROWN, A. M. and GASCOIGNE, J. A. *Nature* **187**, 1010 (1960).
107. BROWN, D. H. *Biochim. Biophys. Acta* **7**, 487 (1951).
108. BROWN, D. H. *Biochim. Biophys. Acta* **16**, 429 (1955).
109. BROWN, D. H. and ILLINGWORTH, B. *Proc. Natl. Acad. Sci., U.S.* **48**, 1783 (1962).
110. BROWN, D. H., ILLINGWORTH, B. and CORI, C. F. *Proc. Natl. Acad. Sci., U.S.* **47**, 479 (1961).
111. BROWN, D. H., ILLINGWORTH, B. and CORI, C. F. *Nature* **197**, 980 (1963).
112. BROWN, D. H., ILLINGWORTH, B. and KORNFELD, R. *Biochemistry* **4**, 486 (1965).
113. BRUMMOND, D. O. and GIBBONS, A. P. *Biochem. Biophys. Res. Commun.* **17**, 156 (1964).
114. BRUNETTI, P., JOURDIAN, G. W. and ROSEMAN, S. *J. Biol. Chem.* **237**, 2447 (1962).
115. BUCHANAN, J. G. *Arch. Biochem. Biophys.* **44**, 140 (1953).
116. BUEDING, E., RUPPENDER, H. and MACKINNON, J. *Proc. Natl. Acad. Sci., U.S.* **40**, 773 (1954).
117. BURGER, M., GLASER, L. and BURTON, R. M. *Biochim. Biophys. Acta* **56**, 172 (1962).
118. BURGER, M. M. and GLASER, L. *J. Biol. Chem.* **239**, 3168 (1964).
119. BURMA, D. P. and HORECKER, B. L. *Biochim. Biophys. Acta* **24**, 660 (1957).
120. BURMA, D. P. and HORECKER, B. L. *J. Biol. Chem.* **231**, 1039 (1958).
121. BURMA, D. P. and MORTIMER, D. C. *Arch. Biochem. Biophys.* **62**, 16 (1956).
122. BURNS, J. J. and KANFER, J. *J. Am. Chem. Soc.* **79**, 3694 (1957).
123. BURTON, K. and KREBS, H. A. *Biochem. J.* **54**, 94 (1953).
124. BURTON, R. M., SODD, M. A. and BRADY, R. O. *J. Biol. Chem.* **233**, 1053 (1958).
125. CABIB, E. and LELOIR, L. F. *J. Biol. Chem.* **206**, 779 (1954).
126. CABIB, E. and LELOIR, L. F. *J. Biol. Chem.* **231**, 259 (1958).
127. CABIB, E., LELOIR, L. F. and CARDINI, C. E. *J. Biol. Chem.* **203**, 1055 (1953).
128. CALVIN, M. *Federation Proc.* **13**, 697 (1954).
129. CALVIN, M. *J. Chem. Soc.* **1956**, 1895.
130. CALVIN, M. *Angew. Chem.* **74**, 174 (1962).
131. CALVIN, M. and BASSHAM, J. A. *The Photosynthesis of Carbon Compounds*, p. 39. W. A. Benjamin, Inc., New York, 1962.
132. CAMPO, R. D. and DZIEWIATKOWSKI, D. D. *J. Biol. Chem.* **237**, 2729 (1962).
133. CANALE-PAROLA, E. and WOLFE, R. S. *Biochim. Biophys. Acta* **82**, 403 (1964).
134. CANDY, D. J., BLUMSOM, N. L. and BADDILEY, J. *Biochem. J.* **91**, 31 (1964).
135. CANDY, D. J. and KILBY, B. A. *Nature* **183**, 1594 (1959).
136. CANDY, D. J. and KILBY, B. A. *J. Exptl. Biol.* **39**, 129 (1962).
137. CAPUTTO, R., LELOIR, L. F., CARDINI, C. E. and PALADINI, A. C. *J. Biol. Chem.* **184**, 333 (1950).
138. CARDINI, C. E. and LELOIR, L. F. *Arch. Biochem. Biophys.* **45**, 55 (1953).
139. CARDINI, C. E. and LELOIR, L. F. *Ciencia e invest.* (*Buenos Aires*) **13**, 514 (1957).
140. CARDINI, C. E. and LELOIR, L. F. *J. Biol. Chem.* **225**, 317 (1957).
141. CARDINI, C. E., LELOIR, L. F. and CHIRIBOGA, J. *J. Biol. Chem.* **214**, 149 (1955).
142. CARDINI, C. E., PALADINI, A. C., CAPUTTO, R., LELOIR, L. F. and TRUCCO, R. E. *Arch. Biochem.* **22**, 87 (1949).

143. CARDINI, C. E. and YAMAHA, T. *Nature* **182**, 1446 (1958).
144. CARLSON, D. M. and HANSEN, R. G. *J. Biol. Chem.* **237**, 1260 (1962).
145. CHAKRAVORTY, M. *Biochim. Biophys. Acta* **85**, 152 (1964).
146. CHATTERJEE, A. N. and PARK, J. T. *Proc. Natl. Acad. Sci., U.S.* **51**, 9 (1964).
147. CHEN, I. W. and CHARALAMPOUS, F. C. *Biochem. Biophys. Res. Commun.* **12**, 62 (1963).
148. CHEN, I. W. and CHARALAMPOUS, F. C. *J. Biol. Chem.* **239**, 1905 (1964).
149. CHESTERS, C. G. C. and BULL, A. T. *Nature* **202**, 454 (1964).
150. CHIANG, C., SIH, C. J. and KNIGHT, S. G. *Biochim. Biophys. Acta* **29**, 664 (1958).
151. CHIU, T. H. and FEINGOLD, D. S. *Biochim. Biophys. Acta* **92**, 489 (1964).
152. CIFONELLI, J. A. and DORFMAN, A. *J. Biol. Chem.* **228**, 547 (1957).
153. CLEGG, J. S. *Comp. Biochem. Physiol.* **14**, 135 (1965).
154. COHEN, A. and FEINGOLD, D. S. *VIth Intern. Congr. Biochem., Abstracts* **1964.**
155. COHEN, S. S. *J. Biol. Chem.* **201**, 71 (1953).
156. COHN, M. *J. Biol. Chem.* **180**, 771 (1949).
157. COHN, M. *Biochim. Biophys. Acta* **20**, 92 (1956).
158. COLOWICK, S. P. and SUTHERLAND, E. W. *J. Biol. Chem.* **144**, 423 (1942).
159. COLVIN, J. R. *Can. J. Biochem. Physiol.* **39**, 1921 (1961).
160. COLVIN, J. R. and BEER, M. *Can. J. Microbiol.* **6**, 631 (1960).
161. COMB, D. G. and ROSEMAN, S. *Biochim. Biophys. Acta* **21**, 193 (1956).
162. COMB, D. G. and ROSEMAN, S. *Biochim. Biophys. Acta* **29**, 653 (1958).
163. COMB, D. G. and ROSEMAN, S. *J. Am. Chem. Soc.* **80**, 497 (1958).
164. COMB, D. G. and ROSEMAN, S. *J. Biol. Chem.* **232**, 807 (1958).
165. COMB, D. G. and ROSEMAN, S. *J. Biol. Chem.* **235**, 2529 (1960).
166. COMB, D. G., SHIMIZU, F. and ROSEMAN, S. *J. Am. Chem. Soc.* **81**, 5513 (1959).
167. CORI, C. F. In *Enzymes: Units of Biological Structure and Function*, p. 573, ed. O. H. Gaebler. Academic Press, New York, 1956.
168. CORI, C. F., COLOWICK, S. P. and CORI, G. T. *J. Biol. Chem.* **121**, 465 (1937).
169. CORI, C. F. and CORI, G. T. *Proc. Soc. Exptl. Biol. and Med.* **34**, 702 (1936).
170. CORI, C. F., CORI, G. T. and GREEN, A. A. *J. Biol. Chem.* **151**, 39 (1943).
171. CORI, C. F. and ILLINGWORTH, B. *Proc. Natl. Acad. Sci., U.S.* **43**, 547 (1957).
172. CORI, C. F., SCHMIDT, G. and CORI, G. T. *Science* **89**, 464 (1939).
173. CORI, G. T., COLOWICK, S. P. and CORI, C. F. *J. Biol. Chem.* **124**, 543 (1938).
174. CORI, G. T. and CORI, C. F. *J. Biol. Chem.* **131**, 397 (1939).
175. CORI, G. T. and CORI, C. F. *J. Biol. Chem.* **135**, 733 (1940).
176. CORI, G. T. and CORI, C. F. *J. Biol. Chem.* **151**, 57 (1943).
177. CORI, G. T. and CORI, C. F. *J. Biol. Chem.* **158**, 321 (1945).
178. CORI, G. T., CORI, C. F. and SCHMIDT, G. *J. Biol. Chem.* **129**, 629 (1939).
179. CORI, G. T. and GREEN, A. A. *J. Biol. Chem.* **151**, 31 (1943).
180. CORI, G. T. and ILLINGWORTH, B. *J. Biol. Chem.* **190**, 679 (1951).
181. CORI, G. T. and ILLINGWORTH, B. *Biochim. Biophys. Acta* **21**, 105 (1956).
182. CORI, G. T., OCHOA, S., SLEIN, M. W. and CORI, C. F. *Biochim. Biophys. Acta* **7**, 304 (1951).
183. CORI, G. T., SWANSON, M. A. and CORI, C. F. *Federation Proc.* **4**, 234 (1945).
184. CORI, O. and LIPMANN, F. *J. Biol. Chem.* **94**, 417 (1952).
185. CORMAN, J. and LANGLYKKE, A. F. *Cereal Chem.* **25**, 190 (1948).
186. COULTHARD, C. E., MICHAELIS, R., SHORT, W. F., SYKES, G., SKRIMSHIRE, G. E. H., STANDFAST, A. F. B., BIRKINSHAW, J. H. and RAISTRICK, H. *Biochem. J.* **38**, 24 (1945).
187. CRAIG, J. W. and LARNER, J. *Nature* **202**, 971 (1964).
188. CRANE, F. L. *Plant Physiol.* **34**, 128 (1959).
189. CUMMINS, J. T., CHELDELIN, V. H. and KING, T. E. *J. Biol. Chem.* **226**, 301 (1957).
190. CUMMINS, J. T., KING, T. E. and CHELDELIN, V. H. *J. Biol. Chem.* **224**, 329 (1957).
191. D'ABRAMO, F. and LIPMANN, F. *Biochim. Biophys. Acta* **25**, 211 (1957).
192. D'ABRAMO, F. and LIPMANN, F. *Proc. Intern. Congr. Biochem., 4th, Vienna, 1958*, **13**, 36.
193. DANFORTH, W. H. *J. Biol. Chem.* **240**, 588 (1965).

194. DANFORTH, W. H. and HARVEY, P. *Biochem. Biophys. Res. Commun.* **16**, 466 (1964).
195. DANFORTH, W. H. and HELMREICH, E. *J. Biol. Chem.* **239**, 3133 (1964).
196. DANFORTH, W. H., HELMREICH, E. and CORI, C. F. *Proc. Natl. Acad. Sci., U.S.* **48**, 1191 (1962).
197. DANKERT, M., GONCALVES, I. R. J. and RECONDO, E. *Biochim. Biophys. Acta* **81**, 78 (1964).
198. DANKERT, M., PASSERON, S., RECONDO, E. and LELOIR, L. F. *Biochem. Biophys. Res. Commun.* **14**, 358 (1964).
199. DARROW, R. A. and CREVELING, C. R. *J. Biol. Chem.* **239**, PC 362 (1964).
200. DAVIDSON, E. A., BLUMENTHAL, H. J. and ROSEMAN, S. *J. Biol. Chem.* **226**, 125 (1957).
201. DAVIDSON, E. A. and RILEY, J. G. *J. Biol. Chem.* **235**, 3367 (1960).
202. DEDONDER, R. A. and HASSID, W. Z. *Biochim. Biophys. Acta* **90**, 239 (1964).
203. DEDONDER, R., JOZON, E., RAPOPORT, G., JOYEUX, Y. and FRITSCH, A. *Bull. Soc. Chim. Biol.* **45**, 477 (1963).
204. DEDONDER, R. and NOBLESSE, C. *Ann. Inst. Pasteur* **85**, 356 (1953).
205. DEDONDER, R. and SLIZEWICZ, P. *Bull. Soc. Chim. Biol.* **40**, 873 (1958).
206. DE LEY, J. and DOUDOROFF, M. *J. Biol. Chem.* **227**, 745 (1957).
207. DE MEIO, R. H. and WIZERKANIUK, M. *Biochim. Biophys. Acta* **20**, 428 (1956).
208. DICKENS, F. and WILLIAMSON, D. H. *Nature* **176**, 400 (1955); *Biochem. J.* **64**, 567 (1956).
209. DOBROGOSZ, W. J. and DE MOSS, R. D. *J. Bacteriol.* **85**, 1350 (1963).
210. DOBROGOSZ, W. J. and DE MOSS, R. D. *J. Bacteriol.* **85**, 1356 (1963).
211. DOI, A., DOI, K. and NIKUNI, Z. *Biochim. Biophys. Acta* **92**, 628 (1964).
212. DOI, K. *Biochim. Biophys. Acta* **94**, 557 (1965).
213. DOI, K. and NIKUNI, Z. *Die Stärke* **14**, 461 (1962).
214. DOMAGK, G. F. and HEINRICH, R. *Biochem. Z.* **341**, 420 (1965).
215. DORFMAN, A. In *Polysaccharides in Biology*, p. 256, Transact. of the 4th Conference, 1958, ed. G. F. Springer. The Josiah Macy, Jr. Foundation, published 1959.
216. DORFMAN, A. *Federation Proc.* **21**, 1070 (1962).
217. DOUDOROFF, M., BARKER, H. A. and HASSID, W. Z. *J. Biol. Chem.* **168**, 725 (1947).
218. DOUDOROFF, M., HASSID, W. Z. and BARKER, H. A. *J. Biol. Chem.* **168**, 733 (1947).
219. DOUDOROFF, M., HASSID, W. Z., PUTMAN, E. W., POTTER, A. L. and LEDERBERG, J. *J. Biol. Chem.* **179**, 921 (1949).
220. DOUDOROFF, M., KAPLAN, N. and HASSID, W. Z. *J. Biol. Chem.* **148**, 67 (1943).
221. DRAPER, P. and KENT, P. W. *Biochem. J.* **86**, 248 (1963).
222. DRUMMOND, G. I., KEITH, J. and GILGAN, M. W. *Arch. Biochem. Biophys.* **105**, 156 (1964).
223. DUTTON, G. J. *Biochem. J.* **64**, 693 (1956).
224. DUTTON, G. J. and STEVENSON, I. H. *Biochim. Biophys. Acta* **31**, 568 (1959).
225. DZIEWIATKOWSKI, D. D. *J. Biol. Chem.* **189**, 187 (1951).
226. DZIEWIATKOWSKI, D. D. *J. Cell Biology* **13**, 359 (1962).
227. DZIEWIATKOWSKI, D. D., BENESCH, R. E. and BENESCH, R. *J. Biol. Chem.* **178**, 931 (1949).
228. EBERT, K. H. and PATAT, F. *Z. Naturforsch.* **17b**, 738 (1962).
229. EDELMAN, J. and BACON, J. S. D. *Biochem. J.* **49**, 529 (1951).
230. EDELMAN, J. and RECALDIN, D. A. C. L. *Biochem. J.* **79**, 12p (1961).
231. EDELMAN, J., RECALDIN, D. A. C. L. and DICKERSON, A. G. *Bull. Research Council Israel* **11A4**, 275 (1963).
232. EDMUNDOWICZ, J. M. and WRISTON, J. C., JR. *J. Biol. Chem.* **238**, 3539 (1963).
233. EDSTROM, R. D. and HEATH, E. C. *Biochem. Biophys. Res. Commun.* **16**, 576 (1964).
234. EICHHORN, M. M. and CYNKIN, M. A. *Biochemistry* **4**, 159 (1965).
235. EISENBERG, F., JR. and BOLDEN, A. H. *Biochem. Biophys. Res. Commun.* **12**, 72 (1963).
236. EISENBERG, F., JR., BOLDEN, A. H. and LOEWUS, F. A. *Biochem. Biophys. Res. Commun.* **14**, 419 (1964).
237. EISENBERG, F., JR. and HESTRIN, S. *Bull. Research Council Israel*, **11A4**, 269 (1963).
238. ELBEIN, A. D. *Proc. Natl. Acad. Sci., U.S.* **53**, 803 (1965).
239. ELBEIN, A. D., BARBER, G. A. and HASSID, W. Z. *J. Am. Chem. Soc.* **86**, 309 (1964).
240. EMERSON, R. *Ann. Rev. Plant Physiol.* **9**, 1 (1958).

241. ESPADA, J. *J. Biol. Chem.* **237**, 3577 (1962).
242. EVANS, T. H. and HIBBERT, H. *Advances Carbohydrate Chem.* **2**, 203 (1946).
243. EYLAR, E. H. and MATIOLI, G. T. *Science* **147**, 869 (1965).
244. FAULKNER, P. and QUASTEL, J. H. *Nature* **177**, 1216 (1956).
245. FEINGOLD, D. S., AVIGAD, G. and HESTRIN, S. *Biochem. J.* **64**, 351 (1956).
246. FEINGOLD, D. S., AVIGAD, G. and HESTRIN, S. *J. Biol. Chem.* **224**, 295 (1957).
247. FEINGOLD, D. S. and GEHATIA, M. *J. Polymer Sci.* **23**, 783 (1957).
248. FEINGOLD, D. S., NEUFELD, E. F. and HASSID, W. Z. *Arch. Biochem. Biophys.* **78**, 401 (1958).
249. FEINGOLD, D. S., NEUFELD, E. F. and HASSID, W. Z. *J. Biol. Chem.* **233**, 783 (1958).
250. FEINGOLD, D. S., NEUFELD, E. F. and HASSID, W. Z. *J. Biol. Chem.* **234**, 488 (1959).
251. FEKETE, M. A. R. DE and CARDINI, C. E. *Arch. Biochem. Biophys.* **104**, 173 (1964).
252. FISCHER, E. H., GRAVES, D. J., CRITTENDEN, E. R. S. and KREBS, E. G. *J. Biol. Chem.* **234**, 1698 (1959).
253. FISCHER, E. H., HURD, S. S., NOVOA, W. B. and KREBS, E. G. *Biochem. J.* **89**, 39P (1963).
254. FISCHER, E. H. and KREBS, E. G. *J. Biol. Chem.* **216**, 121 (1955).
255. FISCHER, W. and WEIDEMANN, G. *Biochim. Biophys. Acta* **93**, 677 (1964).
256. FISCHER, W. and WEIDEMANN, G. *Z. Physiol. Chem.* **336**, 195, 206 (1964).
257. FITTING, C. and DOUDOROFF, M. *J. Biol. Chem.* **199**, 153 (1952).
258. FOSTER, D. W. and GINSBURG, V. *Biochim. Biophys. Acta* **54**, 376 (1961).
259. FRAENKEL, D., OSBORN, M. J., HORECKER, B. L. and SMITH, S. M. *Biochem. Biophys. Res. Commun.* **11**, 423 (1963).
260. FRENCH, D. *Science* **113**, 352 (1951).
261. FRENCH, D., LEVINE, M. L., PAZUR, J. H. and NORBERG, E. *J. Am. Chem. Soc.* **71**, 353 (1949).
262. FRENCH, D., PAZUR, J., LEVINE, M. L. and NORBERG, E. *J. Am. Chem. Soc.* **70**, 3145 (1948).
263. FRENCH, D. and WILD, G. M. *J. Am. Chem. Soc.* **75**, 4990 (1953).
264. FRIEDMAN, D. L. and LARNER, J. *Biochim. Biophys. Acta* **64**, 185 (1962).
265. FRIEDMAN, D. L. and LARNER, J. *Biochemistry* **2**, 669 (1963).
266. FRYDMAN, R. B. *Arch. Biochem. Biophys.* **102**, 242 (1963).
267. FRYDMAN, R. B. and CARDINI, C. E. *Biochem. Biophys. Res. Commun.* **14**, 353 (1964).
268. FRYDMAN, R. B. and CARDINI, C. E. *Biochem. Biophys. Res. Commun.* **17**, 407 (1964).
269. FRYDMAN, R. B. and CARDINI, C. E. *Biochim. Biophys. Acta* **96**, 294 (1965).
270. FRYDMAN, R. B. and HASSID, W. Z. *Nature* **199**, 382 (1963).
271. FRYDMAN, R. B. and NEUFELD, E. F. *Biochem. Biophys. Res. Commun.* **12**, 121 (1963)
272. FRYDMAN, R. B., NEUFELD, E. F. and HASSID, W. Z. *Biochim. Biophys. Acta* **77**, 332 (1963).
273. FUJII, S. and KUSHIDA, H. *Biochim. Biophys. Acta* **69**, 572 (1963).
274. FUJIMOTO, A., INGRAM, P. and SMITH, R. A. *Biochim. Biophys. Acta* **96**, 91 (1965).
275. FUJIMOTO, A. and SMITH, R. A. *Biochim. Biophys. Acta* **56**, 501 (1962).
276. FUKUI, S. and HOCHSTER, R. M. *Biochem. Biophys. Res. Commun.* **11**, 50 (1963).
277. FUKUI, S. and HOCHSTER, R. M. *Can. J. Biochem. Physiol.* **41**, 2363 (1963).
278. FUKUI, S., HOCHSTER, R. M., DURBIN, R., GREBNER, E. E. and FEINGOLD, D. S. *Bull. Research Council Israel* **11A4**, 262 (1963).
279. GABRIEL, O. and ASHWELL, G. *J. Biol. Chem.* **237**, 1400 (1962).
280. GAFFRON, H. In *Autotropic Microorganisms*, p. 152, eds. B. A. Fry and J. L. Peel. Cambridge Univ. Press, London and New York, 1954.
281. GANDER, J. E., PETERSEN, W. E. and BOYER, P. D. *Arch. Biochem. Biophys.* **60**, 259 (1956); **69**, 85 (1957).
282. GANGULI, N. C. *J. Biol. Chem.* **232**, 337 (1958).
283. GHALAMBOR, M. A. and HEATH, E. C. *J. Biol. Chem.* **237**, 2427 (1962).
284. GHALAMBOR, M. A. and HEATH, E. C. *Biochem. Biophys. Res. Commun.* **10**, 346 (1963).
285. GHOSH, H. P. and PREISS, J. *J. Biol. Chem.* **240**, PC 960 (1965).

286. GHOSH, S. and ROSEMAN, S. *Proc. Natl. Acad. Sci., U.S.* **47**, 955 (1961).
287. GHOSH, S. and ROSEMAN, S. *J. Biol. Chem.* **240**, 1525 (1965).
288. GHOSH, S. and ROSEMAN, S. *J. Biol. Chem.* **240**, 1531 (1965).
289. GIBBS, M. *Nature* **170**, 164 (1952).
290. GILBERT, G. A. and PATRICK, A. D. *Biochem. J.* **51**, 181 (1952).
291. GILBERT, J. M., MATSUHASHI, M. and STROMINGER, J. L. *J. Biol. Chem.* **240**, 1305 (1965)
292. GINSBURG, V. *J. Am. Chem. Soc.* **80**, 4426 (1958).
293. GINSBURG, V. *J. Biol. Chem.* **232**, 55 (1958).
294. GINSBURG, V. *J. Biol. Chem.* **235**, 2196 (1960).
295. GINSBURG, V. *J. Biol. Chem.* **236**, 2389 (1961).
296. GINSBURG, V. *Advances in Enzymology* **26**, 35 (1964).
297. GINSBURG, V. and KIRKMAN, H. N. *J. Am. Chem. Soc.* **80**, 3481 (1958).
298. GINSBURG, V., NEUFELD, E. F. and HASSID, W. Z. *Proc. Natl. Acad. Sci. U.S.* **42**, 333 (1956).
299. GINSBURG, V., O'BRIEN, P. J. and HALL, C. W. *Biochem. Biophys. Res. Commun.* **7**, 1 (1962).
300. GINSBURG, V., O'BRIEN, P. J. and HALL, C. W. *J. Biol. Chem.* **237**, 497 (1962).
301. GINSBURG, V., STUMPF, P. K. and HASSID, W. Z. *J. Biol. Chem.* **223**, 977 (1956).
302. GIRI, K. V., NAGABHUSHANAM, A., NIGAM, V. N. and BELAVADI, B. *Science* **121**, 898 (1955).
303. GLASER, L. *Biochim. Biophys. Acta* **25**, 436 (1957).
304. GLASER, L. *J. Biol. Chem.* **232**, 627 (1958).
305. GLASER, L. *Biochim. Biophys. Acta* **31**, 575 (1959).
306. GLASER, L. *J. Biol. Chem.* **234**, 2801 (1959).
307. GLASER, L. *Biochim. Biophys. Acta* **51**, 169 (1961).
308. GLASER, L. *Biochim. Biophys. Acta* **67**, 525 (1963).
309. GLASER, L. *Biochim. Biophys. Acta* **71**, 237 (1963).
310. GLASER, L. *Physiol. Reviews* **43**, 215 (1963).
311. GLASER, L. *J. Biol. Chem.* **239**, 3178 (1964).
312. GLASER, L. *Biochim. Biophys. Acta* **101**, 6 (1965).
313. GLASER, L. and BROWN, D. H. *Proc. Natl. Acad. Sci., U.S.* **41**, 253 (1955).
314. GLASER, L. and BROWN, D. H. *Biochim. Biophys. Acta* **23**, 449 (1957).
315. GLASER, L. and BROWN, D. H. *J. Biol. Chem.* **228**, 729 (1957).
316. GLASER, L. and BURGER, M. M. *J. Biol. Chem.* **239**, 3187 (1964).
317. GLASER, L. and KORNFELD, S. *J. Biol. Chem.* **236**, 1795 (1961).
318. GODMAN, G. C. and PORTER, K. R. *J. Biophys. Biochem. Cytol.* **8**, 719 (1960).
319. GOLDBERG, I. H. and DELBRÜCK, A. *Federation Proc.* **18**, 235 (1959).
320. GOLDBERG, M. L. and RACKER, E. *J. Biol. Chem.* **237**, PC 3841 (1962).
321. GOLDBERG, N. D., DAHL, J. L. and PARKS, R. E., JR. *J. Biol. Chem.* **238**, 3109 (1963).
322. GOLDEMBERG, S. H. *Biochim. Biophys. Acta* **56**, 357 (1962).
323. GOLDEMBERG, S. H. and MARECHAL, L. R. *Biochim. Biophys. Acta* **71**, 743 (1963).
324. GOLDMAN, D. S. and LORNITZO, F. A. *J. Biol. Chem.* **237**, 3332 (1962).
325. GOMPERTZ, S. M. and WATKINS, W. M. *Biochem. J.* **88**, 6P (1963).
326. GONÇALVES, I. R. J. *Enzymologia* **26**, 287 (1963).
327. GONZALES, N. S. and PONTIS, H. G. *Biochim. Biophys. Acta* **69**, 179 (1963).
328. GOTTSCHALK, A. *Advances in Carbohydrate Chem.* **5**, 49 (1950).
329. GOTTSCHALK, A. In *The Enzymes*, vol. I, p. 551, eds. J. B. Sumner and K. Myrbäck. Academic Press, New York, 1950.
330. GOULD, M. F. and GREENSHIELDS, R. N. *Nature* **202**, 108 (1964).
331. GRASSMANN, W., ZECHMEISTER, L., TÓTH, G. and STADLER, R. *Ann.* **503**, 167 (1933).
332. GRAVES, D. J., FISCHER, E. N. and KREBS, E. G. *J. Biol. Chem.* **235**, 805 (1960).
333. GREBNER, E. E., DURBIN, R. and FEINGOLD, D. S. *Nature* **201**, 419 (1964).
334. GREBNER, E. E. and FEINGOLD, S. *Biochem. Biophys. Res. Commun.* **19**, 37 (1965).
335. GREEN, A. A. and CORI, G. T. *J. Biol. Chem.* **151**, 21 (1943).
336. GREEN, M. and COHEN, S. S. *J. Biol. Chem.* **219**, 557 (1956).
337. GREENBERG, E. and PREISS, J. *J. Biol. Chem.* **239**, PC 4314 (1964).

338. GRILLO, T. A. I. and OZONE, K. *Nature* **195**, 902 (1962).
339. GRISBACH, H. and DÖBEREINER, U. *Biochem. Biophys. Res. Commun.* **17**, 737 (1964).
340. GROLLMAN, A. P., HALL, C. W. and GINSBURG, V. *J. Biol. Chem.* **240**, 975 (1965).
341. GROLLMAN, A. P. and LEHNINGER, A. L. *Arch. Biochem. Biophys.* **69**, 458 (1957).
342. GUARINO, A. J. and SABLE, H. Z. *Biochim. Biophys. Acta* **20**, 201 (1956).
343. GUNJA, Z. H., MANNERS, D. J. and MAUNG, K. *Biochem. J.* **75**, 441 (1960).
344. HAGERMAN, D. D., ROUX, J. and VILLEE, C. A. *J. Physiol.* (*London*) **146**, 98 (1959).
345. HAGERMAN, R. H. and ARNON, D. I. *Arch. Biochem. Biophys.* **57**, 421 (1955).
346. HAIGH, W. G. and BEEVERS, H. *Arch. Biochem. Biophys.* **107**, 152 (1964).
347. HANES, C. S. *New Phytologist* **36**, 101, 538 (1937).
348. HANES, C. S. *Proc. Roy. Soc.* (*London*) B **128**, 421 (1939–40); B **129**, 174 (1940).
349. HANN, R. M., TILDEN, E. B. and HUDSON, C. S. *J. Am. Chem. Soc.* **60**, 1201 (1938).
350. HANSEN, R. G., WOOD, H. G., PEETERS, G. J., JACOBSON, B. and WILKEN, J. *J. Biol. Chem.* **237**, 1034 (1962).
351. HARARY, I., KOREY, S. R. and OCHOA, S. *J. Biol. Chem.* **203**, 595 (1953).
352. HARPUR, R. P. and QUASTEL, J. H. *Nature* **164**, 693 (1949).
353. HASEGAWA, E., DELBRUCK, A. and LIPMANN, F. *Federation Proc.* **20**, 86 (1961).
354. HASKELL, T. H. and HANESSIAN, S. *Biochim. Biophys. Acta* **83**, 35 (1964).
355. HASSAN, M. UL and LEHNINGER, A. L. *J. Biol. Chem.* **223**, 132 (1956).
356. HASSID, W. Z. In *Phosphorus Metabolism*, vol. I, p. 11, eds. W. D. McElroy and B. Glass. Johns Hopkins Press, Baltimore, Maryland, 1951.
357. HASSID, W. Z. In *Metabolic Pathways*, vol. I, p. 251, ed. D. Greenberg. Academic Press, New York and London, 1960.
358. HASSID, W. Z., CORI, G. T. and McCREADY, R. M. *J. Biol. Chem.* **148**, 89 (1943).
359. HASSID, W. Z. and DOUDOROFF, M. *Advances in Carbohydrate Chem.* **5**, 29 (1950).
360. HASSID, W. Z. and DOUDOROFF, M. *Advances in Enzymol.* **10**, 123 (1950).
361. HAUK, R. and BROWN, D. H. *Biochim. Biophys. Acta* **33**, 556 (1959).
362. HAUSER, G. and KARNOVSKY, M. L. *J. Biol. Chem.* **224**, 91 (1957).
363. HAUSER, G. and KARNOVSKY, M. L. *J. Biol. Chem.* **233**, 287 (1958).
364. HAWORTH, W. N., HIRST, E. L. and ISHERWOOD, F. A. *J. Chem. Soc.* **1937**, 577.
365. HAWORTH, W. N., HIRST, E. L. and LYNE, R. R. *Biochem. J.* **31**, 786 (1937).
366. HAWORTH, W. N., HIRST, E. L. and RUELL, D. A. *J. Chem. Soc.* **123**, 3125 (1923).
367. HAWORTH, W. N. and LEARNER, A. *J. Chem. Soc.* **1928**, 619.
368. HAWORTH, W. N., PEAT, S. and BOURNE, E. J. *Nature* **154**, 236 (1944).
369. HAYASIDA, A. *Biochem. Z.* **298**, 169 (1938).
370. HEATH, E. C. and ELBEIN, A. D. *Proc. Natl. Acad. Sci., U.S.* **48**, 1209 (1962).
371. HEATH, E. C. and GHALAMBOR, M. A. *J. Biol. Chem.* **237**, 2432 (1962).
372. HEATH, E. C. and GHALAMBOR, M. A. *Biochem. Biophys. Res. Commun.* **10**, 340 (1963).
373. HEATH, E. C., HORECKER, B. L., SMYRNIOTIS, P. Z. and TAKAGI, Y. *J. Biol. Chem.* **231**, 1031 (1958).
374. HEATH, E. C. and ROSEMAN, S. *J. Biol. Chem.* **230**, 511 (1958).
375. HEBER, V. and WILLENBRINK, J. *Biochim. Biophys. Acta* **82**, 313 (1964).
376. HEHRE, E. J. *Science* **93**, 237 (1941).
377. HEHRE, E. J. *Transact. N. Y. Acad. Sci., Ser. II*, **10**, 188 (1948).
378. HEHRE, E. J. *Advances in Enzymol.* **11**, 297 (1951).
379. HEHRE, E. J., CARLSON, A. S. and NEILL, J. M. *Science* **106**, 523 (1947).
380. HEHRE, E. J. and HAMILTON, D. M. *J. Biol. Chem.* **166**, 777 (1946).
381. HEHRE, E. J. and HAMILTON, D. M. *J. Bacteriol.* **55**, 197 (1948).
382. HEHRE, E. J. and HAMILTON, D. M. *Proc. Soc. Exptl. Biol. Med.* **71**, 336 (1949).
383. HEHRE, E. J. and HAMILTON, D. M. *J. Biol. Chem.* **192**, 161 (1951).
384. HEHRE, E. J., HAMILTON, D. M. and CARLSON, A. S. *J. Biol. Chem.* **177**, 267 (1949).
385. HEHRE, E. J. and SUGG, J. Y. *J. Exptl. Med.* **75**, 339 (1942).
386. HEIMER, R. and MEYER, K. *Proc. Natl. Acad. Sci., U.S.* **42**, 728 (1956).
387. HELLE, K. B. and KLUNGSØYR, L. *Biochim. Biophys. Acta* **65**, 461 (1962).
388. HELMREICH, E. and CORI, C. F. *Proc. Natl. Acad. Sci., U.S.* **51**, 131, 536 (1964).
389. HELMREICH, E. and CORI, C. F. *Proc. Natl. Acad. Sci., U.S.* **52**, 647 (1964).

390. HERMANN, S and NEUSCHUL, P. *Biochem. Z.* **233**, 129 (1931).
391. HERS, H. G. *Biochim. Biophys. Acta* **22**, 202 (1956).
392. HERS, H. G. *Biochim. J.* **86**, 11 (1963).
393. HERS, H. G. and KUSAKE, T. *Biochim. Biophys. Acta* **11**, 427 (1953).
394. HESTRIN, S. *J. Biol. Chem.* **179**, 943 (1949).
395. HESTRIN, S. and AVIGAD, G. *Biochem. J.* **69**, 388 (1958).
396. HESTRIN, S. and AVINERI-SHAPIRO, S. *Biochem. J.* **38** 2 (1944).
397. HESTRIN, S., AVINERI-SHAPIRO, S. and ASCHNER, M. *Biochem. J.* **37**, 450 (1943).
398. HESTRIN, S., FEINGOLD, D. S. and AVIGAD, G. *J. Am. Chem. Soc.* **77**, 6710 (1955).
399. HESTRIN, S., FEINGOLD, D. S. and AVIGAD, G. *Biochem. J.* **64**, 340 (1956).
400. HESTRIN, S. and SCHRAMM, M. *Biochem. J.* **58**, 345 (1954).
401. HEYDEMAN, M. T. *Nature* **181**, 627 (1958).
402. HIATT, H. H., GOLDSTEIN, M., LAREAU, J. and HORECKER, B. L. *J. Biol. Chem.* **231**, 303 (1958).
403. HIDY, P. H. and DAY, H. G. *J. Biol. Chem.* **152**, 477 (1944).
404. HILZ, H., KITTLER, M. and KNAPE, G. *Biochem. Z.* **332**, 151 (1959).
405. HILZ, H. and LIPMANN, F. *Proc. Natl. Acad. Sci., U.S.* **41**, 880 (1955).
406. HILZ, H., TARNOWSKI, W. and AREND, P. *Biochem. Biophys. Res. Commun.* **10**, 492 (1963)
407. HIND, G. and JAGENDORF, A. T. *Proc. Natl. Acad. Sci., U.S.* **49**, 715 (1963).
408. HIRST, E. L. *Proc. Chem. Soc. (London)*, **1957**, 193.
409. HIZUKURI, S. and LARNER, J. *Biochim. Biophys. Acta* **73**, 525 (1963).
410. HIZUKURI, S. and LARNER, J. *Biochemistry* **3**, 1783 (1964).
411. HOBSON, P. N., WHELAN, W. J. and PEAT, S. *J. Chem. Soc.* **1950**, 3566.
412. HOCHSTER, R. M. and WATSON, R. W. *Arch. Biochem. Biophys.* **48**, 120 (1954).
413. HOFERT, J., GORSKI, J., MUELLER, G. C. and BOUTWELL, R. K. *Arch. Biochem. Biophys.* **97**, 134 (1962).
414. HOFFMAN, P., MEYER, K. and LINKER, A. *J. Biol. Chem.* **219**, 653 (1956).
415. HOLLMAN, S. and TOUSTER, O. *J. Am. Chem. Soc.* **78**, 3544 (1956).
416. HOLLMANN, S. and TOUSTER, O. *J. Biol. Chem.* **225**, 87 (1957).
417. HOLLMANN, S. and TOUSTER, O. *Biochim. Biophys. Acta* **62**, 338 (1962).
418. HONJO, M., FURUKAWA, Y. and KANAI, Y. *Biochim. Biophys. Acta* **91**, 525 (1964).
419. HORECKER, B. L. In *Phosphorus Metabolism*, vol. 1, p. 117, eds. W. D. McElroy and B. Glass. Johns Hopkins Press, Baltimore, Maryland, 1951.
420. HORECKER, B. L., CHENG, T., GRAZI, E., LAI, C. Y., ROWLEY, P. and TCHOLA, O. *Federation Proc.* **21**, 1023 (1962).
421. HORECKER, B. L., ROWLEY, P. T., GRAZI, E., CHENG, T. and TCHOLA O. *Biochem. Z.* **338**, 36 (1963).
422. HORECKER, B. L. and SMYRNIOTIS, P. Z. *J. Am. Chem. Soc.* **74**, 2123 (1952).
423. HORECKER, B. L., SMYRNIOTIS, P. Z. and KLENOW, H. *J. Biol. Chem.* **205**, 661 (1953).
424. HORWITZ, S. B. and KAPLAN, N. O. *J. Biol. Chem.* **239**, 830 (1964).
425. HOTCHKISS, R. D. and GOEBEL, W. F. *J. Biol. Chem.* **121**, 195 (1937).
426. HULTIN, E. and NORDSTRÖM, L. *Acta Chem. Scand.* **3**, 1405 (1949).
427. HURWITZ, J. and HORECKER, B. L. *J. Biol. Chem.* **223**, 993 (1956).
428. HURWITZ, J., WEISSBACH, A., HORECKER, B. L. and SMYRNIOTIS, P. Z. *J. Biol. Chem.* **218**, 769 (1956).
429. HUSEMANN, E. and WERNER, R. *Makromol. Chem.* **59**, 43 (1963).
430. IGAVE, I. *Agricultural and Biol. Chem., Japan* **26**, 424 (1962).
431. ILLINGWORTH, B., BROWN, D. H. and CORI, C. F. *Proc. Natl. Acad. Sci., U.S.* **47**, 469 (1961).
432. ILLINGWORTH, B. and CORI, C. F. *Biochem. Biophys. Res. Commun.* **19**, 10 (1965).
433. ILLINGWORTH, B., LARNER, J. and CORI, G. T. *J. Biol. Chem.* **199**, 631 (1952).
434. INGELMAN, B. *Acta Chem. Scand.* **2**, 803 (1948).
435. ISBELL, H. S. and PIGMAN, W. W. *J. Research Natl. Bur. Standards* **20**, 773 (1938).
436. ISHII, Y. *J. Biochem., Japan* **55**, 371 (1964).
437. ISSELBACHER, K. Z. *J. Biol. Chem.* **232**, 429 (1958).

438. ISSELBACHER, K. J., ANDERSON, E. P., KURAHASHI, K. and KALCKAR, H. M. *Science* **123**, 635 (1956).
439. ITO, E. and STROMINGER, J. L. *J. Biol. Chem.* **237**, 2689 (1962).
440. ITO, E. and STROMINGER, J. L. *J. Biol. Chem.* **237**, 2696 (1962).
441. JACOBSON, B. and BOSTRÖM, H. *Biochim. Biophys. Acta* **83**, 152 (1964).
442. JACOBSON, B. and DAVIDSON, E. A. *J. Biol. Chem.* **237**, 635 (1962).
443. JACOBSON, B. and DAVIDSON, E. A. *J. Biol. Chem.* **237**, 638 (1962).
444. JACOBSON, B. and DAVIDSON, E. A. *Biochim. Biophys. Acta* **73**, 145 (1963).
445. JAGANNATHAN, V. and LUCK, J. M. *J. Biol. Chem.* **179**, 561 (1949).
446. JAKOBY, W. B., BRUMMOND, D. O. and OCHOA, S. *J. Biol. Chem.* **218**, 811 (1956).
447. JAWORSKI, E., WANG, L. and MARCO, G. *Nature* **198**, 790 (1963).
448. JEANES, A. *A Selected Bibliography.* U.S. Dept. of Agriculture, A.I.C. 288, Peoria, Illinois (1950).
449. JEANES, A. and WATSON, P. R. *Can. J. Chem.* **40**, 1318 (1962).
450. JONES, J. K. N. In *Proc. 4th Intern. Congr. Biochemistry, 1958, Vienna*, vol. I, p. 80, ed. M. L. Wolfrom. Pergamon Press, London (published 1959).
451. JONES, J. K. N., PERRY, M. B. and STOODLEY, R. J. *Can. J. Chem.* **40**, 1798 (1962).
452. JØRGENSEN, O. B. *Acta Chem. Scand.* **18**, 53 (1964).
453. JOURDIAN, G. W., CARLSON, D. M. and ROSEMAN, S. *Biochem. Biophys. Res. Commun.* **10**, 352 (1963).
454. JOURDIAN, G. W. and ROSEMAN, S. *Ann. New York Acad. Sci.* **106**, 202 (1963).
455. JOURDIAN, G. W., SWANSON, A. L., WATSON, D. and ROSEMAN, S. *J. Biol. Chem.* **239**, PC 2714 (1964).
456. KALCKAR, H. M. *Biochem. J.* **33**, 631 (1939).
457. KALCKAR, H. M. *J. Biol. Chem.* **167**, 477 (1947).
458. KALCKAR, H. M. In *The Mechanism of Enzyme Action*, p. 675, eds. W. D. McElroy and B. Glass. Johns Hopkins Press, Baltimore, Maryland, 1954.
459. KALCKAR, H. M. *Science* **125**, 105 (1957).
460. KALCKAR, H. M. *Advances in Enzymol.* **20**, 111 (1958).
461. KALCKAR, H. M. *Federation Proc.* **19**, 984 (1960).
462. KALCKAR, H. M., ANDERSON, E. P. and ISSELBACHER, K. J. *Biochim. Biophys. Acta* **20**, 262 (1956).
463. KALCKAR, H. M., ANDERSON, E. P. and ISSELBACHER, K. J. *Proc. Natl. Acad. Sci.*, *U.S.* **42**, 49 (1956).
464. KALCKAR, H. M., BRAGANCA, B. and MUNCH-PETERSEN, A. *Nature* **172**, 1039 (1953).
465. KALCKAR, H. M. and MAXWELL, E. S. *Biochim. Biophys. Acta* **22**, 588 (1956).
466. KALETTA-GMÜNDER, U., WOLF, H. P. and LEUTHARD, F. *Helv. Chim. Acta* **40**, 1027 (1957).
467. KALINA, M. and AVIGAD, G. *Biochim. Biophys. Acta* **73**, 652 (1963).
468. KAMEYAMA, T. and SHIMAZONO, N. *Biochim. Biophys. Acta* **64**, 180 (1962).
469. KARPATKIN, S., HELMREICH, E. and CORI, C. F. *J. Biol. Chem.* **239**, 3139 (1964).
470. KAUSS, H. *Biochem. Biophys. Res. Commun.* **18**, 170 (1965).
471. KEECH, D. B. and UTTER, M. F. *J. Biol. Chem.* **238**, 2609 (1963).
472. KEILIN, D. and HARTREE, E. F. *Nature* **157**, 801 (1946).
473. KEILIN, D. and HARTREE, E. F. *Biochem. J.* **42**, 221 (1948).
474. KELLER, P. J. and CORI, G. T. *Biochim. Biophys. Acta* **12**, 235 (1953).
475. KENDAL, L. P. and STICKLAND, L. H. *Biochem. J.* **32**, 572 (1938).
476. KENT, A. B., KREBS, E. G. and FISCHER, E. H. *J. Biol. Chem.* **232**, 549 (1958).
477. KENT, P. W. and PASTERNAK, C. A. *Biochem. J.* **69**, 453 (1958).
478. KESSLER, G. K., NEUFELD, E. F., FEINGOLD, D. S. and HASSID, W. Z. *J. Biol. Chem.* **236**, 308 (1961).
479. KHAN, A. W. and COLVIN, J. R. *Science* **133**, 2014 (1961).
480. KHARCHENKO, M. F. and SEITZ, I. F. *Federation Proc.* **24**, T121 (1965).
481. KIESSLING, W. *Biochem. Z.* **302**, 50 (1939); *Naturwissenschaften* **27**, 129 (1939).
482. KING, T. E. and CHELDELIN, V. H. *J. Biol. Chem.* **224**, 579 (1957).
483. KING, T. E. and MANN, T. *Nature* **182**, 868 (1958).
484. KITTENGER, G. W. and REITHEL, F. J. *J. Biol. Chem.* **205**, 527 (1953).

485. Kjölberg, O. and Manners, D. J. *Biochem. J.* **84**, 50P (1962).
486. Kjölberg, O. and Manners, D. L. *Biochem. J.* **86**, 10P (1963).
487. Klenow, H. and Larsen, B. *Arch. Biochem. Biophys.* **37**, 488 (1952).
488. Knox, K. W. *Biochem. J.* **94**, 534 (1965).
489. Knutson, C. A., Watson, P. R. and Jeanes, A. *Abstr. Meeting of Am. Chem. Soc.*, March 1962, p. 4d.
490. Kobata, A. *Biochem. Biophys. Res. Commun.* **7**, 346 (1962).
491. Kobayashi, T. *J. Agr. Chem. Soc. Japan* **28**, 352 (1954).
492. Koepsell, H. J., Tsuchiya, H. M., Hellman, N. N., Kazenko, A., Hoffman, C. A., Sharpe, E. S. and Jackson, R. W. *J. Biol. Chem.* **200**, 793 (1953).
493. Kofler, M., Langemann, A., Rüegg, R., Chopard-dit-Jean, L. H., Rayroud, A. and Isler, O. *Helv. Chim. Acta* **42**, 1283 (1959).
494. Korn, E. D. *J. Biol. Chem.* **234**, 1321 (1959).
495. Korn, E. D. *J. Biol. Chem.* **234**, 1647 (1959).
496. Kornberg, A., Lieberman, I. and Simms. E. S. *J. Biol. Chem.* **215**, 389 (1955).
497. Kornberg, H. L. and Beevers, H. *Biochim. Biophys. Acta* **26**, 531 (1957).
498. Kornberg, H. L. and Beevers, H. *Nature* **180**, 35 (1957).
499. Kornberg, H. L. and Madsen, N. B. *Biochem. J.* **68**, 549 (1958).
500. Kornfeld, R. and Brown, D. H. *J. Biol. Chem.* **237**, 1772 (1962).
501. Kornfeld, R., Kornfeld, S. and Ginsburg, V. *Biochem. Biophys. Res. Commun.* **17**, 578 (1964).
502. Kornfeld, S. and Glaser, L. *Biochim. Biophys. Acta* **42**, 548 (1960).
503. Kornfeld, S. and Glaser, L. *J. Biol. Chem.* **236**, 1791 (1961).
504. Kornfeld, S. and Glaser, L. *Biochim. Biophys. Acta* **56**, 184 (1962).
505. Kornfeld, S. and Glaser, L. *J. Biol. Chem.* **237**, 3052 (1962).
506. Kornfeld, S., Kornfeld, R., Neufeld, E. F. and O'Brien, P. J. *Proc. Natl. Acad. Sci., U.S.* **52**, 371 (1964).
507. Koshland, D. E., Jr. In *The Mechanism of Enzyme Action*, p. 608, eds. W. D. McElroy and B. Glass. Johns Hopkins Press, Baltimore, Maryland, 1954.
508. Kowalsky, A. and Koshland, D. E., Jr. *Biochim. Biophys. Acta* **22**, 575 (1956).
509. Krebs, E. G. and Fischer, E. H. *Biochim. Biophys. Acta* **20**, 150 (1956).
510. Krebs, E. G. and Fischer, E. H. *Advances in Enzymology* **24**, 263 (1962).
511. Krebs, E. G., Graves, D. J. and Fischer, E. H. *J. Biol. Chem.* **234**, 2867 (1959).
512. Krebs, E. G., Kent, A. B. and Fischer, E. H. *J. Biol. Chem.* **231**, 73 (1958).
513. Krebs, H. A. and Hems, R. *Biochem. J.* **61**, 435 (1955).
514. Krebs, H. A. and Lowenstein, J. M. In *Metabolic Pathways*, vol. I, p. 129, ed. D. M. Greenberg. Academic Press, New York and London, 1960.
515. Krisman, C. R. *Biochim. Biophys. Acta* **65**, 307 (1962).
516. Kunitz, M. and MacDonald, M. *J. Gen. Physiol.* **29**, 393 (1946).
517. Kurahashi, K. *Science* **125**, 114 (1957).
518. Kurahashi, K., Pennington, R. J. and Utter, M. F. *J. Biol. Chem.* **226**, 1059 (1957).
519. Lange, C. F. and Kohn, P. *J. Biol. Chem.* **236**, 1 (1961).
520. Larner, J. *J. Biol. Chem.* **202**, 491 (1953).
521. Larner, J. *Federation Proc.* **19**, 971 (1960).
522. Larner, J., Illingworth, B., Cori, G. T. and Cori, C. F. *J. Biol. Chem.* **199**, 641 (1952).
523. Larner, J. and McNickle, C. M. *J. Am. Chem. Soc.* **76**, 4747 (1954).
524. Larner, J., Rosell-Perez, M., Friedman, D. and Craig, J. *Biochem. J.* **89**, 36P (1963).
525. Larner, J. and Villar-Palasi, C. *Proc. Natl. Acad. Sci., U.S.* **45**, 1234 (1959).
526. Larsen, H. In *Autotropic Microorganisms*, p. 186, eds. B. A. Fry and J. L. Peel. Cambridge Univ. Press, London and New York, 1954.
527. Lavintman, N. and Krisman, C. R. *Biochim. Biophys. Acta* **89**, 193 (1964).
528. Layton, L. L. *Proc. Soc. Exptl. Biol. Med.* **73**, 570 (1950).
529. Lazarow, A. *Anat. Record* **84**, 31 (1942).
530. Leloir, L. F. *Arch. Biochem.* **33**, 186 (1951).

531. LELOIR, L. F. In *Phosphorus Metabolism*, vol. I, p. 67, eds. W. D. McElroy and B. Glass. Johns Hopkins Press, Baltimore, Maryland, 1951.
532. LELOIR, L. F. *Biochem. J.* **91**, 1 (1964).
533. LELOIR, L. F. and CABIB, E. *J. Am. Chem. Soc.* **75**, 5445 (1953).
534. LELOIR, L. F. and CARDINI, C. E. *Biochim. Biophys. Acta* **12**, 15 (1953).
535. LELOIR, L. F. and CARDINI, C. E. *J. Am. Chem. Soc.* **75**, 6084 (1953).
536. LELOIR, L. F. and CARDINI, C. E. *J. Biol. Chem.* **214**, 157 (1955).
537. LELOIR, L. F. and CARDINI, C. E. *Biochim. Biophys. Acta* **20**, 33 (1956).
538. LELOIR, L. F. and CARDINI, C. E. *J. Am. Chem. Soc.* **79**, 6340 (1957).
539. LELOIR, L. F., CARDINI, C. E. and CABIB, E. In *Comparative Biochemistry*, vol. II, p. 97, eds. M. Florkin and H. S. Mason. Academic Press, New York and London, 1960.
540. LELOIR, L. F., CARDINI, C. E. and OLAVARRÍA, J. M. *Arch. Biochem. Biophys.* **74**, 84 (1958).
541 LELOIR, L. F., FEKETE, M. A. R. DE and CARDINI, C. E. *J. Biol. Chem.* **236**, 636 (1961).
542. LELOIR, L. F. and GOLDEMBERG, S. H. *J. Biol. Chem.* **235**, 919 (1960).
543. LELOIR, L. F. and MONOZ, J. M. *J. Biol. Chem*, **153**, 53 (1944).
544. LELOIR, L. F., OLAVARRÍA, J. M., GOLDEMBERG, S. H. and CARMINATTI, H. *Arch. Biochem. Biophys.* **81**, 508 (1959).
545. LELOIR, L. F., FEKETE, M. A. R. DE and CARDINI, C. E. *J. Biol. Chem.* **236**, 636 (1961).
546. LEUTHARD, F., TESTA, E. and WOLF, H. P. *Helv. Chim. Acta* **36**, 227 (1953).
547. LEUTHARD, F. and WOLF, H. P. *Helv. Chim. Acta* **37**, 1734 (1954).
548. LIN, E. C. C. *J. Biol. Chem.* **236**, 31 (1961).
549. LIN, T.-Y. and HASSID, W. Z. *J. Biol. Chem.* **239**, PC 944 (1964).
550. LINDAHL, V. and RODÉN, L. *Biochem. Biophys. Res. Commun.* **17**, 254 (1964).
551. LIPMANN, F. *Advances in Enzymol.* **1**, 99 (1941).
552. LIPMANN, F. *Science* **128**, 575 (1958).
553. LISS, M., HORWITZ, S. B. and KAPLAN, N. O. *J. Biol. Chem.* **237**, 1342 (1962).
554. LLOYD, A. G. *Biochim. Biophys. Acta* **58**, 1 (1962).
555. LOCKWOOD, L. B. and NELSON, G. E. N. *J. Bacteriol.* **52**, 581 (1946).
556. LOEWUS, F. A. *Nature* **203**, 1175 (1964).
557. LOEWUS, F. A. and KELLY, S. *Arch. Biochem. Biophys.* **102**, 96 (1963).
558. LOEWUS, F. A., KELLY, S. and NEUFELD, E. F. *Proc. Natl. Acad. Sci., U.S.* **48**, 421 (1962).
559. LORNITZO, F. A. and GOLDMAN, D. S. *J. Biol. Chem.* **239**, 2730 (1964).
560. LOVENBERG, W., BUCHANAN, B. B. and RABINOWITZ, J. C. *J. Biol. Chem.* **238**, 3899 (1963).
561. LOWRY, O. H., SCHULZ, D. W. and PASSONNEAU, J. Y. *J. Biol. Chem.* **239**, 1947 (1964).
562. MADSEN, N. B. *Biochem. Biophys. Res. Commun.* **6**, 310 (1961).
563. MADSEN, N. B. *Biochim. Biophys. Acta* **50**, 194 (1961).
564. MADSEN, N. B. *Can. J. Biochem. Physiol.* **41**, 561 (1963).
565. MALEY, F. and LARDY, H. A. *Science* **124**, 1207 (1956).
566. MALEY, F. and MALEY, F. G. *Biochim. Biophys. Acta* **31**, 577 (1959).
567. MANDELSTAM, P., LOERCHER, R. and STROMINGER, J. L. *J. Biol. Chem.* **237**, 2683 (1962).
568. MANNERS, D. J. and TAYLOR, D. C. *Biochem. J.* **94**, 17P (1965).
569. MANSOUR, T. E. *J. Biol. Chem.* **238**, 2285 (1963).
570. MARÉCHAL, L. R. and GOLDEMBERG, S. H. *Biochem. Biophys. Res. Commun.* **13**, 106 (1963).
571. MARÉCHAL, L. R. and GOLDEMBERG, S. H. *J. Biol. Chem.* **239**, 3163 (1964).
572. MARKOVITZ, A. *Biochem. Biophys. Res. Commun.* **6**, 250 (1961).
573. MARKOVITZ, A. *J. Biol. Chem.* **239**, 2091 (1964).
574. MARKOWITZ, A., CIFONELLI, J. A. and DORFMAN, A. *Biochim. Biophys. Acta* **28**, 453 (1958).
575. MARKOVITZ, A. and DORFMAN, A. *J. Biol. Chem.* **237**, 273 (1962).
576. MARMUR, J. and HOTCHKISS, R. D. *J. Biol. Chem.* **214**, 383 (1955).
577. MARUYAMA, H. and LANE, M. D. *Biochem. Biophys. Res. Commun.* **9**, 461 (1962).

578. MARX-FIGINI, M. *Makromol. Chem.* **68**, 227 (1963).
579. MARX-FIGINI, M. *Makromol. Chem.* **80**, 235 (1964).
580. MASON, H. H. and TURNER, M. E. *Am. J. Diseases Children* **50**, 359 (1935).
581. MATHEWS, M. B. and DEC. HINDS, L. *Biochim. Biophys. Acta* **74**, 198 (1963).
582. MATSUHASHI, M., GILBERT, J. M., MATSUHASHI, S., BROWN, J. G. and STROMINGER, J. L. *Biochem. Biophys. Res. Commun.* **15**, 55 (1964).
583. MATSUHASHI, M. and STROMINGER, J. L. *J. Biol. Chem.* **239**, 2454 (1964).
584. MATSUHASHI, S., MATSUHASHI, M., BROWN, J. G. and STROMINGER, J. L. *Biochem. Biophys. Res. Commun.* **15**, 60 (1964).
585. MAXWELL, E. S. *J. Am. Chem. Soc.* **78**, 1074 (1956).
586. MAXWELL, E. S., KALCKAR, H. M. and BURTON, R. M. *Biochim. Biophys. Acta* **18**, 444 (1955).
587. MAXWELL, E. S., KALCKAR, H M and STROMINGER, J. L. *Arch. Biochem. Biophys.* **65**, 2 (1956).
588. MAXWELL, E. S. and ROBICHON-SZULMAJSTER, H. DE. *J. Biol. Chem.* **235**, 308 (1960).
589. MAXWELL, E. S., ROBICHON-SZULMAJSTER, H. DE and KALCKAR, H. M. *Arch. Biochem. Biophys.* **78**, 407 (1958).
590. MAYAUDON, J., BENSON, A. A. and CALVIN, M. *Biochim. Biophys. Acta* **23**, 342 (1957).
591. MAYER, H., RAPIN, A. M. C. and KALCKAR, H. M. *Proc. Natl. Acad. Sci., U.S.* **53**, 459 (1965).
592. MAYER, R. M. and GINSBURG, V. *Biochem. Biophys. Res. Commun.* **15**, 334 (1964).
593. MCCONNELL, W. B., MITRA, A. K. and PERLIN, A. S. *Can. J. Biochem. and Physiol.* **36**, 985 (1958).
594. MCCORKINDALE, J. and EDSON, N. L. *Biochem. J.* **57**, 518 (1954).
595. MCCORMICK, D. B. and TOUSTER, O. *Biochim. Biophys. Acta* **54**, 598 (1961).
596. MCGEACHIN, R. L., GLEASON, J. R. and ADAMS, M. R. *Arch. Biochem. Biophys.* **75**, 403 (1958).
597. MEADOW, P. M., ANDERSON, J. S. and STROMINGER, J. L. *Biochem. Biophys. Res. Commun.* **14**, 382 (1964).
598. MELO, A. and GLASER, L. *J. Biol. Chem.* **240**, 398 (1965).
599. MELOCHE, H. P. and WOOD, W. A. *J. Biol. Chem.* **239**, 3505 (1964).
600. MELOCHE, H. P. and WOOD, W. A. *J. Biol. Chem.* **239**, 3511 (1964).
601. MENDICINO, J. and PINJANI, M. *Biochim. Biophys. Acta* **89**, 242 (1964).
602. MEYER, K. H. *Natural and Synthetic High Polymers*, Interscience Publishers, Inc., New York, 1950.
603. MEYER, K. H. and BERNFELD, P. *Helv. Chim. Acta* **23**, 875 (1940).
604. MEYER, K. H. and BERNFELD, P. *Helv. Chim. Acta* **24**, 359 E (1941).
605. MEYER, K. H. and FULD, M. *Helv. Chim. Acta* **24**, 375 (1941).
606. MEYER, K. H. and GONON, W. F. *Helv. Chim. Acta* **34**, 308 (1951).
607. MEYER, K. H., WERTHEIM, M. and BERNFELD, P. *Helv. Chim. Acta* **23**, 865 (1940).
608. MEYER, W. L., FISCHER, E. H. and KREBS, E. G. *Biochemistry* **3**, 1033 (1964).
609. MEYERHOF, O. In *The Enzymes*, vol. II, part 1, p. 162, eds. J. B. Sumner and K. Myrbäck. Academic Press, New York, 1951.
610. MILLER, R. M., MEYER, C. M. and TANNER, H. A. *Plant Physiol.* **38**, 184 (1963).
611. MILLER, W. L. and VANDER WENDE, C. *Biochim. Biophys. Acta* **77**, 494 (1963).
612. MILLS, G. T. *Federation Proc.* **19**, 991 (1960).
613. MILLS, G. T., LOCHHEAD, A. C. and SMITH, E. E. B. *Biochim. Biophys. Acta* **27**, 103 (1958).
614. MILLS, G. T. and SMITH, E. E. B. *Federation Proc.* **21**, 1089 (1962).
615. MILNER, Y. and AVIGAD, G. *Israel J. Chem.* **2**, 316 (1964).
616. MINOR, F. W., GREATHOUSE, G. A., SHIRK, H. G., SCHWARTZ, A. M. and HARRIS, M. *J. Am. Chem. Soc.* **76**, 1658 (1954).
617. MITSUHASHI, S. and LAMPEN, J. O. *J. Biol. Chem.* **204**, 1011 (1953).
618. MOLNAR, J., ROBINSON, G. B. and WINZLER, R. J. *J. Biol. Chem.* **239**, 3157 (1964).
619. MOMMAERTS, W. F. H. M., ILLINGWORTH, B., PEARSON, C. M., GUILLORY, R. J. and SERAYDARIAN, K. *Proc. Natl. Acad. Sci., U.S.* **45**, 791 (1959).

620. MONOD, J. and TORRIANI, A. M. *Compt. Rend. Acad. Sci.* **227**, 240 (1948).
621. MONOD, J. and TORRIANI, A. M. *Ann. Inst. Pasteur* **78**, 65 (1950).
622. MORDOH, J., LELOIR, L. F. and KRISMAN, C. R. *Proc. Natl. Acad. Sci., U.S.* **53**, 86 (1965).
623. MORETTI, A. and WOLF, G. *Biochim. Biophys. Acta* **53**, 263 (1961).
624. MORGAN, H. E. and PARMEGGIANI, A. *Biochem. J.* **89**, 39 P (1963).
625. MORGAN, H. E. and PARMEGGIANI, A. *J. Biol. Chem.* **239**, 2435 (1964).
626. MORGAN, K. and WHELAN, W. J. *Nature* **196**, 168 (1962).
627. MORTENSON, L. E., VALENTINE, R. C. and CARNAHAN, J. E. *Biochem. Biophys. Res. Commun.* **7**, 448 (1962).
628. MORTENSON, L. E., VALENTINE, R. C. and CARNAHAN, J. E. *J. Biol. Chem.* **238**, 794 (1963).
629. MOSES, V. and CALVIN, M. *Proc. Natl. Acad. Sci., U.S.* **44**, 260 (1958).
630. MOSES, V. and FERRIER, R. J. *Biochem. J. London*, **83**, 8 (1962).
631. MOSES, V., FERRIER, R. J. and CALVIN, M. *Proc. Natl. Acad. Sci., U.S.* **48**, 1644 (1962).
632. MÜLLER, A., RUMBERG, B. and WITT, H. T. *Proc. Royal Soc., Ser. B*, **157**, 313 (1963).
633. MÜLLER, D. *Biochem. Z.* **199**, 136 (1928).
634. MUNCH-PETERSEN, A. *Acta Chem. Scand.* **10**, 928 (1956).
635. MUNCH-PETERSEN, A., KALCKAR, H. M., CUTOLO, E. and SMITH, E. E. B. *Nature* **172**, 1036 (1953).
636. MURATA, T. and AKAZAWA, T. *Biochem. Biophys. Res. Commun.* **16**, 6 (1964).
637. MURATA, T., MINAMIKAWA, T. and AKAZAWA, T. *Biochem. Biophys. Res. Commun.* **13**, 439 (1963).
638. MURATA, T., MINAMIKAWA, T., AKAZAWA, T. and SUGIYAMA, T. *Arch. Biochem. Biophys.* **106**, 371 (1964).
639. MURATA, T., SUGIYAMA, T. and AKAZAWA, T. *Arch. Biochem. Biophys.* **107**, 92 (1964).
640. MURATA, T., SUGIYAMA, T. and AKAZAWA, T. *Biochem. Biophys. Res. Commun.* **18**, 371 (1965).
641. MURPHY, T. A. and WYATT, G. R. *Nature* **202**, 1112 (1964).
642. MURPHY, T. A. and WYATT, G. R. *J. Biol. Chem.* **240**, 1500 (1965).
643. MYRBÄCK, K. *Biochem. Z.* **285**, 290 (1936).
644 MYRBÄCK, K. and WILLSTAEDT, E. *Acta Chem. Scand.* **3**, 91 (1949).
645. NAJJAR, V. A. *J. Biol. Chem.* **175**, 281 (1948).
646. NAJJAR, V. A. In *Mechanism of Enzyme Action*, p. 731, Symposium by W. D. McElroy and B. Glass, Eds. Johns Hopkins Press, Baltimore, Maryland, 1954.
647. NAJJAR, V. A. and PULLMAN, M. E. *Science* **119**, 631 (1954).
648. NAKAMURA, M. *Bull. Agr. Chem. Soc. Japan* **23**, 398 (1959).
649. NATAKE, M. and YOSHIMURA, S. *Agricult. Biol. Chem. Japan* **27**, 342 (1963).
650. NATHENSON, S. G. and STROMINGER, J. L. *J. Biol. Chem.* **237**, PC 3839 (1962).
651. NATHENSON, S. G. and STROMINGER, J. L. *J. Biol. Chem.* **238**, 3161 (1963).
652. NEAL, G. E. and BEEVERS, H. *Biochem. J.* **74**, 409 (1960).
653. NEELY, W. B. and NOTT, J. *Biochemistry* **1**, 1136 (1962).
654. NEISH, A. C. *Can. J. Biochem. and Physiol.* **33**, 658 (1955).
655. NEISH, A. C. *Can. J. Biochem. and Physiol.* **36**, 187 (1958).
656. NELSON, O. E. and RINES, H. W. *Biochem. Biophys. Res. Commun.* **9**, 297 (1962).
657. NELSON, O. E. and TSAI, C. Y. *Science* **145**, 1194 (1964).
658. NEUFELD, E. F. *Biochem. Biophys. Res. Commun.* **7**, 461 (1962).
659. NEUFELD, E. F. and FEINGOLD, D. S. *Biochim. Biophys. Acta* **53**, 589 (1961).
660. NEUFELD, E. F., FEINGOLD, D. S. and HASSID, W. Z. *J. Am. Chem. Soc.* **80**, 4430 (1958).
661. NEUFELD, E. F., FEINGOLD, D. S. and HASSID, W. Z. *Arch. Biochem. Biophys.* **83**, 96 (1959).
662. NEUFELD, E. F., FEINGOLD, D. S., ILVES, S. M., KESSLER, G. and HASSID, W. Z. *J. Biol. Chem.* **236**, 3102 (1961).
663. NEUFELD, E. F. and HASSID, W. Z. *Advances in Carbohydrate Chem.* **18**, 309 (1963).

664. NIKAIDO, H. *Proc. Natl. Acad. Sci., U.S.* **48**, 1337, 1542 (1962).
665. NIKAIDO, H. and JOKURA, K. *Biochem. Biophys. Res. Commun.* **6**, 304 (1961).
666. NORBERG, E. and FRENCH, D. *J. Am. Chem. Soc.* **72**, 1202 (1950).
667. NORDLIE, R. C. and ARION, W. J. *J. Biol. Chem.* **239**, 1680 (1964).
668. NUSSENBAUM, S. and HASSID, W. Z. *J. Biol. Chem.* **190**, 673 (1951).
669. NUSSENBAUM, S. and HASSID, W. Z. *J. Biol. Chem.* **196**, 785 (1952).
670. O'BRIEN, P. J. and ZILLIKEN, F. *Biochim. Biophys. Acta* **31**, 543 (1959).
671. OCHOA, S. *Physiol. Reviews* **31**, 56 (1951).
672. OCHOA, S. In *Methods in Enzymology*, vol. 1, p. 739, eds. S. P. Colowick and N. O. Kaplan. Academic Press, New York, 1955.
673. OCHOA, S., MEHLER, A. H. and KORNBERG, A. *J. Biol. Chem.* **174**, 979 (1948).
674. OHAD, I., DANON, D. and HESTRIN, S. *J. Cell. Biol.* **12**, 31 (1962).
675. OHLSSON, E. *Compt. Rend. Trav. Lab. Carlsberg Ser. Chim.* **16**, 7 (1926).
676. OHLSSON, E. *Z. Physiol. Chem. Hoppe Seyler's* **189**, 17 (1930).
677. OKAMOTO, K. *J. Biochem., Japan* **53**, 348 (1963).
678. OKAMOTO, K. *J. Biochem., Japan* **53**, 448 (1963).
679. OKAZAKI, T., OKAZAKI, R., STROMINGER, J. L. and SUZUKI, S. *Biochem. Biophys. Res. Commun.* **7**, 300 (1962).
680. OKAZAKI, R., OKAZAKI, T., STROMINGER, J. L. and MICHELSON, A. M. *J. Biol. Chem.* **237**, 3014 (1962).
681. OKUDA, S., SUZUKI, N. and SUZUKI, S. *Biochim. Biophys. Acta* **82**, 436 (1964).
682. OLAVESEN, A. H. and DAVIDSON, E. A. *J. Biol. Chem.* **240**, 992 (1965).
683. ORRELL, S. A., JR. and BUEDING, E. *J. Am. Chem. Soc.* **80**, 3800 (1958).
684. OSBORN, M. J. and D'ARI, L. *Biochem. Biophys. Res. Commun.* **16**, 568 (1964).
685. OSBORN, M. J., ROSEN, S. M., ROTHFIELD, L. and HORECKER, B. L. *Proc. Natl. Acad. Sci., U.S.* **48**, 1831 (1962).
686. PALLERONI, N. J. and DOUDOROFF, M. *J. Biol. Chem.* **218**, 535 (1956).
687. PALLERONI, N. J. and DOUDOROFF, M. *J. Bacteriol.* **74**, 180 (1957).
688. PAN, S. C., NICHOLSON, L. W. and KOLACHOV, P. *J. Am. Chem. Soc.* **73**, 2547 (1951).
689. PAN, S. C., NICHOLSON, L. W. and KOLACHOV, P. *Arch. Biochem. Biophys.* **42**, 421 (1953).
690. PANEK, A. *Arch. Biochem. Biophys.* **98**, 349 (1962).
691. PANEK, A. *Arch. Biochem. Biophys.* **100**, 422 (1963).
692. PARK, J. T. *J. Biol. Chem.* **194**, 877, 885, 897 (1952).
693. PARK, J. T. and STROMINGER, J. L. *Science* **125**, 99 (1957).
694. PARK, R. B. and PON, N. G. *Biochim. Biophys. Acta* **57**, 520 (1962).
695. PARNAS, J. K. and BARANOWSKI, T. *Compt. Rend. Soc. Biol.* **121**, 282 (1936); *Ergeb. Enzymforsch.* **6**, 57 (1937).
696. PASSERON, S., RECONDO, E. and DANKERT, M. *Biochim. Biophys. Acta* **89**, 372 (1964).
697. PASSONNEAU, J. V. and LOWRY, O. H. *Biochem. Biophys. Res. Commun.* **7**, 10 (1962).
698. PATTABIRAMAN, T. N., SEKHARA VARMA, T. N. and BACHHAWAT, B. K. *Biochim. Biophys. Acta* **83**, 74 (1964).
699. PAYNE, W. J. and McRORIE, R. A. *Biochim. Biophys. Acta* **29**, 466 (1958).
700. PAZUR, J. H. *J. Biol. Chem.* **208**, 439 (1954).
701. PAZUR, J. H. and ANDERSON, J. S. *Biochim. Biophys. Acta* **74**, 788 (1963).
702. PAZUR, J. H. and ANDERSON, J. S. *J. Biol. Chem.* **238**, 3155 (1963).
703. PAZUR, J. H. and ANDO, T. *Arch. Biochem. Biophys.* **93**, 43 (1961).
704. PAZUR, J. H. and FRENCH, D. *J. Am. Chem. Soc.* **73**, 3536 (1951).
705. PAZUR, J. H. and FRENCH, D. *J. Biol. Chem.* **196**, 265 (1952).
706. PAZUR, J. H. and KLEPPE, K. *Biochemistry* **3**, 578 (1964).
707. PAZUR, J. H., KLEPPE, K. and CEPURE, A. *Biochem. Biophys. Res. Commun.* **7**, 157 (1962).
708. PAZUR, J. H. and SHADAKSHARASWAMY, M. *Biochem. Biophys. Res. Commun.* **5**, 130 (1961).
709. PAZUR, J. H., SHADAKSHARASWAMY, M. and CEPURE, A. *Arch. Biochem. Biophys.* **94**, 142 (1961).

710. PAZUR, J. H., SHADAKSHARASWAMY, M. and MEIDELL, G. E. *Arch. Biochem. Biophys.* **99**, 78 (1962).
711. PAZUR, J. H. and SHUEY, E. W. *J. Am. Chem. Soc.* **82**, 5009 (1960).
712. PAZUR, J. H. and SHUEY, E. W. *J. Biol. Chem.* **236**, 1780 (1961).
713. PEANASKY, R. J. and LARDY, H. A. *J. Biol. Chem.* **233**, 365 (1958).
714. PEAT, S. *Advances in Enzymol.* **11**, 339 (1951).
715. PEAT, S., TURNEY, J. R. and JONES, G. *J. Chem. Soc.* **1959**, 1540.
716. PEAT, S., WHELAN, W. J. and BAILEY, J. M. *J. Chem. Soc.* **1953**, 1422.
717. PEAT, S., WHELAN, W. J. and REES, W. R. *Nature* **172**, 158 (1953).
718. PEAT, S., WHELAN, W. J. and REES, W. R. *J. Chem. Soc.* **1956**, 44.
719. PÉAUD-LENOËL, C. *Bull. Soc. Chim. Biol.* **39**, 757 (1957).
720. PÉAUD-LENOËL, C. and DEDONDER, R. *Bull. Soc. Chim. Biol.* **39**, 499 (1957).
721. PECK, H. D., JR. *J. Biol. Chem.* **237**, 198 (1962).
722. PERKINS, H. R. *Bacteriol. Reviews* **27**, 18 (1963).
723. PERLMAN, R. L., TELSER, A. and DORFMAN, A. *J. Biol. Chem.* **239**, 3623 (1964).
724. PETROVA, A. N. *Enzymologia* **21**, 23 (1959).
725. PETROVA, A. N. *Biokhimiya* **25**, 355 (1960); *C.A.* **55**, 3681.
726. PHILLIPS, L. L. and CALDWELL, M. L. *J. Am. Chem. Soc.* **73**, 3559, 3563 (1951).
727. PIGMAN, W. In *The Enzymes*, vol. 1, p. 725, eds. J. B. Sumner and K. Myrbäck, Academic Press, New York, 1951.
728. PIRIE, N. W. *Biochem. J.* **28**, 305 (1934).
729. POGELL, B. M. and GRYDER, R. M. *J. Biol. Chem.* **228**, 701 (1957).
730. POGELL, B. M. and GRYDER, R. M. *J. Biol. Chem.* **235**, 558 (1960).
731. PON, N. G., RABIN, B. R. and CALVIN, M. *Bochem. Z.* **338**, 7 (1963).
732. PONTIS, H. G. *J. Biol. Chem.* **216**, 195 (1955).
733. PONTIS, H. G., JAMES, A. L. and BADDILEY. J. *Biochem. J.* **75**, 428 (1960).
734. PONTIS, H. G. and PONTIS, S. M. E. *Biochim. Biophys. Acta* **89**, 554 (1964).
735. POSTERNAK, T. and ROSSELET, J. P. *Helv. Chim. Acta* **37**, 246 (1954).
736. POSTERNAK, T., SCHOPFER, W. H., KAUFMANN-BOETSCH, B. and EDWARDS, S. *Helv. Chim. Acta* **46**, 2676 (1963).
737. POTTINGER, P. K. and OLIVER, I. T. *Biochim. Biophys. Acta* **58**, 303 (1962).
738. PREISS, J. *Biochem. Biophys. Res. Commun.* **9**, 235 (1962).
739. PREISS, J. *J. Biol. Chem.* **239**, 3127 (1964).
740. PREISS, J., SHEN, L. and PARTRIDGE, M. *Biochem. Biophys. Res. Commun.* **18**, 180 (1965).
741. PREISS, J. and WOOD, E. *J. Biol. Chem.* **239**, 3119 (1964).
742. PRITCHARD, G. G., GRIFFIN, W. J. and WHITTINGHAM, C. P. *J. Exptl. Botany* **13**, 176 (1962).
743. PROCHOROFF, N. N., KATTERMANN, R. and HOLZER, H. *Biochem. Biophys. Res. Commun.* **9**, 477 (1962).
744. PULLMAN, M. E. and NAJJAR, V. A. *Federation Proc.* **13**, 277 (1954).
745. QUAYLE, J. R., FULLER, R. C., BENSON, A. A. and CALVIN, M. *J. Am. Chem. Soc.* **76**, 3610 (1954).
746. RABINOWITCH, E. I. *Ann Rev. Plant. Physiol.* **3**, 229 (1952).
747 RABINOWITZ, J. L. and SALL, T. *Biochim. Biophys. Acta* **23**, 289 (1957).
748 RABINOWITZ, M. and GOLDBERG, I. H *J. Biol. Chem.* **238**, 1801 (1963).
749. RACKER, E. *J. Biol. Chem.* **196**, 347 (1952).
750 RACKER, E. *Nature* **175**, 249 (1955).
751. RACKER, E. *Arch. Biochem. Biophys.* **69**, 300 (1957).
752. RACKER, E., DE LA HABA, G. and LEDER, I. G. *J. Am. Chem. Soc.* **75**, 1010 (1953).
753. RACKER, E., DE LA HABA, G. and LEDER, I. G. *Arch. Biochem. Biophys.* **48**, 238 (1954).
754. RACKER, E. and SCHROEDER, E. A. R. *Arch. Biochem. Biophys.* **66**, 241 (1957).
755. RACKER, E. and SCHROEDER, E. A. R. *Arch. Biochem. Biophys.* **74**, 326 (1958).
756. RAFTER, G. W. *J. Biol. Chem.* **235**, 2475 (1960).
757. RALL, T. W. and SUTHERLAND, E. W. *J. Biol. Chem.* **232**, 1065 (1958).
758. RALL, T. W., SUTHERLAND, E. W. and BERTHET, L. *J. Biol. Chem.* **224**, 463 (1957).
759. RALL, T. W., SUTHERLAND, E. W. and WOSILAIT, W. D. *J. Biol. Chem.* **218**, 483 (1956).

760. RAMAIAH, A., HATHAWAY, J. A. and ATKINSON, D. E. *J. Biol. Chem.* **239**, 3619 (1964).
761. RAMAKRISHNAN, C. V., STEEL, R. and LENTZ, C. P. *Arch. Biochem. Biophys.* **55**, 270 (1955).
762. RAMAMURTI, K. and JACKSON, C. P. *J. Biol. Chem.* **237**, 2434 (1962).
763. RAPOPORT, G. and DEDONDER, R. *Bull. Soc. Chim. Biol.* **45**, 493 (1963).
764. RAPOPORT, G. and DEDONDER, R. *Bull. Soc. Chim. Biol.* **45**, 515 (1963).
765. RECONDO, E., DANKERT, M. and LELOIR, L. F. *Biochem. Biophys. Res. Commun.* **12**, 204 (1963).
766. RECONDO, E. and LELOIR, L. F. *Biochem. Biophys. Res. Commun.* **6**, 85 (1961).
767. REESE, E. T. and LEVINSON, H. S. *Physiol. Plantarum* **5**, 345 (1952).
768. REEVES, R. E. and GOEBEL, W. F. *J. Biol. Chem.* **139**, 511 (1941).
769. REICHSTEIN, T. *Helv. Chim. Acta* **17**, 996 (1934).
770. REISSIG, J. L. *J. Biol. Chem.* **219**, 753 (1956).
771. RICHMOND, M. H. and PERKINS, H. R. *Biochem. J.* **85**, 580 (1962).
772. ROBBINS, P. W. and LIPMANN, F. *J. Am. Chem. Soc.* **78**, 2652 (1956).
773. ROBBINS, P. W. and LIPMANN, F. *J. Am. Chem. Soc.* **78**, 6409 (1956).
774. ROBBINS, P. W. and LIPMANN, F. *J. Biol. Chem.* **229**, 837 (1957).
775. ROBBINS, P. W. and LIPMANN, F. *J. Biol. Chem.* **233**, 686 (1958).
776. ROBBINS, P. W., TRAUT, R. R. and LIPMANN, F. *Proc. Natl. Acad. Sci., U.S.* **45**, 6 (1959).
777. ROBERTS, E. C., CAIN, C. K., MUIR, R. D., REITHEL, F. J., GABY, W. L., VAN BRUGGEN, J. T., HOLMAN, D. M., KATZMAN, P. A., JONES, L. R. and DOISY, E. A. *J. Biol. Chem.* **147**, 47 (1943).
778. ROBINSON, G. B., MOLNAR, J. and WINZLER, R. J. *J. Biol. Chem.* **239**, 1134 (1964).
779. RODÉN, L. *Arkiv. Kemi* **10**, 333 (1957).
780. RODÉN, L. and DORFMAN, A. *J. Biol. Chem.* **233**, 1030 (1958).
781. RONGINE DE FEKÉTE, M. A., LELOIR, L. F. and CARDINI, C. E. *Nature* **187**, 918 (1960).
782. ROSELL-PEREZ, M. and LARNER, J. *Biochemistry* **1**, 769 (1962).
783. ROSELL-PEREZ, M. and LARNER, J. *Biochemistry* **3**, 75 (1964).
784. ROSELL-PEREZ, M. and LARNER, J. *Biochemistry* **3**, 81 (1964).
785. ROSELL-PEREZ, M. and LARNER, J. *Biochemistry* **3**, 773 (1964).
786. ROSELL-PEREZ, M., VILLAR-PALASI, C. and LARNER, J. *Biochemistry* **1**, 763 (1962).
787. ROSEMAN, S. *Federation Proc.* **21**, 1075 (1962).
788. ROSEMAN, S. *Proc. Natl. Acad. Sci., U.S.* **48**, 437 (1962).
789. ROSEMAN, S., JOURDIAN, G. W., WATSON, D. and ROOD, R. *Proc. Natl. Acad, Sci., U.S.* **47**, 958 (1961).
790. ROSEN, S. M., OSBORN, M. J. and HORECKER, B. L. *J. Biol. Chem.* **239**, 3196 (1964).
791. RUMBERG, B. *Nature* **204**, 860 (1964).
792. RUTTER, W. J. and ARNOLD, M. L. *Federation Proc.* **20**, 286 (1961).
793. RUTTER, W. J. and HANSEN, R. G. *J. Biol. Chem.* **202**, 323 (1953).
794. SAGARDIA, F. *Biochem. Biophys. Res. Commun.* **17**, 383 (1964).
795. SAITO, M., ISHIMOTO, N. and ITO, E. *J. Biochem. Japan* **54**, 273 (1963).
796. SALITIS, G. and OLIVER, I. T. *Biochim. Biophys. Acta* **81**, 55 (1964).
797. SALTON, M. R. J. *The Bacterial Cell Wall*, p. 191. Elsevier Publishing Company, Amsterdam, 1964.
798. SAMEC, M. and BLINC, M. *Kolloid-Beih.* **47**, 371 (1938).
799. SAMEC, M. and BLINC, M. *Kolloid-Beih.* **49**, 75 (1939).
800. SANDERSON, A. R., STROMINGER, J. L. and NATHENSON, S. G. *J. Biol. Chem.* **237**, 3603 (1962).
801. SATO, T., FUKUYAMA, T., SUZUKI, T. and YOSHIKAWA, H. *Seikagaku* **27**, 672 (1956); *C.A.* **54**, 21236.
802. SAWADA, H. and TAKAGI, Y. *Biochim. Biophys. Acta* **92**, 26 (1964).
803. SAZ, H. J. and HILLARY, E. P. *Biochem. J.* **62**, 563 (1956).
804. SCHILLER, S. *Biochem. Biophys. Res. Commun.* **15**, 250 (1964).
805. SCHILLER, S. and DORFMAN, A. *J. Biol. Chem.* **227**, 625 (1957).
806. SCHILLER, S., MATHEWS, M. B., CIFONELLI, J. A. and DORFMAN, A. *J. Biol. Chem.* **218**, 139 (1956).

807. SCHILLER, S., MATHEWS, M. B., GOLDFABER, L., LUDOWIEG, J. and DORFMAN, A. *J. Biol. Chem.* **212**, 531 (1955).
808. SCHILLER, S., SLOVER, G. A. and DORFMAN, A. *Biochem. Biophys. Res. Commun.* **5**, 344 (1961).
809. SCHLUBACH, H. H. *Experientia* **9**, 230 (1953).
810. SCHLUBACH, H. H. *Biokhimiya* **22**, 96 (1957); *C.A.* **51**, 11484.
811. SCHLUBACH, H. H. and HABERLAND, E. *Ann.* **604**, 22 (1957).
812. SCHMID, R., ROBBINS, P. W. and TRAUT, R. R. *Proc. Natl. Acad. Sci., U.S.* **45**, 1236 (1959).
813. SCHOLDA, R., BILLEK, G. and HOFFMANN-OSTENHOF, O. *Hoppe-Seyler's Z. Physiol. Chem.* **335**, 180 (1964).
814. SCHWARZ, V., GOLDBERG, L. KOMROWER, G. M. and HOLZEL, A. *Biochem. J. (London)* **62**, 34 (1956).
815. SCHWIMMER, S. and GARIBALDI, J. A. *Cereal Chem.* **29**, 108 (1952).
816. SEEGMILLER, C. G., AXELROD, B. and McCREADY, R. M. *J. Biol. Chem.* **217**, 765 (1955).
817. SEEGMILLER, C. G., JANG, R. and MANN, W., JR. *Arch. Biochem. Biophys.* **61**, 422 (1956).
818. SEGAL, H. L. *J. Biol. Chem.* **213**, 161 (1955).
819. SEGAL, H. L. *Biochim. Biophys. Acta* **21**, 194 (1956).
820. SELINGER, Z. and SCHRAMM, M. *Biochem. Biophys. Res. Commun.* **12**, 208 (1963).
821. SHATTON, J. B., GRUENSTEIN, M., SHAY, H. and WEINHOUSE, S. *J. Biol. Chem.* **240**, 22 (1965).
822. SHAW, D. R. D. *Biochem. J.* **64**, 394 (1956).
823. SHAW, D. R. D. *Biochem. J.* **82**, 297 (1962).
824. SHEN, L., GHOSH, H. P., GREENBERG, E. and PREISS, J. *Biochim. Biophys. Acta* **89**, 370 (1964).
825. SHEN, L. and PREISS, J. *Biochem. Biophys. Res. Commun.* **17**, 424 (1964).
826. SHIN, M., TAGAWA, T. and ARNON, D. I. *Biochem. Z.* **338**, 84 (1963).
827. SHOCKLEY, T. E. and PRIDE, H. S. *J. Bacteriol.* **77**, 695 (1959).
828. SHRAGO, E., LARDY, H. A., NORDLIE, R. C. and FOSTER, D. O. *J. Biol. Chem.* **238**, 3188 (1963).
829. SHUKLA, J. P. and PRABHU, K. A. *Naturwissenschaften* **46**, 325 (1959).
830. SIDBURY, J. B., JR. and NAJJAR, V. A. *J. Biol. Chem.* **227**, 517 (1957).
831. SIH, C. J., NELSON, N. M. and McBEE, R. H. *Science* **126**, 1116 (1957).
832. SILBERT, J. E. *Biochem. Biophys. Res. Commun.* **9**, 266 (1962).
833. SILBERT, J. E. *J. Biol. Chem.* **238**, 3542 (1963).
834. SILBERT, J. E. *J. Biol. Chem.* **239**, 1310 (1964).
835. SILBERT, J. E. and HUGHES, E. F. X. *Biochim. Biophys. Acta* **83**, 355 (1964).
836. SIMPSON, F. J. and WOOD, W. A. *J. Am. Chem. Soc.* **78**, 5452 (1956).
837. SIMPSON, F. J. and WOOD, W. A. *J. Biol. Chem.* **230**, 473 (1958).
838. SINOHARA, H. and SKY-PECK, H. H. *Biochim. Biophys. Acta* **101**, 90 (1965).
839. SIU, P. M. L. *Biochim. Biophys. Acta* **63**, 520 (1962).
840. SIU, P. M. L. and WOOD, H. G. *J. Biol. Chem.* **237**, 3044 (1962).
841. SLATER, W. G. and BEEVERS, H. *Plant Physiol.* **33**, 146 (1958).
842. SLEIN, M. W. *J. Biol. Chem.* **186**, 753 (1950).
843. SLEIN, M. W. *J. Am. Chem. Soc.* **77**, 1663 (1955).
844. SLEIN, M. W., CORI, G. T. and CORI, C. F. *J. Biol. Chem.* **186**, 763 (1950).
845. SMILEY, J. D. and ASHWELL, G. *J. Biol. Chem.* **236**, 357 (1961).
846. SMITH, E. E. B., GALLOWAY, B. and MILLS, G. T. *Biochim. Biophys. Acta* **33**, 276 (1959).
847. SMITH, E. E. B., MILLS, G. T., AUSTRIAN, R. and BERNHEIMER, H. P. *J. Gen. Microbiol.* **22**, 265 (1960).
848. SMITH, E. E. B., MILLS, G. T., BERNHEIMER, H. P. and AUSTRIAN, R. *Biochim. Biophys. Acta* **28**, 211 (1958).
849. SMITH, E. E. B., MILLS, G. T., BERNHEIMER, H. P. and AUSTRIAN, R. *Biochim. Biophys. Acta* **29**, 640 (1958).

850. SMITH, E. E. B., MILLS, G. T., BERNHEIMER, H. P. and AUSTRIAN, R. *J. Gen. Microbiol.* **20**, 654 (1959).
851. SMITH, E. E. B., MILLS, G. T., BERNHEIMER, H. P. and AUSTRIAN, R. *J. Biol. Chem.* **235**, 1876 (1960).
852. SMITH, E. E. B., MILLS, G. T. and HARPER, E. M. *Biochim. Biophys. Acta* **23**, 662 (1957).
853. SMITH, E. E. B., MILLS, G. T. and HARPER, E. M. *J. Gen. Microbiol.* **16**, 426 (1957).
854. SMITH, E. E. B., MUNCH-PETERSEN, A. and MILLS, G. T. *Nature* **172**, 1038 (1953).
855. SMITH, R. A. and GUNSALUS, I. C. *J. Am. Chem. Soc.* **76**, 5002 (1954); *Nature* **175**, 774 (1955).
856. SOKATCH, J. R. *Arch. Biochem. Biophys.* **99**, 401 (1962).
857. SOLMS, J., FEINGOLD, D. S. and HASSID, W. Z. *J. Am. Chem. Soc.* **79**, 2342 (1957).
858. SOLS, A. and CRANE, R. K. *J. Biol. Chem.* **210**, 581 (1954).
859. SOMERS, G. F. and COSBY, E. L. *Arch. Biochem.* **6**, 295 (1945).
860. SPOLTER, L. and MARX, W. *Biochim. Biophys. Acta* **32**, 291 (1959).
861. SPOLTER, L., RICE, L. I. and MARX, W. *Biochim. Biophys. Acta* **74**, 188 (1963).
862. SRERE, P. A., COOPER, J. R., KLYBAS, V. and RACKER, E. *Arch. Biochem. Biophys.* **59**, 535 (1955).
863. STAUB, A. and VESTLING, C. S. *J. Biol. Chem.* **191**, 395 (1951).
864. STEINER, D. F. *Biochim. Biophys. Acta* **54**, 206 (1961).
865. STEINER, D. F. and KING, J. *J. Biol. Chem.* **239**, 1292 (1964).
866. STEINER, D. F., RAUDA, V. and WILLIAMS, R. H. *J. Biol. Chem.* **236**, 299 (1961).
867. STEINER, D. F., YOUNGER, L. and KING, J. *Biochemistry* **4**, 740 (1965).
868. STETTEN, M. J. *J. Biol. Chem.* **239**, 3576 (1964).
869. STETTEN, M. R. *J. Am. Chem. Soc.* **81**, 1437 (1959).
870. STETTEN, M. R. and STETTEN, D. *J. Biol. Chem.* **207**, 331 (1954).
871. STETTEN, M. R. and TAFT, H. L. *J. Biol. Chem.* **239**, 4041 (1964).
872. STILLER, M. *Ann. Review Plant Physiol.* **13**, 151 (1962).
873. STILLER, M. L., NEAL, G. E. and BEEVERS, H. *Plant Physiol.* **33**, xxxiv (1958).
874. STOREY, I. D. E. and DUTTON, G. J. *Biochem. J.* **59**, 279 (1955).
875. STRANGE, R. E. *Biochem. J.* (*London*) **64**, 23P (1956).
876. STRANGE, R. E. and DARK, F. A. *Nature* **177**, 186 (1956).
877. STRANGE, R. E. and POWELL, J. F. *Biochem. J.* (*London*) **58**, 80 (1954).
878. STRECKER, H. J. and KORKES, S. *J. Biol. Chem.* **196**, 769 (1952).
879. STROMINGER, J. L. *Biochim. Biophys. Acta* **17**, 283 (1955).
880. STROMINGER, J. L. *Biochim. Biophys. Acta* **30**, 645 (1958).
881. STROMINGER, J. L. *Federation Proc.* **21**, 134 (1962).
882. STROMINGER, J. L. *J. Biol. Chem.* **237**, 1388 (1962).
883. STROMINGER, J. L. and MAPSON, L. W. *Biochem. J.* **66**, 567 (1957).
884. STROMINGER, J. L., MAXWELL, E. S., AXELROD, J. and KALCKAR, H. M. *J. Biol. Chem.* **224**, 79 (1957).
885. STROMINGER, J. L., PARK, J. T. and THOMPSON, R. E. *J. Biol. Chem.* **234**, 3263 (1959).
886. STROMINGER, J. L., SCOTT, S. S. and THRENN, R. H. *Federation Proc.* **18**, 334 (1959).
887. STRUVE, W. G. and NEUHAUS, F. C. *Biochem. Biophys. Res. Commun.* **18**, 6 (1965).
888. STUMPF, P. K. *J. Biol. Chem.* **176**, 233 (1948).
889. SU, J.-C. and HASSID, W. Z. *Biochemistry* **1**, 468 (1962); 474 (1962).
890. SUGAWARA, S., NAKAMURA, Y. and SHIMOMURA, T. *Agricult. and Biol. Chem.* (*Japan*) **26**, 637 (1962).
891. SUSSMAN, M. and OSBORN, M. J. *Proc. Natl. Acad. Sci., U.S.* **52**, 81 (1964).
892. SUTHERLAND, E. W. and RALL, T. W. *J. Biol. Chem.* **232**, 1077 (1958).
893. SUTHERLAND, E. W. and WOSILAIT, W. D. *Nature* **175**, 169 (1955).
894. SUZUKI, S. *J. Biol. Chem.* **237**, 1393 (1962).
895. SUZUKI, S. and STROMINGER, J. L. *Biochim. Biophys. Acta* **31**, 283 (1959).
896. SUZUKI, S. and STROMINGER, J. L. *J. Biol. Chem.* **235**, 257 (1960).
897. SUZUKI, S. and STROMINGER, J. L. *J. Biol. Chem.* **235**, 267 (1960).
898. SUZUKI, S. and STROMINGER, J. L. *J. Biol. Chem.* **235**, 274 (1960).
899. TAGAWA, K. and ARNON, D. I. *Nature* **195**, 537 (1962).

900. TAGAWA, K., TSUJIMOTO, H. Y. and ARNON, D. I. *Proc. Natl. Acad. Sci., U.S.* **49**, 567, 755 (1963).
901. TAKAGI, Y. *Agricult. and Biol. Chem. (Japan)* **26**, 717 (1962).
902. TAKAGI, Y. *Agricult. and Biol. Chem. (Japan)* **26**, 719 (1962).
903. TAKAGI, Y., KANDA, M. and NAKATA, Y. *Biochim. Biophys. Acta* **31**, 264 (1959).
904. TAKAGI, Y. and SAWADA, H. *Biochim. Biophys. Acta* **92**, 10, 18 (1964).
905. TAK HASHI, N. and SUZUKI, S. *Biochim. Biophys. Acta* **63**, 344 (1962).
906. TAKETA, K. and POGELL, B. M. *Biochem. Biophys. Res. Commun.* **12**, 229 (1963).
907. TANNER, H. A., BROWN, T. E., EYSTER, C. and TREHARNE, R. W. *Biochem. Biophys. Res. Commun.* **3**, 205 (1960).
908. TANNER, H. A., BROWN, T. E., EYSTER, C. and TREHARNE, R. W. *Ohio J. Sci.* **60**, 231 (1960).
909. TATA, J. R. *Biochem. J.* **90**, 284 (1964).
910. TAYLOR, W. H. and JUNI, E. *J. Biol. Chem.* **236**, 1231 (1961).
911. TEWFIC, S. and STUMPF, P. K. *Am. J. Bot.* **36**, 567 (1949).
912. TEWFIC, S. and STUMPF, P. K. *J. Biol. Chem.* **192**, 519 (1951).
913. TILDEN, E. B. and HUDSON, C. S. *J. Am. Chem. Soc.* **61**, 2900 (1939).
914. TOLBERT, N. E. *Brookhaven Symposia in Biology* **11**, 271 (1958).
915. TOLBERT, N. E. and ZILL, L. P. *J. Biol. Chem.* **222**, 895 (1956).
916. TOPPER, Y. J. *J. Biol. Chem.* **225**, 419 (1957).
917. TORRIANI, A. M. and MONOD, J. *Compt. Rend. Acad. Sci.* **228**, 718 (1949).
918. TOUSTER, O. *Federation Proc.* **19**, 977 (1960).
919. TOUSTER, O., HUTCHESON, R. M. and RICE, L. *J. Biol. Chem.* **215**, 677 (1959).
920. TOUSTER, O., MAYBERRY, R. H. and McCORMICK, D. B. *Biochim. Biophys. Acta* **25**, 196 (1957).
921. TRAUT, R. R. and LIPMANN, F. *J. Biol. Chem.* **238**, 1213 (1963).
922. TRENNER, N. R., ARISON, B. H., ERICKSON, R. E., SHUNK, C. H., WOLF, D. E. and FOLKERS, K. *J. Am. Chem. Soc.* **81**, 2026 (1959).
923. TREVELYAN, W. E., MANN, P. F. E. and HARRISON, J. S. *Arch. Biochem. Biophys.* **39**, 419 (1952).
924. TRIVELLONI, J. C., RECONDO, E. and CARDINI, C. E. *Nature* **195**, 1202 (1962).
925. TRUCCO, R. E., CAPUTTO, R., LELOIR, L. F. and MITTELMAN, N. *Arch. Biochem.* **18**, 137 (1948).
926. TURNER, D. H. and TURNER, J. F. *Biochem. J.* **69**, 448 (1958).
927. TURNER, J. F. *Nature* **172**, 1149 (1953); **174**, 692 (1954).
928. TURNER, J. F., BLACK, C. C. and GIBBS, M. *J. Biol. Chem.* **237**, 577 (1962).
929. UTTER, M. F. and KEECH, D. B. *J. Biol. Chem.* **238**, 2603 (1963).
930. UTTER, M. F. and KURAHASHI, K. *J. Am. Chem. Soc.* **75**, 758 (1953).
931. UTTER, M. F. and KURAHASHI, K. *J. Biol. Chem.* **207**, 787, 821 (1954).
932. UTTER, M. F., KURAHASHI, K. and ROSE, I. A. *J. Biol. Chem.* **207**, 803 (1954).
933. VALENTINE, R. C., BRILL, W. J. and SAGERS, R. D. *Biochem. Biophys. Res. Commun.* **12**, 315 (1963).
934. VALENTINE, R. C., BRILL, W. J., WOLFE, R. S. and SAN PIETRO, A. *Biochem. Biophys. Res. Commun.* **10**, 73 (1963).
935. VALENTINE, R. C., MORTENSON, L. E. and CARNAHAN, J. E. *J. Biol. Chem.* **238**, 1141 (1963).
936. VAN HEYNINGEN, R. and PIRIE, A. *Biochem. J.* **53**, 436 (1953).
937. VAN NIEL, C. B. *Advances in Enzymology* **1**, 263 (1941).
938. VARDANIS, A. *Biochim. Biophys. Acta* **73**, 565 (1963).
939. VENKATARAMAN, R. and RACKER, E. *J. Biol. Chem.* **236**, 1876 (1961).
940. VERACHTERT, H., BASS, S. T. and HANSEN, R. G. *Biochim. Biophys. Acta* **92**, 482 (1964).
941. VERACHTERT, H., BASS, S. T., and HANSEN, R. G. *Biochem. Biophys. Res. Commun.* **15**, 158 (1964).
942. VERNON, L. P. and KAMEN, M. D. *Arch. Biochem. Biophys.* **44**, 298 (1953).
943. VILLAR-PALASI, C. and LARNER, J. *Biochim. Biophys. Acta* **30**, 449 (1958).
944. VILLAR-PALASI, C. and LARNER, J. *Arch. Biochem. Biophys.* **86**, 61 (1960).
945. VIÑUELA, E., SALAS, M. and SOLS, A. *J. Biol. Chem.* **238**, PC 1175 (1963).

946. VISHNIAC, W., HORECKER, B. A., and OCHOA, S. *Advances in Enzymol.* **19**, 1 (1957).
947. WAHBA, A. J., HICKMAN, J. W. and ASHWELL, G. *J. Am. Chem. Soc.* **80**, 2594 (1958).
948. WAINER, A. *Biochem. Biophys. Res. Commun.* **16**, 141 (1964).
949. WALKER, D. G. and RAO, S. *Biochem. J.* **90**, 360 (1964).
950. WALKER, G. J. *Biochem. J.* **94**, 299 (1965).
951. WALKER, G. J. and WHELAN, W. J. *Biochem. J.* **67**, 548 (1957).
952. WALKER, G. J. and WHELAN, W. J. *Nature* **183**, 46 (1959).
953. WANG, D.-H. and SCHEER, B. T. *Comp. Biochem. Physiol.* **9**, 263 (1963).
954. WANG, J. H. and GRAVES, D. J. *Biochemistry* **3**, 1437 (1964).
955. WARBURG, O. *Science* **128**, 68 (1958).
956. WARBURG, O. and BURK, D. *Arch. Biochem.* **25**, 410 (1950).
957. WARBURG, O. and KRIPPAHL, G. *Acta Chem. Scand.* **17**, Suppl. 1, S1 (1963).
958. WARBURG, O. and KRIPPAHL, G. *Z Physiol. Chem.*, *Hoppe-Seyler's* **332**, 225 (1963).
959 WARBURG, O., KRIPPAHL, G. and BIRKICHT, E. *Biochem. Z.* **340**, 1 (1964).
960. WARBURG, O., KRIPPAHL, G., JETSCHMANN, K. and LEHMANN, A. *Z. Naturforschung* **18b**, 837 (1963).
961. WARBURG, O. and OSTENDORF, P. *Z. Naturforschung* **18b**, 933 (1963).
962. WARBURG, O., SCHRÖDER, W., KRIPPAHL, G. and KLOTZSCH, H. *Angew. Chem.* **69**, 627 (1957).
963. WARD, C. and WRIGHT, B. E. *Biochemistry*, in press.
964. WARREN, L. and BLACKLOW, R. S. *Biochem. Biophys. Res. Commun.* **7**, 433 (1962).
965. WARREN, L. and BLACKLOW, R. S. *J. Biol. Chem.* **237**, 3527 (1962).
966. WARREN, L., BLACKLOW, R. S. and SPEARING, C. W. *Ann. New York Acad. Sci.* **106** 191 (1963).
967. WARREN, L. and FELSENFELD, H. *Biochem. Biophys. Res. Commun.* **5**, 185 (1961).
968. WARREN, L. and FELSENFELD, H. *J. Biol. Chem.* **237**, 1421 (1962).
969. WATKINS, W. M. and HASSID, W. Z. *J. Biol. Chem.* **237**, 1432 (1962).
970. WEIBULL, C. and TISELIUS, A. *Arkiv. Kemi, Mineral. Geol.* **A19**, 1 (1945).
971. WEIMBERG, R. *Biochem. Biophys. Res. Commun.* **8**, 442 (1962).
972. WEIMBERG, R. *Biochim. Biophys. Acta* **67**, 359 (1963).
973. WEIMBERG, R. and DOUDOROFF, M. *J. Biol. Chem.* **217**, 607 (1955).
974. WEISSBACH, A., HORECKER, B. L. and HURWITZ, J. *J. Biol. Chem.* **218**, 795 (1956).
975. WEISSBACH, A., SMYRNIOTIS, P. Z. and HORECKER, B. L. *J. Am. Chem. Soc.* **76**, 5572 (1954).
976. WHATLEY, F. R., TAGAWA, K. and ARNON, D. I. *Proc. Natl. Acad. Sci.*, *U.S.* **49**, 266 (1963).
977. WHEELER, M., HANKE, P. and WEILL, C. E. *Arch. Biochem. Biophys.* **102**, 397 (1963).
978. WHELAN, W. J. and BAILEY, J. M. *Biochem. J.* **58**, 560 (1954).
979. WHELAN, W. J. and ROBERTS, P. J. P. *J. Chem. Soc.* **1953**, 1298.
980. WHISTLER, R. L. and SMART, C. L. *Polysaccharide Chemistry*. Academic Press, Inc., New York, 1953.
981. WHITE, B. N., SHETLAR, M. R., SHURLEY, H. M. and SCHILLING, J. A. *Biochim. Biophys. Acta* **101**, 97 (1965).
982. WHITE, J. W., Jr. and MAHER, J. *Arch. Biochem. Biophys.* **42**, 360 (1953).
983. WHITE, J. W., Jr. and MAHER, J. *J. Am. Chem. Soc.* **75**, 1259 (1953).
984. WHITELEY, H. R. and WOOLFOLK, C. A. *Biochem. Biophys. Res. Commun.* **9**, 517 (1962).
985. WHITTINGHAM, C. P. and PRITCHARD, G. C. *Proc. Royal Soc.*, Ser. B, **157**, 366 (1963).
986. WILLIAMSON, A. R. and ZAMENHOF, S. *J. Biol. Chem.* **238**, 2255 (1963).
987. WILSON, A. T. and CALVIN, M. *J. Am. Chem. Soc.* **77**, 5948 (1955).
988. WILSON, D. B. and HOGNESS, D. S. *J. Biol. Chem.* **239**, 2469 (1964).
989. WILSON, D. M. and AJL, S. *J. Bacteriol.* **73**, 410, 415 (1957).
990. WILSON, E. J., SCHOCH, T. J. and HUDSON, C. S. *J. Am. Chem. Soc.* **65**, 1380 (1943).
991. WILSON, L. G. and BANDURSKI, R. S. *J. Am. Chem. Soc.* **80**, 5576 (1958).
992. WILSON, L. G. and BANDURSKI, R. S. *J. Biol. Chem.* **233**, 975 (1958).
993. WITT, H. T., MÜLLER, A. and RUMBERG, B. *Nature* **197**, 987 (1963).

994. WOLFE, J. B., BRITTON, B. B. and NAKADA, H. I. *Arch. Biochem. Biophys.* **66**, 333 (1957).
995. WOLFF, J. B. and KAPLAN, N. O. *J. Biol. Chem.* **218**, 849 (1956).
996. WOLFROM, M. L., THOMPSON, A. and GALKOWSKI, T. T. *J. Am. Chem. Soc.* **73**, 4093 (1951).
997. WOLFROM, M. L., WEBBER, J. M. and SHAFIZADEH, F. *J. Am. Chem. Soc.* **81**, 1217 (1959).
998. WOLIN, M. J., SIMPSON, F. J. and WOOD, W. A. *Biochim. Biophys. Acta* **24**, 635 (1957).
999. WOLIN, M. J., SIMPSON, F. J. and WOOD, W. A. *J. Biol. Chem.* **232**, 559 (1958).
1000. WOLOCHOW, H. E., PUTMAN, E. W., DOUDOROFF, M., HASSID, W. Z. and BARKER, H. A. *J. Biol. Chem.* **180**, 1237 (1949).
1001. WOOD, H. G., GILLESPIE, R., JOFFE, S., HANSEN, R. G. and HARDENBROOK, H. *J. Biol. Chem.* **233**, 1271 (1958).
1002. WOOD, H. G., JOFFE, S., GILLESPIE, R., HANSEN, R. G. and HARDENBROOK, H. *J. Biol. Chem.* **233**, 1264 (1958).
1003. WOOD, W. A. and SCHWERDT, R. F. *J. Biol. Chem.* **201**, 501 (1953).
1004. WORTMAN, B. *J. Biol. Chem.* **236**, 974 (1961).
1005. WOSILAIT, W. D. and SUTHERLAND, E. W. *J. Biol. Chem.* **218**, 469 (1956).
1006. YAMADA, H., OKAMOTO, K., KODAMA, K. and TANAKA, S. *Biochim. Biophys. Acta* **33**, 271 (1959).
1007. YANKEELOV, J. A., Jr., HORTON, H. R. and KOSHLAND, D. E., Jr. *Biochemistry* **3**, 349 (1964).
1008. YUNIS, A. A., FISCHER, E. H. and KREBS, E. G. *J. Biol. Chem.* **235**, 3163 (1960).
1009. ZELEZNICK, L. D., BOLTRALIK, J. J., BARKULIS, S. S., SMITH, C. and HEYMANN, H. *Science* **140**, 400 (1963).
1010. ZELEZNICK, L. D., ROSEN, S. M., SALTMARSH-ANDREW, M., OSBORN, M. J. and HORECKER, B. L. *Proc. Natl. Acad. Sci., U.S.* **53**, 207 (1965).
1011. ZEVENHUIZEN, L. P. T. M. *Biochim. Biophys. Acta* **81**, 608 (1964).
1012. ZILLIKEN, F., SMITHE, P. N., ROSE, C. S. and GYORGY, P. *J. Biol. Chem.* **208**, 299 (1954).

CHAPTER 7

THE BIOGENESIS OF PROTEINS

THEODORE PETERS†

The Mary Imogene Bassett Hospital (affiliated with Columbia University),
Cooperstown, N.Y.

CONTENTS

I. INTRODUCTION 477
  A. *Structure of proteins* 478
  B. *Unique features of proteins* 480
II. THE STUDY OF PROTEIN BIOSYNTHESIS 481
  A. *Methods employed* 481
  B. *The dynamic state and the nature of turnover* 482
  C. *Some conclusions* 484
III. THE MECHANISM OF PROTEIN BIOSYNTHESIS 489
  A. *Overall scheme* 489
  B. *The genetic code for amino acid sequence* 491
  C. *Activation of amino acids: the adaptor RNA molecule* 494
  D. *Sequence determination: the messenger RNA molecule* 500
  E. *The site of protein formation: the ribosome and polyribosome* 508
  F. *The biosynthetic reaction* 511
  G. *Events subsequent to peptide bond formation* 516
  H. *The role of lipides and membranes* 520
IV. INADEQUACIES OF THE GENERAL MECHANISM; PROTEIN SYNTHESIS
  BY NON-RIBOSOMAL SYSTEMS 521
V. SUMMARY AND CONCLUSIONS 523

I. INTRODUCTION

The name *protein* (from the Greek, *proteios*—primary) ably describes the importance of this class of compounds in biology. Proteins having enzymatic abilities catalyze the great complex of reactions which make up metabolism. Others provide structure to animal cells, furnish muscles with contractility, act as hormones, as antibodies, or as carriers of oxygen.

This chapter will attempt to set forth the unified and exciting picture of

†The author would like to express his appreciation for the support of his research by the United States Public Health Service.

the interplay of nucleic acids and enzymes in the biosynthesis of proteins which is the result of a great volume of research in the past 18 years.

A. *Structure of Proteins*

Recognition that proteins are discrete chemical compounds is essential to the logical study of their structure and synthesis. After elucidation of the complete covalent structure of insulin, Sanger was able to state in 1952[316] his conviction that "a protein is really a single chemical substance, each molecule of one protein being identical with every other molecule of the same pure protein". Subsequent demonstration that other proteins, such as ribonuclease, lysozyme, and hemoglobin, have definite, constant structures has established this view. Although there may be occasional rare errors in assembly of a protein, or modification of some amino acid residues due to later wear and tear, it seems reasonable to contend that each protein is at least intended at its inception to be a distinct molecular species.

Proteins contain α-amino acids linked by peptide bonds into long chains. The number of amino acid residues ranges from about 100 in the smallest true proteins, such as ribonuclease or cytochrome *C*, to several thousand in fibrinogen and collagen. The corresponding physical dimensions are about 30 to 1000 Å. There may be more than one peptide chain in a protein, and its structure may include carbohydrate, lipide or nucleic acid components, prosthetic groups such as heme, phosphorylated derivatives or metals. However, this treatise will of necessity concern itself primarily with the assembly only of the peptide portion of the molecule.

According to the Linderstrøm–Lang concept protein structure can be considered at three levels, termed *primary*, meaning the sequence of amino acid residues in the peptide chain, *secondary*, the restrictions placed on the shape of the molecule due to covalent bonds between amino acid functional groups, and *tertiary*, the folding or association caused by weaker forces.

Primary Structure

The twenty amino acids of which proteins are formed are those in Table 1. The customary abbreviations are also listed. Asparagine and glutamine are derivatives of aspartic and glutamic acids, respectively, in which the carboxyl group farther from the α-amino group has been changed to an amide group. *Cysteine*, the sulfhydryl amino acid, also occurs in proteins as *cystine*, the oxidized form in which two molecules are joined by a disulfide linkage. Cystine is not listed separately since it is apparently the reduced form, cysteine, that is incorporated in the formation of peptide chains.

The order in which these twenty amino acids are linked to each other establishes the identity, and probably all of the properties, of a specific protein, just as the order of the component letters identifies a word. Figure 1 shows the amino acid sequence of bovine ribonuclease, a single-chain protein

TABLE 1. THE TWENTY AMINO ACIDS COMMONLY FOUND IN PROTEINS

Amino acid	Abbreviation
Alanine	Ala
Arginine	Arg
Asparagine	AN or AspNH₂
Aspartic acid	Asp
Cysteine	CySH
Glutamic acid	Glu
Glutamine	GN or GluNH₂
Glycine	Gly
Histidine	His
Isoleucine	Ileu
Leucine	Leu
Lysine	Lys
Methionine	Met
Phenylalanine	Phe
Proline	Pro
Serine	Ser
Threonine	Thr
Tryptophan	Trp
Tyrosine	Tyr
Valine	Val

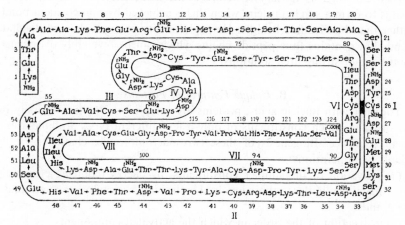

FIG. 1. Complete sequence of amino acid residues in ribonuclease. The four disulfide bonds are shown as dark bands. (From Smyth et al.[348]) Reproduced by courtesy of American Society of Biological Chemists.

with no prosthetic groups. The complete sequence of residues is now known for about twelve proteins. For several of these the interspecies differences have also been identified; they are usually relatively minor and tend to occur at certain regions along the chain.

Secondary Structure

Imposed on the primary structure, or backbone chain, frequently are observed rigid bonds between reactive groups protruding from the peptide chain. Best-known of these bonds are the disulfide bridges, formed by the removal of two hydrogen atoms from the sulfhydryl groups of two cysteine residues to form cystine. Ribonuclease has four such bonds (Fig. 1), which have been demonstrated to occur characteristically between the positions shown. In addition to such intrachain linkages, disulfide bonds may connect two or more peptide chains to form a single protein—insulin and gamma globulin are examples.

Tertiary Structure

Peptide chains without the restrictions of secondary bonding or of the presence of the amino acid, proline, will coil into a helical configuration. The helix has 3·6 amino acid residues per turn, and is stabilized by hydrogen bonding between the oxygen and nitrogen atoms of the peptide groups. In myoglobin, shown in Fig. 2, about 70 per cent of the peptide chain is in the helical form. Myoglobin has no disulfide links, and the major bends in the chain are either caused by the presence of a proline residue, or are strengthened by weak associations between groups of the folded segment and groups on other segments of the chain which become proximal to each other.

Also classified as tertiary structure is the association of several peptide chains to form a single protein, when this is achieved by non-covalent bonds rather than by disulfide bridges. Hemoglobin, for example, has no disulfide bonds but contains four peptide chains which can be reversibly dissociated by the use of strong urea solutions.

B. Unique Features of Proteins

Together with nucleic acids, proteins are unique in attaining diversity by the order in which constituents of only a few different types are linked in a linear sequence. Biogenesis of these two macromolecules characteristically entails two operations:

(a) activation of the simpler constituents, by energy-requiring enzymatic reactions similar to those involved in the biogenesis of other compounds, and

(b) instruction of the order in which the activated components are linked in sequence.

The process by which sequence instruction is transmitted from the genetic material to the formation of a particular protein is an intriguing one. It is based on the Watson–Crick pairings of the purine and pyrimidine bases of the nucleic acids; the forces involved are weak, but a close steric fit gives high specificity in a manner similar to the "lock-and-key" interaction of antigen and antibody or enzyme and substrate.

The very size of proteins and nucleic acids is a unique feature. With the increased use of the electron microscope in biology, visualization of

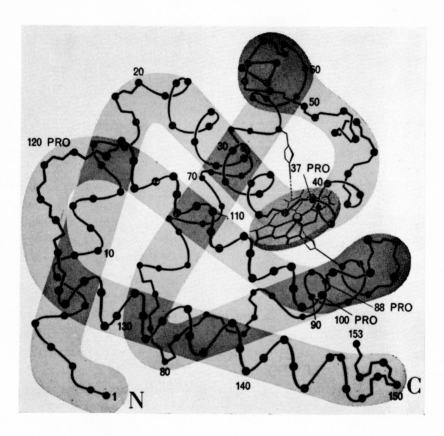

FIG. 2. Three-dimensional model of the myoglobin molecule. (From Perutz.[279] Each dot represents an amino acid residue, and the circle is the heme group. The numbers are the position of the residues in the chain. (N = alpha amino group; C = alpha carboxyl group.) Reproduced by courtesy of Scientific American, Inc.

individual protein molecules has become a reality, permitting correlation of their observed shape and size with that inferred from physical and chemical measurements. Not only the large fibrous molecules such as collagen and fibrin, but the smaller globular proteins such as antibodies, serum albumin and cytochrome *C* have been detected with the electron beam. The ability of the electron microscope to cross the borderline between biology and chemistry has made the study of the biogenesis of proteins an enchanting one, since the site of peptide chain formation can both be observed at the cytological level and studied at the molecular level.

II. THE STUDY OF PROTEIN BIOSYNTHESIS
A. *Methods Employed*

Growth of the plant or animal was initially the only criterion for measuring protein formation, yet this technique gave valuable information on the amino acids which are essential for higher animals. [307] Observation of net gain or loss of nitrogen (nitrogen balance) in the adult animal allowed Folin early in this century [113] to put forth his theory of a separate or exogenous metabolism of proteins of foodstuffs, a concept to be changed in 1935 [41] when Borsook and Keighley proposed that constituent body proteins also can be readily broken down and rebuilt. Measurements based on growth and nitrogen balance have contributed greatly to the understanding of protein malnutrition and of the relative nutritive value of different proteins. [403, 6]

Indispensable to later major advances was the introduction of the use of isotopes as tracers in intermediary metabolism by Schoenheimer and his collaborators in 1939. [328] Isotopes permit experiments on the formation of proteins even when degradation is the predominant process, and have allowed investigators to follow the incorporation of individual amino acids into specific sites within protein chains. Isotopes were first used in the study of protein synthesis in the living animal [328] and in surviving slices of tissues. [376] Winnick managed to eliminate the need for intact cells by demonstrating incorporation of isotopically-labeled amino acids in homogenized preparations of rat liver. [412] Further development yielded protein-synthesizing preparations which contained only ribosomes, with or without attached membranous material, plus an energy source and various soluble components. Important systems used in later work were from rat liver, [431] rabbit reticulocytes [331] and *Escherichia coli*. [209]

As research has probed more deeply into the problems of sequence and of specificity, it has become essential not only to work with proteins in highly purified form, but to be able to answer the question, "Which protein?" Isolation of individual proteins by the classical techniques of fractionation on the basis of solubility has been extended by the use of chromatography, of ion exchange resins, countercurrent distribution, zone electrophoresis, and dextran gel filtration. Specific antibodies have frequently been used to precipitate a desired protein from complex mixtures.

R

The study of protein synthesis and protein structure has been aided materially by the introduction of an automatic analytical system which provides complete separation and determination of microgram quantities of amino acids in mixtures from hydrolyzed proteins, with better than 3 per cent accuracy. [352]

B. *The Dynamic State and the Nature of Turnover*

The use of isotopes has shown that proteins of all types of living organisms take part in Schoenheimer's "dynamic state", [328] in that synthesis and degradation continue throughout the life of the organism. The rate at which these processes occur correlates roughly with the metabolic rate of the species or of the particular organ in question. Thus, the half-life of survival of circulating serum albumin in mammals ranges from 1·9 days in the mouse to 20·7 days in the cow. [5] In adult humans the figure is 18 days. [75, 374] Albumin half-life in 2-day-old rabbits is 2·1 days, but as the animal ages the rate of metabolism falls and the turnover slows to a half-life of 3·8 days when the rabbits are 100 days old. [90]

The rapidity with which the free amino acids of blood plasma "turn over" is phenomenal. Of a tracer dose of leucine injected into the tail vein of a mouse, less than 5 per cent remains in the circulation 2 min later. [42] About half of the leucine is catabolized and excreted as carbon dioxide, water and urea, but the other half is promptly incorporated into tissue proteins. Although the free amino acids of plasma make up a pool small in amount (about 3 mM total concentration in mammals) they compensate for a low inventory by having a rapid turnover.

The relative protein turnover of various organs has been studied either by isolation of protein [42] for determination of radioactivity or by making autoradiographs of sections of the untreated organ. [259, 143, 214] Usually the time after administration of the radioactive amino acid in these studies was only one or two days, but prolonged studies in which rats were exposed to $C^{14}O_2$ [54] or H^3_2O [378] gave very much the same relative results. The rate of protein turnover was found to decrease in the order: lung, liver, small intestinal mucosa, kidney, adipose tissue, muscle, brain, bone collagen. The half life of rat liver protein, for example, is about 3 days, that of muscle protein about 80 days, but collagen, with a half-life of 1000 days, is essentially permanent during the life span of the rat. Collagen is, of course, extracellular and quite resistant to the action of proteases.

Individual cells within an organ also show differences in protein turn-over. [259] The most active cells on autoradiographic examination are those which divide most frequently, such as red cell precursors and reticuloendo-thelial cells, or which secrete protein, such as gastric chief cells or pancreatic acinar cells. Also active are ganglion cells, the epithelium of the choroid plexus, and cells in the adrenal cortex.

Intracellularly there is further diversity in the rate at which amino acids are incorporated. A multitude of reports has demonstrated that, in nearly all tissues examined, the most rapid uptake is by the proteins of the RNA-rich microsomes. [170, 42, 376, 163] Nuclei, mitochondria, and the soluble cytoplasm approach equal labeling after an hour or so. In mitochondria the proteins and lipides disappear with the same half life, which has been interpreted to mean that mitochondria may be formed and destroyed as intact units. [111]

The rate of protein formation and release by microsomes in intact cells appears to be adequate to account for the entire synthesis of protein in the cytoplasm. Fractionation of microsomes reveals that it is particularly the types rich in attached ribosomes which form specific proteins such as serum albumin [283, 180] and catalase, [158] and then pass them along to their ultima'e destinations.

When the cell membrane is broken and the amino acid incorporation is then tested, the importance of the microsomes is seen more clearly. Among the tissues in which the significance of microsomes has been demonstrated are rat liver, [340, 186] rat muscle [413] and chick embryo. [98] Nuclei also retain appreciable ability to carry on protein synthesis when isolated from the cell. [3]

Removal of the membranous portion of microsomes, usually by dissolving it with desoxycholate or other detergent-like compounds, gives a preparation containing essentially pure ribosomes. When properly fortified, ribosomes will conduct protein synthesis, and many of the recent significant findings have been made using such systems.

Protein synthesis by ribosomes is apparently ubiquitous. It has been detected in liver, [219, 199, 372] muscle, [366] reticulocytes, [331, 290] E. coli [209] and many other tissues and organisms. There is evidence that isolated ribosomes can form specific proteins such as serum albumin, [391] and the mechanism by which such synthesis occurs on ribosomes will occupy much of the remainder of this chapter.

The Nature of the Turnover Phenomenon

The meaning of the appearance of tracer amino acids in proteins of adult organisms has caused considerable discussion among protein biochemists. [40, 376] Does the uptake of a single amino acid mean that an entire new protein molecule has been synthesized, or can the peptide chain perhaps open and close to allow the exchange of particular amino acid residues with a pool of free amino acids? The answer now appears to be that the former alternative is correct, but several factors make it not always obvious from observing turnover in the intact animal.

It seems clear that proteins once formed and removed from the site of their synthesis do not undergo incorporation of new amino acids. Antibodies administered in passive immunization take up no labeled amino acids. [149, 55, 173] The red blood cell after maturation does not synthesize protein; its hemoglobin and enzymes do not incorporate amino acids. [5] When serum proteins are administered which have been labeled with two or three different isotopes in different amino acids, the rate of loss of each of the amino acids is the same; [135, 110, 75, 241] it would seem unlikely that the amino acids would be lost at similar rates if exchange were occurring.

When proteins remain in active cells, synthesis and degradation are harder to distinguish. Some of the best evidence that incorporation of amino acids actually indicates formation of complete new protein molecules rather than exchange is the need for a complete amino acid mixture in order for incorporation of a single labeled amino acid to occur in cell-free systems. [43, 23, 290] Recent elegant studies to be discussed in Section III F have substantiated the belief that synthesis means formation of entire new molecules, by observing the linear progression of amino acid incorporation along the protein chain.

Extracellular, circulating proteins are broken down on an exponential time curve in an apparently random manner, [135, 110, 75, 241] that is, unrelated to the age of the molecule. Intracellular enzymes likewise disappear at an exponential rate, at least in the red cell in which continued synthesis does not confuse the picture. [5] Breakdown of proteins in bacteria [197, 227, 114] and in cells in tissue culture [195] is appreciable when the cells are in the resting state, but is minimal during growth. Whether the degradation occurs through the action of proteolytic enzymes or by a more complex process is not clear; a requirement for energy for the degradation of proteins in liver slices favors the more complex mechanism. [360]

The sum of the evidence to date permits one to say with some assurance that synthesis and degradation of proteins are distinct and independent processes, that is, neither involves the other. As a corollary, the pathway of synthesis, as well as of degradation, is seen to be irreversible. *A protein is formed at one site by one irreversible process; its amino acids are not renewed during the life of the molecule; and it is degraded at another site by another irreversible process.*

Several phenomena have been observed which appear at first glance to contradict this view, but which on closer inspection are not examples of protein synthesis in the usual sense. Gale and Folkes [120] reported a rapid exchange of glutamic acid in *Staphylococcus* cells—this was found to occur in the polysaccharide structures of the cell membrane rather than in proteins. An apparent exchange of serine and tyrosine residues in circulating hemoglobin [321] is more logically explained as a conversion of glycine to serine and phenylalanine to tyrosine without rupture of peptide bonds (see also Section III F).

C. Some Conclusions

A few broad conclusions pertinent to the general mechanism of protein synthesis can be drawn from the results of many investigations in this field.

1. *The material for protein synthesis comes from intracellular pools of free amino acids.* The intracellular pools of free amino acids are small, since the body does not store excess amino acids, but converts them into energy, fat and carbohydrate. Hence, like the plasma amino acids with which they interchange, the turnover of the intracellular amino acids is rapid. [42, 190, 308, 19, 26] The lack of a storage capability is attested by the need for the presence of all of the essential amino acids simultaneously for protein synthesis to occur, since there is no mechanism to retain them in the free state until they are needed. [124, 23]

The level of free amino acids within cells is 2 to 60 times that in the plasma. Amino acids reach the intracellular pools either by assimilation as free amino acids through the cell membrane or by manufacture within the cell. Transport across the cell membrane has been shown to be an energy-requiring process which is usually not rate-limiting in the synthesis of proteins; potassium ion and pyridoxal phosphate appear to be required. [71, 303, 151, 274, 242, 302, 308, 22]

Only non-essential amino acids, by definition, can be manufactured within the cell. [100] Synthesis is via well-established pathways of intermediary metabolism, since tagged atoms of carbon in carbon dioxide or acetate appear in the predicted positions in glutamic acid, aspartic acid, alanine and others. [369, 153, 37] The conversion of aspartic and glutamic acids to their amide forms, asparagine and glutamine, probably takes place before incorporation rather than when the amino acids are bound in peptide form. [314]

Recently it has been proposed that the tyrosine formed by liver phenylalanine hydroxylase from phenylalanine derived from protein catabolism is utilized more efficiently than exogenous tyrosine. [176] Amino acids generated metabolically may thus be compartmented in pools which are not in rapid equilibrium with those arriving from the plasma. There is good evidence, however, that within a single organ the same pool of amino acids serves the synthesis of all its proteins. When several radioactive amino acids are administered in tracer experiments, they are incorporated in the same ratio in three enzymes of muscle [150, 341] and two of pancreas. [189] In liver the pool of arginine for serum albumin formation is the same as that for urea production. [295]

Equilibrium between the pools within different organs in the body is less rapid than the utilization of amino acids from these pools. Radioactive glycine appears in liver proteins at a higher level than in muscle proteins for the first seven days after administration of a tracer dose of glycine, but thereafter the level is higher in muscle proteins. [322] The use of glycine to form hippuric acid has demonstrated that equilibrium between the glycine pools of liver and kidney is not attained. [121]

2. *Free peptides are not intermediates in protein synthesis.* With the exception of certain peptides having metabolic functions, free peptides are found in tissues in only very slight amounts. [370, 265] When administered parenterally,

peptides are less effective protein precursors in man than are amino acids [70] and even peptides derived from hemoglobin, e.g. by the use of pepsin, are not taken up by reticulocytes or nucleated red cells and re-used to form hemoglobin. [53, 57]

Some bacteria and plants can utilize peptides more effectively than amino acids, [244, 193] but in bacteria, at least, the peptides are apparently split to amino acids before entering into proteins; it appears that the peptide is simply a form more readily assimilated across the cell membrane. [193] Labeled amino acids supplied in the form of serum proteins can be used for formation of tissue [398, 293] or milk [14] proteins, but again it can be demonstrated that degradation to free amino acids occurs during their incorporation. Even when intact conalbumin, a protein found in egg white, is injected into the blood stream of a laying hen, it is broken to free amino acids before being used in production of proteins of the egg. [226]

When investigators were able to isolate amino acid residues which were situated at different locations within a peptide chain, it was found that these often showed different specific radioactivities in tracer experiments. This was first reported by Muir for the valine residues of hemoglobin and by Askonas for milk proteins, and was later seen with ovalbumin, insulin and ribonuclease (see review by Steinberg et al.). [361] The degree of non-uniformity of labeling of different residues was related to the duration of exposure to the labeled substrate and to the elapsed time between exposure and collection of the protein. The discrepancies decreased with time in all of the proteins examined —hemoglobin, [205, 53, 237, 254] fibrinogen, [82] serum albumin [319] and gamma globulin. [287]

This phenomenon is compatible either with the existence of intermediate peptide pools, which change their specific activity at different rates, or with the assembly of proteins from free amino acids in a sequential manner, provided that the time of synthesis is comparable to the time required to change the specific activity of the free amino acid pool. [361] It has been reasonably well established that the latter is the correct interpretation.

These experiments on intramolecular labeling provided an additional piece of information—the *direction* of synthesis was almost invariably found to be *from the amino terminus toward the carboxyl terminus*. Data that the carboxyl amino acid is incorporated later than the amino terminal one have been reported for hemoglobin-valine [36] and -arginine, [310] amylase-leucine, [427] *E. coli*-leucine [132] and serum albumin-leucine and -glutamic acid. [180, 319] Some earlier results with collagen-glycine [123] and fibroin-glycine and -alanine [339] do not agree with this concept and would seem to be deserving of further study.

3. *Energy for protein synthesis is furnished by high energy phosphate bonds.* Formation of a single peptide bond requires a free energy expenditure of 2600–4100 calories. [40] Observations made with "model systems" producing

simple peptides, such as acetyl amines and hippuric acid, have shown that energy is provided from a high energy bond of ATP to activate the carboxyl group of the amino acid, which then forms the peptide bond without the need for further energy. [217, 218]

The energy needed to lengthen a peptide chain is less than that required to form the initial dipeptide, [117] but ATP bonds are still used to provide energy for polypeptide synthesis. Winnick in 1950 [412] added ATP and restored the amino acid-incorporating activity of a liver homogenate which had been lost upon dialysis. Since that time a great number of experiments, usually on the effects of various metabolic inhibitors, have confirmed the importance of phosphate bond energy for protein synthesis (see review by Borsook [40]). For purified microsome systems, added ATP is not as effective as that produced by added mitochondria or generated *in situ* from added phosphoenol pyruvate plus pyruvate kinase. [431]

4. *The time required for synthesis of a protein is short—2 min or less.* The length of time needed for formation of a protein molecule has been estimated as the time needed for the total incorporation of a tracer amino acid to become linear with time—i.e. for the *rate* of incorporation to increase to a constant value. The reasoning is that up to this time incompletely-labeled molecules are being produced, but subsequently the labeled molecules appearing are saturated with the tracer. Using this criterion, the time for formation of a molecule of a specific protein has been estimated as 5 sec in *E. coli*, [243] 27 sec in yeast, [428] 30 sec in *Azotobacter*, [33] less than 1 min in *Neurospora*, [430] less than 2 min for serum albumin in liver, [282, 283] 2 min for ribonuclease in pancreas [83] and less than 6 min for ferritin in liver. [220, 221] The rate is temperature-sensitive, since lowering the temperature of *E. coli* from 37 degrees to 0 degrees increased the average time of synthesis of a protein molecule from 5 sec to 30 min. [133]

5. *The rate of protein synthesis can change in response to conditions.* Hemoglobin production increases in anoxia, when the need for hemoglobin rises, and plasma protein production output rises after bleeding or plasmapheresis. Loss of serum albumin in experimental nephrosis causes a marked increase in the rate of its formation by liver slices; [234] that the stimulus in this case might be related only to the colloid effect of albumin is suggested by the finding that infusion of dextran conversely causes a *decrease* in albumin production. [309]

Changes in diet can induce the appearance of enzymes needed to catabolize the new constituents. [196, 403, 350, 422] The formation of tryptophan pyrrolase in rat liver after administration of tryptophan is one of the best-studied systems. [106, 198] The level of this enzyme rises several-fold within a few hours after giving tryptophan. Various drugs and carcinogens cause increases in detoxifying enzymes in the liver, and administration of iron will specifically stimulate production of ferritin. [313] Hormones, particularly those of the adrenal cortex, stimulate formation of liver enzymes such as tryptophan pyrrolase,[106] tyrosine-α-ketoglutarate transaminase[191] and others.[297, 405]

In bacterial strains having the proper genetic constitution, enzymes can be induced even though the enzyme itself is not normally present even in low concentrations.[77] From the study of such bacterial systems has come a concept of the control of synthesis of specific proteins via blocking of specific repressor substances. This control mechanism is considered in more detail in Section III c.

6. *Ribonucleic acid is closely involved with protein synthesis.* A connection between RNA and protein formation has been suspected and much sought after since Caspersson[66] and Thorell[379] showed the prevalence of RNA at sites of protein synthesis. Later evidence in support of this relationship has been reviewed by Brachet.[44] The presence of ribosomes, which contain about 50 per cent RNA, can be shown to account for most of the RNA observed where rapid protein formation occurs.

DNA was found not to be obligatory for protein synthesis, since enucleated cells of *Acetabularia* or fetal amnion can still form protein, at least for limited periods.[45, 134, 272] RNA *metabolism*, which ceases in the absence of DNA, is likewise not always needed for protein synthesis. However, when proteins new to the organism are to be produced, as with enzyme induction, prior RNA formation is needed. The first evidence on this important point was Creaser's observation that 8-azaguanine, a purine which inhibits RNA formation, stops the formation of induced β-galactosidase in *Staph. aureus*, but not the formation of other proteins.[86] Chantrenne about the same time[67] reported increased formation of RNA during the induction of catalase in yeast. In this same year (1956) it was determined that the infective properties of tobacco mosaic virus, an agent which induces production of new enzymes in the tobacco leaf, reside entirely in its RNA.[115]

These findings lent support to the theories that it is RNA which directs the sequence of amino acids in proteins. The favorite model for such action was that of an RNA "template" on which the amino acids were assembled.[93, 88] The data on non-uniform labeling of amino acid residues in the peptide chain, for instance, are compatible with a template mechanism.[361] Koshland in 1958[201] proposed a scheme by which peptide bond formation could occur on an RNA template after carboxyl activation of the amino acids.

The main feature lacking in the theory of the action of RNA was a means of fitting amino acids to nucleic acid components in a specific manner. "Adaptor RNA" has now been shown to fulfill this function, and the template has been found to be a "messenger RNA" distinct from the ribosomal RNA. The present scheme of protein synthesis involves an intricate interaction of these three classes of macromolecules.

III. THE MECHANISM OF PROTEIN BIOSYNTHESIS

The features of the mechanism presented here have changed even in the last few months, and will doubtless be modified considerably in the next few years. The version given is that of early 1965. Like the play bill for a Shakesperian production, the scheme is first offered in synopsis form, since it is helpful to have some knowledge of the overall sequence of events in order to follow the detailed action.

A. *Overall Scheme*

The overall pathway of protein biosynthesis is represented in Fig. 3 for four amino acid residues of a peptide chain. The processes of (1) amino acid activation and (2) peptide bond formation can logically be considered separately.

(1) Acyl activation of amino acids occurs by the net reaction:

$$\text{Amino acid} + \text{ATP} + \text{sRNA} \underset{}{\overset{\text{enzyme}}{\longleftrightarrow}} \text{Amino acyl-RNA} + \text{AMP}$$
$$+ \text{PP}_i \quad \text{(I), (II)}$$

In reaction (I) (Fig. 3), an amino acid forms a mixed acyl-phosphoric acid anhydride with the phosphate group of AMP. Energy is provided by the splitting of an AMP-PP bond. The complex remains bound to the enzyme, known as an *amino acyl-RNA synthetase*. In reaction (II) the carboxyl group of the amino acid is transferred to the terminal ribose of a soluble "adaptor" RNA (shown as sRNA_1), which has a site specific for the side chain of that amino acid. Elsewhere on its structure the sRNA bears a particular trinucleotide sequence which is also peculiar to each amino acid species.

(2) The right-hand side of Fig. 3 shows the manner in which individual amino acyl-RNA compounds are aligned in the desired order and the amino acids linked in peptide form. The net reaction for this process is:

$$\text{n(amino acyl-RNA)} \xrightarrow[\substack{\text{2 enzymes} \\ \text{GTP}}]{\substack{\text{mRNA} \\ \text{ribosome}}} \text{(peptide)} + \text{n(sRNA)} \qquad \text{(III–VIII)}$$

The sequence in which the amino acids are to be coupled is directed by a "messenger" RNA molecule, shown as mRNA. The mRNA chain consists of a series of trinucleotide sequences, each specific for an individual amino acid and complementary by Watson–Crick base pairing to the trinucleotide sequence in the corresponding sRNA molecule.

A ribosome first binds to the mRNA at the site coded for the amino terminal residue of the protein, reaction (IX) (Fig. 3). The appropriate amino acyl–RNA complex then binds both to the ribosome and to the mRNA, reaction (III) (Fig. 3), in such a fashion that the complementary trinucleotide sequences on the sRNA and the mRNA link by base pairing. The amino

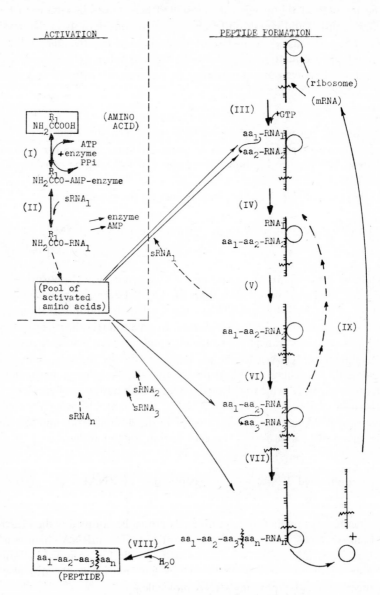

FIG. 3. The overall scheme of protein biosynthesis. (aa_1, aa_2, etc., indicate different amino acids; RNA_1, RNA_2, etc., are the corresponding specific adaptor RNA's.)

acyl–RNA corresponding to the sub-terminal position then binds to the adjacent trinucleotide sequence of the mRNA. The binding is enzymatic, and utilizes GTP in a fashion as yet unknown. Initiation of the protein chain occurs when the acyl group of the first amino acid transfers from its sRNA to form a peptide bond with the (nearby) α-amino group of the sub-terminal amino acid, reaction (IV) (Fig. 3). The enzyme, *peptide synthetase*, catalyzes this reaction. The sRNA which has lost an amino acid is free to detach (reaction (V) (Fig. 3)) and return to the appropriate amino acyl–RNA synthetase to be reused (reaction (II) (Fig. 3)).

Continuation of the chain proceeds in a stepwise fashion as the next amino acyl–RNA complex is guided into the position adjacent to that carrying the new peptide (reaction (VI) (Fig. 3)), another peptide bond is formed (repeat of reaction (IV) (Fig. 3)), and another sRNA is released (repeat of reaction (V) (Fig. 3)). This sequence is repeated for the insertion of each amino and residue in the growing chain. The ribosome moves along the mRNA so that it is always at the site of sRNA binding.

In reaction (VII) (Fig. 3) the chain is completed with the coupling of the carboxyl terminal residue. The newly-formed peptide chain is then detached (reaction (VIII) (Fig. 3)), and the ribosome leaves the mRNA. Both the mRNA and the ribosome can produce further copies of the peptide.

Although Fig. 3 shows only one peptide chain being formed on a messenger at a time, it is not requisite for a ribosome to complete its chain before the next ribosome attaches to the starting site of the mRNA. Actually, as will be seen in Section III E, many ribosomes can utilize a single mRNA at the same time, each bearing a peptide chain in a different stage of completion. Such structures are termed "polyribosomes" or "polysomes".

B. *The Genetic Code for Amino Acid Sequence*

Information for the determination of the amino acid sequence of a protein resides in the linear nucleotide sequence of the DNA of the gene, which is transcribed in complementary form in the mRNA molecule. The sequence of the nucleotides in mRNA then prescribes the order in which the sRNA molecules bearing amino acids will be brought to the growing point of the new peptide chain. The transfer of genetic information to amino acid sequence information is shown diagrammatically in Fig. 4. The action of the mRNA sequence in forming a specific peptide chain is illustrated in Fig. 5. Messenger RNA itself will be considered more fully in Section III D.

The most convincing demonstration that the linear sequence of components of a gene relates to the linear sequence of components of a protein is the work of Yanofsky et al. [424] In studies with the A protein component of the enzyme, tryptophan synthetase, in *E. coli*, they were able to show that the sites at which 16 mutations occurred, determined by careful genetic mapping, correspond linearly with observed changes in amino acid residues within the protein caused by these mutations.

Since there are 20 amino acids and only four common nucleotide bases in RNA, some *combination* of nucleotide bases was felt to be needed to "code" for a single amino acid. Many theories were advanced on the nature of this

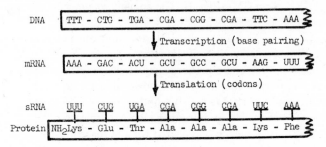

FIG. 4. The two-stage readout of the genetic code. The segment shown is the amino-terminal octapeptide of ribonuclease. *Transcription* refers to the production of messenger RNA as a complementary copy of DNA. *Translation* is the conversion from the four-character language of the messenger to the twenty-character language of proteins.

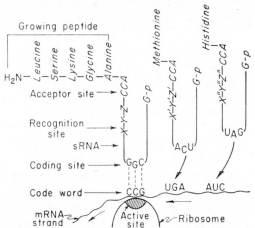

FIG. 5. Diagram of the functioning of the trinucleotide code in protein synthesis. (From Brotman and McGill[52].) The nucleotide sequences selected to correspond with methionine and histidine are not in accord with later findings (Table 2). Reproduced by courtesy of the Mayo Association, Rochester, Minnesota.

code[24] in the period 1954–61, but it was the proposals of Crick *et al.*[87] which have been confirmed by experimental evidence. Basing their conclusions mainly on a consideration of recombination frequencies of mutants of *E. coli*, Crick *et al.* said that:

(a) a sequence of three bases codes for one amino acid,

(b) the sequences along the nucleic acid chain are not overlapping,

(c) the sequence is read from one direction only, and

(d) probably more than one triplet can code for a single amino acid.

The same year Nirenberg and Matthaei [260] and Lengyel et al. [215] observed that the synthetic polynucleotide, polyU, will promote the formation specifically of polyphenylalanine when added to a preparation of E. coli ribosomes. UUU was thus established as the genetic code for the incorporation of phenylalanine.

A current listing of such words, or *codons*, is shown in Table 2. This list is compiled from several sources, and is neither claimed to be complete nor final, as there are still many disagreements between the results with different techniques. Many of these codons were derived by determining the amino

TABLE 2. TENTATIVE ASSIGNMENT OF THE 64 POSSIBLE NUCLEOTIDE CODEWORDS (CODONS) TO THE 20 COMMON AMINO ACIDS

(The nucleotide sequences listed are those proposed to direct the positioning of the amino acyl-adaptor RNA's specific for the corresponding amino acid. The codons UAA and UAG are believed to signal the termination of a peptide chain; the designations "ochre" and "amber" refer to mutants of bacteriophage in which the action of these codons was identified.)

Codon Amino acid	Codon Amino acid	Codon Amino acid	Codon Amino acid
UUU Phenylalanine	CUU Leucine	AUU Isoleucine	GUU Valine
UUC Phenylalanine	CUC Leucine	AUC Isoleucine	GUC Valine
UUA Leucine	CUA	AUA Isoleucine	GUA Valine
UUG Leucine	CUG Leucine (?)	AUG Methionine	GUG Valine
UCU Serine	CCU Proline	ACU Threonine	GCU Alanine
UCC Serine	CCC Proline	ACC Threonine	GCC Alanine
UCA Serine	CCA Proline	ACA Threonine	GCA Alanine
UCG Serine	CCG Proline	ACG Threonine	GCG Alanine
UAU Tyrosine	CAU Histidine	AAU Asparagine	GAU Aspartic acid
UAC Tyrosine	CAC Histidine	AAC Asparagine	GAC Aspartic acid
UAA "Ochre"	CAA Glutamine	AAA Lysine	GAA Glutamic acid
UAG "Amber"	CAG Glutamine	AAG Lysine	GAG Glutamic acid
UGU Cysteine	CGU Arginine	AGU Serine	GGU Glycine
UGC Cysteine	CGC Arginine	AGC Serine	GGC Glycine
UGA Tryptophan (?)	CGA Arginine	AGA Arginine (?)	GGA Glycine
UGG Tryptophan (?)	CGG Arginine	AGG	GGG Glycine

acids most readily incorporated into polypeptides, with synthetic polynucleotides containing two or more different bases, such as polyAG, polyAU. [266, 24, 84, 69] Rather than measuring formation of peptides, an innovation has been to measure the stimulation of binding of specific amino acyl–RNA complexes to ribosomes by *trinucleotides* of known sequence. [32] This technique has been particularly useful in ascertaining the sequence of the three bases within a codon.

Data on codons have also resulted from the study of amino acid substitutions caused by mutations. If it is assumed that a mutation affects only a single nucleotide base (a point mutation), then the codon for the original amino acid should differ in only one of its three nucleotide bases from the codon of its replacement. This reasoning has been applied to the tryptophan synthetase A protein of E. coli, [423] to the naturally occurring mutants of human hemoglobin, [346] and to the amino acid replacements caused in tobacco mosaic virus by the action of nitrous acid. The majority of these nitrous-acid induced changes are consistent with the expected deamination of C to U and A to G. [384, 24] A common substitution, for example, is isoleucine (codon:AUU) for threonine (codon:ACU). In this instance the cytidine residue of the threonine codon was converted to a uracil residue by deamination.

Fitch has deduced other information on codons from comparisons of amino acid compositions of several species of microorganisms with the frequency of occurrence of nucleotide doublets in their DNA. [109]

The triplet nature of the code has also received support from metabolic observations. In rat liver, the average length of the messenger RNA strand between sites of attachment of ribosomes was reported to be about 90 nucleotide residues; movement across this distance by a ribosome was found to lengthen the growing peptide chain by 30 amino acid residues. Hence three nucleotides corresponded to one amino acid. [358]

The code is said to be *degenerate*—that is, there is more than one codon (Table 2), and thus more than one adaptor RNA, which represents a single amino acid. [367] Two different sRNA molecules have been detected in E. coli which are specific for serine, and four for leucine. [25] Two of the latter are apparently restricted in their action to particular leucine residue sites along the chain of hemoglobin. [408]

The code is also apparently "universal". The synthetic polynucleotides give similar results with ribosomal systems of different species, and messenger RNA and adaptor RNA molecules can be interchanged between bacterial, viral and mammalian preparations with little effect on their function. [266]

C. Activation of Amino Acids: The Adaptor RNA Molecule

When it became possible to observe the incorporation of labeled amino acids into proteins in a cell-free system, efforts naturally were turned to isolating the action of the several components of this system. These components were soon resolved into: (a) ribosomes, (b) a source of high energy phosphate bonds, (c) GTP, (d) magnesium, and (e) factors in the particulate-free soluble fraction of the cell. The soluble factors could be precipitated at pH 5 and appeared to be enzymatic in nature. It was also learned that the "pH 5" fraction had the ability to catalyze the carboxyl activation of amino acids by forming amino acid-AMP compounds, which remained attached to the responsible enzyme. [162, 28] Simultaneously there was a consumption of ATP and the appearance of inorganic pyrophosphate (PP_i). The reaction could be followed by changes in either amino acids, the ATP, the PP_i, or by the subsequent addition of hydroxylamine which caused the carboxyl-activated amino acids to form hydroxamates. The reaction was found to be readily reversible.

Connection between the carboxyl activation reaction and the requirement for the pH 5 fraction by the ribosomal system was not apparent, however, until Hultin and Beshow [172] demonstrated the presence of a stable inter-mediate form of amino acids in liver supernatant, and Holley [167] furnished evidence that this was a complex of an amino acid with a soluble RNA present in the preparation.

The two-stage nature of the formation of the amino acid-RNA complexes was proved by Wong and Moldave [418] when they synthesized amino acyl-AMP compounds and showed that these could be bound by the activating enzyme. The complex could then either form amino acid-RNA or, by the reverse of reaction (I), could yield free amino acids and ATP with the consumption of PP_i.

The acyl bond formed with sRNA is an ester linkage between the carboxyl of the amino acid and the 3' (or 2') position (i.e. on the ribosyl group) of AMP. Migration of the acyl group between the 3' and 2' hydroxyl groups occurs readily, and the precise location in the living system is not certain.

Amino acyl-AMP esters or amino acyl-adenosine esters have been isolated following the action of ribonuclease. The bond is heat-stable in 1 M NaCl but is readily split in alkali [409, 429] or by reaction with hydroxylamine. Binding to an amino acid protects the ribosyl hydroxyl groups from the action of periodic acid. Proteolytic enzymes will liberate the amino acids with the same specificity with which these enzymes split amino acid esters. [311]

The equilibrium constants for the overall formation of threonyl-RNA and valyl-RNA are between 0·4 and 0·7, indicating that the acyl bond has some-what higher energy content than the usual ester bond. [163, 29, 30] The reaction is rapid—labeled amino acids appear in peptide form in less than 5 sec in *Azotobacter* [33] and in *E. coli* even at 0° in only 10 sec. [133]

Both reactions (I) and (II) are mediated by a single enzyme, an amino acyl-RNA synthetase. Berg and his associates [30] have shown that during 100-fold purification the abilities to activate valine with ATP and to transfer the activated valyl groups to RNA increase in parallel fashion. The inter-mediate compound, amino acyl-AMP, is not normally released from the enzyme but remains bound until it is transferred to RNA.

It is highly probable that there is a separate enzyme for the activation of each amino acid, [163, 30] but that the mechanism of the catalysis is similar for all of them. Berg *et al.* [30] have demonstrated that discrete enzymes activate leucine, valine, isoleucine and methionine in *E. coli*. Isolation of tryptophyl-RNA and tyrosyl-RNA synthetases from hog pancreas, [332] of a glycyl-RNA-synthetase from silkworms, [105] an alanyl-RNA synthetase from hog liver, [407] and an isoleucyl-RNA synthetase from *E. coli*[264] demonstrated both the existence and the omnipresence of these separate enzymes.

The synthetases are more discriminating in reaction (II) than in reaction (I). Isoleucyl-RNA synthetase will activate both valine and isoleucine, but will transfer only isoleucine to RNA.[29, 264] Valyl-RNA synthetase, on the other hand, will completely distinguish valine from isoleucine even at the activation step. Allo-isoleucine suppresses the formation of both valyl-RNA and isoleucyl-RNA, but does not affect the formation of leucyl-RNA.[222] Other analogs of amino acids, e.g. fluorophenylalanine, are in some cases not differentiated at all from the amino acid and are incorporated into peptide bonds.[29]

The α-amino group of the amino acid is not required for the synthetase reaction. N-acetylation of an amino acid, for instance, does not prevent it from being bound to RNA.[276] The dipeptide, glycyl-tryptophan, is not activated by tryptophyl-RNA synthetase[338] but glycyl-methionine and alanyl-methionine have been reported to substitute for methionine in reaction (I), when activation is measured by hydroxamate formation in crude preparation.[299]

The synthetases of one species will in general react with adaptor RNA molecules of other species, although occasionally with reduced efficiency.[30, 27, 300, 94, 179] The interchangeability appears to depend on the amino acid in question. The amino acyl-RNA products have different properties when heterologous systems are employed, but this has been ascribed to the existence of multiple adaptor RNA's (*vide supra*) for a single amino acid rather than to differences in the synthetases.[30, 179]

The pH optimum of different amino acyl-RNA synthetases varies—for the wheat germ-leucine enzyme optimal activity is observed at pH 6·8–7·1, while for the methionine enzyme it is at pH 8·1–8·5.[250] Synthetases can generally be classed as thiol enzymes, since heavy metal compounds inhibit reaction (I) and (II) in a reversible manner.

The adaptor RNA molecule. The compounds known variously as "soluble RNA" (sRNA), "transfer RNA" (tRNA or T-RNA), or "adaptor RNA" have a leading role in the drama of protein synthesis. Their ability to adapt amino acids so they can be recognized by a trinucleotide codon on the mRNA template is singular among biological molecules. Understandably, adaptor RNA has been the subject of intensive research in the past 6 years.[163, 29, 327]

Since there are multiple sRNA's for at least some of the 20 common amino acids, the number of different types is probably 40 or more. They have been detected in the soluble fraction of all tissues examined.[163] The different types of sRNA have very similar physical and chemical properties and their separation one from the other requires refined techniques. Isolation of individual sRNA species has been accomplished in a number of ways:

extraction with phenol, sodium lauryl sulfate or sodium chloride, followed by fractionation on columns of ECTEOLA-cellulose or methylated albumin, [367] of DEAE-dextran gel, [364] of calcium phosphate, or by countercurrent distribution. [95]

Two techniques have made use of the specific property of amino acid binding to aid the selectivity of purification. Stephenson and Zamecnik [364] oxidized an sRNA mixture with periodic acid while it contained bound valine. Upon removal of the valine and treatment of the then-exposed hydroxyl groups with a naphthol dye, they were able to follow specifically the course of sRNA$_{val}$† during fractionation. Bank et al. similarly [15] charged an sRNA mixture with a single amino acid, methionine, and then precipitated the sRNA$_{met}$† by formation of polymethionine on treatment with methionine-N-carboxyanhydride.

The sRNA species which have been isolated to date have all contained 75–90 nucleotide residues, corresponding to a molecular weight of about 30,000 and a sedimentation rate of about 4·5 S. [432, 267] Their average composition, on a mole percentage basis, is approximately A-18, G-31, C-28 and U-17 (sRNA from E. coli). [267, 327] Unlike other types of RNA, they are consistently found to contain significant quantities of unusual nucleotide bases, among them 2-methyl-adenine, methylguanine, thymine, hypoxanthine, methylaminocytidine and the unusual nucleoside, pseudouridine (5-ribosyluracil). [15, 99]

Holley and his collaborators, in a momentous piece of work, have recently published the complete nucleotide sequence of the alanine transfer RNA (sRNA$_{ala}$) isolated from yeast. [168] This is the first nucleic acid of any type for which the complete sequence is known. The sequence is:

pG—G—G—C—G—U—MeG—G—C—G—C—G—U—A—G—

DiHU—C—G—G—DiHU—A—G—C—G—C—DiMeG—C—U—

C—C—C—U—U—I—G—C—MeI—PsU—G—G—G—A—G—A—

G—U*—C—U—C—C—G(—G—T—PsU—C—G—)A—U—U—C—

C—G—G—A—C—U—C—G—U—C—C—A—C—C—A—OH

(The abbreviations for the unusual bases are: MeG = methylGMP; DiHU = 5,6-dihydroUMP; DiMeG = N^2-dimethylGMP; I = IMP; MeI = 1-methyl-IMP; T = riboTMP; PsU = pseudoUMP; U* = mixture of U and DiHU.) This RNA has a total of 77 nucleotides and a calculated molecular weight of 26,600 (as the sodium salt).

The unusual bases are revealed to be scattered throughout the chain, except that they are not found near the two ends. They tend to occur singly rather than

---

† "sRNA$_{val}$" indicates an adaptor RNA specific for valine, "sRNA$_{met}$" one specific for methionine, etc.

in a particular area. The sequence (—G—T—PsU—C—G—) shown in paren-theses is an interesting one, in that it is believed to be a common feature of acceptor RNA's. [168]

A GMP residue occupies the end having the free 5'-phosphate, and the sequence pCpCpA is found at the other end. These are also universal features of adaptor RNA's. [343] The ribose of the terminal pA residue is the site of the ester bond with the amino acyl group. Loss of one or more nucleotides from the 5'-phosphate terminus destroys the ability to accept amino acids, [72] however, so that both ends of the molecule are implicated in the amino acid binding or *recognition* site. Other regions probably contribute by increasing the specificity of recognition of amino acids or their synthetase enzymes or both. [31]

Secondary structure has been demonstrated to be essential to the function of sRNA. Denaturation by heat or bromination affects physical properties, such as the anomalous rotatory dispersion, and specificity of the recognition of amino acids in a parallel manner. [63, 10, 210] Organic solvents, urea and changes in temperature alter the coding properties of *E. coli* sRNA. [116, 349] X-Ray diffraction [354] and hydrogen exchange [103] studies have implied that as much as 82 per cent of the chain is coiled in a double-stranded helix. The difficulty with the application of these results is that helical structure for nucleic acids requires the Watson–Crick type of base pairing (A—U, G—C), and opportunities for such pairing are limited with the known sequences of nucleotides. [294, 168]

Figure 6 shows two possible conformations for sRNA$_{ala}$ proposed by Holley *et al.* The longest complementary sequences contain only five nucleo-tides, so that the double-stranded regions must be short, or the unusual nucleotides must be included in imperfect base pairing. A choice cannot be made between the two structures shown or other possible structures. The actual conformation of the molecule probably changes during its function.

If the codon for alanine is assumed to be GCU (Table 2), the complement-ary "anti-codon" site of sRNA$_{ala}$ would be CGA or its reverse, AGC. Each of these sequences occurs once in the chain (Fig. 6). In Fig. 6b, CGA is seen to be situated in an exposed position on the left-hand loop.

An alternative codon for alanine is GCC, the anti-codon for which is CGG or GGC. CGG appears in the right-hand loop of Fig. 6b between two dihydroU residues. The IGC sequence in the uppermost loop is another possibility for the coding site, since I would be equivalent to G in coding properties.

That the coding and recognition sites are distinct and not interdependent has been elegantly demonstrated by Chapeville *et al.* [68] and von Ehrenstein *et al.* [394] They charged RNA$_{cysH}$ with cysteine, then converted the attached cysteine group to an alanine group by reduction with Raney nickel. This treatment did not affect the coding site, since the alanine was then incorporated

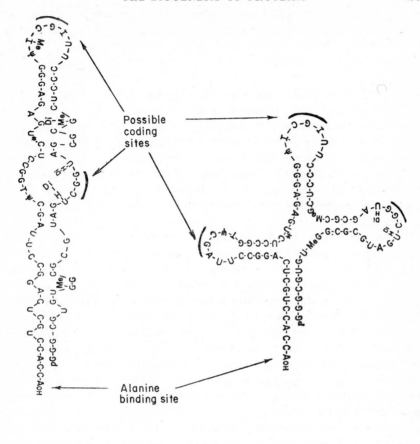

FIG. 6. Two possible configurations of yeast sRNA$_{ala}$, with opportunities for base pairing. (From Holley *et al.* [168]) ψ is pseudouridine; for other abbreviations tsee the text. Reproduced by courtesy of American Association for the Advancement of Science.

as though it were cysteine into rabbit hemoglobin, or into a polypeptide directed by polyUG as messenger. It has also been demonstrated that RNAase action can destroy the transfer function of sRNA's without removing the amino acid binding ability. [261]

Adaptor RNA is not inert, but undergoes some structural changes incident to its functioning. The pCpCpA terminal sequence is lost after the sRNA yields its amino acid and leaves the messenger, and these three nucleotides must be restored before the sRNA is again ready to accept an amino acid. Active methylation of some of the bases of sRNA has also been observed; there are at least six different enzymes which transfer a methyl group from S-adenosylmethionine to different bases of the RNA. [39, 175] Methylation of the sRNA is required before it can act in conjunction with the transferase from yeast, but not for the transferase from *E. coli*. [280] The significance of these metabolic transformations is obscure at present. Further information will be found in Chapter 8.

D. *Sequence Determination*: *the Messenger RNA Molecule*

Messenger RNA might be called the co-star, together with adaptor RNA, in protein production. Its role is to carry the genetic information stored in DNA to the ribosomes, where it acts as a template on which the amino acyl-RNA complexes condense. In addition to the name messenger RNA (mRNA), these compounds have been termed "informational RNA", "complementary RNA", and "DNA-dependent RNA" (D-RNA). The term *messenger RNA*, abbreviated mRNA, has come into the most common usage, and will be employed here.

A messenger RNA strand originates as a complementary copy of a DNA strand, formed through the same type of base pairing that holds the DNA in double-stranded helix. The mRNA then migrates within the cell to the site of protein synthesis, where it is bound to ribosomes and its sequence information is translated to form a new peptide chain. Figures 4 and 5 illustrate this intermediary role of mRNA. The terms "transcription" and "translation" have come into general use for the DNA-RNA and mRNA-protein steps. *Transcription* refers to the rewriting of the genetic information in the formation of mRNA; *translation* of the coded information into another "language", that of amino acid sequence, occurs in the formation of proteins. The one-way flow of information from nuclear DNA via mRNA to protein is called the "Central Dogma".

The present concept of a messenger RNA molecule is an interesting example of the way in which one area of research can benefit from the interpretation of results obtained in a somewhat distant area. The mRNA theory arose as an hypothesis to explain the genetic aspects and temporal features of RNA and protein metabolism incident to the induction of enzymes in bacteria. [178] Most of the proof of the existence of mRNA, however, has come from other systems.

Considerable effort is being expended in attempts to isolate specific mRNA compounds. Techniques employed include centrifugation through density gradients of sucrose or cesium chloride or the use of ECTEOLA-cellulose and other chromatographic media.

A purified RNA should display a number of properties in order to be called a messenger; to be convincing as many criteria as possible ought to be applied to a single preparation. Some of the functional characteristics by which mRNA is identified are:

1. *Metabolic instability*, usually by a rapid uptake of radioactive nucleic acid precursors.

2. *Origination from DNA* and subsequent migration from the DNA or the nucleus.

3. *Size* compatible with the ability to code for peptide chains of the required length.

4. Composition and base sequences which are *complementary to the DNA* from which it was presumably produced.

5. Ability to *bind to ribosomes*, usually with the formation of polyribosomes.

6. Ability to cause the *formation of protein*, particularly of a specific protein, in conjunction with ribosomes and amino acyl-RNA mixtures.

1. *Metabolic instability.* It was partly from the observations of Volkin and Astrachan in 1956 [390] that Jacob and Monod drew [178] their conclusions concerning messenger RNA. Volkin and Astrachan found that infection of *E. coli* with bacteriophage caused the appearance of a minor RNA component complementary in base composition to DNA, and which rapidly incorporated labeled phosphate. Elaboration of such studies has shown that, beginning at 5–7 min after infection, new RNA is formed which is a copy of the viral DNA rather than of the host's DNA. [76, 355] In HeLa cells infected with *Vaccinia* virus a similar phenomenon occurs with an induction period of 30 min. [21]

Enzyme induction in bacteria, like infection by viruses, causes increased RNA metabolism prior to enzyme production. Yeast cells, which produce new enzymes upon changing from a rich to a minimal medium, at the same time exhibit a new RNA which is complementary in composition to DNA. [248]

The rapid uptake of isotopes is the most convenient way to follow messenger RNA during its isolation, and has been widely used for this purpose. In *E. coli* which are neither infected with virus nor undergoing enzyme induction, about 4 per cent of the RNA will incorporate P^{32} after a 10-sec exposure; this RNA has a base composition complementary to the bacterial RNA, and is later found attached to ribosomes. [48, 139] Radioactive RNA fractions fulfilling other criteria for messenger RNA have been isolated from rat liver after 1–7 min doses of radioactive phosphate or orotic acid. [192, 92, 252, 381]

2. *Origination from DNA.* Detection of a newly-formed (radioactive) RNA in close association with DNA has supported the mRNA concept. Kidson *et al.*, for instance, were able to isolate a complex of radioactive RNA with DNA from rat liver after a 7-min labeling period with H^3-orotic acid. [192] The site of synthesis in animal cells appears to be the nucleo-chromatin. [126] Whether the synthesis of the new RNA requires the participation of DNA is often tested by the use of Actinomycin D, an inhibitor of DNA transcription. [130]

DNA normally exists as two paired strands, and it is not clear as yet if or how these strands open to permit transcription, or whether both strands can be copied. Only double-stranded DNA produces free messenger RNA, although single-stranded DNA, such as that of the phage $\phi X174$ or single strands obtained by heat denaturation from double-stranded DNA, can act as primer for the synthesizing enzyme, RNA polymerase.[96, 355, 419] When single strands are used, the RNA formed remains bound to the DNA primer and is not available for a messenger function. There is evidence that, although double-stranded DNA is required for production of mRNA, only one of the complementary DNA strands is normally copied, and the direction of synthesis of the mRNA is *antiparallel* to the DNA. [20]

The *E. coli* ribosomal preparation of Lamborg and Zamecnik[209] attracted investigators of mRNA function when it was learned that protein synthesis in this system was inhibited by removal of DNA, by addition of DNAase or by other means. Subsequent readdition of DNA plus RNA polymerase and nucleoside triphosphates restored the protein synthetic ability. [262, 380, 96, 419] The DNA added could be of bacterial or viral origin. The significant observation for the mRNA theory was that the DNA caused synthesis of RNA before formation of protein occurred.

This *E. coli* system will also produce an inducible enzyme, β-galactosidase, *in vitro*. Upon destruction of the intrinsic DNA, enzyme synthesis ceases. It can be restored by addition of DNA from induced *E. coli* cells, [185] but not by addition of DNA from non-induced cells. Enzyme induction will be considered further in a later section.

3. *Size.* Preparations with sedimentation velocities ranging from 4 to 30 S and judged to contain mRNA have been isolated from sources as varied as yeast,[248] *E. coli*,[355] Neurospora,[397] HeLa cells after *Vaccinia* infection,[21] rabbit reticulocytes,[81, 206, 207, 229] and rat liver ribosomes or nuclei.[268, 252, 253, 273, 381] The broad spectrum of sizes implied by such a range of sedimentation velocities might be expected if each mRNA codes for a different protein chain, since the range of sizes of protein chains is also very broad. However, measurements of the size of an isolated specific mRNA are still lacking.

If all of the nucleotides of an mRNA are involved in the trinucleotide coding, and there is no overlapping of the code, an mRNA would be expected to have a molecular weight 9–10 times that of the protein for which it codes. Otsuka and Terayama[273] found little evidence for mRNA in rat liver as large as 18S, which is the calculated sedimentation velocity for a messenger of molecular weight of 600,000, sufficient to code for the chief protein produced by liver, serum albumin (molecular weight 65,000). However, Marbiax and Burny[229] reported the recovery of a 9-10S "mRNA" from rabbit reticulocytes, which would have a molecular weight of about 160,000 and thus be the proper size to code for one of the chains of hemoglobin (molecular weight 16,500).

Judging by the prevalent strand seen by electron microscopy in reticulocytes, the length of the messenger for a chain of hemoglobin is 1700–2100 Å. If 3·4 Å is assumed as the length of a single nucleotide, the messenger for a chain of hemoglobin would be only 1500 Å long. The discrepancy may reveal that the mRNA strand assumes a more extended form than the usual RNA chain, or it may be due to artefacts inherent in preparing specimens for electron microscopy.

4. *Complementarity to DNA*. Pure mRNA should have a base composition which is exactly complementary to the DNA from which it was made, that is, the relative content of A, C, G and U of the mRNA should correspond to the content of T, G, C, and A respectively of the DNA. This goal is approached in systems making mRNA from added viral DNA,[390, 355] but it has not yet been possible to isolate from rat liver mRNA preparations which are more than 60 per cent complementary to rat liver DNA.[46, 252] The remainder of these preparations has the composition of ribosomal RNA. The rat liver mRNA isolated by Ogata *et al.*[268] and Otsuka and Terayama[273] was not at all complementary to liver DNA in its base composition.

The *sequence* of nucleotides in mRNA, as well as its relative *composition*, should be complementary to that of its parent DNA. Bautz and Heding[20] have found in the mRNA made in response to T4 phage many trinucleotides which are complementary to sequences in the phage DNA. The technique of hybridization has also been useful in demonstrating complementarity between T4 or $\phi X174$ mRNA and its DNA. In this procedure single strands of the DNA are obtained by heating, then mixed with the mRNA strands either in solution, in agar, or attached to a carrier such as acetylated phosphocel-lulose.[140, 355]

5. *Binding to ribosomes*. The rapidly-labeled RNA detected in *E. coli*, with or without phage infection, can be further observed to attach to *E. coli* ribosomes.[139, 48] Addition of mRNA, or of artificial messengers such as polyU, evokes the appearance of polyribosomes.[18, 21] Other aspects of the binding of mRNA to ribosomes and the formation of polyribosomes will follow in Section III D.

6. *Stimulation of protein synthesis*. Ability to direct the appearance of a new, specific protein is the ultimate test of the mRNA concept. While amino acid incorporation into total protein of DNA-free ribosomes from *E. coli*[209] can be stimulated by the addition of TMV-RNA[260] or rat liver nuclear[46, 92, 236] or ribosomal[273] RNA, this is not convincing proof of the existence of specific messenger molecules.

Several reports have dealt in a preliminary fashion, at least, with the production of specific proteins. With the *E. coli* ribosome system, addition of RNA from rabbit reticulocytes could cause amino acids from amino acyl-RNA complexes to be incorporated in a protein with the properties of rabbit hemoglobin.[257] The hemoglobin formed was identified by chromatography of its tryptic peptides, which makes this report the most conclusive demonstration of the existence of mRNA to date. Rabbit or duck reticulocyte ribosomes can also apparently be deceived into producing heterologous hemoglobin by addition of RNA from nucleated red cell precursors of the opposing species. [433] Addition of crude RNA preparations from chicken liver to rat liver ribosomes has been reported to result in some incorporation of labeled amino acids into chicken serum albumin, [391] and nuclear RNA from the epidermis of insect larvae has caused the appearance of DOPA decarboxylase activity in rat liver microsomes. [335]

It is probably wise to accept most of these reports with caution pending substantiation and further evaluation. A searching investigation by chemical and serological methods of the proteins formed when *E. coli* ribosomes are directed by TMV-RNA failed to detect any of the expected viral coat proteins or other proteins formed when the virus infects tobacco leaves. [1] Absolute proof of the action of messenger RNA must be regarded as lacking, pending isolation and characterization of a single RNA species having the correct size, a base sequence complementary to DNA, and which will unequivocably direct the formation of the expected protein in a heterologous system.

The Stimulus for Messenger RNA Production; the Regulation of Protein Synthesis

The control of protein synthesis—which proteins are made by a particular cell and in what quantities—is such an important related question that it deserves consideration in a chapter such as this, although our main concern is the mechanism of how these proteins are made. If the messenger RNA scheme is the general means by which all proteins are formed, then presence or absence of active mRNA might be the significant factor in regulation of protein formation. Messenger RNA does not last indefinitely—its lifespan appears to be related to the rapidity with which it is used to form proteins. Thus, in a rapidly growing and dividing cell such as a bacterium in a rich medium, catabolism of mRNA occurs within minutes, [216, 12, 368] while in adult, non-dividing tissue, such as liver, [381, 389] it lasts several hours. In highly differentiated tissues—reticulocytes, [257] thyroid, [336] lens or feathers [333, 334]—it is stable for a day or more.

It would be expected that an increase in the effective mRNA level would be found when a tissue is called upon to increase its output of a specific protein. Indeed, such appears to be the case in serum albumin production by the liver. Lowering the circulating albumin level, e.g. by experimental nephrosis, causes an increased rate of albumin synthesis by the microsomes of the liver. When the nuclear RNA from the livers of such albumin-deficient rats was added to microsomes, it was found to be somewhat more effective than RNA from normal rats in promoting the appearance of labeled amino acids in albumin. [235] Conversely, a decrease in the level of mRNA has been postulated to be responsible for the decreased activity of rat liver ribosome preparations when the rats are placed on a protein-free diet. [288]

Jacob and Monod [178] originally proposed the mRNA concept to point out a way in which a cell could turn on and off the synthesis of a protein for which it carried the gene, in particular the synthesis of an enzyme induced by the addition of the substrate of that enzyme. The diagram from their original article is reproduced in Fig. 7. The scheme shown has fared well [8, 363] in the four years since it appeared. It proposes the existence of specific

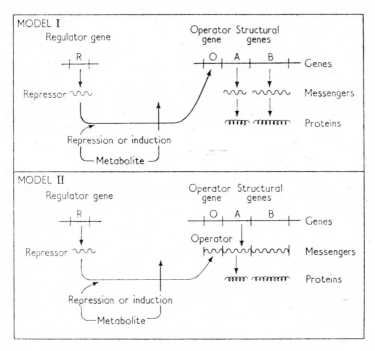

FIG. 7. The repressor–operon concept of Jacob and Monod. [178]
Reproduced by courtesy of Academic Press, New York.

repressor molecules, produced by *regulator genes* which are distinct from the usual *structural genes*. Several functionally-related structural genes are linked to an *operator gene* which initiates the transcription of the structural genes in mRNA form. The repressor normally inhibits the action of the genes by combining with the operator.

When a substrate is added, it combines with the repressor for which it is specific, and prevents the inhibition of the operator. This is termed *de-repression*. The gene then produces messenger(s) for the one or more enzymes needed to metabolize the added substrate, plus ancillary enzymes such as permeases and degradative enzymes which promote its passage through the cell wall or which act on the product of the first enzyme in the chain.

In the case of an enzyme or chain of enzymes which produce a component needed by the cell—histidine in *Salmonella typhinurium*, for example[7]—the repressor (a better term now would be *effector* [363])—has been considered to stimulate rather than inhibit the transcription of the gene via the operator. When there is an excess of histidine in the cell, some of it combines with the corresponding repressor (effector) and prevents its stimulating action. On the other hand, when the cellular histidine is exhausted, the repressor (effector) is freed and acts upon the operator to allow production of the chain of ten enzymes which synthesize histidine in this organism. [7]

Two alternatives are proposed in Fig. 7. The structural genes may form separate messengers (Model I), or the entire unit or *operon* controlled by one operator may be transcribed intact as a polycistronic messenger (Model II). The evidence available favors the latter choice, that is, that the unit of messenger synthesis is the *operon* rather than the *cistron*. [8] The histidine operon in *S. typhimurium*, in controlling the production of a series of ten enzymes, apparently forms only one large mRNA molecule of about 10,000 nucleotides. [7]

Other evidence for the polycistronic nature of mRNA comes from the study of viruses. Virus particles are believed to act as multicistronic operons, and are known to cause a number of new proteins to be formed in their host. Upon infection by TMV-RNA, aggregates of eight ribosomes with the TMV-RNA are seen before appreciable new protein appears. [395] Presumably the ribosomes attach only at points on the messenger where protein chains commence, so that each of the eight ribosomes in this instance may indicate the start of a separate protein on a polycistronic messenger.

The phage *MSϕ2* induces at least three new proteins in infected *E. coli* with a single RNA molecule. [270] One of these three proteins does not appear for 6 min after the other two; the delay has been interpreted as suggesting some regulation of programming at the translation (mRNA functioning) level as well as at the level of the gene.

Ames and Hartman [7] have proposed that the reading of polycistronic messengers may be controlled by special "modulating triplets". These would signal the end of the message for a single enzyme by coding for special adaptor RNA types which would cause the nascent protein to leave the messenger.

A weak point in the repressor scheme of Jacob and Monod is that the repressor itself still eludes investigators. These highly specific molecules were first proposed to consist of RNA, but later the idea appeared that the repressor is a protein, perhaps an enzyme regulating the restoration of the pCpCpA terminus of specific adaptor RNA molecules (with modulating triplets?) required for translation of individual cistrons. [363]

Many enzyme systems inducible in bacteria—in addition to the histidine synthetase already mentioned—fit well on genetic analysis with the operon theory,[8] but detection of the implicated mRNA's has lagged far behind.

The role of mRNA in β-glucosidase induction in yeast, for example, has been substantiated only by kinetic evidence on the appearance of newly formed RNA upon induction. [141] Induction of penicillinase in *Bacillus cereus* can occur even *without* prior RNA synthesis. [146]

Hormones frequently stimulate protein synthesis, and recently it has been proposed that the hormone acts as a "de-repressor" which permits the appearance of the appropriate messengers. [296] In looking over the tabulated evidence, [315] it appears that this mechanism has mainly been inferred from observations that prior administration of actinomycin D—which prevents transcription of DNA—also prevents the formation of newly labeled RNA and of the stimulus of protein synthesis.

Cortisol, for example, causes increased synthesis in the liver of amino acid degradative enzymes such as tryptophan pyrrolase [324] and tyrosine-α-ketoglutarate transaminase. [16] Stimulation of uptake of labeled orotic acid into nuclear RNA preceeds the stimulation of enzyme synthesis; [16, 406] the activity of the nuclear RNA polymerase is found to be increased. Blocking of transcription by actinomycin D is effective only if the inhibitor is supplied shortly after giving the hormone, i.e. while the new messengers presumably are being made. [122] The effects of growth hormone [200] and thyroxine [377] on the rat liver, of estrogen [142] on the rat uterus, of testosterone on rat prostate gland [410] and of aldosterone on sodium transport [285] have been claimed to involve messenger RNA's. Even the plant hormones, indoleacetic acid [74] and gibberellic acid [386] have been included.

The action of actinomycin D is not universal in blocking hormonal stimulation of protein synthesis, however, [351, 420] and it is difficult to separate fact from fancy at this stage of investigation. The most direct findings pertinent to hormone action are that H³-estrogen becomes specifically bound to a macromolecular "receptor" site in rat uterine tissue. [375] This receptor has the capability of inhibiting nuclear RNA polymerase, a function which is blocked by the binding of estrogen. Perhaps the receptor is the sought-for repressor.

Differentiation of tissues implies that, although all somatic cells of a multicellular organism contain the same genetic complement, only certain genes are active in the more highly-differentiated cells. Hence the messenger RNA's of a tissue should be characteristic of that tissue and of its function, and would be expected to differ from tissue to tissue. Hybridization studies in agar support this view; the DNA from 6 mouse tissues showed the occurrence of common complementary strands, while the rapidly-labeled RNA's from these tissues were each distinct. [239] New specific RNA molecules, presumably mRNA, have been detected upon abrupt changes in development of widely diverse organisms: [327] in *Bacillus subtilis* upon sporulation, germination, or "step-down" transition from a rich medium; [97] in peanut cotyledons upon water imbibition; [230] in sea urchin embryos just prior to gastrulation;[78] and in the developing lens of the chick embryo at the time of completion of morphogenesis and the inception of production of a new protein, α-crystallin.[334] Differentiated tissues with low rates of protein turnover, such as striated muscle, have a low content of mRNA.[112] Differentiation of tissues may be related to hormonal action—thyroxine, for example, seems to control the metamorphosis of the tadpole—and so it is not surprising that hormones affect protein synthesis differently in different tissues. Cortisol stimulates protein synthesis in liver but depresses synthesis in thymus.[277] Lack of cortisol causes the activity of mRNA (determined by measuring the amount of ribosomal aggregates) in the anterior pituitary to increase.[202] This is a reflection of the increased output of the polypeptide hormone, adrenocorticotropin.

It has been proposed that drugs, particularly carcinogens such as methylcholanthrene, cause the formation of new enzymes via de-repression and the concomitant formation of new mRNA.[125] There is obvious interest in the possibility that disruption of the control of genetic activity is an early event in carcinogenesis, and that detailed analysis of the changes in specific messenger RNA's will provide information relevant to these events.

Acetylation of nuclear histones has been advanced as a means of regulating the rate of protein synthesis at the messenger level. Acetylated histones bind DNA as do their non-acetylated counterparts, but do not permit transcription of the bound DNA by RNA synthesis.[4] This is one of the first suggestions for a functional role of the protein components of the nucleus. Bonner et al.[38] found that chromatin from pea plant cotyledons would direct the formation of the characteristic "reserve protein" of pea cotyledons in the E. coli ribosome system, but that chromatin from pea buds was inactive unless histone was first removed from it. A link between repressors and histones would be desirable although the search for it may have a somewhat teleological basis.

E. The Site of Protein Formation: The Ribosome and Polyribosome

Named for their high content of RNA, ribosomes are submicroscopic particles which are found in almost every location where protein synthesis is occurring. Pseudonyms are "Palade granules" or "ribonucleoprotein particles". They are indispensable for protein synthesis in cell-free systems,[219] and a great deal of effort has been expended in studying them.

The typical ribosome [163, 30, 305] is a roughly spherical particle measuring about 170×200 Å. It sediments with a velocity of 70–80S, corresponding to a molecular weight of about 4×10^6, of which usually 50 per cent is RNA and the remainder protein.

When the concentration of magnesium ion is lowered to 10^{-4} M, ribosomes dissociate reversibly into two smaller units, usually termed "30S" and "50S" particles for their approximate sedimentation velocities. The 30S *particle* contains RNA of 16–18S and molecular weight 0.55×10^6. It has been described as flat and irregular[163] or as flat and rectangular with horizontal stripes.[356] Its dimensions are about 95×170 Å.

The 50S *particle* contains RNA of 23–28S and molecular weight 1.1×10^6. It measures about 140×170 Å, and its shape has been seen to resemble a dome[163] or a flat cylinder with roughly pentagonal cross-section.[356] The possibility has been raised on the basis of kinetic data that the 50S particle may comprise intertwining strands of used mRNA templates.[240]

The relative nucleotide base composition of the RNA of typical ribosomes is A-25, U-20, G-33, and C-22. There is little difference between the composition of the 30S and 50S subunits. The high guanine content is characteristic. X-ray diffraction photographs imply the presence of about 25 per cent of the total RNA chain in helical form.

The protein of ribosomes has an average molecular weight of only 25,000 based on the proportion of amino terminal amino acid residues.[305] It contains no cysteine.[163] Traces of various enzymatic activities have been observed in ribosomes, but usually these are decreased by further washing. The only enzymes which are likely to be integral parts of the ribosomes are intrinsic RNAase and DNAase.

In mammalian cells ribosomes chiefly occur bound to cytoplasmic membranes, from which they can be removed by the action of various detergents or high concentrations of salt. Ribosomes of bacteria, yeast and reticulocytes are not usually attached to such membranes, and can be obtained simply by rupturing the cell membrane and centrifuging. It has been estimated that there are about 18,000 ribosomes in a single organism of *E. coli*[133] and about 22,000 in a reticulocyte.[238]

Complexing between mRNA and ribosomes. When a ribosome attaches to a messenger RNA molecule, reaction (IX) (Fig. 3), protein synthesis can commence. The site of attachment on the mRNA is the codon corresponding to the amino terminus of the intended protein. It is reported to be at the 3′-OH terminus of the mRNA.[102] Attachment of mRNA is usually detected by the appearance of new particulate species having higher sedimentation velocities. The mRNA of *T*2 phage[304] and the synthetic messenger, polyU, have thus been observed to attach to ribosomes from *E. coli*[17] or reticulocytes.[35]

Single ribosomes attached to messenger can be active in protein synthesis.[147] The nascent protein strand appears to stabilize the complex against dissociation such as that caused by removal of magnesium ion.[326] Attachment of ribosomes to mRNA requires the presence of magnesium and potassium ions, but it is unlikely that it requires energy or is enzymatic in nature.[330] If there is a requirement for energy,[171] it may be to permit synthesis of the first few peptide bonds of the nascent protein strand to give increased stability to the attachment.

A ribosome has only a single site for messenger attachment,[145, 128] and this has been shown to be on the 30S subunit. [271, 358] Figure 8 illustrates the binding diagrammatically. The length of the segment of mRNA which attaches to the ribosome is estimated to be 184 Å, equivalent to 27 nucleotide residues. To determine this figure, Takanami and Zubay [373] took advantage of the finding that mRNA (in this case polyU) is protected from the action of RNAase at sites where it is attached to ribosomes. [144] They caused polyU to attach to *E. coli* ribosomes, then exposed the complex to pancreatic RNAase. Upon removal of the RNAase and the small fragments resulting from the digestion, dissociation of the remaining polyU-ribosome complex yielded primarily 27-nucleotide segments of polyU.

Ribosomes will attach only to single-stranded RNA molecules, those with double strands or a high degree of secondary structure being inactive. While the current theory regards ribosomes as relatively non-specific agents in protein synthesis, this may not be supported by actuality. The affinity for synthetic polynucleotides is not the same for all species—*E. coli* ribosomes will bind polyC, polyA, and polyU with increasing affinity, but reticulocyte ribosomes will bind only polyU. More significantly, the production of β-galactosidase in a cell-free system [185] requires not only DNA from induced bacteria, but also ribosomes from induced cells. It seems that ribosomes have specific properties which have not yet been discovered.

The Polyribosome

While single ribosomes attached to messenger RNA can effect protein synthesis, more commonly the active complexes have been found to be aggregates of three or more ribosomes along a single strand of RNA. [127, 263, 400] These aggregates, termed "polysomes" or "ergosomes" in addition to "polyribosomes", can both be observed visually with the electron microscope or isolated from tissues by centrifugation through density gradients. They have been reported in bacteria, [320] yeast, [231] leaves exposed to light, [73] HeLa cells, [411] liver, [263] reticulocytes [301, 232, 238] and bone marrow cells, heart, [291] skeletal muscle [49] and chick embryo fibroblasts. [203] Their presence correlates with active protein synthesis, since they disappear in inactive *Neurospora* [156] or upon maturation of the rabbit reticulocyte. [232]

In Fig. 9a one can see polyribosomes in the cytoplasm of a nucleated red blood cell of a human fetus. Size of the aggregates ranges from about 3 to 12 ribosomes. Polyribosomes in a rabbit reticulocyte are shown enlarged in Fig. 9b. The proposed mRNA is clearly visible as a thread connecting the ribosomes; the ribosomes number four to five in the most common aggregates in reticulocytes. [232,238]

The length of the mRNA thread in Fig. 9b is 1700–2800 Å. The distance *between* ribosomes along the mRNA strand of reticulocyte polyribosomes is about 300 Å, corresponding to about 90 nucleotides. [358]

Figure 9c, taken from Watson's Nobel Prize lecture in 1962, [404] is a functional diagram of polyribosomes such as those in Figs. 9a and 9b.

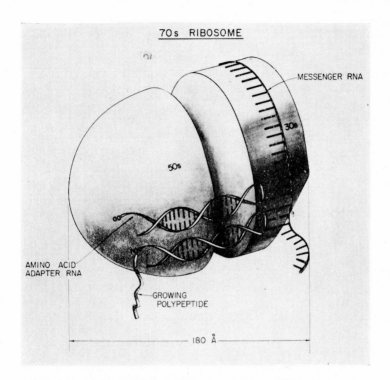

FIG. 8. Hypothetical model of the function of a 70S ribosome in protein synthesis. The helical structure shown for sRNA is diagrammatic and is not intended to represent its true configuration (From Zubay.[435]) Reproduced by courtesy of American Association for the Advancement of Science.

facing page 510

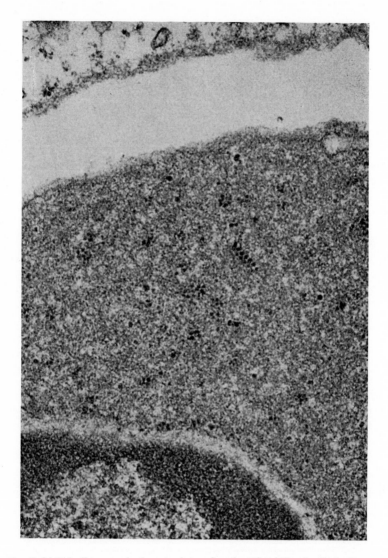

Fig. 9. (a) Polyribosomes in the cytoplasm of nucleated red blood cell of a 9-week human fetus. Electron micrograph courtesy of Dr. C. A. Ashley of the Mary Imogene Bassett Hospital, Cooperstown, N.Y. The tissue was fixed in glutaraldehyde and osmic acid and stained with uranyl acetate and lead acetate. ($\times$ 50,000.)

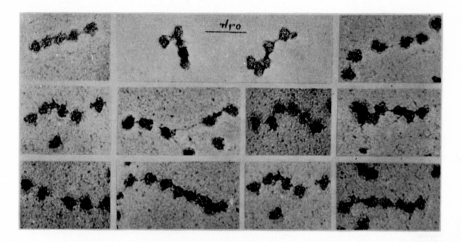

(b) Polyribosomes isolated from rabbit reticulocytes, stained positively with uranyl acetate. (From Rich, Warner and Goodman.[301]) Reproduced by courtesy of Cold Spring Harbor Laboratory for Quantitative Biology.

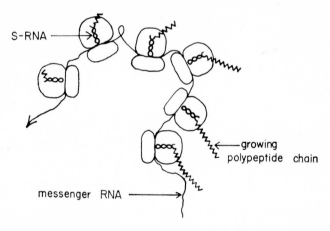

(c) Diagram of the interaction of ribosomes and messenger RNA to form a polyribosome. (From Watson.[404]) Reproduced by courtesy of American Association for Advancement of Science.

Some polyribosomes reach relatively tremendous proportions. Aggregates of 40 ribosomes are seen in HeLa cells [411] and greater than 100-ribosomal units have been reported to occur in muscle [49] and fibroblasts, [203] where they could be presumed to manufacture the long protein chains of myosin and collagen respectively. In general, the rate of amino acid incorporation by polyribosomes increases with increasing number of ribosomes.

F. *The Biosynthetic Reaction*

The ingredients for this climactic stage of protein biosynthesis are the messenger RNA, now linked to a ribosomal particle at the point where a peptide chain is to be started, and a supply of amino acyl-RNA complexes, which are present in soluble form. Synthesis involves three specific events for the incorporation of each amino acid residue (refer to Fig. 3):

reaction (VI)—*attachment* of an sRNA, bearing its amino acyl group, to the mRNA and to the ribosome, adjacent to the sRNA carrying the growing peptide chain.

reaction (IV)—*transfer* of the carboxyl group of the peptide from its sRNA to form a peptide bond with the α-amino group of the newly-added amino acyl-RNA.

reaction (V) —*release* of the sRNA freed of the peptide chain from the ribosome-mRNA complex.

Reaction (III), the attachment of two amino acyl-RNA's, is necessary only at the initiation of a peptide chain. The sequence of reactions (VI)-(V)-(IV) repeats in a cyclical fashion as the mRNA moves with relation to the ribosome by a distance of one codon with each cycle. [327, 330]

The stepwise nature of peptide bond formation has been demonstrated by (a) separating the two enzymes which take part in reactions (VI) and (IV), (b) detection of amino acyl-RNA bound to mRNA-ribosomes, and (c) detection of peptidyl-RNA complexes likewise bound to mRNA-ribosomes. Using the two enzymes alternatingly, Arlinghaus, Schaeffer and Schweet [11] were able to conduct the synthesis of the peptides Phe-Phe and Phe-Phe-Phe with polyU, reticulocyte ribosomes, and Phe-RNA in stepwise fashion. The overall process has been demonstrated in normal and regenerating liver in reticulocytes, *E. coli*, and pea seedlings, and has been shown to yield specific proteins such as hemoglobin [257] and possibly serum albumin. [160]

Attachment of amino acyl-RNA to mRNA-ribosome. Use of labeled sRNA with or without a charge of labeled amino acid permitted Hoagland and Comly [164] to observe that sRNA binds to ribosomes (presumably containing mRNA) and, after forming peptides, is released intact. The intermediate complex, amino acyl-RNA-mRNA-ribosome, has been detected in ribosome and polyribosome preparations from reticulocytes and rat liver. [59, 11, 181] Further investigation showed that the presence of amino acid on the sRNA is not required in order for the sRNA to bind to the ribosome, sRNA alone being attached equally well. The labile pCpCpA terminus (amino acid binding site) of the sRNA must be intact, however, and probably assists with the binding, since the pCpCpA sequence is protected against RNAase action while it is bound. [330]

At least three laboratories have separated the "binding" enzyme (reaction (VI) (Fig. 3)) from the "peptide synthetase", reaction (IV), [107, 255, 11] both of which are present in soluble form in the cell. The exact role of the binding enzyme is not clear; if the $MgCl_2/KCl$ ratio is high, sRNA can attach non-enzymatically [79]—a low $MgCl_2/KCl$ ratio, on the other hand, favors the enzymatic reaction. The action of the enzyme may be related to the concurrent movement of the mRNA relative to the ribosome. [330] GTP is likewise utilized in a manner which is obscure at present; [79] it may participate in the movement of the ribosome, or in preparing the ribosome to receive another sRNA.

The initation of a peptide chain requires attachment of *two* amino acyl-RNA's, reaction (III) (Fig. 3), before the first peptide bond can be joined. The ribosome at this time is situated at the initial codon at the 3'-hydroxyl end of the mRNA. [84, 102] A brief time lag seen before labeled amino acids appear in the form of bound peptides at a linear rate suggests that this initial binding of two sRNA's is slower than the subsequent steps, [2, 79] and that it may be the rate-limiting reaction in chain formation.

The portion of the sRNA which binds to the messenger is presumably the anti-codon (see Fig. 5). Other portions, including that holding the nascent peptide, bind to the 50S *subunit* of the ribosome [62] (Fig. 8). Two sRNA's can be attached per ribosome, [11] one more firmly than the other. Note that, as the cycle of reactions (Fig. 3) proceeds, the sRNA has bound to it, first, a single amino acid, then the entire nascent peptide chain, and finally nothing. The growing peptide chain stabilizes the complex [326] and probably accounts for differences in the firmness of attachment of the sRNA's.

Formation of the peptide bond. The exact nature of this final reaction (reaction (IV) (Fig. 3)) in the path from amino acid to peptide chain is still conjectural. The energy of the amino acyl ester bond to the sRNA may be sufficient in itself to allow the transfer of its carbonyl group to a peptide linkage, or the energy from the observed GTP-GDP split may be used to activate the carbonyl group further. The requirement for GTP in the final reactions of peptide bond formation has been recognized since 1956, [187] but whether it acts in the binding reaction, in the carbonyl transfer, or in the ribosomal movement mentioned previously remains to be seen. [11, 79] Hoagland et al. [165] have presented evidence that GTP antagonizes a normally-occurring thermolabile inhibitor of the last stages of protein synthesis, and may thus provide a means of controlling the rate of synthesis at the ribosomal level.

The soluble enzyme catalyzing reaction (IV), peptide synthetase, is currently under study. [255, 2, 11, 186, 330] It requires thiol groups for activity, [393, 11] and probably attaches to the surface of the 50S segment of the ribosome in the course of its action.

Hawtrey [148] has postulated a credible mechanism for the transfer reaction (IV), which satisfies the observations that GTP is needed and that the growing peptide always remains attached to a molecule of sRNA. [128] (Fig. 10). The acyl carbon of the peptide is visualized to form an orthoester, under direction of the synthetase enzyme, with the 2′ *and* 3′ hydroxyls of the ribose

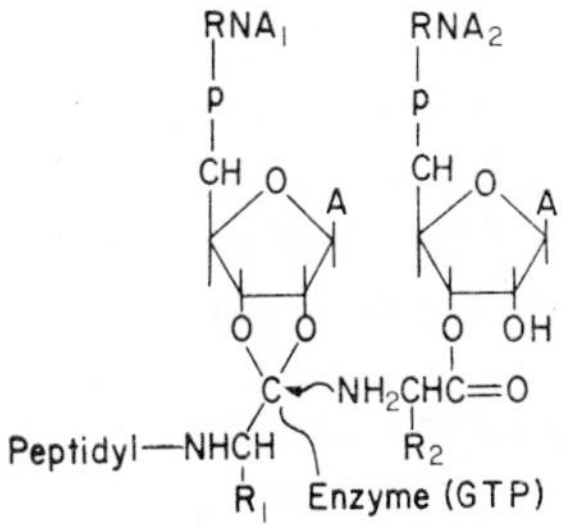

FIG. 10. Possible mechanism for peptide bond formation from amino acyl-RNA compounds, as proposed by Hawtrey. [148]

of the sRNA to which it was formerly attached by a single ester bond. A similar 2,3-ribose orthoester has been shown to be the intermediate in the action of RNAase on RNA. The acidic hydroxyl group of this orthoester is then activated either through direct phosphorylation by GTP, or indirectly by forming a GTP-directed linkage to some group on the synthetase enzyme. The amino group of the oncoming amino acyl residue is then brought into proximity by the binding enzyme, and transfer of the peptide acyl group occurs together with a concomitant hydrolysis of the orthoester.

The recurring sequence of reactions in amino acid incorporation. With each amino acid residue which is incorporated into the growing peptide chain the reactions of binding of amino acyl-RNA (VI), peptide bond formation (IV), and loss of the stripped sRNA (V) occur. There are never more than two sRNA's attached to a ribosome at one time [11] (Fig. 8), which is evidence that only one peptide bond is formed per cycle of the reaction sequence. Earlier postulates which proposed binding of many amino acyl groups to a template simultaneously with closing of peptide bonds in a single wave of reactions (the "zipper" mechanism) are hence disproved.

Schweet [330] has brought together the effects of magnesium ion and potassium ion on the reaction sequence in the following proposal:

(a) the ribosome is brought into a contracted form by an increased level of magnesium ion;

(b) the charged sRNA is bound (reaction IV) (Fig. 3);

S

(c) with an increased KCl (or NH$_4$Cl) level,[224] the active site expands under the action of GTP plus the binding enzyme;

(d) the peptide synthetase enzyme is brought in proximity to the peptidyl group;

(e) the peptide bond is formed, and the active site collapses;

(f) the stripped sRNA is lost, and the cycle is ready to be repeated on the adjacent codon. The ribosome either rolls along the mRNA or the mRNA moves along the ribosome in tape recorder fashion.

The direction in which the peptide chain grows has now been clearly demonstrated for hemoglobin,[36, 258] lysozyme,[61] and RNAase,[225] by correlating the order in which amino acids become labeled with their known positions along the peptide chain. The experiments of Naughton and Dintzis[258] were the first clear demonstration of the direction of chain growth and, indeed, of the stepwise nature of amino acid incorporation. The data from their experiments are shown in Fig. 11. They incubated rabbit reticulocytes with H^3-leucine for various times, then separated the α- and β-chains of the hemoglobin, partially split the chains with trypsin, and determined the relative incorporation of the H^3-leucine in 5 peptides of the α chain and 7 peptides of the β chain. The temperature of incubation was held at 15° in order to slow the reaction. Each line in Fig. 11 is a different incubation time; the ordinate is relative tritium level, and the peptides are arranged horizontally in order of their appearance in the peptide chain, from amino to carboxyl terminus.

At the earliest times of incubation (lowest curves) only the leucines near the carboxyl terminus are newly incorporated. With longer incubation the leucines along the rest of the chains become progressively more highly labeled, and after 60 min (uppermost lines) the labeling of the leucines is nearly uniform. The stepwise sequential addition of amino acids beginning with the amino terminus is thus well established as the mechanism of protein biosynthesis.

The *time* required for synthesis of a protein, discussed earlier, can now be used to estimate the time required for a single amino acid incorporation sequence. If the synthesis of a hemoglobin molecule takes about 2 min (Section II c), and its four 160-amino acid chains are formed concurrently, the rate at which the ribosome moves along the 160-codon messenger for a hemoglobin chain is about one codon (about 10 Å)[233] per second. Each second another amino acid is thus incorporated as the cycle of reactions (VI)-(IV)-(V) repeats.

The sequential mechanism implies that nascent peptide chains could be detected while still bound to sRNA and ribosomes. Such evidence has been forthcoming. [344, 11] Warner and Rich [399] estimate that there is approximately one peptide chain for each active ribosome in reticulocytes (those ribosomes which are in polyribosomal aggregates), and Goldstein and Goldstein [133]

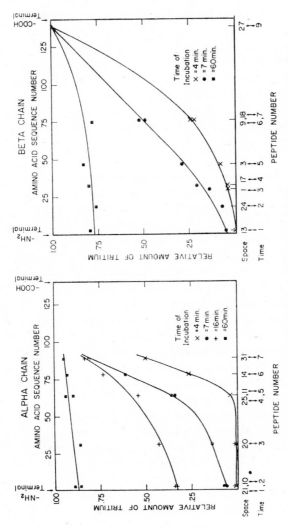

FIG. 11. The experiment of Naughton and Dintzis[258] demonstrating the lineal sequential incorporation of amino acids into the two different chains of rabbit hemoglobin. For details see text. Reproduced by courtesy of National Academy of Science.

calculate that a single *E. coli* organism contains 4000–7000 nascent chains and about 18,000 ribosomes. Traces of antigenic activity of specific proteins, detected on ribosomes, such as serum albumin, [159, 392, 180, 401] β-galactosidase, [434, 194] or *Vaccinia* virus protein, [323] may be nascent chains which have grown sufficiently to include antigenic groups.

The high precision with which the sequential stepwise building of peptide chains occurs is apparent from the reproducibility of protein structure. Some amino acid analogs can escape recognition by the appropriate sRNA and become incorporated in proteins, [387] but the valine analog, α-amino, β-chlorobutyric acid, stops further incorporation at the point where it first enters the template of rabbit hemoglobin in place of a valine residue. [289] Isoleucine, an amino acid which occupies positions farther toward the carboxyl terminus than the first valine residue, is not incorporated in the presence of the valine analog.

Smith [347] has reported the disturbing finding that "slippage" may occur in the reading of the messenger, since he found *tetra*- and *penta*lysine to be produced when the only messenger offered to the ribosomes was nine-unit (i.e. three-codon) polyA. However, this is certainly not a physiological situation, and the evidence for errors in translation of the genetic code is still scanty.

Partial digests of sRNA, [371] or puromycin, an antibiotic which is an analog of a tyrosyl-nucleoside, [426] can cause premature release of incomplete chains. The puromycin is found attached as the C-terminal residue, so that it apparently can be bound to ribosomes and its tyrosyl analog linked to the growing chain, but the complex then leaves the ribosome. When the stepwise synthesis is thus interrupted, the ribosome remains attached to the mRNA and can apparently then initiate a new chain at the next codon and proceed to manufacture this chain which lacks its N-terminal portion. [330] Normally, however, incomplete chains do not detach, and the initiation of a new chain takes place only at the start of a cistron on the mRNA. For instance, if the supply of amino acids is removed from a cell, protein synthesis stops, but the incompleted chains remain attached to the ribosomal complex and their synthesis can be restarted where it left off. [56]

Several antibiotics other than puromycin, among them streptomycin [51] and chloramphenicol, [50] disturb the mechanism of the formation of proteins in cells of higher animals as well as in bacteria. Streptomycin may cause errors in translation of the genetic code, and chloramphenicol may compete with mRNA for binding sites on the ribosomes.

G. *Events Subsequent to Peptide Bond Formation*

When the stepwise incorporation of amino acids has reached the C-terminal residue, reaction (VII) (Fig. 3), the new peptide chain is ready to be released, reaction (VIII), and to assume the function for which it was designed. The events which we will consider are:

(a) release of the peptide chain,

(b) fate of the ribosome, the sRNA and the mRNA,

(c) acquisition of secondary and tertiary structure by the peptide chains, and

(d) (in Section III H) secretion or directed migration within the cell of the new protein, together with the role of lipides and membranes in its biosynthesis.

Release of the peptide chain. If the C-terminal residue is incorporated by the same mechanism as are the other amino acids—and there is no evidence to the contrary—detachment of the peptide chain from its link to the final sRNA, reaction (VIII), requires a hydrolytic cleavage of the peptidyl-RNA ester bond. Release of completed chains can be observed in cell-free systems synthesizing hemoglobin, [211, 145] but it has been difficult to learn the mechanism of the reaction other than that a microsomal "releasing factor" is probably involved. [211] Release does not occur spontaneously or with simple washing of ribosomal preparations, and the action of RNAase is to split the nucleic acid components involved without breaking the peptidyl ester bond. Even if the mRNA is removed, by hydrolysis with RNAase or by lowering the magnesium ion concentration, the nascent protein chains remain "stuck" to the ribosomes. [62, 326]

Fate of the ribosome adaptor RNA, and messenger RNA. When the ribosome reaches the end of the messenger RNA, or a "modulating" codon which terminates synthesis at polycistronic RNA, the ribosome is generally believed to leave the messenger. The breakdown of polyribosomes seen upon maturation of the reticulocyte in vivo [232] is probably an example of the progressive loss of ribosomes from the messenger. It has also been observed in cell free reticulocyte preparations. [212] When re-use of the artificial messenger, polyU, is prevented by the presence of polyA which complexes the polyU, [145] polyribosomes break down as the completed polyPhe chains are released. Phillips, [284] however, has recently made the interesting proposition that the messenger may be *circular*, as polyribosomal aggregates often appear to be on electron microscopy, and that there is no need for the ribosome to detach before starting a new chain.

Adaptor RNA molecules are re-usable after their activity is restored by replacement of the CCA terminal sequence. It has been possible to effect the isolation and re-use of sRNA *in vitro*. [256]

Messenger RNA can be utilized by a succession of ribosomes until it, too, breaks down. The rate of mRNA breakdown bears some relation to the rate at which it is used, since it is more rapid in growing and differentiating cells than in mature ones (see Section III D). mRNA is very sensitive to the action of RNAase—much more so than sRNA or ribosomes—and is probably destroyed by the action of this enzyme within the cell. There is a small amount of "hidden" RNAase in ribosomes and, seeking to employ this fact in a rational explanation of mRNA breakdown, Artman and Engelberg [12] have postulated that only about one of every ten ribosomes has RNAase, and that upon the chance meeting of such a "loaded" ribosome with the messenger, the latter is destroyed. Lest this seem a wasteful and purposeless procedure in the cell's economy, it should be pointed out that it could serve the dual purpose of keeping the rate of production of a specific protein under control of the transcription process in the nucleus, and of providing a means whereby occasional "mistakes" in transcription which produced erroneous messengers would not be long-lasting in the cell.

The *synthesis* of the three nucleic acid-containing agents of protein biogenesis, mRNA, sRNA, and ribosomes, more properly is treated in Chapter 8. It suffices to mention here that these three structures all apparently arise in the nucleus, [430, 126, 327, 358] the sRNA perhaps more specifically from the chromatin and ribosomes and mRNA from the nucleolus. [278] Both sRNA [416] and ribosomal DNA [425] have been shown to have sequences complementary to DNA by hybridization tests. The RNA from the 30S ribosomal subunit has dissimilar sequences from the RNA of the 50S subunit, which implies that these two structures come from separate cistrons. [425] The concept of McCarthy et al., [240, 305] that the 50S subunit originates from a 30S subunit which in turn came from a 14S "eosome", has been challenged [358] by others who postulate that the "eosome" is in reality messenger which has not yet bound to a 30S particle.

In addition to the well-documented increase in ribosomes when protein synthesis increases, and to the production of mRNA when the need for a specific protein arises, there also must be a mechanism for increasing the supply of specific sRNA's when the need increases. When estrogen is administered to a fowl, the liver produces greatly increased amounts of the protein, phosvitin, which is high in serine. The level of RNA_{ser} rises concurrently. [64]

Acquisition of secondary and tertiary properties. The template mechanism just described directly determines only the primary structure of the protein, the linear sequence of its amino acid residues. To assume its biological function, the protein chain must fold in a highly specific and often complex manner (Figs. 1 and 2), held by secondary bonds (disulfide bridges) or tertiary forces (hydrogen bonding). In many cases multiple peptide chains, produced from different cistrons, must be linked together. Experimentation has revealed that the sequence of amino acid residues in a peptide chain uniquely determines its preferred folding—i.e. that the native configuration can be obtained without outside forces. [29, 104, 365]

The exact situation *in vivo* is not known—whether the newly synthesized protein commences folding before synthesis is complete, or exists briefly as a fully-extended chain—whether the association of multiple chains begins before the chains leave their templates—and whether formation of some disulfide bonds is required before the complete tertiary structure is reached. As a chain is synthesized its sulfur is in the reduced form (cysteine is incorporated instead of cystine), which has stimulated investigators to reduce the disulfide bonds of specific proteins and then to observe the reattainment of tertiary structure upon reoxidation. Ribonuclease, lysozyme, serum albumin, pepsinogen, trypsin inhibitor,[362] α-amylase, β-galactosidase,[85] insulin, and antibodies[246] (see Epstein et al.[104] for further references) will all recover at least partial activity when their disulfide bonds are allowed to reform in solution by gentle (air) oxidation after complete reduction. Note that some of these proteins contain multiple chains bound by cystine bridges.

An enzyme has been located in the microsomal fraction of rat liver[131] and pancreas[388] which catalyzes the reoxidation of reduced ribonuclease and lysozyme in vitro. Since newly formed proteins are known to assume their specific properties before leaving the microsome, it seems highly probable that this enzyme functions similarly in vivo. The hydrogen atoms removed from the sulfhydryl groups are probably disposed of through the usual electron transfer pathways.

The helical configuration can be attained spontaneously in the absence of restraining or dissociating influences. Association of chains by tertiary forces, as in the case of hemoglobin, is likewise a spontaneous phenomenon. Reduced antibody chains will associate even without reoxidation.[101] Thyroglobulin, a protein made up of loosely-associated chains, has been observed to appear in microsomes as a consolidation of smaller, 3–8S and 12S units, into the final 19S molecule.[336, 337] Iodination occurs after the 19S molecule is released from the microsomes.

When a protein includes non-amino acid constituents such as heme, the iron of ferritin,[108] or the carbohydrate component of glycoproteins[318, 357, 415] these have been found to be attached after the peptide chains are complete. The existence of the apoproteins usually bound to membranes can be shown by immunological techniques. Incorporation of the additional constituents occurs before the protein leaves the membrane. The phosphate groups of phosphoproteins, which are attached to the hydroxyls of serine residues, are believed to be attached through phosphorylation by ATP after the dephosphoprotein is formed.[291, 317] However, detection of a phosphoserine-RNA complex in chicken liver has raised the question whether some phosphorylation might occur before incorporation of the serine.[64]

The same uncertainty exists at present about the hydroxylation of lysine and proline residues of collagen. Free hydroxylysine[342] and hydroxyproline[417] are not incorporated into collagen, but are formed by oxidation of bound lysine and proline. Peterkofsky and Udenfriend[280] have found that a form of collagen low in hydroxyproline occurs in microsomes, where an enzyme, "proline hydroxylase", oxidizes some of the peptide-bound proline residues. Complexes of hydroxylysine and hydroxyproline with adaptor RNA have also been isolated, however,[80, 228, 177] so there is the possibility that oxidation may occur prior to peptide formation but while the proline and lysine are bound to sRNA.

H. *The Role of Lipides and Membranes*

Proteins which are produced for secretion from the cell are invariably first detected in close association with membranes of the endoplasmic reticulum. The list includes serum albumin [159, 283, 180] antibodies, [13, 152, 269] amylase, [138, 329] pancreatic trypsinogen, chymotrypsinogen and ribonuclease, [189, 91, 402, 65] insulin, [208] thyroglobulins, [336, 337] milk proteins, [385] collagen, [223, 286] and fibroin of silk. [249] These proteins are synthesized with the same rapidity and by the same mechanism as those which are not made for export, but are bound by lipide-containing membranes from the time their formation is complete until they are discharged from the cell. They are synthesized in portions of the endoplasmic reticulum which are rich in attached ribosomes, [283] and then they migrate to cisternal regions devoid of ribosomes and thence across the plasma membrane. The entire process in warm-blooded animals takes about 20 min for serum albumin, a protein not stored within its parent cell. Other proteins can be stored and secreted on demand–insulin and the digestive proenzymes are examples. These are accumulated into special secretory granules through the action of the Golgi apparatus. [214] Upon stimulus the contents of the secretory granules are released through the cell membrane.

Liver catalase is one of the few proteins studied which are of the class which is not secreted but migrates to another cell organelle after synthesis. Newly-formed catalase is first detectable in membranes rich with ribosomes, and it is likely that it passes to a position in mitochondria without leaving the membrane system of the cytoplasm. [158]

A rapid turnover of the phospholipides of the membranes signifies that these structures participate actively in the migration and secretion of proteins. [166] But the action of the membrane is apparently not limited to transportation of completed proteins—ribosomes bound to membranes are usually more active than free ribosomes in protein synthesis, [157, 60] indicating that membranes assist, perhaps in a steric fashion, in peptide bond formation. It is the 50S subunit of the ribosome (Fig. 8) which binds to the cytoplasmic membrane, [312] a location which would orient the membrane in position to receive the nascent peptide as it is formed. Although there has been a temptation to divide cells categorically into secreting types, which contain an extensive endoplasmic reticulum, and non-secreting types, which do not, [34] this distinction may blur on closer inspection. In cells such as *E. coli*[155] and *B. megatherium*,[58, 396, 325, 129] which engage in little protein secretion, membrane-bound ribosomes and polyribosomes have been found to be more active in protein formation than the free forms. Even in reticulocytes, which contain no apparent cytoplasmic membrane structures, the action of lipases irreversibly depresses protein synthesis.[247] The importance of lipide or membrane structures in protein synthesis may be more general than was previously supposed.

Perhaps a clue to the action of lipide components will be found in the lipopeptides[421]—complexes of amino acids and phosphatides. They exhibit rapid turnover of both amino acids[119, 118, 174, 154, 382] and phosphate.[169, 213] There is some evidence that the amino acids of these lipopeptides take up tracer amino acids promptly and then lose them while their level in proteins is still rising—suggestive of a precursor role. Although the quantitative importance of this role has not been established, the possibility should not be discounted that lipides participate in either the early or the late stages of protein biogenesis, perhaps by assisting in the cytological orientation of amino acid or nascent peptide.

IV. INADEQUACIES OF THE GENERAL MECHANISM; PROTEIN SYNTHESIS BY NON-RIBOSOMAL SYSTEMS

The weaknesses of the messenger RNA mechanism just presented have been emphasized by Gray et al.[136] and Roberts et al.[305] They note that the evidence for a messenger, particularly its complementation to a specific DNA segment, is not cogent. Gray et al. studied the base composition of rapidly-labeled RNA in *Rhodopseudomonas spheroides*, and were led to distrust the messenger RNA concept when they found that the base composition of this "mRNA" actually resembled *less* that of DNA in a mutant producing massive amounts of a single protein, catalase, than in the normal strain.

The ease with which environmental conditions can influence the coding properties of adaptor RNA is another disturbing feature. Urea and ethanol cause polyU and polyC to code for leucine and other amino acids in preference to the usual phenylalanine and proline.[349] A simple change of temperature, even in an organism such as *B. stearothermophilus* which flourishes in a wide range of temperatures, can increase the phenylalanine-leucine ambiguity with polyU.[116] A definitive description of the coding mechanism as it functions with natural messengers must apparently await the future.

The technical difficulties of studying compounds as complex as proteins and nucleic acids have not been considered in this article. Extraction of these materials from the mixtures in which they occur is fraught with hazard—proteins[251] and RNA[359] are easily lost into "lipide" solvents, and a mere change of the protein precipitating agent from trichloracetic acid to a trichloracetic acid-tungstic acid mixture alters the apparent results of amino acid incorporation experiments.[137] Improvement of extraction procedures and of techniques for isolating single protein and nucleic acid species without inducing artefacts should in time clear some of the hazier features of the protein synthetic mechanism.

THEODORE PETERS

At the present stage the only function assigned to ribosomes is to act as a workbench where the reacting members in protein formation can meet under favorable steric conditions. Ribosomes appear to bind soluble enzymes important in the peptide bond-forming reactions, and also to contain some enzymes of unknown function. It is probable that their role will be found to be more specific and more significant than it is now.

Other uses of the coding abilities of nucleic acids have been hinted at—information storage and recall in neurones (memory) and immunological recognition and recall in lymphatic cells are examples. When more is understood about these uses, the description of messenger RNA action may have to be broadened considerably.

Protein synthesis by non-ribosomal systems. The scheme of protein biogenesis through interaction of amino acyl-RNA's, mRNA, and ribosomes has been based almost entirely on observations of cytoplasmic preparations, especially of the particulate fractions in the size range of ribosomes or microsomes (ribosomes with attached membranes). The process of incorporation of amino acids in nuclei displays some unique features, such as a requirement for sodium rather than potassium ions, but the present evidence is that ribosomes, activating enzymes, adaptor RNA, and mRNA are all present and that the mechanism evolved for cytoplasmic protein synthesis applies likewise in nuclei. [4] Incorporation of amino acids into cytoplasmic organelles, such as mitochondria and chloroplasts, and into preparations from the soluble cytoplasm may occur by pathways which differ more significantly from that described above.

(a) *Mitochondria.* Isolated plant [89] or mammalian [184, 298] mitochondria will incorporate amino acids, by a process which is dependent on high energy phosphate bond energy and the presence of magnesium ions, but does not require enzymes or RNA from the soluble portion of the cell. Ribonuclease does not depress the incorporation in intact mitochondria, but when the mitochondria are ruptured by sonication or by detergents inhibition by RNAase is observed, [184, 298, 89] suggesting that RNA may normally be protected from the action of the enzyme. Kroon, [204] however, prepared a sub-mitochondrial fraction which was active in incorporating amino acids and which was *not* RNAase-sensitive. The situation seems unclear at present.

The presence of DNA in mitochondria from lamb heart has been reported recently; [183] a DNA-dependent synthesis of RNA was also observed in the same tissue. [414] Actinomycin inhibited both the RNA formation and amino acid incorporation. These interesting findings support the concept that mitochondria have a large amount of autonomy, perhaps to the extent of containing genetic information.

What is becoming clear, at least, is that the proteins formed in mitochondria are of a limited type, namely the structural proteins of the lipoprotein mitochondrial membranes. [306, 383] Only proteins which could be classed as structural on the basis of their solubility were observed to be labeled in isolated mitochondria. Component enzymes, such as catalase, appear to be synthesized elsewhere[158] in the cell. The protein-synthetic apparatus of mitochondria, whether autonomous or controlled, thus makes only the mitochondrial framework.

(b) *Chloroplasts.* Chloroplasts from tobacco leaves[275, 353] or leaves of various vegetables[345] will incorporate amino acids into protein and will form RNA. In most reported cases the incorporation was stimulated by light.[275, 345] No soluble factors are needed except magnesium and nucleoside triphosphates. RNAase was inhibitory. Although the presence of some DNA has been reported in chloroplasts,[47] neither DNAase nor actinomycin, which blocks DNA transcription, is inhibitory. If chloroplasts, like mitochondria, have some measure of autonomy it is not apparent at this time.

Soluble systems. Preparations which incorporate amino acids have been made from the high-speed centrifugal supernate of *E. coli*[182] and rat liver.[161, 182] The largest particle in the *E. coli* system sediments with a velocity of 10S, eliminating the possibility that ribosomes are present. The incorporation has a number of unusual features—only certain amino acids are taken up, and for some of them an external supply of high energy phosphate bonds is dispensable. GTP is not required. Probably the point in question is not the mechanism of protein synthesis in such soluble systems, but whether the incorporation observed is protein synthesis at all. When the labeled proteins are tested with reagents which bind free α-amino groups, it is found that 30 to 90 per cent[161, 182] of the newly-incorporated amino acids are in the N-terminal position! It can probably be safely said that the formation of proteins by mechanisms other than the general scheme presented in this article is limited to certain unusual situations and is quantitatively of slight significance.

V. SUMMARY AND CONCLUSIONS

The present concept of the mechanism of protein biogenesis is based upon solutions to the two major requirements for the formation of proteins from free amino acids—the *activation* of the amino acids and the *direction* of their sequence in the peptide chain (see Fig. 3). Both of these solutions employ nucleic acid molecules of high specificity.

Each of the twenty common amino acids is activated at the carboxyl position to form an amino acyl-RNA compound. The activating enzymes as well as the RNA molecules, termed *adaptor RNA* (sRNA), are specific for individual amino acids, although the mechanism of activation is the same for all of them. The reaction takes place in two steps.

Amino acid + enzyme + ATP $\longleftrightarrow$ amino acyl-AMP-enzyme + PP$_i$ (I)

Amino acyl-AMP-enzyme + sRNA $\longleftrightarrow$ amino acyl-RNA

$$+ \text{AMP} + \text{enzyme} \quad \text{(II)}$$

Each adaptor RNA molecule, in addition to having a site specific for binding one of the different types of amino acid, has at a separate site a particular trinucleotide sequence which is also peculiar to that amino acid.

Information for directing the linear sequence in which the activated amino acids will link is transmitted from the linear sequence of the nucleotides in a DNA cistron by another RNA known as *messenger* or informational RNA (mRNA). Messenger RNA is synthesized along the DNA chain by A-U, T-A, G-C base pairing and so is a complementary copy of the DNA cistron. Sequences of trinucleotides, or *codons*, in the mRNA correspond to or "code" for individual amino acids.

In forming a protein, the mRNA first binds a ribosome at the trinucleotide sequence which codes for the amino terminal residue of the peptide chain.

$$\text{mRNA} + \text{ribosome} \longrightarrow \text{mRNA-ribosome} \qquad \text{(IX)}$$

From the pool of amino acyl-RNA species, which are in soluble form, two complexes bearing trinucleotide sequences complementary to the codons for the terminal and adjacent amino residues prescribed by mRNA attach to the respective codons and to the ribosomes.

$$2 \text{ amino acyl-RNA} + \text{mRNA-ribosome} \longrightarrow$$
$$\text{(amino acyl-RNA)}_2\text{-mRNA-ribosome} \qquad \text{(III)}$$

This binding reaction is enzymatic, as is reaction (IV), in which the first peptide bond is formed by transfer of the carbonyl group of the first amino acid from its sRNA to the amino group of the second amino acid. The first sRNA is released (V).

$$\text{(amino acyl-RNA)}_2\text{-mRNA-ribosome} \longrightarrow$$
$$\text{peptidyl-RNA-mRNA-ribosome} + \text{sRNA} \qquad \text{(IV)} + \text{(V)}$$

The peptide chain grows in a stepwise manner, as with each step:
  (a) the amino acyl-RNA prescribed by the next codon of the mRNA is guided into position on the ribosome, (VI)
  (b) the peptidyl carbonyl group transfers to the new amino group, and (IV)
  (c) the freed sRNA is released from the complex.   (V)

The overall reaction is:

$$\text{peptidyl-RNA-mRNA-ribosome} + \text{amino acyl-RNA} \longrightarrow$$
$$\text{peptidyl'-RNA-mRNA-ribosome} + \text{sRNA} \qquad \text{(VI)} + \text{(IV)} + \text{(V)}$$

The ribosome moves along the mRNA so that it is always at the position where peptide bond formation is taking place. When the peptide chain is completed, it leaves the ribosome complex, often to be held by a lipide-containing membrane. The ribosome, mRNA and sRNA's are not necessarily consumed and can be re-used.

peptidyl-RNA-mRNA-ribosome $\longrightarrow$
$$\text{peptide} + \text{sRNA} + \text{mRNA} + \text{ribosome} \quad \text{(VIII)}$$

This ingenious if somewhat elaborate process has several features analogous to other synthetic mechanisms:

1. *A small molecule is activated at its carboxyl group prior to its coupling into a larger molecule.* The formation of fatty acids from acetyl groups uses the same device, the acyl compound in this case being acetyl-SCoA.
2. *Energy is derived from high energy phosphate bonds, initially in the form of ATP.* This is so general an event in biology, occurring in the formation of nucleic acids, carbohydrates, and lipides alike, that it is hardly surprising.
3. *A "template" mechanism directs the linear sequence of small components in a larger molecule.* DNA reproduces to form complementary copies of itself, and also forms complementary RNA transcriptions, by alignment of the nucleotides on the parent DNA through Watson–Crick base pairing.
4. *The growing peptide chain is never released in a soluble form until it is completed, but remains bound to the template during a repeating cycle of reactions.* This is an interesting analogy to the newly-devised and highly successful method of Merrifield [245] for the laboratory synthesis of oligopeptides. Merrifield has been able to form highly specific peptides with biological activity by keeping the intermediate compound at all times bound to a solid polystyrene resin. The advantage gained is the same in the natural and in the laboratory processes—by restraining the incompleted peptide in an insoluble form, the problem of directing the following amino acid into position is simplified.

Merrifield's method adds amino acids in a stepwise manner, as does the biological process, alternately removing the compound protecting the peptidyl amino group and then adding the next amino acid residue in acyl-activated form.

The repeating sequential action of the two enzymes in coupling amino acyl-RNA's into peptide form is also reminiscent of the repeating cycle which occurs in the synthesis of fatty acids. Here six enzymes in a complex perform their operations in turn on the growing fatty acid molecule. The intermediate form is passed along from enzyme to enzyme and never exists in the free state. With each cycle one acetyl group is added to the carbon chain—then the enzymes repeat the process until the desired length is reached. The similarity to the protein synthetic mechanism is obvious. The main difference is that in protein formation there is not one but twenty types of small constituents to be added, and provision is made for selecting these in the desired order.

Two features are thus far unique to protein biosynthesis:

1. *A component having one type of specificity* (the "R" group specificity of amino acids) *is adapted to another type of specificity* (the trinucleotide codons of the messenger RNA) *by an intermediary "adaptor" molecule which can recognize both determinant classes.* The interesting adaptor RNA molecule performs this function in much the same manner that the more mundane two prong–three prong electrical adaptor binds the two-prong plug at one site and presents another site which recognizes the three-prong socket. Adaptor RNA's are much more versatile than this simple analogy implies, though, since there are separate sRNA's for each different amino acid, and the sRNA's not only bring the bound amino acids to the proper codons on the messenger, but are also bound to the ribosome in such a manner that the amino acid will be in position to link with the growing peptide chain.

2. *A sequence of several members of a language having a small number of characters* (the four nucleotide bases) *is employed to correspond to a single member of a language with a larger number of characters* (the 20 amino acids). One is reminded of the manner in which the information content of the dots and dashes of telegraphy, a language with only two characters, is similarly increased to equal that of our 26-letter alphabet by using sequences of dots and dashes to correspond to individual letters. The "genetic code" translates trinucleotide sequences to amino acid language just as the International Morse code translates dot–dash sequences to letters of the alphabet.

Obviously the picture of how proteins are formed is incomplete and probably to some extent incorrect. But revision is not unexpected in biological theories, particularly in a field in which so much has been learned in such a short time. What started out to be research on the coupling of amino acids into proteins has grown in less than a decade to encompass genetics, nucleic acid metabolism, virology, cell ultrastructure and even the regulation of metabolism. It would be surprising if alterations in the scheme of protein biosynthesis were *not* forthcoming in the years ahead.

REFERENCES

1. AACH, H. G., FUNATSU, G., NIRENBERG, M. W. and FRAENKEL-CONRAT, H. *Biochemistry (N.Y.)* 3, 1362 (1964).
2. ALLENDE, J. E., MONRO, R. and LIPMANN, F. *Proc. Natl. Acad. Sci. U.S.* 51, 1211 (1964).
3. ALLFREY, V. G. *Exptl. Cell Research* 31, Supp 9, 183 (1963).
4. ALLFREY, V. G., FAULKNER R. and MIRSKY, A. E. *Proc. Natl. Acad. Sci. U.S.* 51, 786 (1964).
5. ALLISON, A. C. *Nature* 188, 37 (1960).
6. ALLISON, J. B. *Physiol. Rev.* 35, 664 (1955).
7. AMES, B. N. and HARTMAN, P. E. *Cold Spring Harbor Symp. Quant. Biol.* 28, 349 (1963).
8. AMES, B. N. and MARTIN, R. G. *Ann. Rev. of Biochem.* 33, 235 (1964).

9. Arcos, J. C., Conney, A. H. and Buu-Hoi, Ng. Ph. *J. Biol. Chem.* **236**, 1291 (1961).
10. Arcà, M., Calbori, C., Frontali, L. and Tecce, G. *Biochem. Biophys. Acta* **87**, 440 (1964).
11. Arlinghaus, R., Schaeffer, J. and Schweet, R. *Proc. Natl. Acad. Sci. U.S.* **51**, 1291 (1964).
12. Artman, M. and Engelberg, H. *Biochim. Biophys. Acta* **80**, 517 (1964).
13. Askonas, B. A. and Humphrey, J. H. *Biochim. J.* **68**, 252 (1958).
14. Askonas, B. A., Campbell, P. N. and Work, T. S. *Biochem. J.* **58**, 326 (1954).
15. Bank, A., Gee, S., Mehler, A. and Peterkofsky, A. *Biochemistry (N.Y.)* **3**, 1406 (1964).
16. Barnabei, O. and Sereni, F. *Biochim. Biophys. Acta* **91**, 239 (1964).
17. Barondes, S. H. and Nirenberg, M. W. *Science* **138**, 810, 813 (1962).
18. Barondes, S. H., Dingman, C. W. and Sporn, M. B., *Nature* **196**, 145 (1962).
19. Bassham, J. A., Morawiecka, B. and Kirk, M. *Biochim. Biophys. Acta* **90**, 542 (1964).
20. Bautz, E. K. F. and Heding, L. *Biochemistry (N.Y.)* **3**, 1010 (1964).
21. Becker, Y. and Joklik, W. K. *Proc. Natl. Acad. Sci. U.S.* **51**, 577 (1964).
22. Bégin, N. and Scholefield, P. G. *Biochim. Biophys. Acta* **90**, 82 (1964).
23. Beljanski, M. and Ochoa, S. *Proc. Natl. Acad. Sci. U.S.* **44**, 494, 1157 (1958).
24. Bennett, J. C. and Dreyer, W. J. *Ann. Rev. of Biochem.* **33**, 205 (1964).
25. Bennett, T. P., Goldstein, J. and Lipmann, F. *Proc. Natl. Acad. Sci. U.S.* **53**, 385 (1965).
26. Bent, K. J. *Biochem. J.* **92**, 280 (1964).
27. Benzer, S. and Weisblum, B. *Proc. Natl. Acad. Sci. U.S.* **47**, 1149 (1961).
28. Berg, P. *J. Biol. Chem.* **222**, 1025 (1956).
29. Berg, P. *Ann. Rev. of Biochem.* **30**, 305 (1961).
30. Berg, P., Bergmann, F. H., Ofengand, E. J. and Dieckmann, M. *J. Biol. Chem.* **236**, 1726 (1961).
31. Berg, P., Lagerkvist, U. and Dieckmann, M. *J. Mol. Biol.* **5**, 159 (1962).
32. Bernfeld, M. R. and Nirenberg, M. W. *Science* **147**, 479 (1965).
33. Bernlohr, R. W. and Webster, G. C. *Nature* **182**, 531 (1958).
34. Birbeck, M. S. C. and Mercer, E. H. *Nature* **189**, 558 (1961).
35. Bishop, J. O. *Nature* **203**, 40 (1964).
36. Bishop, J., Leahy, J. and Schweet, R. *Proc. Natl. Acad. Sci. U.S.* **46**, 1030 (1960).
37. Black, A. L., Kleiher, M., Smith, A. H. and Stewart, D. N. *Biochim. Biophys. Acta* **23**, 54 (1957).
38. Bonner, J., Huang, R. C. and Gilden, R. V. *Proc. Natl. Acad. Sci. U.S.* **50**, 893 (1963).
39. Borek, E. *Cold Spring Harbor Symp. Quant. Biol.* **28**, 139 (1963).
40. Borsook, H. *Adv. Protein Chem.* **8**, 127 (1953).
41. Borsook, H. and Keighley, G. C. *Proc. Royal Soc. London B* **118**, 488 (1935).
42. Borsook, H., Deasy, C. L., Haagen-Smit, A. J., Keighley, G. and Lowy, P. H. *J. Biol. Chem.* **187**, 839 (1950).
43. Borsook, H., Fischer, E. H. and Keighley, G. L. *J. Biol. Chem.* **229**, 1059 (1957).
44. Brachet, J. *Bull. soc. chim. biol.* **40**, 1387 (1958).
45. Brachet, J. and Chantrenne, H. *Nature* **168**, 950 (1957).
46. Brawerman, G. *Biochim. Biophys. Acta* **76**, 322 (1963).
47. Brawerman, G. and Eisenstadt, J. M. *Biochim. Biophys. Acta* **91**, 477 (1964).
48. Brenner, S., Jacob, F. and Meselson, M. *Nature* **190**, 576 (1961).
49. Breuer, C. B., Davies, M. C. and Florini, J. R. *Biochemistry (N.Y.)* **3**, 1713 (1964).
50. Brock, T. D. *Bacteriol. Rev.* **25**, 32 (1961).
51. Brock, T. D. *Federation Proc.* **23**, 965 (1964).
52. Brotman, M. and McGill, D. B. *Mayo Clinic Proc.* **39**, 777 (1964).
53. Brown, H. and Brown, J. *Metabolism* **10**, 91 (1961).
54. Buchanan, D. L. and Nakao, N. *J. Biol. Chem.* **200**, 407 (1953).
55. Bulman, N. and Campbell, D. H. *Proc. Soc. Exptl. Biol. Med.* **84**, 155 (1953).
56. Burka, E. R. and Marks, P. A. *J. Mol. Biol.* **9**, 439 (1964).
57. Burnett, J. R., J.P. and Haurowitz, F. *Hoppe Sehlers Z. für physiol. Chem.* **331**, 67 (1963).

58. BUTLER, J. A. V., CRATHORN, A. R. and HUNTER, G. D. *Biochem. J.* **69**, 544 (1958).
59. CAMMARANO, P., GUIDICE, G. and NOVELLI, G. D. *Biochem. Biophys. Research Commun.* **12**, 498 (1963).
60. CAMPBELL, P. N., COOPER, C. and HICKS, M. *Biochem. J.* **92**, 225 (1964).
61. CANFIELD, R. E. and ANFINSEN, C. B. *Biochemistry* (*N.Y.*) **2**, 1073 (1963).
62. CANNON, M., KRUG, R. and GILBERT, W. *J. Mol. Biol.* **7**, 360 (1963).
63. CANTONI, G. L., ISHIKURA, H., RICHARDS, H. H. and TANAKA, K. *Cold Spring Harbor Symp. Quant. Biol.* **28**, 123 (1963).
64. CARLSEN, E. N., TRELLE, C. J. and SCHJEIDE, O. A. *Nature* **202**, 984 (1964).
65. CARO, L. G. and PALADE, G. E. *J. Cell Biology* **20**, 473 (1964).
66. CASPERSSON, T. *Naturwiss.* **29**, 33 (1941).
67. CHANTRENNE, H. *Arch. Biochem. Biophys.* **65**, 414 (1956).
68. CHAPEVILLE, F., LIPMANN, F., VON EHRENSTEIN, G., WEISBLUM, P., RAY, W. J. and BENZER, S. *Proc. Natl. Acad. Sci. U.S.* **48**, 1086 (1962).
69. CHAVCHANIDZE, V. V. and KRINIKHIDZE, K. S. *Svobshch. Akad. Nauk. Gruz. S.S.R.* **32**, 291 (1964).
70. CHRISTENSEN, H. N. *J. Nutrit.* **42**, 189 (1950).
71. CHRISTENSEN, H. N., RIGGS, T. R. and COYNE, B. A. *J. Biol. Chem.* **209**, 413 (1954).
72. CLARK, J. M., EYZAGUIRRE, J.P. and GUNTHER, J. K. *J. Biol. Chem.* **239**, 1877 (1964).
73. CLARK, M. F., MATTHEWS, R. E. F. and RALPH, R. K. *Biochim. Biophys. Acta* **91**, 289 (1964).
74. CLICK, R. E. and HACKETT, D. P. *Federation Proc.* **23**, 525 (1964).
75. COHEN, S., FREEMAN, T. and MCFARLANE, A. S. *Clin. Sci.* **20**, 161 (1961).
76. COHEN, S. S. *Ann. Rev. Biochem.* **32**, 83 (1963).
77. COHN, M. *Bacteriol. Rev.* **21**, 140 (1957).
78. COMB, D. G. and BROWN, R. *Exptl. Cell Research* **34**, 360 (1964).
79. CONWAY, T. W. and LIPMANN, F. *Proc. Natl. Acad. Sci. U.S.* **52**, 1462 (1964).
80. CORONADO, A., MARDONES, E. and ALLENDE, J. E. *Biochem. Biophys. Research Commun.* **13**, 75 (1963).
81. COX, R. A., GOULD, H. and ARNSTEIN, H. R. V. *Proceedings 6th Internatl. Congress of Biochemistry, Symposium I, New York*, 1964, p. 49.
82. CRADDOCK, V. M. and CAMPBELL, P. N. *Biochem. J.* **84**, 340 (1962).
83. CRADDOCK, V. M. and DALGLEISH, C. E. *Biochem. J.* **66**, 250 (1957).
84. CRAMER, F., KUENTZEL, H. and MATTHAEI, J. M. *Angew. Chem.* **76**, 716 (1964).
85. CRAVEN, G. R. and ANFINSEN, C. B. *Proceedings 6th Internatl. Congress of Biochemistry, Symposium IV, New York*, 1964, p. 302.
86. CREASER, E. H. *Biochem. J.* **64**, 539 (1956).
87. CRICK, F. H. C., BARNETT, L., BRENNER, S. and WATTS-TOBIN, R. J. *Nature* **192**, 1227 (1961).
88. DALGLEISH, C. E. *Nature* **171**, 1027 (1953); *Science* **125**, 271 (1957).
89. DAS, H. K., CHATTERJEE, S. K. and ROY, S. C. *Biochim. Biophys. Acta* **87**, 478 (1964).
90. DEICHMILLER, M. P. and DIXON, F. J. *J. Gen. Physiol.* **43**, 1047 (1960).
91. DICKMAN, S. R., HOLTZER, R. L. and GAZZINELLI, G. *Biochemistry* (*N.Y.*) **1**, 574 (1962).
92. DIGIROLAMO, A., HENSHAW, E. C. and HIATT, H. H. *J. Mol. Biol.* **8**, 479 (1964).
93. DOUNCE, A. L. *Enzymologia* **15**, 251 (1952).
94. DOCTOR, B. P. and MUDD, J. A. *J. Biol. Chem.* **238**, 3677 (1963).
95. DOCTOR, B. P., APGAR, J. and HOLLEY, R. W. *J. Biol. Chem.* **236**, 1117 (1961).
96. DOERFLER, W., ZILLIG, W., FUCHS, E. and ALBERS, M. *Hoppe Seyler's z. fur physiol. chem.* **330**, 90 (1962).
97. DOI, R. H. and IGARSKI, R. T. *Proc. Natl. Acad. Sci. U.S.* **52**, 755 (1964).
98. DUCK-CHONG, C., POLLAK, J. K. and NORTH, R. J. *J. Cell Biol.* **20**, 25 (1964).
99. DUNN, D. B., SMITH, J. D. and SPAHR, P. F. *J. Mol. Biol.* **2**, 113 (1960).
100. EAGLE, H., PIEZ, K. A. and LEVY, M. *J. Biol. Chem.* **236**, 2039 (1961).
101. EDELMAN, G. M. and POULIK, J. A. *Proc. Natl. Acad. Sci. U.S.* **51**, 846 (1964).
102. EIKENBERRY, E. F. and RICH, A. *Proc. Natl. Acad. Sci. U.S.* **53**, 668 (1965).
103. ENGLANDER, S. W. and ENGLANDER, J. J. *Proc. Natl. Acad. Sci, U.S.* **53**, 370 (1965).

104. Epstein, C. J., Goldberger, R. F. and Anfinsen, C. B. *Cold Spring Harbor Symp. Quant. Biol.* **28**, 439 (1963).
105. Faulkner, P. and Bheemeswar, B. *Biochem. J.* **76**, 71 (1960).
106. Feigelson, P. and Greengard, O. *J. Biol. Chem.* **237**, 3714 (1962).
107. Fessenden, M. and Moldave, K. *J. Biol. Chem.* **238**, 1479 (1963).
108. Fineberg, R. A. and Greenberg, D. M. *J. Biol. Chem.* **214**, 91, 97, 107 (1955).
109. Fitch, W. M. *Proc. Natl. Acad. Sci. U.S.* **52**, 298 (1964).
110. Fleischer, S., Lietze, A., Walter, H. and Haurowitz, F. *Proc. Soc. Exptl. Biol. Med.* **101**, 860 (1959).
111. Fletcher, M. J. and Sanadi, D. R. *Biochim. Biophys. Acta* **51**, 356 (1961).
112. Florini, J. R. and Breuer, C. B. *Biochemistry (N.Y.)* **4**, 253 (1965).
113. Folin, O. *Am. J. Physiol.* **13**, 117 (1905).
114. Fox, G. and Brown, J. W. *Biochim. Biophys. Acta.* **46**, 387 (1961).
115. Fraenkel-Conrat, H. *J. Am. Chem. Soc.* **78**, 882 (1956).
116. Friedman, S. M. and Weinstein, I. B. *Proc. Natl. Acad. Sci. U.S.* **52**, 988 (1964).
117. Fruton, J. S. *Harvey Lectures*, Series 51, 64 (1955).
118. Fukui, T. and Axelrod, B. *J. Biol. Chem.* **236**, 811 (1961).
119. Gaby, W. L. and Silberman, R. *Arch. Biochem. Biophys.* **87**, 188 (1960).
120. Gale, E. F. and Folkes, J. P. *Biochem. J.* **79**, 661 (1955).
121. Garfinkel, D. and Lajtha, A. *J. Biol. Chem.* **238**, 2429 (1963).
122. Garren, L. D., Howell, R. R., Tomkins, G. M. and Crocco, R. M. *Proc. Natl. Acad. Sci. U.S.* **52**, 1121 (1964).
123. Gehrmann, G., Lauenstein, K. and Altman, K. I. *Arch. Biochem. Biophys.* **62**, 509 (1956).
124. Geiger, E. *Science* **111**, 594 (1950).
125. Gelboin, H. V. and Sokoloff, L. *Biochim. Biophys. Acta* **91**, 122, 130 (1964).
126. Georgiev, G. P., Samauna, U. P., Lerman, M. I., Smirnov, M. V. and Severtzov, A. N. *Nature* **200**, 1291 (1963).
127. Gierer, A. *J. Mol. Biol.* **6**, 148 (1963).
128. Gilbert, W. *J. Mol. Biol.* **6**, 374, 389 (1963).
129. Godson, G. N. and Butler, J. A. V. *Biochem. J.* **93**, 573 (1964).
130. Goldberg, I. H. and Reich, E. *Federation Proc.* **23**, 958 (1964).
131. Goldberger, R. F., Epstein, C. J. and Anfinsen, C. B. *J. Biol. Chem.* **239**, 1406 (1964).
132. Goldstein, A. and Brown, B. *Biochim. Biophys. Acta* **53**, 438 (1961).
133. Goldstein, A. and Goldstein, D. B. *J. Mol. Biol.* **9**, 213 (1964).
134. Goldstein, L., Micou, J. and Crocker, T. T. *Biochim. Biophys. Acta* **45**, 82 (1960).
135. Goldsworthy, P. D. and Volwiler, W. *J. Biol. Chem.* **230**, 817 (1958).
136. Gray, E. D., Haywood, A. M. and Chargaff, E. *Biochim. Biophys. Acta* **87**, 397 (1964).
137. Griffin, A. C., Ward, V., Canning, L. C. and Holland, B. H. *Biochem. Biophys. Research Communs.* **15**, 519 (1964).
138. Gromet-Elhanan, Z. and Winnick, T. *Biochim. Biophys. Acta* **69**, 85 (1963).
139. Gros, F., Gilbert, W., Hiatt, H., Kurland, C., Risebrough, R. W. and Watson, J. D. *Nature*, **190**, 581 (1961).
140. Hall, P. D. and Spiegelman, S. *Proc. Natl. Acad. Sci. U.S.* **47**, 137 (1961).
141. Halvorson, H., Gorman, J., Tauro, P., Epstein, R. and LaBerge, M. *Federation Proc.* **23**, 1002 (1964).
142. Hamilton, T. H. *Proc. Natl. Acad. Sci. U.S.* **51**, 83 (1964).
143. Hansson, E. *Acta Physiol. scand.* **46**, suppl. 161 (1959).
144. Hardesty, B., Arlinghaus, R., Schaeffer, J. and Schweet, R. *Cold Spring Harbor Symp. Quant. Biol.* **28**, 215 (1963).
145. Hardesty, B., Miller, R. and Schweet, R. *Proc. Natl. Acad. Sci. U.S.* **50**, 924 (1963).
146. Harris, H. and Sabath, L. D. *Nature* **292**, 1078 (1964).
147. Haselkorn, R. and Fried, V. A. *Proc. Natl. Acad. Sci. U.S.* **51**, 308 (1964).
148. Hawtrey, A. O. *Nature* **202**, 1179 (1964).

149. HEIDELBERGER, M., TREFFERS, H. P., SCHOENHEIMER, R., RATNER, S. and RITTENBERG, D. *J. Biol. Chem.* **144**, 555 (1942).
150. HEIMBERG, M. and VELICK, S. F. *J. Biol. Chem.* **208**, 725 (1954).
151. HEINZ, E. and PATLAK, C. S. *Biochim. Biophys. Acta* **44**, 324 (1960).
152. HELMREICH, E., KERN, M. and EISEN, H. N. *J. Biol. Chem.* **236**, 464 (1961).
153. HENDLER, R. W. *Nature* **178**, 651 (1956).
154. HENDLER, R. W. *Biochim. Biophys. Acta* **74**, 667 (1963).
155. HENDLER, R. W. and TANI, J. *Biochim. Biophys. Acta* **80**, 279 (1964).
156. HENNEY, H. R. and STORCH, R. *Proc. Natl. Acad. Sci. U.S.* **51**, 1050 (1964).
157. HENSHAW, E. C., BOJARSKI, T. B. and HIATT, H. H. *J. Mol. Biol.* **7**, 122 (1963).
158. HIGASHI, T. and PETERS, T. *J. Biol. Chem.* **238**, 3945, 3952 (1963).
159. HIROKAWA, R. and OGATA, K. *J. Biochem.* (*Tokyo*) **52**, 377 (1962).
160. HIROKAWA, R., OMORI, S., TAKAHASHI, T. and OGATA, K. *Biochim. Biophys. Acta* **49**, 612 (1961).
161. HIRD, H. J., MCLEAN, E. J. T. and MUNRO, H. N. *Biochim. Biophys. Acta* **87**, 219 (1964).
162. HOAGLAND, M. B. *Biochim. Biophys. Acta* **16**, 288 (1955).
163. HOAGLAND, M. B., In *The Nucleic Acids*, eds. E. Chargaff and J. N. Davidson, vol. 3, p. 349, Academic Press, N.Y., 1960.
164. HOAGLAND, M. B. and COMLY, L. T. *Proc. Natl. Acad. Sci. U.S.* **46**, 1554 (1960).
165. HOAGLAND, M. B., SCORNIK, O. A. and PFEFFERKORN, L. C. *Proc. Natl. Acad. Sci. U.S.* **51**, 1184 (1964).
166. HOKIN, M. R. and HOKIN, L. E. *J. Biol. Chem.* **234**, 1381, 1387 (1959).
167. HOLLEY, R. W. *J. Am. Chem. Soc.* **79**, 658 (1957).
168. HOLLEY, R. W., APGAR, J., EVERETT, G. A., MADISON, J. T., MARQUISEE, M., MERRILL, S. H., PENSWICK, J. R. and ZAMIR, A. *Science* **147**, 1462 (1965).
169. HUGGINS, C. G. and COHN, D. V. *J. Biol. Chem.* **234**, 257 (1959).
170. HULTIN, T. *Exptl. Cell Research* **1**, 376 (1950).
171. HULTIN, T. *Exptl. Cell Research* **34**, 308 (1964).
172. HULTIN, T. and BESHOW, G. *Exptl. Cell Research* **11**, 664 (1956).
173. HUMPHREY, J. H. and MCFARLANE, A. S. *Biochem. J.* **57**, 186 (1954).
174. HUNTER, G. D. and GOODSALL, R. A. *Biochem. J.* **78**, 564 (1961).
175. HURWITZ, J., ANDERS, M., GOLD, M and SMITH, I. *J. Biol. Chem.* **240**, 1256 (1965).
176. ITO, T., GUROFF, G. and UDENFRIEND, S. *J. Biol. Chem.* **239**, 3385 (1964).
177. JACKSON, D. S., WATKINS, D. and WINKLER, A. *Biochim. Biophys. Acta* **87**, 152 (1964).
178. JACOB, F. and MONOD, J. *J. Mol. Biol.* **3**, 318 (1961).
179. JACOBSON, K. B. and NISHIMURA, S. *Biochim. Biophys. Acta* **91**, 305 (1964).
180. JUNGBLUT, P. W. *Biochem. Z.* **337**, 267, 285, 297 (1963).
181. KAJI, H. and KAJI, A. *Proc. Natl. Acad. Sci. U.S.* **52**, 1541 (1964).
182. KAJI, H., KAJI, A. and NOVELLI, G. D. *J. Biol. Chem.* **240**, 1192 (1965).
183. KALF, G. F. *Biochemistry* (*N.Y.*) **3**, 1702 (1964).
184. KALF, G. F. and SIMPSON, M. V. *J. Biol. Chem.* **234**, 2943 (1959).
185. KAMEYAMA, T. and NOVELLI, G. D. *Proc. Natl. Acad. Sci. U.S.* **48**, 659 (1962).
186. KELLER, E. B. and FERGER, M. F. *Federation Proc.* **23**, 164 (1964).
187. KELLER, E. B. and ZAMECNIK, P. C. *J. Biol. Chem.* **221**, 45 (1956).
188. KELLER, E. B., ZAMECNIK, P. C. and LOFTFIELD, R. *J. Histochem. Cytochem.* **2**, 378 (1954).
189. KELLER, P. J., COHEN, E. and NEURATH, H. *J. Biol. Chem.* **236**, 1404 (1961).
190. KEMPNER, E. S. and COWIE, D. B. *Biochim. Biophys. Acta* **42**, 401 (1960).
191. KENNEY, F. T. *J. Biol. Chem.* **237**, 3495 (1962).
192. KIDSON, C., KIRBY, K. S. and RALPH, R. K. *J. Mol. Biol.* **7**, 312 (1963).
193. KIHARA, H., IKAWA, M. and SNELL, E. E. *J. Biol Chem* **236**, 172 (1961)
194 KIHO, Y. and RICH, A. *Proc. Natl. Acad. Sci. U.S.* **51**, 111 (1964).
195. KING, D. W., BENSCH, K. G. and HILL, R. B. *Science* **131**, 106 (1960).
196. KNOX, W. E. and BEHRMANN, E. J. *Ann. Rev. Biochem.* **28**, 223 (1959).
197. KOCH, A. L. *J. Biol. Chem.* **217**, 931 (1956).
198. KOIKE, K. and OKUI, S. *J. Biochem.* (*Tokyo*) **56**, 308 (1964).

199. KORNER, A. *Biochem. J.* **81**, 168 (1961).
200. KORNER, A. *Biochem. J.* **92**, 449 (1964).
201. KOSHLAND, D. E. *Proc. Natl. Acad. Sci. U.S.* **44**, 98 (1958).
202. KRAICER, J. *Biochim. Biophys. Acta* **87**, 701 (1964).
203. KRETSINGER, R. H., MANNER, G., GOULD, B. S. and RICH, A. *Nature* **202**, 438 (1964).
204. KROON, A. M. *Biochem. J.* **72**, 391 (1963).
205. KRUH, J., DREYFUS, J.-C. and SCHAPIRA, G. *J. Biol. Chem.* **235**, 1075 (1960).
206. KRUH, J., DREYFUS, J.-C. and SCHAPIRA, G. *Biochim. Biophys. Acta* **91**, 494 (1964).
207. KRUH, J., SCHAPIRA, G., LARSEN, J. and DREYFUS, J.-C. *Biochim. Biophys. Acta* **87**, 669 (1964).
208. LACY, P. E. *Am. J. Med.* **31**, 851 (1961).
209. LAMBORG, M. R. and ZAMECNIK, P. C. *Biochim, Biophys. Acta* **42**, 206 (1960).
210. LAMBORG, M. R., ZAMECNIK, P. C., LI, T., KAGI, J. and VALLEE, B. L. *Biochemistry (N.Y.)* **4**, 63 (1965).
211. LAMFROM, H. *J. Mol. Biol.* **3**, 241 (1961).
212. LAMFROM, H. and KNOPF, P. M. *J. Mol. Biol.* **9**, 558 (1964).
213. LEBARON, F., KISTLER, J. P. and HAUSER, G. *Biochim. Biophys. Acta* **44**, 170 (1960).
214. LEBLOND, C. P. *Am. J. Anat.* **116**, 1 (1965).
215. LENGYEL, P., SPEYER, J. F. and OCHOA, S. *Proc. Natl. Acad. Sci. U.S.* **47**, 1936 (1961).
216. LEVINTHAL, C., KEYNAN, A. and HIGA, A. *Proc. Natl. Acad. Sci. U.S.* **48**, 1631 (1962).
217. LIPMANN, F. *Federation Proc.* **8**, 597 (1949).
218. LIPMANN, F. *Bacteriol. Rev.* **17**, 1 (1953).
219. LITTLEFIELD, J. W., KELLER, E. B., GROSS, J. and ZAMECNIK, P. C *J. Biol. Chem.* **217**, 111 (1955).
220. LOFTFIELD, R. B. and EIGNER, E. A. *J. Biol. Chem.* **231**, 925 (1958).
221. LOFTFIELD, R. B. and HARRIS, A. *J. Biol. Chem.* **219**, 151 (1956).
222. LOFTFIELD, R. B., HECHT, L. and EIGNER, E. A. *Biochim. Biophys. Acta* **72**, 383 (1963).
223. LOWTHER, D. A., GREEN, N. M. and CHAPMAN, J. A. *J. Biochem. Biophys. Cytol.* **10**, 373 (1961).
224. LUBIN, M. and ENNIS, H. L. *Biochim. Biophys. Acta* **80**, 614 (1964).
225. LUCK, D. N. and BARRY, J. M. *J. Mol. Biol.* **9**, 186 (1964).
226. MANDELES, S. and DUCAY, E. D. *J. Biol. Chem.* **237**, 3196 (1962).
227. MANDELSTAM, J. *Biochem. J.* **69**, 103, 110 (1958).
228. MANNER, G. and GOULD, B. S. *Biochim. Biophys. Acta* **72**, 243 (1963).
229. MARBAIX, G. and BURNY, A. *Biochem. Biophys. Research Communs.* **16**, 522 (1964).
230. MARCUS, A. and FEELEY, J. *Proc. Natl. Acad. Sci. U.S.* **51**, 1075 (1964).
231. MARCUS, L., BRETTHAUER, R., HALVORSON, H. and BOCK, R. *Science* **147**, 615 (1965).
232. MARKS, P. A., BURKA, E. R. and RIFKIND, R. A. *Medicine* **43**, 769 (1964).
233. MARKS, P. A., BURKA, E. R. and SCHLESSINGER, D. *Proc. Natl. Acad. Sci. U.S.* **48**, 2163 (1962).
234. MARSH, J. B. and DRABKIN, D. L. *J. Biol. Chem.* **230**, 1073 (1958).
235. MARSH, J. B. and DRABKIN, D. L. *Biochim. Biophys. Acta* **95**, 173 (1965).
236. MARUSHIGE, K. and BONNER, J. *Federation Proc.* **23**, 165 (1964).
237. MASIAR, P. and MURAR, J. *Coll. Czech. Chem. Commun.* **10**, 2562 (1961).
238. MATHIAS, A. P., WILLIAMSON, R., HUXLEY, H. E. and PAGE, S. *J. Mol. Biol.* **9**, 154 (1964).
239. MCCARTHY, B. J. and HOYER, B. H. *Proc. Natl. Acad. Sci. U.S.* **52**, 915 (1964).
240. MCCARTHY, B. J., BRITTEN, R. J. and ROBERTS, R. B. *Biophysical J.* **2**, 35 (1962).
241. MCFARLANE, A. S. *Biochem. J.* **89**, 277 (1963).
242. MCMENAMY, R. H., SHOEMAKER, W. C., RICHMOND, J. E. and ELWYN, D. *Am. J. Physiol.* **202**, 407 (1962).
243. MCQUILLEN, K., ROBERTS, R. B. and BRITTEN, R. J. *Proc. Natl. Acad. Sci. U.S.* **45**, 1437 (1959).
244. MEDVEDEV, ZH. A. and CHIANG-HSIA, S. *Biokhimia* **24**, 709 (1959).
245. MERRIFIELD, R. B. *Biochemistry (N.Y.)* **3**, 1385 (1964).
246. METZGER, H. and MANNICK, M. *J. Exptl. Med.* **119**, 765 (1964).

247. MILLER, A. *Proceedings, 6th Internatl. Congress of Biochemistry, Symposium I,* New York, 1964, p. 74.
248. MITCHISON, J. M. and GROSS, P. R. *Exptl. Cell Research* 37, 259 (1965).
249. MIURA, Y., ITO, H., SUNAGA, K., IKEDA, K., MORIYAMA, Y. and HASEGAWA, S. *J. Biochem.* (*Tokyo*) 55, 623 (1964).
250. MOUSTAFA, E. *Biochim. Biophys. Acta* 91, 421 (1964).
251. MUNRO, H. N. and DOWNIE, E. D. *Arch. Biochem. Biophys.* 106, 516 (1964).
252. MUNRO, A. and KORNER, A. *Nature,* 202, 1194 (1964).
253. MUNRO, A., JACKSON, R. J. and KORNER, A. *Biochem. J.* 92, 289 (1964).
254. MURAR, J. and MASIAR, P. *Coll. Czech. Chem. Communs.* 27, 504 (1962).
255. NAKAMOTO, T., CONWAY, T., ALLENDE, J., SPYRIDES, G. and LIPMANN, F. *Cold Spring Harbor Symp. Quant. Biol.* 28, 227 (1963).
256. NATHANS, D. and LIPMANN, F. *Proc. Natl. Acad. Sci. U.S.* 47, 497 (1961).
257. NATHANS, D., VON EHRENSTEIN, G., MONRO, R. and LIPMANN, F. *Federation Proc.* 21, No. 1, 127 (1962).
258. NAUGHTON, M. A. and DINTZIS, H. M. *Proc. Natl. Acad. Sci. U.S.* 48, 1822 (1962).
259. NIKLAS, A. and OEHLERT, W. *Acta Histochem.* 4, 166 (1957).
260. NIRENBERG, M. W. and MATTHAEI, J. H. *Proc. Natl. Acad. Sci. U.S.* 47, 1588 (1961).
261. NISHIMURA, S. and NOVELLI, G. D. *Proc. Natl. Acad. Sci. U.S.* 53, 178 (1965).
262. NISMAN, B. and FUKUHARA, H. *Compt. rend. acad. sci, Paris* 250, 410 (1960).
263. NOLL, H., STAEHELIN, T. and WETTSTEIN, F. O. *Nature* 198, 632 (1963).
264. NORRIS, A. T. and BERG, P. *Proc. Natl. Acad. Sci. U.S.* 52, 330 (1964).
265. NUTTER, W. E. and SKELTON, D. C. *Federation Proc.* 16, 227 (1957).
266. OCHOA, S. *Bull. N.Y. Acad. Med.* 40, 387 (1964).
267. OFENGAND, E. J., DIECKMANN, M. B. and BERG, P. *J. Biol. Chem.* 236, 1741 (1961).
268. OGATA, K., ISHIKAWA, K., TOMINAGA, H., WATANABE, I., MORITA, T. and SUGANO, H. *Biochim. Biophys. Acta.* 76, 630 (1963).
269. OGATA, K., OMORI, S. and HIROKAWA, R. *J. Biochem.* (*Tokyo*) 49, 660 (1961).
270. OHTAKA, Y. and SPIEGELMAN, S. *Science* 142, 493 (1963).
271. OKAMOTO, T. and TAKANAMI, M. *Biochim. Biophys. Acta* 68, 325 (1963).
272. OLSZEWSKA, M. J. and BRACHET, J. *Exptl. Cell Research* 22, 370 (1961).
273. OTSUKA, H. and TERAYAMA, H. *J. Biochem.* (*Tokyo*) 56, 572 (1964).
274. PAINE, C. M. and HEINZ, E. *J. Biol. Chem.* 235, 1080 (1960).
275. PARTHIER, B. *Z. Naturforsch.* 19b, 235 (1964).
276. PEARLMAN, R. and BLOCH, K. *Proc. Natl. Acad. Sci. U.S.* 50, 533 (1963).
277. PEÑA, R., DVORKIN, B. and WHITE, A. *Biochem. Biophys. Research Communs.* 16, 449 (1964).
278. PERRY, R. P. *Proc. Natl. Acad. Sci. U.S.* 48, 2179 (1962).
279. PERUTZ, M. F. *Scientific American* 211, No. 5, 64 (1964).
280. PETERKOFSKY, A. *Proc. Natl. Acad. Sci. U.S.* 52, 1233 (1964).
281. PETERKOFSKY, B. and UDENFRIEND, S. *Proc. Natl. Acad. Sci. U.S.* 53, 335 (1965).
282. PETERS, T. *J. Biol. Chem.* 229, 659 (1957).
283. PETERS, T. *J. Biol. Chem.* 237, 1181, 1186 (1962).
284. PHILLIPS, G. R. *Nature* 205, 567 (1965).
285. PORTER, G. A., BOGOROCH, R. and EDELMAN, I. S. *Proc. Natl. Acad. Sci. U.S.* 52, 1326 (1964).
286. PORTER, K. R. *Biophysical J.* 4, 167 (1964).
287. PORTER, R. R. *Biochem. J.* 73, 119 (1959).
288. QUIRIN, C., JACOB, M. and MANDEL, P. *Compt. rend. soc. biol.* 258, 6013 (1964).
289. RABINOVITZ, M. and FISHER, J. M. *Biochim. Biophys. Acta* 91, 313 (1964).
290. RABINOVITZ, M. and OLSON, M. E. *J. Biol. Chem.* 234, 2085 (1959).
291. RABINOWITZ, M. and LIPMANN, F. *J. Biol. Chem.* 235, 1043 (1960).
292. RABINOWITZ, M., ZAK, R., BELLER, B., RAMPERSAND, O. and WOOL, I. G. *Proc. Natl. Acad. Sci. U.S.* 52, 1353 (1964).
293. RADOVICH, J., SZANTIVANYI, A. and TALMADGE, D. W. *J. Gen. Physiol.* 47, 297 (1963).
294. RALPH, R. K., YOUNG, R. J. and KHORANA, H. G. *J. Am. Chem. Soc.* 85, 2002 (1963).
295. REEVE, E. B., PEARSON, J. R. and MARTZ, D. C. *Science* 139, 914 (1963).

296. REICH, E., GOLDBERG, I. H. and RABINOWITZ, M. *Nature* **196**, 743 (1962).
297. REID, E. and STEVENS, B. M. *Biochem. J.* **67**, 262 (1957).
298. RENDI, R. *Exptl. Cell Research* **17**, 585 (1959).
299. RENDI, R., DiMILIA, A. and FRONTICELLI, C. *Biochem. J.* **70**, 62 (1958).
300. RENDI, R. and OCHOA, S. *J. Biol. Chem.* **237**, 3707 (1962).
301. RICH, A., WARNER, J. R. and GOODMAN, H. M. *Cold Spring Harbor Symp. Quant. Biol.* **28**, 269 (1963).
302. RIGGS, T. R. and WALKER, L. M. *J. Biol. Chem.* **238**, 2663 (1963).
303. RIGGS, T. R., WALKER, L. M. and CHRISTENSEN, H. N. *J. Biol. Chem.* **233**, 1479 (1958).
304. RISEBROUGH, R. W., TISSIERES, A. and WATSON, J. D. *Proc. Natl. Acad. Sci. U.S.* **48**, 430 (1962).
305. ROBERTS, R. R., BRITTEN, R. J. and McCARTHY, B. J. In *Molecular Genetics*, ed. J. H. Taylor, Part I, p. 291, Academic Press, N.Y., 1963.
306. ROODYN, D. B. *Biochem. J.* **85**, 177 (1962).
307. ROSE, W. L., OESTERLING, M. J. and WOMACK, M. *J. Biol. Chem.* **176**, 753 (1948).
308. ROSENBERG, L. E., BERMAN, M. and SEGAL, S. *Biochim. Biophys. Acta* **71**, 664 (1963).
309. ROTHSCHILD, M. A., ORATZ, M., WIMER, E. and SCHREIBER, S. S. *J. Clin. Invest.* **40**, 545 (1961).
310. RYCHLIK, I. and SORM, F. *Coll. Czech. Chem. Communs.* **27**, 2433 (1962).
311. RYCHLIK, I., DANCHEVA, K. I. and CHERKOVA, M. *Coll. Czech. Chem. Communs.* **30**, 138 (1965).
312. SABATANI, D. and TASHIRO, Y. *Proceedings, 6th Internatl. Congress of Biochemistry, Symposium I, New York*, 1964, p. 84.
313. SADDI, R. and VON DER DECKEN, A. *Biochim. Biophys. Acta* **90**, 196 (1964).
314. SANSOM, B. F. and BARRY, J. M. *Biochem. J.* **68**, 487 (1958).
315. SAMUELS, L. D., *New England J. Med.* **271**, 1252, 1301 (1964).
316. SANGER, F. *Adv. Protein Chem.* **7**, 60 (1952).
317. SANGER, R. and HOCQUARD, E. *Biochim. Biophys. Acta* **62**, 606 (1962).
318. SARCIONE, E. J. *Biochemistry (N.Y.)* **3**, 1686, 1973 (1964).
319. SARGENT, J. R. and CAMPBELL, P. N. *Proceedings, 6th Internatl. Congress of Biochemistry, Symposium I, New York*, 1964 p. 85.
320. SCHAECTER, M. *J. Mol. Biol.* **7**, 561 (1963).
321. SCHAPIRA, G., DREYFUS, J-C. and KRUH, J. *Biochem. J.* **82**, 290 (1962).
322. SCHAPIRA, G., KRUH, J., DREYFUS, J-C. and SCHAPIRA, F. *J. Biol. Chem.* **235**, 1738 (1960).
323. SCHARFF, M. D., SHATKIN, A. J. and LEVINTOW, L. *Proc. Natl. Acad. Sci. U.S.* **50**, 686 (1963).
324. SCHIMKE, R. T., SWEENEY, E. W. and BERLIN, C. M. *J. Biol. Chem.* **240**, 322 (1965).
325. SCHLESSINGER, D. *J. Mol. Biol.* **7**, 569 (1963).
326. SCHLESSINGER, D. and GROS, F. *J. Mol. Biol.* **7**, 350 (1963).
327. SCHMIDT, G. *Ann. Rev. Biochem.* **33**, 667 (1964).
328. SCHOENHEIMER, R., RATNER, S. and RITTENBERG, D. *J. Biol. Chem.* **130**, 703 (1939).
329. SCHRAMM, I. M. and BDOLAH, A. *Arch. Biochem. Biophys.* **104**, 67 (1964).
330. SCHWEET, R. S., ARLINGHAUS, R., SCHAEFFER, J. and WILLIAMSON A. *Medicine* **43**, 731 (1964).
331. SCHWEET, R., BOVARD, F., ALLEN, E. and GLASSMAN, E. *Proc. Natl. Acad. Sci. U.S.* **44**, 173 (1958).
332. SCHWEET, R. S., HOLLEY, R. W. and ALLEN, E. H. *Arch. Biochem. Biophys.* **71**, 311 (1957).
333. SCOTT, R. B. and BELL, E. *Science* **145**, 711 (1964).
334. SCOTT, R. B. and BELL, E. *Science* **147**, 405 (1965).
335. SEKERIS, C. E. and LANG, N. *Life Science* **3**, 625 (1964).
336. SEED, R. W. and GOLDBERG, I. H. *J. Biol. Chem.* **240**, 764 (1965).
337. SELLIN, H. G. and GOLDBERG, I. H. *J. Biol. Chem.* **240**, 774 (1965).
338. SHARLAT, I. V., MOSOLOV, V. V. and AFANAS'ER, P. V. *Dokl. Akad. S.S.R.* **158**, 477 (1964).

339. Shimura, K., Kobayashi, H., Hoshi, R. and Sato, J. *J. Biochem. (Tokyo)* **46**, 849 (1959).
340. Siekevitz, P. *J. Biol. Chem.* **195**, 549 (1952).
341. Simpson, M. V. and Velick, S. F. *Biochim. Biophys. Acta* **20**, 228 (1956).
342. Sinex, M. and van Slyke, D. D. *J. Biol. Chem.* **234**, 918 (1959).
343. Singer, M. F. and Cantoni, G. L. *Biochim. Biophys. Acta* **39**, 182 (1960).
344. Slapikoff, S., Fessenden, J. M. and Moldave, K. *J. Biol. Chem.* **238**, 3671 (1963).
345. Smirnov, B. P. and Rodionova, M. A. *Biokhimia* **29**, 386 (1964).
346. Smith, E. L. *Proc. Natl. Acad. Sci. U.S.* **48**, 859 (1962).
347. Smith, J. D. *J. Mol. Biol.* **8**, 772 (1964).
348. Smyth, D. G., Stein, W. H. and Moore, S. *J. Biol. Chem.* **238**, 227 (1963).
349. So, S. G. and Davie, E. W. *Biochemistry (N.Y.)* **3**, 1165 (1964).
350. Soberón, G. and Sanchez, Q. E. *J. Biol. Chem.* **236**, 1602 (1961).
351. Sokoloff, L., Francis, D. M. and Campbell, P. L. *Proc. Natl. Acad. Sci. U.S.* **52**, 728 (1964).
352. Spackman, D. H., Stein, W. H. and Moore, S. *Anal. Chem.* **30**, 1190 (1958).
353. Spencer, D. and Wildman, S. G. *Biochemistry (N.Y.)* **3**, 954 (1964).
354. Spencer, M., Fuller, W., Wilkins, M. H. F. and Brown, G. L. *Nature*, **194**, 1014 (1962).
355. Spiegelman, S. and Hayashi, M. *Cold Spring Harbor Symp. Quant. Biol.* **28**, 161 (1963).
356. Spirin, A. S. and Kisseler, N. A. *Proceedings 6th Internatl. Congress of Biochemistry, Symposium I, New York*, 1964, p. 32.
357. Spiro, R. G. and Spiro, M. J. *Federation Proc.* **23**, 316 (1964).
358. Staehelin, T., Wettstein, F. O., Oura, H. and Noll, H. *Nature* **201**, 264 (1964).
359. Steele, W. J., Okamura, N. and Busch, H. *Biochim. Biophys. Acta* **87**, 490 (1964).
360. Steinberg, D. *Arch. Biochem. Biophys.* **65**, 93 (1956).
361. Steinberg, D., Vaughan, M. and Anfinsen, C. B. *Science* **124**, 389 (1956).
362. Steiner, R. F. *Nature* **204**, 579 (1964).
363. Stent, G. S. *Science* **144**, 816 (1964).
364. Stephenson, M. and Zamecnik, P. C. *Proc. Natl. Acad. Sci. U.S.* **47**, 1627 (1961).
365. Straub, F. B. *Adv. in Enzymol.* **26**, 89 (1964).
366. Strohman, R. C., Cerwinsky, E. W. and Holmes, D. W. *Exptl. Cell. Research* **35** 617 (1964).
367. Sueoka, N. and Tetsuo, Y. *Proc. Natl. Acad. Sci. U.S.* **48**, 1454 (1962).
368. Svenson, P. A. and Setlow, R. B. *Science* **146**, 791 (1964).
369. Swick, R. W., Buchanan, D. L., and Nakao, N. *J. Biol. Chem.* **203**, 55 (1953).
370. Synge, R. L. M., In *Chemical Structure of Proteins*, ed. G. E. W. Wolstenholme and M. P. Cameron, Ciba Found. Symp., p. 43, Little Brown & Co., Boston, 1954.
371. Takanami, M. *Proc. Natl. Acad. Sci. U.S.* **52**, 1271 (1964).
372. Takanami, M. and Okamoto, T. *Biochim. Biophys. Acta* **44**, 379 (1960).
373. Takanami, M. and Zubay, G. *Proc. Natl. Acad. Sci. U.S.* **51**, 834 (1964).
374. Takeda, Y. and Reeve, E. B. *J. Lab. Clin. Med.* **61**, 183 (1963).
375. Talwar, G. P., Segal, S. J., Evans, A. and Davidson, D. W. *Proc. Natl. Acad. Sci. U.S.* **52**, 1059 (1964).
376. Tarver, H. In *The Proteins*, ed. H. Neurath, Vol. II B, p. 1199, Academic Press, N.Y., 1954.
377. Tata, J. R. *Biochim. Biophys. Acta* **87**, 528 (1964).
378. Thompson, R. C. and Ballou, J. E. *J. Biol. Chem.* **223**, 795 (1956).
379. Thorell, B. *Cold Spring Harbor Symp. Quant. Biol.* **12**, 247 (1947).
380. Tissieres, A. and Hopkins, J. N. *Proc. Natl. Acad. Sci. U.S.* **47**, 2015 (1961).
381. Trakatellis, A. C., Axelrod, A. E. and Montjar, M. *J. Biol. Chem.* **239**, 4237 (1964).
382. Tria, E. and Barnabei, D. *Nature*, **197**, 598 (1963).
383. Truman, D. E. S. *Biochem. J.* **91**, 59 (1964).
384. Tsugita, A. and Fraenkel-Conrat, H. *J. Mol. Biol.* **4**, 73 (1962).
385. Turba, F. and Hilpert, H. *Biochem. Z.* **334**, 487, 501, 507 (1961).

386. VARNER, J. E. and CHANDRA, G. R. *Proc. Natl. Acad. Sci. U.S.* **52**, 100 (1964).
387. VAUGHAN, M. and STEINBERG, D. *Adv. Protein Chem.* **14** 115 (1959).
388. VENETIANER, P. and STRAUB, F. B. *Biochim. Biophys. Acta* **67**, 166 (1963).
389. VILLA-TREVINO, S., FARBER, E., STAEHELIN, T., WETTSTEIN, F. O. and NOLL, H. *J. Biol. Chem.* **239**, 3826 (1964).
390. VOLKIN, E. and ASTRACHAN, L. *Virology* **2**, 149 (1956).
391. VON DER DECKEN, A. *Exptl. Cell Research* **31**, 226 (1963).
392. VON DER DECKEN, A. and CAMPBELL, P. N. *Biochem. J.* **84**, 449 (1962).
393. VON DER DECKEN, A. and HULTIN, T. *Biochim. Biophys. Acta* **45**, 139, 148 (1960).
394. VON EHRENSTEIN, G., WEISBLUM, B. and BENZER, S. *Proc. Natl. Acad. Sci. U.S.* **49**, 669 (1963).
395. VOORMA, H. O., GOUT, P. W., VAN DUIN, J., HOOGENDARN, B. W. and BOSCH, L. *Biochim. Biophys. Acta* **87**, 693 (1964).
396. WACHSMAN, J. T., FUKUHARA, H. and NISMAN, B. *Biochim. Biophys. Acta* **42**, 388 (1960).
397. WAINWRIGHT, S. D. and McFARLANE, E. S. *Biochem. Biophys. Research Communs.* **9**, 529 (1962).
398. WALTER, H. and ZIPPER, H. *Biochem. J.* **84**, 531 (1962).
399. WARNER, J. R. and RICH, A. *J. Mol. Biol.* **10**, 202 (1964).
400. WARNER, J. R., KNOPF, A. and RICH, C. E. *Proc. Natl. Acad. Sci. U.S.* **49**, 122 (1963).
401. WARREN, W. A. and PETERS, T. *J. Biol. Chem.* **240**, 3009 (1965).
402. WARSHAWSKY, H., LeBLOND, C. P. and DROZ, B. *J. Cell Biol.* **16**, 1 (1963).
403. WATERLOW, J. C., CRAVIOTO, J. and STEPHEN, J. M. L. *Adv. Protein Chem.* **15**, 131 (1960).
404. WATSON, J. D. *Science* **140**, 17 (1963).
405. WEBER, G., BANERJEE, G. and BRONSTEIN, S. B. *Biochem. Biophys. Research Communs.* **4**, 332 (1961).
406. WEBER, G., SRIVASTA, S. K. and SINGHAL, R. L. *J. Biol. Chem.* **240**, 750 (1965).
407. WEBSTER, G. C. *Biochim. Biophys. Acta* **49**, 141 (1961).
408. WEISBLUM, B., GONANO, F., VON EHRENSTEIN, G. and BENZER, S. *Proc. Natl. Acad. Sci. U.S.* **53**, 328 (1965).
409. WEISS, S. B., ACS, G. and LIPMANN, F. *Federation Proc.* **17**, 333 (1958).
410. WILLIAMS-ASHMAN, H. G., LIAO, S., HANCOCK, R. L., JURKOWITZ, L. and SILVERMAN, D. A. *Recent Progress Hormone Research* **20**, 247 (1964).
411. WINCKELMAUS, D., HILL, M. and ERRARA, M. *Biochim. Biophys. Acta* **80**, 52 (1964).
412. WINNICK, T. *Arch. Biochem.* **28**, 338 (1950).
413. WINNICK, R. E. and WINNICK, T. *J. Biol. Chem.* **235**, 2657 (1960).
414. WINTERSBERGER, E. *Hoppe Seylers Z. für physiol. Chem.* **336**, 285 (1964).
415. WINZLER, R. J. *Clinical Chem.* **11**, 339 (1965).
416. WOESE, C. R. *Nature* **189**, 920 (1961).
417. WOLF, G. and BERGER, C. R. A. *J. Biol. Chem.* **230**, 231 (1958).
418. WONG, K. G. and MOLDAVE, K. *J. Biol. Chem.* **235**, 694 (1960).
419. WOOD, W. B. and BERG, P. *J. Mol. Biol.* **9**, 452 (1964).
420. WOOL, I. G. and MOYER, A. N. *Biochim. Biophys. Acta* **91**, 248 (1964).
421. WREN, J. J. *Nature* **185**, 295 (1960).
422. WU, C. *Arch. Biochem. Biophys.* **106**, 402 (1964).
423. YANOFSKY, C. *Cold Spring Harbor Symp. Quant. Biol.* **28**, 581 (1963).
424. YANOFSKY, C., CARLTON, B. C., GUEST, J. R., HELINSKI, D. R. and HENNING, U. *Proc. Natl. Acad. Sci. U.S.* **51**, 266 (1964).
425. YANOFSKY, S. A. and SPIEGELMAN, S. *Proc. Natl. Acad. Sci. U.S.* **49**, 538 (1963).
426. YARMOLINSKY, M. B. and DE LA HABA, G. L. *Proc. Natl. Acad. Sci. U.S.* **45**, 1721 (1959).
427. YOSHIDA, A. and TOBITA, T. *Biochim. Biophys. Acta* **37**, 513 (1960).
428. YOUNG, R. J., KIHARA, H. K. and HALVORSON, H. O. *Proc. Natl. Acad. Sci. U.S.* **47**, 1415 (1961).
429. ZACHAU, H. G., ACS, G. and LIPMANN, F. *Proc. Natl. Acad. Sci. U.S.* **44**, 885 (1958).

430. ZALOKAR, M. *Biochim. Biophys. Acta* **46**, 423 (1961).
431. ZAMECNIK, P. C. and KELLER, E. B. *J. Biol. Chem.* **209**, 337 (1954).
432. ZILLIG, W., SCHACHTSCHABEL, D. and KRONE, W. *Hoppe Seylers Z. für physiol. Chem.* **318**, 100 (1960).
433. ZIMMERMAN, E. and TURBA, F. *Biochem. Z.* **339**, 469 (1964).
434. ZIPSER, D. *J. Mol. Biol.* **7**, 739 (1963).
435. ZUBAY, G. *Science* **140**, 1093 (1963).

CHAPTER 8

THE ENZYMIC SYNTHESIS OF NUCLEIC ACIDS

ROGER MANTSAVINOS†

Department of Biochemical Pharmacology and Biochemistry,
State University of New York at Buffalo, Buffalo, New York

and

STEPHEN ZAMENHOF

Department of Medical Microbiology and Immunology,
Department of Biological Chemistry, and Molecular Biology Institute,
University of California, Los Angeles, California

CONTENTS

I. INTRODUCTION — 538

II. GENERAL CONSIDERATIONS — 539
  A. *Primary chemical structure of nucleic acids* — 539
  B. *Secondary structure and general properties of nucleic acids* — 540
    1. Deoxyribonucleic acid — 540
    2. Ribonucleic acid — 542

III. NUCLEOTIDES AS PRECURSORS FOR NUCLEIC ACID SYNTHESIS — 544
  A. *General remarks* — 544
  B. In vivo *studies* — 544
  C. In vitro *studies* — 545

IV. ENZYMIC SYNTHESIS OF POLYDEOXYRIBONUCLEOTIDES — 545
  A. *Bacterial enzymes* — 545
    1. Deoxyribonucleic acid nucleotidyltransferases — 545
    2. Oligodeoxyribonucleotide transferase — 552
  B. *Mammalian enzymes* — 552
    1. Deoxyribonucleic acid nucleotidyltransferases — 553

V. ENZYMIC SYNTHESIS OF POLYRIBONUCLEOTIDES — 555
  A. *Polynucleotide phosphorylase* — 555
  B. *Enzyme systems requiring ribonucleoside 5′-triphosphates* — 560
    1. Introduction — 560

† Deceased.

2. Incorporation of ribonucleotides into terminal positions
of ribonucleic acid   560
3. Incorporation of ribonucleotides into deoxyribonucleic
acid   562
4. Formation of sequences containing one ribonucleotide
residue   562
5. Enzyme systems requiring four ribonucleoside 5′-tri-
phosphates   565
(a) Ribonucleic acid directed synthesis of ribonucleic acid   565
(b) Ribonucleic acid nucleotidyltransferase   567

VI. ENZYMIC METHYLATION OF NUCLEIC ACIDS   571

VII. SUMMARY   574

VIII. REFERENCES   577

I. INTRODUCTION†

Recognition of the basic role of nucleic acids as hereditary determinants of living cells and viruses (for a recent review, see ref. 1) has stimulated a great deal of interest in their biosynthesis. Our current knowledge of the enzymic mechanisms associated with nucleic acid synthesis has been derived largely from isotopic experiments with tissue homogenates, cell-free enzyme extracts, and purified enzymes from various sources. In the present chapter, after a brief discussion of the chemistry and general properties of nucleic acids, we shall discuss the synthesis of these polymers from nucleotide-precursors by various enzyme systems. We wish to emphasize that enzymic reactions formulated as a result of *in vitro* studies should be considered only as possible models for various *in vivo* biosynthetic processes and do not necessarily represent the key reactions that are actually operational in living organisms. In order to assume real significance the conditions under which an enzyme system operates *in vitro* must be ultimately reconciled with observations made in living cells.

† The following abbreviations are used in this chapter, in addition to those listed in the beginning of the volume: t-RNA, "transfer" RNA; m-RNA, "messenger" RNA; r-RNA, ribosomal RNA; poly "X" or poly d"X", a linear 3′-5′ polymer of nucleotide "X" or deoxynucleotide "X", e.g. poly A, polyadenylic acid; poly U, polyuridylic acid; poly C, polycytidylic acid; poly G, polyguanylic acid; poly dT, polydeoxythymidylic acid; poly AU, heteropolymer of adenylic and uridylic acids; poly AGUC, a heteropolymer of adenylic, guanylic, uridylic, and cytidylic acids. Oligoribonucleotides are designated by the system used in the *J. Biol. Chem.* According to this system, the letters A, G, U, I and C represent adenosine, guanosine, uridine, inosine and cytidine, respectively, and a phosphate is designated by "p". When placed to the left of a nucleoside symbol, the phosphate is esterified at carbon-5′ of the ribose moiety; when placed to the right, esterification is at carbon-3′ of the ribose moiety. Thus, ApUp is a dinucleotide with a mono-esterified phosphate on carbon-3′ of the uridine residue and a single 3′,5′ phosphodiester bond between carbon-3′ of the adenosine residue and carbon-5′ of the uridine residue.

II. GENERAL CONSIDERATIONS

A. *Primary Chemical Structure of Nucleic Acids*†

Complete acid hydrolysis of a nucleic acid yields phosphoric acid, a mixture of purine and pyrimidine bases, and a sugar residue. The sugar component of DNA is 2-deoxy-D-ribose and that of RNA is D-ribose. The most prevalent bases of RNA are the purines, adenine and guanine, and the pyrimidines, cytosine and uracil.

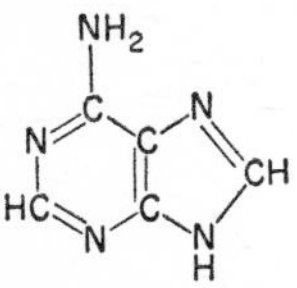

Adenine 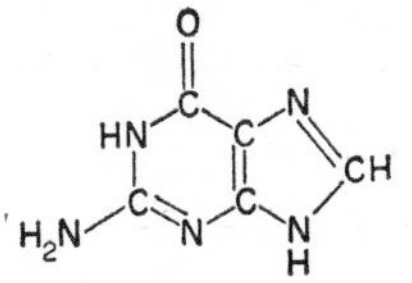   Guanine 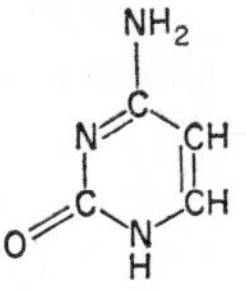   Cytosine 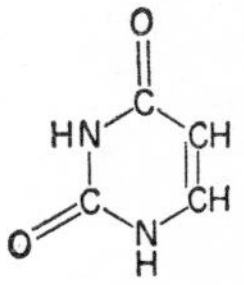   Uracil

Similar bases are also found in DNA with the exception of uracil, which is replaced by the pyrimidine, thymine.

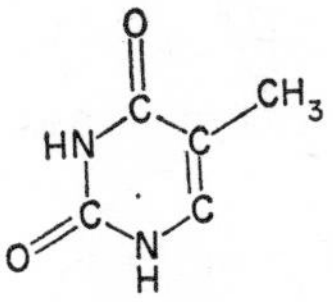

Thymine

In addition to these compounds several other bases and atypical constituents have been detected in nucleic acids as major or minor components (see refs. 6–9, 13–15).

Condensation of a purine or pyrimidine base to ribose or deoxyribose by means of a glycosidic linkage yields a nucleoside. Nucleotides are phosphoric esters of nucleosides and represent the monomeric units of nucleic acids. The chemical formulas for adenosine-5′-monophosphate, a ribonucleotide that has the trivial name adenylic acid, and for the deoxyribonucleotide, thymidine-5′-monophosphate (thymidylic acid) are shown overleaf.

In both RNA and DNA, nucleotides are linked to one another by means of 3′,5′-phosphodiester bonds to form long polynucleotide chains. Thus, RNA is a polyribonucleotide in which the internucleotide linkages are of the phosphodiester type as illustrated below for a portion of an RNA chain. The primary chemical structure for DNA may be likewise depicted.

† For a detailed consideration of the chemistry and physical properties of nucleic acids see refs. 2–5.

Adenosine -5′- monophosphate
(adenylic acid, AMP)

Thymidine -5′- monophosphate
(thymidylic acid, dTMP)

B. Secondary Structure and General Properties of Nucleic Acids

1. Deoxyribonucleic Acid

Early analytical studies on DNA, derived from a variety of sources, revealed that certain regularities exist among the constituent bases. Analysis of the base composition of DNA showed an equivalence of purines to pyrimidines and that the molar ratios of adenine to thymine, and of guanine to cytosine are close to unity (see refs. 18 and 19). On the basis of these analytical studies and X-ray diffraction patterns of DNA,[20, 21] Watson and Crick [22] proposed that the structure of DNA consisted of two linear, but antiparallel, polynucleotide chains intertwined about each other to form a structure as illustrated in Fig. 1. In the model shown, the two poly-nucleotide chains are held together by lateral hydrogen-bonds between specific purine and pyrimidine base pairs, which tend to lie perpendicular to the length of the molecule. Adenine is paired with thymine, and guanine with cytosine. Such an alignment of bases results in a configuration in which the arrangement of bases in one polynucleotide chain determines the order of bases along the complementary chain. The structural features of this model of DNA suggest an interesting scheme for its replication. According to the mechanisms proposed by Watson and Crick [23, 24] (for a recent review see ref. 25) replication occurs by a semi-conservative [26] mechanism in which each polynucleotide chain of the DNA helix serves as a template for the replication of a new complementary chain. Several experimental findings are compatible with a semi-conservative mode of DNA replication (for a review, see ref. 27).

X-ray diffraction studies indicate that the helical structure of DNA also exists in extracted nucleoprotamines and nucleohistones as well as in intact biological specimens such as sperm heads and calf thymus nuclei. [28-30] These results support the view that DNA can also exist as a double-helix in natural sources and that the helical structure of DNA is not an artifact induced by the method of preparation.

The molecular weight of most kinds of native DNA remains uncertain. The values reported for isolated DNA preparations vary widely depending on the source from which the DNA was extracted, the procedure of isolation, and the methodology used in estimating the molecular weight. [3, 31, 32] A commonly quoted value for the average molecular weight of calf thymus DNA is approximately $6 \cdot 0 \times 10^6$, [33] although values ranging from 2×10^6 to 18×10^6 have been reported for this DNA. [31, 34, 35] DNA isolated from cells of higher plants and animals has thus far been reported to represent a heterogeneous mixture of various molecular species. DNA isolated from certain bacterial species and viruses appears to exist as a single structural entity possessing a high molecular weight; however, the rigorous proof that such entity contains nothing else than DNA nucleotides is still lacking. The entire chromosome of T2 bacteriophage is a single molecule of DNA having a molecular weight that lies between 130×10^6 and 160×10^6. [36, 37] Autoradiographic estimates of the minimum length of E. coli DNA liberated after mild lysis of the cell indicate it is a single entity approximately 400μ long with a molecular weight of 10^9 or more. [38] Autoradiographs of some DNA molecules show that the DNA, which represents the entire chromo-some of E. coli, is physically in the form of a circle and that the circular structure is maintained during replication of the DNA. [38, 39] Similarly, electron micrographs of replicating DNA of the phage ϕX-174 [40, 41] and of the DNA from polyoma virus[42, 43] indicate that these double-stranded DNA molecules are also circular, at least in certain stages of the life-cycle.

DNA occurs free in certain viruses, bacteria, and blue-green algae.[44] In cells of higher organisms, however, DNA is found associated with basic proteins by means of ionic linkages between the anionic phosphate groups of DNA and the cationic groups of the basic amino acids.[45] In the sperm of certain species of fish, DNA is found associated with protamines whereas in nuclei of somatic cells histones are the main proteins linked to DNA.[45]

2. *Ribonucleic Acid*

The primary chemical structure of RNA is similar to that of DNA. However, RNA molecules display physical properties characteristic of single-stranded polynucleotides[4, 5] whereas most DNA molecules normally are double-stranded polymers. Nevertheless, under proper conditions a polyribonucleotide chain may assume regions of helical conformation, as a result of intrachain hydrogen-bonding by complementary base pairs, or may interact with other polynucleotide chains to form multi-strand structures.[2, 4, 5] Within cells, most of the RNA is associated with protein and the secondary structure of RNA in nucleoproteins is determined, to a large extent, by the protein component to which it is bound.

Within recent years, several distinct kinds of RNA have been distinguished on the basis of their base composition, molecular size, biological function, and intracellular distribution. Some of the physical properties and functions of m-RNA, t-RNA, and r-RNA are discussed briefly below. These RNAs are involved in the synthesis of proteins (see Chapter 7) and represent the bulk of the cellular RNA.

Recently, the presence of DNA has been reported outside the nucleus especially in chloroplasts.[46, 47]

The genetic code of living cells is assumed to reside in the linear arrangement of purine and pyrimidine bases along the polynucleotide chains of DNA. The sequence of nucleotides in DNA, in turn, dictates the sequence of amino acids in proteins. Messenger RNA is believed to be a complementary copy of a segment of nucleotides in DNA containing information necessary for the synthesis of a specific polypeptide.[48] The assumption that m-RNA serves as a carrier of genetic information from DNA to the ribosomes,[51] where cellular protein synthesis takes place, has gained support from the results of several studies[52–59] including the finding that the incorporation of a given amino acid into polypeptide chains by cell-free enzyme systems containing ribosomes is determined, at least in part, by the nucleotide composition of the polyribonucleotide added to such systems.[63] In bacteria m-RNA has a high rate of turnover.[63] The stability of m-RNA, however, appears to differ in various types of cells. For example, in reticulocytes m-RNA appears to be stable throughout the entire protein synthesizing

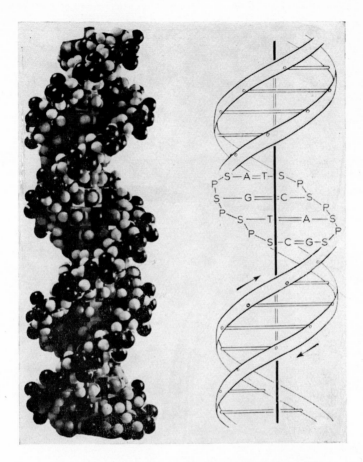

FIG. 1. Molecular models of DNA, from S. S. Cohen.[17]

(*By permission, Academic Press, Inc.*)

To face page 542

period of the cell[60, 61] and there are indications that relatively stable m-RNAs exist in other mammalian cells. [62]

The term "soluble RNA" refers to various low molecular weight species of RNA found in the high speed supernatant fraction cellular homogenates. One kind of soluble RNA is known as "amino acid acceptor" RNA or simply as "transfer" RNA (t-RNA). The general formula for most t-RNAs is pXp . . . pCpCpA, in which "X" is mostly guanosine. [64, 65] A complete sequence of nucleotides in one such t-RNA has been reported recently. [66] The terminal -pCpCpA sequence of t-RNA serves as a functional site for the binding of amino acids. In the process of protein synthesis activated amino acids are bound to the terminal adenosine moiety of specific t-RNAs, by means of ester linkages, and transported to the ribosomes where protein synthesis takes place. [15] The molecular weights of t-RNAs lie in a range of about 23,000 to 28,000. [15] Small amounts of various methylated bases and methylated sugars have also been detected in t-RNA (see Section VI, and ref. 54). Among the atypical nucleosides found in t-RNAs 5-ribosyl-uracil (or pseudouridine) is unique in that it possesses a carbon–carbon ribosyl linkage rather than the common nitrogen–carbon glycosidic linkage. [67, 68]

pseudouridine

Certain lines of evidence suggest that pseudouridine is formed by appropriate rearrangement of uridine residues in the soluble RNA. [69] Other results, however, support the view that the carbon–carbon ribosyl linkages of pseudouridine is formed prior to the incorporation of pseudouridine into RNA. [70]

Ribosomes consist mainly of protein and RNA and contain most of the cellular RNA. [49, 50] In bacteria the quantity of r-RNA is proportional to the growth rate [71] and may account for as much as 90 per cent of the total RNA of rapidly growing bacterial cells. [72] Although r-RNA is the most abundant cellular RNA, relatively little is known about its biosynthesis. Ribosomal RNAs from a wide variety of sources have similar nucleotide compositions characterized by a high content of guanine. [73, 74] RNA obtained from ribosomes of various plant and animal cells consists of two major components with sedimentation coefficients of 17S and 30S corresponding to molecular weights of about 0.5×10^6 and 1.5×10^6, respectively, and bacterial r-RNA has sedimentation coefficients of 16S and 23S corresponding to molecular weights of about 0.6×10^6 and 1.1×10^6, respectively. [50, 75]

For purposes of comparison, it may be mentioned that tobacco mosaic virus RNA has a molecular weight of approximately $2 \cdot 0 \times 10^6$.[76] Methylated bases have also been found in r-RNA [77, 78, 79] (also see Section VI).

III. NUCLEOTIDES AS PRECURSORS FOR NUCLEIC ACID SYNTHESIS

A. *General Remarks*

Several *in vivo* and *in vitro* studies have shown that nucleotides serve as precursors for nucleic acid synthesis. Nucleosides can be synthesized either by *de novo* pathways from simple metabolites, or by so-called "salvage" or "preformed" pathways, from preformed purines, pyrimidines and nucleosides obtained from the intracellular degradation of nucleic acids or from the extracellular environment (see refs. 80–83 and Chapter 2). In each case nucleoside 5′-monophosphates are formed and subsequently phosphorylated to the di- and triphosphate forms [84, 80] which are then utilized for the synthesis of polynucleotides.

The 5′-mono-, di-, and triphosphates of adenosine, guanosine, cytidine, and uridine have been found in a wide variety of cells. [85, 84, 80, 86] The 5′-mono-, di- and triphosphates of TDR and of deoxycytidine have been detected in acid-soluble extracts of calf thymus, [87, 88] and naturally occurring dATP has been isolated from rats bearing the Flexner–Jobling carcinoma. [89] Ribonucleoside 2′- and 3′-phosphates and deoxyribonucleoside 3′-phosphates are regarded as products of nucleic acid degradation and are not known to participate in nucleic acid synthesis. However, the phosphorylation of thymidine 3′-diphosphate to thymidine-3′-triphosphate by extracts of *B. subtilis* has been reported. [90] The significance of this reaction from a biosynthetic point of view has yet to be assessed.

B. In vivo *Studies*

Direct evidence for the role of 5′-nucleotides as building units of nucleic acids has been obtained from *in vivo* experiments with radioactive tracers. [91] When radioactive orotic acid was investigated as a test precursor in rat liver, the labeling of acid-soluble 5′-nucleotides proceeded faster than labeling of nucleotides of nucleic acids of the same tissue. [92] However, owing presumably to metabolic heterogeneity among different kinds of molecules present in isolable nucleic acid specimens, a quantitative precursor–product relationship was not observable in kinetic studies. [93] The carbon–nitrogen skeletons of nucleosides [94, 95] and of nucleoside moieties of exogenous nucleotides [94, 96] enter nucleic acids as units, but the phosphate moiety of an exogenous nucleotide does not accompany the nucleoside portion. [96, 97, 98] The latter phenomenon is apparently a consequence of dephosphorylation of nucleotides at cell walls, followed by independent entry of nucleoside and orthophosphate into the cell. [97, 98] It has been shown that the different theoretical endogenous 5'-nucleotide precursors of RNA of rat liver have markedly different P^{32}-labelings during the first hour of *in vivo* incubations with phosphate P^{32}. [99] Similar studies in which nuclear and cytoplasmic RNA were isolated from the tissue and evaluated, revealed that the pattern of heterogenous P^{32}-labeling among the four major 5'-nucleotide units of RNA closely parallels the heterogenous labeling among theoretical 5'-nucleotide precursors. [100] In contrast, the four 2' (and 3') nucleotide units obtained by alkaline hydrolysis of nuclear RNA are almost equally labeled; a contrast observed also in P^{32} experiments with RNA of tobacco mosaic virus, [98] and DNA of thymine-requiring *E. coli*. [101] The 3'-ribonucleotides obtained by alkaline hydrolysis of cytoplasmic RNA contained cytidine 3'-phosphate of relatively high specific activity, traceable to *in vivo* exchange of very highly labeled adenosine-5'-phosphate units at end positions of soluble RNA molecules that terminate in 5'-esterified cytidine. This type of exchange reaction has also been observed in cell-free extracts of rat liver. [102, 103]

C. In vitro *Studies*

Our present understanding of the enzymic synthesis of polynucleotides has been derived largely from *in vitro* experimental studies with purified enzymes. Such studies have shown that nucleoside 5'-polyphosphates serve as precursors for the synthesis of both polyribonucleotides and polydeoxyribonucleotides. This finding is in agreement with the *in vivo* studies discussed in the preceding section. The remainder of this chapter will be devoted mainly to a consideration of the properties of various enzyme systems that have been implicated in the biosynthesis of RNA and DNA.

IV. ENZYMIC SYNTHESIS OF POLYDEOXYRIBONUCLEOTIDES

A. *Bacterial Enzymes*

1. *Deoxyribonucleic Acid Nucleotidyltransferases*†

The first detailed studies on the enzymic synthesis of DNA were performed by Kornberg and co-workers with the enzymes *E. coli* DNA polymerase. [104] This enzyme has been purified approximately 2000-fold and has a molecular weight estimated to be about 100,000. [105] The enzyme is associated with DNA, in the form of a nucleoprotein complex, in extracts of bacterial cells. [106] *E. coli* DNA polymerase catalyzes the synthesis of a DNA-like product in the presence of Mg^{++} ions, an exogenous supply of DNA (referred to as primer‡ DNA), and the deoxynucleoside 5'-triphosphates of adenine,

---

† At present, these enzymes are better known as "DNA polymerases" and this shorter designation is used in this discussion.

‡ Throughout this discussion the term "primer" is used in a broad sense to denote the ability of DNA to promote the DNA polymerase reaction.

T

thymine, cytosine, and guanine.[104] During the synthetic reaction, PP_i is released in quantities equimolar to the nucleotides incorporated into DNA.[107] This reaction may be represented by the following equation:[107]

$$
\begin{array}{c}
ndATP \\
+ \\
ndCTP + DNA \xrightleftharpoons[]{Mg^{++}} DNA- \\
+ \\
ndGTP \\
+ \\
ndTTP
\end{array}
\begin{bmatrix}
dAP \\
dCP \\
dGP \\
dTP
\end{bmatrix}_n + n(PP_i) \qquad (1)
$$

In equation (1), "n" represents the number of molecules reacting, and dAP, dCP, dGP, and dTP are the deoxynucleotides of adenine, cytosine, guanine, and thymine linked together by means of 3′,5′-phosphodiester bonds, as in native DNA.[108] DNA from viral, bacterial, plant, and animal sources serves equally well as primer for the polymerization reaction provided the molecular weight is sufficiently high.[104] A net synthesis of product greater than 20 times the amount of DNA added as primer may be attained.[109] Hence, the product is derived to the extent of 95 per cent or more from the triphosphates added to the reaction mixture.[104, 109] Omission of any one of the four deoxynucleoside 5′-triphosphates, from an otherwise complete reaction mixture, reduces the rate of incorporation of deoxynucleotides into DNA to approximately 0.5 per cent of the maximal value. Nevertheless, in reaction mixtures containing only a single deoxynucleoside 5′-triphosphate a limited incorporation of one or a few nucleotides onto the ends of DNA chains has been observed.[110] In this "limited" or end addition reaction, the nucleotide incorporated forms a covalent phosphodiester bond with the 3′-hydroxyl ends of the DNA primer.[110]

In the presence of Mg^{++} ions, *E. coli* DNA polymerase utilizes exclusively deoxyribonucleoside 5′-triphosphates as substrates. However, in the presence of Mn^{++} ions, this enzyme catalyzes the synthesis of mixed polymers containing both ribonucleotides and deoxyribonucleotides when provided with DNA primer and ribo- and deoxyribonucleoside 5′-triphosphates.[111] The nucleotide composition and dinucleotide frequencies (see next paragraph) of the mixed polymers formed with one ribonucleotide and three deoxyribonucleotides reflect the base sequence and composition of the primer.[111] Several experimental criteria indicate that the synthesis of mixed polymers is catalyzed by *E. coli* DNA polymerase and not by contaminating enzymic activities.[111] However, it is noteworthy that highly purified DNA polymerase from *B. subtilis* that possesses fundamental properties similar to *E. coli* DNA polymerase does not catalyze the synthesis of mixed polymers.[112]

Several lines of evidence suggest that, in the synthetic reaction catalyzed by *E. coli* DNA polymerase, DNA functions as a template that directs the synthesis of new DNA. Synthetic products reflecting the bases of the DNA primer have been obtained even when the initial concentrations of the substrates are markedly distorted.[109, 113] However, it cannot be assumed that such a synthesis represents an exact replication of the nucleotide sequences of the primer. Unequivocal proof of such replication can only be obtained by determining the sequential arrangement of nucleotides in both the newly synthesized DNA and the DNA primer. At present such an analysis is not possible due to limitations in methodology. Nevertheless, a technique has been developed for determining the "nearest-neighbor" base sequences in DNA.[104, 114, 115] DNA is synthesized from one triphosphate labeled with P^{32} in the alpha phosphate and three nonradioactive triphosphates and subsequently degraded enzymically to 3'-mononucleotides.[104, 114, 115] By hydrolyzing the product to 3'-mononucleotides the labeled phosphate from the original 5'-position of one nucleotide is transferred to the 3'-position of its neighbor along the chain. When this procedure is performed four times with a different radioactive triphosphate each time, the relative frequencies of all the 16 possible kinds of dinucleotide or "nearest-neighbor" sequences can be determined.[104, 114, 115] It has been found that the products synthesized with several different primers possess a unique and nonrandom pattern of the 16 nearest neighbor frequencies.[114, 115] Furthermore, the pattern is unaltered when the primers are denatured by heating. The nearest neighbor frequencies of the product synthesized with either native calf thymus DNA primer or with an enzymically synthesized DNA primer, containing only traces of the original native calf thymus DNA primer, are the same, suggesting that the sequence frequencies in the product are indicative of the sequence frequencies in the native DNA.[114] The distribution of the sequence frequencies in several DNA samples examined indicates that the mechanism of DNA replication involves a sequential alignment of nucleotides along a DNA template and involves hydrogen bonding of adenine to thymine and of guanine to cytosine.[104, 114] Additionally, these results provide experimental evidence for opposite polarity of the strands of the double helix as postulated in the Watson and Crick model for DNA.[104, 114]

Additional evidence favoring the view that DNA replication occurs by a template mechanism involving base-pairing comes from the finding that the natural triphosphate substrates can be replaced by certain purine and pyrimidine analogs[116] providing the structure of the analogs does not interfere with the hydrogen-bonding relationships between the base pairs of DNA as proposed by Watson and Crick.[22] In each case, the analog specifically replaces the triphosphate of the natural base that it most closely resembles chemically. For example, deoxyuridine-5'-triphosphate and 5-*bromodeoxyuridine 5'-triphosphate* each replace dTTP, but not dATP, dCTP or dGTP.[104, 116]† Under proper experimental conditions, several other purine and pyrimidine analogs (e.g. hypoxanthine, 5-bromocytosine, 5-hydroxymethylcytosine, 5-methylcytosine, 5-fluorocytosine, and 5-fluorouracil) can be incorporated into DNA by *E. coli* DNA polymerase when provided as the deoxynucleoside 5′-triphosphates.[104, 116] Similar results are obtained when the triphosphates of analogs are used as substrates for DNA polymerases purified from *B. subtilis*,[112] and from *E. coli* infected with T2 phage.[122]

The secondary structure of the primer DNA influences the rates of the synthetic reactions catalyzed by various DNA polymerases. Single and double-stranded DNAs as well as heat-denatured DNA, can be used as primers by *E. coli* DNA polymerase. However, T2 DNA polymerase, the enzyme induced in *E. coli* after infection by T2 phage, has a requirement for either single-stranded or heat-denatured DNA primers.[122] Native DNA primers obtained from *E. coli*, T2 phage, or animal tissues support from 5 to 10 per cent of the polymerase activity when compared with heat-denatured samples of these same DNAs.[122] The reason for the inability of T2 polymerase to replicate native T2 DNA has not been established. T2 DNA polymerase has been shown, by several criteria, to be a distinct and different enzyme from DNA polymerase purified from uninfected *E. coli*.[122] It is noteworthy that the DNA polymerase obtained from cells of *E. coli* K12 λ that have been induced to form phage λ is similar to the DNA polymerase found in normal uninduced *E. coli* K12 λ.[123] Thus, the synthesis of λ phage DNA does not require the formation of a new DNA-synthesizing enzyme. Bacterial DNA obtained from mitomycin-C-induced cells of *E. coli* K12 λ cells is a poor primer for DNA polymerase and considerably less effective than phage λ DNA.[123, 124] This finding may explain why *E. coli* K12 λ cells preferentially synthesize λ DNA rather than their own DNA after induction.[123] The different priming abilities of various DNAs may be attributable, at least in part, to the nature of their end groups, as well as to the degree of purification of the DNA polymerase. Partial hydrolysis of DNA with purified *E. coli* endonuclease[125] or pancreatic DNA-ase, to produce 3′-hydroxyl and 5′-phosphoryl groups, increases priming activity whereas treatment of DNA with spleen endonuclease[126] or micrococcal endonuclease,[127] to yield 3′-phosphoryl and 5′-hydroxyl termini, inhibits priming activity.[128, 129, 112] Hence, limited enzymic alteration of the chemical structure of DNA may reduce or enhance its priming capacity. An exonuclease that persists in the most highly purified preparations of *E. coli* DNA polymerase is the enzyme designated as exonuclease II.[130] This enzyme attacks

---

† The presence in *E. coli* of kinases that convert 5-bromodeoxyuridylate to the triphosphate form,[116] and of a potent deoxyuridine triphosphatase[117, 118] is consistent with the known ability of this micro-organism to incorporate 5-bromouracil[119, 120] but not uracil[121] into its DNA.

the 3'-hydroxyl termini of polydeoxyribonucleotide chains liberating 5'-mononucleotides. Although attempts to separate the two enzymic activities have been unsuccessful, exonuclease II does not appear to be an obligatory component of the polymerization reaction. [130] Under conditions in which polymerase activity proceeds at nearly an optimal rate contaminating exonuclease II activity in *E. coli* DNA polymerase is barely detectable. [130] Furthermore, highly purified *B. subtilis* DNA polymerase [131] is apparently free of nuclease activity yet does not differ significantly from *E. coli* DNA polymerase in its synthetic properties. [130]

The dAT copolymer is a more effective primer than native DNA for the most highly purified preparations of *E. coli* DNA polymerase. [105] The progressive decrease in the priming ability of native DNA during the course of enzyme purification has been attributed to a removal of the endonuclease [125] mentioned above and a DNA phosphatase-exonuclease [129, 132] that cleaves inhibitory 3'-phosphoryl termini from DNA. The latter enzyme is an exonuclease that carries out a stepwise attack from the 3'-hydroxyl terminus of a DNA chain releasing 5'-mononucleotides. [133] This enzyme preferentially attacks native double-stranded DNA degrading 35 to 45 per cent of its structure and leaving a predominantly single-stranded DNA that is resistant to further attack. [133] The original double-stranded structure of this partially single-stranded molecule can be restored by a repair mechanism [134] that commences by covalent linkage of nucleotides to each 3'-hydroxyl terminus and proceeds with the single strands serving as templates for the sequential addition of nucleotides. [134] The fully repaired product resembles the original native DNA as judged by its denaturability, its appearance in electron micrographs, by CsCl density-gradient analysis, and by genetic activity. [134] Synthesis that follows the repair phase, however, produces a product that is not covalently linked to the primer and that possesses several unusual properties [134] that are not characteristic of native DNA. For example, in electron micrographs it appears as a highly branched material [129, 135, 134] and when separated from the primer DNA, it readily renatures after heating and rapid cooling. [129]

The fate of the product and primer during replication has also been studied. [128, 129] At two replications, when there are two parts product to one part primer, the bulk of the newly synthesized material can be dissociated from the primer by heat or treatment with alkali, [128, 129] indicating that the association of product and primer does not involve a stable covalent linkage. Thus, the synthesis of DNA *in vitro* follows a complex course that is not yet clearly understood and that leads to the synthesis of a DNA-like product that possesses certain properties that do not resemble those of native DNA.

Attempts at synthesizing biologically active DNA with highly purified *E. coli* DNA polymerase have not been successful. [128] After a 5-fold replication of transforming *B. subtilis* DNA no genetic activity was found in the newly synthesized material that could not be accounted for by associated primer DNA. [128] Litman and Szybalski, however, have reported the synthesis of biologically active DNA using heat-denatured bromouracil labeled *B. subtilis* DNA primer and a relatively crude DNA polymerase. [136, 137]

In vivo autoradiographic and genetic studies indicate that DNA synthesis in certain bacteria is a sequential, unidirectional process in which both strands of the parental DNA are replicated simultaneously. [138, 139, 140] If such a scheme applies to *in vitro* systems then two different mechanisms would be required to replicate the two strands of DNA, which are of opposite polarity. One mechanism [81] has already been demonstrated and entails the interaction of a 3'-hydroxyl end group of a DNA chain with the 5'-nucleotidyl phosphorus of the deoxyribonucleoside 5'-triphosphate. [104, 110] Another mechanism was proposed [141] and involves the reaction of the 3'-hydroxyl of the deoxyribonucleoside 5'-triphosphate with the 5'-nucleotidyl phosphorus of a triphosphate terminating a DNA chain. Whether the latter mechanism can be employed by *E. coli* polymerase or is the function of a second polymerase yet to be discovered is, at present, a matter of speculation. [25] Furthermore, the existence of DNA chains terminating in 5'-triphosphate has yet to be demonstrated. Other mechanisms for the replication of DNA have also been proposed [137, 142, 143] but remain to be proven experimentally.

Synthesis of polydeoxyribonucleotide copolymers. Another reaction catalyzed by *E. coli* DNA polymerase is the formation of polydeoxyribonucleotide-copolymers containing only two kinds of nucleotide residues. [104] The synthesis of such polymers is not dependent upon the presence of DNA and the products are formed after an extensive lag period. [104] A copolymer consisting of deoxyadenylate and deoxythymidylate residues (abbreviated dAT) is synthesized from dATP and dTTP, in the presence of Mg^{++} ions, after a lag period, of 3 to 6 hours. [144] The lag period, however, can be eliminated by the addition of enzymically synthesized dAT copolymer to reaction mixtures. [144] With dAT as primer, a limited incorporation of either deoxyadenylate or deoxythymidylate is possible but no detectable incorporation of deoxycytidylate or deoxyguanylate occurs. [104] This finding suggests that the incorporation of a single nucleotide into dAT is governed by hydrogen-bonding between complementary base pairs. [104, 144] Another copolymer containing only deoxyguanylate and deoxycytidylate residues (abbreviated dGdC) has also been synthesized, in the absence of DNA, from dGTP and dCTP. [104, 145] The lag period observed in this reaction can also be eliminated by the addition of enzymically synthesized dGdC to reaction mixtures. [104, 145] It has been proposed that in unprimed reactions a few molecules of each type of copolymer are synthesized *de novo* during the lag period and that these molecules are subsequently replicated autocatalytically. [146]

Viscometric, sedimentation, and spectrophotometric studies indicate that these copolymers are highly ordered double-stranded macromolecules. [104] The dAT copolymer consists of two polynucleotide chains, each of which contains deoxyadenylate and deoxythymidylate residues in alternatings equences, hydrogen-bonded to each other. [104, 144] dAdT Copolymer, consisting of a homopolymeric chain of deoxyadenylate hydrogen-bonded to a homopolymeric chain of deoxythymidylate, has also been synthesized with the helical copolymer dAdU [147] (made up of homopolymeric chains of a poly A and poly U hydrogen-bonded to each other) as a primer (see ref. 148). The dGdC copolymer also consists of two homopolymeric chains, one containing deoxyguanylate residues and the other deoxycytidylate residues, held together by hydrogen-bonds. [104, 145] With dAT and dGdC as primers, several analogous polymers have been synthesized that contain bromouracil in place of thymine, bromocytosine or hydroxymethylcytosine in place of cytosine, or hypoxanthine in place of guanine. [104, 149]

In addition to dAT, oligonucleotides containing sequences of 6 to 14 alternating deoxyadenylate and deoxythymidylate residues (abbreviated $(AT)_x$) are also effective primers for the synthesis of high-molecular weight dAT. [150] Within a temperature-range of 0 to 45°, an optimal temperature was found for the replication of each oligomer that is directly related to the size of the primer. For example, the octanucleotide $(AT)_4$ is replicated most rapidly at 10°, $(AT)_5$ at 20°, and $(AT)_6$ at 37°. [150] In these reactions dAT copolymer is believed to be synthesized by a mechanism involving reiterative replication of the oligonucleotide. It has been proposed that replication of the oligonucleotide primer is followed by "slippage" of the resulting helix by an (AT) dinucleotide pair and that successive steps of replication and "slippage" result in the continuous reiteration of the template and ultimately lead to the synthesis of high molecular weight dAT. [150] The "slippage" step of this mechanism is considered to be temperature dependent. [150]

Certain marine crabs have a DNA component that has a structure similar to enzymically synthesized dAT copolymer. [151–155] The "crab-dAT" copolymer constitutes approximately 30 per cent of the total DNA found in the testis of C. borealis. [151, 154] This type of copolymer has also been found in the muscle, liver, and eggs of this species. [155] The guanine and cytosine content of the "crab-dAT" component of crab testis DNA from C. borealis has been estimated to be about 3 per cent. [155] When "crab-dAT" is employed as a primer for E. coli DNA polymerase, it supports synthesis at a rate comparable to enzymically synthesized dAT copolymer. [115] However, all four triphosphates are required. If dGTP and dCTP are omitted from reaction mixtures, the rate of synthesis is only 19 per cent of that observed with the four triphosphates, owing presumably to the few guanine and cytosine residues interspersed in the primer. [104] The biological function of the dAT copolymer is unknown.

2. Oligodeoxyribonucleotide Transferase

An enzyme, referred to as oligodeoxyribonucleotide transferase, that catalyzes the condensation of oligodeoxyribonucleotides having an average chain length of 18 to 22 nucleotides with polydeoxyribonucleotides has been partially purified from E. coli infected with T2 bacteriophage. [156, 157] The product synthesized appears to be a polynucleotide chain formed by the condensation of the oligodeoxyribonucleotide substrate with the acceptor polymer by 3′,5′-phosphodiester linkages. [156] The reaction is dependent upon the presence of ATP, Mg^{++} ions, and is influenced by the secondary structure of the acceptor polydeoxyribonucleotide. [156] Of the DNA preparations tested for acceptor function, sonicated T2 DNA was found to be at least twice as effective as either native or sonicated DNA from E. coli, calf thymus nuclei, or rainbow trout sperm. [156] Although sonication is not absolutely essential to produce an acceptor polymer, it increases the relative accepting ability by 25 per cent. [156] However, heat-denaturation of sonicated T2 DNA decreases its acceptor ability. RNA cannot substitute for polydeoxyribonucleotides as an acceptor polymer. [156]

DNA polymerase does not appear to be involved in the transfer reaction since the two enzymes can be separated from each other by column chromatography. [156] The partially purified transferase can be separated into two fractions, both of which are necessary for activity and which act in a sequential manner. [156] Although details of the transfer reaction must await further experimentation, it is tempting to associate this reaction with the phenomenon of genetic recombination in bacteriophage. [158, 159]

B. Mammalian Enzymes

The biosynthesis of DNA in mammalian cells from deoxynucleosides and deoxynucleoside 5′-mono- and diphosphates involves the participation of phosphokinases that convert these precursors to their triphosphate forms and enzymes that polymerize nucleotides, derived from triphosphates, to polydeoxyribonucleotides.

Enzymes, that phosphorylate TDR to dTTP, as well as dAMP, dCMP, and dTMP to their corresponding di- and triphosphates have been detected in a wide variety of mammalian tissues. [160–172] Thymidylate kinase warrants some discussion since it has been suggested that this enzyme may play a role in controlling DNA synthesis in mammalian cells. [173] After partial hepatectomy† of normal adult rats the soluble fraction of regenerating rat liver

---

† After partial hepatectomy of adult rats, the enzyme systems in the high speed supernatant fraction of regenerating rat liver homogenates that convert TDR to thymidine nucleotides and incorporate TDR into DNA appear at the same time (approximately 18

contains enzymes that convert dAMP, dCMP, and dTMP to their triphosphate forms whereas a comparable fraction from normal rat liver appears to be deficient in enzymes that convert TDR [160, 174] and dTMP [165, 175] to dTTP.

Thus, the view has been expressed that the extent of DNA synthesis in normal rat liver may be limited by the unavailability of dTTP, [173] an essential precursor for DNA synthesis. [104] However, it has not been established whether the decreased capacity of normal rat liver to synthesize dTTP is due to an actual deficiency of phosphorylating enzymes or to other complicating factors. For example, the activity of dTMP kinase increases in enzyme extracts prepared from normal rat liver if TDR is previously administered parenterally to the animals or if TDR or dTMP are included in the homogenization medium. [176, 177] The latter results have been interpreted in terms of enzyme stabilization. [177] It has been suggested that thymidylate kinase is formed continuously in normal rat liver but that it is rapidly inactivated because of a deficiency of substrate that normally stabilizes the enzyme. [177] More recently, it has been reported that the activity of dTMP kinase in the high speed supernatant fraction of mouse liver represents only a fraction of the total activity of this enzyme and that a major portion of the enzyme is bound to cellular particles. [178] Additionally, the potential activity of this enzyme in normal mouse liver was found to be as high as that found in mouse ascites hepatoma. [178] These findings suggest that resting as well as rapidly proliferating mammalian cells maintain a rather constant level of the enzyme and that association of dTMP kinase with specialized cellular structures, to form inactive enzyme complexes may exert a regulatory influence on the activity of this enzyme. [178] The results of other studies suggest that extracts of normal rat liver contain inhibitory factors, of an unknown nature, which interfere with the enzymic synthesis of dTTP from TDR and the *in vitro* synthesis of DNA. [179, 180]

1. *Deoxyribonucleic Acid Nucleotidyltransferases* (*DNA polymerase*)

After the discovery and characterization of *E. coli* DNA polymerase, several crude enzyme systems that could catalyze the incorporation of radioactive deoxynucleosides and deoxyribonucleotides into DNA were isolated from a wide variety of mammalian cells. Enzyme preparations from regenerating rat liver, [181–184] a variety of other rat tissues, [185, 183, 186] malignant cells, [187, 188, 185, 190, 191, 424, 192] rabbit thymus, [193] and calf thymus gland [189, 193, 194, 195] have been studied for their ability to promote reactions indicative of DNA synthesis. In most cases, the presence of a DNA-synthesizing enzyme, similar to *E. coli* DNA polymerase has been inferred by the

---

hours post-hepatectomy) as DNA synthesis *in vivo* and their activities continue to increase over the period of 18 to 30 hours while DNA synthesis *in vivo* is markedly diminished after about 24 hours. [174]

ability of these enzyme systems to incorporate radioactive precursors into DNA. In general, the incorporation-reactions catalyzed by these relatively crude preparations proceed optimally in the presence of a divalent cation (usually Mg^{++} or Mn^{++}), an exogenous supply of DNA, ATP, and a full complement of the four common deoxynucleotides. Although studies with crude enzyme systems are valuable in helping to establish the over-all fate of radioactive precursors, they do not provide adequate information necessary for a detailed formulation of DNA synthesis. Thus far, only a few attempts have been made to purify enzymes involved in DNA synthesis from mammalian cells.

Purified calf thymus DNA polymerase [196] has been the most extensively studied mammalian DNA polymerase. More recently, an enzyme associated with DNA synthesis has been purified approximately 1000-fold from regenerating rat liver. [197] As in the case of *E. coli* DNA polymerase, the incorporation reactions catalyzed by the mammalian enzymes are dependent upon Mg^{++} ions, the 5'-triphosphates of TDR, CDR, GDR and ADR, and a DNA primer. [196, 197] Omission of any one of these components from reaction mixtures greatly reduce the rate of nucleotide-incorporation into DNA. [196, 197]

Calf thymus DNA polymerase was the first purified polymerase for which an absolute requirement for denatured or single-stranded DNA was demonstrated. [196, 198, 199] In the reaction catalyzed by this enzyme native double-stranded DNA does not serve as a primer unless it is first denatured by physical or chemical means. [196, 199] or treated with trace amounts of pancreatic DNAase. [198] When single-stranded DNA is used as a primer, a complementary polydeoxyribonucleotide chain is synthesized around the primer and the reaction ceases as soon as the amount of primer DNA is doubled. [196, 199] In contrast, the enzyme purified from regenerating rat liver displays a preferential requirement for native double-stranded DNA, which is a more efficient primer than either single stranded DNA or denatured DNA.† Moreover, the dAT copolymer is an excellent primer for the regenerating rat liver enzyme†, but is ineffective as a primer for calf thymus DNA polymerase. [198] Enzymes purified from the Morris Hepatoma 5123, as well as from hepatoma induced in male rats by N-2-fluorenylacetamide display similar DNA-primer requirements as the regenerating rat liver enzyme.‡

Under normal reaction conditions, the product synthesized by calf thymus DNA polymerase is a hydrogen-bonded hybrid of primer and new DNA possessing a high molecular weight. [200] The physical association of product and primer appear to be permanent and strand separation of the hybrid product has not been accomplished. [200] In this respect, the product is not

† R. Mantsavinos, unpublished data.
‡ R. Mantsavinos and H. P. Morris, unpublished data.

identical to native DNA. At present, the biological mechanisms involved in the conversion of double-stranded DNA to primer DNA and in the conversion of the product to "natural" native DNA are not known.

A reaction involving the terminal addition of single deoxyribonucleotides to the 3′-hydroxyl group of oligodeoxyribonucleotides, containing more than two nucleotide residues, has been observed with partially purified preparations of calf thymus DNA polymerase.[201, 202] This reaction was originally believed to be a manifestation of calf thymus DNA polymerase activity but further purification of the enzyme[203] (see refs. 204 and 205) revealed that a second enzyme, referred to as "terminal" DNA nucleotidyltransferase, is responsible for this activity. The reaction catalyzed by "terminal" DNA nucleotidyltransferase is also dependent upon the presence of Mg^{++} ions and DNA primer, but the reaction is depressed in the presence of a full complement of deoxyribonucleoside 5′-triphosphates.[204] The same enzyme also catalyzes the incorporation of single ribonucleotides into terminal positions of DNA.[204]

Highly purified "terminal" DNA nucleotidyltransferase catalyzes the polymerization of deoxyadenylate residues, from dATP, on to oligonucleotide initiators,† to a polydeoxyadenylate copolymer.[203] Although the enzyme preferentially polymerizes dATP, other triphosphates can also be polymerized but at much lower rates.[203] Hence, a large series of polydeoxynucleotides with a definite sequence, structure, and chain length may be prepared. Furthermore, these single chain polymers can be used as templates for the synthesis of complementary, double-stranded products (such as dAdT or dIdC) by calf thymus DNA polymerase, or for the synthesis of complementary polyribonucleotides by RNA polymerase.[203]

V. ENZYMIC SYNTHESIS OF POLYRIBONUCLEOTIDES
A. *Polynucleotide Phosphorylase*

Polynucleotide phosphorylase was discovered by Grunberg-Manago and Ochoa in extracts of *Azotobacter agilis*.[206] This enzyme catalyzes the synthesis of polyribonucleotides from ribonucleoside 5′-diphosphates with the elimination of inorganic orthophosphate as illustrated below:[206–209]

$$n(XRPP) \overset{Mg^{++}}{\rightleftharpoons} (XRP)_n + n(P_i) \qquad (2)$$

In equation (2), "n" is the number of molecules reacting, "X" is a purine or pyrimidine base, R is ribose and $(XRP)_n$ is a long polyribonucleotide.

---

† The term "initiator" as used above, has been defined by Bollum *et al.*[203] as, "a polymer of deoxynucleotides having a free 3′-hydroxyl that will accept the deoxynucleotidyl residue from deoxynucleoside triphosphates". Homologous oligodeoxynucleotides, such as oligodeoxythymidylates (dT_2 to dT_9) and oligodeoxyadenylates (dA_2 to dA_{11}), as well as heterogenous oligodeoxynucleotides (dX_3 to dX_8) prepared by DN-ase I degradation of calf liver DNA, have been used as initiators in the terminal addition reaction.[203]

The reaction is dependent upon Mg^{++} ions and diphosphate substrates; neither ribonucleoside 5′-triphosphates nor deoxyribonucleotides can serve as substrates. [210] Polyribonucleotide phosphorylase also catalyzes the phosphorolytic cleavage of polyribonucleotides; [207, 211, 212] an exchange reaction between P^{32} labeled inorganic orthophosphate and the terminal phosphate of nucleoside 5′-diphosphates; [207, 213] and the arsenolysis of certain polyribonucleotides to mononucleotides. [214, 215] In addition, there are indications that this enzyme catalyzes the transfer of monophosphate units from a polynucleotide donor to a polynucleotide acceptor. [216]

Polynucleotide phosphorylases are widely distributed among aerobic and anaerobic bacteria. [217] The enzyme, however, could not be detected in *L. arabinosus* [218] and *Cl. acetobutylicum.* [219] Similar enzymes have been found in spinach leaves, [219] in yeast, [220] and in animal tissues. [221–6]

The properties of some of the reactions catalyzed by polynucleotide phosphorylase are discussed briefly in the following sections.

1. *Polymerization of Ribonucleoside 5′-diphosphates*

Polynucleotide phosphorylase is capable of catalyzing the formation of homopolymers, [227, 207, 228, 210, 229] containing a linear sequence of one nucleotide residue, and heteropolymers consisting of more than one kind of nucleotide residue. [207, 229] Thus, with ADP as substrate a polymer containing a long sequence of AMP units, called polyadenylic acid (abbreviated poly A), is synthesized. Other substrates that can be polymerized in a similar fashion include CDP, UDP, IDP, [207] GDP, [230] and the nucleoside diphosphate analogs, ribosylthymine diphosphate, [231] 2-thiouridine 5′-diphosphate, [16] 5-fluouridine 5′-diphosphate, [209] pseudouridine 5′-diphosphate, [232] 8-azaguanosine 5′-diphosphate, [217] and 5-bromouridine 5′-diphosphate, and the corresponding chloro- and iodo- compounds. [233] It may be noted that polynucleotide phosphorylase is relatively nonspecific toward the purine and/or pyrimidine base of the substrate and catalyzes the synthesis of several homopolymers that have not been found in natural sources. In general, polynucleotide phosphorylase catalyzes the polymerization of ribonucleoside 5′-diphosphates whose bases can be incorporated into microbial RNAs *in vivo*, [234] with the exception of 5-bromouracil, which is not incorporated into RNA. [120] 1-β-D-Arabinosyl-uracil 5′-diphosphate, [233, 235] adenylyl 5′-methylene diphosphonate, [236] 6-azauridine 5′-diphosphate, [237] and 6-thioinosine 5′-diphosphate [238] actively inhibit the enzyme.

Incubation of polynucleotide phosphorylase with UDP and ADP results in the formation of a heteropolymer containing both AMP and UMP residues (poly AU). [210] Similarly, whenever equimolar amounts of ADP, CDP, UDP, and GDP are used simultaneously as substrates, the product formed is a heteropolymer (poly AGUC) that resembles native RNA. [210] The nucleotide residues of poly AGUC are distributed randomly throughout the hetero-polymer, [239] and the relative amount of each base incorporated is dependent upon the initial concentration of each diphosphate in the reaction mixture. [210] Chemical and enzymic degradation of the polyribonucleotides synthesized by polynucleotide phosphorylase has revealed that they consist of mono-nucleotide units linked together by 3′,5′-phosphodiester bonds as in native RNA and that the polymeric chains are terminated by phosphate groups monoesterified at carbon-5′ of the terminal nucleoside moiety. [208, 221] The polymers synthesized possess molecular weights varying from about 3×10^4 to 2×10^6. [210, 229, 227]

Experimental studies with polynucleotide phosphorylases from *A. agilis*, [209] *M. lysodeikticus*, [240, 241] and *E. coli*, [228] indicate that a single enzyme is responsible for synthesizing various homopolymers and heteropolymers. For example, the relative activity of polynucleotide phosphorylase from *A. agilis* towards various nucleoside diphosphates remained essentially unchanged during the course of a 500-fold purification of the enzyme. [290] However, other studies with enzyme preparations from *M. lysodeik-ticus*, [242, 243] and *Cl. perfringens* [244, 245, 246, 217] suggest that specific enzymes may be responsible for the polymerization of each diphosphate. Hence, the question as to whether polynucleotide phosphorylase is a single enzyme or a mixture of enzymes has yet to be resolved.

2. The Effects of Primers on Polymerization

The polymerization of ribonucleoside 5′-diphosphates by crude enzyme preparations from *A. agilis* proceeds at a linear rate until equilibrium is reached and no apparent stimulation or priming of the reaction can be demonstrated by the addition of various polynucleotides to the reaction mixture. [207, 210] In contrast, whenever highly purified polynucleotide phosphorylase from the same organism is used, a lag period is observed that can be eliminated by certain synthetic polyribonucleotides or oligo-ribonucleotides as well as by natural RNA. [247, 216, 248, 249, 235]

Although priming by polynucleotides demonstrates a certain degree of specificity, [217, 209, 247, 249] there is no evidence that polyribonucleotide primers influence the base composition of the product synthesized. [209] Synthesis of a given homopolymer is generally stimulated by the same kind of homopolymer and not by a complementary homopolymer, [250] suggesting that the primer does not function as a template. Moreover, the polymeriza-tion reaction is inhibited whenever the substrate and primer contribute two bases that are capable of forming complementary hydrogen-bonded base pairs. [251] For example, the polymerization of ADP is inhibited by poly U and the polymerization of UDP is inhibited by poly A. [247] It is not known whether effective synthetic polyribonucleotide primers act by providing end groups for initiating the synthesis of new chains. However, it has been shown that soluble RNA-C^{14} eliminates the lag phase in the synthesis of poly A but is not linked to poly A and can be recovered intact from the reaction mixture. [235]

Singer, Heppel, and Hilmoe have studied the ability of various oligo-ribonucleotides to function as primers in the synthetic reactions catalyzed by purified polynucleotide phosphorylase from *A. agilis*. [248, 252] They found that oligoribonucleotides possessing a monoesterified terminal C-3′ hydroxyl group, such as pApA, ApU, or pApApA, not only serve as primers but are also incorporated intact into the polymer synthesized. [248] In this case, synthesis of a polyribonucleotide chain commences by the addition of monomer units at the free C-3′ hydroxyl group of the primer. [248] Thus, these oligoribonucleotides serve as a nucleus for the formation of new polymer. Dinucleoside monophosphates, e.g. ApA and ApU, containing one 3′,5′-phosphodiester bond represent the minimum size of oligoribonucleotide that can serve as primer in this fashion. [248] Oligoribonucleotides, such as ApUp, with an esterified C-3′ terminal group are also capable of over-coming the lag period in the polymerization of ADP and UDP by the purified *Azotobacter* enzyme, but these oligoribonucleotides are not incorporated into the polymer synthesized. [248] The mechanism by which these oligo-ribonucleotides overcome the lag period in the polymerization of ADP and UDP is not known. These results contrast with the finding that 3′-esterified oligoribonucleotides inhibit the polymerization of ADP, UDP, CDP, or GDP by polynucleotide phosphorylase purified from *M. lysodeikticus*. [253, 254]

3. *Phosphorolysis of Polyribonucleotides and Oligoribonucleotides*

The phosphorolysis of synthetic polyribonucleotides, oligoribonucleotides, and RNA isolated from several sources, has been investigated exten-sively. [207, 255, 256, 257, 216, 212] In general, polynucleotide phosphorylase readily phosphorolyzes synthetic homopolymers having a single-stranded structure but acts more slowly on polymers that can assume a helical configuration. [255] The phosphorolysis of native RNA preparations generally occurs at a slower rate than that of poly A, with the exception of tobacco mosaic virus RNA, which is hydrolyzed at about the same rate as poly A. [255] Soluble RNA, for example, is degraded slowly and to a small extent, [255, 258] owing presumably to its secondary structure.

Oligoribonucleotides bearing a C-3′ phosphomonoester end group are resistant to enzyme hydrolysis,[257] whereas those containing a C-5′ phos-phomonoester group (e.g. pApApA), trinucleotide diphosphates (e.g. ApApA), and tetranucleotide triphosphates (e.g. ApApApU) are readily phosphorolyzed.[208] Oligoribonucleotides bearing a cyclic phosphodiester moiety between C-2′ and C-3′ of the terminal nucleoside residue, dinucleo-tides, and dinucleoside monophosphates resist phosphorolysis.[216, 257]

The phosphorolysis of susceptible oligoribonucleotides proceeds by a stepwise mechanism beginning at the end of the chain having a C-3' hydroxyl, rather than by a random splitting of phosphodiester bonds.[216, 213] Thus, the phosphorolysis of the tetranucleotide pApApApU may be represented as follows:

$$pApApApU \xrightarrow{P_i} pApApA \xrightarrow{P_i} pApA + ADP \qquad (3)$$
$$+$$
$$UDP$$

This reaction shows that phosphorolysis represents a true reversal of the polymerization reaction.

4. P^{32}-Nucleoside Diphosphate Exchange Reaction

Another reaction catalyzed by polynucleotide phosphorylase is the exchange between P^{32} labeled inorganic orthophosphate and the terminal phosphate of a nucleoside diphosphate as illustrated in equation (4).[207, 217, 259, 228, 213]

$$\text{Nucleoside-P-P} + P_i{}^{32} \overset{Mg^{++}}{\rightleftharpoons} \text{Nucleoside-P-P}^{32} + P_i \qquad (4)$$

Under proper experimental conditions, polynucleotide phosphorylase from *A. agilis*, and from *E. coli*, can utilize ADP, CDP, UDP,[207, 228] GDP[213] or ribosylthymine diphosphate[213] as substrates for this reaction. The P^{32} exchange reaction with GDP is stimulated by oligoribonucleotides that serve as primers for its polymerization as well as by oligoribonucleotides that are inactive as primers.[228] Hence, it would appear that the exchange reaction is not related to the polymerization reaction. Other experimental results, however, indicate that the two reactions may be related. For example, homopolymers inhibit the exchange reaction whenever the bases of the substrate and homopolymer form hydrogen-bonding base pairs.[213] As mentioned previously, a similar type of inhibition occurs in the polymerization reaction. At present, the relationship of the exchange reaction to the polymerization reaction is not clearly understood. Furthermore, the exchange between P^{32} and nucleoside diphosphates is not necessarily indicative of polynucleotide phosphorylase activity. A highly purified enzyme from yeast has been shown to catalyze a rapid exchange between $P_i{}^{32}$ and the terminal phosphate of nucleoside diphosphates (both ribose and deoxyribose derivatives) but does not phosphorolyze synthetic polynucleotides or oligoribonucleotides.[235] The yeast enzyme is also active with uridine-5'-phosphosulfate and adenosine-5'-phosphosulfate[235] and is probably the same enzyme as ADP sulfurylase.[260]

5. Function of Polynucleotide Phosphorylase, in vivo

The finding that polynucleotide phosphorylase polymerizes ribonucleoside 5'-diphosphates in a random fashion and that primers have little or no influence on the nucleotide composition of the polymer synthesized indicate that this enzyme may not be involved in a general mechanism for the intracellular synthesis of specific RNAs.[210, 209] The primary function of this enzyme in living organisms is unknown. The ability of polynucleotide phosphorylase to degrade polyribonucleotides to ribonucleoside 5'-diphosphates may represent an indirect mechanism for the generation of DNA precursors. An enzyme has been detected in a wide variety of cells that catalyzes the direct reduction of ribonucleotides to deoxyribonucleotides, at the *diphosphate* stage.[261-265] The deoxyribonucleoside 5'-diphosphates thus formed may then be converted to the corresponding 5'-triphosphates and utilized for DNA synthesis. Additionally, polynucleotide phosphorylase may be involved in the degradation of m-RNA[266] and in controlling the intracellular level of inorganic phosphate[217] in certain organisms.

B. *Enzyme Systems Requiring Ribonucleoside 5'-Triphosphates*
1. *Introduction*
Early studies with crude cell-free enzyme preparations established that radioactive ribonucleotides are incorporated into RNA although the nature of the precursors and mechanisms involved were not determined.[267-270] During the past few years several distinct enzymes have been described that are associated with the synthesis of polyribonucleotides and that are different from polynucleotide phosphorylase. In general, these enzymes display a requirement for a polynucleotide primer and utilize ribonucleoside 5'-triphosphates as substrates. Some enzymes catalyze a limited addition of one or two different ribonucleotides onto the nucleoside termini of the primer. In other reactions, only one kind of ribonucleotide is utilized for the synthesis of homopolymeric chains of various lengths. In a third type of reaction all four of the common ribonucleoside 5'-triphosphates are employed in the synthesis of polyribonucleotides having a nucleotide composition complementary to the base composition of the primer. Examples of each of these different enzyme systems are discussed briefly in the following sections.

2. *Incorporation of Ribonucleotides into Terminal Positions of Ribonucleic Acid*
The formation of the terminal trinucleotide sequence, —pCpCpA, of t-RNA is an example of a reaction in which specific ribonucleotides are incorporated into specific terminal positions of soluble RNA. The enzyme system involved in this reaction modifies a fraction of cytoplasmic soluble RNA to form a species of RNA capable of functioning in protein synthesis. As mentioned previously, the terminal —pCpCpA sequence of t-RNA serves as a functional site for the binding of activated amino acids, which are then transferred to ribosomes where protein synthesis occurs. The earliest experiments indicating that ribonucleotides are incorporated into specific sites in RNA where those of Heidelberger and collaborators who showed that the

cytoplasmic fraction from homogenates of rat liver preferentially incorporated AMP adjacent to CMP units in RNA.[271] Subsequent studies demonstrated that AMP, derived from ATP, is incorporated onto terminal positions of RNA adjacent to CMP residues[272, 273, 274] and that the reaction ceases after AMP is incorporated.[272, 274, 275] The same enzyme system catalyzes the incorporation of CMP, from CTP,[274] and when this system is provided with both ATP and CTP two CMP units and one AMP unit are incorporated sequentially into pyrophosphorolyzed RNA resulting in the formation of the terminal —pCpCpA sequence.[276, 275] The reaction is inhibited by PP_i but not by P_i.[274] In the presence of P^{32}-labeled PP_i this enzyme system causes a pyrophosphorolysis of soluble RNA to which AMP and CMP units have been added with the liberation of P^{32} labeled CTP and ATP from the 3'-hydroxyl end of the RNA.[274, 276] The reaction responsible for the formation [of the —pCpCpA sequence of t-RNAs may be represented by the following equation:[274, 276, 273, 275]

$$RNA + 2CTP + ATP \rightleftharpoons RNA \ldots \ldots pCpCpA + 3\ PP_i \qquad (5)$$

Soluble RNA of the cytoplasm serves as the acceptor RNA to which the ribonucleotides are incorporated.[274] RNA derived from nuclear or microsomal fractions cannot serve in this capacity, nor can the synthetic polyribonucleotides poly A, poly C, poly AGUC, or poly AU.[274] The mechanism by which the reaction proceeds most likely involved a nucleophilic attack by the free 3'-hydroxyl group of the nucleoside terminus of the acceptor RNA on the pyrophosphate-activated AMP and CMP with the formation of 3',5',-phosphodiester bonds and concomitant release of PP_i.[277] The terminal —pCpCpA sequence of t-RNA appears to exist in the form of a single chain without any secondary structure and is readily susceptible to enzymic degradation.[278] The enzyme system associated with the reaction illustrated by equation (5)[279] has been purified from Ehrlich ascites carcinoma,[274] rat liver,[273, 276, 280] E. coli,[281, 282] and extracts of rabbit muscle.[283]

Other cytoplasmic enzyme systems have been described that incorporate GMP or UMP units, from their respective triphosphates, onto the ends of RNA chains resulting in the formation of polyribonucleotides terminating in —pUpU or —pUpUpG sequences.[274, 284, 285] It is conceivable that these enzyme systems function to generate specific terminal sequences on polyribonucleotides that are synthesized by enzymes requiring a DNA or RNA template.

With respect to soluble RNA synthesis mention should also be made of a bacterial enzyme that optically incorporates ribonucleotides into nonterminal positions of RNA in the presence of the four common ribonucleoside 5'-triphosphates and a soluble RNA primer, suggesting that soluble RNA may prime its own synthesis.[286] The significance of this reaction in the synthesis of soluble RNA, however, has yet to be assessed.

3. Incorporation of Ribonucleotides into Deoxyribonucleic Acid

The enzymic incorporation of ribonucleotides into DNA was first demonstrated by Hurwitz with a partially purified enzyme from E. coli that incorporates CMP, derived from CTP, into DNA.[287] It was found that maximal incorporation of cytidylate is obtained in the presence of DNA, Mg^{++} and Mn^{++} ions, and dATP, dGTP, and dTTP and that CMP is interdispersed among the deoxynucleotides of DNA.[287] The requirement for DNA is specific and cannot be met by RNA, and omission of one of the deoxyribonucleotides greatly reduces the extent of incorporation.[287] These findings together with the demonstration that DNA polymerase activity is also required for the incorporation of CMP into DNA[287] suggest that this reaction is similar to the ribonucleotide-incorporation reactions catalyzed by DNA polymerase in the presence of Mn^{++} (see Section V A, 1).

A similar, though different, enzyme that catalyzes a limited incorporation of ribonucleotides (as well as deoxyribonucleotides)[204] into terminal positions of DNA has been isolated from calf thymus nuclei by Canellakis and collaborators.[204, 288] Any one of the four common ribonucleoside 5'-triphosphates can serve as substrates with the following order of activity: GTP > CTP > ATP > UTP. RNA cannot serve as primer in this reaction.[288, 289]   The reaction is self-limiting since it ceases after the addition of one ribonucleotide to the end of a DNA chain resulting in the formation of ribonucleotidyl-DNA.[288] Ribonucleotides are incorporated into DNA by 3'-5'-phosphodiester bonds.[288, 289] The addition of more than one triphosphate to reaction mixtures results in an inhibition of the reaction.[204, 288] The latter finding distinguishes this enzyme from RNA polymerase (see Sections V B, 5 (b)) and other findings have shown that this enzymic activity is distinct from calf thymus DNA polymerase.[288] The ribonucleotidyl DNA formed in this reaction serves as an acceptor for ribonucleotides when added to reaction mixtures containing enzymes that normally incorporate ribonucleotides into RNA but not DNA.[289, 277, 290] The products formed in these reactions are copolymers of DNA with RNA.[289]

4. Formation of Sequences Containing One Ribonucleotide Residue

Edmonds and Abrams[291, 292] have described an enzyme purified from extracts of calf thymus nuclei that utilizes ATP to synthesize a chain of poly A having a minimum average chain length of 25 to 100 AMP units. The incorporation of AMP units from ATP is inhibited by PP_i and by the addition of the remaining three triphosphates singly or in combination. The inhibitory effects of UTP, CTP, and GTP may be due to competitive binding at the active site of the enzyme without subsequent polymerization.[291] Although initial experiments provided no evidence for a primer requirement subsequent studies have shown that the reaction depends on polynucleotide present in the enzyme.[292] The active priming component has been identified as a naturally occurring poly A.[293] It is noteworthy that among polyribonucleotides present in thymus nuclei only poly A is capable of priming further synthesis of poly A.[293]

An enzyme purified from the chorioallantoic membrane of chick embryos that catalyzes the formation of poly A, from ATP, has been studied by Venkataraman and Mahler.[294] The product formed has a chain length of approximately 8 to 10 AMP units and is believed to be bound to the primer RNA. The reaction is dependent upon the presence of a microsomal RNA preparation also isolated from the chorioallantoic membranes.[294] Although DNA cannot replace microsomal RNA as primer, the highly ordered poly A + poly U (1:1) complex serves as primer with twice the efficiency of microsomal RNA. The product formed with the synthetic copolymer as primer is similar to that formed with microsomal RNA primer.[294]

Enzymes capable of synthesizing poly A, from ATP, have also been isolated from E. coli.[277, 295, 296] One of these enzymes is associated with the ribonucleoprotein particles of E. coli.[295, 296] The reaction catalyzed by this enzyme is dependent upon RNA and is inhibited by RNAse but not by DNAse.[295, 296] The RNA requirement can be satisfied by several kinds of RNA including soluble RNA and RNA prepared from rat liver microsomes or E. coli ribosomes, and under proper experimental conditions, poly A is formed in excess of the RNA added as primer to reaction mixtures.[296] After T2, T4, T5, or T6 phage infection of E. coli, the incorporation of AMP units into poly A, by cell-free extracts of E. coli, is markedly reduced.[297] The reason for the loss of this enzymic activity after phage infection has yet to be established.

A similar enzyme purified from E. coli catalyzes the synthesis of poly A containing 25 to 35 AMP units.[277] This enzyme is dependent upon a polynucleotide primer that functions to provide sites of attachment for the newly synthesized poly A. Ribosomal RNA as well as ribonucleotidyl DNA (DNA containing one terminal ribonucleotide) can serve as primers for this reaction. With an RNA primer, the poly A is covalently linked to the RNA, whereas in the presence of ribonucleotidyl DNA primer, the poly A synthesized is covalently linked to the terminal ribonucleotide attached to the DNA. It appears, therefore, that the action of this enzyme is defined primarily by the nature of the terminal nucleoside of the primer rather than the nature of the polynucleotide to which the terminal nucleoside is attached.[277]

The enzyme RNA nucleotidyltransferase (see Section V B, 5 (b)) purified from E. coli also catalyzes the synthesis of poly A in the presence of ATP, a divalent cation, and single-stranded DNA.[298, 299] Addition of another triphosphate to reaction mixtures causes an inhibition of the reaction. The requirement for single-stranded DNA cannot be met by double-stranded DNAs, dAT, RNA or poly A.[298, 299] Destruction of the DNA by DNAse during the course of the reaction blocks further synthesis of poly A, indicating that DNA is required not only to initiate synthesis of poly A but also for the continued synthesis of this homopolymer.[298] It has been proposed that the priming effect of DNA is attributable to a sequence of thymidylate residues in the DNA that prime the synthesis of a corresponding sequence of AMP units and that by subsequent "slippage" of one chain along the other, an elongation of the poly A chain occurs.[298]

The synthesis of short chains of poly A with oligoribonucleotide primers by an enzyme obtainable from rat liver has been reported.[300] Trinucleotides and tetranucleotides terminated by uridine are more efficient primers than either dinucleotides, r-RNA, or poly U.[300] The enzyme displays a specificity for ATP as substrate and neither UTP, CTP, or GTP can be utilized to form the corresponding homopolymers.[300]

From a brief consideration of the properties of these enzyme systems, it may be noted that synthesis of poly A chains, from ATP, can be achieved with either poly A, various polyribonucleotides, ribonucleotidyl DNA, double-stranded DNA, or oligoribonucleotide primers, depending on the primer requirement of the enzyme used. At present, the mechanisms involved in the formation of poly A with various primers are unknown, as is the biological function of poly A chains.

In addition to enzymes that form adenylate sequences from ATP, other enzyme systems are known that catalyze the synthesis of sequences of UMP or CMP units from their respective triphosphates. Burdon and Smellie[301, 302] have studied an enzyme system derived from the soluble cytoplasmic fraction of Ehrlich ascites tumor cells that catalyzes the incorporation of UMP, from UTP, into RNA. This enzyme system has been partially purified and two distinct fractions have been identified. The reactions catalyzed by each fraction are dependent upon an RNA primer—preferably of microsomal origin—and are inhibited by PP_i. The incorporation of UMP, from UTP, by one of these fractions (fraction A) is stimulated by the addition of a mixture of ATP, GTP, and CTP, and the four nucleotides are incorporated into one polyribonucleotide chain.[302] However, when the reaction is carried out by the absence of ATP, GTP, and CTP, most of the UMP units are incorporated adjacent to one another. The second enzyme fraction (fraction B) also incorporates UMP units, from UTP, into RNA but its activity is slightly inhibited by the addition of ATP, GTP, and CTP to reaction mixtures.[302] Experiments with Fraction B and UTP alone have shown that most of the UMP residues are incorporated adjacent to either UMP or AMP residues of the RNA primer and that a substantial portion is located on the 3'-hydroxyl ends of polyribonucleotide chains. The DNA-dependent synthesis of poly U by an enzyme system obtained from nuclei of Landschutz ascites cells has also been reported.[303] This enzymic activity is found in the nuclear residue after removal of the nuclear ribosomes and nuclear sap. The nuclear ribosomes are capable of incorporating uridylate units to existing polyribonucleotides terminating in polyuridylate residues and adenylate units to ribosomal polyribonucleotides terminating in polyadenylate residues.[304] The synthesis of poly U proceeds optimally with heat-denatured DNA and this requirement cannot be satisfied by either RNA or poly U.[303] Although actinomycin D[305] has no effect on this reaction, treatment of heat-denatured DNA with nitrous acid depresses its priming activity indicating that sequences of deoxyadenylate residues in the DNA may prime the formation of corresponding sequences of UMP.[303]

An enzyme that preferentially incorporates UMP units, from UTP, into microsomal RNA with the formation of a sequence of UMP units has been purified from the soluble fraction of rat liver by Klemperer and Kammen.[306]

Other enzymes are known that incorporate CMP, derived from CTP, onto preexisting RNA.[307, 308] Hurwitz and Bresler[309] have purified an enzyme from acetone powders of calf thymus gland that catalyzes the pyrophosphorolytic addition of cytidylate residues onto the ends of RNA chains. This enzyme has specific requirements for CTP and for an RNA primer prepared from thymus gland; DNA is inactive as a primer. The purified enzyme possesses a limited synthetic capacity and catalyzes the incorporation of only a few CMP units onto the free 3'-hydroxyl ends of the RNA primer.[308] A very similar enzyme has been purified from extracts of calf thymus nuclei by other investigators.[309]

5. Enzyme Systems Requiring Four Ribonucleoside 5'-Triphosphates

(a) *Ribonucleic acid directed synthesis of ribonucleic acid.* The extent to which RNA-primed synthesis of RNA participates in normal cellular RNA synthesis is unknown. However, the practically complete inhibition of cellular RNA synthesis by actinomycin D, an antibiotic that inhibits DNA-directed synthesis of RNA[305] (see Section V B, 5 (b)), suggests that RNA-primed synthesis of RNA does not represent a principal enzymic mechanism for the synthesis of various kinds of RNA. Nevertheless, there are indications that several enzyme systems in the presence of RNA, can incorporate simultaneously AMP, CMP, UMP, and GMP units, from their respective triphosphates, in internucleotide linkages of polyribonucleotides although an extensive synthesis is not obtained.[286, 307, 301, 302, 310, 311, 312]† Furthermore, RNA nucleotidyltransferase, which catalyzes the DNA directed synthesis of RNA (see Section V B, 5 (b)), also catalyzes the synthesis of complementary polyribonucleotides with an RNA primer.[313, 314, 315]

RNA directed synthesis of RNA appears to be of primary importance in the replication of RNA viruses. One of the earliest indications for such an enzymic reaction was reported by Reddi[316] who described an enzyme isolated from the soluble cytoplasmic fraction of spinach leaves that catalyzes the synthesis of RNA from GTP, UTP, CTP and ATP in the presence of

† Some of these enzymes have been discussed in the preceding section.

Mg^{++} ions and tobacco mosaic virus RNA. Recently, the synthesis of tobacco virus RNA has been studied by numerous investigators and several claims have been made for the synthesis of infectious tobacco mosaic virus RNA by cell-free extracts from healthy or virus-infected leaves.[425–428]†

Certain lines of experimentation indicate that the replication of viral RNA is not mediated by DNA.[318, 319, 320] For example, actinomycin D prevents the replication of DNA viruses[321, 322, 323, 320] but does not effect the multiplication of viruses containing single-stranded RNA, such as mengo[323] and polio[324] virus, or MS2 bacteriophage.[321] Thus, host cells either contain enzymes capable of replicating viral RNA, or the RNA of the infecting virus induces the formation of a new enzyme or enzymes that are required for its replication. Several experimental studies support the latter of these two possibilities. Infection of susceptible animal,[325, 326] or bacterial[327–31] cells with RNA viruses leads to the formation of RNA-synthesizing enzymes that are not detectable in normal host cells.

The enzyme, RNA synthetase, that is induced in *E. coli* after infection by the RNA bacteriophage MS2, has been partially purified and with ATP, GTP, CTP, and UTP as substrates found to catalyze the synthesis of an RNA product having a base composition analogous to that of MS2 RNA.[327,331,332] The reaction is not inhibited by actinomycin D, DNAase, or inorganic phosphate.[328, 331] The addition of exogenous RNA primer to reaction mixtures is not necessary since RNA synthetase is purified in association with its natural template, the double-stranded replicative form of MS2 RNA.[332] The replicative form serves as an endogenous template which directs the synthesis *in vitro* of new RNA. It has been shown that the multiplication of several single-stranded RNA viruses in susceptible bacterial, animal, and plant cells is accompanied by the synthesis of a replicative form of RNA having the characteristics of a double helix.[333–341, 344] The replicative form consists of complementary RNA strands (one of which is of the parental type), and appears to be an obligatory intermediate in the multiplication of RNA viruses.[333, 336] After incubation of the enzyme with C^{14}-labeled ribonucleoside 5'-triphosphates and phenol extraction, about half of the radioactivity incorporated into acid-insoluble products is present in double-stranded RNA and as much as 85 per cent of the radioactivity incorporated into the double-stranded product is present as parental type MS2 RNA strands,[331] the remainder probably consisting of complementary strands. Since predominantly parental type strands are synthesized an asymmetric replication most likely occurs with the displacement of parental strands from the duplex.[332] On the basis of these findings, it has been proposed that after induction of RNA synthetase the replication of MS2 RNA occurs in two stages. In the first stage single-stranded parental RNA is converted into a double-stranded replicative form, and in the second stage an asymmetric

† For further discussion on this subject, see ref. 317, p. 277.

synthesis of parental type strands occurs with the replicative form acting as a template.[331, 319] Since partially purified RNA synthetase catalyzes predominantly the reaction characteristic of the second stage, it is not known whether one or two enzymes are involved in the synthesis of MS2 RNA.

With respect to viral RNA synthesis, mention may also be made here of the ability of RNA polymerase from *E. coli* B to synthesize RNA *in vitro* with double-stranded reovirus RNA as template.[342] This reaction is discussed in greater detail in Section V B, 5 (b).

(b) *Ribonucleic acid nucleotidyltransferase*.† According to one hypothesis, the synthesis of most, if not all, cellular RNAs is under the control of DNA and originated on a DNA template.[343] This view has gained support from the finding that m-RNA,[344, 345] r-RNA,[346, 347] and t-RNA[348, 349] from *E. coli* contain nucleotide sequences that are complementary to nucleotide sequences in DNA of homologous origin but not to nucleotide sequences in DNA of genetically unrelated species. Furthermore, actinomycin D, an inhibitor of DNA-directed synthesis of RNA,[305] inhibits normal cellular RNA synthesis in bacterial and animal cells.[350] RNA polymerase appears to be the key enzyme concerned with the transcription of the genetic message from DNA to RNA. This enzyme catalyzes the DNA-dependent synthesis of RNA and certain findings suggest that part of the RNA synthesized on a DNA template, *in vitro*, is complementary to homologous 16S and 23S r-RNA, and to homologous t-RNA.[351] RNA polymerase also catalyzes the formation of homopolymeric polynucleotide chains and RNA-directed synthesis of RNA. These reactions are discussed in the following sections.

1. *Heteropolymer Formation*

RNA polymerases have been isolated from animal,[352, 353] plant,[354] and microbial[355, 298, 356, 357] cells. At present, only RNA polymerases of microbial origin have been highly purified and most investigations on the requirements of the enzyme and the properties of the products synthesized have been conducted with bacterial enzymes. In the presence of DNA, RNA polymerase catalyzes the formation of an RNA product that not only reflects the base composition and dinucleotide distribution of the DNA template[298, 356, 358, 359] but that also contains long nucleotide sequences complementary to the nucleotide sequences of the DNA that directs its synthesis.[360, 361, 362] These findings suggest that RNA synthesis proceeds by a copying mechanism that involves base pairings, as in the case of DNA synthesis. In addition to DNA, the synthesis of RNA is dependent upon a divalent cation (usually Mg^{++} or Mn^{++}) and the presence of the four triphosphates, UTP, GTP, CTP and ATP. The addition of polyamines, such

† Abbreviated RNA polymerase.

as spermidine, to reaction mixtures containing RNA polymerase from *M. lysodeikticus* results in a significant enhancement of RNA synthesis.[363] The incorporation of ribonucleotides into RNA proceeds with the elimination of a stoichiometric amount of inorganic pyrophosphate.[343]

RNA polymerase also catalyzes the incorporation of P^{23} labeled inorganic pyrophosphate into ribonucleoside triphosphates.[355, 326] The pyrophosphate exchange reaction requires DNA, at least one triphosphate and a divalent cation.[355, 363] The requirement for triphosphates indicates that the enzyme does not catalyze pyrophosphorolysis of DNA,[343] although high concentrations of RNA polymerase appear to catalyze a slow pyrophosphorolysis of the RNA product.[355]

Analogs of the natural triphosphates can also be incorporated into the RNA product. Each analog specifically substitutes for the natural triphosphate that has corresponding base-pairing properties.[364] As substrates for RNA synthesis, 5-fluoro-UTP, 5-bromo-UTP, and ribosylthymine triphosphate can replace UTP; inosine triphosphate and 6-azaguanosine triphosphate specifically replace GTP; and 5-bromo-CTP replaces CTP.[364] The triphosphates of xanthosine and azauridine do not serve as substrates for RNA synthesis.[364] Substitution of the natural triphosphates by analogs is a complex process, and the rate of incorporation of various analogs into RNA appears to depend on the base composition of the DNA.[343] Nevertheless, the specificity of analog-incorporation may be explained in terms of hydrogen-bond formation between the bases of the analogs and complementary bases in the DNA primer.

Although both single and double-stranded DNAs can function as templates for the synthesis of RNA, native double-stranded DNA is generally a more effective primer.[298, 355, 359] When double-stranded DNA is employed as a template for RNA synthesis, it remains as double-stranded DNA, and stable hybrid intermediates between DNA and RNA do not accumulate.[358, 360, 361, 365, 366] Each strand of the DNA duplex serves as a template for the synthesis of complementary polyribonucleotide chains[351] that can react to assume a highly ordered secondary structure.[361] Hence, in the DNA-directed synthesis of RNA, the nucleotide sequences of the template are copied in a conservative manner; that is, the DNA helix remains intact after directing the synthesis of RNA. However, when single-stranded DNA is used as a template, it is converted to a DNA–RNA hybrid and free RNA does not appear until the composition of the hybrid approaches a limiting value of equal quantities of RNA and DNA.[362, 365, 367, 368] The RNA–DNA hybrid continues to serve as a template for RNA synthesis and a major portion of the RNA of the hybrid template is displaced by newly synthesized RNA.[367]

When single-stranded ϕX-174 DNA is used as a template, the base composition of the product is complementary to that of the DNA, but when double-stranded ϕX-174 DNA (enzymically synthesized with DNA polymerase) is utilized as a template, the base composition of the RNA synthesized is the same as that of the DNA (replacing uracil for thymine).[358, 298] These results indicate that *in vitro* both strands of the DNA are copied. The symmetric character of *in vitro* RNA synthesis by RNA polymerase contrasts with certain results of *in vivo* studies suggesting that only one strand of the DNA duplex is transcribed in living cells.[369, 370, 371] The underlying reason for this apparent difference is not yet clear. Nevertheless, it has been reported[372] that if intact, circular, double-stranded DNA—such as the replication form of ϕX-174 DNA[40]—is used as a template for the *in vitro* synthesis of RNA, only one strand of the DNA is copied, as shown by hybridization tests,[344] and nearest neighbor analysis of the RNA product.[372] However, if circular DNA is fragmented and used as a template, RNA complementary to both strands of the DNA is synthesized.[372] These experiments, however, do not prove that only intact circular DNA retains the strand selection mechanism. Indeed, other experiments show that neither chromosome integrity nor circularity is essential for asymmetric synthesis of RNA *in vitro*.[373] An asymmetric synthesis of RNA has been demonstrated with phage α DNA and with crude supernatant fraction from *B. megatherium*.[373] The ability of phage α DNA to serve as a template for asymmetric synthesis is dependent upon its native conformation but not upon the continuity of the phage chromosome.[373] A clearer understanding of the mechanism involved in the transcription process must await further experimentation.

The DNA dependent synthesis of RNA is inhibited by actinomycin D[305] and by atabrine.[374] Several synthetic polyribonucleotides and natural RNAs also inhibit the rate of the DNA-directed synthesis of RNA catalyzed by *E. coli* RNA polymerase.[314, 315, 375] The inhibition produced by soluble RNA is greater when the soluble RNA is uncharged with amino acids and if native DNA, rather than heat-denatured DNA, is used as a template.[375] The inhibitory effect of soluble RNA appears to be due to a combination of the enzyme with this type of RNA.[375]

In addition to DNA, natural and synthetic polyribonucleotides can be used as templates for the synthesis of polyribonucleotides by RNA polymerase.[313, 314, 315] Synthetic polyribonucleotide-homopolymers are very effective primers and competitively inhibit DNA as a primer, indicating that both DNA and RNA utilize the same enzyme.[314, 315] Complementary polyribonucleotides are synthesized with homopolymeric primers and the appropriate triphosphate substrate.[314] Polyribonucleotide-primed reactions are insensitive to DNAase and are not stimulated by polyamines.[314] Certain lines of evidence suggest that the secondary structure of the polyribonucleotide-primer influences its priming efficiency, as is the case with polydeoxyribonucleotide-primers. With *M. lysodeikticus* RNA polymerase and a poly

A + poly U (1:1) complex as primer, polymerization of either AMP or UMP, from ATP or UTP respectively, proceeds at a faster rate than with either poly A or poly U alone.[313, 314] On the other hand, with RNA polymerase from *A. vinelandii* the double-stranded poly A + poly U (1:1) complex is a better primer than poly A for the incorporation of uridylate but a much less efficient primer than poly U for the synthesis of poly A.[315]

Natural RNAs are usually less effective primers than synthetic polyribonucleotides.[313, 314] The poor priming abilities observed with most natural RNAs may be attributable to their single-stranded structures. Reovirus RNA, which has a double-helical configuration,[376, 377] is a very effective template for RNA polymerase from *E. coli* B.[342] With this RNA as primer, a product reflecting the base composition of reovirus RNA is synthesized.[342] Actinomycin D inhibits the synthesis of RNA when reovirus RNA is used as a primer,[342] but not when single- or double-stranded synthetic polyribonucleotides or native single-stranded RNAs are used as primers.[314, 315] Thus, double-stranded RNA intermediates also appear to be sensitive to the action of actinomycin D. In addition to reovirus replication,[342] actinomycin D inhibits the multiplication of other RNA containing viruses such as influenza virus[378] and Rous-sarcoma virus.[379]

The formation of poly A, by RNA polymerase from *E. coli* B with poly U as template is greatly stimulated by adenine oligonucleotides (dinucleotides to hexanucleotides) that have a free 3'-hydroxyl terminus, such as pApA and ApA.[380] The degree of stimulation is proportional to the chain-length of the oligonucleotide.[380] Oligonucleotides terminating in a 3'-phosphate group do not stimulate this reaction and are inhibitory at high concentrations.[380] Analogous results have been observed with uracil oligonucleotides.[380] Small amounts of stimulatory oligonucleotides are incorporated onto the ends of the products suggesting that these oligonucleotides stimulate the reaction by acting as initiators for the formation of polyribonucleotide-chains.[380] No stimulation is obtained in the formation of heteropolymer with T2 DNA primer or in the synthesis of poly A with heat-denatured T2 DNA.

2. Formation of Homopolymers

RNA polymerase also catalyzes the formation of homopolymeric polyribonucleotide with DNA or polyribonucleotide primers and the appropriate triphosphates.[298, 299, 381, 382, 380] The synthesis of poly A with RNA polymerase from *E. coli*[298, 299] has been discussed previously in Section V 4. In addition to poly A, homopolymers containing either uridylate,[363, 381] cytidylate[363, 381] or guanylate[363] residues have been synthesized. In each case, the addition of more than one triphosphate inhibits the reaction.[299, 363] In contrast to heteropolymer formation, heat-denatured or single-stranded DNA is more effective than double-stranded DNA for the synthesis of homopolymers.[299, 363, 381]

Chemically synthesized polydeoxynucleotides[387-388] can also serve as templates for synthesis of homopolymers by *E. coli* RNA polymerase.[358, 382] Short chain thymidine polynucleotides are efficient templates for the synthesis of poly A, and polydeoxycytidylates larger than dC₈† serve as templates for the synthesis of poly G.[382] Oligodeoxynucleotides as small as the pentonucleotide dT₅ act as templates for the synthesis of poly A and their effectiveness as templates increases with size. Maximal activity is obtained with dT₁₄.[382] The poly A formed with different polydeoxythymidylate templates has, in each case, an average chain length of 50 to 100 adenylate residues.[382] These reactions appear to be catalyzed by a single enzyme and it has been shown that the enzyme does not esterify nucleotides to the terminal 3'-hydroxyl group of the polydeoxythymidylate but initiates the synthesis of new complementary chains.[382] These reactions are believed to proceed by a mechanism involving complementary base-pairing of the Watson–Crick type, although some exceptions have been noted. For example, polydeoxyadenylate homologs of various sizes fail to serve as templates for the synthesis of poly U, and dG₆ is inactive for the formation of poly C. Moreover, the synthesis of poly A can be achieved with a polydeoxyadenylate template.

The DNA directed synthesis of poly A or RNA and the poly U-directed synthesis of poly A by partially purified RNA polymerase from *M. lysodeikticus* is inhibited by 3'-deoxyadenosine 5'-triphosphate.[389, 390] However, the synthesis of poly U with either a DNA or poly A primer is insensitive to this compound.[390] These findings indicate that 3'-deoxyadenosine 5'-triphosphate competes with ATP in polymerization reactions.[390] The inhibition is believed to be brought about by a limited incorporation of 3'-deoxyadenosine 5'-triphosphate into growing polyribonucleotide-chains suppressing further elongation of the chains.[389] Although 3'-deoxyadenine (cordycepin) has been isolated from the culture filtrate of *Aspergillus nidulans*,[391] the natural occurrence of polynucleotides containing 3-deoxyadenosine has not been reported.

VI. ENZYMIC METHYLATION OF NUCLEIC ACIDS

Significant amounts of several methylated bases have been detected in various types of RNA and in DNA. For example, N⁶-methyladenine is found in bacterial DNA[392] and 5-methylcytosine is present in the DNA of certain plants and animals[6, 7] as well as in soluble RNA from *E. coli*.[364] Additionally, soluble RNA from *E. coli* contains 5-methyluracil (thymine), 2-methyladenine, N⁶-methyladenine, N⁶-dimethyladenine, and N'-methylguanine;[393, 394, 395] N'-methyladenine, N⁶-methyladenine, N⁶-dimethyl-

---

† This class of chemically synthesized polynucleotides is designated by the nucleoside initial (d"X") with a subscript indicating the number of nucleosides in the chain. For example, the pentanucleotide, dT₅, is deoxy-pTpTpTpTpT. All of these polydeoxynucleotides possess a 3'-hydroxyl group at one end and a 5'-phosphate group at the opposite end.

adenine, N'-methylguanine, N^2-methylguanine, N^2-dimethylguanine, 5-methyl cytosine and 5-methyluracil (see Fig. 2) are found in soluble RNA from rat liver, and 7-methylguanine is found in RNA of pig liver.[396] Methylated guanosine derivatives have also been detected in bacterial r-RNA.[78] The presence of methylated bases in m-RNA or in viral RNA has not been reported.

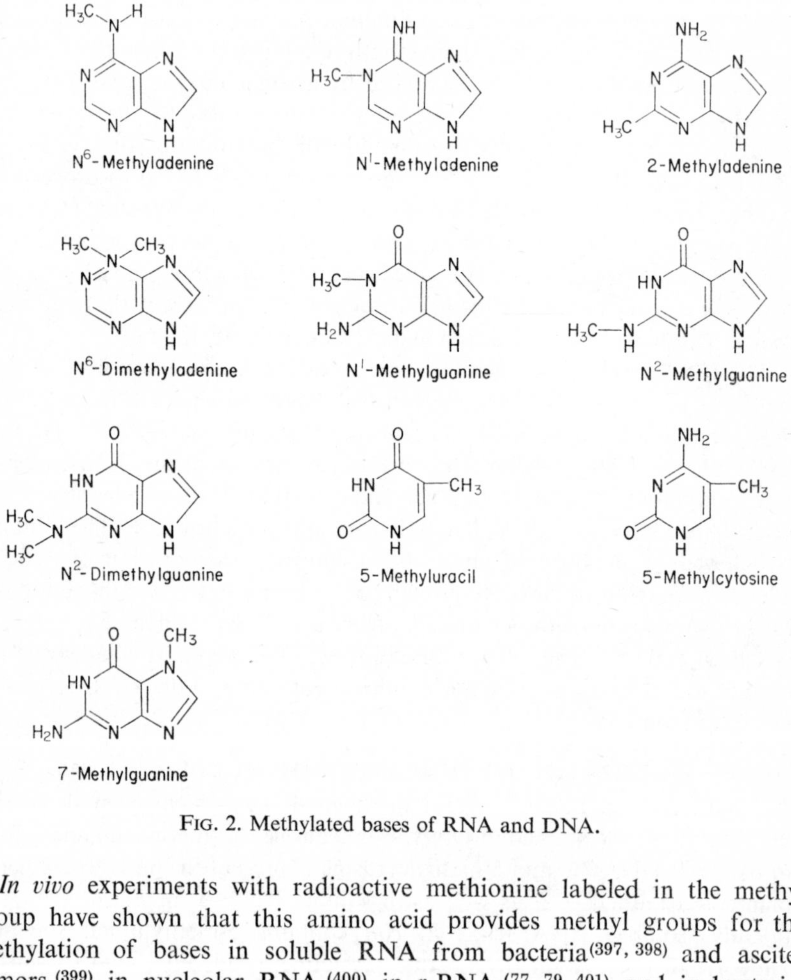

N^6-Methyladenine N^1-Methyladenine   2-Methyladenine

N^6-Dimethyladenine N^1-Methylguanine N^2-Methylguanine

N^2-Dimethylguanine   5-Methyluracil   5-Methylcytosine

7-Methylguanine

FIG. 2. Methylated bases of RNA and DNA.

In vivo experiments with radioactive methionine labeled in the methyl group have shown that this amino acid provides methyl groups for the methylation of bases in soluble RNA from bacteria[397, 398] and ascites tumors,[399] in nucleolar RNA,[400] in r-RNA,[77, 79, 401] and in bacterial DNA.[402, 403]

The *in vitro* methylation of intact polynucleotides with various enzyme systems (RNA and DNA methylases) has also been demonstrated. At the enzymic level S-adenosylmethionine, the activated derivative of methionine, acts as the methyl donor for the methylation of intact soluble RNA,[404, 405] r-RNA,[406] and DNA.[407] The enzymic methylation of nucleic acids may be illustrated by the following equation:[408, 409]

$$\text{methyl-deficient} \left\{ \begin{array}{c} \text{RNA} \\ \text{or} \\ \text{DNA} \end{array} \right\} + \text{S-adenosylmethionine} \rightarrow$$

(6)

$$\text{methylated} \left\{ \begin{array}{c} \text{RNA} \\ \text{or} \\ \text{DNA} \end{array} \right\} + \text{S-adenosylhomocysteine}$$

In each case a methyl group is transferred from S-adenosylmethionine to RNA or DNA by specific enzymes resulting in methylation of each nucleic acid and the formation of S-adenosylhomocysteine.[409] The reactions appear to be irreversible but the possibility of the existence of other enzymes that demethylate at the polynucleotide level has not been excluded.

The methylation of DNA appears to be dependent on the maintenance of its secondary structure, since heat-denaturation of native DNA abolishes its ability to accept methyl groups.[410] Actinomycin D and proflavin inhibit the methylation of adenine and cytosine in DNA.[420] Actinomycin D preferentially inhibits the methylation of adenine and proflavine preferentially inhibits methylation of cytosine.[410]

RNA and DNA methylases are widely distributed in bacteria, plants and animals,[411] and they appear to be species specific.[407, 412] Ordinarily, methylation of nucleic acids does not occur in reaction mixtures containing enzyme and nucleic acid from the same source (homologous systems), but it occurs more readily in heterologous systems (some exceptions to this general rule of homology have been noted).[407, 413] Thus, the methylation of soluble RNA in vitro requires either the use of enzymes from one species and soluble RNA from another, or methyl-deficient RNA such as the soluble RNA extracted from methionine starved E. coli K12 W6.[414, 404, 415, 416, 401, 417]

The methylation of cytosine and adenine in DNA appears to be catalyzed by a single enzyme.[407] However, the methylation of soluble RNA is catalyzed by at least six discrete enzymes, which have been purified from E. coli.[407, 418, 419] All of these enzymes are specific for soluble RNA and each appears to act independently in catalyzing the methylation of specific sites in soluble RNA.[419]

Infection of E. coli by DNA bacteriophages alters the activity of the RNA and DNA methylases in various ways depending on the type of infecting phage.[406] After infection of E. coli with T2 phage more than a 100-fold increase in the DNA-methylation activity of cell-free extracts is observed, whereas no change in the methylation of soluble RNA or r-RNA occurs.[406] It has not been determined whether this increase in enzymic activity is due to de novo synthesis of a phage-directed protein or whether phage infection alters the activity of a preexisting DNA methylase. A smaller increase in activity is observed after infection by T1 or T4 phage, whereas infection by T6 phage produces no change in the methylating activities.[406] Infection with T3 phage results in the appearance of a hydrolase that cleaves S-adenosylmethionine to thiomethyladenosine and homoserine, resulting in a reduction in the methylation of soluble RNA, r-RNA, and DNA by cell-free extracts.[406] Although the enzyme that hydrolyzes S-adenosylmethionine is present in several organisms, it is not normally found in *E. coli* B.

The origin of most of the methylated bases found in nucleic acids is now known, but their biological function still remains obscure.

In some strains of *E. coli* the extent of methylation of adenine depends on thymine starvation and can vary between 1 and 14 per cent of adenine; in other strains of *E. coli* and in other bacteria this extent remains constant.[403] Methylated adenine is not localized at the ends of DNA molecule but distributed throughout its length.[402] A turnover (breakdown and rebuilding) of highly methylated DNA has also been demonstrated.[420]

Kinetic and nearest neighbor studied with RNA and DNA polymerases and enzymically methylated DNA as template have shown that the incorporation of methyl groups on the DNA-template has no effect on the copying of DNA *in vitro*.[410] This finding suggests that methylated bases do not play a role in the replication or transcription of DNA. Other studies on the effects of methylation on transforming DNA and the sensitivity of methylated DNA to a variety of nucleases have not provided any leads as to the biological role of methylated bases in DNA.[410] The function of the methyl groups in t-RNA is also unknown. Preliminary experiments indicate that there is no difference in the ability of methylated or methyl-deficient t-RNA to accept amino acids,[421, 422] and it has also been reported that methylation of s-RNA does not appear to alter its susceptibility to RNAase.[412] High levels of methylated bases have been found in the soluble RNA extracted from certain tumor tissues,[423] and the hypothesis that methylating enzymes may be natural oncogenic agents has been discussed.[411]

VII. SUMMARY

A great deal of our present knowledge on the biosynthesis of nucleic acids has been derived from *in vitro* studies with purified enzymes obtained from bacterial, plant, and animal cells. Polyribonucleotides and polydeoxyribonucleotides may be synthesized by the enzymic polymerization of nucleotide units derived from nucleoside 5′-polyphosphate precursors. In general, enzymes involved in polynucleotide synthesis display specific requirements for one or more specific nucleotide substrates, a divalent cation, usually Mg^{++} or Mn^{++}), and for the presence of a polynucleotide, although certain enzymes can catalyze the synthesis of polynucleotides in the absence of exogenous polynucleotide primers. In some reactions nucleotides are incorporated onto the ends of polynucleotide primers resulting in an elongation of the primer by one or more nucleotides, whereas in other reactions polynucleotides serve as templates that direct the synthesis of complementary polynucleotides that are not covalently linked to the template. The latter reactions appear to proceed by a mechanism involving hydrogen-bond interactions between complementary base pairs of the substrate and the polynucleotide template.

DNA polymerases (DNA nucleotidyltransferases) catalyze the synthesis of polydeoxyribonucleotides and are believed to be associated with the synthesis of DNA *in vivo*. The reactions catalyzed by bacterial and mammalian DNA polymerases are dependent upon Mg^{++} ions, an exogenous supply of DNA and the deoxyribonucleoside 5'-triphosphates of thymidine, deoxyadenosine, deoxycytidine and deoxyguanosine. Some DNA polymerases have a specific requirement for single-stranded or denatured DNA and others utilize either single or double-stranded DNA as primers. The DNA polymerases purified from *E. coli* after T2 phage infection and from calf thymus gland have specific requirements for heat-denatured or single-stranded DNA primers, whereas DNA polymerases purified from *E. coli* and rat liver display a preference for double-stranded primers. *E. coli* DNA polymerase catalyzes an extensive synthesis of a DNA-product that reflects the base composition and dinucleotide distribution of the DNA used to prime the reaction. Several lines of evidence support the view that replication of DNA *in vitro* involves the sequential arrangements of nucleotides along a DNA-template by a complementary base-pairing mechanism. However, the exact mode of DNA replication *in vivo* is unknown. *E. coli* DNA polymerase also catalyzes the *de novo* synthesis of certain copolymers containing only two kinds of nucleotides from appropriate triphosphates and in the absence of polydeoxyribonucleotide primers. The copolymers formed in these reactions possess highly ordered structures consisting of either two homopolymeric or heteropolymeric chains hydrogen-bonded to each other.

The enzyme referred to as oligodeoxyribonucleotide transferase catalyze the condensation of oligodeoxyribonucleotides with polydeoxyribonucleotide acceptors by means of 3'-5'-phosphodiester bonds. This enzyme may be associated with the phenomenon of genetic recombination.

Enzymes have also been described that catalyze a limited incorporation of either ribonucleotides or deoxyribonucleotides onto the ends of polydeoxyribonucleotide chains. DNA containing one terminal ribonucleotide can serve as an acceptor polynucleotide for the incorporation of ribonucleotides when added to reaction mixtures containing enzymes that normally incorporate ribonucleotides into RNA but not DNA.

The enzyme polynucleotide phosphorylase is found widely distributed among bacteria but appears to have a more limited distribution in higher plant and animal cells. This enzyme catalyzes the synthesis of either homopolymers or heteropolymers that contain two or more different kinds of nucleotide residues from ribonucleoside 5'-diphosphates. Although the rates of the polymerization reactions can be altered in various ways by certain polyribonucleotides and oligoribonucleotides, there is no evidence that primers influence the nucleotide composition of the polymers synthesized. Polynucleotide phosphorylase catalyzes the polymerization of ribonucleoside 5'-diphosphates in a random fashion and the base composition of the product formed reflects the initial concentrations of the substrates. This enzyme also catalyzes the phosphorolysis of certain polyribonucleotides and oligoribonucleotides to yield ribonucleoside 5'-diphosphates. The biological role of this enzyme remains to be clarified.

Within recent years, it has become evident that several enzyme systems are associated with the synthesis of various kinds of RNA. In addition to polynucleotide phosphorylase, other enzymes have been discovered that utilize ribonucleoside 5'-triphosphates as substrates and that are dependent upon polynucleotide primers for activity. The results of several studies indicate that the synthesis of cellular RNAs is under control of DNA and originates on a DNA template. RNA polymerase (RNA nucleotidyltransferase) appears to be the key enzyme concerned with the transcription of genetic messages from DNA to RNA. RNA polymerases are widely distributed in nature and have been isolated from bacterial, plant, and animal cells. In the presence of a divalent cation (usually Mg^{++} and Mn^{++}), a DNA template, and the four common ribonucleoside 5'-triphosphates these enzymes catalyze the synthesis of an RNA-product that is complementary in base composition to the DNA template. In addition to DNA, chemically synthesized polydeoxynucleotides as well as synthetic and natural polyribonucleotides can be used as templates for the synthesis of complementary polynucleotides. Homopolymeric polyribonucleotides can also be synthesized with appropriate triphosphates and polynucleotide primers. Homopolymers containing either adenylic, uridylic, cytidylic, or guanylic acid have been synthesized.

In addition to RNA polymerase, other enzyme systems have been described that require triphosphates as substrates and RNA primers. These enzymes may be arbitrarily classified into two groups. Enzymes in the first group catalyze the incorporation of specific ribonucleotides into terminal or sub-terminal positions of RNA. Included in this category are enzymes responsible for the formation of the terminal trinucleotide sequence, —pCpCpA, of transfer RNA. Enzymes of the second group catalyze the incorporation of ribonucleotides predominantly into non-terminal positions of polyribonucleotides, and the newly synthesized product may contain all four ribonucleotides or may consist of a linear sequence of one kind of nucleotide. It is conceivable that the enzymes in both groups modify the structures of polyribonucleotides originating on a DNA template to form polyribonucleotides capable of performing specific cellular functions.

Several enzymes have been described that methylate certain bases in intact nucleic acids. The nucleic acid methylases catalyze the transfer of methyl groups from S-adenosylmethionine to soluble RNA, ribosomal RNA, and DNA. These enzymes are widely distributed in nature and appear to be responsible for the presence of most methylated bases in nucleic acids.

Undoubtedly, other enzymes associated with nucleic acid synthesis will be discovered and some of our current views will have to be revised. A leading question that remains to be answered relates to the extent by which each enzyme is operational in living organisms and the interrelationships of the various enzyme system to each other.

ACKNOWLEDGEMENTS

This study was aided by grants CA-05599-06, CA-08128 and HD-01331 from the National Institutes of Health, U.S. Public Health Service, and E-52 from the American Cancer Society.

REFERENCES

1. GUNSALUS, I. C. and STANIER, R. Y., Eds. In *The Bacteria*, Vol. V. Academic Press, New York, 1964.
2. CHARGAFF, E. and DAVIDSON, J. N., Eds. In *The Nucleic Acids*, Vol. III. Academic Press, New York, 1960.
3. JORDAN, D. O. *The Chemistry of Nucleic Acids*, Butterworth Inc., Washington, 1960.
4. MICHELSON, A. M. In *The Chemistry of Nucleosides and Nucleotides*. Academic Press, New York, 1963.
5. STEINER, R. F. and BEERS, R. F., JR. *Polynucleotides*. Elsevier, New York, 1961.
6. WYATT, G. R. *Nature* **166**, 237 (1950).
7. WYATT, G. R. *Biochem. J.* **48**, 581, 584 (1951).
8. MARSHAK, A. *Proc. Natl. Acad. Sci., U.S.* **37**, 299 (1951).
9. WYATT, G. R. and COHEN, S. S. *Nature* **170**, 1072 (1952).
10. SINSHEIMER, R. L. *Science* **120**, 551 (1954).
11. VOLKIN, E. *J. Am. Chem. Soc.* **76**, 5892 (1954).
12. JESAITS, M. A. *Nature* **178**, 637 (1956).
13. DEKKER, C. A. *Ann. Rev. Biochem.* **29**, 453 (1960).
14. BERG, P. *Ann. Rev. Biochem.* **30**, 293 (1961).
15. BROWN, G. L. In *Prog. Nucleic Acid Res.*, Vol. 2, p. 260, Eds. J. N. Davidson and W. E. Cohn, Academic Press, New York, 1963.
16. LENGYEL, P. and CHAMBERS, R. W. *J. Am. Chem. Soc.* **82**, 752 (1960).
17. COHEN, S. S. In *The Viruses*, Vol. I, p. 15, Eds. F. M. Burnet and W. M. Stanley. Academic Press, London, 1959.
18. CHARGAFF, E. In *The Nucleic Acids*, Vol. I, p. 307, Eds. E. Chargaff and J. N. Davidson. Academic Press, New York, 1955.
19. ZAMENHOF, S. In *Phosphorus Metabolism*, p. 301, Eds. W. D. McElroy and B. Glass. Johns Hopkins Press, Baltimore, 1952.
20. WILKINS, M. H. F., STOKES, A. R. and WILSON, H. P. *Nature* **171**, 738 (1953).
21. FRANKLIN, R. E. and GOSLING, L. G. *Nature* **171**, 740 (1953).
22. WATSON, J. D. and CRICK, F. H. C. *Nature* **171**, 737 (1953).
23. WATSON, J. D. and CRICK, F. H. C. *Cold Spring Harbor Symp. Quant. Biol.* **18**, 123 (1953).
24. WATSON, J. D. and CRICK, F. H. C. *Nature* **171**, 964 (1953).
25. CRICK, F. H. C. *Proc. 6th Int.Congress Biochem.*, p. 109, New York, 1964.
26. DELBRUCK, M. and STENT, G. S. In *The Chemical Basis of Heredity*, p. 699, Eds. W. D. McElroy and G. Glass. Johns Hopkins Press, Baltimore, 1957.
27. TAYLOR, J. H. *Int. Rev. Cytol.* **13**, 39 (1962).
U

28. WILKINS, M. H. F. *Cold Spring Harbor Symp. Quant. Biol.* **21**, 75 (1956).
29. WILKINS, M. H. F. In *Nucleoproteins*, p. 45, Ed. R. Stoops. Interscience, New York, 1959.
30. HAMILTON, L. D., BARCLAY, R. K., WILKINS, M. H. F., BROWN, G. L., WILSON, H. R., MARVIN, D. A., EPHRUSSI-TAYLOR, H. and SIMMONS, N. S. *J. Biophys. Biochem. Cytol.* **5**, 397 (1957).
31. BUTLER, J. A. V. In *Nucleoproteins*, p. 177, Ed. R. Stoops. Interscience, New York (1959).
32. CAVALIERI, L. F., DEUTSCH, J. F. and ROSENBERG, B. H. *Biophys. J.* **1**, 301 (1961).
33. REICHMAN, M. E., RICE, S. A., THOMAS, C. A. and DOTY, P. *J. Am. Chem. Soc.* **76**, 3047 (1954).
34. SADRON, C. and POUYET, J. In *Physical Chemistry of High Polymers of Biological Interest*, p. 52, Ed. O. Kratky. Pergamon Press, London, 1959.
35. BUTLER, J. A. V. In *Physical Chemistry of High Polymers of Biological Interest*, p. 77, Ed. O. Kratky. Pergamon Press, London, 1959
36. RUBENSTEIN, I., THOMAS, C. A., JR. and HERSHEY, A. D. *Proc. Natl. Acad. Sci., U.S.* **47**, 1113 (1961).
37. DAVISON, P. F., FRIEFELDER, D., HEDE, R. and LEVINTHAL, C. *Proc. Natl. Acad. Sci., U.S.* **47**, 1123 (1961).
38. CAIRNS, J. *J. Mol. Biol.* **4**, 407 (1962).
39. CAIRNS, J. *Cold Spring Harbor Symp. Quant. Biol.* **28**, 43 (1963).
40. CHANDLER, B., HAYASHI, M., HAYASHI, M. N. and SPIEGELMAN, S. *Science*, **143**, 47 (1964).
41. KLEINSCHMIDT, A. K., BURTON, A. and SINSHEIMER, R. L. *Science*, **142**, 961 (1963).
42. STOECKENIUS, W. *Proc. Natl. Acad. Sci., U.S.* **50**, 737 (1963).
43. DULBECCO, R. and VOGT, M. *Proc. Natl. Acad. Sci., U.S.*, **50**, 236 (1963).
44. RIS, H. and CHANDLER, B. L. *Cold Spring Harbor Symp. Quant. Biol.* **28**, 43 (1963).
45. BUTLER, J. A. V. and DAVIDSON, P. F. *Adv. Enzymol.* **18**, 161 (1957).
46. BRAWERMAN, G. and EISENSTADT, J. M. *Biochim. Biophys. Acta*, **91**, 477 (1964).
47. RAY, D. S. and HANAWALT, P. C. *J. Molec. Biol.* **9**, 812 (1964).
48. LIPMAN, F. In *Prog. Nucleic Acid. Res.*, Vol. I, p. 135, Eds., J. N. Davidson and W. E. Cohn. Academic Press, New York, 1963.
49. SPIRIN, A. S. In *Prog. Nucleic Acid Res.*, Vol. I, p. 301, Eds., J. N. Davidson and W. E. Cohn. Academic Press, New York, 1963.
50. ARNSTEIN, H. R. V. *Ann. Reports Chem. Soc.* **60**, 512 (1963).
51. JACOB, F. and MONOD, J. *J. Mol. Biol.* **3**, 318 (1961).
52. BRENNER, J., JACOB, F. and MESELSON, M. *Nature*, **190**, 576 (1961).
53. GROS, F., HIATT, H., GILBERT, W., KURLAND, C. G., RISEBROUGH, R. W. and WATSON, J. D. *Nature*, **190**, 581 (1961).
54. BRENNER, S., JACOB, F. and MESELSON, M. *Nature*, **170**, 576 (1961).
55. VOLKIN, E. and ASTRACHAN, L. *Virology*, **2**, 146 (1956).
56. NOMURA, M., HALL, B. D. and SPIEGELMAN, S. *J. Mol. Biol.* **2**, 306 (1960).
57. HAYASHI, M. and SPIEGELMAN, S. *Proc. Natl. Acad. Sci., U.S.* **47**, 1564 (1961).
58. HALL, B. D. and SPIEGELMAN, S. *Proc. Natl. Acad. Sci., U.S.* **47**, 137 (1961).
59. LEVINTHAL, C., KANYAN, A. and HIGA, A. *Proc. Natl. Acad. Sci., U.S.* **48**, 1631 (1962).
60. NATHANS, D. G., VON EHRENSTEIN, G., MONRO, R. and LIPMAN, F. *Federation Proceedings* **21**, 127 (1962).
61. MARKS, P., BURKA, E. R. and SCHLESSINGER, M. J. *Proc. Natl. Acad. Sci., U.S.* **48**, 2163 (1962).
62. REVEL, M. and HIATT, H. H. *Proc. Natl. Acad. Sci., U.S.* **51**, 810 (1964).
63. NIRENBERG, M. W. and MATTHAEI, J. H. *Proc. Natl. Acad. Sci., U.S.* **47**, 1588 (1961).
64. ZILLIG, W. D., SCHACHTSCHABEL, D. and KRONE, W. *Z. Physiol. Chem.* **318**, 100 (1960).
65. SINGER, M. F. and CANTONI, G. L. *Biochim. Biophys. Acta*, **39**, 182 (1960).
66. HOLLEY, R. W., APGAR, J., EVERETT, G. A., MADISON, J. T., MARQUISEE, M., MERRILL, S. H., PENSWICK, J. R. and ZAMIR, A. *Science*, **147**, 1462 (1965).
67. DAVIS, F. F. and ALLEN, F. W. *J. Biol. Chem.* **227**, 907 (1957).
68. COHN, W. E. *Biochim. Biophys. Acta*, **32**, 569 (1959).

69. ROBBINS, P. W. and KINSLEY, B. M. *Federation Proc.* **22**, 229 (1963).
70. HEINRIKSON, R. L. and GOLDWASSER, E. *J. Biol. Chem.* **239**, 1177 (1964).
71. KJELDGAARD, N. O. and KURLAND, C. G. *J. Mol. Biol.* **6**, 341 (1963).
72. BRENNER, S. *Cold Spring Harbor Symp. Quant. Biol.*, **26**, 101 (1961).
73. WALLACE, J. M. and Ts'o, P. O. P. *Biochem. Biophys. Res. Commun.* **5**, 125 (1961).
74. MIDGEY, J. E. M. *Biochim. Biophys. Acta*, **61**, 513 (1962).
75. ELSON, D. In *The Molecular Basis of Neoplasia*, p. 535. University of Texas Press, Austin, 1962.
76. GIERER, A. and SCHRAMM, G. *Nature*, **177**, 702 (1956).
77. STARR, J. L. and FEFFERMAN, R. *J. Biol. Chem.* **239**, 3457 (1964).
78. GORDON, J. and BOMAN, H. G. *J. Mol. Biol.* **9**, 638 (1964).
79. SVENSON, I., BOMAN, H. G., ERIKSSON, K. G. and KJELLIN, K. *Acta Chem. Scand.* **17**, 868 (1963).
80. POTTER, V. R. *Nucleic Acid Outlines*, Vol. I, Burgess, Minneapolis, 1960.
81. KORNBERG, A. In *The Chemical Basis of Heredity*, p. 579, Eds., W. D. McElroy and B. Glass. Johns Hopkins Press, Baltimore, 1957.
82. CROSBIE, G. W. In *The Nucleic Acids*, Vol. 3, p. 323, Eds., E. Chargaff and J. N. Davidson, Academic Press, New York, 1960.
83. BUCHANAN, J. M. In *The Nucleic Acids*, Vol. 3, p. 304, Eds., E. Chargaff and J. N. Davidson, Academic Press, New York, 1960.
84. HURLBERT, R. B. In *Methods in Enzymology*, Vol. III, p. 785, Eds., S. P. Colowick and N. O. Kaplan. Academic Press, New York, 1957.
85. MANDEL, P. In *Prog. Nucleic Acid Res.*, Vol. 3, p. 299, Eds., J. N. Davidson and W. E. Cohn, Academic Press, New York, 1964.
86. HENDERSON, J. F. and LEPAGE, G. A. *Chem. Rev.* **58**, 645 (1958).
87. POTTER, R. L. and SCHLESINGER, S. *J. Am. Chem. Soc.*, **77**, 6714 (1955).
88. POTTER, R. L., SCHLESINGER, S., BUETTNER-JANUSCH, V. and THOMPSON, L. *J. Biol. Chem.* **226**, 381 (1957).
89. LEPAGE, G. A. *J. Biol. Chem.* **226**, 135 (1957).
90. CANELLAKIS, E. S., KAMMEN, H. O. and MORALES, D. R. *Proc. Natl. Acad. Sci., U.S.* **53**, 184 (1965).
91. PRICE, T. D., HUDSON, P. B., HINDS, H. A., DARMSTADT, R. A. and ZAMENHOF, S. *Nature*, **178**, 684 (1956).
92. HURLBERG, R. B. and POTTER, V. R. *J. Biol. Chem.* **209**, 1 (1954).
93. ZILVERSMITH, D. B., ENTENMAN, C. and FISHLER, M. C. *J. Gen. Physiol.* **26**, 325 (1943).
94. ROSE, I. A. and SCHWEIGERT, B. S. *J. Biol. Chem.* **202**, 635 (1953).
95. REICHARD, P. *Acta Chem. Scand.* **11**, 11 (1957).
96. ROLL, P. M., WEINFELD, H. and CARROLL, E. *J. Biol. Chem.* **220**, 455 (1960).
97. LEIBMAN, K. C. and HEIDELBERGER, C. *J. Biol. Chem.* **216**, 823 (1956).
98. STAEHLIN, M. *Biochim. Biophys. Acta*, **29**, 43 (1958).
99. PRICE, T. D., TSUBOI, K. K., HINDS, H. A., and HUDSON, P. B. *Nature*, **186**, 158 (1960).
100. PRICE, T. D., DARMSTADT, R. A., HINDS, H. A. and TSUBOI, K. K. *Federation Proceedings*, **19**, 315 (1960).
101. PRICE, T. D., DARMSTADT, R. A., HINDS, H. A. and HUDSON, P. B. *Federation Proceedings*, **18**, 305 (1959).
102. CANELLAKIS, E. S. *Biochim. Biophys. Acta*, **25**, 217 (1957).
103. HARBERS, E. and HEIDELBERGER, C. *Biochim. Biophys. Acta*, **35**, 381 (1959).
104. KORNBERG, A. *Enzymatic Synthesis of DNA*, J. Wiley and Sons, New York, 1961.
105. RICHARDSON, C. C., SCHILDKRAUT, C. L., APOSHIAN, H. V. and KORNBERG, A. *J. Biol. Chem.* **239**, 222 (1964).
106. BILLEN, D. *Biochim. Biophys. Acta*, **68**, 342 (1963).
107. LEHMAN, I. R., BESSMAN, M. J., SIMMS, E. S. and KORNBERG, A. *J. Biol. Chem.* **233**, 163 (1960).
108. BESSMAN, M. J., LEHMAN, I. R., SIMMS, E. S. and KORNBERG, A. *J. Biol. Chem.* **233**, 171 (1958).
109. KORNBERG, A. *Science*, **131**, 1503 (1960).

110. ADLER, J., LEHMAN, I. R., BESSMAN, M. J., SIMMS, E. S. and KORNBERG, A. *Proc. Natl. Acad. Sci. U.S.* **44**, 641 (1958).
111. BERG, P., FANCHER, H. and CHAMBERLIN, M. In *Symposium on Informational Macromolecules*, Eds., H. J. Vogel, V. Bryson, J. O. Lampen. Academic Press, New York, 1963, p. 467.
112. OKAZAKI, T. and KORNBERG, A. *J. Biol. Chem.* **239**, 259 (1964).
113. LEHMAN, I. R., ZIMMERMAN, S. B., ADLER, J., BESSMAN, M. J., SIMMS, E. S. and KORNBERG, A. *Proc. Natl. Acad. Sci., U.S.* **44**, 1191 (1958).
114. JOSSE, J., KAISER, A. D. and KORNBERG, A. *J. Biol. Chem.* **236**, 864 (1961).
115. SWARTZ, M. N., TRAUTNER, T. A. and KORNBERG, A. *J. Biol. Chem.* **237**, 1961 (1962).
116. BESSMAN, M. J., LEHMAN, I. R., ADLER, J., ZIMMERMAN, S. B., SIMMS, E. S. and KORNBERG, A. *Proc. Natl. Acad. Sci., U.S.* **44**, 633 (1958).
117. BERTANI, L. E., HAGGMARK, A. and REICHARD, P. *J. Biol. Chem.* **236**, PC 67 (1961).
118. GREENBERG, G. R. and SOMERVILLE, R. L. *Proc. Natl. Acad. Sci., U.S.* **48**, 247 (1961).
119. ZAMENHOF, S. and GRIBOFF, G. *Nature*, **174**, 306, 307 (1954).
120. DUNN, D. B. and SMITH, J. D. *Nature*, **174**, 305 (1954).
121. ZAMENHOF, S., REINER, B., DE GIOVANNI, R. and RICH, K. *J. Biol. Chem.* **219**, 165 (1960).
122. APOSHIAN, H. V. and KORNBERG, A. *J. Biol. Chem.* **237**, 519 (1962).
123. PRICER, W. E., JR. and WEISSBACH, A. *J. Biol. Chem.* **239**, 2607 (1964).
124. PRICER, W. E., JR. and WEISSBACH, A. *Biochem. and Biophys. Res. Commun.* **14**, 91 (1964).
125. LEHMAN, I. R., ROUSSOS, G. G. and PRATT, E. A. *J. Biol. Chem.* **237**, 819 (1962).
126. KOERNER, J. F. and SINSHEIMER, R. L. *J. Biol. Chem.* **238**, 1039 (1957).
127. CUNNINGHAM, L., CATLIN, B. W. and DE GARILHE, M. P. *J. Am. Chem. Soc.* **78**, 4642 (1956).
128. RICHARDSON, C. C., SCHILDKRAUT, C. L., APOSHIAN, H. V., KORNBERG, A., BODMER, W. and LEDERBERG, J. In *Symposium on Informational Macromolecules*, p. 13, Eds., H. J. Vogel, V. Bryson, J. O. Lampen. Academic Press, New York. 1963.
129. RICHARDSON, C. C., SCHILDKRAUT, C. L. and KORNBERG, A. *Cold Spring Harbor Symp. Quant. Biol.* **28**, 9 (1963).
130. LEHMAN, I. R. and RICHARDSON, C. C. *J. Biol. Chem.* **239**, 233 (1964).
131. OKAZAKI, T. and KORNBERG, A. *J. Biol. Chem.* **239**, 259 (1964).
132. RICHARDSON, C. C. and KORNBERG, A. *J. Biol. Chem.* **239**, 242 (1964).
133. RICHARDSON, C. C., LEHMAN, I. R. and KORNBERG, A. *J. Biol. Chem.* **239**, 251 (1964).
134. RICHARDSON, C. C., INMAN, R. B. and KORNBERG, A. *J. Mol. Biol.* **9**, 46 (1964).
135. SCHILDKRAUT, C. L., RICHARDSON, C. C. and KORNBERG, A. *J. Mol. Biol.* **9**, 24 (1964).
136. LITMAN, R. M. and SZYBALSKI, W. *Biochem. Biophys. Res. Commun.* **10**, 473 (1963).
137. BALDWIN, R. L. In *The Bacteria*. Vol. V, p. 327, Eds., I. L. Gunsalus, and R. Y. Stanier. Academic Press, New York, 1964.
138. CAIRNS, J. *J. Mol. Biol.* **6**, 208 (1963).
139. NAGATA, T. P. *Proc. Natl. Acad. Sci., U.S.* **49**, 551 (1963).
140. YOSHIKAWA, H. and SUEOKA, N. *Proc. Natl. Acad. Sci., U.S.* **49**, 359 (1963).
141. KORNBERG, A. **18**, 191 (1957).
142. SIBATANI, A. and HIAI, S. *J. Theoret. Biol.* **7**, 393 (1964).
143. SIBATANI, A. *J. Theoret. Biol.* **7**, 558 (1964).
144. SCHACHMAN, H. K., ADLER, J., RADDING, C. M., LEHMAN, I. R. and KORNBERG, A. *J. Biol. Chem.* **235**, 3242 (1960).
145. RADDING, C. M., JOSSE, J. and KORNBERG, A. *J. Biol. Chem.* **237**, 2869 (1962).
146. RADDING, C. and KORNBERG, A. *J. Biol. Chem.* **237**, 2877 (1962).
147. RICH, A. and DAVIES, D. R. *J. Am. Chem. Soc.* **78**, 3548 (1956).
148. LEE-HUANG, S. and CAVALIERI, L. F. *Proc. Natl. Acad. Sci., U.S.* **51**, 1022 (1964).
149. TRAUTNER, T. A., SWARTZ, M. N. and KORNBERG, A. *Proc. Natl. Acad. Sci., U.S* **48**, 449 (1962).
150. KORNBERG, A., BERTSCH, L. L., JACKSON, J. F. and KHORANA, H. G. *Proc. Natl. Acad. Sci., U.S.* **51**, 315 (1964).
151. SUEOKA, N. *J. Mol. Biol.* **3**, 31 (1961).

152. SUEOKA, N. and CHENG, T. Y. *J. Mol. Biol.* **4**, 161 (1962).
153. SUEOKA, N. and CHENG, T. Y. *Proc. Natl. Acad. Sci., U.S.* **48**, 1851 (1962).
154. SMITH, M. *J. Mol. Biol.* **9**, 17 (1964).
155. CHENG, T. Y. and SUEOKA, N. *Science*, **143**, 1442 (1964).
156. MEAD, G. C. *Proc. Natl. Acad. Sci., U.S.* **52**, 1483 (1964).
157. MEAD, G. C. and VOLKIN, E. *Fed. Proc.* **23**, 373 (1964).
158. KOZINSKI, A. W. and KOZINSKI, P. B. *Proc. Natl. Acad. Sci., U.S.* **52**, 111 (1964).
159. KOZINSKI, A. W., KOZINSKI, P. B. and SHANNON, P. *Proc. Natl. Acad. Sci., U.S.* **50**, 746 (1963).
160. HECHT, L. I., POTTER, V. R. and HERBERT, E. *Biochim. Biophys. Acta*, **15**, 134 (1954).
161. SABLE, H. Z., WILBER, P. B., COHEN, A. E. and KANE, M. R. *Biochim. Biophys. Acta*, **13**, 150 (1954).
162. KLOENOW, H. and LICHTER, E. *Biochim. Biophys. Acta*, **23**, 6 (1957).
163. BOLLUM, F. J. *J. Am. Chem. Soc.* **80**, 1766 (1958).
164. CANELLAKIS, E. S. and MANTSAVINOS, R. *Biochim. Biophys. Acta*, **27**, 645 (1958).
165. CANELLAKIS, E. S., JAFFE, J., MANTSAVINOS, R. and KRAKOW, J. S. *J. Biol. Chem.* **234**, 2096 (1959).
166. KEIR, H. M. and SMELLIE, R. M. S. *Biochim. Biophys. Acta*, **35**, 405 (1959).
167. SMELLIE, R. M. S., KEIR, H. M. and DAVIDSON, J. N. *Biochim. Biophys. Acta*, **35**, 389 (1959).
168. FURLONG, N. B. *Arch. Biochem. Biophys.* **87**, 154 (1960).
169. KIELLEY, R. K. *Cancer Res.* **23**, 801 (1963).
170. BELTZ, R. E. *Arch. Biochem. Biophys.* **99**, 304 (1962).
171. FURLONG, N. B. *Anal. Biochem.* **5**, 515 (1963).
172. BEHKI, R. M. and MORGAN, W. S. *Arch. Biochem. Biophys.* **107**, 427 (1964).
173. CANELLAKIS, E. S. *Proc. 4th Intern. Congr. Biochem.*, p. 75, Vienna, 1958.
174. BOLLUM, F. J. and POTTER, V. R. *Cancer Res.* **19**, 561 (1959).
175. MANTSAVINOS, R. and CANELLAKIS, E. S. *J. Biol. Chem.* **234**, 628 (1959).
176. BOJARSKI, T. B. and HIATT, H. H. *Nature*, **188**, 1112 (1960).
177. HIATT, H. H. and BOJARSKI, T. B. *Cold Spring Harbor Symp. Quant. Biol.* **26**, 367 (1961).
178. KIELLEY, R. K. *Biochem. Biophys. Res. Comm.* **10**, 249 (1963).
179. GRAY, E. D., WEISSMAN, S. M., RICHARDS, J., BELL, D., KEIR, H. M., SMELLIE, R. M. S. and DAVIDSON, J. N. *Biochim. Biophys. Acta*, **45**, 111 (1960).
180. GOUTIER, R. and BOLOGNA, I. *Biochim. Biophys. Acta*, **72**, 40 (1963).
181. BOLLUM, F. J. and POTTER, V. R. *J. Am. Chem. Soc.* **79**, 3603 (1957).
182. MANTSAVINOS, R. and CANELLAKIS, E. S. *J. Biol. Chem.* **234**, 628 (1959).
183. BEHKI, R. M. and SCHNEIDER, W. C. *Biochim. Biophys. Acta*, **68**, 34 (1963).
184. SARKAR, N. K., OKADA, S. and DEVI, A. *Exptl. Cell. Res.* **29**, 36 (1963).
185. BOLLUM, F. J. and POTTER, V. R. *J. Biol. Chem.* **233**, 478 (1958).
186. WALWICK, E. R. and MAIN, R. K. *Biochim. Biophys. Acta*, **61**, 876 (1962).
187. GREEN, M., PINA, M. and CHAGOYA, V. *J. Biol. Chem.* **239**, 1188 (1964).
188. GREEN, M. *Cold Spring Harbor Symp. Quant. Biol.* **21**, 31 (1956).
189. HARFORD, C. G. and KORNBERG, A. *Federation Proc.* **17**, 515 (1958).
190. BACH, M. K. *Proc. Natl. Acad. Sci., U.S.* **48**, 1031 (1962).
191. GOLD, M. and HELLEINER, C. W. *Biochim. Biophys. Acta*, **80**, 193 (1964).
192. KEIR, H. M. and GOLD, E. *Biochim. Biophys. Acta*, **72**, 263 (1963).
193. SMITH, M. J., SR. and KEIR, H. M. *Biochim. Biophys. Acta*, **68**, 578 (1963).
194. KEIR, H. M. *Biochem. J.* **85**, 265 (1962).
195. KEIR, H. M. and SMITH, M. J. SR. *Biochim. Biophys. Acta*, **68**, 589 (1963).
196. BOLLUM, F. J. *J. Biol. Chem.* **235**, 2399 (1960).
197. MANTSAVINOS, R. *J. Biol. Chem.* **239**, 3431 (1964).
198. BOLLUM, F. J. In *Progress in Nucleic Acid Research*, Vol. I, p. 1, Eds., J. N. Davidson and W. E. Cohn, Academic Press, New York, 1963.
199. BOLLUM, F. J. *J. Biol. Chem.* **234**, 2733 (1959).
200. BOLLUM, F. J. *J. Cellular Comp. Physiol.* **62**, 61 (1963).
201. BOLLUM, F. J. *J. Biol. Chem.* **235**, PC 18 (1960).

202. BOLLUM, F. J. *J. Biol. Chem.* **237**, 1945 (1962).
203. BOLLUM, F. J., GROENIGER, E. and YONEDA, M. *Proc. Natl. Acad. Sci., U.S.* **51**, 853 (1964).
204. KRAKOW, J., COUTSOGEORGOPOULOS, C. and CANELLAKIS, E. S. *Biochim. Biophys. Acta*, **55**, 639 (1962).
205. KEIR, H. M. and SMITH, S. M. *J. Biochim. Biophys. Acta*, **68**, 589 (1963).
206. GRUNEBERG-MANAGO, M. and OCHOA, S. *J. Am. Chem. Soc.* **77**, 3165 (1955).
207. GRUNEBERG-MANAGO, M., ORTIZ, P. J. and OCHOA, S. *Biochim. Biophys. Acta*, **20**, 269 (1956).
208. HEPPEL, L. A., ORTIZ, P. J. and OCHOA, S. *J. Biol. Chem.* **229**. 679 (1957).
209. OCHOA, S. and MII, S. *J. Biol. Chem.* **236**, 3303 (1961).
210. OCHOA, S. and HEPPEL, L. A. In *The Chemical Basis of Heredity*, p. 615, Eds., W. D. McElroy and B. Glass. Johns Hopkins Press, Baltimore, 1957.
211. HEPPEL, L. A., ORTIZ, P. J. and OCHOA, S. *J. Biol. Chem.* **229**, 695 (1957).
212. OCHOA, S. *Arch. Biochem. Biophys.* **69**, 119 (1957).
213. SINGER, M. F., HILMOE, R. J. and GRUNEBERG-MANAGO, M. *J. Biol. Chem.* **235**, 2705 (1960).
214. SINGER, M. F. and O'BRIEN, B. M. *J. Biol. Chem.* **238**, 328 (1963).
215. HENDLEY, D. D. and BEERS, R. J., JR. *J. Biol. Chem.* **236**, 2050 (1961).
216. SINGER, M. F., HEPPEL, L. A., HILMOE, R. J., OCHOA, S. and MII, S. *Can. Cancer Conf.* **3**, 41 (1959).
217. GRUNEBERG-MANAGO, M. In *Progress in Nucleic Acid Research*, Vol. I, p. 93, Eds., J. N. Davidson and W. E. Cohn, Academic Press, New York, 1963.
218. OCHOA, S., BURMA, D. P., KROGER, H. and EIL, J. D. *Proc. Natl. Acad. Sci., U.S.* **47**, 670 (1961).
219. BRUMMOND, D. O., STRAEHLIN, M. and OCHOA, S. *J. Biol. Chem.* **225**, 835 (1957).
220. GRUNEBERG-MANAGO, M. and FRESCO, J. R. *Federation Proc.* **17**, 235 (1958).
221. HILMOE, R. J. and HEPPEL, L. A. *J. Am. Chem. Soc.* **79**, 4810 (1957).
222. ENTNER, N. and GONZALEZ, C. *Biochem. Biophys. Res. Comm.* **1**, 333 (1956).
223. HAKIM, A. A. *Nature*, **183**, 334 (1959).
224. HAKIM, A. A. *Enzymologia*, **21**, 81 (1959).
225. YAGI, K., OSAWA, T. and KONOGI, H. *Nature*, **184**, 1939 (1959).
226. SMELLIE, R. M. S. In *Progress in Nucleic Acid Research*, Vol. I, p. 27, Eds., J. N. Davidson and W. E. Cohn, Academic Press, New York, 1963.
227. BEERS, R. J., JR. *Nature*, **177**, 790 (1956).
228. LITTAUER, U. Z. and KORNBERG, A. *J. Biol. Chem.* **226**, 1077 (1957).
229. OCHOA, S. In *Physical Chemistry of High Polymers of Biological Interest*, p. 133, Ed. O. Kratky, Pergamon Press, London, 1958.
230. FRESCO, J. R. and SU, D. *J. Biol. Chem.* **237**, PC 3305 (1962).
231. GRIFFIN, B. E., TODD, A. and RICH, A. *Proc. Natl. Acad. Sci., U.S.* **44**, 1123 (1958).
232. PONCHON, F., MICHELSON, A. M., GRUNEBERG-MANAGO, M., DONDON, L. and COHN, W. E. *Federation Proc.* **23**, 218 (1964).
233. MICHELSON, A. M., DONDON, J. and GRUNEBERG-MANAGO, M. *Biochim. Biophys. Acta*, **55**, 529 (1962).
234. SKODA, J., KARA, J. and SORMOVA, Z. *Proc. 5th Intern. Congr. Biochem.*, p. 89. Moscow, 1961.
235. GRUNEBERG-MANAGO, M. In *Acides Ribonucléiques et Polyphosphates*, p. 295, Colloq. Intern. du C.N.R.S., Strasbourg, 1962.
236. SIMON, L. N. and MYERS, T. C. *Biochim. Biophys. Acta*, **51**, 178 (1961).
237. SKODA, J., KARA, J., SORMOVA, Z. and SORM, F. *Biochim. Biophys. Acta*, **33**, 579 (1959).
238. CARBON, J. A. *Biochem. Biophys. Res. Communs.* **7**, 366 (1962).
239. ORTIZ, P. J. and OCHOA, S. *J. Biol. Chem.* **234**, 1208 (1959).
240. SINGER, M. F. and GUSS, J. K. *J. Biol. Chem.* **237**, 182 (1962).
241. BEERS, R. F., JR. *Biochem. J.* **66**, 686 (1957).
242. OLMSTEAD, P. S. and LOWE, G. L. *J. Biol. Chem.* **234**, 2965 (1959).

243. OLMSTEAD, P. S. and LOWE, G. L. *J. Biol. Chem.* **234**, 2971 (1959).
244. DOLIN, M. I. *Biochem. Biophys. Res. Commun.* **6**, 11 (1961).
245. DOLIN, M. I., GODINAUX, E. and GRUNEBERG-MANAGO, M. *Bact. Proc.* **61**, 180 (1961).
246. KNIGHT, E., JR., FITT, P. S. and GRUNEBERG-MANAGO, M. *Biochem. Biophys. Res. Commun.* **10**, 488 (1963).
247. MII, S. and OCHOA, S. *Biochim. Biophys. Acta*, **26**, 445 (1957).
248. SINGER, M. F., HEPPEL, L. A. and HILMOE, R. J. *Biochim. Biophys. Acta*, **26**, 447 (1937).
249. SINGER, M. F., HEPPEL, L. A. and HILMOE, R. J. *J. Biol. Chem.* **235**, 738 (1960).
250. OCHOA, S. In *Nucleoproteins: Proceedings of the 11th Solvay Conference on Chemistry*, Brussels, 1959, p. 241, Wiley, New York, 1959.
251. HEPPEL, L. A. *J. Biol. Chem.* **238**, 357 (1963).
252. SINGER, M. F., HEPPEL, L. A. and HILMOE, R. J. *J. Biol. Chem.* **235**, 751 (1960).
253. SINGER, M. F. and GUSS, J. K. *J. Biol. Chem.* **237**, 182 (1962).
254. BEERS, R. F., JR. *J. Biol. Chem.* **236**, 2703 (1961).
255. GRUNEBERG-MANAGO, M. *J. Mol. Biol.* **1**, 240 (1959).
256. HILMOE, R. J. *Ann. N.Y. Acad. Sci.* **81**, 660 (1959).
257. SINGER, M. F. *J. Biol. Chem.* **232**, 211 (1956).
258. SINGER, M. F., LUBORSKY, S., MORRISON, R. A. and CANTONI, G. L. *Biochim. Biophys. Acta*, **38**, 568 (1960).
259. HEPPEL, L. A., SINGER, M. F. and HILMOE, R. J. *Ann. N.Y. Acad. Sci.* **81**, 635 (1959).
260. ROBBINS, P. W. and LIPMANN, F. *J. Biol. Chem.* **233**, 681 (1958).
261. REICHARD, P. and RUTBERG, L. *Biochim. Biophys. Acta*, **37**, 544 (1960).
262. MOORE, E. C. and HURLBERT, R. B. *Biochim. Biophys. Acta*, **40**, 371 (1960).
263. ABRAMS, R., LIBENSON, L. and EDMONDS, M. *Biochem. Biophys. Res. Commun.* **3**, 272 (1960).
264. REICHARD, P. *J. Biol. Chem.* **237**, 3513 (1962).
265. MOORE, E. C. and REICHARD, P. *J. Biol. Chem.* **239**, 3453 (1964).
266. SEKIGUCHI, M. and COHEN, S. S. *J. Biol. Chem.* **238**, 349 (1963).
267. FRIEDKIN, M. and LEHNINGER, A. L. *J. Biol. Chem.* **177**, 775 (1949).
268. GOLDWASSER, E. *J. Am. Chem. Soc.* **77**, 6083 (1953).
269. POTTER, V. R., HECHT, L. I. and HERBERT, E. *Biochim. Biophys. Acta*, **23**, 217 (1957).
270. CANELLAKIS, E. S. *Biochim. Biophys. Acta*, **23**, 217 (1957).
271. HEIDELBERGER, C., HARBERS, E., LEIBMAN, K. C., TAKAGI, V. and POTTER, V. R. *Biochim. Biophys. Acta*, **20**, 445 (1956).
272. CANELLAKIS, E. S. *Biochim. Biophys. Acta*, **25**, 217 (1957).
273. HERBERT, E. *Ann. N.Y. Acad. Sci.* **81**, 679 (1959).
274. HECHT, L. I., ZAMECNIK, P. C., STEPHENSON, M. L. and SCOTT, J. F. *J. Biol. Chem.* **233**, 954 (1958).
275. HECHT, L. I., STEPHENSON, M. L. and ZAMECNIK, P. C. *Proc. Natl. Acad. Sci., U.S.* **45**, 505 (1959).
276. DANIEL, V. and LITTAUER, U. Z. *J. Biol. Chem.* **238**, 2102 (1963).
277. GOTTESMAN, M. E., CANELLAKIS, Z. N. and CANELLAKIS, E. S. *Biochim. Biophys. Acta*, **61**, 34 (1962).
278. ZUBAY, G. and TAKANAMI, M. *Biochem. Biophys. Res. Commun.* **15**, 207 (1964).
279. ANTHONY, D. D., STARR, J. L., KERR, D. S. and GOLDTHWAIT, D. A. *J. Biol. Chem.* **238**, 690 (1963).
280. CANELLAKIS, E. S. and HERBERT, E. *Biochim. Biophys. Acta*, **45**, 133 (1960).
281. PREISS, J., DIECKMANN, M. and BERG, P. *J. Biol. Chem.* **236**, 1748 (1961).
282. FURTH, J. J., HURWITZ, J., KRUG, R. and ALEXANDER, M. *J. Biol. Chem.* **236**, 3317 (1961).
283. STARR, J. L. and GOLDTHWAIT, D. A. *J. Biol. Chem.* **238**, 682 (1963).
284. CANELLAKIS, E. S. and HERBERT, E. *Proc. Natl. Acad. Sci., U.S.* **46**, 170 (1959).
285. HARBERS, E. and HEIDELBERGER, C. *Biochim. Biophys. Acta*, **35**, 381 (1959).
286. MAJUMDAR, C. and BURMA, D. P. *Biochim. Biophys. Acta*, **76**, 480 (1963).
287. HURWITZ, J. *J. Biol. Chem.* **234**, 2351 (1960).

288. KRAKOW, J. S., KAMMEN, H. O. and CANELLAKIS, E. S. *Biochim. Biophys. Acta,* **53**, 52 (1961).
289. CANELLAKIS, E. S. and CANELLAKIS, Z. N. In *Symposium on Informational Macromolecules,* p. 107, Eds., H. J. Vogel, V. Bryson, J. O. Lampen, Academic Press, New York, 1963.
290. KLEMPERER, H. G., KRAKOW, J. S. and CANELLAKIS, E. S. *Biochim. Biophys. Acta,* **61**, 43 (1962).
291. EDMONDS, M. and ABRAMS, R. *J. Biol. Chem.* **235**, 1142 (1960).
292. EDMONDS, M. and ABRAMS, R. *J. Biol. Chem.* **237**, 2636 (1962).
293. EDMONDS, M. and ABRAMS, R. *J. Biol. Chem.* **238**, PC 1186 (1963).
294. VENKATARAMAN, P. R. and MAHLER, H. R. *J. Biol. Chem.* **238**, 1058 (1963).
295. HURWITZ, J., FURTH, J. J. ANDERS, M., ORTIZ, P. J. and AUGUST, J. T. *Cold Spring Harbor Symp. Quant. Biol.* **26**, 91 (1961).
296. AUGUST, J. T., ORTIZ, P. J. and HURWITZ, J. *J. Biol. Chem.* **237**, 3786 (1962).
297. ORTIZ, P. J., AUGUST, T., WATANABE, M., KAYE, A. M. and HURWITZ, J. *J. Biol. Chem.* **240**, 423 (1965).
298. CHAMBERLAIN, M. and BERG, P. *Proc. Natl. Acad. Sci., U.S.* **48**, 81, (1962).
299. CHAMBERLAIN, M. and BERG, P. *J. Mol. Biol.* **8**, 708 (1964).
300. KLEMPERER, H. G. *Biochem. Biophys. Res. Commun.* **15**, 269 (1964).
301. BURDON, R. H. and SMELLIE, R. M. S. *Biochim. Biophys. Acta,* **47**, 93 (1961).
302. BURDON, R. H. and SMELLIE, R. M. S. *Biochim. Biophys. Acta,* **51**, 153 (1961).
303. BURDON, R. H. *Biochem. Biophys. Res. Commun.* **13**, 37 (1963).
304. BURDON, R. H. *Biochem. Biophys. Res. Commun.* **11**, 472 (1963).
305. GOLDBERG, I. H. and REICH, E. *Federation Proc.* **23**, 958 (1964).
306. KLEMPERER, H. G. and KAMMEN, H. O. *Biochem. Biophys. Res. Commun.* **6**, 244 (1962).
307. STRAUSS, D. B. and GOLDWASSER, E. *J. Biol. Chem.* **236**, 849 (1961).
308. HURWITZ, J. and BRESLER, A. E. *J. Biol. Chem.* **236**, 542 (1961).
309. ABRAMS, R., EDMONDS, M. and BISWAS, B. B. In *Acides Ribonucléiques et Polyphosphates,* p. 323, Colloq. Intern. du D.N.R.S., Strasbourg (1962).
310. CHUNG, C. W. and MAHLER, H. R. *Biochem. Biophys. Res. Commun.* **1**, 232 (1959).
311. CHUNG, C. W., MAHLER, H. R. and ENRIONE, J. *J. Biol. Chem.* **235**, 1448 (1960).
312. GOLDBERG, I. H. *Biochim. Biophys. Acta,* **51**, 201 (1961).
313. NAKAMOTO, T. and WEISS, S. B. *Proc. Natl. Acad. Sci., U.S.* **48**, 880 (1962).
314. FOX, C. F., ROBINSON, W. S., HASELKORN, R. and WEISS, S. B. *J. Biol. Chem.* **239**, 186 (1964).
315. KRAKOW, J. S. and OCHOA, S. *Proc. Natl. Acad. Sci., U.S.* **49**, 88 (1963).
316. REDDI, K. K. *Science,* **133**, 1367 (1961).
317. *Viruses, Nucleic Acids and Cancer,* William and Wilkins, Baltimore (1963).
318. SPIEGELMAN, S. and DOI, R. H. *Cold Spring Harbor Symp. Quant. Biol.* **28**, 109 (1963).
319. COOPER, S. and ZINDER, N. D. *Virology,* **18**, 405 (1962).
320. FRANKLIN, M. and BALTIMORE, D. In *Viruses, Nucleic Acids and Cancer,* p. 310, Williams and Wilkins, Baltimore, 1965.
321. HAYWOOD, A. M. and SINSHEIMER, R. L. *J. Mol. Biol.* **6**, 247 (1963).
322. NAKATA, A., SEKIGUCHI, M. and KAWAMATA, J. *Nature,* **189**, 246 (1961).
323. REICH, E., FRANKLIN, R. M., SHATKIN, J. and TATUM, E. L. *Proc. Natl. Acad. Sci., U.S.* **48**, 1238 (1962).
324. ZIMMERMAN, E. F., HEETER, M. and DARNELL, J. E. *Virology,* **19**, 400 (1963).
325. BALTIMORE, D. and FRANKLIN, R. M. *J. Biol. Chem.* **28**, 3395 (1963).
326. BALTIMORE, D., EGGERS, H. J., FRANKLIN, R. M. and TAMM, I. *Proc. Natl. Acad. Sci., U.S.* **49**, 843 (1963).
327. WEISSMAN, C., SIMON, L. and OCHOA, S. *Proc. Natl. Acad. Sci., U.S.* **49**, 407 (1963).
328. WEISSMAN, C., SIMON, L., BORST, P. and OCHOA, S. *Cold Spring Harbor Symp. Quant. Biol.* **28**, 99 (1963).
329. AUGUST, J. T., COOPER, S., SHAPIRO, L. and ZINDER, N.D. *Cold Spring Harbor Symp. Quant. Biol.* **28**, 95 (1963).
330. HARUNA, I., NOZU, K., OHTAKA, Y. and SPIEGELMAN, S. *Proc. Natl. Acad. Sci., U.S.* **50**, 905 (1963).

331. OCHOA, S., WEISSMAN, C., BORST, P., BURDON, R. H. and BILLETER, A. *Federation Proceedings* **23**, (6), 1285 (1964).
332. WEISSMAN, C., BORST, P., BURDON, R. H., BILLETER, M. A. and OCHOA, S. *Proc. Natl. Acad. Sci., U.S.* **51**, 890 (1964).
333. WEISSMAN, C. and BORST, P. *Science*, **142**, 1188 (1963).
334. MONTAGNIER, L. and SANDERS, F. K. *Nature*, **199**, 664 (1963).
335. BALTIMORE, D., BECKER, Y. and DARNELL, J. E. *Science*, **143**, 1034 (1964).
336. WEISSMAN, C., BORST, P., BURDON, R. H., BILLETER, M. A. and OCHOA, S. *Proc. Natl. Acad. Sci., U.S.* **51**, 682 (1964).
337. FENWICK, M. L., ERICKSON, R. L. and FRANKLIN, R. M. *Federation Proc.* **23**, 319 (1964).
338. LANDRIDGE, R., BILLETER, M. A., BORST, P., BURDON, R. H. and WEISSMAN, C. *Proc. Natl. Acad. Sci., U.S.* **52**, 114 (1964).
339. KELLY, R. B. and SINSHEIMER, R. L. *J. Mol. Biol.* **8**, 602 (1964).
340. MANDEL, H. G., MATTHEWS, R. E. F., MATUS, A. and RALPH, R. K. *Biochem. Biophys. Res. Commun.* **16**, 604 (1964).
341. GOMATOS, A. J. and TAMM, I. *Proc. Natl. Acad. Sci., U.S.* **50**, 878 (1963).
342. GOMATOS, P. J., KRUG, R. M. and TAMM, I. *J. Mol. Biol.* **9**, 193 (1964).
343. HURWITZ, J. and AUGUST, J. T. In *Progress in Nucleic Acid Research*, Vol. I, p. 59, Eds., J. N. Davidson and W. E. Cohn, Academic Press, New York, 1963.
344. HALL, B. D. and SPIEGELMAN, S. *Proc. Natl. Acad. Sci., U.S.* **47**, 187 (1961).
345. HAYASHI, M. and SPIEGELMAN, S. *Proc. Natl. Acad. Sci., U.S.* **47**, 1564 (1961).
346. YANKOFSKY, S. A. and SPIEGELMAN, S. *Proc. Natl. Acad. Sci., U.S.* **48**, 1069 (1962).
347. YANKOFSKY, S. A. and SPIEGELMAN, S. *Proc. Natl. Acad. Sci., U.S.* **48**, 1446 (1962).
348. GIACOMONI, D. and SPIEGELMAN, S. *Science*, **138**, 1328 (1962).
349. GOODMAN, H. M. and RICH, A. *Proc. Natl. Acad. Sci., U.S.* **48**, 2101 (1962).
350. REICH, E., FRANKLIN, R. M., SHATKIN, A. J. and TATUM, E. L. *Proc. Natl. Acad. Sci., U.S.* **48**, 1238 (1962).
351. ROBINSON, W. S., HSU, W. T., FOX, C. F. and WEISS, S. B. *J. Biol. Chem.* **239**, 2944 (1964).
352. WEISS, S. B. and GLADSTONE, L. *J. Am. Chem. Soc.* **81**, 4118 (1959).
353. WEISS, S. B. *Proc. Natl. Acad. Sci., U.S.* **46**, 1020 (1960).
354. HUANG, R. C., MAHESHWARI, N. and BONNER, J. *Biochem. Biophys. Res. Commun.* **3**, 689 (1960).
355. FURTH, J. J., HURWITZ, J. and ANDERS, M. *J. Biol. Chem.* **237**, 2611 (1962).
356. STEVENS, A. *J. Biol. Chem.* **236**, PC 43 (1961).
357. STEVENS, A. and HENRY, J. *J. Biol. Chem.* **239**, 196 (1964).
358. HURWITZ, J., FURTH, J. J., ANDERS, N. and EVANS, A. *J. Biol. Chem.* **237**, 3752 (1962).
359. BURMA, D. P., KROGER, H., OCHOA, S., WARNER, R. C., and WEILL, J. D. *Proc. Natl. Acad. Sci., U.S.* **47**, 749 (1961).
360. GEIDUSCHEK, E. P., NAKAMOTO, T. and WEISS, S. B. *Proc. Natl. Acad. Sci., U.S.* **47**, 1405 (1961).
361. GEIDUSCHEK, E. P., MOOHR, J. W. and WEISS, S. B. *Proc. Natl. Acad. Sci., U.S.* **48**, 1078 (1962).
362. WARNER, R. C., SAMUELS, H. H., ABBOTT, M. T. and KRAKOW, J. S. *Proc. Natl. Acad. Sci., U.S.* **49**, 533 (1963).
363. FOX, F. C. and WEISS, S. B. *J. Biol. Chem.* **239**, 175 (1964).
364. KAHAN, F. M. and HURWITZ, J. *J. Biol. Chem.* **237**, 3778 (1962).
365. CHAMBERLAIN, M., BALDWIN, R. L. and BERG, P. *J. Mol. Biol.* **7**, 334 (1963).
366. CHAMBERLAIN, M. and BERG, P. *Cold Spring Harbor Symp. on Quant. Biol.* **28**, 67 (1963).
367. CHAMBERLAIN, M. and BERG, P. *J. Mol. Biol.* **8**, 297 (1964).
368. SINSHEIMER, R. L. and LAWRENCE, M. *J. Mol. Biol.* **8**, 289 (1964).
369. MARMUR, J. and GREENSPAN, C. M. *Science*, **142**, 387 (1963).
370. GUILD, W. R. and ROBINSON, M. *Proc. Natl. Acad. Sci., U.S.* **50**, 106 (1963).
371. HAYASHI, M., HAYASHI, M. N. and SPIEGELMAN, S. *Proc. Natl. Acad. Sci., U.S.* **50**, 664 (1963).

372. HAYASHI, M., HAYASHI, M. N. and SPIEGELMAN, S. *Proc. Natl. Acad. Sci., U.S.* **51**, 351 (1964).
373. GEIDUSCHEK, E. P., TOCCHINI-VALENTINI, E. P. and SARNAT, M. T. *Proc. Natl. Acad. Sci., U.S.* **52**, 486 (1964).
374. HOCHESTER, R. M. and CHANG, V. M. *Canadian J. Biochem. Physiol.* **41**, 1503 (1963).
375. TISSIERES, A., BOURGEOIS, S. and GROS, F. *J. Mol. Biol.* **7**, 100 (1963).
376. GOMATOS, P. J. and TAMM, I. *Proc. Natl. Acad. Sci., U.S.* **49**, 707 (1963).
377. LANGRIDGE, R. and GOMATOS, P. J. *Science*, **141**, 694 (1963).
378. BARRY, R. D., IVES, D. R. and CRUICKSHANK, J. G. *Nature*, **194**, 1139 (1962).
379. TEMIN, H. M. *Virology*, **20**, 577 (1963).
380. NIYOGI, S. K. and STEVENS, A. *Biochem. Biophys. Res. Commun.* **17**, 272 (1964).
381. STEVENS, A. *J. Biol. Chem.* **239**, 204 (1964).
382. FALASCHI, A., ADLER, J. and KHORANA, H. G. *J. Biol. Chem.* **238**, 3080 (1963).
383. KHORANA, H. G. and VIZSOLYI, J. P. *J. Am. Chem. Soc.* **83**, 675 (1961).
384. KHORANA, H. G., TURNER, A. F. and VIZSOLYI, J. P. *J. Am. Chem. Soc.* **83**, 686 (1961).
385. RALPH, R. K. and KHORANA, H. G. *J. Am. Chem. Soc.* **83**, 2926 (1961).
386. NISHIMURA, S., JACOB, T. M. and KHORANA, H. G. *Proc. Natl. Acad. Sci. U.S.* **52**, 1494 (1964).
387. BYRD, C., OHTSUKA, E., MOON, M. W. and KHORANA, H. G. *Science*, **146**, 423 (1964).
388. BYRD, C., OHTSUKA, E., MOON, M. W. and KHORANA, H. G. *Proc. Natl. Acad. Sci. U.S.* **53**, 79 (1965).
389. SHIGEURA, H. T. and BOXER, G. E. *Biochem. Biophys. Res. Commun.* **17**, 758 (1964).
390. SHIGEURA, H. T. and GORDON, C. N. *J. Biol. Chem.* **240**, 806 (1965).
391. KACZKA, E. A., DULANEY, E. L., GITTERMAN, C. O., WOODRUFF, H. B. and FOLKBERG, K. *Biochem. Biophys. Res. Commun.* **14**, 452 (1964).
392. DUNN, D. B. and SMITH, J. D. *Biochem. J.* **68**, 627 (1958).
393. DUNN, D. B., SMITH, J. D. and SPAHR, P. F. *J. Mol. Biol.* **2**, 113 (1960).
394. LITTLEFIELD, J. W. and DUNN, D. B. *Biochem. J.* **70**, 642 (1958).
395. SMITH, J. D. and DUNN, D. B. *Biochem. J.* **72**, 294 (1959).
396. DUNN, D. B. *Biochem. J.* **86**, 14P (1963).
397. MANDEL, L. R. and BOREK, E. *Biochem. Biophys. Res. Commun.* **6**, 138 (1961).
398. MANDEL, L. R. and BOREK, E. *Biochem.* **2**, 555 (1963).
399. BISWAS, B. B., EDMONDS, M. and ABRAMS, R. *Biochem. Biophys. Res. Commun.* **6**, 146 (1961).
400. SIRLIN, J. L., JACOB, J. and TANDLER, C. J. *Biochem. J.* **89**, 477 (1963).
401. SVENSSON, I., BOMAN, H. G., ERICKSON, K. G. and KJELLIN, K. *Acta Chem. Scand.* **17**, 868 (1963).
402. THEIL, E. C. and ZAMENHOF, S. *J. Biol. Chem.* **238**, 3058 (1963).
403. REMY, C. N. *J. Biol. Chem.* **236**, 2999 (1961).
404. FLEISNER, E. and BOREK, E. *Biochem.* **2**, 1093 (1963).
405. GOLD, M., HURWITZ, J. and ANDERS, M. *Proc. Natl. Acad. Sci., U.S.* **50**, 164 (1963).
406. GOLD, M., HAUSMANN, R., MAITRA, U. and HURWITZ, J. *Proc. Natl. Acad. Sci., U.S.* **52**, 292 (1964).
407. GOLD, M., HURWITZ, J. and ANDERS, M. *Proc. Natl. Acad. Sci., U.S.* **50**, 164 (1963).
408. BOREK, E. *Cold Spring Harbor Symp. Quant. Biol.* **28**, 139 (1963).
409. GOLD, M. and HURWITZ, J. *Cold Spring Harbor Symp. Quant. Biol.* **28**, 149 (1963).
410. GOLD, M. and HURWITZ, J. *J. Biol. Chem.* **239**, 3866 (1964).
411. SRINIVASAN, P. R. and BOREK, E. *Science* **145**, 548 (1964).
412. SRINIVASAN, P. R. and BOREK, E. *Proc. Natl. Acad. Sci., U.S.* **49**, 529 (1963).
413. SRINIVASAN, P. R. and BOREK, E. *Biochem.* **3**, 616 (1964).
414. FLEISNER, E. and BOREK, E. *Proc. Natl. Acad. Sci., U.S.* **48**, 1199 (1962).
415. SVENSSON, I., BOMAN, H. G., ERICSON, K. B. and KJELLIN, K. *J. Mol. Biol.* **7**, 254 (1963).
416. BIRNSTIEL, M. L., FLEISSNER, E. and BOREK, E. *Science* **142**, 1577 (1963).
417. BOREK, E., RYAN, A. and ROCKENBACH, J. *J. Bacteriol.* **69**, 460 (1955).
418. HURWITZ, J., GOLD, M. and ANDERS, M. *J. Biol. Chem.* **239**, 3462 (1964).

419. HURWITZ, J., GOLD, M. and ANDERS, M. *J. Biol. Chem.* **239**, 3474 (1964).
420. THEIL, E. C. and ZAMENHOF, S. *Nature* **199**, 599 (1963).
421. STARR, J. L. *Biochem. Biophys. Res. Commun.* **10**, 428 (1963).
422. LITTAUER, U. F., MUENCH, K., BERG, P., GILBERT, W. and SPAHR, P. F. *Cold Spring Harbor Symp. Quant. Biol.* **28**, 157 (1963).
423. BERQUIST, P. L. and MATTHEWS, R. E. F. *Biochem. J.* **85**, 305 (1962).
424. MANTSAVINOS, R. and CANELLAKIS, E. S. *Cancer Res.* **19**, 1239 (1959).
425. COCHRAN, G. W., DHALIWAL, A. S., WELKIE, G. W., CHIDESTER, J. L., LEE, M. and CHANDRASEKHR, B. *Science* **138**, 46 (1962).
426. KIM, Y. T. and WILDMAN, S. G. *Biochem. Biophys. Res. Commun.* **8**, 394 (1962).
427. KARASEK, M. and SCHRAMM, G. *Biochem. Biophys. Res. Commun.* **9**, 63 (1962).
428. BANDURSKI, R. S. and MAHESHWARI, S. C. *Plant Physiol.* **37**, 556 (1962).

CHAPTER 9

THE BIOGENESIS OF CONJUGATION AND DETOXICATION PRODUCTS

R. T. WILLIAMS

Department of Biochemistry, St. Mary's Hospital Medical School, University of London, London W.2

CONTENTS

I. INTRODUCTION   590
  A. *Mechanistic classification of conjugation reactions*   590
II. GLUCURONIC ACID CONJUGATION   592
  A. *Types of glucuronides formed biologically*   592
  B. *Enzymic mechanism of glucuronide formation*   593
  C. *Zoological distribution of glucuronide synthesis*   597
III. GLUCOSIDE CONJUGATION   598
IV. HIPPURIC ACID SYNTHESIS   598
  A. *Types of acids conjugating with glycine*   599
  B. *Enzymic mechanism of hippuric acid synthesis*   599
  C. *Zoological distribution of hippuric acid synthesis*   599
V. MERCAPTURIC ACID SYNTHESIS   601
  A. *Types of compounds forming mercapturic acids*   601
  B. *Mechanism of mercapturic acid formation*   604
  C. *Zoological distribution of mercapturic acid formation*   607
VI. ORNITHURIC ACID SYNTHESIS   608
  A. *Enzymic mechanism of ornithine conjugation*   608
  B. *Zoological distribution of ornithuric acid synthesis*   608
VII. GLUTAMINE CONJUGATION   609
VIII. SULFATE CONJUGATION   611
  A. *Types of compounds conjugating with sulfate*   611
  B. *Enzymic synthesis of ethereal sulfates*   612
  C. *Zoological distribution of sulfate conjugation*   615
IX. THIOCYANATE SYNTHESIS   615
  A. *The enzymic conversion of cyanide to thiocyanate*   616
X. METHYLATION   619
  A. *Types of compounds undergoing biological methylation*   620
  B. *Enzymic mechanism of methylation*   620

C. *Orientation of methylation of polyhydric phenols*   623
D. *Zoological distribution of methylation*   625
XI. ACETYLATION   625
A. *Types of compounds undergoing acetylation* in vivo   626
B. *Enzymic mechanism of acetylation*   628
C. *Zoological distribution of acetylation*   628
XII. MISCELLANEOUS CONJUGATION REACTIONS   629
XIII. PHYSIOLOGICAL PROPERTIES OF CONJUGATES   632
  The relationship between conjugation and the metabolism of
  foreign compounds generally   633
XIV. SUMMARY   634
REFERENCES   635

I. INTRODUCTION

Our knowledge of the processes of conjugation and detoxication has been obtained from the study of the fate in the body of foreign organic compounds, although there are a number of natural metabolites which can also undergo conjugation and detoxication in the body. Conjugation means the union or coupling of two substances in the body, and detoxication implies the reduction or abolition of the toxicity of a substance during its sojourn in the body. Thus, when phenol is administered to an animal, it is converted in part into phenylglucuronide, and it is said that phenol undergoes conjugation with glucuronic acid. Now phenol is a relatively toxic substance, but its conjugation product, phenylglucuronide, is relatively nontoxic and is regarded as a detoxication product of phenol. A conjugation product is thus made up of two parts, one part being either a compound foreign to the body or a natural metabolite usually unwanted by the organism, and the other part being a compound made by the organism and used under the appropriate circumstances for the detoxication and removal from the body of a foreign compound or useless metabolite. The compound provided by the body for conjugation may be referred to as the conjugating agent and a number of these are known. They are usually substances or groups derived from carbohydrates and amino acids. The known conjugation reactions and conjugating agents are listed in Table 1.

A. Mechanistic Classification of Conjugation Reactions

The reactions listed in Table 1 are all biosynthetic mechanisms and, therefore, require a source of energy for their accomplishment. The detailed mechanism of these syntheses is dealt with in later paragraphs where each reaction is considered separately. However, at this point, it should be noted that those reactions which are more or less fully known (i.e. reactions 1, 2, 3, 5, 6, 7, 9 and 10 of Table 1) can be classified from the point of view of

TABLE 1. CONJUGATION REACTIONS AND CONJUGATING AGENTS

Reaction	Agent	Product†
1. Glucuronic acid conjugation	Glucuronic acid	R—O—CH—(CHOH)$_3$CH—CO$_2$H (with O bridge)
2. Glucoside conjugation	Glucose	R—O—CH—(CHOH)$_3$CH—CH$_2$OH (with O bridge)
3. Hippuric acid synthesis	Glycine	R—CO—NH—CH$_2$—COOH
4. Mercapturic acid synthesis	Cysteine and acetic acid	R—S—CH$_2$—CH(NH—COCH$_3$)COOH
5. Ornithuric acid synthesis	Ornithine	R—CO—NH(CH$_2$)$_3$CH(NH—COR)COOH
6. Glutamine conjugation	Glutamine	R—CO—NH—CH(COOH)(CH$_2$)$_2$CONH$_2$
7. Ethereal sulfate synthesis	Sulfate	R—OSO$_3$H
8. Cyanide-thiocyanate detoxication	Sulfur from thiosulfate	S—CN$^-$
9. Methylation	Methyl group from methionine	R—CH$_3$
10. Acetylation	Acetic acid	R—COCH$_3$

† Where R or R—CO is derived from the foreign compounds.

mechanism into two groups. All these reactions are characterized by the occurrence of activated nucleotides as intermediates in the synthetic process and by a requirement of adenosine triphosphate (ATP) as a source of energy. However, the nucleotide intermediate can contain in its molecule either the conjugating agent or the foreign compound. Therefore, there is one type of conjugation reaction in which an "activated" conjugating agent is involved, and another type in which an "activated" foreign compound is involved, thus:

$$\text{conjugating agent} \xrightarrow[\text{source}]{\text{energy}} \text{``activated'' conjugating agent} \xrightarrow{\text{foreign compound}} \text{conjugated product} \quad (1)$$

$$\text{foreign compound} \xrightarrow[\text{source}]{\text{energy}} \text{``activated'' foreign compound} \xrightarrow{\text{conjugating agent}} \text{conjugated product} \quad (2)$$

It appears that, although the liver is the tissue *par excellence* for carrying out conjugation reactions, reactions of type 1 can occur in other tissues and may be widespread throughout the body, whereas reactions of type 2 occur only in either the liver or the kidney or in both. In Table 2 the reactions listed in Table 1 are classified according to whether the synthesis occurs according to 1 or 2 above. In this table, the activated intermediates are also given.

TABLE 2. MECHANISTIC CLASSIFICATION OF CONJUGATION REACTIONS

Reaction	Intermediate nucleotide	Location
Type 1. *Activated conjugating agent* Glucuronic acid conjugation	Uridinediphosphate glucuronic acid (UDP-glucuronic acid)	Liver, kidney, lung, spleen, urinary bladder, gastrointestinal tract [161, 192]
Glucoside conjugation	Uridinediphosphate glucose (UDP-glucose)	In insects—hepatic caecum. [65]
Ethereal sulfate synthesis	Phosphoadenosinephosphosulfate (PAPS)	Liver, kidney, intestine. [157]
Methylation	S-Adenosylmethionine	Liver, kidney, spleen, brain, small intestine, lung, heart muscle. [1]
Acetylation	Acetyl-CoA	Liver, kidney, brain, lung, pancreas, spleen, blood. [115]
Type 2. *Activated foreign compound* Hippuric acid synthesis	Aroyl-CoA	Liver and/or kidney only. [50, 125],
Ornithuric acid synthesis	Aroyl-CoA	In chickens—kidney only. [106, 125]
Glutamine synthesis	Phenylacetyl-CoA	In man—kidney and liver. [137]

II. GLUCURONIC ACID CONJUGATION

Conjugated glucuronic acids formed as a result of the administration of foreign compounds to animals were first described some 80 to 90 years ago when Mering and Musculus [134] isolated trichloroethyl glucuronide (urochloralic acid) from human urine after the administration of chloral hydrate, and Jaffé [100] isolated *o*-nitrobenzyl glucuronide as a metabolite of *o*-nitrotoluene in dogs. About 120 such glucuronides have been listed by Bray [35] and many more have been described subsequently.

A. *Types of Glucuronides Formed Biologically*

Conjugated glucuronic acids are β-glycosides of D-glucuronic acid which are formed in animals when certain foreign compounds are administered. The structure of these compounds is shown below and they are fully described as β-D-glucopyranuronosides.

In the majority of known glucuronides, X in the above formula is O. A small number of glucuronides are known in which X is NH or S. R is a radicle from the foreign compound.

Glucuronides may be formed *in vivo* if the foreign compound contains (or can acquire during its metabolism):

(a) *a hydroxyl group*, which may be alcoholic (primary, secondary or tertiary), phenolic or enolic. There is also evidence that the hydroxyl group of hydroxylamines can form glucuronides; [53]

(b) *a carboxyl group*, which is usually aromatic, but in special cases aliphatic carboxylic acids form glucuronides. The aromatic carboxyl can occur in carbocyclic or heterocyclic systems, and the aliphatic carboxyl is usually one found in substituted acetic acids;

(c) *an amino group*, which can be aromatic or can occur in certain carboxyamide [203] or sulfonamide groups. [40] A claim has also been made for a glucuronide in which the glucuronic is attached to a ring nitrogen in sulfisoxazole. [206] Glucuronides of amino acids have also been claimed to occur in human urine, but these could be N-glucuronides or carboxylic ester glucuronides. [96, 70]

(d) *a sulfhydryl group*, although very few of these are known. [47, 108]

Examples of compounds which conjugate with glucuronic acid and which contain the above-mentioned groups are listed in Table 3.

The enolic, ester, and N-ether glucuronides show reducing properties towards the usual copper reagents (e.g. Fehling's solution) for reducing sugars.

B. *Enzymic Mechanism of Glucuronide Formation*

The earliest view on the mode of formation of glucuronides in the body was that the glucuronidogenic substance combined with glucose to form a glucoside which was subsequently oxidized at the terminal primary alcohol group to a glucuronide: [72, 196]

$$ROH + C_6H_{12}O_6 \rightarrow RO\overset{\displaystyle \lceil\!-\!-O-\!-\!\rceil}{-CH-(CHOH)_3CH}-CH_2OH \rightarrow$$

$$RO\overset{\displaystyle \lceil\!-\!-O-\!-\!\rceil}{-CH-(CHOH)_3CH}-COOH \qquad (3)$$

TABLE 3. TYPES OF COMPOUNDS FORMING GLUCURONIDES

Type	Example	Formula	Glucuronide type
(a) *Hyroxyl*			O-*Ether type*
Primary alcoholic	Trichloroethanol	$Cl_3C\text{—}CH_2OH$	$R\text{—}CH_2O\text{—}GU$
Secondary alcoholic	Butan-2-ol	$C_2H_5(CH_3)CHOH$	$R(R')\text{—}CHO\text{—}GU$
Tertiary alcoholic	*Tert*-butyl alcohol	$(CH_3)_3COH$	$R(R')(R'')CO\text{—}GU$
Phenolic	Phenol	OH	$ArO\text{—}GU$
Enolic	4-Hydroxycoumarin		$HC\text{=}CO\text{—}GU$ (enol glucuronide)
Hydroxylamine	N-Hydroxy-2-acetyl-aminofluorene		$\text{—}NO\text{—}GU$
(b) *Carboxyl* Aromatic Carbocyclic	Benzoic acid	COOH	*Ester type*
Heterocyclic	Nicotinic acid	COOH	$Ar\text{—}COO\text{—}GU$
Aliphatic Alkyl	2-Ethylhexoic acid	$C_4H_9CH(C_2H_5)COOH$	$R(R')CH\text{—}COO\text{—}GU$
Aryl-alkyl	Phenylacetic acid	CH_2COOH	$Ar\text{—}CH_2COO\text{—}GU$
(c) *Amino* Aromatic	Aniline	NH_2	N—*Ether type* $Ar\text{—}NH\text{—}GU$
Carboxyamide	2-Methyl-2-propyl-1,3-propanediol dicarbamate (meprobamate)	CH_3 $C(CH_2OCONH_2)_2$ $CH_2CH_2CH_3$	$\text{—}CONH\text{—}GU$
Sulfonamide	Sulfadimethoxine		$\text{—}SO_2N\text{—}GU$

TABLE 3—*continued*.

Type	Example	Formula	Glucuronide type
Heterocyclic	Sulfisoxazole	$NH_2C_6H_4SO_2NH$ (CH₃ / CH₃ ring structure)	(CH₃ / CH₃ ring) —N O N—GU
(d) *Sulfhydryl* Sulfhydryl	2-Mercaptobenzo-thiazole	(benzothiazole ring) C—SH	S-*Ether type* Ar—S—GU
Carbodithioic	N,N-Diethyldithio-carbamic acid	$(C_2H_5)_2N.CS.SH$	S-*Ester type* —CS.S—GU

R = aliphatic group.
Ar = aromatic group.
GU = $C_6H_9O_6$ or —CH—(CHOH)₃—CH—CO₂H with —O— bridge

However, it was soon shown that glucosides were not oxidized to glucuronides in the body. The key to the understanding of glucuronide synthesis was not found until 1953, when Dutton and Storey [68] discovered in the liver the heat-stable cofactor necessary for the synthesis. This cofactor, uridine diphosphate glucuronic acid (UDPGA) is the immediate precursor of the glucuronic acid residue found in conjugated glucuronic acids. Consequent upon the discovery of this nucleotide, the source of glucuronic acid could be traced back to glucose, and thus, for the biogenesis of glucuronic acid, any substance which could be converted into glucose or glycogen could, in the normal course of

UDP - Glucuronic acid

metabolism, be also converted into conjugated glucuronic acid. In fact earlier work [61, 69, 122, 141] had shown that lactate, pyruvate, glycerol, glucose and glucogenetic amino acids, but not glucuronic acid itself, could be precursors of the carbohydrate moiety of conjugated glucuronides. The formation of glucuronides takes place according to the following series of reactions:

precursors ———→ glycogen ———→ glucose-1-phosphate
$\underset{\textit{triphosphate}}{\textit{uridine}}$
————————→ uridine diphosphate glucose $\xrightarrow{\textit{oxidation}}$ UDP-glucuronic acid
$\underset{\textit{substance}}{\textit{glucuronidogenic}}$
————————→ β-glucuronide + uridine diphosphate   (4)

The reactions of special interest here are the last two.

The conversion of UDP-glucose to UDP-glucuronic acid is a two-step DPN-linked oxidation which is catalysed by UDP-glucose dehydrogenase, an enzyme which is found in the particle-free supernatant of liver homogenates. In this oxidation the primary alcohol group of the glucose residue is converted into a carboxyl group:

$$R—CH_2OH + 2DPN \xrightarrow{\textit{dehydrogenase}} R—COOH + 2DPNH \qquad (5)$$

The dehydrogenase which has been purified from calf liver[195] and from pea seedlings,[194] has a strict specificity for UDP-glucose, for UDP-galactose is not a substrate for the enzyme. Furthermore, the enzyme catalyses the two possible steps in the oxidation (theoretically the reaction should go via an intermediate aldehyde), for the steps are not separable and no intermediate has yet been found. Such enzymes which catalyse a 4-electron oxidation are rare. Like many other pyridine nucleotide-linked dehydrogenases, UDP-glucose-dehydrogenase is inhibited by incubating it with certain metal chelating agents.[173]

The last step in glucuronide synthesis is the enzymic transfer of the glucuronyl residue from UDP-glucuronic acid to the glucuronyl acceptor or foreign compound:

$$RXH + UDP—C_6H_9O_6 \xrightarrow{\textit{transferase}} RX—C_6H_9O_6 + UDP \qquad (6)$$

(where X = O or N and probably also S)

The enzyme catalysing this reaction is a UDP-glucuronic acid transglycosylase (glucuronyl transferase or UDP-transglucuronylase), and *in vitro* studies have shown that natural and foreign phenols, alcohols, steroids, carboxylic acids and aromatic amines can act as acceptors of the glucuronyl residue[62] (see ref. 173 for further references). The enzyme is located in the microsomal particles of liver homogenates, but at present it is not known whether one enzyme or a number of different enzymes are needed to synthesize various types of glucuronides. However, there is evidence that in mouse liver *o*-aminophenol and *p*-nitrophenol may not necessarily be conjugated with glucuronic acid by the same enzyme. [192] The natural conjugated glucuronides are of the β configuration, whereas the glucuronide link in UDP-glucuronic acid is of the α type. A Walden inversion therefore takes place when glucuronic acid is transferred from UDP-glucuronic acid to an acceptor.

C. *Zoological Distribution of Glucuronide Synthesis*

Glucuronide formation occurs in most mammals, birds, amphibia and probably reptiles, but not in insects [175] and fishes. This statement, however, is subject to certain exceptions. Let us consider first of all the mammals. The synthesis has been shown to occur in man, monkey, dog, rabbit, hamster, rat, mouse, guinea pig, sheep, cattle, pig (see ref. 188 for references) and in marsupials such as the opossum and koala bear. [89, 90] In the domestic cat, glucuronide formation is poorly developed and only occurs to a minor extent compared with other mammals. This has been shown with the intact animal [153] and with tissue slices. [66, 87] Now deficiency in glucuronide formation can be due to a defect in either reaction 5 or reaction 6 above, that is lack of formation of UDP-glucuronic acid or inability to transfer glucuronic acid to the acceptor, due to relative inactivity or deficiency of glucuronyl transferase. In the cat, reaction 5 occurs in both the liver and kidney, but the extent of reaction 6 is almost negligible in these tissues. [63, 66, 87] With birds, glucuronide formation has been shown to occur in all species so far examined, namely, the domestic hen, turkey, goose, duck, domestic pigeon, wood pigeon, dove, carrion crow and parrot; [5] it also occurs in pigeon-liver homogenates. [59] In the amphibia, the conjugation has been observed in frogs (*Rana pipiens*), toads (*Bufo marinus*) and salamanders, [130] but not in tadpoles of frogs and toads. Regarding reptiles, the evidence is limited and uncertain. It is probable that the tortoise, [173] the grass snake (*Natrix*) and the green lizard (*Lacerta*) [173] are capable of forming glucuronides. Insects apparently do not synthesize glucuronides but form glucosides instead (see Section III). According to Maickel, Jondorf and Brodie [130] living fishes (goldfish and perch) are incapable of forming glucuronides, but trout (*Salmo faria*) [67] the chinook salmon (*Oncorhynchus tschawytscha*) [205] and the cod (*Gadus callarias*) [67] are reported to contain UDP-glucuronic acid. Glucuronide formation does occur in trout-liver homogenates, but the transferase is thermolabile and glucuronide formation in such preparations occurs much less readily at 37° than at 22°. [67] In the livers of newborn animals such as man, mouse, guinea pig and rabbit, glucuronide synthesis is at a low level, but this is not true for neonatal rats whose livers are more active in this respect than those from the adult animals. [64]

The occurrence of chrysin and quercetin glucuronides in *Scutellaria* and *Phaseolus vulgaris*, respectively,[119] suggests the possibility of glucuronyl transfer in plant tissues. However, there is at present no evidence that this occurs generally in plants except possibly to special aglycones[65] (see Section III).

III. GLUCOSIDE CONJUGATION

Glucuronide conjugation has not been observed in insects[175] although these organisms are able to detoxicate phenols which they partly convert into β-glucosides.[139, 170, 171] The glucuronide mechanism of mammals is thus replaced by a glucoside mechanism in insects. The details of this mechanism in insects have not been fully worked out. However, it has been shown that the glucose donor is uridine diphosphate glucose and that the probable reaction is

$$\text{UDP-glucose} + \text{phenol} \rightarrow \text{phenol } \beta\text{-glucoside} + \text{UDP} \qquad (7)$$

The reaction has been shown to occur in the fat body of the locust (*Schisto-cerca cancellata*)[201] and the hepatic caecum of the cockroach (*Periplaneta americana*).[65] UDP-glucuronic acid is not utilized by cockroach hepatic caecum and this is in keeping with the absence of glucuronide synthesis in insects. Glucoside conjugation has been observed in a number of species of Coleoptera, Hemiptera, Lepidoptera and Orthoptera.

Glucoside formation from foreign compounds in plants has been known since 1938 when Miller[136] showed that ethylene chlorohydrin was converted into 2-chloroethyl-β-D-glucoside in gladiolus corms. Several authors have shown that the glucose donor in the formation of phenolic and ester glucosides by plants is UDP-glucose.[45, 65, 97, 178] Plant tissues apparently do not utilize UDP-glucuronic acid[65, 217] except possibly in special cases. Chrysin and quercetin glucuronides occur in *Scutellaria* (skullcap) and *Phaseolus vulgaris* (French bean) respectively, and it appears probable that these plants are not only able to form glucosides as in other plants, but also to carry out glucuronyl transfer to specific aglycones.

IV. HIPPURIC ACID SYNTHESIS

The conversion of benzoic acid to hippuric acid in the animal body has been known for a long time and the first proof that this biosynthesis occurred was provided in 1842 by Keller.[109] The formation of hippuric acid is essentially the synthesis of a peptide bond and is a characteristic biochemical reaction of aromatic acids:

$$\text{Ar-COOH} + \text{NH}_2\text{-CH}_2\text{COOH} \rightarrow \text{Ar-CO-NH-CH}_2\text{COOH} \qquad (8)$$

A. *Types of Acids Conjugating with Glycine*

Conjugation with glycine is potentially a reaction of all carboxylic acids. However, most aliphatic acids are readily oxidized in the body and glycine conjugation of an aliphatic acid is rarely observed. The following types of acids have been observed to undergo conjugation with glycine:

(a) aromatic acids, both carbocyclic and heterocyclic,
(b) substituted acetic acids, where one of the substituents is aromatic,
(c) 3-arylpropionic acids (one case known),
(d) β-substituted acrylic acids, and
(e) certain steroid acids.

Examples of these acids are given in Table 4.

B. *Enzymic Mechanism of Hippuric Acid Synthesis*

The synthesis of hippuric acid occurs only in the liver and kidney in rat, rabbit and ox, and in some species such as the dog, only in the kidney. The process, which requires coenzyme A (CoA—SH), is located in the mitochondria† and occurs in three steps. [109, 129, 163]

$$\text{Benzoic acid} + \text{ATP} \rightarrow \text{benzoyl-adenylate} + \text{pyrophosphate} \qquad (9)$$

$$\text{Benzoyl-adenylate} + \text{CoA—SH} \rightarrow \text{benzoyl-CoA} + \text{adenylic acid} \quad (10)$$

$$\text{Benzoyl-CoA} + \text{glycine} \rightarrow \text{hippuric acid} + \text{CoA—SH} \qquad (11)$$

The first two steps result in the activation of benzoic acid, whereby benzoyl-adenylate or adenosine 5′-phosphobenzoate is formed as an intermediate. The activation is catalysed by the enzyme, octanoic thiokinase, to which the benzoyladenylate is firmly attached. Benzoic acid and other aromatic acids are thus activated by means of the same fatty acid-activating enzyme which normally activates fatty acids containing 4 to 12 carbon atoms. Reaction 11 is catalysed by glycine N-acylase [167] which is specific for acylating glycine and no other amino acid, although it will catalyse the conversion of a number of aliphatic acyl thioesters of CoA which contains 2 to 10 carbon atoms, into acylglycines.

C. *Zoological Distribution of Hippuric Acid Synthesis*

Conjugation with glycine has been found with all mammals so far tested including man, dog, cat, rat, rabbit, mouse, cattle, goat, sheep, pig, monkey, guinea pig, horse, camel and elephant. Amongst birds, it occurs in the pigeon family (domestic pigeon, wood-pigeon and dove), [5] but not in common domestic birds such as the hen, goose, duck and turkey. It is also

† Conjugation of cholic acid with glycine to give glycocholic acid occurs in liver microsomes. [39]

TABLE 4. TYPES OF ACIDS FORMING GLYCINE CONJUGATES

$$\text{Reaction: R—COOH} \xrightarrow{\text{glycine}} \text{R—CO—NHCH}_2\text{—COOH}$$

(a) *Aromatic*	*Example*	*R—COOH*
Carbocyclic	Benzoic acid	[benzene ring]—COOH
Heterocyclic	Nicotinic acid	[pyridine ring]—COOH
(b) *Substituted acetic acid* Monosubstituted (arylacetic acids)	Phenylacetic acid	[benzene ring]—CH₂—COOH
Disubstituted	Hydratropic acid	[benzene ring]—CH(CH₃)—COOH
(c) *β-Substituted propionic* *acid*	β-o-Tolylpropionic acid	[benzene ring with CH₃]—CH₂—CH₂—COOH
(d) *Substituted acrylic* *acids* β-Monosubstituted carbocyclic	Cinnamic acid	[benzene ring]—CH=CH—COOH
Heterocyclic	Furylacrylic acid	[furan ring]—CH=CH—COOH
β-Disubstituted	β-Methylcinnamic acid	[benzene ring]—C(CH₃)=CH—COOH
α, β-Disubstituted	Phellandric acid (4-Isopropylcyclohex-1- ene-carboxylic acid)	[structure of 4-isopropylcyclohex-1-ene-carboxylic acid]
(e) *Steroid acids*	Cholic acid Deoxycholic acid	

claimed to occur in certain reptiles (alligators, tortoises, turtles)[173] and in frogs. Glycine conjugation also occurs in insects[74] including the locust, housefly, silkworm, mosquito and rice moth. Fish and marine invertebrates do not appear to have been examined. Glycine conjugation thus seems to have a relatively wide zoological distribution and is found in most species examined except certain birds in which it is replaced by ornithine conjugation.[154] Hippuric acid synthesis is at a lower level in late fetal and early newborn rats.[33]

V. MERCAPTURIC ACID SYNTHESIS

Mercapturic acids are derivatives of N-acetyl-L-cysteine which are formed and excreted when aromatic hydrocarbons and halogenated or nitro aliphatic and aromatic hydrocarbons are administered to animals. They were discovered in 1879 independently by Baumann and Preusse[12] and by Jaffe[99] in the urine of dogs fed bromobenzene and chlorobenzene, respectively.

A. *Types of Compounds Forming Mercapturic Acids*

Mercapturic acids are S-aryl- or S-alkyl-N-acetylcysteines with the general formula (R = aryl or alkyl group):

$$R—S—CH_2—CH—COOH$$
$$\underset{NH—COCH_3}{|}$$

They are formed when the following types of compounds are administered to animals:

(a) aromatic hydrocarbons,
(b) halogenated aromatic hydrocarbons,
(c) halogenated paraffins,
(d) ω-halogenated alkylbenzenes,
(e) halogenated nitrobenzenes,
(f) nitroparaffins,
(g) esters of alkylsulfonic acids,
(h) aromatic amines, and
(i) carbamic ester, particularly urethane.

The overall reaction in the biosynthesis of these compounds is,

$$R—X + HS—CH_2—CH(COOH)NH—COCH_3 \rightarrow$$
$$R—SCH_2CH(COOH)NH—COCH_3 \quad (12)$$

which is, in effect, the replacement of the group X in the foreign compound by an acetylcysteyl group. Thus, the nature of R and X is of importance in the structural requirements for a compound to participate in mercapturic acid synthesis. Up to the present, four kinds of group X are known to be replaced by the acetylcysteyl residue, namely, hydrogen, halogen, nitro, and methane-sulphonoxy ($CH_3—SO_3$). Examples are given in Table 5.

TABLE 5. Types of Compounds forming Mercapturic Acids *in vivo*

Type of compound	Example	Formula	Group replaced by acetylcysteyl residue	Mercapturic acid ($-S-R'$ = acetylcysteyl residue)	Ref.
(a) Aromatic hydrocarbon	Benzene	[benzene ring]	H	[phenyl]$-S-R'$	(218)
(b) Halogenated aromatic hydrocarbon	Chlorobenzene	[chlorobenzene, Cl]	H	[Cl-phenyl]$-S-R'$	(99)
(c) Halogenated paraffin	Bromopropane	C_3H_7Br	Br	C_3H_7-S-R'	(81)
(d) ω-Halogenated alkylbenzene	Benzyl chloride	[benzene]CH_2Cl	Cl	[benzene]CH_2-S-R'	(190)
(e) Halogenated nitrobenzene	(a) p-Fluoronitrobenzene	[benzene, F, NO_2]	F	[benzene, NO_2]$-S-R'$	(38)
	(b) Pentachloronitrobenzene	[benzene, CL CL NO_2 CL CL]	NO_2	[benzene, CL CL CL CL]$-S-R'$	(15)

(f) Nitroparaffin	Nitrobutane	$C_4H_9NO_2$	NO_2	C_4H_9—S—R'	(9)
(g) Alkyl sulphonic ester	Ethyl methanesulphonate	CH_3—SO_3—C_2H_5	CH_3SO_3	C_2H_5—S—R'	(151)
(h) Aromatic amine	Aniline	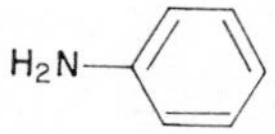 H_2N-⟨benzene ring⟩	H	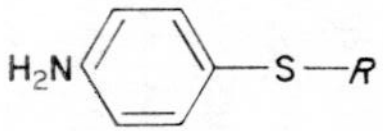 H_2N-⟨benzene ring⟩—S—R	(26)
(i) Carbamic ester	Urethane	$NH_2COOC_2H_5$	NH_2	C_2H_5O—CO—S—R	(28)

$$R' = CH_2CH-CO_2H$$
$$\quad\ \ \ | $$
$$\quad\ \ NH-COCH_3$$

Further comments are necessary regarding Table 5 because not all aromatic hydrocarbons and their halogenated derivatives form mercapturic acids. Benzene, naphthalene and anthracene are converted into mercapturic acids *in vivo*, but polycyclic hydrocarbons such as 3,4-benzopyrene and 1,2,5,6-dibenzanthracene and alkylbenzenes such as toluene are not. Again, *o*- and *m*-dichlorobenzenes form mercapturic acids, but *p*-dichlorobenzene does not. Tetra-, penta- and hexa-chlorobenzenes do not form mercapturic acids, neither does 1,3,5-trichlorobenzene, but 1,2,3- and 1,2,4-trichlorobenzene are mercapturic acid formers to a minor extent (see ref. 102 for references).

B. *Mechanism of Mercapturic Acid Formation*

The mechanism of mercapturic acid formation is almost fully known. However, from the point of view of mechanism, there are two types of mercapturic acid to be considered, namely those formed by apparent replacement of hydrogen and those formed by replacement of halogen or nitro groups in the foreign compound (see Table 5). Mercapturic acids of the first type are now regarded as artifacts derived from precursors known as premercapturic acids, whilst those of the second type appear to be true metabolic products, and the overall mechanism of the formation of these types can be written,

$$\text{foreign compound} \xrightarrow{\text{\textit{in vivo}}} \text{premercapturic acid} \xrightarrow{\text{\textit{in vitro}}} \text{mercapturic acid,} \quad (13)$$

and

$$\text{foreign compound} \xrightarrow{\text{\textit{in vivo}}} \text{mercapturic acid} \quad (14)$$

For the moment let us consider the direct formation of mercapturic acid *in vivo*, reaction 14, and leave the problem of premercapturic acids until later. Bray, Franklin and James[35] had proposed that mercapturic acids may be synthesized in three steps, but recent work has shown that there are actually four, namely,

(i) conjugation of the precursor with glutathione,

(ii) removal of the glutamyl group from the glutathione conjugate by transpeptidation to give an S-arylcysteinylglycine,

(iii) hydrolysis of the S-arylcysteinylglycine by peptidases to give an S-arylcysteine, and

(iv) acetylation of the S-substituted cysteine to a mercapturic acid.

These steps may be formulated as follows (where X in ArX is a halogen or a nitro group):

$$\text{ArX} + \text{HS—CH}_2\text{—}\overset{\displaystyle \text{CO—NHCH}_2\text{CO}_2\text{H}}{\underset{\displaystyle \text{NH—CO(CH}_2)_2\text{CH(NH}_2)\text{CO}_2\text{H}}{\text{CH}}}$$

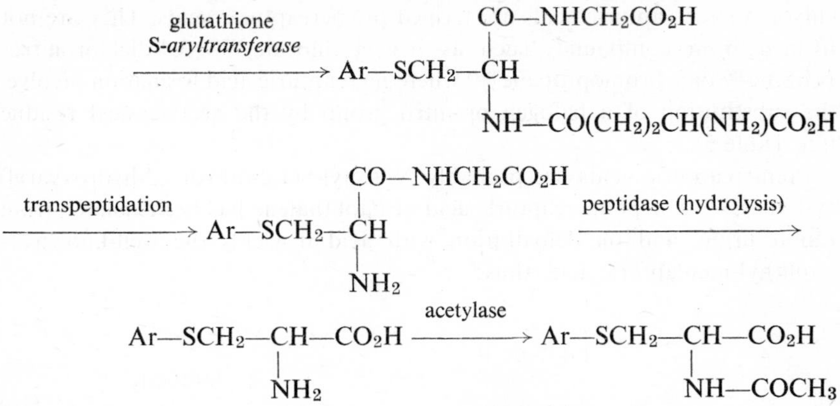

$$\xrightarrow[\text{S-}aryltransferase]{\text{glutathione}} \quad \begin{array}{c} CO-NHCH_2CO_2H \\ | \\ Ar-SCH_2-CH \\ | \\ NH-CO(CH_2)_2CH(NH_2)CO_2H \end{array}$$

$$\xrightarrow{\text{transpeptidation}} \quad \begin{array}{c} CO-NHCH_2CO_2H \\ | \\ Ar-SCH_2-CH \\ | \\ NH_2 \end{array} \quad \xrightarrow{\text{peptidase (hydrolysis)}}$$

$$\begin{array}{c} Ar-SCH_2-CH-CO_2H \\ | \\ NH_2 \end{array} \xrightarrow{\text{acetylase}} \begin{array}{c} Ar-SCH_2-CH-CO_2H \\ | \\ NH-COCH_3 \end{array}$$

$$(15)$$

The activity of the enzyme system catalyzing the first step above has been described by Grover and Sims. [82] It occurs in the supernatant of rat liver homogenates and is concerned with the direct conjugation of aromatic halogen and nitro compounds with glutathione. This enzyme, glutathione S-aryltransferase, does not appear to be involved in the conjugation of glutathione with aliphatic halogen compounds which appear to require a different enzyme. [107]

The next two steps have been discussed by Boyland [23] who points out that all the types of compounds given in the above scheme are to be found in the bile of rats dosed with naphthalene. γ-Glutamyl-S-cysteine derivatives, which could be formed if the glutathione conjugate lost glycine instead of glutamic acid in the second step, have never been detected. The second step appears to be a transfer of glutamyl residues by transpeptidation and is not a hydrolysis. It occurs in kidney homogenates in the rat for only kidney and pancreas can transfer glutamyl residues in this species but in the guinea-pig and rabbit it could also occur in the liver, which in these species can transfer glutamyl residues.

The third step in which a glycine residue is lost from the dipeptide, S-arylcysteinylglycine, is probably carried out by hydrolysis by peptidases occurring in rat kidney, liver or pancreas. The fourth step is supported by many observations on the acetylation of S-arylcysteines *in vivo*, and *in vitro* with rat and rabbit liver slices. [36]

The existence of premercapturic acids was first shown in 1957. [30, 112] Compounds which apparently form mercapturic acids by substitution of hydrogen by the acetylcysteyl group (see Table 5) include benzene, chloro-, bromo- and iodo-benzene, naphthalene and anthracene. Now when these compounds are administered to animals, they are converted into substances which are excreted in the urine and which are converted into mercapturic acids only after the urine has been treated with acid. These acid-labile precursors of mercapturic acids are termed premercapturic acids. They are not formed from compounds such as benzyl chloride, [113] 3,4-dichloronitrobenzene [9] or 1-bromopropane [81] where mercapturic acid formation involve the substitution of a halogen or nitro group by the acetylcysteyl residue (see Table 5).

Premercapturic acids are probably N-acetyl-S(1,2-dihydro-2-hydroxyaryl) cysteines. [29] The premercapturic acid of naphthalene has been isolated from rabbit urine, and on dehydration with acid it yields the well-known 1-naphthyl-mercapturic acid, thus:

$$(16)$$

Premercapturic acids, like mercapturic acids, are formed via glutathione conjugates, but there are, apparently, five steps *in vivo* in their formation instead of four. Compounds such as iodobenzene, naphthalene and phenanthrene will only conjugate with glutathione in liver preparations if a microsomal oxidase system and TPNH are present. From a study of the metabolism of epoxides, such as 1,2-epoxy-1,2,3,4-tetrahydronaphthalene, Boyland [23] has concluded that the first step in premercapturic acid formation is epoxidation. The epoxide then reacts with glutathione in a reaction catalysed by "glutathione S-epoxidetransferase" which is present in rat or ferret liver supernatants, to form the glutathione precursor of the premercapturic acid. [31] "Glutathione S-epoxidetransferase" is different from "glutathione S-aryltransferase", for amongst other things it is readily inactivated at pH 5 whereas the aryltransferase is not. It appears that the first product in the metabolism of naphthalene, for example, is probably 1,2-dihydronaphthalene-1,2-epoxide, which then conjugates with glutathione to form S-(1,2-dihydro-2-hydroxy-1-naphthyl)glutathione. This then undergoes, in order, glutamyl transfer, hydrolysis by peptidases and acetylation to the premercapturic acid. The conversion of the premercapturic acid to the corresponding mercapturic acid does not occur enzymically but is achieved by dilute acid. These reactions are summarized as follows:

Glutamyl transfer
peptide hydrolysis,
acetylation (3 steps)
$\longrightarrow$

$$
\begin{array}{cc}
\text{IV} & \text{V} \\
\text{Premercapturic} & \text{Mercapturic} \\
\text{acid} & \text{acid}
\end{array}
$$

(17)

Epoxidation also appears to be a metabolic reaction of bromo-paraffins, for 1-bromobutane not only gives a butylmercapturic acid by direct replacement of the bromo group, but also N-acetyl-S-2-hydroxybutylcysteine which may be formed via 1,2-butyleneoxide. [102]

It appears, therefore, that the first two types of compounds (a and b) listed in Table 5 give rise to premercapturic acids *in vivo*, and the other types of compounds (c to g) give rise to ordinary mercapturic acids. However, this may not be the whole story for types c to g, for Thompson and Young[200] have recently shown that bromoethane forms not only ethylmercapturic acid in rats, but also ethylmercapturic acid sulfoxide:

$$C_2H_5Br \rightarrow C_2H_5-S-CH_2CH(NHAc)CO_2H +$$

$$C_2H_5-SO-CH_2CH(NHAc)CO_2H \qquad (18)$$

The significance of sulfoxides in the metabolism of mercapturic acid-formers is as yet unknown and it will be particularly interesting to know at what stage the oxygen atom is added to the sulfur.

C. *Zoological Distribution of Mercapturic Acid Formation*

The number of species in which mercapturic acid formation has been investigated is small. The synthesis occurs in man, rat, pig, rabbit, dog, cat, mouse and hamster. Guinea pigs, however, form little mercapturic acid compared with the other mammals listed. [35, 37] This species is unable to acetylate S-aryl- or S-alkyl-cysteines, although sulfanilamide is readily acetylated both by the intact animal and by liver slices. The guinea pig therefore has a defect in the last stage of mercapturic acid synthesis. However, Bray, Franklin and James [35] have reported that guinea pigs do not excrete S-substituted cysteines or S-substituted N-acetylcysteines in response to the administration of various precursors, but that they do excrete an unidentified sulphur-containing metabolite in response to bromobutane. At present, the reason for the low or negligible output of mercapturic acid in guinea pigs in response to the administration of various precursors, including S-substituted cysteines, is unknown. The occurrence of mercapturic acid formation in locusts after the administration of C^{14}-chlorobenzene has been shown by Gessner and

Smith. [77] These insects, however, excrete more S-(chlorophenyl)cysteine than mercapturic acid. Cysteine conjugation may also occur in houseflies in response to the insecticide, benzene hexachloride. [32]

VI. ORNITHURIC ACID SYNTHESIS

The synthesis of ornithuric acid (N:N'-dibenzoylornithine) in hens was discovered by Jaffé in 1877, [98] and it appears to be a process found only in certain birds and reptiles. When benzoic acid is fed to hens, it is partly excreted as dibenzoylornithine; in fact about 40–50 per cent of 250 mg/kg doses of benzoic acid is excreted by hens as ornithuric acid, the rest forming benzoylglucuronide. [5] Compounds such as benzamide and cyclohexane-carboxylic acid which are metabolized to benzoic acid in hens, are also partly excreted as ornithuric acid. [5, 6] The types of compounds which conjugate with ornithine in hens are aromatic acids, such as benzoic and substituted benzoic acids, heterocyclic aromatic acids, such as furoic acid and nicotinic acid, and phenylacetic acid and its nuclear substituted derivatives. No other acids (cf. hippuric acid synthesis) have been tested.

A. Enzymic Mechanism of Ornithine Conjugation

Ornithine conjugation is a typical peptide synthesis probably requiring CoA as a cofactor, but the enzymic details of the process are not fully known. It occurs only in the kidney of hens and not in the liver. The process consists of the addition of two benzoyl groups to L-ornithine thus:

$$
\begin{array}{ccc}
NH_2 & & NH-CO-C_6H_5 \\
| & & | \\
(CH_2)_3 & & (CH_2)_3 \\
| & \xrightarrow{2\ C_6H_5-COOH} & | \\
CH-NH_2 & & CH-NH-CO-C_6H_5 \\
| & & | \\
COOH & & COOH
\end{array}
\tag{19}
$$

It is not known, however, whether the two benzoyl groups are added to ornithine simultaneously or separately. If they were added separately, then N^2- or N^5-monobenzoyl-L-ornithine could be an intermediate in ornithuric acid synthesis.

The enzyme system for the synthesis of ornithuric acid has been located in the particulate fraction of chicken kidney homogenates. [125] These homogenates in the presence of magnesium ions and ATP can benzoylate both N^2- and N^5-monobenzoylornithines, but benzoylation occurs much more readily with the N^5-derivative. It would thus appear that the α-amino group of L-ornithine is more readily benzoylated by kidney homogenates than δ-amino group. Chicken liver homogenates are inactive.

B. Zoological Distribution of Ornithuric Acid Synthesis

Although ornithuric acid synthesis was discovered as a conjugation mechanism in hens and then assumed to be a mechanism for the detoxication of aromatic acids in birds generally, it has been found recently that the process only occurs in certain types of birds. Some birds form hippuric acids, whereas others form neither ornithuric acid nor hippuric acid in response to ingested benzoic acid. [5] Domestic birds such as the hen, goose, duck and turkey convert aromatic acids into ornithine conjugates, but the pigeon family (columbiformes), on the other hand, form exclusively glycine conjugates. In fact, it has been shown that pigeon kidney slices form glycine conjugates, whereas kidney slices from the chicken, goose, duck or turkey do not. [162] The carrion crow and parrot form neither glycine nor ornithine conjugates *in vivo*. In reptiles, which are believed to have evolved from a common ancestor with birds, ornithine conjugation seems to be general (see Table 6), although tortoises and alligators form both ornithine and glycine conjugates from aromatic acid precursors. [173] It has been suggested that ornithine conjugation usually occurs in animals in which uric acid is a major nitrogenous waste. Glycine is necessary for the synthesis of uric acid and this could be a reason for utilization of ornithine rather than glycine for the detoxication of aromatic acids. All the species listed in Table 6 have a uricotelic metabolism, [7] but not all of them form ornithine conjugates. The alligators and tortoises form both glycine and ornithine conjugates, but these species are partly uricotelic and partly ureotelic. It appears at present that ornithine conjugation and uricotelism are not as closely related as formerly suggested.

VII. GLUTAMINE CONJUGATION

Conjugation with glutamine is a process of relatively restricted occurrence, because it has been found to occur only in man and members of the primate sub-order *Anthropoidea*. Furthermore, it appears to be confined to arylacetic acids including phenylacetic, indolyl-3-acetic and 3,4-dihydroxy-5-methoxy-phenylacetic acid, the last being a metabolite of mescaline. [83] The conjugation occurs in man, [198, 199] chimpanzee, [146] rhesus monkey, [212] baboon (*Papio anubis vigilis*), red monkey (*Erythrocebus patas*) and the African monkeys, *Cercopithecus aethiops* and *neglectus*. [144] It probably does not occur in the primate sub-order *Prosimii* of which the ring-tailed lemur (*Lemur catta*) and *Galago senegalensis* have been tested. [144] It does not occur in the dog, rat, rabbit, horse, sheep or hen, for these mammals form the glycine conjugate and the hen, the ornithine conjugate of phenylacetic acid. Glutamine conjugation consists of the combination *in vivo* of phenylacetic acid (or indoleacetic acid) with L-glutamine:

$$
\begin{array}{ccc}
\text{CONH}_2 & & \text{CONH}_2 \\
| & \text{C}_6\text{H}_5\text{CH}_2\text{COOH} & | \\
\text{CH}_2 & \xrightarrow{\hspace{2cm}} & \text{CH}_2 \\
| & & | \\
\text{CH}_2 & & \text{CH}_2 \\
| & & | \\
\text{CHNH}_2 & & \text{CH—NH—COCH}_2\text{C}_6\text{H}_5 \\
| & & | \\
\text{COOH} & & \text{COOH}
\end{array} \quad (20)
$$

x

The process was discovered in man in 1914 by Thierfelder and Sherwin [198, 199] and in the chimpanzee in 1936 by Power. [176] The conjugate,

TABLE 6. ORNITHINE AND GLYCINE CONJUGATION IN BIRDS AND REPTILES

	Ornithine conjugation	Glycine conjugation
BIRDS		
Galliformes		
Domestic fowl	+	−
Turkey	+	−
Anseriformes		
Muscovy duck	+	−
Goose	+	−
Columbiformes		
Domestic pigeon	−	+
Wood pigeon	−	+
Barbary dove	−	+
Passeriformes		
Carrion crow	−	−
Psittaciformes		
Grey African parrot	−	−
REPTILES		
Ophidia		
Grass snake (*Natrix natrix*)	+	−
Lacertilia		
Green lizard (*Lacerta viridis*)	+	−
Slow worm (*Anguis fragilis*)	+	−
Chelonia		
Tortoise (*Testudo gracea*)	+	+
Water tortoise (*Emys orbicularis*)	+	+
Crocadilia		
Alligator (*Caiman sp.*)	+	+

phenylacetylglutamine, occurs normally in human urine (output, 250–500 mg/day) [188] and the phenylacetyl residue probably arises from phenylalanine. Patients with phenylpyruvic oligophrenia excrete increased amounts of this compound. [126, 167]

The mechanism of the formation of this conjugate is analogous to that of hippuric acid and has been shown to consist of three steps. [137]

$$\text{Phenylacetate} + \text{ATP} \rightarrow \text{phenylacetyl-AMP} + \text{pyrophosphate} \qquad (21)$$

$$\text{Phenylacetyl-AMP} + \text{CoA—SH} \rightarrow \text{phenylacetyl-CoA} + \text{AMP} \qquad (22)$$

$$\text{Phenylacetyl-CoA} + \text{L-glutamine} \rightarrow$$
$$\text{phenylacetylglutamine} + \text{CoA—SH} \qquad (23)$$

These three steps occur in human liver and kidney homogenates and in preparations of human liver mitochondria. Rat liver homogenates do not form phenylacetylglutamine but convert phenylacetic acid into phenylacetyl-glycine under the appropriate conditions. The process in the human tissues is essentially the activation of phenylacetate and then the transfer of the phenylacetyl group to L-glutamine. The two-step activation of phenylacetate is analogous to the activation of fatty acids and in fact occurs in beef liver mitochondria as well as in human. The difference between human liver and the liver of other species is in the last step (reaction 23). The reaction between phenylacetyl-CoA and glutamine is apparently catalysed specifically by human tissues, and it appears that human liver and kidney contain an acylating enzyme which is not present in other species. Glutamic acid cannot replace glutamine in the enzyme system. Moldave and Meister [118] also found that indolylacetyl-CoA and p-hydroxyphenylacetyl-CoA were not active in acylating glutamine in the presence of the partly purified acylating enzyme, although glutamine was readily acylated by phenylacetyl-CoA under the same conditions. In this connection it is interesting to note that Jepson [103] has shown that indolylacetylglutamine is a metabolite of indolyl-3-acetic acid in man, but that Thierfelder and Sherwin [198, 199] claimed that p-hydroxyphenylacetic acid was excreted unchanged by man.

VIII. SULFATE CONJUGATION

The formation of mono-esters of sulfuric acid in the body was discovered in 1876 by Baumann [10, 11] who isolated potassium phenyl sulfate from the urine of a patient treated with carbolic acid. Baumann also showed that potassium phenyl sulfate was much less toxic than the phenol from which it was derived. Esters of this type became known as ethereal sulfates, and many of them occur naturally in urine, e.g. urinary indican or potassium indoxyl sulfate.

Phenyl hydrogen   Urinary indican
sulphate

A. Types of Compounds Conjugating with Sulfate

Sulfate conjugation is commonly associated with phenols, but other types of hydroxy compounds can form ethereal sulfates *in vivo*. Compounds containing hydroxyl, amino, or sulfhydryl groups are potentially capable of conjugating with sulfate in the body and the overall reaction of sulfate conjugation is,

$$R—X—H + HOSO_2—OH \rightarrow R—X—SO_2—OH + H_2O \qquad (24)$$

where X is O or NH and possibly S.

This means that sulfate conjugation could result in the formation of ordinary sulfate esters ($RO-SO_3H$), sulfamates or N-sulfates ($RNH-SO_3H$), and possibly thiosulfates ($R-S-SO_3H$). The sulfate conjugation of phenols is well-known and well-documented.[210, 211] The conversion of simple aliphatic alcohols into monoalkyl sulfates has been demonstrated recently[19, 208] when it was shown that rats injected with S^{35}-labeled sodium sulfate immediately after oral doses of alcohols from methyl to amyl, excreted the corresponding labeled mono-alkyl sulfates. Conjugation of the alcohols also occurred *in vitro*, when the alcohols and S^{35}-labeled sulfate were incubated with the particle-free supernatant from the centrifugation of rat liver homogenates, fortified with ATP and Mg ions.

The formation of sulfamates or N-sulfates has only been observed in the rabbit and the rat, and only with the aromatic amines, aniline and naphthylamine.[27, 173] These compounds have the general formula, $Ar-NHSO_3H$. The sulfamates of 1- and 2-naphthylamine and of aniline have been found in the urine of rabbits after administration of the appropriate amines. Sodium 2-naphthylsulfamate has in fact been isolated from urine,[27] and the amount of phenylsulfamic acid excreted by rabbits receiving oral doses (0·2 g/kg) of C^{14}-aniline has been shown by isotope dilution to be about 7–8 per cent.[173] In the rat, aniline and 1-naphthylamine do not produce the corresponding sulfamates in the urine, although 2-naphthylsulfamic acid is excreted to a small extent after 2-naphthylamine. Sulfamates have not been detected in the urine of guinea pigs and hamsters after administration of the above amines, and 4-aminodiphenyl does not apparently form a sulfamate in rats or rabbits.

The formation of S-sulfates or thiosulfates, i.e. $Ar-S-SO_3H$, has not yet been proved unequivocally. Thiophenol administered to rabbits causes an increased output of ethereal sulfate, but no proof has been put forward to show that the ester sulfate is an S-sulfate.[178]

The types of compounds which undergo sulfate conjugation *in vivo* are listed in Table 7.

B. *The Enzymic Synthesis of Ethereal Sulfates*

The synthesis of ethereal sulfates *in vitro* was first demonstrated unequivocally by De Meio and his co-workers[57-60] who found that an activated form of sulfate was formed in liver tissue. Sulfate was then transferred from the active form to an acceptor such as a phenol, under the influence of a transferring enzyme, i.e. a sulfotransferase. Lipmann and his co-workers[129] identified active sulfate as 3′-phosphoadenosine-5′-phosphosulfate (PAPS). Sulfate activation and subsequent formation of ester sulfate occurs in three steps each catalysed by specific enzymes, thus:

$$ATP + SO_4^{2-} \xrightleftharpoons{ATP\text{-}\textit{sulfurylase}}$$
$$\text{adenosine-5′-phosphosulfate} + \text{pyrophosphate} \quad (25)$$
$$\text{(APS)}$$

$$\text{APS} + \text{ATP} \xrightarrow{\text{APS-}phosphokinase}$$

$$\text{3'-phosphoadenosine-5'-phosphosulfate} + \text{ADP} + \text{H}^+ \quad (26)$$
$$\text{(PAPS)}$$

$$\text{PAPS} + \text{ROH} \xrightarrow{\text{}sulfokinase}$$

$$\text{ROSO}_3^- + \text{3'-phosphoadenosine-5'-phosphate} \quad (27)$$

PAPS

TABLE 7. TYPES OF COMPOUND CONJUGATING WITH SULFATE

Hydroxy compounds	Example	Ethereal sulfate
Phenols		
(i) Carbocyclic	Phenol	
(ii) Heterocyclic	3-Hydroxycoumarin	
(iii) Steroidal	Oestrone	
Alcohols		
(i) Primary aliphatic	Ethanol	C_2H_5O—SO_3H
(ii) Secondary steroidal	Dehydroepiandro-sterone	
Amino compounds		
Aromatic amine	Aniline	

These reactions occur in the particle-free supernatant fraction of liver homogenates. [8, 150, 167, 213] The first reaction is catalysed by ATP-sulfurylase, but the equilibrium constant of this reaction is approximately 10^{-8}, so that the amount of APS (sulfuryl adenylate) formed is extremely small. However, APS-phosphokinase catalyses the phosphorylation of APS in the 3-position of the ribose residue and the energetics of reaction 26 are such that reaction 25 is pulled towards formation of APS. The enzyme ATP-sulfurylase is highly specific for ATP, but APS-phosphokinase is active with other nucleotide triphosphates. The major metabolic role of PAPS formed in reaction 26 is to provide sulfate for transfer to various acceptors. The type of acceptor to which sulfate can be transferred is determined by the nature of the transferring enzyme (sulfotransferase or sulfokinase) of reaction 27 and a number of different sulfokinases appear to exist. PAPS in the presence of the appropriate enzyme can transfer sulfate to phenols, phenolic steroids, 3-β-hydroxysteroids, aromatic amines, choline and mucopolysaccharides.

The enzyme for sulfate transfer to phenols, phenol sulfokinase, has a maximum activity at about pH 7–8. [80] It does not catalyse sulfate transfer to the steroids or to the secondary alcohol, cyclohexanol. Salicylic acid, which does not form an ethereal sulfate *in vivo*, is not sulphated by means of the enzyme, but methyl salicylate, which forms an ethereal sulfate in the intact animal, is sulfated in the enzyme system. Phenol sulfokinase also catalyses the transfer of sulfate from p-nitrophenyl sulfate to other phenols, but this transfer depends on the presence of 3-phosphoadenosine-5'-phosphate which acts as a coenzyme. The phenol sulfokinase activity of rabbit liver extracts can be separated from steroid sulfokinase activity by ammonium sulfate fractionation. [140] The steroid sulfokinase fraction thus obtained appears to be a mixture of enzymes, for Nose and Lipmann [140] found evidence that the sulfokinase catalysing the formation of the sulfate esters of 3-β-hydroxy steroids, such as dehydroepiandrosterone, epiandrosterone and pregnenolone, was different from that required to sulfate other steroids, such as androsterone (a 3-α-hydroxysteroid). The distribution of steroid sulfokinase is different from that of phenol sulfokinase, for the former is found only in the liver, whereas the latter has been found in liver, kidney and intestine.

Tyrosine-O-sulfate is a normal constituent of urine, but unlike other phenols, tyrosine itself is not sulfated in mammalian liver. [168] However, if the carboxyl group of tyrosine is blocked as in tyrosine ethyl or methyl ester, then sulfate formation occurs. This suggests that tyrosine-O-sulfate originates *in vivo* from a bound form of tyrosine, and not from free tyrosine.

Another interesting ethereal sulfate is choline sulfate which occurs in fungi. [107] The formation of this sulfate involves transfer of sulfate from PAPS to choline under the influence of a specific transferase, choline sulfokinase, which is not active in sulfating p-nitrophenol. [187, 185] Studies on choline sulfate synthesis have been carried out mainly with *Aspergillus sydowi*[107] but it also occurs in a large number of other fungi. [185]

The formation of sulfamates has also been observed in the soluble fraction of liver. In rabbit and guinea pig liver extracts, both 1- and 2-naphthylamines are converted into the corresponding sulfamates. Aniline also forms a sulfamate in these preparations but less readily than the naphthylamines. Rat liver extracts are less active than those of the rabbit and guinea pig, for they form sulfamates from the naphthylamines but not from aniline. [155] Sulfate for the synthesis of the sulfamates is derived from PAPS and its transfer to arylamines is catalysed by arylamine sulfokinase which differs from phenol sulfokinase in that it requires magnesium ions for optimal activity whereas the phenol sulfokinase does not. [156]

C. *Zoological Distribution of Sulfate Conjugation*

Sulfate conjugation of phenols is a widely distributed biochemical process and has been found to occur in most mammalian species. It is a well-known reaction in man, dog, rabbit, rat, cat, horse, cow and guinea pig. It occurs also in the goat [79] and pig, but according to Stekol [189] and Coombs and Hele [52] the pig does not form ethereal sulfates readily. There is also some evidence that ethereal sulfates are formed in whales. [166] Birds have not been investigated apart from the hen which is known to form ethereal sulfates readily from phenols. [4] Amphibious animals such as frogs, toads and salamanders form ethereal sulfates, but fish apparently do not, [41] although the sulfate of a steroid alcohol, scymnol sulfate, has been found in elasmobranch fish bile. [87]† It seems likely also that molluscs can form sulfates because certain of them contain indoxylsulfate and 5-bromoindoxylsulfate. *Murex trunculus* contains both these sulfates, whilst *Murex brandaris* contains only the bromo derivative. [20] The occurrence of sulfate conjugation in insects has been shown by Smith [172] in four species of Orthoptera (stick insect, and migratory, red and desert locusts), in two species of Coleoptera (cellar beetle and the larva of mealworm), in two species of Lepidoptera (poplar and privet hawk moth) and one species of Hemiptera (the water boatman). The conjugation may also occur in spiders. The existence of the mechanism in fungi is suggested by the occurrence of choline sulfate in a number of fungi and of the sulfate of fusarubin in *Fusarium solanum* cultures. [158] The wide distribution of some form of sulfate conjugation suggests that it may be the most primitive of the detoxication mechanisms.

IX. THIOCYANATE SYNTHESIS

Hydrogen cyanide and the alkali cyanides are highly toxic substances, but the body has an enzymic mechanism for the detoxication of cyanide. This

---

† Sulfate esters of complex alcohols have also been found in fish bile, such as the cyprinol sulfate of carp[85] and the sulfate of an unknown alcohol in the hagfish.[86]

consists of a synthesis which converts the cyanide ion into the relatively non-toxic thiocyanate ion, the overall reaction in the synthesis being,

$$CN^- + S \rightarrow S\text{—}CN^-. \tag{28}$$

Since thiocyanate is some hundred times less toxic than cyanide, the process is a true detoxication. The process was first observed in 1894 by S. Lang [117] and the enzymic aspects were first studied in 1933 by K. Lang [116] who named the enzyme concerned, rhodanese.

The thiocyanate synthesis is specific for the cyanide ion, and organic cyanides or nitriles only give rise to thiocyanate in the body if they are first broken down to cyanide ions. There is no example known of an organic cyanide being converted into an organic thiocyanate *in vivo* and such a reaction is unlikely because it would involve putting a sulphur atom between the organic radicle and the nitrile group (i.e. R—CN → R—S—CN).

Organic cyanides which give rise to thiocyanate in the urine are usually toxic and it is probable that their toxicity is due to the intermediate formation of the cyanide ion:

$$R\text{—}CN \rightarrow CN^- \rightarrow S\text{—}CN^- \tag{29}$$

A list of such cyanides is given in Table 8 and it is to be noted that most of these compounds are readily hydrolysed to HCN. This table also includes compounds which do not yield thiocyanate *in vivo*. The latter compounds contain cyano groups which are relatively stable and such compounds are usually not highly toxic. However, because the cyano group is not released *in vivo*, it does not follow that the compound is not toxic, for the compound may be toxic in its own right. Most of the compounds in list A of Table 8 are relatively toxic, with toxic doses of about 100 mg/kg or less, with the exception of acetonitrile which is much less toxic than the others (see Spector's handbook for toxic doses). [183] This may be related to the rate of hydrolysis to cyanide ions in the body, for if the rate of formation of CN^- is less than the rate at which detoxication to SCN^- takes place, a compound may not be highly toxic despite the fact that it is releasing CN^- *in vivo*. In list B of Table 8, benzonitrile (lethal dose, LD, for rabbits, 200 mg/kg) is much more toxic than cyanacetic acid (LD for rabbits, 2000 mg/kg) [95] but there is no evidence that either of them release CN^- *in vivo*. Presumably benzonitrile is toxic *per se*.

A. *The Enzymic Conversion of Cyanide to Thiocyanate*

Rhodanese, the enzyme which catalyses the conversion of cyanide to thiocyanate, is widely distributed in the body, the highest concentration occurring in the liver. [88] Some animals appear to have more rhodanese activity than

TABLE 8. TYPES OF ORGANIC CYANIDES FORMING THIOCYANATE *in vivo*

A. *Those forming thiocyanate*	
Alkyl cyanides	*Formula*
Acetonitrile	CH_3—CN
Acrylonitrile	CH_2=CH—CN
Arylalkyl cyanides	
Benzyl cyanide	$C_6H_5CH_2CN$
p-Chlorobenzyl cyanide	p-Cl—$C_6H_4CH_2CN$
Cyanohydrins	
Acetone cyanohydrin	$(CH_3)_2$—C(OH)CN
Mandelonitrile	C_6H_5—CHOH—CN
Cyanohydrin glycosides	
Linamarin	$(CH_3)_2$—$C(OC_6H_{11}O_5)$—CN
Lotaustralin	CH_3 >$C(OC_6H_{11}O_5)$—CN C_2H_5
Dinitriles	
Malononitrile	CN—CH_2—CN
Cyanogen	CN—CN
Cyanogen halides	
Cyanogen chloride	Cl—CN
Cyanogen iodide	I—CN
B. *Those which do not form thiocyanate*	
Aryl cyanides	
Benzonitrile	C_6H_5—CN
Tolunitrile	$CH_3C_6H_4CN$
Cyanobenzoic acid	COOH—C_6H_4—CN
Alkyl cyanides	
Cyanacetic acid	CN—CH_2—COOH
Hydracrylonitrile	CN—CH_2—CH_2OH

others, for the livers of rats, rabbits and cows appear to be more active than those of men, dogs and monkeys. Rhodanese activity is widely distributed amongst species and, besides the animals already mentioned, it has been reported in cats, goats, horses, sheep, hens, fish, squids and even in some insects and plants. The enzyme is highly specific and catalyses the transfer of sulfur from thiosulfate to the cyanide ion thus:

$$CN^- + S_2O_3^= \rightarrow SCN^- + SO_3^= \tag{30}$$

It was believed that the enzyme could utilize colloidal sulfur,[116] but Sörbo[181] has shown that purified preparations of rhodanese are without effect on the reaction between colloidal sulfur and cyanide. Under appropriate conditions colloidal sulfur reacts spontaneously with cyanide, and the apparent catalytic effect of liver and muscle preparations and blood serum on this reaction may be due to a facilitation of contact between free sulfur in the solid state and cyanide. [176] The reaction between colloidal sulfur and cyanide is unlikely to be of normal physiological significance, since colloidal sulfur has never been found in the tissues. Apart from thiosulfate, the enzyme can utilize thiosulfonates, especially alkanethiosulfonates, as sulfur donors. The reaction catalyzed is

$$R—SO_2—S^- + CN^- \rightarrow R—SO_2^- + SCN^- \tag{31}$$

and the products are thiocyanate and a sulfinate. *In vitro* experiments have shown that a thiosulfonate, such as sodium ethanethiosulfonate ($C_2H_5SO_2SNa$), is many times more active than thiosulfate. *In vivo*, however, sodium ethanethiosulfonate had little antidotal effect against cyanide in rabbits, but when injected simultaneously with rhodanese it raised the LD_{50} of injected cyanide 10 to 15 times. [49] Thiosulfonates, however, have not been found in body tissues. [164]

Rhodanese has no action on organically bound cyanide as found in acetonitrile or cyanacetic acid, but it may react with complex-bound cyanide such as cyanide-inhibited cytochrome oxidase. Apart from the cyanide ion, it has been found that rhodanese can also catalyse the transfer of sulfur to sulfite with the formation of thiosulfate, but sulfite is much inferior to cyanide as an acceptor of sulfur. [177] The possibility that lipoic acid, which contains a disulfide group, may be a coenzyme for rhodanese has been suggested [57] and this is of interest since Sörbo [180, 181] has shown that rhodanese contains an active disulfide group through which sulfur from thiosulfate is transferred to cyanide:

$$E\big\langle\begin{smallmatrix}S\\|\\S\end{smallmatrix} + S—SO_3^{2-} \longrightarrow E\big\langle\begin{smallmatrix}S—S—SO_3^-\\S^-\end{smallmatrix} + CN^- \longrightarrow E\big\langle\begin{smallmatrix}S\\|\\S\end{smallmatrix} + SO_3^{2-} + SCN^- \tag{32}$$

The source of sulfur for cyanide detoxication *in vivo* is believed to be thiosulfate which is a normal metabolic product in higher animals. In man, the excretion of thiosulfate is 2–17 mg of S per day and it is derived from the sulfur-containing amino acids of dietary protein. [76] The mechanism of thiosulfate formation is at present not known. However, it could be derived from cysteine or cystine for the administration of S^{35}-cystine with cyanide produces labeled thiocyanate. [214] Sörbo [178] has suggested a mechanism using established reactions whereby two molecules of cysteine could give rise to one molecule of thiosulfate *in vivo*. It is known that cysteine can be converted into β-mercaptopyruvate by transamination [132] (see Chapter 1). Furthermore, cysteine can produce sulfite via cysteine sulfinate, [46] and sulfite can be converted into thiosulfate by transfer of sulfur from mercaptopyruvate. [178] An outline of the possible reactions is shown opposite:

$$\begin{array}{ccc}
\text{CO}_2\text{H(NH}_2\text{)CH} \text{—CH}_2\text{SH} & & \text{CO}_2\text{H(NH}_2\text{)CH} \text{——CH}_2\text{SH} \\
\downarrow & & \\
\text{CO}_2\text{H(NH}_2\text{)CH} \text{——CH}_2\text{SO}_2^- & & \downarrow \\
\downarrow & & \\
\text{SO}_3^= & & \text{CO}_2\text{H——CO——CH}_2\text{SH} \\
& \searrow \quad \text{S}_2\text{O}_3^= \quad \swarrow &
\end{array} \tag{33}$$

One of the apparent contradictions of the biochemistry of cyanide is the very high toxicity of cyanide despite the fact that rhodanese occurs abundantly in the body, and thiosulfate does appear to be available. According to Himwich and Saunders [88] the liver of a dog contained enough rhodanese to detoxicate about 4 kg of cyanide in 15 min and the skeletal muscle enough to deal with 1·8 kg of cyanide. Furthermore, Vassel, Partridge and Crossley [207] have shown that well-fed male dogs excrete 50–125 mg of thiosulfate-S and the females 2–15 mg in 24 hr. Yet the oral lethal dose of KCN for dogs is 1·6 mg/kg with death taking place in 155 min or 5·3 mg/kg with death in 21 min. [78] The intravenous lethal dose of NaCN for dogs is given by Lawrence [118] as 2·8–29·0 mg/kg depending upon the rate of injection.

X. METHYLATION

Methylation is a reaction of considerable interest in connection with the metabolism of adrenaline, but it is also a biological reaction of many foreign compounds. In fact it was first discovered as a reaction of foreign compounds in 1887 by His [91] who observed that when pyridine acetate was administered to dogs, a small proportion (4 per cent of the dose) was excreted as the N-methyl-pyridinium ion:

$$\tag{34}$$

Within the last decade or so, methylation has been shown to be a reaction of phenols, especially catechols and possibly of thiols.

A. *Types of Compounds Undergoing Biological Methylation*

Methylation is a potential reaction of compounds containing amino or substituted amino groups (—NH_2, —NHR, —NR—R′), hydroxyl (—OH), or sulfhydryl (—SH) groups. Amongst aliphatic amino compounds, methylation has been observed only with natural amines (primary, secondary and tertiary) such as noradrenaline, glycocyamine (guanidoacetic acid) and dimethylaminoethanol, which are methylated respectively to adrenaline, creatine and choline. These are examples of the following methylation reactions:

$$R—NH_2 \rightarrow R—NH—CH_3 \tag{35}$$

$$R(R′)NH \rightarrow R(R′)N—CH_3 \tag{36}$$

$$R(R′)(R″)N \rightarrow R(R′)(R″)\overset{+}{N}—CH_3 \tag{37}$$

Methylation is not a general reaction of aromatic amines. Aniline for example is not methylated in the rabbit, [173] but according to Miller and Miller [135] certain amines containing azo groups such as 4-aminoazobenzene may undergo methylation to a minor extent *in vivo*. Methylation is also a minor reaction of tertiary nitrogen of heterocyclic aromatic rings as in pyridine, quinoline and isoquinoline, with the formation of quaternary bases. It is also a reaction of the imido nitrogen of the imidazole ring of histamine and possibly of imidazole-4-acetic acid.

Methylation of hydroxy compounds has been observed so far only with certain phenols. The occurrence of 2-methoxyestrone as a metabolite of estradiol in man [114] and of the 8-methyl ether of xanthurenic acid in normal human urine [147] suggests that isolated phenolic hydroxyl groups can be methylated *in vivo*. The only known case of the methylation of a foreign monohydric phenol is that of 4-hydroxy-3,5-di-iodobenzoic acid. [128] The natural monophenol, serotonin, is also methylated to melatonin (N-acetyl-7-methoxytryptamine) in the pineal gland. [3] O-Methylation is usually a reaction of catechol derivatives and polyhydric phenols containing two vicinal hydroxyl groups, and it is confined to one of the hydroxyl groups. The orientation of O-methylation is discussed below.

There is one authentic example of the S-methylation of a foreign compound and this was observed by Sarcione and Sokal [159] who found that 6 per cent of small doses (6 mg) of thiouracil injected into rats is excreted as 2-methylthiouracil.

Table 9 shows a list of compounds which undergo biological methylation.

B. *Enzymic Mechanism of Methylation*

The main souce of methyl groups for the methylation of various compounds *in vivo* is methionine. Methylation, however, requires an active form of

TABLE 9. TYPES OF COMPOUNDS UNDERGOING BIOLOGICAL METHYLATION

Type of compound	Example	Methylated metabolite
N-METHYLATION *Amines (Aliphatic)* (a) Primary	Noradrenaline	
(b) Secondary	Guanidoacetic acid	
(c) Tertiary	Dimethylaminoethanol	
N-Heterocycles (a) Tertiary N	Pyridine	
(b) Secondary N	Histamine	
O-METHYLATION *Phenols* (a) Monohydric	4-Hydroxy-3,5-di-iodo-benzoic acid	
(b) Dihydric	3,4-Dihydroxybenzoic acid	
(c) Trihydric	3,4,5-Trihydroxybenzoic acid	
S-METHYLATION Thiopyrimidine	Thiouracil	

methionine, which is formed enzymically from methionine and ATP. This active form of methionine is a sulfonium compound containing adenosine and methionine, [93] namely S-adenosylmethionine:

S – Adenosylmethionine

Under the influence of a methyltransferase, S-adenosylmethionine transfers its methyl group to an appropriate acceptor and is itself converted into S-adenosylhomocysteine. The steps from methionine to the methylated product are the following:

$$\text{ATP} + \text{methionine} \rightarrow \text{S-adenosylmethionine} + \text{phosphate} +$$
$$\text{pyrophosphate} \qquad (38)$$

$$\text{S-Adenosylmethionine} + \text{acceptor} \xrightarrow{\text{transferase}} \text{methylated acceptor} +$$
$$\text{S-adenosylhomocysteine} \qquad (39)$$

Specificity in methylation depends on the nature of the transferase and several of these enzymes are known to exist, which catalyse various O-methylations, N-methylations and S-methylations.

Different N-methyl transferases have been described for the conversion of noradrenaline to adrenaline, of guanidoacetic acid to creatine and of histamine to 1-methylhistamine. The noradrenaline N-methyl transferase occurs in the adrenal medulla and requires magnesium ions and glutathione for its activity. [111] It catalyses the reaction 35 in noradrenaline. Guanidoacetate-N-methyl transferase which methylates guanidoacetic acid does not require magnesium ions but needs an SH compound for its full activity. [77] It catalyses the reaction 36. Imidazole-N-methyl transferase catalyses the methylation of the ring-NH group of histamine, but it requires neither magnesium ions nor glutathione for its full activity. It is widely distributed and is found in most animal tissues. [42] (The reactions of these three enzymes are described in Table 9). However, it is not known whether these enzymes can methylate foreign compounds similar to their natural substrates.

Two O-methyl transferases have been described, namely catechol-O-methyl transferase [2] and hydroxyindole-O-methyl transferase. [3] The first enzyme monomethylates catechol and its derivatives *in vitro*, but not monohydric phenols. Axelrod and Tomchick [2] tested twelve catechols, both natural and foreign, including d- and l-adrenaline, l-noradrenaline, dopamine, dl-3,4-dihydroxyamphetamine and epinine (3,4-dihydroxyphenyl-ethyl methylamine), and all were methylated by the enzyme system. Furthermore, methylation occurs at the m- or p-hydroxyl, but not in both simultaneously. [55] The enzyme requires for its full activity Mg ions which can be replaced by other divalent cations such as Co^{++} and Mn^{++}, but it is not stimulated by glutathione. It is, however, inhibited by sulfhydryl binding agents such as p-chloromercuribenzoate. It is a widely distributed enzyme occurring in most tissues (especially liver and kidney), except skeletal muscle, and in all the animals (rat, cow, pig, mouse, guinea pig, cat, rabbit and man) so far tested.

The second enzyme, hydroxyindole-O-methyl transferase, is highly localized and appears to occur only in the pineal gland. [3] It is probably concerned with the synthesis of the hormone, melatonin, which blocks the action of the melanocyte-stimulating and adrenocorticotropic hormones. Melatonin is N-acetyl-7-methoxytryptamine which is formed from serotonin thus:

$$\text{Serotonin} \xrightarrow{+ \; CH_3CO} \text{N-acetylserotonin} \xrightarrow{+ \; CH_3} \text{melatonin} \qquad (40)$$

Unlike the catechol enzyme, the hydroxyindole-O-methyl transferase has no requirement for Mg ions and it is not present in liver or kidney. Homogenates of cow pineal gland methylate N-acetylserotonin in the presence of S-adenosylmethionine to melatonin. Serotonin is also methylated to 5-methoxytryptamine by these homogenates but only at one-tenth the rate at which acetylserotonin is methylated. This suggests that serotonin is first acetylated and then methylated to melatonin.

$$(41)$$

N - Acetylserotonin   Melatonin

Recently Axelrod and Daly [1] have found an enzyme in the posterior pituitary gland of mammals (man, cow, rabbit and rat) which methylates water to form methanol. This enzyme converts S-adenosylmethionine into methanol and S-adenosylhomocysteine.

C. Orientation of Methylation of Polyhydric Phenols

Two types of phenols have been investigated from the point of view of orientation of methylation, namely the 4-substituted catechols and some derivatives of pyrogallol.

In the case of the catechols, mono-methylation has been shown to occur *in vitro* and *in vivo* at the m- and p-hydroxyl group, but not at both simultaneously.

$$(42)$$

In vitro, catechol-O-methyl transferase affects both *m*- and *p*-methylation of 3,4-dihydroxyacetophenone (R = $COCH_3$), 3,4-dihydroxyphenylmethylcarbinol (R = CHOH—CH_3), dopamine (R = $CH_2CH_2NH_2$), adrenaline (R = CHOH—CH_2—$NHCH_3$), noradrenaline (R = CHOH—CH_2—NH_2), adrenalone (R = $COCH_2NH$—CH_3) and arterenone (R = $COCH_2NH_2$). [78, 169] When the side chain R is unsaturated, there is nearly as much *m*- as *p*-methylation, but when R is saturated *p*-methylation is much less than *m*-methylation. In the intact rat and mouse, there is no *p*-methylated derivative of adrenaline excreted, only the *m*-compound, metanephrine. With adrenalone, arterenone and 3,4-dihydroxyacetophenone, both *m*- and *p*-methyl ethers are excreted by rats, but the amount of *p*-isomer is very much less than the *m*-isomer excreted. The amount of *p*- and *m*-methyl ethers excreted probably depends on the speed at which *p*- and *m*-methylation and *p*- and *m*-demethylation occur, for the *p*-methyl ethers are more readily demethylated than the *m*-isomers, by the demethylase of the liver. One methyl ether could therefore be converted into the other *in vivo* thus:

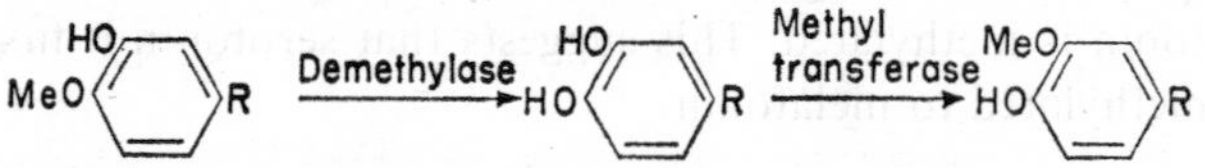

$$(43)$$

In fact the monomethyl ethers of 3,4-dihydroxyacetophenone (i.e. acetovanillone and acetoisovanillone) are interconvertible to a small extent in the rat (about 0·5 per cent *m* to *p*, and 5–6 per cent *p* to *m*), but this is not true for the methyl ethers of adrenaline, for paranephrine is not converted to metanephrine *in vivo*.

Pyrogallol derivatives offer three hydroxyl groups for methylation *in vivo*. 2,3,4- and 3,4,5-Trihydroxybenzoic acids are methylated in rats and rabbits at the central hydroxyl group. [18]

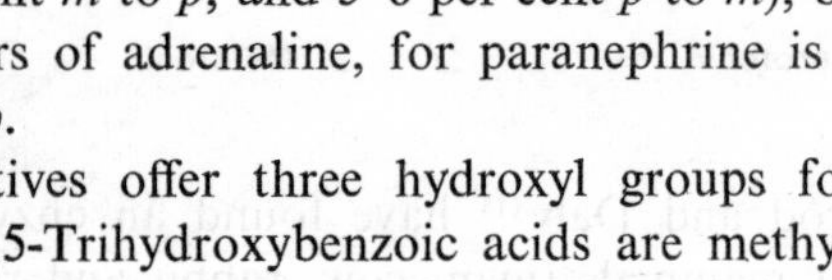

Gallic acid   VII

$$(44)$$

Pyrogallol 4-carboxylic acid

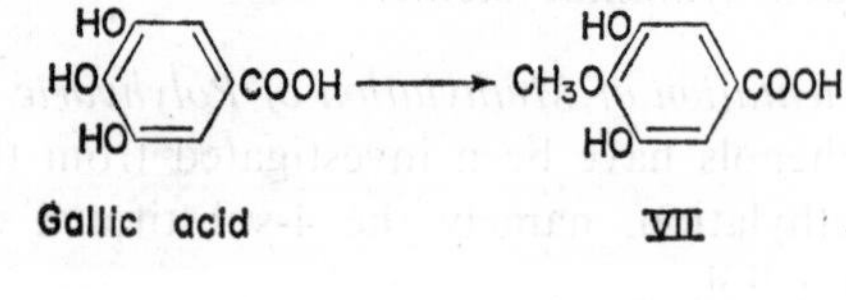

$$(45)$$

The two mono-methyl ethers of gallic acid behave differently. The 4-methyl ether (VII) contains no vicinal pair of hydroxyl groups and when administered to rats and rabbits it is excreted unchanged. It is in fact the metabolite of gallic acid.

The 3-monomethyl ether (VIII), however, gives rise to two methylated metabolites, namely 3-hydroxy-4,5-dimethoxybenzoic acid (IX) and 4-hydroxy-3,5-dimethoxybenzoic acid (X).

$$(46)$$

The metabolism of the 3-methyl ether of gallic acid.

D. *Zoological Distribution of Methylation*

O-Methylation of catechols occurs in man, rat, cow, pig, mouse, guinea pig, cat and rabbit, but no other species have been recorded. [2, 16] Methylation of pyridine derivatives has been reported in the dog, pig, goat, rabbit, frog, rat, mouse, hamster, turtle, hen, and man. According to Baxter and Mason [13] the rat does not methylate pyridine, but Lin and Johnson [120] have shown that the rat can methylate a derivative of pyridine, namely nicotinic acid, quite extensively.

XI. ACETYLATION

Acetylation is a biochemical reaction of compounds containing amino groups, and as far as *foreign* compounds are concerned, no other type of group undergoes this reaction. Amongst *natural* compounds, acetylation of the hydroxyl group, as in the conversion of choline to acetylcholine, and of the sulfhydryl group as in the conversion of CoA into acetyl CoA, is known to occur. As far as amino compounds are concerned, the process consists of the conversion of a primary amine into a monoacetyl compound, thus:

$$R—NH_2 \rightarrow R—NH—COCH_3 \qquad (47)$$

Di-acetylation to form compounds of the type, $R—N(COCH_3)_2$, has not been observed. Acetylation has not been found with secondary amines, $R(R')NH$, or with amides, $R—CO—NH_2$. The first observation of the acetylation of a foreign compound in the animal body was made in 1893 by Cohn [51] who found that m- and p-nitrobenzaldehyde were excreted as the corresponding acetamidobenzoic acids, the route being,

$$NO_2—C_6H_4—CHO \rightarrow NH_2—C_6H_4—COOH \rightarrow$$
$$CH_3CONH—C_6H_4—COOH \quad (48)$$

A. Types of Compound Undergoing Acetylation in vivo

The immediate source of acetyl groups in biological acetylation is acetyl CoA. This compound [121] contains an S-acetyl group (CoA—S—COCH$_3$), [127] and under the influence of the appropriate enzymes, the acetylases, the acetyl group can be transferred to a variety of acceptors which include a number of natural and foreign compounds. Here we shall be concerned

TABLE 10. TYPES OF COMPOUNDS ACETYLATED in vivo

Type	Example	Acetyl derivative
Primary amine Natural (R—CH$_2$NH$_2$)	Histamine	
Amino acid ω-Phenyl-substituted Ar—(CH$_2$)$_n$CH(NH$_2$)COOH	γ-Phenyl-α-amino-butyric acid	
S-Arylcysteine Ar—S—CH$_2$CH(NH$_2$)COOH	S-Phenylcysteine	
Hydrazine derivatives Hydrazine (NH$_2$NH$_2$)	Hydrazine	CH_3CO——NH——NH——$COCH_3$
Hydrazide (R'—CONHNH$_2$)	Isonicotinyl-hydrazide	
Sulfonamide (Ar—SO$_2$NH$_2$)	Sulfanilamide	
Aromatic amine Unsubstituted (Ar—NH$_2$)	Aniline	
Substituted (R—Ar'—NH$_2$)	Sulfanilamide	

mainly with the foreign compounds which, as far as acetylation is concerned, are all amino compounds of one type or another (see Table 10).

An authentic example of the acetylation of a foreign aliphatic amine *in vivo* has not yet been found, although acetylation is a potential reaction of all aliphatic amines. However, acetylation of certain natural amines, such as histamine [197] and serotonin, [126] has been recorded. Amino sugars such as glucosamine and galactosamine are also known to be acetylated *in vivo*. In the case of histamine and serotonin, acetylation is a minor reaction, for the major route of metabolism of these compounds is by deamination. It seems likely, therefore, that foreign amines will be deaminated rather than acetylated *in vivo*, and if acetylation occurs, then it must be a minor reaction. However, the acetylation of other types of non-aromatic amino compounds has been recorded, namely the α-amino group in certain amino acids, the amino groups in hydrazine, the amino group in certain hydrazides and the sulfonamide amino group in sulfanilamide.

Acetylation is a reaction of certain unphysiological phenyl-substituted amino acids. In the homologous series $C_6H_5(CH_2)_nCH(NH_2)COOH$, phenylglycine ($n = 0$) and 2-amino-4-phenylbutyric acid ($n = 2$) are excreted as acetyl derivatives when administered to animals, but the natural L-phenylalanine ($n = 1$) is not acetylated. However, L-hexahydrophenylalanine, which is not a natural product, is acetylated in the dog, [14] as is also its homologue, 2-amino-4-hexahydrophenylbutyric acid. Another series of amino acids which are acetylated *in vivo*, are the derivatives of cysteine and homocysteine of the general formula, $Ar(CH_2)_n$—S—$(CH_2)_mCH(NH_2)COOH$ (where $n = 0$ or 1, and $m = 1$ or 2). It appears probable that any foreign amino acid may be excreted, in part, as an N-acetyl derivative.

Hydrazine is converted to 1,2-diacetylhydrazine, and the hydrazides acetohydrazide and isonicotinic hydrazide are acetylated *in vivo* [93, 127] When hydrazine is fed to rabbits, a small amount is excreted as diacetylhydrazine, but no monoacetylhydrazine is found. Monoacetylhydrazine is also converted to diacetylhydrazine in the rabbit, so that the route of metabolism by way of acetylation is,

$$NH_2—NH_2 \rightarrow CH_3CONH—NH_2 \rightarrow CH_3CONH—NH—COCH_3 \quad (49)$$

Diacetylhydrazine is of relatively low toxicity (intravenous LD_{50} 3000 mg/kg), but monoacetylhydrazine is appreciably toxic (intravenous LD_{50} 175 mg/kg) to mice. Diacetylation of hydrazine is thus necessary for its detoxication. In the case of isonicotinic hydrazide, monoacetylation converts it into a diacyl hydrazine, i.e. 1-acetyl-2-isonicotinyl hydrazine, which is less toxic than its precursor. It is also known that sulfanilamide is acetylated in the rat not only at the aromatic group but also at the sulfonamide group, [22] so that three acetyl derivatives are excreted, namely, N^4-acetyl-, N^1-acetyl- and N^1, N^4-diacetyl sulfanilamide, the last two being minor products.

$$NH\!-\!\!-COCH_3 \qquad\qquad NH_2 \qquad\qquad NH\!-\!\!-COCH_3$$

$$SO_2NH_2 \qquad\qquad SO_2NH\!-\!\!-COCH_3 \qquad SO_2NH\!-\!\!-COCH_3$$

$$\text{XI} \qquad\qquad\qquad \text{XII} \qquad\qquad\qquad \text{XIII}$$

B. Enzymic Mechanism of Acetylation

The acetyl group used in the acetylation of amines and other compounds in the body arises from metabolism generally, that is from carbohydrate, fat or protein sources. From carbohydrate, it is derived via pyruvate, from fat via the two carbon products of fatty acid oxidation and from protein via deaminized residues of amino acids. If these acetyl donors are represented by $CH_3CO\!-\!X$, and the compound acetylated HY, then the general reactions of acetylation are,

$$CH_3CO\!-\!X + CoA\!-\!SH \rightarrow HX + CoA\!-\!S\!-\!COCH_3 \qquad (50)$$

$$CoA\!-\!S\!-\!COCH_3 + HY \rightarrow CoA\!-\!SH + CH_3CO\!-\!Y \qquad (51)$$

Reaction 51 is catalysed by a transacetylase, and it is probable that more than one transacetylase occurs. [197] Acetylation of different groups probably requires different transacetylases. In fact, there is evidence that the enzyme catalysing the acetylation of glucosamine is different from that catalysing the acetylation of aromatic amines. The occurrence of different transacetylases is also supported by species differences in acetylation (see below).

C. Zoological Distribution of Acetylation

The occurrence of the acetylation of aromatic amines in various species of animals has been fairly extensively studied because the methods of detecting acetylation in such amines are fairly simple, but little has been done on the acetylation of other types of amino compounds for the opposite reason.

In mammals, acetylation of amino compounds appears to be general, but there are species differences in the type of amino compound acetylated. Thus, the dog is an animal which appears to be able to acetylate unphysiological amino acids but not aromatic amines. Most studies on the acetylation of aromatic amines have been carried out with sulfanilamide which is acetylated in man, cat, cow, horse, sheep, goat, monkey, mouse, rabbit, rat and guinea pig, but not in the dog including the Dalmatian coach hound. [131] This inability of the dog to acetylate the aromatic amino group, however, does not extend to foreign amino acids for cyclohexylalanine [14] is partly excreted by the dog as N-acetylcyclohexylalanine. A number of other amino acids are also acetylated in the dog including phenyl-substituted amino acids and aryl-cysteines. In the guinea pig we have an example of the opposite situation, for the guinea pig is able to acetylate aromatic amines but seems to have a defect in acetylating arylcysteines. Sulfanilamide is also readily acetylated by guinea pig liver slices, but S-(p-chlorophenyl)-L-cysteine and glucosamine are not. [35]

Acetylation of hydrazine and hydrazides has been shown to occur in man, [93] the rhesus monkey, [94] the rabbit, [127] and the rat, [56] but not in the dog. [127] It thus appears that the dog has a defect in acetylating hydrazine groups as well as aromatic amines.

Ability to acetylate aromatic amines has also been found amongst some of the lower animals. It occurs in the insects, namely the locust, [138] silkworm and waxmoth, [21] in three species of toad (*Bufo bufo, Scaphiopus holbrookii* and *Bufo valliceps*), [71] one frog (tree frog, *Hyla cinerea*), the dogfish [123] and the hen and pigeon [115] but not the green lizard, turtle or the frogs, *Rana pipiens* and *Rana catesbeiana*. [173, 71]

XII. MISCELLANEOUS CONJUGATION REACTIONS

From time to time, there have been reported isolated examples of conjugation reactions which appear to be unique for certain foreign compounds. Little is known about these reactions, and it is for future research to decide whether they are as unique as they appear to be. Three of these conjugations involve amino acids, one carbohydrate, one phosphoric acid and one involving possibly acetic acid. It is not known whether these conjugations have a species specificity, because an insufficient number of animals have been examined.

Serine Conjugation

When xanthurenic acid (4,8-dihydroxyquinoline-2-carboxylic acid) labeled with C^{14} is injected intraperitoneally or given by mouth to rats (dose 3·3 mg per rat), three radioactive metabolites appear in the urine. One of these is unchanged xanthurenic acid and the other two are ether glucuronides with serine attached to the carboxyl group of xanthurenic acid. The structures of these conjugates are shown below.

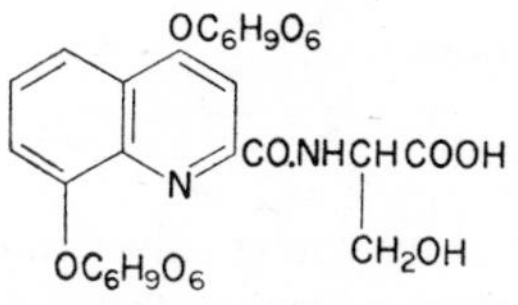

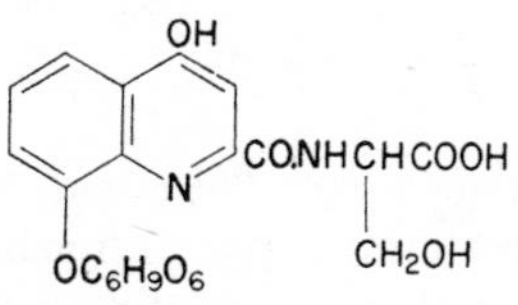

Both conjugates contain serine, but one is an 8-monoglucuronide and the other a 4,8-diglucuronide. [154] Both these serine conjugates are also excreted by vitamin B_6-deficient rats given 30 mg of L-tryptophan by mouth, so that they are formed not only from administered xanthurenic acid, but also from xanthurenic acid formed metabolically from tryptophan. As is well-known, xanthurenic acid excretion after administration of tryptophan is increased in B_6-deficiency. If xanthurenic acid and 1-C^{14}-serine are injected into rats, the serine conjugates in the urine are labeled. It is probable that rabbits also form a serine conjugate of xanthurenic acid. Apparently rabbits excrete only one metabolite besides xanthurenic acid; this metabolite is an ethereal sulfate which contains serine. Rothstein and Greenberg [154] suggest that this conjugate is similar to one of the conjugates excreted by rats (see formulae XIV and XV), but that the glucuronyl residue (or residues) is replaced by an ester sulfate group.

Glycyltaurine Conjugation in Cats

When quinoline-2-carboxylic acid (quinaldic acid) is administered to rats, it is excreted as might be expected as the glycine conjugate quinaldyl-glycine. [105] In cats, however, two-thirds of the administered acid is excreted as a strongly acidic compound which is quinaldylglycyltaurine. This peculiar conjugate is also a minor metabolite of kynurenic acid in the cat. [106]

Formylation

The presence of "active formyl" groups in tissues suggests that the formylation of foreign compounds is possible *in vivo* and that forms of metabolic acylation other than acetylation may exist. 2-Formamido-1-naphthyl hydrogen sulfate has now been found in the urine of rats and dogs as a minor metabolite of 2-naphthylamine. [25]

Peptide Conjugate of Phenothiazine

The anthelmintic, phenothiazine is excreted by young calves (6 weeks old) combined with a polypeptide containing six amino acids, four of which are tyrosine, arginine, glutamic acid and phenylalanine. [48]

Phosphate Conjugation in 2-Naphthylamine Metabolism

The occurrence of a phosphate conjugate in the urine of dogs dosed with 2-naphthylamine has been reported by Troll, Belman and Nelson. [202] This conjugate contains two molecules of 2-amino-1-naphthol to one of phosphoric acid and has been described as bis(2-amino-1-naphthyl) phosphate. Phosphate conjugates do not appear to be excreted by rabbits [202] or rats [24] injected with 2-naphthylamine. It is suggested [202] that this conjugate may be related to the occurrence of bladder cancer in dogs dosed with 2-naphthylamine, for the carcinogenic 2-amino-1-naphthol could be released in the bladder from the conjugate by urinary phosphatases.

Ribose Conjugation

When imidazole-4-acetic acid is administered to rats, it is excreted as an N-riboside. This riboside is also formed as a metabolite of histamine which is degraded to imidazole-4-acetic acid. In rats and mice the riboside is a major metabolite of small doses of histamine, whereas in cats and dogs it is a very minor metabolite. [165]

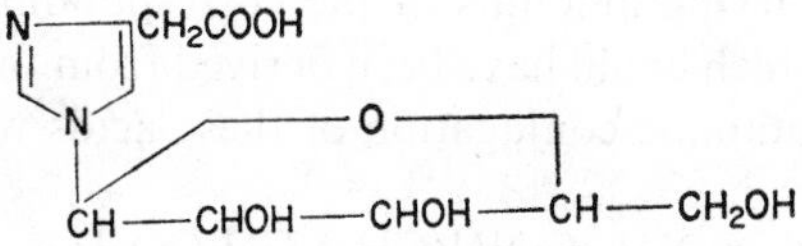

Ribose conjugate of imidazoleacetic acid

The Acrylic Acid Synthesis

This peculiar synthesis has only been found to occur with furfural. [101] When this aldehyde is fed to dogs and rabbits, it gives rise to three metabolites, namely, furoic acid, α-furoylglycine and furylacryloylglycine (furylacryluric acid, XVIII). The first two are expected metabolites of furfural, but the third one appears to be unique for furfural. It is possible that furfural (XVI) undergoes a condensation with acetic acid to yield furylacrylic acid (XVII) which then conjugates normally with glycine:

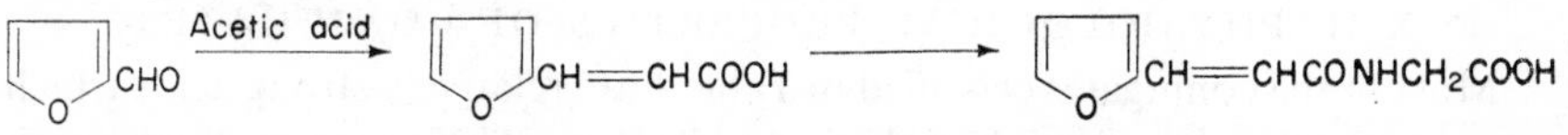

$$\tag{52}$$

The acrylic acid is not formed in hens [101] or in rats [145] and probably not in man. [204] Furylacryluric acid is also a metabolite in dogs of furylacrylic acid, furylpropionic acid and of furoylacetic acid. [75, 160] Presumably furylpropionic acid (XIX) and furoylacetic acid (XX) are metabolized to furylacrylic acid (XVII) by oxidation and reduction, respectively, but not by synthesis.

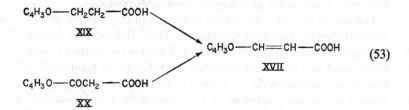

$$\text{(53)}$$

Arginine Conjugation

Aromatic acids are conjugated with glycine in most species (see p. 599) but in the arachnids glycine is apparently replaced by arginine. Three orders of the *Arachnida* have been examined by Hitchcock and Smith[92] namely ticks (*Boophilus decoloratus*, cattle tick), spiders (*Tegenaria* sp., house spider; *Epeira* sp. and *Agelena* sp., garden spiders) and harvestmen (*Mitopus* sp. and *Phalanqium* sp.) and all were found to convert benzoic acid, *p*-aminobenzoic acid, *p*-aminobenzoic acid and *p*-nitrobenzoic acid into the corresponding N^2-aroyl-L-arginines. In some of these species the aroylarginines were accompanied by varying amounts of the corresponding aroyl-glutamic acids and -glutamines, which could have been derived from the arginine derivatives, although direct glutamine conjugation of these acids was not ruled out.

$$\text{NH}_2\cdot\text{C}\cdot\text{NH(CH}_2)_3\text{CH}\cdot\text{CO}_2\text{H}$$

$$\underset{\text{NH}}{\|} \qquad \underset{\text{NHCO}\cdot\text{C}_6\text{H}_5}{|}$$

$$N^2\text{-Benzoylarginine}$$

Detoxication of Metals as Sulfides

This interesting mechanism occurs in the larvae of the clothes-moth (*Tineola biselliella*). Certain metal ions are highly toxic to insects but not the clothes-moth larvae, for these insects convert the metals into insoluble sulfides, apparently using for the purpose the hydrogen sulfide produced by the digestion of wool cystine in the midgut. [209]

XIII. PHYSIOLOGICAL PROPERTIES OF CONJUGATES

Most of the conjugates classified in Table 1 are relatively strong acids which are completely ionized at physiological pH values. The apparent dissociation constants of a number of these compounds have been measured, [152, 210] and the pK_a values of glucuronides are about 3·0–3·5, of glycine conjugates, 3·6–4·0, of mercapturic acids, 3·5–3·8 and ornithuric acid, 3·7. At pH 7, therefore, these conjugates are completely ionized. Ethereal sulfates are even stronger acids than glucuronides, and thiocyanic acid is a much stronger acid than hydrogen cyanide. Furthermore, when heterocyclic compounds such as pyridine and quinoline are methylated to quaternary bases, they are converted into strong bases which are highly ionized at physiological pH values. Acetylation also tends to produce more highly ionized products. It appears, therefore, that most of the conjugation reactions of mammals tend to produce highly ionized products which are readily excreted. Sperber [186, 187] has shown that glucuronides, ethereal sulfates, glycine conjugates, ornithuric acid, the strong base N-methylnicotinamide, and p-acetamidobenzoic acid (the conjugation product of p-aminobenzoic acid) are secreted by the renal tubules, and secretion by the renal tubules is the most rapid method of removing an unwanted compound from the blood. Most conjugated products are also less toxic than their precursors. It appears, therefore, that the function of the conjugation mechanisms is to convert the foreign compound and unwanted natural compounds into products which are non-toxic and which are rapidly removed from the body.

The Relationship between Conjugation and the Metabolism of Foreign Compounds Generally

When foreign compounds enter the body the majority of them are metabolized by oxidation, reduction, hydrolysis or synthesis (conjugation), or any combination of these four processes. The preceding paragraphs of this chapter have dealt specifically with the conjugations, but something must be said about the relationship of conjugation to the other three processes. There are many compounds, examples of which are listed in Tables 3–10, which are metabolized mainly by conjugations of various types. Thus, phenol is metabolized almost entirely by two conjugation mechanisms, namely glucuronide and ethereal sulfate formation. Conjugation, however, depends upon the compound possessing suitable chemical groupings, and should these be absent, then conjugation cannot occur. However, compounds which do not contain groups suitable for conjugation can acquire them by any of the other three processes, that is by oxidation, reduction or hydrolysis. In the metabolism of this type of compound, two phases are necessary, oxidation, reduction or hydrolysis occurring in the first phase and conjugation occurring in the second. Thus, benzene is oxidized in the body to phenol in the first phase of its metabolism, and then phenol is conjugated in the second, thus:

$$\text{Benzene} \xrightarrow{\text{oxidation}} \text{phenol} \xrightarrow{\text{conjugation}} \text{phenyl glucuronide and sulfate} \tag{54}$$

Chloral hydrate is reduced in the first phase to trichloroethanol and then conjugated to trichlorethyl glucuronide:

$$CCl_3\text{—}CH(OH)_2 \xrightarrow{\text{reduction}} CCl_3\text{—}CH_2OH \xrightarrow{\text{conjugation}}$$
$$CCl_3\text{—}CH_2O\text{—}C_6H_9O_6 \tag{55}$$

Procaine is hydrolyzed to *p*-aminobenzoic acid which is then acetylated, thus:

$$NH_2C_6H_4COO—CH_2CH_2NEt_2 \xrightarrow{hydrolysis} NH_2C_6H_4COOH \xrightarrow{conjugation}$$
$$CH_3CO—NH—C_6H_4COOH \qquad (56)$$

During the processes of oxidation, reduction and hydrolysis, the compound may become more toxic or less toxic, so that one cannot regard these processes as detoxications. In the three examples given above, the oxidation of benzene produces phenol which is toxic; the reduction of chloral hydrate produces the active hypnotic drug, trichloroethanol; whereas the hydrolysis of procaine converts an active local anaesthetic into inactive substances. However, in the second phase of the metabolism of all these compounds, non-toxic excretory products are produced by conjugation. Conjugation, whether it occurs directly or as a succeeding reaction to oxidation, reduction and hydrolysis, will result in the formation of a relatively non-toxic excretory product. Conjugations of one kind or another are thus major reactions of most foreign compounds. There are some compounds, however, which are not metabolized in the body and appear to be biochemically inert. These compounds are usually strong organic acids and bases similar in strength to or stronger than conjugation products which are themselves metabolically inert as a rule. There are also known a number of relatively neutral substances which are metabolically inert although pharmacologically active. These include hexachlorobenzene, dieldrin, and aliphatic ethers, such as the cyclopropyl ethers which are used as anaesthetics. Most of these compounds are often chemically stable and inert. [210]

XIV. SUMMARY

Most foreign compounds and a number of natural metabolites, usually unwanted by the body, undergo synthesis or conjugation in the body to produce polar products, usually strongly acidic in nature, but occasionally basic. These conjugation products are relatively non-toxic, water-soluble at physiological pH values, and are eliminated by renal tubular secretion. Part of the conjugated molecule is provided by the body from its carbohydrate and amino acid store, and the syntheses require energy which is provided via adenosine triphosphate. Most of these conjugations require the participation of an intermediate nucleotide which may contain either the carbohydrate or amino acid residue, or the foreign compound. The carbohydrates utilized are glucose, glucuronic acid and possibly ribose, and the amino acids are glycine, cysteine, ornithine, glutamine, methionine and serine. The acetic acid used in acetylations may be derived from carbohydrate, fat or protein. Sulfate for ethereal sulfate synthesis may come from sulfur-containing amino acids or exogenous sulfate. Conjugation processes are intimately connected with the oxidation, reduction and hydrolysis of foreign compounds *in vivo*, for the products of the last three processes usually undergo conjugation in the body to produce excretory products. In general, conjugation reactions result in detoxication of the foreign compound or unwanted natural metabolite.

REFERENCES

1. AXELROD, J. In *Transmethylation and Methionine Biosynthesis*, Shapiro and Schlenk, editors, Univ. Chicago, 1965, p. 71.
2. AXELROD, J. and TOMCHICK, R. *J. Biol. Chem.* **233**, 702 (1958).
3. AXELROD, J. and WEISSBACH, H. *Science* **131**, 1312 (1960).
4. BALDWIN, B. C., ROBINSON, D. and WILLIAMS, R. T. *Biochem. J.* **71**, 638 (1959).
5. BALDWIN, B. C., ROBINSON, D. and WILLIAMS, R. T. *Biochem. J.* **76**, 595 (1960).
6. BALDWIN, B. C., ROBINSON, D. and WILLIAMS, R. T. *Biochem. J.* **76**, 600 (1960).
7. BALDWIN, E. *Dynamic Aspects of Biochemistry*, 3rd ed., p. 309. Oxford University Press, London, 1957.
8. BANDURSKI, R. S., WILSON, L. G. and SQUIRES, C. L. *J. Am. Chem. Soc.* **78**, 6408 (1956).
9. BARNES, M. M., JAMES, S. P. and WOOD, P. B. *Biochem. J.* **71**, 680 (1959).
10. BAUMANN, E. *Pflüger's Arch.* **12**, 63, 69 (1876).
11. BAUMANN, E. *Ber. Deut. Chem. Ges.* **9**, 54 (1876).
12. BAUMANN, E. and PREUSSE, C. *Ber. Deut. Chem. Ges.* **12**, 806 (1879).
13. BAXTER, J. H. and MASON, M. F. *J. Pharmacol.* **91**, 350 (1947).
14. BERNHARD, K. *Z. Physiol. Chem. Hoppe-Seylers* **256**, 49 (1938).
15. BETTS, J. J., JAMES, S. P. and THORPE, W. V. *Biochem. J.* **61**, 611 (1955).
16. BOOTH, A. N., EMERSON, O. H., JONES, F. T. and DeEDS, F. *J. Biol. Chem.* **229**, 51 (1957).
17. BOOTH, A. N., JONES, F. T. and DeEDS, F. *J. Biol. Chem.* **225**, 615 (1957).
18. BOOTH, A. N., MASRI, A. S., ROBBINS, D. J., EMERSON, O. H., JONES, F. T. and DeEDS, F. *J. Biol. Chem.* **234**, 3014 (1959).
19. BOSTRÖM, H. and VESTERMARK, A. *Acta Physiol. Scand.* **48**, 88 (1960).
20. BOUCHILLOUX, S. and ROCHE, J. *Bull. Soc. Chim. Biol.* **37**, 37 (1955).
21. BOULCY-URISON, M. *Bull. Soc. Chim. Biol.* **36**, 525 (1954).
22. BOYER, F., SAVIARD, M. and DECHAVASSINE, M. *Ann. Inst. Pasteur* **90**, 339 (1956).
23. BOYLAND, E. *Proc. 1st Interntl. Pharmacol. Meeting, Stockholm 1961.* Vol. VI, 65 (1962). Pergamon Press.
24. BOYLAND, E. and MANSON, D. *Biochem. J.* **60**, ii (1955).
25. BOYLAND, E. and MANSON, D. *Biochem. J.* **95**, 7P (1965).
26. BOYLAND, E., MANSON, D. and NERY, R. *Biochem. J.* **86**, 263 (1963).
27. BOYLAND, E., MANSON, D. and ORR, S. F. D. *Biochem. J.* **65**, 417 (1957).
28. BOYLAND, E. and NERY, R. *Biochem. J.* **94**, 198 (1965).
29. BOYLAND, E. and SIMS, P. *Biochem. J.* **68**, 440 (1958).
30. BOYLAND, E., SIMS, P. and SOLOMON, J. B. *Biochem. J.* **66**, 41P (1957).
31. BOYLAND, E. and WILLIAMS, K. *Biochem. J.* **94**, 190 (1965).
32. BRADBURY, F. R. and STANDEN, H. *Nature (London)* **183**, 983 (1959).
33. BRANDT, I. K. *Developmental Biol.* **10**, 202 (1964).
34. BRAY, H. G. *Advances in Carbohydrate Chem.* **8**, 251 (1953).
35. BRAY, H. G., FRANKLIN, T. J. and JAMES, S. P. *Biochem. J.* **73**, 465 (1959).
36. BRAY, H. G., FRANKLIN, T. J. and JAMES, S. P. *Biochem. J.* **71**, 690 (1959).
37. BRAY, H. G. and JAMES, S. P. *Biochem. J.* **74**, 394 (1960).
38. BRAY, H. G., JAMES, S. P. and THORPE, W. V. *Biochem. J.* **68**, 561 (1958).
39. BREMER, J. *Acta Chem. Scand.* **9**, 268 (1955).
40. BRIDGES, J. W., KIBBY, M. R. and WILLIAMS, R. T. *Biochem. J.* **96**, 829 (1965).
41. BRODIE, B. B., MAICKEL, R. P. and JONDORF, W. R. *Federation Proc.* **17**, 1163 (1958).
42. BROWN, D. D., AXELROD, J. and TOMCHICK, R. *Nature (London)* **183**, 680 (1959).
43. CANTONI, G. L. *J. Biol. Chem.* **204**, 403 (1953).

44. CANTONI, G. L. and VIGNOS, P. J. *J. Biol. Chem.* **209**, 647 (1954).
45. CARDINI, E. E. and LELOIR, L. F. *Ciencia e invest.* (*Buenos Aires*) **13**, 514 (1957).
46. CHATAGNER, F., BERGERET, B., SÉJOURNÉ, T. and FROMAGEOT, C. *Biochim. Biophys. Acta* **9**, 340 (1952).
47. CLAPP, J. W. *J. Biol. Chem.* **223**, 207 (1956).
48. CLARE, N. T., WHITTEN, L. K. and FILMER, D. B. *Austral. Vet. J.* **23**, 344 (1947).
49. CLEMEDSON, C. J., HULTMAN, H. I. and SÖRBO, B. *Acta Physiol. Scand.* **35**, 31 (1955).
50. COHEN, P. P. and McGILVERY, R. W. *J. Biol. Chem.* **169**, 119 (1947).
51. COHN, R. *Z. Physiol. Chem. Hoppe-Seylers* **17**, 274 (1893).
52. COOMBS, H. I. and HELE, T. S. *Biochem. J.* **21**, 606 (1927).
53. CRAMER, J. W., MILLER, J. A. and MILLER, E. C. *J. Biol. Chem.* **235**, 885 (1960).
54. CUTOLO, E. and REDUZZI, F. *Experientia* **12**, 214 (1956).
55. DALY, J. W., AXELROD, J. and WITKOP, B. *J. Biol. Chem.* **235**, 1155 (1960).
56. DEFRANCHESCHI, A. and ZAMBONI, V. *Biochim. Biophys. Acta* **13**, 304 (1954).
57. DE MEIO, R. H. and ARNOLDT, R. I. *J. Biol. Chem.* **156**, 577 (1944).
58. DE MEIO, R. H. and TKACZ, L. *Arch. Biochem. Biophys.* **27**, 242 (1950).
59. DE MEIO, R. H. and TKACZ, L. *J. Biol. Chem.* **195**, 175 (1952).
60. DE MEIO, R. H., WIZERKANIUK, M. and SCHRIEBMAN, I. *J. Biol. Chem.* **213**, 439 (1955).
61. DOERSCHUK, A. P. *J. Biol. Chem.* **195**, 855 (1952).
62. DUTTON, G. J. *Biochem. J.* **64**, 693 (1956).
63. DUTTON, G. J. *Biochem. J.* **73**, 29P (1959).
64. DUTTON, G. J. *Proc. Eur. Soc. Study of Drug Toxicity* **4**, 121 (1964).
65. DUTTON, G. J. and DUNCAN, A. M. *Biochem. J.* **77**, 18P (1960).
66. DUTTON, G. J. and GRIEG, C. G. *Biochem. J.* **66**, 52P (1957).
67. DUTTON, G. J. and MONTGOMERY, J. P. *Biochem. J.* **70**, 17P (1958).
68. DUTTON, G. J. and STOREY, I. D. E. *Biochem. J.* **53**, xxxvii (1953).
69. DZIEWIATKOWSKI, D. D. and LEWIS, H. B. *J. Biol. Chem.* **153**, 47 (1944).
70. EGI, N. *Hiroshima J. Med. Sci.* **12**, 137 (1963).
71. FAILEY, R. B., ANDERSON, R. C., HENDERSON, F. G. and CHEN, K. K. *J. Pharmacol.* **78**, 366 (1943).
72. FISCHER, E. and PILOTY, O. *Ber. Deut. Chem. Ges.* **24**, 521 (1891).
73. FLORKIN, M., NEUPREZ, R. and ROGERS, J. *Acta Biol. B lg.* **2**, 302 (1941).
74. FRIEDLER, L. and SMITH, J. N. *Biochem. J.* **57**, 396 (1954).
75. FRIEDMAN, E. *Biochem. Z.* **35**, 40 (1911).
76. GAST. J. H., ARAI, K. and ALDRICH, F. L. *J. Biol. Chem.* **196**, 875 (1952).
77. GESSNER, T. and SMITH, J. N. *Biochem. J.* **75**, 165 (1960).
78. GETTLER, A. O. and BAINE, J. O. *Am. J. Med. Sci.* **195**, 182 (1938).
79. GRANT, J. K. *Biochem. J.* **43**, 523 (1948).
80. GREGORY, J. D. and LIPMANN, F. *J. Biol. Chem.* **229**, 1081 (1957).
81. GRENBY, T. H. and YOUNG, L. *Biochem. J.* **75**, 28 (1960).
82. GROVER, P. L. and SIMS, P. *Biochem. J.* **90**, 603 (1964).
83. HARLEY-MASON, J., LAIRD, A. H., and SMYTHIES, J. R., *Confinia Neurol.* **18**, 152 (1958).
84. HASLEWOOD, G. A. D. *Biochem. Soc. Symposia*, No. **6**, 83 (1951).
85. HASLEWOOD, G. A. D. *Biochem. J.* **59**, xi (1955).
86. HASLEWOOD, G. A. D. *Biochem. J.* **78**, 30P (1961).
87. HARTIALA, K. J. V. *Ann. Med. Exp. Biol. Fenn.* **33**, 239 (1955).
88. HIMWICH, W. A. and SAUNDERS, J. P. *Am. J. Physiol.* **153**, 348 (1948).
89. HINKS, N. T. and BOLLIGER, A. *Austral. J. Exptl. Biol. Med. Sci.* **35**, 37 (1957).
90. HINKS, N. T. and BOLLIGER, A. *Austral. J. Sci.* **19**, 228 (1957).
91. HIS, W. *Arch. Exptl. Path. Pharmak.* **22**, 253 (1887).
92. HITCHCOCK, M. and SMITH, J. N. *Biochem. J.* **93**, 392 (1964).
93. HUGHES, H. B. *J. Pharmacol.* **109**, 444 (1953).
94. HUGHES, H. B., BIEHL, J. P., JONES, A. P. and SCHMIDT, L. H. *Amer. Rev. Tuberculosis* **70**, 266 (1954).
95. HUNT, R. In *Handbuch Exptl. Pharmak.*, vol. 1, p. 812, ed. A. Heffter, Berlin, 1923.
96. ISHIDATE, M. *Advances in Glucuronic Acid Research*, 1955–59. Publ. by Chugai Pharmaceutical Co., Tokyo, p. 43 (1960).

97. JACOBELLI, G., TABONE, M. J. and TABONE, D. *Bull. Soc. Chim. Biol.* **40**, 955 (1958).
98. JAFFÉ, M. *Ber. Deut. Chem. Ges.* **10**, 1925 (1877).
99. JAFFÉ, M. *Ber. Deut. Chem. Ges.* **12**, 1092 (1879).
100. JAFFÉ, M. *Z. Physiol. Chem. Hoppe-Seylers* **2**, 47 (1878).
101. JAFFÉ, M. and LEVY, H. *Ber. Deut. Chem. Ges.* **21**, 3461 (1888).
102. JAMES, S. P. and JEFFREY, D. J. *Biochem. J.* **93**, 16P (1964).
103. JEPSON, J. B. *Biochem. J.* **64**, 14P (1956).
104. JOHNSON, M. K. *Biochem. J.* **87**, 9P (1963).
105. KAIHARA, M. *J. Biol. Chem.* **235**, 136 (1960).
106. KAIHARA, M. and PRICE, J. M. *J. Biol. Chem.* **236**, 508 (1961).
107. KAJI, A. and McELROY, W. D. *Biochim. Biophys. Acta* **30**, 190 (1958).
108. KASLANDER, J. *Biochim. Biophys. Acta* **71**, 730 (1963).
109. KELLER, W. *Ann. Chem., Liebigs* **43**, 108 (1842).
110. KELLERMAN, G. M. *J. Biol. Chem.* **231**, 427 (1958).
111. KIRSHNER, N. and GOODALL, McC. *Biochim. Biophys. Acta* **24**, 658 (1957).
112. KNIGHT, R. H. and YOUNG, L. *Biochem. J.* **66**, 55P (1957).
113. KNIGHT, R. H. and YOUNG, L. *Biochem. J.* **70**, 111 (1958).
114. KRAYCHY, S. and GALLAGHER, T. F. *J. Biol. Chem.* **229**, 519 (1957).
115. KREBS, H. A., SYKES, W. O. and BARTLEY, W. C. *Biochem. J.* **41**, 622 (1947).
116. LANG, K. *Biochem. Z.* **259**, 243 (1933).
117. LANG, S. *Arch. Exptl. Path. Pharmak.* **34**, 247 (1894).
118. LAWRENCE, W. S. *Federation Proc.* **6**, 349 (1947).
119. LEVVY, G. A. and MARSH, C. A. *Advances in Carbohydrate Chem.* **14**, 381 (1959).
120. LIN, P. H. and JOHNSON, B. C. *J. Am. Chem. Soc.* **75**, 2974 (1953).
121. LIPMANN, F. *J. Biol. Chem.* **160**, 173 (1945).
122. LIPSCHITZ, W. L. and BUEDING, E. *J. Biol. Chem.* **129**, 333 (1939).
123. LITCHFIELD, J. T. *J. Pharmacol.* **67**, 212 (1939).
124. LYNEN, F., REICHERT, E. and RUEFF, L. *Ann. Chem. Liebigs* **574**, 1 (1951).
125. McGILVERY, R. W. and COHEN, P. P. *J. Biol. Chem.* **183**, 179 (1950).
126. McISAAC, W. M. and PAGE, I. H. *J. Biol. Chem.* **234**, 858 (1959).
127. McKENNIS, H., YARD, A. S., WEATHERBY, J. H. and HAGY, J. A. *J. Pharmacol.* **126**, 109 (1959).
128. MACLAGAN, N. F. and WILKINSON, J. H. *Biochem. J.* **56**, 211 (1954).
129. MAHLER, H. R., WAKIL, S. J. and BOCK, R. M. *J. Biol. Chem.* **204**, 453 (1953).
130. MAICKEL, R. P., JONDORF, W. R. and BRODIE, B. B. *Federation Proc.* **17**, 390 (1958).
131. MARSHALL, E. K. JR. *J. Biol. Chem.* **211**, 499 (1954).
132. MEISTER, A., FRASER, P. E. and TICE, S. V. *J. Biol. Chem.* **206**, 561 (1954).
133. MEISTER, A., UDENFRIEND, S. and BESSMAN, S. P. *J. Clin. Invest.* **35**, 619 (1956).
134. MERING, J. VON and MUSCULUS, O. *Ber. Deut. Chem. Ges.* **8**, 662 (1875).
135. MILLER, J. A. and MILLER, E. C. *Cancer Research* **12**, 283 (1952).
136. MILLER, L. P. *Contr. Boyce Thomson Inst.* **9**, 425 (1938).
137. MOLDAVE, K. and MEISTER, A. *J. Biol. Chem.* **229**, 463 (1957).
138. MYERS, C. M. and SMITH, J. N. *Biochem. J.* **54**, 276 (1953).
139. MYERS, C. M. and SMITH, J. N. *Biochem. J.* **56**, 498 (1954).
140. NOSE, Y. and LIPMANN, F. *J. Biol. Chem.* **233**, 1348 (1958).
141. PACKHAM, M. A. and BUTLER, G. C. *J. Biol. Chem.* **194**, 349 (1952).
142. PARKE, D. V. Ph.D. Thesis. University of London (1952).
143. PARKE, D. V. *Biochem. J.* **77**, 493 (1960).
144. PATEL, R. Z. and CRAWFORD, M. A. *Biochem. J.* **89**, 81P (1963).
145. PAUL, H. E., AUSTIN, F. L., PAUL, M. F. and ELLS, V. R. *J. Biol. Chem.* **180**, 345 (1949).
146. POWER, F. W. *Proc. Soc. Exptl. Biol.* **33**, 598 (1936).
147. PRICE, J. M. and DODGE, L. W. *J. Biol. Chem.* **223**, 699 (1956).
148. PRIDHAM, J. B. and SALTMARSH, M. J. *Biochem. J.* **74**, 42P (1960).
149. ROBBINS, P. W. and LIPMANN, F. *J. Am. Chem. Soc.* **78**, 2652 (1956).
150. ROBBINS, P. W. and LIPMANN, F. *J. Biol. Chem.* **229**, 837 (1957).
151. ROBERTS, J. J. and WARWICK, G. P. *Biochem. Pharmacol.* **1**, 60 (1958).

152. ROBINSON, D., SMITH, J. N. and WILLIAMS, R. T. *Biochem. J.* **55**, 151 (1953).
153. ROBINSON, D. and WILLIAMS, R. T. *Biochem. J.* **68**, 23P (1958).
154. ROTHSTEIN, M. and GREENBERG, D. M. *Arch. Biochem. Biophys.* **68**, 206 (1957).
155. ROY, A. B. *Biochim. Biophys. Acta* **30**, 193 (1958).
156. ROY, A. B. *Biochem. J.* **72**, 19P (1959).
157. ROY, A. B. *Advances Enzymol.* **22**, 211 (1960).
158. RUELIUS, H. W. and GAUHE, A. *Ann. Chem, Liebigs* **570**, 121 (1950).
159. SARCIONE, E. J. and SOKAL, J. E. *J. Biol. Chem.* **231**, 605 (1958).
160. SASAKI, T. *Biochem. Z.* **25**, 272 (1910).
161. SCHACHTER, D., KASS, D. J. and LANNON, T. *J. J. Biol. Chem.* **234**, 201 (1959).
162. SCHACHTER, D., MANIS, J. G. and TAGGART, J. V. *Am. J. Physiol.* **182**, 537 (1955).
163. SCHACHTER, D. and TAGGART, J. V. *J. Biol. Chem.* **203**, 925 (1953).
164. SCHACHTER, D. and TAGGART, J. V. *J. Biol. Chem.* **208**, 263 (1954).
165. SCHAYER, R. W. *Brit. J. Pharmacol.* **11**, 472 (1956).
166. SCHMIDT-NIELSON, S. and HOLMSEN, J. *Arch. Internat. Physiol.* **18**, 128 (1921).
167. SEGAL, H. L. *Biochim. Biophys. Acta* **21**, 194 (1956).
168. SEGAL, H. L. and MALOGNE, L. A. *J. Biol. Chem.* **234**, 909 (1959).
169. SENOH, S., DALY, J., AXELROD, J. and WITKOP, B. *J. Amer. Chem. Soc.* **81**, 6240 (1959).
170. SMITH, J. N. *Nature (London)* **172**, 32 (1953).
171. SMITH, J. N. *Biol. Rev.* **30**, 458 (1955).
172. SMITH, J. N. *Biochem. J.* **60**, 436 (1955).
173. SMITH, J. N. *Biochem. J.* **69**, 509 (1958).
174. SMITH, J. N. In *Comparative Biochemistry*, vol. VI, eds. M. Florkin and H. S. Mason.
175. SMITH, J. N. and TURBERT H. *Biochem. J.* **92**, 127 (1964).
176. SÖRBO, B. *Acta Chem. Scand.* **9** 1656 (1955).
177. SÖRBO, B. *Acta Chem. Scand.* **11**, 628 (1957).
178. SÖRBO, B. *Biochim. Biophys. Acta* **24**, 324 (1957).
179. SÖRBO, B. *Bull. Soc. Chim. Biol.* **40**, 1859 (1958).
180. SÖRBO, B. H. *Acta Chem. Scand.* **5**, 724, 1218, (1951).
181. SÖRBO, B. H. *Acta Chem. Scand.* **7**, 32 (1953).
182. SÖRBO, B. H. *Acta Chem. Scand.* **7**, 238 (1953).
183. SPECTOR, W. S., ed. *Handbook of Toxicology*, vol. 1. Saunders Company, Philadelphia and London, 1956.
184. SPENCER, B. and HARADA, T. *Biochem. J.* **73**, 34P (1959).
185. SPENCER, B. and HARADA, T. *Biochem. J.* **77**, 305 (1960).
186. SPERBER, I. *Ann. Roy. Agric. Coll. Sweden* **16**, 49 (1948).
187. SPERBER, I. *Ann. Roy. Agric. Coll. Sweden* **15**, 108, 317 (1947).
188. STEIN, W. H., PALADINI, A. C., HIRS, C. H. W. and MOORE, S. *J. Am. Chem. Soc.* **76**, 2848 (1954).
189. STEKOL, J. A. *J. Biol. Chem.* **113**, 675 (1936).
190. STEKOL, J. A. *J. Biol. Chem.* **124**, 129 (1938).
191. STEVENSON, I. H. and DUTTON, G. J. *Biochem. J.* **77**, 19P (1960).
192. STOREY, I. D. E. *Biochem. J.* **95**, 209 (1965).
193. STROMINGER, J. L. *Physiol. Rev.* **40**, 66 (1960).
194. STROMINGER, J. L. and MAPSON, L. W. *Biochem. J.* **66**, 567 (1957).
195. STROMINGER, J. L., MAXWELL, E. S., AXELROD, J. and KALCKAR, H. M. *J. Biol. Chem.* **224**, 79 (1957).
196. SUNDVIK, E. *Jahresber Fortschr. Tierchem.* **16**, 76 (1886).
197. TABOR, H., MEHLER, R. A. and STADTMAN, E. R. *J. Biol. Chem.* **204**, 127 (1953).
198. THIERFELDER, H. and SHERWIN, C. P. *Ber. Deut. Chem. Ges.* **47**, 2630 (1914).
199. THIERFELDER, H. and SHERWIN, C. P. *Z. Physiol. Chem. Hoppe-Seylers* **94**, 1 (1915).
200. THOMPSON, A. E. R. and YOUNG, L. *Biochem. J.* **76**, 62P (1960).
201. TRIVELLONI, J. C. *Arch. Biochem. Biophys.* **89**, 149 (1960).
202. TROLL, W., BELMAN, S. and NELSON, N. *Proc. Soc. Exptl. Biol., N.Y.* **100**, 121 (1959).
203. TSUKAMOTO, H., YOSHIMURA, H. and TATSUMI, K. *Life Sci.* **2**, 382 (1963).
204. TSUNOO, S. *J. Biochem. (Tokyo)* **22**, 409 (1935).

205. TSUYUKI, H., CHANG, V. M. and IDLER, D. R. *Canad. J. Biochem. Physiol.* **36**, 465 (1958).
206. UNO, T. and KONO, M. *J. Pharm. Soc., Japan* **82**, 1660 (1962).
207. VASSEL, B., PARTRIDGE, R. and CROSSLEY, M. L. *Arch. Biochem. Biophys.* **4**, 59 (1944).
208. VESTERMARK, A. and BOSTRÖM, H. *Exp. Cell Res.* **18**, 174 (1959).
209. WATERHOUSE, D. F. *Austral. J. Sci. Res.* **B5**, 143 (1952).
210. WILLIAMS, R. T. *Detoxication Mechanisms*, 2nd ed. Chapman & Hall, Ltd., London, 1959.
211. WILLIAMS, R. T. *Pharmacology of Plant Phenolics*, p. 13, ed. J. W. Fairbairn. Academic Press, New York and London, 1959.
212. WILLIAMS, R. T. *Proc. Eur. Soc., Study of Drug Toxicity* **4**, 13 (1964).
213. WILSON, L. G. and BANDURSKI, R. S. *Arch. Biochem. Biophys.* **62**, 503 (1956).
214. WOOD, J. L. and COOLEY, S. L. *Federation Proc.* **11**, 314 (1952).
215. WOOD, J. L. and FIEDLER, H. *J. Biol. Chem.* **205**, 231 (1953).
216. WOOLF, L. I. *Biochem. J.* **49**, ix (1951).
217. YAMADA, T. and CARDINI, C. E. *Arch. Biochem. Biophys.* **86**, 127, 133 (1960).
218. ZBARSKY, S. H. and YOUNG, L. *J. Biol. Chem.* **151**, 487 (1943).

CHAPTER 10

THE BIOSYNTHESIS OF CAROTENOIDS AND VITAMIN A

C. O. CHICHESTER and T. O. M. NAKAYAMA*

Department of Food Science and Technology,
University of California, Davis, California

CONTENTS

I. INTRODUCTION   641
II. STRUCTURES   642
III. FORMATION OF THE 40 CARBON CHAIN   643
IV. ALTERATIONS OF THE 40 CARBON CHAIN   651
V. XANTHOPHYLLS   661
VI. STERIC MODIFICATIONS   669
VII. VITAMIN A   670
VIII. SUMMARY   672
    REFERENCES   672

I. INTRODUCTION

The complete synthesis of β-carotene was achieved by at least three independent investigators in 1950.[100, 117, 150] Continuing work in synthetic organic chemistry has led to unambiguous confirmation of known structures, correction of erroneous ones and discovery of new types.[214, 103] It remains for the biochemist to delineate the process by which nature accomplishes the same feat. The general area of carotenoid chemistry has been the subject of numerous reviews, notably the more recent ones by Goodwin, Mackinney, Stanier, and Mackinney and Chichester.[132, 139, 74-88, 188, 141, 82]

The ubiquitous occurrence of carotenoids in nature has made a study of environmental factors a confusing one for comparative purposes. Carotenoids are often found concentrated in reproductive organs, a fact which has led to the postulation of sexual functions; their various properties associated with light absorption have earned them assignments as energy filters, receptors and directors. Under other conditions of occurrence they have been called storage material, antioxidants and have even been relegated to the role of metabolic wastes. While a protective role has been suggested

*The authors would like to acknowledge the help of PHS Grant GM 8869 and NSF Grant GB 558.

as the primary function of carotenoids, especially in photosynthetic systems, [89] it is not unlikely that other secondary functions exist. An excellent discussion of these has been presented by Burnett. [24] Their function as provitamins for animals must certainly be ascribed as a secondary adaptation, inasmuch as vitamin A *per se* is neither found in plants nor utilized by them. Similarly, it is only in plants where carotenoid synthesis *de novo* has been shown, although animals may ingest carotenoids and modify them selectively, in a manner paralleling that in plants. In this review we will attempt to limit consideration of the experimental evidence involving the overall investigation of cultural and environmental conditions controlling synthesis and instead direct our attention to the molecular level with a view of relating the synthesis to the metabolic processes of the organisms. The discussion of the intermediates centred around mevalonic acid is intentionally brief, since this is covered intensely elsewhere in this volume under sterols (see Chapter 4).

II. STRUCTURES

Although the number of modifications and modes of occurrence of carotenoids described in the literature are large and varied, it can be seen that structurally they are all related to lycopene. Thus, γ-carotene can be considered as lycopene with one terminal β-ionone group introduced by ring closure, while β-carotene has two such groups. α-Carotene has one α and one β-ionone group. The numbering system as employed in this chapter will be that proposed by the American Chemical Society committee on nomenclature as illustrated for trans α-carotene and γ-carotene in Fig. 1. [9]

There has been some confusion as to the classification of the C_{40} polyenes. They are highly unsaturated and, because of their conjugated double-bond

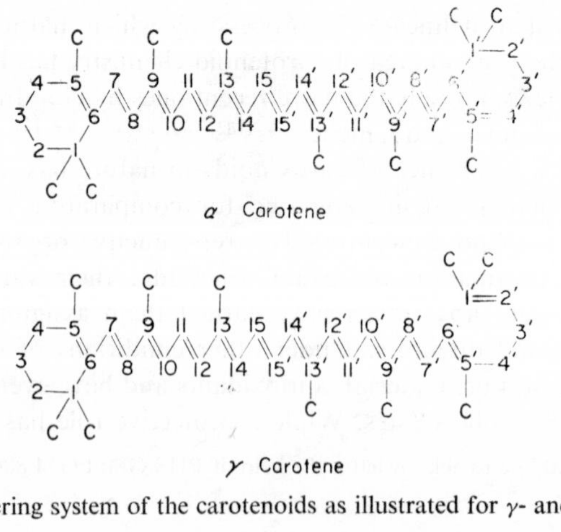

α Carotene

γ Carotene

FIG. 1. Numbering system of the carotenoids as illustrated for γ- and α-carotenes.

systems, may be colored. All have strong absorptions in the blue or ultraviolet portions of the spectrum. All of these compounds are polyenes and are composed of eight isoprenoid units, but by strict definition, only the polyenes which have absorptions in the visible spectrum are named carotenoids. [118] Because of the close biosynthetic relationships, however, we will in this review refer to all of the C_{40} isoprenoids as carotenoids.

It is assumed that the 40 carbon isoprenoid chain with the reversal of direction in the center is basic to all carotenoids. This central change of direction or plane of symmetry is also shared by a number of other shorter chain isoprenoid compounds; the most notable of these is squalene and the sterols related to it.

III. FORMATION OF THE 40 CARBON CHAIN

In recent investigations of the biosynthesis of carotenoids at the molecular level, microorganisms have been utilized almost exclusively although a limited amount of work has been done with the tomato fruit. Early studies on fungi attempted to delineate the effect of various carbon sources upon the synthesis of carotenoids. [64] In a typical study, it was found that maltose and glucose are equally effective in promoting carotenoid synthesis in *Phycomyces blakesleeanus* while other carbohydrates such as xylose or fructose were less effective. Substances such as glycerol and related compounds were tested, and changes in the net synthesis of carotenoids were observed in their presence. Schopfer and Grob in 1950 showed that the mold *Phycomyces* could be grown on a completely synthetic medium containing only thiamine and ammonium lactate. [180] This medium would support growth but not the formation of carotenoids. When the lactate of the medium was replaced by acetate, carotenoids were formed, but growth was somewhat inhibited. The total carotenoids formed were lower, however, than those normally produced on a medium containing glucose and added cofactors. Later it was observed that acetate in the presence of ammonium nitrate was sufficient to support both growth and carotenogenesis. With the establishment of a medium which was strictly defined, it was possible for Schopfer et al. [180, 182] to grow the mold *P. blakesleeanus* on media containing C^{14}-labeled acetate and to show that approximately 70 per cent of the carotene carbons were derived from acetate. [181, 182, 92] In another series of experiments, Grob and Butler [93] grew *Mucor hiemalis* on a medium which contained C^{14} acetate as the sole carbon source. In one case the acetate was labeled in the methyl position and the second case in the carboxyl. Under the conditions of these experiments the organism produced approximately 90 per cent of its carotenoids in the form of β-carotene. After isolation of the β-carotene by chromatographic means, Grob and Butler degraded the compound by chromate oxidation in one case and by permanganate oxidation in a second. Figure 2 illustrates the fragments obtained under both oxidizing conditions. Upon radioactive analysis of the fragments obtained from the degradation by either procedure, these authors were able to assign the origin of each of the 40 carbons to either the carboxyl or the methyl carbon of acetate. Figure 3

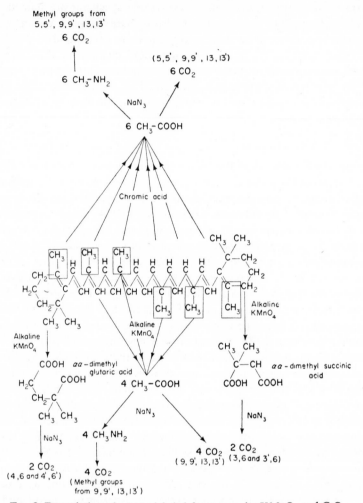

FIG. 2. Degradation of acetate labeled β-carotene, by $KMnO_4$ and CrO_3.

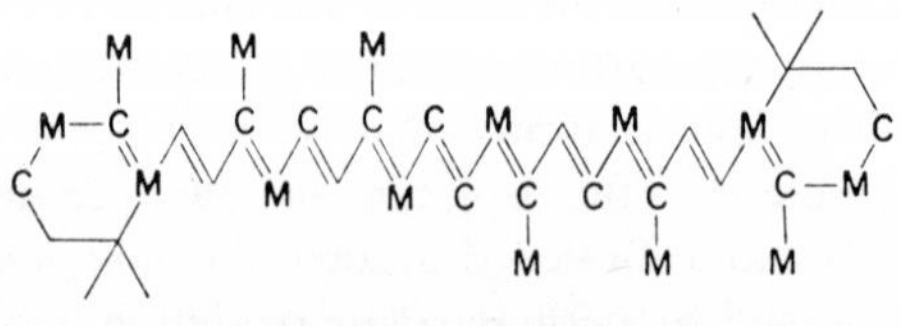

FIG. 3. Positions of carboxyl and methyl carbons in β-carotene synthesized from acetate by *Mucor hiemalis*.

illustrates the results of the labeling experiments. They then postulated that the basic repeating unit above the level of acetate could follow the formal pattern of β-methyl, β-hydroxyglutaric acid, or a similar 5 carbon acid.

Another hint as to the nature of the repeating unit arose from the observation of Goodwin and Lijinsky[68] that when *Phycomyces* was forced to metabolize leucine or valine, by providing only a suboptimal amount of assimilable carbohydrate, the production of β-carotene was stimulated almost five-fold, although the growth was limited.

In the same series of experiments the authors tested a wide range of other compounds such as β-methylcrotonaldehyde, isovaleraldehyde, 2-hydroxy-isocaproic acid, 2-ketoisocaproic acid, β-methylcrotonic acid, etc. All of these compounds could conceivably give rise to a carbon fragment of such a form that, when condensed with others of like type, a pattern similar to that found in the carotenoids would result. The compounds tested were not all caroteno-genic, but enough similarities were found to conclude that the most likely isoprenoid unit building block was β-methylcrotonaldehyde. This could be produced from the degradation of leucine or valine by previously postulated paths. Although leucine and valine are often cited as amino acids which will promote carotene synthesis, they are not, however, universally carotenogenic. Little or no effect was observed in *Rhodospirillum rubrum*,[71] *Corynebacterium poinsettiae*[189] and *Sarcina lutea*.[11] In *Rhodotorula shibatana*,[101] leucine but not valine stimulated carotenoid biogenesis.

In their experiments Reichel and Wallis found that β-methylcrotonic acid gave a substantial increase in carotenoid production in *Phycomyces*.[171, 172] This is in direct contrast to Goodwin's original results, in which it has no effect. The same investigators also obtained an increase in carotenoid formation with β-hydroxyisovaleric acid, β-hydroxyisovaleraldehyde and β-hydroxy-β-methylglutaric acid.

The situation was confusing enough so that a direct test of the function of leucine in carotenoid stimulation was needed. Goodwin *et al.*[31] used C^{14} leucine labeled in the 1 and 2 positions in a growth medium for *Phycomyces*; they found that the β-carotene derived from C-1 labeled leucine contained no significant activity, although it was apparent that the leucine was metabolized as witnessed by the radioactivity in the carbon dioxide respired. β-Carotene from C-2 labeled leucine, although slightly active, could not be shown to have been produced selectively from the leucine.

A systematic series of experiments was conducted by Yokoyama *et al.*[221, 228–32, 32, 33] Specifically labeled 3-C^{14}, 4-C^{14} and 5,5'-C^{14} leucines were used to supply 50 per cent of the nitrogen requirement of *Phycomyces*. The β-carotene produced was isolated, degraded and analyzed. The results showed that the iso-3 carbon unit was incorporated into β-carotene selectively to a significant degree. Thus, while the basis of the leucine stimulation became apparent, the source of the other two carbons remained indefinite.

In later experiments it was shown chromatographically in extracts of the mold *Phycomyces* that there was an increase in the production of β-hydroxy-β-methylglutarate when leucine was added to the culture media of *Phycomyces*. It was further shown that the stimulating effect of β-hydroxy-β-methylglutarate upon carotenoid synthesis, when added to a culture medium, was of the same magnitude as leucine. However, the addition of a large quantity of leucine to the growth media suppressed growth whereas β-hydroxy-β-methylglutarate actually increased growth above that experienced in a minimal medium.

Coon and co-workers, in studies of leucine catabolism in liver preparations established the sequential modifications of leucine by decarboxylation and deamination to β-hydroxyisovaleryl-CoA. [12, 13, 46, 27] They observed that β-hydroxy-β-methylglutaryl-CoA was formed and simultaneously found evidence of the uptake of CO_2. A pathway for the addition of CO_2 to β-hydroxyisovaleryl-CoA was postulated to give β-hydroxy-β-methylglutaryl-CoA. Later, the details of this mechanism were invalidated by the same workers, but the existence of the CO_2 fixing system was substantiated. The CO_2 acceptor is now thought to be β-methylcrotonyl-CoA and the product is thus β-methylglutaconyl-CoA. Upon the addition of water this substance will give β-hydroxy-β-methylglutaryl-CoA. In the same manner, Yokoyama *et al.* have shown that the stimulation of carotenoid synthesis by leucine follows the general pathway established by Coon *et al.* [12, 27, 32, 33] The leucine is converted by a series of deaminations and decarboxylations to β,β-dimethylacrylyl-CoA. CO_2 is added to the complex by means of a biotin reaction and β-hydroxy-β-methylglutaryl-CoA is formed. [130] The latter compound is thus a key intermediate when leucine is the metabolically stimulating carotenogenic agent and no doubt remains as to its importance in carotenoid synthesis.

In the carboxylation of β,β-dimethylacrylyl-CoA, the CO_2 would form the carboxyl at the C-5 "active isoprene unit". However, Rudney has demonstrated the formation of β-hydroxy-β-methylglutaryl-CoA from acetoacetyl-CoA and acetyl-CoA, and also the reverse reaction to acetyl-CoA and acetoacetate. [175, 176, 54] Since both acetate and acetoacetate are convertible to carotenoids it is not surprising to find that $C^{14}O_2$ is utilized in the formation of β-carotene, particularly in the presence of leucine.

The similarity between synthesis of compounds of basically isoprenoid structure has been alluded to previously. There is no reason to exclude, at least at the initial stages of formation, an identity of precursors. Thus, β-hydroxy-β-methylglutarate was implicated in sterol synthesis very heavily before being tested in the synthesis of carotenoids. Upon the discovery of an acetate-replacing factor for *Lactobacillus* by Folkers *et al.*, the establishing of its structure and synthesis, and the experiments by Tavormina, Gibbs and Huff, and others implicating it heavily in cholesterol synthesis, it was apparent that the next compound to be investigated in carotenoid synthesis would be mevalonic acid. [195, 49, 43, 218, 219] Several workers had shown that β-hydroxy-β-methylglutaryl-CoA was convertible to mevalonic acid in systems capable of synthesizing both sterols and carotenoids. [176, 55, 232] Mackinney et al. first reported its incorporation into carotene. [140] Goodwin tested its ability to suppress the incorporation of active acetate into carotene by Phycomyces, [72] Zabin and Shneour tested the incorporation of 2-C^{14} mevalonic acid into lycopene in tomatoes, [183] Yokoyama et al. tested the direct incorporation of 2-C^{14} mevalonic acid into carotene in Phycomyces, [33] and Grob investigated its utilization in carotenoid synthesis in Mucor hiemalis. [94] In all cases there was a ready incorporation of the labeled material and a dilution of labeled acetate by inactive mevalonic acid in the synthesis of carotene. [23] Investigations too numerous to recount have confirmed the utilization of mevalonic acid for carotene synthesis in many other organisms. [190, 165, 4, 124] Its incorporation and utilization are higher by several fold than acetate of β-hydroxy-β-methylglutarate. Although some randomization of label has been reported when 2-C^{14}-mevalonic acid was tested in intact organisms or homogenates, the primary labeling pattern was as suspected (Fig. 4). There is little doubt that mevalonic acid is an obligatory intermediate in the biosynthesis of carotene.

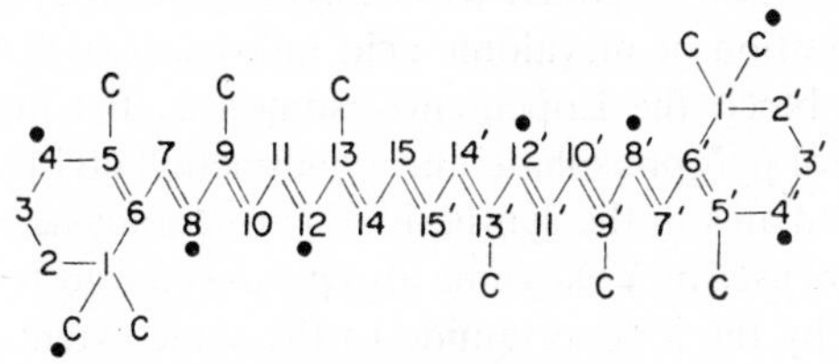

FIG. 4. Position of the 2 carbon of mevalonic acid in β-carotene synthesized by Phycomyces.

By analogy to work reported by investigators in the sterol field, the next step in the synthetic pathway would require the phosphorylation of mevalonic acid through the agency of adenosine triphosphate. [196, 160, 28] The initial phosphate ester was shown to be attached at the five-hydroxy group of mevalonic acid. [98] The 5-phosphomevalonic acid is subsequently rephosphorylated to give 5-pyrophosphorylmevalonic acid (ATP requirement). After this sequence of reactions, the pyrophosphorylmevalonic acid is decarboxylated to form Δ^3-isopentenol pyrophosphate. The decarboxylation and isomerization requires an additional molecule of ATP and results in a compound still containing a pyrophosphate, which has no hydroxyl group but contains a double bond at positions 3–4. [160, 129] No phosphorus from the ATP is incorporated; however, it is postulated that a 3-phosphate ester is an intermediate. The phosphate ester at position C-3 would facilitate cleavage of the C—O bond and would result in the concerted removal of the 3-OH as well as the carboxyl group. The postulated Δ^3-isopentenol pyrophosphate has been synthesized chemically.[131] It has been shown in the sterol field that Δ^3-isopentenol pyrophosphate is the condensing unit with the isomeric γ,γ-dimethylallyl pyrophosphate, the latter is formed by the action of iso-pentenol isomerase.[1] The isomerase yielding diallyl pyrophosphate is mediated by a sulfhydryl enzyme and is blocked by iodoacetamide. The two units, one nucleophilic and one electrophilic in character, are condensed to give a 10-carbon unit.[99, 216, 217] This is thought to be utilized in a condensa-tion with another Δ^3-isopentenol pyrophosphate to give as a result farnesyl pyrophosphate.[131] A pair of farnesyl pyrophosphates are condensed after an isomerization reaction to yield squalene with the loss of the phosphates. Evidence indicates that the final condensation is mediated by TPNH.[161]

Varma et al. demonstrated the incorporation of 1-C^{14}-isopentenol-pyro-phosphate (prepared by the procedure of Bloch et al.[17] using an enzyme extract of yeast) into β-carotene by mold extracts and into lycopene in tomato homogenates.[210] The percentage incorporation was significantly higher than that of 2-C^{14} mevalonic acid and thus would indicate an identity of metabolic pathways in both sterols and carotenoids, at least as far as the isopentenol compound. Yokoyama et al. previously had found that in a cell-free enzyme preparation obtained from Phycomyces, iodoacetamide, would block the incorporation of mevalonic acid into carotenoids.[233] Since iodo-acetamide would block the isopentenol isomerase, the implication here is that the isopentenol pyrophosphate and γ,γ-dimethylallyl pyrophosphate are obligatory intermediates in the synthesis of carotenoids as well as of sterols. The cell-free system used by Yokoyama also produced ergosterol, and its forma-tion was blocked by the iodoacetamide to the same extent as was the caro-tenoid synthesis, further substantiating the similarity of precursors in the two systems. A significant difference between the metabolism of β-carotene and sterols was observed. DPN was not required for carotene synthesis but was required for the formation of sterols.

In contrast to the formation of sterols with their C_{30} skeleton, the analo-gous formation of carotenoids would presumably require a C_{20} condensing unit. The most frequently suggested unit has been geranylgeranyl pyro-phosphate. This had not been shown directly to be an intermediate in caro-tenoid biosynthesis. It has been shown, however, that geranylgeranyl pyro-phosphate can be synthesized by pig liver enzymes, as well as carrot dia-lysates.[215] Geranyl pyrophosphate has been shown to be formed from dimethylallyl pyrophosphate and isopentenol pyrophosphate by the action of the enzyme farnesyl pyrophosphate synthetase. A schematic for the formation of geranyl pyrophosphate is shown in Fig. 5.[95]

Using the cell-free system described by Yokoyama, it has been possible to demonstrate incorporation of C^{14}-labeled farnesyl pyrophosphate (obtained from a rat liver preparation) into β-carotene and other polyenes. The utilization is enhanced by the presence of inactive mevalonic acid, suggesting that in the case of the C_{40} compounds the condensing unit is a 20 carbon unit. [234] This has been confirmed by Anderson and Porter [6] in a plastid system, and later the investigation was expanded by Beeler and

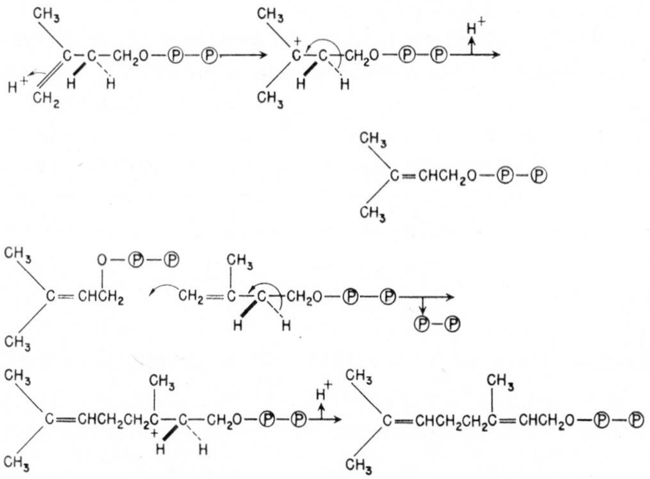

FIG. 5. Goodwin's scheme for the isomerization of isopentenyl pyrophosphate to dimethylallyl pyrophosphate and its condensation with isopentenyl pyrophosphate.

Porter to include the analysis of the specific radioactivities of carotenes synthesized from farnesyl pyrophosphate. In this case using highly radioactive substrates, it was found that the maximum incorporation of radioactivity was in phytoene, and both the specific activity and the specific activity of carotenoids decreased with the increasing desaturation. [16] Using the same system, Beeler et al. [16] followed the formation of squalene from mevalonic acid and farnesyl pyrophosphate in carrots and tomato plastids as well as rat liver microsomal systems and a dialyzed preparation obtained from tomato plastids. TPNH and magnesium were required as co-factors.

In the condensations of mevalonic acid to yield ultimately farnesyl or geranyl pyrophosphate an isomerization takes place, to form, as referred to previously, the dimethylallyl pyrophosphate. The hydrogen loss occurs from carbon 4 referred to mevalonic acid. Cornforth et al. in 1964 [44] synthesized two species of mevalonic acid $[2-C^{14}]$—4R $[4T]$ MVA and $[2-C^{14}]$—4S $[4-T]$ MVA in which the absolute configuration at carbon 4 was R and S. [25] By measuring the T/C^{14} ratio of products derived from stereo-specifically labeled mevalonic acids, it was possible to show the loss of hydrogen in the condensation and isomerization reaction was stereospecific. [79] Cornforth *et al.* [44] showed that the same specificity existed in the formation of squalene synthesized by rat liver preparation. In both cases [44] the 4R hydrogen was specifically retained, or alternately, the 4S hydrogen was lost, in these condensations. Archer [10] showed, however, that in rubber, which has the *cis* configuration, the 4R hydrogen is lost, in contrast to squalene or carotenoids having in general a *trans* configuration.

The conversion of mevalonic acid to squalene during sterol synthesis is a net reductive process. [197] If mevalonic acid is utilized for the synthesis of carotenoids, the conversion to the highly unsaturated compounds such as β-carotene and lycopene would require that the overall process be an oxidative one. In contrast, that for carotenoids such as dihydrophytoene is reductive. The conversion to phytoene, however, which has been suggested as the immediate precursor to all of the colored carotenoids, occurs without change in oxidation state. Phytoene is found relatively widespread in plants producing colored carotenoids, but the existence of the dihydrophytoene (lycopersene) has only recently been claimed. [91, 155] If lycopersene is presumed to be the intermediate in the formation of the C_{40} carotenoids, the postulated

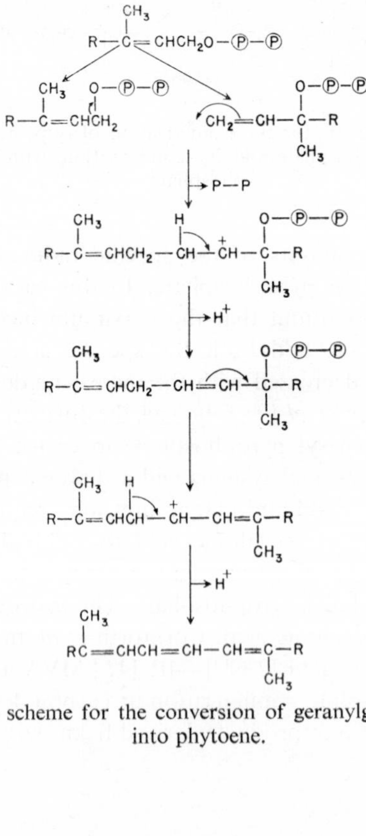

FIG. 6. Goodwin's scheme for the conversion of geranylgeranyl pyrophosphate into phytoene.

pathway from mevalonic acid to any carotenoid would require a net reduction initially followed by a subsequent oxidation of the chain.

The molecule of squalene formed as an intermediate during sterol synthesis has its six double bonds completely isolated one from another. This allows comparatively free rotation of the entire molecule. By contrast, the most saturated carotenoid commonly found in nature is phytoene which, on the basis of recent evidence, has a central double bond in conjunction with two double bonds immediately adjacent. It thus contains a total of nine double bonds. The placement of the double bonds of this molecule requires that the central position be fixed, and this leaves only the ends of the chain containing the three isolated double bonds on either side of the center free to rotate. Two of these would be immobilized during cyclization of β-carotene, thus leaving only a single double bond and associated carbons free to rotate. It is extremely attractive to suggest that differentiation between sterol and carotenoid synthesis is centered to a large measure about the central rigidity of the chain and the limited ability of the ends for rotation. This is in obvious contrast to the intermediate in sterol synthesis, squalene, which has essentially free rotation about a great number of its carbons.

A scheme for the condensation of a compound such as geranylgeranyl pyrophosphate into phytoene has been suggested by Goodwin. [80] This scheme is presented in Fig. 6.

IV. ALTERATIONS OF THE 40 CARBON CHAIN

In all plant tissues examined to date there exists a series of carotenoids differing one from another by their ratio of carbon to hydrogen. The common biological assumption is that all of the members of the series are derived from a common C_{40} precursor, which is now believed to be phytoene.

The most saturated C_{40} compound phytoene ($C_{40}H_{64}$) contains nine double bonds, three of which are in conjugation, and phytoene's structure is similar to that of squalene except that the central bond is unsaturated. It can be dehydrogenated to bis-dehydrolycopene ($C_{40}H_{52}$, containing fifteen double bonds all in conjugation) by treatment with N-bromosuccinimide. The compounds intermediate between phytoene and bis-dehydrolycopene are also found in nature. Thus, we have the series for the aliphatic carotenes, phytoene ($C_{40}H_{64}$), phytofluene ($C_{40}H_{62}$), ζ-carotene ($C_{40}H_{60}$), neurosporene ($C_{40}H_{58}$), lycopene ($C_{40}H_{56}$), dehydrolycopene ($C_{40}H_{54}$), and bis-dehydrolycopene ($C_{40}H_{52}$). Most theories of biogenesis consider the precursor to be more saturated than the ultimate carotenoid and no serious proponent of a reductive theory of biogenesis has been heard. Thus, the major queries left are concerned with the initial C_{40} compound, the points of ring closure to form the alicyclic compounds, the nature of the cyclization products, the formation of aromatic end-groups, and the structures of some of the less well-defined members.

An early unifying theory of biogenesis was advanced by Porter and Lincoln assigning the role of the initial compound to tetrahydrophytoene which was then dehydrogenated successively to phytoene, phytofluene, ζ-carotene, tetrahydrolycopene (neurosporene) and lycopene. [162] Lycopene was assigned the pivotal role, and it was suggested that it in turn gives rise to γ- and β-carotenes by ring closure at one or both ends (γ-carotene is thus an intermediate in β-carotene formation; [165] α-carotene arises by isomerization of β-carotene, and the xanthophylls are formed by oxidation of the hydrocarbons. Each step in the sequential transformations postulated requires the removal of four hydrogens. The theory was supported by experimental work on tomato varieties which were shown in each case to contain all of the more saturated members of the series as compared to the most unsaturated compound present. As an example, if a tomato contained ζ-carotene as the most unsaturated carotenoid, then the theory would require that only ζ-carotene, phytofluene, and phytoene could exist in the total carotene extract. [162]

The actual mechanism by which the transformations of the basic saturated precursor is converted to the unsaturated carotenoids was envisioned by Porter and Lincoln to occur by either of two mechanisms. In the first case, a separate enzyme would be required for each step, the production of the enzyme being controlled by one gene. In the second case, only one enzyme would be required for all of the steps, but a particular and specific hydrogen acceptor would be necessary at each. Figure 7 outlines the transformations of the original hypothesis.

A somewhat different point of view was taken by Goodwin, who favored parallel pathways of synthesis. [65, 69, 74] After the publication of the Porter–Lincoln work, Goodwin investigated the synthesis of lycopene in tomatoes. He measured the amount of different carotenoids produced in the fruit ripened at 30°C. Under such circumstances, very little lycopene but normal amounts of carotene are produced. At low temperatures, β-carotene synthesis was much less affected than the lycopene synthesis. Based upon these experiments and those of Tomes, [203] Goodwin argued that if the synthesis of β-carotene occurred at the expense of lycopene, it would not be possible to accumulate β-carotene with little or no production of lycopene, particularly at the lower temperatures. If the synthesis were sequential, one would expect that the synthesis of β-carotene would be affected in the same manner and to a like degree as that of lycopene. [67]

As an argument against the sequential pathway of synthesis, Goodwin also cited some work on tomatoes containing the lutescent gene. Fruit containing the lutescent gene ripened in about 2 weeks as yellow tomatoes with normal amounts of carotene but very little lycopene. Suddenly, within a very short period of time, 36 hours at the most, relatively large amounts of lycopene were synthesized. In other tomato varieties, genetic blocks were cited as causing a marked increase in the synthesis of β-carotene at the expense of lycopene. [132] These experimental facts were used to conclude that the synthesis of β-carotene, at least its final steps, cannot go through lycopene, thus in a sense demolishing the latter part of the Porter–Lincoln hypothesis.

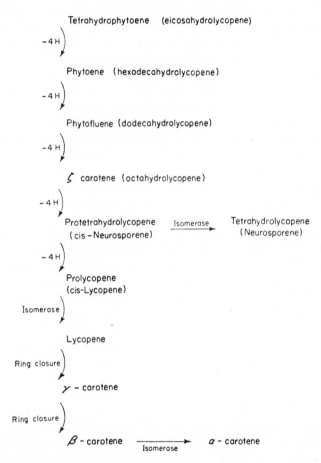

Fig. 7. Sequential formation of carotenes from a saturated C_{40} precursor as proposed by Porter and Lincoln. [162]

Mackinney, Jenkins, Rick, and Tomes, in a number of publications, [133, 137–9, 201–3] reported upon the interactions of a number of genes found in wild and domesticated types of tomatoes. In some investigations, the effects of the lutescent gene upon β-carotene and lycopene synthesis were studied. Additionally, investigations were made of the genes R+, T+, B+, at and gh in crosses of *Lycopersicon esculentum*. This further work resulted in the statement: "When the effects of R, T, and B on fruit carotenoids are examined, we must conclude that the gene interactions are complex." [142] All three of the genes affect lycopene synthesis; other genes affect β-carotene synthesis, others affect phytoene and still others the stereochemistry of the pigments produced. At the present time, it must be concluded that the work with genetic crosses of tomatoes and mutant tomatoes cannot substantiate an argument either for or against the step-wise synthesis of the unsaturated from the saturated carotenoids. One portion of this work, however, apparently bears directly upon the scheme, and the summations of the various investigations would substantiate that it is unlikely that β-carotene is produced solely from lycopene in any of the plant tissues so far investigated although an enzyme system has been reported which will convert lycopene to β-carotene. [74, 47]

In the fungus *Rhizophlyctis rosea*, lycopene is synthesized under experimental conditions between 7 and 14 days, while the synthesis of the second major pigment of the organism, γ-carotene, is initiated at the time the lycopene concentration reaches a steady-state level. When C^{14}-labeled mevalonate was used as a substrate during the entire growth period, the label in both carotenoids were equal. If, however, mevalonate were added early and then removed prior to the formation of γ-carotene, the lycopene acquired a very high specific activity, while the γ-carotene formed later did not acquire any comparable level of radioactivity. If the reverse experiment were performed, i.e. that the mevalonate was added after the formation steady-state concentration of lycopene was reached, very little activity was incorporated into the lycopene, while a high level of activity appeared in the γ-carotene. This experiment was cited as an argument against the conversion of lycopene to a cyclic structure. [81]

Beeler and Porter reported data indicating that cyclization may take place at neurosporene in addition to lycopene. [16] Porter and Anderson have published a revised pathway which requires the removal of two hydrogens per step, and includes the conversion of lycopene to β-carotene through γ-carotene. [163]

Mackinney *et al.*, on the basis of experiments with tomatoes and *Phycomyces*, proposed a very general scheme which divided the formation of carotenoids into three steps. [29] Step 1 was the formation of an intermediate substance common to all subsequent mechanisms of carotenoid synthesis. Step 2 was considered a branch point where part of the precursor leads to the formation of aliphatic compounds and the remainder to alicyclic substances. [30] This would imply that phytoene and phytofluene are precursors of the more unsaturated carotenoids but only of those of an aliphatic nature. Conversely, the alicyclic carotenoids would be formed in an independent pathway. In this generalization, there would be no necessity for the ring closure to occur after the formation of the C_{40} chain, but could conceivably occur at the C_{20} level. [142]

One of the basic difficulties with the schemes of Porter–Lincoln and others was the uncertainty of some of the structures of the carotenoids supposed as intermediates. At the present time, the proposed elementary structures, phytoene $C_{40}H_{64}$, phytofluene $C_{40}H_{62}$, ζ-carotene $C_{40}H_{60}$, and neurosporene $C_{40}H_{58}$, appear to have reconciled the results of various dehydrogenation procedures. [167, 168, 74] These structures are strongly supported by nuclear magnetic resonance data, although they no longer fit the original proposal for a stepwise removal of four hydrogen atoms at a time. [45]

The problem posed by the conversion of one carotenoid to another is exemplified in the extreme phase by the question of ring closure. Lycopene, in order to give rise to β-carotene, must undergo a cyclization and must lose a double bond. If one attempts to cyclize lycopene directly, it is found to be impossible owing to the steric hindrance of the terminal methyl groups, unless the isopropylidene group is first hydrogenated, allowing effective rotation about the single bond. If the squalene-lanosterol analogy is followed, it would seem that the mechanism required would be an acid catalyzed proton attack on the terminal double bond. This double bond, unlike the rest in the central chain of the lycopene molecule, is an isolated one, and since it is terminal it possesses the most basic characteristics. The proton attack would then occur between carbons 1 and 2 of the lycopene molecule, and provided there is a double bond at the 5,6 position as in lycopene, the resulting carbonium ion would attach at carbon 6, followed by a proton discharge. The cyclization product in this case will be a six-membered ring. [17] As pointed out by Mackinney, this hypothesis has not been tested by labeling techniques. [142] In the case cited, the proton would be discharged at carbon 5 of the β-carotene, rather than the charge carried along the chain as in the squalene cyclization.

This hypothesis has now been tested by Goodwin and Williams. Utilizing doubly-labeled, i.e. 2-C^{14}, 4 or 3T mevalonic acid, they incubated *Phycomyces blakesleeanus* with the substrate and analyzed both the phytoene and β-carotene for the ratios of tritium to C^{14}. The ratio of T to C^{14} in phytoene with 8 isoprene residues and open rings should be 8:8. If the ring closure of phytoene to give ultimately β-carotene were to occur by the removal of 1 tritium per end group, the ratio should amount to 6:8 in β-carotene. After crystallization and analysis, they found a ratio of 8:8 in phytoene, 6:6 in squalene, and 6:8 in β-carotene. This would confirm to a very large extent the mechanism postulated above. [84, 83]

Considering the various suggestions cited against the completely sequential system, Rabourn postulated a unifying theory of carotenoid biogenesis which is shown in Fig. 9. [168, 143–8] This theory overcomes most of the objections to the original scheme, although it still retains its salient features. It differs primarily in the later stages where the pivotal carotene is ζ-carotene. The subsequent lines follow different pathways and lead to lycopene, γ-carotene, and β-carotene. Neurosporene is thought to be $C_{40}H_{58}$ and nuclear magnetic resonance studies show that it has the formula of a dihydrolycopene, whereas it was previously thought to be a tetrahydrolycopene. [52, 153, 45] In this sense, the scheme separates the formation of the aliphatic from the alicyclic carotenoids and avoids the very great difficulties of placing lycopene ahead of β-carotene in a sequential pathway. The presence in natural sources of many minor pigments, generally in small amounts, may find an explanation by this

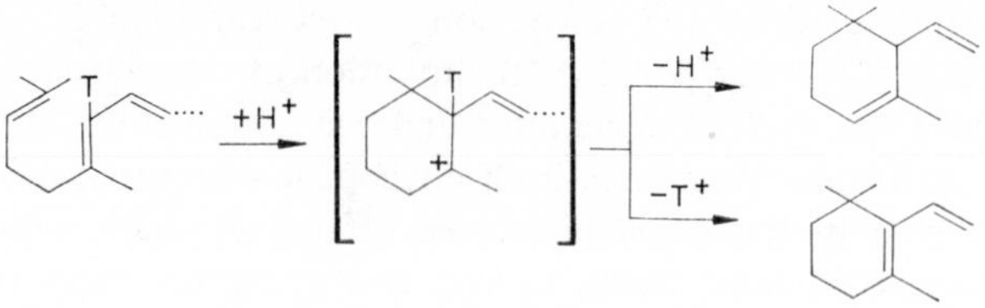

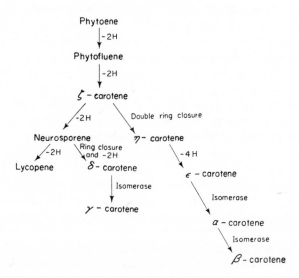

FIG. 8. Cyclization of carotenes.

Phytoene

$\downarrow$ -2H

Phytofluene

$\downarrow$ -2H

ζ – carotene

-2H   Double ring closure

Neurosporene η – carotene

-2H   Ring closure
      and -2H   -4H

Lycopene δ – carotene

                              ϵ – carotene

      Isomerase

γ – carotene

                Isomerase

                α – carotene

                Isomerase

                β – carotene

FIG. 9. Rabourn's proposed pathway for the C_{40} carotenes. Note that most dehydrogenations involve two H atoms, and ring closure results in an α ionone ring. A simultaneous closure of both rings of carotene is postulated.

scheme. It must be noted, however, that no definite assignments can be given to these pigments as to their positions within the sequence until their structures are confirmed. These minor pigments are found in almost all natural systems, but in extremely minute concentrations. Their presence was largely overlooked until recently, since their separation was difficult and their identification even more complicated. The fact that they accumulate in systems only to a very limited extent, of course, does not mean that they do not serve a significant relation to the synthetic pathway. One could postulate that the mere fact that they occur in such small quantities under normal conditions indicates that they are extremely active metabolically, have a high turnover and exist in small pools.

The results cited previously and the hypothesis based upon them have originated largely from experiments under static conditions in which the carotenoids of a tissue were analyzed quantitatively after the cessation of growth or synthesis. Their relation to one another is postulated on the basis of the amount of accumulation and of the differences in structural character-istics of the various pigments. It is instructive then to turn to the evidence with respect to the rearrangement of normal carotenoid biosynthesis, making the assumption that accumulation of related isoprenoids represents normal intermediates and not by-products. The agents of rearrangement are mutation, chemical inhibition, or normal stages of growth wherein the full complement of pigments is not reached.

The effect of diphenylamine upon carotenogenesis was first noticed by Kharasch as early as 1936. [119] Specific inhibitions of the colored com-pounds with accompanying stimulation of the saturated group was found in *Mycobacterium phlei* by Turian and by Turian and Haxo. [205, 206] Other investigators have studied the effect of inhibitors on the production of colored pigments in *Rhodospirillum rubrum*, *Allomyces javanicus* and *Chroma-tium* (spp.) where there is a marked trend toward the formation of the more reduced carotenoids. [73, 207, 74] In other organisns, the addition of diphenyl-amine has no specific antichromogenic effects. [70, 76] In general, the effect of diphenylamine, when added to a growing culture, is to inhibit the produc-tion of the β-carotene group of pigments and concurrently to enhance the production of the aliphatic carotenoids, such as phytoene and phytofluene. In most instances, there is less effect on growth than there is on carotenoid production.

In the static experiments the effect was interpreted as showing a specific inhibition of a dehydrogenation reaction, and thus is used as evidence for the conversion of the hydrocarbons to the unsaturated carotenes.

Kinetic experiments were performed by Jensen et al., using *Rhodospirillum rubrum* in which the carotenoid synthesis was inhibited by the addition of diphenylamine. [105] The diphenylamine was added initially to the cultures which were allowed to produce the phytoene group extensively. The inhibitor was then removed by washing, and the rate of synthesis of unsaturated carotenoids was determined. The results of these experiments showed that there is stoichiometric relation between the loss of phytofluene and ζ-caro-tene, and the production of unsaturated carotenoids. This indicates that, as far as phytofluene is concerned, there is an apparent conversion of one C_{40} compound to another. If one considers this result with respect to phytoene, the relationship is not as direct. The experiment showed little or no loss of the excess phytoene produced and consequently led to the proposal that phytoene, when produced in large quantities, becomes metabolically inactive. In addition to the sequential build-up of the highly coloured compounds from the hydrocarbons, similar concurrent transformations of hydroxylated derivatives of the hydrocarbons were detected. The authors pointed out the possibility that these mono- and dihydroxy compounds could be (i) intermediates in the dehydrogenation reactions or (ii) by-products of the main biosynthetic chain. A number of possible routes to the main pigment produced by *Rhodospirillum*, spirilloxanthin (rhodoviolascin) have been proposed. [159, 208, 116, 114] In other words, for each hydrocarbon there appear under the experimental conditions a mono- and a dihydroxy-derivative. It would not be unreasonable to suppose that the hydroxylations of these hydrocarbons could take place at any time during the conversion, if structural determinations show that the hydroxyls are at the end of the hydrocarbons. This has been shown for hydroxylycopene and demethylated spirilloxanthin. [2, 4, 111, 112] The compounds could remain in the synthetic chain after the hydroxylations take place and could be carried along in the conversion without affecting the final outcome of the sequence.

In all experiments cited, the effect of diphenylamine is considered to be a specific one—this is, the blocking of a dehydrogenation reaction. Rilling has recently suggested that diphenylamine is a competitive inhibitor for the carotenoid dehydrogenase in the sequential conversion of the saturated to the unsaturated compounds by virtue of its steric resemblance to the saturated segments of the isoprenoid molecule. [174] Presumably the diphenylamine would adhere to an enzyme surface in lieu of the carotenoid, and thus prevent the effective dehydrogenation of the central portion of the carotenoid molecule competitively. In *in vitro* systems, diphenylamine is a powerful antioxidant and prevents, under various environmental conditions, the oxidation of carotenoids. In one report, using rather special culturing conditions, Varma *et al.* showed that diphenylamine could effectively increase the production of the alicyclic carotenoid in *Phycomyces* which is in contrast with other experiments. [211] The effect here was ascribed to the prevention of β-carotene turnover under oxidizing conditions.

Numerous other chemical agents have been implicated as affecting carotenoid synthesis. Among these may be listed adenosine monophosphate, which is reported to reverse the diphenylamine effect in *Phycomyces*. [70] The compounds β-ionone and methylheptenone have been shown to effect the stimulation of the alicyclic carotenoids and of the aliphatic ones, respectively. [134–6] β-Ionone is used to stimulate carotene synthesis on a commercially feasible scale by employing selected strains of fungi. [7, 8]

The effect of β-ionone on carotenoid synthesis has at least partially been explained by Reyes in recent years. It was suggested that in *Phycomyces* the isoprenoid acts as an inhibitor by blocking a negative feedback mechanism.

It was postulated that the rate of formation of β-carotene in fungi was determined by the level of carotenoid formed previously. Thus an increase in carotenoid concentration would decrease its rate of formation and eventually result in a steady state. β-Ionone resembling the terminal portions of the carotenoid molecule could substitute for it in the feedback mechanism and thus block its regulatory function. In a series of experiments it was shown that this indeed was the case. Although β-ionone is not incorporated into carotenoids, it is an extremely effective promoter of carotenogenesis in several fungi. Interestingly enough, the β-ionone effect can also be shown in sterol synthesis, since it promotes the synthesis of these compounds in a manner similar to the carotenoids. Experimental evidence indicated that the point of feedback control was at the level of the isomeric C_5 pyrophosphates.

In other organisms, β-ionone acts as an inhibitor. Thus in *Rhodotorula* yeasts, the effect is to stimulate the precursors of the carotenoids such as phytoene at the expense of β-carotene. [187]

Other compounds such as streptomycin, ferrous sulfate, thiamine, ergosterol, glycerol and biotin have also been used to modify the formation of polyenes. [181, 182, 205, 189, 164, 58, 120] The primary difficulty in interpreting the results based upon their use is that often these effects are limiting either to a particular species or in some cases to specific organisms.

Light has a stimulating effect on carotenogenesis in fungi. It has been shown that exposure to light during any stage of growth of *Phycomyces* will trigger carotene production. [30, 59] The effect of light and oxygen on carotenoid synthesis by *Neurospora crassa* has been studied by Zalokar [235] who determined the rates of formation of phytoene, an acidic pigment (neurosporaxanthin), β-carotene, γ-carotene, lycopene, neurosporene and other members of the aliphatic series, after exposing the organisms to light. His results showed that β-carotene, lycopene and neurosporene appear simultaneously and at the same rate, just after exposure. This would indicate that these pigments are formed via independent pathways by separate sequential reactions. In this case, a definite decrease in phytoene occurred during the formation of the other pigments. In another experiment, a restriction in the oxygen supply was found to cause *Neurospora* to decrease in phytoene content. This decrease was not related to the formation or change in concentration of any other carotenoid. [236]

Rilling, in a study on photoinduction, found in *Mycobacterium* spp. that phytoene and phytofluene were photoinduced initially, followed by more highly unsaturated carotenoids, and postulated that the photoinduction of carotenoid synthesis depended upon inducing a carotenogenic enzyme as a result of exposure to light and oxygen. [173]

The mutations of microorganisms have been used by a number of investigators to study the path of carotenoid synthesis. Bonner *et al.* used mutants of *Rhodotorula rubra*. [18] The normal wild type produced primarily a red pigment, torulene, while the series of seven ultraviolet mutants produced various combinations of red, brown, orange, and colorless colonies. The red mutants had increased synthesis of all components, e.g. γ-carotene, β-carotene, neurosporene, torulene and phytofluene. The orange mutants contained primarily γ- and β-carotenes, neurosporene and phytofluene, whereas the colorless contained no polyenes. Based upon the assumption that each mutant represented an enzymatic block, Bonner proposed phytofluence as the immediate precursor of both torulene, and β- and γ-carotenes. It might be noted that the colorless mutants were not checked for the presence of phytoene, since it was not known at the time.

Haxo examined the polyene composition of eight different strains of *Neurospora*.[96, 97] Three categories of polyene dearrangement were noted: (1) the complete absence of acidic polyenes, (2) general reduction in the synthesis of hydrogenated polyenes, elimination of xanthophylls and most carotenes but normal phytoene production, and (3) the loss of all colored carotenoids with enhanced phytoene production. As Haxo pointed out in his review, the patterns of polyene deficiency observed can equally be explained by the two opposing theories of carotenoid synthesis, i.e., by the assumption that carotenoids are formed either sequentially or through parallel syntheses from a common precursor. In either case, none of the blocks observed was absolute in the sense that in most instances there was some leakage around the blocks. The only exception was an absolute block preventing the formation of the acidic carotenoids.

Using *Rhodopseudomonas spheroides*, Griffiths and Stanier isolated fifty mutants which represented varying degrees of inhibition of carotenoid synthesis. One was designated the blue-green mutant and contained only phytoene.[90] In this case there appeared to be a complete block of all other carotenoids. Another designated as the green mutant contained predominately neurosporene, hydroxyneurosporene and ζ-carotene, but produced small amounts of more highly unsaturated compounds. The brown mutants contained the pigments of the parent strain, pigment Y and pigment R (spheroidenone), but the latter pigment was present in much reduced amounts.[154, 112a] The evidence developed indicated that there is a possibility of a sharp block between phytoene and the less saturated carotenoids. Secondary blocks are possible, but these were seldom complete in the sense that they merely reduced, but not completely eliminated compounds on one side of the block while allowing accumulation on the other. The results supply additional substantiation to the theory of interconvertibility of the saturated to the less saturated carotenoids, but here again an alternate postulation is possible. No information on the point of ring closure was afforded because purple bacteria generally contain no cyclic forms, with the only known exception of traces of alicyclic carotenoids in *Rhodomicrobium vannieleii* whose morphology is also atypical.[51, 212]

Claes described a series of *Chlorella* X-ray mutants in which chlorophyll synthesis is almost completely blocked and the synthesis of plastid carotenoids rearranged to varying degrees. [37-41] In the mutants there appeared a number of more saturated carotenoids than are normally found in wild types. In one case, mutant 5/871 produced phytoene alone; a complete block existed between it and the rest of the polyenes. Mutant 5/515 produced phytoene, phytofluene, ζ-carotene and no additional carotenoids. The others produced varying amounts of most of the carotenoids. Mutant 5/520 produced different carotenoids depending on whether it was grown in light or dark. In contrast with other mutant experiments, this group of mutants showed a block higher up in the sequence of carotenoids, as compared to those examined previously.

If the mutant 5/520 is grown in the dark aerobically, it accumulates phytoene, phytofluene, ζ-carotene, protetrahydrolycopene, and prolycopene, and if then transferred to an illuminated anaerobic system, there is a mass production of α-carotene, β-carotene and carotene X (possibly β-zeacarotene). [158] Simultaneously, there is a linear decrease of the accumulated ζ-carotene with the increase in the three more desaturated carotenes. The phytofluene content in contrast to the work reported by Jensen *et al.*, does not change. These results might be interpreted as strong evidence for the formation of the unsaturated from the saturated one, but one wonders why in one case photofluene seems to be utilized and in another only ζ-carotene.

Allen has isolated a series of ultraviolet mutants of *Chorella pyrenoidosa* in which the carotenoid synthesis has been deranged. [2] These mutants were examined by Goodwin who reported that they were closely similar to Claes' mutants and again showed a sharp block at the phytoene level. [77] The others showed blocks at phytofluene and β-carotene.

In contrast, the mutant of *Chlamydomonas reinhardii* studied by Sager and Zalokar, although showing a block in carotenoid as well as chlorophyll synthesis, showed no accumulation of the more saturated hydrocarbons. [179] The carotenes present were the usual types except in greatly reduced amounts.

In the photosynthetic green bacteria, the structures of chlorobactene and hydroxy chlorobactene show them to have a trimethyl aromatic end-group, similar to isorenieratene and others similar to lycopene and 1′,2′-dihydro-1′-hydroxy, respectively. The identity of leprotene from *Mycobacterium phlei* and isorenieratene from the sponge *Reniera japonica* shows the diversity of bacterial carotenoids. [113] Yamaguchi indicated that the aromatic groups in renieratene, isorenieratene, and renierapurpurin were trimethylphenyl groups. It is, however, premature to speculate on the biochemical significance of the aromatic carotenoids. [222-7]

V. XANTHOPHYLLS

The oxygenated carotenoids, generally called xanthophylls, exhibit the greatest variation in structure. The ability of animals to ingest and modify carotenoids contributes in large measure to the variability in structure found. The resultant compounds that can be isolated from animal sources are on occasions identical to those found in plants. Although the area of animal modification of carotenoids is an important one, it is nevertheless one in which an organism serves only as a modifying medium. Thus, we will concern ourselves here with those organisms which synthesize the entire carotenoid *de novo*.

The groups attached to the C_{40} carotenoid skeleton consist of hydroxyls, carbonyls, methoxyl, epoxy and carboxyl groups. No functional groups containing elements other than carbon, hydrogen, or oxygen are known to occur naturally. The organic chemistry of most of the well-characterized xanthophylls are discussed in detail by Karrer. [118]

Considering first the hydroxyl groups of carotenoids, these are generally of the secondary type and they occur almost exclusively in positions 3 and 3'. Positions 4 and 4' are next in abundance in higher plants. There exist other possibilities, of course, and there is evidence that hydroxyls may be attached to the 5 and 5' positions in alicyclic carotenoids; these hydroxyl groups are of importance because of their tertiary character. [118] Weedon and Jensen have shown that in the purple bacteria, hydroxyls occur in the 1 and 1' positions, and since the carotenoids in this organism are aliphatic, these hydroxyls too are tertiary in character. [14, 107]

Unlike the theories of formation of the various carotenoids, there is general agreement that the xanthophylls are formed from a parent carotenoid and do not arise independently of the related compounds. This then presupposes a mechanism for the addition of oxygen, or of oxygen and other groupings to a series of compounds having the carbon configuration of the xanthophyll to be produced. In higher plants, the ratio of xanthophylls to carotenoids varies rather widely from as low as 1:1 to as high as 1:15. The hydroxylated compounds occur free in green tissue but are often esterified in the cytoplasm.

A comprehensive work on the xanthophylls is to be found in an extensive set of publications by Strain who studied the fading of leaves and the xanthophyll content of various higher plants. [192, 193] Qualitatively, when the leaves fade, there is a loss of chlorophyll and a general fall in the level of non-oxygenated carotenoids. Quantitatively, it can be shown that there is a net synthesis of zeaxanthin (3,3'-dihydroxy-β-carotene).

While many theories have been proposed for the oxygenation of the carotenes to form xanthophylls, no direct evidence was presented until Claes, using a *Chlorella* mutant (5/520), was able to separate carotene biosynthesis from xanthophyll synthesis in a closed system. [40, 41] The mutants, when grown aerobically in the dark, produce carotene precursors. Upon illumination with red light anaerobically, the carotene precursors were transformed into three carotenes, α, β, and carotene-X. Subsequent aeration in the dark, produced xanthophylls at the expense of the carotenes previously formed. This evidence pointed strongly to molecular oxygen as being instrumental in the formation of hydroxyl groups.

In the purple bacterium, *Rhodospirillum rubrum*, the main pigment is spirilloxanthin which contains, instead of hydroxyl groups, methoxyl groups. These methoxyl groups arise from hydroxyl groups as shown by Jensen. [108–10, 112] In the kinetic experiments described previously, the mono- and dihydroxy-derivatives of the carotenes were formed simultaneously with the carotenes. Recent work by the same author has revealed that the hydroxyl groups of the immediate precursors are located at positions 1 and 1' exclusively. [111, 112] Strong evidence for the formation of spirilloxanthin from a 1,1'-dihydroxy-derivative was obtained by isolation of the 1,1'-dihydroxy-derivative from a strain of *Halobacterium*. [111, 112] This derivative was subsequently chemically methylated, and the resulting product was found to be identical to spirilloxanthin. Goodwin also showed that the carbon of the methoxyl group can arise from a 1 carbon source. [22]

The xanthophylls of bacterial species differ considerably from those of the higher plants, whereas the biogenetic precursors of lycopene are presumed identical. Liaaen Jensen and her colleagues [114] have formulated a biosynthetic scheme for photosynthetic bacteria based upon the structures of the individual pigments. The reaction type includes dehydrogenation, cyclization, hydroxylation, hydration, methylation, oxidation (aerobic) and an anaerobic oxidation (dehydrogenation of a secondary alcohol). The latter reaction explains the occurrence of a keto group in warmingone and okenone, pigments occurring in the obligate anaerobes *Chromatium warmingii migula* and *C. okenii*, respectively, whereas the conjugated carbonyl group generally occurs in the 2,2' position in photosynthetic bacteria and is dependent for its formation on the presence of molecular oxygen. The postulated pathway for these changes in photosynthetic bacteria is shown in Fig. 10.

Direct evidence for the utilization of aerobic oxygen in the formation of xanthophylls is given by Yamamoto. [229] When O^{18}-water was used in a medium on which *Chlorella vulgaris* was grown in the dark, the major xanthophyll, lutein, was shown to contain no O^{18} from the water. In contrast the alternative experiment, e.g. growth in an O^{18} enriched atmosphere, indicated that the same xanthophyll accumulated O^{18} from the molecular oxygen.

Several theories for the interrelationship of oxygen-containing carotenoids have been published. A scheme, illustrating the function of carotenoids in oxygen transport, has been proposed by Cholnoky *et al.* [34, 35] Initially, carotenoids with the β-configuration are formed, that is β-carotene and zeaxanthin. These are converted to the epoxides and, after reduction, are reconverted to their original forms or α-carotene and lutein, respectively.

The proposal thus explains the curious situation that carotenes of green leaves are predominantly of the β type, whereas the xanthophylls are of the α structure. The proposal would also explain the presence of large amounts of individual pigments at different times and relate them to the physiological activities of the plant. There is, however, one objection to this scheme which will be discussed under the formation of epoxides.

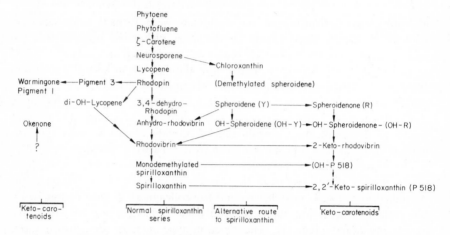

FIG. 10. Pathway of carotenoid biosynthesis in photosynthetic bacteria as postulated by S. L. Jensen.

Krinsky suggests that the conversion of the 5,6-epoxy to the β-ionone derivative would proceed through the 5-hydroxy, 6-dihydro derivatives by the reduction of the epoxide group. He further postulates that this compound could be dehydrated into either the α- or the β-ionone configuration. [123]

Losev, in experiments utilizing $C^{14}O_2$ in barley and wheat seedlings, found that lutein is formed most rapidly, followed by lutein epoxide, zeaxanthin, violaxanthin and, finally, neoxanthin. Based upon these observations, he suggests that neoxanthin cannot be a precursor of violaxanthin or lutein, and that violaxanthin is not a precursor of lutein. [127]

Redfearn, in experiments using CO_2 labeled with C^{14}, found that there was an equal distribution of activity between β-carotene and the xanthophylls. [169, 170] This is in contrast with the work reported by Anderson et al., who found that the β-carotene activity under similar circumstances was 10 times that of the xanthophylls. [5] In either case, however, there is a ready incorporation of activity into both carotene and the xanthophylls in green photosynthetic tissues.

The proposal that the carotenoids in green tissue may be used as an antioxidant has been made by Stanier. [89] Calvin, on the basis of the same data, postulated a direct energy absorption mechanism. [26] Oxygen transport has also been suggested by Calvin, [50, 5] but it was further suggested that the protective action of carotenoids consists in the prevention of the oxidation of an SH-enzyme system vital to photosynthesis.

In green photosynthetic tissues, where one can demonstrate the existence of hydroxylated carotenoids, there is in addition an almost universal occurrence of epoxy compounds. These compounds, in general, have an oxygen bridge between carbon atoms 5,6 and 5',6' and, as illustrated previously, these oxygen bridges have been implicated with the hydroxylated compounds in an oxygen transport function.

Anderson et al., as well as Cholnoky, have suggested that the epoxides may serve as an oxygen carrying system and believe that there is a direct oxygenation of the xanthophylls by molecular oxygen. [5, 34] Yamamoto et al., in experiments utilizing $O_2{}^{18}$, have recently shown that the oxygen in the epoxy carotenoid antheraxanthin obtained from spinach leaves is derived from oxygen. [230a]

Under conditions of the Hill Reaction (chloroplast reaction) carried out in the presence of O^{18} water no significant labeling was found in the xanthophylls. The isotope was transferred from the water to molecular oxygen without the mediation of the xanthophylls. Thus, these compounds cannot be assigned a major role in photosynthetic oxygen transport. [228, 230] These results were later confirmed by Shneour and Calvin. [185]

Redfearn and Glover showed that in detached leaves held in the dark, there as a coincidental production of carotene epoxides with a drop in β-carotene. [170] They suggested that the β-carotene was the most labile of the carotenoids and the first stage in its destruction was the formation of epoxides. When the leaves were subsequently illuminated, the β-carotene increased to its normal level and the epoxides disappeared. The interpretation in this case was that the β-carotene was formed by a new synthesis rather than by a reversal of the dark reaction.

Yamamoto, in studying the formation of xanthophylls, found that the formation of their epoxides was not simultaneous with the formation of xanthophylls, the latter preceding the former. In bean leaves the addition of water-derived oxygen proceeded in two steps; oxygen was added to zeaxanthin to yield first antheraxanthin and secondly the antheraxanthin was oxidized to violaxanthin. A proposed scheme for the formation of the xanthophylls and epoxy pigments is shown in Fig. 11.

In an analysis of a portion of the scheme proposed in Fig. 11, Krinsky observed the conversion of antheraxanthin to zeaxanthin in the light under anaerobic condition, and the reverse under non-illumination. [122] He was also able to observe the same conversion in lyophilized cells *Euglena gracilis* to which FMN and NADPH were added. Recently, the same group has demonstrated the conversion of antheraxanthin to zeaxanthin in chloroplasts isolated by sonic oscillation. In this case malic acid was required to obtain full activity, and was postulated to be the source of reducing power.

Again, it may be pointed out that there is general agreement among the workers in this portion of the carotenoid field that the epoxides are derived from xanthophylls, and this suggestion is now supported by experimental evidence. While it is clear that the xanthophylls as a class do not function directly in photosynthetic oxygen transport, it may still be suggested that they act as mediators or storage units in the process.

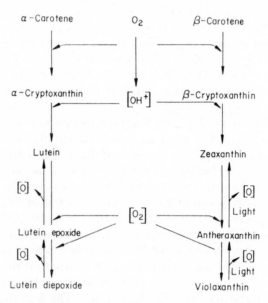

FIG. 11. Proposed interrelationships of leaf xanthophylls.

Peroxide formation in carotenoids has been suggested for a great many years. It was first speculated upon by Lumry and then experimentally investigated by Dorough and Calvin. [128, 50] These authors suggested that the two oxygen atoms from a carotenoid diepoxide could meet in the center of the carotene molecule to form a peroxide. On decomposition, the oxygen would be evolved and the original carotene regenerated.

Carotenoids with carbonyl groups are not normally found in the green leaves of higher plants. Their primary occurrence is in fungi, algae, bacteria, fruits and in animal tissues. The carbonyl linkages are most often found at the end of the chromophoric chain in the 4,4′ positions. Cholnoky has shown that capsorubin is an exception to the 4,4′ position placement of carbonyls in that it is presumably at the 6,6′ position. [36] However, in this case the cyclohexenyl ring has undergone a rearrangement to a cyclopentanyl, a saturated five carbon ring. [15] Fucoxanthin is a rather peculiar carotenoid in that it possesses an allene grouping at one end of its chromophore. The only occurrence of this type of linkage has so far been in this principal pigment of the brown algae. [204, 126, 104, 19] The addition of a carbonyl grouping to the long conjugated chromophore reinforces it considerably, and the carbonyl pigments are characterized by having maxima of their absorption spectra at longer wavelengths than their parent compounds. They also lack the fine structure found in most of the other carotenoids.

When carbonyls occur adjacent to a hydroxyl group as in astaxanthin, acidic properties of enols are conferred. [118] Astaxanthin, which is considered the primary coloring matter of crustacea, is thought of as primarily an animal pigment, but it also occurs in encysted algae such as *Euglena* and *Hematococcus*. [199, 200] This pigment constitutes an example of an animal modification of carotenoid. Locusts, crustacea, and flamingos, produce astaxanthin which is identical to the carotenoid found in plants. [66, 60, 56] There is no information as to whether the method of production of astaxanthin is the same in animals as it is in plants.

The origin of the oxygen atoms in the carbonyl group appears to be similar to that of the hydroxyl. Van Niel demonstrated a quantitative conversion of pigment Y to pigment R in *Rhodopseudomonas spheroides*. [209] The *Rhodopseudomonas* was grown anaerobically to yield a brownish yellow microorganism. Upon the introduction of air, the organism exhibits an observable color change within 15 minutes and at the end of several hours, there is almost a quantitative conversion of the yellow pigment to the red one. This might be pointed out as one of the very few examples where there is unequivocal conversion of one carotenoid to another. Shneour has confirmed by direct experiment that the carbonyl oxygen is obtained from atmospheric oxygen. [184] Stokke and Sorenson present additional evidence that a ketone is produced from a parent carotenoid. [191] In this experiment, 3,3'-diketo-β-carotene, rhodoxanthin, appears in the leaves of *Reseda* when it is illuminated at $0°C$ with light of a wavelength longer than 500 mμ. The production of rhodoxanthin is quantitatively related to the decrease of lutein in the leaves. The mechanism of this conversion has not been closely studied but it would appear most interesting. The simplest chemical reaction that could be envisioned would be the removal of the two hydrogens from the hydroxyl of lutein to produce a carbonyl. The two examples stated constitute two different modes of modification, either by a direct aerobic oxidation or by the removal of hydrogen from hydroxyl groups already existent on the pigment.

There are several examples of the production of carbonyl-like pigments in algae, but since the structure of these compounds has not been established, it is difficult to ascribe metabolic conversions to their production. In experiments with *Neurospora*, Haxo showed that one of the mutant strains possessed a block between the neutral xanthophylls and the acidic xanthophylls. [96] Presumably this would constitute a conversion of the methoxylated or hydroxylated xanthophylls to the acidic form. The structure of the acidic compounds was not established. Similarly, Zalokar could demonstrate a decrease in the phytoene level with an increase in the production of acidic xanthophylls. [235] Since again the structure of these compounds is not known, it is hard to ascribe a mechanism to such a conversion if it exists. This last finding is contrary to most of the other theories of formation since in Zalokar's case, there was no note of changes in concentration of the neutral xanthophylls. If the two events are to be correlated and are not in conflict with previously reported results, it can be assumed that the metabolic scheme must possess a rather large number of steps.

Carboxyl groups have been generally associated with apocarotenoids such as azafrin, crocetin and bixin. [118] These compounds, since they contain less than forty carbon atoms, are by nature thought to be oxidation products of the carotenoids. A number of investigators have implicated lipoxidase as the agent which actively oxidizes the carotenoids in plants. [20, 213, 57] It is assumed that the enzyme acts directly on unsaturated fatty acids and the carotene is indirectly oxidized by the unstable peroxides they form.

Recently, torularhodin, the pigment of red yeast and *Sporobolomyces*, has been shown to be a C_{40} compound with a carboxyl group attached to the $1'$ position. [177] Hithertofore, it has been considered to belong in the same class as bixin and azafrin. The compound has been assigned a provisional structure with $C_{37}H_{48}O_2$. [118] It has been considered to be a compound in which one ring of the β-carotene molecule had been opened by oxidation.

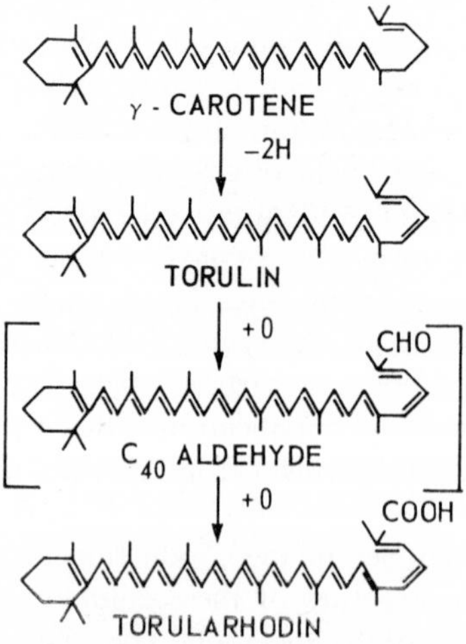

Fig. 12. Simpson *et al.*'s proposed pathway for biosynthesis of yeast carotenoids.

Thus, under the present structure, it is now believed to be dehydro-γ-carotene in which one of the terminal methyl groups attached to the open end is replaced by a carboxyl group.

With the confirmation of the structure of torulin as a dehydro-γ-carotene, [178] Simpson postulated that γ-carotene in *Rhodotorula gracilis* gives rise to torulin and subsequently, torularhodin, in the manner illustrated in Fig. 12. [186] He also demonstrated that one of the oxygens of torularhodin arises from molecular oxygen. [186]

VI. STERIC MODIFICATIONS

Zechmeister's work on *cis-trans* isomerization laid the basis for the identification of steric isomers which have markedly different light absorption characteristics. [237–9] Almost all of the carotenoids which are found in plant sources are in the *trans* configuration. This configuration, as well as that of the all-*cis* configuration requires that the chain of the carotenoid lies in a plane, and comparatively little energy is required to change the *trans* bond to the *cis* bond. [118] The investigations of *cis-trans* isomerization have been largely confined to an identification of the isomers and to the study of their chemical properties. There has been very little work upon the biological significance of these isomers. The degree of conversion to vitamin A is definitely known to be a function of the shape of the molecule. Thus, the introduction of a single *trans* or *cis* rotation can reduce the potency of the vitamin A precursor by 75 per cent. [3]

It has been shown by Mackinney and Jenkins that in the tomato the configurations of the carotenoids produced are controlled by a single gene. [133] This is in line with the generality that upon mutation, there is under most conditions an increase in the isomeric form of the carotenoids produced.

In the postulated pathways for the formation of β-carotene by dehydrogenation, there is a requirement that the shape of the molecule must change rather radically since the saturated molecule allows moderately free rotation about each of its bonds and the introduction of a double bond or the removal of hydrogen requires that the chain become more rigid. Thus, unless the original molecule is held in a specific configuration as an enzyme complex, the coiled form of the saturated C_{40} compound must be gradually straightened out during the hydrogenation to form the final all-*trans* β-carotene.

This problem is further complicated by the postulation that the central double bond in phytoene is a *cis* bond and would require, if this is to be transformed to the unsaturated carotenoid, that the bond be inverted to the *trans* configuration. [166] Along similar lines, phytofluene which occurs naturally, is in the *cis* form, and only upon chemical treatment is it converted to the *trans* configuration. In these two instances, the postulated immediate precursors to the highly unsaturated carotenoids have a steric configuration which is different from their so-called products.

Jungalwala and Porter[115] have recently confirmed the structures of natural phytoene and phytofluene to be 15,15' *cis* compounds, while natural ζ-carotene is all *trans*.

Claes, in an investigation of the X-ray mutants, described one which contained both all-*trans* and poly-*cis* lycopenes, as well as neurosporene and poly-*cis* neurosporene.[38] If grown in the dark, the *cis* forms appear but, when illuminated with blue light, the respective all-*trans* isomers are formed. Claes and Nakayama showed that for one mutant the *cis* forms are converted to the all-*trans* forms in red light, provided the irradiation is done in the absence of oxygen.[42] They suggested that the stereo configuration of the carotenoids in the chloroplast may be controlled by the chlorophyll. The conversion of the poly-*cis* to the all-*trans* isomers can be accomplished under the same conditions *in vitro*, using solutions of chlorophyll and carotenoids. This can be contrasted to the illumination of carotene solutions having no chlorophyll, in which circumstances there is no transformation of isomers at the same wavelenths. In other cases, under normal conditions if the irradiating wavelength is lowered, an equilibrium mixture of isomers is formed.

VII. VITAMIN A

The provitamin A activity of carotenoids is based on the presence of an unsubstituted β-ionylidene ring and is quite specific for this group. Growth tests are used to indicate the presence of such groups in carotenoids. The subject of vitamin A and details as to potency, storage, physiological responses, clinical manifestations, and pathology are covered in the excellent works of Moore, Ames, Deuel and Goodwin,[152, 3, 48, 78a] and in recent symposia.[156, 157]† We will not attempt to duplicate these discussions here, but merely point out some of the areas of interest.

Carotene is converted to vitamin A in the intestinal wall and is esterified and stored in the liver. The mechanism of the transformation of β-carotene → vitamin A is still in some doubt. Data are available indicating both central fission and terminal oxidation. The difficulty in examining the pathway is that the absolute yields and the rate of turnover are low.[62] About 90–95 per cent of the total body supply of vitamin A is in the liver; the remaining portions are found in other organs. The vitamin A function in vision is extremely important, yet the total supply in the retina is only 0·1 per cent of the total amount of vitamin A in the body. The biochemistry of photoreception and the participation of vitamin A derivatives in its function are discussed in a symposium on photoreception sponsored by the New York Academy of Sciences.[220]

A study of the various modifications of vitamin A is a subject of a number

† *Vitamins and Hormones* 18 (eds. R. S. Harris and D. S. Ingle), Academic Press, N.Y. (1960).

of recent papers. The C_{41}, C_{42} and C_{46} hydrocarbon analogues of vitamin A have been shown to possess biological activity for growth and liver storage. [194] The C_{25} substance likewise showed vitamin A activity and has been shown to give rise to vitamin A. [61, 53] Of considerable interest are the modifications of the β-ionone moiety which will still permit vitamin A activity. Although most modifications of this ring decrease the activity, it is rather surprising that some activity can still be displayed. The discovery of vitamin A_2 has suggested examination of carotenoids with 3,4-dehydro grouping. The synthesis of 3,4-monodehydro- and 3,4,3′,4′-dehydro-β-carotene has been described and their activities recorded to be 75 and 38 per cent of the activity of β-carotene. [102] Similarly, deoxylutein (3-hydroxy-3-dehydro-β-carotene) was shown to have 10 per cent of the activity of β-carotene in rat growth. [240]

The course of these transformations is not clear as apparently vitamin A_1 and A_2 are not interconvertible in the animal. Thus, it would appear that when the provitamin is broken, it results in a specific precursor for vitamin A_1 or A_2.

Recent work of Lakshmanan et al. [125] has shown that the 5,6 monoepoxide of vitamin A aldehyde had identical biological activity as vitamin A aldehyde. They also isolated a new visual pigment from the retinas of the rats which had a λ_{max} of 480 mμ and suggested that it was analogous to rhodopsin and porphyropsin.

Vitamin A activity has been ascribed to astaxanthin by Grangaud. [85–88] Subsequently, it has been shown that the vitamin A activity has been restricted to astaxanthin esters, and although these were capable of restoring growth, they did not support reproduction in white albino rats. [149]

The recent work of Thompson et al. [198] has shown that in the rat there are at least three functions of vitamin A in vision, in reproduction, and a systemic function. It was shown that vitamin A acid, retinoic acid could replace retinal in only the systemic functions.

Goldsmith [63] has shown the presence of vitamin A, retinene and retinene reductase in the heads of honey bees. Vitamin A appears to be related to the visual system showing increases during light adaptation and decreases during dark adaptation.

Work by Moatti on the formation of vitamin A in the fish Gambusia holbrookii showed that in this particular organism astaxanthin is a provitamin for both vitamins A_1 and A_2. [88, 151] It has been postulated that the formation of both vitamins A_1 and A_2 is through β-carotene, as this is found as a transient compound during the conversion. [88] Retinal in the same organisms is claimed to give rise to dehydroretinal. [151] Similar results were found in the red fish Crassius auratus. Kon and Fisher, in contrast, have shown that the guppy (Lebistes reticulatus) does not convert pure crystalline astaxanthin into vitamin A, although under the same conditions β-carotene is converted readily. [121] These interesting and rather conflicting results await confirmation by tracer studies.

VIII. SUMMARY

The work of the last ten years on the formation of the basic structure of carotenoids illustrates the close similarity between the biosynthesis of the various isoprenoid compounds. The data accumulated thus far indicate an identity of precursors in both sterol and carotenoid synthesis, at least as far as the basic repeating unit. The individual steps leading to the formation of the C_{40} chain have not been examined as minutely as they have in sterol synthesis and the particular enzymes concerned in the various steps have not been characterized. One of the divergences in the sterol and carotenoid synthesis is centered about major condensing units; it is likely that a C_{20} rather than a C_{15} unit is the condensing moiety.

The transformation of the basic C_{40} chain leading to the diverse carotenes and xanthophylls has been generally characterized, but the mechanism for the individual transformations have yet to be elucidated. The predominance of the evidence indicates that pathways for the interconversion of different carotenoids exist, while it has not been shown that all the carotenoids are formed from a single saturated precursor. Several alternate theories have been proposed, but none are unequivocal, since naturally occurring exceptions can be found for many of the individual steps in the suggested transformations. One of the biggest difficulties in the biochemical interpretation of the postulated pathways is the uncertainty of the chemical structures of compounds proposed as intermediates.

There is general agreement that the oxygenated carotenoids arise from the hydrocarbon types. The mechanisms for such conversions have had little study and only meagre data are available in the literature to indicate even the origin of the oxygen-containing groups attached. As a consequence, there is a need for additional investigations on the mechanism for the oxygenation of the carotenes.

The conversion of β-carotene and its isomers to vitamin A has been the subject of numerous researches, and in general the process is well known. The conversion of the various carotenoid derivatives to vitamin A active units, however, still require extensive investigation, particularly in the case of marine organisms.

REFERENCES

1. AGRANOFF, B. W., EGGERER, H., HENNING, V. and LYNEN, F. *J. Am. Chem. Soc.* **81**, 1254 (1959).
2. ALLEN, M. B., GOODWIN, T. W. and PHAGPOLNGARM, S. *J. Gen. Microbiol.* **23**, 93 (1960).
3. AMES, S. In *Ann. Rev. Biochem.*, p. 375, ed. J. M. Luck. Stanford University Press, Stanford, California, 1958.

4. ANDERSON, D. G., NORGARD, D. W. and PORTER, J. W. *Arch. Biochem. Biophys.* **88**, 68 (1960).
5. ANDERSON, J. M., BLASS, U. and CALVIN, M. *Plant Physiol.* **34**, 329 (1959).
6. ANDERSON, D. G. and PORTER, J. W. *Arch. Biochem. Biophys.* **97**, 509 (1962).
7. ANDERSON, R. F. U.S. Patent 2 890 989, June 15, 1959.
8. ANDERSON, R. F., ARNOLD, M., NELSON, G. E. N. and CIEGLER, A. J. *Agr. and Food Chem.* **6**, 543 (1958).
9. ANON. *Chem. Eng. News* **24**, 1235 (1946).
10. ARCHER, B. L., BARNARD, D. and COCKBAIN, E. G. *Proc. Roy. Soc.* B **1964** (in press). Cited in *Chemistry and Biochemistry of Plant Pigments*, p. 164, ed. T. W. Goodwin. Academic Press, London, 1965.
11. ARNAKI, M. and STANY, Z. *Biochem. Z.* **323**, 376 (1952).
12. BACHHAWAT, B. K., ROBINSON, W. G. and COON, M. J. *J. Biol. Chem.* **216**, 727 (1955).
13. BACHHAWAT, B. K., ROBINSON, W. G. and COON, M. J. *J. Biol. Chem.* **219**, 539 (1956).
14. BARBER, M. S., JACKMAN, L. M. and WEEDON, B. C. L. *Proc. Chem. Soc.* **1959**, 96.
15. BARBER, M. J., JACKMAN, L. M., WARREN, C. K. and WEEDON, B. C. L. *Proc. Chem. Soc.* **1960**, 19.
16. BEELER, D. A. and PORTER, J. W. *Arch. Biochem. Biophys.* **100**, 167–70 (1963).
17. BLOCH, K. In *Currents in Biochemical Research*, p. 477, ed. D. E. Green. Interscience Publishers, N.Y., 1956.
18. BONNER, J., SANDOVAL, A., TANG, Y. W. and ZECHMEISTER, L. *Arch. Biochem.* **10**, 113 (1946).
19. BONNETT, R., SPARK, A. A., TEE, J. L. and WEEDON, D. C. L. *Proc. Chem. Soc.* **1964**, 419.
20. BOOTH, V. H. *Qualitas Plantarum* **3/4**, 317 (1958).
21. BRAITHWAITE, G. D. and GOODWIN, T. W. *Biochem. J.* **66**, 31p (1957).
22. BRAITHWAITE, G. D. and GOODWIN, T. W. *Nature* **182**, 1304 (1958).
23. BRAITHWAITE, G. D. and GOODWIN, T. W. *Biochem. J.* **76**, 55 (1960).
24. BURNETT, J. H. In *Chemistry and Biochemistry of Plant Pigments*, chap. 14, ed. T. W. Goodwin. Academic Press, London, 1965.
25. CAHN, R. S., INGOLD, C. K. and PRELOG, V. *Experientia* **12**, 81–93 (1956).
26. CALVIN, M. *Nature* **176**, 1215 (1955).
27. CAMPILLO-CAMPBELL, A. DEL, DEKKER, E. E. and COON, M. S. *Biochim. Biophys. Acta* **31**, 290 (1959).
28. CHAYKIN, S., LAW, J., PHILLIPS, A. H., TCHEN, T. T. and BLOCK, K. *Proc. Natl. Acad. Sc. U.S.* **44**, 998 (1958).
29. CHICHESTER, C. O., WONG, P. S. and MACKINNEY, G. *Arch. Biochem. Biophys.* **53**, 479 (1954).
30. CHICHESTER, C. O., WONG, P. S. and MACKINNEY, G. *Plant Physiol.* **29**, 238 (1954).
31. CHICHESTER, C. O., NAKAYAMA, T., MACKINNEY, G. and GOODWIN, T. W. *J. Biol. Chem.* **214**, 515 (1955).
32. CHICHESTER, C. O. and YOKOYAMA, H. Abstracts of *4th Int. Cong. Biochem. Vienna*, p. 102 (1958).
33. CHICHESTER, C. O., YOKOYAMA, H., NAKAYAMA, T. O. M., LUKTON, A. and MACKINNEY, G. *J. Biol. Chem.* **234**, 598 (1959).
34. CHOLNOKY, L., GYORGYFY, C., NAGY, E. and PANCZEL, M. *Nature* **178**, 410 (1956).
35. CHOLNOKY, L., SZABOLCS, J. and NAGY, E. *Ann. Chem. Liebigs.* **616**, 207 (1958).
36. CHOLNOKY, L. and SZABOLCS, J. *Experientia* **16**, 483 (1960).
37. CLAES, H. *Z. Naturforsch.* **9b**, 461 (1954).
38. CLAES, H. *Z. Naturforsch.* **11b**, 260 (1956).
39. CLAES, H. *Z. Naturforsch.* **12b**, 401 (1957).
40. CLAES, H. *Z. Naturforsch.* **13b**, 222 (1958).
41. CLAES, H. *Z. Naturforsch.* **14b**, 4 (1959).
42. CLAES, H. and NAKAYAMA, T. O. M. *Nature* **183**, 1053 (1959).
43. CORNFORTH, J. W., CORNFORTH, R. H., POPJÁK, G. and YOUHOTSKY-GORE, I. *Biochem. J.* **66**, 10p (1957).

44. CORNFORTH, J. W., CORNFORTH, R. H., DONNIGER, C. and POPJÁK, G. J. *Proc. Roy. Soc.* B **1964** (in press). Cited in *Chemistry and Biochemistry of Plant Pigments*, p. 164, ed. T. W. Goodwin. Academic Press, London, 1965.
45. DAVIS, J. B., JACKMAN, L. M., SIDDONS, P. T. and WEEDON, B. C. L. *Proc. Chem. Soc.* **1961**, 261.
46. DEKKER, E. E., SCHLESINGER, M. J. and COON, M. J. *J. Biochem.* **233**, 434 (1958).
47. DEKKER, K. and UEHLEKE, H. *Z. Physiol. Chem.* **323**, 61 (1961).
48. DEUEL, H. J. In *The Lipids*, vol. III, p. 421, ed. H. J. Deuel. Interscience, New York, 1957.
49. DITURI, F., GURIN, S. and RABINOWITZ, J. L. *J. Am. Chem. Soc.* **79**, 2650 (1957).
50. DOROUGH, G. D. and CALVIN, M. *J. Am. Chem. Soc.* **73**, 2362 (1951).
51. DUCHOW, E. and DOUGLAS, H. C. *J. Bacteriol.* **58**, 409 (1949).
52. EUGSTER, C. H., LINNER, E., TRIVEDI, A. H. and KARRER, P. *Helv. Chim. Acta* **39**, 690 (1956).
53. FAZAKERLEY, S. and GLOVER, J. *Biochem. J.* **65**, 38p (1957).
54. FERGUSON, J. J., DURR, F. and RUDNEY, H. *Federation Proc.* **17**, 219 (1958).
55. FERGUSON, J. J. and RUDNEY, H. *J. Biol. Chem.* **234**, 1072 (1959).
56. FOX, D. L. In *Comparative Biochemistry of Photoreactive Systems*, p. 25, ed. M. B. Allen. Academic Press, New York, 1959.
57. FRIEND, J. *Chemistry and Industry* **1958**, 597.
58. FROMAGEOT, C. and TSCHANG, J. L. *Arch. f. Mikrobiol.* **9**, 424 (1938).
59. GARTON, G. A., GOODWIN, T. W. and LIJINSKY, W. *Biochem. J.* **48**, 154 (1951).
60. GILCHRIST, BARBARA M. and GREEN, J. *Proc. Roy. Soc.* **152**, 9B, 118 (1960).
61. GLOVER, J. and REDFEARN, E. R. *Biochem. J.* **58**, XV (1955).
62. GLOVER, J. In *Vitamins and Hormones*, vol. 18, p. 371, eds. R. S. Harris and D. J. Ingle. Academic Press, New York (1960).
63. GOLDSMITH, T. H. *J. Gen. Physiology* **47**, 433 (1964).
64. GOODWIN, T. W. *Biochemistry of Carotenoids*, pp. 110–11. Chapman & Hall Ltd., London,l 952.
65. GOODWIN, T. W. *Biochem. J.* **50**, 550 (1952).
66. GOODWIN, T. W. *Biol. Revs. Cambridge Phil. Soc.* **27**, 439 (1952).
67. GOODWIN, T. W. and JAMIKORN. *Nature* **170**, 104 (1952).
68. GOODWIN, T. W. and LIJINSKY, W. *Biochem. J.* **50**, 268 (1952).
69. GOODWIN, T. W. *J. Sci. Food Agric.* **4**, 209 (1953).
70. GOODWIN, T. W., JAMIKORN, M. and WILLMER, J. S. *Biochem. J.* **53**, 531 (1953).
71. GOODWIN, T. W. and OSMAN, H. G. *Arch. Biochem. Biophys.* **47**, 215 (1953).
72. GOODWIN, T. W. *Experientia* **10**, 213 (1954).
73. GOODWIN, T. W. and OSMAN, H. G. *Biochem. J.* **56**, 222 (1954).
74. GOODWIN, T. W. In *Ann. Rev. Biochem.*, vol. 24, p. 497, ed. J. M. Luck. Annual Reviews, Inc., Palo Alto, 1955.
75. GOODWIN, T. W. In *Handbuch der Pflanzenphysiologie*, vol. X, p. 186, ed. W. Ruhland. Springer-Verlag, Berlin–Göttingen–Heidelberg, 1958.
76. GOODWIN, T. W. *Advances Enzymol.* **21**, 295 (1959).
77. GOODWIN, T. W. In *Comparative Biochemistry of Photoreactive Systems*, p. 1, ed. M. B. Allen. Academic Press, New York, 1960.
78. GOODWIN, T. W. In *Handbuch der Pflanzenphysiologie*, vol. V/I, p. 394, ed. W. Ruhland. Springer-Verlag, Berlin–Göttingen–Heidelberg, 1960.
78a GOODWIN, T. W. In *The Biosynthesis of Vitamins and Related Compounds*, chap. 14. Academic Press, London, 1963.
79. GOODWIN, T. W. and WILLIAMS, R. J. H. *Proc. Roy. Soc.* B **1964** (in press). Cited in *Chemistry and Biochemistry of Plant Pigments*, p. 164, ed. T. W. Goodwin. Academic Press, London, 1965.
80. GOODWIN, T. W. In *Chemistry and Biochemistry of Plant Pigments*, p. 153, ed. T. W. Goodwin. Academic Press, London, 1965.
81. GOODWIN, T. W. In *Chemistry and Biochemistry of Plant Pigments*, p. 157, ed. T. W. Goodwin, Academic Press, London, 1965.

82. GOODWIN, T. W. In *Chemistry and Biochemistry of Plant Pigments*, chap. 5, ed. T. W. Goodwin. Academic Press, London, 1965.
83. GOODWIN, T. W. *Biochem. J.* **96**, 2P (1965).
84. GOODWIN, T. W. and WILLIAMS, R. J. H. *Biochem. J.* **94**, 5C (1965).
85. GRANGAUD, R. *Actualites Biochim.* **15**, 1 (1951).
86. GRANGAUD, R. and MASSONET, R. *Compt. Rend.* **241**, 1087 (1955).
87. GRANGAUD, R., VIGNAIS, P., MASSONET, R. and MOATTI, M. P. *Compt. Rend.* **243**, 1170 (1956).
88. GRANGAUD, R., VIGNAIS, P., MASSONET, R. and MOATTI, J. P. *Bull. Soc. Chim. Biol.* **39**, 1271 (1957).
89. GRIFFITHS, M., SISTROM, W. R., COHEN-BAZIRE, G. and STANIER, R. Y. *Nature* **176**, 1211 (1955).
90. GRIFFITHS, M. and STANIER, R. Y. *J. Gen. Microbiol.* **14**, 698 (1956).
91. GROB, E. C. and BOSCHETTI, A. *Chimia (Switz.)* **16**, 15 (1962).
92. GROB, E. C., PORETTI, C. G., MURALT, A. V. and SCHOPFER, W. H. *Experientia* **7**, 218 (1951).
93. GROB, E. C. and BUTLER, R. *Helv. Chim. Acta* **39**, 197 (1956).
94. GROB, E. C. *Chimia (Switz.)* **2**, 338 (1957).
95. GROB, E. C., KIRSCHNER, K. and LYNEN, F. *Chimia (Switz.)* **15**, 308 (1961).
96. HAXO, F. *Biol. Bull.* **103**, 216 (1952).
97. HAXO, F. *Fortschr. Chem. Org. Naturstoffe* **12**, 159 (1956).
98. HENNING, V., KESSEL, I. and LYNEN, F. *Abstr. Intern. Cong. Biochem.*, 4th Congr., Vienna, **1958**, p. 47.
99. HENNING, V. Unpublished data as cited in paper by Lynen, F. (ref. 130).
100. INHOFFEN, H. H., BOHLMAN, F., BARTRAM, K., RUMMERT, G. and POMMER, H. *Ann. Chem. Liebigs.* **570**, 54 (1950).
101. ISHII, K. *J. Fermentation Technol. (Japan)* **30**, 350; 390 (1952).
102. ISLER, O., LINDLAR, H., MONTAVON, M., RÜEGG, R. and ZELLER, P. *Helv. Chim. Acta* **39**, 274 (1956).
103. ISLER, O. and SCHUDEL, P. *Adv. Org. Chem.* **4**, 115 (1963), Interscience, N.Y.
104. JENSEN, A. *Acta Chemia Scand.* **18** (8), 2005–7 (1964).
105. JENSEN, S. L., COHEN-BAZIRE, G., NAKAYAMA, T. O. M. and STANIER, R. Y. *Biochim. Biophys. Acta* **29**, 477 (1958).
106. JENSEN, S. L. *Acta Chem. Scand.* **12**, 1698 (1958).
107. JENSEN, S. L. *Acta Chem. Scand.* **13**, 381 (1959).
108. JENSEN, S. L. *Acta Chem. Scand.* **13**, 842 (1959).
109. JENSEN, S. L. *Acta Chem. Scand.* **13**, 2142 (1959).
110. JENSEN, S. L. *Acta Chem. Scand.* **13**, 2143 (1959).
111. JENSEN, S. L. *Acta Chem. Scand.* **14**, 950–2 (1960).
112. JENSEN, S. L. *Acta Chem. Scand.* **14**, 953–5 (1960).
112a JENSEN, S. L., COHEN-BAZIRE, G. and STANIER, R. Y. *Nature* **192**, 1168 (1961).
113. JENSEN, S. L., HEGGE, E. and JACKAM, L. M. *Acta Chemia Scand.* **18**, 1703–18 (1964).
114. JENSEN, S. L. In *Bacterial Photosynthesis*, pp. 19–36, eds. H. Gest, A. San Pietro and L. P. Vernon. Antioch Press, Yellow Spring, Ohio, 1963.
115. JUNGALWALA, F. B. and PORTER, J. W. *Arch. Biochem. Biophys.* **110** (2), 291–9 (1965)
116. KARRER, P. and SOLMSSEN, U. *Helv. Chim. Acta* **18**, 1306 (1935).
117. KARRER, P. and EUGSTER, C. H. *Helv. Chim. Acta* **33**, 1172 (1950).
118. KARRER, P. and JUCKER, E. *Carotenoids*. Elsevier Publ. Co. Inc. Amsterdam (1950).
119. KHARASCH, M., CONWAY, E. and BLOOM, W. *J. Bacterol.* **32**, 533 (1936).
120. KIZEN, M., MATSUMOTO, K. and NEDATE, S. *Hakko Kyokai Shi* **9**, 143 (1951).
121. KON, S. K. and FISHER, L. R. Personal communication.
122. KRINSKY, N. I. *Federation Proc.* **21**, 92 (1962).
123. KRINSKY, N. *Biochim. Biophys. Acta* **88**, 487–91 (1964).
124. KRZEMINSKI, L. F. and QUACKENBUSH, F. W. *Arch. Biochem. Biophys.* **88**, 287 (1960).
125. LAKSHMANAN, M. R., JUNGALWALA, F. B. and CAMA, H. R. *Biochem. J.* **95**, 27 (1965).
126. LIAAEN, S. and SORENSON, N. A. In *Second International Seaweed Symposium*, p. 25, eds. T. Braarud and N. A. Sorenson. Pergamon Press, London, 1956.

676   C. O. CHICHESTER AND T. O. M. NAKAYAMA

127. Losev, A. P. and Shlyk, A. A. *Biokhimiya* **29** (3), 396–400 (1964) (Eng. trans.).
128. Lumry, R., Spikes, J. D. and Eyring, H. *Ann. Rev. Plant. Physiol.* **5**, 271 (1954).
129. Lynen, F., Eggerer, H., Henning, V. and Kessel, I. *Angew. Chem.* **70**, 738 (1958).
130. Lynen, F. J. *Cellular Comp. Physiol.* **54**, Supplement 1, 45 (1959).
131. Lynen, F. In *Biosynthesis of Terpenes and Sterols*, p. 95, eds. G. E. W. Wolstenholme and C. M. O'Connor. Little, Brown & Co., Boston, 1959.
132. Mackinney, G. In *Ann. Rev. Biochem.*, p. 473, vol. 21, ed. J. M. Luck. Annual Reviews, Inc., Palo Alto, 1952.
133. Mackinney, G. and Jenkins, J. A. *Proc. Natl. Acad. Sci. U.S.* **38**, 48 (1952).
134. Mackinney, G., Nakayama, T., Buss, C. D. and Chichester, C. O. *J. Am. Chem. Soc.* **74**, 3456 (1952).
135. Mackinney, G., Nakayama, T., Chichester, C. O. and Buss, C. D. *J. Am. Chem. Soc.* **75**, 236 (1953).
136. Mackinney, G., Chichester, C. O. and Wong, P. S. *J. Am. Chem. Soc.* **75**, 5428 (1953).
137. Mackinney, G., Rick, C. M. and Jenkins, J. A. *Proc. Natl. Acad. Sci. U.S.* **40**, 569 (1954).
138. Mackinney, G., Rick, C. M. and Jenkins, J. A. *Proc. Natl. Acad. Sci. U.S.* **42**, 404 (1956).
139. Mackinney, G. *Qualitas Plant. Materiae Vegetabiles* **3**, 281 (1958).
140. Mackinney, G., Chandler, B. V. and Lukton, A. *Abstr. Intern. Congr. Biochem.*, *4th Congr.*, Vienna, **1958**, p. 130.
141. Mackinney, G. and Chichester, C. O. In *Comparative Biochemistry of Photoreactive Systems*, p. 205, ed. Mary Belle Allen. Academic Press, N.Y., 1959.
142. Mackinney, G. In *Metabolic Pathways*, p. 481, ed. D. M. Greenberg. Academic Press, N.Y., 1960.
143. Mase, Y. *Vitamins (Japan)* **15**, 182 (1958).
144. Mase, Y. *Vitamins (Japan)* **15**, 185 (1958).
145. Mase, Y. *Vitamins (Japan)* **15**, 193 (1958).
146. Mase, Y. *Vitamins (Japan)* **15**, 196 (1958).
147. Mase, Y. *Vitamins (Japan)* **15**, 199 (1958).
148. Mase, Y. *J. Vitaminol.* **5**, 161 (1959).
149. Massonet, R. *Compt. Rend. Soc. Biol.* **150**, 529 (1950).
150. Milas, N. A., Davis, P., Belic, I. and Fles, D. A. *J. Am. Chem. Soc.* **72**, 4844 (1950).
151. Moatti, M. P. (Thesis) Université d'Alger, Contribution à l'Étude de la Biogénèse de la Vitamine des Poissons (1959).
152. Moore, T. *Vitamin A.* Elsevier Publ. Co., London (1957).
153. Nakayama, T. O. M. *Arch. Biochem. Biophys.* **75**, 352 (1958).
154. Nakayama, T. O. M. *Arch. Biochem. Biophys.* **75**, 356 (1958).
155. Nusbaum-Cassuto, E. and Villoutreix, J. *Compt. Rend.* **260** (3), 1013–15 (1965).
156. Olson, J. A. *Am. J. Clin. Nutr.* **9** (4), Pt. 2, 1 (1961).
157. Olson, J. A. *J. Lipid Research* **5**, 281 (1964).
158. Petzold, E. N., Quackenbush, F. W. and McQuistan, Marilyn. *Arch. Biochem. Biophys.* **82**, 117 (1959).
159. Polgar, A., van Niel, C. B. and Zechmeister, L. *Arch. Biochem.* **5**, 243 (1944).
160. Popják, G., Gosselin, L., Gore, I. Y. and DeWaard, A. *Abstr. Intern. Congr. Biochem.*, *4th Congr.*, Vienna, **1958**, p. 203.
161. Popjáck, G., Goodman, DeWitt, S., Cornforth, S. W., Cornforth, R. H. and Ryhage, R. *J. Biol. Chem.* **236**, 1934 (1961).
162. Porter, J. W. and Lincoln, R. E. *Arch. Biochem.* **27**, 390 (1950).
163. Porter, J. W. and Anderson, D. G. *Arch. Biochem. Biophys.* **97**, 520 (1962).
164. Prickett, P. S. and Massengale, O. N. *J. Infectious Diseases* **49**, 297 (1952).
165. Purcell, A. E., Thompson, G. A., Jr. and Bonner, J. *J. Biol. Chem.* **234**, 1081 (1959).
166. Rabourn, W. J. and Quackenbush, F. W. *Arch. Biochem.* **44**, 159 (1953).
167. Rabourn, W. J. and Quackenbush, F. W. *Arch. Biochem. Biophys.* **61**, 111 (1956).
168. Rabourn, W. J. *132nd Meeting, American Chemical Society*, Sept. 8–13, Abstract of Papers, p. 88c (1957).

169. REDFEARN, E. In *Comparative Biochemistry of Photoreactive Systems*, p. 225, ed. M. B. Allen. Academic Press, New York, 1959.
170. REDFEARN, E. and GLOVER, J. *Biochem. J.* **54**, VIII (1953).
171. REICHEL, L. and WALLIS, M. *Angew. Chem.* **68**, 181 (1956).
172. REICHEL, L. and WALLIS, M. *Naturwiss.* **44**, 234 (1957).
173. RILLING, H. C. *Biochim. Biophys. Acta* **79**, 464–75 (1964).
174. RILLING, H. D. *Arch. Biochem. Biophys.* **110**, 39–46 (1965).
175. RUDNEY, H. and FERGUSON, J. J. *J. Biol. Chem.* **234**, 1076 (1959).
176. RUDNEY, H. In *Biosynthesis of Terpenes and Sterols*, p. 75, eds. G. E. W. Wolstenholme and C. M. O'Connor. Little, Brown & Co., Boston, 1959.
177. RÜEGG, R., GUEX, W., MONTAVON, M., SCHWIETER, A., SAVEY, G. and ISLER, O. *Chimia.* (*Switz.*) **12**, 327 (1958).
178. RÜEGG, R., SCHWIETER, U., RYSER, G., SCHUDEL, P. and ISLER, O. *Helv. Chim. Acta* **44**, 994 (1961).
179. SAGER, R. and ZALOKAR, M. *Nature* **182**, 98 (1958).
180. SCHOPFER, W. H. and GROB, E. C. *Experientia* **6**, 419 (1950).
181. SCHOPFER, W. H., GROB, E. C., BESSON, G. and KELLER, V. *Arch. Sci.* (*Geneva*) **5**, 1 (1952).
182. SCHOPFER, W. H., GROB, E. C. and BESSON, G. *Arch. Sci.* (Geneva) **5**, 5 (1952).
183. SHNEOUR, E. A. and ZABIN, I. *J. Biol. Chem.* **234**, 770 (1959).
184. SHNEOUR, E. A. *Biochim. Biophys. Acta, Previews* **2**, 2 (1962).
185. SHNEOUR, E. A. and CALVIN, M. *Nature* **196**, 439 (1962).
186. SIMPSON, K. L., NAKAYAMA, T. O. M. and CHICHESTER, C. O. *Biochem. J.* **92**, 508–10 (1964).
187. SIMPSON, K. L., NAKAYAMA, T. O. M. and CHICHESTER, C. O. *J. Bact.* **88**, 1688–94 (1964).
188. STANIER, R. Y. *Harvey Lectures*, 1958–9, p. 219 (1960).
189. STARR, M. P. and SAPERSTEIN, S. *Arch. Biochem. Biophys.* **43**, 157 (1953).
190. STEELE, W. J. and GURIN, S. *J. Biol. Chem.* **235**, 2778 (1960).
191. STOKKE, K. and SORENSON, N. A. As quoted by Arnulv Stabursvik in *A Phytochemical Study of* Narthecium ossifragum (*C*) *Huds.* Norges Tekniske vitenskapsakademi, Oslo Univ. Press, Olso (1959), Series 2, No. 6, p. 41.
192. STRAIN, H. H. *Leaf Xanthophylls.* Carnegie Inst. Wash. Publ. No. 490, 1938.
193. STRAIN, H. H. *Chloroplast Pigments and Chromatographic Analysis*, pp. 1–180. Penn. State Univ. Press, University Park, Pennsylvania, 1959.
194. SURMATIS, J. D., MARIEQ, J. and OFNER, A. 131*st Meeting Am. Chem. Soc.*, 0–20. Miami, Fla., April 1957.
195. TAVORMINA, P. A., GIBBS, M. H. and HUFF, J. W. *J. Am. Chem. Soc.* **78**, 4498 (1956).
196. TCHEN, T. T. *J. Am. Chem. Soc.* **79**, 6344 (1957).
197. TCHEN, T. T. In *Metabolic Pathways*, p. 403, ed. D. M. Greenberg. Academic Press, New York, 1960.
198. THOMPSON, J. H., McC. HOWELL, J. and PITT, G. A. J. *Proc. Roy. Soc.* B **159**, 510–35 (1964).
199. TISCHER, J. *Z. Physiol. Chem.* **281**, 143 (1944).
200. TISCHER, J. *Z. Physiol. Chem.* **267**, 281 (1941).
201. TOMES, M. L., QUACKENBUSH, F. W., NELSON, O. E. and NORTH, B. *Genetics* **38**, 117 (1953).
202. TOMES, M. L., QUACKENBUSH, F. W. and McQUISTAN, M. *Genetics* **39**, 810 (1954).
203. TOMES, M. L., QUACKENBUSH, F. W. and KARGL, T. E. *Botan. Gaz.* **117**, 248 (1956).
204. TORTO, F. G. and WEEDON, B. C. L. *Chemistry and Industry* **1955**, 1219.
205. TURIAN, G. *Helv. Chim. Acta* **33**, 1988 (1950).
206. TURIAN, G. and HAXO, F. *J. Bacteriol.* **63**, 690 (1952).
207. TURIAN, G. and HAXO, F. *Botan. Gaz.* **119**, 254 (1954).
208. VAN NIEL, C. B. and SMITH, J. H. C. *Arch. Microbiol.* **6**, 219 (1935).
209. VAN NIEL, C. B. *Antonie van Leeuwenhoek, J. Microbiol. Serol.* **12**, 156 (1947).
210. VARMA, T. N. R. and CHICHESTER, C. O. *Arch. Biochem. Biophys.* **96**, 265 (1962).
211. VARMA, T. N. R., CHICHESTER, C. O. and MACKINNEY, G. *Nature* **183**, 188 (1959).

212. VOLK, W. A. and PENNINGTON, D. J. Bacteriol. 59, 169 (1950).
213. WALSH, K. A. and HAUGE, S. M. J. Agric. Food Chem. 1, 1001 (1955).
214. WEEDON, B. C. L. In Chemistry and Biochemistry of Plant Pigments, chap. 3, ed. T. W. Goodwin. Academic Press, London, 1965.
215. WELLS, L. W., SCHEIBLE, W. J. and PORTER, J. W. Federation Proc. 23, 426 (1964).
216. WITTING, L. A. and PORTER, J. W. J. Biol. Chem. 234, 2841 (1959).
217. WITTING, L. A. and PORTER, J. W. Biochem. Biophys. Res. Commun. 1, 341 (1959).
218. WOLF, D. E., HOFFMAN, C. H., ALDRICH, P. E., SKEGGS, H. R., WRIGHT, L. D. and FOLKERS, K. J. Am. Chem. Soc. 78, 4499 (1956).
219. WOLF, D. E., HOFFMAN, C. H., ALDRICH, P. E., SKEGGS, H. R., WRIGHT, L. D. and FOLKERS, K. J. Am. Chem. Soc. 79, 1486-7 (1957).
220. WOLKEN, J. J. Ann. N.Y. Acad. Sci. 74, 161 (1958).
221. WUHRMANN, J. J., YOKOYAMA, H. and CHICHESTER, C. O. J. Am. Chem. Soc. 79, 4569 (1957).
222. YAMAGUCHI, M. Bull. Chem. Soc. Japan 30, 111 (1957).
223. YAMAGUCHI, M. Bull. Chem. Soc. Japan 30, 979 (1957).
224. YAMAGUCHI, M. Bull. Chem. Soc. Japan 31, 51 (1958).
225. YAMAGUCHI, M. Bull. Chem. Soc. Japan 31, 739 (1958).
226. YAMAGUCHI, M. Bull. Chem. Soc. Japan 32, 1171 (1959).
227. YAMAGUCHI, M. Bull. Chem. Soc. Japan 33, 1560 (1960).
228. YAMAMOTO, H. Y., CHICHESTER, C. O. and NAKAYAMA, T. O. M. Arch. Biochem. Biophys. 96, 645 (1962).
229. YAMAMOTO, H. Y., NAKAYAMA, T. O. M. and CHICHESTER, C. O. Arch. Biochem. Biophys. 97, 168 (1962).
230. YAMAMOTO, H. Y., CHICHESTER, C. O. and NAKAYAMA, T. O. M. Photochem. and Photobiology 1, 53 (1962).
230a YAMAMOTO, H. Y. and CHICHESTER, C. O. Biochim. Biophys. Acta 109, 303 (1965).
231. YOKOYAMA, H., CHICHESTER, C. O., NAKAYAMA, T. O. M. and MACKINNEY, G. J. Am. Chem. Soc. 79, 2029 (1957).
232. YOKOYAMA, H., CHICHESTER, C. O. and MACKINNEY, G. Nature 185, 687 (1960).
233. YOKOYAMA, H., NAKAYAMA, T. O. M. and CHICHESTER, C. O. J. Biol. Chem. 237, 681 (1962).
234. YOKOYAMA, H., YAMAMOTO, H., NAKAYAMA, T. O. M., SIMPSON, K. and CHICHESTER, C. O. Nature 191, 1299 (1961).
235. ZALOKAR, M. Arch. Biochem. 50, 71 (1954).
236. ZALOKAR, M. Arch. Biochem. Biophys. 70, 561 (1957).
237. ZECHMEISTER, L. and POLGAR, A. J. Am. Chem. Soc. 65, 1522 (1954).
238. ZECHMEISTER, L., LEROSEN, A. L., SCHROEDER, W. A., POLGAR, A. and PAULING, L. J. Am. Chem. Soc. 65, 1940 (1943).
239. ZECHMEISTER, L. Chem. Revs. 34, 267 (1944).
240. ZECHMEISTER, L. and PETRACEK, F. J. Arch. Biochem. Biophys. 61, 243 (1956).

CHAPTER 11

THE BIOSYNTHESIS OF THE WATER-SOLUBLE VITAMINS

VERNON H. CHELDELIN* and ANNETTE BAICH

Department of Chemistry and Science Research Institute,
Oregon State University, Corvallis, Oregon

CONTENTS

I.	THIAMINE	680
II.	NICOTINIC ACID (NIACIN)	682
III.	PANTOTHENIC ACID	694
IV.	RIBOFLAVIN	699
V.	FOLIC ACID	704
VI.	CYANOCOBALAMINS	711
VII.	BIOTIN	718
VIII.	PYRIDOXAL	722
IX.	INOSITOL	724
X.	ASCORBIC ACID	727
XI.	INTERCONVERSIONS AMONG THE VITAMINS	730
XII.	CONCLUSION	731
	REFERENCES	732

The notable transformations that have taken place in biochemical research during the past 35 years are well exemplified by the corresponding changes in the field of vitamin research. In 1930, only a very few persons paid attention to the term "vitamin". As new vitamins were discovered and as knowledge grew concerning the already known members of the group, awareness developed of the essential character of these substances in the diet. As new species were tested and the concept grew of the universality of requirements for the various vitamins, it was natural that a study of *biosynthesis* of these compounds would hardly be a popularly held idea. Even later, as researchers began to raise the question of biogenesis of vitamins in species that seemed not to be dependent on them in the diet, it was noted by one reviewer of this subject [47] that the study tended to lag further because of the difficulty of finding systems that would synthesize sufficient amounts of these substances to examine; this called for the development of ultramicro methods

* Deceased.

which have come to the fore only in recent years. Progress has now been made with some of the biosynthetic studies, to the point that plausible stories may be told of some of the means whereby individual vitamins may arise, in those species that normally synthesize them.

I. THIAMINE

This vitamin (aneurin, vitamin B_1) is usually discussed initially because of its greater seniority, despite the fact that the biosynthetic pathways involving some of the other vitamins, notably nicotinic acid, are better known.

Thiamine has the structure indicated in Fig. 1. It is a compound molecule, being composed of a pyrimidine and a thiazole moiety, joined by a methylene bridge. The pyrimidine moiety, called "pyrimidine" for convenience, is 2-methyl-4-amino-5-hydroxymethyl pyrimidine; the thiazole, called "thiazole" for short, is 4-methyl-5(2-hydroxyethyl)-thiazole.

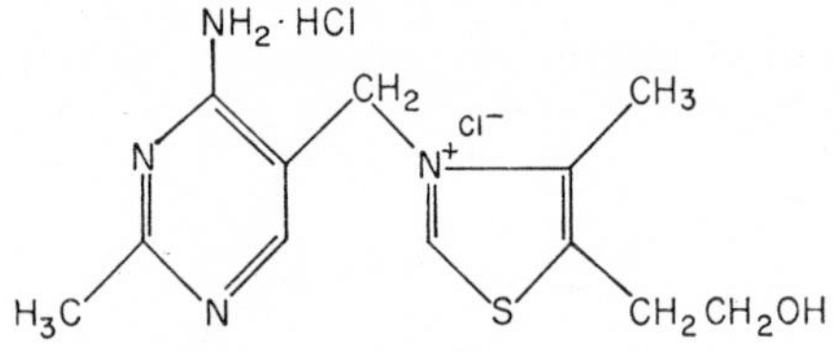

A. Thiamine chloride hydrochloride

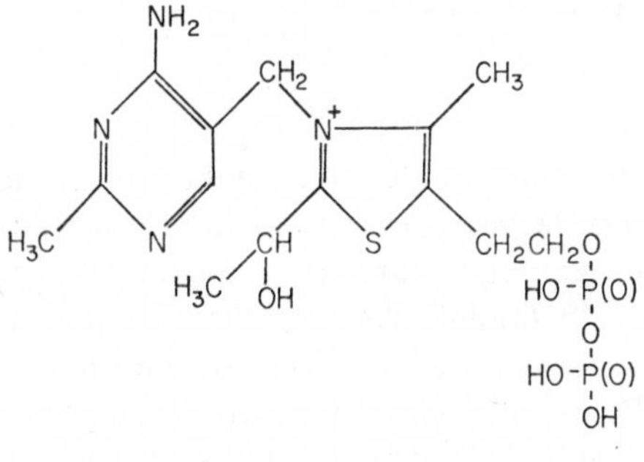

B. Hydroxyl ethyl thiamine pyrophosphate

Fig. 1. Structures in the thiamine series.

Early speculations on biogenesis of thiamine were probably stimulated by studies with different organisms. In some strains of yeast, for example,[435, 377] either the pyrimidine or thiazole moiety is sufficient for growth; this means that biosynthesis of the opposite moiety proceeds, as well as coupling of the two portions to form the intact vitamin. *Lactobacillus fermenti*[369, 72] behaves somewhat similarly, and the mold *Phycomyces blakesleeanus* [375, 152] can synthesize the complete vitamin when both halves are present in the growth medium.

These observations suggest the next noteworthy experiment: Bakers' yeast catalyzed the coupling of pyrimidine phosphate and thiazole to form thiamine activity (measured by thiochrome assay) when incubated in the presence of ATP and Mg^{++}. [316] This notion, that the two moieties are synthesized first, then joined together, was indeed derived earlier from the work of Tatum and Bell [404] and Harris. [155] The work was extended by Camiener and Brown [61] to furnish the slightly revised conclusion that the two moieties undergo the following series of transformations:

Hydroxymethylpyrimidine + ATP → pyrimidine pyrophosphate
Thiazole + ATP → thiazole monophosphate
Pyrimidine pyrophosphate + thiazole monophosphate → thiamine
                                                                monophosphate
Thiamine monophosphate → thiamine
Thiamine + ATP → thiamine pyrophosphate

This sequence, somewhat unexpected, is supported by direct enzymatic experiments. The question as to why thiamine monophosphate should precede formation of the free vitamin is left unexplained, although the postulate that the unphosphorylated form should precede the monophosphate in the cellular assembly line, may not be wholly justifiable even on theoretical grounds.

Beyond this, information on biosynthesis of each ring from simpler precursors is scanty. It is tempting, perhaps even reasonable, to suppose that the pyrimidine half is fabricated in a manner analogous to most other pyrimidines, but this may be an erroneous notion. The pyrimidine portion is unusual in that important substituents appear (in thiamine) at C-2 and C-5. There are few other naturally occurring pyrimidines of similar structure recorded. [137] Thiazole can be replaced in *Escherichia coli* and *Neurospora* mutants by cystine or thiazolidinedicarboxylic acid; [307] it (thiazole) can be formed from formamide and 4-ketopentanol [31] in pea roots. This conversion is disputed, however. [31] Such observations mean little regarding the origin of the complete carbon skeleton, however (cf., for example, the need for the glutamine molecule in order to obtain nitrogen for the biosynthesis of purines). It is clear that the pathway of biosynthesis of thiamine is ripe for investigation.

Appearance of Cocarboxylase

This coenzyme, also called diphosphothiamine and thiamine pyrophosphate, has been formed from thiamine and any of several nucleoside triphosphates [216] by the enzyme thiaminokinase, with ATP being the most effective. The enzyme has been purified about 100-fold from yeast. Thiamine monophosphate was inactive as substrate for this enzyme, thus confirming again the absence of the monophosphate from this synthetic sequence.

A close relative of cocarboxylase has been studied by Carlson and Brown.[63] It has a hydroxyethyl group substituted on the 2-position of the thiazole ring and is believed to have the structure indicated in Fig. 1B. The corresponding hydroxyethyl analog of thiamine has been proposed by Breslow[38] as the biologically active form of acetaldehyde, and this compound in the hands of Krampitz et al.,[236] yielded acetaldehyde when acted upon by thiaminokinase and then decomposed by yeast carboxylase. Hydroxyethyl thiamine pyrophosphate is able to substitute for cocarboxylase in the yeast carboxylase[175] and pyruvic oxidase[174] systems, and it donates its hydroxyethyl group to the enzymatic synthesis of acetoin.[63]

It seems likely that hydroxyethyl thiamine pyrophosphate may be "active acetaldehyde", or at least a very close relative. 2-Acyl derivatives of thiamine have been found by Ingraham et al.[308] to possess "high energy" configurations, presumably about the 2-acyl position of 2-acetyl-thiamine pyrophosphate. This group may supposedly arise en route to the formation of acetyl phosphate from ketopentose phosphates.[162] As the persuasive reports [63, 38, 236, 174, 175, 308, 162] are borne out by further study in this connection, this work ranks as the most exciting in the thiamine field for some time. Although it does not shed new light on the question of biosynthesis of the vitamin, it is nonetheless of paramount importance in understanding the mechanism of biosynthetic mechanisms in general. When taken together with information on acetyl transfer (CoA), formyl transfer (folic acid coenzymes) and methyl transfer (B_{12} coenzymes) we can recognize that the field has indeed progressed during the past quarter century.

II. NICOTINIC ACID (NIACIN)

Nicotinic acid, like vitamin D, is not an obligatory component of animal diets if adequate amounts of the proper precursors are present. Such a precursor is tryptophan, which is convertible by many animal, plant and microbial species into nicotinic acid. The conversion ratio in humans is estimated at roughly one mole vitamin per 60 moles of tryptophan.[179] In various microorganisms, the biosynthesis of the vitamin has been traced back even further, to anthranilic acid, shikimic acid and to sugar derivatives that form precursors of the aromatic ring. The steps prior to anthranilic acid are discussed in Chapter 1, Sections VI B and C, in connection with aromatic ring formation.

The biosynthesis of nicotinic acid from anthranilic acid and tryptophan is an elaborate process, which may strike the newcomer to the field as logically unnecessary.[238] However, the literature of enzymology is replete with examples of deviously connected enzymic sequences, which may only occasionally run the same course as corresponding syntheses planned by the

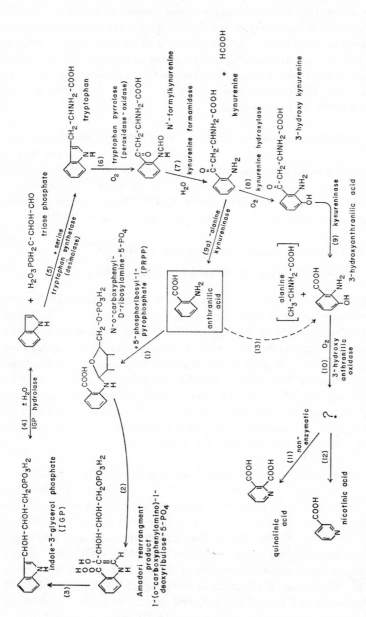

FIG. 2. Biosynthesis of nicotinic acid. Care should be exercised, however, in interpreting this diagram to mean that (a) this pathway prevails in all species tested, or that (b) the reactions represented are exclusive. A considerable literature has been accumulated, which indicates that probably three or more separate, distinct pathways may exist; however their extent, or their exclusiveness in tissue metabolism, cannot be answered.

organic chemist. The scheme in Fig. 2 is a general one which summarizes the bulk of the known reaction steps leading to nicotinic acid. Actually, three (and perhaps more) different pathways of niacin genesis are known to exist. [49] These are often well documented; yet no one who is familiar with the field would be prepared to expect a definite *limit* on the extent of the violations that may exist *en route* to niacin formation in any new organism. The actual extent to which individual reactions are known to occur will be pointed out below. There may likely be deviations from this scheme, as will be pointed out; others may be yet undiscovered.

REACTION 1: *Anthranilic acid + PRPP → N-o-Carboxyphenyl-D-ribosyl-amine-5-PO$_4$.*

This reaction has been carried out in cell-free extracts of a mutant strain of *Escherichia coli* that requires tryptophan for growth; [87, 453] also in a corresponding culture of *Aerobacter aerogenes.* [99] The phosphate group in the product corresponds to the 5' (ortho) phosphate group in PRPP.

REACTION 2: *N-o-carboxyphenyl-D-ribosylamine-5-PO$_4$ $\xrightarrow[\text{rearrangement}]{\text{Amadori}}$*
1-(o-carboxyphenylamino)-l-deoxyribulose-5-PO$_4$

The indicated product in reaction 1 has not been rigorously characterized structurally; however, the product of reaction 2 has been indirectly established through the 2,4-dinitrophenylhydrazone, [391, 98] and agreement with behavior of model compounds. The product from reaction 2 accumulated in the cultures used; [99] its identity with a synthetic material, derived by Amadori rearrangement of N-o-carboxyphenyl-D-ribosylamine, seems probable. Its lability is not surprising, and the unavailability of authentic crystalline Amadori rearrangement compounds of pentoses [169] make this absence of unequivocal proof of structure seem more reasonable. The Amadori rearrangement, if it occurs *in vivo*, may not be enyzmatic.

REACTION 3: *1-(o-carboxyphenylamino)-1-deoxyribulose-5-PO$_4$ → indole-3-glycerol phosphate*

Here the evidence for the postulated sequence is somewhat better, at least with respect to the overall reaction, anthranilic acid → indole-3-glycerol phosphate: Yanofsky [454] has shown that anthranilic acid and PRPP are converted quantitatively to indole-3-glycerol phosphate (IGP) and further that appropriate tryptophan auxotrophs of *E. coli* lack the enzyme [391] to carry out this conversion. Cyclization of the product from reaction 2 (or a similar compound) and loss of the carboxyl group are to be expected. In the overall conversion (reactions 1 through 3), ATP, inorganic P and ribose-5-PO$_4$ may substitute for PRPP, and anthranilic acid may be replaced by several ring-substituted derivatives.

REACTIONS 4 and 5: *Indole-3-glycerol phosphate → indole; indole + serine →*
tryptophan

In *E. coli* the synthesis of tryptophan from IGP (tryptophan synthetase) appears to operate in two steps, as shown in Fig. 2, [78, 77, 457] or as follows:

$$\text{Indole} + \text{serine} \rightarrow \text{tryptophan} \qquad (5)$$
$$\text{IGP} + \text{serine} \rightarrow \text{tryptophan} + \text{triose-PO}_4 \qquad (4a)$$
$$\text{IGP} \leftrightarrow \text{indole} + \text{triose-P} \qquad (4)$$

Reactions 5 and 4a require pyridoxal phosphate; [77] reaction 4a is probably common to a variety of organisms; [458] reaction 4 can be demonstrated to occur if serine is absent, in *E. coli.* [77] However, in the mold *Neurospora*, free indole appears not to be an intermediate in the synthesis of tryptophan. [459] The explanation for the difference in behavior appears to hinge on the report [78, 457] that *E. coli* synthetase is composed of two separable proteins, whereas *N. crassa* synthetase activity is associated with a single protein. The two *separate* proteins alone catalyze reactions 4 and 5, respectively, at low rates; together they effect the complete synthesis at a rapid rate.

The *Neurospora* enzyme is specific for L-serine, but is not completely specific for indole, responding also to the 6-methyl and 7-hydroxy derivatives. [456]

Doy [98] has proposed the scheme shown in Fig. 3 to summarize the terminal steps in tryptophan biosynthesis in *Neurospora* and *E. coli.*

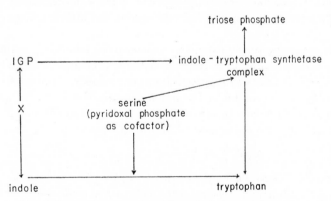

FIG. 3. Terminal steps in tryptophan biosynthesis in neurospora and *E. coli*
(after Doy [98]).

The demonstrated need (on genetic grounds) for both reactions 4 and 5 in the same organism [458] may be somewhat unexpected in that the glycerol phosphate side chain is hydrolyzed off and serine is then incorporated as a new side chain. Other *Neurospora* mutants appear able to convert imidazole-glycerol phosphate to histidine by appropriate alteration of the glycerol residue. [10]

REACTION 6: (*Tryptophan pyrrolase*) *L-Tryptophan → formylkynurenine*

This degradation, first observed by Kotake and Masayama, [235] has been described for several years (about 1951–9) as a coupled peroxidase-oxidase reaction, in which tryptophan was converted in two stages to an unidentified intermediate, [226, 84] followed by the formation of formyl kynurenine. Although two separate enzymes were at first conjectured, other work with the system from rat liver revealed [224] that a single enzyme may catalyze both reactions, with the final step producing peroxide to drive the first reaction: tryptophan $+ H_2O_2 →$ intermediate $+ O_2 →$ formylkynurenine $+ H_2O_2$. The enzyme preparations used were relatively crude, and the precise mechanism of the reaction 5 remains unclear. The enzyme is inhibited by Cu^{++} and by CO, with the latter inhibition reversed by light. Similar activity has been demonstrated in bacteria. [159]

On the other hand, a similar, if not precisely corresponding enzyme has been studied in a *Pseudomonas* sp. [402] Here the enzyme has been partially purified and shown to be an iron porphyrin protein. Peroxide was not involved in the reaction, although this compound was necessary to activate the enzyme; this was considered due to the need for reduction of the inactive ferric enzyme to the active ferrous form. The ferrous enzyme then served as an oxygenase to carry oxygen directly to tryptophan. The authors now suggest that the name for the enzyme, tryptophane pyrrolase, [235] originally suggested by Kotake and Masayama [235] may be more appropriate than peroxidase-oxidase in view of the now recognized different function of this enzyme.

In the rat, tryptophane pyrrolase appears to be adaptive, i.e. the concentrations present in the liver respond rapidly to changes in dietary tryptophan. [227, 103] It has been suggested that maintenance of normal tissue levels of the enzyme may be under hormonal control. [227, 225, 133, 406] There is no evidence for the presence of a dissociable cofactor in this enzyme: purification was attended by loss of hematin, [144] during a reported purification of 300- to 1000-fold.

REACTION 7: (*Kynurenine formamidase* (*formylase*)).

Formylkynurenine → HCOOH + kynurenine

This enzyme, which has been purified eight-fold from rat liver [291] and 17-fold from *Neurospora*, [199] hydrolyzes a number of aromatic formamido compounds. The "natural" substrate, N′-formyl-L-kynurenine, is cleaved most rapidly. The affinity of these substrates for the enzyme is also the greatest for formyl kynurenine, as shown by the Michaelis constant: the K_m value is $1·1 \times 10^{-4}$ compared to approximately 3×10^{-3} for the other compounds tested. [199] Kynurenine formamidase activity has also been shown in *Pseudomonas*, [159] where the reaction appears specific for the L-isomer of formylkynurenine.

REACTION 8: (*Kynurenine hydroxylase*). *Kynurenine* → *3-hydroxykynurenine*.
This reaction, dependent upon TPNH, was demonstrated in cat- and rat-liver mitochondria by de Castro *et al.* [88] The enzyme was further purified by Saito *et al.*, [367] who showed that the oxygen incorporated into 3-hydroxy kynurenine was derived from atmospheric oxygen rather than from water; the enzyme is thus of the oxygenase type. Some of the best evidence for the participation of hydroxykynurenine in the tryptophan breakdown scheme includes its formation from tryptophan in pyridoxine-deficient rats, [80] in insects, [59, 397, 269] and in urine of human fever patients. [83]

REACTION 9: (*Kynureninase*). *3-Hydroxy kynurenine* → *3-hydroxy anthranilic acid + alanine*
This reaction has been demonstrated in a variety of organisms. The enzyme has been concentrated 20-fold from liver, [223] 7-fold from *Pseudomonas*, [160] and 70-fold from *Neurospora*. [197] Kynureninase from all three sources utilizes pyridoxal phosphate as the coenzyme, and the *Neurospora* preparation has been shown to be Mg-dependent. All three are inhibited by carbonyl reagents such as semicarbazide, cyanide and hydroxylamine. Specificity is not complete, [223, 160, 197, 439, 158] since the 5-hydroxy- and N'-formyl derivatives, as well as kynurenine itself are degraded in an analogous manner to yield 5-hydroxy-anthranilic acid, formyl anthranilic acid and anthranilic acid, respectively. The enzyme is in fact named for the last reaction.

Whereas reaction 6 above was adaptive in the rat, in bacteria kynureninase is adaptive, being induced by culture on tryptophan-containing media. [160]

REACTION 9a:
The ability of kynureninase to cleave kynurenine and formyl kynurenine naturally raises the question of the function of such reactions in the cell. An "anthranilate cycle" could hardly be of value in the biosynthesis of nicotinic acid, nor of aromatic (including indole) derivatives, since removal of the latter would prevent the formation of hydroxy anthranilate by the usual kynureninase reaction. This type of cycle has in fact been reported [324] to play no significant role under conditions of normal tryptophan synthesis in *Neurospora*, and thus may be of importance (in this organism at least) only when the tryptophan content of the medium is abnormally high.

REACTIONS 10, 11 AND 12:
Several groups of workers have made significant and nearly simultaneous contributions to the problem. Details of the conversion of *3-hydroxyanthranilate* to nicotinic acid are still unclear. An enzyme, *3-hydroxyanthranilate oxidase*, has been described in mammalian liver, [347, 290, 437, 189a, 88a, 414] which consumes two gram atoms of oxygen per mole of substrate and produces one mole of an unstable oxidation product that may spontaneously

rearrange to form quinolinic acid. [290, 440] This intermediate has been viewed as a product formed by cleavage between carbon atoms 3 and 4 of the aromatic ring, [154] with structure I indicated below: [290, 82]

I

I - Amino - 4 - Formyl
buta -1,3 - diene -1,2 - dicarboxylic
acid
(2-acroleyl-3-aminofumarate)

II

α-Aminomethyl
muconic acid

An alternate proposal, with structure II pictured, has been offered; [156] it can replace nicotinic acid in the nutrition of *Xanthomonas pruni*, [156] whereas compound I appears to give rise to quinolinic acid [292] and picolinic acid. [289]

Further relationships among these compounds are not clear. Picolinic acid is not significantly utilized by rats, [293] and quinolinic acid is biologically much less effective than niacin or 3-hydroxyanthranilate. [367] Solution of these relationships will have to wait more definitive experiments with purified enzyme systems, using substrates of known composition. The instability of the product of reaction 10 has undoubtedly slowed progress in this area, although the results obtained by Wilson and Henderson [431] using isotopic tryptophan and 3-hydroxyanthranilate, indicate that quinolinic acid is a true intermediate in the pathway proposed, in the developing chick. The possibility also exists that reactions 10, 11 and 12 may in part represent various side paths of tryptophan metabolism. In the cell, niacin occurs primarily as the amide, and in turn, chiefly as DPN and TPN. It seems likely, on the basis of experience with other nucleotides, that ribosides or ribotides may be formed much earlier than is pictured in Figs. 2 and 4. Some of these points are covered in the review articles by Yanofsky [455] and Dalgliesh. [81]

REACTION 13: *Possible direct pathway from anthranilate to hydroxyanthranilate*

Although mammals and *Neurospora* are able to utilize dietary tryptophan as a source of niacin, *E. coli*, *M. tuberculosis* [7] and *Bacillus subtilis* apparently do not. [458] In *E. coli* nicotinic acid appears to be derived from C^{14}-labeled succinate and glycerol. [321] Some mutants of *Aspergillus* have been reported to respond to anthranilate and 3-hydroxyanthranilate, but not to compounds in the tryptophan series, and a direct conversion of anthranilate has been postulated. [344] Support for this idea has been provided by the observation [284] that cell-free *E. coli* extracts can hydroxylate anthranilate in the 3-position. The ability is reportedly lost among aged cells, but can be regained by incubating them with *p*-amino benzoic acid.

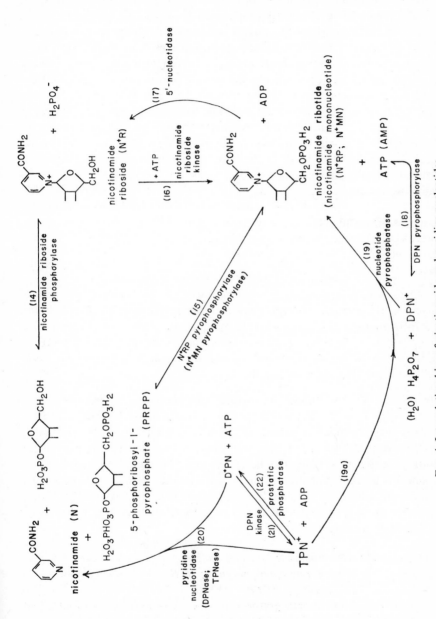

Fig. 4. Interrelationships of nicotinamide and pyridine nucleotides.

Miscellaneous Pathways

Other evidence has been obtained in some plants that argues against the scheme presented in Fig. 2: tryptophan-3-C^{14}, unlike nicotinic acid, is not converted to trigonelline in garden peas,[248] and 3-hydroxy anthranilic acid-7-C^{14} does not appear as trigonelline in soy bean leaves.[14] Similar negative information has been observed in other plants;[247, 146] neither labeled tryptophan nor 3-hydroxy anthranilic acid is converted to nicotinic acid by germinating corn, nor by tobacco,[164] nor by a *Bacillus* species isolated from soil.[113] It seems reasonable to conclude that many plants as well as bacteria[418] and mammalian liver[315] may use different routes for biosynthesis of niacin from that employed by *Neurospora* and most mammalian systems tested. Some of these routes may represent minor variations wherein certain enzymes or reaction steps are emphasized[12, 134, 135, 190] either by variations in growth stimulation or through differences in the effect of repressor agents, whereas others show larger divergences. Thus, for example, Hayaishi and his colleagues have shown[190] that in the cat, synthesis of NAD is retarded (from tryptophan) by excessive synthesis of picolinic carboxylase.

Conversion of Niacin to Pyridine Nucleotides

Whereas most species are unable to carry out a complete synthesis of niacin in the absence of tryptophan or other precursors already discussed, the incorporation of this vitamin into pyridine nucleotides is a property of all but a very few organisms. A conversion sequence has been constructed from reactions occurring in yeast and various mammalian preparations, which follows the outline given in Fig. 4.

REACTION 14: (*Nicotinamide riboside phosphorylase*). *Nicotinamide* + *ribose*-1-PO_4 ⇌ *nicotinamide riboside* (*NR*) + $H_2PO_4^-$

This enzyme, which is named for the reverse reaction, has been found in erythrocytes and liver.[365] Salt fractionation and adsorption provided a 60-fold purification from the latter source. The equilibrium constant is about 0·1. Purified preparations do not attack other pyridinium compounds, but do phosphorolyze inosine. Inosine inhibits phosphorolysis of N^+R, and it has been suggested[365] that the same enzyme may catalyze the cleavage of both nucleotides.

REACTION 15: (*Nicotinamide mononucleotide pyrophosphorylase*). (*N^+MN pyrophosphorylase; N^+R pyrophosphorylase*). $N + H^+ + PRPP$ ⇌ $N^+RP + PP_i$.

An enzyme from human erythrocytes has been purified 600-fold which catalyzes the synthesis of N^+RP from nicotinamide.[345] The reaction is slow, reversibility is somewhat doubtful and the affinity for the substrate is unusually low (K_m for nicotinamide = 0·1), so that it seems possible that this reaction may normally employ other components. Nevertheless, the N^+RP synthesizing enzyme appears different from those catalyzing the formation of inosinic, adanylic or guanylic acids. This is similar to the observed formation [306a] of N^+RP, discribed by Nakamura *et al.* from quinolinate. Purification of up to 5000-fold of the enzyme has been claimed, from beef liver.

REACTION 16: (*Nicotinamide riboside kinase*).

> (N^+R *kinase*). $N^+R + ATP \rightarrow$ nicotinamide ribotide (N^+RP, N^+MN) $+ ADP$.

This enzyme has been reported in liver, [365] but it has not been purified or studied extensively. ATP was found to be a necessary component of the reaction; N^+R could not be replaced by combinations of nicotinamide, ribose-1-PO_4 and ribose-5-PO_4.

REACTION 17: (*5'-nucleotidase*). $N^+RP + H_2O \rightarrow N^+R + P_i$.

This reaction, although not the reverse of reaction 16, serves to degrade the ribotides of nicotinamide and several purines and pyrimidines to the corresponding ribosides. The enzyme has been observed in a variety of mammalian sources [358, 274] and in snake venoms. [147] It has been purified 50-fold from semen [165] using salt, alcohol and protamine fractionations and adsorption on alumina. It is specific for the ribose-5-PO_4 moiety of phosphate esters. The reaction is stimulated by Mg^{++} and inhibited by Ca^{++}.

REACTION 18: (*DPN pyrophosphorylase*). *Nicotinamide ribotide* (N^+RP; N^+MN) $+ ATP \rightleftharpoons DPN + PP_i$.

This enzyme (named for the reverse reaction) has been purified 110-fold from liver and 1800-fold from yeast, [230] chiefly through salt fractionation procedures. Both preparations are Mg^{++}-dependent, with slight stimulation by Mn^{++}. The Michaelis constants for the liver and yeast enzymes are reported as 2×10^{-4} and 5×10^{-4}, respectively, with an equilibrium constant of about 0·4 for the reaction as written. The specificity requirements for this enzyme are sharp; only the reduced nucleotides (NRPH and DPNH) have been found to replace NRP and DPN. In the forward direction, this enzyme is a prominent one for the synthesis of DPN in the cell, although nicotinic acid or nicotinamide riboside may serve as precursors of the coenzyme. [185]

REACTION 19: (*Nucleotide pyrophosphatase*). $DPN + H_2O \rightarrow \overset{+}{N}RP(\overset{+}{NMN}) +$ adenosine-5'-PO_4 (5'-AMP).

This reaction differs from the reverse of reaction 17 in that DPN is hydrolyzed rather than phosphorylyzed. One of the products, nicotinamide ribotide, is the same in both reactions; however, in reaction 19 the bond energy of the terminal group in ATP is presumably dissipated as heat, into the reaction mixture.

Pyrophosphatase is found in animal and plant tissue, [232] and has been concentrated over 700-fold from potatoes by salt and ethanol fractionations followed by calcium phosphate adsorption. The purest preparations of the enzyme also hydrolyze the pyrophosphate bond in other nucleotides, including flavin-adenine dinucleotide and ATP, as well as TPN, so that the same enzyme may possibly be involved in all of these degradations. The pH range for optimum activity is fairly broad, from 6·5 to 8·5. Unlike the phosphatase in reaction 17, this enzyme appears to be unaffected by Mg^{++} or Ca^{++}. Specificity of action toward DPN and DPNH varies; in the potato, DPN is split more readily, [230] whereas in the kidney the reverse is true. [232]

Pyrophosphatase acts on TPN in a similar manner, to form NRP and adenosine-2',5'-diphosphate (reaction 19a).

REACTION 20: (*Pyridine nucleotidase; PNase; DPNase; TPNase*).
$$\begin{cases} N^+RPPRA \ (=DPN^+) + H_2O \rightarrow N + RPPRA + H^+ \\ N^+RPPRPA \ (=TPN^+) + H_2O \rightarrow N + RPPRPA + H^+ \end{cases}$$

Broken cell extracts of many tissues suffer a rapid breakdown of DPN or TPN to free nicotinamide. [272, 153, 285] In *Neurospora*, the enzyme responsible is a *hydrolase* which acts as shown in the foregoing equation. In animal tissues another enzyme exists which is reported [463] to function not only as a hydrolase but also as a *transglycosidase*, according to equation 20a:

$$N^+RPPRA + X \rightarrow X^+RPPRA + N \tag{20a}$$

Where X = other pyridinium compounds related to nicotinamide.

The specificities of the two enzymes differ considerably, as do their susceptibilities to inhibitors. In addition, there is variability in the properties of animal tissue DPNases. When *Neurospora* is grown on a medium deficient in zinc and biotin, DPNase accumulates in the cells to nearly 100 times its normal concentration.

The ability of nicotinamide to inhibit DPNase is often utilized to prevent the destruction of added pyridine nucleotide in *in vitro* experiments. Inasmuch as no evidence exists for reversibility of the reaction, the action of nicotinamide should not be interpreted as inhibition by a reaction product (mass action effect). Instead, it has been suggested [463] that nicotinamide competes with water for attachment to an intermediate complex formed between DPN and the enzyme.

Interconversions of DPN and TPN
REACTION 21: (*DPN kinase*). $DPN + ATP \rightarrow TPN + ADP$ [291, 212]

DPN kinase has been observed in mammalian and avian tissues and in yeast. [419] It has been purified 45-fold from pigeon liver [422] and 25-fold from yeast; [231] however, the final product from yeast exhibits higher specific activity. The enzyme is Mg^{++} or Mn^{++} dependent, and is highly specific; in addition to DPN, only the 3-acetyl pyridine analog is attacked by the liver enzyme. [423] Other nucleotides with structures resembling DPN are inhibitory. An exception is DPNH which, while reversibly inhibiting the liver preparation, stimulates the yeast enzyme.

REACTION 22: (*Prostatic phosphatase*). *TPN $\rightarrow$ DPN $+$ P_i.*

A relatively non-specific phosphatase from the prostate gland, which preferentially hydrolyzes 2'- and 3'-phosphate groups from nucleotides, [373] can degrade TPN or DPN. [205] The importance of this reaction in other tissues or organisms is unknown.

Pyridine nucleotide transhydrogenase [206] catalyzes the reaction, DPN $+$ TPNH $\rightarrow$ TPN $+$ DPNH. This reaction is not reversible. It seems to afford a route in many organisms for the oxidation of TPNH, in the absence of suitable electron transport systems to link TPNH to the cytochrome system; the transhydrogenase enzyme merely converts TPNH to DPNH, then the organism oxidizes the latter. This route has been suggested [208] as a common one; it may, however, not be the exclusive pathway for oxidation of TPNH in tissues. [203]

Interconversion of Nicotinic Acid and Nicotinamide

The reader may now ask: how is *nicotinic acid* converted to the ribose derivatives shown in Fig. 4? This is not clearly defined, although a suggestion of an interconversion pattern has been given. [370a] Although both the free vitamin and its amide are readily utilized by nearly all organisms, and although there are certain other pyridines that can give rise to DPN (β-picoline, pyridine-3-carbinol or aldehyde, [207]) the direct enzymatic conversion of nicotinic acid to its amide seems not to occur readily. The work of Preiss and Handler [346] and Imsande and Handler [192b] rather suggests that, starting with nicotinic acid, nucleosides and nucleotides corresponding to the compounds listed in Fig. 4 are first formed; when the acid corresponding to DPN appears ("desamido-DPN"), it is converted through the action of glutamine or NH_3, ATP and Mg^{++}, to the desired product (DPN). Handler, [346] has reported that dietary nicotinamide is hydrolyzed to nicotinic acid, then incorporated into desamido DPN (the nicotinic acid analog of DPN) and finally converted to the co-enzyme. Work by Nishizuka and Hayaishi [315] proposes that free niacin is not formed *per se* but that NAD (DPN) is formed instead, directly. Finally, studies by Imsande [192a] and Imsande and Pardee [192c] equating the overall DPN (NAD) synthesizing abilities of *E. coli* preparations with the corresponding abilities of several of the individual enzymes, gives a reassuring view of the plausibility of the scheme that is presented in Fig. 2.

Despite these reservations and the still incomplete knowledge of the tryptophan → niacin reaction scheme, the work performed to date with a variety of organisms represents a splendid integration of nutritional, genetic and enzymatic studies, including isotope tracer experiments, which demonstrate unquestionably the link between these two nutrients (see also Chapter 17, Section V).

III. PANTOTHENIC ACID

This vitamin, discovered by R. J. Williams and co-workers [433] in 1933, was characterized in 1940, [434, 432, 396] but its function was not recognized until after 1947, when Lipmann et al. [257] demonstrated that a conjugated form of the vitamin was the coenzyme of acetylation, or Coenzyme A (CoA). Other conjugates (pantetheine, pantothenyl cysteine, pantetheine-4'-PO_4 [53, 52, 220, 51, 19]) have been described since that time; some of these figure in the biosynthesis of CoA. [44, 47, 317] Still other derivatives, such as pantothenic acid-4'-PO_4, are reported not to be biologically active. [221, 18]

The structures of pantothenic acid and some of its congeners are give in Fig. 5, and several conjugates of the vitamin, including CoA, are shown in Fig. 6. The vitamin is a compound molecule, composed of the amino acid β-alanine and α,γ-dihydroxy-β,β-dimethyl butyric acid, called pantoic acid. Most organisms require the intact vitamin, which is widely distributed in nature; the name (Greek, *from everywhere*) implies this. However, a few organisms such as yeast [436, 429] and several species of *Corynebacterium* [304,251] synthesize pantoic acid; *Acetobacter suboxydans*, [411, 370] some hemolytic streptococci, [443] and a *Clostridium* species [394] manufacture their own β-alanine. Wild type *E. coli* is an example of a microorganism that synthesizes both halves of the vitamin. With the advent of methods for preparing mutant strains of organisms, auxotrophs of *E. coli* have been developed that synthesize either moiety alone, or, by contrast, require intact pantothenic acid for growth.

Synthesis of Pantoic Acid

Kuhn and Wieland [241] developed an organic synthesis for pantoyl lactone from α-ketoisovaleric acid ("ketovaline") via α-keto-β,β-dimethylbutyric acid ("ketopantoic acid"). They reported that ketopantoic lactone could be converted to pantoyl lactone, and suggested a similar route *in vivo*. This has been shown to be similar to, but not identical with, the biosynthetic route; in the latter scheme ketovaline gives rise to both pantoic acid and valine, as shown in Fig. 5, reactions 1 and 4. Evidence for the entire sequence has not been gained with cell-free systems, however mutant strains blocked between ketovaline and valine were able to form pantoic acid. [267] Valine appears not to be a usual precursor of pantoic acid, since one strain of *E. coli*, when offered either ketovaline or ketopantoate, accumulated valine. [267]

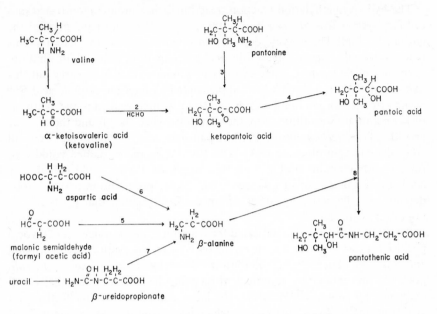

FIG. 5. Origin of pantothenic acid (after Maas[265]).

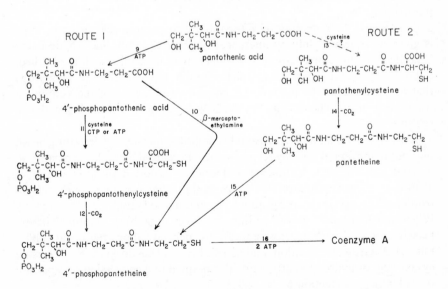

FIG. 6. The biosynthesis of CoA (after Brown[46]). Reaction 13 is the only one shown for which no enzyme has yet been found.

The hydroxymethylation reaction, reaction 2, has been demonstrated in a cell-free system from *E. coli* by McIntosh *et al.*, [286] who have purified the enzyme 36-fold. The enzyme depends on divalent cations for activity. This reaction would seem to suggest folic acid participation; although this has not been rigorously verified, crude extracts of *E. coli* were able to carry out this hydroxymethylation better when supplemented with tetrahydrofolic acid. [348] Some evidence for *p*-aminobenzoic acid (PABA) involvement in the synthesis of ketopantoate was afforded by these authors when they found that for the growth of *Bacterium linens*, PABA, pantoate and ketopantoate were all equivalent to pantothenate (PA). The PA intermediates named could also reverse sulfanilamide inhibition in this organism. PABA could presumably act here as a precursor of folic acid; the further presumption is that a folic derivative is the active agent, as outlined. The situation that exists in this organism is still unclear

Pantonine, the substrate indicated for reaction 3, has a somewhat equivocal position. It was so placed mainly on the basis of an observation by Ackermann and Shive, [4] that a growth inhibition caused by salicylic acid vs. *E. coli*, normally preventable by pantoic acid or pantothenic acid, was equally well overcome by pantonine. However, the latter compound was ineffective as a growth promoter for *A. suboxydans*, which needs pantothenate or pantoic acid for growth. Moreover, its conjugate with β-alanine is ineffective as a replacement for pantothenate in the nutrition of lactic acid bacteria. [348] Maas [265] has concluded that pantonine may not be a normal precursor of pantoate in most organisms.

Reaction 4, the reduction of ketopantoate to pantoic acid or its lactone, is given as shown mainly by inference; presumably, only one reaction step is needed for this conversion. The product, pantoic acid, is well established, not only by breakdown of the complete vitamin, but also from the knowledge that it can serve as the jumping-off place for resynthesis of the vitamin in several organisms. The weight of evidence with mutants is also in line with this scheme. [138]

The origin of β-alanine is reasonably well documented, at least in general outline; it appears to arise by several routes. Perhaps the best known pathway is from aspartic acid. Virtanen and Laine [416] reported the presence of β-alanine as a fermentation product, presumably from aspartate, by *Rhizobium trifolii*. The enzyme bringing about the decarboxylation was observed by Billen and Lichstein, [25] both in this and other organisms. As might be expected, these decarboxylases appear to depend upon pyridoxal phosphate. [281] Growth inhibition studies by Shive and co-workers, [388, 354] using cysteic acid or hydroxyaspartic acid, also pointed to a conversion of aspartate to β-alanine, see reaction 6.

Evidence of β-alanine formation by other routes has come from several sources. Roberts and Bregoff [362] report a transamination in mammalian tissues between glutamate and malonic semialdehyde (formyl acetic acid); one of the products was β-alanine. Formyl acetic acid, in turn, according to Coon and co-workers [242, 359] may arise from propionate. The reverse reaction (β-alanine to formylacetic acid) has been suggested in the rat. [334] Finally, Maas [265] reports that in E. coli, at pH 7–8 there exists a glutamate-dependent synthesis of β-alanine. From these reactions, the diagram shown in Fig. 5, reaction 5, seems reasonable.

Reaction 7 describes a pathway that occurs in certain Clostridia: C. uracilicum was observed to degrade uracil to β-alanine, CO_2 and NH_3 via dihydrouracil and β-ureidopropionic acid. [62] A similar degradation may occur in rat liver. [118] Finally, the Clostridium culture studied by Stadtman [394] appears to oxidize propionyl CoA to β-alanyl CoA via acrylyl CoA as an intermediate. This CoA derivative may play a role in the biosynthesis of carnosine and anserine. It would appear that biosynthesis of β-alanine is a fairly common occurrence in organisms; yet it is curious to reflect on how very small is the total number of species that do not require intact pantothenic acid as a preformed vitamin.

The final condensation of the PA moieties, reaction 8, is based on the indirect evidence already discussed; in addition there is more direct evidence from Brucella abortus [9] and from E. coli [264] that extracts contain an enzyme that synthesizes pantothenate directly from β-alanine and pantoate. The E. coli enzyme has been partly purified, and shown to require ATP and Mg^{++}, Mn^{++}, K^+ or NH_4^+ as activators; it produces equimolar amounts of AMP and pyrophosphate. The work of Maas [265] and Maas and Novelli [266] has revealed that the coupling may take place in two steps, as follows:

Enzyme $+$ ATP $+$ pantoate $\rightarrow$
$$\text{Enzyme-pantoyladenylate} + \text{pyrophosphate} \qquad (8a)$$

Enzyme-pantoyladenylate $+$ β-alanine $\rightarrow$
$$\text{Enzyme} + \text{AMP} + \text{pantothenate} \qquad (8b)$$

A peptide bond is thus fabricated, in which the second phosphate of ATP is used. This is unusual; the mechanism resembles the activation of amino acids and the formation of acetyl CoA.

Biosynthesis of CoA

Coenzyme A is one of the most complex vitamin-nucleotide combinations yet discovered. It has been shown to be involved in a large number of biological reactions, mostly associated with activation of acyl groups. No significant biological activity has been reported for any other conjugate of pantothenic acid, except as it may lead toward the appearance of CoA. Several intermediates in the biosynthesis have been reported; they are arranged in Fig. 6 to demonstrate their interrelationships. Most of our present knowledge in this area has been accumulated by Lipmann and Novelli and Snell, Brown and their co-workers, with occasional assists from other laboratories. The outline presented is quite different, as might be anticipated, from the course of an elegant total organic synthesis of this nucleotide that has been described. [299]

The reaction scheme in Fig. 6 is essentially that outlined by Brown; [46] others, somewhat older, have been presented by Novelli. [317] Coenzyme A arises, as may be seen, after a series of phosphorylations and joining of amide bonds; the exact sequence may differ under various circumstances, although of the two main pathways presented, route 1 has been better documented in general than route 2. The enzymes along route 1 have been verified, at least in part, in *Proteus morganii*, *E. coli*, *L. arabinosus*, and *N. crassa*; moreover, the decarboxylase for PA-cysteine catalyzing reaction 14 could not be shown in any of them. [44] When these organisms (as well as a few others) grew in high concentrations of PA, they accumulated 4′-phospho PA, which lies on route 1, reaction 9. [46] *Lactobacillus helveticus*, on the other hand, for which pantetheine is a superior growth stimulant, [76] also utilizes PA-cysteine more readily than the free vitamin. PA-cysteine is similarly preferred over free PA by *A. suboxydans*, [52, 220] and this conjugate occurs naturally in mammalian liver. [79] Finally, *L. bulgaricus* contains PA-cysteine decarboxylase. It might appear, therefore, that these organisms are capable of employing route 2: *L. helveticus*, for example, when forced to grow on free PA, might be pictured as employing this means of producing CoA for cellular activities. As pointed out by Brown, [46] however, the lack of unequivocal proof in any organism of the existence of reaction 13 makes questionable the entire argument for the existence of route 2.

Brown [46] raises the interesting point that pantetheine, despite its demonstrated superiority in *A. suboxydans* nutrition, may lie off the main biosynthetic pathway toward CoA formation. This is based on the finding that PA-cysteine appears relatively inert when fed to animals, being neither hydrolyzed nor phosphorylated, and only very slightly decarboxylated. Pantetheine can, on the other hand, arise readily from degradation of either CoA or pantetheine-PO_4, and Brown has reported further that this is probably the route of formation of pantetheine in most natural materials. Once formed, it may again be converted to CoA by kinases that are present in these materials. [252, 424]

It is noteworthy that CTP is required for the synthesis of pantetheine-PO_4 from pantothenic acid-PO_4 + cystamine, reaction 10. It can be replaced by ATP, and Brown has suggested that CTP may play a role in amide formation that is analogous to the ATP-dependent coupling of β-alanine and pantoate in PA synthesis, reaction 8. Alternately, it is possible that cytidine diphosphate pantothenic acid may be an intermediate in a two-stage reaction. Verification of either of these possibilities will have to await further purification of the coupling enzyme or enzymes.

The effectiveness of route 16 as pictured in Fig. 6 seems to occur as expected, almost to the point that it seems nearly not to be noteworthy. It has been studied by Hoagland and Novelli [167] and has been shown to occur in two steps, with the intermediate formation of dephospho CoA. Purification of about 100-fold of the enzymes has been reported, from hog liver.

IV. RIBOFLAVIN

Riboflavin (vitamin B_2), although required by man and some bacteria is produced by many organisms in amounts sufficient for growth. Many organisms produce an excess [430] and in some unusual fungi *Eremothecium ashbyii*, *Ashbya gossypii*, and *Candida flareri*, such large excesses of riboflavin are produced that the vitamin crystallizes out of the medium. It is these organisms which have been most useful for the elucidation of the mechanism of synthesis of riboflavin.

That riboflavin arises from some purine precursor, or from some intermediate common to both was first suggested by the work of MacLaren, [268] who found that the addition of adenine, guanine, xanthine or thymine to the culture medium of *E. ashbyii* increased the yield of riboflavin without affecting growth of the organism. Brown, Goodwin, and Jones [43] confirmed these observations in a similar series of experiments. In addition, this group [139] found serine to function as a precursor—presumably by way of degradation to glycine and formate. Goodwin and McEvoy [140] found adenine did not stimulate riboflavin synthesis in *C. flareri*, and attributed this lack of activity to the lack of adenine deaminase. Urea, arginine, and ornithine promote riboflavin synthesis in *C. flareri*, although these compounds are ineffective in *E. ashbyii*. The observation by Brown, Goodwin and Pendlington [42] that aminopterin inhibits growth of *E. ashbyii* but promotes riboflavin synthesis further indicated a relationship between riboflavin and the purines. Howells and Plaut [181] studied the synthesis of riboflavin in a strain of *E. coli* which requires purines for growth. In this strain, there was no significant incorporation of carbon-14 from glycine into the riboflavin, or into nucleic acids. There was appreciable incorporation of label into 5-aminoimidazole-4-carboxamide. When guanine-6-C^{14} was used, the riboflavin isolated was radioactive. These authors concluded that a purine precursor was an obligatory intermediate in riboflavin synthesis.

Direct contribution of the carbon skeleton of adenine to riboflavin was demonstrated by McNutt [288, 287] in *E. ashbyii*, who found radioactive adenine to be incorporated into the isoalloxazine ring of riboflavin. In agreement with the idea that adenine is used less extensively than guanine for riboflavin synthesis in *C. flareri*, Audley and Goodwin [17] obtained only a 19 per cent incorporation of adenine-U-C^{14} into riboflavin, compared to an 85 per cent incorporation of guanine-U-C^{14}. Under suitable conditions, up to 70 per cent of the added guanine was converted to riboflavin. [143] McNutt found that carbon-8 of radioactive adenine was not incorporated into the isoalloxazine ring, as would be expected if 4,5-diamino uracil were a precursor.

The pattern of labeling in riboflavin is very similar to that found in purines. Radioactive formate offered to *A. gossypii* yields riboflavin labeled in carbon-2, bicarbonate-C^{14} yields products with label in carbon-4, and glycine-1- or 2-C^{14} yields riboflavin labeled almost completely in carbons-4a and 9a (see Fig. 7). [181, 335, 336] Although evidence for the involvement of purines or

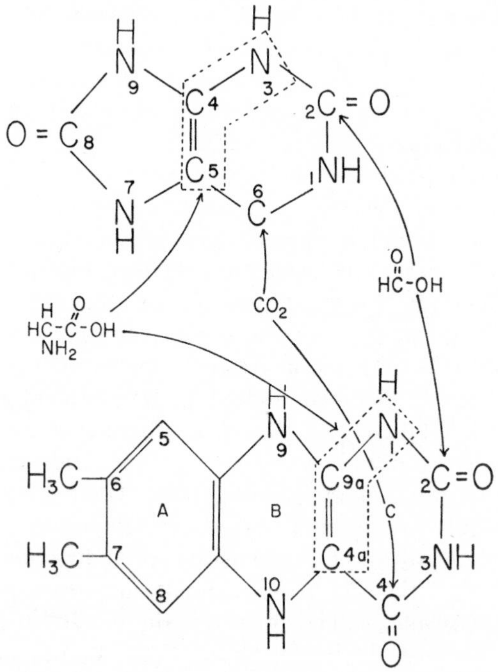

FIG. 7. Incorporation of C^{14} compounds into the B and C rings of riboflavin (after Plaut [335]).

some purine metabolite in the synthesis of riboflavin is extensive, the mechanism by which this conversion proceeds is still unknown. 4,5-Diamino uracil has been suggested as a possible intermediate in the synthesis, and its detection as a metabolite of *E. ashbyii* has been reported by Goodwin and Treble [141] who trapped the compound with diacetyl and glyoxal. Kuwada, Masuda, Kishi and Asai [243] report however that the addition of 4,5-diamino-uracil inhibits the formation of riboflavin. [268] Birch and Moye [26, 27] achieved the condensation of diacetyl with 4,5-diamino uracil chemically. Both lumichrome and lumiflavin were obtained by this condensation, and they suggest the biochemical synthesis may be similar to the chemical one. Goodwin and Treble [142] found labeled acetoin incorporated in ring A of riboflavin, when the former compound was incubated with *E. ashbyii*. They suggested that acetoin condenses with a diamino uracil derivative, to form 6,7-dimethyl-8-ribityllumazine. Kishi, Asai, Masuda and Kuwada [222] proposed 4-ribityl amino-5-amino uracil as the active intermediate which condenses with acetoin in the reaction, as shown in Fig. 8.

Guanine-2-C^{14} serves as a precursor of riboflavin, but it is not converted to adenine of nucleic acids. [8] This observation suggests that guanine is utilized directly, or at least, it is not first converted to adenine before being used for riboflavin biosynthesis.

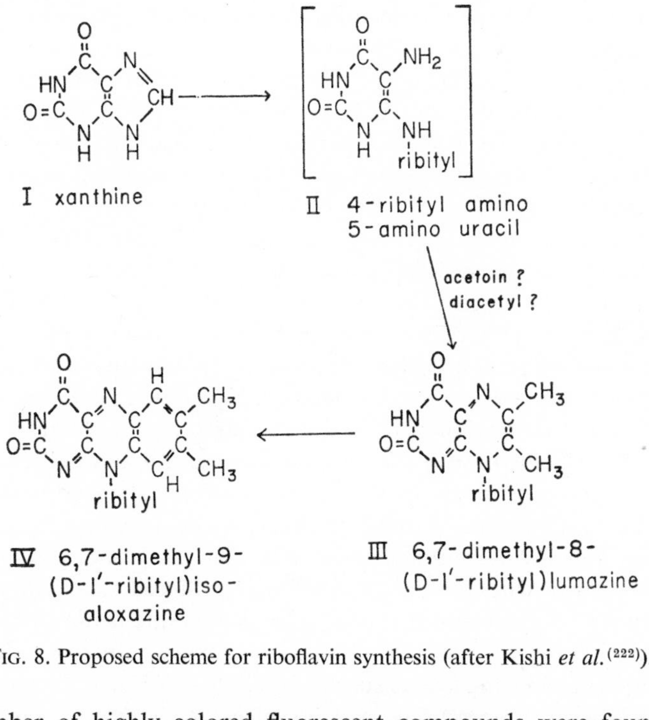

I   xanthine

II   4-ribityl amino
5-amino uracil

acetoin ?
diacetyl ?

IV   6,7-dimethyl-9-
(D-1'-ribityl)iso-
aloxazine

III   6,7-dimethyl-8-
(D-1'-ribityl)lumazine

FIG. 8. Proposed scheme for riboflavin synthesis (after Kishi *et al.* [222]).

A number of highly colored fluorescent compounds were found in an examination of products formed by *E. ashbyii* and *C. acetobutylicum*, and these compounds were examined for metabolic acitivity in the synthesis of riboflavin. Blue and violet compounds found by McNutt and Forest, [289, 124] Asai, Masuda and Kuwada [15] and Katagiri, Takeda and Imai [209] and Hotta and Ando [180] appear to be the products of side reactions, rather than precursors of riboflavin. However, Katagiri, Takeda and Imai [209] found several green fluorescent compounds in the culture filtrate of *C. acetobutyli-cum*, one of which, when added to the organism, promoted the synthesis of riboflavin *in vivo*. Asai, Masuda and Kuwada [15] made similar observations on the activity of a green compound found in *E. ashbyii*, and Maley and Plaut [272] found a corresponding substance in mycelia of *A. gossypii*. The most active riboflavin precursor was identified by several groups [15, 272, 143, 211] as 6,7-dimethyl-8-ribityllumazine. Maley and Plaut [270] further demonstrated the metabolic activity of this compound by using formate-C^{14} and glycine-C^{14}. The specific activity of the lumazine formed from these precursors was higher than that of riboflavin, supporting the hypothesis that riboflavin is derived from lumazine.

6,7-Dimethyl-8-ribityllumazine has been found to be a precursor of riboflavin in *E. ashbyii* [282, 244] *A. gossypii*, [337, 272, 271, 340] *C. acetobutylicum* [210] *E. coli*, [337, 210] bovine liver, [245] and green leaves. [297]

The conversion of the intermediate to riboflavin has been the subject of recent intensive study. In a preliminary series of experiments in extracts of *A. gossypii*, Maley and Plaut [271] reported the synthesis of riboflavin from lumazine using pyruvate and ATP, in addition to a mixture of coenzymes. Specific activities of the synthesized riboflavin and lumazine added were quite similar (61,000 cpm/μmole and 67,200 cpm/μmole, respectively). In later reports Plaut [341, 342, 420, 337] found no stimulation of synthesis by acetoin, butane-2,3-dione, pyruvate, acetate, ethanol, acetyl phosphate, acetyl CoA, ATP, ADP, ribose-5-phosphate, DPN or TPN. Acetate-1 or -2-C^{14} or uniformly labeled glucose was not incorporated. He suggested that the lumazine acts as both donor and acceptor of carbon atoms, and in this series of experiments found that one mole of 6,7-dimethyl-8-ribityllumazine led to the formation of $\frac{1}{2}$ mole of riboflavin. In addition, he found incubation of 6,7-dimethyl-8-ribityllumazine-C^{14} with extracts of *A. gossypii* led to the formation of riboflavin with label in positions 5 and 8 and in the two methyl groups. The ratio of molar specific activities of lumazine and riboflavin was 1 : 2·2. Using an enzyme purified 177 times from *A. gossypii* extracts Plaut found 6,7-dimethyl-8-ribityllumazine was converted to microbiologically active riboflavin. The amount of riboflavin produced was proportional to the amount of enzyme added. The *A. gossypii* enzyme had a Michealis constant of $2·9 \times 10^{-5}$ M, while the yeast enzyme had a *Km* of 4×10^{-5}. Only the addition of reducing agents such as bisulfate stimulated the reaction, and NaF, arsenicals, or mercurials had no effect. While Plaut found that the addition of metals did not influence the enzymic reaction, Rowan and Wood [364] reported the addition of metals improved the rate at which they were able to convert 6,7-dimethyl-8-ribityllumazine to riboflavin chemically. They achieved a 55 per cent yield of riboflavin by refluxing the lumazine precursor for 15 hours under nitrogen. A mechanism in which the pyrazine ring is opened under the influence of a nucleophilic attack at position 7 was proposed by these workers. This reaction may provide a model system for the determination of the mechanism of the biosynthetic reaction. Kuwada, Masuda, Kishi and Asai [244] found that cell-free extracts of *E. ashbyii* mycelia could also convert 6,7-dimethyl-8-ribityllumazine to riboflavin in the absence of any added carbon source, in agreement with the observations made by Plaut [337] in the *A. gossypii* system. Plaut [342] found that although conversion of lumazine to riboflavin proceeded without dilution of the label, the ratio of the disappearance of lumazine to formation of riboflavin had an average value of 2.3, and a small amount of 6-methyl-7-hydroxy-8-ribityllumazine was formed as a by-product. Mitsuda, Kawai, Suzuki and Satani [298] detected this compound when they treated 6,7-dimethyl-8-ribityllumazine with NaOH and Asai, Mizumo and Kuwada [16] found it when they treated the lumazine with acid.

The final reaction in the synthesis of riboflavin can thus be written:

2 (6,7-dimethyl-8-ribityllumazine) → riboflavin +

4-(1'-D-ribitylamino)-5-amino-2,6-dihydroxylpyrimidine.

The second product of the reaction was identified by Wacker, Harvey, Weinstock and Plaut. [420] Addition of glyoxal to 6-ribitylamino-5-aminouracil yielded 8-ribityllumazine, which could then presumably, be converted to additional riboflavin. Identification of this last reaction may explain the previously described stimulation of riboflavin biosynthesis by small carbon units. [210, 222]

Synthesis of the ribityl side chain has been studied by Plaut and Broherg [339] who found incorporation of both carbons 1 and 6 of glucose in this moiety. Although a greater incorporation was obtained when glucose-6-C^{14} was used, sufficient glucose-1-C^{14} was incorporated to make it clear that there was not a direct incorporation of ribose from the pentose cycle. They suggest randomization of carbon-1 of glucose *via* the glycolytic pathway.

Many vitamins have been found to function as parts of coenzymes in the body, and to do so, they are usually phosphorylated. Riboflavin is no exception, and its phosphorylation to flavin mononucleotide was described by Kearney and England [217] long before the synthesis of riboflavin was formulated. Interestingly enough, the phosphorylation reaction catalyzed by flavokinase is almost irreversible—perhaps a mechanism for retaining the vitamin in a useful form in the cell.

Biosynthesis of Flavin Nucleotides
ATP + riboflavin → riboflavin-phosphate (FMN)

Isoriboflavin, 5,6-dimethyl-9-(D-1'-ribityl)-isoalloxazine is not attacked by this enzyme.

The synthesis of flavin adenine dinucleotide from flavin mononucleotide is reversible. This synthesis, as described by Schrecker and Kornberg, [376] involves the reversible combination of flavin mononucleotide with ATP to yield flavin adenine dinucleotide and pyrophosphate.

$$FMN + ATP \rightleftharpoons FAD + PP_i$$

Riboflavin itself is inactive in the system. Although the FAD synthesizing activity in yeast is only 1 per cent of the DPN synthesizing enzyme, this may be rationalized to some extent on the basis that FAD is present in considerably lower amounts than is DPN.

Riboflavin appears to be synthesized from either a purine metabolite or from purines themselves, and, as will be seen in a later section, folic acid appears to be derived from a similar source. The elaborate synthetic procedure for the synthesis of purines may thus be used in many organisms, not only for the synthesis of major metabolites, nucleic acids, but also for the synthesis of minor, vital components, the coenzymes.

Control of riboflavin synthesis appears to be less exact than control in other pathways, and Wilson and Pardee [430] found the flavins to be greatly overproduced. The ratio of flavin excreted to flavin in the cells varied from 0·8 to 8·0. Since the synthesis of riboflavin is so interconnected with the synthesis of purines, it is possible that an examination of the intimate details of its biosynthesis may disclose types of control which depend upon the concentrations of several end products, similar to those described by Freundlich, Burns and Umbarger [127] for the control of the valine-isoleucine pathway in *E. coli*.

V. FOLIC ACID

Folic acid is a complex vitamin which consists of a pteridine moiety, *p*-aminobenzoic acid (PABA), and one or more molecules of glutamic acid attached in peptide linkages (Fig. 9).

Synthesis of Pteridine Ring

The pteridine ring of folic acid appears to be synthesized either from a purine precursor, or from a purine metabolite. Indirect evidence for the involvement of purines in the synthesis of the pteridine ring comes from the work of Dewey and coworkers [91] who found that 2,4,5-triamino-6-hydroxy-pyrimidine replaced the biopterin requirement for *Crithidia fasciculata*. Esposito and Fletcher [115] found that pteridines, guanine and xanthine but not adenine acted as antagonists to copper-8-hydroxyquinolate inhibition of spore germination in fungi. And, Andreeva [11] reports that the addition of purines to wheat embryos accelerates the synthesis of folic acid.

A more direct involvement of purines in folic acid biosynthesis was demonstrated by Weygand and Waldschmidt[428] who found incorporation of glycine and formate-C^{14} into leucopterin of butterfly wings after these radioactive substrates had been injected into the larvae. Formate-C^{14} was found in carbon-2 of leucopterin, and glycine-1-C^{14} in carbons 4 and 6. This

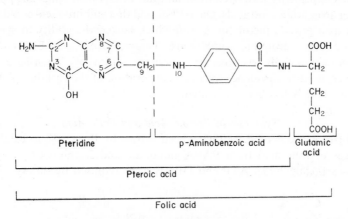

Fig. 9. The structure of folic acid.

labeling pattern is similar to that found in the purine nucleus, except for the radioactivity in carbon-6 from glycine-1-C^{14}. The direct conversion of xanthopterin to folic acid has been reported by Korte, Schicke and Weitkamp[234] in *Streptococcus faecalis*, *Pichia membranefaciens* and *Candida albicans*. Viera and Shaw[415] found that growing cultures of *Corynebacterium* were able to use radioactive adenine for the synthesis of pteridine. Radioactive carbon from adenine-2-14-C was incorporated into folic acid, but radioactive carbon from adenine-8-C^{14} was not. Reynolds and Brown[360, 361] extended these observations and found that cell-free extracts of *E. coli* converted guanosine, and guanosine nucleotides to folic acid. These authors found that guanosine mono-, di- and tri-phosphate could all serve as precursors for the synthesis of microbiologically active vitamin. In the presence of cell extract and *p*-aminobenzoic acid-glutamate, radioactive guanosine added at a level of 700 cpm/mμmole gave rise to radioactive dihydrofolate, which had a specific activity of 500 cpm/mμmole. While guanosine-8-C^{14} also gave rise to a microbiologically active product under these conditions, the folate isolated was not radioactive. In contrast to the observations of Korte, Schicke and Weitkamp[234] neither xanthopterin nor reduced xanthopterin could function as folate precursors in the *E. coli* system. Baugh and Shaw[23] and Krumdieck, Baugh and Shaw[240] found that *Corynebacterium* was able to convert guanine to the expected intermediate, 2,4,5-triamino-6-hydroxypyrimidine, which appears to be intimately involved in folate synthesis.

2A

Albert[6] found that 2-hydroxy purine and glyoxal could be condensed chemically at 37° to yield pteridine, and it is suggested that a similar mechanism occurs in the synthesis of naturally occurring pteridines (see Fig. 10).

Synthesis of PABA

PABA appears to be derived from shikimic acid, which is also the precursor of other aromatic amino acids. Davis [86] found that shikimic acid could replace PABA as a growth factor for E. coli which lacked the ability to synthesize this and other aromatic compounds. Tatum, Gross and Ehrensvärd [405] reported similar observations in a mutant strain of Neurospora crassa. However, no direct evidence for the incorporation of the carbons of shikimic acid into PABA has been presented.

Synthesis of Pteroic Acid and Folic Acid

Cell-free extracts of E. coli have been shown by Brown [45] to catalyze the synthesis of folic acid from PABA-glutamate and 2-amino-4-hydroxypteridine-6-carboxaldehyde. ATP and DPNH were required by this system as is

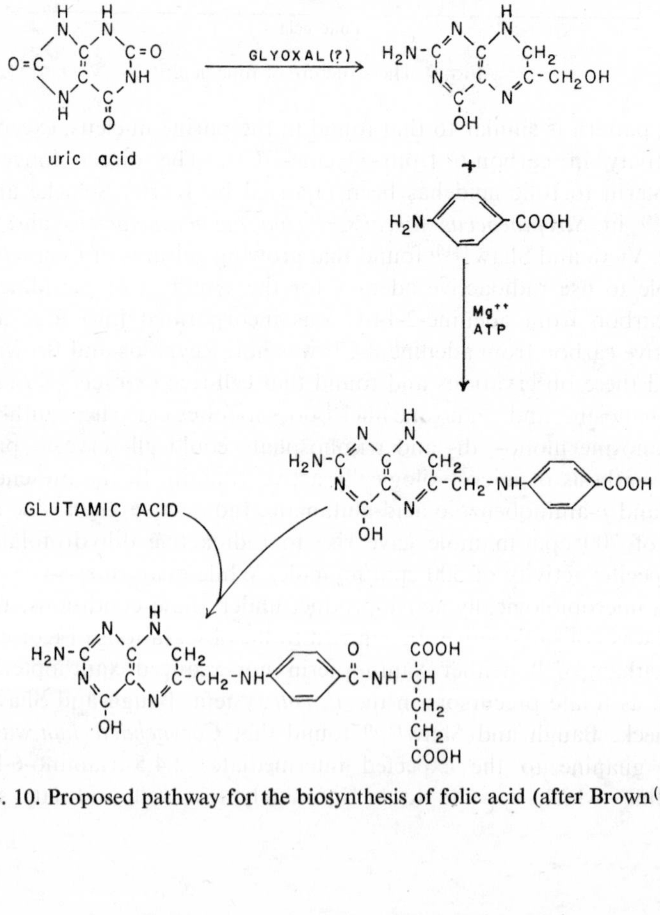

FIG. 10. Proposed pathway for the biosynthesis of folic acid (after Brown[54]).

shown in Fig. 10. Similar results have been obtained by Shiota [385] who found that extracts of *L. arabinosus* would utilize 2-amino-4-hydroxyl-6-hydroxymethyl and 6-carboxaldehyde pteridine for the synthesis of folic acid in the presence of ATP and Mg^{++}. He found reduction of the pteridines with zinc made these compounds more active in the enzyme system. Further support of the efficacy of reduced pteridines was found by Jaenicke and Chan [198] who reported the enzymic condensation of PABA-glutamate with 2-amino-4-hydroxy-6-hydroxymethyl dihydropterin in extracts of yeast, *E. coli*, and *Corynebacterium* sp. Preincubation of the pteridine with ATP satisfied the ATP requirement in this system. The authors propose that for condensation to occur, the pteridine must have a pyrophosphate linkage on carbon 9, and isotope exchange experiments with P_i^{32} and ATP^{32} support the existence of this phosphorylated intermediate. A recent report by Brown, Weisman and Molnar [54] describes the coupling of hydroxymethyldihydropteridine to PABA directly to yield dihydropteroic acid in cell-free extracts of *E. coli*. These authors suggest that glutamic acid is added later to the pteroic acid to form dihydrofolic acid. Alternatively, Katunuma, Shoda and Noda [213] found evidence for the synthesis of PABA-glutamate directly in extracts of *Mycobacterium avium*. In the presence of ATP and CoA, a CoA derivative of PABA is formed, which condenses with glutamic acid. They suggest the series of reactions shown in Fig. 11. Recently, more evidence has accumulated relating to the reactions by which folic acid is synthesized from pteridine. Weisman and Brown, [427] Griffin and Brown, [145] and Jones, Reynolds and Brown [202] working with *E. coli* extracts, and Shiota, Disraely and McCann, [387] working with *Lactobacillus plantarum* have presented data to support the following sequence of reactions:

1. reduced   pteridine(2-amino-4-hydroxy-6-hydroxymethyl   dihydropteridine) + *p*-aminobenzoic acid + ATP $\xrightarrow{Mg^{++}}$ pteroic acid
2. pteroic acid + glutamic acid → folic acid.

Shiota and Disraely [386] obtained similar results with extracts of *Lactobacillus plantarum* although these workers used *p*-amino-benzoyl-glutamate as a substrate. Griffin and Brown [145] found that in *E. coli* extracts, *p*-aminobenzoic acid was utilized ten times as effectively as aminobenzoyl-glutamate.

Shiota, Disraely, and McCann [387] prepared pteridine diphosphate which, after reduction to the dihydro form, was active in forming folic acid in the presence of *p*-aminobenzoic acid. Phosphorylation of the pteridine eliminated the requirement of ATP in reaction 1.

Further evidence for the formation of a pteroic acid derivative has been presented by Rauen, Hess and Mechery [353] who find pteroic acid to be the most active substance in reversing the inhibition of growth of *N. crassa* with sulfathiazole, although rhizopterin, folic acid, 1-formylfolic acid, PABA, and PABA-glutamate are also effective. This work is in agreement with that of Brown [48, 47] who found that sulfonamides are strong inhibitors of reaction 2 in *E. coli* extracts. Pato and Brown [325] isolated sulfathiazole-resistant strains of *E. coli* which were able to carry out these reactions both in the presence and absence of the sulfa drug. Wolf and Hotchkiss [442] isolated several strains of *Pneumococcus* in which there were found genetically controlled alterations of the affinity in the substrate binding groups in the enzyme which controls reaction 1. These authors found that sulfanilimides changed the K_m for the reaction, while not affecting the V_{max}. They also found that PABA was more effective than PABA-glutamate.

It is interesting to observe that Forrest and Mitchell [125] and van Baalen and Forrest [413] find pteridines in eye pigments of *Drosophila*, 2-amino-4-hydroxy-6-(1′,2′-dihydroxypropyl)-pteridine, 2-amino-4-hydroxy pteridine,

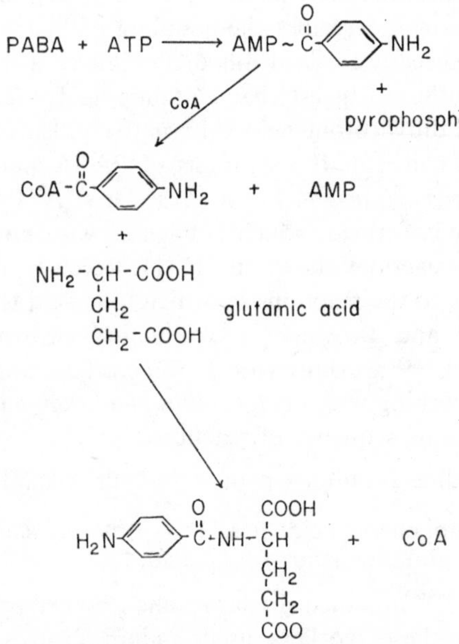

FIG. 11. Proposed pathway for the synthesis of PABA-glutamate (after Katunuma, Shoda and Noda [213]).

isoxanthopterin and 2,6-diamino-4-hydroxypteridine, which are similar to intermediates active in folic acid biosynthesis.

Conjugated forms of folic acid, in which there are three to seven glutamic acid residues, have been found in some organisms. Three glutamic acid residues in folic acid have been found by Hakala and Welch [149] in *Bacillus subtilus*, by Zakrzewski and Nichol [461] in *Streptococcus faecalis*, and by Wright, Anderson and Herman [444] in *Clostridium sticklandii*, and seven glutamic acid residues in yeast by Pfiffner, Calkins, Bloom and O'Dell. [333]

The significance of the extra glutamic acid residues is still unknown, but Sirotnak, Donata and Hutchison[389] reported that practically all of the synthesis of the glutamyl peptides moieties of folate occurred prior to folic acid in *Diplococcus pneumoniae*. In this organism, sulfanilamide inhibition was reversed with dihydrofolate only, not with folic acid.

Direct enzymatic formation of dihydrofolic acid (DHFA) has been observed

$$\text{folic acid} + \text{TPNH} + \text{H}^+ \to \text{DHFA} + \text{TPN}$$

$$\text{DHFA} + \text{TPNH} + \text{H}^+ \rightleftharpoons \text{THFA} + \text{TPN}$$

by Wright, Anderson and Herman[444] in extracts of *C. sticklandii*, and the further enzymic reduction of dihydrofolic acid to tetrahydrofolic acid (THFA) in chicken liver extracts has been reported by Osborn and Huennekens,[322] Futterman[130] Zakrzewski and Nichol[462] and Zakrzewski.[460] It appears likely that although folic acid may be synthesized in the reduced form, mechanisms exist for its reduction should it become oxidized in the cell. The mechanism for the formation of a primary oxidation product was studied by Kaufman,[214] using the artificial pteridine, 2-amino-4-hydroxyl-6,7-dimethyl, 5,6,7,8-tetrahydropteridine as a cofactor for the oxidation of phenylalanine to tyrosine by a rat liver enzyme. The "oxidized" pteridine formed in this reaction was reduced with TPNH and a sheep liver enzyme to the original compound. Kaufman excluded a 5,6-dihydropteridine intermediate in the reaction by use of tritium labeled TPNH, and he concluded the "oxidized" pteridine probably had a quinoidal structure.

Formyl Derivatives of THFA

The formation of formyl derivatives of folic acid has been observed in both bacterial and mammalian systems. An extensive review of the earlier work is presented by Huennekens and Osborn in the *Advances of Enzymology*.[182] The synthesis of N^5-formyl THFA, the citrovorum factor, was observed *in vitro* by Doctor and Trummell[97] who fed homocysteine, cysteine and folic acid to rats. When rats were given 100 μg per day of folic acid, there was a six-fold increased excretion of N^5-formyl THFA acid in the urine. The yield of N^5-formyl THFA was increased when the urine was autoclaved with ascorbic acid.[96] Broquist, Kohler, Hutchison and Burchenal[39] using *S. faecalis* also found folic acid to be converted to N^5-formyl THFA in the presence of reducing conditions and a source of formate. A similar synthesis has been obtained by Heisler and Schweigert[163] in extracts of *L. casei*. These authors observed that the omission of ascorbic acid decreased the yield of N^5-formyl THFA several fold. Couch and Reid [75] found that chicken liver homogenates could also catalyze the formation of N^5-formyl THFA from folic acid:

$$\text{folic acid} \xrightarrow[\text{ATP, Mg}^{++}\text{ DPN}]{\text{ascorbic acid formate}} N^5\text{-formyl THFA}$$

Their enzyme system was stimulated by ATP, DPN and Mg^{++}. Glycine exerted an inhibitory effect on this conversion. Kay, Osborn, Hatefi and Huennekens [215] report an enzyme in chicken liver which requires ATP and Mg^{++} to catalyze the isomerization of N^5-formyl THFA to the N^{10}-formyl form:

$$N^5\text{-formyl THFA} + \text{ATP} \rightarrow \text{ADP} + P_i + N^{10}\text{-formyl THFA}$$

ADP and inorganic phosphate are formed during the reaction. In this system the authors obtained no evidence for the formation of the N^5,N^{10}-methenyl THFA intermediate. In contrast to these observations, Rabinowitz and Pricer, [350] using purified extracts of *Clostridium cylindrosporum*, found three enzymes involved in the formation of N^{10}-formyl THFA from THFA and formiminoglycine. 5-Formimino-THFA is formed by the action of the first enzyme, and this product is converted to N^5,N^{10}-methenyl THFA by the action of the second enzyme. The third enzyme generates N^{10}-formyl THFA. Himes and Rabinowitz [166] in examining the mechanism of this reaction were unable to find evidence for a phosphorylated derivative. An interesting observation was made by Peters and Greenberg [330] who found that sheep liver acetone powders contained an enzyme which would catalyze the conversion of N^5-formyl THFA to a compound which is similar to, but whose absorption spectrum is different from N^5, N^{10}-methenyl THFA. The maximum absorption of N^5, N^{10}-methenyl THFA occurs at 354 mμ, but that of the unknown compound at 343 mμ. ATP is necessary for this conversion.

The interrelationships between folic acid, purines and other vitamins are still obscure. In four strains of lactobacilli, Bolinder and Kurz [30] found that a requirement for folic acid could be met by thymidine or thymidine monophosphate, and Lieberman and Ove [255] found in mammalian cell cultures that a requirement for folic acid was satisfied by a mixture of glycine, adenine and thymidine. Brown, Silva, Gardiner and Silverman [41] found rats deficient in folic acid and B_{12} excreted formimido glutamic acid in large amounts while methionine in excess prevented this excretion. It has been reported [318] that germ-free animals excrete folic acid in large quantities when they are fed biotin.

The synthesis of folic acid in some organisms may be self-regulating, since this vitamin functions in an important capacity in the synthesis of purines, which also appear to serve as precursors in its biosynthesis.

VI. CYANOCOBALAMINS*

The B_{12} vitamins are a numerous and unusual family whose members have the same general structure. This structure consists of a novel porphyrin-like ring with cobalt in the center (Fig. 12) attached by a carbon chain with a peptide-like linkage to aminopropanol, which in turn is bound to phosphate. Phosphate is connected to ribose in the 3 position and ribose is bound to a

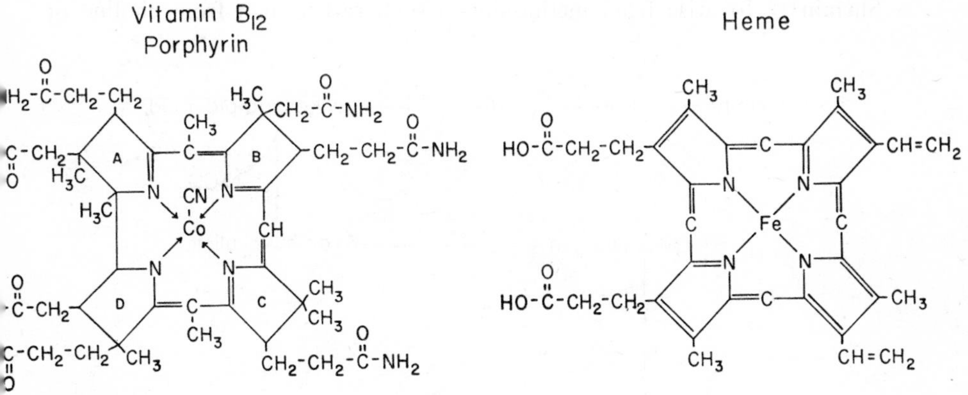

FIG. 12.

benzimidazole or to a purine. [390, 368, 13, 32] The four-ring complexes differ from other porphyrins in that rings A and D are joined directly rather than through a usual methylene bridge.

Similarities found between hydrolysis products of vitamin B_{12} and the more usual porphyrin suggested a relationship between these two kinds of compounds. The incorporation of glycine and succinate first into δ-aminolevulinic acid and then into porphyrins was traced by a number of investigators in a large group of elegant experiments (Fig. 13). [352, 441, 305, 381, 382. 116, 312, 29, 138, 383, 451, 372, 384] Shemin, Corcoran, Rosenblum and Miller [380] found that if δ-aminolevulinic acid-1,4-C^{14} was offered bacteria, the B_{12} synthesized was also highly radioactive. And, more recently, DiMarco and Spalla, [93] and Bykhovskii and coworkers [60] have also found δ-aminolevulinic acid acts as a precursor of B_{12} synthesis. Corcoran and Shemin [14] also demonstrated the biosynthesis of the porphyrin moiety of B_{12} from δ-aminolevulinic acid by isolating the vitamin from *actinomycetes* offered the

* See also Chapter 5.

compound. These authors found there was good indication that most, although not all, of the radioactive carbon was in the atoms as indicated in Fig. 14. Schwartz, Ikeda, Miller and Watson [378] reported the utilization of porphobilinogen-C^{14} in the synthesis of vitamin B_{12} and indicated that in these experiments one-half to one-third of the porphyrin moieties obtained were derived from the added porphobilinogen. Many organisms synthesize porphyrins quite readily and the point of divergence by which B_{12} is synthesized as opposed to the more usual porphyrins is not known. This divergent pathway is of particular interest since the synthesis of this vitamin by other than microorganisms has not been reported.

Methyl groups on the porphyrin ring (Fig. 14) were found by Bray and Shemin [36] to arise from methionine-methyl, rather than from choline or

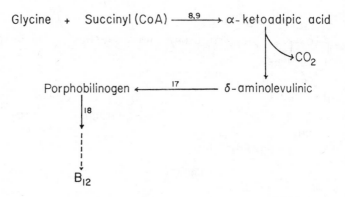

FIG. 13. Synthesis of factor B porphyrin moiety of B_{12}.

betaine, as measured by isotope labeling experiments. More recently, these authors [37] found that the two gem-methyl groups in ring A of the corrin ring system were derived from two different sources, namely, methionine and the δ-carbon of δ-aminolevulinic acid (Fig. 14). They suggest the odd placement of this last methyl group arises from the fact that there is no methylene bridge between rings A and D in B_{12}, as there is in the porphyrins. Krasna, Rosenblum and Sprinson [239] found the aminopropanol portion of B_{12} synthesized by *Streptomyces griseus* in the presence of threonine-N^{15} contained a high concentration of heavy nitrogen. Apparently, threonine was decarboxylated, and the amine formed used directly, without breakage of the carbon chain. Additional evidence for an isopropanolamine precursor for this part of the vitamin comes from the work of Koenigk [228] who was able to replace hydrogen in this moiety with fluorine. The fluoride analogue was obtained when cobanamide was allowed to react with 1,2,3-trifluoro isopropanolamine. The ribose moiety of B_{12} is derived from 1-pyrophosphorylribose-5'-phosphate by way of nicotinic acid mononucleotide (NaMN). The reaction, studied by Friedmann[129] and Harris[128] is:

5,6-Dimethylbenzimidazole + NaMN → 5,6-Dimethyl-
benzimidazole-5'-phosphate + nicotinic acid + H⁺.

There are a number of interesting aspects of this reaction, including the

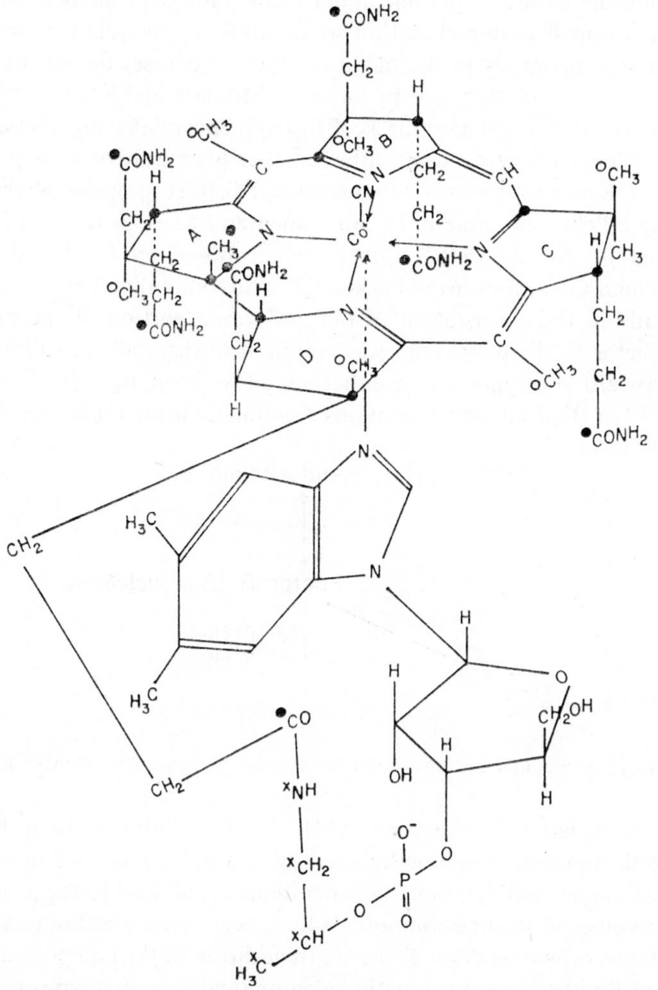

FIG. 14. Labeling pattern in vitamin B_{12}.
● When δ-aminolevulinic acid —1,4—C^{14} is used (after Corcoran and Shemin[74]).
○ When methionine —C^{14} is used (after Bray and Shemin[36, 37]).
× When threonine —C^{14} is used (after Krasna, Rosenblum and Spinson[239]).

observation that nicotinic acid mononucleotide is much more effective as a ribose source than is nicotinamide mononucleotide. In addition, the enzyme involved in this reaction catalyzes a single displacement with the formation of an N-α-glycosidic bond, a novel reaction, since other *trans*-N-glycosidases apparently catalyze double displacement reactions. The lack of absolute specificity of this enzyme suggests that it may play an essential role in the guided biosynthesis of various B_{12} vitamers, that is, the ability of bacteria to incorporate a wide variety of bases into analogues of the vitamin. With this idea in mind the nature of the remainder of the molecule, the benzimidazole or purine, is thus determined, within some limits, by the relative concentrations of usable materials in the medium, and, of course, the nature of the organism involved, as suggested by Sahashi, Mikdata and Sakao. [366]

Sahashi *et al.* [366] found a synthesis of B_{12} from a postulated prosthetic group, 5,6- dimethylbenzimidazole, using either chicken liver paste or a *Streptomyces* strain. Ford, Kon and Porter [123] found several distinct compounds which had B_{12} activity by chromatography of calf rumen and feces. A relation between the various B_{12} factors (see Fig. 15) was proposed by Ford and Holdsworth, [121] and Gant, Smith and Parker, [132] who found that these compounds differed only in the constitution of the nucleotide portion of the molecule and that factor B, the porphyrin, was common to them all. *E. coli* was thus directed toward the synthesis of either pseudovitamin B_{12}, which contains adenine, [300] or B_{12} itself, which contains 5,6-dimethylbenzimidazole. Adenine

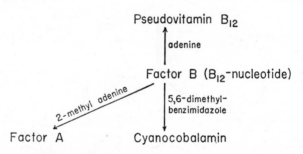

FIG. 15. Some interrelationships in the B_{12}-like vitamins (after Kon[229]).

could not be replaced by adenosine, AMP or ATP. With riboflavin, B_{12} itself is produced. 1-Amino-3,4-dimethyl-6-ribityl-aminobenzene, 4,5-dimethyl-*o*-phenylenediamine, and 5,6-dimethylbenzimidazole, all lead to the production of B_{12}. A number of B_{12}-like compounds have been synthesized in this way by several groups of workers (see Table 1). In addition to the compounds listed, Brown and Smith [50] found 2-methyladenine, and 2-methylhypoxanthine in the B_{12} compounds isolated from pig manure. Because of the ease with which *E. coli* can make B_{12}-like materials from the offered nucleotides, Ford, Holdsworth and Kon [122] suggest that the B_{12} requirements of this organism are imposed by a defect in the synthesis of factor B. From the list of compounds synthesized by *Propionibacterium arabinosum*, the same defect appears to be present in this organism.

Although many microorganisms are able to utilize assorted nucleotides for the synthesis of B_{12} vitamers, *Nocardia rugosa* appears to make more specific demands. In contrast to reactions observed in *P. shermanii* and in

TABLE 1. SYNTHESIS OF B_{12}-LIKE COMPOUNDS

Nucleotide	Organism	Reference
5,6-dimethylbenzimidazole	Streptomyces x-28	366
	Chicken liver	
	Propionibacterium arabinosum	328
Adenine	*E. coli*	121, 122
Benzimidazole	*E. coli, P. arabinosum*	122, 328
5,6-dichlorobenzimidazole	*E. coli*	122
5-methylbenzimidazole	*E. coli, P. arabinosum*	122, 328
4-chloro-1,2-benztriazole	*E. coli*	122
Benztriazole	*E. coli*	122, 328
2,6-diaminopurine	*E. coli, P. arabinosum*	122, 328
2,8-dichloroadenine	*E. coli*	122
o-phenylenediamine	*Streptococcus griseus*	117
	Streptococcus olivaceus	131
5-nitrobenzimidazole	*P. arabinosum*	328
5-trifluoromethylbenzimidazole	*P. arabinosum*	328
Phenazine	*P. arabinosum*	328
2-hydroxyphenzaine	*P. arabinosum*	328
4-bromo-6-methoxybenzimidazole	*P. arabinosum*	328
3,4-dihydro-4-oxoquinazoline	*P. arabinosum*	328
Quinoxaline	*P. arabinosum*	328

E. coli, this organism appears to be unable to utilize analogues for synthetic purposes. This may be due to the fact that the mechanisms by which the purine base is in fact incorporated into B_{12} differs from that used by other microorganisms.[20, 33, 296, 92] In *N. rugosa*, the α-glycosidic nucleoside of dimethylbenzimidazole is incorporated into cobalamin by attachment to bound phosphate, and guanosine diphosphate cobinamide is a likely intermediate.

Nocardia rugosa produces several B_{12} compounds, two of which have activity only for *E. coli*. One active compound is suggested by Barchielli et al.[21] to have the structure:

Factor B-O-P-O-P-O-ribose-guanine

That is, it is a guanosine-diphospho-derivative of factor B. In the presence of benzimidazole in the medium, none of the guanosine compound accumulates.

On the basis of these data, Barchielli et al.[21] suggest that guanosine triphosphate may take an active part in the synthesis of B_{12} as is shown in Fig. 16.

The addition of purines and purine analogues has been reported by several workers to have an effect on the total amount of B_{12} vitamers produced. Shaposhnikov and coworkers[379] found addition of 5,6-dimethylbenzimidazole increased the B_{12} excretion by 50 per cent from *Streptomyces olivaceus*. However, addition of this same compound at the beginning of the fermentation evidently caused a decrease in the yield of corrinoids by several species, including *P. shermanii*, although if it was added late in the fermentation, B_{12} production was stimulated.[464] This observation was also made in six strains of *S. faecalis*,[151] where the addition of 0·5 per cent mg of 5,6-dimethylbenzimidazole decreased the yield of B_{12}.

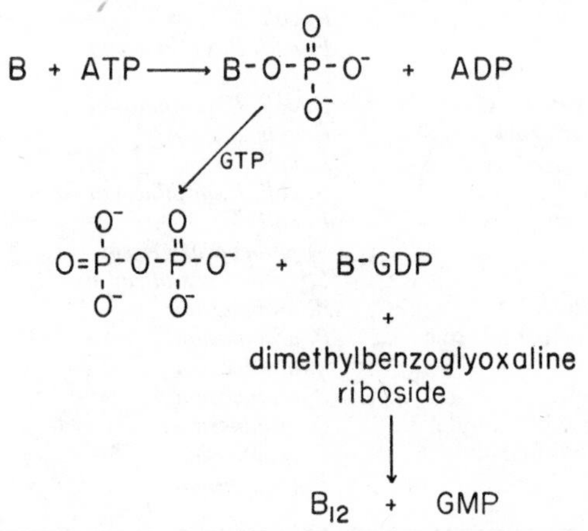

FIG. 16. Proposed synthesis of B_{12} from factor B (after Barchielli et al.[21]).

The effect of phenylenediamine on the synthesis of B_{12} vitamins in *Streptococcus griseus* is unusual. Fantes and O'Callaghan[117] found a variation in the amount of synthesis of B_{12} with the concentration of added phenylene diamine. The authors concluded that the presence of this compound in the growth medium causes the formation of a new analogue which is more active for *E. coli* and *Lactobacillus leichmannii*, rather than an actual stimulation of synthesis. A consideration of these data suggests that one possible source of inhibition by the numerous benzimidazoles tested by Epstein[114] and by Blackwood and Shorb[28] is that these compounds are incorporated into B_{12}-like compounds antagonistic to the active ones.

In examining some of the chemical properties of vitamin B_{12}, Smith and Mervyn[392] found a grey-green reduction product, which they believe to be a cobalt hydride. Müller and Müller[306] also found a cobalt-hydride to be formed by reduction. Smith and Mervyn found that treatment of the hydride with any alkylating agent, such as methyl iodide or methyl sulfate caused the compound to become red. Apparently the nature of the reducing agent is vital, since Hufham and coworkers[184] found that B_{12} reduced anaerobically with *P. rubescens* gives a different absorption spectrum from that of B_{12} reduced by catalytic reduction, or by photolysis.

The coenzyme form of B_{12} was reported by Weissbach, Toohey and Barker[425] to contain 2 moles of adenine, only one of which is attached to ribose. This would suggest that the coenzyme is actually a derivative of pseudovitamin B_{12}. *Clostridium tetanomorphum* can utilize benzimidazole and 5,6-dimethylbenzimidazole to form coenzymes, and under these circumstances the pseudovitamin B_{12} is not produced. However, one mole of adenine is still present in the coenzyme form of the molecule. With all the B_{12} coenzymes, cyanide treatment causes rapid liberation of one mole of adenine, and the formation of the corresponding vitamin. For the catalysis of the conversion of glutamate to β-methylaspartate, the benzimidazole is the most active, and 5,6-dimethyl form least so, and Barker, Weissbach and Smythe[22] report vitamin B_{12} and pseudovitamin B_{12} to be completely inactive in the system. A detailed X-ray analysis of the 5,6-dimethylbenzimidazole cobamide coenzyme performed by Lenhert and Hodgkin[249] revealed that the adenosyl-3'-hydroxyl was bonded to a phosphate of a neighboring molecule, while the NH_2 group of adenine was in contact with the phosphate of another molecule. From the structure, these workers suggested that the cobalt atom is in a trivalent state in the coenzyme molecule. Johnson and Shaw[201] and Bernhauer, Gaiser and Muller[24] came to the conclusion that the cobalt in the coenzyme is divalent, on the basis of magnetic susceptibility studies, which showed the coenzyme to be paramagnetic, compared to B_{12} itself, which is diamagnetic. Hogenkamp, Barker and Mason[172] determined that the coenzyme had no electron spin resonance spectrum, and they concluded that it is diamagnetic, rather than paramagnetic. These authors suggest that the cobalt atom in the coenzyme is trivalent, in agreement with the conclusion from the X-ray findings, and that the paramagnetism observed by other workers is a property of one or more of the photolysis[171] products of the coenzyme.

The coenzyme form of vitamin B_{12} has recently been synthesized by Brady and Barker[34] and Peterkofsky, Redfield and Weissbach[329, 426] in *Propionibacterium shermanii* and *Clostridium tetanomorphum* extracts, respectively. Synthesis of the coenzyme form of B_{12} requires ATP, FAD, glutathione, DPNH and $MgCl_2$ as well as B_{12}. Hydrolysis data[329] show that the ribose moiety is derived from ATP, and not FAD. Brady, Castanera and Barker[35] purified an enzyme from *P. shermanii* which catalyzed this reaction:

Hydroxo benzimidazole cobamide $+$ ATP $+$ FADH$_2$ $+$ e $\longrightarrow$
    benzimidazole cobamide coenzyme $+$ PP$_i$ $+$ P$_i$ $+$ FAD

Vitols, Walker and Huennekens[417] found that reduced B_{12} was a more effective substrate for this reaction, and presumably $FADH_2$ is present to reduce the vitamin. However, Vitols and coworkers found that lipoic acid served as the reducing agent in *C. tetanomorphum*, rather than $FADH_2$. Although the vitamin appears to be synthesized only by bacteria, Uchino and coworkers[408] report that the coenzyme can be synthesized in the intact rat. Both the hydroxo- and cyano-cobalamin forms of B_{12} are active.

B_{12} has been implicated in protein biosynthesis by Mehta, Wagle and Johnson[294] who found that the addition of B_{12} cofactor increased the incorporation of radioactive phenylalanine in a cell-free system prepared from B_{12} deficient animals. B_{12} has also been implicated in the conversion of ribose to deoxyribose by Spell and Dinning[393] and Manson.[275] They found in *Lactobacillus leichmannii* that the addition of ribose-1-C^{14} led to rapid labeling of RNA of the organisms, and in the presence of added B_{12}, the DNA sugar was also radioactive. In the same organism, Floyd and Whitehead[120] found B_{12} to be involved in the conversion of uridine to deoxyuridine. Dinning and Hogan[94] found that B_{12} stimulates the conversion of formate to thymine, and they suggest that the vitamin may function in hydroxymethyl THFA dehydrogenase, since the activity of this enzyme is decreased in B_{12} deficient chicks. Carbon dioxide exchange with carbon-1 of pyruvate in *Clostridium acidi-urici* and *Clostridium cylindrosporum* in the presence of CoA, thiamine pyrophosphate, inorganic phosphate and B_{12} has been reported by Rabinowitz,[349] but the mechanism for this reaction is still unknown. An interesting reaction was found by Abeles and Lee[2] who discovered that extracts of *Aerobacter aerogenes* convert 1,2-propanediol to propionaldehyde, and ethyleneglycol to acetaldehyde. Light sensitive B_{12} coenzymes are required for these reactions.

Finally, Larrabee and Buchanan[246] and Brot and Weissbach[40] found methionine synthesis from N^5,N^{10}-methenyl-THFA and homocysteine to take place in the presence of a B_{12} coenzyme. The reaction of alkyl halides with 5-methyl tetrahydrofolate-homocysteine transferase enzyme in the presence of a reducing system and S-adenosylmethionine to form an inhibited enzyme was described by the latter authors, and this inhibition was reversed by exposure of the system to light. This last reaction is interesting not only because it describes an interrelationship between folic acid and vitamin B_{12} (also observed at the synthetic level by Nathan and coworkers,[309] but because the reaction does not depend upon the coenzyme form of the vitamin, in contrast to all the other reactions in which B_{12} has coenzyme function.

VII. BIOTIN

The chemical structure of biotin includes 2 unusual saturated double heterocyclic rings, one of which contains a sulfur atom (Fig. 17).

Pimelic acid has been intimately connected with biotin since du Vigneaud *et al.* [100] showed that biotin could replace a pimelic acid growth stimulation in *Corynebacterium diphtheria* found by Mueller. [303] Eakin and Eakin [102] found pimelic acid stimulatory for the synthesis of biotin in *Aspergillus niger*, which required neither of these compounds for growth. The addition of cysteine and cystine doubled their yield of biotin from added pimelic acid, although the amino acids were ineffective alone. Of the dicarboxylic acids only the C_7, pimelic, the C_8, suberic and C_9, azelaic acids showed growth promoting activity. These results were verified by Wright, Cresson and Driscoll [447] who found pimelic and azelaic acids effective for the promotion of biotin synthesis in this organism. They suggested that azelaic acid is probably converted to pimelic acid by the loss of a two-carbon fragment, before being used for biotin synthesis, since the C_9 acid is not effective in stimulating growth of *C. diphtheriae*.

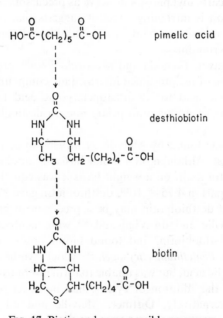

FIG. 17. Biotin and some possible precursors.

Recently, Eisenberg, [105, 106, 107] Iwahara, Tochikura and Ogata, [195] Elford, [112] and Elford and Wright [111] found that pimelic acid $1,7\text{-}C^{14}$ is incorporated into biotin. Elford and Wright [111] offered *Aspergillus niger* radioactive pimelic acid, and recovered radioactive biotin. Degradation of the biosynthesized vitamin led the authors to the conclusion that pimelic acid was incorporated as a unit into biotin. Eisenberg [106] found that *Phycomycees blakesleeanus* fed radioactive pimelic acid produced several biotin vitamers;

biotin sulfoxide, desthiobiotin, and an unidentified component. Calculation of the specific activity of the biotin demonstrated that the biotin had twice the specific activity of the added pimelic acid, on a molar basis, indicating that two molecules of radioactive precursor had been utilized.

Elford [112] in his study of the effect of pimelic acid on *Aspergillus niger* found that lipoic acid added to the medium improved the incorporation of pimelic acid into the vitamin. Lipoic acid alone was ineffective. The lipoic acid did not yield its sulfur to the vitamin, and its function in the system is still unknown.

Lezius, Ringelmann and Lynen [254] isolated radioactive biotin from a culture of *Achromobacter* grown in cysteine 3-C^{14}, in contrast to Wright [445] who considered cysteine not to be incorporated into the molecule. Lezius *et al.* [254] found $C^{14}O_2$ incorporated in the ureido carbon, and in the carboxyl carbon of biotin. This group postulated a mechanism in which cysteine, pimelyl CoA and carbamyl phosphate serve as precursors for biotin synthesis. This last suggestion is intriguing, since it suggests that organisms deficient in the ability to synthesize carbamyl phosphate should require biotin, as well as arginine and pyrimidines.

Okumura, Tsugawa, Tsunoda and Motozaki [319, 320] proposed a pathway, based on utilization of the presumed intermediate compounds. Their pathway proceeds from oleic acid to 7,8-diketopelargonic acid to 7-amino 8-keto-pelargonic acid, to 7-keto-8-amino pelargonic, to desthiobiotin, and thence to biotin.

Desthiobiotin was found by Melville *et al.* [295a] to be an effective growth stimulator for yeast. Although on a molar basis, desthiobiotin was not quite as effective as biotin itself, on a weight basis it was equally active. In a concentration of one part in $4 \cdot 75 \times 10^{10}$, desthiobiotin gave $\frac{1}{2}$ maximum growth. An indication that desthiobiotin may be a precursor of biotin was obtained by Dittmer, Melville and du Vigneaud [95] who incubated *Saccharomyces cerevisiae* with desthiobiotin, and found biotin produced. Tatum [403] observed a strain of *Penicillium chrysogenum* which synthesized desthiobiotin when offered pimelic acid, but was unable to form biotin from this compound. In this organism, the addition of cystine had no effect on the synthesis of desthiobiotin. Alternatively, Dittmer, Melville and du Vigneaud [95] and Tatum [403] found that *L. casei* could not use desthiobiotin, but required the preformed vitamin. Lilly and Leonian [256] discovered that desthiobiotin in high concentrations competes with biotin and thus acts as a growth inhibitor in this organism, and in *Ceratostomella pini*.

Nimura, Suzuki and Sahashi [313, 314] found the addition of sulfur compounds did not increase the synthesis of biotin from desthiobiotin. This group concluded that methionine sulfoxide and methionine were the best sources of biotin sulfur, with Na_2SO_4, Na_2SO_3 and Na_2S less effective sources.

Oxybiotin, the oxygen analogue of biotin (Fig. 18), is active as a vitamin in yeast, and Hofmann and Winnick [170] report that *Saccharomyces cerevisiae* and *Rhizobium trifolii* grown in oxybiotin do not convert this compound to biotin. Evidently, the sulfur atom is not essential for activity.

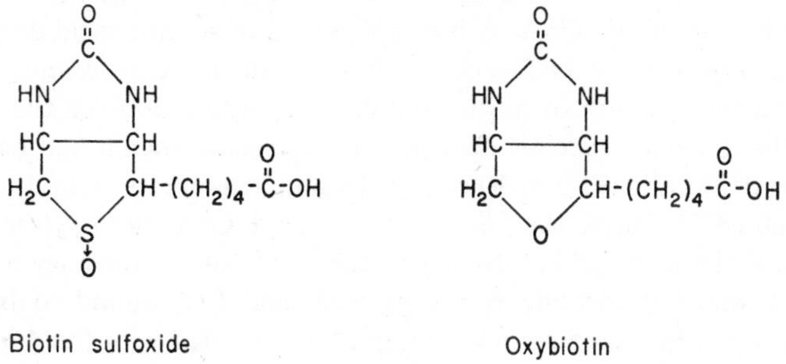

Biotin sulfoxide   Oxybiotin

FIG. 18.

The existence of a biotin-like material in the culture filtrate of *A. niger* was first recognized by Wright and Cresson [446] when an avidin-combinable compound was found which was not chromatographically identical to biotin. Biotin sulfoxide (Fig. 18) was isolated from culture filtrates of *A. niger* grown in pimelic acid by Wright and co-workers. [449, 448] The compound is optically active, and the *dextro* form was found to be as active as biotin itself for the growth of *L. arabinosus* and *Saccharomyces cerevisiae*. The *levo* form was found to be only 5 per cent as active for *L. arabinosus*, and only one thousandth as active for yeast. In a later note, Wright and Driscoll [450, 447] reported conversion of desthiobiotin to biotin L-sulfoxide in *A. niger in vivo*. They added desthiobiotin to the culture medium and isolated biotin sulfoxide as a product. A chemical oxidation of biotin was devised by Melville [295] who used hydrogen peroxide as the oxidizing agent. The chemical oxidation yields both optical isomers, however, while *in vivo* only the *dextro* form is produced. Biocytin (N-biotyl-L-lysine), which is found in yeast autolysates [445] does not appear more active than free biotin for many organisms, and may be a breakdown product of biotin bound to cell protein.

An unusual replacement for biotin was reported by Aaronson [1] in *Micrococcus sodonensis*, which requires this vitamin for growth. This organism could also utilize polyoxyethylene sorbitan monoöleate ("Tween 80") or sodium oleate, if these were offered in very large amounts. Plaut [338] recently observed that *L. arabinosus* can also utilize the latter compound instead of biotin for growth. Wright, Cresson and Driscoll [447] tested unsaturated dicarboxylic acids and found them inactive as biotin replacements. The effect of unsaturated fatty acids caused them nevertheless, to suggest that biotin may function in the biosynthesis of these compounds.

Control of biotin synthesis was shown by Pai and Lichstein, [323] who found the total amount of biotin synthesized was inversely proportional to the amount of the vitamin in the medium; the amount in the cells was constant.

In agreement with predictions derived from nutritional studies, Wakil, Titchener and Gibson [421] found biotin to be involved in the synthesis of fatty acids from acetyl CoA. A biotin function in succinic acid decarboxylation was observed by Delwiche [89] in *Propionibacterium pentosaceum*. He noted that the addition of biotin to a cell suspension doubled the release of carbon dioxide from succinic acid by this organism, when it had been grown in biotin deficient medium. Recently, Lynen, Knappe, Lorch, Jütting, and Ringelmann [262] found that β-methyl crotonyl CoA carboxylase contains biotin, and the biotin is involved with the active site of the enzyme. A CO_2-biotin enzyme intermediate was suggested, and CO_2 bound to biotin was obtained when the three-member complex was treated with free biotin. That biotin is involved in the functioning of enzymes concerned with CO_2 fixation is further substantiated by reports by Utter and Keech [412] who found an oxalacetic acid decarboxylase from avian and beef liver inhibited by avidin, by Swick and Wood [399] who observed avidin to inhibit carboxylation of propionyl CoA, and by Stadtman, Overath, Eggerer and Lynen [395] who proposed a CO_2 biotin complex in the conversion of succinate to propionate. Biotin has also been implicated by Swick [398] in the conversion of methylmalonyl CoA to succinyl CoA in *P. shermanii*.

Although the coenzyme functions of biotin are being rapidly elucidated, the details of the synthesis of this interesting compound are still essentially unknown.

VIII. PYRIDOXAL

Pyridoxal, pyridoxamine and pyridoxine are the three biologically interconvertible forms of vitamin B_6 (Fig. 19). Although all of these are effective

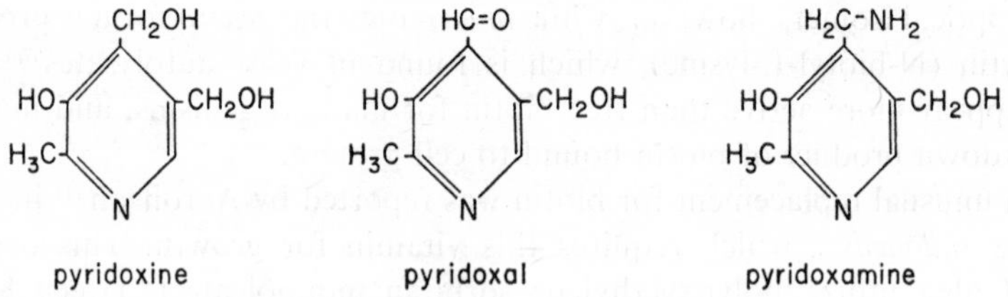

pyridoxine   pyridoxal   pyridoxamine

FIG. 19. The three forms of vitamin B_6.

as vitamins, the active form in the cell is presumably the oxidized form, pyridoxal.

Most microorganisms synthesize sufficient vitamin B_6 for their needs, but some mutant strains are known which require the addition of pyridoxal for growth. Morris[301] and Morris and Woods[302] found that *E. coli* B166, which requires pyridoxal as a growth factor, synthesizes as much pyridoxal on a medium containing serine, or glycine and glycolaldehyde as does the wild type. Suspensions of *E. coli* grown in serine, and in glycine and glycoladlehyde, when incubated with glucose and ammonia, synthesize pyridoxal only when additional glycolaldehyde is added. However, this mixture of nutrients has little effect on pyridoxal production in the wild type strain. Recently, Sate, Suzuki and Sahaskhi[371] found the addition of aspartic acid and glutamic acid to the growth medium of *Candida albicans* markedly stimulated the production of pyridoxal. Fumaric acid was produced in the aspartate fortified medium, and also when malic acid was the supplement.[371] All the carboxylic acids in the Krebs' cycle, particularly malic and citric acids increased the amount of pyridoxal excreted by this organism. It would be interesting to investigate the possibility that pyridoxal production is stimulated because of its requirement as a cofactor for transamination, since it appears that the aspartic acid was deaminated. No other observations have been made on the biosynthesis of this vitamin. One factor that has undoubtedly restrained progress in this field has been the failure of researchers to find systems that synthesize workable amounts of vitamin B_6. This general fact was alluded to in the introductory paragraphs of this chapter; the biosynthesis of B_6, as well as B_{12} and folic acid, are cases especially in point.

Oxidation of pyridoxamine to pyridoxal has been observed in rabbit liver extracts by Pogell[343] and in *S. faecalis* by Hurwitz.[187] In rabbit liver, the reaction involves a flavoprotein and both pyridoxamine and pyridoxamine-5-phosphate can function as substrates:

$$\text{pyridoxamine} + \tfrac{1}{2} O_2 \rightarrow \text{pyridoxal} + NH_3$$
$$\text{pyridoxamine-5-phosphate} + \tfrac{1}{2} O_2 \rightarrow \text{pyridoxal-5-phosphate} + NH_3$$

Gunsalus, Bellamy and Umbreit[148] found that pyridoxal is active as a coenzyme for decarboxylation in *S. faecalis* only after it is phosphorylated. Although ATP is the biological phosphorylating agent, chemically phosphorylated pyridoxal can function equally well. Hurwitz[186] observed that not only pyridoxal itself, but analogues of the vitamin could be phosphorylated by yeast extracts. Umbreit and Waddell[410] found that 2,4-dimethyl-3-hydroxy-5-hydroxymethyl pyridine acts as a pyridoxal antagonist in *S. faecalis*. This compound does not prevent phosphorylation of pyridoxal, but is itself phosphorylated and in this form interferes with the combination of pyridoxal phosphate with the apoenzyme of tyrosine decarboxylase.

Hurwitz[187, 188] reported that adenine, adenosine, adenylic acid, adenosine diphosphate, inosine triphosphate and pyrophosphate acted as competitive inhibitors of pyridoxal kinase in *S. faecalis*. Pyridoxal kinase of human brain was examined by McCormick and Snell,[283] who found this tissue to be an extremely rich source of the enzyme. The kinase was active with all three forms of the vitamin, and in contrast to most kinases, was activated more effectively by Zn^{++} than by Mg^{++} or Mn^{++}. These authors found the enzyme to be strongly inhibited by hydrazine derivatives, particularly iso-nicotinic acid hydrazide (isoniazid). Hoare[168] found that isoniazid also inhibits the action of lysine and diaminopimelic decarboxylase of *Aerobacter aerogenes* and *E. coli* respectively, and Jenkins, Orlowski and Sizer[200] demonstrated the inhibitory effect of this compound on glutamic-aspartic transaminase. However, the inhibition of pyridoxal kinase requires 1000 times less isoniazid than does inhibition of other enzyme reactions.

Degradation of pyridoxal by mammals appears to involve preliminary oxidation of the aldehyde group. Korte and Bannuscher[233] found an enzyme in liver homogenate which causes the formation of 4-pyridoxine lactone from pyridoxal phosphate while pyridoxine itself is not affected. Huff and Perl-zweig[183] reported the presence of a fluorescent compound in the urine of humans who had ingested pyridoxine, and identified the compound as 2-methyl-3-hydroxy-4-carboxy-5-hydroxymethyl-pyridine (4-pyridoxic acid). Rabinowitz and Snell[351] and Reddy, Reynolds and Price[357] also found this compound in human urine. Ikawa, Rodwell and Snell[189] and Rodwell, Volcani, Ikawa and Snell[363] examined the oxidation products of pyridoxine by a *Psuedomonas* sp. which utilized the vitamin as its sole carbon source. Isopyridoxal, 5-pyridoxic acid, and α-hydroxymethyl-α-(N-acetylaminomethe-lene)-succinic acid were identified as breakdown products of the vitamin. The significance of oxidation products of the vitamin as possible precursors in biosynthesis is unknown, but it is interesting that neither 4-pyridoxic acid, nor its lactone show B_6 activity for *L. casei*, *S. faecalis* or yeast.

Structurally, the B_6 vitamins appear quite simple; they are formally iso-nicotinic acid derivatives. However, the synthesis of nicotinic acid involves a long and difficult pathway in many organisms and pyridoxal may be equally difficult to synthesize.

Control of pyridoxine biosynthesis in *E. coli* has been reported by Demp-sey,[90] who found that addition of pyridoxal to the medium at a final con-centration of 4×10^{-7} M completely stopped pyridoxine biosynthesis by the organisms. His findings suggest that the biosynthesis is controlled by a rapidly acting mechanism which is not dependent upon protein synthesis.

IX. INOSITOL

Inositol is a vitamin with a simple structure, shown in Fig. 20. As a growth factor, it is unusual in that it is synthesized to some extent in most organisms; yet it is presumably needed in the diet in relatively enormous amounts. Ana-lysis of the inositol content of foods[73] has shown, for example, that this vitamin comprises up to 1·6 per cent of the dry weight of oranges.

Needham[310] found no change in the inositol content of rat tissues after the animals had been fed an inositol-free diet for 8 months, and this author furthermore found a vigorous and lasting excretion of inositol during polyuria induced by salt feeding. The question arises, of course, whether the inositol was being synthesized by rat tissue, or by the intestinal bacteria. Halliday and Anderson [150] injected glucose-1-C^{14} into rats and isolated labeled inositol.

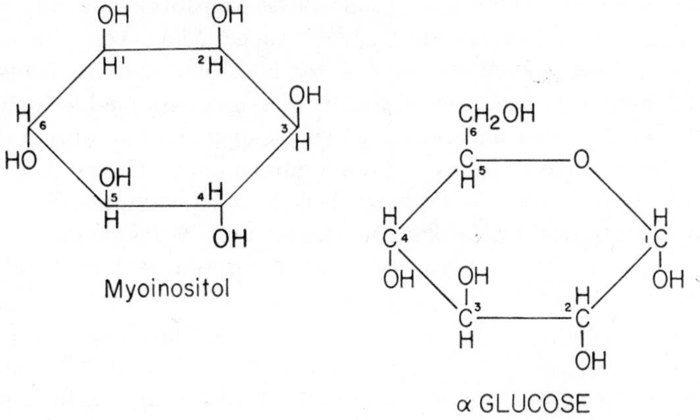

FIG. 20. The structure of myoinositol.

From the rate of synthesis of the vitamin, they concluded that rat tissue itself carries out the synthesis, rather than the intestinal bacteria. Freinkel and Dawson [126] in a carefully conducted experiment, injected glucose-C^{14} into germ-free and normal mice, and found the amount of inositol-C^{14} recovered from these animals was of the same order of magnitude. These authors also concluded that mice were able to synthesize the vitamin in the absence of bacteria. The incorporation of randomly labeled glucose into inositol in immature rats and in chick embryos was found by Daughaday, Larner and Hartnett. [85]

By a careful selection process, Leonian and Lilly [250] isolated a strain of *Saccharomyces cerevisiae* which could synthesize all of the vitamins, including inositol, and Lewis [253] found inositol to be synthesized in another yeast, *Torulopsis utilis* (*Candida utilis*). An iron deficiency decreased the synthesis of inositol in this organism. The synthesis of inositol in mammalian cells was demonstrated by Eagle, Agranoff and Snell [101] who observed that HeLa and KB cell cultures could produce one-fourth their requirement of inositol, although most cell strains, including these, required addition of this vitamin for growth.

The biosynthesis of inositol has been suggested to occur directly from glucose, partly perhaps because of the close structural similarities between these two compounds, as shown in Fig. 20. Fischer [119] suggested cyclization of glucose-6-phosphate to inositol by analogy with the cyclization of a chemically similar compound, glucose-6-nitrate. Imai [191, 192] found that glucose and galactose were utilized directly as precursors of inositol in rats, and found no significant relation between the position of the labeled carbon and the incorporation of radioactivity into inositol. Kindl and Hoffmann-Ostenhof [218, 219] found glucose 2-C^{14} was converted to the vitamin in *Sinapis alba* and that in this system, also, the glucose is transformed directly, without prior fragmentation. Loewus and Kelly [258] suggested a 5-keto-glucose intermediate in parsley leaves. In contrast to these observations, Hauser and Finelli [157] found the carbon-6 of glucose was used less readily for vitamin synthesis than carbon-1 and carbon-2, which suggested that during the synthesis the carbon chain of glucose did not remain intact. Hauser and Finelli's conclusions are similar to those reached by Charalampous [64] although the data are reversed: Charalampous found that in *Torulopsis* (*Candida*), carbon-1 and carbon-2 of glucose were incorporated less readily than carbon-6.

More recently, Chen and Charalampous working with *Candida utilis* [69, 70] and Eisenberg and Bolden [108, 110] and Eisenberg, Bolden and Loewus [109] working with rat testis, reported cell free synthesis of inositol from glucose. Chen and Charalampous [69, 70] found glucose-6-phosphate served as a substrate and DPN acted as a cofactor in the reaction. These authors found the accumulation of inositol-1-phosphate during biosynthesis of the vitamin from glucose-6-phosphate. [71] The presence of magnesium ion in the mixture prevented accumulation of the phosphate ester, presumably by stimulating a phosphatase. Neubacher, Kindl and Hoffmann-Ostenhof [311] working also with *Candida utilis*, found that glucose, adenosine, and FAD were required for cell-free synthesis of the vitamin.

Cleavage of inositol to D-glucuronic acid by an enzyme isolated from rat kidney has been extensively examined by Charalampous and Lyras, [67] Charalampous, Bumiller and Graham, [68] and Charalampous. [65, 66] When inositol-2-C^{14} is used in the system, glucuronic acid-5-C^{14} is obtained, thus, the oxidation involves a cleavage between carbon-1 and carbon-6 of inositol. Oxygen for this reaction comes from the gaseous phase, rather than from the water.

The exact function of inositol in the body is still unknown. It has not been implicated as a coenzyme, in contrast to most of the B vitamins. Inositol is, however, involved in the synthesis of phosphatides, and Paulus and Kennedy [326, 327] suggest the following series of reactions for the synthesis of inositol monophosphatides:

$$L\text{-glycerophosphate} + R\text{---}\overset{\displaystyle O}{\overset{\|}{C}}\text{---SCoA} \rightarrow \text{phosphatidic acid}$$

$$\text{Phosphatidic Acid} + \text{CTP} \rightleftharpoons \text{CDP-diglyceride}$$

$$\text{CDP-diglyceride} + \text{inositol} \rightleftharpoons \text{inositol monophosphatide} + \text{CMP}$$

Although the synthesis of inositol from glucose appears to be a simple reaction, inositol is still required from external sources for adequate functioning of many organisms (see also Chapter 3, Section B, b, v).

X. ASCORBIC ACID (VITAMIN C)

This vitamin is required in relatively large quantities. Whether the British[331] or American[356] recommendations as dietary supplement in humans (10–20 mg vs. 75–100 mg daily) are followed, the dietary intake is from 10 to several hundred times the required amount of, for example, thiamin or vitamin B_{12}.

The inclusion of discussions on ascorbic acid in the same context with the B vitamins, not only in these pages but also in other recent reviews, [276, 47, 56] indicates the growing maturity of the entire field. During the decades of the 1930's and 1940's, for example, vitamins were roughly classified into (a) fat-soluble vitamins, (b) water-soluble vitamins, and (c) ascorbic acid. This classification has been fairly rigid; persons who worked with any one of the three groups seldom worked with the other two, and the literature surrounding each group has tended to grow independently. Justification for this distinction was of course relatively easy between the first two groups; but the separate classification of ascorbic acid and the B vitamins continued for years despite increasing recognition that these vitamins were all similar with respect to water solubility (riboflavin and vitamins B_6 and B_{12} are much *less* soluble than ascorbic acid). The groups are also similar with respect to ubiquity of occurrence, at least in plants. Also the structural formulas of inositol and ascorbic acid are similar; this may imply a possible metabolic relationship. As knowledge of the functions of the vitamins has grown, it is true that ascorbic acid has not found a niche in metabolism comparable to those of the other water-soluble members, yet on the other hand there is a growing tendency to recognize the essential metabolite character of all the vitamins and their conjugates, and to consider them all together as dietary essentials, for one or more animal species.

Studies on the biosynthesis of vitamin C probably received their earliest stimulus from the recognition that it was a dietary requirement for species in only two common orders: primates and guinea pigs. The albino rat, in particular, does not require ascorbic acid in the diet. For several years the possibilities were considered that this animal might either (a) receive ascorbic acid via bacterial synthesis, or (b) not require the compound in its metabolism. These studies tended to be aided by the fact that, in contrast to biotin and like vitamins, this compound is synthesized in much larger amounts, so that experiments with ascorbic acid, while not easy, have nonetheless been relatively less tedious.

Direct formation of ascorbic acid from hexoses in plants was noted by Ray,[355] who found that in excised pea roots, administration of hexoses increased the production of the vitamin. Mannose and several other sugars, especially fructose and glucose, [3, 5, 278, 401] were effective. Glucose has indeed universally served to produce ascorbic acid. [331] Later, as isotopically labeled glucose became available, King and his co-workers[196, 176, 177] demonstrated clearly this precursor-product relationship, together with inversion of the carbon chain; D-glucose-1-C^{14} gave rise to L-ascorbic acid-6-C^{14}, and D-glucose-6-C^{14} yielded L-ascorbic acid-1-C^{14}. This was true both in normal rats and in animals that had been treated with chloretone* to stimulate ascorbic synthesis.

The studies just described, as well as numerous others to be recounted below,[56] serve to underline the scheme presented in Fig. 21 for the biosynthesis of ascorbic acid. Glucuronolactone was established as an intermediate in rats by isotope experiments, [178, 57] in cell-free microsomal preparations, [409] and in plants. [193] The reduction product, L-gulonolactone, was also identified in rat studies [57] and plants; [193] the participation of TPNH in this conversion was demonstrated [58] as well as an (aldono) lactonase [452, 55, 194] that occurs in the soluble fraction of rat liver and which converts free D-glucuronic acid or L-gulonic acid to the corresponding lactones; the latter step is also an essential one in ultimate ascorbate synthesis. [57] Oxidation of L-gulonolactone to ascorbic acid is then carried out by the appropriate enzyme in the microsomal fraction. [55, 56, 204] No dissociable coenzyme could be demonstrated in this last-named reaction, which was dependent on oxygen, in the manner of an autoxidizable protein.

Figure 21 also indicates that galactose may give rise to ascorbic acid. This was discovered by Isherwood et al., [193] and confirmed by ul Hassan and Lehninger [409] and Kanfer and co-workers; [204] these workers found that in rat liver enzymes and in intact cress seedlings, the lactones of D-galacturonic, L-gulonic, or L-galactonic acids were converted to ascorbic acid. A TPNH-dependent reduction of methyl-D-galacturonate to L-galactonate was also observed in pea seedlings, [278] corresponding to the glucuronate conversion described above in the rat.

Conversion of L-gulonolactone to L-galactonolactone, a reaction that might be assumed from the scheme presented in Fig. 21, is equivocal. L-gulonolactone cannot serve as a source of ascorbic acid in mitochondria from pea seedlings or cauliflower, [277, 280] despite the fact that intact plants can utilize both this compound and D-glucuronolactone, as well as D-galacturonolactone. [193, 280] Further study on the specificity of the enzyme that converts appropriate lactones to ascorbic acid in plants eliminated L-gulonolactone as a substrate. This enzyme, a flavoprotein that cooperates with cytochrome c, [277] is different from the corresponding one in the rat; the latter is apparently not a flavoprotein and is cytochrome c-independent.

* 1,1,1,-Trichloro-2-methyl-2-propanol.

Yet the hypothetical interconversion of the lactones of L-gulonic and L-galactonic acids has not been ruled out; as pointed out by Brown,[47] the possibility exists that an appropriate accessory enzyme might have been lost in the preparation of mitochondria in the plant experiments. Meanwhile, the reaction schemes listed in Fig. 21 will serve to rationalize the formation of ascorbic acid, in both animals and plants.

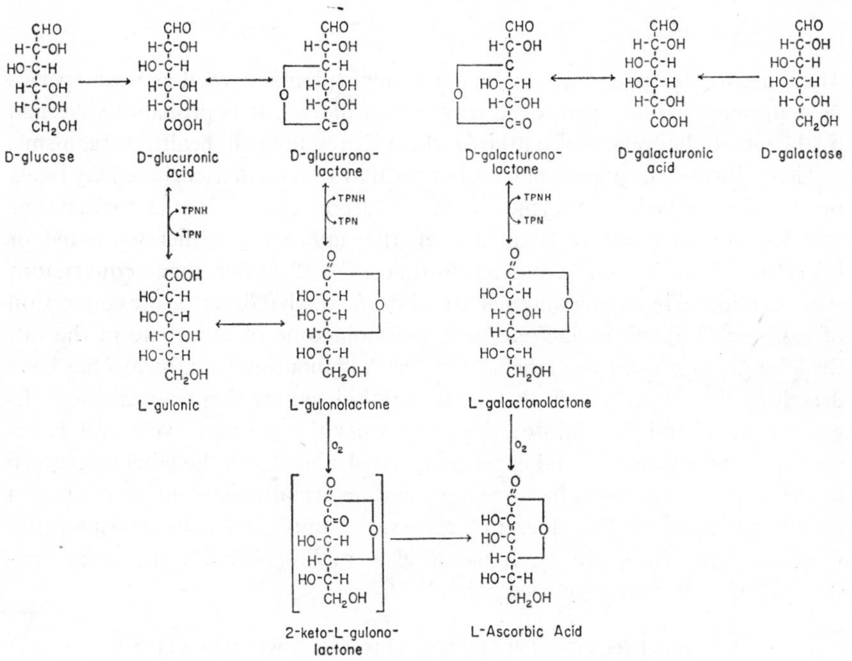

$$
\begin{array}{cccccc}
\text{CHO} & \text{CHO} & \text{CHO} & \text{CHO} & \text{CHO} & \text{CHO} \\
\text{H-C-OH} & \text{H-C-OH} & \text{H-C-OH} & \text{H-C-OH} & \text{H-C-OH} & \text{H-C-OH} \\
\text{HO-C-H} & \text{HO-C-H} & \text{C-H} & \text{C} & \text{HO-C-H} & \text{HO-C-H} \\
\text{H-C-OH} & \text{H-C-OH} & \text{H-C-OH} & \text{HO-C-H} & \text{HO-C-H} & \text{HO-C-H} \\
\text{H-C-OH} & \text{H-C-OH} & \text{H-C-OH} & \text{H-C-OH} & \text{H-C-OH} & \text{H-C-OH} \\
\text{CH}_2\text{OH} & \text{COOH} & \text{C=O} & \text{C=O} & \text{COOH} & \text{CH}_2\text{OH} \\
\text{D-glucose} & \text{D-glucuronic acid} & \text{D-glucurono-lactone} & \text{D-galacturono-lactone} & \text{D-galacturonic acid} & \text{D-galactose}
\end{array}
$$

TPNH, TPN (↑↓)   ↓ TPNH, TPN   ↓ TPNH, TPN

$$
\begin{array}{ccc}
\text{COOH} & \text{(L-gulonolactone)} & \text{(L-galactonolactone)} \\
\text{HO-C-H} & \text{HO-C-H} & \text{HO-C-H} \\
\text{HO-C-H} & \text{HO-C-H} & \text{H-C-OH} \\
\text{H-C-OH} & \text{H-C} & \text{H-C} \\
\text{HO-C-H} & \text{HO-C-H} & \text{HO-C-H} \\
\text{CH}_2\text{OH} & \text{CH}_2\text{OH} & \text{CH}_2\text{OH} \\
\text{L-gulonic} & \text{L-gulonolactone} & \text{L-galactonolactone}
\end{array}
$$

O₂ ↓   O₂ ↓

2-keto-L-gulono-lactone   L-Ascorbic Acid

FIG. 21. Biosynthesis of L-ascorbic acid (after Brown[47]).

The probability that other pathways of ascorbate synthesis may exist is heightened by the work of Loewus et al.[261, 260, 259] They observed that in plants, C-1 of glucose gives rise to C-1 of ascorbate, in other words there is no inversion of the carbon chain. On the basis of this observation they have proposed a conversion sequence that involves fructuronic acid, a diketo oxidation product, then enolization followed by hydrogenation to yield ascorbic acid. However, no experimental evidence has been advanced to support this scheme.

Evidence has also been presented[56] for the cyclic production and reuse of L-ascorbate in a pathway that also involves glucose. It is in part constructed from well-known transformations among carbohydrate residues:

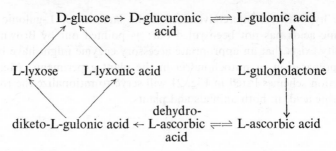

Thus, ascorbate appearance in such a system (plants, as well as most species of mammals) would seem to be very casual indeed. It is probably governed by the metabolic control of synthesis which is present in all (healthy) organisms.

The failure of the guinea pig, and of primates, to form ascorbate may likely be due to the lack of enzymes in the final conversion. L-galactonolactone and L-gulonolactone are both inert in the guinea pig, either when fed or injected, [276] or in guinea pig microsomes. [409, 58] Other sugar conversions seem to abound in most mammals; in experiments that describe the conversion of isotopic D-glucuronolactone or L-gulonolactone to ascorbate in the rat, the liver glycogen was also labeled. [104, 408] A "glucuronate pathway" has been described [104, 173] in which glucose is metabolized *via* D-glucuronic acid, L-gulonic acid, and L-xylulose; the last enters the pentose cycle and is re-converted to glucose. In the experiment cited above, [104] the labeling pattern in the liver glycogen was in agreement with expectations based on operation of this cycle. While this does not necessarily imply extensive consumption of glucose via this pathway, it nonetheless makes plausible the ready syn-thesis of the vitamin in most species.

XI. INTERCONVERSIONS AMONG THE VITAMINS

Although we do not commonly think of chemical events as involving one vitamin in support of another, this is precisely what may happen where bio-syntheses are involved. A number of interesting relationships have been un-covered not only among the various vitamins, but also between the vitamins and the major metabolites, and in the manner in which both of these are synthesized and utilized in living organisms. Probably one of the best known examples of interdependence of this sort lies in the well known tryptophan-niacin relationship (see Fig. 2).

The four main groups of biochemical, non-polymeric compounds syn-thesized and used in living cells, namely, carbohydrates, amino acids, nitro-genous bases, and fatty acids, have all been implicated in the biosynthesis of water-soluble vitamins. Carbohydrates give rise to ascorbic acid, inositol, and some parts of B_{12} and riboflavin. Amino acids act as precursors for pantothenic acid, and *p*-aminobenzoic acid, as well as for nicotinic acid mentioned above. Purines are an essential part of vitamin B_{12}, and act as precursors for riboflavin and folic acid, and a pyrimidine is a precursor of thiamine (see Fig. 1). Biotin is synthesized from pimelic acid, which can be regarded as a fatty acid. In the synthesis of folic acid and riboflavin, for example, guanine loses carbon-8, and is converted into a pteridine, and eventually into a vitamin (see Fig. 22).

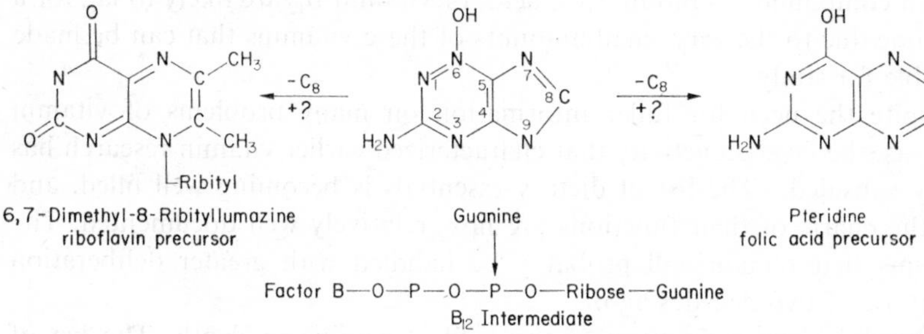

6,7-Dimethyl-8-Ribityllumazine   Guanine   Pteridine
riboflavin precursor   folic acid precursor

Factor B—O—P—O—P—O—Ribose—Guanine
B_{12} Intermediate

FIG. 22. Interrelationships between vitamins and purines.

Many vitamins are involved in the biosynthesis of their own precursors, and folic acid is vital in the synthesis of purines and cobalamin in the synthesis of methionine. The recently reported relationship between NaMN and vitamin B_{12} demonstrates interconversions at the vitamin level alone. Others, selected more or less in the order discussed, would be the hydroxymethylation reaction that was suggested by Maas,[263] in which ketopantoate is formed from HCHO and ketovaline in *E. coli*. This synthesis may also involve participation of PABA, in a manner that is yet unclear, as is also the decarboxylation reaction that appears possibly to be involved in rat liver, described in reaction 7, Fig. 5. The participation of coenzymes that deal with single atoms, as in the transfer of hydrogen (in DPNH or TPNH) in folic acid or ascorbic acid creation are further examples.[56] Such examples are not now numerous, but they will probably grow in number as enzyme systems are purified and the cofactors are sought. A final notation may be made that apparently involves the joint participation of pantothenic acid and vitamin B_6, in the observed transamination reaction between β-alanine and pyruvic acid[161] in the formation of pantothenic acid.

Because of the manifold interrelationships between the vitamins, and the major metabolites in the cell, control of vitamin biosynthesis may become a fairly difficult task to disentangle. Control may be a complex function involving the concentrations of several metabolites, as well as the physiological state of the organism.

XII. CONCLUSION

As might have been expected, advances in our knowledge of vitamin biosynthesis have been far from uniform. The great effort that has been poured into the problems of nicotinic acid formation, for example, is largely a by-product of exercises in biochemical genetics, controlled enzyme synthesis, and the fascinating realization that one dietary essential (tryptophan) could give rise to another. These efforts are not likely to be matched soon on behalf of other vitamins. Also, as has been pointed out, similar advances in research on such compounds as biotin, folic acid, or vitamin B_{12} are likely to lag for a long time due to the very small amounts of these vitamins that can be made available for study.

Despite the need for fuller information on many problems of vitamin synthesis, the feverish activity that characterized earlier vitamin research has largely subsided. The list of dietary essentials is becoming well filled, and even the charts of their functions are now relatively well documented. The problems that remain will probably be handled with greater deliberation than those of two decades ago.

Meanwhile, our perception of the field is gaining in depth. The list of vitamins is a short one, compared to the total number of cellular entities; all but the most fastidious species are very nearly autotrophic with respect to carbon (half a hundred biosynthetic lesions out of perhaps ten thousand reactions throughout an organism). It has become more fully appreciated that the chief common property among the vitamins is the fact that one or another synthetic ability has become lost in some species, presumably during the long evolution of living things. These losses have made organisms dependent upon the environment for the preformed compounds that they have lost the ability to synthesize. These compounds are relatively simple ones, such as coenzymes or amino acids. That the list of synthetic imperfections is so short may in part be due to the lethality of many other types of failures; loss of the ability to make structural proteins, for example, might well cause the organism to perish. (Derangement in hemoglobin leading to sickle-cell anemia is a case in point; although not immediately lethal, the general tendency is plain.)

Other common features among the vitamins are lacking, and there is good ground for the feeling that the synthesis of vitamins may be a small part of the larger related problem of the synthesis of proteins. Meanwhile, continuing advances should serve to further illuminate the problem of synthesis of cellular components in general.

REFERENCES

1. AARONSON, S. *J. Bacteriol.* **69**, 67 (1955).
2. ABELES, R. H. and LEE, H. A. *J. Biol. Chem.* **236**, PC 1 (1961).
3. ÅBERG, B. *Ann. Roy. Agr. Coll. Sweden* **20**, 136 (1953).
4. ACKERMANN, W. W. and SHIVE, W. *J. Biol. Chem.* **175**, 867 (1948).
5. AHMAD, B., QURESHI, A. A., BABBAR, I. and SAWHNEY, P. C. *Ann. Biochem. Exptl. Med.* (*Calcutta*) **6**, 29 (1946).

6. ALBERT, A. *Biochem. J.* **57**, x (1954).
7. ALBERTSON, J. N. and MOAT, A. G. *J. Bacteriol.* **89**, 540 (1965).
8. AL-KHALIDI, U. *Federation Proc.* **17**, 180 (1958).
9. ALTENBERN, R. A. and GINOZA, H. S. *J. Bacteriol.* **68**, 570 (1954).
10. AMES, B. N. and MITCHELL, H. K. *J. Biol. Chem.* **212**, 687 (1955).
11. ANDREEVA, N. A. *Doklady Akad. Nauk SSSR* **134**, 457 (1960); *CA.* **35**, 13502 (1961).
12. ANDREOLI, A. J., IKEDA, M., NISHIZUKA, Y. and HAYAISHI, O. *Biochem. Biophys. Res. Commun.* **12**, 92 (1963).
13. ARMITAGE, J. B., CANNON, J. R., JOHNSON, A. W., PARKER, L. F. J., SMITH, E. L., STAFFORD, W. H. and TODD, A. R. *J. Chem. Soc.* **1953**, 3849.
14. ARONOFF, S. *Plant Physiol.* **31**, 355 (1956).
15. ASAI, M., MASUDA, T. and KUWADA, S. *Chem. & Pharm. Bulletin (Japan)* **9**, 85 (1961).
16. ASAI, M., MIZUMO, K. and KUWADA, S. *Chem. & Pharm. Bulletin (Japan)* **10**, 243 (1962).
17. AUDLEY, B. J. and GOODWIN, T. W. *Biochem. J.* **84**, 587 (1962).
18. BADDILEY, J. and THAIN, E. M. *J. Chem. Soc.* **1951**, 3421.
19. BADDILEY, J. and THAIN, E. M. *J. Chem. Soc.* **1953**, 1610.
20. BARBIERI, P., BORETTI, G., diMARCO, A., MIGLIACCI, A. and SPALLA, C. *Biochim. Biophys. Acta* **57**, 599 (1962).
21. BARCHIELLI, R., BORETTI, G., diMARCO, A., JULITA, P., MIGLIACCI, A., MINGHETTI, A. and SPALLA, C. *Biochem. J.* **74**, 382 (1960).
22. BARKER, H. A., WEISSBACH, H. and SMYTHE, R. D. *Proc. Natl. Acad. Sci.* **44**, 1093 (1958).
23. BAUGH, C. M. and SHAW, E. *Biochem. Biophys. Res. Commun.* **10**, 28 (1963).
24. BERNHAUER, K., GAISER, P. and MULLER, O. *Biochem. Z.* **333**, 560 (1961).
25. BILLEN, D. and LICHSTEIN, H. C. *J. Bacteriol.* **58**, 117 (1949).
26. BIRCH, A. J. and MOYE, C. J. *J. Chem. Soc.* **1957**, 412.
27. BIRCH, A. J. and MOYE, C. J. *J. Chem. Soc.* **1958**, 2622.
28. BLACKWOOD, U. B. and SHORB, M. S. *Poultry Science* **37**, 1185 (1958).
29. BOGARD, L. and GRANICK, S. *Proc. Natl. Acad. Sci.* **39**, 1176 (1953).
30. BOLINDER, A. E. and KURZ, W. G. *Acta Chem. Scand.* **14**, 1173 (1960).
31. BONNER, J. and BUCHMAN, E. R. *Proc. Natl. Acad. Sci.* **24**, 431 (1938).
32. BONNETT, R., CANNON, J. R., JOHNSON, A. W., SUTHERLAND, I. and TODD, A. R. *Nature* **176**, 328 (1955).
33. BORETTI, B., diMARCO, A., FUOCO, L., MARNATI, M. P., MIGLIACCI, A. and SPALLA, C. *Biochim. Biophys. Acta* **37**, 379 (1960).
34. BRADY, R. O. and BARKER, H. A. *Biochem. Biophys. Res. Commun.* **4**, 464 (1961).
35. BRADY, R. O., CASTANERA, E. C. and BARKER, H. A. *J. Biol. Chem.* **237**, 2325 (1962).
36. BRAY, R. and SHEMIN, D. *Biochim. Biophys. Acta* **30**, 647 (1958).
37. BRAY, R. C. and SHEMIN, D. *J. Biol. Chem.* **238**, 1501 (1963).
38. BRESLOW, R. *J. Am. Chem. Soc.* **80**, 3719 (1958); in *The Mechanism of Action of Water-Soluble Vitamins*, eds. A. V. S. de-Rueck and M. O'Connor (1961), p. 65.
39. BROQUIST, H. P., KOHLER, A. R., HUTCHISON, D. J. and BURCHENAL, J. H. *J. Biol. Chem.* **202**, 59 (1953).
40. BROT, N. and WEISSBACK, H. *J. Biol. Chem.* **240**, 3064 (1965).
41. BROWN, D. D., SILVA, O. L., GARDINER, R. C. and SILVERMAN, M. *J. Biol. Chem.* **235**, 2058 (1960).
42. BROWN, E. G., GOODWIN, T. W. and PENDLINGTON, S. *Biochem. J.* **61**, 37 (1955).
43. BROWN, E. G., GOODWIN, T. W. and JONES, O. T. G. *Biochem. J.* **68**, 40 (1958).
44. BROWN, G. M. *Federation Proc.* **12**, 675 (1953).
45. BROWN, G. M. *Federation Proc.* **18**, 19 (1959).
46. BROWN, G. M. *J. Biol. Chem.* **234**, 370, 379 (1959).
47. BROWN, G. M. *Physiol. Rev.* **40**, 331 (1960).
48. BROWN, G. M. *J. Biol. Chem.* **237**, 536 (1962).
49. BROWN, G. M. and REYNOLDS, J. J. *Ann. Rev. Biochem.* **32**, 419 (1963).
50. BROWN, F. B. and SMITH, E. L. *Biochem. J.* **56**, xxxiv (1954).
51. BROWN, G. M. and SNELL, E. E. *J. Am. Chem. Soc.* **75**, 2782 (1953).
52. BROWN, G. M. and SNELL, E. E. *J. Bacteriol.* **67**, 465 (1954).

53. BROWN, G. M., CRAIG, J. A. and SNELL, E. E. *Arch. Biochem.* **27**, 473 (1950).
54. BROWN, G. M., WEISMAN, R. A. and MOLNAR, D. A. *J. Biol. Chem.* **236**, 2435 (1961).
55. BUBLITZ, C. and LEHNINGER, A. L. *Biochim. Biophys. Acta* **32**, 290 (1959).
56. BURNS, J. J. In GREENBERG, D. *Metabolic Pathways*, p. 341, 1960. Academic Press, New York; in *Vitamin C, Ann. N.Y. Acad. Sci.* **92**, 1 (1961).
57. BURNS, J. J., EVANS, C. and MOSBACH, E. H. *Federation Proc.* **15**, 406 (1956); BURNS, J. J. and EVANS, C. *J. Biol. Chem.* **223**, 897 (1956).
58. BURNS, J. J., PEYSER, P. and MOLTZ, A. *Science* **124**, 1148 (1956).
59. BUTENANDT, A., WEIDEL, W. and SCHLOSSBERGER, H. G. *Z. Naturforsch.* **4b**, 242 (1949).
60. BYKHORSKII, V. Y., ZAITSEVA, N. I. and MANTROVA, G. V. *Doklady Akad. Nauk. SSSR* **157** (3), 692 (1964) [*C.A.* **61**: 9794 (1964).
61. CAMIENER, G. W. and BROWN, G. M. *J. Biol. Chem.* **235**, 2404, 2411 (1960).
62. CAMPBELL, L. L. *J. Bacteriol.* **73**, 220 (1957).
63. CARLSON, G. L. and BROWN, G. M. *J. Biol. Chem.* **236**, 2099 (1961).
64. CHARALAMPOUS, F. C. *J. Biol. Chem.* **225**, 595 (1957).
65. CHARALAMPOUS, F. C. *J. Biol. Chem.* **234**, 220 (1959).
66. CHARALAMPOUS, F. C. *J. Biol. Chem.* **235**, 1286 (1960).
67. CHARALAMPOUS, F. C. and LYRAS, C. *J. Biol. Chem.* **228**, 1 (1957).
68. CHARALAMPOUS, F. C., BUMILLER, S. and GRAHAM, S. *J. Am. Chem. Soc.* **80**, 2022 (1958).
69. CHEN, I. W. and CHARALAMPOUS, F. C. *Biochem. Biophys. Res. Commun.* **12**, 62 (1963).
70. CHEN, I. W. and CHARALAMPOUS, F. C. *J. Biol. Chem.* **235**, 1905 (1964).
71. CHEN, I. W. and CHARALAMPOUS, F. C. *Biochem. Biophys. Res. Commun.* **19**, 144 (1965).
72. CHELDELIN, V. H., BENNETT, M. J. and KORNBERG, H. A. *J. Biol. Chem.* **166**, 779 (1946).
73. CHELDELIN, V. H. and WILLIAMS, R. J. The University of Texas Publication No. 4237, p. 105 (1942).
74. CORCORAN, J. W. and SHEMIN, D. *Biochim. Biophys. Acta* **25**, 661 (1957).
75. COUCH, J. R. and REID, B. L. *Federation Proc.* **14**, 197 (1955).
76. CRAIG, J. A. and SNELL, E. E. *J. Bacteriol.* **61**, 283 (1951).
77. CRAWFORD, I. P. *Biochim. Biophys. Acta* **45**, 405 (1960).
78. CRAWFORD, I. P. and YANOFSKY, C. *Proc. Natl. Acad. Sci.* **44**, 1161 (1958).
79. CUMMINS, J. T., CHELDELIN, V. H. and KING, T. E. *Proc. Soc. Exptl. Biol. Med.* **90**, 658 (1955).
80. DALGLIESH, C. E. *Biochem. J.* **52**, 3 (1952).
81. DALGLIESH, C. E. *Proc. IVth Internat. Biochem. Congr. Vienna 1958*, **11**, 32 (1959).
82. DALGLIESH, C. E. and TABECHIAN, H. *Biochem. J.* **62**, 625 (1956).
83. DALGLIESH, C. E. and TEKMAN, S. *Biochem. J.* **56**, 458 (1954).
84. DALGLIESH, C. E., KNOX, W. E. and NEUBERGER, A. *Nature* **168**, 20 (1951).
85. DAUGHADAY, W. H., LARNER, J. and HARTNETT, C. *J. Biol. Chem.* **212**, 869 (1955).
86. DAVIS, B. D. *Experientia* **6**, 41 (1950).
87. DAVIS, B. D. and MINGIOLI, E. S. *J. Bacteriol.* **60**, 17 (1950).
88. DE CASTRO, F. T., PRICE, J. M. and BROWN, R. R. *J. Am. Chem. Soc.* **78**, 2904 (1956).
88a DECKER, R. H., KANG, H. H., LEACH, F. R. and HENDERSON, L. M. *J. Biol. Chem.* **236**, 3076 (1961).
89. DELWICHE, E. A. *J. Bacteriol.* **59**, 439 (1950).
90. DEMPSEY, W. B. *J. Bacteriol.* **90**, 431 (1965).
91. DEWEY, V. C., KIDDER, G. W. and BUTLER, F. P. *Biochem. Biophys. Res. Commun.* **1**, 25 (1959).
92. diMARCO, A., MARNATI, M. P., MIGLIACCI, A., RUSCONI, A. and SPALLA, C. *2 Europ. Vitamin B12, Intrinsic Factor Symp.* **1961**, 69 (Pub. 1962) [through *C.A.* **58**: 14465 (1963)].
93. diMARCO, A. and SPALLA, C. *Giorn. Microbiol.* **9**, 237 (1961).
94. DINNING, J. S. and HOGAN, R. *Federation Proc.* **19**, 418 (1960).
95. DITTMER, K., MELVILLE, D. B. and DU VIGNEAUD, V. *Science* **99**, 203 (1944).
96. DOCTOR, V. M. *J. Biol. Chem.* **233**, 982 (1958).
97. DOCTOR, V. M. and TRUNNELL, J. B. *Proc. Soc. Exptl. Biol. Med.* **87**, 498 (1954).

98. Doy, C. H. *Rev. Pure and Appl. Chem.* **10**, 185 (1960); *Nature* **189**, 461 (1961).
99. Doy, C. H. and Gibson, F. *Biochem. J.* **72**, 586 (1959).
100. Du Vigneaud, V., Dittmer, K., Hague, E. and Long, B. *Science* **96**, 186 (1942).
101. Eagle, H., Agranoff, W. and Snell, E. E. *J. Biol. Chem.* **235**, 1891 (1960).
102. Eakin, R. E. and Eakin, E. A. *Science* **96**, 187 (1942).
103. Efimochkina, E. F. *Biokhimiya* **19**, 68 (1954); *C.A.* **48**, 8366 (1954).
104. Eisenberg, F., Dayton, P. G. and Burns, J. J. *J. Biol. Chem.* **234**, 250 (1959).
105. Eisenberg, M. A. *Federation Proc.* **21**, 467 (1962).
106. Eisenberg, M. A. *Biochem. Biophys. Res. Commun.* **8**, 437 (1962).
107. Eisenberg, M. A. *J. Bacteriol.* **86**, 673 (1963).
108. Eisenberg, F. Jr. and Bolden, A. H. *Biochem. Biophys. Res. Commun.* **12**, 72 (1963).
109. Eisenberg, F. Jr., Bolden, A. H. and Loewus, A. *Biochem. Biophys. Res. Commun.* **14**, 419 (1964).
110. Eisenberg, F. Jr. and Bolden, A. H. *Nature* **202**, 599 (1964).
111. Elford, H. L. and Wright, L. D. *Biochem. Biophys. Res. Commun.* **10**, 373 (1963).
112. Elford, H. L. *Diss. Abst.* **23**, 4519 (1963).
113. Ensign, J. C. and Rittenberg, S. C. *J. Biol. Chem.* **239**, 2285 (1964).
114. Epstein, S. S. *Nature* **188**, 143 (1960).
115. Esposito, R. G. and Fletcher, A. M. *Arch. Biochem. Biophys.* **93**, 369 (1961).
116. Falk, J. E., Dresel, E. I. B. and Rimington, C. *Nature* **172**, 292 (1953).
117. Fantes, K. H. and O'Callaghan, C. H. *Biochem. J.* **59**, 79 (1955).
118. Fink, R. M., Fink, K. and Henderson, R. B. *J. Biol. Chem.* **210**, 349 (1953).
119. Fischer, H. O. L. *The Harvey Lectures* **40**, 156 (1945).
120. Floyd, K. W. and Whitehead, R. W. *Biochem. Biophys. Res. Commun.* **3**, 220 (1960).
121. Ford, J. E. and Holdsworth, E. S. *Biochem. J.* **56**, xxxv (1954).
122. Ford, J. E., Holdsworth, E. S. and Kon, S. K. *Biochem. J.* **58**, xxiv (1954).
123. Ford, J. E., Kon, S. K. and Porter, J. W. G. *Biochem. J.* **50**, ix (1951).
124. Forrest, H. S. and McNutt, W. S. *J. Am. Chem. Soc.* **80**, 739 (1958).
125. Forrest, H. S. and Mitchell, H. K. *J. Am. Chem. Soc.* **77**, 4865 (1955).
126. Freinkel, N. and Dawson, R. M. C. *Biochem. J.* **81**, 250 (1961).
127. Freundlich, M., Burns, R. O. and Umbarger, H. E. *Proc. Natl. Acad. Sci. U.S.* **48**, 1804 (1962).
128. Friedmann, H. C. and Harris, D. L. *J. Biol. Chem.* **240**, 406 (1965).
129. Friedmann, H. C. *J. Biol. Chem.* **240**, 413 (1965).
130. Futterman, S. *J. Biol. Chem.* **228**, 1031 (1957).
131. Ganguly, S. and Roy, S. C. *Arch. Biochem. Biophys.* **64**, 67 (1956).
132. Gant, D. E., Smith, E. L. and Parker, L. F. *J. Biochem. J.* **56**, xxxiv (1954).
133. Geschwind, I. I. and Li, C. H. *J. Clin. Endocrinol. Metab.* **14**, 789 (1954).
134. Gholson, R. K., Ueda, I., Ogasawara, N. and Henderson, L. M. *J. Biol. Chem.* **239**, 1208 (1964).
135. Gholson, R. K. and Kori, J. *J. Biol. Chem.* **239**, PC 2399 (1964).
136. Goodwin, T. W. *Recent Advances in Biochemistry.* Churchill, London (1960).
137. Goodwin, T. W. *The Biosynthesis of Vitamins and Related Compounds.* Academic Press, New York (1963).
138. Gibson, K. D., Neuberger, A. and Scott, J. J. *Biochem. J.* **58**, xli (1954).
139. Goodwin, T. W. and Jones, O. T. G. *Biochem. J.* **64**, 9 (1956).
140. Goodwin, T. W. and McEvoy, D. *Biochem. J.* **71**, 742 (1959).
141. Goodwin, T. W. and Treble, D. H. *Biochem. J.* **67**, 10P (1957).
142. Goodwin, T. W. and Treble, D. H. *Biochem. J.* **70**, 14P (1958).
143. Goodwin, T. W. and Horton, A. A. *Nature* **191**, 772 (1961).
144. Greengard, O. and Feigelson, P. *J. Biol. Chem.* **237**, 703, 1908 (1962).
145. Griffin, N. J. and Brown, G. M. *J. Biol. Chem.* **239**, 310 (1964).
146. Grimshaw, J. and Marion, L. *Nature* **181**, 112 (1958).
147. Gulland, J. M. and Jackson, E. M. *Biochem. J.* **32**, 597 (1938).
148. Gunsalus, I. C., Bellamy, W. D. and Umbreit, W. W. *J. Biol. Chem.* **155**, 685 (1944).
149. Hakala, M. T. and Welch, A. D. *Federation Proc.* **14**, 222 (1955).

150. HALLIDAY, J. W. and ANDERSON, L. J. Biol. Chem. 217, 797 (1955).
151. HAMADA, K. and SASAKI, M. Igaku To Seibutsugaku 55, 191 (1960) [through C.A. 60: 12394 (1964)].
152. HAMNER, K. C., STEWART, W. S. and MATRONE, G. Food Res. 8, 44 (1943).
153. HANDLER, P. and KLEIN, J. R. J. Biol. Chem. 143, 49 (1942).
154. HANKES, L. V. and HENDERSON, L. M. J. Biol. Chem. 225, 349 (1957).
155. HARRIS, D. L. Arch. Biochem. Biophys. 57, 240 (1955).
156. HARRIS, J. O. and BINNS, F. Nature 179, 475 (1957).
157. HAUSER, G. and FINELLI, V. N. J. Biol. Chem. 238, 3224 (1963).
158. HAYAISHI, O. In Amino Acid Metabolism, p. 914, eds. W. D. McElroy and B. Glass. Johns Hopkins Press, Baltimore, 1955.
159. HAYAISHI, O. and STAINIER, R. Y. J. Bacteriol. 62, 691 (1951).
160. HAYAISHI, O. and STAINIER, R. Y. J. Biol. Chem. 195, 735 (1952).
161. HAYAISHI, O., NISHIZUKA, Y., TATIBANA, M., TAKESHITA, M. and KUNO, S. J. Biol. Chem. 236, 781 (1961).
162. HEATH, E. C., HURWITZ, J. and HORECKER, B. L. J. Am. Chem. Soc. 78, 5449 (1956).
163. HEISLER, C. R. and SCHWEIGERT, B. S. Federation Proc. 14, 436 (1955).
164. HENDERSON, L. M., SOMEROSKI, J. F., RAO, D. R., WU, P.-H. L., GRIFFITH, T. and BYERRUM, R. U. J. Biol. Chem. 234, 93 (1959).
165. HEPPEL, L. A. and HILMOE, R. J. J. Biol. Chem. 188, 665 (1951).
166. HIMES, R. H. and RABINOWITZ, J. C. Federation Proc. 19, 47 (1960).
167. HOAGLAND, M. B. and NOVELLI, G. D. J. Biol. Chem. 207, 767 (1954).
168. HOARE, D. S. Biochim. Biophys. Acta 19, 141 (1956).
169. HODGE, J. E. Advances in Carbohydrate Chem. 10, 169 (1955).
170. HOFMANN, K. and WINNICK, T. J. Biol. Chem. 160, 449 (1945).
171. HOGENKAMP, H. P. C., LADD, J. N. and BARKER, H. A. J. Biol. Chem. 237, 1950 (1962).
172. HOGENKAMP, H. P. C., BARKER, H. A. and MASON, H. S. Arch. Biochem. Biophys. 100, 353 (1963).
173. HOLZER, H. Ann. Rev. Biochem. 28, 171 (1959).
174. HOLZER, H. and BEAUCAMP, K. Angew. Chem. 71, 776 (1959).
175. HOLZER, H., GOEDDER, H. W., GOGGEL, K. H. and ULRICH, B. Biochem. Biophys. Res. Commun. 3, 599 (1960).
176. HOROWITZ, H. H., DOERSCHUK, A. P.and KING, C. G. J. Biol. Chem. 199, 193 (1952).
177. HOROWITZ, H. H. and KING, C. G. J. Biol. Chem. 200, 125 (1953).
178. HOROWITZ, H. H. and KING, C. G. J. Biol. Chem. 205, 815 (1953).
179. HORWITT, M. K. Am. J. Clin. Nutrition 3, 244 (1955).
180. HOTTA, K. and ANDO, O. Bitamin 27 (3), 205 (1963) [through C.A. 61: 3413 (1964)].
181. HOWELLS, D. J. and PLAUT, G. W. E. Biochem. J. 94, 775 (1965).
182. HUENNEKENS, F. M. and OSBORN, M. J. Advan. Enzymol. 21, 393 (1959).
183. HUFF, J. W. and PERLZWEIG, W. A. J. Biol. Chem. 155, 345 (1945).
184. HUFHAM, J. B., BURGUS, R. C., SCOTT, W. M. and PFIFFNER, J. J. J. Bacteriol. 88, 538 (1964).
185. HUGHES, D. E. and WILLIAMSON, D. H. Biochem. J. 51, 330 (1952).
186. HURWITZ, J. Biochim. Biophys. Acta 9, 496 (1952).
187. HURWITZ, J. J. Biol. Chem. 205, 935 (1953).
188. HURWITZ, J. Symposium on Vitamin Metabolism, p. 49. Nutrition Symposium Series 13, New York, Natl. Vitamin Foundn., March 6, 1956.
189. IKAWA, M., RODWELL, V. W. and SNELL, E. E. J. Biol. Chem. 233, 1555 (1958).
189a IACCARINO, M., BOERI, E. and SCARDI, V. Biochem. J. 78, 65 (1961).
190. IKEDA, M., TSUJI, H., NAKAMURA, S., ICHIYAMA, A., NISHIZUKA, Y. and HAYAISHI, O. J. Biol. Chem. 240, 1395 (1965).
191. IMAI, Y. J. Biochem. (Tokyo) 53, 50 (1963).
192. IMAI, Y. J. Biochem. (Tokyo) 55, 126 (1964).
192a IMSANDE, J. J. Biol. Chem. 236, 1494 (1961).
192b IMSAMDE, J. and HANDLER, P. J. Biol. Chem. 236, 525 (1961).
192c IMSANDE J. and PARDEE, A. B. J. Biol. Chem. 237, 1305 (1962).
193. ISHERWOOD, F. A., CHEN, Y. T. and MAPSON, L. W. Biochem. J. 56, 1 (1954).

194. ISHERWOOD, F. A., MAPSON, L. W. and CHEN, Y. T. *Biochem. J.* **76**, 157 (1960).
195. IWAHARA, S., TOCHIKURA, T. and OGATA, K. *Agr. Biol. Chem.* **29**, 262 (1965) [through *C.A.* **63**: 2144 (1965)].
196. JACKEL, S. S., MOSBACH, E. H., BURNS, J. J. and KING, C. G. *J. Biol. Chem.* **186**, 569 (1950).
197. JACOBY, W. B. and BONNER, D. M. *J. Biol. Chem.* **205**, 699 (1953).
198. JAENICKE, L. and CHAN, P. C. *Angew. Chem.* **72**, 752 (1960).
199. JAKOBY, W. B. *J. Biol. Chem.* **207**, 657 (1954).
200. JENKINS, W. T., ORLOWSKI, S. and SIZER, J. W. *J. Biol. Chem.* **234**, 2657 (1959).
201. JOHNSON, A. W. and SHAW, N. *Proc. Chem. Soc.* **420**, Dec. 1960.
202. JONES, T. H. D., REYNOLDS, J. J. and BROWN, G. M. *Biochem. Biophys. Res. Commun.* **17**, 486 (1964).
203. JOSHI, S., NEWBURGH, R. W. and CHELDELIN, V. H. *J. Biol. Chem.* **229**, 779 (1957).
204. KANFER, J., BURNS, J. J. and ASHWELL, G. *Biochim. Biophys. Acta* **31**, 556 (1959).
205. KAPLAN, N. O., COLOWICK, S. P. and CIOTTI, M. N. *J. Biol. Chem.* **194**, 579 (1952).
206. KAPLAN, N. O., COLOWICK, S. P., NEUFELD, E. F. and CIOTTI, M. N. *J. Biol. Chem.* **205**, 17 (1953).
207. KAPLAN, N. O., GOLDIN, A., HUMPHREYS, S. R. and STOLZENBACH, F. E. *J. Biol. Chem.* **226**, 365 (1956).
208. KAPLAN, N. O., SWARTZ, M. N., FRECH, M. E. and CIOTTI, M. N. *Proc. Natl. Acad. Sci.* **42**, 481 (1956).
209. KATAGIRI, H., TAKEDA, I. and IMAI, K. *J. Vitaminology* **4**, 207 (1958).
210. KATAGIRI, H., TAKEDA, I. and IMAI, K. *J. Vitaminology* **4**, 211 (1958).
211. KATAGIRI, H., IMAI, K. and TAKEDA, I. *Bitamin* **20**, 361 (1960) [through *C.A.* **61**: 1647 (1964)].
212. KATCHMAN, B., BETHEIL, J. J., SCHEPARTZ, A. I. and SANADI, D. R. *Arch. Biochem. Biophys.* **34**, 437 (1951).
213. KATUNUMA, N., SHODA, T. and NODA, H. *J. Vitaminology* **3**, 77 (1957).
214. KAUFMAN, S. *J. Biol. Chem.* **239**, 332 (1964).
215. KAY, L. D., OSBORN, M. J., HATEFI, Y. and HUENNEKENS, F. M. *J. Biol. Chem.* **235**, 195 (1960).
216. KAZIRO, Y. and SHIMAZONO, N. *J. Biochem. (Japan)* **46**, 963 (1959).
217. KEARNEY, E. B. and ENGLAND, S. *J. Biol. Chem.* **193**, 821 (1951).
218. KINDL, H. and HOFFMANN-OSTENHOF, O. *Monatsh.* **95**, 548 (1964).
219. KINDL, H. and HOFFMANN-OSTENHOF, O. *Biochem. Z.* **339**, 374 (1964).
220. KING, T. E. and CHELDELIN, V. H. *Proc. Soc. Exptl. Biol. Med.* **84**, 591 (1953).
221. KING, T. E. and STRONG, F. M. *J. Biol. Chem.* **189**, 315 (1951); **191**, 515 (1951).
222. KISHI, T., ASAI, M., MASUDA, T. and KUWADA, S. *Chem. & Pharm. Bulletin (Japan)* **7**, 515 (1959).
223. KNOX, W. E. *Biochem. J.* **53**, 379 (1953).
224. KNOX, W. E. *Biochim. Biophys. Acta* **14**, 117 (1954).
225. KNOX, W. E. and AUERBACH, V. H. *J. Biol. Chem.* **214**, 307 (1955).
226. KNOX, W. E. and MEHLER, A. H. *J. Biol. Chem.* **187**, 419 (1950).
227. KNOX, W. E. and MEHLER, A. H. *Science* **113**, 237 (1951).
228. KOENIGK, E. *Biochem. Z.* **341**, 123 (1964).
229. KON, S. K. In *Biochemistry of Vitamins B_{12}*, p. 17, ed. R. T. Williams, Bioch. Soc. Symposia No. 13, 1955.
230. KORNBERG, A. *J. Biol. Chem.* **182**, 779 (1950).
231. KORNBERG, A. *J. Biol. Chem.* **182**, 805 (1950).
232. KORNBERG, A. and LINDBERG, O. *J. Biol. Chem.* **176**, 665 (1948); KORNBERG, A. and PRICER, W. E. *J. Biol. Chem.* **182**, 763 (1950).
233. KORTE, F. and BANNUSCHER, H. *Angew. Chem.* **69**, 97 (1957).
234. KORTE, F., SCHICKE, H. G. and WEITKAMP, H. *Angew. Chem.* **69**, 96 (1957).
235. KOTAKE, Y. and MASAYAMA, T. *Z. Physiol. Chem.* **243**, 237 (1936).
236. KRAMPITZ, L. O., GREULL, G., MILLER, C. S., BICKING, J. B., SKEGGS, H. R. and SPRAGUE, J. M. *J. Am. Chem. Soc.* **80**, 5893 (1958).

2B

237. KRAMPITZ, L. O., SUZUKI, I. and GRUELL, G. *Federation Proc.* **20**, 971 (1961).
238. KREHL, W. A., TEPLY, L. J., SARMA, P. S. and ELVEHJEM, C. A. *Science* **101**, 489 (1945).
239. KRASNA, A. J., ROSENBLUM, C. and SPRINSON, D. B. *J. Biol. Chem.* **225**, 745 (1957).
240. KRUMDIECK, C. L., BAUGH, C. M. and SHAW, E. N. *Biochim. Biophys. Acta* **90**, 573 (1964).
241. KUHN, R. and WIELAND, T. *Ber.* **75B**, 121 (1942).
242. KUPIECKI, F. P. and COON, M. J. *J. Biol. Chem.* **229**, 743 (1957).
243. KUWADA, S., MASUDA, T., KISHI, T. and ASAI, M. *J. Vitaminology* **4**, 217 (1958).
244. KUWADA, S., MASUDA, T., KISHI, T. and ASAI, M. *Chem. & Pharm. Bulletin (Japan)* **6**, 618 (1958).
245. KUWADA, S., MASUDA, T. and ASAI, M. *Chem. & Pharm. Bulletin (Japan)* **8**, 792 (1960).
246. LARRABEE, A. R. and BUCHANAN, J. M. *Federation Proc.* **20**, 9 (1961).
247. LEETE, E. *Chem. and Ind. (London)* 1270 (1957).
248. LEETE, E., MARION, L. and SPENSER, I. D. *Can. J. Chem.* **33**, 405 (1955).
249. LENHERT, P. G. and HODGKIN, D. C. *Nature* **192**, 937 (1961).
250. LEONIAN, L. H. and LILLY, V. G. *Science* **95**, 658 (1942).
251. LEVEQUE, P. Master's Thesis, Oregon State Univ. 18 pp. (1951).
252. LEVINTOW, L. and NOVELLI, G. D. *J. Biol. Chem.* **207**, 761 (1954).
253. LEWIS, J. C. *Arch. Biochem.* **4**, 217 (1944).
254. LEZIUS, A., RINGELMANN, E. and LYNEN, F. *Biochem. Z.* **336**, 510 (1963).
255. LIEBERMAN, I. and OVE, P. *J. Biol. Chem.* **235**, 1119 (1960).
256. LILLY, V. G. and LEONIAN, L. H. *Science* **99**, 205 (1944).
257. LIPMANN, F., KAPLAN, N. O., NOVELLI, G. D., TUTTLE, L. C. and GUIRARD, B. M. *J. Biol. Chem.* **167**, 869 (1947).
258. LOEWUS, F. A. and KELLY, S. *Biochem. Biophys. Res. Commun.* **7**, 204 (1962).
259. LOEWUS, F. A. In *Vitamin C. Ann. N.Y. Acad. Sci.* **92**, 57 (1961).
260. LOEWUS, F. A. and JANG, R. *Biochim. Biophys. Acta* **23**, 205 (1957).
261. LOEWUS, F. A., JANG, R. and SEEGMILLER, C. G. *J. Biol. Chem.* **222**, 649 (1956).
262. LYNEN, F., KNAPP, J., LORCH, E., JÜTTING, G. and RINGELMANN, E. *Angew. Chem.* **71**, 481 (1959).
263. MAAS, W. K. *Natl. Vitamin Found. Nutr. Symp. Ser.* 13, March 1956, 75; *Abstr. 3rd Internat. Congress Biochim.* (1955), pp. 4–36.
264. MAAS, W. K. *J. Biol. Chem.* **198**, 23 (1952).
265. MAAS, W. K. *IVth Internat. Congr. Biochem., Vienna 1958,* **11**, 161 (published 1959).
266. MAAS, W. K. and NOVELLI, G. D. *Arch. Biochem. Biophys.* **43**, 236 (1953).
267. MAAS, W. K. and VOGEL, H. J. *J. Bacteriol.* **65**, 388 (1953).
268. MACLAREN, J. *J. Bacteriol.* **63**, 233 (1952).
269. MAKINO, K., TAKAHASHI, H., SATOH, K. and INAGAMI, K. *Nature* **173**, 586 (1954).
270. MALEY, G. F. and PLAUT, G. W. E. *Federation Proc.* **17**, 268 (1958).
271. MALEY, G. F. and PLAUT, G. W. E. *J. Am. Chem. Soc.* **81**, 2025 (1959).
272. MALEY, G. F. and PLAUT, G. W. E. *J. Biol. Chem.* **234**, 641 (1959).
273. MANN, P. J. G. and QUASTEL, J. H. *Biochem. J.* **35**, 502 (1941).
274. MANN, T. *Biochem. J.* **39**, 451 (1945).
275. MANSON, L. A. *J. Biol. Chem.* **235**, 2955 (1960).
276. MAPSON, L. W. *Proc. IVth Internat. Congr. Biochem. Vienna 1958,* **11**, 1 (published 1959).
277. MAPSON, L. W. and BRESLOW, E. *Biochem. J.* **68**, 395 (1958).
278. MAPSON, L. W. and ISHERWOOD, F. A. *Biochem. J.* **64**, 13 (1956).
279. MAPSON, L. W., CRUICKSHANK, E. M. and CHEN, Y. T. *Biochem. J.* **45**, 171 (1949).
280. MAPSON, L. W., ISHERWOOD, F. A. and CHEN, Y. T. *Biochem. J.* **56**, 21 (1954).
281. MARDESHEV, S. R. and ETINGOF, R. N. *Biokhimiya* **13**, 402 (1948); through Ref. No. 264, Maas 1958/1959, *op. cit.*
282. MASUDA, T. *Pharm. Bull. (Tokyo)* **5**, 136 (1957).
283. MCCORMICK, D. B. and SNELL, E. E. *Proc. Natl. Acad. Sci. U.S.* **45**, 1371 (1959).
284. MCCULLOGH, W. G. *Abstr. 131st Meeting Am. Chem. Soc.* **1957**, 26C.
285. MCILWAIN, H. and RODNIGHT, R. *Biochem. J.* **44**, 470 (1949).

286. McINTOSH, E. N., PURKO, M. and WOOD, W. A. *J. Biol. Chem.* **228**, 499 (1957).
287. McNUTT, W. S. *J. Biol. Chem.* **210**, 511 (1954).
288. McNUTT, W. S. *J. Biol. Chem.* **219**, 365 (1956).
289. McNUTT, W. S. and FORREST, H. S. *J. Am. Chem. Soc.* **80**, 951 (1958).
290. MEHLER, A. H. *J. Biol. Chem.* **218**, 241 (1956).
291. MEHLER, A. H. and KNOX, W. E. *J. Biol. Chem.* **187**, 431 (1950).
292. MEHLER, A. H., KORNBERG, A., GRISOLIA, S. and OCHOA, S. *J. Biol. Chem.* **174**, 961 (1948).
293. MEHLER, A. H. and MAY, E. L. *J. Biol. Chem.* **223**, 449 (1956).
294. MEHTA, R., WAGLE, S. R. and JOHNSON, B. C. *Biochim. Biophys. Acta* **35**, 286 (1959).
295. MELVILLE, D. B. *J. Biol. Chem.* **208**, 495 (1954).
295a MELVILLE, D. B., DITTMER, K., BROWN, G. B. and DU VIGNEAUD, V. *Science* **98**, 497 (1943).
296. MIGLIACCI, A. and RUSCONI, A. *Biochim. Biophys. Acta* **50**, 370 (1961).
297. MITSUDA, H., KAWAI, F. and MORITAKA, S. *J. Vitaminology* **7**, 128 (1961).
298. MITSUDA, H., KAWAI, F., SUZUKI, Y. and SATANI, E. *J. Vitaminology* **8**, 178 (1962).
299. MOFFAT, J. G. and KHORANA, H. G. *J. Am. Chem. Soc.* **83**, 663 (1961).
300. MONTGOMERY, J. A. and THOMAS, H. J. *J. Am. Chem. Soc.* **85**, 2672 (1963).
301. MORRIS, J. G. *J. Gen. Microbiol.* **20**, 597 (1959).
302. MORRIS, J. G. and WOODS, D. D. *J. Gen. Microbiol.* **20**, 576 (1959).
303. MUELLER, J. H. *J. Biol. Chem.* **119**, 121 (1937).
304. MUELLER, J. H. and COHEN, S. *J. Bacteriol.* **34**, 381 (1937).
305. MUIR, H. M. and NEUBERGER, A. *Biochem. J.* **47**, 97 (1950).
306. MÜLLER, O. and MÜLLER, G. *Biochem. Z.* **336**, 299 (1962).
306a NAKAMURA, S., IKEDA, M., TSUJI, H., NISHIZUKA, Y. and HAYAISHI, O. *Biochem. Biophys. Res. Commun.* **13**, 285 (1963).
307. NAKAYAMA, H. *Vitamins (Japan)* **11**, 169 (1956); *C.A.* **51**, 18091 (1957).
308. NASH, C. P., OLSEN, C. W., WHITE, F. G. and INGRAHAM, L. L. *J. Am. Chem. Soc.* **83**, 4106 (1961).
309. NATHAN, H. A., BAKER, H. and FRANK, O. *Nature* **188**, 35 (1960).
310. NEEDHAM, J. *Biochem. J.* **18**, 891 (1924).
311. NEUBACHER, J., KINDL, H. and HOFFMANN-OSTENHOF, O. *Biochem. J.* **92**, 56P (1964).
312. NEUBERGER, A. and SCOTT, J. J. *Nature* **172**, 1093 (1953).
313. NIMURA, T., SUZUKI, T. and SAHASHI, Y. *Bitamin* **26**, 38 (1962) [*C.A.* **61**: 16482 (1964)].
314. NIMURA, T., SUZUKI, T. and SAHASHI, Y. *Bitamin* **27**, 355 (1963) [*C.A.* **61**: 996 (1964)].
315. NISHIZUKA, Y. and HAYAISHI, O. *J. Biol. Chem.* **238**, PC 483, 3369 (1963).
316. NOSE, Y., UEDA, K. and KAWASAKI, T. *Biochim. Biophys. Acta* **34**, 277 (1959).
317. NOVELLI, G. D. *Physiol. Rev.* **33**, 525 (1953); *J. Cellular Comp. Physiol.* **43**, Supp. 1, 67 (1953); *IVth Internat. Congr. Biochem.*, *Vienna 1958*, **11**, 169 (published 1959).
318. *Nutrition Reviews* **14**, 116 (1956) (anonymous).
319. OKUMURA, S., TSUGAWA, R., TSUNODA, T. and MOTOZAKI, S. *Nippon Nogei Kagaku Matsui* **36** (2), 141 (1962) [through *C.A.* **61**: 7656 (1964)].
320. OKUMURA, S., TSUGAWA, R., TSUNODA, T. and MOTOZAKI, S. *Nippon Nogei Kagaku Matsui* **36**, 506 (1962) [through *C.A.* **61**: 15064 (1964)].
321. ORTEGA, M. V. and BROWN, G. M. *J. Am. Chem. Soc.* **81**, 4437 (1959); *J. Biol. Chem.* **235**, 2939 (1960).
322. OSBORN, M. J. and HUENNEKENS, F. M. *J. Biol. Chem.* **233**, 969 (1958).
323. PAI, C. H. and LICHSTEIN, H. C. *Biochim. Biophys. Acta* **65**, 159 (1962).
324. PARTRIDGE, C. W. H., BONNER, D. M. and YANOFSKY, C. *J. Biol. Chem.* **194**, 269 (1952).
325. PATO, M. L. and BROWN, B. M. *Arch. Biochem. Biophys.* **103**, 443 (1963).
326. PAULUS, H. and KENNEDY, E. P. *J. Am. Chem. Soc.* **80**, 6689 (1958).
327. PAULUS, H. and KENNEDY, E. P. *J. Biol. Chem.* **235**, 1303 (1960).
328. PERLMAN, D. and BARRETT, J. M. *Can. J. Microbiology* **4**, 9 (1958).
329. PETERKOFSKY, A., REDFIELD, B. and WEISSBACH, H. *Biochem. Biophys. Res. Commun.* **5**, 213 (1961).
330. PETERS, J. M. and GREENBERG, D. M. *J. Am. Chem. Soc.* **80**, 2719 (1958).

331. PETERS, R. A., COWARD, K. H., KREBS, H. A., MAPSON, L. W., PARSONS, L. G., PLATT, B. S., SPENCE, J. C. and O'BRIEN, J. R. P. *Lancet* **254**, 853 (1948).
332. PETERS, V. J., BROWN, G. M., WILLIAMS, W. L. and SNELL, E. E. *J. Am. Chem. Soc.* **75**, 1688 (1953).
333. PFIFFNER, J. J., CALKINS, D. G., BLOOM, E. S. and O'DELL, B. L. *J. Am. Chem. Soc.* **68**, 1392 (1946).
334. PIHL, A. and FRITZSON, P. *J. Biol. Chem.* **215**, 345 (1955).
335. PLAUT, G. W. E. *J. Biol. Chem.* **208**, 513 (1954).
336. PLAUT, G. W. E. *J. Biol. Chem.* **211**, 111 (1954).
337. PLAUT, G. W. E. *J. Biol. Chem.* **235**, PC 41 (1960).
338. PLAUT, G. W. E. *J. Biol. Chem.* **236**, 61 (1961).
339. PLAUT, G. W. E. and BROHERG, P. L. *J. Biol. Chem.* **219**, 131 (1956).
340. PLAUT, G. W. E. and MALEY, G. F. *Archiv. Biochem. Biophys.* **80**, 219 (1959).
341. PLAUT, G. W. E. *J. Biol. Chem.* **238**, 2224 (1963).
342. PLAUT, G. W. E. *J. Biol. Chem.* **238**, 2235 (1963).
343. POGELL, B. M. *J. Biol. Chem.* **232**, 761 (1958).
344. PONTECORVO, G. *Advances in Genet.* **5**, 141 (1953).
345. PREISS, J. and HANDLER, P. *J. Biol. Chem.* **225**, 759 (1957).
346. PREISS, J. and HANDLER, P. *J. Am. Chem. Soc.* **79**, 1514 (1957); *J. Biol. Chem.* **233**, 488 (1959); HANDLER, P. *Proc. IVth Internat. Congr. Biochem., Vienna 1958*, **11**, p. 39 (published 1959).
347. PRIEST, ROBERT E., BOKMAN, A. H. and SCHWEIGERT, B. S. *Proc. Soc. Exptl. Biol. Med.* **78**, 477 (1951).
348. PURKO, M., NELSON, W. O. and WOOD, W. A. *Abstr. 126th Meeting, Am. Chem. Soc.* **1954**, 57c; *J. Biol. Chem.* **207**, 51 (1954).
349. RABINOWITZ, J. C. *J. Biol. Chem.* **235**, PC 50 (1960).
350. RABINOWITZ, J. C. and PRICER, W. E., JR. *J. Am. Chem. Soc.* **78**, 5702 (1956).
351. RABINOWITZ, J. C. and SNELL, E. E. *Proc. Soc. Exptl. Biol. Med.* **70**, 235 (1949).
352. RADIN, N. S., RITTENBERG, D. and SHEMIN, D. *J. Biol. Chem.* **184**, 745 (1950).
353. RAUEN, H. M., HESS, G. and MECHERY, J. *Z. Physiol. Chem.* **315**, 60 (1959).
354. RAVEL, J. M. and SHIVE, W. *J. Biol. Chem.* **166**, 407 (1946).
355. RAY, S. N. *Biochem. J.* **28**, 996 (1934).
356. Recommended Dietary Allowances, Washington, D.C., Natl. Acad. Sci.—Natl. Res. Council, Publ. No. 302, p. 22 (1953).
357. REDDY, S. K., REYNOLDS, M. S. and PRICE, J. M. *J. Biol. Chem.* **233**, 691 (1958).
358. REIS, J. *Bull. Soc. Chim. Biol.* **22**, 36 (1940).
359. RENDINA, G. and COON, M. J. *J. Biol. Chem.* **225**, 523 (1957).
360. REYNOLDS, J. J. and BROWN, G. M. *J. Biol. Chem.* **237**, PC 2713 (1962).
361. REYNOLDS, J. J. and BROWN, G. M. *J. Biol. Chem.* **239**, 317 (1964).
362. ROBERTS, E. and BREGOFF, H. M. *J. Biol. Chem.* **201**, 393 (1953).
363. RODWELL, V. W., VOLCANI, B. E., IKAWA, M. and SNELL, E. E. *J. Biol. Chem.* **233**, 1548 (1958).
364. ROWAN, T. and WOOD, H. C. S. *Proc. Chem. Soc.* 21 (1963).
365. ROWEN, J. W. and KORNBERG, A. *J. Biol. Chem.* **193**, 497 (1951).
366. SAHASHI, Y., MIKATA, M. and SAKAO, H. *Bull. Chem. Soc. (Japan)* **23**, 247 (1950); cf. *C.A.* **46**, 8210 (1952).
367. SAITO, Y., HAYAISHI, O. and ROTHBERG, S. *J. Biol. Chem.* **229**, 921 (1957).
368. SANDERS, F. and SEAMAN, G. R. *Biochem. J.* **73**, 580 (1959).
369. SARETT, H. P. and CHELDELIN, V. H. *J. Biol. Chem.* **155**, 153 (1944).
370. SARETT, H. P. and CHELDELIN, V. H. *J. Biol. Chem.* **159**, 311 (1945).
370a SARMA, D. S. R., RAJALAKSHMI, S. and SARMA, P. S. *Biochem. Biophys. Res. Commun.* **6**, 389 (1961).
371. SATO, K., SUZUKI, T. and SAHASHI, Y. *Bitamin* **31**, 356 (1965) [through *C.A.* **63**: 2152 (1965)].
372. SCHMID, R. and SHEMIN, D. *J. Am. Chem. Soc.* **77**, 506 (1955).
373. SCHMIDT, G., CUBILES, R., ZOELLNER, N., HECHT, L., STRICKLER, N., SERAIDARIAN, K., SERAIDARIAN, M. and THANNHAUSER, S. J. *J. Biol. Chem.* **192**, 715 (1951).

374. SCHOPFER, W. H. *Plants and Vitamins*, *Cronika Botanika*, Waltham, Massachusetts (1943).
375. SCHOPFER, W. H. and JUNG, A. *Compt. Rend.* **204**, 1500 (1937).
376. SCHRECKER, A. W. and KORNBERG, A. *J. Biol. Chem.* **182**, 795 (1950).
377. SCHULTZ, A. S., ATKIN, L. and FREY, C. N. *Ind. Eng. Chem. Anal. Ed.* **14**, 35 (1942).
378. SCHWARTZ, S., IKEDA, K., MILLER, I. M. and WATSON, C. J. *Science* **129**, 40 (1959).
379. SHAPOSHNIKOV, V. N., KONOVA, I. V. and BORISOVA, A. I. *Mikrobiologiya* **32**, 598 (1963) [through *C.A.* **59**: 11915 (1963)].
380. SHEMIN, D., CORCORAN, J. W., ROSENBLUM, C. and MILLER, I. M. *Science* **124**, 272 (1956).
381. SHEMIN, D. and KUMIN, S. *J. Biol. Chem.* **198**, 827 (1952).
382. SHEMIN, D. and RUSSELL, C. S. *J. Am. Chem. Soc.* **75**, 4873 (1953).
383. SHEMIN, D., RUSSELL, C. S. and ABRAMSKY, T. *J. Biol. Chem.* **215**, 613 (1955).
384. SHEMIN, D. and WITTENBERG, J. *J. Biol. Chem.* **192**, 315 (1951).
385. SHIOTA, T. *Arch. Biochem. Biophys.* **80**, 155 (1959).
386. SHIOTA, T. and DISRAELY, M. N. *Biochim. Biophys. Acta* **52**, 467 (1961).
387. SHIOTA, T., DISRAELY, M. N. and MCCANN, M. P. *Biochem. Biophys. Res. Commun.* **7**, 194 (1962).
388. SHIVE, W. and MACOW, J. *J. Biol. Chem.* **162**, 451 (1946).
389. SIROTNAK, F. M., DONATI, G. J. and HUTCHISON, D. J. *J. Bacteriol.* **85**, 658 (1963).
390. SMITH, E. L. In *The Biochemistry of Vitamin B*$_{12}$, p. 3, ed. R. T. Williams. Biochem. Soc. Symposia No. 13, 1955.
391. SMITH, O. H. and YANOFSKY, C. *J. Biol. Chem.* **235**, 2051 (1960).
392. SMITH, E. L. and MERVYN, L. *Biochem. J.* **86**, 2P (1963).
393. SPELL, W. H. and DINNING, J. S. *J. Am. Chem. Soc.* **81**, 3804 (1959).
394. STADTMAN, E. R. *J. Am. Chem. Soc.* **77**, 5765 (1955).
395. STADTMAN, E. R., OVERATH, P., EGGERER, H. and LYNEN, F. *Biochem. Biophys. Res. Commun.* **2**, 1 (1960).
396. STILLER, E. T., HARRIS, S. A., FINKELSTEIN, J., KERESZTESY, J. C. and FOLKERS, K. *J. Am. Chem. Soc.* **62**, 1785 (1940).
397. SUNDARAM, T. E. and SARMA, P. S. *Nature* **172**, 627 (1953).
398. SWICK, R. W. *Federation Proc.* **20**, 80 (1961).
399. SWICK, R. W. and WOOD, H. G. *Proc. Natl. Acad. Sci.* **46**, 28 (1960).
400. TABOR, H. and RABINOWITZ, J. C. *J. Am. Chem. Soc.* **78**, 5705 (1956).
401. TADOKORO, T. and NISIDA, M. *J. Agr. Chem. Soc. Japan* **16**, 963 (1940).
402. TANAKA, T. and KNOX, W. E. *J. Biol. Chem.* **234**, 1162 (1959).
403. TATUM, E. L. *J. Biol. Chem.* **160**, 455 (1945).
404. TATUM, E. L. and BELL, T. T. *Am. J. Botany* **33**, 15 (1946).
405. TATUM, E. L., GROSS, S. R., EHRENSVÄRD, G. and GARNJOBST, L. *Proc. Natl. Acad. Sci.* **40**, 271(1954).
406. THOMPSON, J. F. and MIKUTA, E. T. *Proc. Soc. Exptl. Biol. Med.* **85**, 29 (1954).
407. TOUSTER, O. *Ann. Rev. Biochem.* **31**, 407 (1962).
408. UCHINO, H., YAGIRI, Y., YOSHINO, T., KONDO, M. and WAKISAKA, G. *Nature*, **205**, 176 (1965).
409. UL HASSAN, M. and LEHNINGER, A. L. *J. Biol. Chem.* **223**, 123 (1956).
410. UMBREIT, W. W. and WADDELL, J. G. *Proc. Soc. Exptl. Biol. Med.* **70**, 293 (1949).
411. UNDERKOFLER, L. A., BANTZ, A. C. and PETERSON, W. H. *J. Bacteriol.* **45**, 183 (1943).
412. UTTER, M. F. and KEECH, D. B. *J. Biol. Chem.* **235**, PC 17 (1960).
413. VAN BAALEN, C. and FORREST, H. S. *J. Am. Chem. Soc.* **81**, 1770 (1959).
414. VESCIA, A. and DI PRISCO, G. *J. Biol. Chem.* **237**, 2318 (1962).
415. VIERA, E. and SHAW, E. *J. Biol. Chem.* **236**, 2507 (1961).
416. VIRTANEN, A. I. and LAINE, T. *Enzymologia* **3**, 266 (1937).
417. VITOLS, E., WALKER, G. and HUENNEKENS, F. M. *Biochem. Biophys. Res. Commun.* **15**, 372 (1964).
418. VOLCANI, B. E. and SNELL, E. E. *Proc. Soc. Exptl. Biol. Med.* **67**, 511 (1948).
419. VON EULER, H. and ADLER, E. *Z. Physiol. Chem.* **252**, 41 (1938).

420. WACKER, H., HARVEY, R. A., WEINSTOCK, C. H. and PLAUT, G. W. E. *J. Biol. Chem.* **239**, 3493 (1964).
421. WAKIL, S. J., TITCHENER, E. B. and GIBSON, D. B. *Biochim. Biophys. Acta* **29**, 225 (1958).
422. WANG, T. P. and KAPLAN, N. O. *J. Biol. Chem.* **206**, 311 (1954).
423. WANG, T. P., KAPLAN, N. O. and STOLZENBACH, *J. Biol. Chem.* **211**, 465 (1954).
424. WARD, G. B., BROWN, G. M. and SNELL, E. E. *J. Biol. Chem.* **213**, 839 (1955).
425. WEISSBACH, H., TOOHEY, J. and BARKER, H. A. *Proc. Natl. Acad. Sci.* **45**, 521 (1959).
426. WEISSBACH, H., REDFIELD, B. and PETERKOFSKY, A. *J. Biol. Chem.* **236**, PC40 (1961).
427. WEISMAN, R. A. and BROWN, G. M. *J. Biol. Chem.* **239**, 326 (1964).
428. WEYGAND, F. and WALDSCHMIDT, M. *Angew. Chem.* **67**, 328 (1955).
429. WIELAND, T. and MOLLER, E. F. *Z. Physiol. Chem.* **269**, 227 (1941).
430. WILSON, A. C. and PARDEE, A. B. *J. Gen. Microbiol.* **28**, 283 (1962).
431. WILSON, R. G. and HENDERSON, L. M. *J. Biol. Chem.* **235**, 2099 (1960).
432. WILLIAMS, R. J. *Biol. Rev. Cambridge Phil. Soc.* **16**, 49 (1941).
433. WILLIAMS, R. J., LYMAN, C. M., GOODYEAR, G. H., TRUESDAIL, J. H. and HOLADAY, D. *J. Am. Chem. Soc.* **55**, 2912 (1933).
434. WILLIAMS, R. J. and MAJOR, R. T. *Science* **91**, 246 (1940).
435. WILLIAMS, R. J., MCMAHAN, J. R. and EAKIN, R. E. University of Texas Publ. No. 4137, 31 (1941).
436. WILLIAMS, R. J. and ROHRMANN, E. *J. Am. Chem. Soc.* **58**, 695 (1936).
437. WISS, O. *Proc. Internat. Symp. Enzyme Chem. Tokyo and Kyoto* **2**, 200 (1957).
438. WISS, O. and BETTENDORF, G. *Z. Physiol. Chem.* **306**, 145 (1957).
439. WISS, O. and FUCHS, H. *Experientia* **6**, 472 (1950).
440. WISS, O., SIMMER, H. and PETERS, H. *Z. Physiol. Chem.* **304**, 221 (1956).
441. WITTENBERG, J. and SHEMIN, D. *J. Biol. Chem.* **185**, 103 (1950).
442. WOLF, B. and HOTCHKISS, R. D. *Biochemistry* **2**, 145 (1963).
443. WOOLLEY, D. W. *J. Biol. Chem.* **130**, 417 (1939).
444. WRIGHT, B. E., ANDERSON, M. L. and HERMAN, E. C. *J. Biol. Chem.* **230**, 271 (1958).
445. WRIGHT, L. D. *Symposium on Vitamin Metabolism*, p. 104. Nutrition Symposium Series 13, New York, Natl. Vitamin Foundn., March 6, 1956.
446. WRIGHT, L. D. and CRESSON, E. L. *J. Am. Chem. Soc.* **76**, 4156 (1954).
447. WRIGHT, L. D., CRESSON, E. L. and DRISCOLL, C. A. *Proc. Soc. Exptl. Biol. and Med.* **89**, 234 (1955).
448. WRIGHT, L. D., CRESSON, E. L., VALIANT, J., WOLF, D. E. and FOLKERS, K. *J. Am. Chem. Soc.* **76**, 4160 (1954).
449. WRIGHT, L. D., CRESSON, E. L., VALIANT, J., WOLF, D. E. and FOLKERS, K. *J. Am. Chem. Soc.* **76**, 4163 (1954).
450. WRIGHT, L. D. and DRISCOLL, C. A. *J. Am. Chem. Soc.* **76**, 4999 (1954).
451. WRISTON, J. C., LACK, L. and SHEMIN, D. *J. Biol. Chem.* **215**, 603 (1955).
452. YAMADA, K., ISHIKAWA, S. and SHIMAZONO, N. *Biochim. Biophys. Acta* **32**, 253 (1959).
453. YANOFSKY, C. *Biochim. Biophys. Acta* **20**, 438 (1956).
454. YANOFSKY, C. *J. Biol. Chem.* **223**, 171 (1956).
455. YANOFSKY, C. *J. Biol. Chem.* **224**, 783 (1957).
456. YANOFSKY, C. In *Methods in Enzymology*, vol. 2, p. 233, eds. S. P. Colowick and N. O. Kaplan, Academic Press, New York, 1955.
457. YANOFSKY, C. and CRAWFORD, I. P. *Proc. Natl. Acad. Sci.* **45**, 1016 (1959).
458. YANOFSKY, C. In *Amino Acid Metabolism*, p. 930, eds. W. D. McElroy and B. Glass. Johns Hopkins Press, Baltimore, 1955; *J. Bacteriol.* **68**, 577 (1954).
459. YANOFSKY, C. and RACHMELER, M. *Biochim. Biophys. Acta* **28**, 640 (1958).
460. ZAKRZEWSKI, S. F. *J. Biol. Chem.* **235**, 1776 (1960).
461. ZAKRZEWSKI, S. F. and NICHOL, C. A. *Federation Proc.* **14**, 311 (1955).
462. ZAKRZEWSKI, S. F. and NICHOL, C. A. *Biochim. Biophys. Acta* **27**, 425 (1958).
463. ZATMAN, L. J., KAPLAN, N. O. and COLOWICK, S. P. *J. Biol. Chem.* **200**, 197 (1953).
463a ZATMAN, L. J., KAPLAN, N. O., COLOWICK, S. P. and CIOTTI, M. N. *J. Biol. Chem.* **209**, 453 (1954).
464. ZODROW, K. and ZODROW, H. *Acta Microbial. Polon.* **12**, 61 (1963).

CHAPTER 12

THE BIOSYNTHESIS OF PHENOLIC PLANT PRODUCTS

T. A. GEISSMAN

Department of Chemistry, University of California,
Los Angeles, California

CONTENTS

INTRODUCTION	743
EARLIER STUDIES	745
GENETIC EVIDENCE	746
THE BIOSYNTHESIS OF THE C_6—C_3 UNIT	748
Cinnamic acids	750
THE USE OF TWO-CARBON UNITS IN AROMATIC BIOSYNTHESIS	751
THE ACETATE HYPOTHESIS	751
THE BIOSYNTHESIS OF PARTICULAR GROUPS OF COMPOUNDS	755
Phenols, resorcinol derivatives, salicylic acid derivatives	755
Extension of acyl residues by C_2 units	760
The lichen compounds	764
Anthraquinones	769
Naphthoquinones	770
Compounds derived from 1-phenylpropane precursors	772
Flavonoid compounds	772
Isoflavones	777
Stilbenes and dihydroisocoumarins	779
Carbon alkylation	781
Isoprenoid substituents	784
The furan ring	787
Coumarins	788
Hydroxylation of aromatic rings	791
Oxidative metabolism in biosynthesis	792
SUMMARY	796
REFERENCES	797

INTRODUCTION

The phenolic compounds elaborated by plants range in structural type over a wide spectrum, from such simple phenols as hydroquinone (1), *p*-hydroxy-acetophenone (2) and anethole (3), to such complex compounds as emodin (4) and the dianthrone hypericin (5).

Hydroquinone
(1)

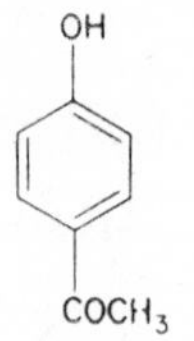

p-Hydroxyacetophenone
(2)

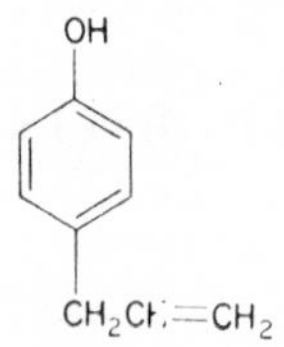

Anethole
(3)

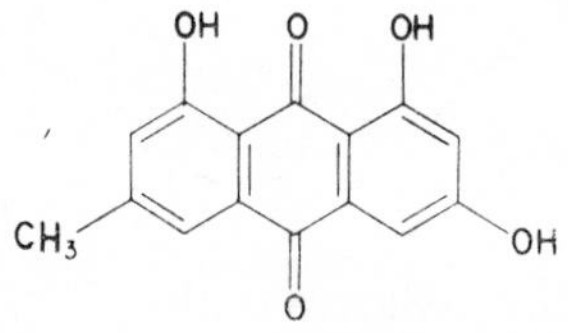

Emodin
(4)

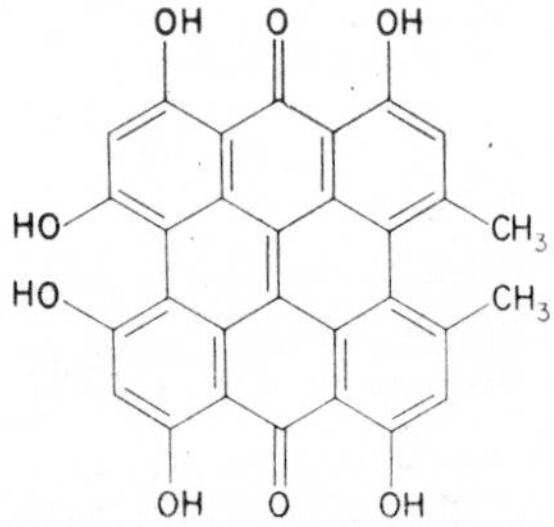

Hypericin
(5)

Present-day knowledge of the main routes by which phenolic compounds of these and many other types are synthesized in the plants, is based in part upon direct experimental evidence obtained with the use of radioactive tracer technics and in part upon systematic and compelling speculations that possess an impressive degree of coherence and consistency. While the origins of some plant phenols are open to alternative interpretations, a large number of them can be described with a high degree of assurance; but much remains to be done to establish speculative routes of biosynthesis by experimental verification. In particular, little is known about the nature of the multitude of individual steps through which small structural details are elaborated: the addition and removal of hydroxyl groups, the introduction and saturation of multiple bonds, the introduction of "extra" carbon atoms, the occasional skeletal rearrangements; these and other changes can often be recognized as un-doubted steps in biosynthetic sequences without it being possible to specify the point or the order in which they occur.

In the following pages the biosynthesis of the plant phenolic compounds will be dealt with largely from the point of view of the theories of biosyn-thesis that have received experimental support. While experiment has established routes that may be regarded as prototypes for many as yet un-investigated biosyntheses, a great many classes of substances have not yet come under direct experimental scrutiny. Of these, many can be accommodated into a few simple but compelling hypotheses about the essential soundness of which there can be little doubt. In some cases alternative hypotheses exist. Occasionally these can be seen to be but different expressions of a single idea; in others, they represent quite different viewpoints.

EARLIER STUDIES

Even before the advent of modern technics for the thorough study of plant constituents and of tracer methods using radioactive compounds, theories of biosynthesis were not wanting. The lack of experimental methods necessitated approaches that were based upon hypothesis and speculation, and before 1930 a considerable body of literature had been built up around the theme of plant biogenesis. Much of this dealt with the biosynthesis of plant alkaloids and included the fruitful and prophetic ideas of Robinson[1] and Schöpf,[2] some of which received support in elegant *in vitro* syntheses under conditions comparable to those obtaining in living cells. While theories of the biogenesis of terpenoid compounds are not within the scope of this chapter, it is to be recalled that the possible role of isoprene in the formation of terpenes has been a recurring theme,[3] and a number of terpenoid hydrocarbons were early synthesized[4] in the course of attempts to demonstrate that isoprene was at least a plausible, if not obligatory, precursor of this class of substances. Schemes have been devised to account for the biogenesis of carbohydrates,[5] steroid sapogenins,[6] cinnamic acids,[7] flavones,[8] and other aromatic compounds;[9] but these early speculations can now be regarded as part of the historical development of the subject, and attention can be turned to the more sophisticated theories of recent years.

Before leaving consideration of these early speculations, it is appropriate to recall the part they played in the development of what is now known about plant biogenesis. Schöpf[10] gave the clearest expression of a point of view regarding an attack upon the problem by using a reconstructive approach based upon a "comparative anatomy" of plant compounds. By considering the structures of groups of compounds closely related in their botanical occurrence, and assuming that certain common intermediates or precursors lie at the start of the synthetic sequences, Schöpf was able to devise rational schemes of biosynthesis that were based upon permissible grounds. The *in vitro* syntheses (under "conditions possible in the cell") of a group of quinoline alkaloids in *Angostura* bark[11] was one example of the validity of this approach. Schöpf's studies, and those of Robinson,[12] were the forerunners of many others in which highly reactive intermediates, whose presence in the living cell could be regarded as reasonably likely, were shown to condense to give naturally occurring compounds or products only a step or two away from natural substances.

This reconstructive approach lies at the base of much of our present-day knowledge of biosynthesis. The chief difference between modern investigations and those of thirty years ago is that the older theories were supported chiefly by the compelling weight of coincidence while at the present time it is possible to test theory by experiments on the living plant itself. The use of radioactive tracers and the separation of enzyme systems capable of carrying out distinct stages of a synthetic sequence have made it possible to put biosynthetic theory to direct test.

GENETIC EVIDENCE

A fruitful avenue of investigation of the chemical processes occurring in plants has been the combined chemical–genetical approach. Studies of this kind were first carried out by Wheldale and Bassett [13] and later extended by a school of geneticists and chemists at the John Innes Institution. [14] Evidence from the study of chemical structures of the anthocyanin pigments of plants of known genetic composition showed clearly that single factors ("genes") controlled specific chemical reactions in the elaboration of the anthocyanins. Genes specific for the establishment of nuclear hydroxylation patterns, for methylation of phenolic hydroxyl groups, for the attachment of sugar residues and for the control of the amount of pigment, were recognized. Evidence from the effects of interaction and competition between genes suggested that anthocyanins of various structural types were synthesized from common precursors.

After the advent of methods that permitted the systematic study of noncyanic plant pigments, genetic studies were extended to the examination of all of the flavonoid constituents of selected genotypes. [15] These studies showed that the genetic control of the positions of hydroxylation in the anthocyanin pigments was exerted as well upon the hydroxylation patterns of the accompanying flavones. These findings offered additional support for the concept of parallel synthetic paths for the flavonoid constituents, starting from a common early precursor.

Numerous other chemical genetical studies have confirmed this general picture of flavonoid biosynthesis; but the genetical approach has so far failed to provide clear evidence for the detailed sequence of synthetic transformations by which flavones, aurones, flavanones, and anthocyanins are derived from their precursors, or whether these compounds are directly interconvertible by simple oxidation or reduction processes.

A significant observation was made in the study of an albino mutant of *Antirrhinum majus*, the garden snapdragon. This mutant contains no flavonoid (i.e. C_6—C_3—C_6) substances in the colorless flower petals. Instead, esters of caffeic, *p*-coumaric and ferulic acids are present. [16, 17, 18] The conclusion from these observations that the mutant lacks the capacity for coupling of a C_6—C_3 unit to a C_6 unit (6) to provide the flavonoid precursor has been borne

(6)

out in the subsequent development of what is today an accepted overall view of flavonoid biosynthesis. The nature of the six-carbon fragment to which the phenylpropane-derived unit became attached to form the C_{15} unit of the flavonoids was not revealed in the studies on the mutant snapdragon. That these six carbon atoms are derived from three molecules of acetic acid is now known. Evidence for this conclusion will be described in the sequel.

The extension of the C_6—C_3 unit of phenylpropane-derived precursors (such as the cinnamic acids) by the attachment of two-carbon units can easily be discerned in the 6-styryl-α-pyrones, kawain (7) and methysticin (8).

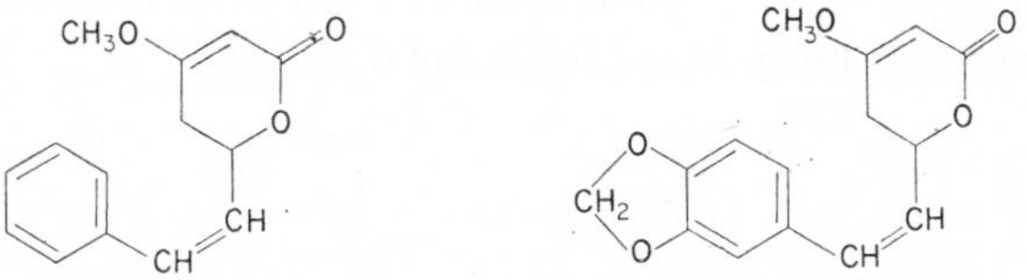

Kawain   Methysticin
(7)   (8)

Kawain (7) is a methyl ether of the cyclized form of the hypothetical C_6—C_3— C_2—C_2 precursor (9). [18]

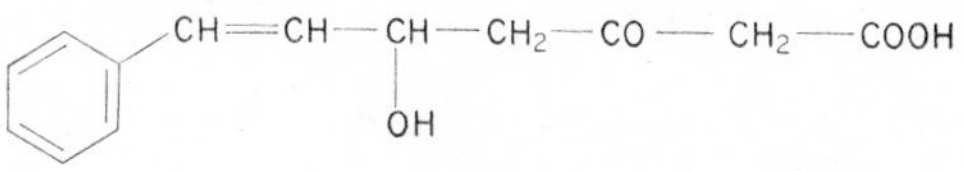

(9)

Paracotoin (10) is similarly related to the C_6—C_3—C_2 precursor (11).

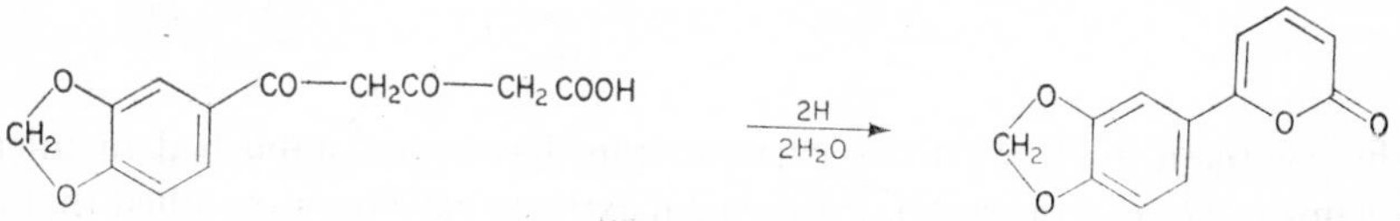

(10)   (11)

A summary of the evidence from the reconstructive and genetic approaches gave strong support for a view of biosynthesis of many plant phenols that contained two fundamental ideas: (a) a nine-carbon atom unit with a 1-arylpropane skeleton is one of the widely occurring building units in plant biosynthesis; and (b) the extension of the three-carbon side chain by two-carbon units can account for the elaboration of eleven-, thirteen- and fifteen-carbon atom compounds. This hypothesis was later enunciated with explicit application to compounds of widely differing structural types by Birch and Donovan,[20] and now embodies the essential idea of a generally accepted view of plant phenol biosynthesis. Its elaboration to include modifications of the C_6—C_3 unit and of pathways involving only C_2 condensations has led to the development of the comprehensive view of plant biosynthesis that will be dealt with in the following sections.

THE BIOSYNTHESIS OF THE C_6—C_3 UNIT

The origin of the aromatic ring of the many natural phenylpropanoid compounds is now regarded to be the cyclohexane derivatives that arise by carbohydrate cyclization. The key compound in this series is shikimic acid (14), which is formed as shown in the following diagram:

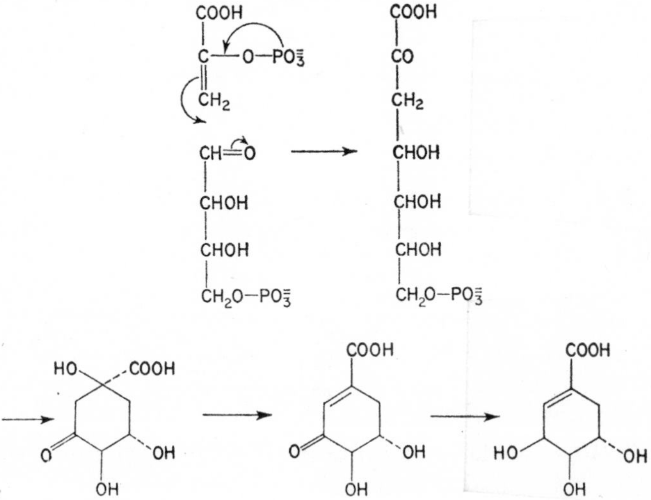

Dehydroquinic acid	Dehydroshikimic acid	Shikimic acid
(12)	(13)	(14)

This synthetic pathway from carbohydrate has been established in microorganisms (*E. coli* mutants), from which extracts have been obtained that are capable of carrying out the combination of phosphoenolpyruvate with erythrose-4-phosphate to give shikimic acid (by way of dehydroquinic (1 and dehydroshikimic (13) acids.[21-23])

The synthesis of aromatic compounds of the general pattern C_6—C—C—C, such as phenylalanine and tyrosine, takes place in microorganisms by the following pathway:

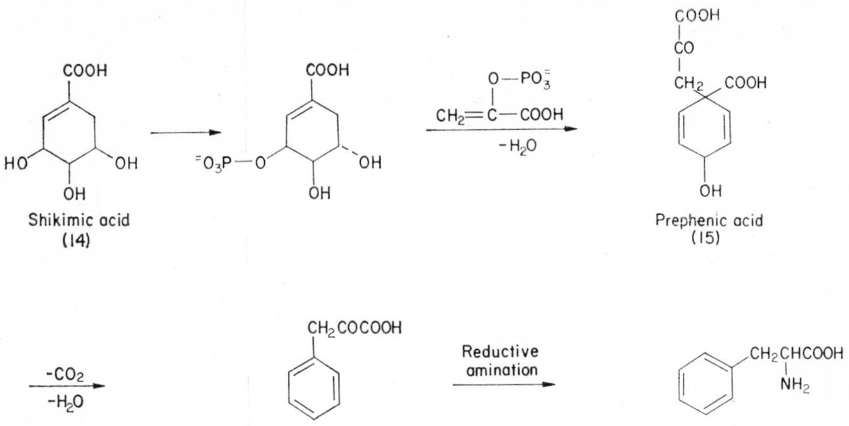

Shikimic acid
(14)

Prephenic acid
(15)

$-CO_2$
$-H_2O$

Reductive
amination

The formation of tyrosine from prephenic acid (15) appears to take place by way of p-hydroxyphenyllactic acid (16): [24]

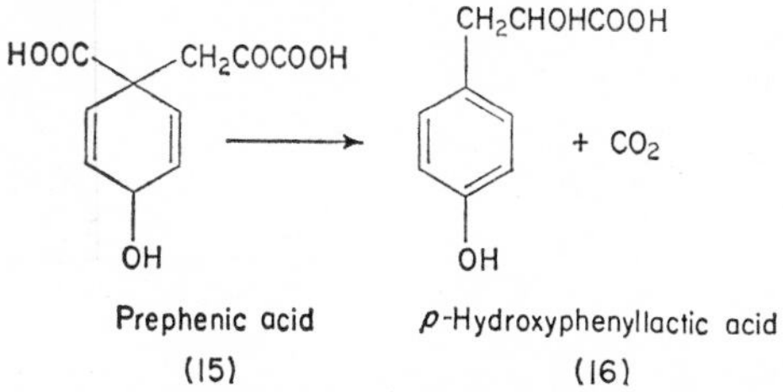

Prephenic acid
(15)

p-Hydroxyphenyllactic acid
(16)

Tyrosine is formed from phenylalanine in mammals, but that the hydroxylation of phenylalanine is the route by which tyrosine is formed in plants is not indicated by the results of experiments to test this suggestion. [25] However, that shikimic acid is the precursor in plants of the C_6—C_3 compounds that occur so widely, and indeed of phenylalanine and tyrosine, [25] has been well substantiated by a number of investigators.

Early experiments to test this hypothesis were directed to the study of the biogenesis of lignin. Lignin, a polymeric substance of still undefined structure, is the product of the condensation of nine-carbon units—for example, coniferyl alcohol—into a high molecular weight substance. When wheat and maple cuttings were fed with radioactive (carbon-14) L-phenylalanine and shikimic acid, it was found that both of these precursors were incorporated into lignin with about equal facility. [26] Subsequent experiments showed that the specific labeling patterns were preserved: cinnamic acid-3-C^{14} was incorporated into lignin in such a way as to provide formyl-labeled vanillin and syringaldehyde on degradation. [27] The biosynthesis of lignin is discussed further in Chapter 15.

A generalized scheme that has been proposed for the biosynthesis of shikimic acid-derived compounds in higher plants is represented as follows: [28]

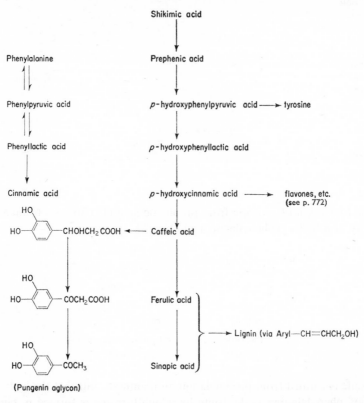

(Pungenin aglycon)

While certain details of this scheme remain to be demonstrated, it represents a working hypothesis that embodies the present information about the chief synthetic role of the cinnamic acids and their precursors in plant metabolism.

Cinnamic Acids

The conversion of phenylalanine into caffeic acid in plants, with specific retention of the position of isotopic labeling, was first found in experiments on tobacco. [29] The biosynthetic relationships between caffeic and p-coumaric ferulic and sinapic acids were studied in *Salvia splendens*, [25] with findings that led to the conclusion that the course of synthesis is the following:

p-coumaric → caffeic → ferulic → sinapic.

Salvia could convert the simpler members of this series into the more complex compounds. The reverse process did not occur readily (but see p. 791).

When shikimic acid (labeled generally) was fed to *Salvia*, caffeic acid labeled only in the ring was obtained. This and other results have disposed of the possibility that an important pathway to the cinnamic acids is by extension of a substituted benzoic acid by the addition of a two-carbon unit.

THE USE OF TWO-CARBON UNITS IN
AROMATIC BIOSYNTHESIS

The discoveries in the past ten years of the importance of acetic acid, in the form of its thioester, acetyl CoA, as a building unit in cellular synthesis have clarified and pointed the way toward the ultimate solution of a host of questions concerning biosynthetic pathways. We can distinguish three distinct routes of synthesis in which "acetate" is involved:

(I) The condensation of acetate fragments into the branched chain compound mevalonic acid (17) and the ultimate conversion of this into such building units as (18) and (19):

$$^-O_6P_2 - OCH_2CH_2C \underset{CH_3}{\overset{CH_2}{<}} \longrightarrow \left\{ \begin{array}{l} \text{Steroids} \\ \text{Cartenoids} \\ \text{Terpenes} \\ \text{O-and C-Prenylations} \end{array} \right.$$

(18)

$$CH_3COOH \longrightarrow \underset{\substack{| \quad | \\ COOH \; CH_2OH}}{\overset{\substack{HO \diagdown C \diagup CH_3 \\ CH_2 \quad CH_2}}{}}$$

Mevalonic acid
(17)

$$^-O_6P_2 - OCOCH = C \underset{CH_3}{\overset{CH_3}{<}} \longrightarrow \text{(O-and C-acylations)}$$

(19)

(II) The linear condensation of acetate fragments into chains, with or without ultimate cyclization into benzene, naphthalene or anthracene derivatives.

(III) The addition of two-carbon units to a precursor that may or may not be acetate-derived. This route is most commonly recognized in the addition of $-CH_2CO-$ units to a carboxyl group (20):

$$R-COOH \rightarrow R-COCH_2COOH \rightarrow R-COCH_2COCH_2COOH \quad (20)$$

The first of these routes will not be discussed here. Although numerous plant phenolic compounds are terpenoid, and may be regarded as arising by route I, a discussion of their biogenesis is to be found in Chapter 14.

THE ACETATE HYPOTHESIS

Plant biosynthesis by way of routes II and III was suggested by Birch and Donovan[20] as a general hypothesis. Collie, in 1907, was the first to propose a role for polyketomethylene intermediates in the biosynthesis of aromatic compounds;[9] and the possible role of two-carbon atom units in the biosynthesis of the fatty acids, characteristically even-numbered chains of carbon atoms, has been a prevalent theme for many years.

Many instances of biosynthesis by the acetate route—the linear condensation of two-carbon units into (hypothetical) poly-β-ketomethylene chains followed by cyclization in one or another way—have now been studied, with the use of labeled compounds, in microorganisms, fungi and higher plants. The results of these studies leave no doubt about the essential validity of the broad outlines of the theory, although many details remain to be explained.

The general outlines of the theory, with respect to both routes II and III, may be presented first as a prelude to a more detailed description of individual examples. In the simplest formulation, the polycondensation of C_2 units could proceed as follows (21):

$$CH_3COOH \rightarrow CH_3COCH_2COOH \rightarrow CH_3COCH_2COCH_2COOH \rightarrow$$
$$CH_3CO(CH_2CO)_nCH_2COOH \qquad (21)$$

Cyclization of an intermediate of this kind could take place in many ways:

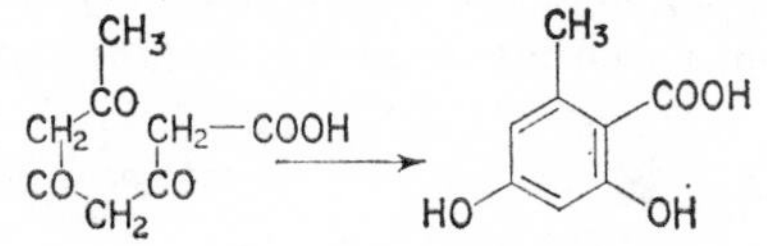

(22)

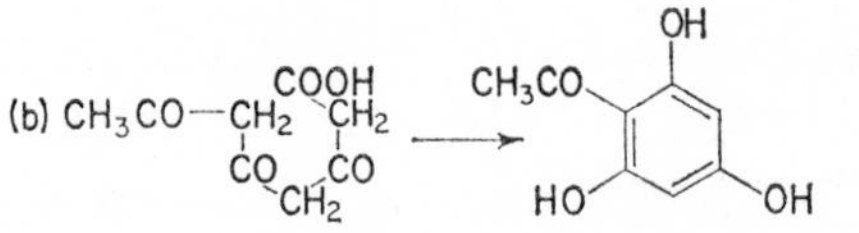

(23)

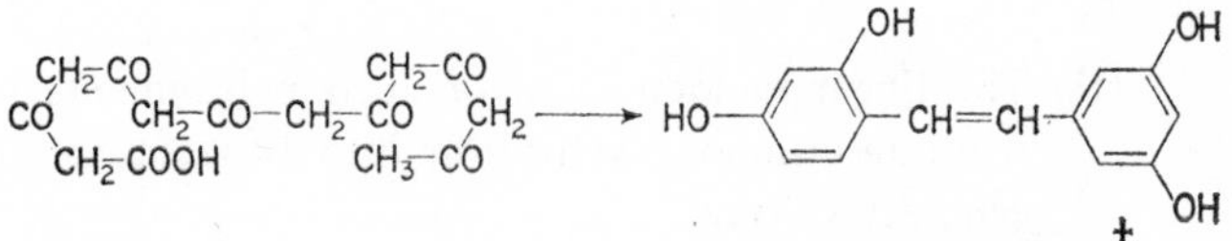

(24) Resveratrol †

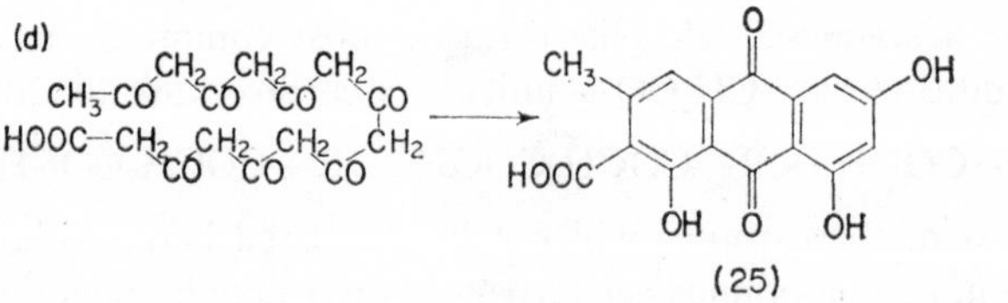

(25)

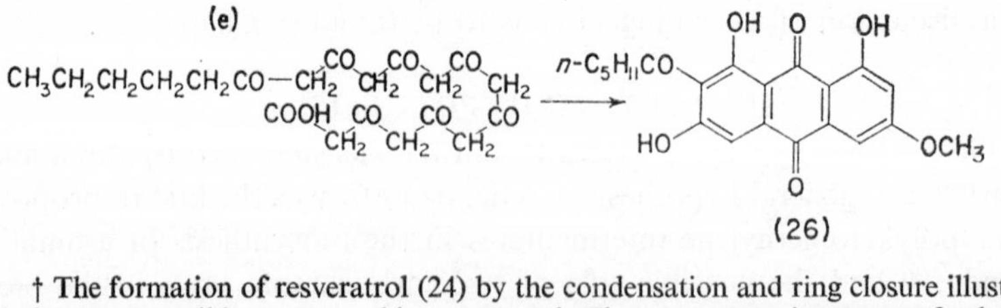

(26)

† The formation of resveratrol (24) by the condensation and ring closure illustrated here is but one possible route to this compound. The occurrence in nature of other stilbenes with different hydroxylation patterns suggests an alternative course of synthesis in which one ring is phenylpropane-derived, the other acetate-derived. This will be discussed in the sequel.

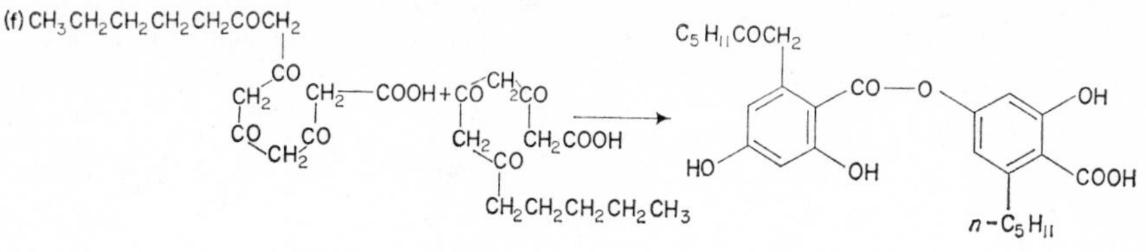
(f) CH3CH2CH2CH2CH2COCH2
CO
CH2
CH2
COOH+CO
CH2
CO
CO
CO
CH2
CH2
CH2COOH
CO
CH2CH2CH2CH2CH3
C5H11COCH2
CO—O
OH
HO
OH
COOH
n-C5H11

(27)

Examples of route III are typified by the biosynthesis of compounds in which one structural element is the 1-arylpropane-derived unit which will be referred to as C_6—C—C—C, or C_6—C_3. Combination of this with a single C_2 unit can lead to the intermediate (28); addition of successive C_2 units provide, in turn, the precursor substances (31) and (34). As is shown in the following generalized schemes, various natural substances have structures that can be directly related to these intermediates:†

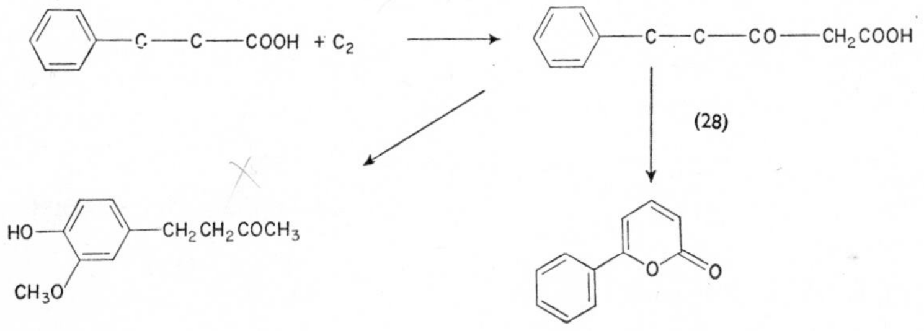
C—C—COOH + C2
C—C—CO—CH2COOH
(28)
HO
CH2CH2COCH3
CH3O
O
O

(29) (30)

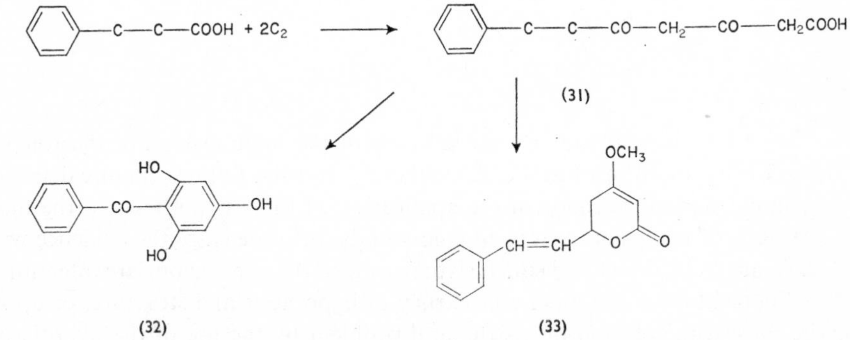
C—C—COOH + 2C2
C—C—CO—CH2—CO—CH2COOH
(31)
HO
CO
OH
HO
OCH3
CH=CH
O
O

(32) (33)

† The presence or absence of 4- and 3,4-hydroxylation in the final products used as illustrations is irrelevant to the point in question. This structural feature relates to the C_6—C_3 portion of the molecules.

$$\text{Ph}-\text{C}-\text{C}-\text{COOH} + 3C_2 \longrightarrow \text{Ph}-\text{C}-\text{C}-\text{CO}-\text{CH}_2\text{CO}-\text{CH}_2\text{CO}-\text{CH}_2\text{COOH} \quad (34)$$

$$\downarrow$$

$$\text{Ph}-\text{C}-\text{C}-\text{CO}-\underset{\text{HO}}{\overset{\text{HO}}{\bigcirc}}-\text{OH} \quad (35)$$

The elaboration of a phenolic ring as a terminal unit on what is clearly a fatty acid-derived side chain, as in (36), presents a question to which no unequivocal answer can be given. The short polyketomethylene "end" could be added to the preformed fatty acid (37), or could conceivably be the unreduced residue of a long polyketomethylene chain (38). The former of these is certainly the most likely, but the question remains open. For example, anacardic acid (39) is related to the intermediate (36):

$$CH_3(CH_2)_5\,CH{=}CH\,(CH_2)_7COCH_2\;COCH_2\,COCH_2\,COOH$$
$$(36)$$

$$\leftarrow\!-\!-\!\overset{?}{-}\!-\!\rceil 3C_2$$
$$CH_3(CH_2)_5\,CH{=}CH\,(CH_2)_7COOH$$
$$(37)$$

$$\downarrow$$

$$CH_3\,(CH_2)_5\,CH{=}CH{-}(CH_2)_7$$

$$\underset{\text{OH}}{\overset{\text{COOH}}{\bigcirc}}$$

$$(39)\quad\text{Anacardic Acid}$$

$$-\!-\,CH_3\,(COCH_2)_7\,COOH$$
$$(38)$$

The foregoing presents an overall view of the main aspects of the role of acetate (C_2 units) in phenolic biosynthesis.† In what follows, a more detailed examination will be made of the application of these hypotheses to the biosynthesis of particular groups of compounds. In some cases the evidence will be found to be direct and conclusive; in others, the conclusions are inferential and depend upon the inner consistency of hypothesis and structure, or upon the successful solution of a structural problem by the use of the hypothesis as a predictive device.

† See p. 760.

THE BIOSYNTHESIS OF PARTICULAR GROUPS OF COMPOUNDS

Phenols, Resorcinol Derivatives, Salicylic Acid Derivatives

Perhaps the simplest of the natural acetate-derived phenols is 6-methylsalicylic acid (40), the derivation of which can be written as follows:

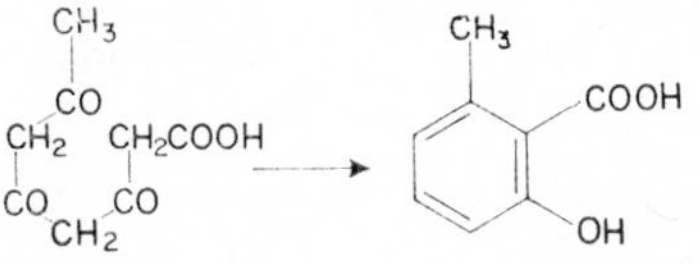
CH3
CO
CH2 CH2COOH
CO CO
CH2
CH3
COOH
OH

6-Methylsalicylic acid

(40)

That the sequence of carbon atoms indicated by this mode of formation is correct was shown[31] by the study of 6-methylsalicylic acid produced by *Penicillium griseofulvum* supplied with carboxyl-C^{14} acetic acid. Degradation of the salicylic acid gave results that were fully in accord with the following scheme:

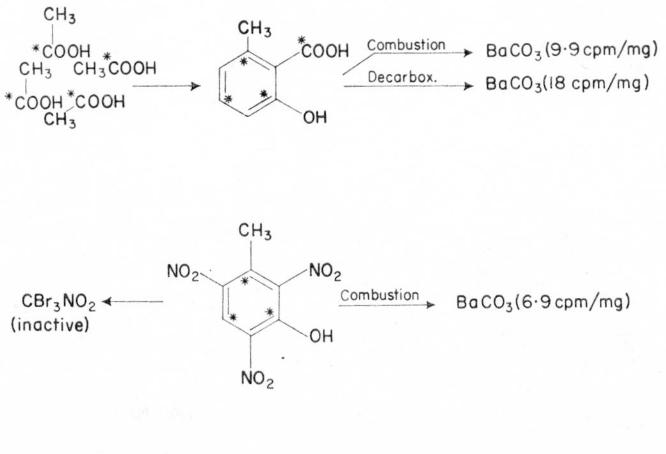
CH3
*COOH *
CH3 CH3COOH
*COOH *COOH
CH3
CH3
*COOH
OH
Combustion
BaCO3(9·9 cpm/mg)
Decarbox.
BaCO3(18 cpm/mg)
CH3
NO2
NO2
NO2
OH
CBr3NO2
(inactive)
Combustion
BaCO3(6·9 cpm/mg)

Further transformations, probably starting from 6-methylsalicylic acid, are brought about by *Penicillium* strains to produce a variety of related compounds:[32]

(40a) Patulin

The formation of various related aromatic compounds by various strains of the ascomycete *Daldinia concentrica* is illustrated by the following: [33]

Dihydroxyperylene quinone
(40b)

To the foregoing examples can be added many others drawn from studies on the biosynthetic activities of microorganisms. Griseofulvin (41) is formed from acetate units according to the scheme: [34]

Griseofulvin
(41)

Another mold metabolite, curvularin, has the structure (42), and has been shown to be derived by head-to-tail linkage of eight acetate units: [35]

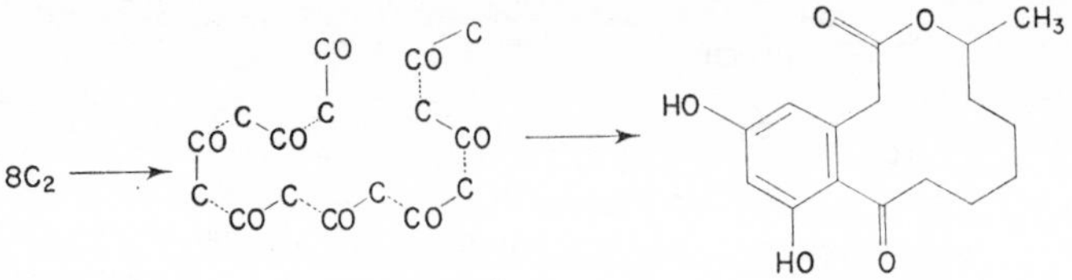

Curvularin
(42)

The formation of compounds derived from head-to-tail combination of acetate units in higher plants has received far less attention. Much of what is postulated about phenolic biosynthesis in plants is based largely upon the ability of the acetate hypothesis to assist in structural investigations by predicting which of two or more plausible structures is the most likely. An early example of this is found in the revision [36] of the structure of eleutherinol (43), first formulated [37] as (44):

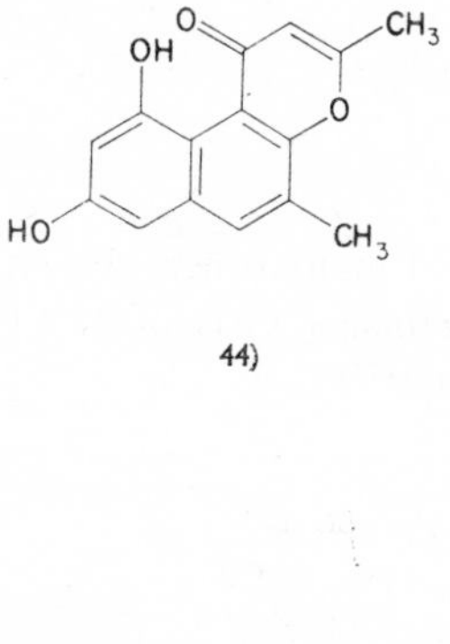

44)

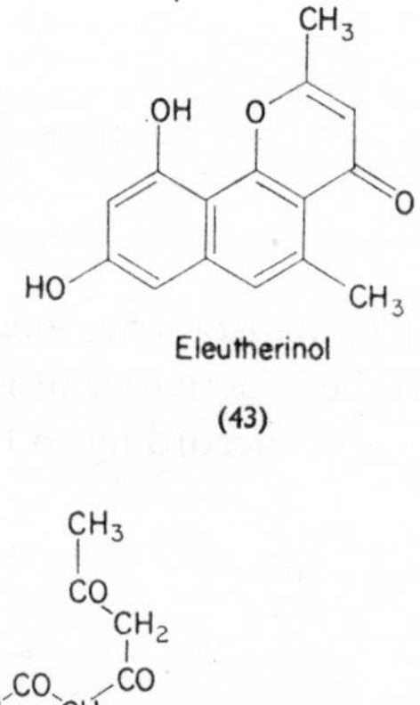

Eleutherinol
(43)

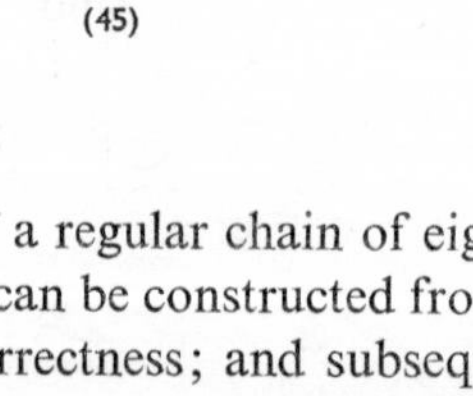

(45)

Structure (43) can be constructed of a regular chain of eight acetate units in head-to-tail linkage (45). While (44) can be constructed from acetate units, its irregularity casts doubt upon its correctness; and subsequent chemical evidence furnished support for (43). It is also to be noted that eleutherol (46) and eleutherin (47), which occur along with eleutherinol in *Eleutherine bulbosa*, follow the "regular" pattern of head-to-tail linkage of acetate units (with modifications due to oxidation and reduction reactions):

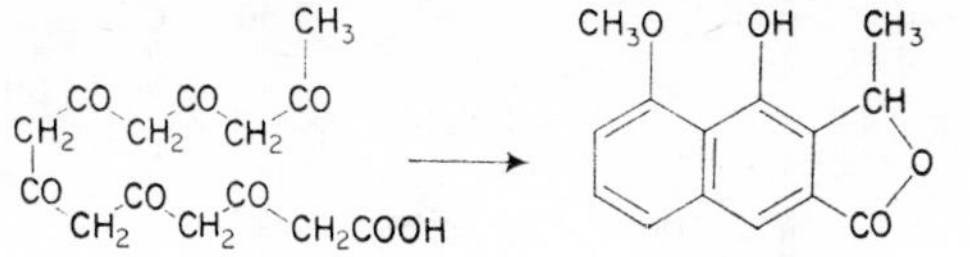

Eleutherol
(46)

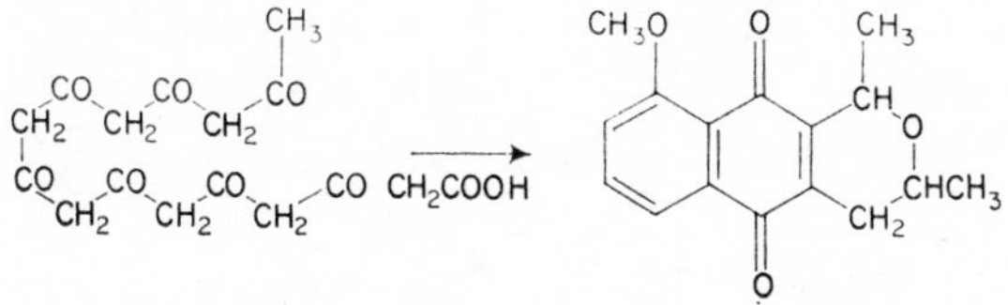

Eleutherin
(47)

Similar consideration led to the alteration of the structure (48) first proposed [38] for α-sorigenin to (49), which was subsequently confirmed by chemical means. The hypothetical precursor (50) would lead more readily to (49) than to (48):

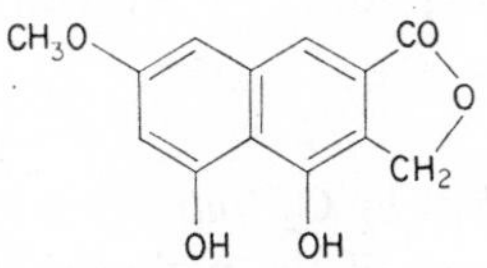

(48)

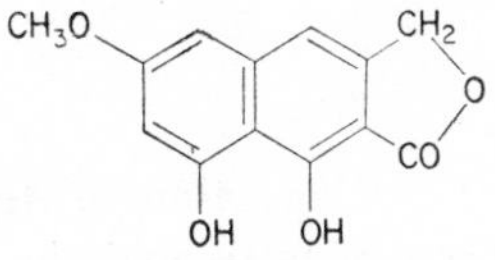

α-Sorigenin

(49)

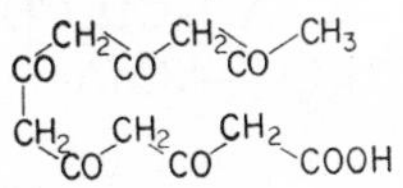

(50)

It is to be noted that a feature of the hypothesis, as expressed in the structures of compounds 43, 46, 47 and 49, is the placing of phenolic hydroxyl groups in the positions called for by the arrangement of acetate residues in the postulated precursors. A case that demonstrates the usefulness of this feature of the theory is that of flaviolin (51), for which the alternative structure (52) was at first also in consideration:

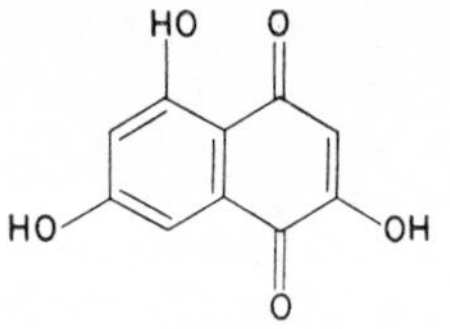

Flaviolin
(51)

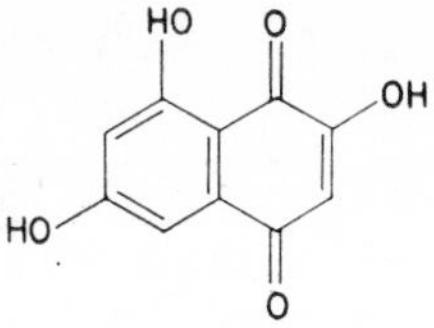

(52)

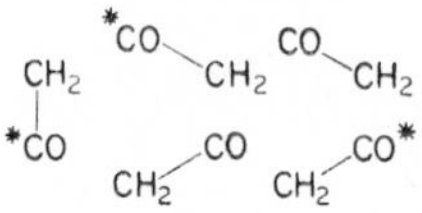

(53)

The placing of the oxygen atoms (*) in the ten-carbon atom precursor (53) is in better accord with (51). The synthesis of flaviolin trimethyl ether has established (51) as the correct structure. [40, 41]

It must be admitted that because of the ability of living systems to introduce and remove oxygen atoms in compounds of the types being considered here, arguments such as the ones that have been presented are not always compelling. They have, however, served as useful guides in directing degradative and synthetic experiments in one of several alternative directions, and have been of value in furnishing working hypotheses in structural investigations.

Extension of Acyl Residues by C_2 Units

The synthesis of fatty acids by the reverse of the pathways of oxidative degradation can be summarized as follows (54):

$$RCH_2CO\text{—}SCoA + CH_3CO\text{—}SCoA \rightleftharpoons RCH_2COCH_2CO\text{—}SCoA + HSCoA$$

$$RCH_2COCH_2CO\text{—}SCoA + DPNH + H^+$$
$$\rightleftharpoons RCH_2CHOHCH_2CO\text{—}SCoA + DPN^+$$

$$TPNH + H^+$$

$$RCH_2CH_2CH_2CO\text{—}SCoA \longleftarrow RCH_2CH=CHCO\text{—}SCoA$$

$$(54)$$

where the various steps are catalyzed by specific enzymes. [42]

That this simple picture may not represent the only, or even the most important, route to long-chain fatty acids is suggested by the recent observation that an essential primary step in fatty acid biosynthesis involves the reaction of acetyl-CoA with carbon dioxide to form malonyl-CoA which is then converted into long-chain acids. The overall scheme that has been suggested is the following (55): [43]

$$CH_3CO-SCoA + CO_2 + ATP \longrightarrow \underset{\underset{COOH}{|}}{CH_2CO-SCoA}$$

$$\left\{ CH_3CO-SCoA + \underset{\underset{COOH}{|}}{CH_2CO-SCoA} \longrightarrow \underset{\underset{COOH}{|}}{CH_3COCH-CO-SCoA} \right.$$

$$\xrightarrow[\quad]{TPNH} \underset{\underset{COOH}{|}}{\overset{\overset{OH}{|}}{CH_3CH-CH-CO-SCoA}} \longrightarrow \underset{\underset{COOH}{|}}{CH_3CH=C-CO-SCoA}$$

$$\xrightarrow{\quad} \underset{\underset{COOH}{|}}{CH_3CH_2CH-CO-SCoA} \longrightarrow \underset{\downarrow \text{ malonyl-CoA}}{CH_3CH_2CH_2CO-SCoA} + CO_2$$

$$\text{etc.}$$

(55)

The acetate hypothesis of the biosynthesis of plant substances implies a reaction such as the following, without, however, the necessary intervention of the reduction of —CO— to —CH₂— between successive acylations (56):

$$RCH_2COOH + CH_3COOH \longrightarrow RCH_2COCH_2COOH$$
$$RCH_2COCH_2COOH + CH_3COOH \longrightarrow RCH_2COCH_2COCH_2COOH$$

(56)

It should be emphasized, however, that in many of its applications the "acetate" theory has so far remained as a structural hypothesis, and none of its proponents have spelled out the details (as in (56)) of the process of chain extension. If a process such as (56) is to be assumed, the use of coenzyme A derivatives instead of the free acids would, of course, be implied. For the present the simpler scheme (54, 56) will be used for the purposes of this discussion.

The extension of the fatty acid chain by the addition of a single C_2 unit has been shown by the incorporation of radioactivity into arachidonic acid (58) by rats fed with γ-linolenic acid (57) and acetate:

$$CH_3(CH_2)_4CH=CHCH_2CH=CHCH_2CH=CH(CH_2)_4COOH$$

(57)

COOH-labeled (57) + $CH_3COOH \rightarrow$
$$CH_3(CH_2)_4(CH=CHCH_2)_4\overset{*}{C}H_2CH_2COOH$$

unlabeled (57) + $CH_3\overset{*}{C}OOH \rightarrow CH_3(CH_2)_4(CH=CHCH_2)_4CH_2CH_2\overset{*}{C}OOH$

(58)

A group of compounds whose biosynthesis may be represented by an extension of this process is that which includes a number of phenols found in the Anacardiaceae. These are urushiol (59), anacardic acid (60), cardol (61) and cardanol (62):†

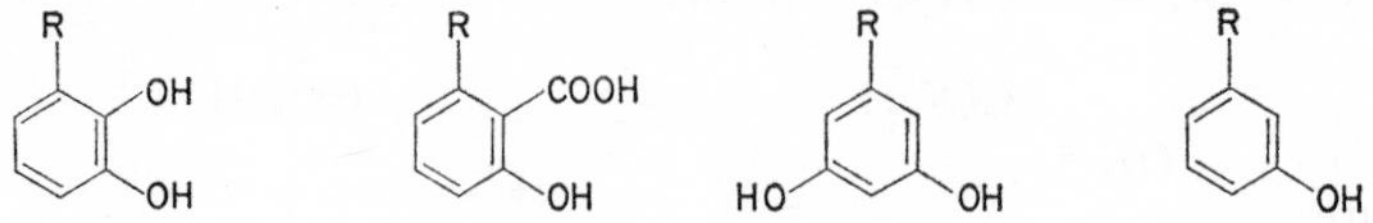

(59) Urushiol   (60) Anacardic acid   (61) Cardol   (62) Cardanol

$R = n\text{-}C_{15}$

The biosynthesis of these phenols may be formulated by the following scheme:

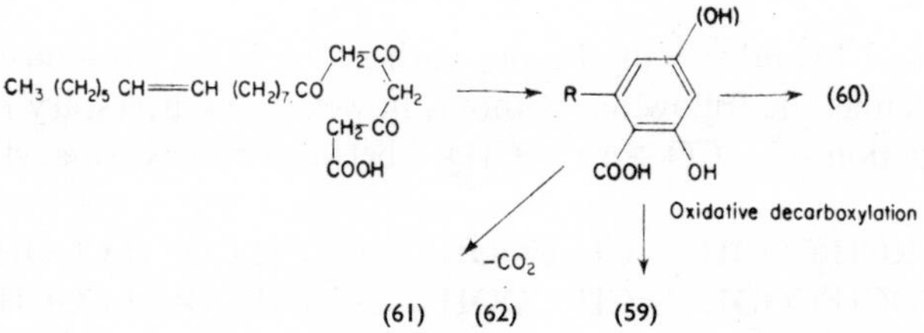

A most striking example of biosynthesis by this route is found in a group of compounds isolated from the oil of the anacardiaceous plant *Campnosperma brevipetiolata* (Tigaso).[44] The phenol campnospermonol (63) was the first phenolic compound found in this oil:

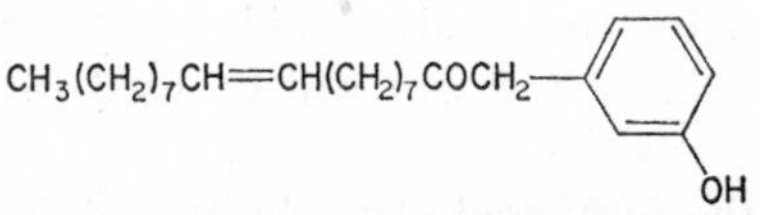

$$CH_3(CH_2)_7CH\!=\!CH(CH_2)_7COCH_2\!-\!\!\!\!\!\bigcirc$$

Campnospermonol (63)

Later studies showed the presence in Tigaso oil of oleyl methyl ketone (64)

$$CH_3(CH_2)_7CH\!=\!CH(CH_2)_7COCH_3$$
$$(64)$$

and the cyclic ketone (65).

---

† The side chains (R) in these natural phenols are mono-, di- and tri-unsaturated, with double bonds at 8, 8 : 11, or 8 : 11 : 14. For the present purposes, the mono-olefins will be chosen for discussion; this side chain is that of the natural fatty acid palmitoleic acid, $CH_3(CH_2)_5CH\!=\!CH(CH_2)_7COOH$.

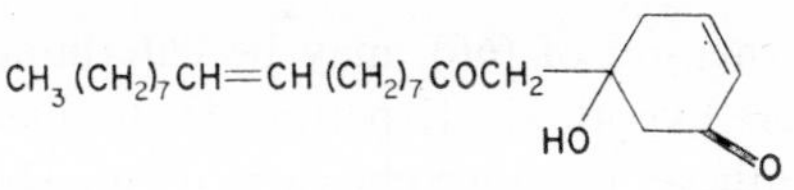

$$CH_3(CH_2)_7CH=CH(CH_2)_7COCH_2$$

(65)

The latter appears to be the aldol derived by ring closure of the intermediate (66):

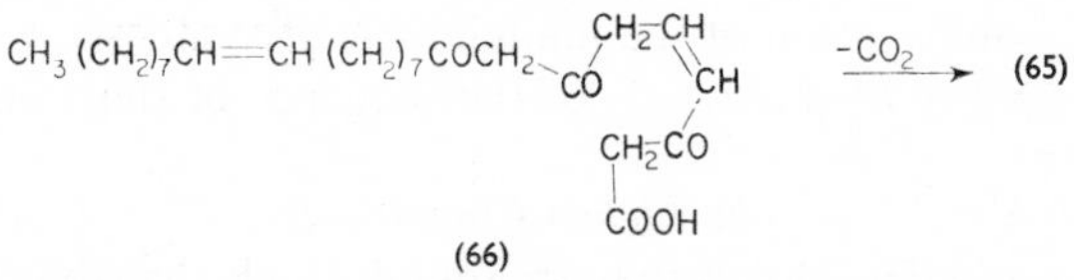

$$CH_3(CH_2)_7CH=CH(CH_2)_7COCH_2 \quad \xrightarrow{-CO_2} \quad (65)$$

(66)

The significance of this observation is two-fold: the cyclic ketone (65) is only a reduction–dehydration step removed from the oxidation stage of the tetra-keto precursor (66a):

$$CH_3(CH_2)_7CH=CH(CH_2)_7COCH_2COCH_2COCH_2COCH_2COOH$$
(66a)

and the presence of the double-bond in the ring at a stage prior to that of complete aromatization indicates that the phenol (63) is not derived by removal of a nuclear hydroxyl group from the resorcinol that corresponds to cardol (61). Thus, removal of the phenolic hydroxyl group is probably not a stage in the synthesis of the monophenols (60) and (62).

In another species of *Campnospermum* are found the related compounds (67)

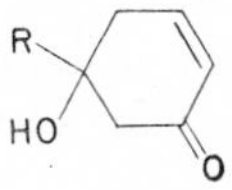

67)

in which R represents unsaturated side-chains that can be reduced to the n-$C_{19}H_{39}$-residue. The positions of unsaturation are unknown. [45]

The modifications of structure in the phenols of the Anacardiaceae include catechols and resorcinols, with C_{15}, C_{17} and C_{19} side chains. Moreacol and thitsiol are 4-alkyl (or alkenyl) catechols (68) and may arise by hydroxylation

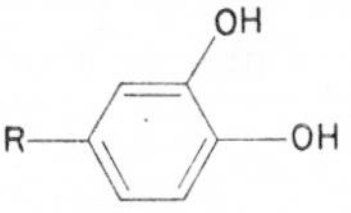

(68)

of the "parent" 3-substituted phenols, of which (62) and (63) are prototypes.

It is clear that these phenols form a group of compounds that provide excellent support for the hypothesis of synthesis by the acetate route. While alternative hypotheses, for example that a crotonyl fragment is incorporated in the course of formation of (66), may be entertained, these are obvious variants of the acetate hypothesis. Experimental studies to establish the steps in these involved syntheses remain to be carried out. There can be little doubt that the *positions* of labeling that would result from the experimental incorporation of, say, methyl-labeled acetic acid into the phenols of one of these plants could be predicted with considerable assurance. Such demonstrations, while valuable confirmation of the main course of synthesis, would add little to the understanding of the details of the sequence of steps involved.

The Lichen Compounds

The depsides and depsidones that are found widely distributed and in great structural variety in the lichens provide another closely integrated group of compounds, many of whose structures fit into the general scheme of biosynthesis by linear combination of C_2 units.

The depsides are esters formed between the carboxyl group of one, and a phenolic hydroxyl group of another di- or tri- hydroxybenzoic acid. The simplest of the depsides is lecanoric acid (69):

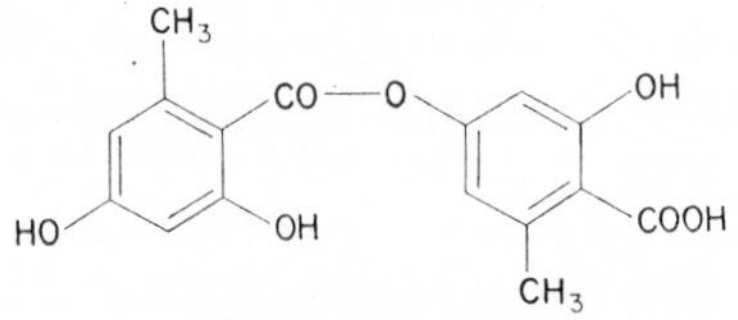

(69) Lecanoric acid

Orsellinic acid (22), into which lecanoric acid is converted by hydrolysis, could be formed by the cyclization of a precursor derived from four acetate units. The resemblance of this scheme to that proposed for the synthesis of

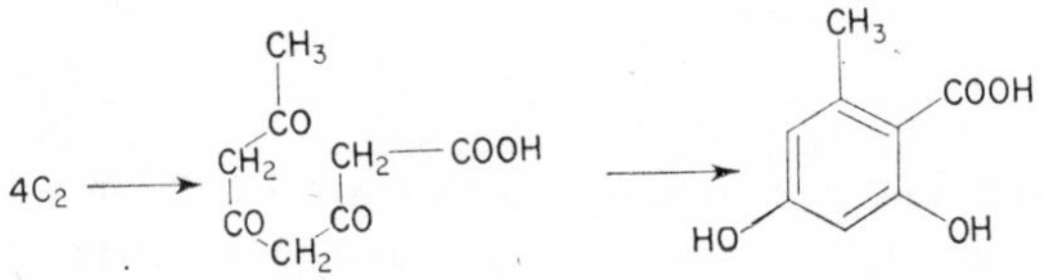

Orsellinic acid   (22)

6-methyl-salicylic acid (40) is apparent. The formation of (22) is more direct; all of the oxygen atoms, except the one lost in the ring closure, are retained.

Divaricatic acid (70) is an example of a compound formed from a $5 \times C_2$ precursor:

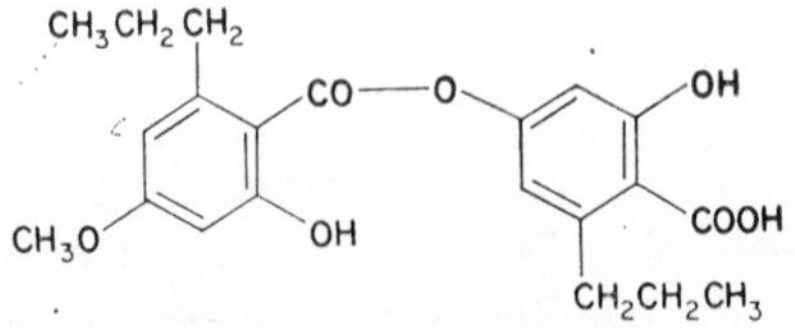

Divaricatic acid
(70)

The theory provides no basis for deciding whether the unit $CH_3CH_2CH_2CO-$ forms the starting point, or whether the carbonyl group in a hypothetical compound CH_3COCH_2-Aryl is later reduced to a $-CH_2$ group.

Anziaic (71) and perlatolic (72) acids possess structures similar to that of divaricatic acid, but with $CH_3CH_2CH_2CH_2CH_2-$ residues on the aromatic rings. Sphaeropherin contains a methyl group in one ring, a *n*-heptyl group in the other (73):

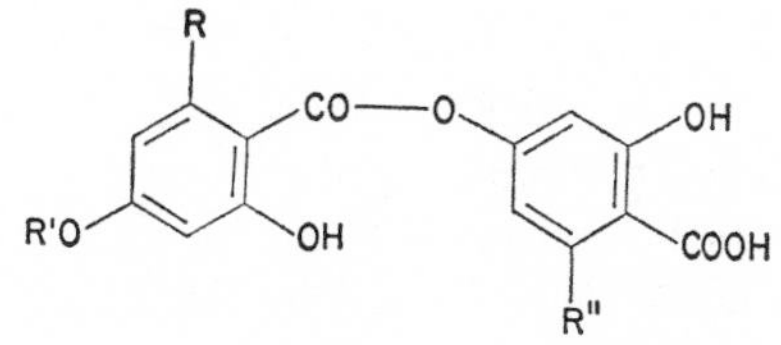

(71) R = R" = n-C_5H_{11}; R' = H; Anziaic acid
(72) R = R" = n-C_5H_{11}; R' = CH_3; Perlatolic acid
(73) R = R' = CH_3 ; R"= n-C_7H_{15}; Sphaeropherin

Numerous additional compounds with the same fundamental structure as lecanoric and similar acids, varying in the nature of the R groups (as in 71–73), are known.

That these esters are formed by combination of the separate aromatic monomers is indicated by the occurrence of triesters typified by gyrophoric acid (74):

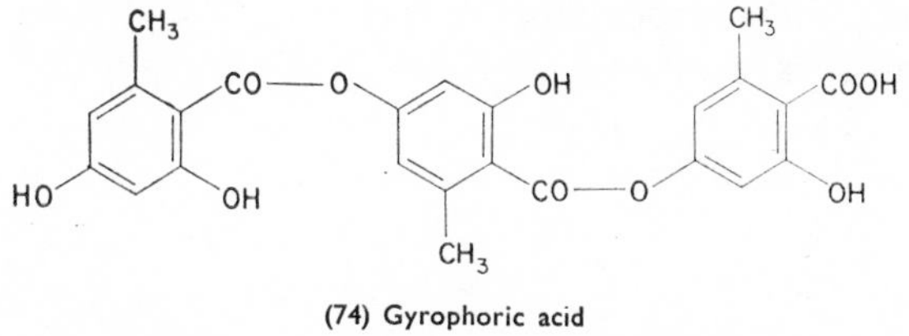

(74) Gyrophoric acid

Ring closure at a different point in the hypothetical linear precursor can account for the depsides of the type exemplified by olivetoric acid (75):

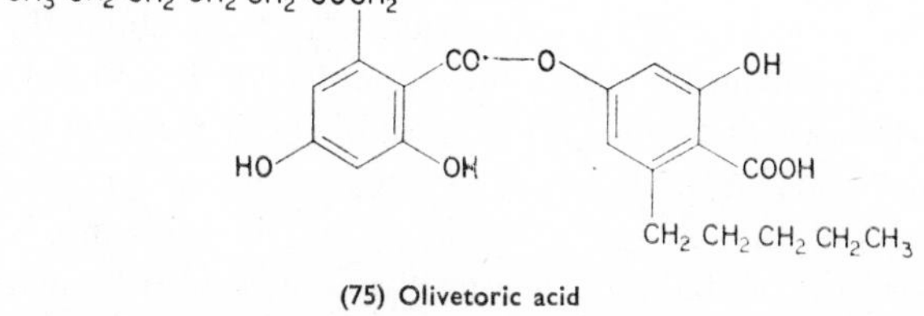

(75) Olivetoric acid

The precursor (76) can account for the formation of the left-hand ring of

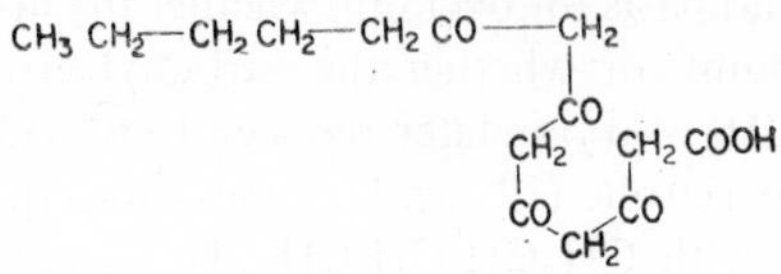

$$CH_3\ CH_2-CH_2\ CH_2-CH_2\ CO-CH_2$$

(76)

(75); the other ring would be derived by ring closure of the orsellinic acid type.

Although little has yet been done in the experimentally difficult field of lichen biosynthesis, Mosbach[46] has observed that gyrophoric acid (74) is formed in *Umbilicaria pustulata* by the usual acetate-malonate pathway. The three orsellinic acid units in (74) had identical specific activities when radioactive ethyl malonate was utilized by the lichen. Shibata and his collaborators[47] have found that the acetate-malonate pathway can account for the formation of lecanoric acid and atranorin in *Parmelia tinctorum*. In this case it was also observed that C^{14}-formate is incorporated into atranorin (and chloroatranorin), presumably to provide the —CH_3 and —CHO groups in these depsides.

Mosbach[48] and Maas, Towers and Neish[49] have shown that pulvinic and vulpinic acids are formed by way of polyporic acid, which is derived from a C_6-C_3 precursor in the shikimic acid-phenylalanine pathway of aromatic biosynthesis. Cinnamic acid was not utilized by the lichen (*Pseudocyphellaria crocata*).

A group of depsides whose structures depart from the simple $(C_2)_x$ pathway contain an additional carbon atom in each ring. The phenolic acids that are found as component parts of compounds in this group include the following (77–79):

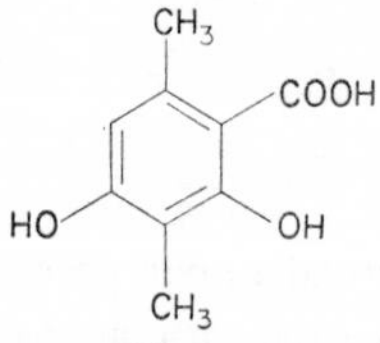

(77) 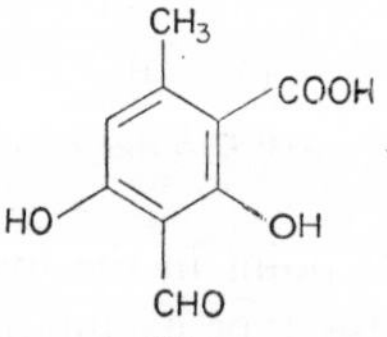   78) 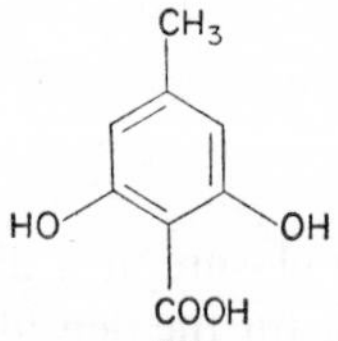   (79)

It is not possible to make a categorical statement about the origin of the "additional" carbon atom in the compounds 77–79. It is found in the position at which carbon-alkylation would be most likely to occur; and, as will be seen in the sequel, carbon-methylation is a common biosynthetic process. An alternative possibility is that a single propionic acid unit is incorporated during the process of chain-extension. Propionic acid is known to participate in biosynthetic processes in a manner very similar to that in which acetate units take part. Erythromycin (80), for example, is synthesized by *Strepto-myces erythreus* from propionic acid units, and not from acetate units with accompanying C-methylation. [50] The oxidation of —CH$_3$ to —CHO and

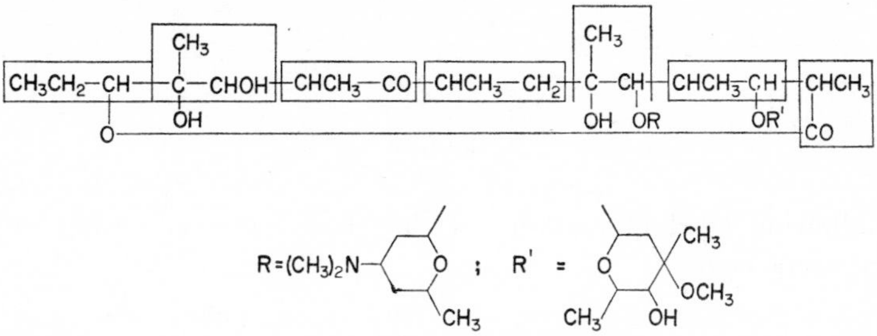

(80) Erythromycin

—COOH, as in 77–79 is unexceptional; many comparable examples are known (see, for example, patulin (40a)).

The occurrence of depsides containing the trihydroxytoluic acid residue (81) represents another departure from strict adherence to an acetate "rule".

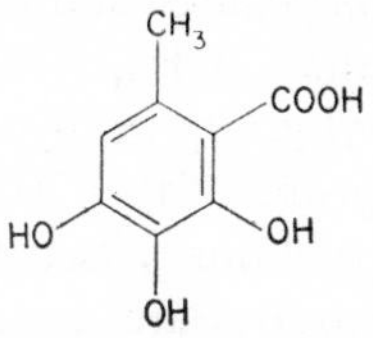

(81)

However, the introduction and removal of hydroxyl groups are processes that are not necessarily relevant to considerations of the biosynthesis of the carbon skeleton. The relationship between (79) and (81) is reminiscent of that be-tween anacardic acid (60) and urushiol (59).

In this connection, evidence concerning the origin of the "extra" carbon atoms (in —CH$_3$, —CHO and —COOH) in compounds (77–79) may be drawn from studies on a product of mold metabolism, mycophenolic acid (82):

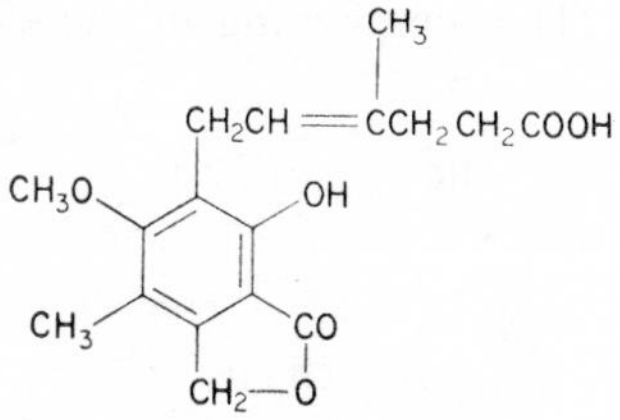

(82) Mycophenolic acid

Mycophenolic acid may be regarded as being a nuclear dialkylation product (see 83) of an acetate-derived derivative of orsellinic acid (or its precursor).

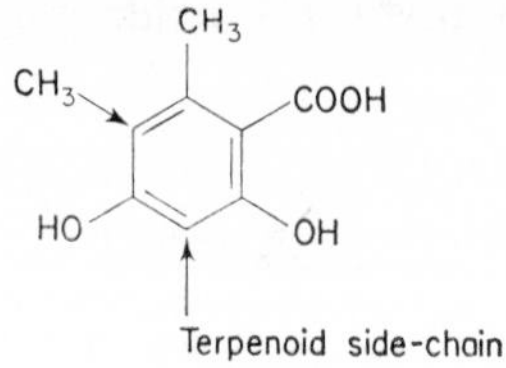

$$CH_3$$

CH_3 / COOH

HO / OH

Terpenoid side-chain

(83)

The following labeling pattern (84) has been observed, using carboxyl-labeled acetic acid:[51]

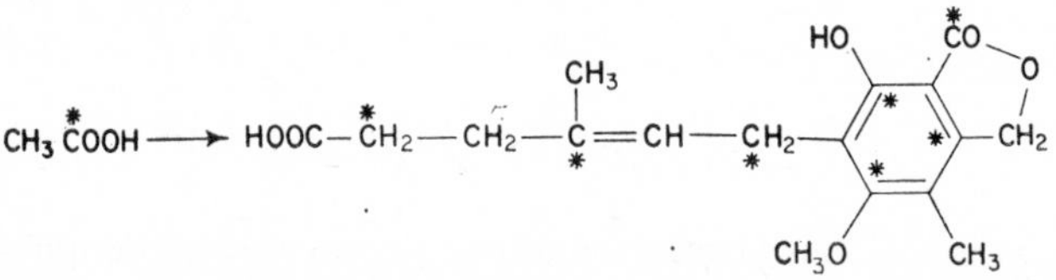

$$CH_3 \overset{*}{C}OOH \longrightarrow HOOC-\overset{*}{C}H_2-CH_2-\underset{*}{C}=CH-CH_2-\cdots$$

(84)

The labeling in the isoprenoid side-chain does not concern us here (other experiments[51] establish its origin as from mevalonic acid), but the fact that it was found to represent an *introduced* substituent is of importance, since it corresponds in position to the —CH₃, —CHO and —COOH groups in (77–79). The additional methyl group in mycophenolic acid is derived from methionine (as is the methyl group of the CH₃O—),[52] and thus is the result of carbon-alkylation by a methyl donor (see p. 781).

The conclusion that the depsides are acetate-derived, and that orsellinic acid and such related dihydroxy-benzoic acids as those found in (70) and (75) are the primary substances which may undergo further elaboration, seems to be well supported by both direct labeling studies and by the structural correlations that exist with these groups of compounds.

Alternative schemes have, however, been proposed. Aghoramurthy and Seshadri[53] have put forward a theory of biosynthesis of compounds of these types in which the recognition of a C_8 unit as the fundamental unit of the depsides and depsidones forms the basis of the proposal. The derivation of orsellinic acid by the condensation of a hexose and a biose is formulated in the following way (85). The lengthening of the side chain by further con-

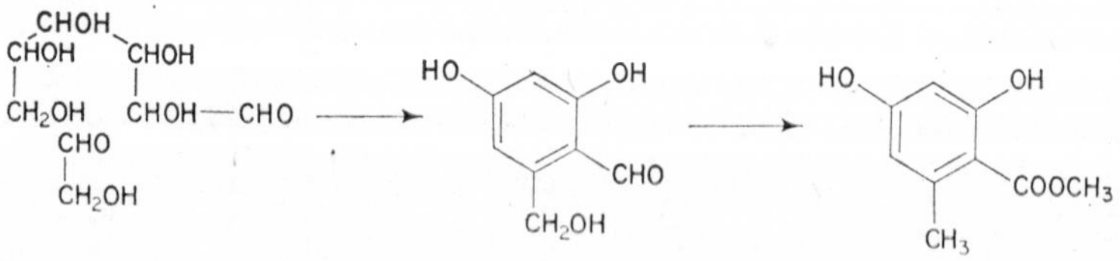

(85)   (and other compounds)

densations of the methyl group of orsellinic acid (or a derivative, such as an ester) with additional biose residues accounts for the production of the *n*-alkyl derivatives described earlier.

The frequent occurrence of erythritol in lichens both as the free sugar and as in erythrin, the erythritol ester of lecanoric acid, has led Robinson [30] and Asahina and Shibata [54] to suggest that two four-carbon units combine (86) to form the fundamental orsellinic acid (22):

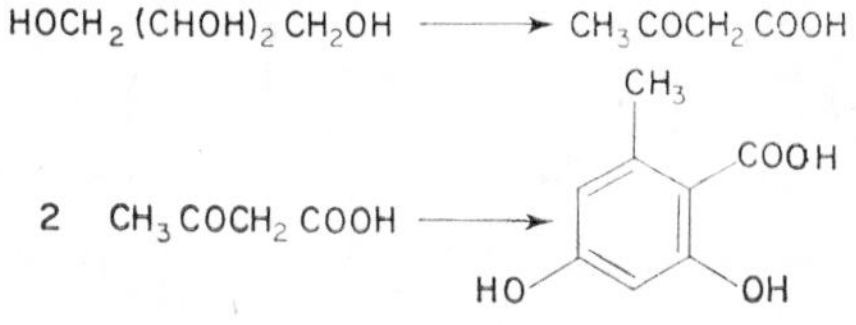

It is apparent that these older theories bear a similarity to the acetate hypothesis, and it is worthy of note that they were devised at a time when the recognition of the role of two-carbon units in biosynthesis was gaining widespread acceptance. They are still worth noting, however, because, despite the satisfactory manner in which the acetate hypothesis can be used to account for the synthesis of these lichen acids, its very facility can tend to quiet critical inquiry. Until further experimental demonstration of the ways in which acetate units are utilized in the formation of these complex substances, alternatives or modifications of the theory must be held as worthy of consideration.

Anthraquinones

Anthraquinones (and some of the related anthrones) are common metabolic products of higher plants, lichens, and microorganisms. The perfect adherence of certain of these compounds to the acetate hypothesis is striking indeed. For example, endocrocin (87, R = COOH), a component of the lichen *Nephromopsis endocrocea*, can be related directly to the poly-β-ketomethylene acid (88):

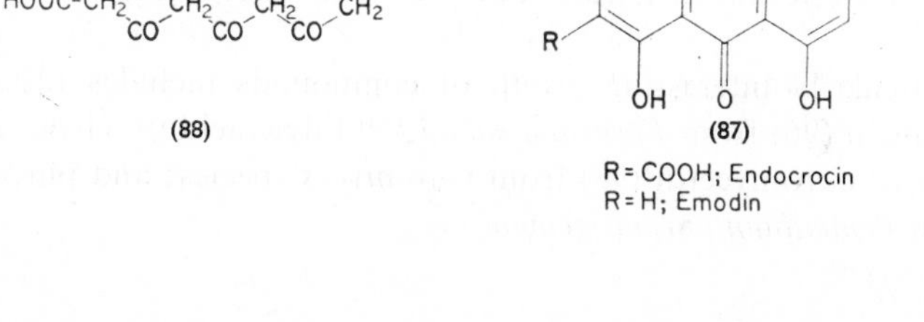

2C

Emodin (87, R = H), an anthraquinone of a higher plant, lacks only the carboxyl residue of endocrocin, but bears the same pattern of oxidation.

Alteration by oxidation (at some unknown stage in the overall synthesis) of the side-chain residue, and removal of nuclear hydroxyl groups (perhaps before cyclization), are processes that can be invoked to account for the structures of such anthraquinones as aloe-emodin (89) and rhein (90):

89) Aloe-emodin   (90) Rhein

In addition to these "regular" anthraquinones, there are a number whose derivation from a precursor such as (88) involves stages that cannot be so simply related to the acetate hypothesis. Alizarin (91), rubiadin (92) and morindadiol (93) are examples.

(91) Alizarin   (92) Rubiadin   (93) Morindadiol

Finally, the genesis of solorinic acid (94) from a precursor (95) represents an obvious extension of the synthetic scheme:

(95)   (94) Solorinic acid

Naphthoquinones

Flaviolin, sorigenin and the naphthalene derivatives from *Eleutherine* species have been dealt with earlier. Besides these, numerous naphthalene derivatives are found in nature, many of them the products of mold metabolism.

A particularly interesting group of compounds includes fusarubin (95) and javanicin (96) from *Fusarium solani*;[40] fulvic acid (97) from *Penicillium griseofulvin*; citromycetin (98) from *Citromyces* species; and purpurogenone (99) from *Penicillium purpurogenum*.

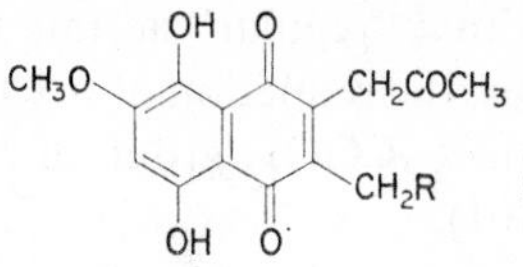

(95) R = OH Fusarubin
(96) R = H   Javanicin

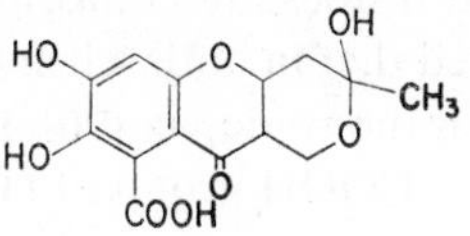

(97) Fulvic acid

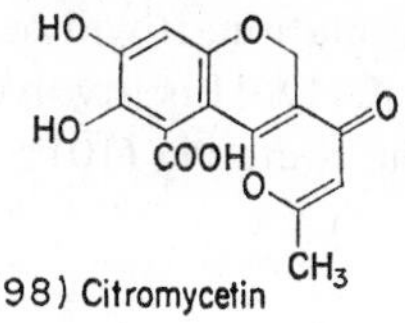

(98) Citromycetin

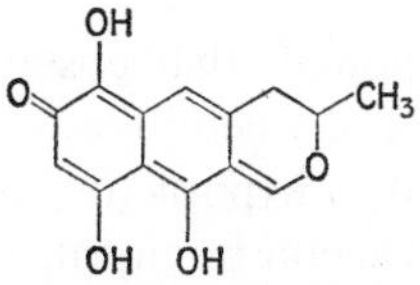

(99) Purpurogenone

The derivation of fusarubin and javanicin by the acetate pathway is strongly suggested by the presence of the acetonyl residue. If the following pathway is followed (100) the —CH_3 (—CH_2OH) group would be the result of reduction of the terminal —COOH group:

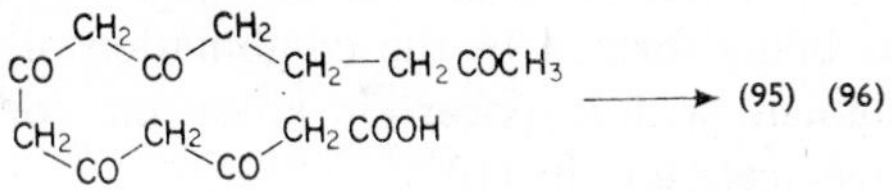

(100)

It has been suggested [55, 56] that the relationship of javanicin and fusarubin to the compounds (97) and (98) is to be found in the hypothetical structure (101):

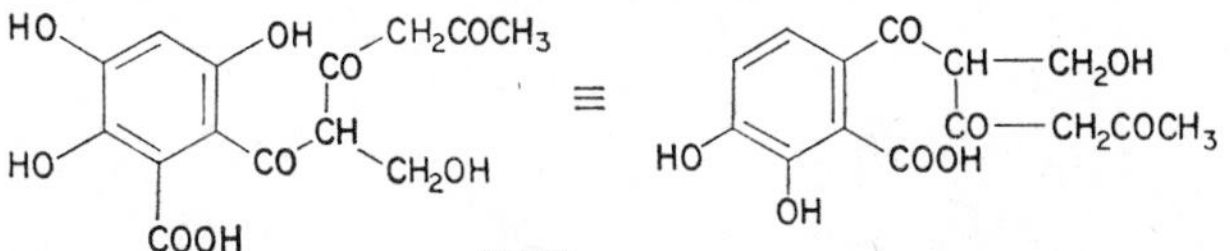

(101)

The relationship of (101) to (95) and (96) could be through the cleavage of one aromatic ring; or, as Whalley has suggested, (101) could be the primordial precursor from which (95) and (96), as well as (97), (98) and (99) are

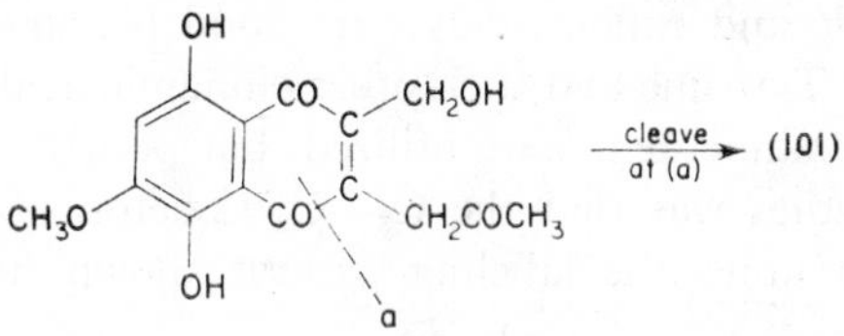

(96)

formed despite the fact that it does not conform to a "regular" acetate route of formation. It will be noted that in both schemes, the reduction of —COOH to —CH$_2$OH is involved: in the route via (96), the —COOH group of (100); in the route via (101), the —COOH group of (101).

Compounds Derived from 1-Phenylpropane Precursors
Flavonoid Compounds

The biosynthesis of compounds that possess the structural unit (102) has been discussed earlier (p. 747), where it was remarked that numerous compound classes can be related to hypothetical precursors derived by extension of the C$_6$—C$_3$ unit by two-carbon fragments.

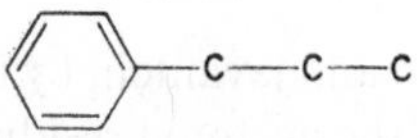

(102)

The largest and most varied class of substances of this kind is that of the flavonoid compounds. These are described as C$_6$—C$_3$—C$_6$ compounds, and may be regarded as being formed by the combination of the shikimic acid-derived C$_6$—C$_3$ fragment with a six-carbon atom unit formed by the linear combination of three acetate units (103):

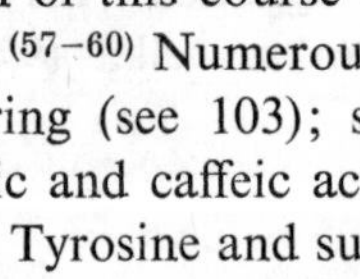

(103)

The substantiation of this course of synthesis has been accomplished by a number of studies. [57-60] Numerous phenylpropanoid precursors serve as the source of the B-ring (see 103); shikimic acid, phenylalanine, p-hydroxycinnamic, cinnamic and caffeic acids were good precursors of quercetin in buckwheat plants. Tyrosine and such other cinnamic acids as sinapic, ferulic and m-methoxycinnamic acid were utilized, but poorly. The most revealing result of these studies was that the C$_6$—C$_3$ skeleton of the precursor was incorporated as a unit; the labeling pattern shown in (104) was established: [57, 59]

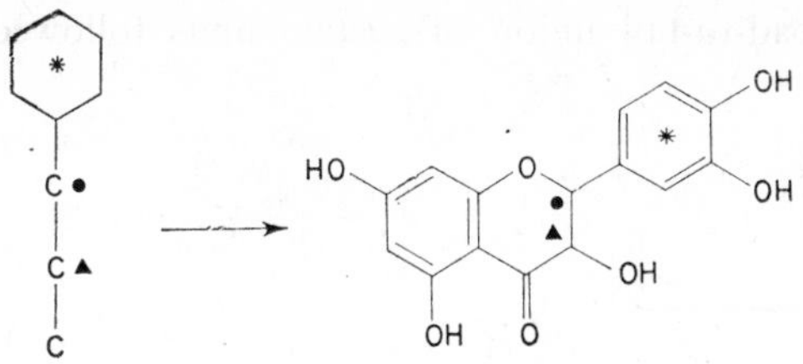

(104)

When uniformly-labeled phenylalanine was fed to buckwheat plants, seven-ninths of the activity of the precursor was recovered in the veratric acid formed by methylation and cleavage of the quercetin; two-ninths was found in the acetophenone derivative formed along with veratric acid (105): [57]

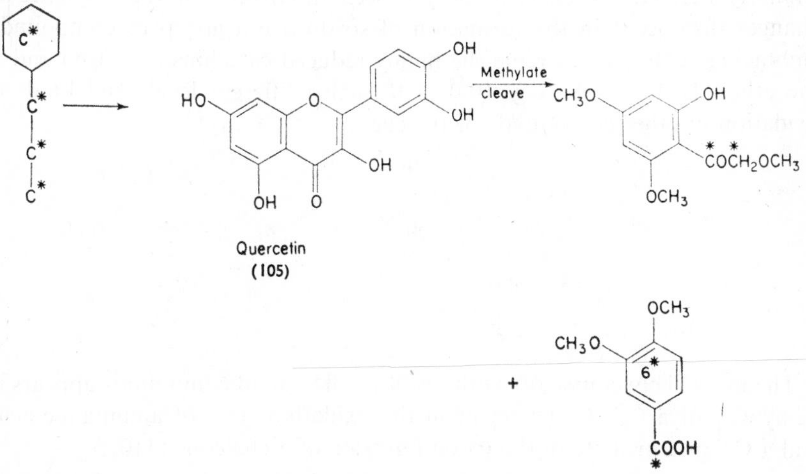

Quercetin
(105)

Surprisingly, Grisebach observed that coniferin-3-C^{14} did not give radio-active cyanidin in red cabbage seedlings, although a flavone present in the plants was radioactive.

Experiments with labeled sodium acetate showed that this was incorporated exclusively (except for slight randomization) into the A-ring of the flavone (106)

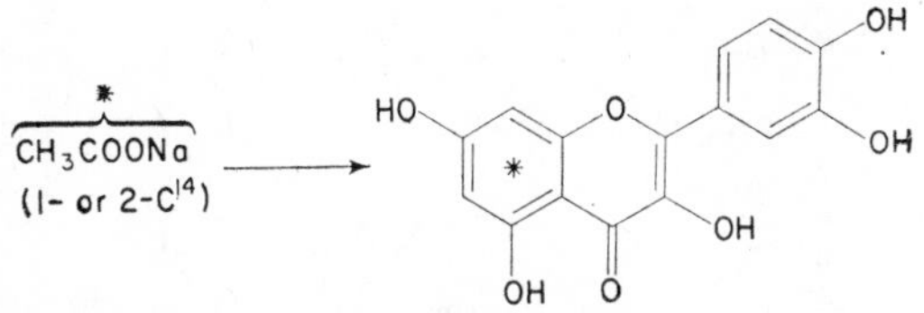

(106)

When cyanidin is produced by red cabbage seedlings fed with labeled sodium acetate, the A-ring labeling is consistent with the view that this ring is formed by head-to-tail union of acetate units followed by cyclization (107): [60]

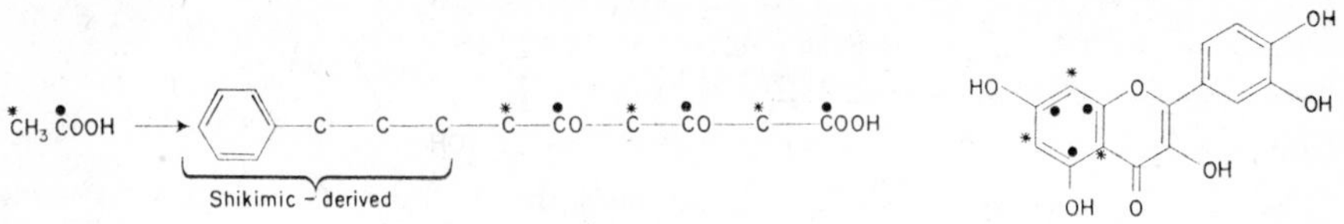

(107)

While the biogenesis of the numerous flavonoid compounds related to the flavones, but differing only in the state of oxidation of the C_3 part of the molecule and in the number of hydroxyl groups on the aromatic rings, has not been established with equally definitive experiments, there can be little doubt that, so far as the source of the carbon skeletons is concerned, they are similarly derived. What has not yet been discovered in the sequence of changes that occur in the formation of so diverse a group of compounds, embracing at the one extreme the highly reduced catechins (e.g. 108) and at the other the flavonols (e.g. 109), with many different levels and kinds of oxidation in other compounds of the class.

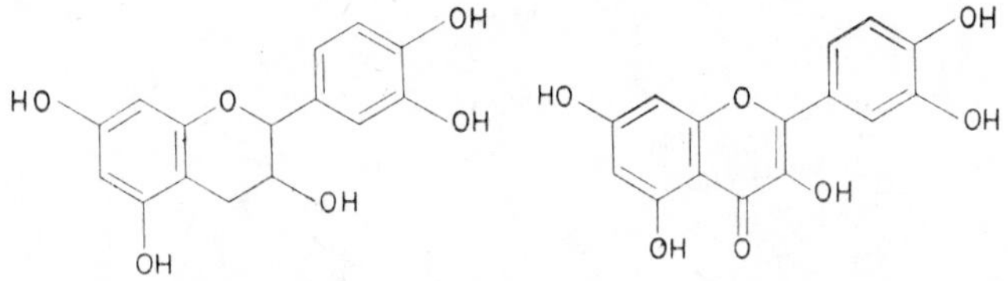

(108)   (109)

The most likely course of synthesis of the flavonoid compounds appears to be by way of a C_6—C_3 fragment in the oxidation state of a cinnamic acid, and a C_{15} intermediate in the oxidation state of a chalcone (110):†

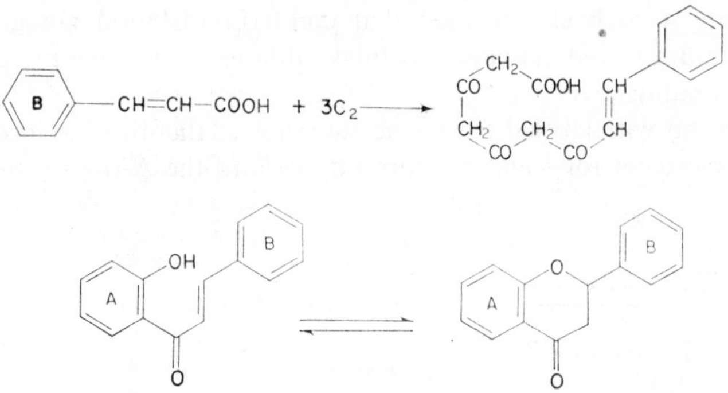

(110)

† Only the *o*-hydroxyl group of the A-ring is shown in the final product of sequence (110) because it is only this position that is invariably hydroxylated. Other hydroxylation patterns are discussed further on.

Information as to the order in which hydroxyl groups are introduced or removed from rings A and B is still lacking, and only speculation can be offered to define the stages in the overall synthesis at which such changes occur. Indeed, the evidence from many observations fails to provide a clear and compelling hypothesis. It might be argued that since baicalein (111) and wagonin (112) occur in the same plant, the common open-chain precursor (113) precedes them in the synthetic order:

(111) Baicalein   (a)   (b)   (112) Wagonin

(113)

On the other hand, the co-occurrence in a single plant of quercimeritrin (114) and gossypitrin (115) suggests that hydroxylation occurs at a stage after ring formation has been completed. This suggestion depends upon the conclusion that glycosylation is a late development in flavone biosynthesis, a conclusion supported by the co-occurrence in single plants of numerous glycosides of a given aglycon. [61]

(114)
Quercimeritrin   R = glucosyl   (115)
Gossypitrin

Genetic studies have given strong support to the view that the flavonoid compounds of various levels of oxidation derive from a common precursor. [63] Single genetic factors ("genes") are known to control whether 4'- or 3',4'-hydroxylation of the B-ring occurs, the presence of absence of methoxyl groups, the position and degree of glycosylation. There is no doubt that the processes by which the simple precursors (ultimately, shikimic acid and acetate units) are converted into the many flavones, anthocyanins, aurones, etc., that are found in plants are very complex, and represent competing and interacting pathways of oxidation and reduction. The concept of the central role assigned to chalcones in flavonoid biosynthesis embraces dihydrochalcones as well, as seen by the demonstration that apple leaves contain a reductase capable of converting 2',4',6',4-tetrahydroxychalcone-2'-glycoside into phloridzin. [62]

The view that the precursor at the C_6—C_3—C_6 level is indeed represented best by (110), that is, by the chalcone, finds support from a number of observations, none, however, of a compelling nature. Studies on the chemical genetics of pigmentation in *Antirrhinum* flowers[63] have disclosed the suggestive fact that anthocyanin formation, governed by a specific dominant gene (P), is always accompanied by flavonol formation; in acyanic flowers flavones, but not flavonols, are present. Moreover, the production of the aurone, aureusidin (as 116) takes place in all non-albino flowers, but in increased amount in the absence of the dominant gene Y. Finally, a gene M (dominant) produces 3',4'-dihydroxy flavones and anthocyanin; and in the absence of the dominant gene N, cinnamic acids, but no flavonoid compounds, are produced. Flavanones are also present in many genotypes.

While any scheme that attempts to use these observations for the construction of a detailed scheme of the total path of pigment biosynthesis would be a very tenuous one, certain possibilities suggest themselves. The co-occurrence of flavonol and anthocyanin may mean that a step in pigment synthesis, governed by factor P, is the production of the flavanonol (117) from a primordial chalcone:

(116) Aurone

It is worthy of comment that the flavanonol (117) is at the oxidation level of the anthocyanidin; the transformation can be represented (formally only) as follows:†

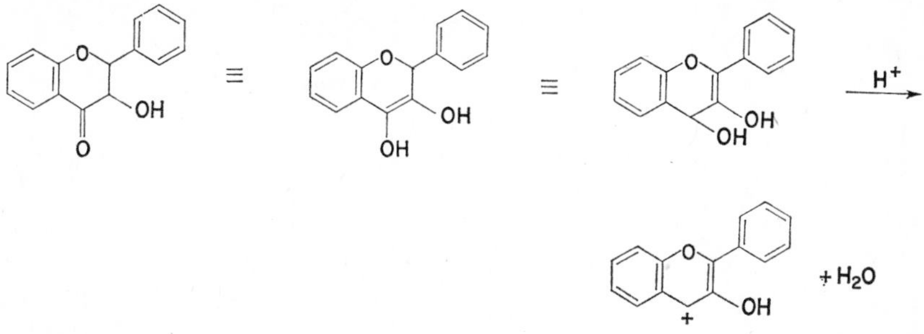

The transformation of chalcones into aurones by hydrogen peroxide oxidation, presumably by way of the epoxy intermediates, is a well-known transformation,[71] although in the laboratory it is governed by rather strict structural requirements.

In the following section another possible role of a chalcone epoxide or flavanonol in a different biosynthetic sequence will be considered.

Isoflavones

The biogenesis of isoflavones has been found[64] to proceed by way of a C_6—C_3—C_6 intermediate and involves at some point in the sequence a rearrangement of the aryl B-ring to the adjacent carbon atom (117a):‡

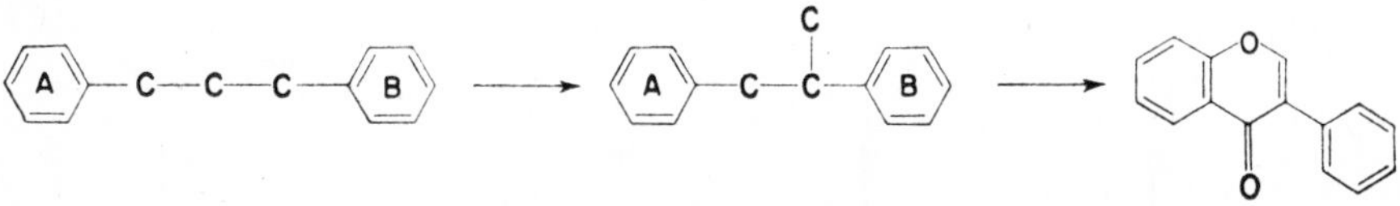

(117a)

The sequence (117a) is shown in outline only. It was demonstrated for the case of formononetin (in clover)[64] and for biochanin-A in *Cicer arietinum* (see refs. 59, 60 and footnote). It is not known with certainty at which point in the synthetic process the rearrangement occurs. It has been suggested that the chalcone oxide (117b) is the intermediate, and rearranges according to recognized mechanisms put forward to explain acid-catalyzed rearrangements of α,β-oxidoketones.[67]

---

† Again the hydroxyl groups normally present in the natural compounds are not shown that attention may be confined to the particular processes under discussion.

‡ The report[65, 66] that a different course is followed was withdrawn after repetition of the experiments confirmed the original observation of Grisebach.[64]

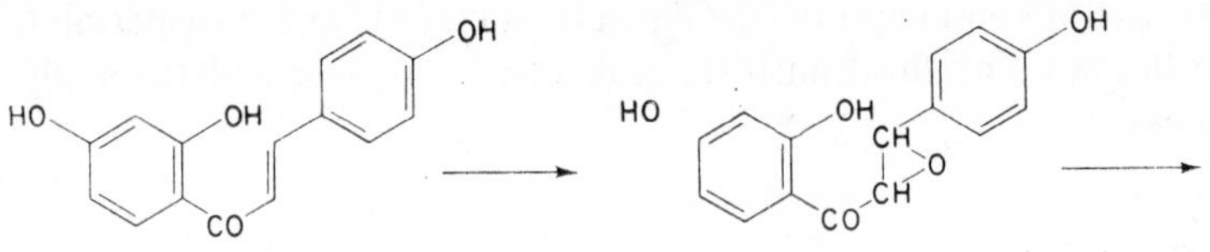

(117b)

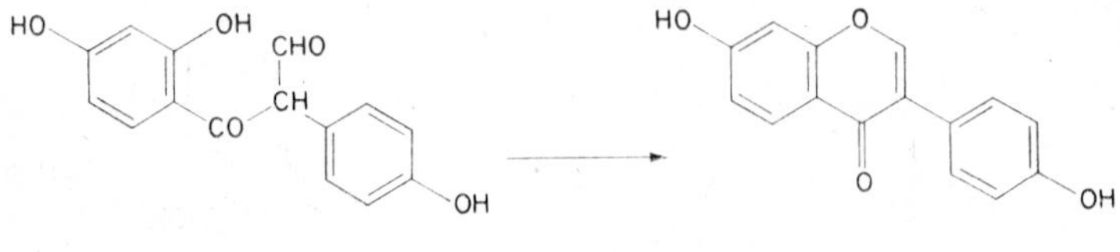

The mechanistic details of the rearrangement of the aryl group from position 2 to 3 are still a matter for conjecture. That the oxide (e.g. 117b) itself is not an obligatory intermediate is shown by the conversion of 3,4',7-trihydroxyflavanone (garbanzol)[68] into formononetin in *Cicer arietinum* seedlings.[69] It should be noted, however, that the interconversion 2'-hydroxychalcone epoxide ⇌ 3-hydroxyflavanone is a clear mechanistic possibility, and so the question of the exact nature of the immediate natural progenitor of the isoflavone skeleton remains unsettled.

The possible intervention of chalcone epoxides in flavonoid interconversions *in vivo* is rendered plausible by the results of many studies on the chemistry of compounds of this kind. The following reactions (in which only the prototype skeleton is used for illustration) show some of the alterations that have been observed (118):

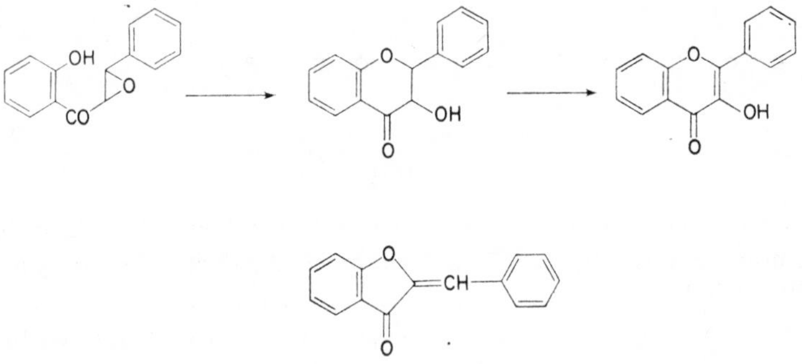

(118)

No case of rearrangement of a chalcone epoxide of the kind found in nature to an isoflavone has been observed, however.

The occurrence in nature of angolensin (119)[70] suggests that the postulated rearrangement can occur before closure of the heterocyclic ring:

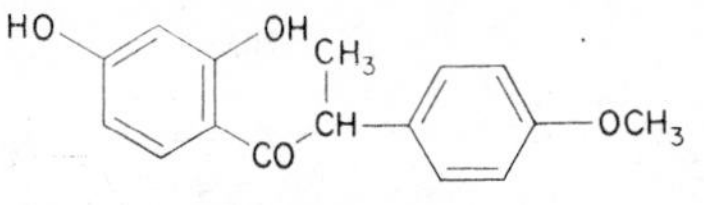

(119) Angolensin

Stilbenes and Dihydroisocoumarins

The naturally occurring stilbene derivatives form a group of compounds of which certain structural features suggest their biogenetic origins. Hydrangenol, a dihydroisocoumarin, may be regarded as the isomer, by a simple ring closure, of a stilbene-carboxylic acid, and, further, appears to be derived from a cyclization of a C_6—C_3—C_6 precursor (120):

(120)

(121) Hydrangenol

Early experiments[72] supported this view, but were not conclusive. An alternative theory of stilbene and dihydroisocoumarin biosynthesis, put forward by Seshadri,[73] suggests that the building units of hydrangenol are an orsellinic acid-derived fragment (122) and the C_8 fragment (123) formed by the degradation of a C_6—C_3 precursor (phenylalanine, etc.):

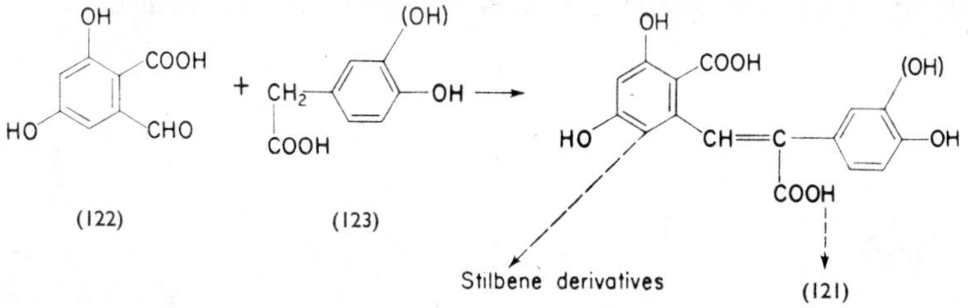

(122)

(123)

Stilbene derivatives

(121)

Since (122) would be derived from four acetate units (see 22), the labeling of the hydrangenol skeleton should distinguish clearly between these alternative paths of synthesis. For example, 2-C^{14}-labeled phenylalanine would give unlabeled hydrangenol according to the scheme $122 \rightarrow 123 \rightarrow 121$, but 4-labeled hydrangenol by the route $120 \rightarrow 121$. Similar comments would apply to the natural stilbenes, the structures of several examples of which—pinosylvin (124), resveratrol (125), hydroxyresveratrol (24), (126) and (127)—are shown:†

† A number of other natural stilbenes are methyl ethers of these. Compounds (126) and (127) are named systematically.

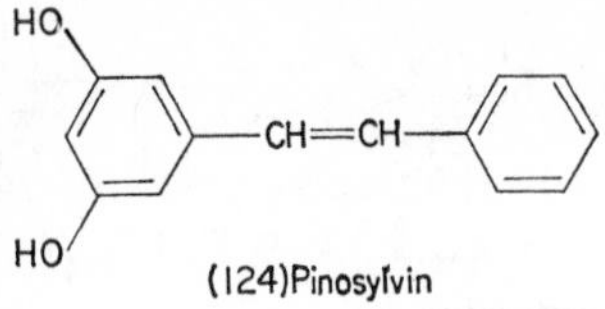

(124)Pinosylvin

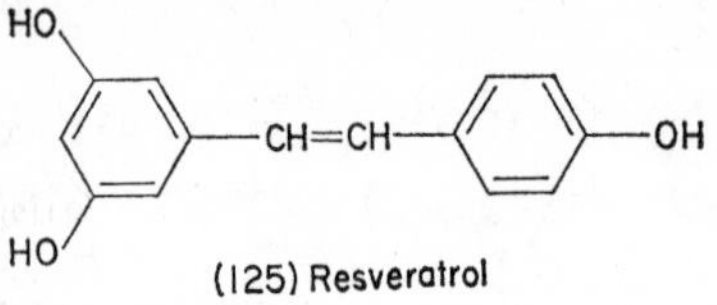

(125) Resveratrol

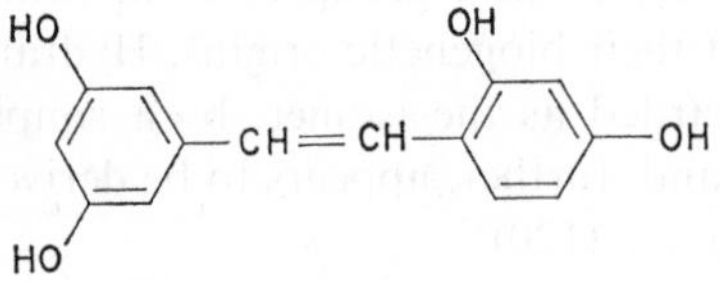

(24) Hydroxyresveratrol

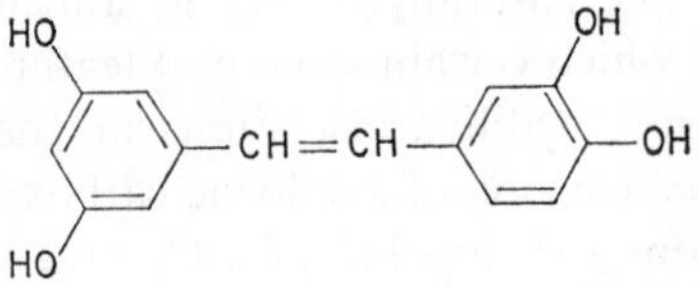

(126)

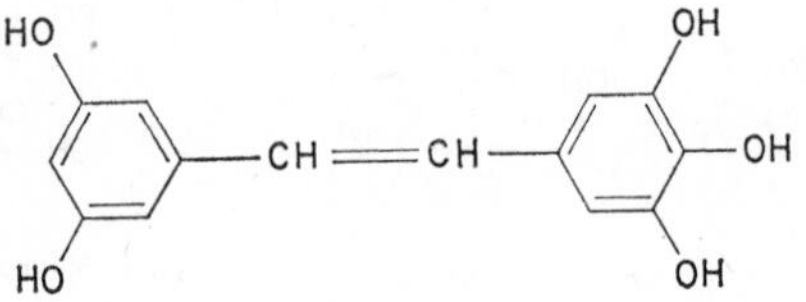

(127)

Recent studies [74, 75] have confirmed that hydrangenol and the stilbenes are formed from a shikimic acid-acetate-derived C_6—C_3—C_6 precursor. The following scheme represents the manner in which hydrangenol and (probably by decarboxylation of (128)), the stilbenes are formed:

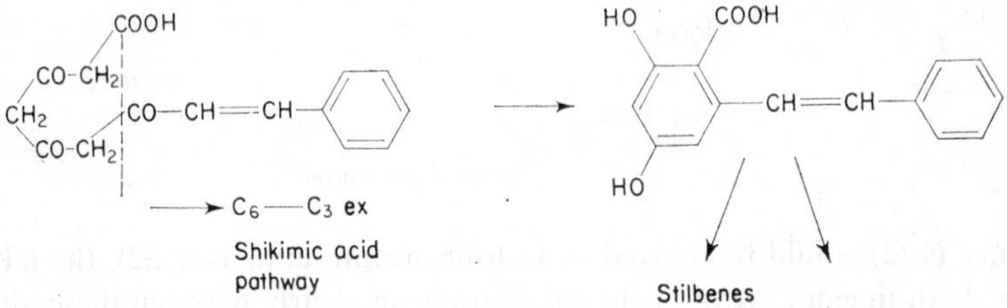

$\longrightarrow C_6$—C_3 ex

Shikimic acid pathway

(128)

Stilbenes

(121)

Again it should be pointed out that the inclusion or exclusion of hydroxyl groups from these formulas entails no suggestion as to the point at which hydroxylation (or reduction) takes place in the synthesis of the end product.

Much remains to be done in working out the many final details of the biosynthesis of the isocoumarins and stilbenes, and very little experimental work involving the feeding of labeled compounds to plants has yet been done.

Carbon Alkylation

Prominent among the processes carried out in the course of biosynthesis in many organisms is the introduction, by the formation of carbon-carbon linkages, of substituents into one or another of the fundamental classes of compounds that have already been discussed. The two kinds of substituents most often encountered are (a) the methyl group and (b) alkyl groups of iso-prenoid origin. In some cases the latter may undergo subsequent degradation to smaller fragments. Examples of these will be given in the discussion. It must be noted, however, that few experiments have been performed to provide positive evidence of the biological source of such "extra" carbon atoms. It is nevertheless very probable that living organisms possess the synthetic mechanisms for the carbon-alkylation of carbon atoms of at least two kinds: those alpha to, or flanked by, carbonyl groups, and those in phenolic rings, especially when in the 2-position to 1,3-di-hydroxyl groups. It is evident that in many cases these two situations are mechanistically equivalent.

Numerous C-methylated chromones are known in nature. [76] An interesting group of compounds is that found in *Eugenia caryophyllata*; these are eugenin (129), eugenitin (130), isoeugenitin (131), and isoeugenitol (132). There also exists in nature, but in another plant (*Backhousia angustifolia* Benth.), the related compound angustifolionol (133).

(129) Eugenin   (130) Eugenitin   131) Isoeugenitin

(132) Isoeugenitol   (133) Angustifolionol

The origin of these compounds by the carbon-methylation of an acetate-derived parent substance seems too probable to be doubted. Whether the introduction of the C-methyl group takes place after the chromone system (as in 129) has been formed, or at the earlier stage of the hypothetical poly-ketomethylene precursor, or at the state just prior to the closure of the hetero-cyclic ring, cannot be stated with assurance. The co-occurrence of (130) and

(131) finds a ready explanation in the assumption that the precursor (134) undergoes ring closure in two ways:[77]

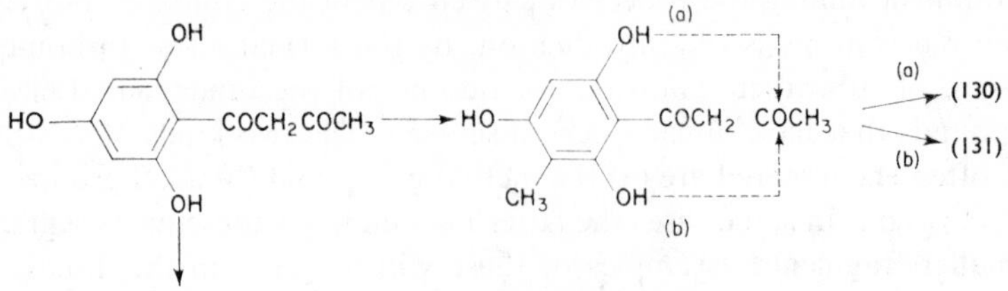

(129)   (134)

Carbon methylation in 2-arylchromones (flavones) is also quite common in nature. Pinoquercetin (135) and pinomyricetin (136) occur in a species of

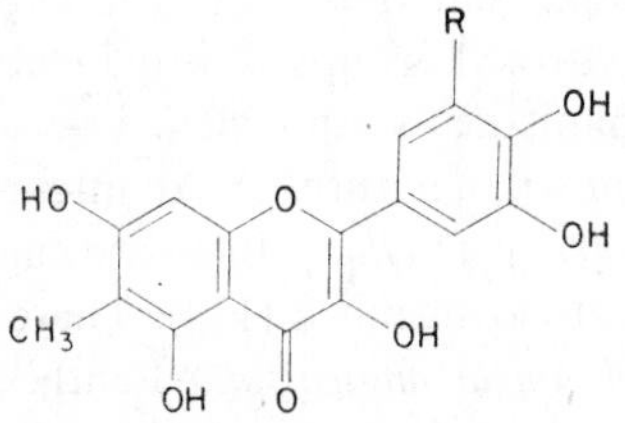

(135) R=H   Pinoquercetin
(136) R=OH Pinomyricetin

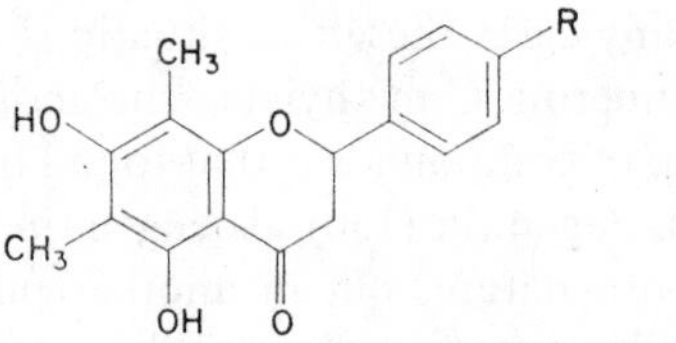

(137) R=OCH₃ Matteucinol
(138) R=H Demethoxy matteucinol

Pinus, while the C-methylated flavanones matteucinol (137) and demethoxy-matteucinol (138) are components of *Matteucia orientalis.* A number of C-methylated flavones and dihydroflavonols occur in various *Pinus* species, and further examples are given in the review cited.[76]

An interesting example of C-methylation in a C_6—C_3—C_6 compound is found in ceroptene (139), a constituent of a fern.[78] In this compound alkylation of the phloroglucinol ring has proceeded to the stage of dimethylation and

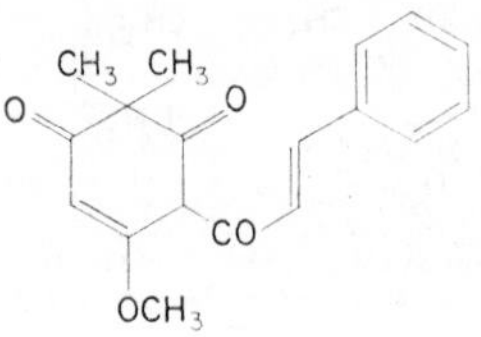

(139) Ceroptene

preservation of the triketo structure of the A-ring. It is known that C-dimethylation of phloroglucinol derivatives can occur under treatment with methyl iodide and alkali; and the C-dialkylation of 1,3-diketones is a well-known reaction. Thus, it is still open to future investigation to determine at which state the biological alkylation takes place.

The occurrence of C-methylated and C-dimethylated phloroacetophenones is common in nature. Angustione (140) and dehydroangustione (141) occur in the same plant along with angustifolionol (133).

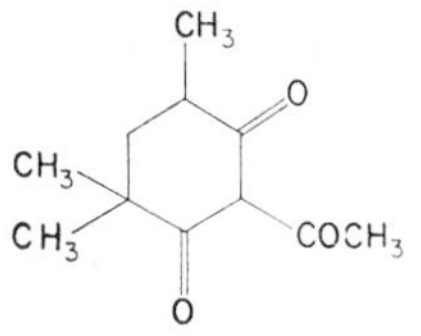

(140) Angustione 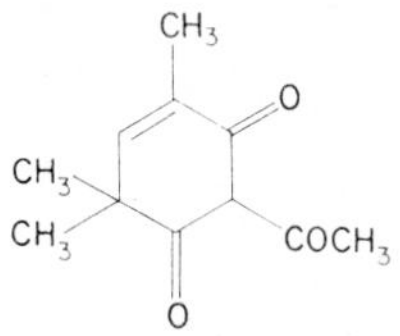   (141) Dehydroangustione

Essential oils of *Leptospermum* species contain leptospermone (142); and male fern contains albaspidin (143) and flavaspidic acid (144):

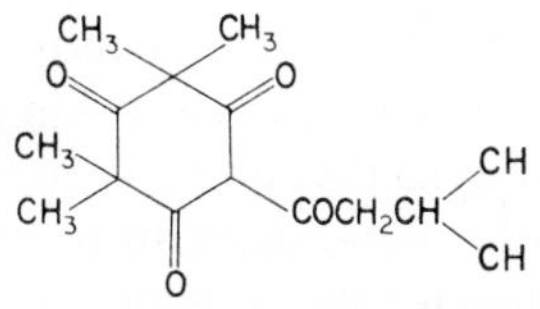

(142) Leptospermone

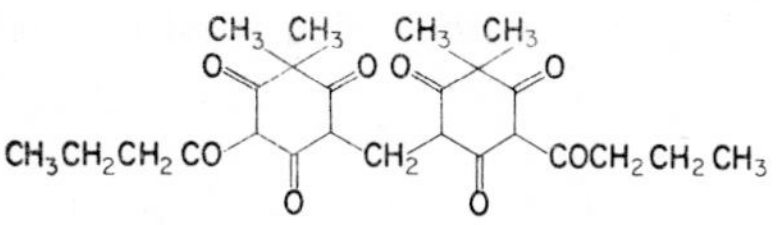

(143) Albaspidin

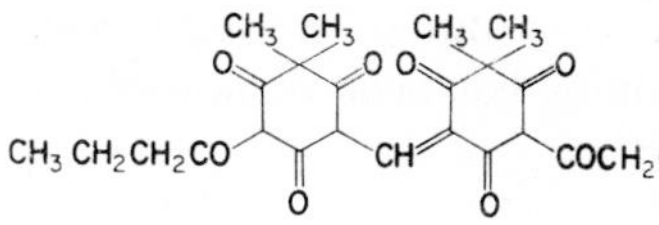

(144) Flavaspidic acid

Usnic acid (145) is formed by the oxidative coupling of two molecules of C-methylphloroacetophenone:

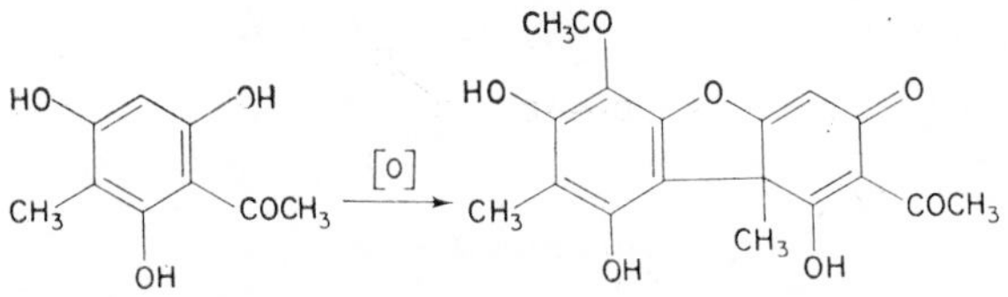

(145) Usnic acid

The source of both O-methyl and C-methyl groups is probably the same as that of the N-methyl groups so common in plant alkaloids, namely, the methyl-transfer systems that involve methionine and the compounds associated with it. The active methylating agent, at least in animal organisms, is S-adenosylmethionine (146):

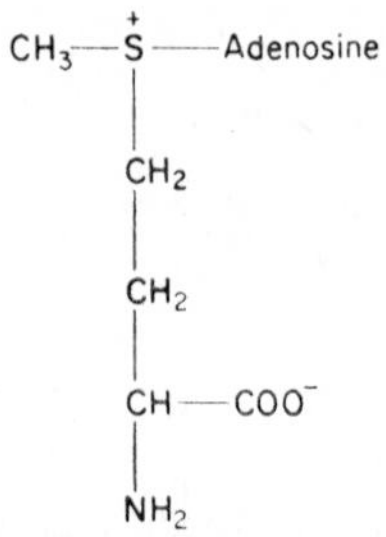

$$CH_3 \!-\! \overset{+}{S} \!-\!\!-\! Adenosine$$

$$CH_2$$

$$CH_2$$

$$CH \!-\! COO^-$$

$$NH_2$$

(146) S-Adenosylmethionine

The attack of an anionic carbon, oxygen or nitrogen atom upon the methyl group brings about its attachment to the attacking atom.

The ultimate genesis of the methyl groups can take place by a number of routes, in which, among other substances, formate can serve as a precursor. Biogenetic studies have shown that formate can often serve to introduce single methyl groups; the best examples of this are found in the field of alkaloid biosynthesis, which is discussed in Chapter 17. The incorporation of a C-methyl group of mycophenolic acid (82) by feeding of methyl-labeled methionine has been demonstrated. [52]

Isoprenoid Substituents [79]

The widespread occurrence in plants and other organisms (e.g., see 84) of compounds that contain, as both C— and O— linked substituents, the typical isoprenoid residue (147) strongly suggests that there exists in many living

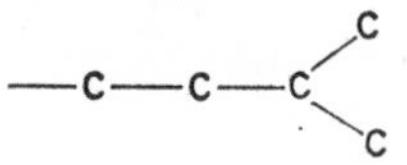

$$-C \!-\! C \!-\! C \!\!\Big\langle\!\!\begin{array}{c} C \\ C \end{array}$$

(147) Isoprenoid residue

organisms a source of this (and higher isoprenoid) grouping in a biological form that permits its introduction by alkylation or acylation.

The ultimate source of these isoprenoid units is mevalonic acid (17) (via acetate), which eventually gives rise to the active synthetic fragment,

isopentenyl-pyrophosphate (148). The elaboration of this fragment into terpenes and polyterpenes is beyond the scope of the present discussion. However, the availability of (148) or its isomeric 3-methyl-2-butenyl fragment, as

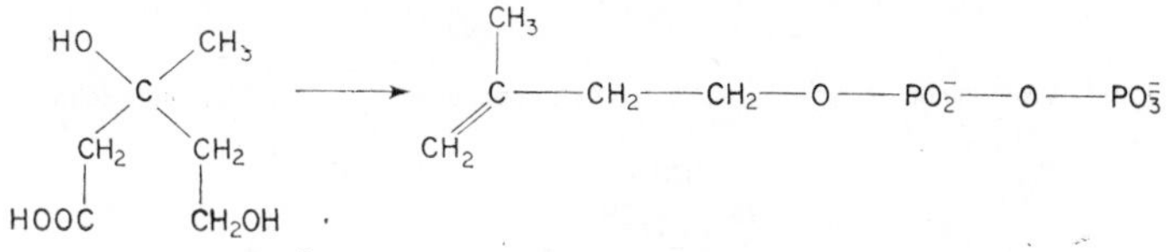

(17) Mevalonic acid   (148) Isopentenyl-pyrophosphate

an alkylating agent provides a ready solution to the question of the biosynthesis of such compounds as, for example, suberosin (149), peucenin (150)
and brayleyanin (151):

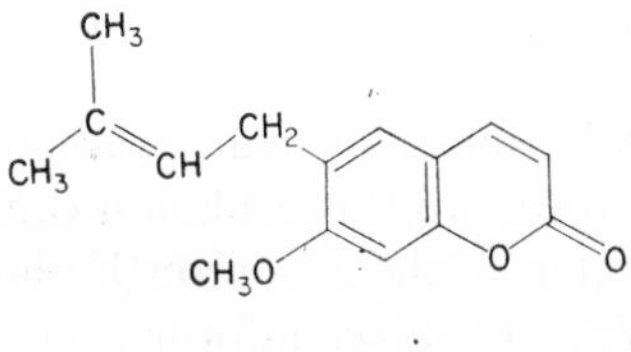

(149) Suberosin 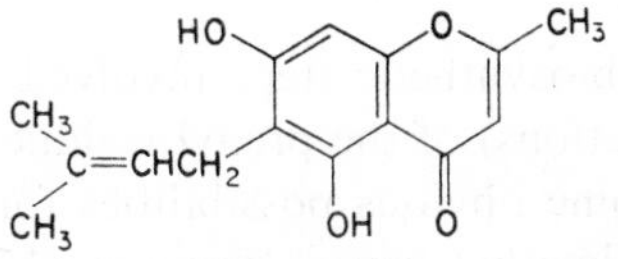   (150) Peucenin

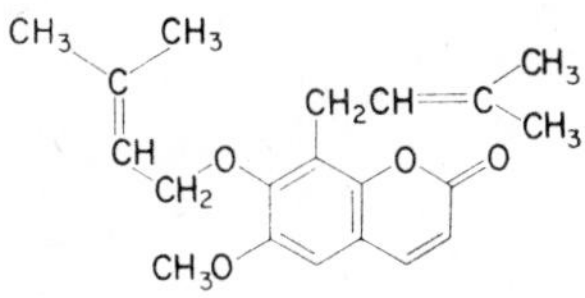

(151) Brayleyanin

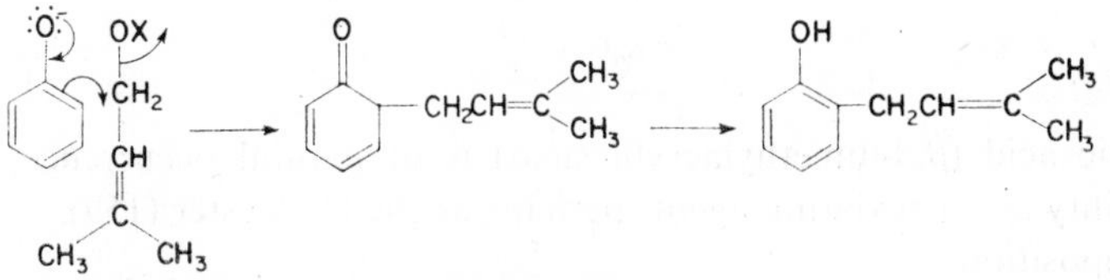

(152) C-Prenylation

Attack by anionic oxygen, to produce prenyl ethers (e.g. 151) can proceed by
a completely analogous course.

Numerous derived forms of the prenyl residue occur in nature. A few
respresentative examples are visamminol (153), lapachenol (154), xanthyletin
(155) and the flavone, amurensin (156):

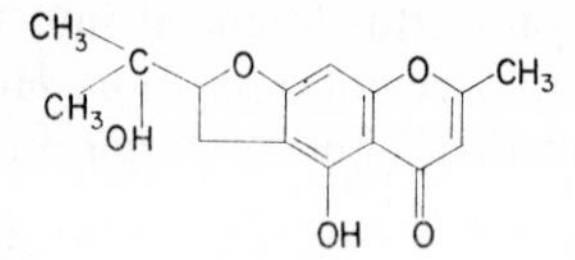

(153) Visamminol

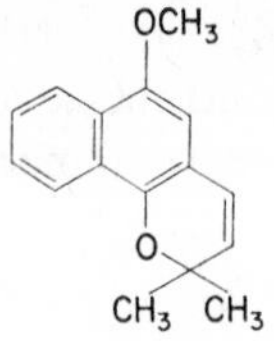

(154) Lapachenol

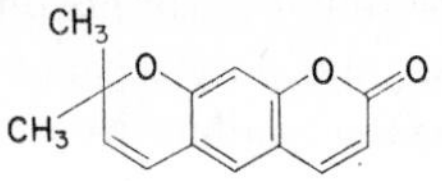

(155) Xanthyletin

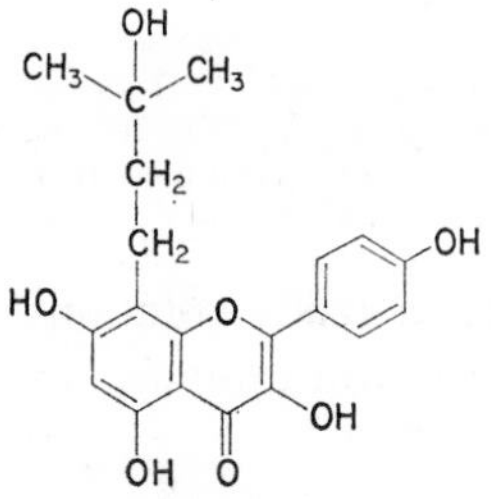

(156) Amurensin

The biosynthetic steps involved in these hydrations and hydroxylations (or oxidations) of the prenyl residue are not known; while speculation can lead to some obvious possibilities for the formation of the 2-isopropylfuran and 2,2-dimethylchrome rings of (153) and (155), no direct information exists regarding the course of these transformations.

The senecioyl residue, as in the C-acylated glabra lactone (157) and the O-acylated samidin (158), appears frequently in natural compounds.

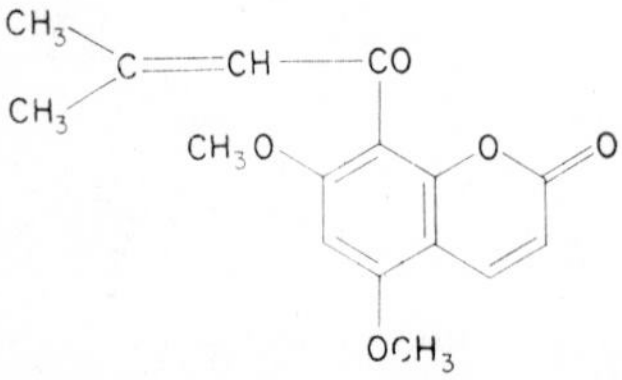

(157)

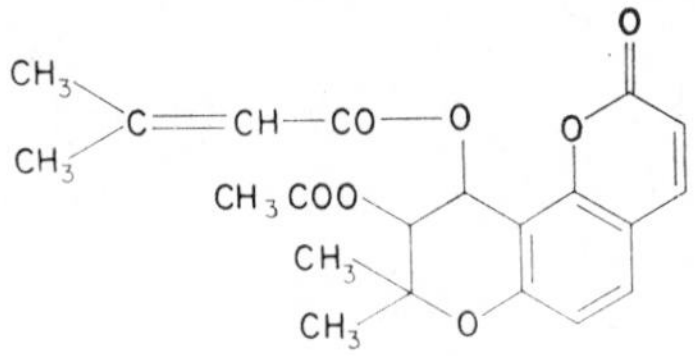

(158)

Senecioic acid (β,β-dimethylacrylic acid) is of natural occurrence, and its availability as an acylating agent, perhaps as the CoA ester (159), is a plausible supposition:

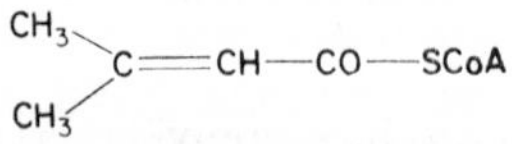

(159) Senecioyl CoA

Indeed, the structure of leptospermone (142) invites the supposition that the senecioyl residue (or its dihydro derivative) can serve as a starting point for elaboration by the linear condensation of acetate units:

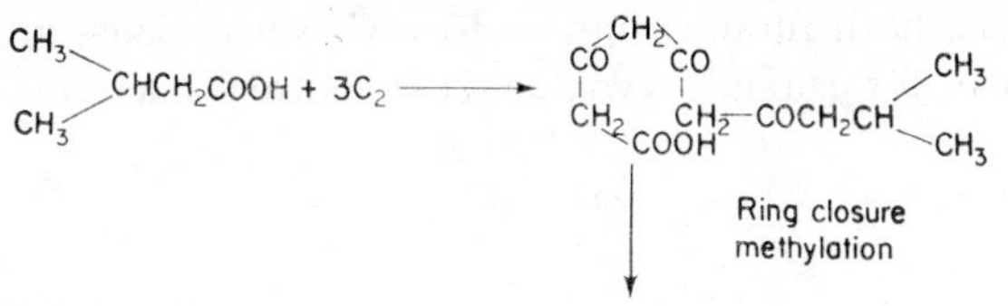

(142)

In concluding this discussion of carbon-alkylation it must be emphasized that most of what can be said about biosynthetic pathways rests upon structural correlations. In very few instances (e.g. mycophenolic acid (82), where the seven-carbon-atom side chain has been shown to be derived from mevalonic acid, and the C-methyl group from methionine) has the source of the alkylating agents, or the biosynthetic stage at which alkylation occurs, been demonstrated by the use of labeled precursors. It seems very probable that the course of synthesis described in this section represents the essential nature of these processes but direct confirmation is still to be desired.

The Furan Ring

Numerous natural substances, of which dictamnine (160) and psoralene (161) are simple examples, contain the unsubstituted furan ring:

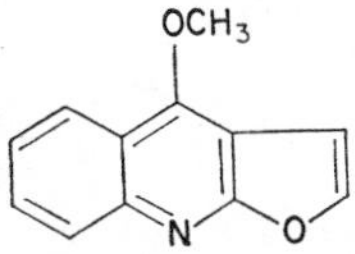

(160) Dictamnine

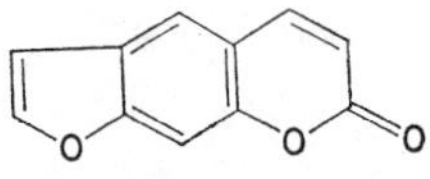

(161) Psoralene

The origin of this ring has been discussed by Aneja *et al.*,[79] who take the very reasonable view that it represents a degradation of a C_5 unit, possibly by way of a dihydroxyisopentyl substituent. The high incidence, especially in the Umbelliferae and Rutaceae, of furano compounds that contain, as C— and O— substituents, prenyl or modified prenyl groups, makes this suggestion an attractive one. A notable example of the association of compounds related in this way is found in the occurrence in *Flindersia* species of such compounds as flindersine (162) and maculosidine (163):

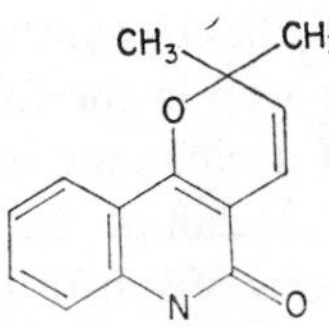

(162) Flindersine

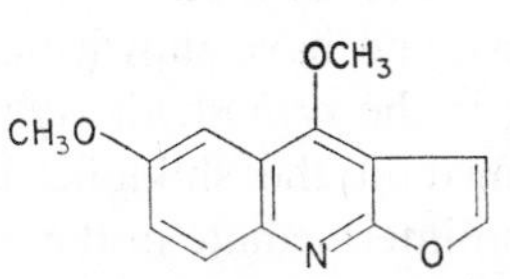

(163) Maculosidine

In other cases, both furano rings and iso-C_5 substituents are found in the same molecule; for example, evoxine (164) and oxypeucedanin (165):

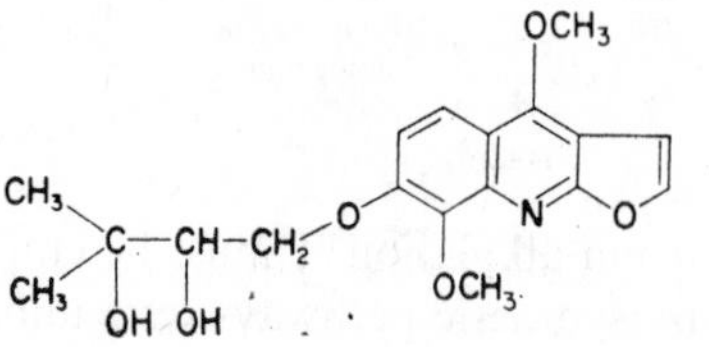

(164) Evoxine 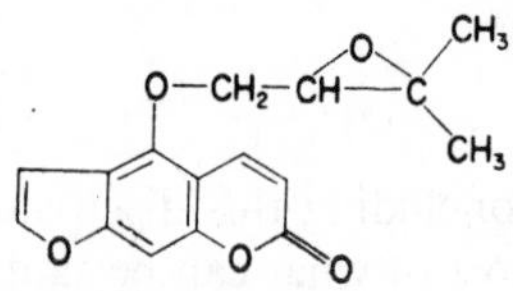   (165) Oxypeucedanin

Coumarins

The biosynthesis of the coumarin ring system has only recently been investigated experimentally. An early proposal of Haworth's was that the fundamental reaction in coumarin biosynthesis is the oxidative ring closure (166) of p-coumaric acid. This hypothesis served to account for the common occurrence in coumarins of the 7-hydroxyl group and for the introduction of the lactonic oxygen atom:

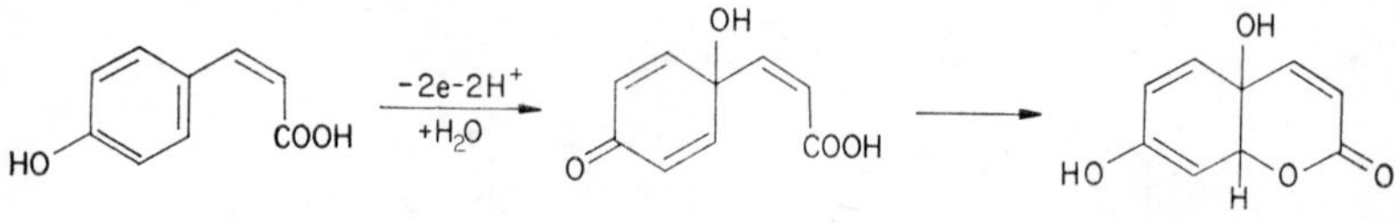

(166)

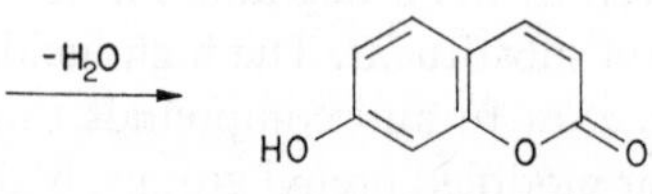

7-Hydroxycoumarin

A similar scheme, involving the intermediate formation of a spirolactone, has also been proposed. [69a]

Recent studies have defined the course of the biosynthesis of several natural coumarins, and have shown that a key step in the formation of the heterocyclic ring is the *ortho*-hydroxylation of a cinnamic acid. [80–89] Cinnamic acid, formed in the shikimic acid-phenylalanine pathway, appears to be the common intermediate in the biosynthesis of substituted coumarins. In the biosynthesis of the many 7-hydroxylated coumarins, the first step is the conversion of *trans*-cinnamic acid into *trans-p*-coumaric acid. The succeeding steps in the synthesis of umbelliferone in *Hydrangea macrophylla* can be represented as follows:

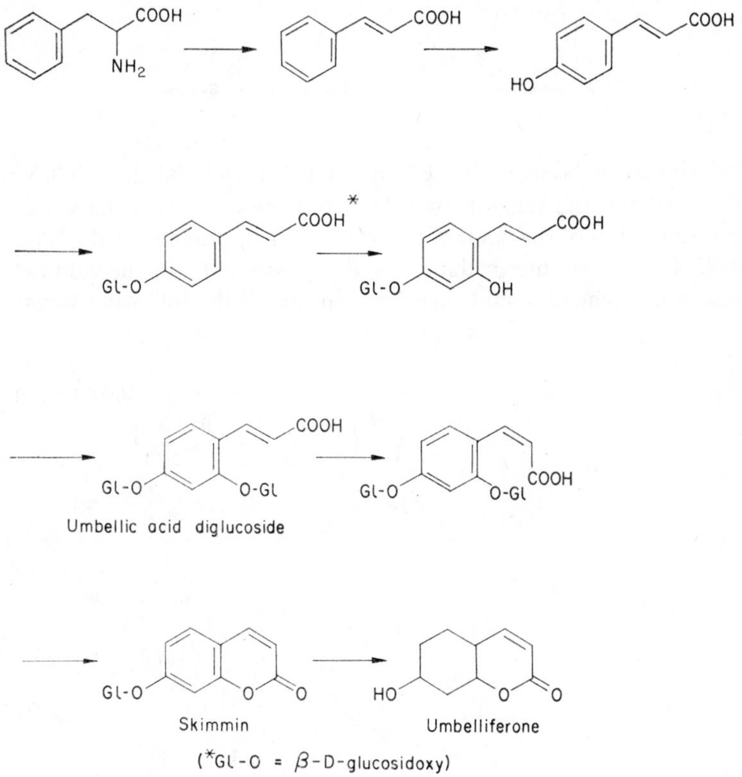

Umbellic acid diglucoside

Skimmin   Umbelliferone

(*Gl-O = β-D-glucosidoxy)

Coumarin itself is formed from cinnamic acid administered to *Melilotus albus*. The presence in higher plants of cinnamic acid-*cis-trans*-isomerase is indicated by the efficiency of *trans*-cinnamic and *trans*-p-coumaric acids as precursors for natural coumarins, and by the demonstration that a heat-labile extract prepared from *M. alba* was able to carry out the conversion of *trans*- into *cis*-cinnamic acid. [90]

The biosynthesis of furocoumarins appears to follow a similar course. Radioactive feeding experiments using *Pimpinella magna* led to the conclusion that furocoumarins are formed by way of *p*-coumaric acid and not by the further elaboration of coumarin itself. [91]

It is interesting to note that both isopimpinellin (167) and khellin (168) are found in umbelliferous plants (although not, so far as has been reported, in the same plant).

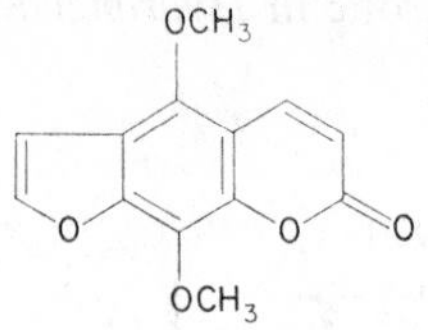

(167) Isopimpinellin

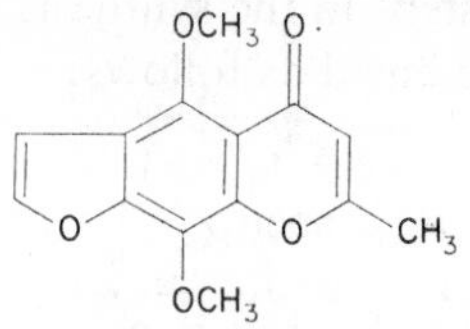

(168) Khellin

The similarity between the coumarin (167) and the 2-methylchromone (168) is striking, and suggests that the two heterocyclic rings have a common origin. Extension of the cinnamic acid side-chain, possibly at the stage of the *ortho*-hydroxylated intermediate (as the glucoside), by the addition of a two-carbon fragment, could take place in one of the following ways:

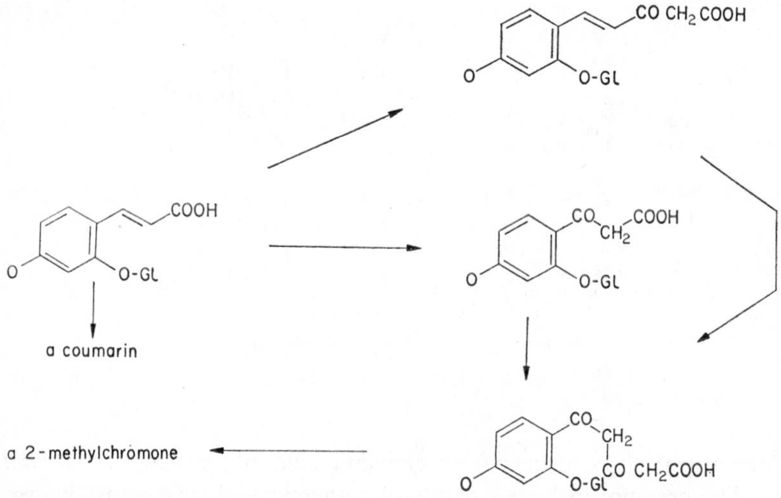

(169)

The addition of a two-carbon fragment (from malonate-CoA) to either —CH=CHCOSCoA or —COCH$_2$COSCoA can be viewed as unexceptional.

It is worth recalling in this connection that the glucoside pungenin (p. 750) has been shown to be formed from such C$_6$—C$_3$ compounds as caffeic, *p*-coumaric, cinnamic, phenyllactic and shikimic acids and phenylalanine. [92] This finding indicates that the α,β-unsaturated acids, the α-hydroxy acid and the amino acid can be converted into the β-keto acid and thence into the acetophenone:

$$ArCH_2CHCOOH \dashrightarrow ArCH_2CHCOOH \dashrightarrow ArCH{=}CHCOOH$$
$$| |$$
$$OH NH_2$$

$$\dashrightarrow ArCHCH_2COOH \dashrightarrow ArCOCH_2COOH \dashrightarrow ArCOCH_3$$
$$|$$
$$OH$$

$$(170)$$

Hydroxylation of Aromatic Rings

The conversion of cinnamic acid into *p*-coumaric acid, a reaction which plays a fundamental role in the biosynthesis of naturally occurring coumarins, appears to be a process common to many biosynthetic sequences in higher plants. The efficiency with which phenylalanine, cinnamic acid and their congeners are utilized in the synthesis of lignins, flavonoid compounds, coumarins, and other substances containing the C_6—C_3 unit or products derived from it by chain elongation or degradation, shows clearly that the introduction of hydroxyl groups into the aromatic nucleus is a general biosynthetic process.

The hydroxylation of other aromatic compounds has been observed as well. Stem tissue of *Avena sativa* converts phenoxyacetic acid into 4-hydroxyphenoxyacetic acid. [93]

Salicylic acid can be formed in higher plants either by *ortho*-hydroxylation of benzoic acid (in *Helianthus anuus*, *Solanum tuberosum*, and *Pisum sativum*, but not in wheat coleoptiles), [94] or of cinnamic acid (and subsequent side-chain degradation) in *Gaultheria procumbens* [95, 96] and in other plants. [97]

The phenylalanine-cinnamic acid-*p*-coumaric acid route, followed by side-chain degradation, leads to the formation of *p*-hydroxybenzoic acid in *Catalpa ovata* and *C. bignonoides*. [98]

Many cases of what is surely hydroxyl group introduction into aromatic nuclei are found in the flavonoid compounds, in which 5 and 8-hydroxylation in the A-ring and 2'-hydroxylation in the B-ring are probably the result of the late introduction of oxygen into the fundamental 5,7-dihydroxy A-ring and the 4'-hydroxy B-ring.

Although the removal of hydroxyl (or methoxyl) groups from aromatic rings is not a common or general process in phenolic biosynthesis, it has been observed in a number of cases. Sinapic acid is converted into coniferyl lignin as well as into sinapyl lignin, [99, 100] and *Hordeum*, *Triticum* and *Oryza* can demethoxylate sinapic acid to form ferulic acid. [97] (see also Chapter 15).

There is no indication that flavonoid compounds possessing a resorcinol-derived A-ring (butein, formononetin, etc.) are formed by way of the corresponding phloroglucinol-derived compounds by loss of the 5- (or corresponding) hydroxyl group. Indeed, the loss of oxygen where there are hydroxyl groups "missing" from the normal acetate-derived aromatic rings is probably to be accounted for by the following sequence:

$$-COCH_2CO- \longrightarrow -CH-CH_2CO \longrightarrow -CH=CHCO-$$
$$\underset{\displaystyle OH}{|}$$

at the polyketomethylene level of elaboration (see pp. 760–761).

Oxidative Metabolism in Biosynthesis

The elaboration of complex compounds by the oxidative coupling of simpler molecules has been proposed by many investigators to account for the biosynthesis of compounds of a number of different classes. The origin of such compounds as hypericin (5) and the perylene quinone (40b) found in *Daldinia concentrica* from the corresponding anthracene and naphthalene compounds is readily explicable. Simple oxidative changes that lead to compounds in which the carbon skeletons of their progenitors are immediately apparent are exemplified by chebulic acid (172), derived from ellagic acid (171); and the bisflavones, such as sotetsuflavone (173); [101]

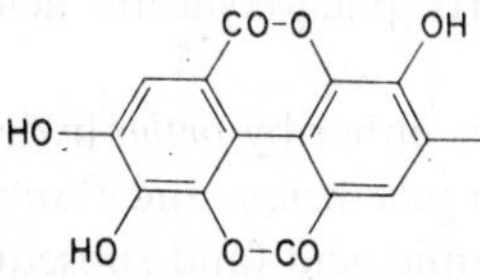

(171) Ellagic acid

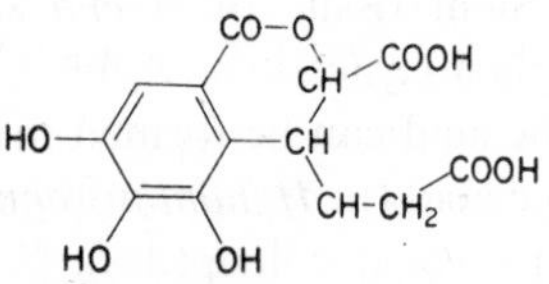

(172) Chebulic acid

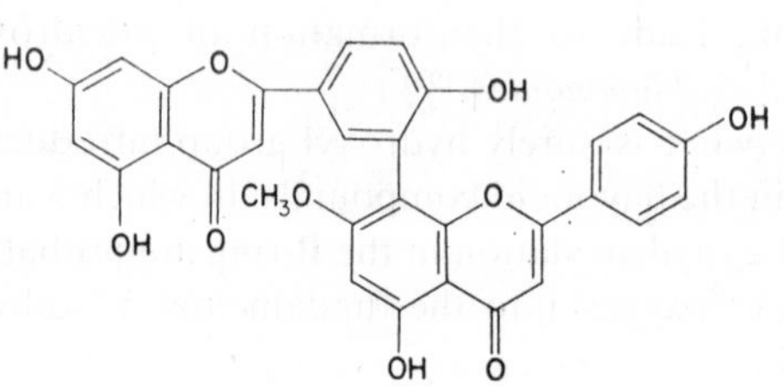

(173) Sotetsuflavone

A widely occurring class of natural phenols whose origins and interrelationships are readily inferred on structural grounds are the lignans. (See also Chapter 15.) Lignans are C_{18} compounds that may be regarded as C_6—C_3—C_3—C_6 compounds in which the bond between the two phenylpropane-derived residues is at the point shown in (174):

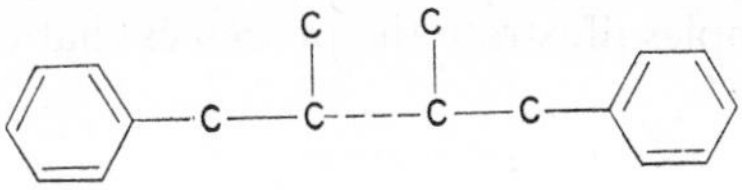

(174)

These are known in a variety of modifications, including diarylbutanes such as guaiaretic acid (175), tetrahydrofurans such as olivil (176), and α-phenyltetralins such as conidendrin (177):

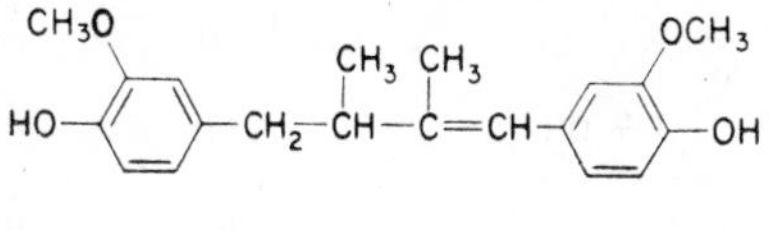

(175) Guaiaretic acid

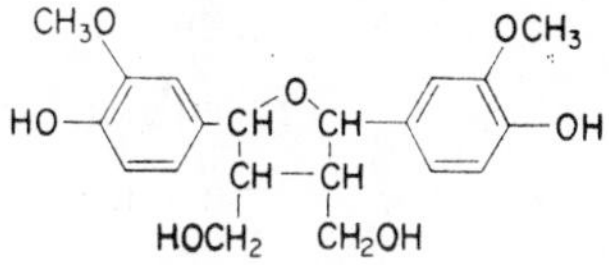

(176) Olivil

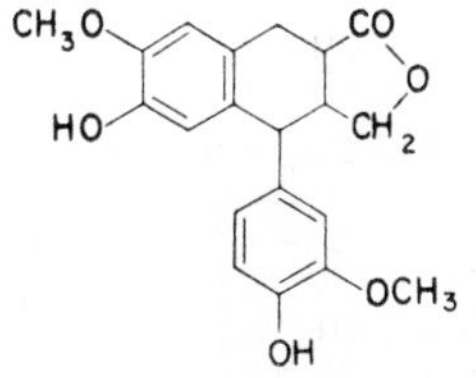

(177) Conidendrin

A general theory of the biosynthesis of the lignans is that first outlined by Erdtman, [102] and reinforced by experimental findings of Freudenberg. [103] The essential features of the hypothetical scheme of the biosynthesis of the lignans can be represented in the following somewhat simplified form. It can be seen that the process of condensation depends for its initiation upon an oxidation of a 4-propenylphenol, of which a natural prototype may be coniferyl alcohol (178). In the equations below a generalized p-hydroxystyrene (179) is used as the example, and a two-electron oxidation is chosen for convenience in representation. (Erdtman [102] discusses these reactions in terms of a one-electron oxidation.)

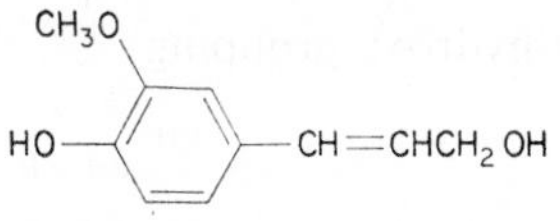

(178) Coniferyl alcohol

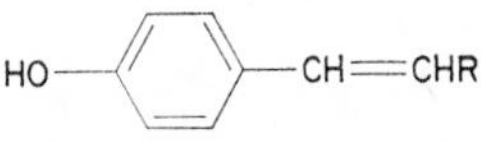

(179) p–Hydroxystyrene derivative

$$\frac{-2e}{-H^+}$$

(180)

The following examples illustrate the processes that can lead to representative lignan structures:

(a)

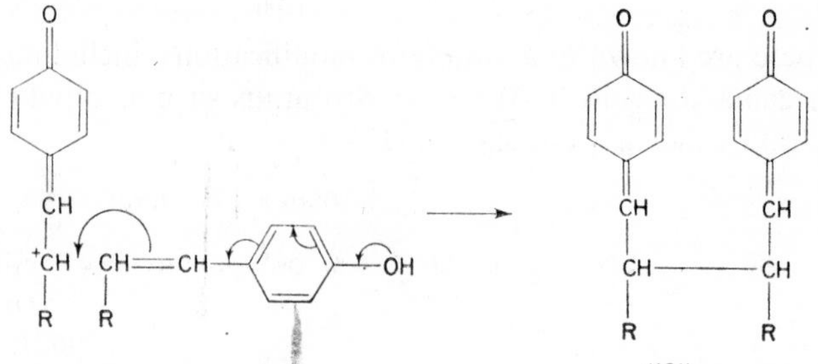

(181)

(b)   (181) + H₂O ⟶

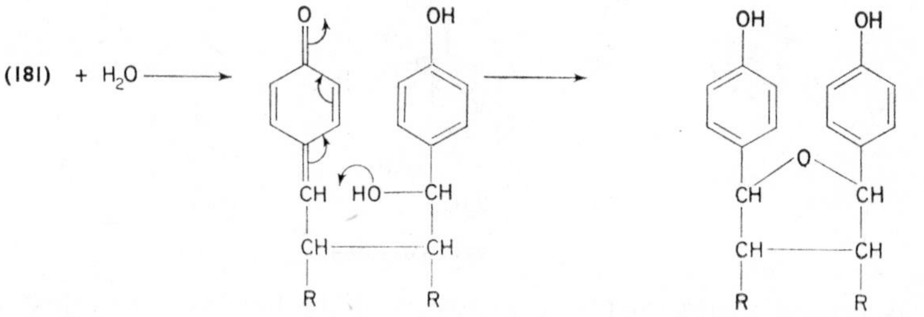

(182)

(c)

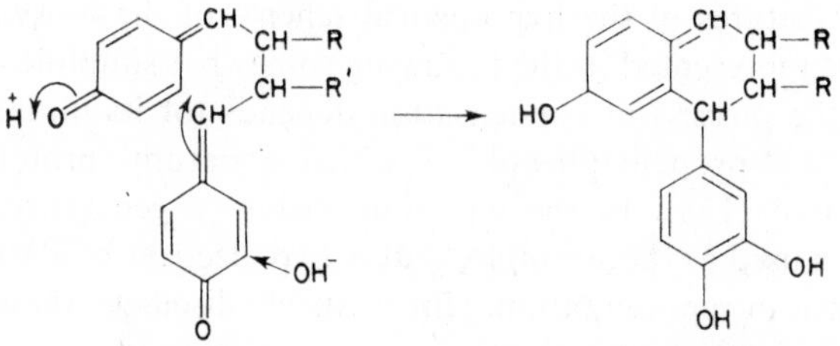

(181)   183)

or **(d)** if (181) already contains the *o*-dihydroxy grouping:

(d)

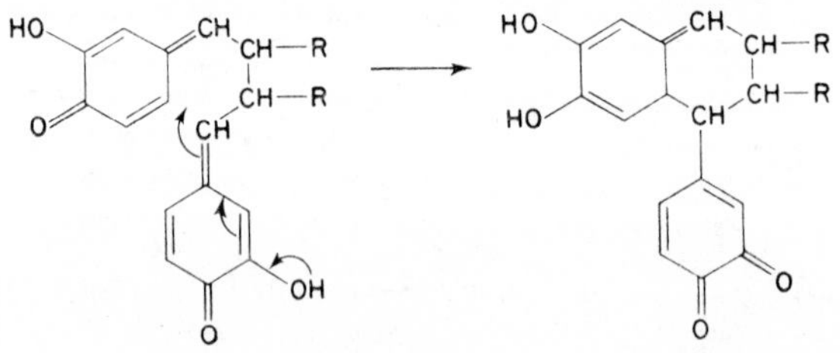

(181a)   (184)

Freudenberg discovered that if coniferyl alcohol (178) is oxidized in the presence of an enzyme preparation there are formed, in addition to a polymer, "synthetic lignin", a number of intermediate oxidation products. These are (185–188):

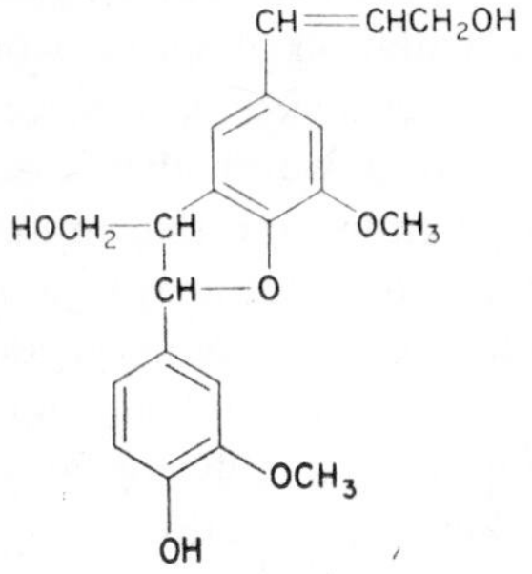

(185) 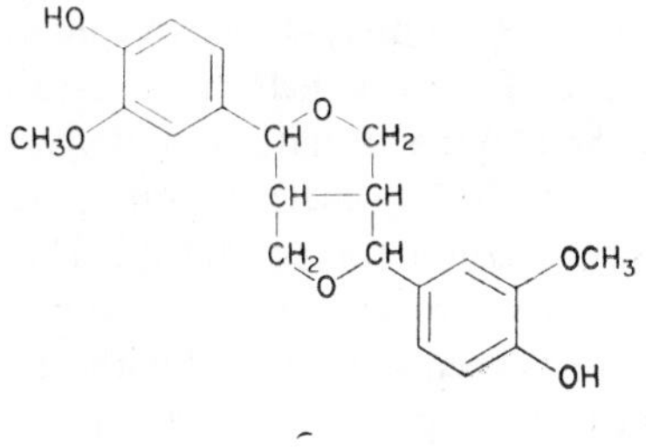 (186)

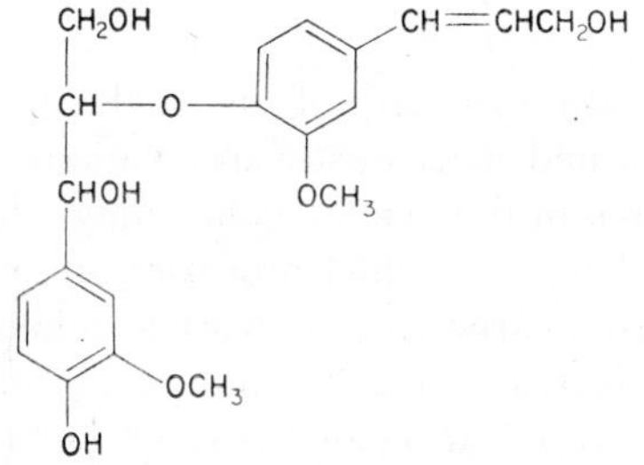

(187) 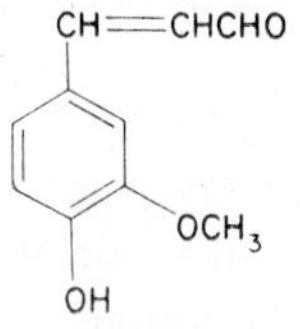 (188)

The derivation of these by way of an initial oxidation of the type (179 → 180) is readily understood; for example:

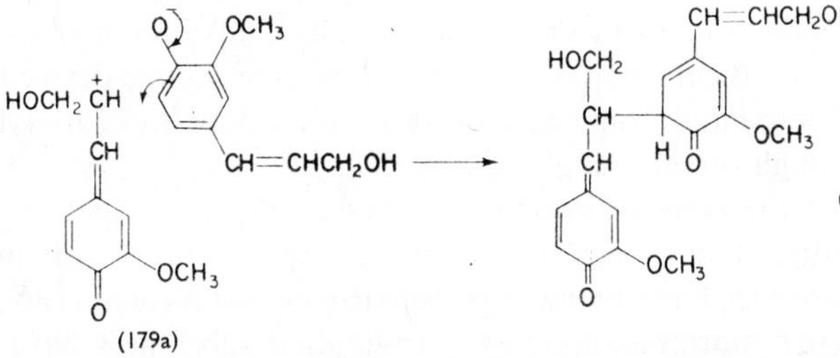

(179a) (185)

The attack upon (179a) by the anionic oxygen of (178) (rather than by the ring) leads to (187); and (186) is derived as described earlier for (182), with the modification that the furan ring closure occurs by attack of the terminal —CH$_2$OH groups.

A continuation of processes of oxidation and condensation such as these outlined above can lead to complex, polymeric molecules. Freudenberg takes the view that lignin owes its formation to such a course, a view that is supported by the observations that (a) coniferyl alcohol can be enzymatically oxidized to a polymer that is indistinguishable from lignin, (b) coniferyl alcohol—C^{14} is incorporated into lignin in spruce saplings, (c) the number of hydroxyl groups in lignin is less than one per C_9 unit, and (d) the production of as much as 25 per cent of vanillin by the oxidation of spruce wood indicates that the 3-methoxy-4-hydroxyphenyl residue makes up a large part of the structure of the wood. It must be recognized, however, that it is difficult to prove the identity of natural and synthetic lignins, and that in nature the exact point at which O-methylation occurs need not necessarily be at the level of coniferyl alcohol (or coniferin). The evidence that coniferyl alcohol is indeed the real precursor is however, substantial, and no alternative hypothesis has been put forward with the support of equally cogent evidence.

The ultimate origin of lignin from the shikimic acid pathway seems clear from the evidence: all that is still in need of further clarification is the nature of the steps at and beyond the C_6—C_3 level of elaboration. [26, 104]

SUMMARY

In the foregoing pages is found a summary of the results of experimental findings, structural correlations, and mechanistic speculations as they have led to the development of present-day views concerning the origins of phenolic substances in higher plants. The chief processes are, basically, few in number: (a) The synthesis, from carbohydrate and via shikimic acid, of a C_6—C_3 (a 1-phenylpropane derivative) unit; (b) the joining of C_2 (acetate) units into linear chains and the cyclization of these, by aldolization, into carbocyclic rings. Other kinds of ring closures, leading to oxygen heterocyclic rings, also occur: (c) the lengthening of the C_6—C_3 unit by addition of C_2-units, or shortening by degradation to C_6—C_2 and C_6—C_1 structures; (d) the modification of the basic structures derived as in (a), (b) and (c), by oxidation or reduction, or by the attachment, by C-alkylation or C-acylation, of side chains; (e) the incursion into the shikimic- or acetate-derived synthetic pathways of terpenoid fragments derived from β-methylcrotonyl residues produced through the mevalonic acid pathway.

For most of the *types* of synthetic processes, direct substantiation of the route of synthesis has been obtained by experiments involving labeled precursors introduced into living organisms (higher plants or microorganisms), but most of the enormous number of individual substances have not been studied in detail. Existing views as to the biosynthesis of most of the known plant phenolics depend upon the structural kinship to those few whose biosynthesis has been established by experiment. Nevertheless, the remarkable degree of structural coincidence that exists within this large and diverse group of compounds makes it very likely that the fundamental synthetic processes are relatively few in number. The least that can be said is that to undertake the study of the biogenesis of most of the plant phenolics would be to start with a working hypothesis that would in most cases turn out to be correct.

Concerning the many details of structural alteration, such as the oxidation of methyl groups, the reduction of carbonyl and carboxyl groups, the introduction and removal of hydroxyl groups, the cleavage of rings and the formation of new ones, there is little but speculation. The time has come to penetrate below the level of the intact plant and to seek the enzymatic systems that bring about the sequential stages in synthesis. Until this is accomplished our knowledge of the processes of biosynthesis will remain confined to knowledge of the origin of the carbon atoms of the skeletons of the molecules.

REFERENCES

1. ROBINSON, R. *J. Chem. Soc.* **111**, 876 (1917).
2. SCHÖPF, C. *Ann. Chem.* **497**, 1 (1923).
3. BOGERT, M. T. *Chem. Rev.* **10**, 265 (1932).
4. WAGNER-JAUREGG, T. *Ann. Chem.* **496**, 52 (1932).
5. GARDNER, T. S. *J. Org. Chem.* **8**, 111 (1943).
6. MARKER, R. E. *J. Am. Chem. Soc.* **69**, 2383 (1947).
7. HALL, J. A. *Chem. Rev.* **20**, 305 (1937).
8. ULLAL, V. V., SHAH, R. C. and WHEELER, T. S. *J. Chem. Soc.* **1940**, 1499.
9. COLLIE, J. N. *J. Chem. Soc.* **91**, 1806 (1907).
10. SCHÖPF, C., LEHMAN, G., ARNOLD, W., KOCH, K., BAYERLE, H., FALK, K., OECHLER, F. and STEUER, H. *Z. Angew. Chemie* **50**, 779; 797 (1937).
11. SCHÖPF, C. and THIERFELDER, K. *Ann. Chem.* **518**, 127 (1935).
12. ROBINSON, R. *J. Chem. Soc.* **111**, 762 (1917).
13. WHELDALE, M. and BASSETT, H. L. *Biochem. J.* **7**, 441 (1913); **8**, 204 (1919).
14. LAWRENCE, W. J. C. Biochem. Soc. Symposia, Cambridge, Engl., No. 4 (1950).
15. GEISSMAN, T. A., JORGENSEN, E. C. and JOHNSON, B. L. *Arch. Biochem. Biophys.* **49**, 368 (1954).
16. GEISSMAN, T. A. and HARBORNE, J. B. *Arch. Biochem. Biophys.* **55**, 447 (1955).
17. HARBORNE, J. B. Private communication, 1960. To be published.
18. SCHMIDT, H. *Bioch. Zentr.* **81**, 213 (1962).
19. GEISSMAN, T. A. and HINREINER, E. H. *Botan. Rev.* **18**, 77 (1952); p. 149.
20. BIRCH, A. J. and DONOVAN, F. W. *Australian J. Chem.* **6**, 360 (1953).
21. DAVIS, B. D. *Advances in Enzymol.* **16**, 247 (1955).
22. SRINAVASAN, P. R., SHIGEURA, H. T., SPRECHER, M., SPRINSON, D. B. and DAVIS, B. D. *J. Biol. Chem.* **220**, 477 (1956).
23. SRINAVASAN, P. R., SPRINSON, D. B., KALAN, E. B. and DAVIS, B. D. *J. Biol. Chem.* **223**, 913 (1956).
24. GHOSH, J. J., ADAMS, E. and DAVIS, B. D. *Federation Proc.* **15**, 261 (1956).
25. McCALLA, D. R. and NEISH, A. G. *Can. J. Biochem. Physiol.* **37**, 531 (1959).
26. BROWN, S. A. and NEISH, A. C. *Nature* **175**, 688 (1955).
27. BROWN, S. A. and NEISH, A. C. *Can. J. Biochem. Physiol.* **33**, 948 (1955).
28. WATKIN, J. E., BROWN, S. A. and NEISH, A. C. *Chemistry in Canada*, March 1960.
29. GEISSMAN, T. A. and SWAIN, T. *Chem. and Ind. London*, **1957**, 984.
30. ROBINSON, R. In *Structural Relations of Natural Products*. Oxford Press, 1955.
31. BIRCH, A. J., MASSY-WESTROPP, R. A. and MOYE, C. J. *Australian J. Chem.* **8**, 539 (1955).
32. TANENBAUM, S. W. and BASSETT E. W. *Biochim. Biophys. Acta* **28**, 21 (1958); *J. Biol. Chem.* **234**, 1861 (1959).

33. ALLPORT, D. C. and BU'LOCK, J. D. *J. Chem. Soc.* **1960**, 654.
34. BIRCH, A. J., MASSY-WESTROPP, R. A., RICKARDS, R. W. and SMITH, H. *J. Chem. Soc.* **1958**, 640.
35. BIRCH, A. J., MUSGRAVE, O. C., RICKARDS, R. W. and SMITH, H. *J. Chem. Soc.* **1959**, 3146.
36. BIRCH, A. J. and DONOVAN, F. W. *Australian J. Chem.* **6**, 373 (1953).
37. EBNÖTHER, A., MEIGER, TH. M. and SCHMID, H. *Helv. Chim. Acta* **35**, 910 (1952).
38. NIKUNI, J. *J. Agr. Chem. Soc. Japan* **18**, 496, 714 (1942).
39. HABER, R. G., NIKUNI, J., SCHMID, H. and YOGI, K. *Helv. Chim. Acta* **39**, 1654 (1956).
40. BIRCH, A. J. and DONOVAN, F. W. *Chem. and Ind. London*, **1954**, 1047; *Australian J. Chem.* **8**, 529 (1955).
41. DAVIES, J. E., KING, F. E. and ROBERTS, J. C. *Chem. and Ind. London*, **1954**, 1110.
42. WHITE, A., HANDLER, P., SMITH, E. L. and STETTEN, DE W. In *Principles of Biochemistry*, 2nd ed., p. 466. McGraw-Hill, 1959.
43. WAKIL, S. J. and GANGULY, J. *J. Am. Chem. Soc.* **81**, 2597 (1959).
44. DALTON, L. K. and LAMBERTON, J. A. *Australian J. Chem.* **11**, 46 (1958).
45. LAMBERTON, J. A. *Australian J. Chem.* **12**, 224 (1959).
46. MOSBACH, K. *Acta Chem. Scand.* **18**, 329 (1964).
47. YAMAZAKI, M., MATSUO, M., KASHIDO, Y. and SHIBATA, S. *Chem. Pharm. Bull. (Japan)*, in press (1965).
48. MOSBACH, K. *Bioch. Bioph. Res. Commun.* **17**, 363 (1964).
49. MAAS, W. S. G., TOWERS, G. H. N. and NEISH, A. C. *Ber. Deutsch. Bot. Ges.* **77**, 157 (1964).
50. GRISEBACH, H., ACHENBACH, H. and GRISEBACH, U. C. *Naturwiss.* **47**, 206 (1960).
51. BIRCH, A. J., ENGLISH, R. J., MASSY-WESTROPP, R. A. and SMITH, H. *J. Chem. Soc.* **1958**, 369.
52. BIRCH, A. J., ENGLISH, R. J., MASSY-WESTROPP, R. A., SLAYTOR, M. and SMITH, H. *J. Chem. Soc.* **1958**, 365.
53. AGHORAMURTHY, K. and SESHADRI, T. R. *J. Sci. Ind. Res. (India)* **13A**, 114 (1954).
54. ASAHINA, Y. and SHIBATA, S. *Chemistry of Lichen Substances*. Japan Soc. for Promotion of Science, Ueno, Tokyo, 1954.
55. DEAN, F. M., EADE, R. A., MOUBASHIER, R. A. and ROBERTSON, A. *Nature* **179**, 366 (1957).
56. WHALLEY, W. B. *Chem. and Ind. London*, **1958**, 131.
57. UNDERHILL, E. W., WATKIN, J. E. and NEISH, A. C. *Can. J. Biochem. Physiol.* **35**, 219 (1957).
58. WATKIN, J. E., UNDERHILL, E. W. and NEISH, A. C. *Can. J. Biochem. Physiol.* **35**, 229 (1957).
59. GEISSMAN, T. A. and SWAIN, T. *Chem. and Ind. London*, **1957**, 984.
60. GRISEBACH, H. *Z. Naturforschung.* **12b**, 227, 597 (1957); **13b**, 335 (1958); **14b**, 485 (1959).
61. SIEGELMAN, H. W. *J. Biol. Chem.* **213**, 647 (1955).
62. GRISEBACH, H. and PATSCHKE, L. *Z. Naturforsch.* **17b**, 857 (1962).
63. GEISSMAN, T. A., JORGENSEN, E. C. and JOHNSON, B. L. *Arch. Biochem. Biophys.* **49**, 368 (1959).
64. GRISEBACH, H. and DOERR, N. *Z. Naturforsch.* **14b**, 802 (1959); **15b**, 284 (1960).
65. GEISSMAN, T. A., MASON, J. W. and ROWE, J. R. *Chem. and Ind. London*, **1959**, 1577.
66. GEISSMAN, T. A. and MASON, J. W. *Chem. and Ind. London*, **1960**, 291.
67. HOUSE, H. O., REIT, D. J. and WASSON, R. L. *J. Am. Chem. Soc.* **79**, 2490 (1957).
68. WONG, E., MORTIMER, P. I. and GEISSMAN, T. A. *Phytochemistry* **4**, 89 (1965).
69. IMASEKI, H., WHEELER, R. and GEISSMAN, T. A. *Tetrahedron Letters*, **1965**, 1785.
70. KING, F. E., KING, T. J. and WARWICK, A. *J. J. Chem. Soc.* **1952**, 1920.
71. GEISSMAN, T. A. and FUKUSHIMA, D. *J. Am. Chem. Soc.* **70**, 1686 (1948).
72. IBRAHAM, R. K. and TOWERS, G. H. N. *Can. J. Biochem. Physiol.* **38**, 627 (1960).
73. SESHADRI, T. R. *Current Science* **26**, 310 (1957).
74. BILLEK, G. and ZIEGLER, W. *Monatsh.* **93**, 1430 (1962).
75. VON RUDLOFF, E. and JORGENSEN, E. *Phytochemistry* **2**, 297 (1963).

76. JAIN, A. C. and SESHADI, T. R. *Quant. Rev. London* **10,** 169 (1956).
77. SCHMID, H. and BOLLETER, A. *Helv. Chim. Acta* **32,** 1358 (1949).
78. NILSSON, M. *Acta Chem. Scand.* **13,** 750 (1959).
79. ANEJA, R., MUKERJEE, S. K. and SESHADRI, T. R. *Tetrahedron* **4,** 256 (1957).
80. BROWN, S. A. Personal communication.
81. BROWN, S. A., TOWERS, G. H. N. and WRIGHT, D. *Can. J. Biochem. Physiol.* **38,** 143 (1960).
82. KOSUGE, T. and CONN, E. *J. Biol. Chem.* **234,** 2133 (1950).
83. KOSUGE, T. and CONN, E. E. *J. Biol. Chem.* **236,** 1617 (1961).
84. BROWN, S. A. *Can. J. Biochem. Physiol.* **40,** 607 (1962).
85. BROWN, S. A. *Lloydia* **26,** 211 (1963).
86. BROWN, S. A. *Phytochemistry* **2,** 137 (1963).
87. BROWN, S. A., TOWERS, G. H. N. and CHEN, D. *Phytochemistry* **3,** 469 (1964).
88. AUSTIN, D. J. and MEYERS, M. B. *Phytochemistry* **4,** 245 (1965).
89. AUSTIN, D. J. and MEYERS, M. B. *Phytochemistry* **4,** 255 (1965).
90. STOKER, J. R. *Bioch. Biophys. Res. Commun.* **14,** 17 (1964).
91. FISOS, H. G. and MOTHES, U. *Z. Naturforsch.* **19b,** 770 (1964).
92. NEISH, A. C. *Can. J. Botany* **37,** 1085 (1959).
93. THOMAS, E. W., LOUGHMAN, B. C. and POWELL, R. G. *Nature* **199,** 73 (1963).
94. KLAEMBT, H. D. *Nature* **196,** 491 (1962).
95. GRISEBACH, N. and VOLLMER, K. *Z. Naturforsch.* **18b,** 753 (1963).
96. GRISEBACH, N. and VOLLMER, K. *Z. Naturforsch.* **19b,** 781 (1964).
97. EL-BASYOUNI, S. Z., CHEN, D., IBRAHIM, R. K., NEISH, A. C. and TOWERS, G. H. N. *Phytochemistry* **3,** 485 (1964).
98. ZENK, M. H. and MUELLER, G. *Z. Naturforsch.* **19b,** 398 (1964).
99. HIGUCHI, T. and BROWN, S. A. *Can. J. Biochem. Physiol.* **41,** 65 (1963).
100. HIGUCHI, T. and BROWN, S. A. *Can. J. Biochem. Physiol.* **41,** 613 (1963).
101. KAWANO, N. and YAMADA, M. *J. Am. Chem. Soc.* **82,** 1505 (1960).
102. ERDTMAN, H. In *Modern Methods of Plant Analysis*, p. 428, eds. Paech and Tracey. Springer Verlag, Berlin, 1955.
103. FREUDENBERG, K. *Ibid.*, p. 499.
104. BROWN, S. A., NEISH, A. C., CLAIRE, F. M. and CHISHOLM, M. D. *Can. J. Biochem. Physiol.* **33,** 948 (1955); **37,** 25 (1959).

CHAPTER 13

THE BIOSYNTHESIS OF TANNINS

S. G. Humphries

British Leather Manufacturers' Research Association,
Milton Park, Egham, Surrey

CONTENTS

I. Introduction   801
II. Biogenesis of the Possible Phenolic and Other Precursors
     of Tannins   802
     A. *Hydrolyzable tannins*   802
     B. *Condensed tannins*   804
III. Concepts of Tannin Formation from Phenolic and Other
     Precursors   808
     A. *Hydrolyzable tannins*   808
     B. *Condensed tannins*:   812
         (i) Acid catalyzed polymerizations   812
         (ii) Quinone type polymerizations   815
         (iii) Possible polyleucoanthocyanidins of unknown structure   819
         (iv) The possible mode of origin of tannins   820
IV. Some Factors Influencing the Formation of Tannin in
     Plants   821
V. Summary   823
     Acknowledgements   823
     References   823

I. INTRODUCTION

The term "tannin" dates from 1796 when it was first used [161] to denote substances present in plant extracts which possessed the property of converting animal skins into leather. This definition implies a limitation, and many examples in the literature of substances which give those reactions characteristic of polyphenols, but which have no tanning action, may be excluded. Thus, simple phenols such as chlorogenic and gallic acids, and catechin are ineligible although they may precipitate gelatin under unselective conditions and are partially retained by hide powder; properties which are associated with tannins. In general most natural tannins are regarded as having molecular weights within the range 1000 and 5000. As tannin extracts are in general

2D

complex mixtures of substances it has in many cases to date, not been possible
to single out a particular tannin as being the characteristic one of a particular
plant source. Most authors prefer to speak of "tannin extracts" rather than
"tannins". In recent years, chromatographic studies have assisted greatly in
confirming the heterogeneity of the composition of the tannin extracts and in
some cases the simple polyphenols, present in small amounts, have been
identified. These are important because the complex tannins are generally
considered to arise from the simple phenols by a polymerization mechanism.
In view of the fact that condensed tannins have never been isolated or
characterized, very little is positively known about their biogenesis, but it is
possible to mention some of the mechanisms by which the tannins may arise.
A brief mention regarding the biogenesis of some of the phenolic and non-
aromatic precursors of tannins is relevant, but these compounds are treated
more extensively in Chapters 12 and 15 of this volume and elsewhere. [121, 170]
For the sake of convenience the hydrolyzable tannins, which are easily
broken down by the action of acids, alkalis or enzymes to give gallic acid
and in most cases a sugar, and the condensed tannins which are not hydrolyzed in this way, are treated separately.

II. BIOGENESIS OF THE POSSIBLE PHENOLIC AND
OTHER PRECURSORS OF TANNINS

A. *Hydrolyzable Tannins*

The initial approach involved a search for families of related polyphenolic
carboxylic acids, to which the hydrolyzable tannins and hydrophilic conjugates of phenols might be related in the polyphenol and tannin fractions of
plant extracts. Gallic and ellagic acids stand in this relationship to the hydrolyzable tannins, chebulinic and chebulagic acids and corilagin, the structural
formulae for which have been elucidated. [148, 156, 159, 160]

A related approach has been concerned with investigating the occurrence
of intermediates of aromatic biosynthesis among fractions of plant extracts
other than those containing tannins. This may be illustrated with reference
to the studies of Hathway [68] concerning myrobalans, the dried fruit of
Terminalia chebula Retz. From the tannin-free methanolic extract were
separated, as the principal acids present, shikimic acid and quinic acid
whilst evidence for 5-dehydroshikimic acid was obtained. The probable
biochemical significance of the occurrence in the same plant source of cyclohexanecarboxylic acids with configurations at carbon atoms C_3, C_4 and C_5
identical [35] with those of three carbon atoms of glucose present in the combined form, chebulinic acid [148, 156] was noted. The possibility of shikimic
acid or one of its derivatives serving as a biosynthetic precursor of the gallate
unit of these tannins was suggested by Hathway [69] and this idea has also

been put forward by others.[23] When the structures of shikimic and quinic acids were originally established, their functions as intermediates in biosynthesis of aromatic natural products was thought a possibility.[33, 34] Several workers have reported on the formation of gallic acid and of protocatechuic acid by the mold *Phycomyces blakesleeanus* when grown on glucose media,[13, 21] and more recent studies,[67] intended as a preliminary to the study of the biosynthesis of gallic acid and gallotannins in plants, have confirmed the earlier results. Two possible biosynthetic pathways were considered for the formation of gallic acid (IV), namely the oxidation of protocatechuic acid (III), and the dehydrogenation of 5-dehydroshikimic acid (II) derived from shikimic acid (I) (Fig. 1). Although the former route has several chemical

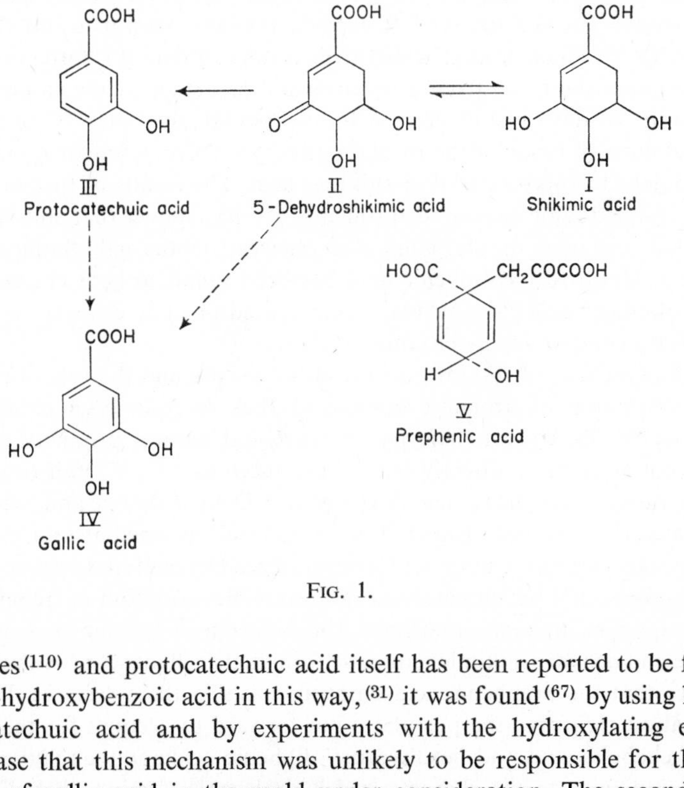

FIG. 1.

analogies[110] and protocatechuic acid itself has been reported to be formed from *p*-hydroxybenzoic acid in this way,[31] it was found[67] by using labeled protocatechuic acid and by experiments with the hydroxylating enzyme tyrosinase that this mechanism was unlikely to be responsible for the biogenesis of gallic acid in the mold under consideration. The second route considered involved the dehydrogenation of 5-dehydroshikimic acid (II) followed by enolization, as it had previously been shown[65] that protocatechuic acid (III) may be formed in microorganisms by elimination of the 3-hydroxyl group of (II). 5-Dehydroshikimic acid can be oxidized to gallic acid by aeration in alkaline solution and both 5-dehydroshikimic acid (II) and shikimic acid (I) were isolated from old cultures of *Phycomyces blakes-leeanus*.[67] Growth experiments on glucose media supplemented by one of several possible precursors showed 5-dehydroshikimic acid to be a direct precursor of gallic acid, with shikimic acid and 5-dehydroquinic acid as near but not immediate precursors. Brücker and Hashem[22] however maintain that deamination of the aromatic amino acid tyrosine plays an important part in the formation of gallic acid in *P. blakesleeanus*. The biosynthesis of gallic acid in higher plants has recently been studied by Conn and Swain.[27] Glucose proved to be the best precursor of this acid, the shikimic acid pathway being operative, rather than a route involving β oxidation of a trihydroxylated C_9 molecule derived from phenylalanine. Zenk[184] has proposed that gallic acid is formed in Sumac (*Rhus typhina*) by β-oxidation of the C_3 side chain of 3,4,5-trihydroxycinnamic acid. However from radioactive tracer studies on leaf discs of *R. typhina* Haslam, Haworth and their co-workers[28, 66] conclude that whilst their results to date do not conclusively support either the route from a nonaromatic precursor of the shikimic acid type or the oxidative route from a C_9 compound, they may be interpreted as being more in favor of the former pathway involving dehydrogenation of either 5-dehydroshikimic acid or shikimic acid. The results of further studies will be awaited with interest. Zaprometov[181] has shown that shikimic acid is a good precursor of the gallic acid esterified in the gallotannins of the tea plant. Hexahydroxydiphenic acid has been found to be a chemical precursor of ellagic acid[70] which is also produced in some cases from gallates and related compounds by enzymic oxidation.[71]

The biosynthesis of shikimic acid from D-glucose and the role of this acid in the formation of aromatic compounds has recently been reviewed by Sprinson.[167] In a great majority of benzenoid natural products, shikimic acid is not aromatised directly but is introduced as a C_6-C_3 unit originating in a derivative of prephenic acid (V) (Fig. 1). 5-Dehydroquinic and 5-dehydroshikimic acids have been found[29] to be normal intermediates in microbial aromatic biosynthesis. Quinic acid is only utilized by reactions involving quinic dehydrogenase[118] which catalyses the reversible oxidation of quinate to 5-dehydroquinate in some organisms. The isolation of the enzymes dehydroquinase and dehydroshikimic reductase from higher plants[4] provides further evidence that the prephenic acid pathway exists in these systems. Relevant information regarding the postulates put forward to account for the formation of chebulic acid and hexahydroxy diphenic acid and the relationship of these compounds to the characterized hydrolyzable tannins, chebulinic and chebulagic acids has been more favorably included in Section IIIA.

B. *Condensed Tannins*

At present the supposition is widely held that the relatively small amounts of the simple polyphenols which occur simultaneously with the condensed tannins in the barks and heartwoods of forest trees are in some way biogenetic precursors of the tannins themselves.[77] In this connection, the catechin and leucoanthocyanidin types of compounds are important. Other flavonoid molecules which are present, for example in quebracho heartwood, [179] may also participate in the reactions which these monomeric substances undergo in forming the natural polymers which are regarded as tannins. The behavior of a tannin extract is considered to be related to its complexity and each individual component, large or small, of the extract is thought to play a part. Thus it has been said to be unlikely[179] that any single structural formula can be conceived to represent completely a single condensed tannin extract.

At this juncture mention should be made of the possible mode of formation of some of the simple phenolic substances which are of special relevance to plant extracts. For the sake of convenience consideration might be given to different classes of condensed tannins defined as:

(1) those where the major monomeric phenols isolated from the tannin extract are flavan-3-ols, i.e. catechin;

(2) those where the major monomeric phenols isolated are flavan-3,4-diols akin to some leucoanthocyanidins;

(3) those where neither of the above phenolic substances are found, but where other compounds, e.g. hydroxystilbenes, occur.

There are examples of tannin extracts which do not fit easily into the broad classification, where more than one type of monomeric phenol occurs. Thus, in consideration of the simple phenols and their possible mode of formation, mention might be made in particular of catechin and related flavonoid compounds, leucoanthocyanidins and the related anthocyanidins and the hydroxystilbenes.

Catechin (VI) bears a close structural relationship to cyanidin (VII) and to the flavonol quercetin (VIII) (Fig. 2), and although studies concerning the formation of catechin have been few, the results obtained tend to be in agreement with the observations leading to the biosynthetic route deduced for cyanidin and quercetin. Kursanov and Zaprometov [108] have investigated the formation of catechin by following the photosynthetic assimilation of $C^{14}O_2$ in the tea plant. The results and those of experiments wherein solutions of $(1-C^{14})$ acetate and labeled shikimic acid were fed to young tea shoots [181] agree with the general conclusions obtained for quercetin formation in buckwheat. [173] Comte and his co-workers [25, 26] have found that catechin labeled in ring B is formed when cinnamic acid-β-C^{14} was incorporated into young wild cherry trees. meso-Inositol-C^{14} is not converted into catechins in tea leaves or into cyanidin in red cabbage seedlings. [178]

Studies on the biosynthesis of quercetin have been carried out by various workers [53, 164, 173] and it has been established that the acetate pathway [14, 15] operates in the formation of ring A of this compound. Grisebach [60, 62] came to a similar conclusion with regard to cyanidin, which conformed with the postulated head to tail linking of acetate units. Various compounds have been found to behave in varying degree as precursors of the $C_6(B)$-C_3 unit of quercetin and cyanidin, and it is generally recognized that this unit is formed from shikimic acid or from such C_6-C_3 compounds as phenylalanine whose origin may be traced to shikimic acid. Shikimic acid itself has been found to be a good precursor of quercetin, [173] p-coumaric and caffeic acids also being reasonably good, and phenylpyruvic acid has been suggested as a

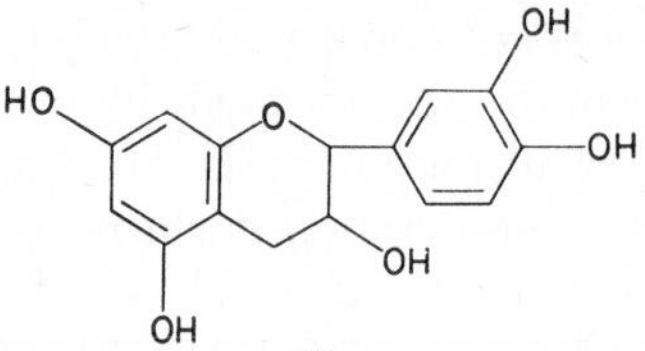

VI
Catechin

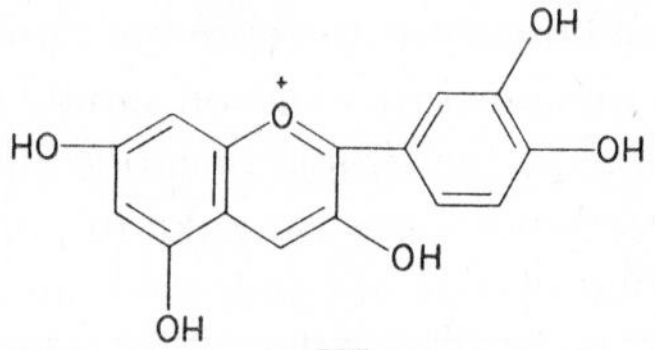

VII
Cyanidin

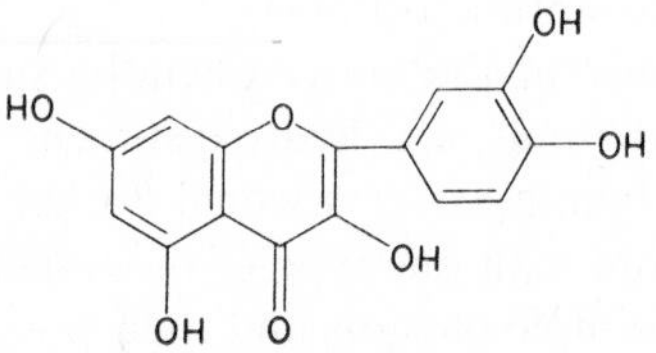

VIII
Quercetin

Fig. 2.

key intermediate in flavonol synthesis. Phenylalanine has been found to contribute notably to the B ring of cyanidin [61] and the phenolic cinnamic acids have been found to be biosynthesized from L-phenylalanine in Salvia [116] and in tobacco, [53, 123] and it is believed that all species can carry out this transformation. Speculations regarding the role of cinnamic acids in flavonoid and related biosynthesis have recently been put forward by Grisebach and Ollis [64] and the reviews of Bogorad [16] and of Neish [120, 121] are of noteworthy interest. The possible transformation of one flavonoid to another in the plant has been considered [16, 162] with the alternative that different flavonoids may arise from a key intermediate. The occurrence of both quercetin and cyanidin in *Fagopyrum esculentum* [63] indicates that there is no interconversion of flavonol and anthocyanidin as might be expected from their structures and they both arise independently from similar or related precursors. It is also considered probable that catechin may be formed before the flavonols in the biosynthetic path. [94]

Investigations have shown [6-11, 87, 88, 132, 133] leucoanthocyanidins to occur widely in nature, particularly in all *Eucalyptus* species and in mangrove barks, of those materials commonly used for tannin extracts, and these substances give many of the diagnostic chemical reactions considered to be characteristic of tannins. Leucoanthocyanidins as well as catechins have been suggested as prototypes of condensed tannins. [11] These leucoanthocyanidins yield mainly cyanidin and delphinidin on treatment with mineral acid, and chemical studies have led [12, 168] to the idea that certain leucoanthocyanidins have a flavan-3,4-diol type of structure, since this would be capable of being converted to the corresponding anthocyanidins under the influence of mineral acid. Leucoanthocyanidins and synthetic flavan-3,4-diols usually give low yields of the anthocyanidin in this reaction. [130, 138] Examples of flavan-3,4-diols have been shown to exist in nature [17,97,100] but evidence is available that the natural leucoanthocyanidins are not simple flavan-3,4-diols but are much more complicated. [36, 37, 101] Recently a scheme of systematic nomenclature for flavonoids has been suggested [48] in which the term "proanthocyanidin" is proposed for all colorless anthocyanidin-forming substances. These include the simple flavan 2:3- and 3:4-diols and 2,3,4-triols in addition to those of a more complex type. Weinges has also given further consideration to the simple and polymeric substances of this nature. [174] In a consideration of the biosynthesis of leucoanthocyanidins, reference should be made to the review of Bogorad [16] where the possible deviation of these compounds from flavonols has been indicated. For some years leucoanthocyanidins have been considered as being the immediate precursors of the naturally occurring anthocyanidins [131, 166] and biological evidence for this biosynthetic relationship has been summarized. [16] Bate-Smith and his coworkers [6, 9-11] suggested that since leucoanthocyanidins are mainly confined to woody species which do not contain appreciable amounts of anthocyanidins, the pathways leading to anthocyanidins differ from those leading to leucoanthocyanidins. Krugma [107] has found that leucoanthocyanidins are not direct precursors of anthocyanidins in *Pinus*, and this is in good agreement with Hillis's observation that the leucoanthocyanidins of some Eucalypts are synthesized *in situ*. [89]

Hydroxystilbenes have also been found in the heartwoods of various *Eucalyptus* species [81] and in the bark of spruce (*Picea excelsa*) [55-58] concomitant with the condensed tannin. The occurrence in *Eucalyptus* species of flavonoids which are related to the 3,5,4'-trihydroxystilbenes in the same way as the flavonoids of the genus *Pinus* are related to the 3,5-dihydroxystilbenes, draws attention to the probable similarity of the biosynthetic routes to these two classes of compounds. [15, 94] In connection with the work on quercetin biosynthesis [53, 173] it appears that the resorcinol ring of the 3,5,4'-trihydroxy- and of the 3,5-dihydroxystilbenes originates from acetate and possibly related units (e.g. malonate) [121] and the remaining phenylethane residue of the C skeleton is formed by the shikimic acid pathway. The two possible modes of ring closure of the intermediate derived from the condensation of a cinnamic acid with three acetate groups, or related units lead to stilbenes or to flavonoids. [15, 125]

III. CONCEPTS OF TANNIN FORMATION FROM PHENOLIC AND OTHER PRECURSORS

A. *Hydrolyzable Tannins*

The origin of the hydrolyzable tannins has been the subject of considerable speculation. Michel-Durand suggested that they could be synthesized from carbohydrate, [117] whereas Frey-Wyssling [52] favored amino acid precursors. Other workers suggested reaction sequences similar to those implicated in lignin formation and in photosynthesis. The microbial studies of Davis and his co-workers [29] on aromatic biosynthesis and recent knowledge regarding the structures of several hydrolyzable tannins has clarified the biosynthesis of the phenolic units of which these tannins are partly composed but the biosynthesis of a complete hydrolyzable tannin has not been accomplished.

The isolation of the gallotannin, chebulinic acid (IX) and the ellagitannins chebulagic acid (X) and corilagin (XI) and the elucidation of their structures has been carried out by Schmidt and his co-workers [148, 156, 159, 160] in a series of distinguished researches (Fig. 3). Chebulic acid (XII), one of the hydrolysis products of both chebulinic acid and chebulagic acid has been shown by Schmidt, Heitler and Mayer [155] and by Schmidt and Mayer [158] to have the dihydroisocoumarin structure indicated, and further evidence for this structure was obtained by Haworth and his co-workers. [59, 82, 83] The relationship of this acid to gallic acid (IV), ellagic acid (XIV) and to the hexahydroxydiphenic acid grouping (XIII) of chebulagic acid and corilagin is clear. (The hexahydroxy acid has been shown to be a chemical precursor of ellagic acid. [70]) Free ellagic acid may be formed in the fruit of *Terminalia* after abscission, by aerobic oxidation of gallates, of chebulinic acid or by hydrolysis of chebulagic acid. [71] In view of the unstable nature of free hexahydroxy diphenic acid [153] it is not considered very likely that this molecule is preformed in the plant and then esterified to the sugar. A more plausible mechanism has been suggested wherein the hexahydroxydiphenic acid group of, for example, chebulagic acid, may be formed from two adjacent galloyl residues attached at suitable positions to the sugar as in chebulinic acid, by a dehydrogenation step. [151]

Wenkert [177] has suggested that the structural units common to many diphenyl or diphenylether systems and to acyclic or heterocyclic systems do not necessarily arise biosynthetically by oxidative coupling but may be formed by carbohydrate type condensation and fission reactions of hydroaromatic precursors. Thus, a reaction between 5-dehydroshikimate with its gallate

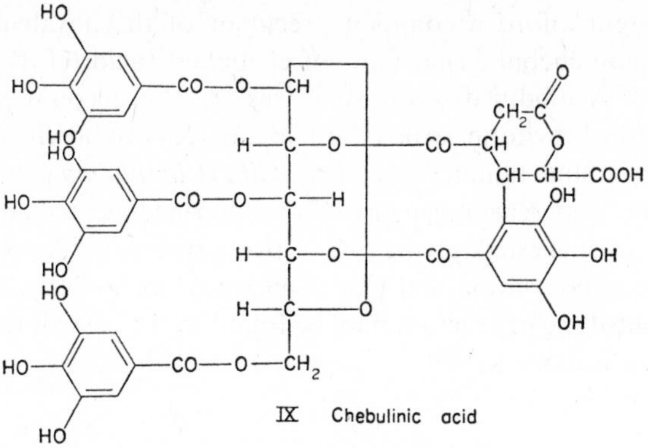

IX Chebulinic acid

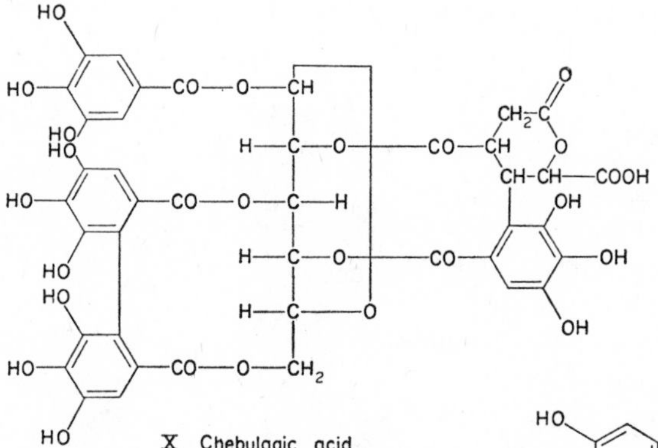

X Chebulagic acid

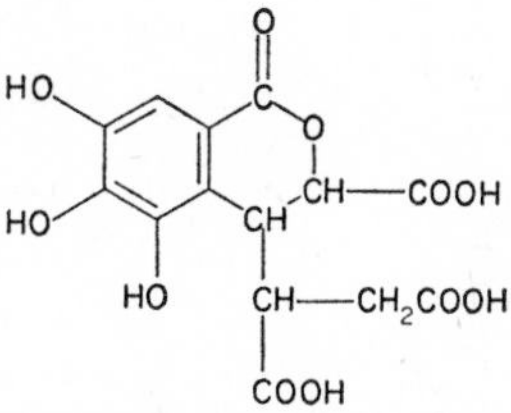

XI Corilagin

XII Chebulic acid

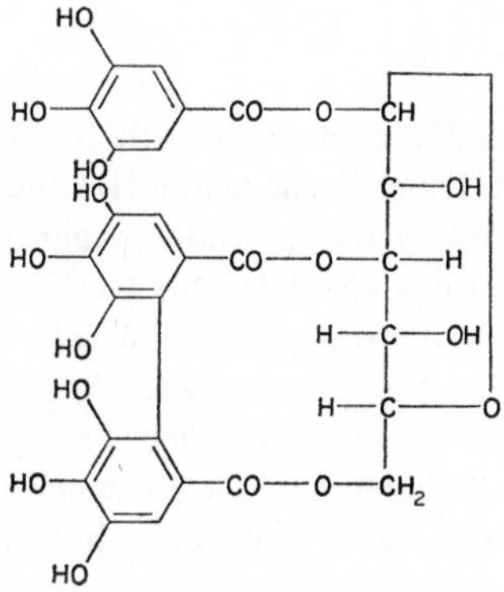

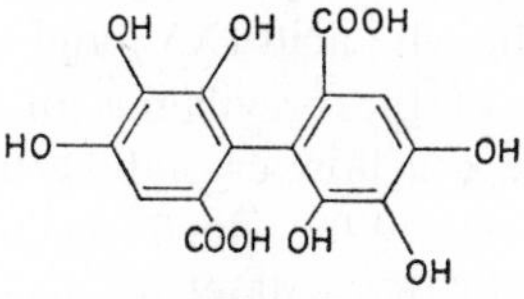

XIII Hexahydroxydiphenic acid

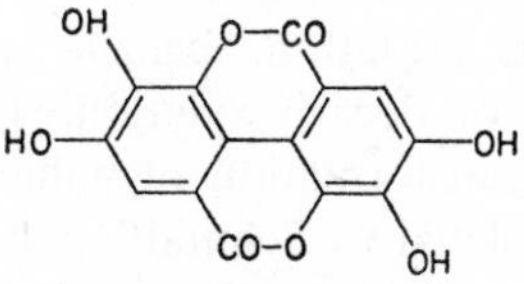

XIV Ellagic acid

FIG. 3.

oxidation product might afford a common precursor of the hexahydroxy-diphenic acid and of the chebulic acid units of chebulagic acid (cf. the suggestion of Swain [169]). A modified scheme [177] was used to account for the possible formation of the brevifolin carboxylic acid unit (XV) of brevilagin [154] (Figs. 4 and 5), the crystalline tannin from *Algarobilla* (*Caesalpinia brevifolia*) extract. [152] A benzilic acid rearrangement of the intermediate triketone in the original scheme was suggested, giving one of two α-hydroxy-β-keto acids, either of which on decarboxylation and oxidation would yield (XV). A biochemical parallel of this type of reaction may be found in the case of the biosynthesis of valine and isoleucine. [171]

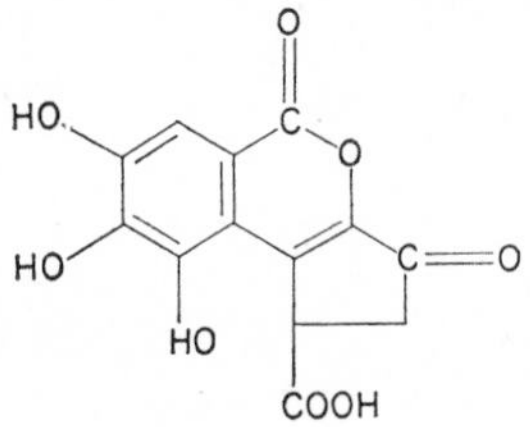

XV
Brevifolin carboxylic acid

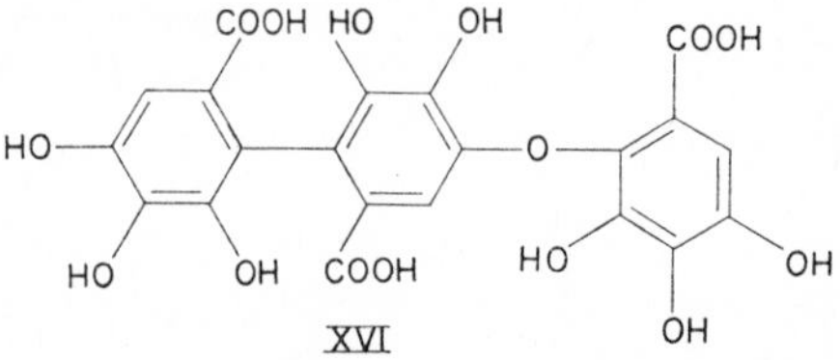

XVI
Valonic acid

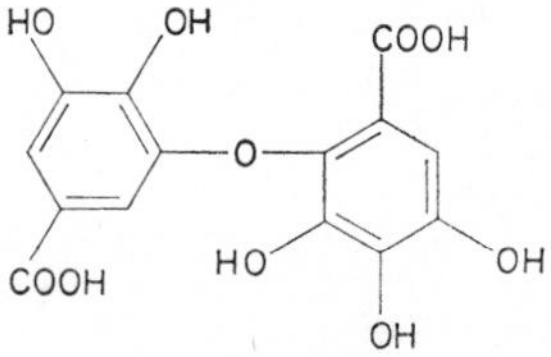

XVII
Dehydrodigallic acid

FIG. 4.

The hypothesis of Schmidt [149] is similarly concerned with relating the structures of hexahydroxydiphenic acid (XIII), chebulic acid (XII) and brevifolin carboxylic acid (XV) and is supported by recent studies regarding the structure of the brevilagins of part structures (XVIII) and (XIX) and of terchebin, a yellow crystalline tannin isolated from myrobalans (*Terminalia chebula*) [150, 151] for which structure (XX) has been put forward. An oxidative coupling of two galloyl residues either free or in the bonded state yields a diester type of derivative of hexahydroxydiphenic acid, from which derivatives of chebulic acid or brevifolin carboxylic acid might arise by processes involving oxidation, benzilic acid rearrangement and either hydrolytic cleavage or decarboxylation. The work of Mayer and his colleagues [112] on the transformation of gallic acid to 2-hydroxy-4-carboxyadipic acid is closely related to Schmidt's reaction scheme. [149] The intermediate steps in the proposed biosynthetic scheme involve an oxidation reaction leading to

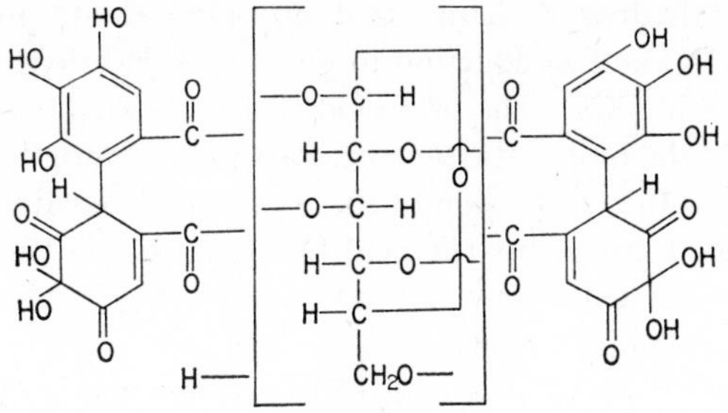

XVIII
Brevilagin I

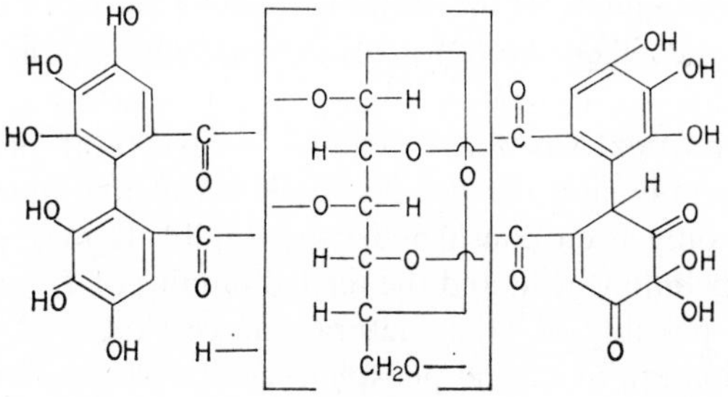

XIX
Brevilagin II

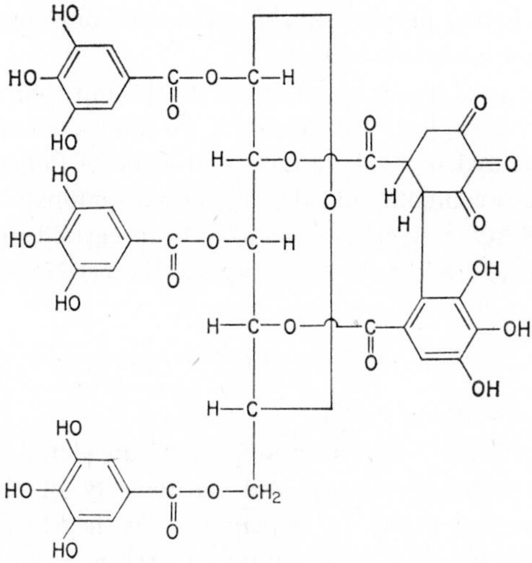

XX
Terchebin

FIG. 5.

the dehydrohexahydroxydiphenic acid grouping found in the brevilagins (XVIII) and (XIX) and a reduction to give the isohexahydroxydiphenic acid unit as in terchebin (XX). The proposed structures of these compounds thus strongly support the biogenetic scheme. Paper chromatographic evidence has been obtained for the conversion of the isohexahydroxydiphenic acid unit of terchebin to brevifolin carboxylic acid (XV) and to chebulic acid (XII) and whilst Wenkert's scheme may not be entirely ruled out the experimental evidence favors Schmidt's route.

The isolation [157] of valonic acid (XVI) from valonia (*Quercus aegilops*) extract and of the closely related dehydrodigallic acid (XVII) from chestnut leaves [111] (Fig. 4) is noteworthy as these are probably formed by an oxidative coupling with the formation of carbon-oxygen-carbon linkages. The relationship of these compounds to brevifolin carboxylic acid (XV), brevifolin, and to gallic (IV) and ellagic (XIV) acids is important to the biosynthesis of tannins by plants.

The above postulations relate mainly to structural units only of the hydrolyzable tannins and the possible build-up of the units into the larger molecules has only been considered superficially. It may well be that the formation of chebulinic acid and the related tannins of *Terminalia chebula* in particular and possibly of other natural sources, takes place by way of a stepwise combination of several phosphorylated cyclohexane carboxylic acid units of the shikimic acid type with a glucose molecule. Subsequent conversion of some of these alicyclic units into gallate units and simultaneous condensations of the type discussed above, of the other alicyclic units would give the chebulic acid residue or the hexahydroxy diphenic residue of the complex acids. Further progress in this interesting biosynthetic field depends in all probability on enzymic studies.

The observations of King and White [103, 104] concerning three *Schinopsis* (*Quebracho*) species appear to indicate a possible connection between the occurrence of the hydrolyzable tannins and some of the compounds related to their probable precursors, and the condensed tannins in these species, and are of interest. Similar investigations have been carried out regarding some *Eucalyptus* species [92] and to a lesser degree, the *Terminalia chebula* tree. [119]

B. *Condensed Tannins*

(i) *Acid Catalyzed Polymerizations*

The catechins (flavan-3-ols) have long been considered to be the phenolic precursors of condensed tannins and particularly of those occurring in *Uncaria gambir* extract and in *Acacia catechu* heartwood. The possible types of condensation or polymerization reactions that these flavan-3-ols and related compounds, such as the flavan-3,4-diols, might undergo under certain conditions may indicate how the reactivity of these compounds could be a pointer to the mode of linkage existing in tannins. The sensitivity of flavans, flavan-3-ols and flavan-3,4-diols to acids has been considered by Freudenberg and his co-workers, [38, 44-46] and for a smooth catalytic polymerization hydroxyl groups are required in the 7 and 4' positions, i.e. a p-hydroxybenzyl ether hydroxylation pattern on ring B and a resorcinol pattern on ring A. The idea that the condensed tannins derived from the barks of many forest trees and those of the heartwood of *Acacia catechu* and of *Schinopsis* species consist of catechins polymerized *post mortem* under the influence of plant acids has often been advanced by the Heidelberg school. [38, 42-46, 113, 159] Freudenberg and Maitland [42, 43] suggested that polymerization proceeded by the opening of the pyran ring to give a secondary benzyl alcohol and the electrophilic carbon atom C_2 then condensed with either of the nucleophilic carbon atoms C_6 or C_8 of another molecule to give, without elimination of water, a bifunctional dimer capable of further polymerization with possible branch chain formation. This mechanism has been found by Brown and his co-workers [19, 20] to be plausible in the light of their chemical studies of simple model compounds, whilst Freudenberg and Alonso de Lama [41] and Freudenberg and Weinges [47] have advanced chemical evidence for the formation of a catechin dimer. In this connection the studies of Mayer and Merger are worthy of mention, [114, 115] the structure of one of the catechin dimerization products obtained by Mayer and Merger being recently formulated more conclusively as (XXI) by Freudenberg, Weinges and co-workers [51, 176] following their proposed structure for a catechin dimer obtained from *Uncaria gambir*. Other similar structures are also possible. A less likely mechanism, of catechin reacting as a pair of tautomeric diphenyl-propenes has also been suggested. [38] Although the formation of a carbon-carbon linkage is a chemical possibility under the acidic conditions used [45] it is unlikely that such conditions of low pH and relatively high temperature would occur in dead or living plant tissue, and Freudenberg's acid catalyzed reaction would not appear to be a possible biogenetic route to the tannins assumed to be derived from catechin. Satisfactory comparisons of artificially produced condensation products of catechin obtained under acidic conditions and the natural tannins have not been forthcoming. Where polymerization of a flavan derivative occurs under considerably less drastic conditions [45] this type of reaction may possibly account for the formation of some condensed tannins, but the relevant studies of Hathway and Seakins [78, 80] and of Hathway [72] regarding the polymers formed by the oxidation of catechin are of considerable importance and these will be dealt with later in this section.

The flavan-3,4-diol type of leucoanthocyanidins are acid sensitive and some of these substances may form self-condensation products, in addition to the anthocyanidins, under mild conditions of pH and temperature. As previously mentioned the term proanthocyanidins has been put forward for compounds

of this nature [48, 174] and this thus includes other related structures such as
the flavan-2,3,4-triols which may be considered possible. [170, 174] Freudenberg
has reviewed [40] the possibilities of catechins and flavan-3,4-diols, being
tannin precursors, and the possible modes of linkage arising from an acid
catalyzed self-condensation have been considered. Following this author's
catechin polymerization hypothesis, a similar carbon–carbon linkage of

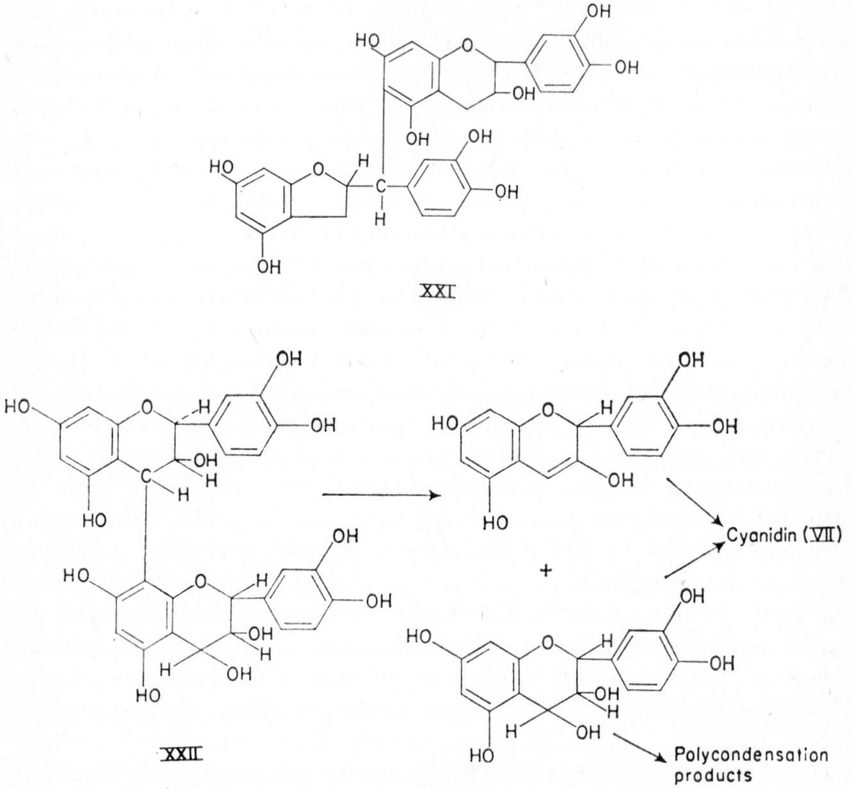

FIG. 6.

position 4 of one flavan-diol molecule with either position 6 or 8 of a second
molecule has been postulated, [40] initially yielding a structure of the type (XXII)
(Fig. 6). This view has recently been substantiated by Hergert [84] by studies
of the acid catalyzed polymerization of monomeric leucocyanidin (5,7,3',4'-
tetrahydroxyflavan-3,4-diol). The formation of anthocyanidin from such a
structure would follow from a reaction sequence [40, 47] involving rupture of
the C—C bond of this C-substituted phloroglucinol with the formation of a
true leucocyanidin and a flavan-3,4-diol, both of which would be expected to

yield the same anthocyanidin, only small amounts, however, arising from the diol. Evidence for the existence in nature of a carbon–carbon linked compound of this particular type has very recently been provided. [175] Roux [136] has advanced another postulate for the type of structures that might be derived by the self-condensation of flavan diol units. As a secondary hydroxyl group of a 7-hydroxy substituted flavan-3,4-diol might behave similar to that of a ρ-hydroxybenzyl alcohol, which readily undergo condensations giving benzyl-aryl-ethers, Roux envisages the formation of an ether bridge between the hydroxyl group of position 4 of one flavan-3,4-diol molecule and either positions 6 or 8 of a second molecule. Such linkages have been favored to some extent by Hillis and Urbach, [96] and by Hergert [84] in connection with pine bark tannin. Forsyth and Roberts describe a naturally occurring compound considered as having an ether linkage [36, 37] and recently three other similar compounds have been reported [50, 174] one of which is closely related to the substance isolated by Forsyth and Roberts. The structures of these dimeric compounds involve the linkage of a catechin or epi-catechin with one of the simple precursors of the anthocyanidins as discussed by Weinges. [174] Information is not available regarding the formation and mode of cross-linkage in such polyleucoanthocyanidins considered as being related to the condensed tannins and the ideas put forward can only be regarded as hypotheses. An acid-catalyzed mechanism seems unlikely to be responsible for the polymerization process but oxidative coupling (dehydrogenation) of flavonoid units, via a free radical mechanism may be involved (cf. refs. 5, 39, 49).

(ii) *Quinone Type Polymerizations*

Post-mortem oxidation, whether atmospheric or enzymic is known to affect the composition of polyphenols present in plant extracts and to be associated with the well-known browning phenomenon. (+)Catechin and (−)epi-catechin obtainable from the leaves of *Uncaria gambir* and the heartwood of *Acacia catechu*, respectively, are known to be associated with the dark colored condensed tannins of these species. The autoxidation of (+) catechin has been studied by Hathway and Seakins [78, 79] and by Hathway, [72] two different types of autoxidation polymers being recognized. In agreement with Freudenberg's interpretations [38, 42, 43, 46] of phlobaphene formation, at pH < 2 and elevated temperatures, a buff colored polymer was rapidly formed both in the presence and absence of oxygen. In the pH range 4–8 in the presence of oxygen, catechin was autoxidized to a red catechin tannin but when oxygen was excluded from the system, only epimerization occurred. Similar results have more recently been obtained by Evelyn, Maihs and Roux. [32] Manometric and spectroscopic evidence led Hathway and Seakins [78] to suggest that the main reaction sequence involved the initial formation of an *o*-quinone probably by a free radical mechanism, followed by an oxidative condensation to give the resulting polymer. Further work involving autoxidation of catechin and related flavans at 35°C in neutral solution [79] served to confirm the earlier view, constitutional differences tending to modify the process in some cases. Polymerization through quinones of catechol and

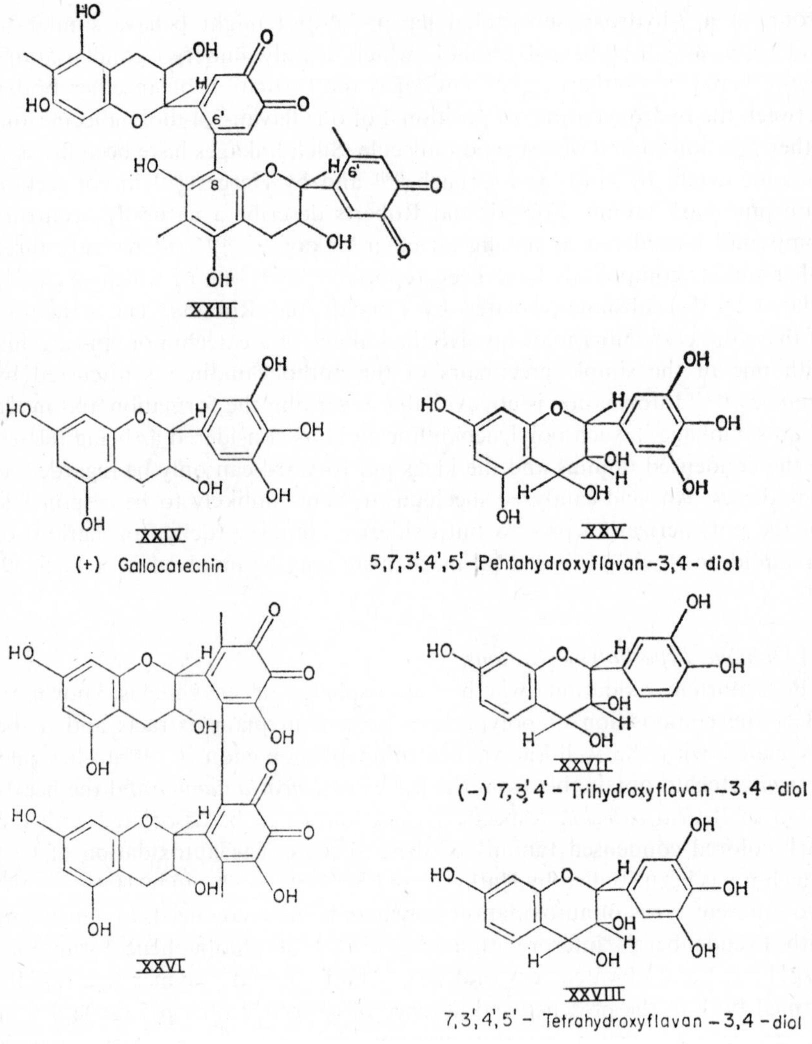

XXIII

XXIV
(+) Gallocatechin

XXV
5,7,3',4',5'-Pentahydroxyflavan-3,4-diol

XXVI

XXVII
(−) 7,3',4'-Trihydroxyflavan−3,4-diol

XXVIII
7,3',4',5'-Tetrahydroxyflavan−3,4-diol

FIG. 7.

3',4'-dihydroxyflavan involving coupling of the catechol units yielded products, the spectra of which resembled closely that of the polymer derived from 5,7-di-O-methylcatechin indicating a common autoxidation mechanism. The spectra exhibited by the autoxidation polymers of catechin and 5,7,3',4'-

tetrahydroxyflavan were found to differ considerably from those of the basic catechol-type condensation products, suggesting that catechin polymerization resulted in the formation of a product containing at least some head-to-tail linkages of the type indicated in the partial formula (XXIII) (Fig. 7) involving position 6' of the first and either 6 or 8 of the second catechin-*o*-quinone molecule. The observations of Kostanecki and his co-workers [105, 106] would possibly suggest that position 8 may be the more favored one. Evidence for the proposed linkage was obtained by Hathway, [72] an oxidative degradation of the methylated hydrogenated autoxidation polymer yielding *inter alia* small amounts of *m*-hemipinic acid.

Enzymic oxidation of catechin under mild conditions using different plant polyphenoloxidases [80] resulted in the formation of a polymer precisely similar to that produced by autoxidation. Additional evidence for the head-to-tail polymerization pattern of this compound was obtained by studying the oxidation, by polyphenol-oxidase, of a mixture of model phenolic substrates. The enzymic oxidation polymer of catechin gave several of the tests associated with tannins such as the gelatin precipitation test and being partially retained by hide powder. It had identical tannin properties to, and similar absorption spectra and elementary analysis as the main tannin extractives of *Uncaria gambir* leaves and *Acacia catechu* heartwood, and clearly a close structural relationship exists between the catechin polymer and these natural tannins, and it is highly probable that these tannins arise by similar oxidations of catechin type precursors. Phlobatannins differing considerably from those considered above, have been isolated from *Acacia mollisima* bark, and it is obviously not possible [80, 97] to regard the phlobatannins as members of a closely related chemical family although they may well arise through free radical polymerization.

A related investigation has been carried out by Hathway [73] concerning the tannins of *Quercus* species, in the leaves and bark of which (+)catechin and (+)gallocatechin (XXIV) (Fig. 7) occur together with several leucoanthocyanidins. It has been suggested that metabolites of these compounds originate in the leaves by reaction sequences of the type considered by Neish and his co-workers [173] and by Hathway. [68, 69] A polyphenoloxidase present in the cambium acted more readily on the pyrogallol type phenols [(+)gallocatechin and a leucodelphinidin (5,7,3',4',5'-pentahydroxy-flavan-3,4-diol) (XXV)] than on the catechol type [(+)catechin] to form polymeric products. Aerobic oxidation of (+)gallocatechin by the oak cambium polyphenoloxidase was found to proceed by quinone polymerization, the product being considered to have tail-to-tail linked units, since its spectrum agreed closely with the spectra of the polymers obtained from the basic catechol systems. [79] A partial structure is indicated (XXVI) for what is considered to be the first change that occurs in the initial quinone polymerization. [76, 77] Roberts [127] and Roberts and Myers [129] in connection with tea fermentation processes have found tail-to-tail linkages to be most probably formed by enzymic oxidation of *epi*-gallo-catechin and of *epi*-gallocatechin gallate, *o*-quinone formation being the initial step[126] the process however terminating at the dimeric product (theaflavin) stage, [128] these compounds appearing to be relatively stable to further oxidation. In view of the latter fact the further polymerization of gallocatechin beyond the two-units stage by a tail to tail process is considered to be somewhat unlikely. [170] The higher-molecular-weight tannin might contain linkages of all the other types discussed involving other positions on the molecules. Hathway[73] concluded that the pyrogallol phenols formed in the leaves of *Quercus* species, are translocated to the cambium where they are oxidized by the polyphenoloxidase present, the resulting phlobatannins being stored in the bark. The recently established structures of ginkgetin and related compounds of the biflavonyl type [2, 3] which are found in some cases along with the polymeric leucoanthocyanidins [9] indicate the existence in nature of compounds of this type with C—C and ether linkages. Whilst an oxidative coupling mechanism [3, 5] of flavonoid precursors seems very plausible for the production of these biflavonyls and therefore of related compounds considered to have similar linkages [147] some criticism has been directed [84] at the quinone type structures suggested for some condensed tannins. However, evidence consistent with the quinone polymerization mechanism has been provided by Rex[124] who showed by electron para-magnetic resonance studies, the presence of free radicals in, *inter alia*, con-densed tannin extracts. Further investigations are obviously required but the experimental approach involving oxidative enzymes is, however, likely to prove useful in providing a key to the structures of many of the polymeric flavonoid type compounds allied to the condensed tannins. It has been considered probable that since a polyphenoloxidase occurs in the cambium of the spruce (*Picea excelsa*)†, the stem bark tannins of this species may originate by aerobic oxidation through quinone, of such hydroxystilbene aglycones [55, 58] and possibly flavonoids present, by this enzyme.

It is therefore reasonable to suppose that various condensed tannins are synthesized in forest trees by aerobic oxidation of flavan-3-ol and possibly flavan-3,4-diol type precursors although the physiological processes are not defined. Some copolymerization [85, 89, 91] of these types of compounds is not beyond the realms of possibility (cf. ref. 36, 37), and in the case of the que-bracho tannins both classes of compounds appear to be intermediates as indicated by the studies of King and White, [103, 104] Roux and Evelyn [141] and Roux, [134] thus supporting the original suggestion of Bate-Smith and Swain. [11]

It is not considered timely‡ to exclude the possibility of various condensed

---

† W. Grassmann; personal communication to D. E. Hathway.

‡ D. E. Hathway and R. D. Haworth; personal communication.

tannins being some form of polymer derived from the precursors of the flavan-3-ol, and of flavan-3,4-diol and other types of polyphenols with which the condensed tannins are concomitant in several cases. [89, 92, 103, 104] As no really general procedure has yet been devised for the isolation of a true condensed tannin and the subsequent elucidation of a detailed structure, it would be difficult to obtain evidence for such a possibility. The recent studies of Roux and Paulus [145, 146] are of considerable interest and importance in this respect as these authors have isolated by countercurrent distribution and chromatographic procedures small amounts of various polymeric leucofisetinidin tannins from extracts of black wattle (*Acacia mearnsii* [18]) heartwood. It has been adduced that the 4-hydroxyl group is most likely implicated in ether linkages of flavonoid limits in these tannins but the presence of more than one type of linkage is considered highly probable in these condensed leucofisetinidin tannins of biological origin.

(iii) *Possible Polyleucoanthocyanidins of Unknown Structure*

A number of authors have put forward ideas regarding the possible relevance of leucoanthocyanidins to some of the condensed tannins, and these ideas apply to eucalypt and mangrove tan barks which are exceptionally rich in leucoanthocyanidins. [86–88, 102] Hillis[87, 88] suggested that leucoanthocyanidins originate in the leaves of plants and are the immediate precursors of bark and heartwood extractives. The studies of Roux and co-workers [135, 139–141] have indicated the possible association of the monomeric and more complex leucoanthocyanidins of similar hydroxylation pattern in the extractives from black wattle and quebracho. Presumptive evidence for the transformation in the sapwood of quebracho of the monomeric leucofisetinidin [(−)7,3′,4′-trihydroxyflavan-3,4-diol] (XXVII) to the various polymeric forms present in the heartwood led to this compound being regarded by Roux [135, 144] as a highly significant precursor in this species (cf. refs. 103, 104). Chemical evidence for the presence of flavan-3,4-diol groups in quebracho tannin extract [134, 140, 141] has been presented, and the transformation referred to by Roux [135, 144] appears to be one of the most important which occurs in this complex mixture of extractives. Some of the black wattle bark (*Acacia mollissima*) now renamed *Acacia mearnsii* [18] tannins (cf. ref. 80) are considered to be related in the main to the monomeric leucorobinetinidin (7,3′,4′,5′-tetrahydroxyflavan-3,4-diol) (XXVIII) and to leucofisetinidin both of which occur in small amounts in the bark [137] and another monomeric leucoanthocyanidin, (+)mollisacacidin [(+)7,3′4′-trihydroxyflavan-3,4-diol] is stated to be of significance in considering the complex tannins of black wattle heartwood (cf. refs. 145, 146). The catechin, (−)7,3′,4′,5′-tetrahydroxy-flavan-3-ol [(−)robinetinidol] has long been regarded as a possible prototype of the wattle tannins, [142] but there is no chemical or biochemical evidence for this supposition. The presence of the related (−)7,3′,4′-trihydroxyflavan-

3-ol [(−)fisetinidol] in black wattle heartwood has however been demonstrated. [143] Although both simple and complex leucoanthocyanidins could originate from common precursors, Roux [135] states that the polymeric leucoanthocyanidins of wattle and quebracho extracts arise from the monomeric flavan-3,4-diols by enzymic condensation *in vivo*. From a consideration of the interrelationships of flavonoid compounds of wattle bark extract, Drewes and Roux [30] state that the high concentration of polymeric leucorobinetinidin and leucofisetinidin tannins in the bark compared with the low concentration of the simple flavan-3,4-diols and other flavonoids, suggests that enzymic polymerization of the flavan-3,4-diol to tannin occurs more rapidly and completely in the bark than in the heartwood where the ratio of the amounts of the flavonoids to tannins present is often reversed. The flavandiol units must remain intact or potentially available in the polymers since anthocyanidins are formed on treatment with acids. If such a polymerization of monomeric leucoanthocyanidins is possible, it certainly accounts for only a small proportion of the tanning action of wattle and quebracho extracts. The whole subject needs much more work before the underlying suppositions can be regarded as final.

(iv) *The Possible Mode of Origin of Tannins*

The results of several of the researches quoted earlier have indicated the probable regions of maximum accumulation or deposition of tannins in certain species. The work on the tannins of *Quercus* species involving ringing experiments led Hathway [73, 75] to the conclusion that the pyrogallol phenols formed in the leaves are translocated downwards by the sieve tube system to the cambium where they undergo oxidation through quinone, by the cambium polyphenoloxidase, and the resulting tannins are subsequently stored in the outer bark. Studies on the distribution of tannins in oak stem bark confirm this view and are in accordance with the suppositions of Hergert and Goldschmid. [84] The fact that phlobatannin occurs in the bark and not the heartwood of this species is taken as implying that the cambium does not take part in the formation of heartwood extractives. Tannins are products of secondary metabolism. From studies of *Eucalyptus marginata* [87, 88] Hillis has shown that most of the phenolic materials (leucoanthocyanidins) are in the sapwood and the amount increases at the sapwood–heartwood boundary where they are converted to the less soluble tannins. As a result of similar work, King and White [103, 104] and Roux [135] observe that in the sapwood–heartwood transformation of constituents of *Schinopsis* (*Quebracho*) species, carbohydrates and related moieties are probably metabolized in the living cells of the sapwood with formation of the flavan-type precursors. Roux and Evelyn [141] suggest that after the deposition of these flavans they are converted into tannins or related substances, a view also supported by Hillis. [89] Further studies [93] indicate the wide variety of polyphenols that exist in the various tissues of *Eucalyptus astringens* and *E. marginata*. Hillis[90] has recently compiled a comprehensive review of the existing data regarding the formation and distribution of polyphenols within the tree. Whilst the possibility of translocation of alicyclic precursors of the shikimic acid type is not excluded, an explanation in better accord with the recently obtained data is that sucrose and related oligosaccharides are translocated and are converted *in situ*[89, 91, 92] together with stored carbohydrate into the relevant polyphenols by the local enzyme systems.

IV. SOME FACTORS INFLUENCING THE FORMATION OF TANNIN IN PLANTS

Many factors affect the rate of biosynthesis of tannin and its accumulation in the barks and wood of forest trees. Some of the evidence is conflicting and in general the effect of these factors is little understood.[90] Forest trees, particularly in temperate zones, are fairly high demanders and are reasonably selective where suitable sites for growth and cultivation are concerned. High nutrient status favors rapid growth of the trees and, in the case of tannin-bearing species, the formation and accumulation of a high concentration of tannin.

An investigation of the tannin content of the butt and crown regions of the stem bark of both dominant and suppressed Douglas fir (*Pseudotsuga taxifolin*) trees at five different localities showed[74] that the dominant trees contain a significantly higher proportion of tannin and other extractives than the suppressed trees. The figures were comparable with those given by Kurth and Chan[109] for indigenous trees in the United States. This supports the suggested correlation of tannin content with rate of growth of the tree, since suppression results from low nutrient status and inadequate sunlight during subsequent growth. It has been cited that oak trees which grow at high elevation appear to require deeper soil and a larger proportion of humus than those at a lower altitude, which depend more on the mineral content of the soil than on its texture.[172] In contrast to these suppositions, it is interesting that the botanist, Howes[98] suggests that the barks of European oak trees which grow in poor, dry soil have a higher tannin content than those growing in the damp lowlands, but the statement is vague and may have arisen from observations which were not made on a statistical basis and for which proper allowance for controls were not made. Another study[1] of the factors influencing the variation of tannin content of the bark of the oak (*Quercus sessiliflora*) indicated that the most important factor in tannin formation appeared to be the histological structure of the bark and in this work the amount of tannin was significantly higher in young and old trees, but these observations do not agree with the bulk of the evidence.[75, 98]

Vogel[172] cites a mild climate, the maximum amount of strong sunlight and a high nutrient status of the soil as the requirements for rapid growth of the chestnut tree (*Castanea sativa*) and for a high tannin content of the heart-wood, and in agreement with this, Norway spruce (*Picea abies*) has a thin bark of low tannin content when grown on poor, stony and dry soil, but on a moist soil of high nutrient level, the spruce grows quite rapidly and the bark is strong and rich in tannin. Altitude may affect tannin production since the tree is then growing under unfavorable conditions where its rate of growth would be low. [54] Variations in the tannin content due to the locality of the trees have been quoted for some species. [1, 75, 90] The bark of trees of Acacia species grown in high rainfall areas has been found to contain less tannin than that from trees grown in a lower rainfall area. [163] More recently the percentage of non-tannins was found to decrease with increasing rainfall and the ratio of tannin to non-tannin varied directly with rainfall. This effect and other factors have been further studied over an extended period by Zeijlemaker. [183] Observations made with Sitka spruce trees [74] all of which were 27 years old, indicated that there is probably no significant seasonal variation in tannin content of the stem bark of trees of this age. It is considered likely that any increase in tannin with increase in age is balanced by an increase in the bark tissue, the net result being that the tannin level remains without any significant variation throughout the season. It is concluded that there is seemingly no connection between the sap streaming season and the maximum tannin content of the bark as has often been recorded in the literature of forestry.

An investigation of American sumac has been carried out by Sievers and Clarke [165] who record a high seasonal change in the tannin content of the leaves, the samples taken in mid-summer having considerably more tannin. Heredity or genetic factors were also found important, and plants with high nutrient status contained less tannin than those grown on poor soil. This is all very complicated, however, as the tannin of sumac shrubs is laid down annually in the leaves and the tannin content of sumac leaves (*Rhus copallina* and *R. glabra*) is supposed to vary inversely with the height of leaves from the ground. [24] The height factor has been quoted for black wattle (*Acacia mollissima*) bark, that near the top of the tree having appreciably less tannin than the bark from around the base [180] and further examples illustrating this point have been quoted by Hillis. [90] Seasonal and growth variations as related to the amount of leucoanthocyanidins and other polyphenols present in Eucalyptus [87, 91] and Acacia species [182, 183] have been recorded and Hillis and Swain [95] have studied the effect of light in stimulating the formation of polyphenols in various tissues of Prunus species. Black wattle grows well in soils that are well drained even if the humus content is low and a definite correlation between bark thickness and tannin content has been claimed. Individual trees show variations in tannin content which are attributable to genetical causes. [122]

In this connection mention might also be made of the effect of the cation concentration of the medium on mangrove trees where the stem barks contain up to 35 per cent tannin. These trees frequent sheltered swamps and poorly aerated mud flats in tropical areas, and the mixture of fresh and salt water gives rise to the ideal conditions in which the mangrove thrives. Growth is often so rapid that seedlings have been noted as growing at the seemingly record rate of up to 20 in. in as many hours. Mangrove barks contain a considerable amount of salt as a result of their salt-water environment but this does not adversely affect the formation and accumulation of water soluble tannin. In quebracho trees (*Schinopsis balansea* and *S. lorentzii*), the heartwood contains up to 25 per cent tannin and these trees grow in the Chaco slightly above sea level, and in soils of high potassium content such that the fibrous roots are largely in fresh water but the main roots reach into salt water. In lesser degree a cation concentration is necessary for the rapid growth and high tannin yield of oak forests.

V. SUMMARY

The biogenesis of some of the phenolic and non-aromatic precursors of tannins is briefly considered and mechanisms by which the tannins may arise are surveyed. Reference is made to the possible mode of origin of tannins and to some of the factors influencing the formation of tannin in plants.

ACKNOWLEDGEMENTS

The author wishes to thank the Director and Council of the British Leather Manufacturers' Research Association for permission to publish this chapter, and Dr. D. E. Hathway for many helpful discussions and suggestions.

REFERENCES

1. ALEXA, G., SIRETEANU, L., BURGHELEA, G. and CHIRIȚĂ, A. *Acad. Rep. Populare Romine, Filiala Iasi, Studii Cercetări Stiint. Chim.* **9**, 93 (1958).
2. BAKER, W., FINCH, A. C. M., OLLIS, W. D. and ROBINSON, K. W. *J. Chem. Soc.* **1963**, 1477.
3. BAKER, W. and OLLIS, W. D. In *Recent Developments in the Chemistry of Natural Phenolic Compounds*, p. 152, ed. W. D. Ollis. Pergamon Press, London, 1961.
4. BALINSKY, D. and DAVIES, D. D. *Biochem. J.* **80**, 292; 295; 300 (1961).
5. BARTON, D. H. R. and COHEN, T. In *Festschrift A. Stoll*, p. 117. Birkhauser, Basel, 1957.
6. BATE-SMITH, E. C. *J. Exptl. Botany* **4**, 1 (1952).
7. BATE-SMITH, E. C. *Biochem. J.* **58**, 122 (1954).
8. BATE-SMITH, *Chem. and Ind.* (*London*) **1954**, 1457.
9. BATE-SMITH, E. C. and LERNER, N. H. *Biochem. J.* **58**, 126 (1954).
10. BATE-SMITH, E. C. and METCALFE, C. R. *J. Linnean Soc. London, Botany* **60**, 669 (1957).
11. BATE-SMITH, E. C. and SWAIN, T. *Chem. and Ind.* (*London*) **1953**, 377.
12. BAUER, L., BIRCH, A. J. and HILLIS, W. E. *Chem. and Ind.* (*London*) **1954**, 433.
13. BERNHARD, K. and ALBRECHT, H. *Helv. Chim. Acta* **30**, 627 (1947).
14. BIRCH, A. J. *Fortschr. Chem. Org. Naturstoffe* **14**, 186 (1957).
15. BIRCH, A. J. and DONOVAN, F. W. *Australian J. Chem.* **6**, 360 (1953).
16. BOGORAD, L. *Ann. Rev. Plant Physiol.* **9**, 417 (1958).

17. Bottomley, W. *Chem. and Ind. (London)* **1954**, 516.
18. Brenan, J. P. M. and Melville, R. *Kew Bulletin* **14**, 17 (1960).
19. Brown, B. R., Cummings, W. and Somerfield, G. A. *J. Chem. Soc.* **1957**, 3757.
20. Brown, B. R. and Cummings, W. *J. Chem. Soc.* **1958**, 4302.
21. Brücker, W. *Planta* **48**, 627 (1957).
22. Brücker, W. and Hashem, M. *Flora* **157**, 57 (1962).
23. Burton, D. and Nursten, H. E. In *The Chemistry of Vegetable Tannins*, p. 57. Symposium Soc. Leather Trades' Chemists, Croydon, 1956.
24. Clarke, I. D., Rogers, J. S., Sievers, A. F. and Hopp, H. *U.S. Dep. Agr. Tech. Bull.* No. 986 (1949).
25. Comte, P., Ville, A., Zwingelstein, G., Favre-Bonvin, J. and Mentzer, C. *Bull. Soc. Chim. Biol.* **40**, 1117 (1958).
26. Comte, P., Ville, A., Zwingelstein, G., Favre-Bonvin, J. and Mentzer, C. *Bull. Soc. Chim. Biol.* **42**, 1079 (1960).
27. Conn, E. E. and Swain, T. *Chem. and Ind. (London)* **1961**, 592.
28. Cornthwaite, D. and Haslam, E. *J. Chem. Soc.* **1965**, 3008.
29. Davis, B. D. In *Amino Acid Metabolism*, p. 799, eds. W. D. McElroy and B. Glass. Johns Hopkins Press, Baltimore, 1955.
30. Drewes, S. E. and Roux, D. G. *Biochem. J.* **87**, 167 (1963).
31. Evans, W. C. *Biochem. J.* **41**, 373 (1947).
32. Evelyn, S. R., Maihs, E. A. and Roux, D. G. *Biochem. J.* **76**, 23 (1960).
33. Fischer, H. O. L. and Dangschat, G. *Ber.* **65**, 1008 (1932).
34. Fischer, H. O. L. and Dangschat, G. *Helv. Chim. Acta* **18**, 1206 (1935).
35. Fischer, H. O. L. and Dangschat, G. *Biochim. Biophys. Acta* **4**, 199 (1950).
36. Forsyth, W. G. C. and Roberts, J. B. *Chem. and Ind. (London)* **1958**, 755.
37. Forsyth, W. G. C. and Roberts, J. B. *Biochem. J.* **74**, 374 (1960).
38. Freudenberg, K. *Sci. Proc. Roy. Dublin Soc.* **22**, 153 (1956).
39. Freudenberg, K. *Nature* **183**, 1152 (1958).
40. Freudenberg, K. *Experientia* **16**, 101 (1960).
41. Freudenberg, K. and Alonso de Lama, J. M. *Ann.* **612**, 78 (1958).
42. Freudenberg, K. and Maitland, P. *Ann.* **510**, 193 (1934).
43. Freudenberg, K. and Maitland, P. *Collegium* **776**, 656 (1934).
44. Freudenberg, K., Stocker, J. H. and Porter, J. *Ber.* **90**, 957 (1957).
45. Freudenberg, K. and Weinges, K. *Ann.* **590**, 140 (1954).
46. Freudenberg, K. and Weinges, K. *Fortschr. Chem. Org. Naturstoffe* **16**, 1 (1958).
47. Freudenberg, K. and Weinges, K. *Chem. and Ind. (London)* **1959**, 486.
48. Freudenberg, K. and Weinges, K. *Tetrahedron* **8**, 336 (1960).
49. Freudenberg, K. and Weinges, K. In *The Chemistry of Flavonoid Compounds*, p. 214, ed. T. A. Geissman. Pergamon Press, London, 1962.
50. Freudenberg, K. and Weinges, K. *Angew. Chem. Internat. edit.* **1**, 158 (1962).
51. Fruedenberg, K. and Weinges, K. *Ann.* **668**, 92 (1963).
52. Frey-Wyssling, A. *Naturwiss.* **26**, 624 (1938).
53. Geissman, T. A. and Swain, T. *Chem. and Ind. (London)* **1957**, 984.
54. Gnamm, H. *Die Gerbstoffe und Gerbmittel.* Wissenschaftliche Verlagsgesellschaft m.b.H. Stuttgart 1933.
55. Grassmann, W., Deffner, G., Schuster, E. and Pauckner, W. *Ber.* **89**, 2523 (1956).
56. Grassmann, W., Endres, H., Brockhaus, R. and Merkle, K. *Ber.* **90**, 2416 (1957).
57. Grassmann, W., Endres, H. and Pauckner, W. *Ber.* **91**, 136 (1958).
58. Grassmann, W., Endres, H., Pauckner, W. and Mathes, H. *Ber.* **90**, 1125 (1957).
59. Grimshaw, J., Haworth, R. D., Pindred, H. K. and Silva, L. B. *Chem. and Ind. (London)* **1954**, 1508.
60. Grisebach, H. *Z. Naturforsch.* **12b**, 227, 597 (1957).
61. Grisebach, H. *Z. Naturforsch.* **13b**, 335 (1958).
62. Grisebach, H. In *Proc. Intern. Congr. Biochem., 4th Congr. Vienna*, vol. 2, p. 56. Pergamon Press, London, 1958.
63. Grisebach, H. and Bopp, M. *Z. Naturforsch.* **14b**, 485 (1959).
64. Grisebach, H. and Ollis, W. D. *Experientia* **17**, 4 (1961).

65. GROSS, S. R. *J. Biol. Chem.* **233**, 1146 (1958).
66. HASLAM, E. and HAWORTH, R. D. *Progress in Organic Chemistry* **6**, 1 (1964).
67. HASLAM, E., HAWORTH, R. D. and KNOWLES, P. F. *J. Chem. Soc.* **1961**, 1854.
68. HATHWAY, D. E. *Biochem. J.* **63**, 380 (1956).
69. HATHWAY, D. E. In *The Chemistry of Vegetable Tannins*, p. 57, Symposium Soc. Leather Trades' Chemists, Croydon, 1956.
70. HATHWAY, D. E. *J. Chem. Soc.* **1957**, 519.
71. HATHWAY, D. E. *Biochem. J.* **67**, 445 (1957).
72. HATHWAY, D. E. *J. Chem. Soc.* **1958**, 520.
73. HATHWAY, D. E. *Biochem. J.* **70**, 34 (1958).
74. HATHWAY, D. E. In *Report on Forest Research* 1958–59, p. 115, H.M.S.O., London.
75. HATHWAY, D. E. *Biochem. J.* **71**, 533 (1959).
76. HATHWAY, D. E. Lecture given to Intern. Union Leather Chemists Societies, 6th Congr. Munich, 1959.
77. HATHWAY, D. E. In *Wood Extractives*, p. 191, ed. W. E. Hillis, Academic Press, New York, 1962.
78. HATHWAY, D. E. and SEAKINS, J. W. T. *Nature* **176**, 218 (1955).
79. HATHWAY, D. E. and SEAKINS, J. W. T. *J. Chem. Soc.* **1957**, 1562.
80. HATHWAY, D. E. and SEAKINS, J. W. T. *Biochem. J.* **67**, 239 (1957).
81. HATHWAY, D. E. and SEAKINS, J. W. T. *J. Biochem.* **72**, 369 (1959).
82. HAWORTH, R. D., PINDRED, H. K. and JEFFRIES, P. R. *J. Chem. Soc.* **1954**, 3617.
83. HAWORTH, R. D. and SILVA, L. B. *Chem. and Ind. (London)* **1954**, 1506.
84. HERGERT, H. L. In *The Chemistry of Flavonoid Compounds*, p. 553, ed. T. A. Geissman. Pergamon Press, London, 1962.
85. HERGERT, H. L. and GOLDSCHMID, O. *J. Org. Chem.* **23**, 700 (1958).
86. HILLIS, W. E. *Nature* **175**, 597 (1955).
87. HILLIS, W. E. *Australian J. Biol. Sci.* **9**, 263 (1956).
88. HILLIS, W. E. In *The Chemistry of Vegetable Tannins*, p. 121. Symposium Soc. Leather Trades' Chemists, Croydon, 1956.
89. HILLIS, W. E. *Nature* **182**, 1371 (1958).
90. HILLIS, W. E. In *Wood Extractives*, p. 59, ed. W. E. Hillis, Academic Press, New York, 1962.
91. HILLIS, W. E. and CARLE, A. *Holzforschung* **12**, 136 (1958).
92. HILLIS, W. E. and CARLE, A. *Biochem. J.* **74**, 607 (1960).
93. HILLIS, W. E. and CARLE, A. *Biochem. J.* **82**, 435 (1962).
94. HILLIS, W. E. and HASEGAWA, M. *Biochem. J.* **83**, 503 (1962).
95. HILLIS, W. E. and SWAIN, T. *J. Sci. Food Agric.* **10**, 135 (1959).
96. HILLIS, W. E. and URBACH, G. *J. Appl. Chem. (London)* **9**, 665 (1957).
97. HILLIS, W. E. and URBACH, G. *Nature* **187**, 657 (1958).
98. HOWES, F. N. *Vegetable Tanning Materials*, p. 6. Butterworth, London, 1953.
99. KEPPLER, H. H. *Chem. and Ind. (London)* **1956**, 380.
100. KING, F. E. and BOTTOMLEY, W. *Chem. and Ind. (London)* **1953**, 1368.
101. KING, F. E. and CLARK-LEWIS, J. W. *J. Chem. Soc.* **1955**, 3384.
102. KING, H. G. C. and WHITE, T. In *The Chemistry of Vegetable Tannins*, p. 31, Symposium Soc. Leather Trades' Chemists, Croydon, 1956.
103. KING, H. G. C. and WHITE, T. *J. Soc. Leather Trades' Chemists* **41**, 368 (1957).
104. KING, H. G. C. and WHITE, T. *Proc. Chem. Soc.* **1957**, 341.
105. KOSTANECKI, ST. V. and LAMPE, V. *Ber.* **39**, 4007 (1906).
106. KONSTANECKI, ST. V. and TAMBOR, J. *Ber.* **35**, 1867 (1902).
107. KRUGMA, S. *Forest Sci.* **2**, 273 (1956).
108. KURSANOV, A. L. and ZAPROMETOV, M. N. *Atompraxis* **4**, 280 (1958).
109. KURTH, E. F. and CHAN, F. L. *J. Am. Leather Chemists Assoc.* **48**, 20 (1953).
110. LOUDON, J. D. and SUMMERS, L. A. *J. Chem. Soc.* **1954**, 1134.
111. MAYER, W. *Ann.* **518**, 34 (1952).
112. MAYER, W., BACHMANN, R. and KRAUS, F. *Ber.* **88**, 316 (1955).
113. MAYER, W. and BAUNI, G. *Leder* **7**, 35 (1956).
114. MAYER, W. and MERGER, F. *Chem. and Ind. (London)* **1959**, 485.

115. MAYER, W. and MERGER, F. *Ann.* **644**, 70; 79 (1961).
116. McCALLA, D. R. and NEISH, A. C. *Can. J. Biochem. and Physiol.* **37**, 537 (1959).
117. MICHEL-DURAND, E. *Rev. Gén. Botan.* **44**, 161 (1932).
118. MITSUHASHI, S. and DAVIS, B. D. *Biochim. Biophys. Acta* **15**, 268 (1954).
119. NAYUDAMMA, Y., RAO, J. B. and SASTRY, K. N. S. *Bull. Central Leather Research Inst. Madras (India)* **5**, 495 (1959).
120. NEISH, A. C. *Ann. Rev. Plant. Physiol.* **11**, 55 (1960).
121. NEISH, A. C. In *Biochemistry of Phenolic Compounds*, p. 295, ed. J. B. Harborne. Academic Press, London, 1964.
122. PHILP, J. and SHERRY, S. P. *J. South African Forestry Assoc.* **14**, 1 (1946).
123. REID, W. W. *Chem. and Ind. (London)* **1958**, 1439.
124. REX, R. W. *Nature* **188**, 1185 (1960).
125. RICKARDS, R. W. In *Recent Developments in the Chemistry of Natural Phenolic Compounds*, p. 1, ed. W. D. Ollis. Pergamon Press, London, 1961.
126. ROBERTS, E. A. H. *Biochem. J.* **34**, 500 (1940).
127. ROBERTS, E. A. H. *Chem. and Ind. (London)* **1957**, 1355.
128. ROBERTS, E. A. H. In *The Chemistry of Flavonoid Compounds*, p. 468, ed. T. A. Geissman. Pergamon Press, London, 1962.
129. ROBERTS, E. A. H. and MYERS, M. *J. Sci. Food Agr.* **10**, 167 (1959).
130. ROBERTSON, A. V. *Can. J. Chem.* **37**, 1946 (1959).
131. ROBINSON, R. *Nature* **137**, 172 (1936).
132. ROBINSON, R. and ROBINSON, G. M. *Biochem. J.* **27**, 206 (1933).
133. ROBINSON, R. and ROBINSON, G. M. *J. Chem. Soc.* **1935**, 744.
134. ROUX, D. G. *Chem. and Ind. (London)* **1958**, 161.
135. ROUX, D. G. *Nature* **181**, 1454 (1958).
136. ROUX, D. G. *J. Am. Leather Chemists' Assoc.* **54**, 614 (1959).
137. ROUX, D. G. *Chem. and Ind. (London)* **1962**, 278.
138. ROUX, D. G. and BILL, M. C. *Nature* **183**, 42 (1959).
139. ROUX, D. G. and EVELYN, S. R. *Biochem. J.* **69**, 530 (1958).
140. ROUX, D. G. and EVELYN, S. R. *Biochem. J.* **70**, 344 (1958).
141. ROUX, D. G. and EVELYN, S. R. *Biochem. J.* **76**, 17 (1960).
142. ROUX, D. G. and MAIHS, E. A. *Nature* **182**, 1798 (1958).
143. ROUX, D. G. and PAULUS, E. *Biochem. J.* **78**, 120 (1961).
144. ROUX, D. G. and PAULUS, E. *Biochem. J.* **78**, 785 (1961).
145. ROUX, D. G. and PAULUS, E. *Biochem. J.* **80**, 476 (1961).
146. ROUX, D. G. and PAULUS, E. *Biochem. J.* **82**, 320 (1962).
147. ROUX, D. G. and PAULUS, E. *Biochem. J.* **84**, 416 (1962).
148. SCHMIDT, O. T. In *The Chemistry of Vegetable Tannins*, Leather Trades' Chemists, Croydon, 1956.
149. SCHMIDT, O. T. In *Recent Developments in the Chemistry of Natural Phenolic Compounds*, p. 139, ed. W. D. Ollis. Pergamon Press, London, 1961.
150. SCHMIDT, O. T. *Proceedings Chemical Society Symposium Sheffield*, 1962. *Proc. Chem. Soc.* **1962**, 204.
151. SCHMIDT, O. T. *Leder* **14**, 40 (1963).
152. SCHMIDT, O. T. and BERNAUER, K. *Ann.* **588**, 211 (1954).
153. SCHMIDT, O. T. and DEMMLER, K. *Ann.* **586**, 179 (1954).
154. SCHMIDT, O. T. and ECKERT, R. *Ann.* **618**, 71 (1958).
155. SCHMIDT, O. T., HEINTZELER, M. and MAYER, W. *Ber.* **80**, 510 (1947).
156. SCHMIDT, O. T., HEUSLER, R. and STEPHAN, P. *Ann.* **609**, 186 (1957).
157. SCHMIDT, O. T. and HOMERECK, E. *Ann.* **591**, 156 (1955).
158. SCHMIDT, O. T. and MAYER W. *Ann.* **571**, 1 (1951).
159. SCHMIDT, O. T. and MAYER, W. *Angew. Chem.* **68**, 103 (1956).
160. SCHMIDT, O. T., SCHMIDT, D. M. and HEROK, J. *Ann.* **587**, 67 (1954).
161. SEGUIN, A. *Ann. Chim. (Paris)* **20**, 15 (1796).
162. SESHADRI, T. R. XIV Int. Congr. Pure Appl. Chem. Zurich; *Experientia*, Suppl. No. 2, 270 (1955).
163. SHERRY, S. P. *Wattle Research Inst., Univ. Natal, S. Africa Report* No. 4–5, 64 (1952).

164. SHIBATA, S. and YAMAZAKI, M. *Pharm. Bull.* (*Tokyo*) **6**, 42 (1958).
165. SIEVERS, A. F. and CLARKE, I. D. *J. Am. Leathers Chemists' Assoc.* **39**, 293 (1944).
166. SIMMONDS, N. W. *Nature* **173**, 402 (1954).
167. SPRINSON, B. D. *Advances in Carbohydrate Chem.* **15**, 235 (1961).
168. SWAIN, T. *Chem. and Ind.* (*London*) **1954**, 1144.
169. SWAIN, T. In *The Chemistry of Vegetable Tannins*, p. 106. Symposium Soc. Leather Trades' Chemists, Croydon, 1956.
170. SWAIN, T. In *Wood Extractives*, p. 277, ed. W. E. Hillis. Academic Press, New York, 1962.
171. UMBARGER, H. E. and BROWN, B. *J. Biol. Chem.* **233**, 1156 (1958).
172. VOGEL, W. In *Handbuch der Gerbereichemie und Lederfabrikation*, vol. II, part 1, ed. M. Bergmann. Springer, Vienna, 1931.
173. WATKIN, J. E., UNDERHILL, E. W. and NEISH, A. C. *Can. J. Biochem. Physiol.* **35**, 219, 229 (1957).
174. WEINGES, K. *Ber.* **94**, 3032 (1961).
175. WEINGES, K. and FREUDENBERG, K. *Chem. Comm.* **1965**, 220.
176. WEINGES, K., NAYA, Y. and TORIBIO, F. *Ber.* **96**, 2870 (1963).
177. WENKERT, E. *Chem. and Ind.* (*London*) **1959**, 906.
178. WEYGAND, F., BRUCKER, W., GRISEBACH, H. and SCHULZE, E. *Z. Naturforsch.* **12b**, 222 (1957).
179. WHITE, T. In *The Chemistry and Technology of Leather*, vol. 2, p. 98, eds. F. O'FLA-HERTY, W. T. RODDY and R. M. LOLLAR, Reinhold, New York, 1958.
180. WILLIAMS, C. O. *Sci. Bull. South African Dep. Agric.* No. 74 (1930).
181. ZAPROMETOV, M. N. *Biokhimia* **27**, 366 (1962).
182. ZEIJLEMAKER, F. C. J. *Wattle Research Inst., Univ. Natal, S. Africa, Report 1962–1963*, 36.
183. ZEIJLEMAKER, F. C. J. *Wattle Research Inst., Univ. Natal, S. Africa, Report 1963–1964*, 30.
184. ZENK, M. H. *Z. Naturforsch.* **19b**, 83 (1964).

CHAPTER 14

THE BIOGENESIS OF TERPENES IN PLANTS

HAROLD J. NICHOLAS

Institute of Medical Education and Research, Max C. Starkloff Memorial
Hospital, and Department of Biochemistry, St. Louis University School of
Medicine, St. Louis, Missouri

CONTENTS

INTRODUCTION: DEFINITION AND GENERAL DISCUSSION OF THE PROBLEM   829
EARLY SPECULATION ON THE NATURE OF A BASIC FIVE-CARBON UNIT
   IN TERPENE BIOGENESIS   833
OTHER EARLY SPECULATIONS ON THE BIOGENESIS OF PLANT TERPENES   835
MISCELLANEOUS APPROACHES TO THE PROBLEM OF TERPENE BIO-
   GENESIS IN PLANTS   835
CURRENT BROAD CONCEPT OF TERPENE BIOGENESIS   842
BIOGENESIS OF MONOTERPENES   845
BIOGENESIS OF SESQUITERPENES   855
BIOGENESIS OF DITERPENES   863
   Phytol   865
   The cyclic diterpenes   866
BIOGENESIS OF PLANT STEROLS AND TRITERPENES   873
   Squalene   879
   β-Sitosterol and related steroids   880
   Cholesterol   883
   Steroid hormones   883
   Cardiac glycosides   884
   Sapogenins   885
   The tetra- and pentacyclic triterpenes   886
POLYTERPENES: SOLANESOL   890
THE CONTROL OF TRITERPENE AND STEROL BIOGENESIS   890
THE FUTURE FOR STUDIES ON THE BIOGENESIS OF TERPENES IN PLANTS   892
SUMMARY   893
REFERENCES   894

INTRODUCTION: DEFINITION AND GENERAL DISCUSSION
OF THE PROBLEM

Widely distributed throughout the plant and animal kingdom in exceptionally diversified forms there exists a group of substances known collectively

as terpenes. Through the years the word "terpene" has become associated with fragrant, steam-volatile substances from higher plants (essential oils), but, with the advent of modern biochemistry and recognition of the significance of isoprenoid structures to animal physiology, this association has diminished. There is perhaps no more descriptive and precise definition of "terpenes" than that given by Haagen-Smit† who designated terpenes as ".... all compounds which have a distinct architectural and chemical relation to the simple C_5H_8 (isoprene) molecule . . .".[1] Included are compounds containing multiples of this group, and the terpenes are now classically grouped as follows:

hemiterpenes	C_5H_8
monoterpenes	$C_{10}H_{16}$
sesquiterpenes	$C_{15}H_{24}$
diterpenes	$C_{20}H_{32}$
triterpenes	$C_{30}H_{48}$
tetraterpenes	$(C_5H_8)_8$
polyterpenes	$(C_5H_8)_n$

Structural formulas of representative members of the hemi-, mono-, sesqui-, di- and triterpene groups will be found on figures preceding the individual sections in which the biogenesis of the group is discussed; the tetra- and polyterpenes have been discussed elsewhere in this book (see Chapters 10 and 16). Wallach's original concept of the terpene family included only hydrocarbons;[2] members of the C_{10} camphor family were considered separately. Terpenes, as we now know them, may contain any number of different functional groups, and based on structural requirements, there appears no valid reason for excluding the camphor series. No definition is all-inclusive. Thus, there are compounds which do not contain multiples of five carbon atoms like (see Fig. 1) the ionones (I, C_{13}), angustione (II, C_{11}), polyporenic acid A (III, C_{31}), considered terpenes because of their obvious isoprenoid structure, although they cannot be divided totally into distinct isopentane units. The steroids, a large number of them containing twenty-seven or twenty-nine carbon atoms, are isoprenoid structures as we now know from their biosynthetic origin.

Frequently the isoprene-like nature of a compound may be masked or the isopentane unit may appear only as a portion of the total molecule. For example, only part of the molecule of osthol (IV), found in the roots

---

† Definition taken in part: an interesting discussion of the origin of the word terpene (essentially from the French *terebenthine* or German *Terpentin* for turpentine) is given by Kremers.[3]

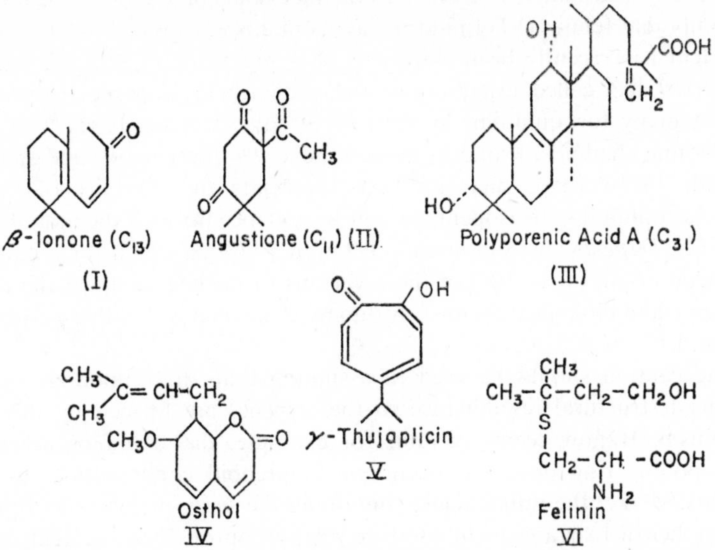

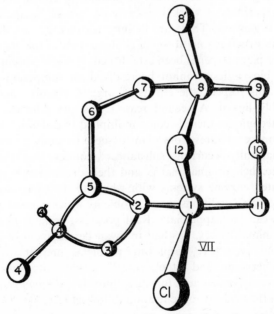

β-Ionone (C₁₃)

(I)

Angustione (C₁₁) (II).

Polyporenic Acid A (C₃₁)

(III)

Osthol

IV

γ-Thujaplicin

V

Felinin

VI

FIG. 1. Some isoprenoid substances which do not contain multiples of 5 carbons, which contain the isoprenoid nature "masked", or substances only partly isoprenoid in nature.

FIG. 2. Perspective view of the caryophyllene molecule (as the chloride), after Robertson and Todd.[21] (*By courtesy of the Society of Chemical Industry*).

of *Imperatori ostruthium*, [4] contains a distinct isopentane group. The interesting compound felinin (VI) found in cats contains an isoprenoid unit. Mevalonic acid has recently been shown to be a precursor of this substance. [5] Wenkert [6] has called attention to the presence of isoprene (isopentane) units in many furoquinoline systems, [7] in some tropane bases [8] in some isoquinoline alkaloids, [9] and in monoterpene, [10] diterpene [11] and steroidal alkaloids. [12]† Perhaps one can best appreciate the diversity of natural products containing the isopentane unit by a glance through the monumental series *The Terpenes*, by Simonsen and Owen. [13–15] A search for a common biogenetic origin of the unit in these various forms has occupied the efforts of organic and biological chemists for many years, and is rapidly approaching fruition.

Some caution should be used in assuming that all compounds bearing superficial structural resemblance to the terpenes are formed by the same mechanism. It now seems certain, for example, that the biosynthesis of the tropolone ring does not occur via isoprenoid condensation, at least in molds. [16] Yet the thujaplicins, containing the seven-membered tropolone ring, by benzil rearrangement produce methylisopropylbenzoic acid derivatives which suggest an isoprenoid origin for the tropolones from higher plants. Additional illustrations for other ring systems have been given by Wenkert [17] and Leete. [18]

Although terpenes are particularly abundant in higher plants, comparatively little experimental work has been performed on their biosynthesis within these organisms. There are definite reasons for this. Only in recent years have the structure and absolute configuration of the major representatives of higher plant terpenes been established. It is self evident that complex problems of biosynthesis cannot be resolved on compounds of unknown structure. In this respect, the efforts of organic chemists and biochemists are inseparably linked. A second reason exists in difficulties inherent in problems of technique; these become multiplied in isolating, separating and purifying complex mixtures from plant tissues. To study properly the metabolism of naturally-occurring substances requires that they eventually be returned to their original matrix and their disposition evaluated, unless one has isolated enzyme systems with which to work. To accomplish this under quantitative conditions poses problems which anyone working with higher plants can best appreciate. Real progress, perhaps more so than in studies with animal tissues, has had to await development of isotope tracer techniques and even here perplexing problems present themselves. For example, Sandermann and Stockmann [19] could not introduce geranic, farnesic or geranylgeranic acid for study into *M. pulegium* roots because of the toxicity of the acids in concentration as low as 1:10,000. Numerous other

---

† The nitrogen-containing terpenoid substances have been considered outside the scope of this chapter (See Chapter 17, Section XI).

examples could be presented. The pioneering efforts of Fujita, beginning as early as 1938 (before the introduction of the isotope technique), are noteworthy and will be discussed later. A more pertinent reason for much speculation and little experimentation in the field of higher plant terpene biogenesis has been the competitive and more immediate needs in the field of medicine, particularly in the area of steroid biogenesis. Thus, we find geraniol,[20] farnesol,[21] and nerolidol[22] assuming critical importance before their function in plant physiology has been experimentally assessed, even though we ordinarily think of these substances as plant products. The recent monograph *Biosynthesis of Terpenes and Sterols*[23] indicates how much studies on the biogenesis of terpenes of vegetable origin will owe to those initiated by steroid biogenetic mechanisms. Finally, there is the problem of terpene source. A number of complex and interesting terpenes are known to occur only in select plants, frequently in bushes or trees. Laboratory limitations of this kind of problem are obvious.

In discussing the problem of terpene biogenesis at this time two facets appear outstanding. Despite marked advances in our knowledge of the initial stages of terpene biogenesis, the subject, when viewed broadly, appears as fascinating and challenging as it must have appeared to organic chemists and physiologists of sixty or seventy years ago. Consider, for example, the structure of caryophyllene (Fig. 2, VII) and the numerous biogenetic problems its nucleus suggests. Secondly, it appears essential that a large body of theoretical information now embodied in the "isoprene rule" and adjacent areas of study in higher plants should be subjected to *experimental observation*. With a wide diversity of isotope techniques and tools such as vapor phase and thin layer chromatography this important phase can now progress in a deserving manner.

EARLY SPECULATION ON THE NATURE OF A BASIC FIVE-CARBON UNIT IN TERPENE BIOGENESIS

The "isoprene rule" states in principle that a number of naturally-occurring compounds can be divided into distinct isoprenoid (isoprene or isopentane) units. The rule probably first came into being with the observations of Bertholet[25] in 1860 wherein he commented on the periodicity in the architecture of the molecules of some terpenes.[1] The rule became of fundamental merit, however, under the guidance of Otto Wallach,[2] who classified the then known terpenes on the basis of C_5H_8 units, thus bringing considerable order into the field. He showed that the monocyclic monoterpenes could be "built up" (constructed on paper) by the union of two isoprene units coiled in the proper fashion. Later studies made it evident that similar construction from isoprene units could be envisioned for more complex terpenes. It was a natural step to speculate on how such a building process might occur in plant tissues. The nature of the basic five-carbon unit which, by

TABLE 1. TERPENE BIOGENESIS:
EARLY SPECULATIONS ON THE NATURE OF THE BASIC 5-CARBON UNIT

5-Carbon unit	Structure	Suggested origin	References
Isoprene	VIII	Condensation of acetone or dihydroxy acetone with acetaldehyde	26, 27, 22
β-Methylcroton-aldehyde (3-methylbut-2-enal)	IX	Condensation of acetone and acetaldehyde or acetone and pyruvic acid, followed by decarboxylation; decarboxylation of α-keto iso-caproic acid (via isoleucine)	1, 29
Isoamyl alcohol	X	Degradation of carbohydrate, protein	30
Isovaleraldehyde	XI	From leucine	31, 32, 33, 34
Isovaleric acid	XII	Condensation of acetone and pyruvic acid followed by decarboxylation; from leucine	1
β-Hydroxyiso-valeraldehyde	XIII	Condensation of acetone and acetaldehyde; decarboxylation of α-ketoiso-caproic acid (via isoleucine)	35, 36
Apiose	XIV	From carbohydrates	37
Isoamylene	XV	From leucine by loss of NH_3 and CO_2	38
β-Methylcrotonic acid	XVI	Condensation of acetone and acetic acid	36
Tiglic acid	XVII		36
Angelic acid	XVIII		36

repeated condensation, would form the more complex terpenes, has been the source of much speculation; some of the forms suggested are shown on Table 1. The rationale leading to the suggestion of these substances as the "primary" repeating unit has been discussed in several excellent reviews† and need not be reiterated here. It will be noted that all of the five-carbon precursors were suggested as the result of speculations on the biogenesis of terpenes in higher plants. It is interesting that isoprene itself has recently been subjected to test as the critical C-5 unit. [44] The position of β-methyl-crotonic acid, perhaps still undecided, will be discussed in the section on Diterpene Biogenesis. In view of our present concept of isopentyl pyrophosphate as "active isoprene" [21] some of the early guesses were not grossly inept (compare Table 1 and Fig. 5). However, knowledge of phosphorylated intermediates as active precursors had not yet been developed, and most of the suggestions of how the C-5 units were united were based on probable aldol condensations followed by dehydrations, reductions and other transformations. Had the hypothetical precursors been subjected to experimentation with living tissues, it is unlikely that any positive results would have been obtained without the use of isotopes.

OTHER EARLY SPECULATIONS ON THE BIOGENESIS OF PLANT TERPENES

Several early approaches to terpene biogenesis by-passed the question of a basic five-carbon precursor and considered possible direct ring closures of prominent acyclic monoterpenes to cyclic terpenes in association with oxidations, reductions and dehydrations. Also suggested were elaborate condensations of elementary units such as acetone and acetaldehyde to hypothetical larger units of ill-defined constitution which might subsequently fold and condense. Early suggestions and hypothetical precursors are listed on Table 2. Cyclizations of acyclic monoterpenes to cyclic products are common in the field of terpene chemistry and, by analogy, might be assumed to occur under physiological conditions with special enzymes. Such analogy forms the basis of much speculation in the field of terpene biogenesis. By and large, however, the early mechanisms considered in Table 2 were quite hypothetical and were based on little or no experimental background. It will be noted, again, that these early approaches were based on mechanisms which might occur in higher plants.

MISCELLANEOUS APPROACHES TO THE PROBLEM OF TERPENE BIOGENESIS IN PLANTS

It will be of value to review briefly some additional approaches to the general problem of terpene biogenesis as used by various investigators. It will be noted that these studies also deal with higher plants, because of the

† Suggested leading references for this and the following section: 1, 39, 40, 41, 42, 43.

2DD*

TABLE 2. TERPENE BIOGENESIS:
SOME EARLY SUGGESTED PRECURSORS AND MECHANISMS

Precursor	Mechanism	Reference
Carbohydrates	Degradation to levulinic acid, coupling of the latter, loss of CO_2, etc.	45
Branched monosaccharides or acids therefrom (e.g. quinic acid)	Condensations and eventual cyclization of a pre-formed terpene-like unit	46
Carbohydrates, via simple sugar units		47
Proteins	Degradation to amino acids which in turn give rise to isoprenoid units (see also Table 1)	48, 41, 49
Straight carbon chain (e.g. acrolein)	Stepwise addition of single carbon units to form acyclic terpenes	50
Acetone and acetaldehyde	Multiple condensations followed by dehydrations and reductions, etc.	51, 52
Citral	Cyclization to monoterpenes	29
Geraniol	Cyclization to monoterpenes	32, 53
Nerol	Cyclization to monoterpenes	54
Limonene	Internal polymerization	55
Linalool	Cyclization to monoterpenes	56

abundance of terpenes in the latter organisms. Although largely of historical interest, some of the studies have particular bearing on specific areas of higher plant metabolism which must be considered even with present-day isotope work.

What we would consider the "direct approach" appears to have been used only by Fujita. [57] This investigator injected d-citronellal, isovaleraldehyde, geraniol, citral and linalool, respectively, into holes bored in living *Ficus retusa* L. trees. The holes were sealed and after many months the tree was cut and appropriate fractions were obtained by steam distillation. Several biochemical reductions were indicated by changes in composition of the distillates, e.g. the conversion of isovaleraldehyde to isoamyl alcohol and of geraniol to d-methyl heptanol; oxidations and cyclization were indicated also. The rationale for this type of experiment was presumably the fact that the trees into which the injections were made ordinarily contained little or none of the metabolites isolated. Parallel reactions in yeast were cited as

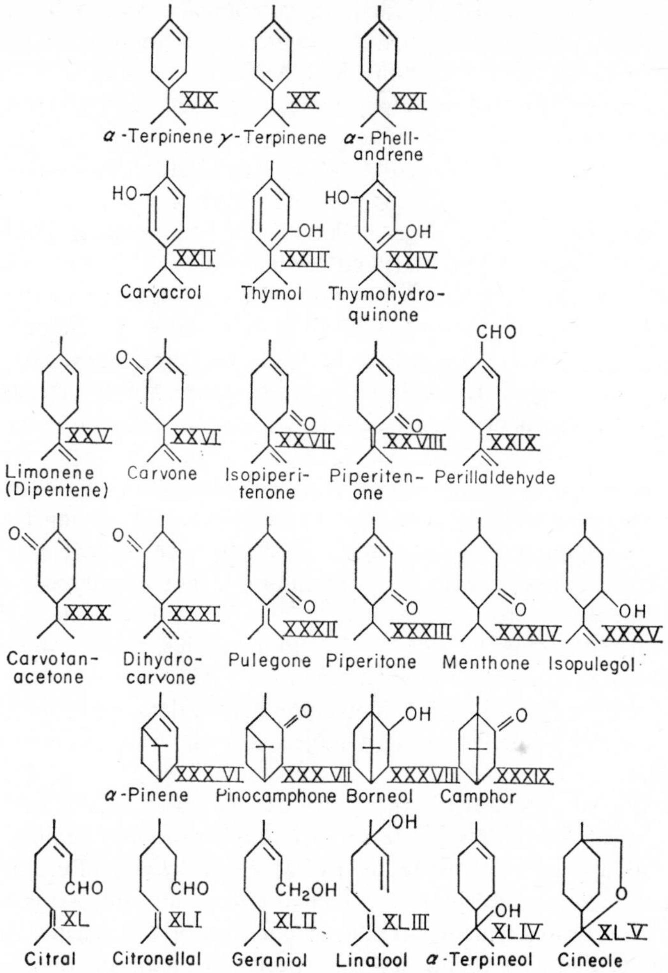

FIG. 3. Monoterpene members of the Labiatae family; after Naves.[57]

analogous experiments: Neuberg's reduction of citral to geraniol[58] and of isovaleraldehyde to isoamyl alcohol.[59] The difficulties associated with this type of experimentation are obvious and it is expected that confirmation by more precise modern techniques will be necessary.

A second approach has involved structural comparison of various terpenes within a particular plant, or plant genus or species on the "not too improbable assumption", paraphrasing Haagen-Smit,[1] that terpenes closely allied in structure may be related biogenetically. This line of reasoning has proved fruitful in almost all fields of biochemistry where specific structures can be allocated to individual compounds. An example from the older literature will serve to illustrate the use of this approach in the monoterpene series. Naves [60] studied in detail the volatile terpenes of the *Labiatae* family, members of which are rich in substances such as linalool, geraniol, citral and cyclic products like the terpinenes, carvacrol, pinene, etc. A chart of these constituents is presented in Fig. 3. Arranged in this manner various patterns immediately present themselves. Naves, for example, suggested the ultimate formation of α-terpineol (XLIV) and cineole (XLV) from citral, and piperitenone (XXVIII) and perillaldehyde (XXIX) from limonene (XXV). No tenable explanation was given for the formation of the bicyclic monoterpenes (e.g. α-pinene (XXXVI) in this series. In lemongrass oil, acetaldehyde, citral *a*, citronellal, linalool, the dipentenes and methylheptenone occur together, and Francesconi [30] attempted to interrelate these substances from their obvious structural correlation. This work has recently been reviewed. [61] In a similar manner, based on the essential oil content of flora of East Africa, isoamyl alcohol, isovaleraldehyde and isovaleric acid have been interrelated with isoamyl alcohol presumably giving rise to the latter two compounds. More recently, on the basis of the co-occurrence of ascaridole and α-terpinene in Chenopodium oil, the latter terpene was presumed to be the precursor of ascaridole. [62] Observations such as these are not limited to the monoterpene family and numerous fruitful examples may be found in the diterpene and triterpene series. Although information from this type of approach provides valuable preliminary data, in the final analysis the relationships suggested must be subjected to the tracer technique in the living plant.

Intimately concerned with the previous discussion is the question of genetic control. Within a given genus of a number of plant families studied, the terpenes appear to be distributed rather selectively within certain species. If one may exclude local conditions such as climate and soil status, then this distribution is probably under specific genetic control. In the genus *Monarda*, for example, Fujita [63] found that one species, *M. didyma*, contained large quantities of linalool and little or no phenolic constituents like *p*-cymene or thymol, whereas in other species of this genus the reverse was found. Fujita developed from these observations a biogenetic scheme envisioning linalool as the parent compound of the cyclic intermediates (see Haagen-Smit [39]). The influence of specific genetic factors is markedly apparent in the studies of Penfold and Morrison [64] on the *Eucalyptus* genus. The story is told [65] that Penfold, while waiting in Australia for a tire to be changed, crumbled the leaves of several *Eucalyptus* trees and noticed that the odor of the leaves from one was distinctly different from that of two others. From this chance observation was developed the broad study of some 230 species of the genus *Eucalyptus* which permitted grouping into four principal types: those producing largely (1) cineole, (2) piperitone, (3) phellandrene or (4) acyclic terpenes like geraniol. In a group of such trees growing but a few feet apart (thus eliminating the possibility of climatological influence) some contained essential oil consisting predominantly of cineole; others contained predominantly piperitone. Mirov[66] in a study of the genus *Pinus* gives similar examples where individual species could not be differentiated morphologically but differed in terpene content. Of fundamental interest to the field of triterpene biogenesis are the observations of Wildman *et al.*[67] Using two *Cryptostegia* species, one of which produces rubber and the other the pentacyclic triterpene lupeol, it was found by crossbreeding that production of either rubber or the triterpene was inherited as a simple Mendelian

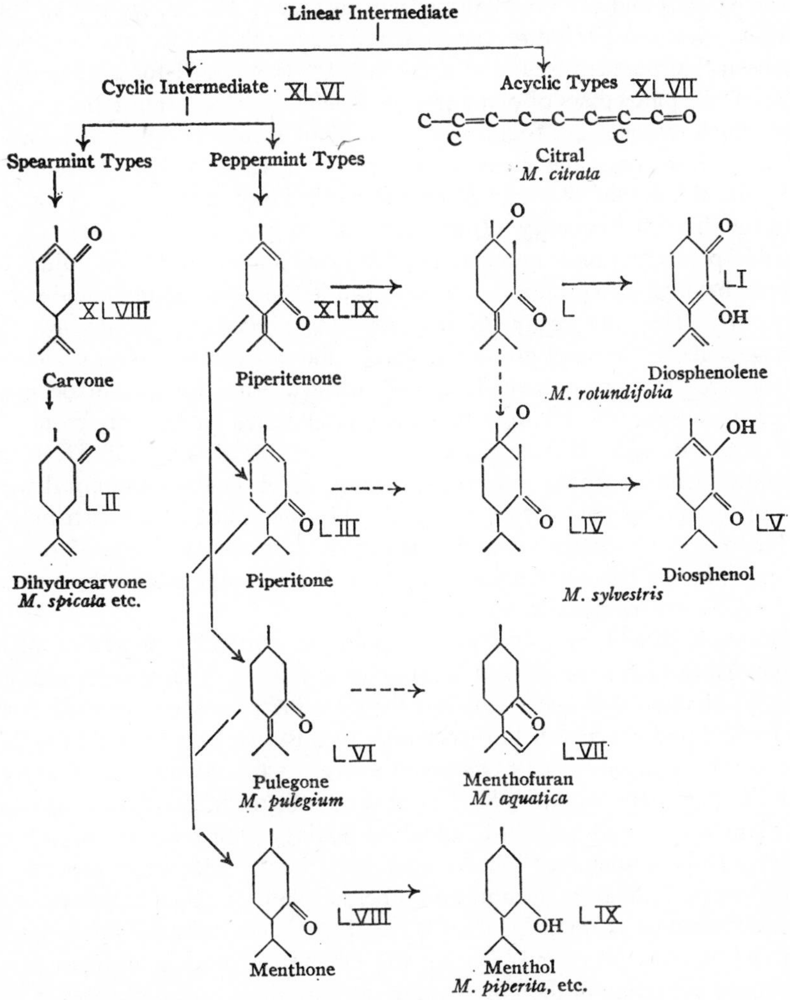

FIG. 4. Biogenesis of monoterpenes in the Mint species, according to Reitsma.[69]

factor with rubber formation predominant. Recently, Kremer's hypothesis on the origin of terpenes in the mint family [29] has been re-evaluated by Rovth and Hegnauer. [68] In an examination of the essential oil content of various *Mentha* species a genetic factor was suggested. For a high carvone or menthol content, genes from two species were felt essential. Reitsma [69] has presented evidence of how the presence or absence of a particular enzyme system (genetically controlled) may influence the terpene content of certain mint species also. A biogenetic scheme arising from his deductions is shown in Fig. 4. According to this projection, cyclizing reactions are not promoted in *M. citrata* so that acyclic terpenes like citral and linalool predominate in this species and are essentially absent in species like *M. spicata* and *M. pulegone*. Still another indirect approach to the problem of terpene biogenesis has been that pursued by Fujita and others [70] (see ref. 71 for similar treatment of phenolic ethers of plant origin). Briefly, the "occurrence frequency" with which terpenes are found in certain plant species is tabulated; such a list, taken from Thies and Wehmer, [72] is shown in Table 3. This list, according to Fujita, shows that all terpenes can be classified into three groups: (1) those found with great frequency, (2) an intermediate group, and (3) those distributed in plants in limited number. The following quotation is from Fujita: [42] "Those belonging to group I are widespread in the plant kingdom and occur frequently. They are easily formed from the precursor, but are not the precursor itself. Those of group III, that is, the terpenes which do not occur frequently, are the compounds hardly formed from the precursor itself either. Consequently, the real precursor is expected to exist in group II, and it may be selected from the compounds of this group. . . ." From the aliphatic members of the group II, geraniol, nerol, linalool and citral were chosen for further consideration. Based on further study of the distribution of linalool in *Gymnosperms* and *Angiosperms*, linalool was considered by Fujita to be the basic precursor. Like most indirect approaches these views will require experimental confirmation.

Attention should be called at this point to particular phases of plant metabolism which have marked bearing on any study of terpene biogenesis, namely: changes that occur between the time the plants are removed from the ground and processed. Earlier studies in this area have been thoroughly reviewed by Haagen-Smit. [1] Of special interest is the summary by Haagen-Smit of Charabot's work. [73] Several of the problems involved seem specific for plant tissues and have little apparent analogy with reactions in animal tissues. Thus, Littlejohn [41] has stated that, in the enfleurage process of extracting perfume from jasmine and tuberose plants, a much higher yield of fragrant material is obtained than if the flowers are extracted immediately and the extracts processed. During the enfleurage process, changes must have been occurring in the flowers after cutting. Biochemical changes in the terpene content of *Orris* rhizomes, on standing for long periods, are well

TABLE 3. FREQUENCY OF OCCURRENCE OF MONOTERPENE COMPOUNDS
(IN HIGHER PLANTS)

Group	Terpene	Number of species in which the terpene occurs
I	α-pinene	412
	cineole	281
	limonene (dipentene)	272
II	phellandrene (α-, β-)	152
	geraniol	123
	borneol	108
	linalool	96
	α-terpineol	86
	camphene	85
	ρ-cymene	71
	citral	67
	β-pinene	67
	camphor	62
III	thymol	43
	carvacrol	40
	terpinene (α-, γ-)	36
	citronellol	33
	piperitone	33
	menthol	32
	menthone	30
	pulegone	27
	citronellal	26
	thujone	24
	sabinene	22
	carvone	16
	myrcene	16
	terpinenol-(4)	14
	carene (Δ^3-, Δ^4-)	11
	methylheptenone	11
	thujyl alcohol	11
	ocimene	10
	dihydrocumic alcohol	9
	fenchone	8
	piperitol	8
	fenchyl alcohol	6
	fenchene	4
	methylheptenol	4
	perillaldehyde	4
	terpinolene	4

From Fujita,[42] after Thies and Wehmer.[72]

known in the perfume industry.[74] Kalitzki[75] performed studies on changes that occur in the volatile oil of peppermint at various stages of growth and after removal of leaves for wilting. Evidence was obtained that the volatile oils are affected by the metabolic changes occurring in the plant during wilting. It must be kept in mind, then, that following removal from the ground, or in the case of isolation of particular organs from the main plant section, the parts are still viable tissue undergoing an active, although altered, metabolism for some time. The lipid content of plants changes as the organisms mature, both in concentration and frequently in the nature of the lipid. It seems possible that, in some cases, clues to the biogenesis of compounds may be obtained from an examination of changes in terpene content as maturity is reached. The *Labiatae* family, because of its rich supply of volatile terpenes, has been the frequent source of material for such studies [76] (see also section on Monoterpene Biogenesis). Recently, Ahlgrim, [77] in a study of certain mint species, found much menthone and little menthol in young mint leaves, and a reversal of this ratio as the plants reached maturity. A common origin, rather than interconversion of menthol and menthone, was expressed as the reason for the change. Studies of this type should prove particularly interesting in the diterpene and triterpene-containing plants, but are as yet largely limited to observation of changes in monoterpenes during growth.

Littlejohn [41] has called attention to Naves's observation of the absence of caryophyllene from cloves if the latter are extracted with benzene, as opposed to recovery of the terpene when the cloves are subjected to steam distillation. Also cited was the probability that carvotanacetone is not found in thuja oil as such, but arises from thujone on steam distillation. The latter are not examples of biochemical changes, of course, and are not unique to plant tissues, but indicate some areas for caution in isolation studies.

CURRENT BROAD CONCEPT OF TERPENE BIOGENESIS

Before proceeding to recent and more critical work, it will be advisable to review briefly our current concepts of terpene biogenesis emanating from recent marked advances in steroid biogenesis.† Although developed largely from work with animal tissues and yeast, a universal mechanism applicable to terpene biogenesis in all organisms possessing these substances appears to be forming, at least regarding the initial stages.

Two marked advances might be attributed to general consideration of problems relevant to terpene biogenesis in the plant kingdom. One of these was the observation of Bonner [36, 78] relating acetone and acetic acid condensation to the formation of β-methylcrotonic acid, a likely isoprenoid precursor of rubber in guayule plants (see also Chapter 16). Because of the terpenoid relationship between rubber and squalene, attention was again directed to a possible common origin of these substances from some basic intermediate larger than acetate. Although β-methylcrotonic acid subsequently did not appear to be the basic unit [79, 80] since it is degraded first to acetic acid, it appears likely that the suggestion sparked renewed interest in a

† See Chapter 4 for more detailed discussion relating to steroid biogenesis.

search for "active isoprene". A second development, leading largely from extensive pioneering investigations in the determination of plant terpene structure, was the publication by Ruzicka of the "biogenetic isoprene rule".[81] According to this rule, certain key acyclic terpenes, or hypothetical substances closely related to them, can condense by ionic or radical mechanisms to form all of the known mono-, sesqui- and diterpenes, and, in the case of squalene as the acyclic precursor, can give rise to all of the known sterols and triterpenes of plant and animal tissues. The principal value of this rule lies in its broad unifying concept which implies a rational sequence of events for the biogenesis of all terpenes. We shall have occasion to refer to Ruzicka's biogenetic isoprene rule frequently in subsequent sections.

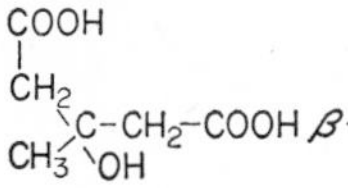

β-Hydroxy-β-methyl glutaric acid

LX

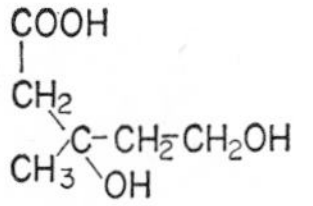

Mevalonic acid (3,5-dihydroxy-3-methyl pentanoic acid)

LXI

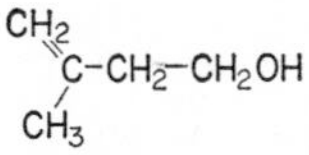

Δ^3-isopentol (3-methyl-Δ^3-1-butenol)

LXII

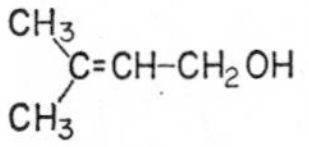

Dimethyl allyl alcohol (3-methyl-Δ^2-butenol)

LXIII

FIG. 5. Biologically active hemiterpenes (C_5) and closely related active compounds.

As has been duly credited,[23] a giant step forward in studies of terpene biogenesis came with the discovery of mevalonic acid[82] (Fig. 5, LXI) and recognition of it as a markedly efficient cholesterol precursor.[83] The incorporation of this substance when labeled in the C-2 position with carbon 14 (but not the C-1 position, which is lost in the formation of cholesterol)[84] into carotenoids,[85] rubber†[86] and other terpenoid substances rapidly indicated that from it "active isoprene" was probably formed in plant and animal tissues.

Mevalonic acid is formed from acetic acid in tissues. The mechanism involves condensation of acetyl CoA and acetoacetyl CoA to β-hydroxy-β-methylglutaryl CoA. The latter on reduction of the thiolester group yields mevalonic acid. Only (+)-mevalonic acid is a precursor of squalene,[89]

† See, however, Barlow and Patrick,[87] and Gascoigne and Jones.[88]

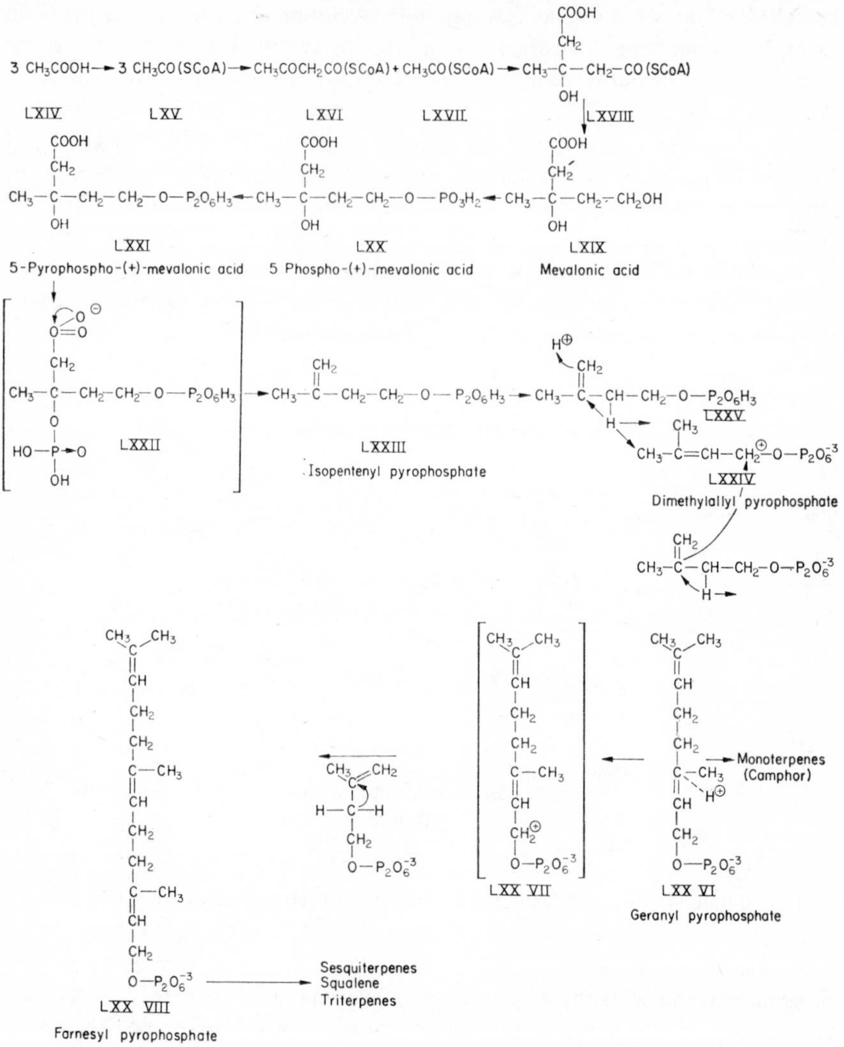

FIG. 6. Biogenesis of terpenes, Cornforth et al.[97] and after Lynen et al.[27]

and therefore only this isomer will serve as a precursor of other terpenes. After the observation by Tchen[90] that the first intermediate in the biosynthesis of squalene from mevalonic acid is a monophosphate ester of the latter, rapid progress was made. On incubation of this ester (5-phospho-mevalonic acid, Fig. 6, LXX) with adenosine triphosphate, a new ester was formed and was demonstrated to be mevalonic acid-5-pyrophosphate (LXXI).[91, 92] Subsequently, both the laboratories of Bloch[93] and Lynen[21] established that a phosphate ester of Δ^3-isopentenol (isopentenyl pyrophosphate, LXXIII) was critical in the sequence of events leading to the biogenesis of farnesol, as farnesyl pyrophosphate, from mevalonic acid. Recently it has been shown [94, 95] that in the formation of farnesyl pyrophosphate, the first reaction is the isomerization of isopentenyl pyrophosphate to the pyrophosphate ester of dimethylallyl alcohol (LXXV). This reaction is reversible with the equilibrium lying far in the direction of dimethylallyl pyrophosphate formation. The unique scheme involved in the transformation of mevalonic acid to farnesyl pyrophosphate had been previously postulated by Bloch [96] on mechanistic grounds and from studies on the conversion of mevalonic acid to squalene in a D_2O medium. The biogenesis of elongated isoprenoid chains, therefore, unlike condensations of the aldol, α-acyloin, or Claisson types established for the biogenesis of straight chain compounds, proceeds via the participation of phosphate. Hydroxyl groups are removed not by dehydration but by elimination of phosphate or pyrophosphate anion. [91] The allylic nature of dimethylallyl pyrophosphate permits it to act as an alkylating agent so that condensation with a second molecule of isopentenyl pyrophosphate occurs to form farnesyl pyrophosphate which has been established as a precursor of squalene. The presently accepted overall sequence for the biogenesis of terpenoid substances is shown in Fig. 6. If it may be assumed that the initial steps in terpene biogenesis through squalene are the same in all living tissues, then, in the biogenesis of terpenes in higher plants, our principal areas of ignorance lie in the cyclizing mechanism and subsequent steps, as the next sections will indicate.

Since publication of the first edition of *Biogenesis of Natural Compounds*, an excellent monograph has appeared discussing the origin of many naturally occurring compounds from acetic acid. [98] The reader is referred to the chapter on terpene biogenesis in this monograph for additional theoretical approaches to many of the mechanisms reviewed in the following sections. In addition, Ruzicka [99] has again concisely summed the existing theory on isoprenoid condensation. See also the comprehensive reviews by Clayton [99a] and Sandermann. [110]

BIOGENESIS OF MONOTERPENES

Some concept of the magnitude of monoterpene biogenesis by vegetation over the earth's surface may be obtained by considering recent evidence—not entirely new—that the blue haze over forests is the result of many tons of submicroscopic particles given to the atmosphere by trees and other plants. [100] If we add to this observation a consideration of the numerous cyclopentanoid monoterpenes found in the insect kingdom [101] and the numerous plant types to be discussed in this section, there is certainly much justification for a detailed study of how these substances are formed biogenetically. A recent observation that nepetalactone from catnip has insect repelling properties may give some impetus for investigating monoterpene biogenesis at a more rapid pace. [102]

Structural formulas of some of the more prominent monoterpenes (C_{10}) are shown in Fig. 7. They include acyclic, monocyclic, bicyclic and tricyclic types. A large percentage of them occur in higher plants as hydrocarbons, but alcohols, aldehydes, ketones, acid lactones, oxides and peroxides have been found. Most of them can be divided into head-to-tail combinations of two

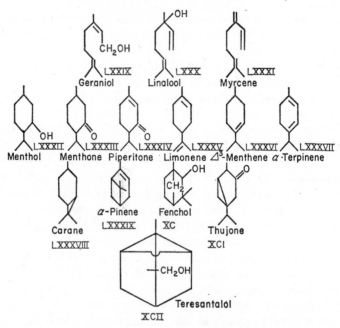

FIG. 7. Prominent members of the monoterpene (C_{10}) family.

isopentane units (as in XCIII, XIV, Fig. 8) but some exceptions, in which the isopentane units are irregularly arranged, are known (artemesia ketone (XCV, XCVI), and lavandulol (XCVII, XCVIII)). These exceptions are puzzling, but it appears likely that biochemical experimentation will readily lead to a clear answer. Clemo [104] suggested that artemesia ketone might form by "breaking" of Δ^3-carene as shown by the dotted lines in (XCIX), but there appears little biochemical rationale for this suggestion. Crabbe [105] has suggested what appears to be a more plausible origin by methyl migration in a cationic intermediate common to artemesia ketone, linalool and menthone (Fig. 9). Both artemesia ketone and linalool occur together in the same plant. [80]

The biogenesis of geraniol, linalool and nerol (*cis-geraniol*) from mevalonic acid in animal tissues has more or less clearly delineated the origin of these substances from "active isoprene" within these tissues. [22] Experimental evidence is accumulating to the effect that the origin of these substances within higher plant tissue will follow same course. It is interesting that these alcohols did not occur in the free form, but were probably present as the pyrophosphates.

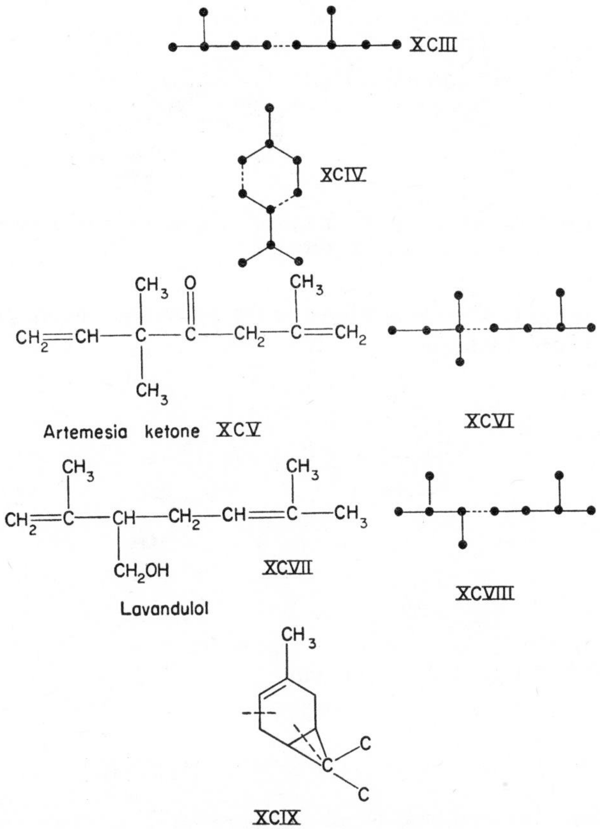

FIG. 8. Irregular monoterpenes.

The cyclic monoterpenes are limited in their occurrence to the higher plant kingdom (with the exception of numerous cyclopentanoid terpenes found in insects). [101] Insufficient data are available to discuss the biogenesis of the cyclopentanoid substances, but some C^{14} experiments have been reported. [103] Speculations have been made regarding the formation of cyclic monoterpenes in the past. It was considered that these substances are derived biogenetically from an acyclic precursor such as geraniol or linalool. Analogous chemical formation of six-membered rings by the acid-catalyzed cyclization of dienes

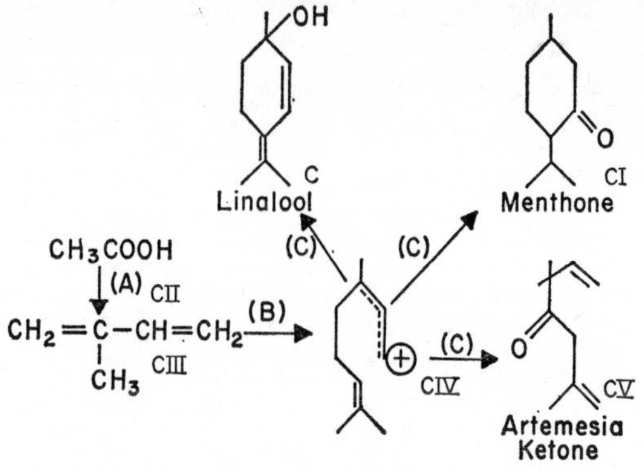

FIG. 9. Possible biogenesis of the "irregular" terpene artemesia ketone; after Crabbe.[105]

are known; a representative example is the formation of α-terpineol from geraniol (CVI → CVII).

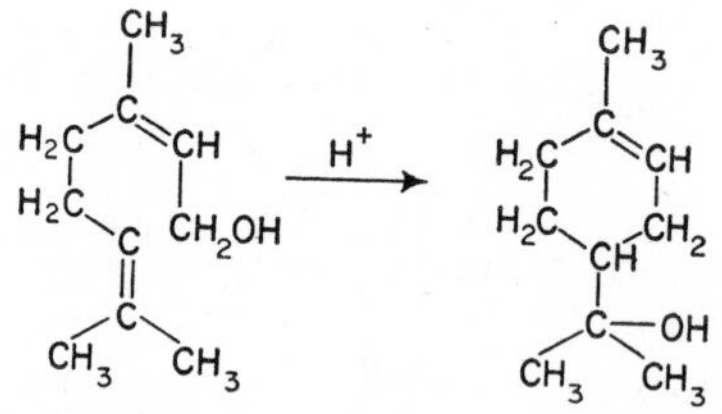

CVI CVII

Clemo[104] has suggested that the unit

$$\mathrm{C{-}\overset{\overset{C}{|}}{C}{=}C{-}C{-}C{=}\overset{\overset{C}{|}}{C}{-}C{=}CH_2}\quad \mathrm{(CVIII)}$$

(as in ocimene) can give rise to all the monocyclic terpenes, since double bonds at the positions indicated are essential for cyclization. Stork and Burghstahler have pointed out[106] that the cyclizing olefin may not necessarily be a 1,5-diene providing that under acidic conditions it can produce the same cationic species that can be obtained from the 1,5-diene. Ruzicka, in developing the "biogenetic isoprene rule", has suggested a series of ionic mechanisms for the formation of cyclic monoterpenes from geraniol (or linalool or myrcene)[81] (Fig. 10) or radical mechanisms for similar cyclization of the hydrocarbons ocimene or myrcene (Fig. 11). Basically these suggestions envision cyclization of an acyclic precursor to a cyclic form which by Wagner–Meerwein rearrangements, extensive in the field of terpene chemistry,[107] give rise to the more complex cyclic terpenes. Gascoigne[108]

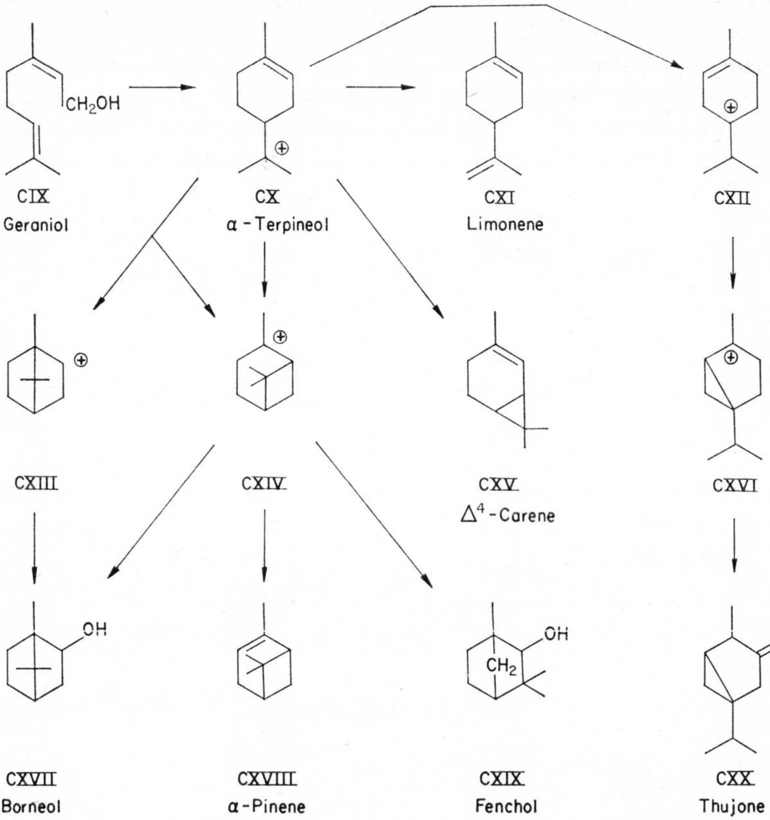

Fig. 10. Ionic mechanisms in the biogenesis of monoterpenes (Ruzicka[81]).

has noted the probability that *in vivo* the conversion of a monocyclic to a bicyclic hydrocarbon would involve a positive free energy change, a rather unlikely situation to occur within the living organism. He concluded that the bicyclic monoterpenes are likely to be formed in a single concerted reaction from an acyclic prototype rather than from a monocyclic hydrocarbon.

Within the framework of such a closely related series of monoterpenes as the menthol and terpinene types (Fig. 7) the similarities are striking; it is always tempting to develop a biogenetic relationship between compounds so closely allied in structure. Early experiments of Charabot† indicated that terpene alcohols are the first condensation products to arise in higher plants and that esters and terpene hydrocarbons are derived from them by dehydration. Reitsma, presumably on the basis of his suggested derivation of mint

† Cited in ref. 52.

terpenes,[69] stated: "It appears that the proposal of a hydrocarbon as an intermediate compound in the biosynthesis of the oxygenated compounds is unnecessary." Penfold noted[109] that the concentration of oxygenated terpenes increases in concentration with the age of the leaves in several species of eucalypts, whereby hydrocarbons decrease. Perhaps these observations are a measure of the limitation of such approaches to the problem of

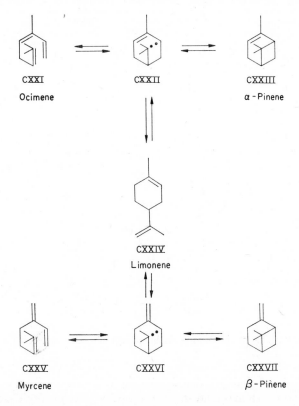

FIG. 11. Radical mechanisms in the biogenesis of monoterpenes (Ruzicka[81]).

terpene biogenesis. Several additional references relevant to this problem are cited from recent German literature in the review by Sandermann.[110] The question remains to be answered whether the various cyclic monoterpene forms all arise independently from a single cyclic precursor or are derived stepwise by oxidations, dehydrations and Wagner–Meerwein rearrangements from a single or a few common basic forms.

Approaches to the general problem of monoterpene biogenesis, using the isotope technique have appeared. Birch *et al.*[111] fed 2-C^{14}-sodium acetate and 2-C^{14}-mevalonic lactone to isolated terminal branches of *Eucalyptus citriodora* and *E. globulus Lab.* respectively. By steam distillation, citronellal was isolated from the *E. citriodora* as the 2,4-dinitrophenylhydrazone and cineole from the *E. globulus* as the resorcinol complex. Radioactivity was detected in both isolates; degradation indicated the expected distribution pattern for biogenesis from an isoprenoid unit (Fig. 12). Considerable

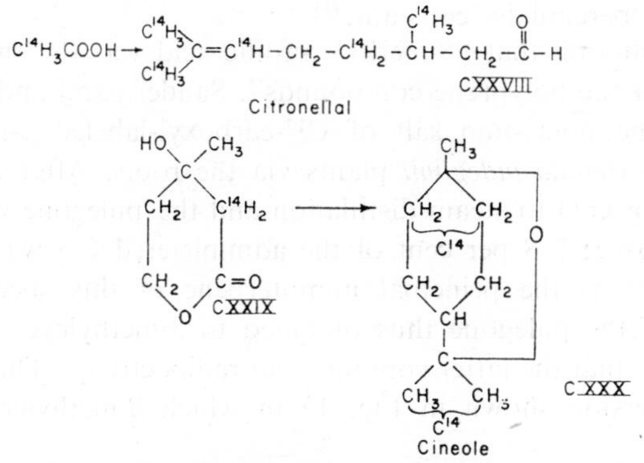

FIG. 12. Biogenesis of C^{14}-citronellal and cineole from 2-C^{14}-sodium acetate and 2-C^{14}-mevalonic acid lactone. [110]

randomization had occurred in the incorporation of acetate into citronellal. For reasons which are not clear, the incorporation of C^{14} was unexpectedly low. Stanley [112] gave 2-C^{14}-sodium acetate and 2-C^{14}-mevalonic acid to shoot tips of *Pinus attenuata*, the turpentine from which contains 98 per cent α-pinene. The latter was isolated as the nitrosochloride. The amount of C^{14} from the mevalonic acid was considerably more than that incorporated from the acetic acid for a given period of time, but as the author states "... acetate can be metabolized in many ways in pine tissues. It would therefore be erroneous to conclude from these preliminary studies that mevalonic acid is incorporated in preference to acetate."

Sukhov [113] followed the path of $C^{14}O_2$ disposition in large *Pinus sylvestris* trees (see also section on Diterpene Biogenesis). The monoterpenes from this species of tree consist almost totally of α-pinene and carene. The latter were isolated in radioactive form as the nitrosocholoride and nitrosate, respectively. The rate of biosynthesis of the terpenes studied did not appear to be influenced perceptibly by the tapping required to periodically obtain samples from the trees.† Particularly pertinent to the present discussion was the observation that the radioactivity of the monoterpenes studies was characterized by a comparatively swift rise (within 8–15 days) followed by a gradual fall. The author concluded that such terpenes are "continually re-

† Wounding of pine trees produces an abundant exudate which might unduly influence the metabolism of the tree under investigation. [114]

newed and take place in metabolism", a conclusion strikingly different from earlier suggestions that the volatile terpenes are inert products of metabolism. [41] Neither in the work of Stanley nor in that of Sukhov has the detailed biogenetic pathway of the monoterpenes been disclosed, but such preliminary experiments are indeed needed. Germane to the problem of monoterpene biogenesis is the recent report that monoterpene synthesis in *P. ponderosa* is perennially constant. [115]

On the assumption that "β-methylcrotonic acid was the smallest specific building unit of the polyprene compounds", Sandermann and Stockman [19] administered the potassium salt of C^{14}-carboxyl-labeled β-methylcrotonic acid to young *Mentha pulegium* plants via the roots. After 2–3 weeks the plants were subjected to steam distillation and the pulegone was isolated as the semicarbazone; 7–8 per cent of the administered C^{14} was found in the pulegone, which is the principal monoterpene of this species. Chemical degradation of the pulegone thus obtained to 3-methylcyclohexanone and acetone showed that the latter contained no radioactivity. This is consistent with the conversion shown in Fig. 13 in which β-methylcrotonic acid is

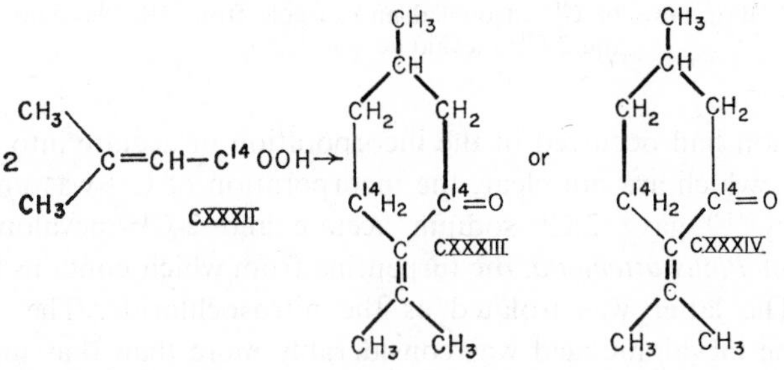

FIG. 13. Biogenesis of C^{14}-Pulegone from 1-C^{14}-β-methylcrotonic acid. [19]

converted intact into the terpene molecule. The pulegone was also degraded to the non-homogeneous pulegenic acid via the dibromide and treatment with alkali, with decarboxylation accomplished by distillation† (Fig. 14). A comparison of the specific activities of the original pulegone and CO_2 and pulegene obtained by degradation caused the authors to conclude that the β-methylcrotonic acid had been incorporated into the terpene intact without any prior conversion of the β-methylcrotonic acid to acetic acid. In view of evidence from other areas that β-methylcrotonic acid is degraded to acetic acid [79, 80] this important observation bears further investigation.

Attention should be called to the labeling of mycelianamide and mycophenolic acid following the feeding of labeled substrates to the molds yielding these metabolites, [116] Mycelianamide contains a methylgeraniolene side

† Presumably according to the method described in Simonsen and Owen, vol. I. [13]

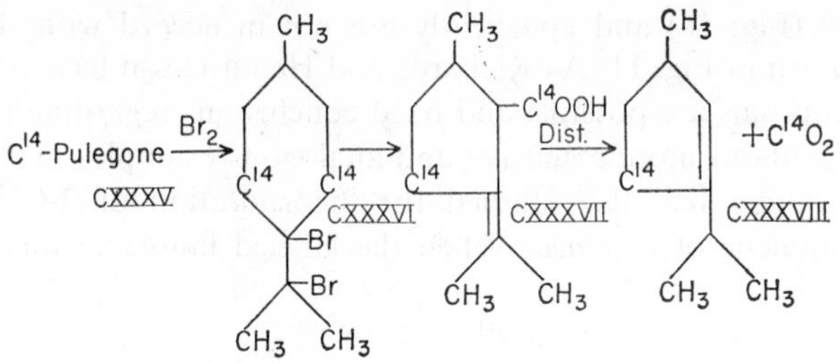

Fig. 14.

chain and mycophenolic acid, a side chain representing the residue of an oxidized geranyl group. Feeding the mold. *P. griseofulvum* carboxyl-labeled β-methylcrotonic acid yielded mycelianamide and mycophenolic acid labeled according to the pattern shown in Fig. 15. The pattern shown by the myco-phenolic acid was the same as that following the administration of carboxyl-labeled acetic acid, from which Birch *et al.* concluded that the β-methyl-crotonic acid was not incorporated directly into a biologically active iso-pentane unit, but was first degraded to acetic acid.

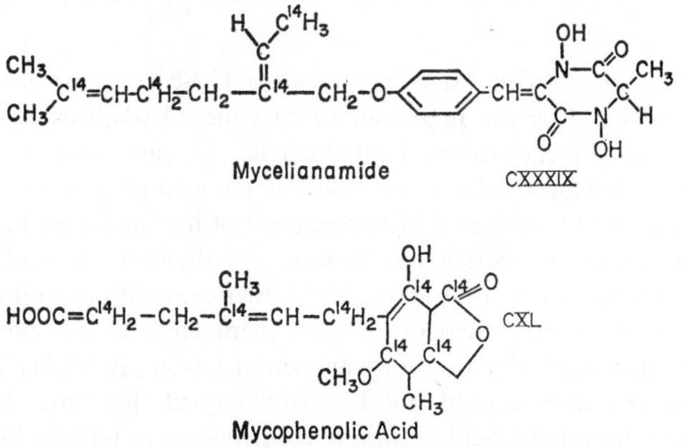

Mycelianamide   CXXXIX

Mycophenolic Acid

Fig. 15. Labeling of mycelianamide and mycophenolic acid following the feeding of $1\text{-}C^{14}\text{-}\beta$-methylcrotonic acid to molds.

In addition to previously mentioned data $2\text{-}C^{14}$-mevalonic acid has now been established as a precursor of α-pinene in *Pinus nigra austriaca*[117, 118] and of thujone in *Thuja occidentalis.*[118, 119] Degradation of the labeled α-pinene gave norpinic acid of the same specific activity, and degradation of the labeled thujone gave 2-methyl-heptanedione-3,6 of approximately the same specific activity as the thujone-C^{14}. Both results have been interpreted as an electrophilic attack of an intermediate carbonium ion upon an allylic hydrogen [98] (Fig. 16) and apparently are not in accord with the Ruzicka proposal shown in Fig. 11. As Richards and Hendrickson have indicated, [98] alternate proposals are possible and fixed conclusions regarding the intrinsic mechanism without more extensive and analogous examples may be premature. Sandermann has also studied the incorporation of 2-C^{14}-mevalonic acid into limonene of *P. pinea*. When the labeled limonene was vigorously

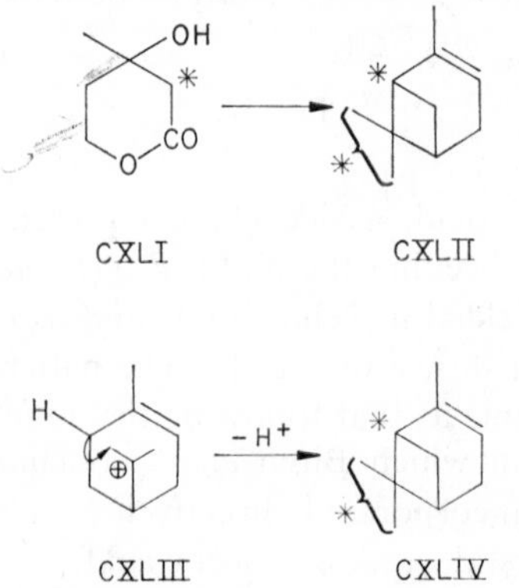

CXLI   CXLII

CXLIII   CXLIV

FIG. 16. Biosynthesis of α-pinene (after Richards and Hendrickson [98]).

mixed and incubated with *Anethum graveolens*, C^{14}-carvone was obtained. [120] Limonene is therefore the precursor of carvone. Ozonolysis of the labeled limonene gave non-radioactive formaldehyde, which is consistent with the labeling pattern expected from 2-C^{14}-mevalonic acid (Fig. 17).

In contrast to the successful incorporations of mevalonic acid cited above, neither this terpene precursor nor labeled α-methylcrotonic acid was incorporated into terpenes of mint leaves. [121] Other examples of failure of mevalonic acid to be incorporated into higher plant terpenes will be cited later. In view of the complexity of "compartmentalization" in higher green plant tissue these examples should not be disturbing at this time. Despite this problem with mevalonic acid, a unique contribution to terpene biochemistry was obtained by the use of $C^{14}O_2$ and the radioautograph technique. [121]

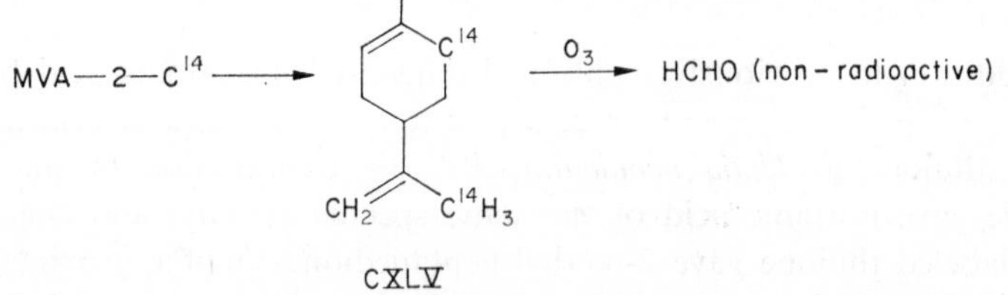

MVA—2—C^{14} $\longrightarrow$ ... $\xrightarrow{O_3}$ HCHO (non-radioactive)

CXLV

FIG. 17. Biosynthesis of limonene.

The results were consistent with earlier suggestions of Reitsma [69, 122] (see Fig. 4). The conversion of piperitenone to piperitone, of pulegone to menthone and of pulegone to menthofuran was demonstrated. Only young leaves of peppermint were capable of synthesizing terpenes. The Battaile and Loomis work has in general been supported by another laboratory, [123] which also demonstrated the conversion of menthone to menthol. Steam volatile C^{14}-labeled material which must have been largely monoterpenes was obtained from *Salvia sclarea* to which 2-C^{14}-mevalonic acid was administered. [124] The nature of the volatile material was not examined, however. The spontaneous aromatization of γ-terpinene to *p*-cymene in the presence of oxygen has been recorded, [125] another reason for exercising caution in interpreting biosynthetic experiments. In this work a rise of *p*-cymene content in *Thymus vulgaris* L. accompanied the fall in content of γ-terpinene.

Although no C^{14} experiments have been performed with the "irregular" artemesia ketone (Fig. 9), the incorporation of 2-C^{14}-mevalonic acid into chrysanthemum carboxylic acid, which possesses in part an artemesia-like skeleton, has been studied. This acid is a portion of a pyrethrin insecticide from *Chrysanthemum cinerariaefolium*. Condensation of two isoprene units as indicated in Fig. 18, followed by ring closure to give the cyclopropane

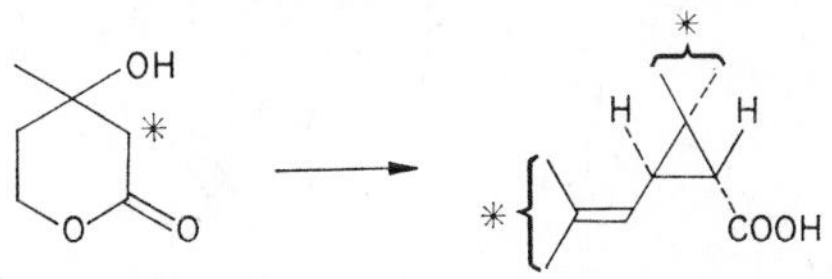

CXLVI   CXLVII

FIG. 18. Biosynthesis of chrysanthemum carboxylic acid.

ring, would account for the formation of the acid. When 2-C^{14}-mevalonic acid was fed to ovules of *C. cinerariaefolium* and the isolated chrysanthemum carboxylic acid was degraded, the C^{14} was found in positions consistent with the suggested condensation of two C_5-units. [126] Pyrethric acid is also formed biogenetically from two molecules of 2-C^{14}-mevalonic acid. [127] Degradation indicated that the side-chain carboxyl was obtained from C-2 of the mevalonic acid as predicted (Fig. 18). Thus the origin of these unusual terpenoid substances from an isoprenoid precursor has been amply verified.

The conversion of C^{14}-citral to C^{14}-geraniol in carrot root slices has been reported, [128] confirming a similar observation on yeast. [58]

BIOGENESIS OF SESQUITERPENES

Structural formulas of some of the more prominent sesquiterpenes found in the plant kingdom are shown in Fig. 19. Like the monoterpenes, they

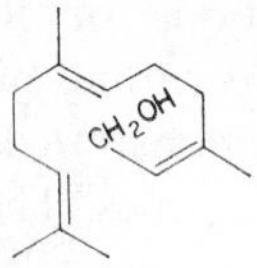

CXLVIII	CXLIX	CL
Farnesol	Nerolidol	Farnesene

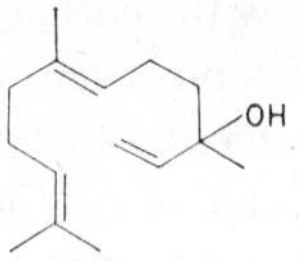

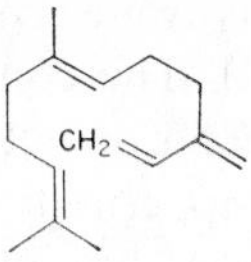

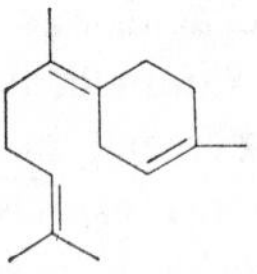

CLI	CLII	CLIII	CLIV
γ – Bisabolene	Lanceol	γ – Curcumene	Zingiberene

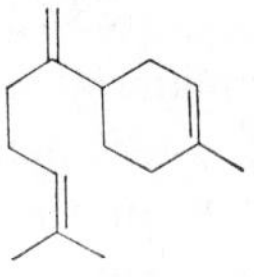

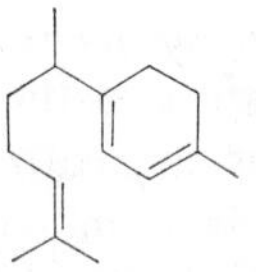

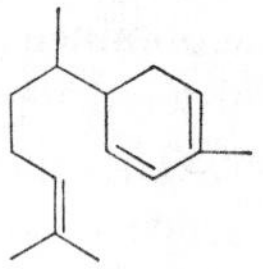

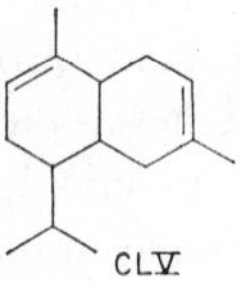

CLV	CLVI	CLVII	CLVIII	CLIX
α – Cadinene	α – Eudesmol	Vetivone	Guaiol	β – Caryophyllene

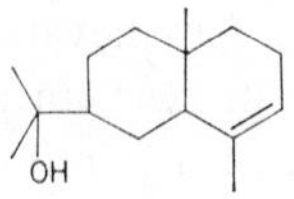

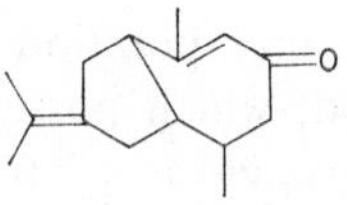

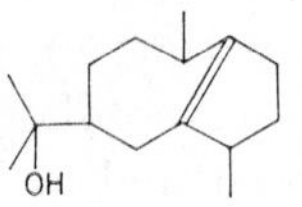

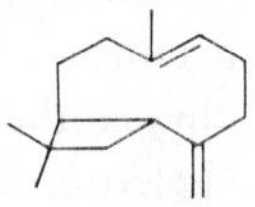

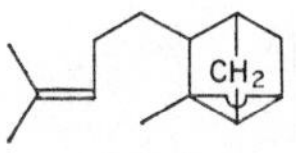

CLX	CLXI
α – Santalene	Cedrene

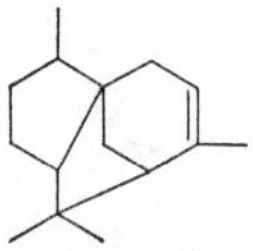

Fig. 19. Prominent members of the sesquiterpene (C_{15}) family.

may occur in acyclic, bicyclic and tricyclic forms. Most of them can be divided into three isopentane units connected head-to-tail (CLXII and CLXIII). An exception is carotol (CLXV, Fig. 20) from carrot oil, in which the isopentane units are irregularly arranged. An additional exception is eremophilone (CLXVII), in that no sequence can be established for three isopentane units. Robinson [129] has suggested that by methyl migration of a hypothetical precursor (Fig. 21), the structure of eremophilone becomes more tenable with that of other terpenes (see also Hendrickson [130] and Zalkow et al. [131] Biochemical studies of this problem should prove interesting; the present known source of eremophilone (and the related hydroxy- and hydroxydihydroeremophilone), the shrub *Eremophila mitchelli*, [132] grows in the Far East.

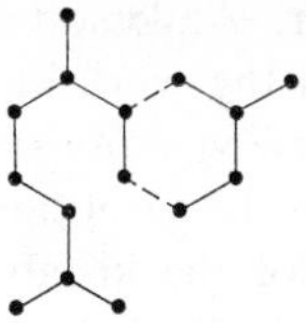

CLXII

Bisabolene type

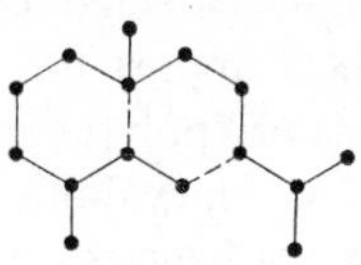

CLXIII

Eudolesmol type

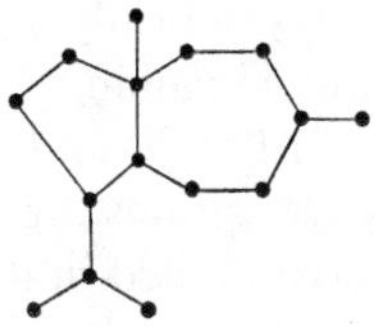

CLXIV

Carotol skeleton

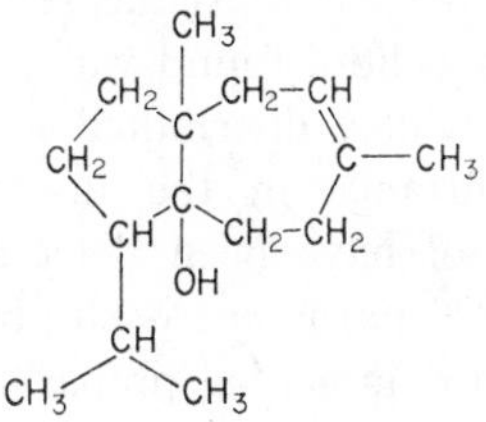

CLXV

Carotol

FIG. 20.

CLXVI

Hypothetical precursor

CLXVII

Eremophilone

FIG. 21. Suggested origin of eremophilone, a ketone that does not follow the isoprene rule.[127]

The most important acyclic sesquiterpene is farnesol (CXLVIII), which bears the same structural relationship to nerolidol that geraniol does to linalool. Regarding the actual biogenetic formation of farnesol itself, Emde's suggested origin from plant sugars[45] had no experimental support. A more sound suggestion (according to present biochemical concepts) was made by Haagen-Smit,[133] who envisioned acetyl CoA as starting material. Recent identification of farnesyl pyrophosphate[21] as an intermediate in the biogenesis of squalene in animal tissues and yeast has established the role of this substance as an important intermediate in terpene biogenesis. As in the case of geraniol, it seems quite likely that the biogenesis of farnesol in higher plants will proceed through a mechanism suggested for its origin in the other tissues, although the presence of a phosphorylated farnesol in higher plant tissues has yet to be detected (see, however, Anderson and Porter[134]). A point of particular import has arisen from the work of Popják,[22] who studied the synthesis of "polyprenols" in liver enzyme preparations following incubation with 2-C[14]-mevalonic acid. Both farnesol and nerolidol (as pyrophosphates) were detected, and in view of the instability of esters of allylic alcohols in the presence of acid (used in the isolation), the question arose as to whether the nerolidol found was a genuine enzymatic product or merely resulted from rearrangement of an ester of farnesol. The point was resolved with the use of snake venom phosphatase; it was concluded that much of the nerolidol found was actually enzymatically synthesized.

Farnesol is widely distributed in the plant kingdom.[135] It has recently assumed importance in the insect kingdom[136–9] and *trans,trans-* and *cis,trans*-farnesol have been detected in yeast strains by thin layer chromatography.[140] Farnesene itself appears to be limited in its occurrence.[141] In one case† a commercial preparation of farnesol, when chromatographed on active alumina, gave a small amount of hydrocarbon comparable in yield and properties to that reported for the isolation of farnesene from a plant source by alumina chromatography.[142] A word of caution seems advisable in isolating this unstable hydrocarbon by passage over active alumina (see also, Stedman *et al.*[143]). Unequivocal identification of farnesene from the natural coating of apples has recently been made.[144]

Farnesol has been implicated as a biogenetic precursor of higher plant cyclic terpenes by virtue of its isoprenoid structure, which permits facile folding to cyclic terpenes on paper, and because of established chemical cyclizations of it or allied substances. A representative transformation is the synthesis of the bisabolenes (CLXIX, CLI, CLXIII) (via farnesene) from nerolidol (CLXVIII) (see also discussion relevant to the conformational fixation and acid-catalyzed cyclization of farnesic acids[145]). A detailed presentation of how farnesol, nerolidol or farnesene might serve as precursors of a wide variety of sesquiterpenes has been given by Ruzicka[81] as part of his "biogenetic isoprene rule". Suggested sequences through a

CLXVIII
Nerolidol

CLXIX
Bisabolene

† Nicholas, H. J., unpublished observations.

series of ionic and radical mechanisms for the formation of ten- or eleven-membered ring terpenes (for example, caryophyllene) or six-membered ring terpenes of the bisabolene type were given. The ionic mechanisms for the latter type are shown in Fig. 22. Theoretical discussion of the possible course of farnesol cyclization, complementing that of Ruzicka, has been presented by Hendrickson. [130] According to the latter, either *cis*-farnesol or *trans*-farnesol can be envisioned as a reasonable precursor of all cyclic sesquiterpenes. The hypothesis of a ten-membered ring as a precursor of many of the sesquiterpenes has been abandoned by Barton and De Mayo. [146]

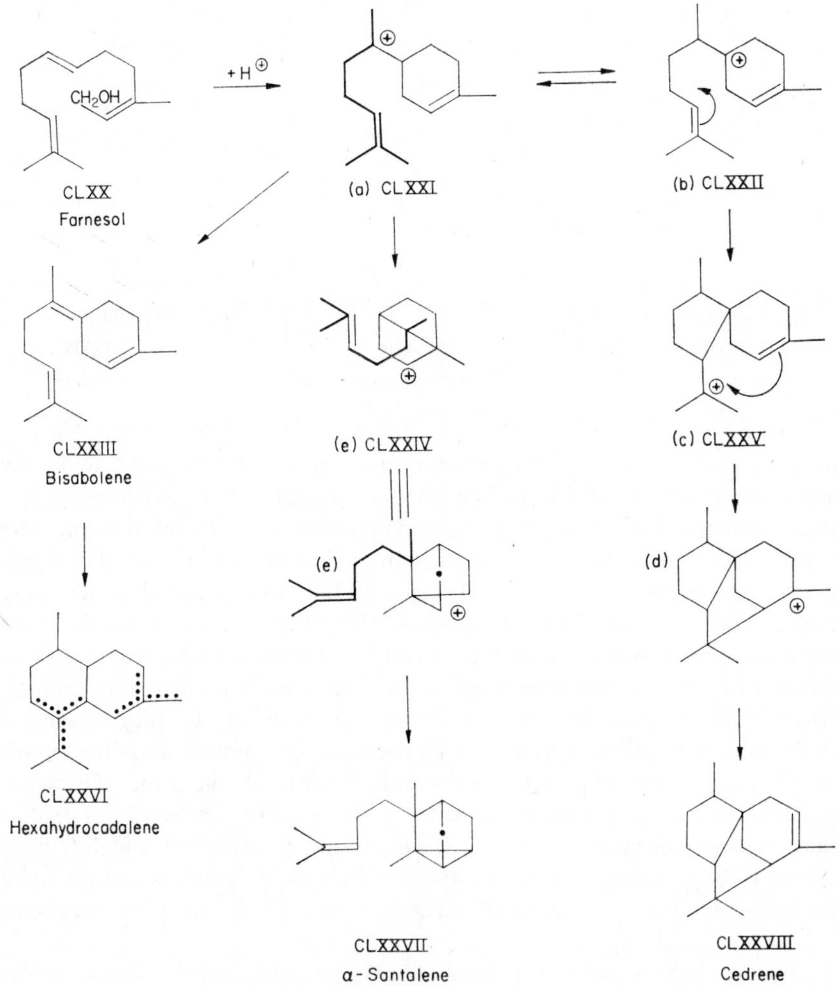

FIG. 22. Ionic mechanisms in the biogenesis of sesquiterpenes (6-membered ring intermediate); Ruzicka. [81]

In recent years, several interesting sesquiterpenes have been isolated from the Mexican shrub *Iresin celosioides* in the laboratories of Djerassi. [147] These include iresin (Fig. 23, CLXXIX), its hydrogenated companion dihydroiresin (CLXXX), and dihydroiresone (CLXXXI), and isoiresin (CLXXXII). The particular arrangement of isopentane units found in this group of substances is represented by the bicyclofarnesol skeleton (CLXXXIII) and is typical of rings A and B of the cyclic diterpenes, triterpenes and (with ring A demethylated) the steroids. The basic form is strikingly reminiscent of the

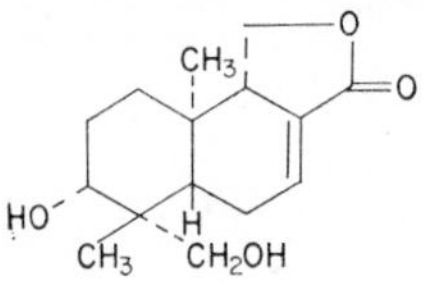

| CLXXIX | CLXXX | CLXXXI |
| Iresin | Dihydroiresin | Dihydroiresone |

| CLXXXII | CLXXXIII | CLXXXIV |
| Isoiresin | Bicyclofarnesol skeleton | Drimenol |

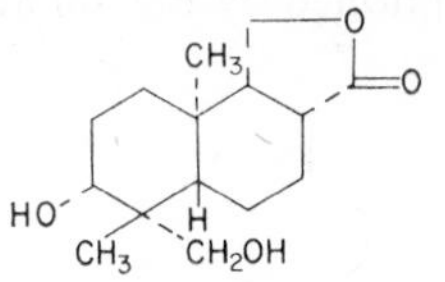

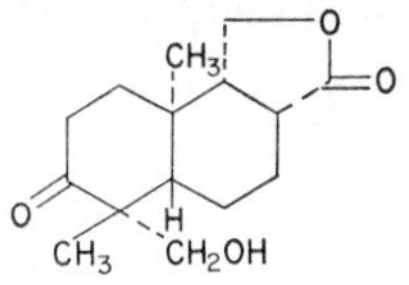

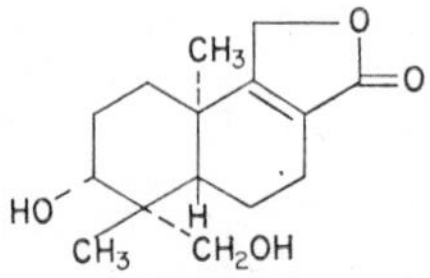

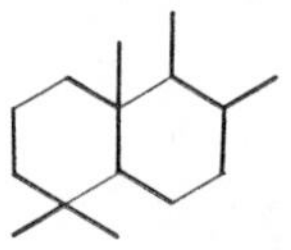

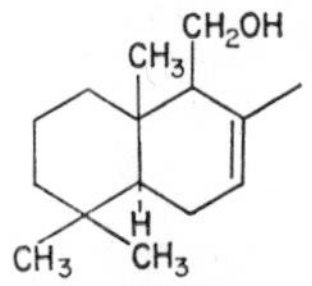

FIG. 23. Prominent members of the iresin family of sesquiterpenes.

products formed by acid-catalyzed cyclization of the farnesic acids, [145] and correspondingly different from the ring systems of the cyclic sesquiterpenes shown in Fig. 19. The iresin group of substances is therefore formed by a basic mechanism different from that by which the majority of the higher plant sesquiterpenes are formed. Haagen-Smit has suggested that they may arise by degradation of higher terpenes.† [133] However, iresin and its companions were shown to have the "wrong" absolute configuration, that is, 5β,10α instead of 5α,10β as in most of the diterpenes, triterpenes and sterols. Attention was called by Djerassi [149] to the rarity of the bicyclofarnesol skeleton with a hydroxyl group at C-3, the iresin compounds and farnesiferol A [150] being the only such compounds known at the time. Drimenol (CLXXXIV), a sesquiterpene from the bark of *Drimys winteri* Forst., has the conventional steroid absolute configuration (5α,10β) [151] and has been shown to be identical in structure and stereochemistry with an acid obtained by acid-catalyzed cyclization of farnesic acid.‡ [145] Djerassi [149] suggested

† See also comments by Brieskorn. [148]

‡ The C_{16} terpenoid acid alcohol identified by Ogilvie and Langdon [152] as a metabolite of mevalonic acid in rat liver can be folded to resemble an acyclic sesquiterpene ready for cyclization; according to Crabbé [105] the formation of this compound may be the result of a side reaction.

that the formation of these "wrong"-configuration sesquiterpenes is governed by some special stereochemical requirement of the enzyme system promoting the cyclization. Biochemical exploration of the origin and disposition of the iresin group of substances within plants should prove to be an especially fruitful area for research.

Experimental tracer work on the biogenesis of either acyclic or cyclic sesquiterpenes in higher plants is limited but informative. Preliminary results have been obtained with the mold metabolite trichothecin (Fig. 24),

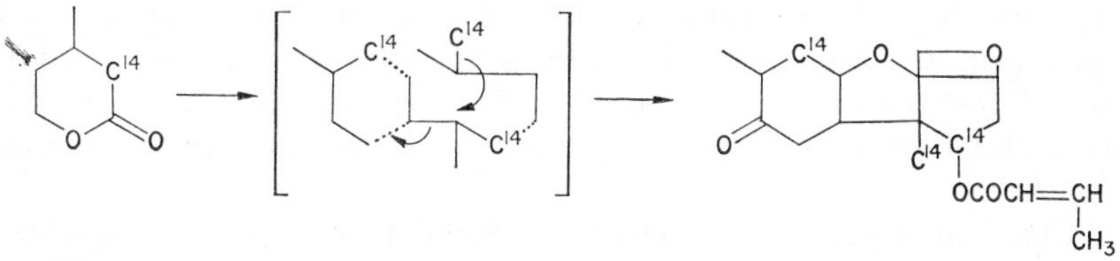

CLXXXV	CLXXXVI	CLXXXVII
Mevalonic acid	Intermediate	Trichothecin
lactone	precursor	

FIG. 24. Labeling of the mold metabolite trichothecin by 2-C^{14}-mevalonic acid lactone.

from the mold *Trichothecium roseum* Link. Mild hydrolysis of trichothecin yields *cis*-crotonic acid and a C_{15} moiety which superficially bears little resemblance to the classical type of sesquiterpene. This portion does not obey the isoprene rule, yet it can be derived from a hypothetical precursor composed of three isoprenoid groups by two 1,2-methyl or one 1,3-methyl group migrations. Fishman et al.[153] studied the incorporation of 2-C^{14}-mevalonic acid lactone into the metabolite and found the labeling pattern as indicated in Fig. 24. Little or no C^{14} was found in the crotonate side chain. With labeled acetic acid administered, the reverse was found (i.e. good in-

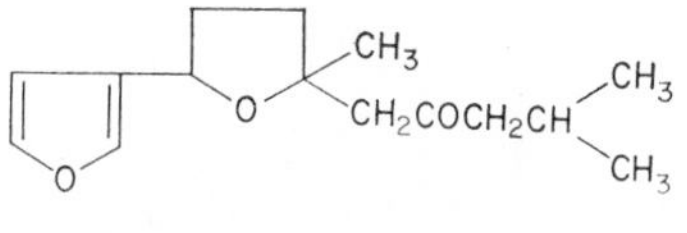

FIG. 25. Ipomeamarone.

corporation into the isocrotonate side chain, none in the nucleus). The suggested origin shown by the labeling pattern necessitated two methyl group migrations rather than a single 1,3-shift.

The incorporation of 2-C^{14}-mevalonic acid into the furanoterpenoid ipomeamarone from sweet potato roots infected with the black rot fungus *Ceratocystis timbriata* has been reported. Part of ipomeamarone (Fig. 25) can be derived (from farnesol) without cyclization by head-to-tail linkage of three isoprene units, with the terminal unit becoming the carbon skeleton of the furan ring. The incorporation of mevalonic acid was found to be considerably less than incorporation of 2-C^{14}-sodium acetate, [154] reminiscent of other examples which have been cited. No degradation experiments have as yet been reported.

Helminthosporal (Fig. 26) is a sesquiterpene fungal toxin isolated from the mold *Helminthosporum sativum*. 2-C^{14}-Mevalonic acid was incorporated into the molecule to the extent of 5 per cent. [155] Degradation of the labeled sesquiterpene indicated that the unsaturated aldehyde group contained approximately 38 per cent of the total C^{14} present. The source of the sesquiterpene has been visualized [98] as a 10-ring cation that can be formed from *cis*-farnesyl pyrophosphate (Fig. 26). The degradation that has been performed on the C^{14}-labeled sesquiterpene is consistent with the suggested formation.

Chemical aspects of Wagner–Meerwein rearrangements possible in the longifolene type of sesquiterpenes has recently been reviewed. [156] The biogenesis of this fascinating terpene has been given some initial study

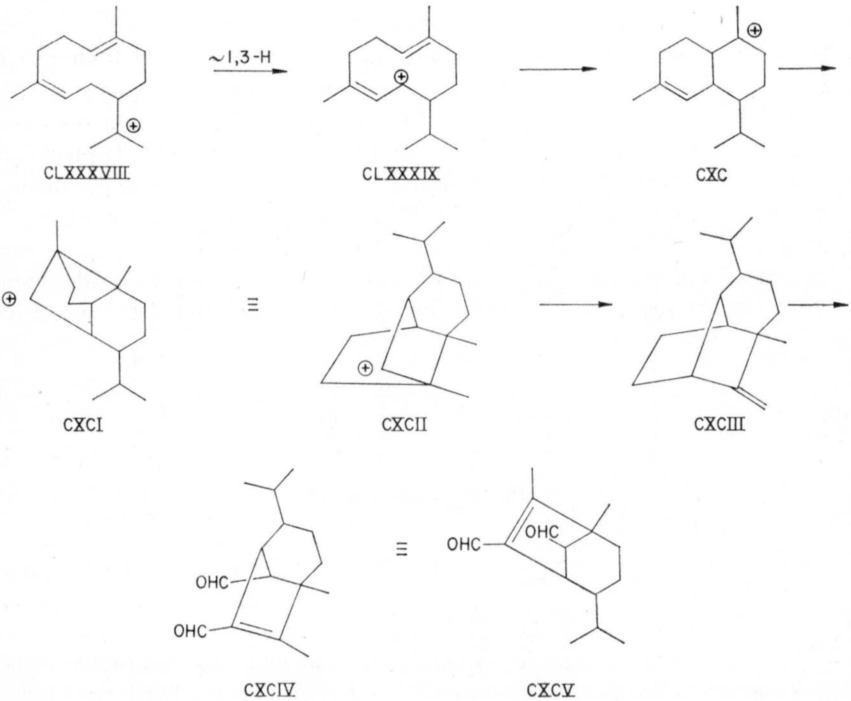

FIG. 26. Biosynthesis of helminthosporal, after Richards and Hendrickson. [98]

by administering 1-C^{14}-sodium acetate to *Pinus longifolia* Roxb.[117] When the sesquiterpene was ozonized, the exocyclic methylene group was found to be essentially devoid of radioactivity. This result was consistent with the sequence of reactions shown in Fig. 27, which begins[98] with the hypothetical ion (CXCVI) arising from farnesol.

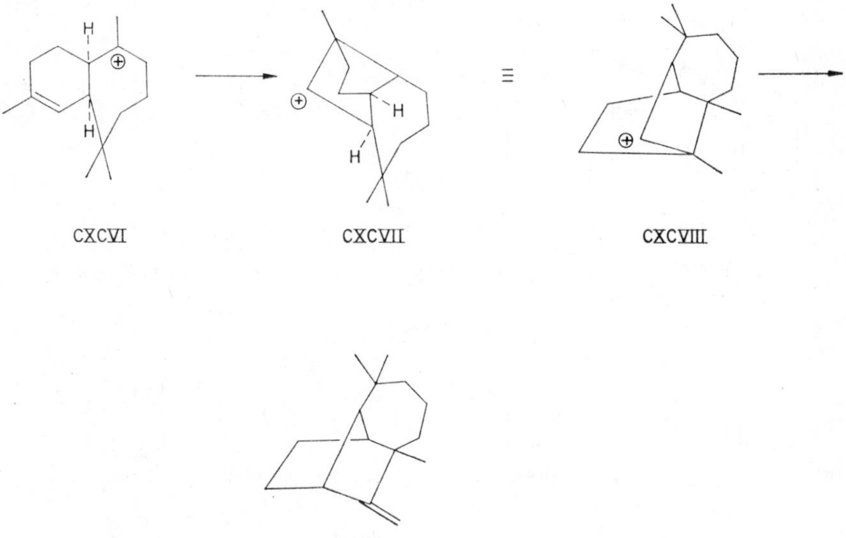

CXCVI   CXCVII   CXCVIII

CXCIX

FIG. 27. Biosynthesis of longifolene, after Richards and Hendrickson.[98]

BIOGENESIS OF DITERPENES

Because the diterpenes basically consist of four isopentane units combined the possibilities for structural complexity become correspondingly greater, as reflected in some of the more prominent forms shown in Fig. 28. Mono-cyclic forms are rare,† and this may have some biochemical significance. However, acyclic, bi-, tri-, tetra- and pentacyclic forms are known. With the exception of the abietic acid type of resin acid‡ with an irregular sequence of four isopentane units, all of the higher plant diterpenes can be constructed on paper from a phytol-like tetramer consisting of the four units linked head-to-tail. Ruzicka suggested a hypothetical geranylgeraniol (or geranyl-linalool, recently isolated from jasmine oil,[159] or geranylmyrcene) type of structure as a possible biogenetic precursor of the diterpenes,[81] through ionic mechanisms as indicated in Fig. 29.

† Two representatives are axerophthol of the vitamin A series[81] (animal tissues) and the partially aromatic wormwood diterpene of Sorm.[105] (See also Dauben *et al.*[157])

‡ Abietic acid is a "derived" acid formed by the isomerizing action of heat or acid on the "primary resin acids" present in the original oleoresin.[158]

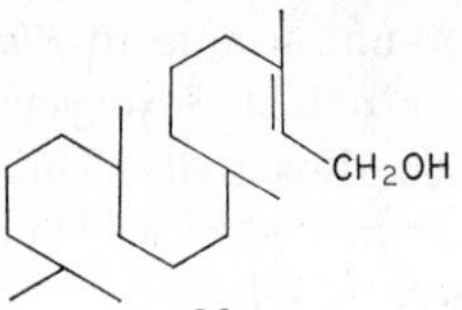

CC
Phytol

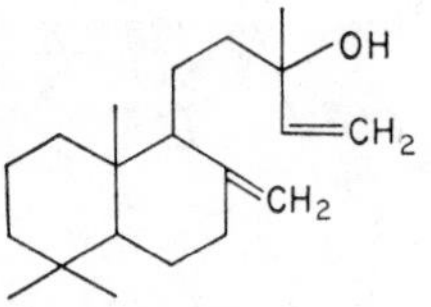

CCI
Manool

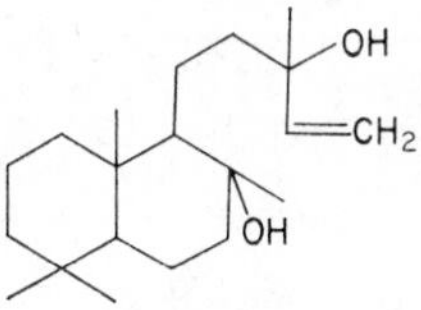

CCII
Sclareol

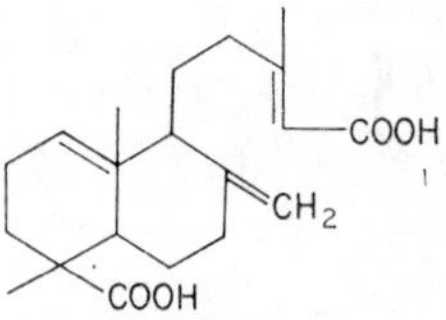

CCIII
Agathic acid

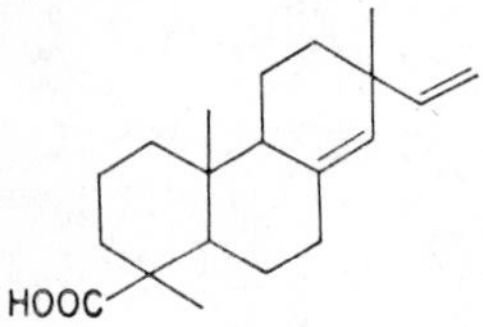

CCIV
Dextropimaric acid

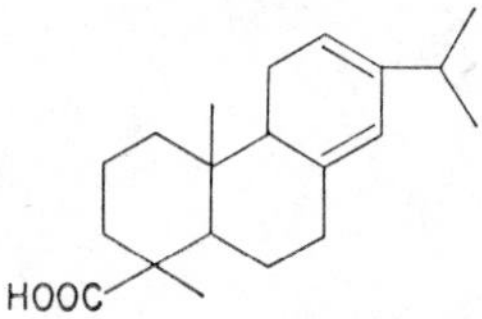

CCV
Levopimaric acid

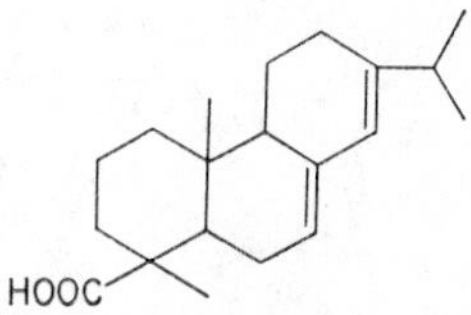

CCVI
Abietic acid

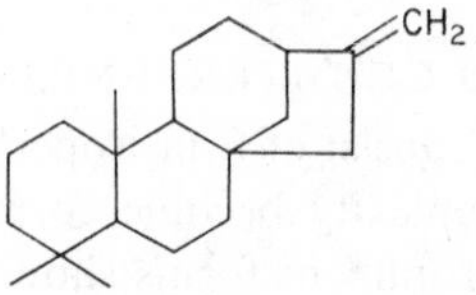

CCVII
Phyllocladene

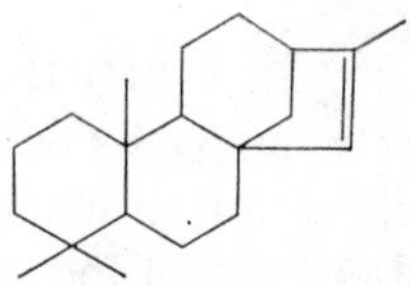

CCVIII
Isophyllocladene

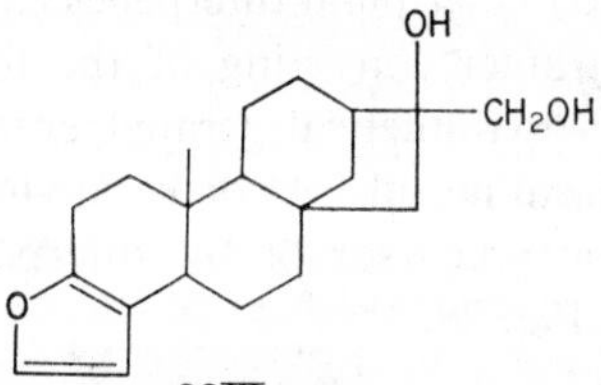

CCIX
Cafestol

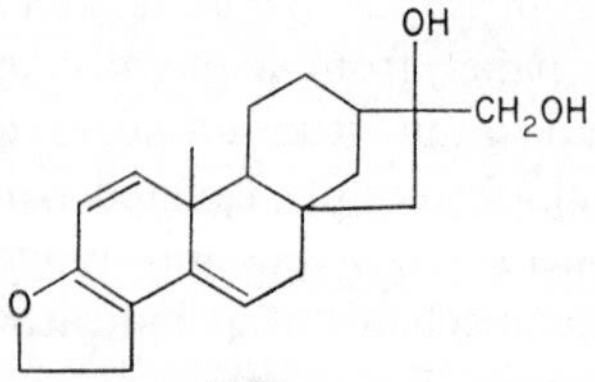

CCX
Kahweol

FIG. 28. Prominent members of the diterpene (C_{20}) family.

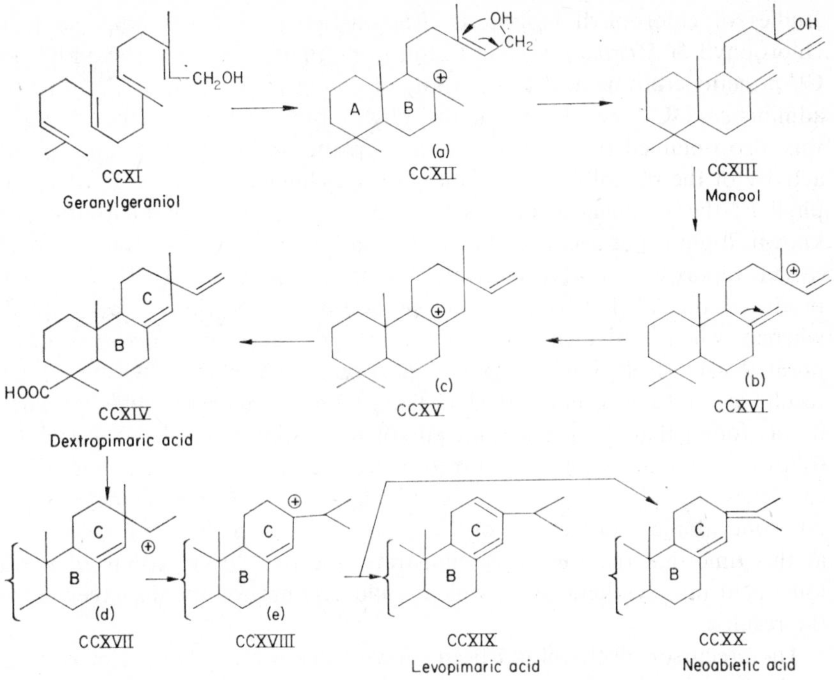

FIG. 29. Ionic mechanisms in the biogenesis of diterpenes; after Ruzicka.[81]

Phytol

The acyclic phytol occurs throughout the higher plant kingdom as a constituent of chlorophyll, and in the vitamins K and E. A hydrocarbon neophytadiene (the γ-phytadiene of Onishi[160]) has been isolated from flue-cured tobacco and has been assigned the following structure:[161]

$$CH_3-\underset{\underset{CH_3}{|}}{CH}-(CH_2)_3-\underset{\underset{CH_3}{|}}{CH}-(CH_2)_3-\underset{\underset{CH_3}{|}}{CH}-(CH_2)_3-\underset{\underset{CH_2}{\|}}{C}-CH=CH_2$$

3-methylene-7,11,15-trimethyl-1-hexadecene (neophytadiene)

A series of isomeric conjugated phytadienes related to the above substance have also been isolated from cigarette smoke;[162] they are presumed to arise from the thermal isomerization of neophytadiene during the smoking process. According to Fujita,[163] neophytadiene probably does not arise by simple dehydration of phytol itself, but rather by dehydration of a tertiary alcohol type of phytol (analogous to linalool) which has not been found in nature.

Studies on the biogenesis of phytol are of necessity intimately bound to studies of chlorophyll biogenesis. Radioactive phytol was obtained from chlorophyll of *Mentha pulegium* L. following the feeding of carboxyl-labeled C^{14}-β-methylcrotonic acid to the roots of young plants; 2·93 per cent of the administered C^{14} was found in the phytol isolated. [19] C^{14}-labeled phytol was also obtained from several types of plants fed $C^{14}O_2$. [164] The specific activity of the phytol from chlorophyll *a* was higher than that from chlorophyll *b*; the significance of this for the biogenesis of phytol itself is not known. Light is not necessary for the formation of phytol, [165] contrary to an earlier report.[166] Barley cultivated in the presence of 2-C^{14}-acetic acid produced the label principally in the non-phytol portion of chlorophyll, whereas when cultivated with 2-C^{14}-mevalonic acid the latter was incorporated exclusively into the phytol portion of the chlorophyll. [167] These results are not consistent with data from another laboratory,[168, 169] where it was found that β-carotene and phytol were appreciably labeled with C^{14} following administration of $C^{14}O_2$ to maize, oat, pea and lettuce, but neither carotenes nor phytol were significantly labeled following incubation with 2-C^{14}-mevalonic acid lactone (or 2-C^{14}-mevalonic acid). It seems most likely at this time that these examples illustrate selective "penetration" of mevalonic acid into synthetic sites, which could account for the disagreement in the results.

The precursor of phytol has been shown to be geranylgeraniol or geranyllinalool. In tritiated form both were incorporated in high percentages into phytol of maize seedlings. [170] Previously the same laboratory had shown by isotopic dilution experiments utilizing 2-C^{14}-sodium acetate fed to maize seedlings that geranylgeraniol was a common precursor of both β-carotene and phytol. Thus, the original suggestion of Ruzicka [81] on the hypothetical role of these substances as diterpene precursors has been confirmed.

In concluding our present knowledge of phytol biogenesis it may be in order to cite recent evidence that phytol itself is the precursor of the interesting hydrocarbon pristane, which may have originated in a prehistoric era. [171, 172] Phytol in chlorophyll, in contrast to the porphyrin nucleus, may undergo turnover. [173]

The Cyclic Diterpenes

The cyclic diterpenes have presented a particularly challenging field for research. Their occurrence in nature is limited to the plant kingdom, where some of them in the form of gibberellins have assumed great economic importance while they also provide considerable scientific interest. An original concept of cyclic diterpene biogenesis stems from the suggestion of Ruzicka, [81] involving cyclization of an initial isoprenoid tetramer (e.g. geranylgeraniol) to a hypothetical cyclic precursor from which all of the known diterpenes subsequently develop by methyl migrations characteristic

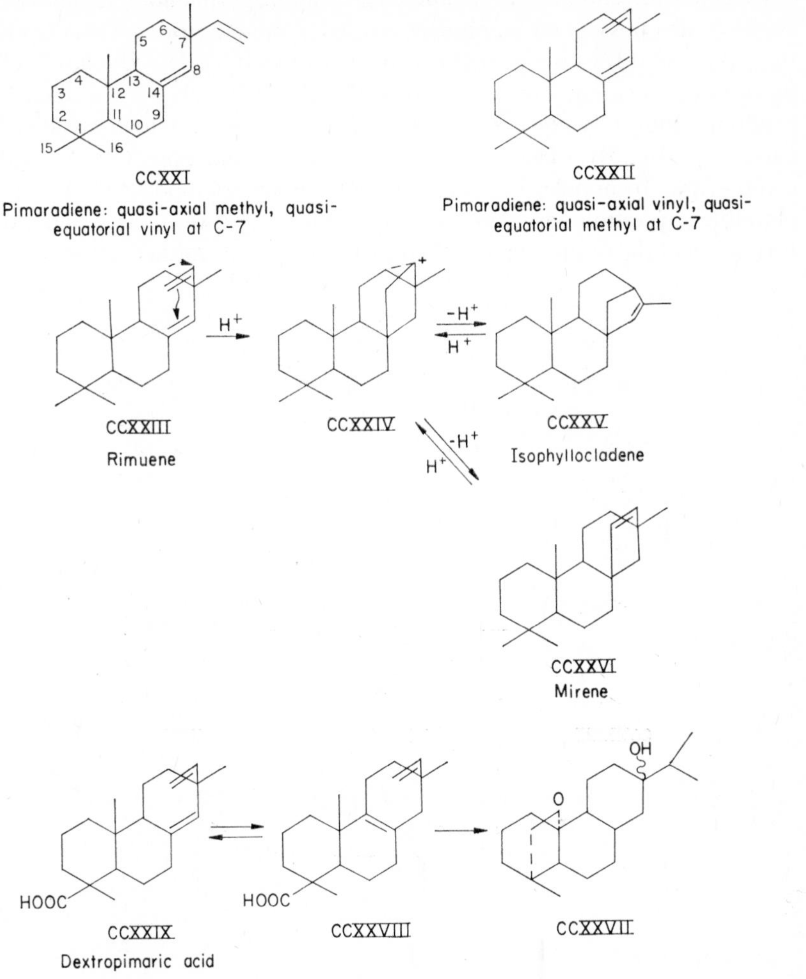

CCXXI

Pimaradiene: quasi-axial methyl, quasi-
equatorial vinyl at C-7

CCXXII

Pimaradiene: quasi-axial vinyl, quasi-
equatorial methyl at C-7

CCXXIII

Rimuene

CCXXIV

CCXXV

Isophyllocladene

CCXXVI

Mirene

CCXXIX

Dextropimaric acid

CCXXVIII

CCXXVII

FIG. 30. Transformation in the resin acid series, according to Wenkert.[190]

of the terpene series (Fig. 30). Early suggestions that the resin acids are
formed by cyclization of a phytol isomer[174] or by copolymerization of
isoprene and vinylacrylic acid[114] were interesting but premature, since
knowledge of the structure of the rings was incomplete at the time. It is
interesting that the majority of the presently known cyclic diterpenes contain
no hydroxyl at C-3 and possess the conventional $5\alpha,10\beta$ configuration of
rings A and B as in the steroids and triterpenes. An exception, according to
Djerassi,[175] is the diterpenoid cassaine, which possesses the conventional
steroid ring A/B configuration but does have a hydroxyl at C-3. Cafestol

(CCIX), darutigenol, [176] (—)-kaurene, [177] andrographolide [178] and eperuic acid [179] also possess the opposite, "wrong" configuration ($5\beta,10\alpha$); some of them possess at least a potential hydroxyl group at C-3. The generation of the furan ring in cafestol (CCIX) and kahweol (CCX) has been visualized as resulting from a Wagner–Meerwein rearrangement of a hydroxylated precursor [175] (Fig. 31). The proposed formation is analogous to the origin of menthofuran from pulegone, for which there is some support. [122] An equally plausible suggestion has been made by Wenkert, [179] who has visualized the formation of the furan ring by oxidation of an α,β-unsaturated ketone through

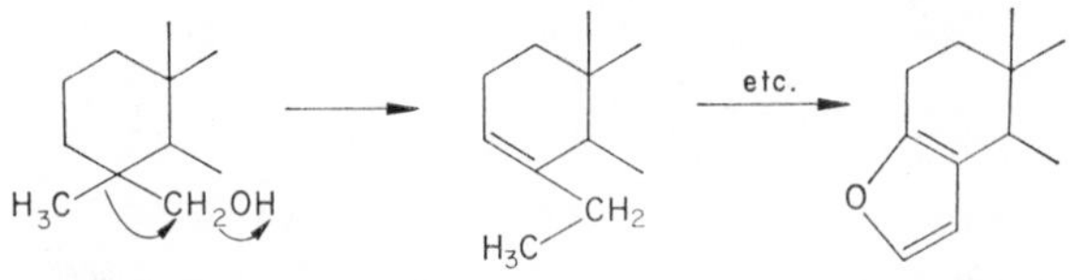

H₃C CH₂OH CCXXX   CH₂ H₃C CCXXXI   O CCXXXII   etc.

FIG. 31. Biosynthesis of furan ring of kahweol. [175]

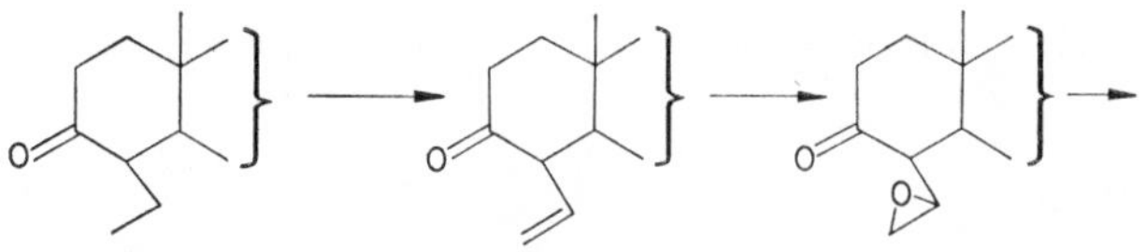

O CCXXXIII   O CCXXXIV   O CCXXXV

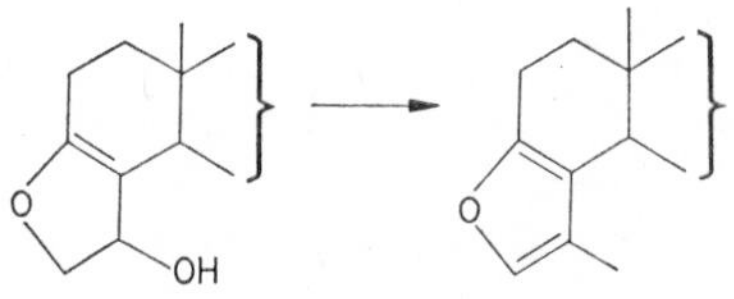

O OH CCXXXVI   O CCXXXVII

FIG. 32. Biosynthesis of furan ring of kahweol and cafestol. [179]

an intermediate epoxide (Fig. 32). None of these suggestions for the formation of the extra-nuclear portion of diterpenes like cafestol has as yet been supported by tracer work.

The origin of the diterpene nucleus has received its greatest support from experiments on two mold products. Following the feeding of 2-C^{14}-mevalonic acid lactone to *Trichothecium roseum* L., Birch [180] and Arigoni [181] independently demonstrated that the diterpene rosenonolactone isolated contained the C^{14} pattern indicated in Fig. 33, the biogenesis presumably proceeding through the hypothetical precursor (CCXXXIX) composed of four isoprenoid units. It will be noted that rosenonolactone itself does not obey the classical isoprene rule in that it cannot be divided into four regular isopentane units. A point of particular note borne out by both laboratories was the detection of radioactivity in the C-15 methyl group of ring A and the

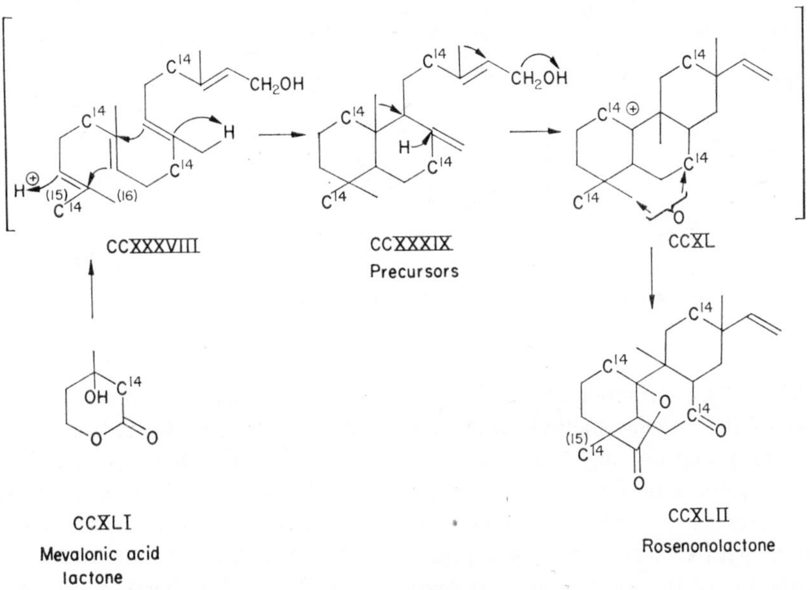

FIG. 33. Biogenesis of rosenonolactone from 2-C^{14}-mevalonic acid lactone.

absence of radioactivity in the carbon from the lactone ring, a finding which indicated that the C-15 was derived specifically from the C-2 of the mevalonic acid with carbons C-2 and C-3 of the mevalonic acid at no time becoming equivalent (the stereochemistry remaining select).

The other "mold product" which has proved of great value in biogenetic studies of the diterpene nucleus in gibberellic acid. It now appears that this substance and many closely related metabolites are endogenous higher plant hormones, and their significance can be partly assessed by the enormous literature that has accumulated on their varied forms and physiological effects.[182, 183] Birch,[180] utilizing 2-C^{14}-mevalonic acid, obtained C^{14}-gibberellic acid from the mold *Gibberella fujikuroi*. Degradation of the diterpene gave results consistent with its probable origin by condensation of four mevalonic acid units (Fig. 34). According to a proposed scheme,[184] geranylgeraniol pyrophosphate from mevalonic acid cyclizes to a bicyclic intermediate (CCXLV), then to the tricyclic diterpenoid (CCXLVI). Gibberellic acid then arises by formation of ring D from the side chain of

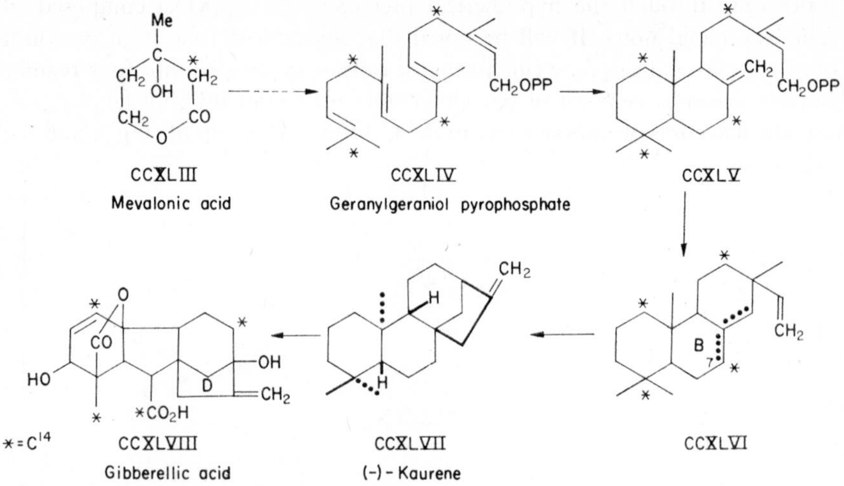

FIG. 34. Biosynthesis of gibberellin.[184]

(CCXLVI), contraction of ring B with extrusion of C-7 as the carboxyl group,† loss of the angular methyl group, and hydroxylation and formation of the lactone group on ring A. In the course of further biosynthetic studies using *G. fujikuroi* a number of C_{20} compounds were isolated.[184] One of these, (—)-kaurene, (CCXLVII) when chemically labeled in the exocyclic methylene group with C^{14}, proved to be a precursor of gibberellin and therefore represents one of the intermediates between (CCXLVI) and gibberellin (Fig. 34). Kaurene, previously only isolated from New Zealand trees of the Podocarpus species, is thus not limited to the fungi. In fact, recent investigations into the biological activity of kaurene-like compounds [185, 186] have indicated that several of them, including the higher plant diterpene steviol [187] (but not kaurene itself) are active in sheath and leaf elongation teets. C^{14}-Labeled steviol, prepared from 2-C^{14}-acetate by administration of the latter to growing *Stevia rebaudiana* plants, [188] when incubated with *G. fujikuroi* did not serve as a precursor of any of the known gibberellins, but was converted to a substance having gibberellin activity.

At least one experiment has been reported on the biosynthesis of gibberellins in higher plants. The pyrophosphate ester of 2-C^{14}-geranylgeraniol was incubated with endosperm-nucellar preparations from the seed of the wild cucumber *Echinocystis macrocarpa* Greene. [189] Evidence was obtained that the acylic terpenoid was incorporated into gibberellins A_4 and A_7.

These important developments, while clarifying the overall schemes suggested for diterpene biogenesis, leave some areas which need further biogenetic experimentation. They do not explain in any detail, for example,

† Using the numbering system common to the sterol ring system.

the formation of the phyllocladene type of ring D, nor the interrelationship between the resin acids of the dextropimaric (pimarane) type and the levopimaric (abietane) type. It will be noted that in acids of the pimarane type four isopentane units are combined in "regular" formation, whereas in those of the abietane type, the fourth unit is bound in an irregular manner (Fig. 30). Sandermann originally suggested [174, 189] that both types of resin acids would arise from a common precursor through a final Wagner–Meerwein rearrangement of dextropimaric acid to levopimaric acid. The problem of the biogenesis of these substances was re-examined by Wenkert. [190] According to this investigator, acid-catalyzed rearrangement of the pimarane to the abietane or phyllocladene type should be especially influenced by the stereochemistry of the functional groups involved, in this case C-7 in particular (Fig. 30). Pimaradienes may possess either a quasi-axial methyl and a quasi-equatorial vinyl function (CCXXI) or the opposite conformation (CCXXII).† On mechanistic grounds it was concluded that the conformation which would most likely be the one involved would be that in which the pimaradiene possessed the quasi-axial vinyl and quasi-equatorial groups; the transformation of rimuene‡ (CCXXIII) to isophyllocladene (CCXXV) and mirene (CCXXVI) was then envisioned as occurring as shown in Fig. 30. The acid-catalyzed transformation of dextropimaric acid to the abietane type was believed to occur as indicated in Fig. 30 (CCXVIII → CCXXIX), the mechanism being more complex because of the carboxyl of the dextropimaric acid. Biogenetic mechanisms were presumed to occur by the same type of sequence. The general approach to this problem was later modified [192] and the actual acid-catalyzed conversion of pimaradiene to an abietadiene demonstrated. It will be noted that by the suggested mechanism, the formation of the phyllocladene ring system occurs through migration of the C-6 carbon atom and not the angular C-20 methyl group. According to Briggs et al. [193] a similar mechanism had been proposed earlier by Wilmshurst. [194, 195] Briggs and associates provided additional evidence to substantiate the structural relationships between these complex diterpenes by establishing the absolute configuration of phyllocladene, mirene, rimuene, cuppressene and kaurene, utilizing the new tool of optical rotatory dispersion developed by Djerassi [196] (see also Wenkert and Beak, [197] and Djerassi et al. [198]). The final biogenetic scheme suggested was supported by the observation that phyllocladene and isophyllocladene co-occur in *Araucaria excelsa* and *Phyllocladus trichomanoides* and the co-occurrence of ferruginol, sugiol (isomiropinic acid), isopimaric (miropinic) acid, phyllocladene, mirene and kaurene in *Podocarpus ferrugineus* (the miro pine), growing in New Zealand.

† See Barton et al.[191] for nomenclature.
‡ The quasi-axial vinyl was inferred here and subsequently established[193] for these diterpenes.

The formic acid catalyzed conversion of rimuene to a mixture containing isophyllocladene and abieta-7,9-diene [14] has been reported. [199-201] Unfortunately, the stereochemistry of rimuene is at present in doubt, [182] which limits effective interpretation of the results.

Sandermann and Stockman [19] subjected their suggestions of a common precursor for the dextropimaric and levopimaric acid diterpenes to experimental observation by supplying a 1 m high pine tree with carboxyl-labeled C^{14}-methylcrotonic acid through the roots. After 6 weeks "resin acids", turpentine, phytol (from the chlorophyll) and "phytosterols" were found to contain radioactivity. Degradation of the resin acids was performed by heating with $KMnO_4$ and periodic acid in the presence of ethanol, which procedure is said to give only formaldehyde with acids of the abietic acid type. C^{14} was found in both formaldehyde and acetone (examined as the 2,4-dinitrophenylhydrazones) indicating, according to the authors, that the resin acids arose from a common intermediate.

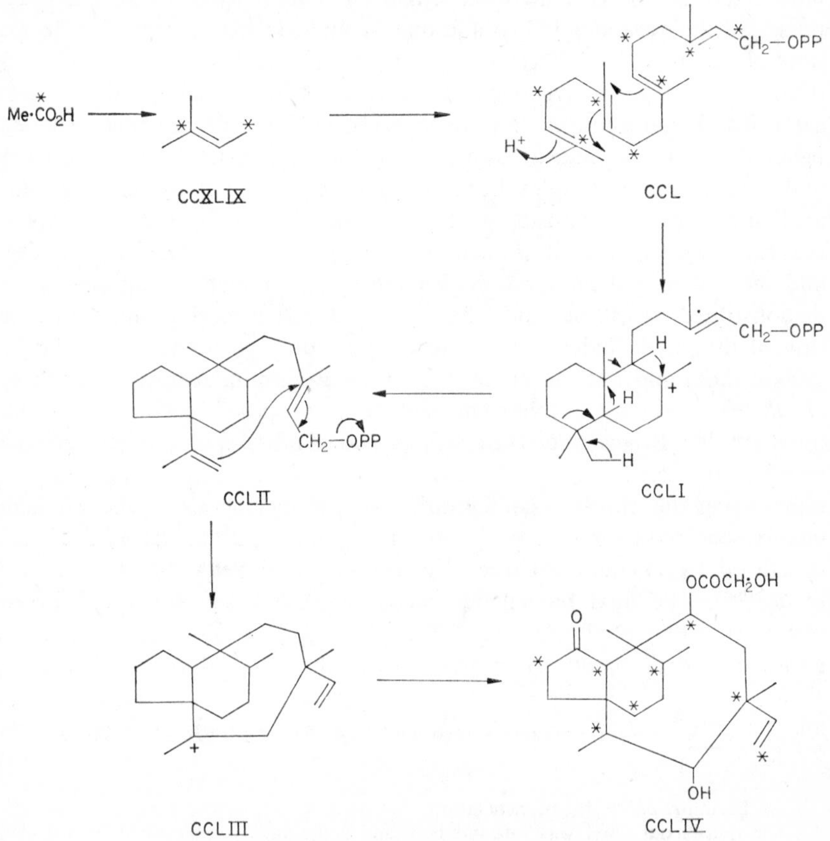

FIG. 35. Biosynthesis of pleuromutilin. [202]

How fantastically nature can vary its diterpenoid forms is illustrated well by the structural formula for pleuromutilin (Fig. 35), from the Bacidiomycete *Pleurotus mutilis*. Tracer studies utilizing 2-C^{14}-mevalonic acid, with subsequent degradation of the diterpene, validated the biogenetic mechanism suggested for its formation. [202, 98]

Finally, mention should be made of some ancillary experiments which may have later bearing on biosynthetic studies. By feeding $C^{14}O_2$ to 10- or 12-year-old pine trees enclosed in plastic film, Sukhov [113] presented evidence that "resin acids" undergo a relatively high rate of turnover. The maximum specific activity of resin acids was obtained 14 days after the introduction of C^{14}, followed by a relatively rapid decrease. It was concluded that the resin acids undergo a continuous metabolism like the monoterpenes investigated. The magnitude of this work and the implications for the diterpenes are impressive, although it would be desirable that more experimental data be given on purification of the acids. If the cyclic diterpenes represented by the resin acids are not inert substances, it would seem of considerable importance to determine what the nature of their conversion products are. The plant *Salvia sclarea* (Labiatae family) contains sclareol, β-sitosterol and some acidic pentacyclic triterpenes. [203, 204] Thus, it is a convenient plant with which to study diterpene, sterol and triterpene metabolism simultaneously. When 2-C^{14}-mevalonic acid was fed to cut flowering section of *S. sclarea* and the sections were allowed to dry, the sclareol isolated contained only negligible amounts of C^{14}, whereas the β-sitosterol and acidic triterpenes were appreciably labeled. [205] Interpretation of these findings cannot be made until further experimentation is performed. C^{14}-Sclareol of high specific activity has been obtained by exposing cut sections of *S. sclarea* to high concentrations of $C^{14}O_2$. [206] Unfortunately this observation has not provided much information as to the course of the biosynthetic mechanism involved.

In general, it may be concluded that the theoretical origin of the cyclic diterpenes appears fairly well documented by tracer work, despite some gaps to be filled in. It appears likely that the fascinating questions raised by the coordinated study of fungal and higher plant diterpenes will open many new areas for exploration into the physiological function of terpenes in plants.

BIOGENESIS OF PLANT STEROLS AND TRITERPENES

In 1926 Heilbron and his collaborators made the cryptic comment: "That squalene is intimately connected with metabolic processes is self evident, and in this connection we desire to direct attention to a possible relationship between this hydrocarbon, stigmasterol ($C_{30}H_{50}O$) and cholesterol." [207] In the intervening years, not only was the correct formula for stigmasterol established but the role of squalene in animal and fungal sterol biosynthesis has been thoroughly elucidated by Bloch [208, 209] and others. It has been a natural step to assume that squalene is also the precursor of

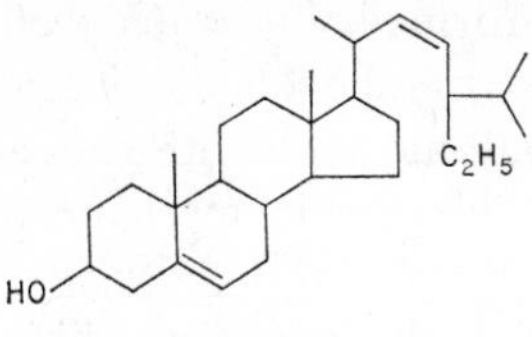

CCLV
Stigmasterol

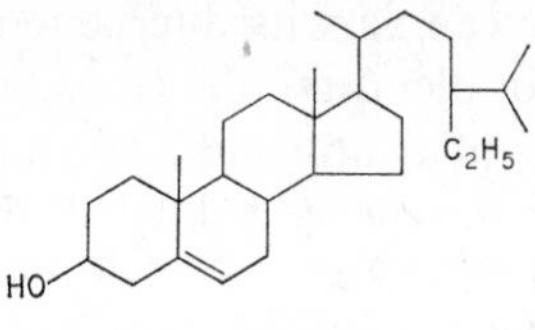

CCLVI
β-Sitosterol

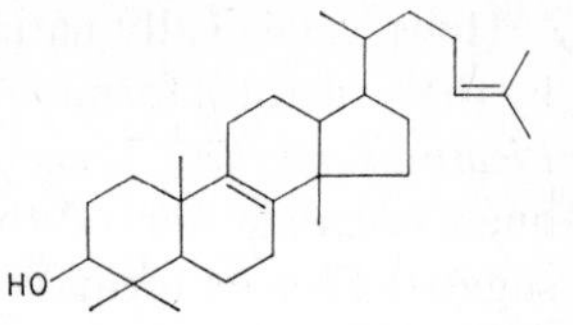

CCLVII
Euphol

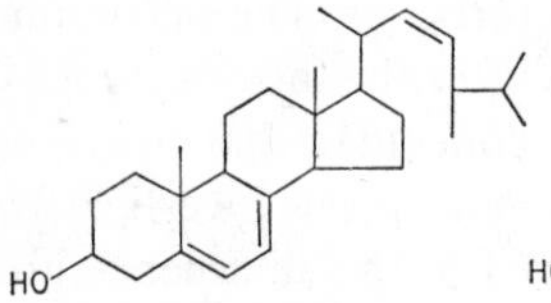

CCLVIII
Ergosterol

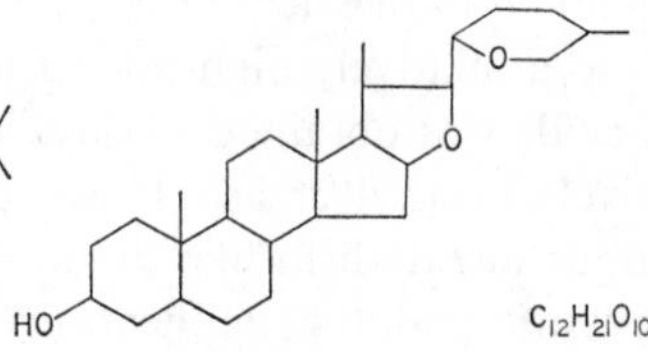

CCLIX
Tigogenin

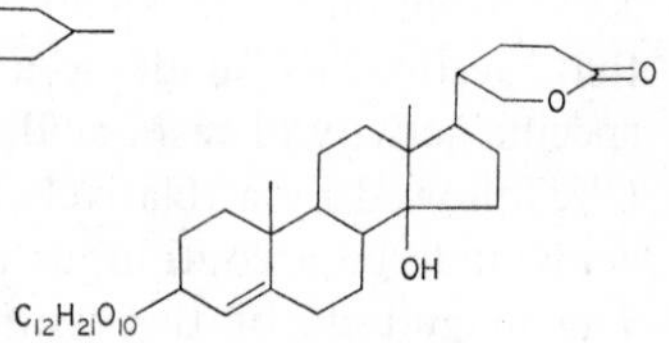

CCLX
Scillaren A

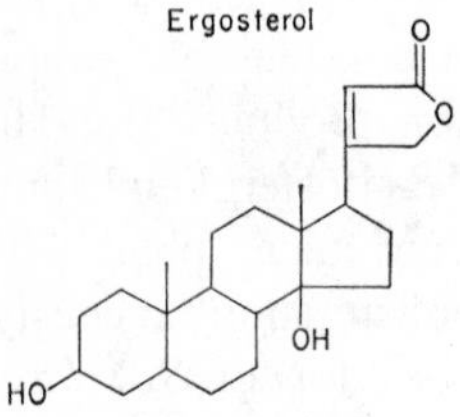

CCLXI
Digitoxigenin

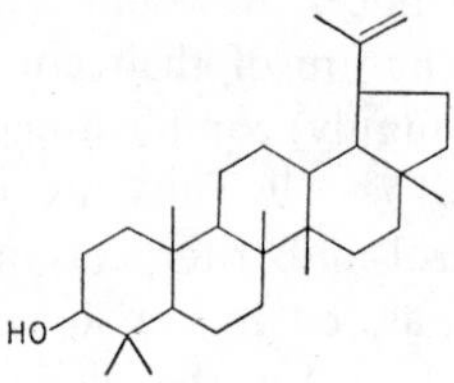

CCLXII
Lupeol

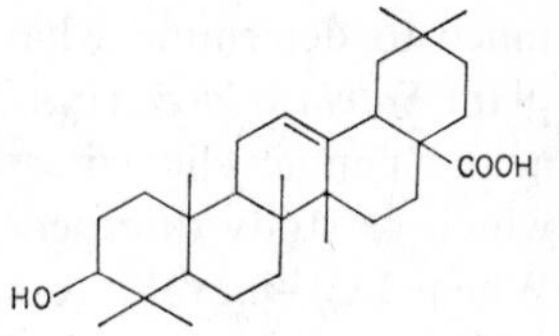

CCLXIII
Oleanolic acid

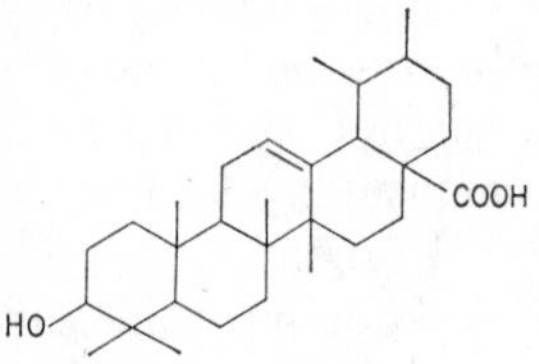

CCLXIV
Ursolic acid

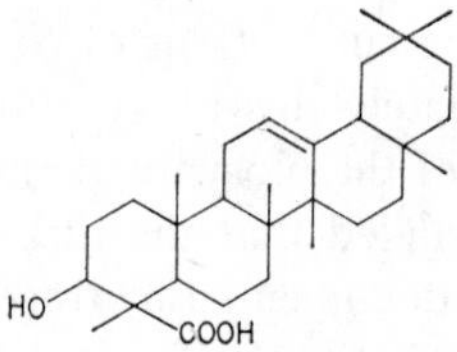

CCLXV
α- Boswellic acid

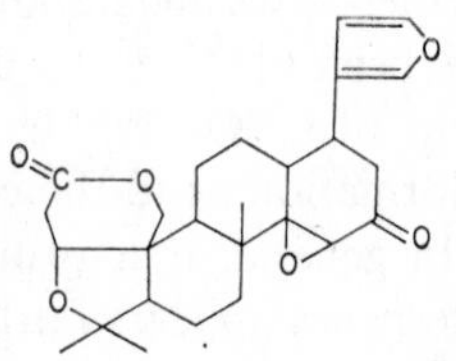

CCLXVI
Limonin

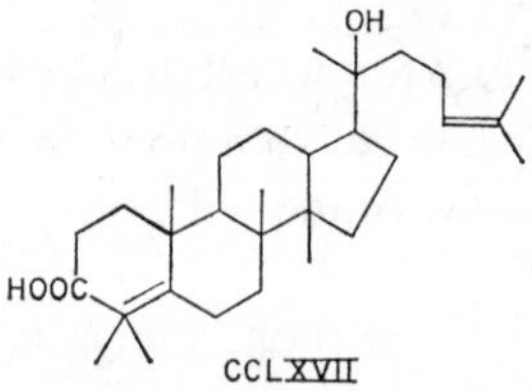

CCLXVII
Dammarenolic acid

FIG. 36. Sterols and triterpenes of the plant kingdom. Considerable liberty has been taken in calling sapogenins and butadienolides (etc.) "sterols".

sterols and triterpenes in higher plants and most experimental work to date has been based on this assumption.

Squalene has been reported present in a number of plant seed oils. [210, 211] If squalene is indeed a universal precursor of sterols and triterpenes, including those in higher plants, then following the initial cyclization, a number of further transformations must occur. This is evident in most of the representative sterols and triterpenes shown in Fig. 36. The stereochemical requirements for the folding of the squalene molecule to conform with cyclization to the different types of sterols and triterpenes have been discussed in detail by Ruzicka [81] and Eschenmoser et al., [212] who set the general theory underlying modern experimental approaches to the problem, and more recently by Ruzicka [99] and Richards and Hendrickson [98] and will not be repeated here. A few comments are essential, however. According to Ruzicka, the cyclization is initiated by attack of a cation (OH^+) at one end of the molecule and cyclization proceeds through a series of ionic (carbonium ion) intermediates as indicated in Fig. 37. Critical in subsequent transformations is a Wagner–Meerwein rearrangement of CCLXX to CCLXXI and an additional rearrangement to CCLXXII for the lupeol type of triterpene. Since lupeol has been converted by chemical treatment to germanicol, a triterpene of the

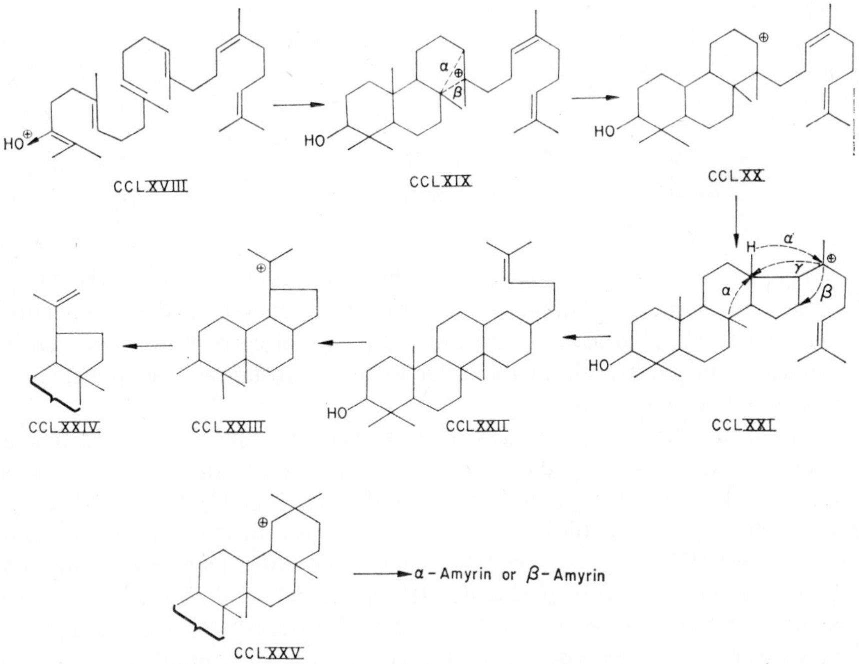

FIG. 37. Biogenesis of the pentacyclic triterpenes according to Ruzicka. [81]

β-amyrin type, a biogenetic origin of the β-amyrin class of triterpenes was implied, given the correct enzymatic and physiological conditions. Eschenmoser *et al.*[212] have indicated that, in such biochemical transformations, the reactions are fully concerted (non-stop) and that no transitory intermediates can be isolated. Gascoigne,[108] in considering the thermodynamic stabilities of certain pentacyclic triterpenes, has given some support to the principal that each representative triterpene is formed directly from squalene by a single concerted reaction.

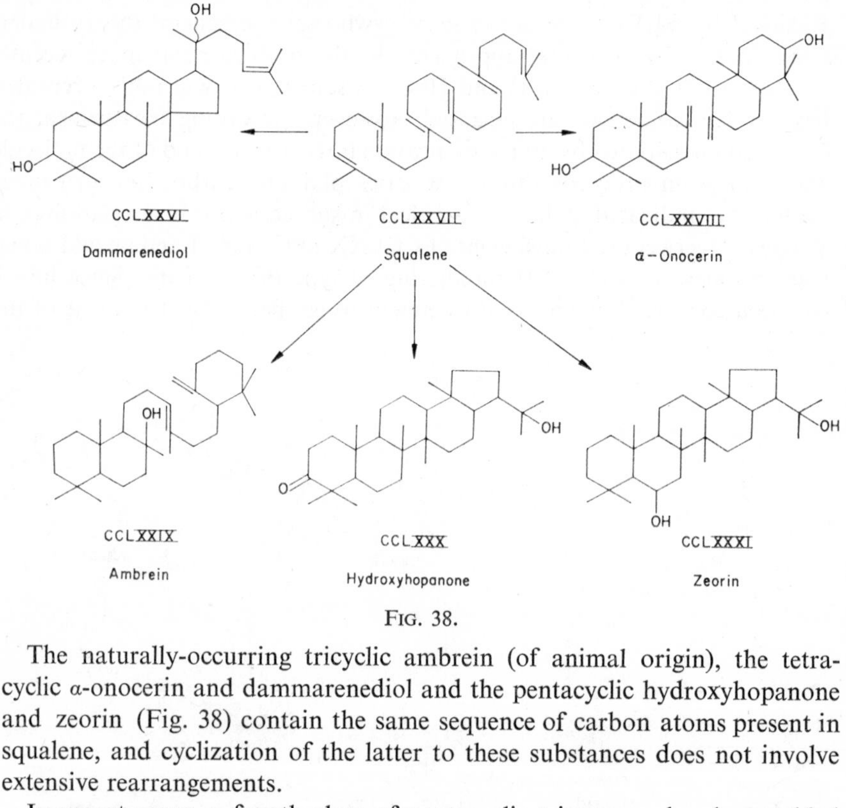

CCLXXVI
Dammarenediol

CCLXXVII
Squalene

CCLXXVIII
α−Onocerin

CCLXXIX
Ambrein

CCLXXX
Hydroxyhopanone

CCLXXXI
Zeorin

FIG. 38.

The naturally-occurring tricyclic ambrein (of animal origin), the tetracyclic α-onocerin and dammarenediol and the pentacyclic hydroxyhopanone and zeorin (Fig. 38) contain the same sequence of carbon atoms present in squalene, and cyclization of the latter to these substances does not involve extensive rearrangements.

In recent years, a fourth class of pentacyclic triterpenes has been added to the already-characterized α-amyrin, β-amyrin and lupeol types.† This class includes the cork triterpenes friedelin and cerin (Fig. 39), the structures of which have been established by the elegant investigations of Corey and Ursprung. [213, 214] A direct correlation of friedelin with β-amyrin was indicated by reduction of the former with $LiAlH_4$ to friedelan-3β-ol, which on treatment with HCl in phenol at 110° gave olean-13(18)-ene, identical with material prepared from β-amyrin. The conversion is essentially as shown in

† See also Ref. 212a for a recently recognized additional type.

Fig. 40. These interesting triterpenes should not be confused with the 4-methyl sterols of the lophenol or citrostadienol types. According to Corey and Ursprung, [214] the structure of the friedelin triterpenes suggests a biochemical conversion of lupeol to friedelin via β-amyrin as previously suggested by Ruzicka [81] for the biogenesis of the α- and β-amyrins from lupeol. The

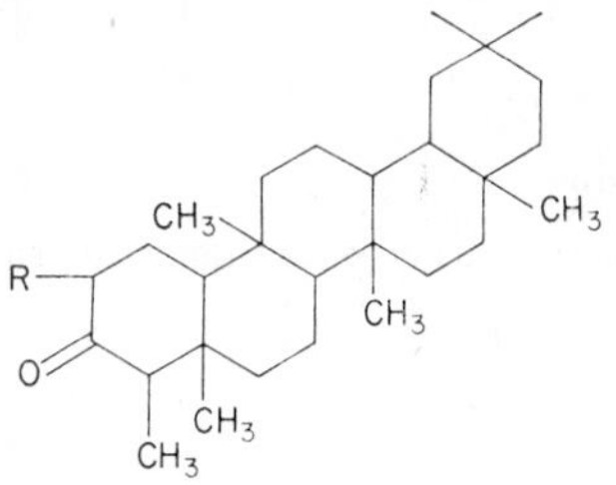

Friedelin CCLXXXII (R = H)

Cerin CCLXXXIII (R = OH)

FIG. 39.

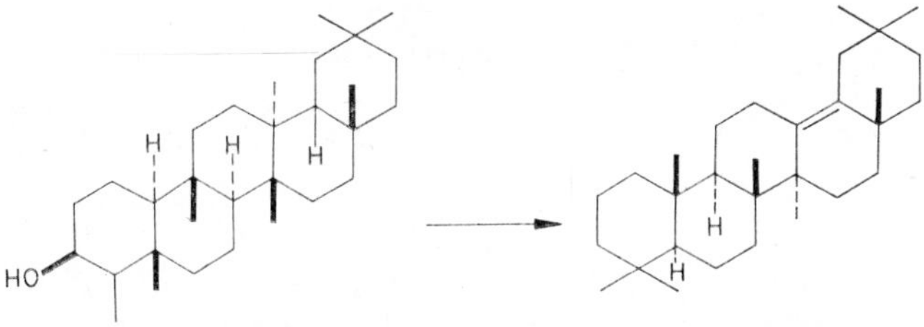

CCLXXXIV   CCLXXXV

FIG. 40. Chemical transformation of friedelan-3β-ol to olean-13(18)-ene; Corey and Ursprung. [213]

biogenetic sequences from β-amyrin is envisioned to occur as in Fig. 41 and is essentially a sequence of 1,2-shifts of methyl groups and hydrogen atoms away from ring A and towards ring E. Some possible biochemical functions for the friedelin compounds have been suggested. [214] No biochemical experiments have as yet been reported on these interesting compounds.

One of the significant discoveries in the field of plant steroid biogenesis has been the isolation and characterization of compounds like citrostadienol and lophenol (Fig. 42). Lophenol was isolated from the giant cactus *Lophocereus schotti* along with 7-stigmasten-3β-ol and lupeol by Djerassi *et al.*, [215, 216] and Mazur *et al.* [217] isolated citrostadienol along with β-sitosterol from grapefruit peel.

By analogy with the loss of the ring A methyl groups of lanosterol in the biosynthesis of cholesterol, these 4α-methyl derivatives represent stepwise

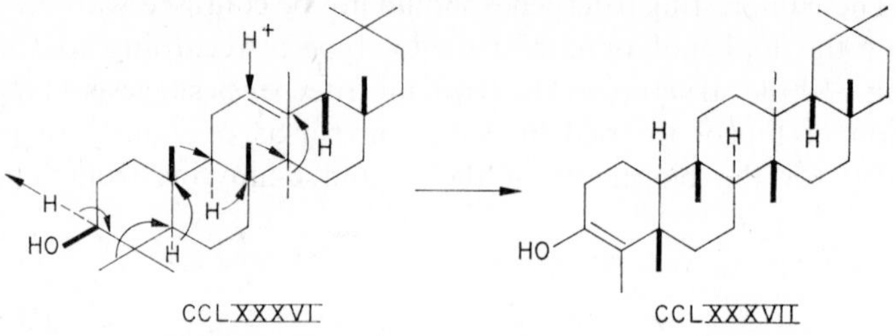

CCLXXXVI   CCLXXXVII

β-Amyrin   Friedelin (enol)

FIG. 41. Biogenesis of the friedelin triterpenes from β-amyrin; Corey and Ursprung.[214]

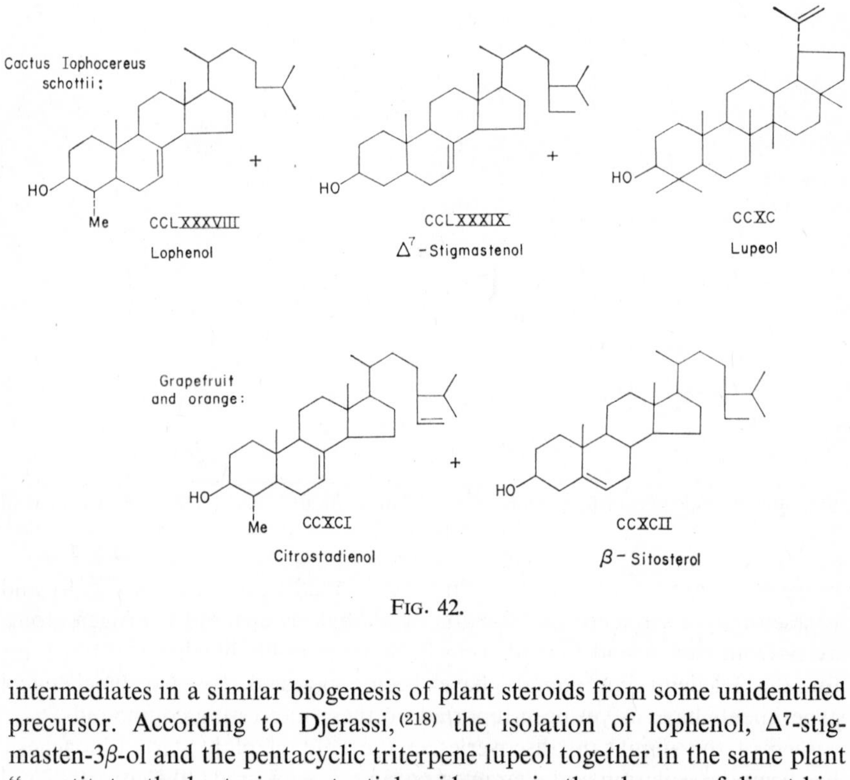

Cactus Iophocereus
schottii:

HO   Me   CCLXXXVIII   CCLXXXIX   CCXC

Lophenol Δ^7-Stigmastenol   Lupeol

Grapefruit
and orange:

HO   Me   CCXCI   CCXCII

Citrostadienol   β-Sitosterol

FIG. 42.

intermediates in a similar biogenesis of plant steroids from some unidentified precursor. According to Djerassi, [218] the isolation of lophenol, Δ^7-stigmasten-3β-ol and the pentacyclic triterpene lupeol together in the same plant "constitutes the best circumstantial evidence—in the absence of direct biochemical experimentation—that demethylation of squalenoid cyclization products represents a biosynthetic route to sterols in the plant". Demonstration of the conversion of methostenol† to cholesterol in animal tissues is additional evidence of the likelihood of the corresponding mechan-

† Methostenol is a 4α-methyl-Δ^7-cholesterol.[219] The Δ^8-isomer has been implicated as a cholesterol precursor in preputial gland tumor and liver *in vitro*.[220]

ism in plant tissues (see also Crabbe [105]). If 4α-methyl sterols of the lophenol type do prove to be precursors of plant sterols like β-sitosterol, then it may be tacitly assumed that they will play a similar role in the biogenesis of tetracyclic triterpenes of the euphol type. Theoretical aspects of squalene cyclization to the latter type of triterpene have been discussed in detail by Ruzicka [81] and Crabbé. [105] This cyclization involves the same 1-2 methyl shifts required for the formation of lanosterol from squalene.

Sufficient tracer work has been recorded to merit discussion of individual sterol and triterpenoid biogenesis. The reader is referred to the excellent review by Heftmann [221] for some of the earlier observations relevant to this problem.

Squalene†

Arigoni [222] suggested the possible detection of radioactive squalene in activity growing plant tissue, but unequivocal identification was not made. Since then, C^{14}-squalene has been identified by several different laboratories and attempts have been made to relate its formation to steroid or triterpene biogenesis. Following the feeding of 2-C^{14} mevalonic acid to cut stems of *Ocimum basilicum* a non-polar fraction was prepared by chromatography on alumina of ethanol extracts of the tissues. [124] On dilution of this non-polar fraction with non-radioactive squalene, preparation of a hexahydrochloride and crystallization to constant radioactivity, C^{14}-squalene was indicated. The time sequence of formation and disappearance were similar to the turnover of squalene in liver tissue. C^{14}-squalene has been obtained without dilution by non-radioactive material in germinating pea seedlings. [223] Nes subsequently degraded C^{14}-squalene prepared in this manner. [224] The results were consistent with the labeling pattern found previously for squalene formed in liver tissue. C^{14}-Squalene has also been detected in isolated higher plant incubated with C^{14}-terpenol pyrophosphates obtained by incubating 2-C^{14}-mevalonic acid with a soluble rat liver enzyme system. [225] At least two laboratories have indicated that C^{14}-squalene synthesized by plant tissues is converted to C^{14}-cholesterol by animal tissues, [226, 227] good evidence that both the plant and animal product are identical (all *trans*-squalene). Recently the conversion of C^{14}-squalene to β-amyrin has been observed [228,228a] with use of an enzyme system from peas pre-germinated with water for 24 hours. C^{14}-Squalene has also been identified in tobacco tissue cultures following incubation with 1-C^{14}-sodium acetate [229] and in cut tobacco stems following administration of 2-C^{14}-mevalonic acid. [230]

No intermediate between squalene and lanosterol has as yet been identified.‡ Dehydrosqualene is present as an impurity in commercial squalene, but evidence for the formation of this substance as an intermediate in the biosynthesis of squalene was not obtained. [227,231] Evidence has been obtained,

† See also Chapter 4.
‡ See, however, Refs. 230a and 230b.

however, for the formation of an enzyme-bound C_{30} intermediate in squalene synthesis by a mammalian enzyme. [232]

The biogenesis of C^{14}-squalene in higher plants has thus been well documented, and in one case has been shown to be a direct precursor of a pentacyclic triterpene, and plant sterol (see p. 882).

β-Sitosterol and Related Steroids

β-Sitosterol is the most widely distributed of the plant sterols, and its general structure (Fig. 43) places it in the key position of representing a plant sterol whose biogenesis should follow the general steps allocated for cholesterol, i.e. via cyclization of squalene to lanosterol, etc. The additional ethyl group as C-24 which is not supplied by squalene cyclization, however, implies a step not required for cholesterol biosynthesis. According to Arigoni [222]

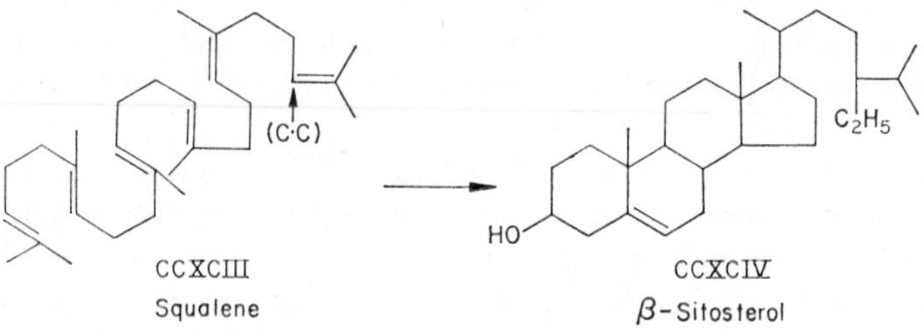

FIG. 43.

some analogy with the formation of the methyl group at C-24 in ergosterol from methionine or formate would be expected. [232, 233] This indeed has proved to be the case. 2-C^{14}-Mevalonic acid, 1-C^{14}-L-ethionine-ethyl, C^{14}-sodium formate and C^{14}-L-methionine-methyl respectively were fed to cut stems of *Salvia officinalis*. [234] β-Sitosterol was isolated by chromatography on alumina and subsequent purifications, then pyrolyzed as the chloride in a reaction similar to that employed in early studies on cholesterol biosynthesis. [235] The percentage of C^{14} in a volatile fraction representing the side chain was highest in the β-sitosterol biosynthesized from formate and methionine, presumptive evidence that a large portion of the label must have been in the "extra" ethyl group of the side chain. Nes and co-workers subsequently presented a mechanism [236] shown in Fig. 44 which is consistent with their and other data for elaboration of the ethyl group from two C_1-units supplied by the active methyl group of methionine. The mechanism provides for the formation of several other naturally occurring sterols containing saturated and unsaturated -methyl and -ethyl groups in the side chains. Where and at what stage a double bond is introduced in this side chain has not yet been determined. Since β-sitosterol and stigmasterol differ only by a double bond

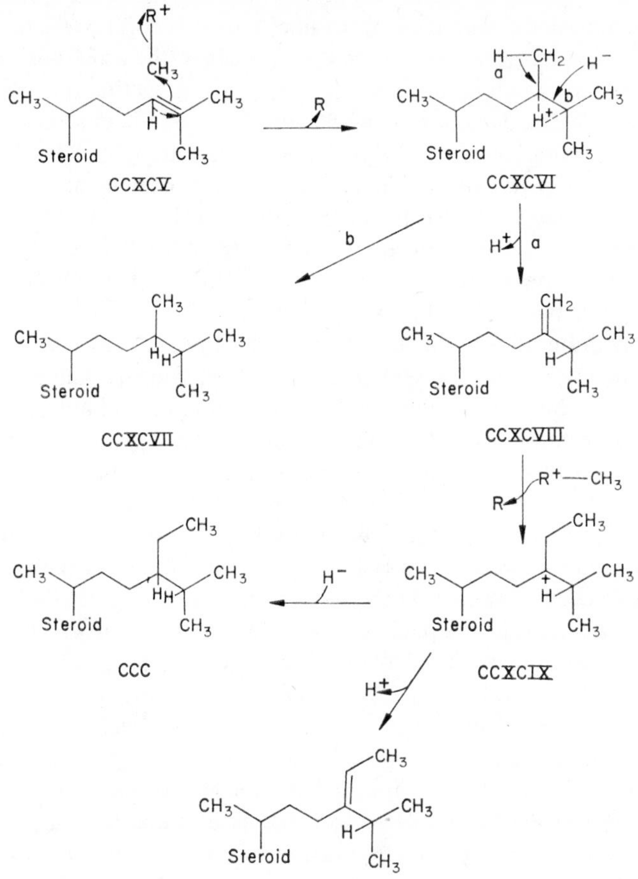

FIG. 44. Origin of the ethyl group of β-sitosterol.[236]

at C-24 (in stigmasterol, Fig. 36), this latter problem is of general interest. In studying the incorporation of 2-C^{14}-mevalonic acid into sterols of *Solanum tubersum* it was found[237] that at any given growth period, total and specific activity of stigmasterol was almost always less than in the case of β-sitosterol. A similar ratio of specific activity was found in these sterols in *Dioscorea spiculiflora*,[238] suggesting that stigmasterol may be formed by dehydrogenation of β-sitosterol. This would be contrary to the formation of animal sterols, where unsaturated compounds are the precursors of the more saturated sterols. The incorporation of 2-C^{14}-mevalonic acid into stigmasterol of tomato fruits has been noted[239] but the level of radioactivity of the stigmasterol obtained in these experiments was too low to permit degradation experiments. Indirect evidence has been presented that the "extra" ethyl group of stigmasterol also arises from methionine. [240] Since β-sitosterol has no point of attack for ozonization in the side chain, the exact position of the label in the side chain following biogenesis from methionine or formate presents a problem. This has been solved by systematic degradation of the side chain of spinasterol [241] following administration of DL-methyl-C^{14}-methionine to *Menyanthes trifoliata* and similar treatment of fucosterol [242] from the algae *Lamineria saccharina*. In both cases the C^{14} label from methionine was located in high percentage in the degraded "extra" ethyl group. There is no reasoning for doubting that a similar mechanism holds for β-sitosterol, stigmasterol and all similar plant sterols, e.g. double alkylation involving methionine as the methyl donor. This linkage of two C_1-units is the first biogenetic evidence presented for the formation of an ethyl group, which occurs widely distributed in plant and animal metabolites.

The incorporation of 2-C^{14}-sodium acetate into β-sitosterol of *Salvia officinalis* L. has been reported. [243] The data gave no information as to the biogenetic precursors or mechanism of formation of the sterol. However, it was presumed from this study that the synthetic capacity of higher plants for sterols (and triterpenes) is not limited to a strict area of the plants. In a more extensive study essentially the same results were found. [244] An attempt to demonstrate the role of squalene in β-sitosterol and triterpene biosynthesis by direct absorption of the C^{14}-labeled acyclic triterpene into living plant tissue was unsuccessful. [124] Relevant to the problem of β-sitosterol biogenesis is the observation that the sterol is present in *Ocimum basilicum* and *S. officinalis* at all stages of growth, [245] and in increasing concentration up to the flowering stage. In addition, it has been noted that sterols, including β-sitosterol or those closely related to it increase in quantity in pine needles with increasing age. [246] The incorporation of 2-C^{14}-acetate and 2-C^{14}-mevalonic acid into Δ^{22}-stigmasterol by the slime mold *Dictyostelium discoideum* has been observed, with mevalonic acid incorporated with greater efficiency than the acetate. [247] Several other reports on the incorporation of either labeled acetate or mevalonate into β-sitosterol or closely allied sterols ("phytosterols") are now existent. [230, 248, 249]

With the origin of the ethyl group in the side chain of the C_{29} plant sterols solved, only proof for origin of the nucleus from cyclization of squalene remains to be established. A start on this problem has been made by Kuhn-Roth oxidation of C^{14}-β-sitosterol (from *Rauwolfia serpentina*) prepared biosynthetically from 1-C^{14}-acetate and 2-C^{14}-mevalonate respectively. [250] The results indicated that the acetate→mevalonate→β-sitosterol pathway through biosynthetic reactions common to cholesterol is responsible for the origin of β-sitosterol.†

† Added in press: The *in vivo* conversion of squalene to β-sitosterol has now been reported. [250a]

Cholesterol

Cholesterol and closely related sterols have been isolated from algae and protozoa (see Heftmann [221] for review). It now appears that cholesterol may also be common to higher plants, possibly more common than anticipated, based on reports appearing in the literature. A compound identified as 22-hydroxycholesterol was isolated several years ago from a Norwegian lily, *Nartiecium ossifragum*. [251] The first report of the isolation of cholesterol itself was recently made by Johnson *et al.*, [252] who detected C^{14}-cholesterol in young potato plants (*Solanum tuberosum*) and *Dioscorea spiculiflora* by gas-liquid and thin layer chromatographic techniques following administration of 2-C^{14}-mevalonic acid. C^{14}-cholesterol of high specific activity was again detected by the same procedures in *D. spiculiflora* along with several radioactive sapogenins and sterols. [238] A trace of cholesterol has been detected in cotyledons and axial parts of beans, along with β-sitosterol, stigmasterol and possibly campesterol. [253] If, as suggested by Johnson *et al.*, [237] the possibility exists of a biogenetic relationship between cholesterol and the sapogenins—or other steroids—in plants, then it is anticipated that increasing reports will be made of the "animal sterol" cholesterol in higher plants (see also Chapter 4).

Steroid Hormones†

Since cholesterol plays a critical role in animal tissues as the precursor of steroid hormones and bile acids, perhaps its isolation from higher plants will give more impetus to assume that analogous degradations can and do occur in plant tissues. Estrone [254] and estriol [255, 256] were isolated from palm kernel oil and willow flowers respectively many years ago. Recently one of these findings has been subjected to re-evaluation when no estrogenic activity was detected in examining seeds of the African oil palm. [257] Since the estrogens may have physiological activity of considerable import in plant tissues, [258, 220] the question of whether or not they do form in plant tissues merits thorough investigation. In defense of the original observations of Butenandt [254] and Skarzynski, [256] whose work will be difficult to reproduce even with modern techniques,‡ it may be stated that it is not uncommon for plant constituents to vary extremely in amount from one species to another, and to undergo similar variations in concentration with changes in season and time of collection.

Progesterone (Fig. 45) has recently been isolated from the leaves of *Holarrhena floribunda* along with the steroid alkaloid holaphylline and (possibly) pregna-4-en-20α-ol-3-one. [259] It would be rather difficult to envision a hormonal role for progesterone (or any other pregnane or allopregnane metabolite for that matter) in higher plant tissues. Nevertheless, its identification in this

---

† See also Chapter 4.

‡ Estrone has recently been isolated from dates and pomegranate seeds. [256a, 256b]

plant again lowers the metabolic boundaries that are sometimes placed between concepts of plant and animal metabolism (see also next section).†

Cardiac Glycosides

Arigoni et al. [260] in commenting on the biogenesis of limonin (Fig. 36), a citrus bitter principle, suggested that the biogenesis of the cardiac aglycones may proceed in a similar manner in that a triterpenoid of the euphol type loses four carbon atoms at the end of the side chain and carbon 20 and 23 are converted to a furan ring. Tschesche [261] suggested that the aglycone portion could result from condensation of a C_{19} steroid with a C_4 unit (2 molecules of acetic or one of malic acid) rather than by direct degradation of a C_{27} steroid. Later, [263] on the basis of the common occurrence of "digitanol" glycosides like xysmalogenin (CCCV) and uzarigenin (CCCVI) (Fig. 46) with 5α-pregnane-3β-ol-20-one and its Δ^5-unsaturated glycoside [263] in Digitalis, a C_{21}-steroid was envisioned as a precursor. A number of tracer experiments have been recorded in efforts to elucidate the biosynthetic mechanism involved. Radioactive digitoxin was prepared from D. purpurea grown in $C^{14}O_2$ almost twenty years ago. [264] A low incorporation of C^{14} into D. purpurea glycosides was obtained by feeding 1-C^{14}-sodium acetate through the roots. [265] Following the injection of 2-C^{14}-mevalonic acid into a young

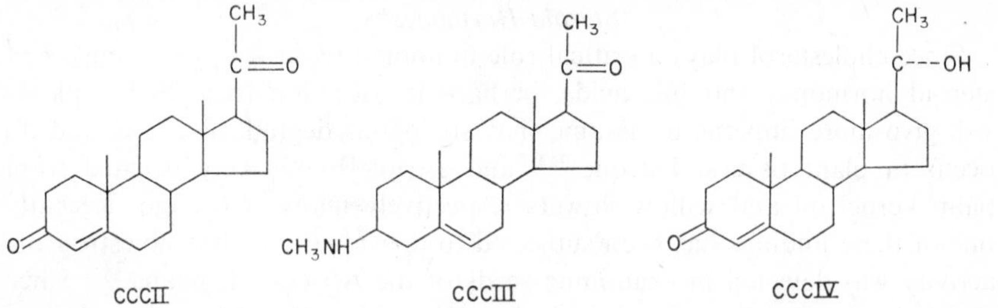

CCCII   CCCIII   CCCIV

Progesterone   Holaphylline   Pregna – 4 – en – 20α – ol – 3 – one

FIG. 45.

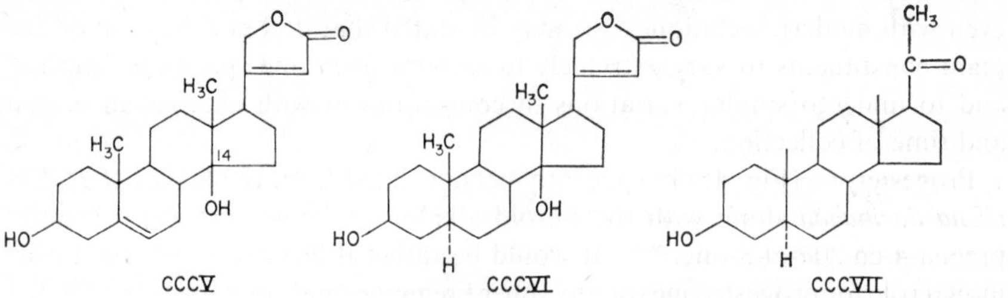

CCCV   CCCVI   CCCVII

Xysmalogenin   Uzarigenin   5α – pregnane – 3β – ol – 20 – one

FIG. 46.

† See addendum on page 893.

digitalis plant C^{14} was found in the lanatoside A portion of digitoxigenin and some in the sugar residues. [266] Digitoxigenin of sufficiently high specific activity for chemical degradation was obtained by wick feeding of *Digitalis* [267] with 2-C^{14}-mevalonic acid or 1-C^{14}-acetate. Degradation showed that C-20 and C-23 were labeled by the acetate but not C-21 and C-22. The digitoxigenin obtained from feeding mevalonate was not labeled at position 22, which would have occurred if the cardenolide had been formed from a C_{27} steroid. The evidence was interpreted as favoring Tschesche's hypothesis [262] that a C_{19} steroid precursor condenses with a C_4 fragment. The conversion of cholesterol to a bufadienolide has been demonstrated. [268] Without delineating the detailed pathway, it would not be surprising if degradation of this cholesterol to a C_{21} steroid first occurred, analogous to a reaction common to certain animal tissues, followed by formation of the characteristic lactone ring. Yet in a recent presentation (as of this writing only in Abstract) a number of C_{21} steroids were tested (not listed) as bufadienolide precursors in the toad, but none was found effective. [269] 3β-Hydroxy-Δ^5-cholenic acid proved to be as effective a precursor as cholesterol, but this does not rule out prior degradation to a C_{21} compound. That C_{21} steroids are, indeed the source of the cardenolides has now been shown† by the direct isolation of C^{14}-digitoxigenin, C^{14}-xysmalogenin, C^{14}-gitoxigenin and C^{14}-digoxigenin (with a combined total of 6 per cent of the administered C^{14} incorporated) following the administration of 21-C^{14}-Δ^5-pregnene-3β-ol-20-one glucoside to *Digitalis lanata*. [270] The above combined experiments suggest rather conclusively that the route cholesterol→C_{21} steroid→cardenolides (and bufadienolides(?)) is the correct one.

Presumably these steroids, especially if the above conclusions are correct, arise from cyclization of squalene, and the distribution of C^{14} in the nucleus should be characteristic of this cyclization if formed from 2-C^{14}-mevalonic acid. This problem has recently been attacked by Leete. [271] Digitoxigenin biosynthesized from 2-C^{14}-mevalonic acid through the squalene route should be labeled in positions 1,7 and 15 (Fig. 47). Preliminary evidence showed that activity was indeed present in 15 and 1 and at this writing some progress had been indicated in attempts to determine the C^{14} content of position 7.

Sapogenins

Despite the economic importance of the steroidal sapogenins (e.g. diosgenin), little effort has been expended on determining how they are formed in plants. Attention should be called to Marker's early efforts in which changes in the sapogenin content with age of the plants was studied in detail. [221] Presumably the nucleus is formed by squalene condensation following the pathway indicated for other sterols. Tschesche [262] has suggested

---

† See also Euw, J. V. and Reichstein, T. *Helv. Chim. Acta* **47**, 711 (1964).

2F

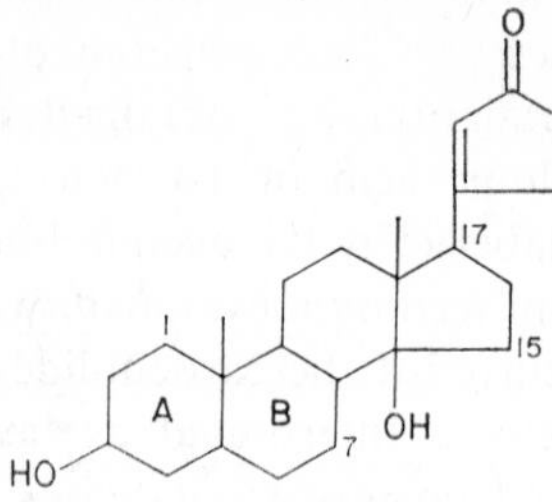

CCCVIII

Digitoxigenin

FIG. 47.

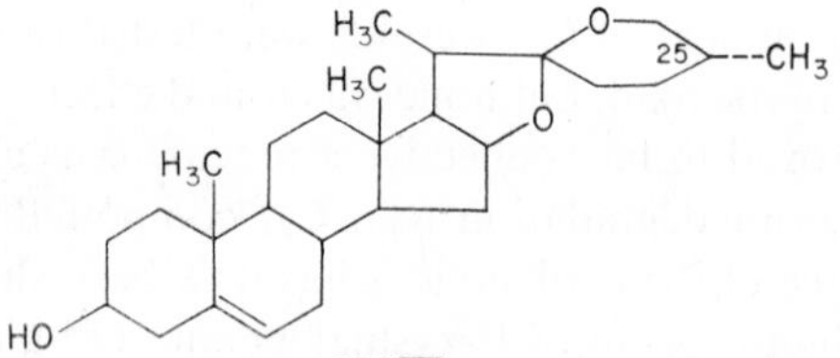

CCCIX

Diosgenin

FIG. 48.

that the sapogenins are formed from sterols following oxidation at C-16, C-22 and C-27 followed by ring closure. Only a few tracer studies are recorded dealing with their biogenetic origin. Incubation of homogenates of *Dioscorea* tubers [272] with radioactive acetate produced weakly labeled diosgenin (Fig. 48). The same experiment conducted with labeled mevalonate produced no C^{14} in the isolated sapogenin. In a later publication [238] the same group administered 2-C^{14}-mevalonic acid to growing roots, leaves and stems of *Dioscorea spiculiflora*. In addition to some informative observations on the translocation of steroids within plant organs, it was observed that the steroids exist wholly in the form of conjugates (glycosides). The specific activities of the 25α isomers diosgenin and yamogenin from various parts of the plant were always higher than the 25β isomers gentrogenin and correllogenin. Full publication of recent abstract [273] in which the statement is made that the general route cholesterol→kryptogenin→diosgenin holds will be looked to with interest.

The Tetra- and Pentacyclic Triterpenes

The squalene→tetracyclic triterpene hypothesis does not require extensive transformations in the cyclization process. Dauben and associates [274] studied the biogenesis of the fungus metabolite eburicoic acid (Fig. 49). The latter was obtained labeled with C^{14} by growing *P. sulfureus* on a medium containing 1- or 2-C^{14}-sodium acetate. Degradation indicated a labeling pattern consistent with the cyclization of squalene to this triterpene. The "extra" C-28 carbon atom was not supplied by acetate, but was supplied by formate.[275] Cycloartanol and 24-methylene-cycloartanol (Fig. 50) have been detected [276, 276a, 276b] in tobacco tissue cultures incubated with 1-C^{14}-sodium

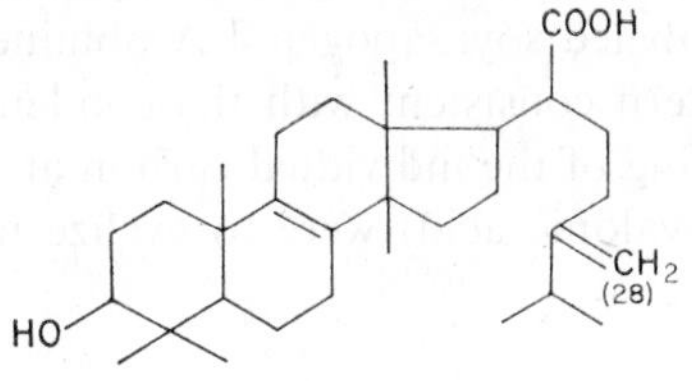

CCCX

Eburicoic acid

FIG. 49.

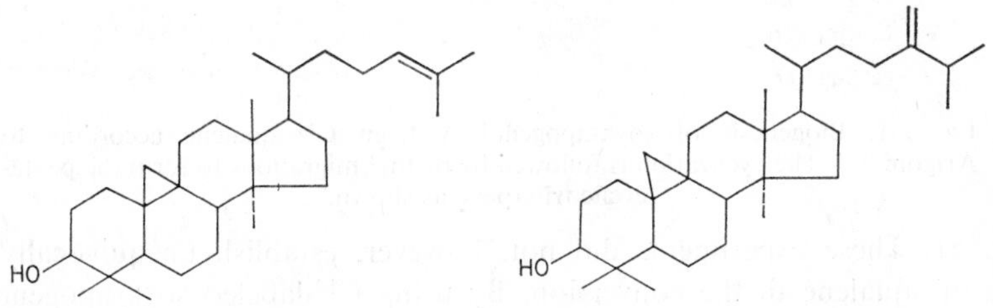

CCCXI

Cycloartanol

CCCXII

Methylene − 24 − cycloartanol

FIG. 50.

acetate. In this interesting work labeled lanosterol could not be detected. Since lanosterol should be a very critical intermediate in the formation of the tetracyclic triterpenes and the phytosterols, these experiments are of particular merit and deserve critical evaluation. C^{14}-lanosterol, presumably a precursor of sterols like β-sitosterol and stigmasterol, has been detected in the organism *C. malhemensis* [240] following incubation with C^{14}-acetate, and in maize seedlings presented with 2-C^{14}-mevalonic acid. [248] With increased interest in the biogenesis of higher plant terpenoids it is anticipated that the labeled substance will be reported with greater frequency in coming years. Lanosterol and dihydrolanosterol have recently been isolated from coffee beans along with squalene and the unusual tetracyclic coffeasterene. [277]

Arigoni [222] has provided the first experimental evidence for the biogenetic origin of the pentacyclic triterpenes. By feeding 1-C^{14}- and 2-C^{14}-sodium acetate, respectively, and 2-C^{14}-mevalonic acid to young soy bean seedlings, C^{14}-labeled "sterols" (presumably largely β-sitosterol) and soyasapogenol A were obtained. As expected, the efficiency of incorporation of label into both sterol and triterpene was greatest with mevalonic acid, and the close correspondence of the specific activities of the sterol and triterpene was felt to lend some support to a common origin through the cyclization of squalene. Degradation of the labeled soyasapogenol A obtained by feeding mevalonic acid, indicated a pattern consistent with the condensation of six mevalonic acid groups and labeling of the individual carbon atoms expected if squalene (formed from the mevalonic acid) were to cyclize in the manner shown in

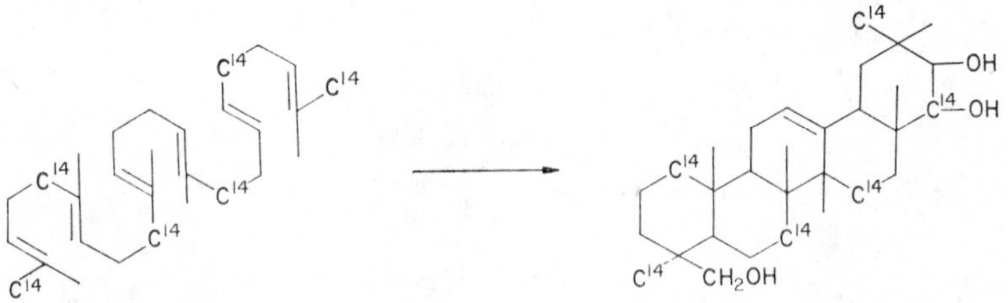

CCCXIII
Squalene

CCCXIV
Soyasapogenol A

FIG. 51. Biogenesis of soyasapogenol A from C^{14}-squalene according to Arigoni. [222] The cyclization is followed by methyl migrations to form the pentacyclic triterpene as shown.

Fig. 51. These experiments did not, however, establish unequivocally the role of squalene in the conversion. By using C^{14}-labeled soyasapogenol D obtained as indicated for soyasapogenol A, a point of particular note was made. Oxidation of the labeled soyasapogenol D, containing a 1,3-glycol system in ring A, gave an unstable β-keto acid which lost CO_2 according to the sequence shown in Fig. 52. The C^{14} values obtained for the CO_2 from the original carbon atom 24 were essentially negligible, indicating that, during the condensation of mevalonic acid to squalene, carbon atom 2 of

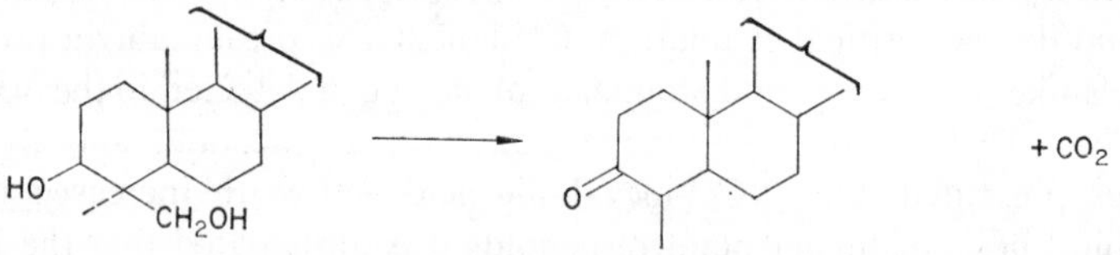

CCCXV

CCCXVI

CCCXVII

+ CO_2

FIG. 52.

mevalonic acid retained its individuality such as to restrict the label to that of the two methyl groups (of ring A) which bears a *cis* relationship to the hydrogen of the double bond (see also section on Diterpene Biogenesis). This excellent study again indicated the remarkable stereospecificity of biochemical conversions.

Despite the widespread occurrence in plants of the acidic pentacyclic triterpenes oleanolic acid and ursolic acid (Fig. 36, CCLXIII and CCLXIV), comparatively few biochemical observations have been made with them. Sando [278] noted an increase in the concentration of ursolic acid in the cuticle of apples as the latter were allowed to stand. Brieskorn *et al.* [279] have called attention to the high concentration of ethereal oils and oleanolic and ursolic acids in members of the Labiatae family and indicated an inverse relationship between the oils and acidic triterpenes as growth of the plants progressed. The conversion of the more soluble oleanolic acid into the less soluble ursolic acid was suggested from their observations. An increase in concentration of β-sitosterol, oleanolic acid and ursolic acid (all occurring together) in *Ocimum basilicum* and *Salvia officinalis* with increasing maturity of the plants has been reported. [245] At least one of the triterpenes was present at all stages of growth (including 5-day-old seedlings). The incorporation of 2-C^{14}-sodium acetate into β-sitosterol, oleanolic acid and ursolic acid of *S. officinalis* L. by isolated leaves and flowering stems devoid of leaves has been reported. [243] The data gave no information as to the respective biogenetic origin of the triterpenes because of the diverse metabolic disposition of acetate itself. However, it may be presumed from this study and others that the synthetic capacity of higher plants for sterols *and* the pentacyclic triterpenes is not limited to a strict area of the plant. In a more extensive study essentially the same results were found. [244, 280, 281]

The ring E area of lupeol and betulin prepared biosynthetically from C^{14}-acetate or C^{14}-mevalonate has been subjected to extensive degradation. [282] Most of the results were consistent with the original Ruzicka hypothesis [8] for the formation of the pentacyclic triterpenes via cyclization of squalene and subsequent transformations (Fig. 37). When not consistent (e.g. unusually low incorporation of 2-C^{14}-sodium acetate into C-29 and C-30 of betulic acid), the results were credited to randomization by the Krebs cycle. Ursolic acid was prepared biosynthetically from 1-C^{14}-sodium or 2-C^{14}-acetate, 2-C^{14}-mevalonic acid, C^{14}-sodium formate and C^{14}-methyl-L-methionine, respectively.† The triterpene acid was then subjected to the Schmidt reaction to detect C^{14} in the carboxyl group. Only ursolic acid prepared biosynthetically from C^{14}-formate gave radioactive $C^{14}O_2$. Since the Ruzicka transformations (Fig. 37) predict the labeling of the ursolic acid carboxyl from 2-C^{14}-sodium acetate, these data are puzzling.

† Nicholas, H. J., *Phytochemistry*: In press.

Finally, attention must again be directed to a report—unfortunately only in abstract at this writing—that squalene is converted to β-amyrin by a solubilized enzyme preparation from germinating peas. [228] Full publication of this important observation is awaited with interest. [228a]

POLYTERPENES: SOLANESOL

The biosynthesis of ubiquinones, carotenoids and other polyisoprenoids widely distributed throughout plant and animal tissues has been discussed in other chapters of this book. (see Chapters 4, 10, 16, 17 and 18). It seems appropriate to discuss the interesting polyterpenoid solanesol (Fig. 53) here, however. Although it has been detected in small quantities in rat liver, [283] at the moment it seems more characteristically a component of plant tissue, being a major constituent of tobacco resin. However, should evidence be

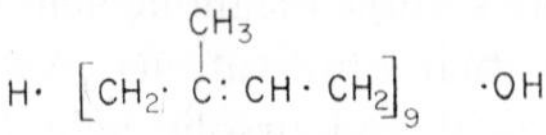

$$H \cdot \left[CH_2 \cdot \underset{\underset{CH_3}{\mid}}{C} : CH \cdot CH_2 \right]_9 \cdot OH$$

CCCXVIII

Solanesol

FIG. 53.

obtained that solanesol itself can directly provide the source of the isoprenoid side chain of ubiquinone, [284] then this conclusion is invalid. The biosynthesis of solanesol was first investigated by Reid, [285] who found that 15 per cent of 2-C^{14}-mevalonic acid was incorporated into phytosterols (principally β-sitosterol) when cut tobacco stems were given mevalonate. The solanesol was not labeled. The incorporation of C^{14}-labeled acetate under similar conditions was considerably less. Squalene was not labeled with either precursor, but since the plants were examined 3 days after administration of the precursors, it is unlikely that it would be found labeled because of its rapid turnover. In a later investigation, [230] 30 days after administration of mevalonic acid, the C^{14} content of isolated solanesol was practically negligible. The significance of these observations remain to be determined. The distribution of solanesol in subcellular fractions of tobacco plants has been studied. [286] Only unesterified solanesol was found, and it was concentrated in the chloroplasts (along with plastoquinone), though some was present in "supernatant" fraction from which mitochondria had been separated.

THE CONTROL OF TRITERPENE AND STEROL BIOGENESIS

Mevalonic acid is a very efficient precursor of terpenoid substances because its formation from β-hydroxy-β-methylglutaryl-CoA is irreversible and, unlike acetic acid, it is not diverted to non-terpenoid biosynthetic pathways. [23] Yet, almost all experiments utilizing 2-C^{14}-mevalonic acid in conjunction with higher plants have resulted in very poor yields in terms of incorporation of C^{14} label into terpenoids. While this will not necessarily influence interpretation of biosynthetic pathways utilizing mevalonic acid, it seems logical that considerably more information could be gained if this efficient terpenoid precursor were permitted to gain access to all its reactions unimpeded, which is probably one reason for the low yields reported. What are the sub-cellular sites to which mevalonic acid must gain access for biosynthesis of various terpenoids? Some progress has been made toward this problem by Goodwin and co-workers. [249] In a series of experiments utilizing maize seedlings grown in the dark, excised from their roots and incubated with 2-C^{14}-mevalonic acid under illumination, considerable C^{14} was found in two compounds identified as β-amyrin and lanosterol and a third compound, probably a Δ^7-sterol. Neither β-carotene nor the phytyl portion of chlorophyll were labeled, however. In short, the mevalonic acid appeared to have selectively labeled the sterols but not other terpenoid substances. When the same experiments were performed with $C^{14}O_2$ rather than mevalonate, β-carotene and phytol were labeled but not the "sterols". These and other experiments suggested that the regulation of sterol, carotenoid and phytol biosynthesis in the early stages of germination occurs by a process of "compartmentalization". The problem appears to be quite complex and somewhat confused at the time of this writing. The Goodwin experiments indicate that the chloroplastidic site is responsible for the formation of chlorophylls, carotenes, plastoquinones, tocopherols and vitamin K_1, all more or less implicated in photosynthesis, while an "extra chloroplastidic site" synthesizes sterols and triterpenes. Somewhat the same results—with perhaps the same interpretation—were found when $C^{14}O_2$ was administered to flowering *Salvia sclarea* plants. [206] After 24 hours in the presence of $C^{14}O_2$ the diterpene sclareol was heavily labeled with $C^{14}O_2$; the β-sitosterol was not labeled. 2-C^{14}-Mevalonic acid, however, gave C^{14}-β-sitosterol heavily labeled (after 24 hours) but the sclareol, even after longer exposures of the plant to the terpenoid precursor, never became labeled. It does not clarify the problem by attributing these results to failure of mature tissue to synthesize terpenes or to localization of terpenes in specific oil glands. A more fundamental problem appears involved.

None of these experiments locate specifically the sub-cellular site of sterol or triterpene biosynthesis, except in general terms. Shifts from "extra plastidic" sites or vice versa are implied but not clarified. The biosynthesis of squalene from 2-C^{14}-mevalonic acid by isolated tomato and carrot plastids has been demonstrated, [227] but no sterol synthesis from the squalene within the plastids was indicated. Isolated lettuce chloroplasts were not capable of synthesizing hydrocarbons or sterols from 2-C^{14}-sodium acetate, whereas under the conditions employed (light, ATP, CoA, CO_2 and P_i) saturated fatty acids from C_{18} to C_{18} and oleic acid were readily labeled. [287] Recently the distribution of C^{14} in lettuce subcellular particles following incubation of chopped lettuce with 2-C^{14}-mevalonic acid was studied. Labeled sterol (material precipitated by digitonin) was highest in mitochondria, next highest in microsomes and about equally distributed in chloroplasts and 112,000 × g supernatant fractions. All of these experiments seem to eliminate the chloroplast as the site of sterol synthesis, with the exception of the Porter work demonstrating squalene formation in plastids. To add to the confusion there is the recent demonstration [228] that an enzymatic preparation, presumably free of chloroplasts and mitochondria, can synthesize squalene (from mevalonic acid) and in turn permit the direct cyclization of this substance to β-amyrin. Here indeed is an area which demands active exploration.†

One other factor should be considered in evaluating the incorporation of mevalonic acid into terpenoids of higher plants since it may have special bearing on the control of terpene biogenesis as studied with intact plants. This is the question of "competition" of substrate for the mevalonate administered. For example, in a higher plant in which five or more biogenetically unrelated terpenoids may be present in quantity—and there are frequently many more—which will command greater utilization of the mevalonic acid? This may partially be the answer for the selective labeling of β-sitosterol by mevalonic acid while a diterpene remained unlabeled. [206] In a similar study‡ 2-C^{14}-mevalonic acid was presented to cut stems of *Marrubium vulgare* L. A marrubiin (diterpene) fraction was isolated by a procedure which ordinarily gave the diterpene in pure form [288] after one or two crystallizations from a selected solvent. Thin-layer chromatography of the crude marrubium fraction followed by preparation of a radioautograph indicated that at least eleven labeled companions were present in addition to the marrubium. The plant also contains at least one sterol and several sesquiterpenes. [288] It is suggested that it would be helpful, for evaluation of tracer work in studying a particular terpenoid, if companion terpenoids within the plant were investigated also.

THE FUTURE FOR STUDIES ON THE BIOGENESIS OF TERPENES IN PLANTS

Two of the most intriguing problems of terpene metabolism in the plant kingdom are (1) the function of the frequently bizarre structures which occur in plant tissues and (2) the manner in which these structures are formed within the tissue. It seems unlikely that satisfactory answers for the first problem will be found until the latter has been surveyed in all its ramifications. Some progress in this area has been made, as this chapter has indicated. A detailed study of turnover rates of various individual terpenes might provide a reasonable approach to the question of function within the plant tissue. Due to the impact of progress in the field of steroid biogenesis, the initial

† See also Goodwin's excellent discussion. [228b]
‡ Nicholas, H. J.: unpublished observations.

steps in terpene biogenesis within all kinds of tissue have been outlined. A vast field for exploration still exists in the realm of terpene biogenesis in higher plants, partly because of the number of structures unique to these organisms. The indispensable contributions of theoretical organic chemistry and structural determination of newly discovered compounds must continue. Yet, in the final analysis, biogenetic mechanisms should be studied with living tissue and it is here that the greatest promise lies for future work.

Within the category of classical terpene types it is not difficult to select outstanding problems. For example, the cyclization mechanism for all classes or terpenes still remains an enigma. It will be noted that most of the cyclization mechanisms proposed have been drawn from analogy with acid-catalyzed reactions. The limitations of this analogy have been outlined elsewhere. [145] In the monoterpene series it is of interest to know whether the varied bi- and tricyclic forms arise from a monocyclic precursor or are produced independently from some other prototype. Studies on the biogenesis of the important camphor series are indeed in order. In the sesquiterpene family there is the question of why cyclization stops in the bisabolene type of terpene, or why cyclization may continue with the formation of either the cadinene, eudesmol or iresin types. In the diterpene series a firm decision is needed from experimentation in plants on the question of transformations that may occur *in vivo* among the pimarane, abietane and phyllocladane types. In the cyclic triterpene series the origin of the various types of pentacyclic triterpenes presents challenging problems. Extensive transformations that must occur in the formation of the more complex plant steroids are also virtually an untouched area. It seems reasonable to postulate that findings of considerable fundamental importance will emerge from these studies. Studies have begun on the subcellular site of terpenoid biogenesis; these could have great practical as well as fundamental significance.

Added in press: Recently an excellent series of manuscripts have added considerably to our knowledge in the area of steroid hormones. These include documentation of the biosynthesis of progesterone from pregnenolone in *Holarrhena floribunda*[259a] and the biosynthesis of *Holarrhena* steroidal alkaloids from cholesterol.[259b] The exact relationship between cholesterol, progesterone, pregnenolone and the *Holarrhena* alkaloids was not entirely clarified. The reversible interconversion of pregnenolone and *Holarrhena* alkaloids has been demonstrated.[259c, 259d] The conversion of cholesterol to pregnenolone in *Digitalis purpurea* has also been shown.[259e]

SUMMARY

Slow development of studies on terpene biogenesis in plants has been accelerated by the use of the carbon 14 isotope technique and the discovery of mevalonic acid. The field has also received considerable aid from prior studies on terpene biogenesis in animal tissues. Some special problems peculiar to plant terpene studies have been discussed and areas for future work have been outlined. Where labeled mevalonic acid has been applied to plant tissues, degradation of the terpenes has given full support to the "biogenetic isoprene rule".

REFERENCES

1. HAAGEN-SMIT, A. J. In *The Essential Oils*, vol. 1, p. 17, ed. E. Guenther. Van Nostrand Co., Inc., New York, 1948.
2. WALLACH, O. *Terpene und Campher*, 2nd ed. Vit & Co., Leipzig, 1914.
3. KREMERS, E. *J. Am. Pharm. Assoc.* **22**, 227 (1933).
4. BUTENANDT, A. and MARTEN, A. *Ann. Chem.* **495**, 187 (1932).
5. AVIZONIS, P. V. and WRISTON, J. C. *Biochim. Biophys. Acta* **34**, 279 (1959).
6. WENKERT, E. In *Experimentia* **15**, 165 (1959).
7. ROBINSON, R. In *The Structural Relations of Natural Products*, p. 95. Clarendon Press, Oxford, England, 1955.
8. DECKERS, W. and MAIER, J. *Ber.* **86**, 1423 (1953).
9. DJERASSI, C., FIGDOR, S. K., BOBBITT, J. M. and MARKLEY, F. X. *J. Am. Chem. Soc.* **79**, 2203 (1957).
10. WIESNER, K., VALENTA, Z., HURLBERT, B. S., BICKELHAUPT, F. and FOWLER, L. R. *J. Am. Chem. Soc.* **80**, 1521 (1958).
11. WIESNER, K., ARMSTRONG, R., BARTLETT, M. F. and EDWARDS, J. A. *J. Am. Chem. Soc.* **76**, 6068 (1954).
12. ROBINSON, R. In *The Structural Relations of Natural Products*, p. 97. Clarendon Press, Oxford, England, 1955.
13. SIMONSEN, J. L. and OWEN, J. N. In *The Terpenes*. Cambridge University Press, Cambridge, England. Vol. I (1953); vol. II (1957).
14. SIMONSEN, J. and BARTON, D. H. R. In *The Terpenes*, vol. III. Cambridge University Press, Cambridge, England, 1952.
15. SIMONSEN, J. and ROSS, W. C. J. In *The Terpenes*, vols. IV and V. Cambridge University Press, Cambridge, England, 1957.
16. TANENBAUM, S. W. and BASSETT, E. W. *Biochim. Biophys. Acta* **59**, 524 (1962).
17. WENKERT, E. *J. Am. Chem. Soc.* **84**, 98 (1962).
18. LEETE, E., GHOSAL, S. and EDWARDS, P. N. *J. Am. Chem. Soc.* **84**, 1068 (1962).
19. SANDEMANN, W. and STOCKMANN, H. *Fette, Seifen, Anstrichmittel* **59**, 852 (1957).
20. WITTING, L. A. and PORTER, J. W. *Biochem. Biophys. Res. Commun.* **1**, 341 (1959).
21. LYNEN, F., EGGERER, H., HENNING, U. and KESSEL, I. *Angew. Chem.* **70**, 738 (1958).
22. POPJÁK, G. *Tetrahedron Letters* **19**, 19 (1959).
23. *A Ciba Foundation Symposium on the Biosynthesis of Terpenes and Sterols.* J. & A. Churchill, London, 1959.
24. ROBERTSON, J. M. and TODD, G. *Chem. and Ind.* (*London*) **1953**, 437.
25. BERTHOLET, M. P. E. In *Chimie Organique Fondée sur la Synthèse*, p. 733. Millet-Bachelier, Paris, 1860.
26. ASCHAN, O. In *Naphtenverbindungen, Terpene und Campherarten*, p. 127. Walter De Gruter and Co., Berlin and Leipzig, 1929.
27. PROKOFIEV, A. A. *Bull. Acad. Sci. U.S.S.R.* **908** (1939).
28. FAVORSKY, A. E. and LEBEDEVA, A. I. *Bull. Soc. Chim. Belges* **6**, 1350 (1939).
29. KREMERS, E. *J. Biol. Chem.* **50**, 31 (1922).
30. FRANCESCONI, L. *Riv. Ital. Essenzee Profumi* **10**, 33 (1928).
31. ASTENGO, R. *Riv. Ital. Essenzee Profumi* **7**, 5 (1925).
32. READ, J. *Chem. and Ind.* (*London*) **48**, 786 (1929).
33. LEEMAN, A. *Nature* **124**, 946 (1929).
34. HUZITA, Y. *J. Chem. Soc. Japan* **60**, 1025 (1939).
35. KUZIN, A. and NEVRAJEVA, N. *Biokhimia* **6**, 261 (1941).
36. BONNER, J. and GALSTON, A. W. *Botan. Rev.* **13**, 543 (1947).

37. STEWART, A. W. and GRAHAM, H. In *Recent Advances in Organic Chemistry*, vol. 2, p. 414. Longmans, Green & Co., 1948.
38. FREY-WYSSLING, A. *Naturwiss.* **26**, 624 (1938).
39. HAAGEN-SMIT, A. J. In *Ann. Rev. Plant Physiol.*, vol. 4, p. 305. Annual Reviews, Inc., Stanford, California, 1953.
40. GASCOIGNE, J. A. and OVEREND, W. G. *Perfumery Essent. Oil Record* **45**, 324 (1954).
41. LITTLEJOHN, W. R. *Perfumary Essent. Oil Record* **41**, 281 (1950).
42. FUJITA, Y. *Kagaku (Kyoto)* **11**, 874 (1956).
43. CRABBÉ, P. and OURISSON, G. *Ind. Chim. Belge* **22**, 1309, 1418 (1957).
44. RILLING, H., TCHEN, T. T. and BLOCH, K. *Proc. Natl. Acad. Sci. U.S.* **44**, 167 (1958).
45. EMDE, H. *Helv. Chim. Acta* **14**, 881 (1931).
46. HALL, J. A. *Chem. Revs.* **20**, 305 (1937).
47. HAAGEN-SMIT, A. J. and SIU, R. *J. Am. Chem. Soc.* **66**, 2068 (1944).
48. POLAK, E. H. *Perfumery Essent. Oil Record* **46**, 369 (1955).
49. ARMSTRONG, H. *Chem. and Ind. (London)* **51**, 359 (1932).
50. BEETS, M. G. J. *Perfumery Essent. Oil Record* **56**, 377 (1950).
51. SMEDLEY, I. *J. Chem. Soc.* **1911**, 1627.
52. SINGLETON, F. *Chem. and Ind. (London)* **50**, 989 (1931).
53. READ, J. *Chem. Revs.* **7**, 44 (1930).
54. HORIUCHI, Y. *Nippon Gakujyutsu Kyokai Hokoku (Reports of the Japanese Assoc. Advance. Sci.)* **10**, 953 (1934); quoted in ref. 41.
55. WALKER, J. *Chem. and Ind. (London)* **54**, 55 (1935).
56. GANAPARTI, K. *Current Sci.* **6**, 19 (1937); *C.A.* **31**, 7939.
57. FUJITA, Y. In *Fundamental Studies of Essential Oils* (in Japanese). The Ogawa Perfume Times, Ogawa and Co., Ltd., Osaka and Tokyo, No. 202, Sept. 1951, pp. 107, 315, 331, 469.
58. MAYER, P. and NEUBERG, C. *Biochem. Z.* **71**, 174 (1915).
59. NEUBERG, C. and KERB, E. *Biochem. Z.* **92**, 111 (1918).
60. NAVES, Y. *Technik Industrie Schweizer Chemiker* **203** (1942).
61. ROVESTI, P. *Parfumerie* **47**, 61 (1955); *C.A.* **49**, 16359e.
62. HALPERN, A. *J. Am. Pharm. Assoc., Sci. Ed.* **40**, 68 (1951).
63. FUJITA, Y. In *Fundamental Studies of Essential Oils* (in Japanese). The Ogawa Prefume Times, Ogawa and Co., Ltd., Osaka and Tokyo. No. 202, Sept. 1951, p. 502.
64. PENFOLD, A. R. and MORRISON, F. R. *J. Proc. Roy. Soc. N.S. Wales* **61**, 54 (1927).
65. TRADE NOTES AND NEWS, *Perfumery Essent. Oil Record* **45**, 144 (1954).
66. MIROV, N. T. In *Ann. Rev. Biochem.*, vol. 17, p. 521. Annual Reviews, Inc., Stanford, California, 1948.
67. WILDMAN, S. G., ABEGG, F. A., ELDER, J. A. and HENDRICKS, S. B. *Arch. Biochem.* **10**, 141 (1946).
68. ROVTH, A. G. and HEGNAUER, R. *Pharm. Weekblad* **90**, 33 (1955); *C.A.* **49**, 7814h.
69. REITSMA, R. H. *J. Am. Pharm. Assoc., Sci. Ed.* **47**, 267 (1958).
70. FUJITA, Y. *Kagaku (Tokyo)* **20**, 514 (1950).
71. FUJITA, Y. *Kagaku (Tokyo)* **20**, 419 (1950).
72. THIES, W. and WEHMER, C. In *Handbuch der Pflanzen Analyse*, III/II, p. 571, ed. G. KLEIN. Springer, Vienna, Austria, 1932.
73. HAAGEN-SMIT, A. J. In *The Essential Oils*, p. 70, E. Guenther. Van Nostrand Co., Inc., New York, 1948.
74. NAVES, Y. and ARDIZIO, P. *Perfumery Essent. Oil Record* **45**, 225 (1954).
75. KALITZKI, M. *Pharmazie* **9**, 61, 155 (1954); *C.A.* **49**, 16357f.
76. GRAHLE, A. *Pharmazie* **10**, 494 (1955); *C.A.* **50**, 16997d.
77. AHLGRIMM, E. D. *Planta* **47**, 255 (1956); *C.A.* **50**, 13180c.
78. BONNER, J. *J. Chem. Education*, **26**, 628 (1949).
79. BIRCH, A. J., ENGLISH, R. J., MASSY-WESTROPP, R. A. and SMITH, H. *Proc. Chem. Soc. (London)* **1957**, 233.
80. BIRCH, A. J., ENGLISH, R. J., MASSY-WESTROPP, R. A. and SMITH, H. *J. Chem. Soc.* **1958**, 369.
81. RUZICKA, L. *Experientia* **9**, 357 (1953).

82. WOLF, D. E., HOFFMAN, C. H., ALDRICH, P. E., SKEGGS, H. R., WRIGHT, L. D. and FOLKERS, K. *J. Am. Chem. Soc.* **78**, 4499 (1956).
83. TAVORMINA, P. A., GIBBS, M. H. and HUFF, J. W. *J. Am. Chem. Soc.* **78**, 4498 (1956).
84. TAVORMINA, P. A. and GIBBS, M. H. *J. Am. Chem. Soc.* **78**, 6210 (1956).
85. BRAITHWAITE, G. D. and GOODWIN, T. W. *Biochem. J.* **67**, 13 (1957).
86. PARK, R. B. and BONNER, J. *J. Biol. Chem.* **233**, 340 (1958).
87. BARLOW, G. B. and PATRICK, A. D. *Nature* **182**, 662 (1958).
88. GASCOIGNE, J. A. and JONES, P. *Nature* **183**, 819 (1959).
89. FOLKERS, K., SHUNK, C. H., LINN, B. O., ROBINSON, F. M., WITTREICH, P. E., HUFF, J. W., GILFILLAN, J. L. and SKEGGS, H. R. In *A Ciba Foundation Symposium on the Biosynthesis of Terpenes and Sterols*, p. 20. J. & A. Churchill, Ltd., London, 1959.
90. TCHEN, T. T. *J. Am. Chem. Soc.* **79**, 6345 (1957).
91. BLOCH, K. In *Biochemistry of Steroids*, p. 50. Proc. 4th Internatl. Congr. Biochem., ed. E. Mosettig, Pergamon Press, New York, 1958.
92. HENNING, U., MOSLEIN, E. M. and LYNEN, F. *Arch. Biochem. Biophys.* **83**, 259 (1959).
93. CHAYKIN, S., LAW, J., PHILLIPS, A. H., TCHEN, T. T. and BLOCH, K. *Proc. Natl. Acad. Sci., U.S.* **44**, 998 (1958).
94. AGRANOFF, B. W., EGGERER, H., HENNING, U. and LYNEN, F. *J. Am. Chem. Soc.* **81**, 1254 (1959).
95. AGRANOFF, B. W., EGGERER, H., HENNING, U. and LYNEN, F. *J. Biol. Chem.* **235**, 326 (1960).
96. BLOCH, K. In *A Ciba Foundation Symposium on the Biosynthesis of Terpenes and Sterols*, p. 4. J. & A. Churchill, Ltd., London, 1959.
97. CORNFORTH, J. W., CORNFORTH, R. H., PELTER, A., HORNING, M. G. and POPJÁK, G. *Tetrahedron* **5**, 311 (1959).
98. RICHARDS, J. H. and HENDRICKSON, J. B. *Biosynthesis of Terpenes, Steroids and Acetogenins*, Frontiers in Chemistry Series, W. A. Benjamin, Inc., New York, 1964.
99. RUZICKA, L. *Pure Appl. Chem.* **6**, 493 (1963).
99a. CLAYTON, R. B. *Quart. Revs. London* **19**, 201 (1965).
100. WENT, F. W. *Nature* **187**, 641 (1960).
101. CAVILL, G. W. K. *Rev. Pure Appl. Chem.* **10**, 169 (1960).
102. EISNER, T. *Science* **146**, 1318 (1964).
103. CASINOVI, G. C. and MARINI-BETTOLO, G. B. Abstracts A, *Meeting of Internatl. Union Pure and Appl. Chem.*, London (1963), p. 285. Quoted in LEETE, E. *Science*, **147**, 1000 (1965).
104. CLEMO, G. R. *Perfumery Essent. Oil Record* **41**, 435 (1950).
105. CRABBÉ, P. *Record Chem. Prog. Kresge-Hooker Sci. Lib.* **20**, 189 (1959).
106. STORK, G. and BURGSTAHLER, A. W. *J. Am. Chem. Soc.* **77**, 5068 (1955).
107. OWEN, L. N. *Perfumery Essent. Oil Record* **41**, 4 (1950).
108. GASCOIGNE, R. M. *J. Chem. Soc.* **1958**, 879.
109. PENFOLD, A. R. *Perfumery Essent. Oil Record* **45**, 213 (1954).
110. SANDERMANN, W. In *Comparative Biochemistry*, vol. 3, p. 591, ed. Florkin, M. and Mason, H. S. Academic Press, New York, 1962.
111. BIRCH, A. J., BOULTER, D., FRYER, R. I., THOMPSON, P. J. and WILLIS, J. L. *Tetrahedron Letters* **3**, 1 (1959).
112. STANLEY, R. G. *Nature* **182**, 738 (1958).
113. SUKHOV, G. V. *Radioisotopes in Scientific Research*, vol. 4, p. 535. First Internatl. Conf., Pergamon Press, New York, 1958.
114. HASSELSTROM, T. *Paper Trade J.* **128**, 55 (1949).
115. SMITH, R. H. *Nature*, 202, 4927 (1964).
116. BIRCH, A. J. and SMITH, H. In *A Ciba Foundation Symposium on the Biosynthesis of Terpenes and Sterols*, p. 245. J. & A. Churchill Ltd., London, 1959.
117. SANDERMANN, W. and SCHWEERS, W. *Tetrahedron Letters* **257** (1962).
118. SANDERMANN, W. *Holzforschung* **16**, 65 (1962).
119. SANDERMANN, W. and SCHWEERS, W. *Tetrahedron Letters* **259** (1962).
120. SANDERMANN, W. Personal communication.
121. BATTAILE, J. and LOOMIS, W. B. *Biochim. Biophys. Acta* **51**, 545 (1961).

122. REITSMA, R. H. *J. Pharm. Sci.* **47**, 267 (1958).
123. CAMPBELL, A. N. Thesis, University Microfilms, Inc., Ann Arbor, Michigan (1961).
124. NICHOLAS, H. J. *J. Biol. Chem.* **247**, 1485 (1962).
125. GRANGER, R., PASSET, J. and VERDIER, R. *Compt. Rend.* **258**, 5539 (1964).
126. CROWLEY, M. P., GODIN, P. J., INGLIS, H. S., SNAREY, M. and THAIN, E. M. *Biochim. Biophys. Acta* **60**, 312 (1962).
127. GODIN, P. J., INGLIS, H. S., SNAREY, M. and THAIN, E. M. *J. Chem. Soc.* **5878** (1963).
128. VARNA, T. N. R. and CHICHESTER, C. O. *Arch. Biochem. Biophys.* **96**, 419 (1962).
129. Cited in PENFOLD, A. R. and SIMONSEN, J. L. *J. Chem. Soc.* **87** (1939).
130. HENDRIKSON, J. B. *Tetrahedron* **7**, 82 (1959).
131. ZALKOW, L. H., MARKLEY, F. X. and DJERASSI, C. *J. Am. Chem. Soc.* **82**, 6354 (1960).
132. BRADFIELD, A. E., PENFOLD, A. R. and SIMONSEN, J. L. *J. Chem. Soc.* **1932**, 2744.
133. HAAGEN-SMIT, A. J. In *Progress in the Chemistry of Organic Natural Products*, vol. 12, p. 1. Springer, Vienna, Austria, 1955.
134. ANDERSON, D. G. and PORTER, J. W. *Federation Proc.* **20**, 350 (1961).
135. SIMONSEN, J. and BARTON, D. H. R. In *The Terpenes*, vol. III, p. 115. Cambridge University Press, Cambridge, England, 1952.
136. STEIN, G. *Biol. Zentr.* **82**, 345 (1963).
137. O'FARRELL, A. F. and STOCK, A. *Life Sciences* **3**, 491 (1964).
138. LEWALLEN, L. L. *Mosquito News* **24**, 43 (1964).
139. DEARDEN, M. J. *Insect Physiol.* **10**, 195 (1964).
140. TYCHAK, E. and MOLNAR, G. *Z. Allgam. Mikrobiol.* **4**, 161 (1964).
141. Ref. 135, p. 119.
142. SORM, F., MLEVISA, V., ARNOLD, Z. and RHIZA, J. *Coll. Czech. Chem. Comp.* **14**, 699 (1949).
143. STEDMAN, R. L., SWAIN, A. P. and RUSANIWSKYJ, W. *J. Chromatography* **4**, 252 (1960).
144. MURRAY, K. E., HUELIN, F. E. and DAVENPORT, J. B. *Nature* **204**, 80 (1964).
145. ESCHENMOSER, A., FELIX, D., GUT, M., MEIER, J. and STADLER, P. In *A Ciba Foundation Symposium on the Biosynthesis of Terpenes and Sterols*. J. & A. Churchill Ltd., London, 1959.
146. BARTON, D. H. R. and DEMAYO, P. *J. Chem. Soc.* **1957**, 150.
147. DJERASSI, C. and BURSTEIN, S. *Tetrahedron* **7**, 37 (1959).
148. BRIESKORN, C. and WENGER, E. *Arch. Pharmazie* **293**, 21 (1960).
149. DJERASSI, C., CAIS, M. and MITSCHER, L. A. *J. Am. Chem. Soc.* **81**, 2386 (1959).
150. CAGLIOTI, L., NAEF, H., ARIGONI, D. and JEGER, O. *Helv. Chim. Acta* **41**, 2278 (1958).
151. BROOKS, C. J. W. and OVERTON, K. H. *Proc. Chem. Soc. (London)* **1957**, 322.
152. OGILVIE, J. W. and LANGDON, R. G. *J. Am. Chem. Soc.* **81**, 754, 756 (1959).
153. FISHMAN, J., JONES, E. R. H., LOWE, G. and WHITING, M. C. *Proc. Chem. Soc. (London)* **1959**, 127.
154. AKAZAWA, T., URITANI, I. and AKAZAWA, Y. *Arch. Biochem. Biophys.* **99**, 52 (1962).
155. DE MAYO, P., ROBINSON, J. R., SPENCER, E. Y. and WHITE, R. W. *Experientia* **18**, 359 (1962).
156. OURISSON, G. *Chem. Soc. Proceedings (London)* **274** (1964).
157. DAUBEN, W. G., THIESSEN, W. E. and RESNICK, P. R. *J. Am. Chem. Soc.* **84**, 2015 (1962).
158. SIMONSEN, J. and BARTON, D. H. R. In *The Terpenes*, vol. III, p. 380. Cambridge University Press, Cambridge, England, 1952.
159. LEDERER, E. *France Parfums* **3**, 28 (1960); *C.A.* **54**, 1457d (1960).
160. ONISHI, I., NAGASAWA, M., TOMITA, H. and FUKUZUMI, T. *Bull. Agr. Chem. Soc., Japan* **22**, 57 (1958).
161. ROWLAND, R. L. *J. Am. Chem. Soc.* **79**, 5007 (1957).
162. RODGMAN, A. *J. Org. Chem.* **24**, 1916 (1959).
163. FUJITA, Y. *Kagaku (Kyoto)* **14**, 794 (1959).
164. SCHLYK, A. A. and GODNEV, T. N. In *Radioisotopes in Scientific Research*, vol. 4, p. 479. Proc. First Internatl. Conf., Pergamon Press, New York, 1958.

165. SHLYK, A. A. and STANISHEVSKAYA, E. M. *Biokhimia* **27**, 984 (1962).
166. FISHER, F. G. and RUDIGER, W. *Ann. Chem.* (Liebig's) **627**, 35 (1959).
167. FISHER, F. G., MARKL, G. and HONEL, H. *Ann. Chem.* (Liebig's) **657**, 199 (1962).
168. MERCER, E. I. and GOODWIN, T. W. *Biochem. J.* (Proceedings), **85**, 13P (1962).
169. TREHARNE, K. J., MERCER, E. I. and GOODWIN, T. W. *Biochem. J.* (Proceedings) **90**, 39P (1964).
170. COSTES, C. *6th Internatl. Biochem. Congress*, New York, N.Y. (1964): Abstract, p. 569.
171. *Chem. and Eng. News*, Special Report, June 1964, p. 25A.
172. ORO, J. and NOONER, D. W. *Federation Proc.* **24**, 663 (1965).
173. ARONOFF, S. and WICKLIFF, J. L. *Plant Physiol.* **37**, 590 (1962).
174. SANDERMAN, W. *Ber.* **71**, 2005 (1938).
175. DJERASSI, C., CAIS, M. and MITSCHER, L. A. *J. Am. Chem. Soc.* **81**, 2386 (1959).
176. CROSS, B. E., HANSON, J. R., BRIGGS, L. H., CAMBIE, R. C. and RUTLEDGE, P. S. *Proc. Chem. Soc.* **17** (1963).
177. CHAN, W. R., WILLIS, C., CARA, M. P. and STEIN, R. P. *Chem. and Ind.* (*London*) **495** (1963).
178. BARLTROP, J. A. and BIGLEY, D. B. *Chem. and Ind.* (*London*) **1447** (1959).
179. WENKERT, E. and CHAMBERLAIN, J. W. *J. Amer. Chem. Soc.* **81**, 688 (1959).
180. BIRCH, A. J. and SMITH, H. In *A Ciba Foundation Symposium on the Biosynthesis of Terpenes and Sterols*, p. 245. J. & A. Churchill, Ltd., London, 1959.
181. ARIGONI, D. *ibid.*, p. 231.
182. *Gibberellins*, Advances in Chemistry Series, No. 28, The Amer. Chem. Soc., Washington, D.C., 1961.
183. CROSS, B. E., GALT, R. H. B. and HANSON, J. R. *J. Chem. Soc.* 2569 (1963).
184. CROSS, B. E., GALT, R. H. B. and HANSON, J. R. *Colloq. Intern. Centre Natl. Rich. Sci.* (*Paris*) **123**, 265 (1963).
185. JEFFRIES, P. R. and HENRICK, C. A. *Science* **144**, 849 (1964).
186. RUDDAT, M., LANG, A. and MOSETTIG, *Naturwissenschaften* **50**, 23 (1963).
187. HEFTMAN, E., RUDDAT, M. and LANG, A. *Federation Proc.* **24**, 294 (1965).
188. WEST, C. A., DENNIS, D. T., UPPER, C. D. and LEW, F. Abstracts *6th Internatl. Biochem. Congress.* New York, N.Y. (1964), p. 601.
189. SANDERMANN, W. *Österr. Chemiker-Zg.* **45**, 49 (1942).
190. WENKERT, E. *Chem. and Ind.* (*London*) **282** (1955).
191. BARTON, D. H. R., COOKSON, R. C., KLYNE, W. and SHOPPEE, C. W. *Chem. and Ind.* (*London*) **21** (1954).
192. WENKERT, E. and CHAMBERLAIN, J. W. *J. Am. Chem. Soc.* **81**, 688 (1959).
193. BRIGGS, L. H., CAIN, B. F., DAVIS, B. R. and WILSMHURST, J. K. *Tetrahedron Letters* **8**, 13 (1959).
194. WILMSHURST, J. K. Thesis, University of New Zealand (1953).
195. BRIGGS, L. H., CAIN, B. F. and CAMBIE, R. C. *Tetrahedron Letters* **8**, 17 (1959).
196. DJERASSI, C. *Bull. Soc. Chim. France* **1957**, 741.
197. WENKERT, E. and BEAK, P. *J. Am. Chem. Soc.* **83**, 998 (1961).
198. DJERASSI, C., WARAWA, E. J., BERDAHL, J. M. and EISENBRAUN, E. J. *J. Am. Chem. Soc.* **83**, 3720 (1961).
199. BRIGGS, L. H., CAIN, B. F., CAMBIE, R. C. and DAVIS, B. R. *J. Chem. Soc.* **1840** (1962).
200. BRIGGS, L. H., CAIN, B. F., DAVIS, B. R. and WILMSHURST, J. K. *Tetrahedron Letters* **13** (1959).
201. GRANT, P. K. and HODGES, R. *Tetrahedron* **8**, 261 (1960).
202. BIRCH, A. J., CAMERON, D. W., HOLZAPFEL, C. W. and RICKARDS, R. W. *Chem. and Ind.* (*London*) **374** (1963).
203. NICHOLAS, H. J. *J. Am. Pharm. Assoc., Sci. Ed.* **47**, 731 (1958).
204. NICHOLAS, H. J. *J. Pharm. Sci.* **50**, 504 (1961).
205. NICHOLAS, H. J. *Nature* **189**, 143 (1961).
206. NICHOLAS, H. J. *Biochim. Biophys. Acta* **84**, 80 (1964).
207. HEILBRON, I. M., KAMM, E. D. and OWENS, W. M. *J. Chem. Soc.* **129**, 1630 (1926).
208. LANGDON, R. G. and BLOCH, K. *J. Biol. Chem.* **200**, 135 (1953).

209. CLAYTON, R. B. and BLOCH, K. *J. Biol. Chem.* **218**, 305, 319 (1956).
210. FITELSON, J. *J. Assoc. Offic. Agr. Chemists* **26**, 506 (1943).
211. DICKHART, W. *Am J. Pharm.* **127**, 359 (1955).
212. ESCHENMOSER, A., RUZICKA, L., JEGER, O. and ARIGONI, D. *Helv. Chim. Acta* **38**, 1890 (1955).
212a. ROWE, J. W. *Tetrahedron Letters* **34**, 2347 (1964).
213. COREY, E. J. and URSPRUNG, J. J. *J. Am. Chem. Soc.* **77**, 3667, 3668 (1955).
214. COREY, E. J. and URSPRUNG, J. J. *J. Am. Chem. Soc.* **78**, 5041 (1956).
215. DJERASSI, C., MILLS, J. S. and VILLOTTI, R. *J. Am. Chem. Soc.* **80**, 1005 (1958).
216. DJERASSI, C., KRAKOWER, G. W., LEMIN, A. J., LIU, L. H., MILLS, J. S. and VILOTTI, R. *J. Am. Chem. Soc.* **80**, 6284 (1958).
217. MAZUR, Y., WEIZMANN, A. and SONDHEIMER, F. *J. Am. Chem. Soc.* **80**, 1007 (1958).
218. DJERASSI, C. In *Biochemistry of Steroids*, p. 1. Proc. 4th Internatl. Congr. Biochem., ed. E. Mosettig, Pergamon Press, New York, 1958.
219. WELLS, W. W. and LORAH, C. L. *J. Am. Chem. Soc.* **81**, 6089 (1959).
220. KANDUTSCH, A. A. and RUSSELL, A. E. *J. Biol. Chem.* **235**, 2256 (1960).
221. HEFTMANN, E. *Ann. Rev. Plant Physiol.* **14**, 225 (1963), Ann. Revs., Inc., Palo Alto, California.
222. ARIGONI, D. In *A Ciba Foundation Symposium on the Biosynthesis of Terpenes and Sterols*, p. 231. J. & A. Churchill Ltd., London, 1959.
223. BAISTED, D. J., CAPSTACK, E., JR. and NES, W. R. *Biochemistry* **1**, 537 (1962).
224. NES, W. R. and ROSIN, N. L. *Abstract 6th Internatl. Biochem. Congr.*, New York, N.Y. (1964), p. 588.
225. ANDERSON, D. G. and PORTER, J. W. *Arch. Biochem. Biophys.* **97**, 509 (1962).
226. CAPSTACK, E., JR., BAISTED, D. J., NEWSCHWANDER, W. W., BLONDIN, G., ROSIN, N.L. and NES, W. R. *Biochemistry* **1**, 1178 (1962).
227. BEELER, D. A., ANDERSON, D. G. and PORTER, J. W. *Arch. Biochem. Biophys.* **102**, 26 (1963).
228. NES, W. R., CAPSTACK, E. and BLONDIN, G. A. *Federation Proc.* **24**, 660 (1965).
228a. CAPSTACK, E., JR., ROSIN, N., BLONDIN, G. A. and NES, W. R. *J. Biol. Chem.* **240**, 3258 (1965).
228b. GOODWIN, T. W., In *Biosynthetic Pathways in Higher Plants*, ed. by Pridham, J. B. and Swain, T., Academic Press, New York (1965), p. 57.
229. BENVENISTE, M. P., DURR, A., HIRTH, L. and OURISSON, G. *Compt. Rend.* **259**, 2005 (1964).
230. BERNARD, M., VALENTINE, C. and REID, W. W. Tobacco Research Conf., Canberra, Australia (1964); Reid, Personal communication.
230a. BARTON, D. H. R. and MOSS, G. P. *Chem. Commun.* 261 (1966).
230b. COREY, E. J., RUSSEY, W. E. and DE MONTELLANO, P. R. O., *J. Amer. Chem. Soc.* **88**, 4750 (1966).
231. PORTER, J. W. Personal communication.
232. KRISHNA, G., FELDBRUEGGE, D. H. and PORTER, J. W. *Biochem. Biophys. Res. Commun.* **14**, 363 (1964).
233. ALEXANDER, J. A., GOLD, A. M. and SCHENK, E. *J. Biol. Chem.* **232**, 599 (1958).
234. NICHOLAS, H. J. and MORIARTY, S. *Federation Proc.* **22**, 529 (1963).
235. LITTLE, H. N. and BLOCH, K. *J. Biol. Chem.* **183**, 33 (1950).
236. CASTLE, M., BLONDIN, G. and NES, W. R. *J. Amer. Chem. Soc.* **85**, 3306 (1963).
237. JOHNSON, D. F., HEFTMANN, E. and HOUGHLAND, G. V. C. *Arch. Biochem. Biophys.* **104**, 102 (1964).
238. BENNETT, R. D., HEFTMANN, E., PRESTON, W. H., JR. and HAUN, J. R. *Arch. Biochem. Biophys.* **103**, 74 (1963).
239. BENNETT, R. D., HEFTMANN, E., PURCELL, A. E. and BONNER, J. *Science* **134**, 671 (1961).
240. BAZZANO, G., HAMILTON, J. G., MILLER, O. N. and HANSEN, J. H. *Federation Proc.* **23**, 425 (1964).
241. BADER, S., GUGLIELMETTI, L. and ARIGONI, D. *Proceedings Chem. Soc.* (*London*) **16** (1964).

242. VILLANEUVA, V. R., BARBIER, M. and LEDERER, E. *Bull. Soc. Chim.* **1423** (1964).
243. NICHOLAS, H. J. *J. Pharm. Sci.* **50**, 623 (1961).
244. NICHOLAS, H. J. *J. Biol. Chem.* **237**, 1476 (1962).
245. NICHOLAS, H. J. *J. Pharm. Sci.* **50**, 645 (1961).
246. DAVID, R., BERNARD-DAGAN, C. and CALLIDE-SIEUZAC, C. *Compt. Rend.* **254**, 1668 (1962).
247. JOHNSON, D. F., WRIGHT, B. E. and HEFTMANN, E. *Arch. Biochem. Biophys.* **97**, 232 (1962).
248. HERBERT, E. J. and KIRBY, G. W. *Tetrahedron Letters* **1505** (1963).
249. GOODWIN, T. W. and MERCER, E. I. *The Control of Lipid Metabolism, Biochem. Soc. Symp.* No. 24. Academic Press, N.Y. (1963).
250. BATTERSBY, A. R. and PARRY, G. V. *Tetrahedron Letters* **787** (1964).
250a. BENNETT, R. D. and HEFTMANN, E. *Phytochemistry* **4**, 475 (1965).
251. STABURSKIV, A. *Chem. Scand.* **7**, 1220 (1953).
252. JOHNSON, D. F., BENNETT, R. D. and HEFTMANN, E. *Science* **140**, 198 (1963).
253. DUPERON, R. *Compt. Rend.* **157**, 2268 (1963).
254. BUTENANDT, A. and JACOBI, H. *Z. Physiol. Chem.* **218**, 104 (1933).
255. SKARZYNSKI, B. *Nature* **131**, 766 (1933).
256. SKARZYNSKI, B. *Polska Gazeta Lekarska* **37**, 657 (1935).
256a. BENNETT, R. D., KO, S. and HEFTMANN, E. *Phytochemistry* **5**, 231 (1966).
256b. HEFTMANN, E., KO, S. and BENNETT, R. D. *Phytochemistry* **5**, 1337 (1966).
257. JACOBSON, G. M., FREY, M. J. and HOCHBERG, R. B. *Abstracts, Amer. Chem. Soc.* 148th Meeting, Chicago, Ill., Sept. 1964. *Div. Biol. Chem.*, p. 28C.
258. HELMKAMP, G. and BONNER, J. *Plant Physiol.* **28**, 428 (1953).
259. LEBOEUF, M., CAVE, A. and GOUTAREL, R. *Compt. Rend.* **259**, 3401 (1964).
259a. BENNETT, R. D. and HEFTMANN, E. *Science* **149**, 652 (1965).
259b. BENNETT, R. D. and HEFTMANN, E. *Arch. Biochem. Biophys.* **112**, 616 (1965).
259c. BENNETT, R. D., HEFTMANN, E. and KO, S. *Phytochemistry* **5**, 517 (1966).
259d. BENNETT, R. D. and HEFTMANN, E. *Phytochemistry* **4**, 873 (1965).
259e. CASPI, E., LEWIS, D. O., PIATAK, D. M., THIMANN, K. V. and WINTER, A. *Experientia* **22**, 506 (1966).
260. ARIGONI, D., BARTON, D. H. R., COREY, E. J. and JAGER, O. and collaborators. *Experientia* **16**, 41 (1960).
261. TSCHESCHE, R. In *Progress in the Chemistry of Organic Natural Products*, vol. 12, p. 131. Springer, Vienna, Austria, 1955.
262. TSCHESCHE, R. *Angew. Chem.* **73**, 727 (1961).
263. TSCHESCHE, R. and SNATZKE, G. *Ann. Chem.* **636**, 105 (1960).
264. GEILING, E. M. K., KELSEY, F. E., MCINTOSH, B. J. and GANZ, A. *Science* **108**, 558 (1948).
265. DJAO, E. H. and YOUNGKEN, A. H. W., JR. *J. Amer. Pharm. Assoc., Sci. Ed.* **44**, 321 (1955).
266. RAMSTAD, E. and BEAL, J. L. *J. Pharm. Pharmacol.* **12**, 552 (1960).
267. GREGORY, H. and LEETE, E. *Chem. and Ind.* (*London*) 1242 (1960).
268. SIPERSTEIN, M. D., MURRAY, A. W. and TITUS, E. O. *Arch. Biochem. Biophys.* **67**, 154 (1957).
269. CHEN, C., OSUCH, M. V. and BOECK, L. H. *Abstracts, 6th Internatl. Biochem. Congr.*, New York, N.Y. (1964).
270. TSCHESCHE, R. and LILIENWEISS, G. *Z. für Naturforsch.* **19b**, 265 (1964).
271. LEETE, E. and GROS, E. G. *Abstracts, Div. of Biol., Amer. Chem. Soc.*, 148th Meeting, Chicago, Ill. (1964).
272. HEFTMANN, E., BENNETT, R. D. and BONNER, J. *Arch. Biochem. Biophys.* **92**, 13 (1961).
273. BENNETT, R. D. and HEFTMANN, E. Abstracts, *6th Internatl. Biochem. Congr.*, New York, N.Y. (1964), p. 565.
274. DAUBEN, W. G., BAN, Y. and RICHARDS, J. H. *J. Amer. Chem. Soc.* **79**, 968 (1957).
275. DAUBEN, W. G., FONKEN, G. J. and BOSWELL, G. A. *J. Amer. Chem. Soc.* **79**, 1000 (1957).
276. BENVENISTE, P., HIRTH, L. and OURISSON, G. *Compt. Rend.* **259**, 2284 (1964).

276a. BENVENISTE, P., HIRTH, L. and OURISSON, G. *Phytochemistry* **5**, 31 (1966).
276b. BENVENISTE, P., HIRTH, L. and OURISSON, G. *Phytochemistry* **5**, 45 (1966).
277 KAUFMANN, H. P. and SAN GUPTA, A. K. *Fette, Seifen. Anstrichmittel* **66**, 461 (1964).
278. MARKLEY, K. S. and SANDO, C. E. *J. Agr. Research* **46**, 403 (1933).
279. BRIESKORN, C. H., BRINER, M., SCHLUMPRECHT, L. and EBERHARDT, K. H. *Arch. Pharm.* **285**, 290 (1952).
280. NICHOLAS, H. J. *J. Biol. Chem.* **237**, 1481 (1962).
281. NICHOLAS, H. J. *Ibid.*, p. 1485.
282. GUGLIELMETTI, L. Thesis: Federal Polytechnic School, Zurich (1962).
283. GLOOR, U. and WISS, O. *Biochem. Biophys. Res. Commun.* **8**, 294 (1964).
284. STOFFEL, W. and MARTIUS, C. *Biochem. Z.* **333**, 440 (1960).
285. REID, W. W. *Chem. and Ind.* **1489** (1961).
286. STEVENSON, F. J., HEMMING, F. W. and MORTON, R. A. *Biochem. J.* **88**, 52 (1963).
287. STUMPF, P. K. and JAMES, A. T. *Biochim. Biophys. Acta* **70**, 20 (1963).
288. NICHOLAS, H. J. *J. Pharm. Sci.* **53**, 895 (1964).

CHAPTER 15

THE BIOGENESIS OF LIGNINS†

F. F. NORD and WALTER J. SCHUBERT

Laboratory of Organic Chemistry and Enzymology,
Fordham University, Bronx, New York 10458

CONTENTS

I. INTRODUCTION   903
II. THE AROMATIZATION PROCESS IN MICROORGANISMS   907
  A. *Aromatic amino acid biosynthesis in bacteria*   907
  B. *Aromatic amino acid biosynthesis in fungi*   908
  C. *Methyl* p-*methoxycinnamate metabolism in* Lentinus lepideus   909
    1. Biogenesis of methyl p-methoxycinnamate   909
    2. Metabolism of methyl p-methoxycinnamate   912
III. LIGNIFICATION IN HIGHER PLANTS   916
  A. *Lignin formation from carbon dioxide*   917
  B. *Carbohydrate precursors*   918
  C. *The shikimic acid pathway*   922
  D. *Genesis of the lignin building stones*   925
  E. *Conversions of the lignin building stones*   930
  F. *The enzymes involved*   934
IV. CONCLUSION   936
V. REFERENCES   937
  ADDENDUM   939

I. INTRODUCTION

During the growth of woody plant tissues, the carbohydrate constituents are formed first. Then the formation of another component, lignin, begins,

† Contribution No. 407. The experimental results from this laboratory were obtained with the aid of grants or fellowships of the Office of Naval Research, the National Science Foundation, the U.S. Public Health Service, the U.S. Atomic Energy Commission, the Research Corporation and the Procter & Gamble Co. Parts of this report were discussed at the Gordon Research Conferences, New Hampton, N.H., 1963, at the Symposium on the Degradation of Lignin, London, 1963, at the Ann. Meeting of the Tech. Assoc. of the Pulp and Paper Industry, New York, 1964, at the Internatl. Symposium on Lignin, Cellulose and Hemicelluloses, Grenoble, France, 1964, and at the Second Internat. Symposium on the Chemistry and Technology of Cellulose and Lignin, Yassi, Romania, 1965.

a process called "lignification". As a result of this transformation, the spaces previously existing between the polysaccharide fibers are gradually filled in with lignin, or perhaps, certain of the carbohydrates already present may be converted somehow into lignin. The purpose of lignification appears to be twofold. It cements and anchors the cellulose fibers together, and simultaneously, it stiffens and protects them from physical and chemical damage. Thus, the completely lignified fiber no longer plays an active role in the life of the plant, but serves principally as a supporting structure. [104]

Although over one hundred years have passed since the discovery of lignin, and although a tremendous amount of research has been performed on it, a complete elucidation of its structure has still not been achieved. Due to this unsatisfactory state of knowledge of the chemistry of lignin,† it is difficult to describe it. The term "lignin" can no longer be considered the designation of a chemically defined compound, but is rather a collective term for a group of high molecular, amorphous compounds which are related chemically in the same way as are many other natural high molecular products, such as cellulose, the hemicelluloses, and starch. In the light of earlier knowledge of lignin chemistry, lignin has been defined [10a] as: "that incrusting material of the plant which is built up mainly, if not entirely, of phenylpropane building stones; it carries the major part of the methoxyl content of the wood; it is unhydrolyzable by acids, readily oxidizable, soluble in hot alkali and bisulfite, and readily condenses with phenols and thio compounds".

On the basis of more recent results, the definition of lignin can now be somewhat amplified. Thus, since lignin yields aldehydes when it is treated with nitrobenzene in alkali at 160°, it may be further stipulated as "that wood constituent which, when oxidized with nitrobenzene, yields vanillin in the case of coniferous woods, vanillin and syringaldehyde in the case of deciduous woods, and p-hydroxybenzaldehyde, vanillin, and syringaldehyde, in the case of monocotyledons". [13] In addition, lignin may be considered as "that plant component which, when refluxed with ethanol in the presence of catalytic amounts of hydrogen chloride, gives a mixture of ethanolysis products—'Hibbert's monomers'—such as α-ethoxypropioguaiacone, vanillin, vanilloyl methyl ketone from coniferous woods and, in addition, the corresponding syringyl derivatives from deciduous wood". [13]

Lignin never occurs alone in nature, but always coexists with cellulose, or some other carbohydrate. Although it appears to be physically associated with these carbohydrates, this does not imply that lignin forms a chemical compound in the plant with the carbohydrates, and, in fact, the opposite may be the case. [82, 92] Indeed, much of the difficulty involved in studying the chemistry of lignin can be attributed to the fact that, until relatively recently, no method was known by which it could be separated in an unchanged form

† Progress in the chemistry of lignin has been reviewed by Nord and de Stevens,[82] by Brauns and Brauns[13] and by Kürschner.[74a]

from the coexisting carbohydrates. Whatever method was employed, a preparation was obtained which was no longer identical with lignin as it exists in nature. [104]

Accordingly, it is premature at the present time to attempt to suggest a structural formula for lignin. However, on the basis of experimental results, it is possible to indicate certain structural features which a formula for lignin must accommodate. [11]

The results of the hydrogenation of lignin, whereby up to 50 per cent of cyclohexylpropane-type derivatives can be obtained, show that a large part of the lignin structure is composed of phenylpropane skeletons, since there is little doubt that the cyclohexyl ring of these products results from the hydrogenation of benzene rings in lignin. [23, 22, 93, 94] That benzene rings do in fact occur in lignin is further indicated by its chemical analysis, which reveals a high degree of unsaturation, and also by the fact that, upon mild oxidation, up to 25 per cent of vanillin has been obtained. The formation of vanillin from lignin further indicates that, in at least a part of the lignin structure, the benzene ring contains a methoxyl group in the position *meta* to, and a hydroxyl group (or phenyl ether linkage) in the position *para* to the propyl side chain.

Furthermore, there is little doubt that lignin is a high polymer which is formed to a great extent (perhaps entirely) of phenylpropane building stones. In what way these building stones are joined to each other, whether they are combined according to a single pattern, or in different ways, are questions whose answers are still unknown. Thus, before an authentic structural formula for lignin can be proposed, we must first know the structures of all the lignin building stones, and then we must characterize the building units, i.e. the di- and trimerized building stones, in order to learn the mode of combination of the building stones, one to another, with the sum-total forming the lignin polymer. [104]

The mechanism of the biogenesis of lignin has also intrigued lignin chemists ever since the discovery of this complex substance. Simply stated, the process of lignification is that transformation which occurs in plants whereby the aromatic polymer, lignin, is synthesized, ultimately from carbon dioxide, probably by way of intermediates of a carbohydrate nature. Accordingly then, lignification is but one illustration of the more general phenomenon of aromatization, i.e., the conversion by living cells of nonaromatic precursors into compounds containing benzenoid-type rings. Noteworthy advances have indeed been made in the elucidation of the biogenesis of the benzene rings of the aromatic amino acids, tyrosine, phenylalanine and tryptophane. [27]

Many suggestions have been advanced in the past in an effort to explain the nature of the precursors of lignin and the mechanism of its synthesis in plants, but these suggestions have been justly referred to as either purely speculative, or else as based on evidence of an indirect or fragmentary character. [92] Basically, the problem of the biogenesis of lignin is this: by what enzymic pathway is this aromatic compound of high degree of polymerization formed from substances preexisting in the plant?

A comprehensive answer to this question requires the consideration of two fundamental assumptions. First, this complex material must have its ultimate origin in certain relatively simpler compounds. Second, the biogenesis of lignin probably involves the functioning of not one enzyme system, but rather, there is indicated the functioning of several different systems, each exerting its influence on its substrates in a systematized and integrated sequence, with the sum-total of the reactions giving rise to a product, or group of products (lignin) which is required for the existence of the mature plant. Thus, in such a biosynthetic study, both the source material of the final product and the energetics of the reactions involved must be considered. Too often, these concepts are neglected, with the result that conclusions derived frequently are not unequivocal. [89, 87, 86, 106]

Although our knowledge of the total scheme of biogenesis of lignin is still incomplete,† there can be little doubt that it originates ultimately from the carbohydrates which are formed from atmospheric carbon dioxide by the process of photosynthesis. The "lignification problem" may then be considered to include the elucidation of the identity of the ultimate carbohydrate precursors (or derivatives thereof) of lignin, together with the enzymic mechanisms operative, and intermediate compounds formed, whereby the carbohydrate precursors are eventually transformed into the aromatic polymer, lignin. Obviously, this transformation cannot occur by a direct conversion, but must proceed by way of the polymerization of some simpler, monomeric unit (or units), referred to as the "primary building stones". However, the almost complete disparity of chemical nature between a carbohydrate on the one hand, and an aromatic polymer on the other, clearly implies an extended series of far-reaching enzyme reactions in order to effect this profound transformation.

The complexity of the structure of lignin precludes the possibility of the existence of one simple building unit for lignin in the sense in which glucose or cellobiose may be considered the building units of cellulose. Accordingly, for lignin formation, it becomes necessary to postulate the existence of certain dimeric "secondary building stones". The formation of lignin itself finally may be considered to be either the direct polymerization of the secondary building stones as such, or else, there may conceivably be additional modifications (such as trimerizations, etc.), before the final polymerization results in the formation of the complex polymer we regard as lignin.

---

† Older theories on the origin and mode of formation of lignin were reviewed by Brauns. [12, 13]

The over-all picture of the lignification process may therefore be presented schematically as follows:

$$CO_2 \xrightarrow{\text{photosynthesis}} \text{Carbohydrates} \xrightarrow{\text{aromatization}} \text{Primary Building Stones}$$

$$\xrightarrow{\text{dimerization}} \text{Secondary Building Stones} \xrightarrow{\text{polymerization}} \text{Lignin.}$$

II. THE AROMATIZATION PROCESS IN MICROORGANISMS

Biochemists have long speculated about the mechanism by which plants and microorganisms are able to accomplish the feat of synthesizing benzenoid compounds from non-aromatic precursors. The investigation of the biogenesis of the aromatic lignin building stones, and of lignin itself in higher plants, had met with experimental difficulty. However, the opportunity for an experimental approach to the general problem of "aromatization" arose from the isolation of aromatic polyauxotrophs of the microorganisms *Escherichia coli*[26] and of *Neurospora*,[119] i.e. mutants of the microorganisms that require a supplementary mixture of aromatic compounds for their metabolic activities.

A. *Aromatic Amino Acid Biosynthesis in Bacteria*

The researches of B. D. Davis[27] and collaborators on the above-mentioned mutants of *E. coli* established a partial pathway for the biosynthesis of the aromatic amino acids from carbohydrate precursors. This work has been reviewed,[28, 79, 112] and an accepted pathway for the biogenesis of phenylalanine and tyrosine is presented in Fig. 1.

Thus, the carbon atoms of the two aromatic amino acids are derived from one mole of D-erythrose-4-phosphate (II) and two moles of phosphoenol-pyruvate (I). The second mole of phosphoenol-pyruvate is incorporated by a reaction with 5-phospho-shikimic acid (III) to give compound Z_1 which then rearranges to form prephenic acid (IV). Prephenic acid then serves as a "branching point"; thus, it may be converted either to phenylpyruvic acid (V), or to *p*-hydroxyphenylpyruvic acid (VII), and these compounds give phenylalanine (VI) and tyrosine (VIII), respectively, by a transamination reaction.

A new intermediate in aromatic biosynthesis has recently been found,[51] for which the trivial name chorismic acid was suggested. It lies in the metabolic sequence after 3-enol pyruvyl shikimic acid-5-phosphate (IX), and can be converted enzymically to prephenic acid (IV), anthranilic acid and 4-hydroxybenzoic acid. While further work may be necessary to provide a final proof of its structure and stereochemistry, chorismic acid has been formulated [51] as the 3-enol-pyruvic ether of *trans*-3,4-dihydroxycyclohexa-1,5-diene carboxylic acid (X).

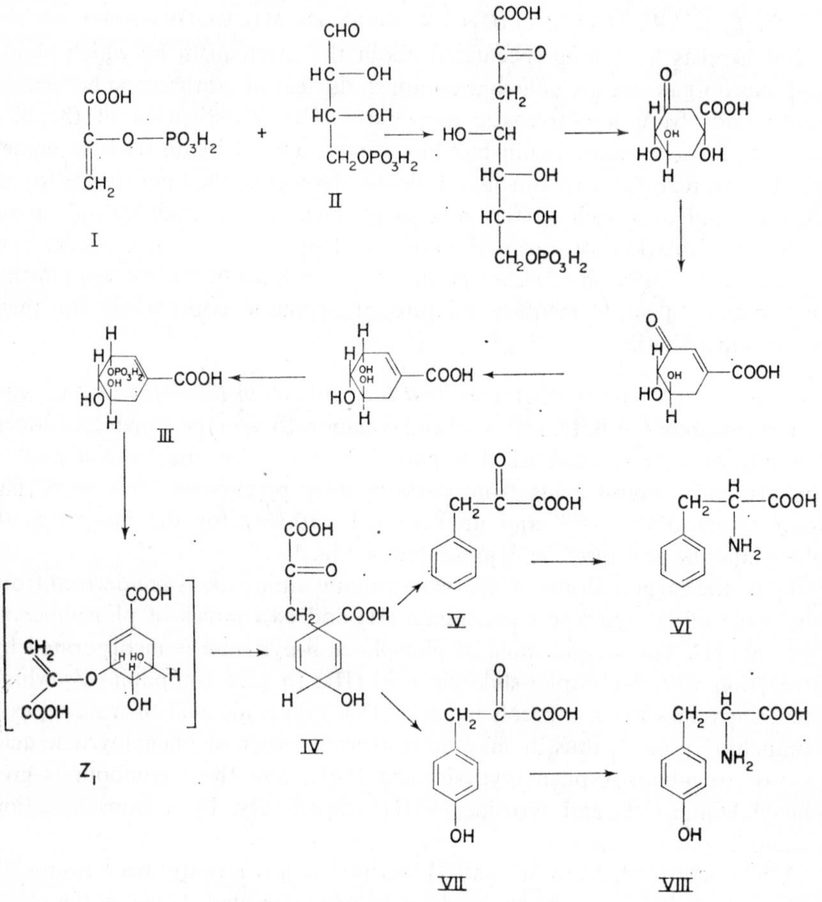

Fig. 1.

B. *Aromatic Amino Acid Biosynthesis in Fungi*

The mold *Neurospora crassa* also appears to utilize the shikimic acid pathway for the biosynthesis of its aromatic amino acids. Thus, Tatum *et al.* [119] obtained a mutant of this organism which demonstrated a multiple nutritional requirement for aromatic amino acids, and this requirement could be satisfied by added shikimic acid. [38]

Thus, it does seem that *N. crassa* also synthesizes its aromatic amino acids by a pathway similar to that found in *E. coli*, although it is not proven that the two pathways are identical in all respects. [79] Other fungi have not been investigated to any great extent, although added shikimic acid has been found [5] to cause an increased yield of 6-methyl salicylic acid in experiments with *Penicillium patulum*.

C. *Methyl* p-*Methoxycinnamate Metabolism in* Lentinus lepideus

Among the several species of wood-destroying fungi, *Lentinus lepideus* produces "brown rot" in wood, i.e. during its growth on wood, a preferential attack is made on the carbohydrate components with the lignin remaining unaffected, as contrasted with "white rot", in which the lignin seems to be the main substrate of the fungus.

It was observed [9] that the metabolic processes associated with the decay of wood by this organism give rise to certain aromatic esters, namely, methyl anisate (XI), methyl cinnamate (XII), and methyl p-methoxycinnamate (XIII).

Furthermore, it has long been noted [90] that if growing cultures of *Lentinus lepideus* are allowed to incubate in the presence of the produced crystalline deposit of methyl p-methoxycinnamate, after a sufficient period of time, the crystals eventually disappeared. This clearly indicated a further metabolism of the ester by the fungus. [91]

1. *Biogenesis of Methyl* p-*Methoxycinnamate*

Investigations have shown that it is possible to grow *L. lepideus* on media containing glucose, xylose, or ethyl alcohol as sole carbon source, [90] whereby methyl p-methoxycinnamate appears as a crystalline deposit in the culture medium after several weeks of growth. From this observation, it was concluded that the ester is not a product of the degradation of lignin, which might conceivably have been effected by the organism during its growth on wood, for the fungus is capable of synthesizing the aromatic ester either from carbohydrates or ethyl alcohol.

Results obtained from experiments on the biogenesis of methyl p-methoxycinnamate by *L. lepideus* have importance in theorizing on the formation of lignin building stones, if we assume the existence of similar pathways in the formation of the ester, and of the building stones. [92] The assumption of the similarity of the biogenesis of the ester and of the lignin building stones is based upon the structural relationship of methyl p-methoxycinnamate and p-hydroxycinnamyl alcohol, which is one of the three fundamental building stones of lignin. [104]

The following experiments were therefore undertaken as part of an investigation of the problem of the biogenesis of lignin building stones. As a result of these studies, a number of products of the metabolism of L. lepideus was detected. [31] Specifically, these were: pyruvic acid, acetoacetic acid, oxaloacetic acid, α-ketoglutaric acid, ribose, glucose, p-hydroxyphenyl-pyruvic acid (XIV), sedoheptulose (XV), and 5-phosphoshikimic acid (XVI).

XIV   XV   XVI

The origin of methyl p-methoxycinnamate from glucose was indicated by the fact that the organism, when grown on ethanol as substrate, synthesized glucose, and also, by the results of certain competition experiments. In these experiments, ribose, sodium acetate and shikimic acid were tested for their ability to serve as competitors in the biogenesis of methyl p-methoxy-cinnamate. In each case, the ester derived from the competition experiment did not show any dilution of activity when compared with the activity of the product of the control experiment. [30]

The detection of the keto-acids implied the functioning of the citric acid cycle. Acetic acid can be introduced into this cycle. However, the result of an experiment employing methyl-C^{14}-labeled sodium acetate, in addition to unlabeled glucose, did not show any significant incorporation of C^{14} into methyl p-methoxycinnamate. This result was interpreted as meaning that neither the keto-acids nor acetic acid are directly involved in the formation of methyl p-methoxycinnamate. [30]

Thus, the experiments indicated the origin of methyl p-methoxycinnamate from glucose. This conversion then prompted a comparison with the biogenesis of the aromatic amino acids. Davis [27] showed that the synthesis of tyrosine takes place via glucose and shikimic acid. Sedoheptulose, to which some importance had been attributed in the biogenesis of shikimic acid, appeared among the metabolic products of *L. lepideus*. Furthermore, *p*-hydroxyphenylpyruvic acid has been considered as an intermediate in the biogenesis of tyrosine. [27] This compound was also identified in the medium of *L. lepideus* cultures, and might be considered a precursor of *p*-hydroxy-cinnamic acid. [30]

These findings then indicated the possibility of a relationship between the formation of methyl *p*-methoxycinnamate by *L. lepideus* and the biogenesis of the aromatic amino acids by bacteria. [83, 105]

Lentinus lepideus was next grown in media containing D-glucose-1-C^{14} and D-glucose-6-C^{14}. The activities of both were significantly incorporated into methyl *p*-methoxycinnamate. The comparative distributions of activity in the ester derived from the two differently labeled forms of D-glucose were determined [110] by specific degradation reactions which permitted the selective isolation of several of the individual carbon atoms of methyl *p*-methoxy-cinnamate (XVII).

The relative distributions of activity of C^{14} from the two glucose samples are summarized in Table 1.

The percentage distributions in each carbon of the side chain were nearly identical, when comparing the esters obtained from the 1-C^{14} and 6-C^{14}-labeled D-glucose, but the observed absolute differences were attributable to

TABLE 1. DISTRIBUTIONS OF ACTIVITY IN METHYL *p*-METHOXYCINNAMATE FORMED FROM D-GLUCOSE-1-C^{14} AND D-GLUCOSE-6-C^{14} [110]

Positions in methyl *p*-methoxycinnamate: Carbon no.	Percentage of total activity of ester	
	from Glucose-1-C^{14}	from Glucose-6-C^{14}
1	—	3·2
2 + 6	—	39·1
3 + 5	—	4·9
4	—	4·2
7	14·1	17·6
8 + 9	5·4	5·0
10	14·5	13·4
11	13·2	12·6

a uniformly greater dilution of C-1. In the ester produced from D-glucose-6-C^{14}, significant activity was incorporated into carbons 7 and 2 or 6 of the phenylpropane moiety of the ester. In general, these results were very similar to those obtained for tyrosine[27] and shikimic acid[114] biosyntheses from glucose.

Relating the results of the ester biosynthesis from D-glucose-6-C^{14} to those of tyrosine synthesis, the probability that methyl p-methoxycinnamate is synthesized by *L. lepideus* from glucose via shikimic acid was apparent. However, in the ester biogenesis, the specific activity of carbon 1 underwent greater dilution, when compared with carbon 6. This can be accounted for by an alternative oxidative decarboxylation of carbon 1 of glucose.[110]

It was also observed that carbon 6 of glucose was markedly incorporated into the methoxyl carbon and the ester methyl carbon of the product. The nonequivalent incorporation of carbons 1 and 6 of glucose into these positions gave further support of the occurrence in *L. lepideus* of a pathway other than glycolysis.[110]

These findings then confirmed the existence of a relationship between the formation of methyl p-methoxycinnamate by *Lentinus lepideus* and the biogenesis of aromatic amino acids by bacteria. The structural relationship existing between methyl p-methoxycinnamate and the lignin building stones has already been indicated. Hence, it seemed possible that the lignin building stones might also be synthesized by a similar pathway.[104]

2. *Metabolism of Methyl* p-*Methoxycinnamate*

As indicated above, *Lentinus lepideus* produces large amounts of crystalline methyl p-methoxycinnamate in its culture medium. It was then observed[108] that when the culture flasks in which the deposit had accumulated were shaken, the amount of crystals in the medium diminished rapidly, and after a few days, they had almost completely disappeared. Simultaneously, the color of the medium turned brown. When, after one or two days of shaking the flasks, the medium was extracted with ether, the presence of a small amount of a hitherto undetected phenolic compound was established. This compound was isolated and identified[108] as methyl p-coumarate (XVIII).

XVIII

The methyl p-coumarate produced was easily oxidized by a mycelial extract of the mold. [108] It was therefore suggested that methyl p-coumarate might be regarded as an intermediate in the metabolism of methyl p-methoxycinnamate by *Lentinus lepideus*, and also possibly in the biosynthesis of that compound. It was further considered that, in the first step of the metabolism of methyl p-methoxycinnamate, this compound may be demethylated to methyl p-coumarate, and then, the latter may be oxidized by a phenolase, possibly tyrosinase. [108]

In a subsequent study, [107] the occurrence in the culture medium of the phenolic ester, methyl isoferulate (XIX), was established, together with

XIX

methyl p-coumarate and methyl p-methoxycinnamate. It was further noted that methyl p-coumarate was accumulated only in small amounts and under certain special conditions, since this compound was rapidly oxidized by the phenolase present in the mold to a colored, oxidized material. Accordingly, methyl p-coumarate was regarded as an intermediate in the biosynthesis of methyl p-methoxycinnamate by *Lentinus lepideus*.

When methyl p-coumarate-carboxyl-C^{14} was added to the culture medium, about 60 per cent of the total isotopic activity was recovered in the methyl p-methoxycinnamate isolated. The isotopic activity of the carbon in the original position of methyl p-coumarate did not migrate to other carbons of methyl p-methoxycinnamate. The loss of 40 per cent of the original isotopic activity was accounted for on the basis of: (a) mechanical loss during the isolation and purification of the ester; (b) oxidation of some of the methyl p-coumarate added to the medium by the enzyme present in the mycelium of the mold; and (c) dilution of the methyl p-coumarate-carboxyl-C^{14} added to the medium with that synthesized by the mold. Nevertheless, the significant recovery of the isotopic activity demonstrated that methyl p-coumarate was a direct precursor of methyl p-methoxycinnamate in the biosynthesis of that compound. [107]

Twenty per cent of the total activity of added DL-methionine-methyl-C^{14}

was recovered from the methyl *p*-methoxycinnamate isolated. Here, the isotopic activity was found principally in the ethereal methoxyl carbon, and (to the same extent) in the ester methyl carbon, indicating the absence of migration to other positions. This significant incorporation of the methionine-methyl carbon into the two methyl carbons of the ester indicates the possibility that methionine (or some related compound) might be the methyl donor to the ethereal and ester methyl groups of this compound. [107]

Accordingly, in the biosynthesis of methyl *p*-methoxycinnamate by *Lentinus lepideus*, it is believed that the intermediate, methyl *p*-coumarate, is methylated to methyl *p*-methoxycinnamate by methionine (or a related compound). However, the reverse of this might occur under different cultural conditions. Thus, while methyl *p*-coumarate does not accumulate in the medium (except under special conditions), small amounts of methyl isoferulate do accumulate, along with methyl *p*-methoxycinnamate.

Two possibilities for the formation of methyl isoferulate were considered. One is the O-methylation of methyl caffeate, which could be formed from methyl *p*-coumarate by the action of phenolase. The other is the hydroxylation of methyl *p*-methoxycinnamate by an enzyme other than phenolase.

In the metabolism of the *p*-methoxyaromatic esters, methyl *p*-methoxycinnamate and methyl isoferulate, it is believed that the methoxyl groups of these esters are first demethylated to the free phenolic compounds. This would be the reverse of their biosynthesis. Then the free phenols formed are subject to the action of the phenolase present in the mold mycelium, whereupon the colored oxidized products are formed. These transformations are summarized in Fig. 2.

The three phenolic compounds identified were accumulated in the medium of *Lentinus lepideus* in the form of esters, and not as free acids. The accumulation of such compounds in the medium is not frequently encountered in microorganisms. Accordingly, the mechanism of O-methylation of phenols in the realm of microbial metabolism cannot yet be fully explained. [107, 95]

In a related investigation, [109] the transformations of anisic acid and methyl anisate by another wood-destroying fungus, *Polystictus* (*Polyporus*) *versicolor*, were studied. This organism does not accumulate significant amounts of aromatic compounds in its culture medium. However, when methyl anisate was added to its medium, transformations analogous to those undergone in the methyl *p*-methoxycinnamate metabolism of *Lentinus lepideus* were observed.

Thus, when methyl anisate was added to the culture medium of *P. versicolor*, demethylation and (simultaneously) hydroxylation were observed, and the color of the medium gradually turned brown. However, if the culture flasks were first heated, and then methyl anisate was added to the medium and shaken, no hydroxylated compounds could be detected. But, the conversion of methyl anisate to hydroxylated compounds was observed when an ascorbic

acid system was employed. [109] Accordingly, it was assumed that these transformations were achieved by a similar system inherent in these molds.

However, significantly, if anisic acid, rather than methyl anisate, was added
to the medium of this fungus, no hydroxylated derivatives of anisic acid
could be detected, and the color of the medium did not turn brown. The
anisic acid was rapidly converted into anisaldehyde and anisyl alcohol,
both identified in the medium. Thus, changes in the ultraviolet absorption
patterns showed that anisic acid was converted to anisaldehyde, and that the
major portion of the aldehyde produced was reduced to anisyl alcohol. [109]

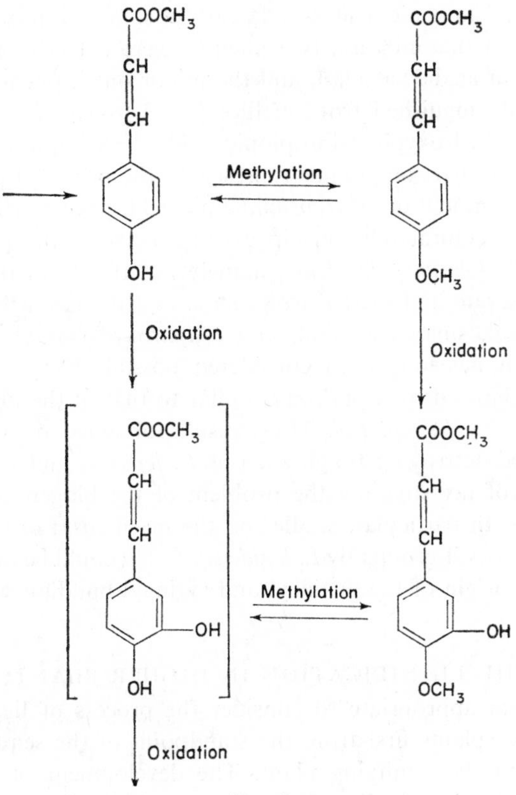

FIG. 2.

The differences between the observed transformations of methyl anisate
and of anisic acid by *P. versicolor* indicated that added methyl anisate could
not be significantly hydrolyzed; hence, the ester accumulates. However, a
slow demethylation and hydroxylation of methyl anisate were achieved by the
fungus during hydrolysis, and these were followed by reduction of a portion
of the resultant products. The hydroxylated derivatives of methyl anisate

are believed to be partially transformed by the general oxidizing processes of the organism, whereby the color of the medium becomes brown. [109]

When p-hydroxybenzoic acid was added to the medium of *P. versicolor*, p-hydroxybenzaldehyde was isolated (as its 2,4-dinitrophenylhydrazone). Hence, it is believed probable that p-hydroxybenzoic acid, possibly originating from methyl anisate, is reduced to p-hydroxybenzaldehyde and to the corresponding alcohol. [109]

W. C. Evans [37] also believes that the microbiological degradation of benzenoid compounds involves the production of phenolic compounds at some stage. For example, when soil *Pseudomonads* were grown in a liquid culture containing *trans*-cinnamic acid as sole carbon source, a mixture of phenols was obtained. In this mixture, two phenols were detected, the major constituent being an acidic catechol, and the minor one a phenolic acid. These could not be distinguished from melilotic acid (o-hydroxyphenylpropionic acid) and 2,3-dihydroxyphenylpropionic acid. [24] Accordingly, it was concluded that these two compounds represented the principal products of the *Pseudomonads* degradation of *trans*-cinnamic acid, prior to ring fission.

Again, the structural relationship existing between the products of the metabolism of *Lentinus lepideus*, namely, methyl p-methoxycinnamate, methyl p-coumarate and methyl isoferulate, and the lignin building stones, coniferyl alcohol, sinapyl alcohol, and p-hydroxycinnamyl alcohol, is obvious. Hence, it has long been considered possible [92] that lignin building stones are synthesized by a pathway similar to that of the biogenesis of the aromatic esters by *L. lepideus*. Thus, results obtained on the metabolism of certain wood-destroying fungi, such as *L. lepideus* and *P. versicolor*, do offer a means of investigating the problem of the biogenesis of the lignin building stones. In particular, studies on the mechanism of the methylation of phenolic hydroxyl groups by *L. lepideus* [108, 107] could be of significance in relation to the origin of the guaiacyl and syringyl building stones of lignin.

III. LIGNIFICATION IN HIGHER PLANTS

It would seem appropriate to consider the process of lignification as it occurs in higher plants first from the standpoint of the sequence of events which occurs in the lignifying plant. The development of mature wood-fiber has been divided [122] into four phases: cell division, cell enlargement, cell wall thickening, and lignification. However, these stages are not strictly consecutive and should not be considered as separate and distinct phases.

Many suggestions have been made regarding the origin of lignin in plants, [12, 13] but in general, these hypotheses fall into three groups: [122]

(1) Lignin may arise *in situ* in the cell wall by the transformation of other cell wall constituents already present.

(2) The lignin precursor(s) may arise in the cambial zone, diffuse away, and be incorporated into the differentiating cells of the xylem and phloem.

(3) Lignin, or its precursors, may originate within the differentiating cell wall, and subsequently be incorporated into the cell wall.

Wardrop[122] has rejected the idea of molecular transformations within the cell wall, and he believes that the lignin precursor or precursors diffuse outward from the interior of the cell.

The biochemical pathway of lignin formation in plant tissues has been divided[3] into two distinct parts: (1) the formation of the primary lignin building stones, such as p-coumaryl alcohol, coniferyl alcohol and sinapyl alcohol, and (2) their conversion into lignin itself. We may then ask, with Adler[3] "How does nature synthesize molecules of that structural type?"

Although a wide variety of plant constituents has been postulated as lignin precursors, in most cases, the experimental evidence supporting these hypotheses has been meager. On the basis of recent findings, the most tenable theory would appear to be that lignin is a polymer of some compound or compounds with a phenylpropane skeleton, as for example, one or more of the above three lignin building stones.[104, 82]

Although some information on the final steps of lignin formation has been available, the biochemical reactions leading ultimately from carbon dioxide, via carbohydrate intermediates, to the primary lignin building stones long remained obscure. Accordingly, the following studies were undertaken in an effort to elucidate the overall pathway by which lignin is synthesized in growing plants.

A. *Lignin Formation from Carbon Dioxide*

After the exposure of Sugar cane plants to radioactive carbon dioxide in the dark, the lignin fraction of these plants was found to contain radioactivity.[53]

In a study of lignin biosynthesis in wheat plants, Stone *et al.*[118] found that the greatest increase in the production of lignin, syringaldehyde, and vanillin was evidenced 45–70 days after seeding. The methoxyl content of the plants was also found to increase as the plants matured.

Stone[117] then subjected the wheat plants to $C^{14}O_2$ in a "long-term" experiment. The $C^{14}O_2$ was fed at a stage of growth corresponding to rapid lignification. The plants were harvested every few days until maturity, and were then oxidized with nitrobenzene in alkali, and the resulting vanillin, syringaldehyde, and p-hydroxybenzaldehyde were separated by paper chromatography. The results indicated that $C^{14}O_2$ was still respired from the plants at maturity. All the $C^{14}O_2$ which was incorporated into the lignin did so within 24 hr after administration. The total activity originally acquired by

2G

the syringaldehyde portion of the lignin remained constant throughout the growth of the plant. From these results, Stone concluded that lignin is an end product of plant growth, and is not involved in the respiratory system.

In "short-term" experiments, [16] wheat plants, again at a stage of rapid lignification, were exposed for 20 min to $C^{14}O_2$ in a closed chamber, and were then grown for 1 to 24 hr in a normal atmosphere before harvesting. The results showed that the synthesis of lignin was most rapid from 4 to 6 hr after $C^{14}O_2$ administration. Syringyl residues appeared to be formed more slowly than were guaiacyl residues. A slower rate of formation persisted for the remainder of a 1-day period, possibly as a result of recycling in the carbon pool. After 24 hr, C^{14} appeared in the lignin to the extent of about 1·5–2·0 per cent of that administered.

B. *Carbohydrate Precursors*

The problem of the mechanism of lignification includes the elucidation of the identity of the carbohydrate precursor(s) from which lignin is ultimately derived, together with the nature of the enzymic reactions operative during the process. As a result of these transformations, the carbohydrate precursor(s), photosynthetically derived from atmospheric carbon dioxide, are eventually converted into lignin. [104]

With regard to the identity of the carbohydrate precursor(s), many suggestions have been advanced relative to their nature, viz., cellulose, pentosans, [99] soluble carbohydrates such as pentoses, [67] methyl pentoses, sucrose, [97] and hexoses such as fructose. [123] These suggestions have been justly referred to as either purely speculative, or else as based on evidence of an indirect or fragmentary character. [92]

In a preliminary experiment, [102] uniformly labeled D-glucose was fed to a Norway spruce tree, and, after a suitable period of metabolism, radioactivity was detected in the cambium layer of the tree. The lignin of this layer was isolated and found to be radioactive (Table 2).

TABLE 2. DISTRIBUTION OF ACTIVITY IN NORWAY SPRUCE PLANT MATERIALS AFTER FEEDING UNIFORMLY LABELED D-GLUCOSE-C^{14} [102]

Plant material	Activity (counts/min/mg C)
Stem	460
Lignin	240

From the data of Table 2, it was obvious that the radioactivity of the labeled D-glucose fed to the tree was incorporated to a considerable extent into the lignin. Thus, it was also obvious that the tree was able to convert glucose into lignin. Considering the central place that D-glucose occupies in plant biochemistry, both as a product of photosynthesis and as the monomeric unit of cellulose, it was considered significant that the tree also possessed the enzymic equipment necessary to convert this monosaccharide into lignin. [102] Obviously, however, in the case of lignin, an aromatization process is also required. This will be considered in a later section.

In a subsequent investigation, [2] the fate in lignification of glucose samples which were labeled with C^{14} specifically in their number 1 and 6 positions (XX) was also studied.

HC——OH
|2
HC——OH
|3   O
HO——CH
|4
HC——OH
|5
HC—
|6
CH$_2$OH

XX

In these experiments, D-glucose-1-C^{14} and D-glucose-6-C^{14} were fed separately to individual Norway spruce trees. The method of feeding the tagged compounds and the isolation of lignins have been described. [84, 101] The lignin was subjected to alkaline nitrobenzene oxidation, [100] and vanillin was isolated. Carbons 1, 2, 5, 6, 7 and 8 of the vanillin were isolated by means of the degradation reactions shown in Fig. 3. The activities of the compounds obtained by the degradation of the lignins from the specifically labeled D-glucose preparations are given in Table 3.

TABLE 3. PERCENTAGE DISTRIBUTION OF ACTIVITY IN VANILLIN
OBTAINED FROM D-GLUCOSE-1-C^{14} AND D-GLUCOSE-6-C^{14} EXPERIMENTS [2]

Positions in vanillin	Percentage of total activity in vanillin	
	D-Glucose-1-C^{14} experiment	D-Glucose-6-C^{14} experiment
Total molecule	100·0	100·0
C-1	2·6	4·5
C-2	18·2	16·1
C-5	3·1	3·9
C-6	11·4	18·1
C-7	28·5	22·0
C-8	31·1	24·7
C-3, 4†	5·1	10·7

† Calculated values.

The comparative distribution of activity in the vanillin from the two experiments shows that appreciable activity was incorporated into carbons 2, 6-7 and 8 of the vanillin, whereas considerably lesser amounts were incorporated into the other positions. These results are therefore similar to those obtained for the biosyntheses of shikimic acid [114] and methyl p-methoxycinnamate [110] from glucose, and have since been amply confirmed. [70, 71]

Previously, it has been asserted [104, 82, 92] that both fungal and plant biosyntheses of phenylpropane moieties follow a similar pathway. The similarity of C^{14} distribution from D-glucose-1-C^{14} and D-glucose-6-C^{14} in the aromatic rings of methyl p-methoxycinnamate formed by *Lentinus lepideus* and of the vanillin derived from lignin oxidation shows that a marked similarity in metabolic pathways does indeed exist in the two systems. This is apparent when we compare the percentage distributions of C^{14} from D-glucose-6-C^{14} in the ester (XXI) derived from *L. lepideus* and the vanillin (XXII) derived from the lignin of Norway spruce, using the corresponding position designations, as in XXI and XXII:

TABLE 4. COMPARISON OF RELATIVE DISTRIBUTIONS OF ACTIVITY IN
METHYL p-METHOXYCINNAMATE AND VANILLIN

Positions in ester and vanillin	Percentage distribution of C^{14}	
	in Ester [110]	in Vanillin [2]
C-1	3·2	4·5
C-2	19·5†	16·1
C-3	3·5†	5·4†
C-4	4·2†	5·4†
C-5	3·5†	3·9
C-6	19·5†	18·1
C-7	17·6	22·0
C-8	12·6	24·7

† Calculated values.

The comparison in Table 4 reveals a remarkable agreement in the distribution of radioactivity. From the data, it is apparent that both the ester and the vanillin incorporated most of the activity in carbons 2, 6, 7 and 8.

The mode of formation of shikimic acid from glucose [114] indicates that glucose is converted into this acid by the condensation of a triose derived via glycolysis, with a tetrose derived via the pentose phosphate pathway.

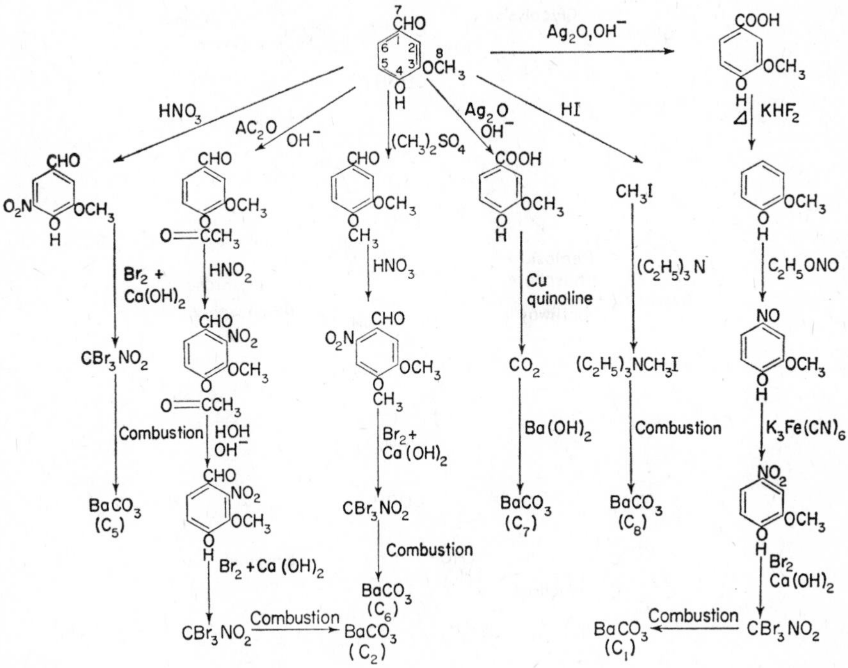

FIG. 3.

Further, there is evidence that phosphoenolpyruvate and D-erythrose-4-phosphate, required for the synthesis of shikimic acid, can be formed in higher plants. [79] Thus, the Embden–Meyerhof pathway produces phospho-enolpyruvate, while D-erythrose-4-phosphate can be derived from the pentose phosphate pathway.

Evidence for the formation of D-erythrose-4-phosphate in plants rests in part on its function as a substrate for the enzymes, transketolase and trans-aldolase. These enzymes are believed to form D-erythrose-4-phosphate as a transitory intermediate during oxidation by the pentose phosphate path-way, [113] and also in the operation of the photosynthetic carbon cycle. [19] It is necessary to include the formation of D-erythrose-4-phosphate to explain the cyclic nature of these two processes. [79] Furthermore, there exists direct evidence [78] for the formation of D-erythrose-4-phosphate during photosynthesis by *Chlorella*.

These considerations then provide an explanation for the observed activity in positions 2 and 6 of the rings of shikimic acid [114] derived from glucose, and of vanillin [2] obtained as described above, i.e.

Glucose $\xrightarrow{\text{Glycolysis}}$

$$\begin{array}{c} CH_2 \\ \parallel \\ C\!-\!\!-\!O\!-\!\!-\!PO_3H_2 \\ \mid \\ COOH \end{array}$$ Phosphoenol pyruvate

Glucose $\xrightarrow[\text{pathway}]{\substack{\text{Pentose} \\ \text{phosphate}}}$

$$\begin{array}{c} CHO \\ \mid \\ HC\!-\!\!-\!OH \\ \mid \\ HC\!-\!\!-\!OH \\ \mid \\ CH_2OPO_3H_2 \end{array}$$ D – erythrose 4 – phosphate

$\xrightarrow[\text{Figure I}]{\text{As in}}$ Shikimic acid

Thus, the ultimate organic source of lignin is the carbohydrate photo-synthetically formed by the plant from atmospheric carbon dioxide. Phospho-enolpyruvate and D-erythrose-4-phosphate may serve as the proximate precursors of the aromatic rings of lignin, while D-glucose has been demon-strated [2] to be an ultimate carbohydrate source.

Recently, fully labeled xylitol was infused into spruce wood, and was found to be incorporated into the lignin as well as the polysaccharides. [72] After isolation of the radioactive wood constituents, they were chemically degraded, and the radioactivity distribution was quantitatively determined. Thus, the conversion of xylitol to lignin was demonstrated. [72] This then indicates that glucose is not necessarily the only carbohydrate precursor which is convertible to lignin.

C. *The Shikimic Acid Pathway*

As indicated above, the studies of Davis, [27] and of Katagiri [65, 64] confirmed that shikimic acid plays an important role in bacteria and fungi as a precursor of aromatic amino acids, and that the enzyme systems which bring about the transformation of glucose, via shikimic acid and other intermediates, into these aromatic acids are to be found in microorganisms. Furthermore, the presence of the enzyme system responsible for the synthesis of shikimic acid was confirmed, not only in microorganisms, but also in higher plants, such as spinach and pea. [77] These investigations then suggested that other aromatic products, such as lignin, which is widely distributed in higher plants, may also be formed from shikimic acid via a similar pathway.

Accordingly, in connection with the biosynthesis of lignin, it is of importance to consider the distribution of shikimic acid in higher plants, and particularly in woody plants. Hasegawa et al. [54] investigated the distribution of shikimic acid in the leaves of 164 plant species, and found shikimic acid in 82 of the species. Further, T. Higuchi [57] studied the distribution of shikimic acid in the leaves and cross-sections of the young stems of 96 species of woody plants. Shikimic acid was detected in 70 species. Hence, there can be no doubt that the shikimic acid pathway does indeed function in higher plants. [79, 57]

The following results prove that shikimic acid, without any rearrangement of the carbon atoms of its six-membered ring, is also to be considered a precursor of the aromatic rings of the lignin building stones, and accordingly, that their formation parallels the mechanism of formation of the aromatic amino acids by microorganisms.

Specifically labeled shikimic acid was prepared by fermentation of D-glucose-6-C^{14} by Escherichia coli mutant 83–24. As shown in Table 5, such shikimic acid contains 44 per cent of its total activity in position 2, and 52 per cent in position 6. [114]

TABLE 5. DISTRIBUTION OF THE C-6 CARBON ATOM OF GLUCOSE IN SHIKIMIC ACID [114]

Position of label in glucose	Activity of shikimate carbon atoms (in % of labeled glucose atom)							
	Total	S-1	S-2	S-3	S-4	S-5	S-6	S-7
C-6	115	0	51	0	0	0	60	7

An aqueous solution of this specifically labeled shikimic acid was incorporated into a growing sugar cane plant. After several days of metabolism, the leaves were removed, the stem of the plant was cut, dried and pulverized, and the resulting powder thoroughly extracted with water.

Activity measurements of the plant material (Table 6) indicated that, upon introduction of the specifically labeled shikimic acid into the plant, the active material was incorporated into non-water-extractable components of the stem. Counting of the isolated Klason lignin indicated that the radioactivity, to its greatest extent, was located in the lignin.

The plant material was first submitted to treatment with Schweizer's reagent to remove the cellulose, and then to an alkaline nitrobenzene oxidation,[100] and the resulting vanillin isolated. The distribution of radioactivity in the ring carbons of the vanillin was determined according to the reactions shown in Fig. 4. The activities in positions 2, 5 and 6 of the ring, determined according to these degradations, are shown in Table 7. From the data, it can be seen that there was a distribution of activity in the aromatic ring of vanillin which agreed well with the original distribution of C^{14} in the six-membered ring of the incorporated shikimic acid.[32]

TABLE 6. DISTRIBUTION OF ACTIVITY IN THE SUGAR CANE

Plant material	Activity (counts/min)
Stem (ground and water-extracted)	6
Klason lignin (10% of weight of stem)	42
Vanillin	58

No attempt was made to equate carbon-2 of vanillin with the corresponding position in shikimic acid, or carbon-6 of vanillin with this position in the acid, since one cannot distinguish these two positions, and since the two positions may be interconvertible.

Thus, after absorption of specifically labeled shikimic acid into a sugar cane plant, it was established that this compound was metabolized by the plant, and was incorporated to a great extent into the lignin.

The degradation of the lignin, via vanillin, revealed that the distribution of activity in the aromatic rings of the product was comparable to the distri-

TABLE 7. DISTRIBUTION OF ACTIVITY IN THE VANILLIN

Vanillin	Activity (counts/min)	Percentage distribution of total activity
Total Molecule	58	100
C-6	204	44
C-2	190	41
C-5	0	0

bution of activity in the incorporated shikimic acid. From these results, it was concluded that shikimic acid is an intermediate on the pathway from carbohydrates, formed from atmospheric CO_2 by photosynthesis, to the aromatic rings of the lignin building stones.[85]

D. *Genesis of the Lignin Building Stones*

The use of the term "primary lignin building stone" is based upon the widely accepted assumption that the lignin molecule, like cellulose and starch, is a long chain, composed of simple "building stones" which, in turn, are linked in some way (or perhaps in several ways) to form a "lignin building

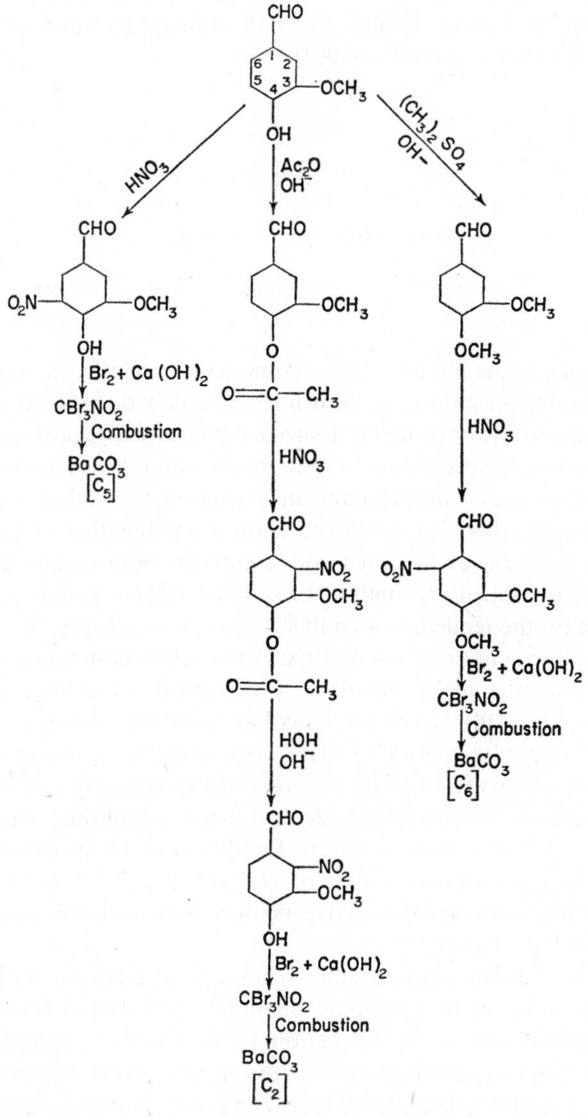

FIG. 4.

unit". [104, 10] This then is similar to the concept of "glucose anhydride" as the building stone for cellulose and starch.

The building stones of lignin, however, possess the phenylpropane carbon structure, and at least four of these are linked together to form a "lignin building unit". A series of lignin building units then makes up the lignin molecule. But, unlike the building stones of cellulose and starch, lignin building stones, although they all have the same basic phenylpropane carbon structure, may be of the vanillyl (XXIII), syringyl (XXIV), or p-hydroxyphenylmethyl (XXV) type. [104, 82, 10, 96]

XXIII   XXIV   XXV

The phenolic cinnamic acids have come to be regarded as potential precursors of lignin, since they are known to be widely distributed in plants, [6] and also because they are highly ionized under physiological conditions. [28] In addition, much speculation about lignification has centered on coniferyl alcohol as a key intermediate in a process of oxidation-polymerization. Historically, this idea developed from a combination of three circumstances: (a) isolation of the glucoside, coniferin, from certain conifers; (b) the similarity in elementary analysis of isolated Klason lignins and coniferyl alcohol, and (c) the tendency of coniferyl alcohol to resinify. [74]

However, since coniferyl alcohol (XXVI) itself was not found in plants, this hypothesis was really based on the natural occurrence of coniferin (XXVII), the glucoside of coniferyl alcohol. Similarly, syringin (XXIX), the glucoside of sinapyl alcohol (XXVIII), is regarded as a precursor of lignin in hardwoods. A survey [73] of the recorded occurrences of coniferin revealed that the presence of this glucoside has been established predominantly in coniferous wood species, with six families and 15 species represented. Regarding the reported occurrences of syringin, except for one finding of its presence in black locust, this glucoside has been isolated only from five genera of the olive family. [73]

The results of many tracer studies from several laboratories have amply supported the concept that phenolic cinnamic alcohols and acids are indeed important precursors in the formation of lignin. For example, coniferyl alcohol has been synthesized with radioactive carbon in several known positions of the molecule [69, 40, 45] and then fed to growing plants. Of equal importance has been the elaboration of degradation procedures employed to recover the radioactivity from the isolated lignin, or more particularly, from the vanillin obtained by the oxidation of lignin, [2, 32] or from the "Hibbert ketones" obtained by ethanolysis. [69]

The synthesized radioactive compounds have been administered to plants in various ways: they may be fed directly to the plant or to excised shoots, [79] or solutions of them may be absorbed through the ends of freshly cut stems, branches, leaves or needles. [2, 32] The localization of the introduced radioactive material may then be followed if desired by radioautography. The plant is allowed a certain time for metabolism; it is then worked up, and the specific activity of the lignin is measured.

The fact that the radioactive material actually is incorporated into the lignin is assured by pre-extraction of the plant tissue with solvents in which the originally synthesized compound is known to be soluble. Usually, the lignin is then isolated by some conventional method, prior to the degradative recovery of the radioactivity.

Data obtained in this fashion have been accepted as proof that precursors such as coniferyl alcohol do mediate in lignin biosynthesis. [3, 101] Analogous studies have also been made with sinapyl alcohol and with *p*-hydroxycinnamyl alcohol. A large number of other C^{14}-labeled compounds has also been studied for their efficiency to serve as precursors of lignin.[79] Experiments of this type have produced the scheme shown in Fig. 5.

It may be noted from this scheme that the cinnamic acid derivatives may be derived from the aromatic amino acids, phenylalanine and tyrosine, and may serve as intermediates in the biosynthesis of a number of phenolic metabolites peculiar to plants, including lignin.[79, 14]

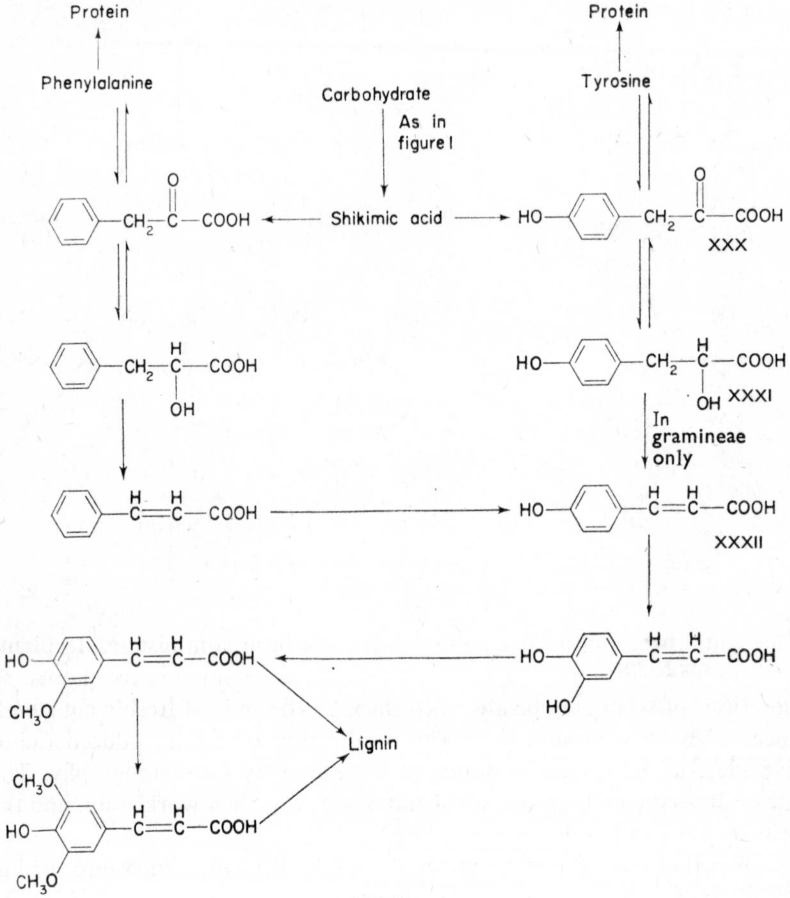

FIG. 5. Reactions leading to the formation of lignin.[79]

The compounds shown as intermediates in Fig. 5 were fed by Neish *et al.* to excised shoots of wheat and maple and were found to be readily converted to lignin.[15, 17] In these investigations, certain taxonomic differences were noted. Thus, out of 11 species representing 10 plant families, only two converted tyrosine to lignin, although all utilized phenylalanine as a lignin precursor. The two species using tyrosine were both members of the *Gramineae* family. In this connection, it was suggested [17] that the failure of (non-*Gramineae*) species to use tyrosine for synthesizing lignin is due to their enzymic inability to dehydrate p-hydroxyphenyllactic acid (XXXI).

It was mentioned earlier that during the course of the investigations on the biogenesis of methyl p-methoxycinnamate by *Lentinus lepideus*, p-hydroxyphenylpyruvic acid was detected in the culture medium. [31] The structural relationship of this acid to the suggested building stones of lignin prompted an investigation of the possible role of this acid in the mechanism of lignification by growing sugar cane plants.

p-Hydroxyphenylpyruvic acid-$C^{14}OOH$ was incorporated into a growing sugar cane plant by employing essentially the same technique used with D-glucose and shikimic acid. [88] A comparison of the activity measurements of the introduced p-hydroxyphenylpyruvic acid, of the isolated lignin, and of barium carbonate obtained on combustion of the latter, revealed that most of the activity of the introduced acid was incorporated into the lignin. [103]

The radioactive lignin obtained was subjected to alkaline nitrobenzene oxidation and the vanillin formed was isolated, and, in this instance, was found to be non-radioactive. On the other hand, subjection of this lignin to alkaline fusion produced oxalic acid which was also isolated and found to contain the radioactivity. [1] It was concluded that the three-carbon side chain of the introduced p-hydroxyphenylpyruvic acid, which contained the radioactivity, was retained as a unit, possibly affording a connecting link between the several aromatic rings of the lignin polymer. [83, 105] Accordingly, it was concluded that p-hydroxyphenylpyruvic acid is an intermediate on the pathway between shikimic acid, derived from carbohydrates, and the lignin building stones, in the biogenesis of lignin by growing sugar cane plants. [85]

However, G. Billek [8] later reported that p-hydroxyphenylpyruvic acid was not converted into lignin by spruce trees. This apparent discrepancy was resolved by Neish [80] who noted that p-hydroxyphenylpyruvic acid-3-C^{14} can be converted to guaiacyl or syringyl lignin in wheat, but not in buckwheat or sage. This difference in biosynthetic abilities among different species was then interpreted [17] as follows: Neither p-hydroxyphenylpyruvic acid (XXX) nor p-hydroxyphenyllactic acid (XXXI) is a *general* intermediate in lignification, and differences noted (as here) between grasses and non-grasses probably result from the unique ability of grasses to convert p-hydroxyphenyllactic acid (XXXI) to p-hydroxycinnamic acid (XXXII). Since the sugar cane plants employed in the experiments described above are grasses, they *are* able to utilize p-hydroxyphenylpyruvic acid (XXX) for lignin biosynthesis, as has been emphasized. [20]

The direct precursor of the propyl side-chains of the phenylpropanoid-derived aromatic amino acids, phenylalanine and tyrosine, has been reported [75] to be phosphoenolpyruvic acid, which has also been proposed [115] as an intermediate in shikimic acid formation. While it would be of interest to determine whether phosphoenolpyruvate is similarly operative in lignin biogenesis, reported difficulties in the permeability of many phosphorylated compounds prompted the substitution of pyruvic acid.

Thus, uniformly labeled sodium pyruvate-C^{14} was incorporated into a birch sapling by forced feeding. After isolation of the "milled-wood" lignin, the distribution of radioactivity in the propyl side-chain of its building units was studied [21] by hydrogenation, hydrogenolysis and vapor phase chromatography. The results indicated that pyruvate was not a direct precursor of the propyl moieties of lignin. Rather, it appeared that the fate of the C^{14} derived from the incorporated radioactive pyruvate was varied, and that C-atoms which found their way into the propyl moieties of lignin did so predominantly by carbon dioxide fixation *via* the "dicarboxylate shuttle". [21]

E. *Conversions of the Lignin Building Stones*

As mentioned above, the hypothesis that lignin is biogenetically derived from coniferyl alcohol is suggested by the presence of the glucoside, coniferin, in precambial tissues. [121]

The structure of coniferin was clarified by F. Tiemann in 1875. Shortly thereafter, Tiemann and Mendelsohn [120] concluded that coniferyl alcohol, the aglucone of coniferin, bore a structural relationship to lignin. Then, in 1899, Klason [66] expressed the opinion that lignin is a condensation or polymerization product of coniferyl alcohol. Later, he suggested [68] that coniferyl aldehyde may be the fundamental building stone of lignin.

But the nature of the polymerization of such monomers remained obscure until Cousin and Hérissey [25] in 1908 found that isoeugenol would dimerize in the presence of air under the influence of the oxidase enzymes present in a glycerol extract of the mushroom *Russula delicia*. The product of the dimerization, dehydrodiisoeugenol, was found by Erdtman [33] to have the structure of a phenylcoumarane derivative.

This discovery led Erdtman to a concept for an explanation of the mechanism for the polymerization of monomers into lignin. He postulated [34] that *p*-hydroxyphenylpropane compounds, unsaturated in their side chains, on oxidation, would initiate coupling reactions, not only in the position *ortho* to the phenolic hydroxyl group, but also at the β-carbon atom of the side chain. Lignin might then originate from guaiacylpropane units which first become oxidized in the side-chain, and are then dehydrogenated. Erdtman concluded that lignin is very probably formed from precursors similar to coniferyl alcohol. [34] Following these suggestions, it has generally become accepted [36] that lignin is produced by the dehydrogenation of such compounds, with conifer lignin probably being formed mainly from coniferyl alcohol.

About 10 years later, these ideas were adopted by K. Freudenberg who then subjected them to experimental verification. Freudenberg found that D-coniferin, labeled with C^{14} in the side-chain, when incorporated into a spruce twig, was deposited in the stem in the form of a high-molecular product. [39] Ethanolysis of the latter yielded (radioactive) Hibbert ketones. In a similar experiment, L-coniferin remained unchanged. [47] This indicated that D-coniferin may be hydrolyzed by a β-glucosidase; the liberated coniferyl alcohol might then polymerize to lignin. Accordingly, Freudenberg suggested the following overall scheme of lignin formation:

$$\text{Coniferin} \xrightarrow{\beta\text{-glucosidase}} \text{Coniferyl Alcohol} \xrightarrow[\text{dehydrogenase}]{\text{phenol-}} \text{Lignin.}$$

Freudenberg then tried to obtain polymeric products with lignin-like properties by the *in vitro* treatment of so-called "primary lignin building stones" with air, in the presence of a mushroom oxidase. [49] Of the compounds tested, the dehydrogenation product of coniferyl alcohol (so-called DHP†) seemed to show some similarity to lignin. [40]

According to Freudenberg then, spruce lignin is some kind of a dehydrogenation polymer of coniferyl alcohol. By the action of enzymes, coniferyl alcohol is dehydrogenated, thereby forming reactive quinone-methide radicals. [40]

However, it has long been recognized [124] that quinone methides readily undergo polymerization.

Such radicals would then be able to combine in various ways, thereby forming a variety of carbon–carbon and carbon–oxygen–carbon linkages, which would seem typical for lignin.

Freudenberg then isolated from the reaction mixture, at an intermediary stage, three "secondary lignin building stones", viz., dehydrodiconiferyl

† This dehydrogenation product of coniferyl alcohol is referred to in the following as DHP.

alcohol (XXXIII), D,L-pinoresinol (XXXIV) and guaiacylglycerol-β-coni-feryl ether (XXXV).

These "secondary lignin building stones" [41] were condensible to the DHP polymer by subsequent treatment with dehydrogenating enzymes. Further-more, these building stones were reported to be found in cambial sap. [42] Accordingly, Freudenberg seems to feel that the final phases of lignin forma-tion are explainable [44] in terms of the oxidation and condensation of coniferyl alcohol by plant enzymes.

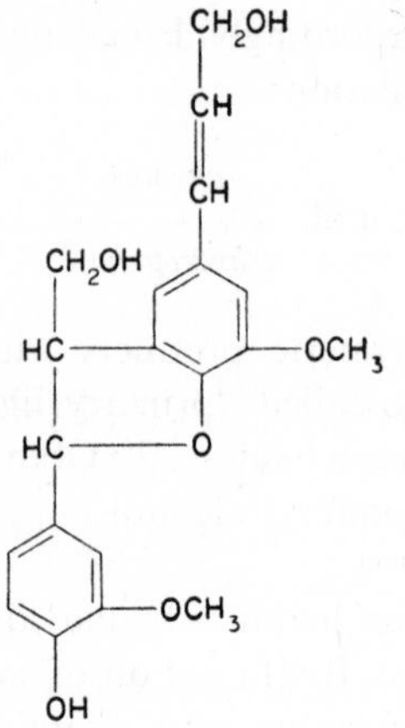

XXXIII

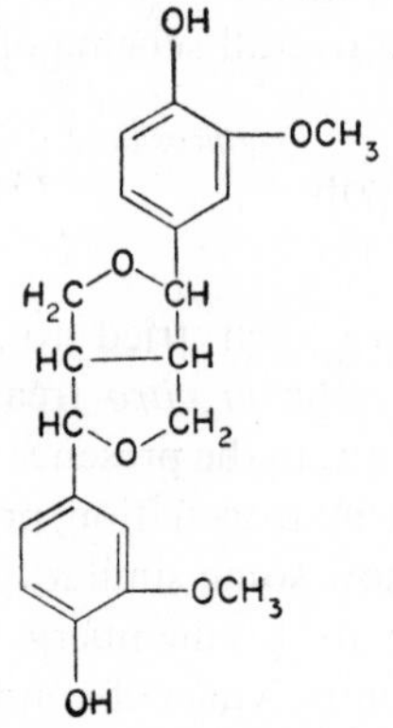

XXXIV

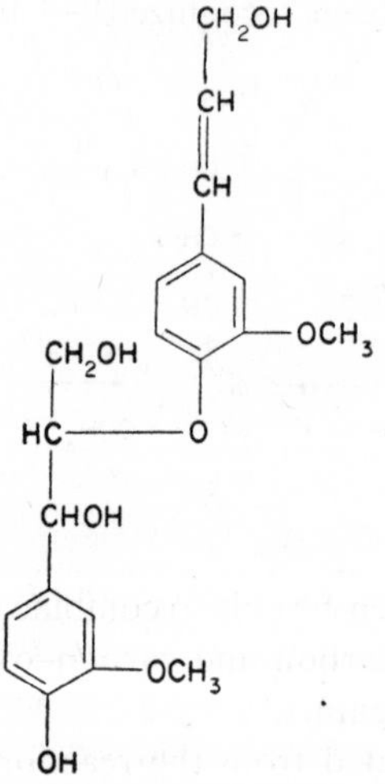

XXXV

Thus, the "dimeric intermediates" are phenol, which might also be enzymically dehydrogenated to form other radicals, which might combine together, or with the monomeric radicals. One such product would be the trimer guaiacylglycerol-β-pinoresinol ether. Freudenberg[46] claims to have identified several such trimers. After further dehydrogenation, the dimers might combine to form tetramers, as implied by the formation of bisdehydropinoresinol. Freudenberg[46] calls this process "progressive dehydrogenation".

However, many reservations and objections to these considerations have been raised in recent years. For example, since Nord and de Stevens found that the oxidation products of certain native and enzymically liberated lignins contain p-hydroxybenzaldehyde,[82, 29] they have concluded that coniferyl alcohol cannot be the *only* lignin precursor, or else, that it may be preceded in the process of lignification by some simpler, less substituted aromatic system.

In addition, H. Erdtman[35] has pointed out that, while in some respects Freudenberg's DHP's are similar to lignins, in other respects they are distinctly different. Aulin-Erdtman considers the ill-defined[4] DHP's mainly as "stabilization products" of quinone methides. She also indicates that it has not been demonstrated that the DHP's are really formed by further dehydrogenation of the dimeric dehydrogenation products of coniferyl alcohol. And while Freudenberg claims that these dimers are present in cambial sap, the sap had already been drawn from the tree, and consequently, these compounds may actually be non-physiological dehydrogenation products[35] or artifacts.

Further, Kremers[74] has asked whether the accumulation of coniferin is a part of the lignification process, or merely an incidental offshoot of some more general biochemical pathway? In this connection, it must be noted that numerous other substances, such as eugenol, ferulic acid and several related compounds, which may be lignin intermediates, but are at least in part structurally somewhat different from lignin itself, have been tested as lignin progenitors with some success.[116]

On the assumption that compounds which are believed to be intermediates in the formation of lignin should be present in the zone adjacent to the cambium of a tree in which lignin is being synthesized, Goldschmid and Hergert[52] initiated an examination of Western hemlock cambial constituents in an attempt to find such intermediates. Compounds identified in the cambium included quinic acid, shikimic acid, coniferin, sucrose, fructose, glucose, and certain depsides and glucosides. However, compounds proposed by Freudenberg as lignin intermediates, such as coniferyl alcohol, dehydrodiconiferyl alcohol and guaiacyl glycerol-β-coniferyl ether, were *not* found in the cambial zone.

Finally, Baylis[7] has correctly pointed out that while Freudenberg has obtained evidence for the transitory existence of quino-methide type compounds, he has not found direct evidence for the existence of his postulated free radical intermediates. Obviously, much still remains to be done in this area. For example, some of the more recent postulations of Freudenberg,

Lehmann and Sakakibara [50] regarding the mode of adduct formation had to be retracted and revised by Freudenberg and Friedmann. [48]

One of the principal aspects of the structure of lignin which requires elucidation is knowledge of the nature of the linkages which join the phenylpropane building stones together. Although a variety of reactions have been applied to lignin in an effort to degrade it to oligomeric units, the reactions employed are drastic, and destroy the linkages to be studied. Alternatively, the "depolymerization" of lignin might be accomplished enzymically, rather than chemically.

In such investigations, three "white rot" fungi, namely, *Fomes fomentarius*, *Poria subacida* and *Trametes pini* were found to form fifteen degradation products from the native and milled-wood lignins of pine and spruce woods. [60] Compounds identified included coniferaldehyde, *p*-hydroxycinnamaldehyde, ferulic acid, 3-methoxy-4-hydroxy phenylpyruvic acid, *p*-hydroxycinnamic acid, guaiacylglycerol and guaiacylglycerol-β-coniferyl ether. Thus, the existence of guaiacylglycerol-β-coniferyl ether as one of the dimeric building units of the lignins of pine and spruce woods is indicated. [60, 61]

To gain an understanding of the metabolism of these lignin degradation products by white-rot fungi, a study was made of the enzymic conversion by *Polyporus versicolor* and *Fomes fomentarius* of certain aromatic compounds structurally related to softwood lignin. As a result of these studies, a scheme [62] was evolved (Fig. 6) for the enzymic degradation of the guaiacyl lignin by white-rot fungi.

F. *The Enzymes Involved*

Parallel with the interest in the chemical structures of the precursors of lignin is the biochemical problem of the nature of the enzymes which convert these precursors into lignin. The biosynthetic pathways for the formation of aromatic compounds in plants have been actively investigated by tracer experiments using C^{14}-labeled compounds. It has been assumed that in plants the universally occurring aromatic amino acids are formed from carbohydrate by essentially the same pathway, "Davis' scheme of aromatic biosynthesis", as in microorganisms, and that other characteristic aromatic compounds such as lignin are derived by secondary reactions from the aromatic amino acids, or intermediates occurring in their biosynthesis. The enzymes involved in aromatic biosynthesis from non-aromatic compounds which are operative in microorganisms have recently been thoroughly reviewed. [81]

As mentioned above, Freudenberg [43] has suggested that coniferyl alcohol may be dehydrogenated by either a mushroom or cambial sap oxidoreductase, or by peroxidase with dilute hydrogen peroxide, to a polymer which has a lignin-like appearance.

T. Higuchi [59, 55] investigated the properties of a phenol oxidase responsible for lignification in the tissues of bamboo-shoots, and found that the enzyme had a substrate specificity similar to that of a laccase. Accordingly, he suggested that Freudenberg's enzyme is also probably a laccase.

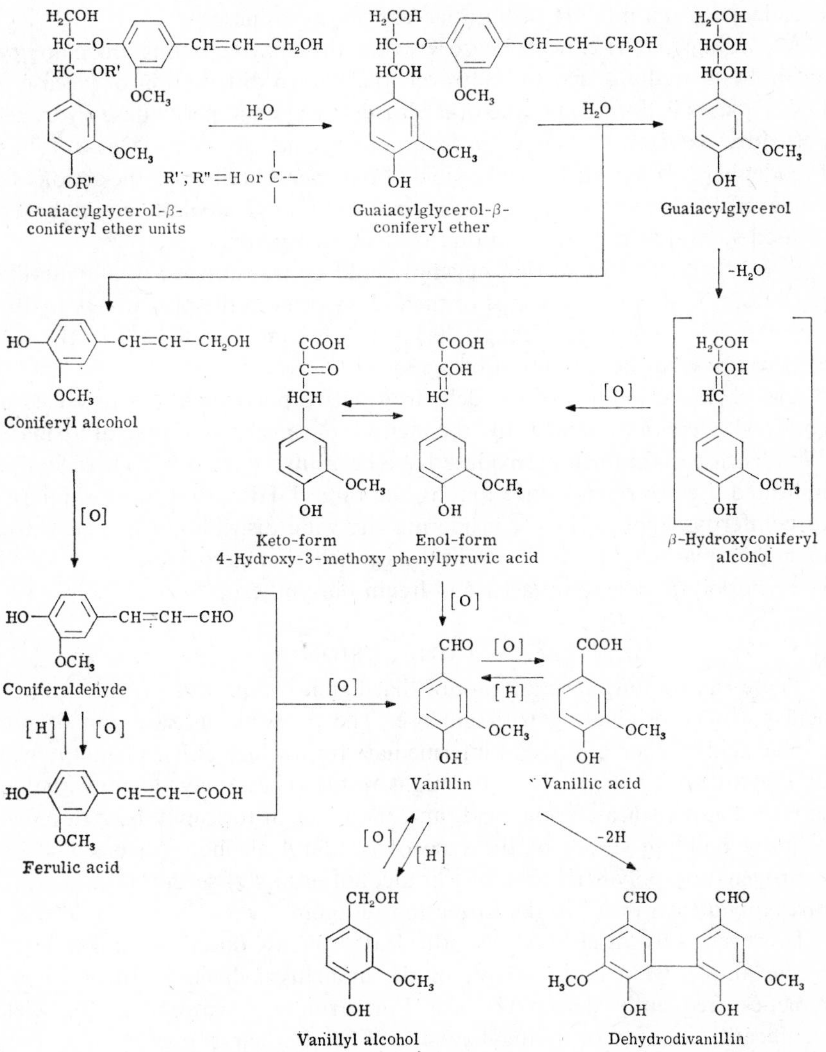

FIG. 6. A scheme for the enzymic degradation of the guaiacylglycerol-β-coniferyl ether units present in softwood lignin by white-rot fungi.

The oxidation of coniferyl alcohol by crude mushroom extracts has been confirmed, [76] but, with a purified mushroom polyphenol oxidase (tyrosinase), the oxygen consumption was negligible. Accordingly, it was concluded that, although there is present in crude mushroom extracts a heat-labile system which does catalyze the consumption of oxygen by coniferyl alcohol, it is not "polyphenol oxidase" which does this. Higuchi[57] has suggested that the enzyme obtained from mushroom according to the procedure used by Freudenberg is a mixture of both laccase and tyrosinase.

Accordingly, it is now believed[57] that the enzyme acting on coniferyl alcohol is actually a laccase. However, the known distribution of laccase in higher plants is limited. On the other hand, the system, peroxidase-hydrogen peroxide, oxidizes the same types of compounds as does laccase. Thus, Freudenberg[49] reported that the yield of polymer, obtained by the action of a crude enzyme from *Araucaria excelsa* on coniferyl alcohol, could be increased several fold by the addition of hydrogen peroxide.

S. M. Siegel[111] found that eugenol could be transformed to a lignin-like product by embryonic root tips of the kidney bean in the presence of hydrogen peroxide, and he accordingly has attached some significance to the role of peroxidase in the formation of lignin.

The chemical natures of the dehydrogenative polymerization products of coniferyl alcohol obtained by the action of mushroom phenol oxidase, *Rhus* laccase and radish peroxidase have been investigated.[56] These studies indicated a close resemblance among the three DHP's, and some similarity to coniferous lignin. Thus, considering the wide distribution of peroxidase in higher plants, Higuchi[57, 56] has suggested that peroxidase may play a more important role than laccase in lignin biosynthesis.

IV. CONCLUSION

There can no longer be any doubt that lignin is a product of the shikimic acid pathway originating with glucose. The probable intervention of prephenic acid[98] then affords an intermediate from which either phenylpyruvic or p-hydroxyphenylpyruvic acids might result. These may be converted to intermediates such as ferulic acid, and the latter in turn may be reduced to primary building stones of the type of coniferyl alcohol. An enzymic dehydrogenation-polymerization of this alcohol or any of several related structures might then result in the formation of lignin.

However, this brief analysis still leaves many questions unanswered. For example, what is the source of the unmethyoxylated p-hydroxyphenyl moieties frequently detected?[82, 29] Furthermore, hardwood lignins yield significant amounts of syringyl nuclei. What is their source? It has been suggested[18] that the required methylation of guaiacyl nuclei can occur through the intervention of methionine, but this is surely not the only possible explanation.

And lastly, it cannot be overlooked that the precise number and nature of the primary and secondary building stones of lignin are still not known with certainty, and this is definitely also true of the structure of the final product itself.

REFERENCES

1. ACERBO, S. N., SCHUBERT, W. J. and NORD, F. F *J. Am. Chem. Soc.* **80**, 1990 (1958).
2. ACERBO, S. N., SCHUBERT, W. J. and NORD, F. F. *J. Am. Chem. Soc.* **82**, 735 (1960).
3. ADLER, E. *Tappi* **40**, 294 (1957).
4. AULIN-ERDTMAN, G. and HEGBOM, L. *Svensk Papperstidn.* **59**, 363 (1956).
5. BASSETT, E. W. and TANENBAUM, S. W. *Biochim. Biophys. Acta* **28**, 247 (1958).
6. BATE-SMITH, E. C. *Scientific Proceedings, Royal Soc. of Dublin* **27**, 165 (1956).
7. BAYLIS, P. E. T. *Science Progress* **48**, 409 (1960).
8. BILLEK, G. In *Proceedings of the Fourth Internatl. Congr. of Biochemistry*, vol. II, p. 207. *Biochemistry of Wood*. Pergamon Press, London, 1959.
9. BIRKINSHAW, J. H. and FINDLAY, W. P. K. *Biochem. J.* **34**, 82 (1940).
10. BRAUNS, F. E. In *The Chemistry of Lignin*. Academic Press, Inc., New York, 1952.
10a *Ibid.*, p. 15.
11. *Ibid.*, p. 669.
12. *Ibid.*, p. 694.
13. BRAUNS, F. E. and BRAUNS, D. A. In *The Chemistry of Lignin Supplement Volume*. Academic Press, Inc., New York, 1960.
14. BROWN, S. A. *Science* **134**, 305 (1961).
15. BROWN, S. A. and NEISH, A. C. *Can. J. Biochem. Physiol.* **33**, 948 (1955).
16. BROWN, S. A., TANNER, K. G. and STONE, J. E. *Can. J. Chem.* **31**, 755 (1953).
17. BROWN, S. A., WRIGHT, D. and NEISH, A. C. *Can. J. Biochem. Physiol.* **37**, 25 (1959).
18. BYERRUM, R. V., FLOKSTRA, J. M., DEWEY, L. J. and BALL, C. D. *J. Biol. Chem.* **210**, 633 (1954).
19. CALVIN, M. In *Horizons in Biochemistry*, eds. Kasha and Pullman, p. 23. Academic Press, New York, 1962.
20. COSCIA, C. J. *Experientia* **16**, 81 (1960).
21. COSCIA, C. J., RAMIREZ, M. I., SCHUBERT, W. J. and NORD, F. F. *Biochemistry* **1**, 447 (1962).
22. COSCIA, C. J., SCHUBERT, W. J. and NORD, F. F. *J. Org. Chem.* **26**, 5085 (1961).
23. COSCIA, C. J., SCHUBERT, W. J. and NORD, F. F. *Tappi* **44**, 360 (1961).
24. COULSON, C. B. and EVANS, W. C. *Chem. and Ind., London* **1959**, 543.
25. COUSIN, H. and HÉRISSÉY, H. *Compt. Rend.* **147**, 247 (1908); *J. Pharm. Chim.* (6) **28**, 193 (1908).
26. DAVIS, B. D. *Experientia* **6**, 41 (1950).
27. DAVIS, B. D. *Advances in Enzymol.* **16**, 247 (1955).
28. DAVIS, B. D. *Arch. Biochem. Biophys.* **78**, 497 (1958).
29. DE STEVENS, G. and NORD, F. F. *Proc. Natl. Acad. Sci. U.S.* **39**, 80 (1953).
30. EBERHARDT, G. *J. Am. Chem. Soc.* **78**, 2832 (1956).
31. EBERHARDT, G. and NORD, F. F. *Arch. Biochem. Biophys.* **55**, 578 (1955).
32. EBERHARDT, G. and SCHUBERT, W. J. *J. Am. Chem. Soc.* **78**, 2835 (1956).
33. ERDTMAN, H. *Biochem. Z.* **258**, 172 (1933); *Ann.* **503**, 283 (1933).
34. ERDTMAN, H. *Svensk Papperstidn.* **42**, 115 (1939); *ibid.* **44**, 249 (1941); *Research, London* **3**, 63 (1950); ERDTMAN, H. and WACHTMEISTER, C. A. In *Festschr. A. Stoll*, p. 145. Birkhäuser Verlag, Basel, 1957.
35. ERDTMAN, H. *Ind. Eng. Chem.* **49**, 1385 (1957).
36. ERDTMAN, H. In *Proceedings of the Fourth Internatl. Congr. of Biochem.*, vol. II, p. 10. *Biochemistry of Wood*. Pergamon Press, London, 1959.
37. EVANS, W. C. In *Encyclopedia of Plant Physiology*, vol. X, p. 454. Springer-Verlag, Berlin, 1958.
38. EYKMAN, J. F. *Berichte* **24**, 1278 (1891).
39. FREUDENBERG, K. *Holz als Roh- u. Werkstoff* **11**, 267 (1953).
40. FREUDENBERG, K. *Fortschr. Chem. Org. Naturstoffe* **11**, 43 (1954).
41. FREUDENBERG, K. *J. Polymer Sci.* **16**, 155 (1955).
42. FREUDENBERG, K. *Angew. Chem.* **68**, 84 (1956).
43. FREUDENBERG, K. *Angew. Chem.* **68**, 508 (1956).

44. FREUDENBERG, K. *Ind. Eng. Chem.* **49**, 1384 (1957).
45. FREUDENBERG, K. *See* COSCIA, C. J. *Experientia* **16**, 81 (1960), ref. 20.
46. FREUDENBERG, K. In *Formation of Wood in Forest Trees*, ed. M. H. Zimmermann, p. 203. Academic Press, New York, 1964.
47. FREUDENBERG, K. and BITTNER, F. *Ber.* **86**, 155 (1953).
48. FREUDENBERG, K. and FRIEDMANN, M. *Ber.* **93**, 2138 (1960).
49. FREUDENBERG, K., KRAFT, R. and HEIMBERGER, W. *Ber.* **84**, 472 (1951); FREUDENBERG, K., REZNIK, H., BOESENBERG, H. and RASENACK, D. *Ibid.* **85**, 641 (1952).
50. FREUDENBERG, K., LEHMANN, B. and SAKAKIBARA, A. *Ber.* **93**, 1354 (1960); *Ann.* **623**, 129 (1959).
51. GIBSON, F. and JACKMAN, L. M. *Nature* **198**, 388 (1963).
52. GOLDSCMID, O. and HERGERT, H. L. *Tappi* **44**, 858 (1961).
53. HARTT, C. E. and BURR, G. O. *Proc. Internatl. Bot. Congr. Stockholm*, 1950, **7**, 748 (1953).
54. HASEGAWA, M., NAKAGAWA, T. and YOSHIDA, S. *J. Japan. Forestry Soc.* **39**, 159 (1957).
55. HIGUCHI, T. *Plant Physiol.* **10**, 364 (1957).
56. HIGUCHI, T. *J. Biochem.* **45**, 575 (1958).
57. HIGUCHI, T. In *Proceedings of the Fourth Internatl. Congr. of Biochem.*, vol. II, p. 161. *Biochemistry of Wood.* Pergamon Press, London, 1959.
58. HIGUCHI, T. and KAWAMURA, I. In *Modern Methods of Plant Analysis*, eds. M. F. Linskens, B. D. Sanwal and M. V. Tracey, vol. VII, p. 260. Springer-Verlag, Berlin, 1964.
59. HIGUCHI, T., KAWAMURA, I. and ISHIKAWA, H. *J. Japan. Forest Soc.* **35**, 258 (1953); HIGUCHI, T., KAWAMURA, T. and MORIMOTO, I. *Ibid.* **37**, 446 (1955).
60. ISHIKAWA, H., SCHUBERT, W. J. and NORD, F. F. *Life Sciences* **1**, 365 (1962).
61. ISHIKAWA, H., SCHUBERT, W. J. and NORD, F. F. *Arch. Biochem. B iophys.* **100**, 131 (1963).
62. *Ibid.* **100**, 140 (1963).
63. *Idem, Biochem. Z.* **338**, 153 (1963).
64. KATAGIRI, M. *J. Biochem.* **40**, 629 (1953).
65. KATAGIRI, M. and SATO, R. *Science* **118**, 250 (1953).
66. KLASON, P. *Svensk Kem. Tidskr.* **9**, 133 (1899).
67. KLASON, P. *Arkiv. Kemi Mineral. Geol.* **6**, No. 15 (1917).
68. KLASON, P. *Ber.* **B53**, 706 (1920).
69. KRATZL, K. and BILLEK, G. *Tappi* **40**, 269 (1957).
70. KRATZL, K. and FAIGLE, H. *Monatsh. Chem.* **90**, 768 (1959).
71. KRATZL, K. and FAIGLE, H. *Z. Naturforsch.* **15b**, 4 (1960).
72. KRATZL, K. and ZAUNER, J. *Holzforschung u. Holzverwertung* **14**, 108 (1962).
73. KREMERS, R. E. *Tappi* **40**, 262 (1957).
74. KREMERS, R. E. *Ann. Rev. Plant Physiol.* **10**, 185 (1959).
74a. KÜRSCHNER, K. *Chemie des Holzes.* Verlag Herbert Cram, Berlin, 1966.
75. LEVIN, J. G. and SPRINSON, D. B. *Biochem. Biophys. Research Communs.* **3**, 157 (1960).
76. MASON, H. S. and CRONYN, M. *J. Am. Chem. Soc.* **77**, 491 (1955).
77. MITSUHASHI, S. and DAVIS, B. D. *Biochim. Biophys. Acta* **15**, 54 (1954).
78. MOSES, V. and CALVIN, M. *Arch. Biochem. Biophys.* **78**, 598 (1958).
79. NEISH, A. C. *Ann. Rev. Plant Physiol.* **11**, 55 (1960); *idem* in *The Formation of Wood in Forest Trees*, ed. M. H. Zimmerman, p. 219. Academic Press, New York, 1964.
80. NEISH, A. C. In the Discussion of the paper of G. Billek (8), *loc. cit.*, p. 213.
81. NORD, F. F. *Geochim. et Cosmochim. Acta* **28**, 1507 (1964); *Tappi* **47**, 624 (1964).
82. NORD, F. F. and DE STEVENS, G. In *Handbuch d. Pflanzenphysiol.* X, 389 (1958).
83. NORD, F. F. and SCHUBERT, W. J. *Tappi* **40**, 285 (1957).
84. NORD, F. F. and SCHUBERT, W. J. *Experientia* **15**, 245 (1959).
85. NORD, F. F. and SCHUBERT, W. J. In *Proceedings of the Fourth Internatl. Congr. of Biochem.*, vol. II, p. 189. *Biochemistry of Wood.* Pergamon Press, London, 1959.
86. NORD, F. F. and SCHUBERT, W. J. *Holzforschung* **15**, 1 (1961).
87. NORD, F. F. and SCHUBERT, W. J. In Mason's *Comparative Biochemistry*, vol. IV, p. 65. Academic Press, New York, 1962.

88. NORD, F. F., SCHUBERT, W. J. and ACERBO, S. N. *Naturwiss.* **44**, 35 (1957).
89. NORD, F. F., SCHUBERT, W. J. and OLCAY, A. In *Chemistry of Natural and Synthetic Colouring Matters*, p. 413. Academic Press, New York, 1962.
90. NORD, F. F. and VITUCCI, J. C. *Arch. Biochem.* **14**, 243 (1947).
91. NORD, F. F. and VITUCCI, J. C. *Arch. Biochem.* **15**, 465 (1947).
92. NORD, F. F. and VITUCCI, J. C. *Advances in Enzymol.* **8**, 253 (1948).
93. OLCAY, A. *J. Org. Chem.* **27**, 1783 (1962).
94. OLCAY, A. *Holzforschung* **17**, 105 (1963).
95. PACLT, J. *Biologia* (Lahore) **6**, 137 (1960).
96. PEPPER, J. M. *Tappi* **42**, 793 (1959).
97. PHILLIPS, M. and GOSS, M. J. *J. Agr. Res.* **51**, 301 (1935).
98. PLIENINGER, H. *Angew. Chem.* **74**, 423 (1962).
99. RASSOW, B. and ZSCHENDERLEIN, A. *Z. Angew. Chem.* **34**, 204 (1921).
100. SCHIMMEL & Co., German Patent No. 693350 (1940). U.S. Patent No. 2187366 (1940).
101. SCHUBERT, W. J. In *Methods in Enzymology*, vol. V, p. 402. Academic Press, N.Y., 1961.
102. SCHUBERT, W. J. and ACERBO, S. N. *Arch. Biochem. Biophys.* **83**, 178 (1959).
103. SCHUBERT, W. J., ACERBO, S. N. and NORD, F. F. *J. Am. Chem. Soc.* **79**, 251 (1957).
104. SCHUBERT, W. J. and NORD, F. F. *Advances in Enzymol.* **18**, 349 (1957).
105. SCHUBERT, W. J. and NORD, F. F. *Ind. Eng. Chem.* **49**, 1387 (1957).
106. SCHUBERT, W. J. and NORD, F. F. *Tappi* **44**, 355 (1961).
107. SHIMAZONO, H. *Arch. Biochem. Biophys.* **83**, 206 (1959).
108. SHIMAZONO, H. and NORD, F. F. *Arch. Biochem. Biophys.* **78**, 263 (1958).
109. SHIMAZONO, H. and NORD, F. F. *Arch. Biochem. Biophys.* **87**, 140 (1960).
110. SHIMAZONO, H., SCHUBERT, W. J. and NORD, F. F. *J. Am. Chem. Soc.* **80**, 1992 (1958).
111. SIEGEL, S. M. *Physiol. Plantarum* **6**, 134 (1953); *ibid.* **7**, 41 (1954); **8**, 20 (1955); *J. Am. Chem. Soc.* **78**, 1753 (1956); *Quart. Rev. Biol.* **31**, 1 (1956).
112. SPRINSON, D. B. *Adv. Carbohydrate Chem.* **15**, 235 (1960).
113. SRERE, P. A., COOPER, J. R., KLYBAS, V. and RACKER, E. *Arch. Biochem. Biophys.* **59**, 535 (1955).
114. SRINIVASAN, P. R., SHIGEURA, M. T., SPRECHER, M., SPRINSON, D. B. and DAVIS, B. D. *J. Biol. Chem.* **220**, 477 (1956).
115. SRINIVASAN, P. R. and SPRINSON, D. B. *J. Biol. Chem.* **234**, 716 (1959).
116. STAFFORD, H. A. *Plant Physiol.* **35**, 108, 612 (1960).
117. STONE, J. E. *Can. J. Chem.* **31**, 207 (1953).
118. STONE, J. E., BLUNDELL, M. J. and TANNER, K. G. *Can. J. Chem.* **29**, 734 (1951).
119. TATUM, E. L., GROSS, S. R., EHRENSVAERD, G. and GARNJOBST, L. *Proc. Natl. Acad. Sci. U.S.* **40**, 271 (1954).
120. TIEMANN, F. and MENDELSOHN, B. *Ber.* **8**, 1127, 1136, 1139 (1875).
121. VON WACEK, A., HÄRTEL, O. and MERALLA, S. *Holzforschung* **7**, 58 (1953); *ibid.* **8**, 65 (1954).
122. WARDROP, A. B. *Tappi* **40**, 225 (1957).
123. WISLICENUS, H. *Kolloid Z.* **27**, 209 (1920).
124. ZINCKE, T. and HAHN, O. *Liebig's Ann. Chem.* **329**, 1 (1903).

ADDENDUM

The following publications could not be dealt with in this report:

NORD, F. F. Biochemistry of Lignin. *Buletinul Institutului Politehnic, Din Iasi*, Serie Noua XI (XV), Fasc. spec. 35 (1965).

REALE, M. J. Fast Determination of Aromatic Aldehydes. *Anal. Biochem.* **13**, 162 (1965).

HATA, K., SCHUBERT, W. J. and NORD, F. F. Fungal Degradation of the Lignin and Phenolic Acids of the Bark of Western Pine. *Arch. Biochem. Biophys.* **113**, 250 (1966).

REALE, M. J., CLARKE, D. D., SCHUBERT, W. J. and NORD, F. F. Investigations on Lignins and Lignification. XXXI. Characterization of Metasequoia "Milled-Wood" Lignin. *Holzforschg.* **20**, 31 (1966).

NORD, F. F. and HATA, K. Fungal Degradation of Pine Bark Lignin. Lignin Series XXXII. In *Current Aspects of Biochemical Energetics*—Fritz Lipmann Dedicatory volume (eds. N. O. Kaplan and E. P. Kennedy), p. 315. Academic Press, New York, 1966.

HATA, K. Investigations on Lignins and Lignification. XXXIII. Studies on Lignins Isolated from Spruce Wood Decayed by *Poria subacida B11*. *Holzforschg.* **20**, No. 5 (1966).

NORD, F. F. Biochemistry of Lignin (Symposium: Wood and Organisms, Berlin, 1965). *Materials and Organisms* **1**, Sept. 1966.

TROJANOWSKI, J., LEONOWICZ, A. and HAMPEL, B. Exoenzymes in Fungi Degrading Lignin. II. Demethoxylation of lignin and vanillic acid. *Acta Microbiol. Polonica* **15**, 17 (1966).

CHAPTER 16

RUBBER BIOGENESIS

JAMES BONNER

Division of Biology, California Institute of Technology,
Pasadena, California

CONTENTS

I. NATURAL DISTRIBUTION OF RUBBER   941
II. LATEX   942
III. STRUCTURE OF RUBBER   942
IV. ACETATE AS THE PRECURSOR OF RUBBER   943
V. NATURE AND GENESIS OF THE ISOPRENOID MONOMER   943
VI. POLYMERIZATION OF THE ISOPRENOID MONOMER TO RUBBER   948
VII. STERIC CONSIDERATIONS   949
VIII. FURTHER PROBLEMS   949
REFERENCES   951

THE path of carbon in the biogenesis of rubber and of other isoprenoids has been among the last of the major biosynthetic pathways to be elucidated. All of our information concerning isoprenoid biogenesis has been obtained in the years since 1949, most of it since 1956. We are today, however, able to plot out in detail not only the course of the biogenesis of rubber but also the courses of the related pathways which lead to terpenes, carotenoids, steroids, and indeed of all isoprenoid materials.

I. NATURAL DISTRIBUTION OF RUBBER

Every species of higher plant possesses, so far as we know today, the ability to make several kinds of isoprenoids. These widely distributed isoprenoids include carotenoids, steroids, and the exotic long-chain alcohols which form the tails of the electron-transporting ubiquinones and of phytol. Ability to produce the polyterpene rubber is, however, scattered in a random fashion through the plant kingdom and is possessed by only about 2000 species of the 400,000 species or so of higher plants. [15] Rubber formation is not known to occur in any monocotyledonous plant nor in any gymnosperm, but is confined to the dicotyledonous branch of the higher plants, including particularly the families Moraceae, to which *Ficus elastica*, the rubber plant belongs; the Euphorbiaceae, to which *Hevea brasiliensis*, the rubber tree of commerce belongs; the Apocynaceac, the Asclepiadaceae and the Compositae which includes the guayule, *Parthenium argentatum*, and *Taracacum kok saghyz*, the Russian dandelion. Gutta which, like rubber, is a polyisoprenoid, is produced by a small number of tropical species, including *Palaquium gutta* and *Mimusops balata*. Chicle, a mixture of gutta and triterpene alcohols, is produced principally by the tropical tree *Achras sapota*.

II. LATEX

Rubber is in general produced in the plant in the form of microscopic particles contained in the protoplasm of specialized cells—the latex cells, or vessels. Since latex represents and is protoplasm, it contains in addition to rubber and proteins, a great mixture of low molecular weight metabolites as well as nucleic acid and other materials. Rubber is present in only low concentration in the latex of most rubber-bearing plants. Its concentration in latex may, however, attain the extraordinarily high value of 30 per cent as in the case of *Hevea brasiliensis*. The proteins of the latex include, as will be shown below, the enzymes responsible for rubber synthesis.

In *Hevea brasiliensis* and in many other latex-producing species, the latex vessels, which are contained in the bark, are interconnected into an anastomosing continuous system. When an opening into this system is made, as for example by a tapping cut, latex is exuded through the open vessels because of the hydrostatic pressure of the vessel contents. Latex flows from such a tapping cut for minutes or hours, depending upon the species involved, after which coagulation of the latex takes place, probably in general due to the activity of the microorganisms. Once latex flow has stopped, the latex vessel again takes up water, and in some species, as in *Hevea brasiliensis*, rubber is again synthesized. The important and characteristic feature of *Hevea brasiliensis* which differentiates it from all other rubber plants is the rapid regeneration of rubber in the latex vessel after tapping. [15] In general, the rubber tree may be tapped on alternate days throughout most of its life, yielding a constant or increasing amount of rubber over the course of 30 or more years.

III. STRUCTURE OF RUBBER

Rubber and the related gutta are merely polyterpenes in which isoprene residues are linked together through 1,4 linkages. The resultant chains are of the order of 500 to 5000 residues long in the case of rubber, and of the order of 100 residues long in the case of gutta. [13] The double bonds of the individual isoprenoid units are all of *cis* configuration in rubber, all of *trans* configuration in gutta. No hybrid molecules containing both *cis* and *trans* double bonds are detectable in either rubber or gutta. [22] Strangely enough, there is at present no knowledge of the end-groups of the polyisoprenoid chains of rubber.

IV. ACETATE AS THE PRECURSOR OF RUBBER

The cornerstone of our present knowledge concerning the biogenesis of rubber, and indeed of all isoprenoids, is the fact that all carbon atoms of rubber are derived from acetate. [12, 14] The evidence consists in part of the fact that when rubber-producing plants are supplied with large amounts of uniformly C^{14}-labeled acetate, the acetate carbon is not only preferentially deposited in rubber, but in addition the carbon of the rubber formed possesses a specific radioactivity equal to that of the acetate supplied. [6, 12] It is clear, therefore, that the carbon atoms of acetate are transformed without great dilution into the carbon atoms of rubber. That acetate is also the source of carbon for that other great group of isoprenoids, the sterols, was first demonstrated by Bloch [11] for the case of cholesterol and by Ottke et al. [39] for ergosterol synthesis by the fungus Neurospora, and in fact it is now clear that acetate serves as a source of carbon in the biosynthesis of all isoprenoids.

The early work on rubber biosynthesis was carried on with the guayule, Parthenium argentatum. It is now clear, however, that acetate forms the basic precursor for rubber biosynthesis in all rubber plants. Thus, acetate carbon is rapidly converted to rubber in vivo, by the Russian dandelion, Kok saghyz, [40] by Hevea, [52, 40] and in fact by all rubber-producing plants yet tested—19 in all. [51]

V. NATURE AND GENESIS OF THE ISOPRENOID MONOMER

The principal task of rubber biochemistry has been to determine the nature of the isoprenoid monomer and the path by which this monomer is synthesized in the plant from the carbon atoms of acetate. Bloch [11] first established the positions occupied in the isoprenoid carbon skeleton by the carboxyl and methyl carbons of acetate, and all subsequent work has confirmed the validity of his initial observations (see Fig. 1).

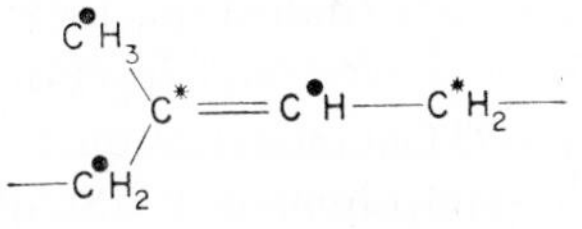

Fig. 1. Contribution of carboxyl (C*) and methyl (C•) carbons of acetate to isoprenoid carbon skeleton.

The 5 carbon isoprenoid monomer contains 2 carbon atoms derived from the carboxyl carbon of acetate and 3 carbon atoms derived from the methyl carbon of acetate. That this is true for rubber as for cholesterol, with which

Bloch[11] worked, has been shown by Teas et al.[52] and by Park and Bonner.[40] It is, however, a long jump from the 2 carbon acetate molecule to the 5 carbon isoprene molecule, one which must clearly involve condensation of 3 acetate molecules together with elimination of one carbon atom. The steps by which 3 acetate molecules are linked into branched chain structures involve the acyl transferring coenzyme, CoA, and elucidation of these steps required knowledge of CoA chemistry, the basis of which was laid by Lipmann.[29] That CoA functions as a carrier of active acetyl groups was established by Lynen et al.[34] The plant contains enzymes not only for the formation of active acetyl CoA[38] but for the conduct of two successive acetyl condensing reactions which, as shown in Fig. 2, result in the formation

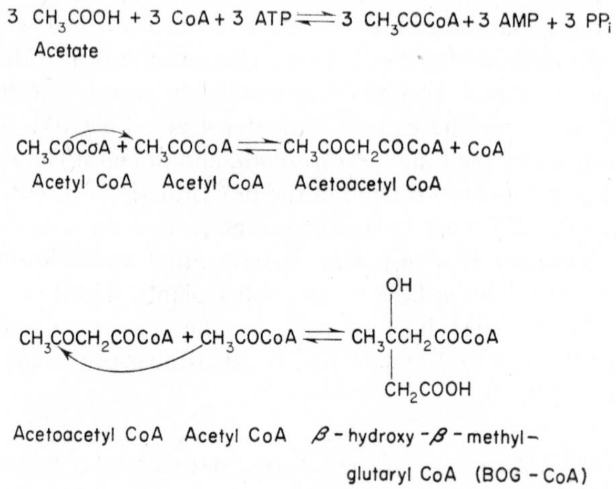

$$3 \ CH_3COOH + 3 \ CoA + 3 \ ATP \rightleftharpoons 3 \ CH_3COCoA + 3 \ AMP + 3 \ PP_i$$

Acetate

$$CH_3COCoA + CH_3COCoA \rightleftharpoons CH_3COCH_2COCoA + CoA$$

Acetyl CoA   Acetyl CoA   Acetoacetyl CoA

$$
CH_3COCH_2COCoA + CH_3COCoA \rightleftharpoons CH_3\underset{\underset{CH_2COOH}{|}}{\overset{\overset{OH}{|}}{C}}CH_2COCoA
$$

Acetoacetyl CoA   Acetyl CoA   β-hydroxy-β-methylglutaryl CoA (BOG – CoA)

FIG. 2. Formation of β-hydroxy-β-methylglutaryl CoA (BOG-CoA) from acetate.

first of acetoacetyl CoA[38] and by addition of a further acetyl moiety, of the 6 carbon, branched chain, β-hydroxy-β-methylglutaryl CoA.[25] The first two of these steps, acetate activation and acetoacetyl CoA formation are common to many pathways of acetate metabolism in addition to that leading to isoprenoids and have been studied in many organisms. Characterization of the acetate activating enzyme and reaction is due first to Lipmann et al.[30] and to Beinert et al.[10] Characterization of the acetoacetyl synthesizing reaction is due to Chow and Lipmann,[17] Stadtman et al.[46] and Lynen et al.[35] The step of β-methyl-β-hydroxyglutaryl (BOG) formation is the first in the series which is more nearly (although not entirely) unique to isoprenoid metabolism, and BOG-CoA is therefore a key intermediate in this process. BOG was first suspected as an intermediate in isoprenoid metabolism by a leaf enzyme preparation.[9] BOG was shortly thereafter isolated as a natural product from flax.[28] The enzymatic system responsible for condensation of acetyl CoA with acetoacetyl CoA to yield BOG-CoA has been characterized by Johnston *et al.* [25] for a plant system and for animal systems by Rabinowitz *et al.* [44] and by Bachhawat *et al.* [8] That the labeling in BOG is that expected by the formulation of the reaction as shown in Fig. 3 has been elegantly demonstrated by Rudney. [45]

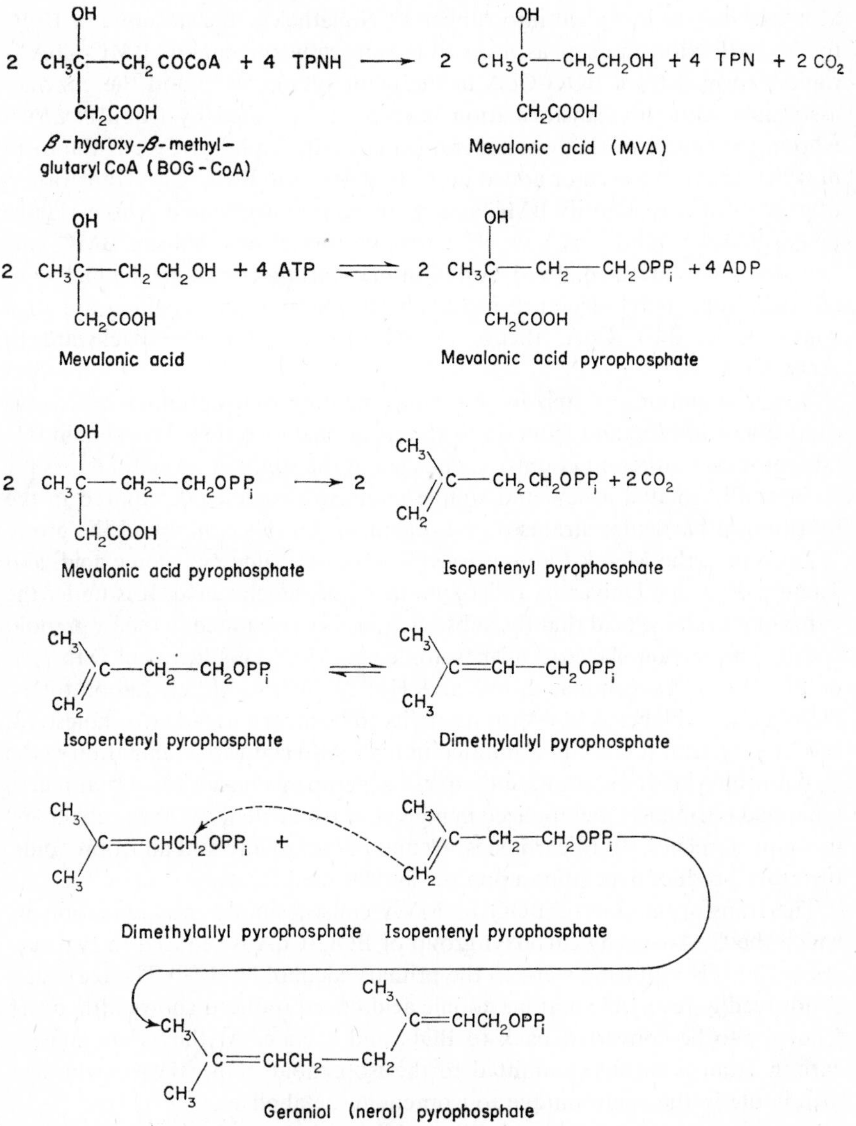

FIG. 3. Formation of geraniol (or nerol) pyrophosphate from β-hydroxy-β-methylglutaryl CoA.

It must now be noted that BOG-CoA is subject to further metabolism by 2 pathways of which one is that leading to isoprenoids while the other is that leading to β-methylcrotonyl (BMC) CoA with the elimination of CO_2. BMC, long known as a natural product under the name of senecioic acid, [7] possesses a 5 carbon skeleton identical to that of the isoprenoid unit, and, if supplied as a C^{14}-labeled material to a rubber-making plant, is incorporated although only in low yield into rubber. [6] Nonetheless, the structure of BMC focused attention upon it as a possible isoprenoid precursor. BMC-CoA is rapidly formed from BOG-CoA in the plant system, [6, 25] and the enzymes associated with the transformation have been separated by Coon et al. [18] who in the course of this work identified adenylphosphoryl CO_2 as the form in which CO_2 is released or added in the BOG-CoA to BMC-CoA transformation. All efforts to identify BMC as a participant in isoprenoid synthesis have failed, however, and it is now clear that in normal metabolism, BMC participates as an intermediate in oxidation of 5-carbon compounds which contain the isopentenyl structure including leucine and valine which are then converted to BMC-CoA, thence to BOG-CoA and thence backward to acetyl CoA.

The next important step in our understanding of isoprenoid biogenesis came about in 1956 and from quite an unexpected direction. Workers in two laboratories in different countries, engaged in the study of growth factors for lactobacilli, isolated a new and simple monocarboxylic acid required in the nutrition of particular strains of the organism. To this compound the group of Folkers at the Merck Laboratories [49] gave the name mevalonic acid, and Tamura [48] at the University of Tokyo the name, hiochic acid. It is under the name of mevalonic acid that the substance has become noted in the isoprenoid world. The carbon skeleton of mevalonic acid (MVA) is identical with that of BOG, and Tavormina, Gibbs and Huff [49] in the Merck Laboratories, therefore tested labeled MVA for its ability to be incorporated into cholesterol in a liver system. It is so incorporated in high yield and with elimination of the C_1 or carboxyl carbon atom. Subsequent experiments have shown that mevalonic acid is similarly metabolized in high yield to squalene, [2, 20] to rubber, [40] to simple terpenes, [47] to carotenes, [43] and in fact to any and all isoprenoids, the exact product depending upon the system used.

The transformations of BOG to MVA consist simply in a reduction by which the CoA-bearing carboxyl group of BOG-CoA is reduced in two successive TPNH requiring steps to the primary alcohol level. [21] The reduction is not readily reversible and mevalonic acid once produced shows little or no tendency to be converted back to BOG and acetate. At the MVA stage a carbon atom is firmly committed to the isoprenoid path. MVA is the first metabolite in the chain unique to isoprenoid metabolism.

It is now pertinent to consider the evidence that synthesis of rubber does in fact proceed from acetate through MVA and without randomization of the carbon atoms of MVA. The pertinent experiments are those of Park and Bonner [40] and of Kekwick et al., [27] using as the enzymatic system the latex of *Hevea*. To such latex MVA-2-C^{14} is supplied together with ATP which, as will be shown, is required as a source of energy. After a brief

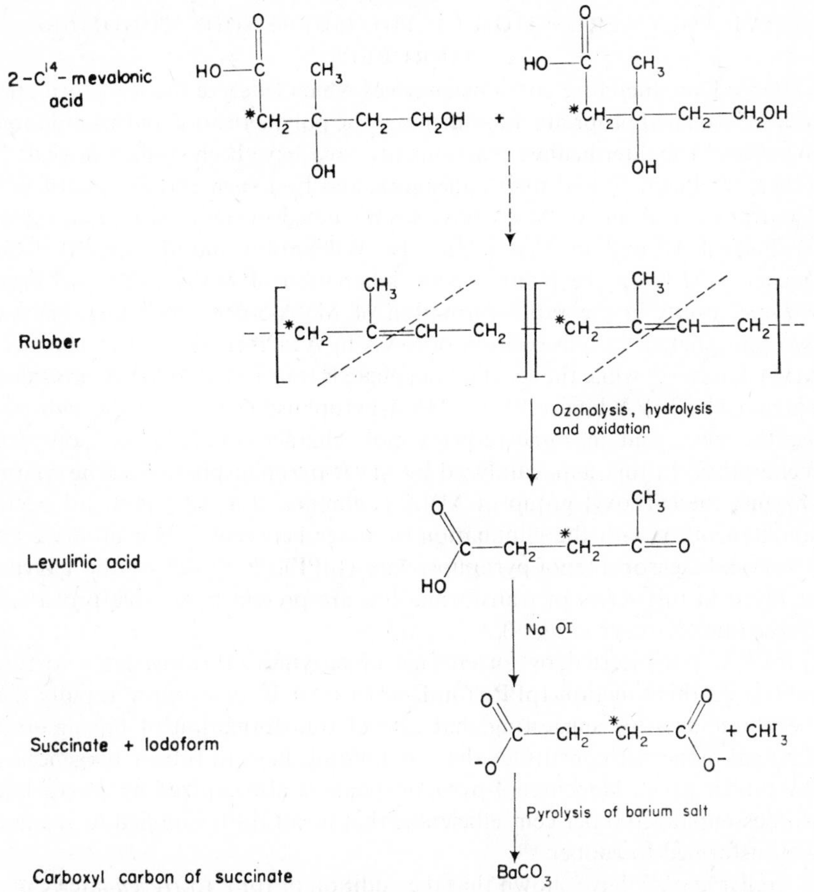

FIG. 4. The enzymatic synthesis and chemical degradation of rubber from latex incubated with 2-C^{14}-MVA. The labeled rubber is degraded by ozonolysis to yield labeled levulinic acid. The levulinic acid is degraded to iodoform (un-labeled) and succinate (labeled). The succinate is degraded by pyrolysis to yield its carboxyl groups as $BaCO_3$ (unlabeled). The label of 2-C^{14}-mevalonic acid is therefore transformed into rubber as expected on the basis of the above formulation. C* indicates C^{14} labeled carbon atom.

incubation period, the rubber enzymatically produced in the reaction mixture is isolated and degraded by reactions appropriate for the separate collection of the individual carbon atoms of the isoprene moiety. The results indicate that substantially all of the label of the C-2 atom of MVA is contained specifically in the 4 positions of the isoprene moieties of rubber. The MVA has therefore been incorporated without randomization and in a way consistent with that found for the incorporation of the label of acetate into rubber and into the carbon skeleton of BOG and MVA (see Fig. 4).

VI. POLYMERIZATION OF THE ISOPRENOID MONOMER TO RUBBER

Hevea latex therefore contains enzymes which catalyze the transformation of MVA to an appropriate monomer and the polymerization of this monomer to rubber. The intermediate reactions involved have been studied in yeast by Tchen, [50] Bloch [11] and their colleagues, and by Lynen and associates. [1, 23] The transformations of MVA have been studied in the higher plant system by Pollard, [41] and in *Hevea* latex by Williamson and Rockwith [54] and Archer *et al.* [5] In the plant system, incubation of MVA, ATP and crude enzyme results in the rapid formation of MVA-5-phosphate and MVA-5-pyrophosphate. Phosphorylation of MVA by ATP is catalyzed by the enzyme MVA-kinase [50] while the second phosphate is transferred to MVA-phosphate by phospho-MVA-kinase. [16, 23] MVA-pyrophosphate forms the substrate for the next, and in some respects most characteristic step of isoprenoid metabolism. In this step, catalyzed by MVA-pyrophosphate-decarboxylating enzyme, the carboxyl group of MVA is eliminated as CO_2 and this occurs simultaneously with the elimination of water between carbon atoms 2 and 3 to yield Δ^3-isopentenol-pyrophosphate (IpPP). [16, 32] All of the enzymes involved in this series of transformations are present as soluble proteins in *Hevea* latex (Archer *et al.* [5]).

IpPP is polymerized by an enzyme or enzymes of *Hevea* latex to form rubber. In this function IpPP is utilized at least 10 times more rapidly than mevalonic acid, [33] suggesting that rate of transformation of precursors to the final monomer constitutes the rate limiting steps in rubber biogenesis in the rubber plant. Isopentenol-pyrophosphate is also utilized by *Hevea* latex with essentially 100 per cent efficiency, that is, all IpPP supplied to the latex is transformed to rubber. [4]

Archer *et al.* [5] have shown that the addition of IpPP to *Hevea* latex causes only chain expansion of rubber molecules already present. Initiation of new chains results, however, when dimethylallyl pyrophosphate is added to the system. How does this polymerization proceed? The first step appears to be the production from IpPP of its isomer (by double bond shift), dimethylallyl-pyrophosphate and is accomplished by the enzyme IpPP-isomerase. [1] One molecule of dimethylallyl-pyrophosphate then serves as an acceptor for one molecule of IpPP with the elimination of pyrophosphate and the formation of one molecule of 10-carbon diisoprenoid-alcohol-pyrophosphate. In all probability this polymerization proceeds by loss by the dimethylallyl-pyrophosphate of its pyrophosphate group and temporary formation of an electron deficient species of dimethylallyl molecule which then attacks IpPP with resultant shift of the double bond of the latter. [19]

The further growth of the polyisoprene chain appears to involve merely the addition of further IpPP units. Thus, in yeast and liver the sesquiterpene alcohol pyrophosphate farnesol pyrophosphate is enzymatically produced from geraniol pyrophosphate. In the case of the plant systems studied by Pollard, [41] geraniol pyrophosphate, farnesol pyrophosphate, and a diterpene alcohol pyrophosphate containing 4 isoprenoid units are sequentially produced. The further polymerizations may be thought of as precisely analogous to the first. Thus, a 10-carbon unit, geraniol pyrophosphate for example, may attack a further molecule of IpPP, and we presume this mode of repeated stapling of an IpPP residue to the growing chain is the general mode of isoprenoid polymerization.

VII. STERIC CONSIDERATIONS

In the case of yeast and liver systems, the polymerization of IpPP to form the terpene-alcohol-pyrophosphates involves the production of the *trans* geraniol pyrophosphate as well as the *trans-trans* farnesol-pyrophosphate. In the case of the plant systems, studied by Pollard [41] and concerned with the production of carotene molecules, the polymerization involves exclusively the production of *trans* isomers. In the biogenesis of rubber, however, each new C_5 unit added must assume the *cis* configuration. The enzymatic polymerases thus far studied, other than that of rubber latex itself, would, if they proceeded to the level of polyisoprenoid production, produce gutta rather than rubber. The determination of the configuration of each C_5 unit as it is added to the growing terpene chain is presumably enzymatically determined. This determination is in turn made by the geometry of the proton shift which takes place as the new allyl double bond is produced. It depends only upon which of the two protons is transferred in the formation of this double bond. It will clearly be of interest to rigorously separate and characterize the enzymes responsible for the formation of *cis* and *trans* polymers. It will be of interest to discover in what way the enzyme which makes the *trans* geraniol-pyrophosphate, is different from that which makes the *cis* nerol-pyrophosphate.

VIII. FURTHER PROBLEMS

A further unsolved question concerning rubber biogenesis is how many polymerization enzymes are involved. Is the enzyme which adds IpPP to nerol-pyrophosphate identical with that which forms nerol-pyrophosphate from dimethylallyl-pyrophosphate and IpPP? And this same question must be asked concerning the formation of the higher oligo-isoprenoids. Does a single enzyme suffice for the polymerization of the entire rubber molecule or are there lower, middle, and higher chain length polymerases, or what?

2H

And finally, we wish to know what determines where chain growth stops. In yeast and liver it stops at three isopentenyl residues, farnesol-pyrophosphate; in the tomato at four residues, the 20-carbon precursor of carotenes, [43] in rubber only at many (500 to 5000) residues. Is cessation of chain growth associated with the absence of the enzyme for further chain growth? Is it due to the presence of an enzyme which specifically dephosphorylates or otherwise deactivates the growing chain when it reaches a specific length? Thus, there are still important and interesting problems of rubber biogenesis. But in main outline the path of carbon in rubber biogenesis may now be considered as solved.

Further important problems of rubber biosynthesis are, however, posed by the phenomena which accompany the regeneration of rubber in the latex vessel of *Hevea* after the cessation of rubber flow from a tapping cut. When an incision is made into the lactiferous system, rubber-containing latex gushes out. This latex contains not only rubber but, as indicated above, all of the enzymes required for the conversion of acetate to IpPP and rubber as well as mitochondria for the generation of the ATP needed in the mevalonic acid pathway. After the cessation of latex flow, rubber is again formed. *Hevea*, under tap on each second day, can continue to synthesize rubber at an undiminished rate for many years. It is clear, therefore, that the rubber synthesizing system must be reversed during the periods between tappings.

The synthesis of enzyme molecules requires that ribosomes be present in the latex. Their presence has been demonstrated by McMullen. [36, 37] The twenty amino acids which are also required are also present in latex, as is ATP synthesized presumably by the mitochondria of latex (Andrew and Dickenson [3]). The m-RNA required by the ribosomes for enzyme synthesis has not been demonstrated in latex.

The renewal in latex after a tapping cut of rubber-forming enzymes, of m-RNA, and of ribosomes, requires the activity of nuclei. These are not swept from the latex vessels during latex flow but remain appressed to the vessel walls. The nuclei are then ready to repopulate the vessel contents with ribosomes, m-RNA, and thence enzymes after the cessation of latex flow. In the genetic material of these nuclei we must envisage that most genes are repressed. The latex vessel has no need of those enzymes which are required for the specialized functions of leaves, roots, etc. Those genes concerned with the making of m-RNA, for the making of the enzymes of rubber synthesis must be derepressed, turned on. Similarly for the genes which have to do with the synthesis of the globulin which stabilizes rubber particles. An important aspect of keeping the latex vessel concentrated on the rubber-making task must consist in complete repression of those genes not concerned with this task.

And finally, as regeneration of the enzymes concerned in rubber synthesis proceeds in the latex vessel, and as more and more rubber is synthesized, a final new and interesting problem of molecular biology presents itself. The enzymes concerned with the accumulation of rubber must cease to exert themselves once the rubber concentration has reached the required and predetermined level. The genes concerned with the synthesis of the enzyme molecules concerned with rubber synthesis must also cease to exert themselves once the predetermined level of rubber concentration has been achieved. The very production of ribosomes by the nucleus must close else the latex would ultimately become a solid mass of ribosomes. The whole rubber-making process appears to be regulated by the concentration of rubber in the latex vessel. When this concentration is low, the production of enzymes for rubber synthesis and rubber synthesis itself proceed full tilt. As the rubber concentration in the vessel approaches the predetermined maximum level, all of the processes concerned with rubber-making slow down and stop. Here we see before our eyes the processes of genetic regulation and of regulation of enzyme activity at work. How is this regulation exerted in the latex vessel? How do the genes concerned with making the messenger RNAs for making the rubber-making enzymes sense and respond to rubber concentration in the latex vessel? These are today's interesting and important questions of rubber biochemistry.

REFERENCES

1. AGRANOFF, B., EGGERER, H., HENNING, U. and LYNEN, F. *J. Biol. Chem.* **235**, 326 (1960).
2. AMDUR, B., RILLING, H. and BLOCH, K. *J. Am. Chem. Soc.* **79**, 2646 (1957).
3. ANDREWS, E. H. and DICKENSON, P. B. *Proc. Nat. Rubber Res. Conference, Kuala Lumpur, 1960*, p. 756.
4. ARCHER, B. L., AYREY, G., COCKBAIN, F. G. and McSWEENEY, G. P. *Nature* **189**, 663 (1961).
5. ARCHER, B. L., AUDLEY, B. G., COCKBAIN, E. G. and McSWEENEY, G. P. *Biochem. J.* **89**, 565 (1963).
6. ARREGUIN, B., BONNER, J. and WOOD, B. J. *Arch. Biochem. Biophys.* **31**, 234 (1951).
7. ASAHINA, Y. *Arch. Pharm.* **251**, 355 (1915).
8. BACHHAWAT, B. K., ROBINSON, W. G. and COON, M. J. *J. Am. Chem. Soc.* **76**, 3098 (1954).
9. BANDURSKI, R., COYLE, T. and BONNER, J. *Biology* 1953. California Inst. Tech., p. 118.
10. BEINERT, H., GREEN, D. E., HELE, P., HIFT, H., von KORFF, R. W. and RAMAKRISHRAN, C. V. *J. Biol. Chem.* **203**, 35 (1953).
11. BLOCH, K. *Recent Progress in Hormone Research* **6**, 111 (1951).
12. BONNER, J. *J. Chem. Ed.* **26**, 628 (1949).
13. BONNER, J. In *Plant Biochemistry*, p. 27. Academic Press, New York, 1950.
14. BONNER, J. and ARREGUIN, B. *Arch. Biochem.* **21**, 109 (1949).
15. BONNER, J. and GALSTON, A. W. *Bot. Rev.* **13**, 543 (1947).
16. CHAYKIN, S., LAW, J., PHILLIPS, A., TCHEN, T. and BLOCH, K. *Proc. Natl. Acad. Sci. U.S.* **44**, 998 (1958).
17. CHOW, T. C. and LIPMANN, F. *J. Biol. Chem.* **196**, 89 (1952).
18. COON, M. J., ROBINSON, W. G. and BACHHAWAT, B. K. In *Amino Acid Metabolism*, p. 431. John Hopkins Press, 1955.
19. CORNFORTH, J. and POPJÁK, G. *Tetrahedron Letters* **19**, 23 (1959).
20. DITURI, F., RABINOWITZ, J., HULLIN, R. and GURIN, S. *J. Biol. Chem.* **229**, 825 (1957).
21. FERGUSON, J., DUER, I. and RUDNEY, H. *Proc. Natl. Acad. Sci. U.S.* **45**, 499 (1959).

22. HENDRICKS, S. B., WILDMAN, S. G. and JONES, E. J. *Arch. Biochem.* **7**, 427 (1945).
23. HENNING, U., MOSLEIN, E. M. and LYNEN, F. *Arch. Biochem. Biophys.* **83**, 259 (1959).
24. HOFFMAN, C. H., WAGNER, A. F., WILSON, A. N., WALTON, E., SHENCK, C. H., WOLF, D. E., HOLLY, F. W. and FOLKERS, K. *J. Am. Chem. Soc.* **79**, 2316 (1957).
25. JOHNSTON, J. A., RACUSEN, D. W. and BONNER, J. *Proc. Natl. Acad. Sci. U.S.* **40**, 1031 (1954).
26. KAPLAN, N. O. and LIPMANN, F. *J. Biol. Chem.* **174**, 37 (1948).
27. KEKWICK, R. G., ARCHER, B., BARNARD, D., HIGGINS, G., MCSWEENEY, G. and MOORE, C. *Nature* **184**, 268 (1959).
28. KLOSTERMANN, H. J. and SMITH, F. *J. Am. Chem. Soc.* **76**, 1229 (1954).
29. LIPMANN, F. *J. Biol. Chem.* **160**, 173 (1945).
30. LIPMANN, F., JAMES, M. E., BLACK, S. and FLYNN, K. *J. Am. Chem. Soc.* **74**, 2384 (1952).
31. LYNEN, F., AGRANOFF, B. W., EGGERER, H., HENNING, U. and MOSLEIN, E. M. *Angew. Chem.* **71**, 657 (1959).
32. LYNEN, F., EGGERER, H., HENNING, J. and KESSEL, I. *Angew. Chem.* **70**, 738 (1958).
33. LYNEN, F. and HENNING, U. *Angew. Chem.* **72**, 820 (1960).
34. LYNEN, F., REICHART, E. and RUEFF, L. *Ann.* **574**, 1 (1951).
35. LYNEN, F., WESSELY, L., WIELAND, O. and RUEFF, L. *Angew. Chem.* **64**, 687 (1952).
36. MCMULLEN, A. I. *Biochim. Biophys. Acta* **41**, 314 (1960).
37. MCMULLEN, A. I. *Biochem. J.* **85**, 491 (1962).
38. MILLERD, A. and BONNER, J. *Arch. Biochem. Biophys.* **49**, 343 (1954).
39. OTTKE, R. C., TATUM, E. L., ZABIN, I. and BLOCH, K. *Federation Proc.* **9**, 212 (1950).
40. PARK, R. B. and BONNER, J. *J. Biol. Chem.* **233**, 340 (1958).
41. POLLARD, C., BONNER, J., HAAGEN-SMIT, A. J. and NIMMO, C. *Plant Physiol.*, in press.
42. POPJÁK, G. *Tetrahedron Letters* **19**, 19 (1959).
43. PURCELL, A. E., THOMPSON, G. A., JR. and BONNER, J. *J. Biol. Chem.* **234**, 1081 (1959).
44. RABINOWITZ, J. L. and GURIN, S. *J. Biol. Chem.* **208**, 307 (1954).
45. RUDNEY, H. *J. Am. Chem. Soc.* **76**, 2595 (1954).
46. STADTMAN, E. R., DOUDOROFF, M. and LIPMANN, F. *J. Biol. Chem.* **191**, 377 (1951).
47. STANLEY, R. G. *Nature* **182**, 738 (1958).
48. TAMURA, G. *J. Gen. Appl. Microbiol., Tokyo* **2**, 431 (1956).
49. TAVORMINA, P., GIBBS, M. H. and HUFF, J. B. *J. Amer. Chem. Soc.* **78**, 4498 (1956).
50. TCHEN, T. T. *J. Biol. Chem.* **233**, 1100 (1958).
51. TEAS, H. J. and BONNER, J. *Rev. Gen. Caoutchouc* **37**, 1143 (1960).
52. TEAS, H. J., POLHAMUS, L. and MONTERMOSO, J. C. Abstr., Conference on Radioactive Isotopes in Agriculture, January 1956.
53. THOMPSON, G. A., JR., PURCELL, A. E. and BONNER, J. *Plant Physiol.* **35**, 678 (1960).
54. WILLIAMSON, I. P. and ROCKWITH, R. *Biochem. J.* **88**, 18P (1963).
55. WITTING, L. and PORTER, J. *Biochem. Biophys. Res. Commun.* **1**, 341 (1959).
56. WRIGHT, L. D., CRESSON, E. L., SKEGGS, H. R., MACRAE, G. D., HOFFMAN, C. H., WOLF, D. E. and FOLKERS, K. *J. Bacteriol.* **72**, 519 (1956).

CHAPTER 17

ALKALOID BIOGENESIS

EDWARD LEETE

School of Chemistry, University of Minnesota, Minneapolis

CONTENTS

I.	INTRODUCTION	953
II.	NON-HETEROCYCLIC AMINES AND RELATED COMPOUNDS	955
III.	PYRROLIDINE ALKALOIDS	958
IV.	TROPANE ALKALOIDS	959
V.	PYRIDINE AND PIPERIDINE ALKALOIDS	961
VI.	PYRROLIZIDINE ALKALOIDS	971
VII.	QUINOLIZIDINE ALKALOIDS	972
VIII.	ISOQUINOLINE ALKALOIDS	975
IX.	COLCHICINE AND RELATED ALKALOIDS	984
X.	AMARYLLIDACEAE ALKALOIDS	985
XI.	ERYTHRINA ALKALOIDS	988
XII.	INDOLE ALKALOIDS	989
XIII.	ERGOLINE ALKALOIDS	1004
XIV.	QUINOLINE, QUINAZOLINE, AND ACRIDONE ALKALOIDS	1006
XV.	TERPENOID AND STEROIDAL ALKALOIDS	1009
XVI.	MISCELLANEOUS ALKALOIDS	1014
XVII.	SUMMARY	1014
	REFERENCES	1015

I. INTRODUCTION

Alkaloids are a very heterogeneous class of natural products. We shall see that some are formed from α-amino acids, others are plausibly derived from acetic acid, whereas others are obviously related to the terpenes or steroids. It is not possible to give a general definition which will encompass all alkaloids. However, we can state that the majority of alkaloids are basic, nitrogen-containing organic compounds found in plants. The nitrogen is usually part of a heterocyclic system. Some exceptions to this statement are illustrated in Fig. 1. Thus ricinine (1) and colchicine (2) are neutral compounds. Some alkaloids are quaternary salts and others are tertiary amine oxides. The indole alkaloid bufotenine (3) is found in plants (*Piptadenia peregrina*), fungi (*Amanita mappa*), and toads (*Bufo vulgaris*). Many of the nitrogen containing products of molds and bacteria could be termed alkaloids. Some examples are gliotoxin (4) (from the fungus *Trichoderma viride*), pyocyanine (5) (from the bacteria *Pseudomonas aeruginosa*), and erythromycin (6) (from certain strains of *Streptomyces*).

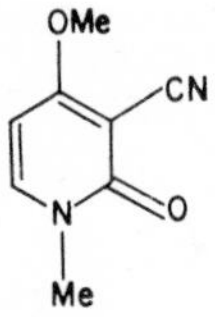

(1)
Ricinine

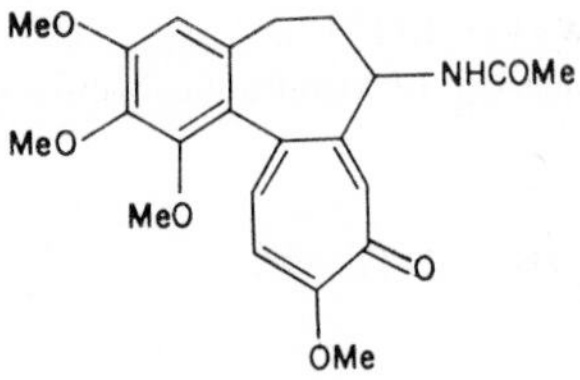

(2)
Colchicine

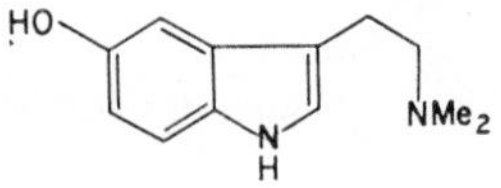

(3)
Bufotenine

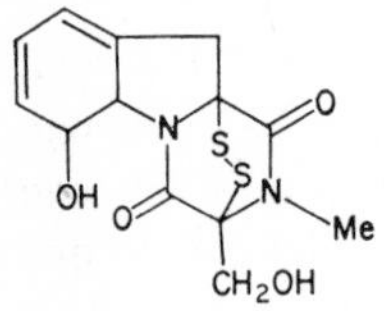

(4)
Gliotoxin

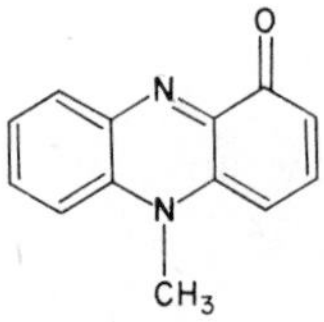

(5)
Pyocyanine

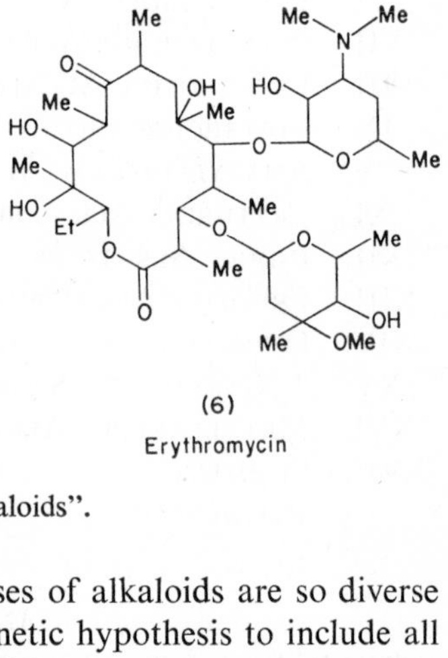

(6)
Erythromycin

Fig. 1. Some "atypical alkaloids".

The structural types found in different classes of alkaloids are so diverse that it is impossible to develop a single biogenetic hypothesis to include all alkaloids. For the same reason, it is not possible to assign a common biological role to all alkaloids. In fact we know very little about the function of alkaloids in plants. Several suggestions have been made. Some have attempted to relate alkaloid formation with protein synthesis or with carbohydrate metabolism. Others have proposed that alkaloids serve to protect plants, from attack by insects. An area of study which is receiving increasing attention is the relationship between the age of the plant and the alkaloid content and distribution. This aspect of alkaloid biosynthesis has been reviewed by Mothes, [210, 211] and in this chapter we shall concern ourselves mainly with a discussion of the mode of formation of the carbon skeletons of the various classes of alkaloids.

Ever since the structures of alkaloids were first elucidated, organic chemists have speculated on their biosynthesis. A classical paper on this subject is that of Sir Robert Robinson [241] who has collected his ideas and those of others in a book. [243] Several other reviews on alkaloid biosynthesis have appeared in recent years. [17, 18, 26, 27, 198, 214, 234] Five years have passed since the chapter on alkaloid biogenesis was written for the first edition of this book. We are now able to present a much more complete story on the biosynthesis of several classes of alkaloids. This progress has resulted from the extensive use of isotopically labeled organic compounds. Subtle points relating to the biosynthesis of particular alkaloids have been settled by feeding relatively complex intermediates, often labeled in several positions with C^{14}, H^3 and N^{15}. Some of the speculative biosynthetic schemes which at present have no experimental justification have been omitted from this edition.

II. NON-HETEROCYCLIC AMINES AND RELATED COMPOUNDS

Several alkaloids which are formed from phenylalanine or its hydroxylated derivatives are illustrated in Fig. 2. It should be stressed that the conversion of phenylalanine to tyrosine does not occur in some plants. [29, 33, 171b, 190] However, in barley (*Hordeum distischum*) this transformation is apparently possible. [204] Hordenine (13) and N-methyltryamine (11) which are produced by germinating barley have been shown to be metabolites of tyrosine. [183] Tyramine (10) is presumably an intermediate in this transformation since radioactive alkaloids were obtained when tyramine-α-C^{14} was fed to barley, [179] however it must occur in very low concentrations since none could be isolated from the normal plant. The N-methyl groups of these alkaloids are derived from the S-methyl group of methionine [185, 205] and also from formate. [146, 185] An enzyme has been isolated from barley roots which catalyses the reaction of S-adenosylmethionine with tyramine yielding N-methyltyramine. [200] To avoid repetition it may be stated at this time that the S-methyl group of methionine or formate has been shown to serve as the source of O- and N-methyl groups of many alkaloids, namely ajmaline, [25, 34] berberine, [20, 123] caffeine, [7] cephaeline, [34] colchicine, [33, 191] damascenine, [220] delpheline, [133] demecolcine, [191] hydrastine, [123] hyoscyamine, [201] ephedrine, [268] gliotoxin, [281] gramine, [185] nicotine, [68, 83] codeine, morphine, thebaine, [42] narcotine, [47] quinine, [174] stachydrine, [239] ricinine, [85] and the ergoline alkaloids. [51] The methylene bridge in the methylenedioxy group, which occurs in protopine and numerous other alkaloids, is also derived from the methyl group of methionine. [277] It has been established [24, 29] that the methylenedioxy group in haemanthamine and lycorine is formed by the oxidative cyclization of an ortho-methoxy phenol. Mescaline (14) is also formed from tyrosine. [157, 171] Phenylalanine is a precursor of ephedrine (9) in *Ephedra distachya* [267] and d-nor-Ψ-ephedrine (8) in *Catha edulis*. [155] Radioactive ω-aminoacetophenone (7) was converted into ephedrine when fed to *Ephedra* plants and is a plausible intermediate between phenylalanine and

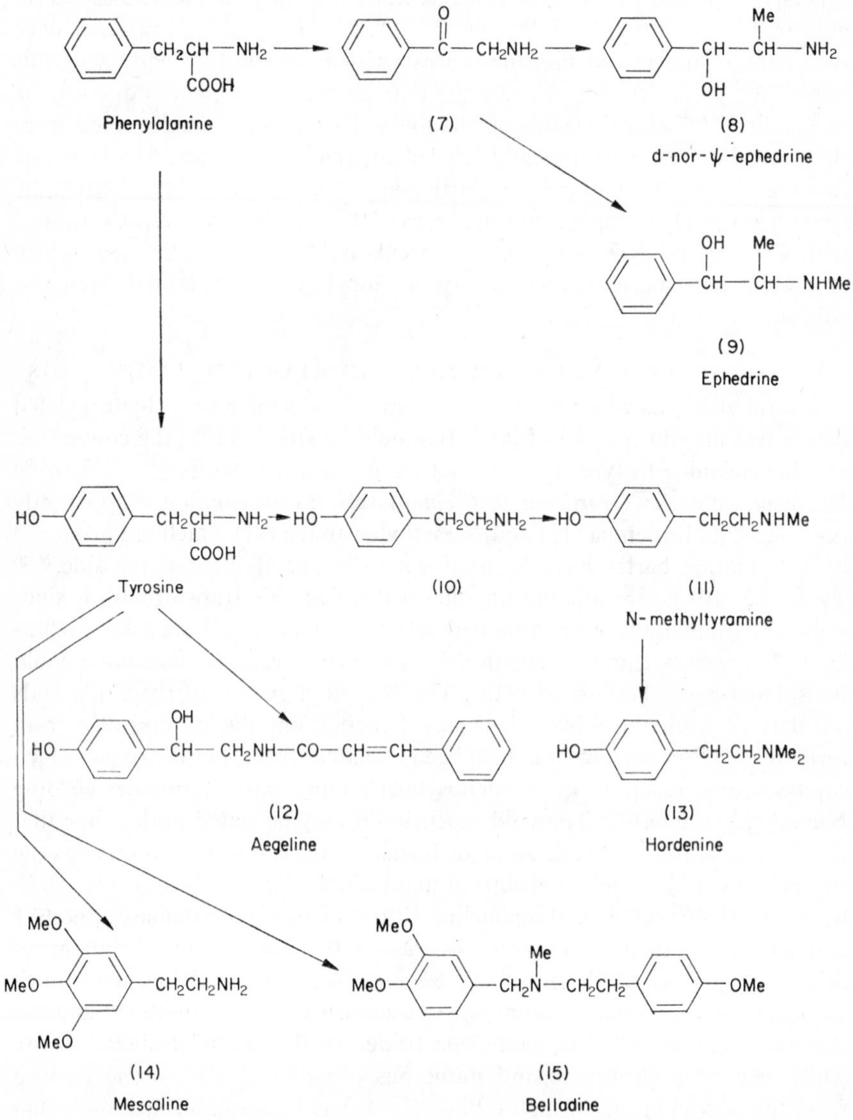

FIG. 2. Some amines related to phenylalanine.

ephedrine. [140] It is surprising that the C-methyl group of ephedrine is derived from formate [269] but not from the methyl group of methionine. [268] Aegeline (12) is presumably derived from tyrosine by hydroxylation of the side chain. The amine moiety of this alkaloid is acylated with cinnamic acid which is a metabolite of phenylalanine. [148, 222] The tyramine half of belladine (15) is derived from tyrosine, whereas the benzylamine half is formed from phenylalanine. [29, 282, 312] Norbelladine is a precursor of many heterocyclic *Amaryllidaceae* alkaloids and its biosynthesis from these two amino acids is discussed in detail in Section X of this chapter.

Some tryptamine derivatives which have been isolated from plants are illustrated in Fig. 3. These amines are presumably derived from tryptophan

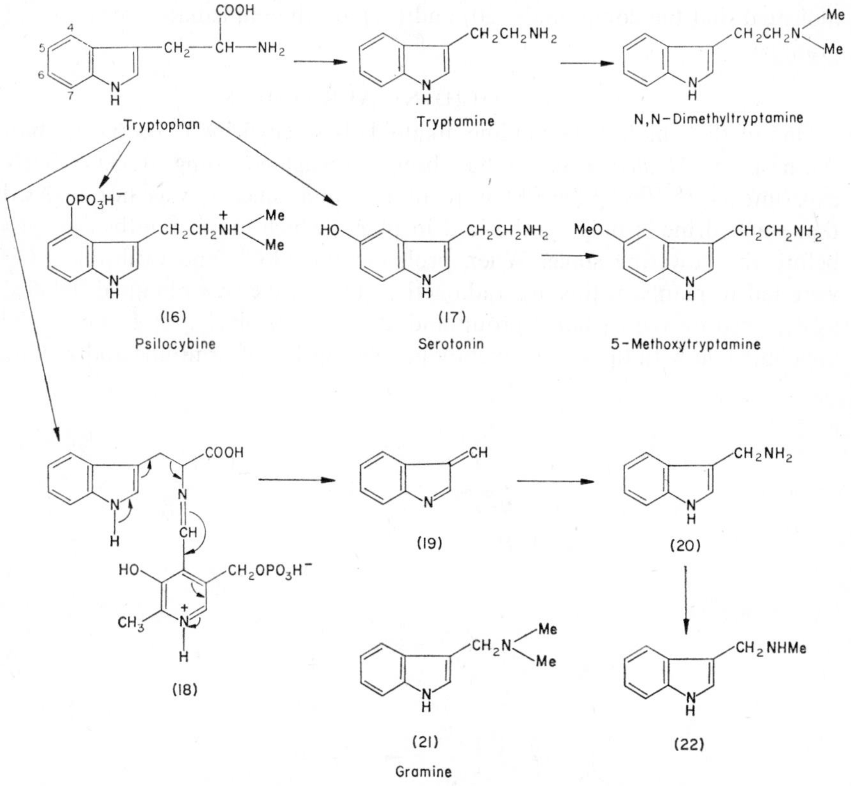

FIG. 3. Some simple derivatives of tryptophan.

by decarboxylation. Several are hydroxylated at the C_5-position, for example, serotonin (17), and these amines could be derived from 5-hydroxytryptophan. Psilocybine (16) which is a 4-hydroxytryptamine derivative has been shown to be derived from tryptophan in the fungus *Psilocybe semperiva*. [63] Tryptophan is also a precursor of gramine (21),(62, 63a, 64, 184, 304) an alkaloid found in the leaves of germinating barley. The methylene group of the tryptophan side chain maintains its integrity in this biosynthesis,(229) and this result is consistent with Wenkert's hypothesis for the origin of this alkaloid,(299) illustrated in Fig. 3. Tryptophan and pyridoxal phosphate condense affording the Schiff base (18), which undergoes a reverse Michael reaction yielding 3-methylene-indolenine (19). Amination of this compound then yields 3-aminomethylindole (20) which is then methylated to give gramine. Mudd(219) has detected 3-aminomethylindole and 3-methylaminomethylindole (22) in the shoots of young barley. He has also been able to methylate these two compounds to gramine with S-adenosylmethionine in the presence of a crude enzyme isolated from barley shoots. Tracer experiments(106) have also indicated that the compounds (20) and (22) are the immediate precursors of gramine.

III. PYRROLIDINE ALKALOIDS

One of the simplest pyrrolidine alkaloids is stachydrine (23), and its biosynthesis in *Medicago sativa* has been investigated using tracers. Early experiments(188, 208, 239, 240, 303) were of no value since it was not realized that stachydrine is only synthesized in plants which are 6 months old, just before the flowering stage. When proline-carboxyl-C^{14} and ornithine-2-C^{14} were fed to plants of this age radioactive stachydrine was obtained, labeled as expected on the carboxyl group and at C-2 respectively.(88) These results are consistent with the known metabolic relationship of ornithine and proline

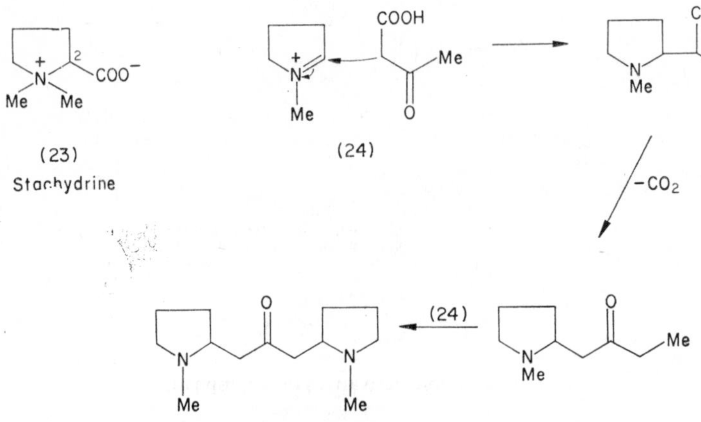

(23) Stachydrine

(24)

(25) Cuscohygrine

(26) Hygrine

FIG. 4. Some pyrrolidine alkaloids.

(see also Section V of this chapter in which the biosynthesis of the pyrrolidine ring of nicotine is discussed).

Hygrine (26) is plausibly formed by a condensation between acetoacetic acid and N-methyl-Δ'-pyrrolinium salt (24) (derived from ornithine or α-N-methylornithine) as illustrated in Fig. 4. Cuscohygrine (25) is obtained by reaction of hygrine with a second molecule of (24). The biosynthesis of hygrine and cuscohygrine seems to be closely related to that of the tropane alkaloids, and it is of interest to note that cuscohygrine has been detected in several of the *Solanaceous* plants which produce the tropane alkaloids. [238]

IV. TROPANE ALKALOIDS

The most widely distributed alkaloid of this group is hyoscyamine (34) and is an ester of tropine and tropic acid. Tropine is formed from ornithine [186, 196] and acetic acid. [145] Recently it has been shown that the N-methyl group of tropine is introduced at an early stage in the biosynthesis. α-N-Methylornithine (27) was incorporated into the tropine moiety of hyoscyamine without loss of the N-methyl group. [224a] The incorporation of ornithine is stereospecific, the α-carbon of ornithine becoming C_1 of hyoscyamine. [60, 164, 169a] Carbons-2 and -4 of tropine are derived from the methyl group of acetic acid, and C_3 from the carboxyl group. A hypothetical biosynthetic scheme consistent with these results is illustrated in Fig. 5. Ornithine is methylated to the α-N-methylornithine which undergoes δ-trans-amination affording α-N-methylglutamic-γ-aldehyde (28). Cyclization affords the N-methylpyrrolinium salt (29) which condenses with acetoacetic acid to give the intermediate (32). Oxidative decarboxylation yields compound (31) which undergoes a second cyclization to the tropanone carboxylic acid (30) which may be a common precursor of tropine and ecgonine, the basic moiety of cocaine (33). The administration of putrescine-1,4-C^{14} (35) to *Datura* species also yielded radioactive tropine having activity at C_1 and C_5. [144, 181, 195a, 196] This result is inconsistent with the stereospecific incorporation of ornithine, and may simply represent an aberrant synthesis, or possibly there may be two different routes to tropine. [195] Hyoscyamine is a precursor of hyoscine (38), and intermediates in this transformation are apparently 6,7-dehydro-hyoscyamine (36) and 6-hydroxyhyoscyamine (37). [245, 246, 286b] The tropic acid moiety of hyoscyamine and hyoscine is derived from phenylalanine by an intramolecular rearrangement of the side chain indicated schematically in Fig. 6. [120, 162, 182, 197, 288] Phenylacetic acid also serves as a precursor of tropic acid. [288] However, since phenylalanine is a much more efficient precursor it seems probable that the phenylacetic acid is converted to the amino acid prior to its incorporation into tropic acid. The carboxylation of phenyl-acetic acid to phenylpyruvic acid and thence to phenylalanine has been demonstrated in some bacteria. [5] The report [104] that tryptophan serves as a precursor of tropic acid was not substantiated by other workers. [182] Phenyl-alanine was also found to be the source of the benzoic acid moiety of cocaine. [120]

Tiglic acid esters of hydroxytropanes constitute a group of minor alkaloids

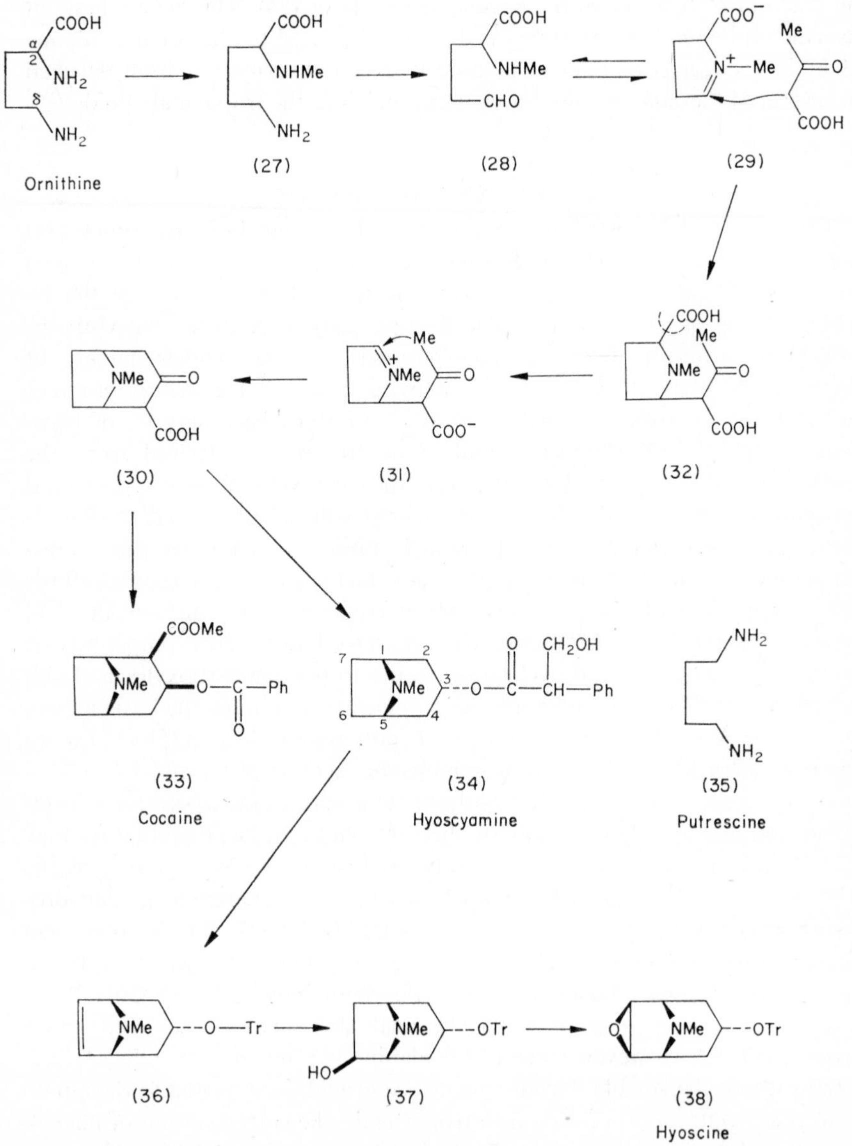

FIG. 5. Biosynthesis of the tropane alkaloids (Tr = tropic acid residue).

of *Datura* and *Duboisia* species. In *Datura ferox* and *D. innoxia* 7-hydroxy-3,6-ditigloyloxytropane (39) is formed in the roots and is then translocated to the leaves where hydrolysis occurs yielding meteloidine (40) and teloidine (41).[89] Tiglic acid (45) is derived from isoleucine (42)[90, 189a] and a metabolic sequence similar to that established in animals[244] seems probable (Fig. 6).

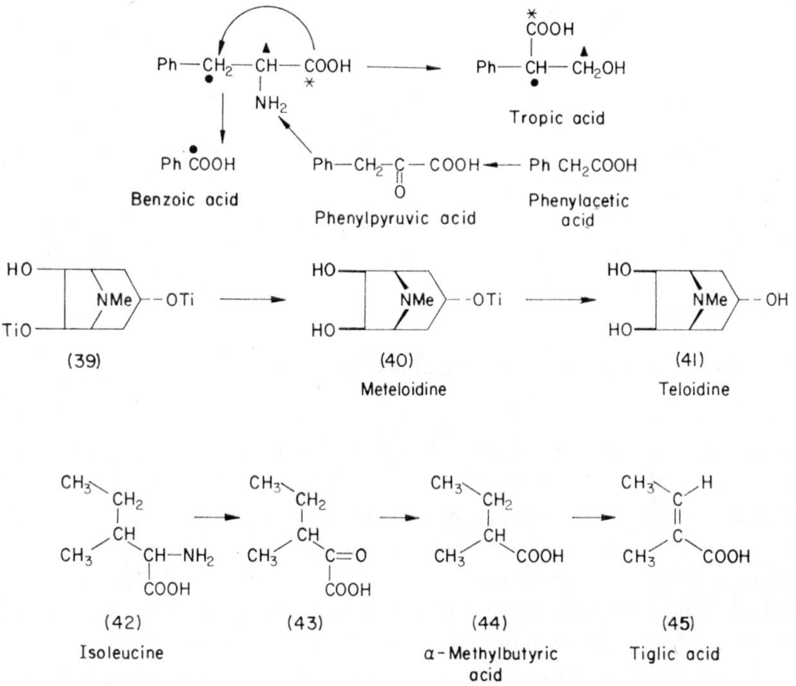

FIG. 6. Biosynthesis of the acid moieties of the tropane alkaloids (Tr = tiglic residue).

It is probably significant that one of the intermediates in this suggested transformation, namely α-methylbutyric acid (44), is found esterified with tropane bases in some *Duboisia* species.

V. PYRIDINE AND PIPERIDINE ALKALOIDS

Pyridine and piperidine rings occur in a wide variety of alkaloids and it is now clear that more than one biosynthetic route exists for their formation.[168] It has been established that nicotinic acid is a precursor of the pyridine ring of anabasine (48)[272] and nicotine (49),[77, 81] the carboxyl group being lost at some step in the biosynthesis.[79] Nicotinic acid is also a precursor of ricinine (47),[180, 295] an alkaloid found in the castor bean

(*Ricinus communis*). In this case the carboxyl group of nicotinic acid becomes the cyano group of ricinine, nicotinamide being an intermediate. [296, 296a]

Nicotinic acid is formed from tryptophan in some microorganisms such as *Neurospora*, and in animals by the route illustrated briefly in Fig. 7.

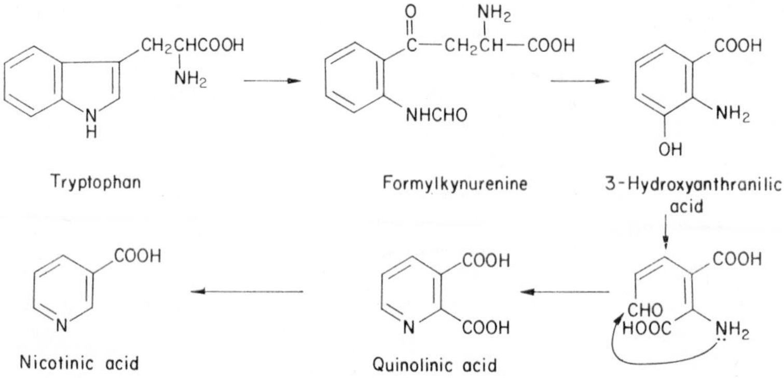

Fig. 7. Biosynthesis of nicotinic acid in animals and some microorganisms.

However, several investigators [12, 111, 131, 154, 187] have shown that this metabolic sequence apparently does not occur in higher plants. As a result of feeding experiments with many different precursors it has been established that carbons-4, -5, and -6 of nicotinic acid are derived from a three-carbon compound closely related to glycerol. [71, 96b, 143, 109, 173] The other carbons are derived from succinic acid or a closely related compound. [87, 100, 107, 108, 110, 140a, 142a, 156, 249, 285a] A tentative biosynthetic scheme based on these tracer results is illustrated in Fig. 8. It is suggested that the heterocyclic ring is formed by a condensation between glyceraldehyde-3-phosphate and aspartic acid. The resultant piperidine derivative then undergoes dehydration and dehydrogenation to yield quinolinic acid, which is then decarboxylated affording nicotinic acid. Quinolinic acid is indeed a precursor of nicotinic acid in corn and castor bean plants. [128, 310a] It is also incorporated into nicotine in tobacco plants. [78, 310] In *Escherichia coli* glycerol and succinic acid are also precursors of nicotinic acid. [230] Mothes and co-workers have studied the biosynthesis of nicotinic acid in *Mycobacterium tuberculosis*. [121, 209] By feeding aspartic acid-1,4-C^{14}-N^{15}, they showed that the pyridine nitrogen was derived from the amino group of aspartic acid, and the carboxyl group was derived from the γ-carboxyl of aspartic acid. Glycerol also served as a precursor of nicotinic acid in this same organism. [119a]

The piperidine and pyrrolidine rings of anabasine and nicotine are derived from lysine and ornithine respectively. In the case of anabasine tracer results [108a, 158, 176] unambiguously favor the biogenetic scheme illustrated in Fig. 9.

Lysine undergoes α-transamination affording α-keto- ε-aminocaproic acid (50) which cyclizes to Δ'-piperideine-2-carboxylic acid (51). Decarboxylation affords Δ'-piperideine (55). Cadaverine (52) which also serves as a precursor of the piperidine ring of anabasine [160] may be converted to Δ'-piperideine by

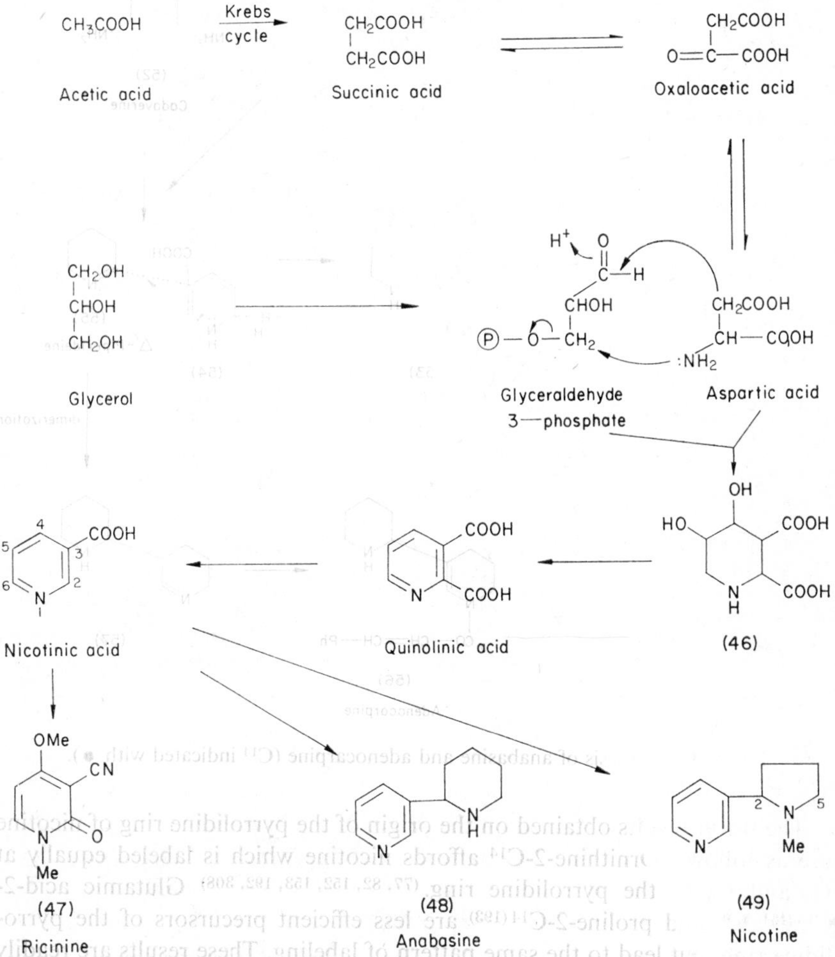

FIG. 8. Tentative biosynthetic scheme for the formation of nicotinic acid in plants.

oxidative deamination. It is then suggested that the imine (55) condenses with a reduced nicotinic acid (54). Since Dawson and co-workers [80] have shown that nicotinic acid labeled at C_6 with tritium was less efficiently incorporated than the other hydrogen-labeled nicotinic acids, we suggest that the active intermediate is a 1,6-dihydronicotinic acid. Oxidative decarboxylation of the intermediate (53) affords anabasine. Adenocarpine, cinnamoyl-tetrahydroanabasine(56), is apparently formed via intermediate (57) from Δ′-piperideine derived from cadaverine. [257]

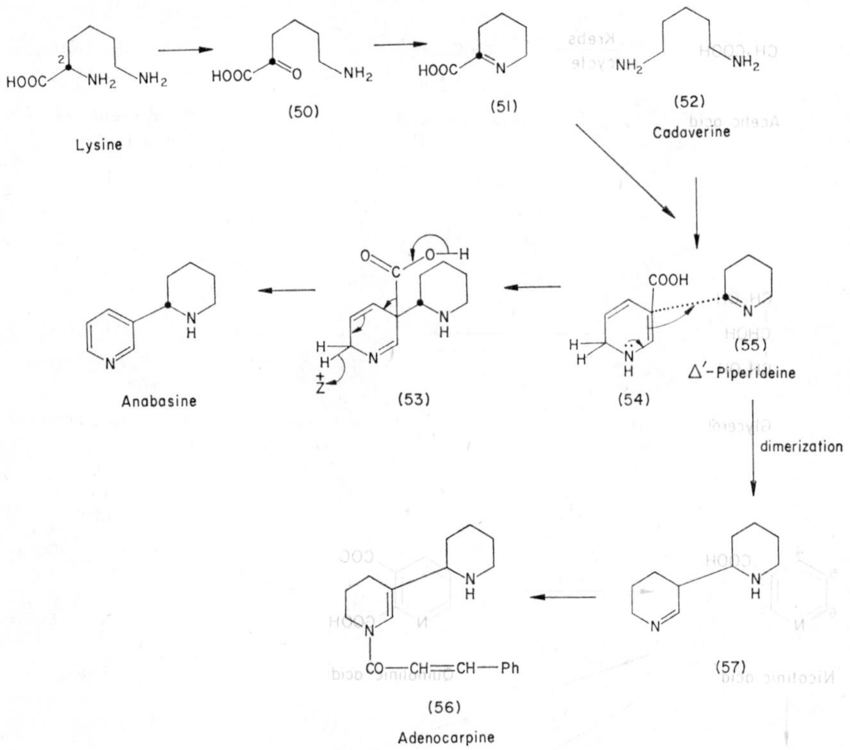

FIG. 9. Biosynthesis of anabasine and adenocarpine (C^{14} indicated with ●).

The tracer results obtained on the origin of the pyrrolidine ring of nicotine are as follows. Ornithine-2-C^{14} affords nicotine which is labeled equally at C_2 and C_5 of the pyrrolidine ring. [77, 82, 152, 153, 192, 308] Glutamic acid-2-C^{14} [151, 159] and proline-2-C^{14} [193] are less efficient precursors of the pyrrolidine ring, but lead to the same pattern of labeling. These results are readily rationalized on the basis of the known biochemical relationship of these three amino acids which is illustrated in Fig. 10. Experiments with N^{15} labeled ornithine indicated that only the σ-amino group was utilized for the formation of the pyrrolidine ring. [177] However, Schröter and Neumann [249a] have found that α-N-methylornithine (59) is a precursor of the N-methylpyrrolidine ring of nicotine, incorporation occurring without loss of the N-methyl group. Putrescine is also an efficient precursor of the pyrrolidine ring.[159, 213] A reasonable explanation of these results is illustrated in Fig. 10. It is suggested that an N-methyl-Δ'-pyrrolinium salt (63) is the active intermediate which condenses with a nicotinic acid derivative to yield nicotine analogous to the formation of anabasine illustrated in Fig. 9. The inter-

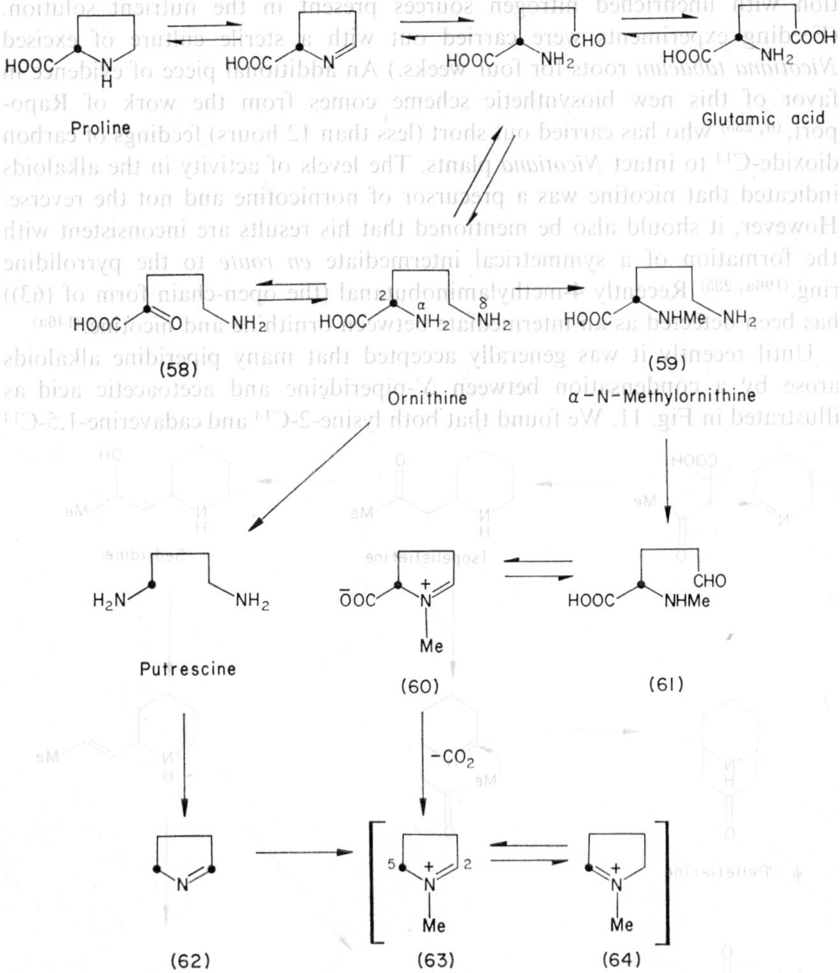

HOOC–[Proline]–N(H)   HOOC–[N]   HOOC–[CHO/NH₂]   HOOC–[COOH/NH₂ Glutamic acid]

HOOC–[O/NH₂] (58)   HOOC–[NH₂/NH₂ Ornithine] (α)   HOOC–[NHMe/NH₂ α-N-Methylornithine] (59)

H₂N–[Putrescine]–NH₂   ⁻OOC–[N⁺/Me] (60)   HOOC–[CHO/NHMe] (61)

[N] (62)   –CO₂   [5 N⁺ 2 / Me] (63) ⇌ [N⁺/Me] (64)

FIG. 10. Precursors of the pyrrolidine ring of nicotine (C^{14} indicated with •).

mediate (63) is formed from ornithine, via α-N-methylornithine and compounds (61) and (60). Randomization of activity between C_2 and C_5 in the ultimate pyrrolidine ring of nicotine is achieved by postulating a tautomeric equilibrium between (63) and (64). The positive charge on the nitrogen would favor such tautomerism. An alternate route to (63) would be via putrescine and Δ'-pyrroline (62). In order to explain the lack of incorporation of α-N^{15} labeled ornithine we suggest that the N^{15} is lost by an α-transamination to α-keto-δ-aminovaleric acid (58). Ornithine containing no excess N^{15} at the α-position could then be formed by a reversal of this transamination with unenriched nitrogen sources present in the nutrient solution. (Feeding experiments were carried out with a sterile culture of excised *Nicotiana tabacum* roots for four weeks.) An additional piece of evidence in favor of this new biosynthetic scheme comes from the work of Rapoport, [6, 235] who has carried out short (less than 12 hours) feedings of carbon dioxide-C^{14} to intact *Nicotiana* plants. The levels of activity in the alkaloids indicated that nicotine was a precursor of nornicotine and not the reverse. However, it should also be mentioned that his results are inconsistent with the formation of a symmetrical intermediate *en route* to the pyrrolidine ring. [196a, 235] Recently 4-methylaminobutanal (the open-chain form of (63)) has been detected as an intermediate between ornithine and nicotine. [146a]

Until recently it was generally accepted that many piperidine alkaloids arose by a condensation between Δ'-piperideine and acetoacetic acid as illustrated in Fig. 11. We found that both lysine-2-C^{14} and cadaverine-1,5-C^{14}

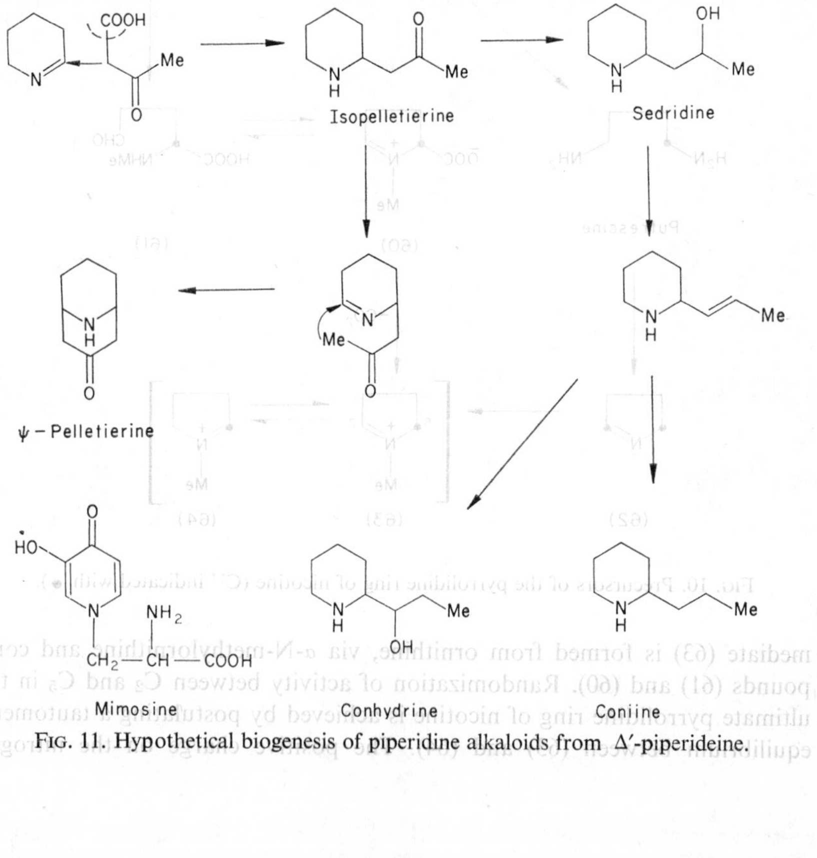

Fig. 11. Hypothetical biogenesis of piperidine alkaloids from Δ'-piperideine.

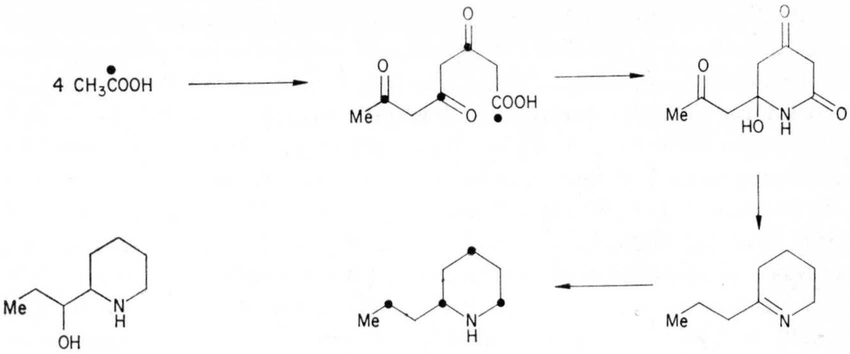

Conhydrine Coniine γ-coniceine

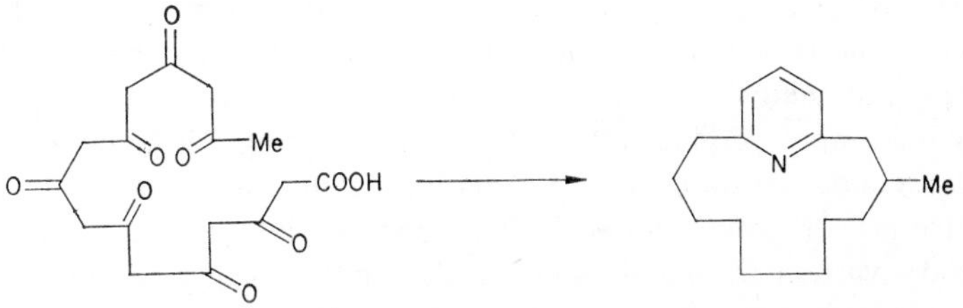

(65)
Muscopyridine

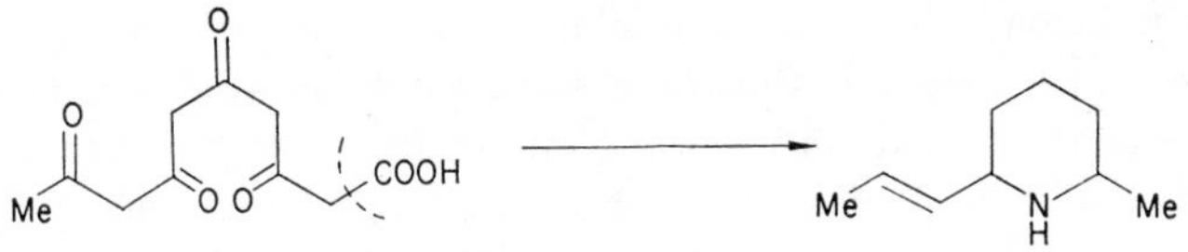

(66)
Pinidine

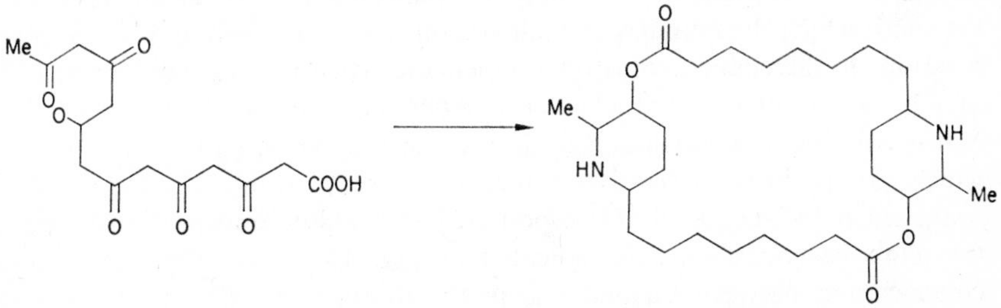

(67)
Carpaine

FIG. 12. Biosynthesis of some piperidine and pyridine alkaloids from poly-β-ketoacids.

(potential precursors of Δ'-piperideine) were very poor precursors of coniine and other hemlock alkaloids. However, the administration of acetate-1-C^{14} to hemlock plants yielded radioactive coniine and conhydrine which were labeled on alternate carbons as illustrated in Fig. 12.[167] Cromwell[75] obtained radioactive γ-coniceine from hemlock plants which had been fed uniformly labeled lysine-C^{14}, cadaverine-1,5-C^{14} or Δ'-piperideine-U-C^{14}. The significance of these results will not be apparent until the isolated alkaloids have been systematically degraded in order to discover whether activity was confined to the piperidine ring. Cromwell has found[76] that acetate-1-C^{14} is a much more efficient precursor of γ-coniceine than lysine. Thus his first results, and those of Schiedt and Hoss,[249] who reported the incorporation of lysine-U-C^{14} into coniine, may be explained by postulating that the lysine was degraded to acetate prior to incorporation into the hemlock alkaloids. The work of Fairbairn[93, 94] suggests that γ-coniceine plays a central role in the biosynthesis of the other hemlock alkaloids. This has been confirmed by feeding radioactive γ-coniceine to hemlock when labeled coniine and Ψ-conhydrine were produced.[171a] We therefore consider that γ-coniceine arises by a condensation of ammonia with an eight-carbon poly-β-keto acid derived from four acetate units as illustrated in Fig. 12. The formation of pyridine derivatives from poly-β-ketoacids was first suggested by Büchi[58] to rationalize the structure of muscopyridine (65), an alkaloid found in the animal *Moschus moschiferus*. Pinidine (66) would be formed hypothetically from five acetate units, and carpaine (67), which has recently been shown[276] to have a dimeric structure, from fourteen acetate units. Preliminary tracer work[56] has indicated that acetate is a much more efficient precursor of carpaine than lysine. Figure 13 illustrates some alkaloids which are plausibly formed from benzoic acid and varying numbers of acetate units. Thus sedamine (68) could be formed from benzoic acid and three acetate units, sedinine (69) from benzoic acid and five acetate units, and lobelanine (70) from two molecules of benzoic acid and four acetate units. However, recent tracer work on the biosynthesis of sedamine is incompatible with this hypothesis.[123a] Himbacine (71) may be plausibly derived from a poly-β-ketoacid which has undergone alkylation with one-carbon units at two positions in the chain as illustrated schematically in Fig. 13. Dioscorine (72) may be derived from a branched acetate chain as illustrated.

It is convenient at this point to discuss the *Lycopodium* alkaloids, some of which are pyridine derivatives, since they are plausibly derived from a branched poly-β-ketoacid (73) produced by an aldol condensation between two eight-carbon chains as indicated in Fig. 14.[73] A subsequent aldol condensation between C_4 and C_{14} in the intermediate (73) together with oxidation of the methyl group at C_5 yields compound (76). A Mannich reaction involving C_8, the carbonyl at C_{12} and ammonia yields compound (80) after lactamization. Unexceptional steps then afford annotinine (84). An

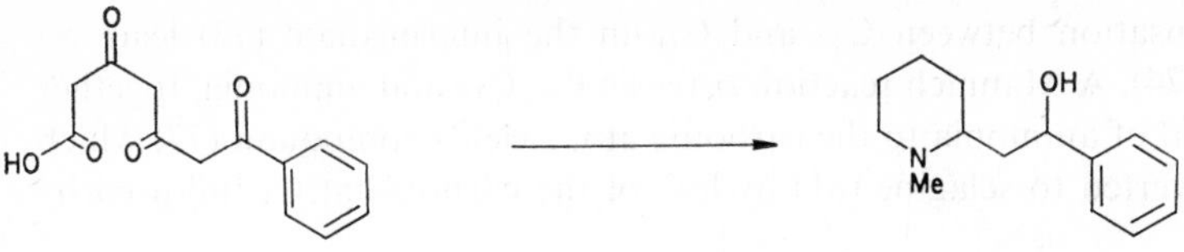

(68)
Sedamine

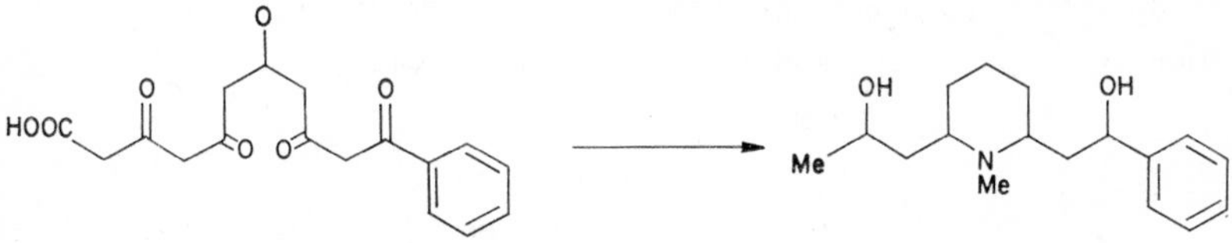

(69)
Sedinine

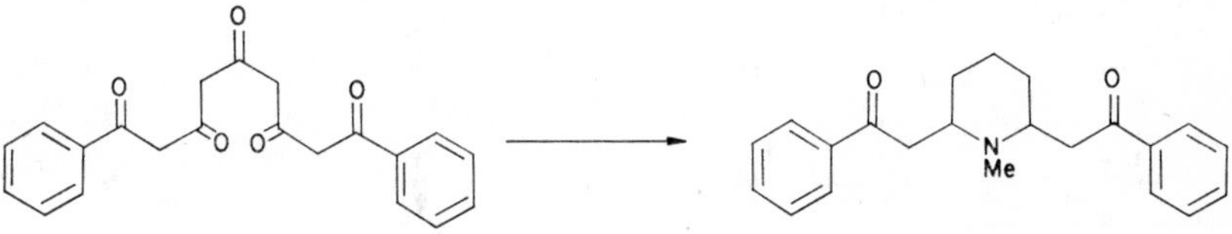

(70)
Lobelanine

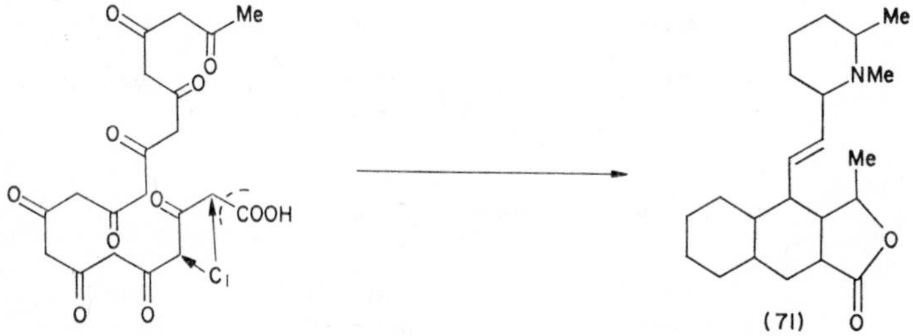

(71)
Himbacine

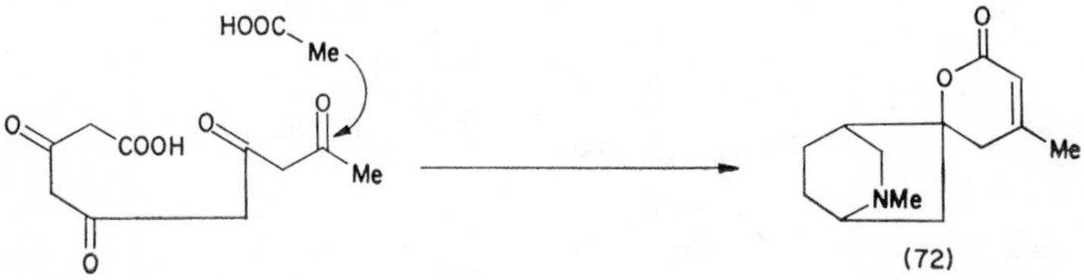

(72)
Dioscorine

FIG. 13. Hypothetical formation of more piperidine alkaloids from poly-β-keto-acids.

aldol condensation between C_{14} and C_{16} in the intermediate (73) leads to compound (74). A Mannich reaction between C_8, C_{12} and ammonia, together with addition of ammonia to the carbonyl at C_7 yields compound (77) which may be converted to selagine (81) by loss of the carboxyl at C_1 followed by

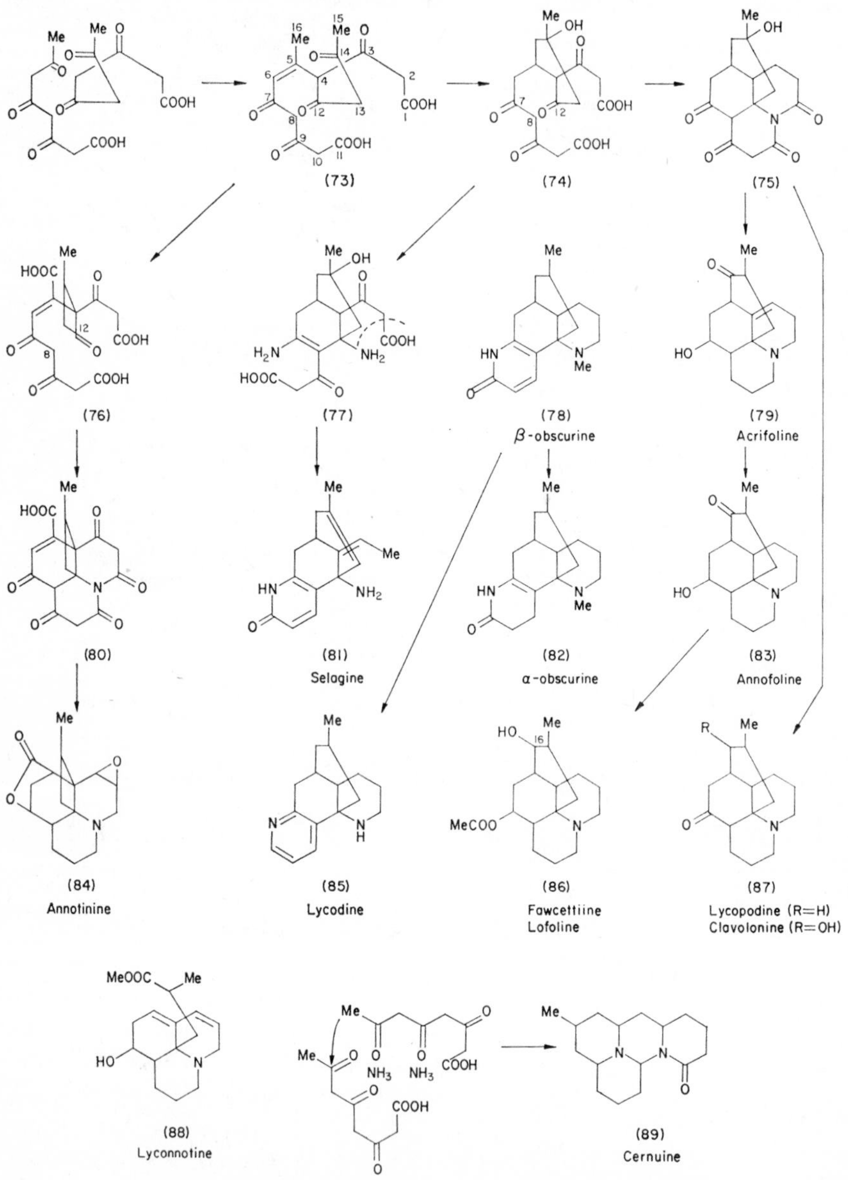

FIG. 14. Hypothetical biosynthesis of the lycopodium alkaloids.

unexceptional reductions and dehydrations. By retention of the carboxy group at C_1, the structures of the obscurines (78, 82) and lycodine (85) may be arrived at. It is of interest to note that the correct structure of lycodine was predicted on the basis of this biosynthetic scheme. [9, 13] Compound (75) is also formed from (74) by a Mannich reaction followed by lactamization. Lycopodine (87), annofoline (83), acrifoline (79) and related alkaloids may be plausibly formed from this compound by unexceptional steps. Fawcettiine and lofoline (86) are epimeric at C_{16}. Lyconnotine (88) may be formed by an oxidative cleavage of acrifoline (79). [8] Cernuine (89) represents another structural type and was isolated from *Lycopodium cernuum*. [14] Here also it seems reasonable to predict that this alkaloid is derived from two eight-carbon chains as illustrated in Fig. 14.

Mimosine (illustrated in Fig. 11) is apparently derived from lysine; [137, 225, 286a] however, the intermediates in this remarkable transformation are not known.

Isolated pyridine and piperidine rings are found in alkaloids such as acti-nidine, skytanthine, jervine and veratramine. It seems almost certain that these alkaloids are derived from terpenoid precursors and they are discussed in Section XV of this chapter.

VI. PYRROLIZIDINE ALKALOIDS

One of the simplest alkaloids of this class is 1-methylenepyrrolizidine (90) found in various *Crotalaria* species. However, most of the alkaloids are esters of the amino-alcohols platynecine (91), retronecine (92), heliotridine (93) and rosmarinecine (94), with the necic acids which are a rather miscellaneous collection of compounds. It has been suggested that the pyrrolizidine bases are formed by an intramolecular Mannich reaction involving the dialde-hydeimine (95) derived from ornithine or putrescine as illustrated in Fig. 15. Such a Mannich reaction has been achieved *in vitro*, [15, 194] and tracer experiments are consistent with this hypothesis. [228] The administration of ornithine-2-C^{14}, ornithine-5-C^{14}, or putrescine-1,4-C^{14} to *Senecio* plants yielded radioactive retronecine, or its N-oxide, which had 25 per cent of its activity located at C_9. [61, 135a, 297] It is assumed that the other 75 per cent will be distributed equally between C_3, C_5 and C_8. Hughes and Warren [136] have reported on the biosynthesis of retronecic acid which is esterified with retronecine in the alkaloid retrosine (96). Mevalonic acid was not a precursor of this ten-carbon acid which might possibly have been a monoterpene. Acetate was incorporated and the pattern of labeling was consistent with the biosynthetic scheme illustrated in Fig. 15. Acetoacetic acid is alkylated with a one-carbon fragment and then the two branched five-carbon units join to yield retronecic acid. Little is known about the origin of the other necic acids. It is possible to arrive at their structures by plausible condensations involving acetic acid units and the occasional one-carbon fragment. [3] Thus

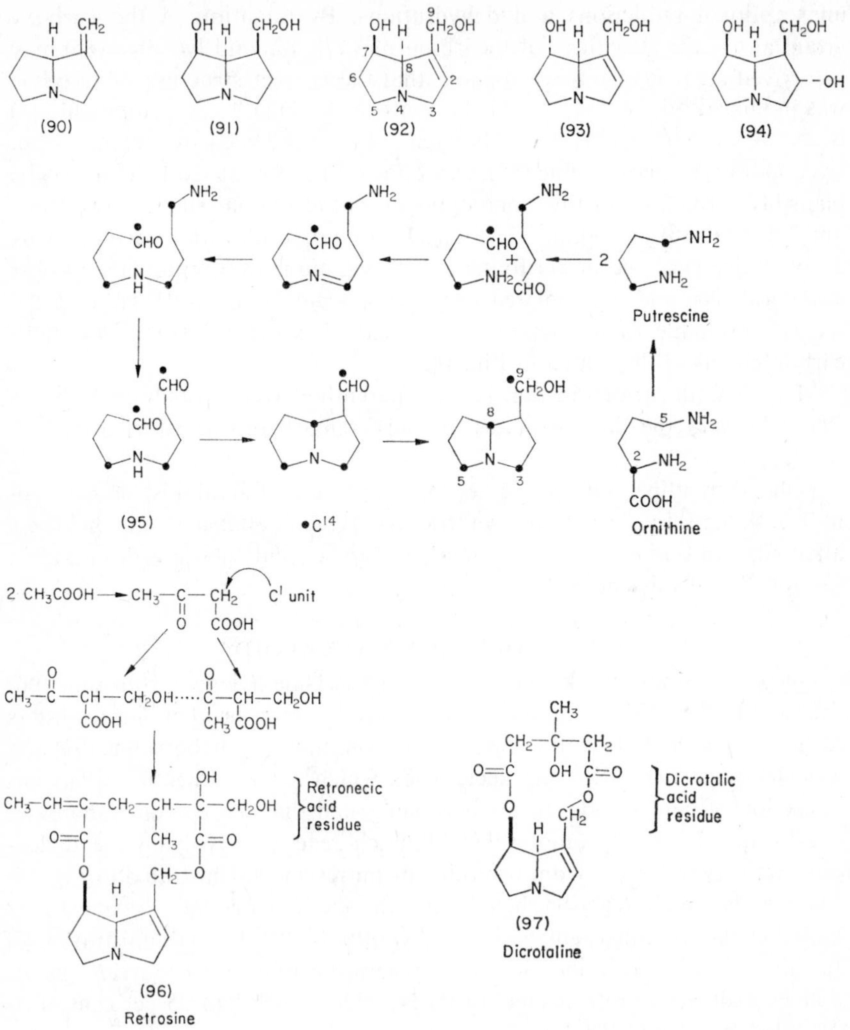

FIG. 15. Pyrrolizidine alkaloids and their biosynthesis.

it seems highly probable that dicrotalic acid found in the alkaloid dicrotaline (97) is derived from three acetate units. The coenzyme A ester of this acid is, of course, an intermediate in the formation of mevalonic acid (see Chapter 4). Work has been reported on the biosynthesis of the necic acids: echimidinic,[76a] and seneciphyllic.[76b]

VII. QUINOLIZIDINE ALKALOIDS

Many of the *Lycopodium* alkaloids contain the quinolizidine nucleus; however, these alkaloids are derived from acetate and their biosynthesis is discussed in Section V of this chapter. The alkaloids in this section are often referred to as the Lupin alkaloids and they are now known to be derived from lysine via cadaverine. Tracer results are consistent with the schemes outlined in Fig. 16 for the biosynthesis of lupinine, matrine, sparteine, cytisine and related alkaloids. The dialdehydeimine (98) results from lysine via cadaverine by a route analogous to the formation of (95) from putrescine

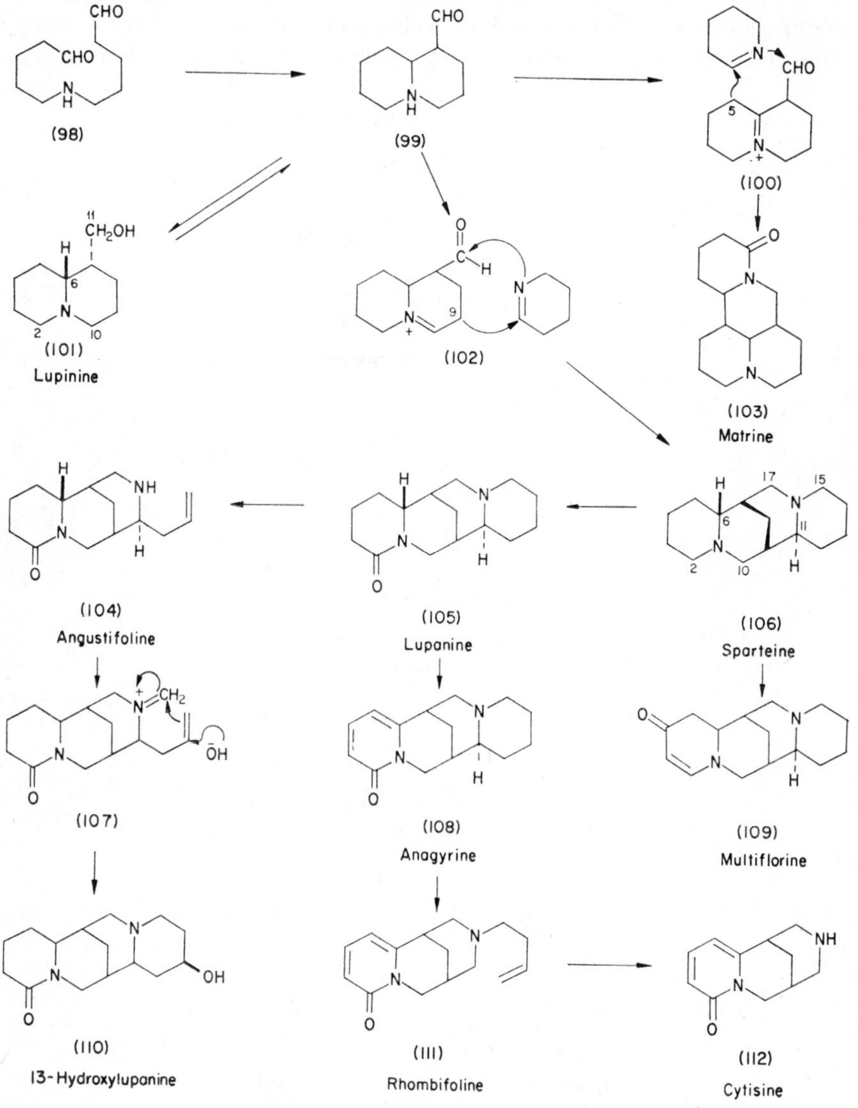

(98)

(99)

(100)

(101) Lupinine

(102)

(103) Matrine

(104) Angustifoline

(105) Luponine

(106) Sparteine

(107)

(108) Anagyrine

(109) Multiflorine

(110) 13-Hydroxyluponine

(111) Rhombifoline

(112) Cytisine

Fig. 16.

outlined in Fig. 15. An intramolecular Mannich reaction affords the quinolizidine (99). This cyclization has also been achieved *in vitro*. [291] Reduction of this intermediate yields lupinine (101). The administration of cadaverine-1,5-C^{14} to *Lupinus luteus* plants yielded radioactive lupinine which had 25 per cent of its activity located at C_2, C_{10} and C_{11}, a result consistent with this hypothesis. [250, 273, 261] Dehydrogenation of the intermediate (99) affords compound (100) which is suitably activated at C_5 for condensation with Δ'-piperideine to afford the carbon skeleton of matrine (103). The distribution of activity in radioactive matrine isolated from *Sophora flavescens* or

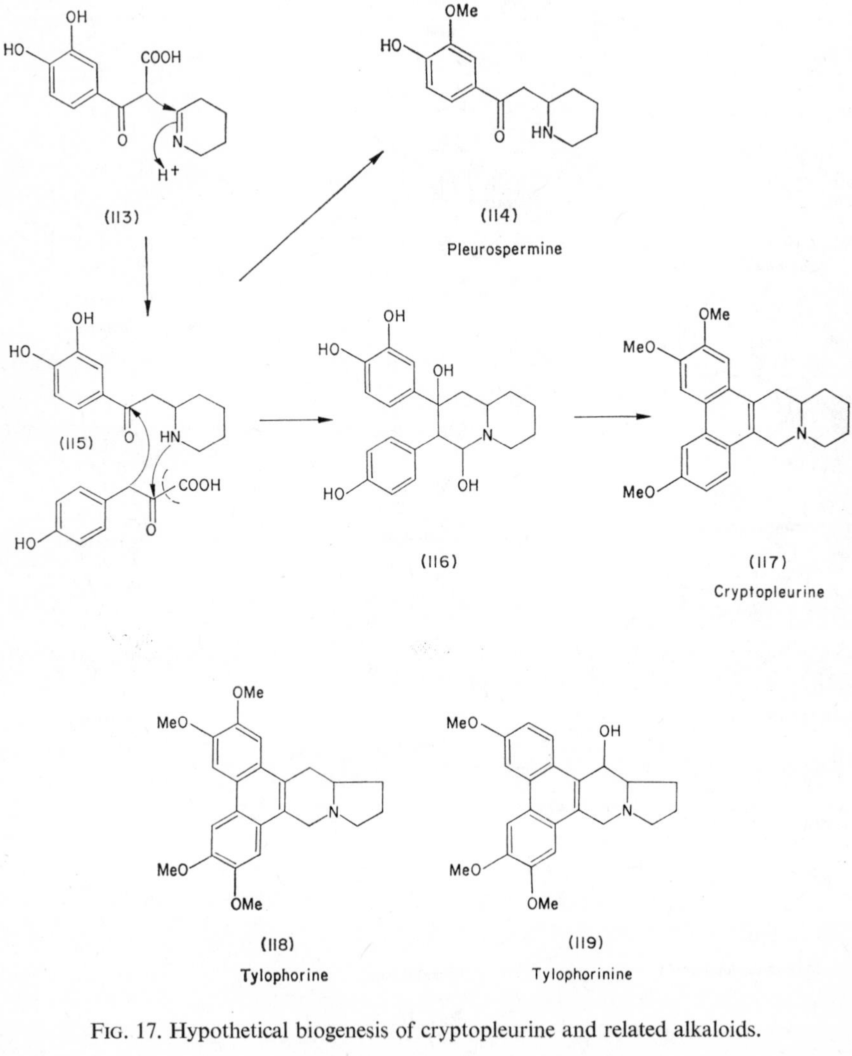

FIG. 17. Hypothetical biogenesis of cryptopleurine and related alkaloids.

tetraptera which had been fed cadaverine-1,5-C[14] agreed with this scheme. [252, 258a, 270]   An alternative dehydrogenation of (99) yields compound (102) which on condensation with Δ'-piperideine affords the carbon skeleton of sparteine (106). Extensive degradations have been carried out on sparteine derived from lysine-2-C[14] and cadaverine-1,5-C[14] and all the results [227, 251, 253, 255, 259, 262] indicated that the six carbon atoms C-2, 6, 10, 17, 11 and 15, were labeled equally. Especially significant were the experiments carried out with lysine-2-C[14]-α-N[15]. [256] The hypothesis in Fig. 16 requires that the specific incorporation of C[14] should be three times that of the N[15], and the experimental results were very close to this value. Sparteine and related alkaloids are usually found in the Papilionacae family, and almost all the tracer experiments have been carried out with plants of this family. However, sparteine also occurs along with benzophenanthridine alkaloids in the plant *Chelidonium majus*, a member of the Papaveracae. It was thus of considerable interest to discover that sparteine is apparently produced by the same biosynthetic route from cadaverine in *C. majus*. [254]

Sparteine is a precursor of cytisine (112) and N-methylcytisine, possible intermediates being lupanine (105), anagyrine (108), and rhombifoline (111). [253a, 258, 260, 263] Lupanine is converted to angustifoline (104) and 13-hydroxylupanine (110) in *Lupinus albus*. [59, 260] A possible intermediate between these last two alkaloids being the aldimine (107), and this transformation has been achieved in the laboratory. [202] Another oxidation product of sparteine is multiflorine (109). [226]

Cryptopleurine (117), which contains the quinolizidine nucleus, is plausibly formed by the route illustrated in Fig. 17. [243] The 3,4-dihydroxybenzoylacetic acid (113), which could arise from acetic acid and shikimic acid, condenses with Δ'-piperideine to yield compound (115). Reaction of (115) with p-hydroxyphenylpyruvic acid, a precursor or metabolite of tyrosine, yields compound (116) which is converted to cryptopleurine by unexceptional steps. Pleurospermine (114), the monomethyl ether of intermediate (115), has been found in the leaves of *Cryptocarya pleurosperma*, the bark of which yields cryptopleurine. Tylophorine (118) and tylophorinine (119) are presumably biogenetically related to cryptopleurine, Δ'-pyrroline instead of Δ'-piperidene being involved in the initial condensation.

The alkaloid nupharidine contains a quinolizidine nucleus, but it is probably related to the terpenes and is discussed in Section XV.

VIII. ISOQUINOLINE ALKALOIDS

There are several simple 1,2,3,4-tetrahydroisoquinoline alkaloids which are plausibly formed by a Mannich reaction involving a hydroxylated phenylalanine or phenylethylamine and an appropriate aldehyde. Some examples are illustrated in Fig. 18. Tracer experiments have confirmed this hypothesis. Thus Battersby obtained radioactive pellotine (N-methyl anhalonidine) from the cactus *Anhalonium lewinii* which had been fed tyrosine-2-C^{14}. We[171] have degraded radioactive anhalonidine (120) obtained from the same plant which had also been fed tyrosine-2-C^{14} and found all the activity located, as expected, at C_3. The aldehyde involved in the formation of lophocerine (122) may be derived from leucine or mevalonic acid. Pilocereine (123) is a tri-isoquinoline alkaloid and is plausibly formed by the oxidative coupling of three molecules of lophocerine.[84] These two alkaloids occur together in the same cactus *Lophocereus schottii*.

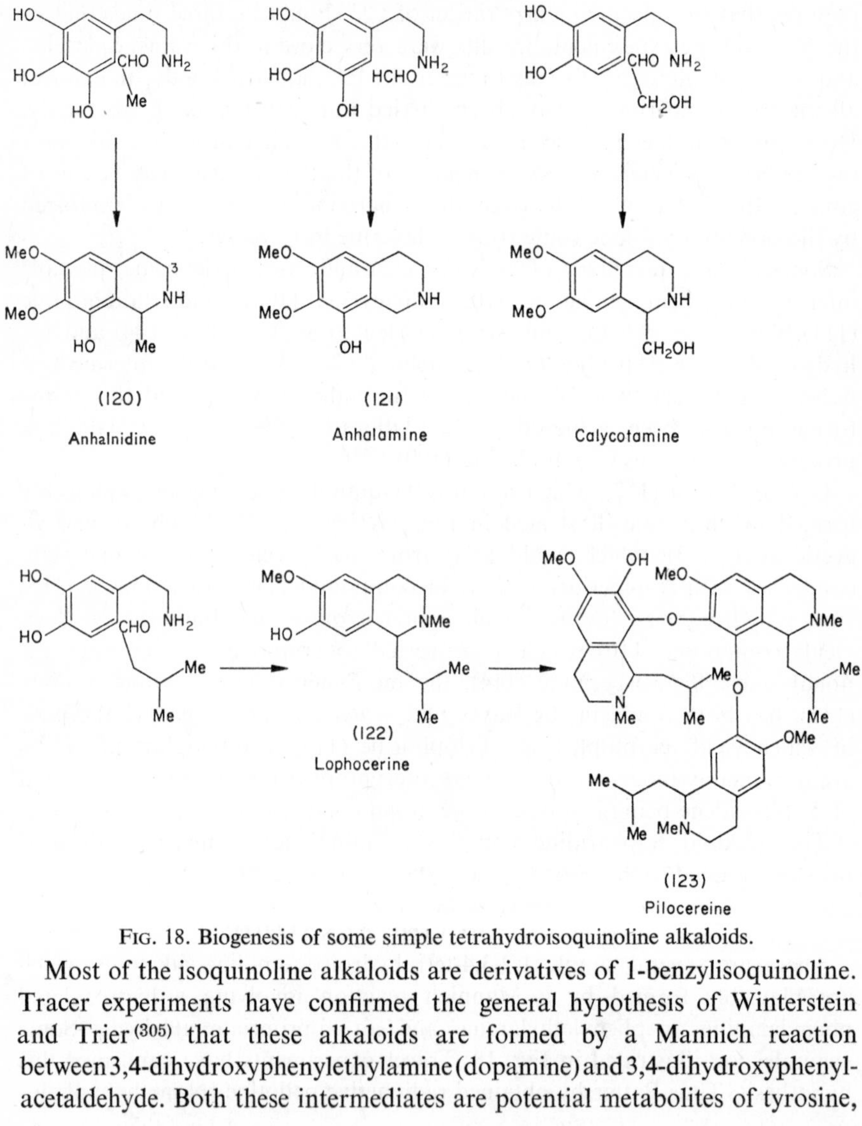

(120)   (121)
Anhalnidine   Anhalamine   Calycotamine

(122)
Lophocerine

(123)
Pilocereine

FIG. 18. Biogenesis of some simple tetrahydroisoquinoline alkaloids.

Most of the isoquinoline alkaloids are derivatives of 1-benzylisoquinoline. Tracer experiments have confirmed the general hypothesis of Winterstein and Trier[305] that these alkaloids are formed by a Mannich reaction between 3,4-dihydroxyphenylethylamine (dopamine) and 3,4-dihydroxyphenylacetaldehyde. Both these intermediates are potential metabolites of tyrosine, and it was shown by Battersby [43] that the administration of tyrosine-2-C^{14} to *Papaver somniferum* plants (opium poppies) yielded papaverine (127) labeled at C_1 and C_3. Later tracer work [39, 102, 207] has shown that dopamine serves only as the precursor of the isoquinoline half of the 1-benzyliso-

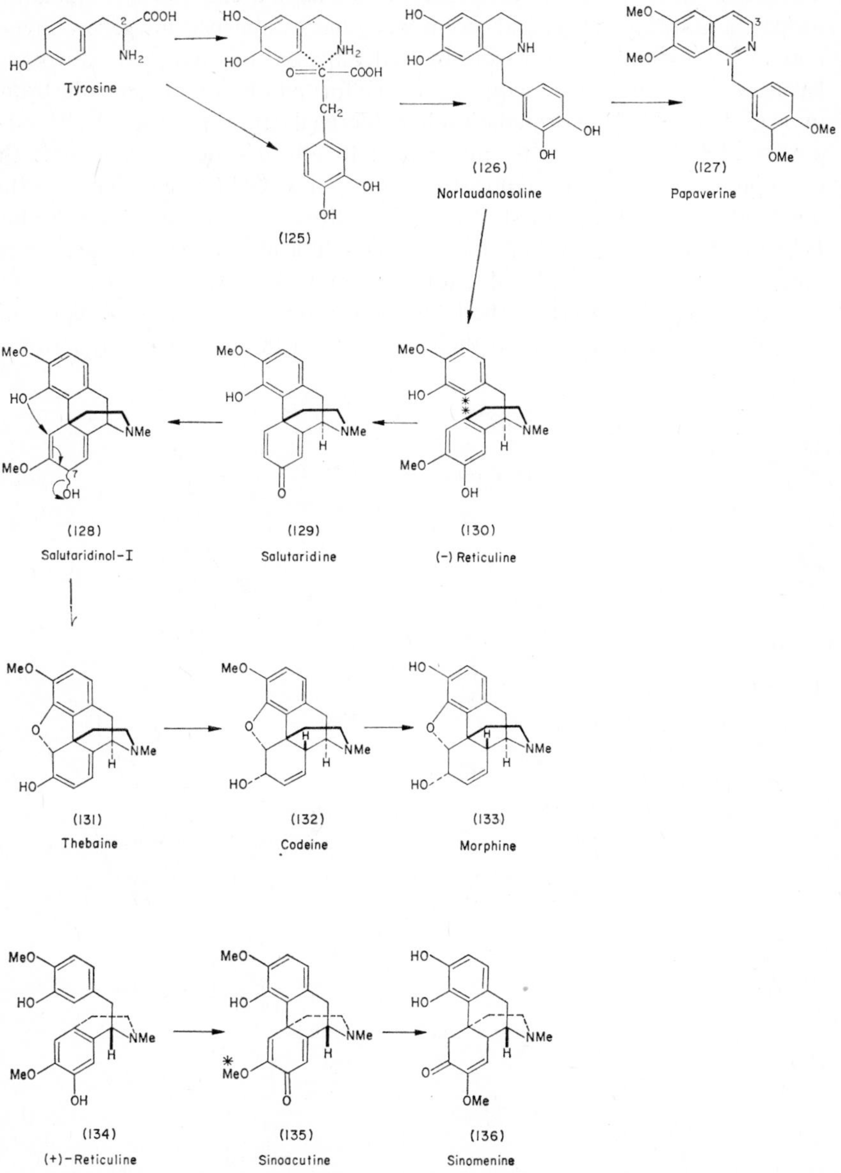

FIG. 19. Biosynthesis of the opium and related alkaloids.

quinoline alkaloids. We therefore suggest that the compound involved in the initial Mannich reaction is 3,4-dihydroxyphenylpyruvic acid (125) and not 3,4-dihydroxyphenylacetaldehyde, which we feel should be readily formed in the plant by the oxidation of dopamine. Robinson[122] suggested that norlaudanosoline (126) was the precursor of a large number of other alkaloids including morphine (133) and recent work has established his general hypothesis.[274a] Extensive tracer work by Battersby, Barton and their co-workers has led to the biosynthetic sequence for the formation of morphine illustrated in Fig. 19.[31, 32, 38] Norlaudanosoline (derived from tyrosine[147, 161] and dopamine[39, 189]) is partially methylated to afford reticuline and it is the (−)-epimer (130) which is converted to morphine. Oxidative coupling of this diphenol between the asterisked positions affords salutaridine (129). Reduction of this dienone yields the dienol salutaridinol. Two isomers were obtained by the chemical reduction of salutaridine. One of these, named salutaridinol-I (128) (having the hydroxy group at C_7 cis to the ethanamine bridge[145a]), was converted to thebaine (131) in the opium poppy 30 times

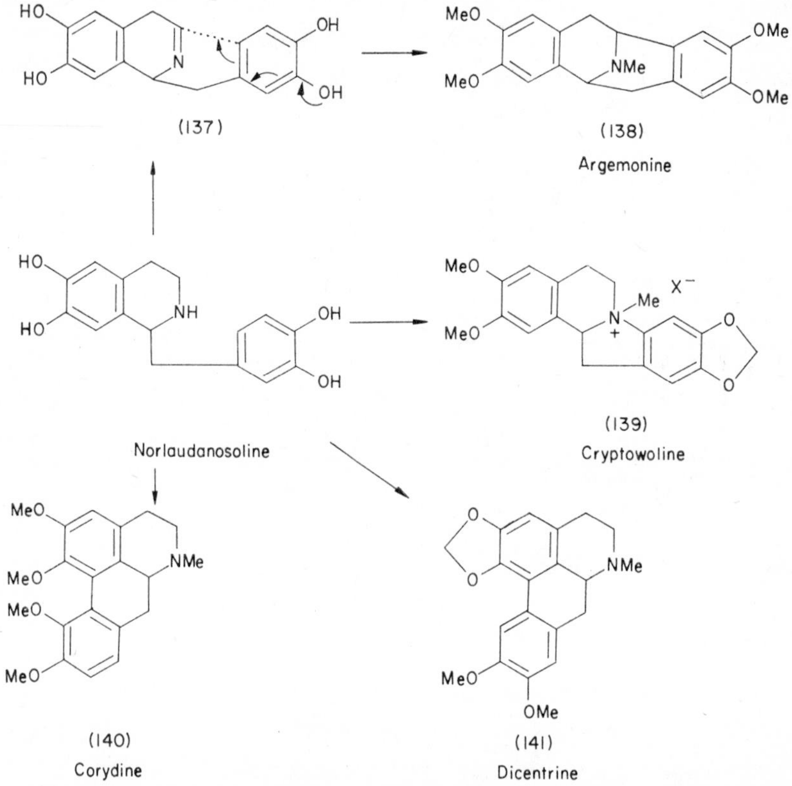

(137)

(138)
Argemonine

Norlaudanosoline

(139)
Cryptowoline

(140)
Corydine

(141)
Dicentrine

Fig. 20. Some alkaloids hypothetically derived from norlaudanosoline.

more efficiently than its C_7-epimer.[23] Several studies[44, 91, 92, 203, 237, 279] have indicated that thebaine is the first of the major alkaloids produced in *Papaver somniferum*. It is then converted to codeine (132) and finally to morphine. Some *Papaver* species apparently lack the enzymes which catalyse these last two steps. Thus *P. bracteatum* contains a large amount of thebaine but no morphine or codeine.[223, 224] Reticuline and salutaridine, first isolated from other plants, have now been found in opium poppies in very low concentration.[23, 36f, 65, 66, 67] In a crude enzyme preparation obtained from young *P. somniferum* seedlings, Rapoport[235] has demonstrated the conversion of (—)-reticuline to thebaine.

Sinomenine (136) is formed in the plant *Sinomenium acutum* from (+)-reticuline, an intermediate being sinoacutine (135), the enantiomer of salutaridine. [21] It is not at present known whether the O-methyl group in the non-aromatic ring of this alkaloid is derived from the methyl group indicated with an asterisk in sinoacutine.

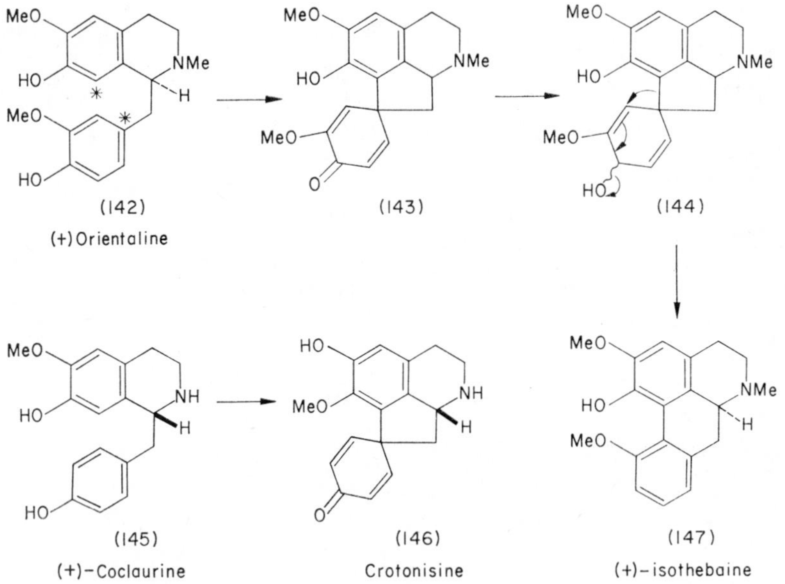

FIG. 21. Biosynthesis of isothebaine and related alkaloids.

Argemonine (138) is plausibly formed in nature by the cyclization of a 2,3-dehydro-norlaudanosoline, as illustrated in Fig. 20. An alternative oxidative cyclization of norlaudanosoline hypothetically leads to the carbon skeleton of cryptowoline (139). The aporphine type of alkaloid results from a third type of oxidative coupling leading to hydroxylation patterns represented by the alkaloids corydine (140) and dicentrine (141). (+)-Isothebaine (147) with an "abnormal" hydroxylation pattern is derived from (+)-orientaline (142) in *P. orientale*. [36, 36e] Oxidative coupling of orientaline at the asterisked

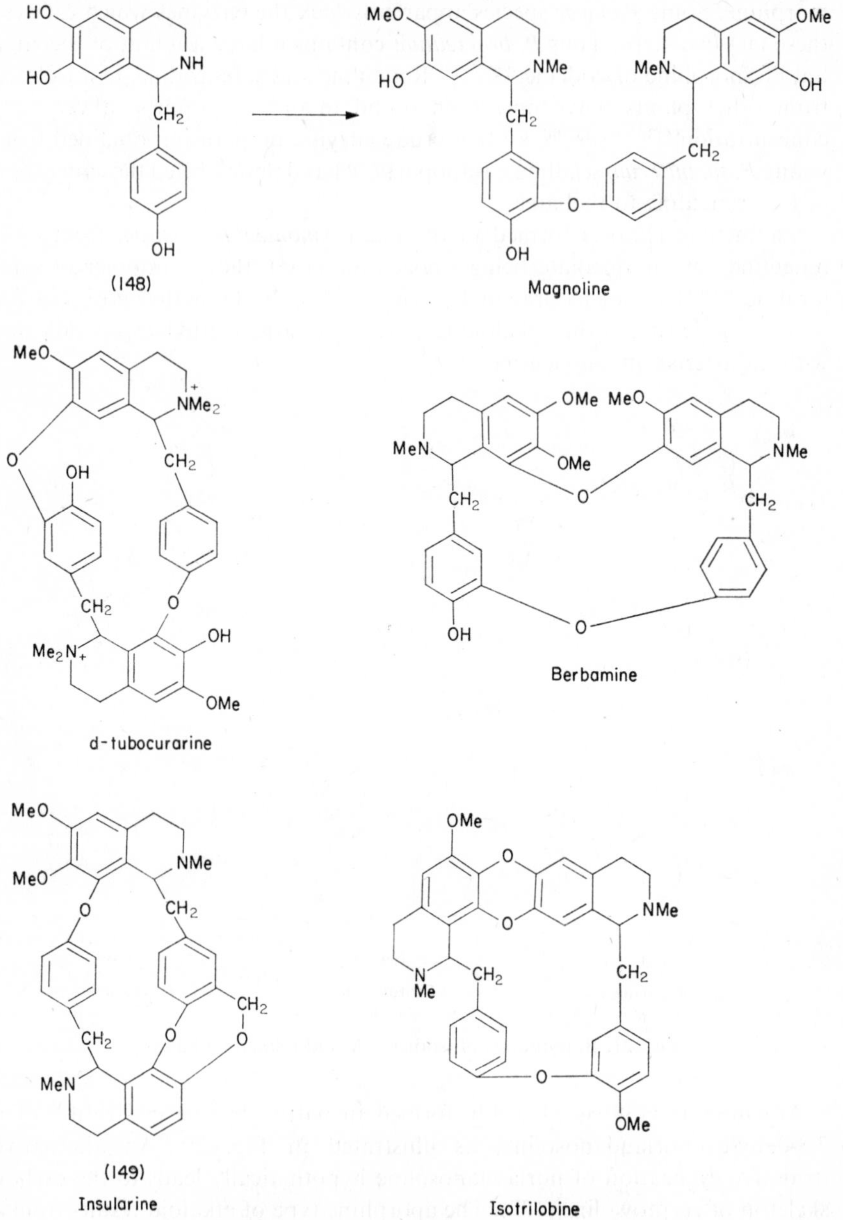

FIG. 22. Some bis-benzylisoquinoline alkaloids.

positions affords the dienone (143), which is reduced to the dienol (144). A dienol-benzene rearrangement then affords isothebaine as illustrated in Fig. 21. Several dienones of the type (143) have been recently found in nature. One of these, crotonisine (146), has been shown to arise in the plant *Croton linearis* by the oxidative coupling of (+)-coclaurine (145).[130] Tracer results indicated that the coclaurine was not demethylated prior to its conversion to crotonisine. There is the possibility[18] that methyl migration occurs during the biosynthesis. Roemerine is formed by a similar dienol-benzene rearrangement.[18a]

Many of the bis-benzylisoquinoline alkaloids are plausibly formed by the oxidative coupling of two molecules of the trihydroxybenzylisoquinoline (148), which could be formed from dopamine and p-hydroxyphenylpyruvic acid. Representative examples from this large class are illustrated in Fig. 22. Detailed mechanisms for the formation of some of these alkaloids have been discussed by Barton,[19] and tracer experiments on the biosynthesis of epistephanine are consistent with these hypotheses.[25a] An extra one-carbon fragment must be involved in the biosynthesis of insularine (149) which contains a seven-membered depsidan ring. Cyclization of the benzylisoquinoline (151), which has an uncommon hydroxylation pattern, leads to the alkaloid cularine (152, Fig. 23). Petaline (150) having the hydroxyls at C_7 and C_8 in the isoquinoline nucleus, has been recently isolated.[206]

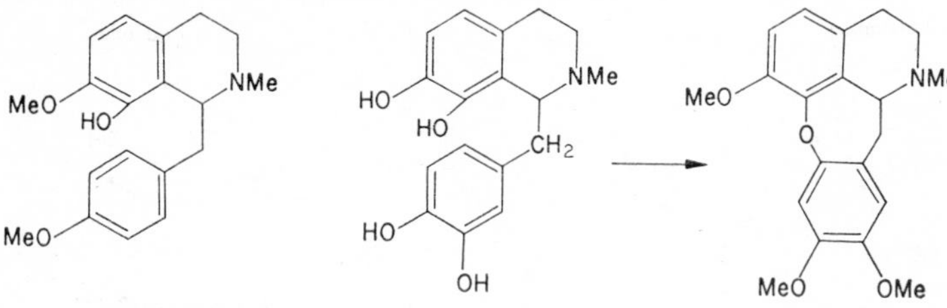

(150)   (151)   (152)
Petaline   Cularine

FIG. 23. Hypothetical biogenesis of cularine.

Another group of alkaloids arises by reaction of the norlaudanosoline skeleton with a one-carbon unit. It has been shown that this extra carbon is in fact the N-methyl group of (+)-reticuline, which undergoes an oxidative cyclization, possibly via the hypothetical imine (153), giving rise to alkaloids such as (−)-stylopine (156),[41] canadine (154) and berberine (155).[20, 40, 54, 139, 101] Protopine (159) is also formed from reticuline,[20] plausible intermediates being stylopine and compounds (157) and (158). Chelidonine (161), a benzophenanthridine alkaloid, is a rearrangement product of stylopine and the formation of the hypothetical intermediate (160) is consistent with tracer results.[41, 165, 189a]

2I

The phthalide-isoquinoline alkaloids, such as narcotine (162) and hydrastine (163), are also apparently degradation products of the berberine type of alkaloid. It was found that (+)-reticuline is a precursor of narcotine in the opium poppy, the lactone-carbonyl group being derived from the N-methyl group of reticuline. [47] Hydrastine is apparently formed by a similar route in *Hydrastis canadensis* plants. [20, 101, 123] Berberastine (164) is un-

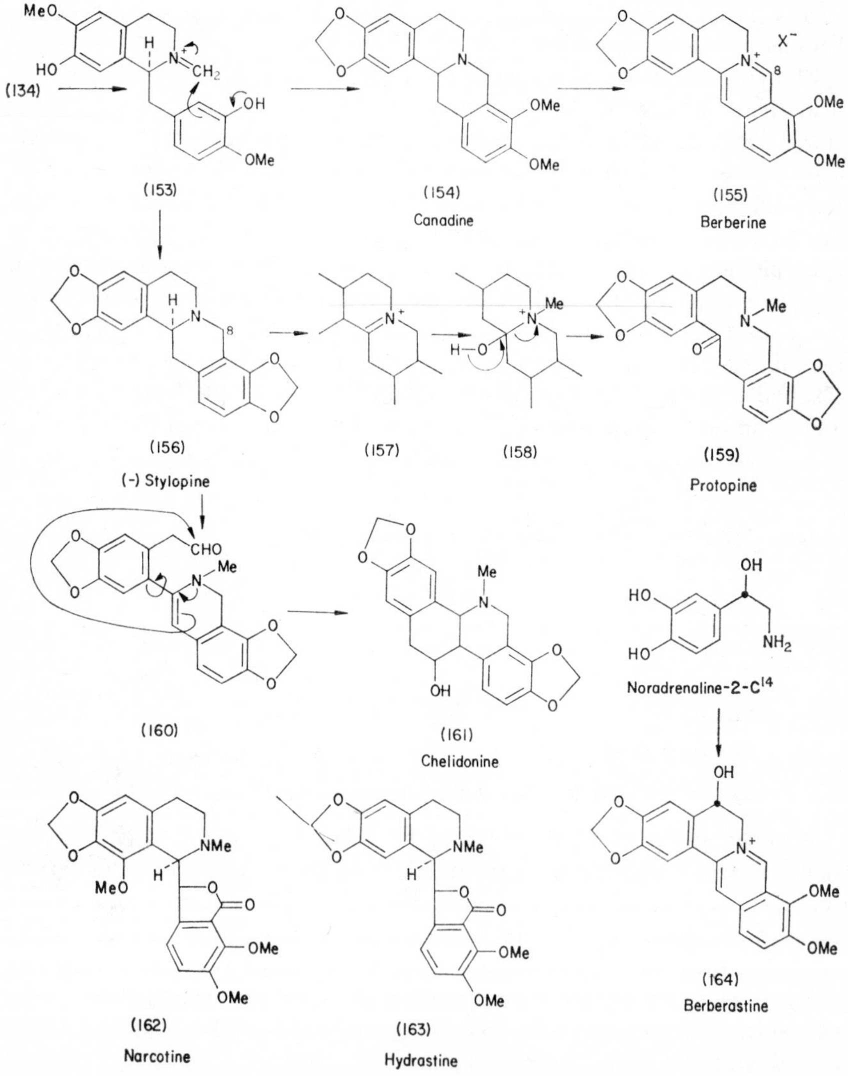

FIG. 24. Alkaloids derived from the protoberberines.

expectedly not derived from berberine, and tracer experiments [207a] indicate that the benzylic hydroxyl group is introduced at an early stage in the biosynthesis before the formation of the benzylisoquinoline skeleton. Noradrenaline-2-C^{14} was incorporated into the alkaloid without randomization of activity.

The alkaloid taspine (166) may be plausibly formed by the oxidation of the aporphine alkaloid (165) followed by dilactonization of the carboxylic acid. [271]

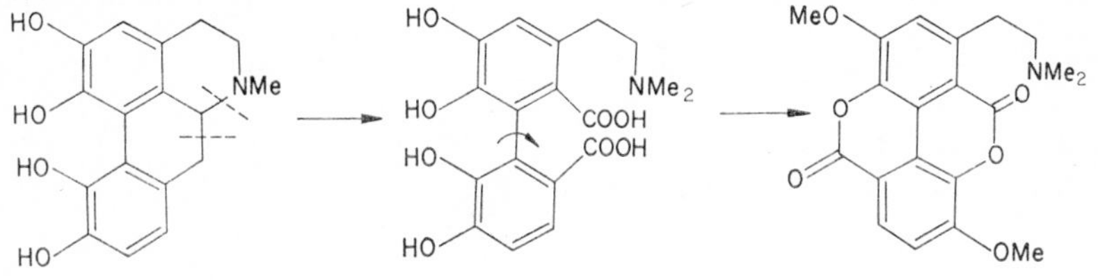

(165)

(166)

Taspine

FIG. 25. Hypothetical biogenesis of taspine.

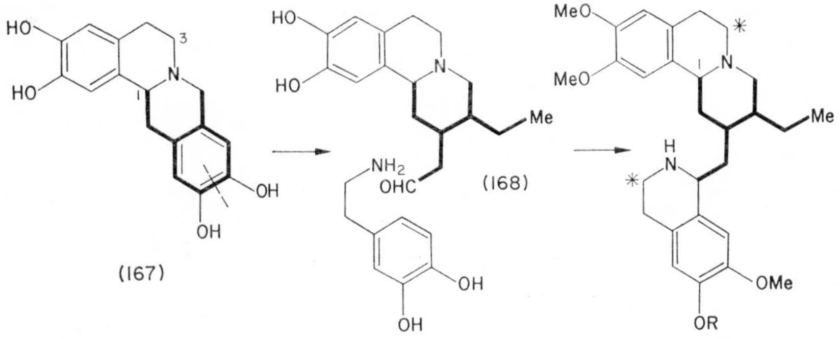

(167)

(168)

(169)

Emetine (R = Me)
Cephaeline (R = H)

FIG. 26. Biosynthesis of emetine.

Emetine (169) is an isoquinoline alkaloid found in *Cephaelis ipecuanha* and Robinson suggested [242] the biogenetic scheme illustrated in Fig. 26. Fission of the catechol ring of the protoberberine (167) could give rise to the intermediate (168), which on condensation with dopamine yields the carbon skeleton of emetine. Battersby [28, 34a] has shown this hypothesis to be incorrect. Tyrosine-2-C^{14} was fed to *C. ipecuanha* plants and radioactive cephaeline obtained. However, activity was located only at the asterisked carbons. A protoberberine derived from tyrosine-2-C^{14} would be labeled at C_1 and C_3 and should have yielded cephaeline with label at C_1. The origin of the central C-9 unit of emetine thus remains in doubt. This same C-9 unit is found in many indole alkaloids (see Section XII) and may be derived from the same precursors.

IX. COLCHICINE AND RELATED ALKALOIDS

It is appropriate to discuss the biosynthesis of colchicine (175) at this time since it is now clear that this alkaloid, once thought to have a unique type of

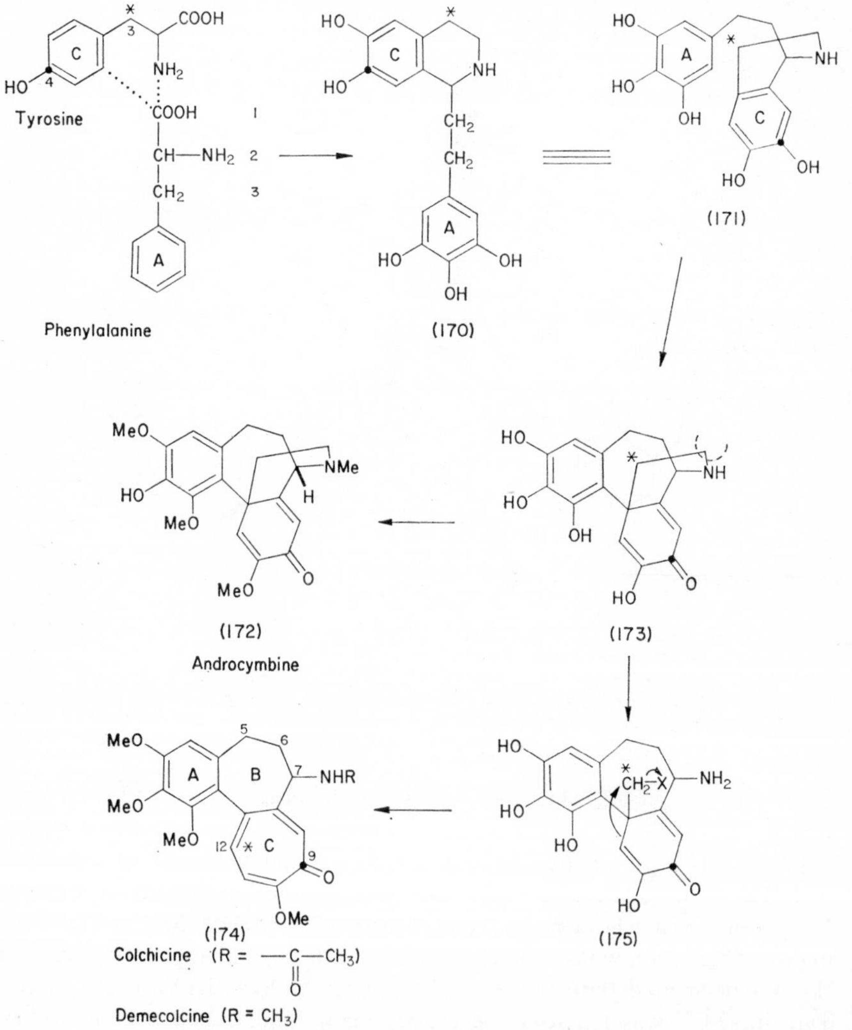

FIG. 27. Biosynthesis of colchicine and related alkaloids.

structure, is related to the isoquinoline alkaloids. This relationship is evident in Fig. 27 where a biosynthetic scheme for colchicine and related alkaloids is outlined. Compounds metabolically close to tyrosine and phenylalanine condense to yield the hydroxylated 1-phenylethyltetrahydroisoquinoline (170). The immediate precursors of this compound may be dopamine and β-(3,4,5-trihydroxyphenyl)propionaldehyde. Redrawing the structure of this isoquinoline as (171) makes it easy to follow the next step which is an oxidative coupling affording the dienone (173). Androcymbine (172), which is found along with colchicine in *Androcymbium melanthioides*,[46] is a methylated derivative of this hypothetical intermediate. It is likely that the actual oxidative coupling actually occurs on a methylated derivative of the isoquinoline (170).[45a] Loss of a carbon from the ethano-bridge in compound (173) affords the intermediate (175), where X is a good leaving group such as phosphate. A ring enlargement of this dienone then affords the tropolone ring of colchicine, having the correct oxygenation pattern. Feeding experiments which substantiate this hypothesis are as follows. Phenylalanine labeled with C^{14} at C-1, -2 and -3 of the side chain afforded colchicine or demecolcine labeled at C-7, -6 and -5, respectively.[33, 35, 166, 190] Cinnamic acid could also replace phenylalanine as a precursor of this part of the colchicine molecule.[33, 135] Tyrosine labeled at C-3 of the side chain and at C-4 in the benzene ring yielded colchicine labeled at C-12 and C-9, respectively.[35, 45, 170] It should be noted that in the *Colchicum* plant phenylalanine and tyrosine are not interconvertible. Acetic acid served as a precursor of the N-acetyl group of colchicine.[33, 191]

X. AMARYLLIDACEAE ALKALOIDS

O-Methylnorbelladine (179) plays a central role in the biosynthesis of the *Amaryllidaceae* alkaloids.[24, 26] This compound is formed from phenylalanine and tyrosine by the route illustrated in Fig. 28.[29, 282, 312] Phenylalanine is a precursor of protocatechuic aldehyde (176) which condenses with tyramine, derived from tyrosine, to yield the Schiff base (177). Reduction affords norbelladine (178) which is methylated to (179). The enzyme which catalyzes this methylation has been isolated by Mudd and co-workers[95] from the plant *Neriine bowdenii*. Suhadolnik has also isolated some of the enzymes which catalyze earlier steps in this sequence.[280] Para-ortho oxidative coupling of O-methylnorbelladine yields the transient intermediate (182). Nucleophilic attack of the amino group on the dienone yields norpluviine (181). Allylic oxidation at C_2 and formation of the methylenedioxy group leads to lycorine (180). Much ingenious tracer work has confirmed this hypothesis.[29, 30, 145b] Lycorine is a precursor of hippeastrine (185)[280] and plausible intermediates are (183) and (184).

Para-para coupling of O-methylnorbelladine leads to (186) and then by unexceptional steps to alkaloids such as crinamine (187). Further oxidation yields haemanthamine (190), [24, 37, 141] which has been shown to be a precursor of haemanthidine (193) and tazzetine (194). [96] The conversion of compound (192) to (191) involves an intramolecular hydride transfer, and has been demonstrated in the laboratory. [221] The non-heterocyclic alkaloid ismine (188), which is found along with tazzetine in several *Amaryllidaceae*

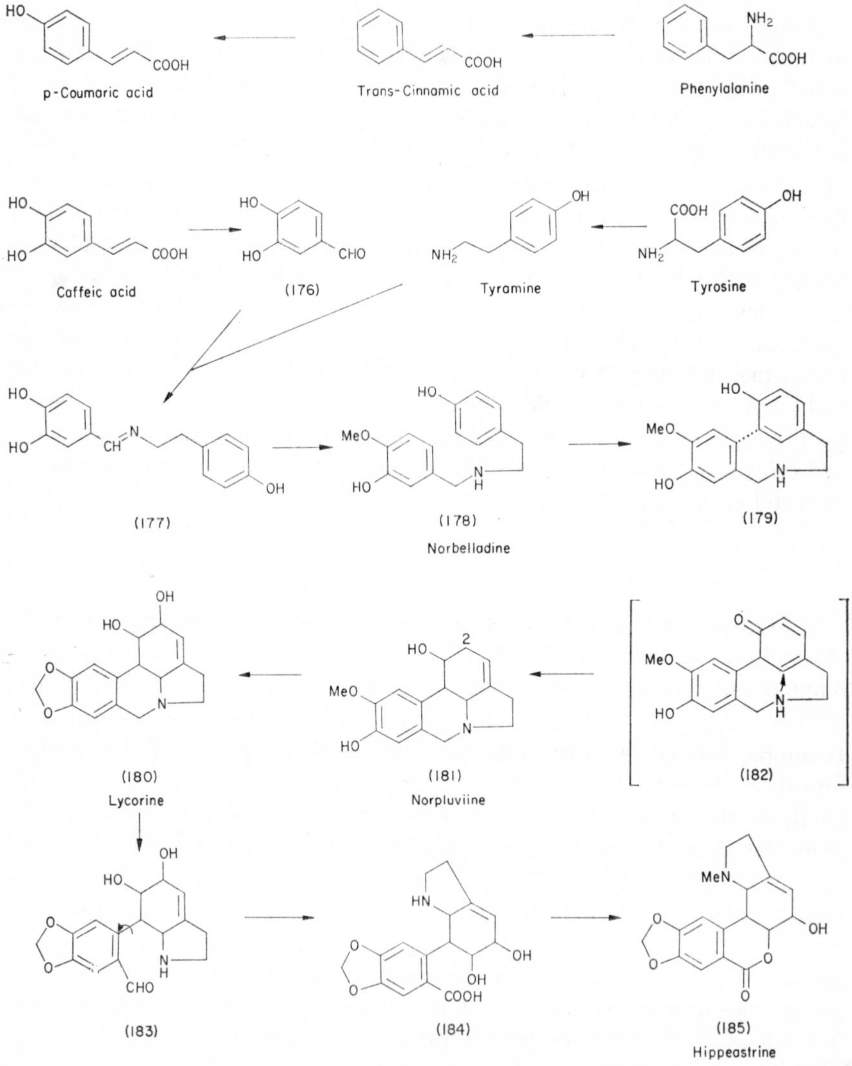

FIG. 28. Biosynthesis of lycorine and related alkaloids.

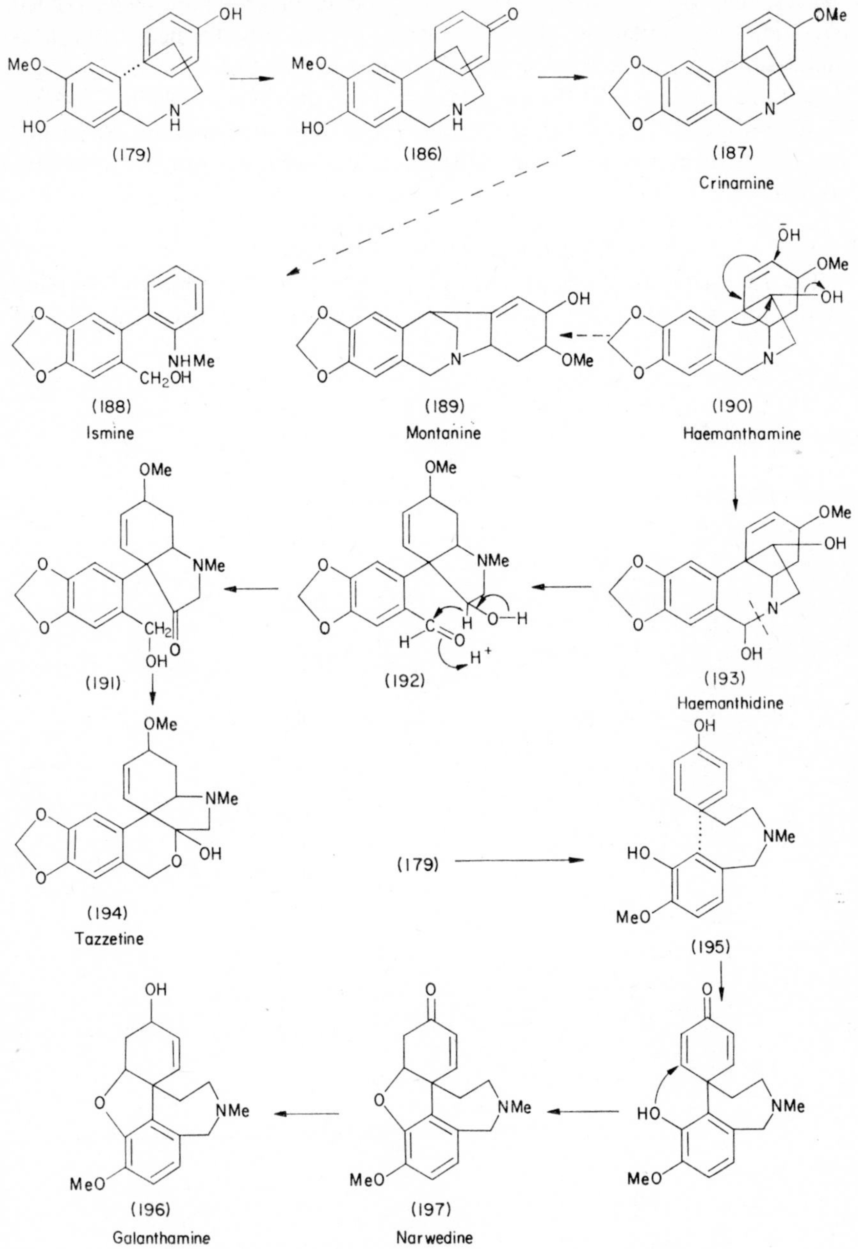

(179)

(186)

(187)
Crinamine

(188)
Ismine

(189)
Montanine

(190)
Haemanthamine

(191)

(192)

(193)
Haemanthidine

(194)
Tazzetine

(179) ⟶

(195)

(196)
Galanthamine

(197)
Narwedine

FIG. 29. Biosynthesis of tazzetine, galanthamine and related alkaloids.

species, may be a natural degradation product of crinamine or a related alkaloid. [134] Montanine (189) is also hypothetically formed from hae- manthamine by the rearrangement illustrated in Fig. 29.

A third mode of oxidative coupling of O-methylnorbelladine leading to narwedine (197) and galathamine (196) is illustrated in Fig. 29. In this case N-methylation to (195) is apparently essential prior to oxidative coupling. [17, 18, 22, 24]

XI. ERYTHRINA ALKALOIDS

The Erythrina alkaloids are plausibly derived by the oxidative coupling of the intermediate (198), which could be formed from two molecules of

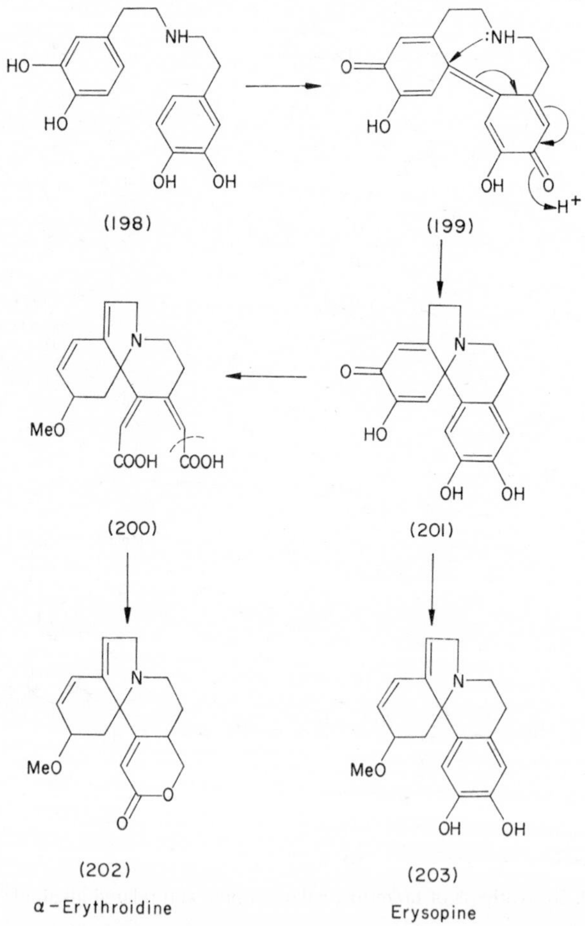

FIG. 30. Hypothetical biogenesis of the *Erythrina* alkaloids.

dopamine.[19] Nucleophilic addition of the amino group to the quinonoid system in (199) leads to compound (201). Unexceptional steps then yield the aromatic *Erythrina* alkaloids represented in Fig. 30 by erysopine (203). A dimethyl derivative of (198) has been oxidized *in vitro* to a compound containing the tetracyclic ring system of erysopine.[21a, 102a, 206a] The non-aromatic alkaloids of this family, represented by α-erythroidine (202), may be formed by the oxidative fission of the catechol ring of (201) to yield (200), followed by appropriate modifications of the side chains and ultimate lactonization. The pattern of labeling found in α- and β-erythroidine after administering tyrosine-2-C^{14} to *Erythrina berteroana* plants was consistent with this biosynthetic sequence.[171b] Wenkert's suggestion[298] that these alkaloids are formed from prephenic acid is now untenable.

XII. INDOLE ALKALOIDS

The majority of these alkaloids contain two nitrogen atoms; one is the indolic nitrogen, and the second almost invariably is separated from the β-position of the indole nucleus by a two-carbon unit. Some examples are

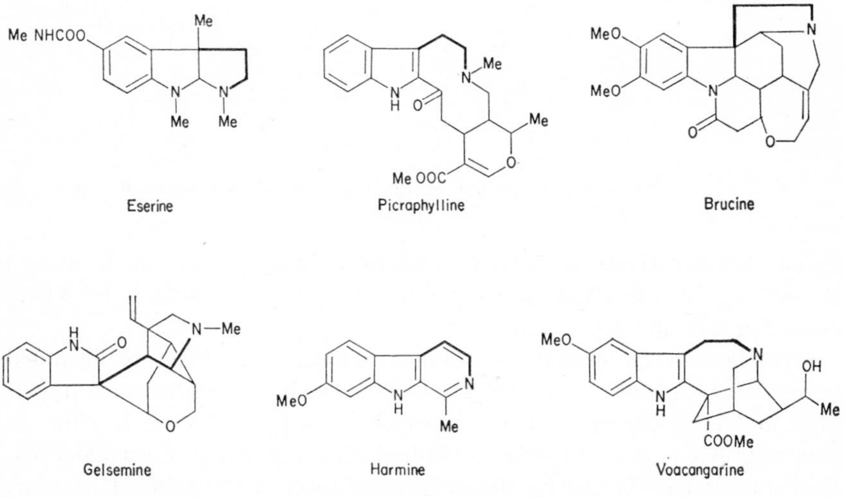

FIG. 31. Some indole alkaloids.

illustrated in Fig. 31, the bonds joining the β-position of the indole nucleus to the second nitrogen being indicated with heavy lines. It was thus suggested many years ago that the indole alkaloids are derived in part from tryptophan or its decarboxylation product tryptamine. Radioactive ajmaline,[163] cinchonamine,[174] reserpine,[169] serpentine,[169] vindoline,[118, 172] ibogaine,[309] and harmine,[117] were obtained from radioactive tryptophan, and degradations indicated that the alkaloids were labeled in the expected positions.

The benzene ring of the indole nucleus in these alkaloids is quite commonly hydroxylated. We do not know the mechanism of this hydroxylation, or at what stage in the biosynthesis of these alkaloids these hydroxyl groups are introduced. Therefore in the biosynthetic schemes which follow, hydroxyl groups will be introduced into this benzene ring without further comment.

A large number of indole alkaloids are hypothetically produced by a Mannich reaction involving the α- or β-position of the indole nucleus of tryptamine, an aldehyde or α-ketoacid, and the primary amino group of the tryptamine side chain, as illustrated in Fig. 32. An α-condensation leads

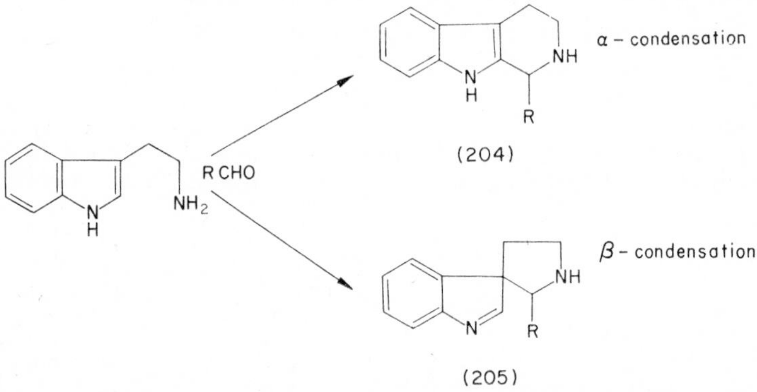

FIG. 32. Schematic representation of the hypothetical biogenesis of some indole alkaloids.

to β-carboline derivatives (204). This reaction is analogous to the formation of the isoquinoline alkaloids from dopamine. The product of the β-condensation is an indolenine (205).

Plausible routes to several of the simple β-carboline alkaloids are illustrated in Fig. 33. Eleagnine (206) is the product of a condensation between tryptamine and acetaldehyde, a reaction which is readily achieved *in vitro*. In plants pyruvic acid could serve as the biological equivalent of acetaldehyde. Harman (207) is formed by the dehydrogenation of eleagnine. Harmaline (209) is a 3,4-dihydro-β-carboline and it has been suggested[274] that this type of alkaloid arise by the dehydration and tautomerization of a 1-hydroxymethyltetrahydro-β-carboline (208) as illustrated in Fig. 33. This hydroxymethyl derivative could be formed from tryptamine and glycolaldehyde. The tetracyclic alkaloid canthin-6-one (210) could be formed from tryptamine and 3-formylpropionic acid, [243] a plausible metabolite of glutamic acid.

The quinazolone alkaloids which also contain an indole nucleus are probably formed from anthranilic acid and 1-oxo-1,2,3,4-tetrahydro-β-carboline (211) by unexceptional steps illustrated in Fig. 34.[308a]

It was suggested many years ago by Barger[16] and Hahn[127] that indole

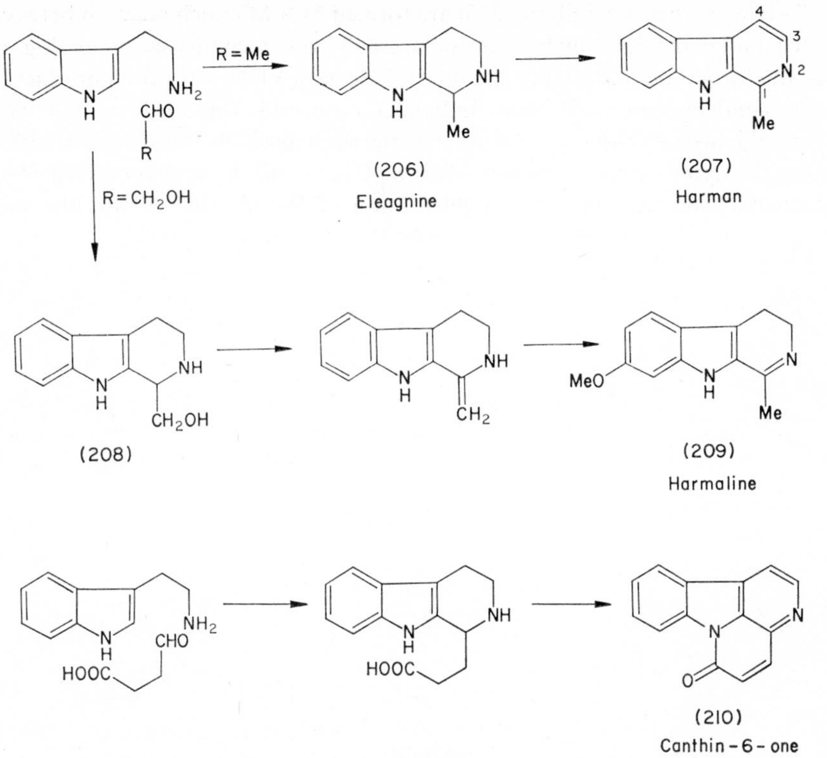

FIG. 33. Hypothetical biogenesis of some simple β-carboline derivatives.

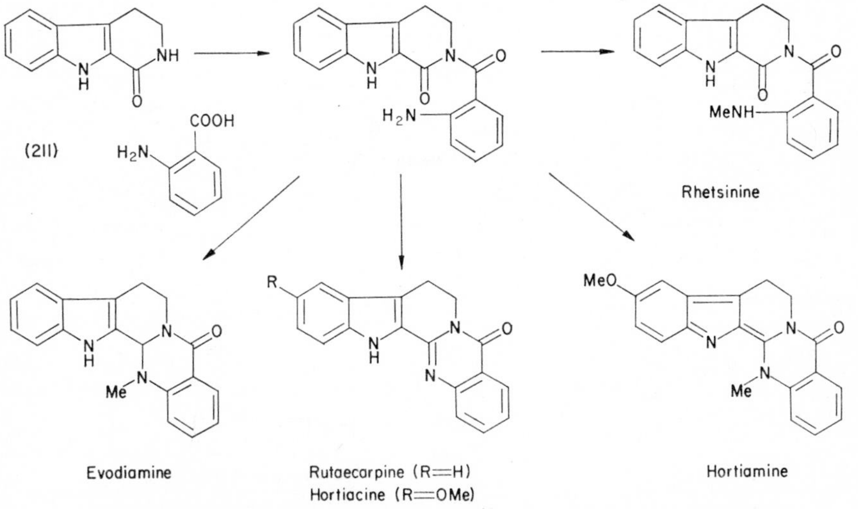

FIG. 34. Hypothetical biogenesis of some quinazolino-β-carboline alkaloids.

alkaloids such as yohimbine (215) are formed by a Mannich reaction between tryptamine and 3,4-dihydroxyphenylacetaldehyde, a condensation analogous to the formation of norlaudanosoline (cf. Section VIII). The initial product of this condensation (212) then undergoes a second Mannich reaction with formaldehyde yielding the pentacyclic intermediate (213). It was suggested [243] that the extra carbon, which is often at C_{16} in ring E, is also derived from formaldehyde. An important contribution of Woodward [306] was the sug-

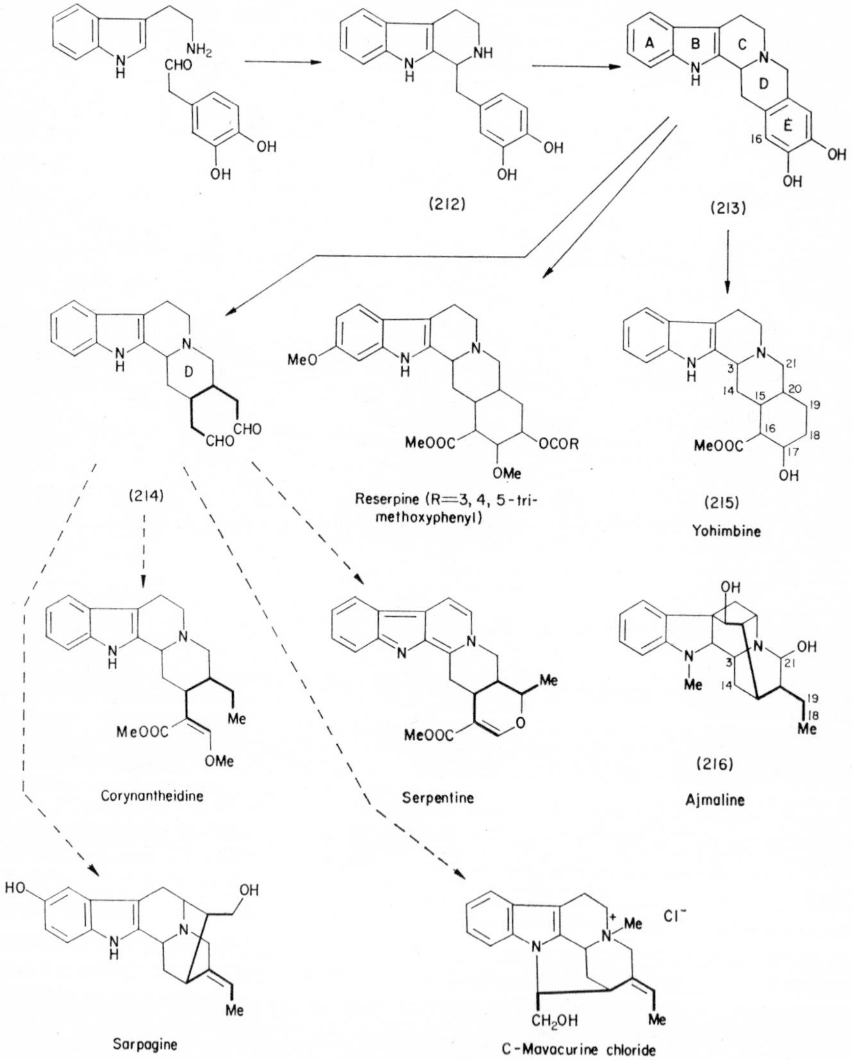

FIG. 35. Some indole alkaloids belonging to the α-series.

gestion that the catechol ring E could undergo fission to yield an intermediate such as (214). The two side chains attached to ring D in this compound can then undergo plausible condensations with each other or with other parts of the molecule to give rise to various structural types, some of which are illustrated in Fig. 35. The bonds joining the atoms which were originally part of ring E in the intermediate (213) are indicated by heavy lines in these alkaloids.

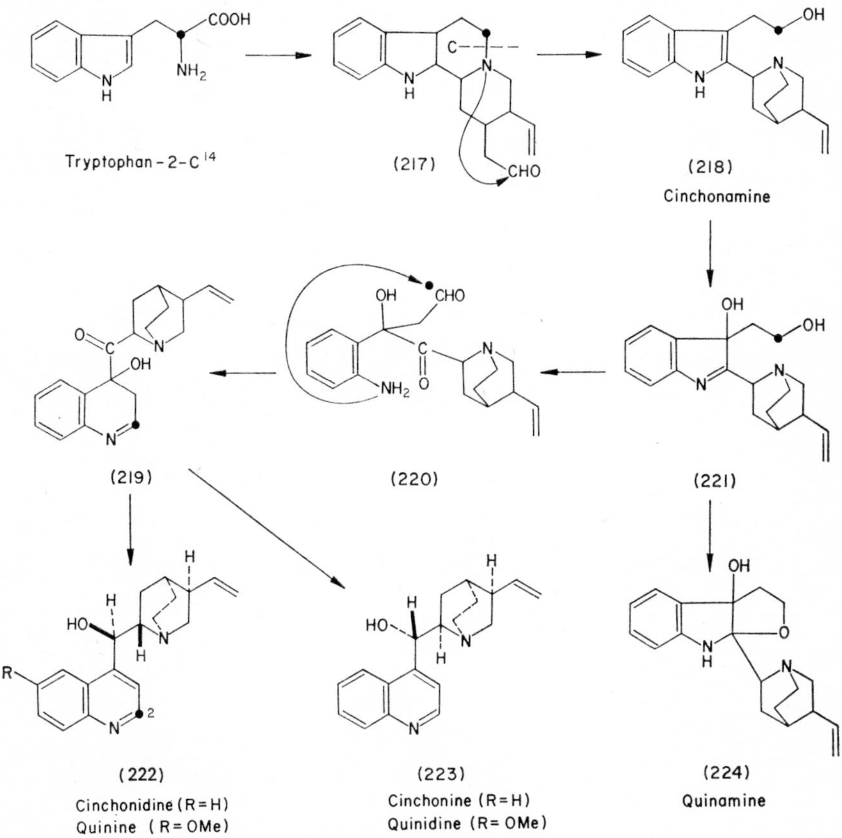

FIG. 36. Biosynthesis of the cinchona alkaloids.

It has also been suggested [105] that the *Cinchona* alkaloids (Fig. 36) are derived from an intermediate of the type (217). Cleavage of ring C and formation of the quinuclidine ring affords cinchonamine (218). The indolenine derivative (221) results from oxidative attack of the β-position of cinchonamine. Oxidation of the primary alcohol group and opening of the indolenine ring yields compound (220). Recyclization of the amino group on the aldehyde carbonyl affords the dihydroquinoline (219). Unexceptional steps then yield the main *Cinchona* alkaloids (222) and (223). Quinamine (224) could arise from intermediate (221). Tracer experiments are consistent with this hypothesis. The administration of tryptophan-2-C¹⁴ to *Cinchona succirubra*

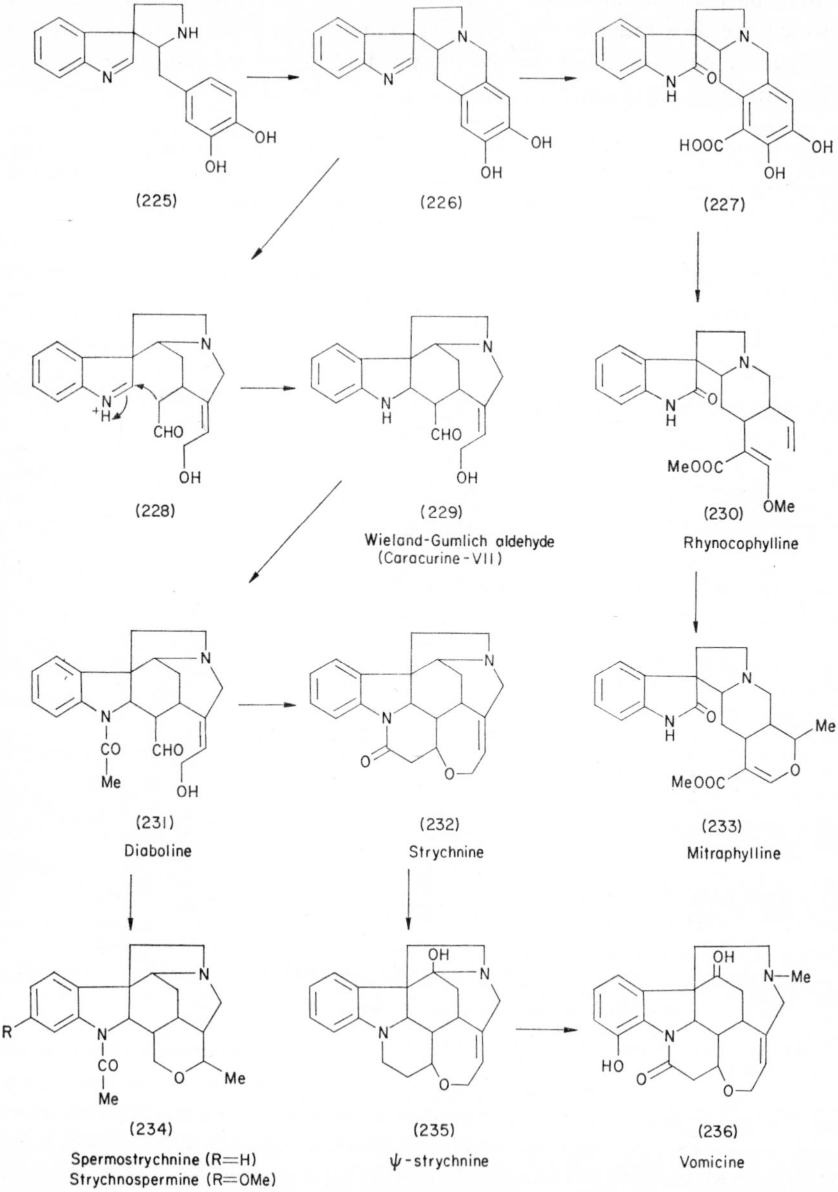

(225)

(226)

(227)

(228)

(229)
Wieland-Gumlich aldehyde
(Caracurine-VII)

(230)
Rhynocophylline

(231)
Diaboline

(232)
Strychnine

(233)
Mitraphylline

(234)
Spermostrychnine (R=H)
Strychnospermine (R=OMe)

(235)
ψ-strychnine

(236)
Vomicine

FIG. 37. Hypothetical biogenesis of strychnine and related alkaloids.

plants yielded radioactive quinine, labeled as expected at C-2 of the quinoline nucleus. [149] An *in vitro* conversion of 2-methyltryptophan to 4-acetyl-quinoline has been achieved. [293]

Woodward [306] rationalized the structure of strychnine (232) on the basis of the biogenetic scheme illustrated in Fig. 37. An initial β-condensation of tryptamine and 3,4-dihydroxyphenylacetaldehyde affords the intermediate (225). A second Mannich reaction involving formaldehyde yields compound (227). Fission of the catechol ring affords the intermediate (228), which undergoes the condensation illustrated in Fig. 37 yielding the Wieland–Gumlich

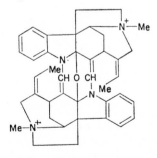

C – fluorocurarine   Akuammicine

Caracurine Ⅴ   Toxiferine I

C – alkaloid H   C – curarine – I

Fig. 38. Some alkaloids biogenetically related to the Wieland–Gumlich aldehyde.

aldehyde (229). This compound, which exists mainly as the hemiacetal, was first obtained as a degradation product of strychnine. However, it has been found that the curare alkaloid, caracurine-VII, is identical with it. Acetylation yields the alkaloid diaboline (231), which is converted into strychnine by dehydration. Condensations analogous with this biogenetic scheme have

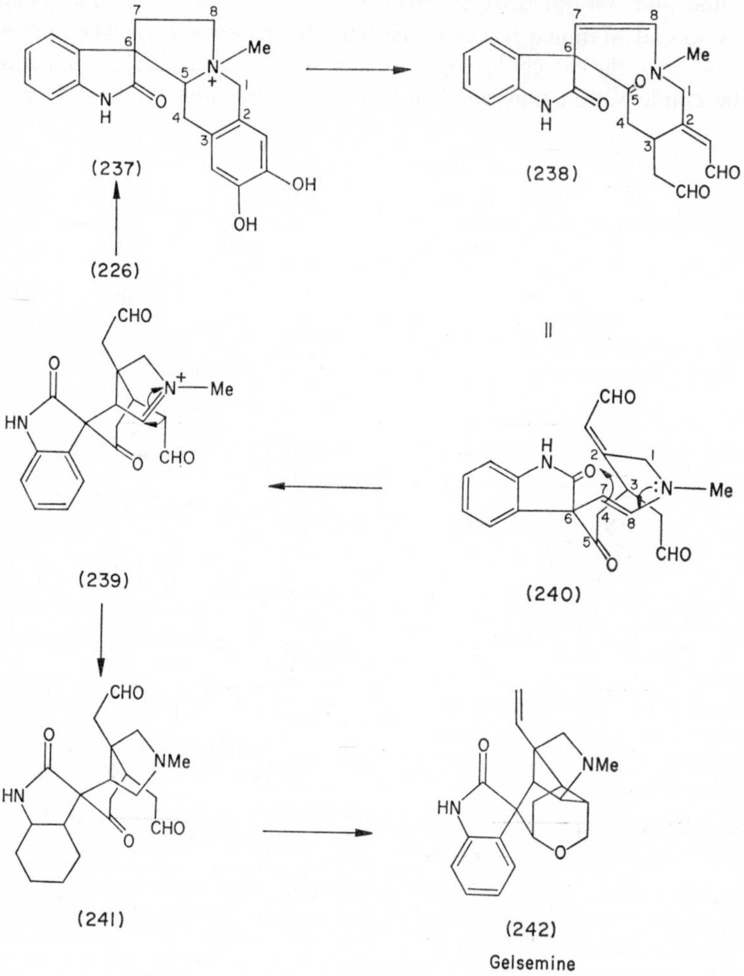

FIG. 39. Hypothetical biogenesis of gelsemine.

been achieved in the laboratory. [129, 290] The oxindole alkaloids, rhynoco-phylline (230) and mitraphylline (233) may be derived from the intermediate (227) by fission of the catechol ring and appropriate reactions of the fragments produced. The intermediate (227) could be formed by reaction of the catechol ring with a one-carbon fragment, with concomitant oxidation of the indolenine to an oxindole. Alternatively, the initial Mannich reaction could involve 3-aminoethyloxindole rather than tryptamine. Spermostrychnine and strychnospermine (234) could be derived from intermediates closely related to diaboline. Vomicine (236) could be formed from strychnine via ψ-strychnine (235). Some other alkaloids which are obviously closely related biogenetically to the Wieland–Gumlich aldehyde are illustrated in Fig. 38. Several of the dimeric C_{40} alkaloids have been synthesized *in vitro* from two molecules of a C_{20} alkaloid, and it seems probable that similar reactions occur in plants.

Gelsemine (242) is another alkaloid which is plausibly derived from the strychnine precursor (226) as illustrated in Fig. 39. [74] Oxidation of the intermediate (226) and N-methylation yields compound (237). Woodward fission of the catechol ring, dehydrogenation of the 7,8-bond, and oxidative cleavage of the bond joining C_5 with the quarternary nitrogen leads to compound (238) which may be redrawn as (240). A new bond is formed between C_2 and C_7 by a Michael addition of the enamine to the α,β-unsaturated aldehyde affording (239). An internal Mannich reaction affords compound (241), gelsemine then being obtained by unexceptional steps.

It is now opportune to discuss Wenkert's ideas on the biogenesis of the indole alkaloids. [298, 299, 300] He suggests that the hydroaromatic compound (245) (Fig. 40) is the one involved in a Mannich reaction with tryptamine and a one-carbon unit. This compound may be formed from prephenic acid (243) via the intermediate (244), or directly from shikimic acid. [300] The carbon atoms in (245) are numbered as they are predicted to occur in an alkaloid such as yohimbine (215, Fig. 35). This hypothesis has several attractive features. It accounts for the presence of the carboxyl group at C_{16} and also rationalizes the fact that the hydrogen attached to C_{15} in yohimbine, reserpine, and related alkaloids almost always has an α-configuration. Wenkert suggests that the α-configuration of the hydrogen at C_{15} in the intermediate (245) is the result of a stereospecific migration of the pyruvate side chain in compound (244). Furthermore, there is little chance for racemization at C_{15} in subsequent modifications of (245) to yield the various types of structure found in the indole alkaloids. Some possible transformations of (245) are illustrated in Fig. 40. A reverse aldol condensation involved in the conversion of (248) to (247) is equivalent to "Woodward fission" of the older hypothesis.

More hypotheses regarding the origin of the non-tryptophan derived portion of the indole alkaloids are illustrated in Fig. 41. The "monoterpene" hypothesis was suggested independently by Thomas [286] and Wenkert. [299] Here the cyclopentanomonoterpene (249), derived from two molecules of mevalonic acid, undergoes cleavage at the dotted line yielding the desired carbon skeleton (250) which is numbered as it would appear in yohimbine and related alkaloids. The "acetate" hypothesis was developed to rationalize

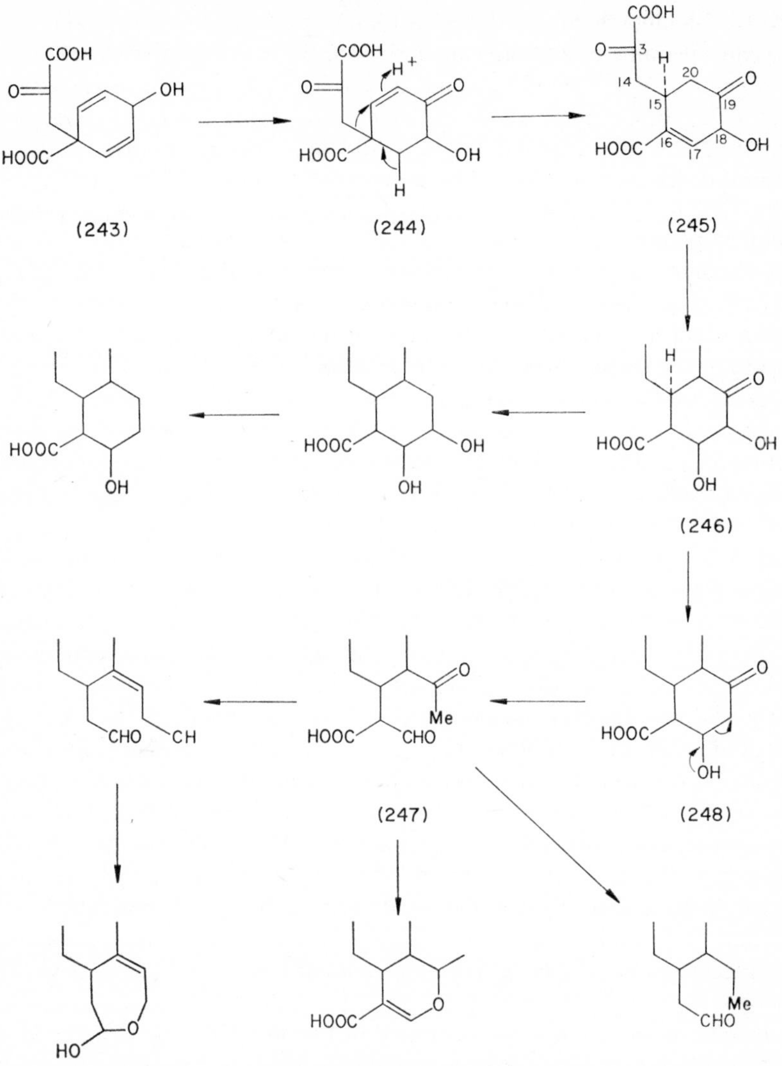

Fig. 40. Wenkert's hypothesis for the origin of the "E ring" of the indole alkaloids.

preliminary tracer results. [175] A six-carbon chain derived from three acetate units condenses with malonic acid and a one-carbon unit (biologically equivalent to formaldehyde) yielding the desired C-10 unit (251). Hendrickson [132] suggested a modification of this scheme. A ten-carbon chain (252) undergoes oxidation at the terminal methyl group, reaction with a one-carbon unit, and an aldol cyclization to yield (253). A retroactive aldol (at the dotted line) then affords (254). The intermediate (253) is essentially the same as the one which Wenkert derived from prephenic acid.

Until recently the origin of this C-9 or C-10 unit remained one of the major unsolved problems in the alkaloid biosynthesis field.[285] Experiments with radioactive tracers are summarized as follows. Ajmaline (216, Fig. 35) isolated from *Rauwolfia serpentina* plants which had been fed tyrosine-2-C^{14}

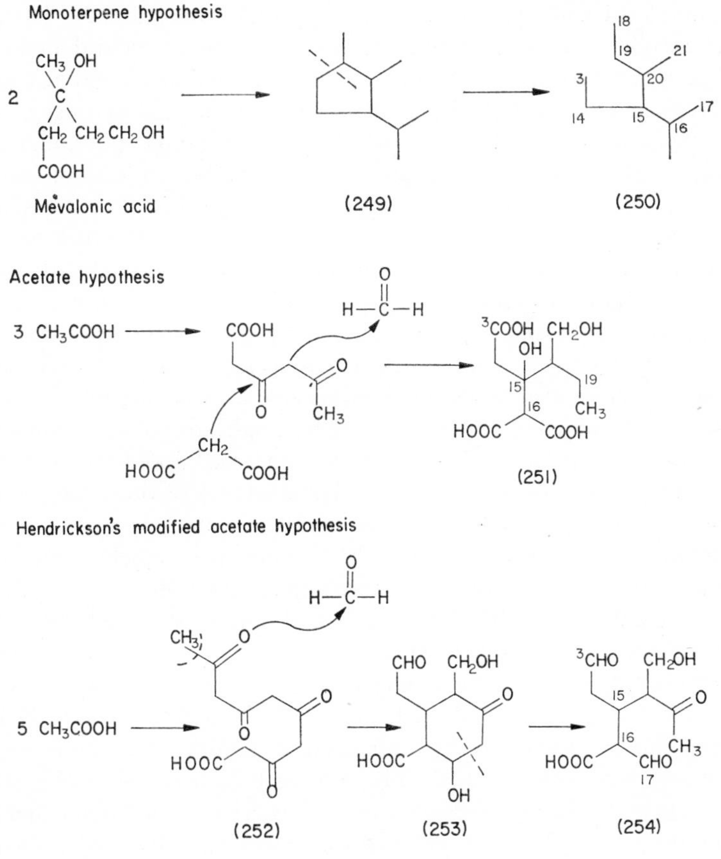

Fig. 41. Hypothesis for the origin of the C-10 unit of yohimbine and related alkaloids.

was completely inactive.[175] Negative results from feeding experiments must be interpreted with caution, and it could be argued that the plant was unable to convert tyrosine to the required 3,4-dihydroxyphenyl-acetaldehyde. Wenkert's prephenic acid hypothesis has not yet been adequately tested. We fed alanine-2-C^{14} to *R. serpentina* and obtained no specific labeling of ajmaline.[175] We had assumed that the pyruvate formed from alanine by transamination would be incorporated into prephenic acid. However, the actual precursor of the side chain of prephenic acid is phosphoenolpyruvate which is not readily formed from pyruvic acid *in vivo*. [103, 150, 278] Uniformly labeled shikimic acid-C^{14} (the precursor of prephenic acid) was fed to *Vinca rosea* plants and radioactive vindoline obtained (260, Fig. 42). However, degradations indicated that the activity was confined to the indole moiety, which is derived from shikimic acid via anthranilic acid and tryptophan.[118a, 279a] Initially we claimed[175] that the administration of acetate-1-C^{14} to *R. serpentina* plants yielded radioactive ajmaline which had 25 per cent of its activity located at C_3 and at C_{19} with no activity at C_{14} and C_{18}. It was these results which led us to suggest the acetate hypothesis (Fig. 41). Later work [175a] apparently substantiated this hypothesis. However, Battersby, also studying the biosynthesis of ajmaline, reported results[34] which were not consistent with ours. His degradations carried out on ajmaline isolated from *R. serpentina* plants which had been fed acetate-1-C^{14} indicated that the alkaloid was uniformly labeled. We[178] have also obtained radioactive ajmaline which is apparently uniformly labeled from *R. serpentina* plants which were fed acetate-1-C^{14}. Reserpine isolated from the same plant which had been fed acetate-1-C^{14} yielded on hydrolysis reserpic acid and trimethoxybenzoic acid having relative specific activities of 63·5 and 31·5 per cent respectively, indicative of uniform labeling. These recent results have caused me to be concerned about the authenticity of our earlier published work.[175, 175a] However, no obvious deception has been detected and the matter is still under investigation. Arigoni also observed that the administration of acetate-1-C^{14} to *Vinca* plants yielded radioactive reserpinine and vincamedine which were apparently uniformly labeled.[103b]

In preliminary work both Battersby[34] and ourselves[175] failed to obtain any significant radioactivity in ajmaline, when mevalonic acid-2-C^{14} or its lactone was fed to *R. serpentina* plants. However, exciting results have been obtained by Arigoni[103a] and A. I. Scott.[205b, 206b] Arigoni fed mevalonic acid-2-C^{14} to *R. canescens* and obtained a significant incorporation of activity into isoreserpinine (259, Fig. 42), and 25 per cent of the activity was located at the position indicated with an asterisk. Both Arigoni and Scott fed mevalonic acid-2-C^{14} to *Vinca rosea* plants and obtained radioactive vindoline which also had 25 per cent of its activity located on the carbomethoxy group. No activity was detected on the C-ethyl group or the O-acetyl group of vindoline. These observations favor the monoterpene hypothesis. To rationalize the results one has to postulate that randomization of activity occurs between the terminal methyl groups in the intermediate terpene (255) as illustrated in Fig. 42. This distribution of activity was in fact obtained in the terpene plumieride (258) isolated from *Plumiera acutifolia* plants which had been fed mevalonic acid-2-C^{14}. [311] To arrive at the carbon skeleton required for vindoline a rearrangement of (256) to (257) is postulated. We[172] fed acetate-1-C^{14} to *V. rosea* plants and obtained radioactive ajmalicine (262, Fig. 43), catharanthine (263) and vindoline. Degradations indicated that these alkaloids were apparently uniformly labeled, except that the O-acetyl group of vindoline was labeled almost entirely on the carbonyl carbon. If the monoterpene hypothesis is correct, it is not clear why acetate-1-C^{14} should not also afford specifically labeled indole alkaloids,

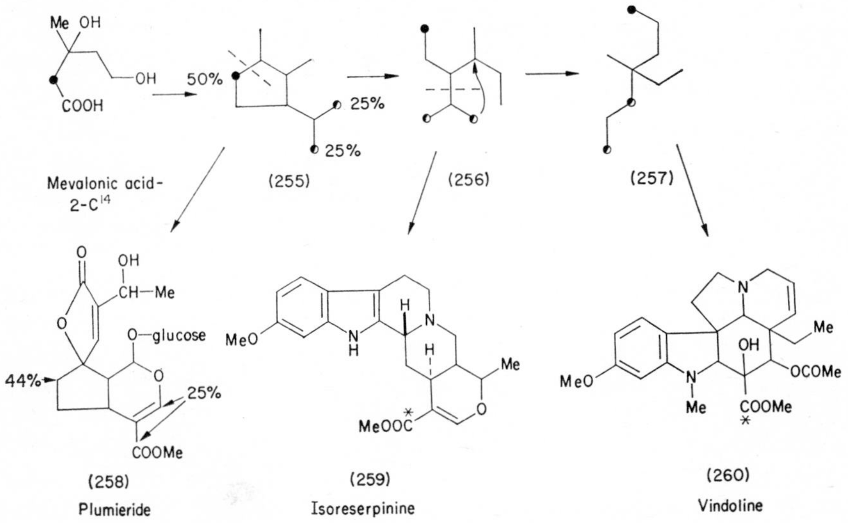

FIG. 42. Incorporation of mevalonic acid into the indole alkaloids and related compounds.

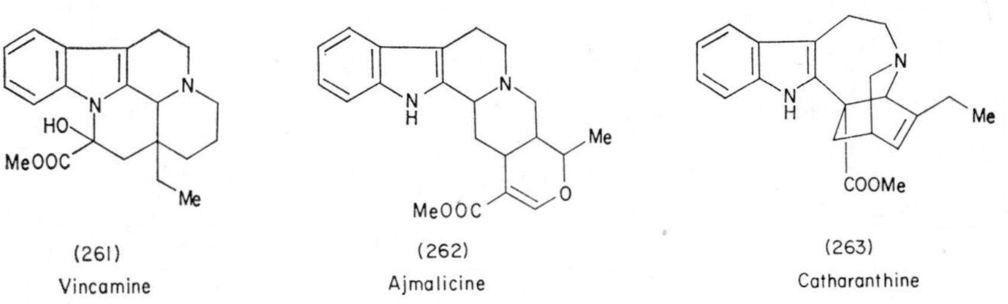

FIG. 43. Some vinca alkaloids.

since acetate is a direct precursor of mevalonic acid. It should also be pointed out that the β-sitosterol (a plant steroid derived from mevalonic acid) isolated from *R. serpentina* plants which had been fed acetate-1-C^{14} was labeled at the expected specific positions, [49] whilst the ajmaline from the same plants was uniformly labeled. It is also relevant to mention that all the hypotheses, except the monoterpene one, require that at least one of the carbons (C_{21} in ajmaline) in the C-10 unit should be derived from a one-carbon source.

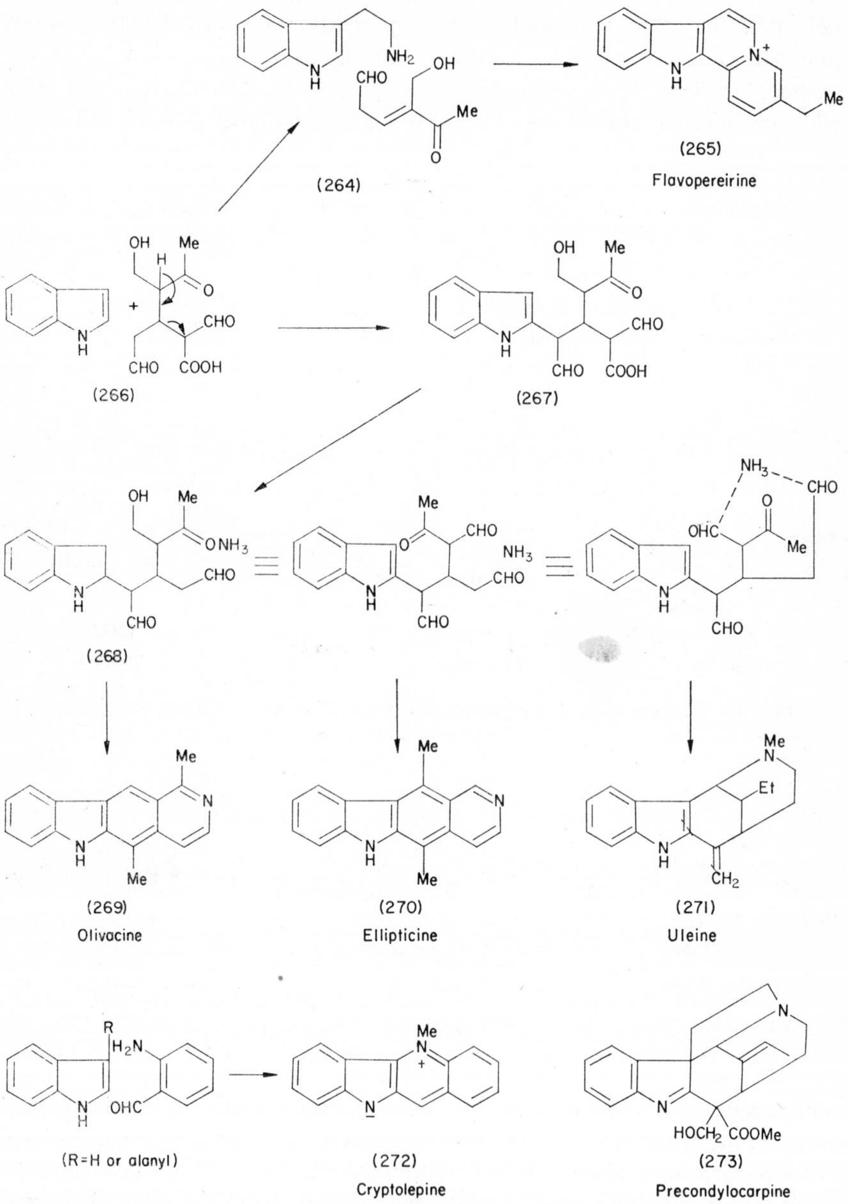

(264)

(265)
Flavopereirine

(266)

(267)

(268)

(269)
Olivacine

(270)
Ellipticine

(271)
Uleine

(R=H or alanyl)

(272)
Cryptolepine

(273)
Precondylocarpine

FIG. 44.

Formate-C^{14} and methionine-methyl-H^3 have been fed to *Rauwolfia* plants [25, 34, 86] and the resultant ajmaline either had no activity at C_{21} or a rather small amount compared with the activity at the N-methyl group, which is known to be derived from one-carbon sources.

Further degradations of vindoline and related alkaloids derived from various labeled mevalonic acids have supported the monoterpene hypothesis for the origin of the non-tryptophan derived portion of these alkaloids.[36a, 36c] Finally the direct incorporation of labeled geraniol into the alkaloids of *Vinca rosea*[36d, 127a, 192a, 196b] and *Cinchona* [36a, 192b] has provided convincing proof for this hypothesis. There are obviously many metabolic steps between geraniol and the final indole alkaloid, and Battersby[36b] has shown that loganin is an important intermediate in the biosynthesis of the alkaloids of *Vinca rosea*.

The C-10 unit present in vindoline is also found in several other *Vinca* alkaloids. One example is vincamine (261) where condensation has occurred at the α-position of the indole nucleus.

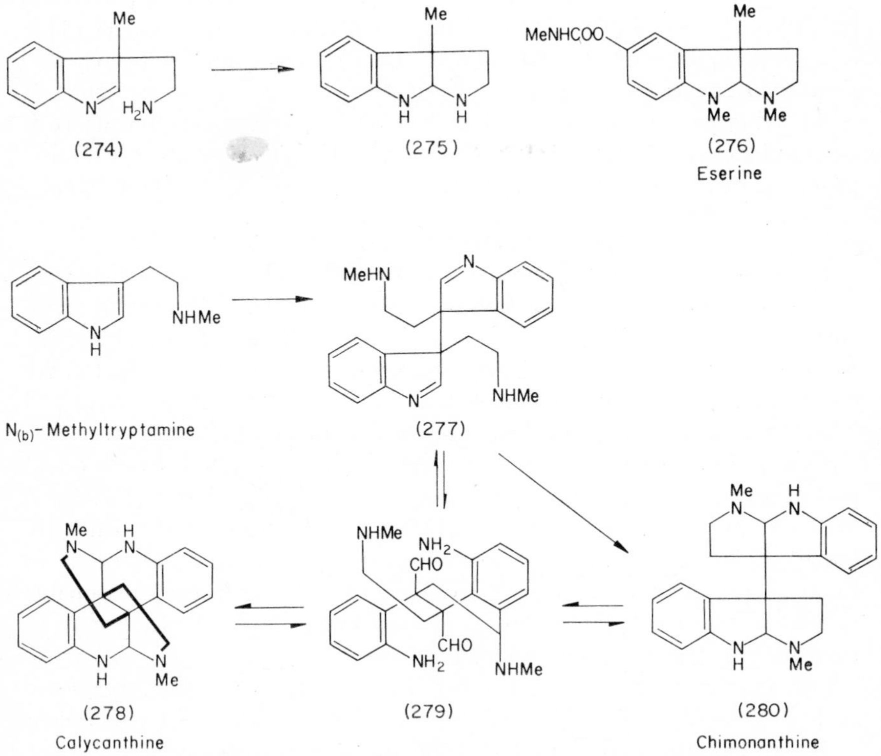

FIG. 45. Hypothetical biosynthesis of eserine and related alkaloids.

Flavopereirine (265) is plausibly formed from tryptamine and a C-7 fragment (264) produced by a reverse Michael reaction on the ubiquitous C-10 intermediate (266). Wenkert [299] has suggested that several indole alkaloids may be derived by the reaction of the C-10 unit (266) with indole as illustrated in Fig. 44. The initial product of coupling (267) after decarboxylation to (268) can undergo gyrations and unexceptional reactions affording olivacine (269), ellipticine (270) and uleine (271). Alternatively tryptophan could be involved in the initial condensation, and then the two-carbon bridge from the β-position of the indole nucleus to $N_{(b)}$ could be eliminated at some stage in the biosynthesis. [307] Circumstantial evidence in favor of the latter scheme has been provided by the isolation of precondylocarpine (273), which may be biogenetically related to a precursor of uleine. Cryptolepine (272) is plausibly formed by reaction of indole with o-aminobenzaldehyde (derived from anthranilic acid). [243]

It seems highly probable that eserine (276) is formed from tryptophan or a hydroxylated tryptophan by the route shown in Fig. 45. C-Methylation at the 3-position of tryptophan, with subsequent decarboxylation yields the indolenine (274). Cyclization yields (275) which on methylation and urethane formation (biochemical mechanism unknown) affords eserine. Calycanthine (278) and chimonanthine (280), two of the alkaloids found in *Calycanthus floridus*, are plausibly formed by the oxidative coupling of two molecules of N-methyltryptamine as illustrated in Fig. 45.[265] Tracer experiments have substantiated this hypothesis.[228a, 258b] The indolenine derivative (277) first formed is hydrolyzed to (279) which then condenses to form calycanthine.

XIII. ERGOLINE ALKALOIDS

These alkaloids are often referred to as the Ergot alkaloids since they were first isolated from the fungus *Claviceps purpurea*, commonly known as ergot. However, since alkaloids having similar structures have been found in quite unrelated higher plants, [138] it seems most reasonable to classify them under the chemical name of the structure which is common to almost all of them. [287] The first alkaloids isolated from ergot were amides of lysergic acid (289) or isolysergic acid (epimeric at C_8) such as ergotamine (292). Abe [2] found that the saprophytic cultures of various *Claviceps* strains led to the formation of new alkaloids such as agroclavine (285) and elymoclavine (288), which are known as the clavine alkaloids. Little work has been done on the origin of the cyclic peptide portion of the ergot alkaloids, however it seems reasonable to assume that the peptide portion of ergotamine, for example, is derived from proline, phenylalanine and alanine. [231]

The ergoline skeleton is formed from tryptophan and mevalonic acid. [50, 51, 115, 116, 216, 233, 283, 284] All tracer work indicates that L-tryptophan is directly incorporated being the precursor of the indole nucleus, carbons 4, 5, and the nitrogen at position-6. [97, 98] The carboxyl group of tryptophan

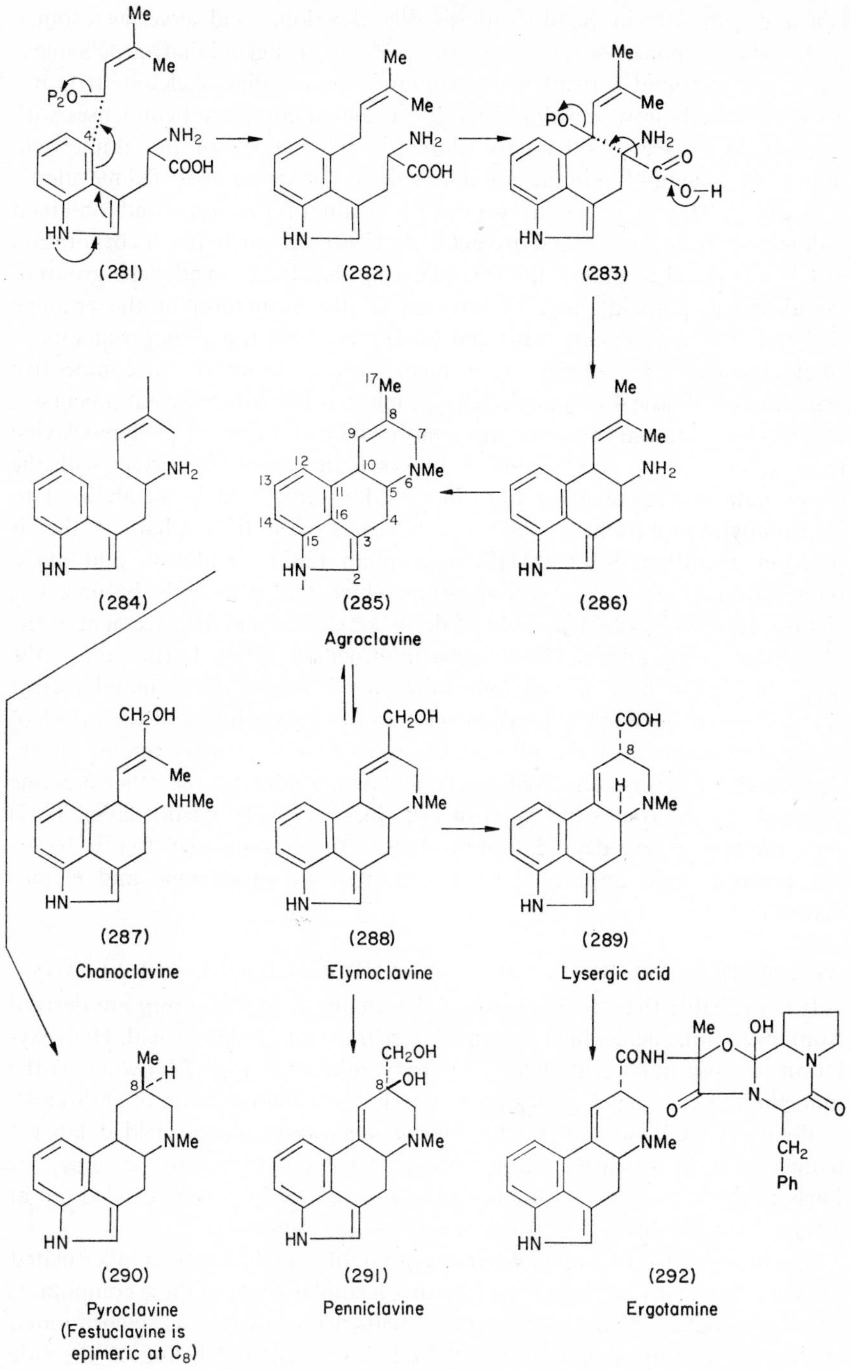

FIG. 46. Biosynthesis of the ergoline alkaloids.

is lost at some step in the biosynthesis. [115] Mevalonic acid serves as a source of the other carbons. Most investigators [1, 3a, 301] are agreed that agroclavine is the first compound formed which contains the ergoline skeleton. It is not yet clear exactly how mevalonic acid or a related compound condenses with tryptophan. Tracer results have shown [52, 57] that C_2 of mevalonic acid ultimately becomes C_{17} in the ergoline skeleton. Baxter *et al.* [53] fed mevalonic acid-2-(C^{14}, H^3) to a clavine producing strain of *Claviceps* and obtained radioactive festuclavine and pyroclavine (290) in which the incorporation of C^{14} was equal to that of the H^3 indicating that the C_2-methylene group of mevalonic acid maintained its integrity in the formation of the ergoline skeleton. The compounds (284) and (282) have been tested as precursors of elymoclavine. [233, 302] Both were incorporated, however in competitive experiments [302] the 4-dimethylallyltryptophan is the more efficient precursor. On the other hand, tryptophan was a more efficient precursor of elymoclavine than either of these compounds. A biosynthetic scheme consistent with the tracer data is illustrated in Fig. 46. [53] Mevalonic acid is metabolized to isopentenylpyrophosphate (281) which reacts with tryptophan at the 4-position affording 4-dimethylallyltryptophan (282). Oxidation and phosphorylation at the allylic carbon atom which will ultimately become C_{10} yields intermediate (283). Concerted decarboxylation and displacement of the phosphate group affords the tricyclic intermediate (286). Formation of the final ring could be achieved by oxidation of one of the terminal methyl groups to hydroxymethyl, phosphorylation of the alcohol, and then nucleophilic displacement of the phosphate group by the primary amino group. Agroclavine (285) is converted to elymoclavine (288) and the other ergoline alkaloids by the routes indicated in Fig. 46. [1, 4, 217, 218] Chanoclavine (287) once thought to be a degradation product of the ergoline skeleton, [1, 112, 217] has recently been implicated as a precursor of agroclavine and elymoclavine. [96a, 112a]

XIV. QUINOLINE, QUINAZOLINE, AND ACRIDONE ALKALOIDS

It is probable that the majority of the alkaloids in this group are derived from anthranilic acid which is formed in plants from shikimic acid. Hydroxylation of anthranilic acid yields 3-hydroxyanthranilic acid (293) which is the immediate precursor of damascenine (294). The administration of anthranilic acid-carboxyl-C^{14}, amino-N^{15} to *Nigella damascena* plants yielded labeled damascenine in which the incorporation of C^{14} and N^{15} were the same. [220] Early negative results [294] were not valid because feedings were carried out at a time when the plant was not producing damascenine.

The biosynthesis of 2-alkyl-4-hydroxyquinolines (300) has been investigated in microorganisms, [199] and it may be that a similar route to these compounds exists in higher plants. Anthranilic acid-carboxyl-C^{14} was incorporated leading to activity at C_4. Acetate-1 and -2-C^{14} led to labeling of the side

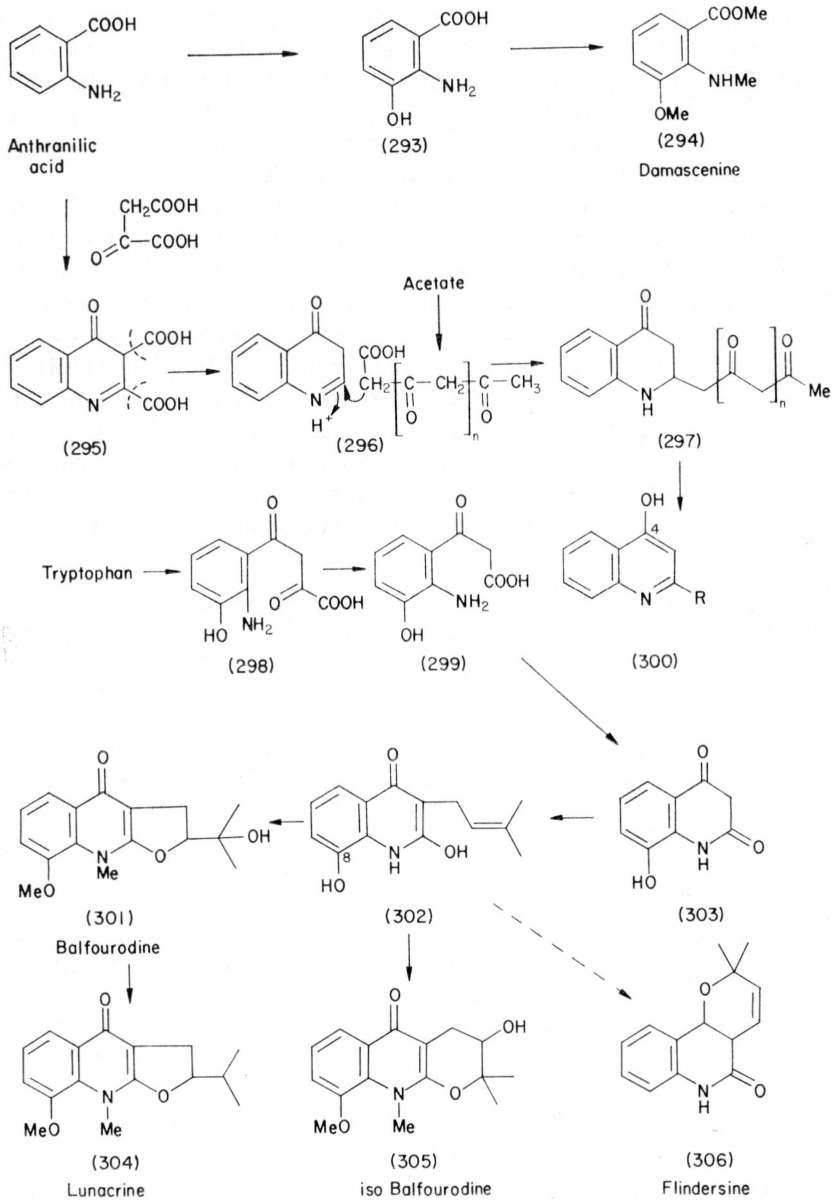

FIG. 47. Some alkaloids related to anthranilic acid.

chain R, but not C_2 and C_3 of the quinoline ring. It is suggested that the quinoline nucleus is built up from anthranilic acid and oxaloacetate as illustrated in Fig. 47, yielding first compound (295) and then the quinoline (296). Condensation with an acetate derived poly-β-ketoacid yields (297) which is then reduced to the alkylquinoline (300). A small amount of activity was detected at C_2 and C_3 from the acetate-2-C^{14}, and this would be expected since oxaloacetate is formed from acetate via the Krebs cycle.

Several furano- and pyrano-quinolines found in *Lunasia* species are plausibly formed by oxidative cyclization of the intermediate (302), which is tentatively [72] formed from tryptophan by the route indicated in Fig. 47. The isoprene side chain could be introduced by reaction of isopentenyl-pyrophosphate with intermediate (303). The *in vitro* oxidation of methylated derivatives of (302) has actually led to the formation of balfourodine (301). [72] Flindersine (306) would be plausibly derived from a precursor similar to (302), but lacking the hydroxyl group at C_8. Tracer experiments on the biosynthesis of the furoquinoline alkaloids dictamnine [207b] and skimmia-nine [205a] favor this hypothesis. However, it seems that intermediates of the type (299) are derived directly from anthranilic acid and acetic acid.

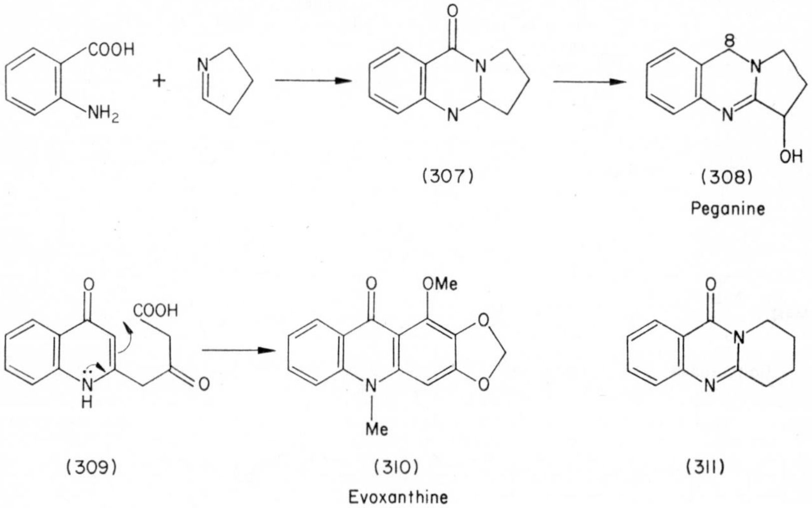

(307)

(308)
Peganine

(309)

(310)
Evoxanthine

(311)

Fig. 48. Biosynthesis of peganine and related alkaloids.

The biosynthesis of peganine (308) has been studied in *Peganum har-mala* [114] and *Adhatoda vasica*. [112, 113] The administration of anthranilic acid-carboxyl-C^{14} yielded peganine labeled at C_8. Radioactive putrescine and proline were incorporated into the alkaloid, presumably via Δ'-pyrroline, which also served as a good precursor of peganine. It is suggested that anthranilic acid and Δ'-pyrroline condense yielding (307) which undergoes oxidation and reduction to afford peganine. It seems reasonable to propose that the pyrido-quinazolinone (311) isolated from *Mackinlay* species [142] is formed in a similar way from anthranilic acid and Δ'-piperideine.

Acridones such as evoxanthine (310) are plausibly formed by the cyclization of intermediates such as (309) which could arise from 4-quinoline and acetoacetic acid.

XV. TERPENOID AND STEROIDAL ALKALOIDS

Inspection of the structures of some alkaloids immediately suggests that they are terpenoid, presumably being derived from mevalonic acid (see also

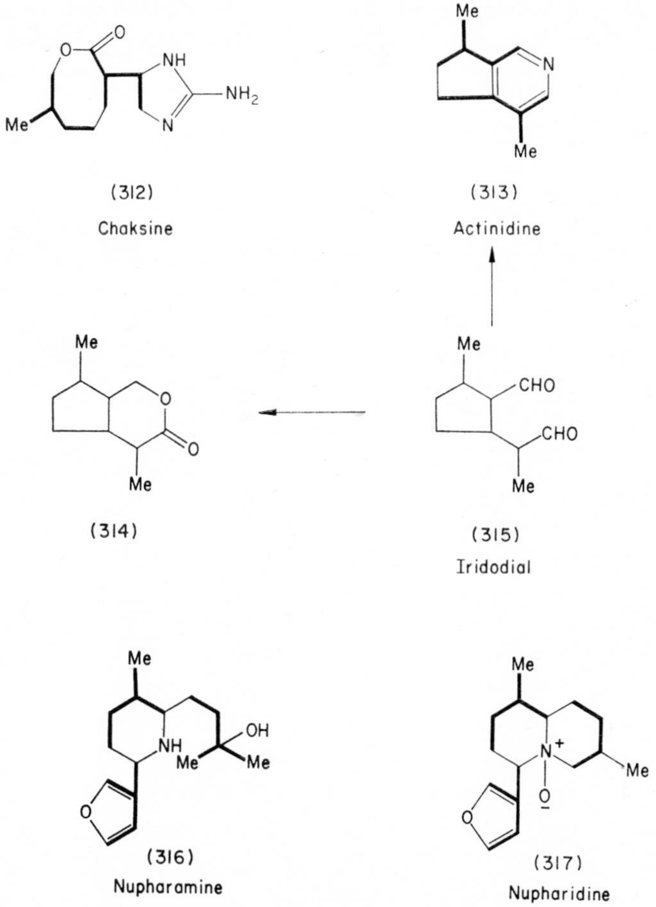

FIG. 49. Some terpenoid alkaloids.

Chapter 14). Chaksine (312) and actinidine (313) are examples of monoterpenes. The lactone metatabilactone (314) occurs with actinidine in the

plant *Actinidia polygama* and both compounds are plausibly derived from
iridodial (315) which is also found in nature. [70] Preliminary tracer work [69, 86a]
has indicated that mevalonic acid is an excellent precursor of this class of
alkaloid. Napharamine (316) and nupharidine (317) occur together and are
sesquiterpenes. The isoprene units present in these alkaloids are indicated
by heavy lines in the structures illustrated in Fig. 49.

The carbon skeleton of atisine and the *Garrya* alkaloids may be derived

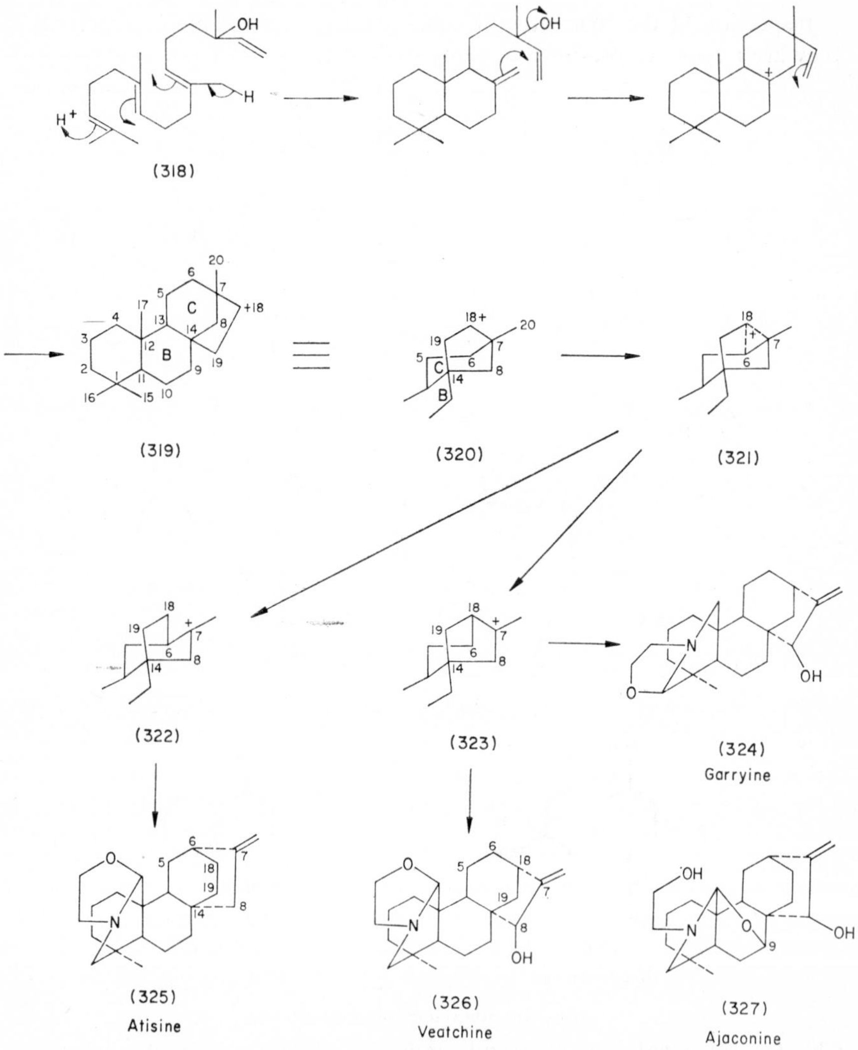

FIG. 50. Hypothetical biogenesis of atisine and the Garrya alkaloids.

from the acyclic diterpene nerolidol (318) by plausible cyclizations illustrated in Fig. 50. The carbonium ion intermediate (319) may be represented by the three-dimensional partial structure (320). This is then transformed to the non-classical bridged ion (321) which can collapse to yield the ions (322) and (323), which may then be converted into the alkaloids atisine (325), veatchine (326), garryine (324) and related alkaloids by unexceptional steps. The oxazolidine ring present in these alkaloids could be formed in part from β-ethanolamine, a metabolite of serine. Ajaconine (327) contains a carbinolamine ether involving a hydroxyl group at C_9. Atisine and related alkaloids have absolute configurations which are opposite to those depicted in Fig. 50.

The possible biogenetic relationship of atisine to lycoctonine (329) and related alkaloids has been pointed out by Wiesner, [289] and is illustrated briefly in Fig. 51. Tracer experiments which have so far been carried out are ambiguous. Kirby [133] found that delpheline (328) isolated from *Delphinium*

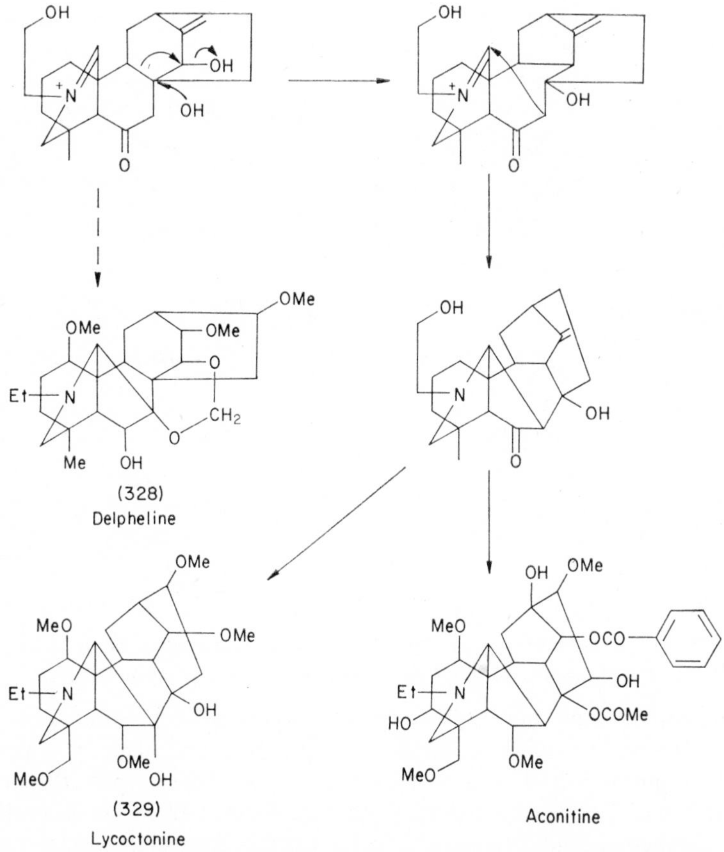

(328)
Delpheline

(329)
Lycoctonine

Aconitine

FIG. 51. Hypothetical biogenesis of lycoctonine and related alkaloids.

elatum plants which had been fed mevalonic acid-2-C^{14} had negligible activity. On the other hand, radioactive delpheline was obtained from plants which had been fed methionine-methyl-C^{14}, indicating that alkaloid synthesis was actually occurring at the time of feeding. Benn[55] reported that the administration of acetate-1, or -2-C^{14}, or mevalonic acid-2-C^{14} to *Delphinium brownii* plants yielded lycoctonine having a small, but significant, activity. No degradations have yet been carried out.

Possible biosynthetic routes to the steroidal alkaloids have been outlined by Schreiber.[266] There are several alkaloids found in the *Apocynanaceae* which may be regarded as derivatives of pregnenolone (330). Some typical examples are illustrated in Fig. 52. Pregnenolone-4-^{14}C was converted to

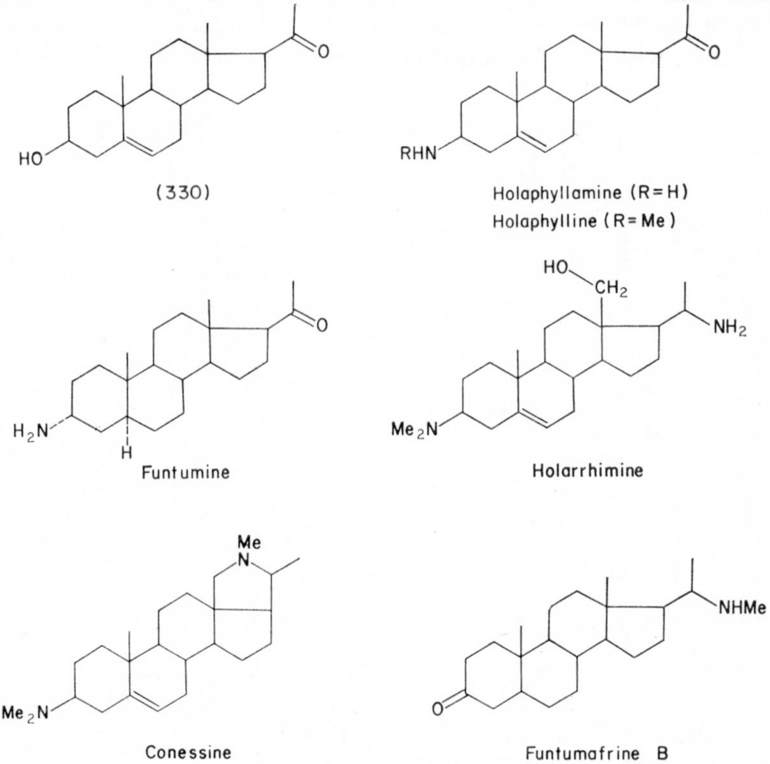

(330)

Holaphyllamine (R = H)
Holaphylline (R = Me)

Funtumine

Holarrhimine

Conessine

Funtumafrine B

FIG. 52. Some alkaloids biogenetically related to pregnenolone.

holaphyllamine and holaphylline in the leaves of the plant *Holarrhena floribunda*.[55a] The aglycone moieties of the *Solanum* alkaloids which are found in potatoes and tomato plants have the same carbon skeleton as cholesterol and it is assumed that they are formed from cholesterol or a closely related steroid. Preliminary tracer work is consistent with this hypothesis. When radioactive acetic acid was fed to sprouting potatoes[124, 125] or tomato plants[247] radioactive alkaloids were obtained and the majority of the activity was located in the aglycones, solanidine (329) and tomatidine (332). Mevalonic acid-2-C^{14} was also incorporated into these steroidal alkaloids, somewhat more efficiently than acetate.[126]

The alkamine moieties of the ester alkaloids of *Veratrum* species also contain the same number of carbons as cholesterol and have the same branched side chain at C_{17}. However, in these compounds ring C is five-membered. A plausible mechanism for this transformation is illustrated in Fig. 53. Hydroxy-

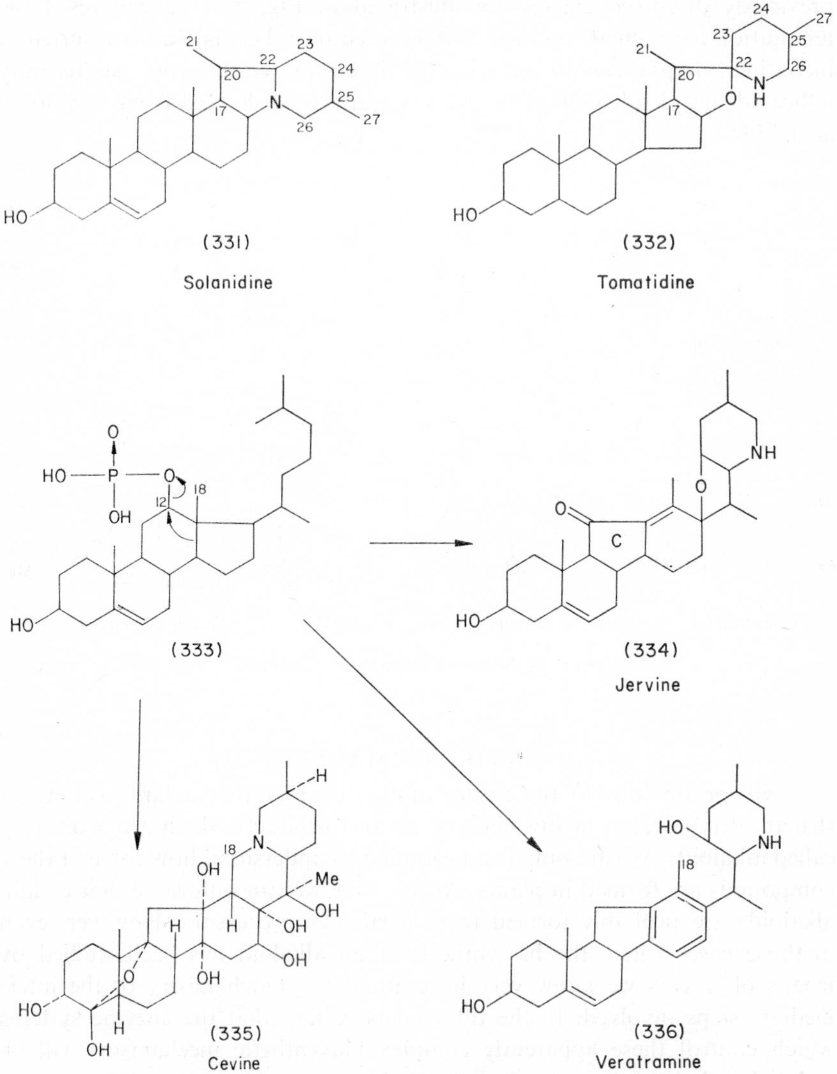

(331)
Solanidine

(332)
Tomatidine

(333)

(334)
Jervine

(335)
Cevine

(336)
Veratramine

FIG. 53. Some steroidal alkaloids from *Solanum* and *Veratrum* species.

2K

lation and phosphorylation occurs at C_{12} in the steroid molecule affording (333) which rearranges leading to alkaloids such as jervine (334), cevine (335) and veratramine (336).

XVI. MISCELLANEOUS ALKALOIDS

Organic chemists continue to isolate alkaloids having "novel" structures and there is no shortage of research problems for those who wish to investigate the biosynthesis of alkaloids. Some alkaloids which do not readily fit into the previously discussed classes are illustrated in Fig. 54. We will resist the temptation to speculate on their biosynthesis since there is already a surfeit of incontinent hypotheses in the scientific literature. Tracer work has recently indicated that dendrobine is in fact a sesquiterpene derived from mevalonic acid.[308b]

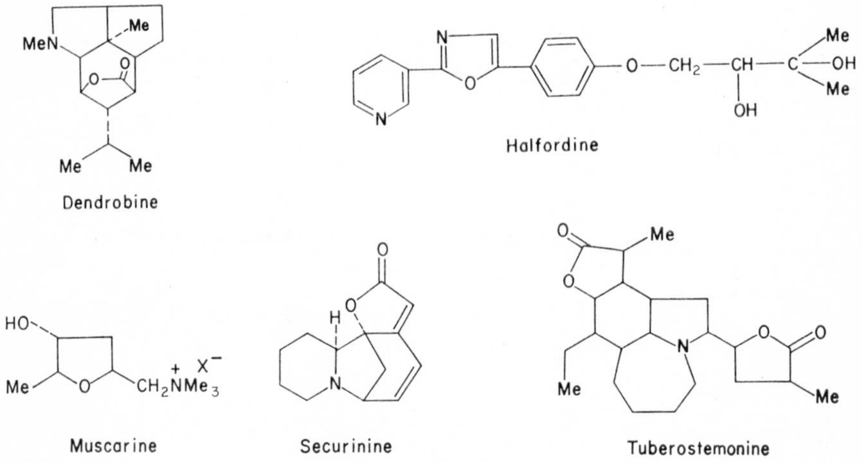

FIG. 54. Some miscellaneous alkaloids.

XVII. SUMMARY

It will be obvious to the reader of this chapter that a large variety of structural types exist in this class of natural products which are arbitrarily called alkaloids. We are only just beginning to understand how some of these compounds are formed in plants. At this time we can only state that certain alkaloids are probably formed from particular precursors. However, even in those cases where the biosynthesis of an alkaloid has been studied by means of tracers we know very little about the biochemistry of the intermediate steps involved. In the future it is certain that the enzyme systems which control these apparently complex biosynthetic mechanisms will be isolated and characterized.

REFERENCES

1. ABE, M. *Abhandl. Deut. Akad. Wiss. Berlin Kl. Chem. Geol. Biol.* N. 3, 393 (1966).
2. ABE, M. *J. Agr. Chem. Soc. (Japan)* 22, 2 (1948).
3. ADAMS, R. and GIANTURCO, M. In *Festschrift Arthur Stoll*, p. 72. Birkhäuser, Basel, 1957.
3a. AGURELL, S. *Acta Pharm. Suecica* 3, 71 (1966).
4. AGURELL, S. and RAMSTAD, E. *Tetrahedron Letters* 501 (1961); *Arch. Biochem. Biophys.* 98, 457 (1962).
5. ALLISON, M. J. *Biochem. Biophys. Res. Comm.* 18, 30 (1965).
6. ALWORTH, W. L., LIEBMAN, A. A. and RAPOPORT, H. *J. Am. Chem. Soc.* 86, 3375 (1964).
7. ANDERSON, L. and GIBBS, M. *J. Biol. Chem.* 237, 1941 (1962).
8. ANET, F. A. L., HAQ, M. Z., KHAN, N. H., AYER, W. A., HAYATSU, R., VALVERDE-LOPEZ, S., DESLONGCHAMPS, P., RIESS, W., TERNBAH, M., VALENTA, Z. and WIESNER, K. *Tetrahedron Letters* 751 (1964).
9. ANET, F. A. L. and RAO, M. V. *Tetrahedron Letters* 20, 9 (1960).
10. ARCHER, D. A., BREUER, S. W., BINKS, R., BATTERSBY, A. R. and WILDMAN, W. C. *Proc. Chem. Soc.* 168 (1963).
12. ARONOFF, S. *Plant Physiol.* 31, 355 (1956).
13. AYER, W. A. and IVERACH, G. G. *Tetrahedron Letters* 10, 19 (1960).
14. AYER, W. A., JENKINS, J. K., VALVERDE-LOPEZ, S. and BURNELL, R. H. *Tetrahedron Letters* 2201 (1964).
15. BABOR, K., JEŽO, I., KALÁČ, V. and KARVAŠ, M. *Chem. Zvesti* 13, 163 (1959).
16. BARGER, G. and SCHOLZ, C. *Helv. Chim. Acta* 16, 1343 (1933).
17. BARTON, D. H. R. *Proc. Chem. Soc.* 293 (1963).
18. BARTON, D. H. R. *Pure and Applied Chem.* 9, 35 (1964).
18a. BARTON, D. H. R., BHAKUNI, D. S., CHAPMAN, G. M. and KIRBY, G. W. *Chem. Commun.* 259 (1966).
19. BARTON, D. H. R. and COHEN, T. In *Festschrift Arthur Stoll*, p. 117. Birkhäuser, Basel, 1957.
20. BARTON, D. H. R., HESSE, R. H. and KIRBY, G. W. *Proc. Chem. Soc.* 267 (1963); *J. Chem. Soc.* 6379 (1965).
21. BARTON, D. H. R., KIRBY, A. J. and KIRBY, G. W. *Chem. Comm.* 52 (1965).
21a. BARTON, D. H. R., JAMES, R., KIRBY, G. W., TURNER, D. W. and WIDDOWSON, D. A. *Chem. Commun.* 294 (1966).
22. BARTON, D. H. R. and KIRBY, G. W. *Proc. Chem. Soc.* 392 (1960).
23. BARTON, D. H. R., KIRBY, G. W., STEGLICH, W., THOMAS, G. M., BATTERSBY, A. R., DOBSON, T. A. and RAMUZ, H. *J. Chem. Soc.* 2423 (1965).
24. BARTON, D. H. R., KIRBY, G. W., TAYLOR, J. B. and THOMAS, G. M. *Proc. Chem. Soc.* 179 (1962); *J. Chem. Soc.* 4545 (1963).
25. BARTON, D. H. R., KIRBY, G. W., PRAGER, R. H. and WILSON, E. M. *J. Chem. Soc.* 3990 (1965).
25a. BARTON, D. H. R., KIRBY, G. W. and WIECHERS, A. *J. Chem. Soc.* (C) 2313 (1966).
26. BATTERSBY, A. R. *Proc. Chem. Soc.* 189 (1963).
27. BATTERSBY, A. R. *Quart. Rev. (London)* 15, 259 (1961).
28. BATTERSBY, A. R. *The Donegani Lectures on Biosynthesis, Milan, Sept. 1962*; Acad. Naz. dei Lincei, vii° Corso Estivo di Chimica, 1964, p. 47.
29. BATTERSBY, A. R., BINKS, R., BREUER, S. W., FALES, H. M., WILDMAN, W. C. and HIGHET, R. J. *J. Chem. Soc.* 1595 (1964).
30. BATTERSBY, A. R., BINKS, R., BREUER, S. W., FALES, H. M. and WILDMAN, W. C. *Proc. Chem. Soc.* 243 (1961).
31. BATTERSBY, A. R., BINKS, R., FRANCIS, R. J., McCALDIN, D. J. and RAMUZ, H. *J. Chem. Soc.* 3600 (1964).
32. BATTERSBY, A. R., BINKS, R. and HAPER, B. J. T. *J. Chem. Soc.* 3534 (1962).
33. BATTERSBY, A. R., BINKS, R., REYNOLDS, J. J. and YEOWELL, D. A. *J. Chem. Soc.* 4257 (1964).

34. BATTERSBY, A. R., BINKS, R., LAURIE, W., PARRY, G. V. and WEBSTER, B. R. *Proc. Chem. Soc.* 369 (1963).

34a. BATTERSBY, A. R., BINKS, R., LAWRIE, W., PARRY, G. V. and WEBSTER, B. R. *J. Chem. Soc.* 7459 (1965).

35. BATTERSBY, A. R., BINKS, R. and YEOWELL, D. A. *Proc. Chem. Soc.* 86 (1964).

36. BATTERSBY, A. R., BROWN, R. T., CLEMENTS, J. H. and IVERACH, G. G. *Chem. Comm.* 230 (1965).

36a. BATTERSBY, A. R., BROWN, R. T., KAPIL, R. S., KNIGHT, J. A., MARTIN, J. A. and PLUNKETT, A. O. *Chem. Commun.* 888 (1966).

36b. BATTERSBY, A. R., BROWN, R. T., KAPIL, R. S., MARTIN, J. A. and PLUNKETT, A. O. *Chem. Commun.* 890 (1966).

36c. BATTERSBY, A. R., BROWN, R. T., KAPIL, R. S., PLUNKETT, A. O. and TAYLOR, J. B. *Chem. Commun.* 46 (1966).

36d. BATTERSBY, A. R., BROWN, R. T., KNIGHT, J. A. and PLUNKETT, A. O. *Chem. Commun.* 346 (1966).

36e. BATTERSBY, A. R. and BROWN, T. H. *Chem. Commun.* 120 (1966).

36f. BATTERSBY, A. R., EVANS, G. W., MARTIN, R. O., WARREN, M. E. and RAPOPORT, H. *Tetrahedron Letters* 1275 (1965).

37. BATTERSBY, A. R., FALES, H. M. and WILDMAN, W. C. *J. Am. Chem. Soc.* **83**, 4098 (1961).

38. BATTERSBY, A. R., FOULKES, D. M. and BINKS, R. *J. Chem. Soc.* 3323 (1965).

39. BATTERSBY, A. R. and FRANCIS, R. J. *J. Chem. Soc.* 4078 (1964).

40. BATTERSBY, A. R., FRANCIS, R. J., HIRST, M. and STAUNTON, J. *Proc. Chem. Soc.* 268 (1963).

41. BATTERSBY, A. R., FRANCIS, R. J., RUVEDA, E. A. and STAUNTON, J. *Chem. Comm.* 89 (1965).

42. BATTERSBY, A. R. and HARPER, B. J. T. *Chem. and Ind. (London)* 365 (1958).

43. BATTERSBY, A. R. and HARPER, B. J. T. *Proc. Chem. Soc.* 152 (1959); *J. Chem. Soc.* 2526 (1962).

44. BATTERSBY, A. R. and HARPER, B. J. T. *Tetrahedron Letters* **27**, 21 (1960).

45. BATTERSBY, A. R. and HERBERT, R. B. *Proc. Chem. Soc.* 260 (1964).

45a. BATTERSBY, A. R., HERBERT, R. B., McDONALD, E., RAMAGE, R. and CLEMENT, J. H., *Chem. Commun.* 603 (1966).

46. BATTERSBY, A. R., HERBERT, R. B., PIJEWSKA, L. and SANTAVÝ, F. *Chem. Comm.* 228 (1965).

47. BATTERSBY, A. R. and HIRST, M. *Tetrahedron Letters* 669 (1965).

48. BATTERSBY, A. R. and McCALDIN, D. J. *Proc. Chem. Soc.* 365 (1962).

49. BATTERSBY, A. R. and PARRY, G. V. *Tetrahedron Letters*, 787 (1964).

50. BAXTER, R. M., KANDEL, S. I. and OKANY, A. *Chem. and Ind., London* 266 (1960); *Nature* **185**, 241 (1960).

51. BAXTER, R. M., KANDEL, S. I. and OKANY, A. *Chem. and Ind., London* 1453 (1961).

52. BAXTER, R. M., KANDEL, S. I. and OKANY, A. *J. Am. Chem. Soc.* **84**, 2997 (1962); *Tetrahedron Letters* 596 (1961).

53. BAXTER, R. M., KANDEL, S. I., OKANY, A. and TAM, K. L. *J. Am. Chem. Soc.* 4350 (1962).

54. BEAL, J. L. and RAMSTAD, E. *Naturwiss.* **47**, 206 (1960).

55. BENN, M. H. and MAY, J. *Experientia* **20**, 252 (1964).

55a. BENNETT, R. D. and HEFTMANN, E. *Phytochemistry* **4**, 873 (1965).

56. BEVAN, C. W. and OGAN, A. U. *Phytochemistry* **3**, 591 (1964).

57. BHATTACHARJI, S., BIRCH, A. J., BRACK, A., HOFMANN, A., KOBEL, H., SMITH, D. C. C., SMITH, H. and WINTER, J. *J. Chem. Soc.* 421 (1962).

58. BIEMANN, K., BÜCHI, G. and WALKER, B. H. *J. Am. Chem. Soc.* **79**, 5558 (1957).

59. BIRECKA, H. and SEBYLA, T. *Bul. Acad. Pol. Sci.*, Cl. II, **8**, 183 (1960).

60. BOTHNER-BY, A. A., SCHUTZ, R. S., DAWSON, R. F. and SOLT, M. L. *J. Am. Chem. Soc.* **84**, 52 (1962).

61. BOTTOMLEY, W. and GEISSMAN, T. A. *Phytochemistry* **3**, 357 (1964).

62. BOWDEN, K. and MARION, L. *Can. J. Chem.* **29**, 1037 (1951).

63. BRACK, A., HOFMANN, A., KALBERER, F., KOBEL, H. and RUSCHMANN, J. *Arch. Pharm.* **292**, 230 (1961).
63a. BRECCIA, A. and CRESPI, A. M. *Z. Naturforsch.* **21b**, 832 (1966).
64. BRECCIA, A. and MARION, L. *Can. J. Chem.* **37**, 1066 (1959).
65. BROCHMANN-HANSSEN, E. and FURUYA, T. *J. Pharm. Sci.* **53**, 575 (1964).
66. BROCHMANN-HANSSEN, E. and FURUYA, T. *Planta Med.* **12**, 328 (1964).
67. BROCHMANN-HANSSEN, E. and NIELSEN, B. *Tetrahedron Letters* 1271 (1965).
68. BROWN, S. A. and BYERRUM, R. U. *J. Am. Chem. Soc.* **74**, 1523 (1952).
69. CASINOVI, C. G., GIOVANNOZZI-SERMANNI, G. and MARINO-BETTOLO, G. B. *Gazzetta* **94**, 1356 (1964).
70. CAVILL, G. W. K. *Rev. Pure Appl. Chem.* **10**, 169 (1960).
71. CHRISTMAN, D. R. and DAWSON, R. F. *Biochemistry* **2**, 182 (1963).
72. CLARKE, E. A. and GRUNDON, M. F. *J. Chem. Soc.* 807 (1964).
73. CONROY, H. *Tetrahedron Letters* **10**, 34 (1960).
74. CONROY, H. and CHAKRABARTI, J. *Tetrahedron Letters* **4**, 6 (1959).
75. CROMWELL, B. T. and ROBERTS, M. F. *Phytochemistry* **3**, 369 (1964).
76. CROMWELL, B. T. Private communication.
76a. CROUT, D. H. G. *J. Chem. Soc.* (C) 1968 (1966).
76b. CROUT, D. H. G., BENN, M. H., IMASEKI, H. and GEISSMAN, T. A. *Phytochemistry* **5**, 1 (1966).
77. DAWSON, R. F. *American Scientist* **48**, 321 (1960).
78. DAWSON, R. F. and CHRISTMAN, D. R. *J. Am. Chem. Soc.* **87**, 4187 (1965).
79. DAWSON, R. F., CHRISTMAN, D. R. and ANDERSON, R. C. *J. Am. Chem. Soc.* **75**, 5114 (1953).
80. DAWSON, R. F., CHRISTMAN, D. R., D'ADAMO, A. F., SOLT, M. L. and WOLF, A. P. *Chem. and Ind., London* 100 (1958); *J. Am. Chem. Soc.* **82**, 2628 (1960).
81. DAWSON, R. F., CHRISTMAN, D. R., SOLT, M. L. and WOLF, A. P. *Arch. Biochem. Biophys.* **91**, 144 (1960).
82. DEWEY, L. J., BYERRUM, R. U. and BALL, C. D. *Biochim. Biophys. Acta* **18**, 141 (1955).
83. DEWEY, L. J., BYERRUM, R. U. and BALL, C. D. *J. Am. Chem. Soc.* **76**, 3997 (1954).
84. DJERASSI, C., BREWER, H. W., CLARK, C. and DURHAM, L. J. *J. Am. Chem. Soc.* **84**, 3210 (1962).
85. DUBECK, M. and KIRKWOOD, S. *J. Biol. Chem.* **199**, 307 (1952).
86. EDWARDS, P. N. and LEETE, E. *Chem. and Ind., London* 1666 (1961).
86a. EISENBRAUN, E. J., AUDA, H., JUNEJA, H. R., WALLER, G. R. and APPEL, H. *Abs. 150th Meeting of the Am. Chem. Soc.* Sept. p. 115c (1965).
87. ESSERY, J. M., JUBY, P. F., MARION, L. and TRUMBULL, *J. Am. Chem. Soc.* **84**, 4593 (1962); *Can. J. Chem.* **41**, 1142 (1963).
88. ESSERY, J. M., McCALDIN, D. J. and MARION, L. *Phytochemistry* **1**, 209 (1962).
89. EVANS, W. C. and GRIFFIN, W. J. *J. Pharm. Pharmacol.* **16**, 337 (1964); *Phytochemistry* **3**, 503 (1964).
90. EVANS, W. C. and WOOLEY, J. G. *Abhandl. Deut. Akad. Wiss. Berlin Kl. Chem. Geol. Biol.* **Nr. 3**, 507, 531 (1966).
91. FAIRBAIRN, J. W. and WASSEL, G. *Phytochemistry* **3**, 583 (1964).
92. FAIRBAIRN, J. W., PATTERSON, A. and WASSEL, G. *Phytochemistry* **3**, 577 (1964).
93. FAIRBAIRN, J. W. and SUWAL, P. N. *Phytochemistry* **1**, 38 (1961).
94. FAIRBAIRN, J. W. *Abhandl. Deut. Akad. Wiss. Berlin Kl. Chem. Geol. Biol.* **Nr. 3**, 141 (1966).
95. FALES, H. M., MANN, J. and MUDD, S. H. *J. Am. Chem. Soc.* **85**, 2025 (1963).
96. FALES, H. M. and WILDMAN, W. C. *J. Am. Chem. Soc.* **86**, 296 (1964).
96a. FEHR, T., ACKLIN, W. and ARIGONI, D. *Chem. Commun.* 801 (1966).
96b. FLEEKER, J. and BYERRUM, R. U. *J. Biol. Chem.* **240**, 4099 (1965).
97. FLOSS, H.-G. and GROGER, D. *Z. Naturforsch.* **19b**, 393 (1964).
98. FLOSS, H.-G., MOTHES, U. and GÜNTHER, H. Z. *Naturforsch.* **19b**, 794 (1964).
99. FLOSS, H.-G., MOTHES, U. and RETTIG, A. *Z. Naturforsch.* **19b**, 1106 (1964).
100. FRIEDMAN, A. R. and LEETE, E. *J. Am. Chem. Soc.* **85**, 2141 (1963).
101. GEAR, J. R. and SPENSER, I. D. *Can. J. Chem.* **41**, 783 (1963).

102. GEAR, J. R. and SPENSER, I. D. *Nature* **191**, 1393 (1961).
102a. GERVAG, J. E., McCAPRA, F., MONEY, T., SHARMA, G. M. and SCOTT, A. I. *Chem. Commun.* 142 (1966).
103. GILVARG, C. and BLOCH, K. *J. Biol. Chem.* **193**, 339 (1951).
103a. GOEGGEL, H. and ARIGONI, D. *Chem. Commun.* 538 (1965).
103b. GOEGGEL, H. and ARIGONI, D. *Experientia* **21**, 369 (1965).
104. GOODEVE, A. M. and RAMSTAD, E. *Experientia* **17**, 124 (1961).
105. GOUTAREL, R., JANOT, M.-M., PRELOG, V. and TAYLOR, W. I. *Helv. Chim. Acta* **33**, 150 (1950).
106. GOWER, B. G. and LEETE, E. *J. Am. Chem. Soc.* **85**, 3683 (1963).
107. GRIFFITH, T. and BYERRUM, R. U. *Biochem. Biophys. Res. Comm.* **10**, 293 (1963).
108. GRIFFITH, T. and BYERRUM, R. U. *Science* **129**, 1485 (1959).
108a. GRIFFITH, T. and GRIFFITH, G. D. *Phytochemistry* **5**, 1175 (1966).
109. GRIFFITH, T., HELLMAN, K. P. and BYERRUM, R. U. *Biochemistry* **1**, 336 (1962).
110. GRIFFITH, T., HELLMAN, K. P. and BYERRUM, R. U. *J. Biol. Chem.* **235**, 800 (1960).
111. GRIMSHAW, J. and MARION, L. *Nature* **181**, 112 (1958).
112. GRÖGER, D., *Fortschr. chem. Forsch.* **6**, 159 (1966).
112a. GRÖGER, D., ERGE, D. and FLOSS, H. G. *Z. Naturforsch.* **21b**, 827 (1966).
113. GRÖGER, D., JOHNE, S. and MOTHES, K. *Experientia* **21**, 13 (1965).
114. GRÖGER, D. and MOTHES, K. *Arch. Pharm.* **293**, 1049 (1950).
115. GRÖGER, D., MOTHES, K., SIMON, H., FLOSS, H.-G. and WEYGAND, F. *Z. Naturforsch.* **15b**, 141 (1960).
116. GRÖGER, D., MOTHES, K., SIMON, H., FLOSS, H.-G. and WEYGAND, F. *Z. Naturforsch.* **16b**, 432 (1961).
117. GRÖGER, D. and SIMON, H. *Abh. Dtsch. Akad. Wiss. Berlin*, 1963, Nr. 4, p. 343.
118. GRÖGER, D., STOLLE, K. and MOTHES, K. *Tetrahedron Letters* 2579 (1964).
118a. GRÖGER, D., STOLLE, K. and MOTHES, K. *Z. Naturforsch.* **21b**, 206 (1966).
119. GRÖGER, D., WENDT, H. J., MOTHES, K. and WEYGAND, F. *Z. Naturforsch.* **14b**, 355 (1959).
119a. GROSS, D., FEIGE, A., STECHER, R., ZÜRECK, A. and SCHÜTTE, H. R. *Z. Naturforsch.* **20b**, 1116 (1965).
120. GROSS, D. and SCHÜTTE, H. R. *Arch. Pharm.* **296**, 1 (1963).
121. GROSS, D., SCHÜTTE, H. R., HÜBNER, G. and MOTHES, K. *Tetrahedron Letters* 451 (1963).
122. GULLAND, J. M. and ROBINSON, R. *Mem. Proc. Manchester Lit. and Phil. Soc.* **69**, 79 (1925).
123. GUPTA, R. M. and SPENSER, I. D. *Can. J. Chem.* **43**, 133 (1965).
123a. GUPTA, R. M. and SPENSER, I. D. *Chem. Commun.* 893 (1966).
124. GUSEVA, A. R., BORIKHINA, M. G. and PASESHNICHENKO, V. A. *Biokimiya* **25**, 282 (1960).
125. GUSEVA, A. R. and PASESHNICHENKO, V. A. *Biokimiya* **23**, 412 (1958).
126. GUSEVA, A. R., PASESHNICHENKO, V. A. and BORIKHINA, M. G. *Biokhimiya* **26**, 723 (1961).
127. HAHN, G. and LUDEWIG, H. *Ber.* **67**, 203 (1934).
127a. HALL, E. S., McCAPRA, F., MONEY, T., FUKUMOTO, K., HANSON, J. R., MOOTOO, B. S., PHILLIPS, G. T. and SCOTT, A. I. *Chem. Commun.* 348 (1966).
128. HARDWIGER, L. A., BADIEI, S. E., WALLER, G. R. and GHOLSON, R. K. *Biochem. Biophys. Res. Comm.* **13**, 466 (1963).
129. HARLEY-MASON, J. and WATERFIELD, W. R. *Chem. and Ind., London* 1477 (1960).
130. HAYNES, L. J., STUART, K. L., BARTON, D. H. R., BHAKUNI, D. S. and KIRBY, G. W. *Chem. Comm.* 141 (1965).
131. HENDERSON, L. M., SOMEROSKI, J. F., RAO, D. R., WU, P. L., GRIFFITH, T. and BYERRUM, R. U. *J. Biol. Chem.* **234**, 93 (1959).
132. HENDRICKSON, J. B. In *The Biosynthesis of Steroids, Terpenes and Acetogenins*, eds. J. H. Richards and J. B. Hendrickson, p. 120. W. A. Benjamin, New York, 1964.
133. HERBERT, E. J. and KIRBY, G. W. *Tetrahedron Letters* 1505 (1963).
134. HIGHET, R. J. *J. Org. Chem.* **26**, 4767 (1961).

135. HILL, R. D. and UNRAU, A. M. *Can. J. Chem.* **43**, 709 (1965).
135a. HUGHES, C. A., LETCHER, R. and WARREN, F. L. *J. Chem. Soc.* 4974 (1964).
136. HUGHES, C. and WARREN, F. L. *J. Chem. Soc.* 34 (1962).
137. HYLIN, J. W. *Phytochemistry* **3**, 161 (1964).
138. HYLIN, J. W. and WATSON, D. P. *Science* **148**, 499 (1965).
139. IMASEKI, I., ONEYAMA, R. and TAJIMA, M. *J. Pharm. Soc. Japan* **80**, 1802 (1960).
140. IMASEKI, I., SHIBATA, S. and YAMAZAKI, M. *Chem. and Ind., London* 1625 (1958).
140a. JACKANICZ, T. M. and BYERRUM, R. U. *J. Biol. Chem.* **241**, 1296 (1966).
141. JEFFS, P. W. *Proc. Chem. Soc.* 80 (1962).
142. JOHNS, S. R. and LAMBERTON, J. A. *Chem. Comm.* 267 (1965).
142a. JOHNS, S. R. and MARION, L. *Can. J. Chem.* **44**, 23 (1966).
143. JUBY, P. F. and MARION, L. *Can. J. Chem.* **41**, 117 (1963).
144. KACZKOWSKI, J. and MARION, L. *Can. J. Chem.* **41**, 2651 (1963).
145. KACZKOWSKI, J., SCHUTTE, H. R. and MOTHES, K. *Biochim. Biophys. Acta* **46**, 588 (1961).
145a. KIRBY, G. W. *Science*, **155**, 170 (1967).
145b. KIRBY, G. W. and TIWARI, H. P. *J. Chem. Soc.* (C) 676 (1966).
146. KIRKWOOD, S. and MARION, L. *Can. J. Chem.* **29**, 30 (1951).
146a. KISAKI, T., MIZUSAKI, S. and TAMAKI, E. *Arch. Biochem. Biophys.* **117**, 677 (1966).
147. KLEINSCHMIDT and MOTHES, K. *Z. Naturforsch.* **14b**, 52 (1959); *Arch. Pharm.* **293**, 948 (1960).
148. KOUKOL, J. and CONN, E. E. *J. Biol. Chem.* **236**, 2692 (1961).
149. KOWANKO, N. and LEETE, E. *J. Am. Chem. Soc.* **84**, 4919 (1962).
150. KRIMSKY, I. *J. Biol. Chem.* **234**, 232 (1959).
151. LAMBERTS, B. L. and BYERRUM, R. U. *J. Biol. Chem.* **233**, 939 (1958).
152. LAMBERTS, B. L., DEWEY, L. J. and BYERRUM, R. U. *Biochim. Biophys. Acta* **33**, 22 (1959).
153. LEETE, E. *Chem. and Ind., London* 537 (1955).
154. LEETE, E. *Chem. and Ind., London* 1270 (1957).
155. LEETE, E. *Chem. and Ind., London* 1088 (1958).
156. LEETE, E. *Chem. and Ind., London* 1477 (1958).
157. LEETE, E. *Chem. and Ind., London* 604 (1959).
158. LEETE, E. *J. Am. Chem. Soc.* **78**, 3520 (1956).
159. LEETE, E. *J. Am. Chem. Soc.* **80**, 2162 (1958).
160. LEETE, E. *J. Am. Chem. Soc.* **80**, 4393 (1958).
161. LEETE, E. *J. Am. Chem. Soc.* **81**, 3948 (1959).
162. LEETE, E. *J. Am. Chem. Soc.* **82**, 612 (1960).
163. LEETE, E. *J. Am. Chem. Soc.* **82**, 6338 (1960).
164. LEETE, E. *J. Am. Chem. Soc.* **84**, 55 (1962).
165. LEETE, E. *J. Am. Chem. Soc.* **85**, 473 (1963).
166. LEETE, E. *J. Am. Chem. Soc.* **85**, 3666 (1963).
167. LEETE, E. *J. Am. Chem. Soc.* **86**, 2509 (1964).
168. LEETE, E. *Science* **147**, 1000 (1965).
169. LEETE, E. *Tetrahedron* **14**, 35 (1961).
169a LEETE, E. *Tetrahedron Letters* 1619 (1964).
170. LEETE, E. *Tetrahedron Letters* 333 (1965).
171. LEETE, E. *J. Am. Chem. Soc.* **88**, 4218 (1966).
171a. LEETE, E. and ADITYACHAUDHURY, N. *Phytochemistry* **7** (in press) (1967).
171b. LEETE, E. and AHMAD, A. *J. Am. Chem. Soc.* **88**, 4722 (1966).
172. LEETE, E., AHMAD, A. and KOMPIS, I. *J. Am. Chem. Soc.* **87**, 4168 (1965).
173. LEETE, E. and FRIEDMAN, A. R. *J. Am. Chem. Soc.* **86**, 1224 (1964).
174. LEETE, E., FRIEDMAN, A. R. and KOWANKO, N., unpublished work.
175. LEETE, E., GHOSAL, S. and EDWARDS, P. N. *J. Am. Chem. Soc.* **84**, 1068 (1962).
175a LEETE, E. and GHOSAL, S. *Tetrahedron Letters* 1179 (1962).
176. LEETE, E., GROS, E. G. and GILBERTSON, T. J. *J. Am. Chem. Soc.* **86**, 3907 (1964).
177. LEETE, E., GROS, E. G. and GILBERTSON, T. J. *Tetrahedron Letters* 587 (1964).
178. LEETE, E. and GEAR, J. R., unpublished work.

179. Leete, E., Kirkwood, S. and Marion, L. *Can. J. Chem.* **30**, 749 (1952).
180. Leete, E. and Leitz, F. H. B. *Chem. and Ind., London* 1572 (1957).
181. Leete, E. and Louden, M. C. L. *Chem. and Ind., London* 1725 (1963).
182. Leete, E. and Louden, M. T. L. *Abhandl. Deut. Akad. Wiss. Berlin Kl. Chem. Geol. Biol.* **Nr. 3,** 538 (1966).
183. Leete, E. and Marion, L. *Can. J. Chem.* **31,** 126 (1953).
184. Leete, E. and Marion, L. *Can. J. Chem.* **31,** 1195 (1953).
185. Leete, E. and Marion, L. *Can. J. Chem.* **32,** 646 (1954).
186. Leete, E., Marion, L. and Spenser, I. D. *Nature* **174,** 650 (1954); *Can. J. Chem.* **32,** 1116 (1954).
187. Leete, E., Marion, L. and Spenser, I. D. *Can. J. Chem.* **33,** 405 (1955).
188. Leete, E., Marion, L. and Spenser, I. D. *J. Biol. Chem.* **214,** 71 (1955).
189. Leete, E. and Murrill, Sister J. B. *Tetrahedron Letters* 147 (1964).
189a. Leete, E. and Murrill, Sister J. B., unpublished work.
190. Leete, E. and Németh, P. E. *J. Am. Chem. Soc.* **82,** 6055 (1960).
191. Leete, E. and Németh, P. E. *J. Am. Chem. Soc.* **83,** 2192 (1961).
192. Leete, E. and Siegfried, K. J. *J. Am. Chem. Soc.* **79,** 4529 (1957).
192a. Leete, E. and Ueda, S. *Tetrahedron Letters* 4915 (1966).
192b. Leete, E. and Wemple, J. N. *J. Am. Chem. Soc.* **88,** 4743 (1966).
193. Leete, E., unpublished work, referred to in footnote 5, reference (177).
194. Leonard, N. J. and Blum, S. W. *J. Am. Chem. Soc.* **82,** 503 (1960).
195. Liebisch, H. W., Maier, W. and Schütte, H. R. *Tetrahedron Letters,* 4079 (1966).
195a. Liebisch, H. W., Ramin, H., Schöfinius, I. and Schütte, H. R. *Z. Naturforsch.* **20b,** 1183 (1965).
196. Liebisch, H. W., Schütte, H. R. and Mothes, K. *Annalen* **668,** 139 (1963).
196a. Liebman, A. A., Morsingh, F. and Rapoport, H. *J. Am. Chem. Soc.* **87,** 4399 (1965).
196b. Loew, P., Goeggel, H. and Arigoni, D. *Chem. Commun.* 347 (1966).
197. Louden, M. L. and Leete, E. *J. Am. Chem. Soc.* **84,** 4507 (1962).
198. Luckner, M. *Die Pharmazie* **14,** 121, 177 (1959); **18,** 93 (1963); **19,** 1 (1964).
199. Luckner, M. and Ritter, C. *Tetrahedron Letters* 741 (1965).
200. Mann, J. D. and Mudd, S. H. *J. Biol. Chem.* **238,** 381 (1963).
201. Marion, L. and Thomas, A. F. *Can. J. Chem.* **33,** 1853 (1955).
202. Marion, L., Wiewiorowski, M. and Bratek, M. D. *Tetrahedron Letters* **19,** 1 (1960).
203. Martin, R. O., Warren, M. E. and Rapoport, H. *J. Am. Chem. Soc.* **86,** 4726 (1964).
204. Massicot, J. and Marion, L. *Can. J. Chem.* **35,** 1 (1957).
205. Matchett, J., Marion, L. and Kirkwood, S. *Can. J. Chem.* **31,** 488 (1953).
205a. Matsuo, M., Yamazaki, M. and Kasida, Y. *Biochem. Biophys. Research Comm.* **23,** 679 (1966).
205b. McCapra, F., Money, T., Scott, A. I., and Wright, I. G. *Chem. Comm.* 537 (1965).
206. McCorkindale, N. J., Magrill, D. S., Martin-Smith, M., Smith, S. J. and Stenlake, J. B. *Tetrahedron Letters* 3841 (1964).
206a. Mondon, A. and Ehrhardt, M. *Tetrahedron Letters* 2557 (1966).
206b. Money, T., Wright, I. G., McCapra, F. and Scott, A. I. *Proc. Natl. Acad. Sci. U.S.* **53,** 901 (1965).
207. Monkovic, I. and Spenser, I. D. *Proc. Chem. Soc.* 223 (1964).
207a. Monkovic, I. and Spenser, I. D. *J. Am. Chem. Soc.* **87,** 1137 (1965); *Can. J. Chem.* **43,** 2017 (1965).
207b. Monkovic, I. and Spenser, I. D. *Chem. Commun.* 205 (1966).
208. Morgan, A. and Marion, L. *Can. J. Chem.* **34,** 1704 (1956).
209. Mothes, E., Gross, D., Schütte, H. R. and Mothes, K. *Naturwiss.* **48,** 623 (1961).
210. Mothes, K. In *The Alkaloids,* vol. VI, p. 1, ed. R. H. F. Manske. Academic Press, New York, 1960.
211. Mothes, K. *J. Pharm. Pharmacol.* **11,** 193 (1959).
213. Mothes, K. and Schroter, H.-B. *Arch. Pharm.* **294,** 99 (1962).
214. Mothes, K. and Schütte, H. R. *Angew. Chemie* **75,** 265, 357 (1963).
215. Mothes, K., Schütte, H. R., Simon, H. and Weygand, F. *Z. Naturforsch.* **14b,** 49 (1959).

216. MOTHES, K., WEYGAND, F., GROGER, D. and GRISEBACH, H. Z. Naturforsch. 13b, 41 (1958).
217. MOTHES, K. and WINKLER, K. Tetrahedron Letters 1243 (1962).
218. MOTHES, K., WINKLER, K., GROGER, D., FLOSS, H.-G., MOTHES, U. and WEYGAND, F. Tetrahedron Letters 933 (1962).
219. MUDD, S. H. Nature 189, 489 (1961).
220. MUNSCHE, D. Abhandl. Deut. Akad. Wiss. Berlin Kl. Chem. Geol. Biol. Nr. 3, 611 (1966).
221. MURPHY, C. F. and WILDMAN, W. C. Tetrahedron Letters 3863 (1964).
222. NEISH, A. C. Phytochemistry 1, (1961).
223. NEUBAUER, D. Planta Med. 12, 43 (1964).
224. NEUBAUER, D. Abhandl. Deut. Akad. Wiss. Berlin Kl. Chem. Geol. Biol. Nr. 3, 341 (1966).
224a. NEUMANN, D and SCHRÖTER, H. B. Tetrahedron Letters, 1273 (1966).
225. NOTATION, A. D. and SPENSER, I. D. Can J. Biochem. 42, 1802 (1964).
226. NOWACKI, E. Genetica Polonica 5, 189 (1964).
227. NOWACKI, E. and BYERRUM, R. U. Biochem. Biophys. Res. Comm. 7, 58 (1958).
228. NOWACKI, E. and BYERRUM, R. U. Life Sciences 5, 157 (1962).
228a. O'DONOVAN, D. and KEOGH, M. F. J. Chem. Soc. (C) 1570 (1966).
229. O'DONOVAN, D. and LEETE, E. J. Am. Chem. Soc. 85, 461 (1963).
230. ORTEGA, M. W. and BROWN, G. M. J. Am. Chem. Soc. 81, 4437 (1959); J. Biol. Chem. 235, 2939 (1960).
231. PAUL, A. G. Ph.D. dissertation, University of Connecticut, 1957.
232. PLIENINGER, H., FISCHER, R., KEILICH, G. and ORTH, H. D. Annalen 642, 214 (1961).
233. PLIENINGER, H., FISCHER, R. and LIEDE, V. Angew. Chem. 74, 430 (1962); Annalen 672, 233 (1964).
234. RAMSTAD, E. and AGURELL, S. Ann. Rev. Plant Physiol. 15, 143 (1964).
235. RAPOPORT, H. Abhandl. Deut. Akad. Wiss. Berlin Kl. Chem. Geol. Biol. Nr. 3, 111 (1966).
237. RAPOPORT, H., STERMITZ, F. R. and BAKER, D. R. J. Am. Chem. Soc. 82, 2765 (1960).
238. REINOUTS, P. VAN HAGA. Nature 174, 833 (1953).
239. ROBERTSON, A. V. and MARION, L. Can. J. Chem. 37, 1197 (1959).
240. ROBERTSON, A. V. and MARION, L. Can. J. Chem. 38, 396 (1960).
241. ROBINSON, R. J. Chem. Soc. 111, 876 (1917).
242. ROBINSON, R. Nature 162, 524 (1948).
243. ROBINSON, R. The Structural Relations of Natural Products. Clarendon Press, Oxford, 1955.
244. ROBINSON, W. G., BACHHAWAT, B. K. and COON, M. J. J. Biol. Chem. 218, 391 (1956).
245. ROMEIKE, A. Planta Med. 8, 491 (1960); Naturwiss. 49, 281 (1962).
246. ROMEIKE, A. and FODOR, G. Tetrahedron Letters 22, 1 (1960).
247. SANDER, H. and GRISEBACH, H. Z. Naturforsch. 13b, 755 (1958).
248. SCHIEDT, U. and BOECKH-BEHRENS, G. Z. Physiol. Chem. 330. 58 (1962).
249. SCHIEDT, U. and HÖSS, H. G. Z. Naturforsch 13b, 691 (1958); Z. Physiol. Chem. 330, 74 (1962).
249a. SCHRÖTER, H. B., and NEUMANN, D. Tetrahedron Letters 279 (1966).
250. SCHÜTTE, H. R. Arch. Pharm. 293, 1006 (1960).
251. SCHÜTTE, H. R. Atompraxis 7, 91 (1961).
252. SCHÜTTE, H. R., ASHANOW, H. and SCHAFER, Ch. Arch. Pharm. 295, 34 (1962).
253. SCHÜTTE, H. R., BOHLMANN, F. and REUSCHE, W. Arch. Pharm. 294, 610 (1961).
253a. SCHÜTTE, H. R. and HINDORF, H. Annalen 685, 187 (1965).
254. SCHÜTTE, H. R. and HINDORF, H. Naturwiss. 51, 463 (1964).
255. SCHÜTTE, H. R. and HINDORF, H. Z. Naturforsch. 19b, 855 (1964).
256. SCHÜTTE, H. R., HINDORF, H., MOTHES, K. and HUBNER, G. Annalen 680, 93 (1964).
257. SCHÜTTE, H. R., KELLING, K. L., KNÖFEL, D. and MOTHES, K. Phytochemistry 3, 249 (1964).
258. SCHÜTTE, H. R. and LEHFELDT, J. J. Prakt. Chem. 24, 143 (1964); Z. Naturforsch. 19b, 1085 (1964).

258a. SCHÜTTE, H. R., LEHFELDT, J. and HINDORF, H. *Annalen* **685,** 194 (1965).
258b. SCHÜTTE, H. R., and MAIER, B., *Arch. Pharm.* **298,** 459 (1965).
259. SCHÜTTE, H. R. and NOWACKI, E. *Naturwiss.* **46,** 493 (1959).
260. SCHÜTTE, H. R., NOWACKI, E., KOVACS, H. P. and LIEBISCH, H. W. *Arch. Pharm.* **296,** 438 (1963).
261. SCHÜTTE, H. R., NOWACKI, E. and SCHAFER, Ch. *Arch. Pharm.* **295,** 20 (1962).
262. SCHÜTTE, H. R., SANDKE, G. and LEHFELDT, J. *Arch. Pharm.* **297,** 118 (1964).
263. SCHÜTTE, H. R. and SCHAFER, CH. *Naturwiss.* **48,** 669 (1961).
265. SCOTT, A. I. *Quart. Rev. London*, **19,** 1 (1965).
266. SCHREIBER, K. *Abhandl. Deut. Akad. Wiss. Berlin Kl. Chem. Geol. Biol.* **Nr. 3,** 65 (1966).
267. SHIBATA, S. and IMASEKI, I. *Pharm. Bull. Tokyo* **4,** 277 (1956).
268. SHIBATA, S., IMASEKI, I. and YAMAZAKI, M. *Pharm. Bull. Tokyo* **5,** 71 (1957).
269. SHIBATA, S., IMASEKI, I. and YAMAZAKI, M. *Pharm. Bull. Tokyo* **5** 594 (1957).
270. SHIBATA, S. and SANKAWA, U. *Chem. and Ind. London* 1161 (1963).
271. SMITH, G. F. *Ann. Rep. Chem. Soc.* **53,** 242 (1956).
272. SOLT, M. L., DAWSON, R. F. and CHRISTMAN, D. R. *Plant Physiol.* **35,** 887 (1960).
273. SOUCEK, M. and SCHÜTTE, H. R. *Angew. Chemie* **74,** 901 (1962).
274. SPENSER, I. D. *Can. J. Chem.* **37,** 1851 (1959).
274a. SPENSER, I. D. *Lloydia* **29,** 71 (1966).
275. SPENSER, I. D. and GEAR, J. R. *J. Am. Chem. Soc.* **84,** 1059 (1962); *Proc. Chem. Soc.* 228 (1962).
276. SPITELLER-FRIEDMAN, M. and SPITELLER, G. *Monatsch.* **95,** 1234 (1964).
277. SRIBNEY, M. and KIRKWOOD, S. *Nature* **171,** 931 (1953).
278. SPRINSON, D. B. *Adv. Carbohydrate Chem.* **15,** 235 (1960).
279. STERMITZ, F. R. and RAPOPORT, H. *J. Am. Chem. Soc.* **83,** 4045 (1961).
279a. STOLLE, K., GRÖGER, D. and MOTHES, K. *Chem. and Ind. London* 2065 (1965).
280. SUHADOLNIK, R. J. *Abhandl. Deut. Akad. Wiss. Berlin Kl. Chem. Geol. Biol.* **Nr. 3,** 369 (1966).
281. SUHADOLNIK, R. J. and CHENOWETH, R. G. *J. Am. Chem. Soc.* **80,** 4391 (1958).
282. SUHADOLNIK, R. J., FISCHER, A. G. and ZULALIAN, J. *Biochem. Biophys. Res. Comm.* **11,** 208 (1963); *J. Am. Chem. Soc.* **84,** 4348 (1962); *Proc. Chem. Soc.* 132 (1963).
283. TABOR, W. A. and VINING, L. C. *Chem. and Ind. London* 1218 (1959).
284. TAYLOR, E. H. and RAMSTAD, *Nature* **188,** 484 (1960).
285. TAYLOR, W. I. *Science* **153,** 954 (1966).
285a. THOMAS, P. R., BARNES, M. F. and MARION, L. *Can. J. Chem.* **44,** 1997 (1966).
286. THOMAS, R. *Tetrahedron Letters* 544 (1961).
286a. TIWARI, H. P. and SPENSER, I. D. *Can. J. Biochem.* **43,** 1687 (1965).
286b. TURNER, F. A. and GEARIEN, J. E. *J. Pharm. Sci.* **53,** 1309 (1964).
287. TYLER, V. E. *J. Pharm. Sci.* **50,** 629 (1961).
288. UNDERHILL, E. W. and YOUNGKEN, H. W. *J. Pharm. Sci.* **51,** 121 (1962).
289. VALENTA, Z. and WIESNER, K. *Chem. and Ind. London* 354 (1956).
290. VAN TAMELEN, E. E., DOLBY, L. J. and LAWTON, R. G. *Tetrahedron Letters*, **19,** 30 (1960).
291. VAN TAMELEN, E. E. and FOLTZ, R. L. *J. Am. Chem. Soc.* **82,** 503 (1960).
293. VAN TAMELEN, E. E. and HAARSTAD, V. B. *Tetrahedron Letters* 390 (1961).
294. VISHIN, M. L., MOTHES, K, ENGELBRECHT, L. and SCHROTER, H.-B. *Nature*, **188,** 4744 (1960).
295. WALLER, G. R. and HENDERSON, L. M. *Biochem. Biophys. Res. Comm.* **5,** 5 (1961).
296. WALLER, G. R. and HENDERSON, L. M. *J. Biol. Chem.* **236,** 1186 (1961).
296a. WALLER, G. R., YANG, K. S., GHOLSON, R. K., HARDWIGER, L. A. and CHAYKIN, S. *J. Biol. Chem.* **241,** 4411 (1966).
297. WARREN, F. L. *Abhandl. Deut. Akad. Wiss. Berlin Kl. Chem. Geol. Biol.* **Nr. 3,** 571 (1966).
298. WENKERT, E. *Experientia* **15,** 165 (1959).
299. WENKERT, E. *J. Am. Chem. Soc.* **84,** 98 (1962).
300. WENKERT, E. and BRINGI, N. V. *J. Am. Chem. Soc.* **81,** 1474 (1959).
301. WEYGAND, F. and FLOSS, H.-G. *Angew. Chem. Int. Ed.* **2,** 243 (1963).

302. WEYGAND, F., FLOSS, H.-G., MOTHES, U., GRÖGER, D. and MOTHES, K. Z. Natur-forsch. **19b**, 202 (1964).
303. WIEHLER, G. and MARION, L. J. Biol. Chem. **231**, 799 (1958).
304. WIGHTMAN, F, CHISHOLM, M. D. and NEISH, A. C. Phytochemistry **1**, 30 (1961).
305. WINTERSTEIN, E. and TRIER, G. Die Alkaloide, p. 307. Gebr. Bornträger, Berlin, 1910.
306. WOODWARD, R. B. Nature, **162**, 155 (1948).
307. WOODWARD, R. B., IACOBUCCI, G. A. and HOCHSTEIN, F. A. J. Am. Chem. Soc. **81**, 4434 (1959).
308. WU, P. L. and BYERRUM, R. U. Biochemistry **4**, 1628 (1965).
308a. YAMAZAKI, M. and IKUTA, A. Tetrahedron Letters 3221 (1966).
308b. YAMAZAKI, M., MATSUO, M. and ARAI, K. Chem. Pharm. Bull. Tokyo **14**, 1058 (1966).
309. YAMAZAKI, M. and LEETE, E. Tetrahedron Letters 1499 (1964).
310. YANG, K. S., GHOLSON, R. K. and WALLER, G. R. J. Am. Chem. Soc. **87** 4184 (1965).
310a. YANG, K. S. and WALLER, G. R. Phytochemistry **4**, 881 (1965).
311. YEOWELL, D. A. and SCHMID, H. Experientia **20**, 250 (1964).
312. ZULALIAN, J. and SUHADOLNIK, R. J. Proc. Chem. Soc. 422 (1964).

CHAPTER 18

THE BIOSYNTHESIS OF FUNGAL METABOLITES†

W. Basil Whalley

Department of Chemistry, School of Pharmacy, The University of London

CONTENTS

Introduction	1025
Biosynthesis from Acetic Acid	1026
The Origin of "Extra" Carbon Atoms	1038
Quinones	1043
Terpenes	1046
Structural Units derived from Amino Acids and Shikimic Acid	1052
Structural Correlations	1055
Conclusion	1060
References	1060

INTRODUCTION

This chapter is concerned with the biosynthesis of metabolites of microorganisms, particularly the fungi. Investigations in this field have contributed substantially to the understanding of biosynthetic processes in general, and the information thus derived may be applied, with appropriate caution, to related fields of biosynthesis and particularly to those in the higher plants.

The rapid advance in this area of biosynthetic knowledge since 1956 has been facilitated by two principal factors. Firstly, an extensive body of information concerning the chemistry of a wide variety of fungal metabolites had been made available by the research groups of Harold Raistrick and Alexander Robertson. Secondly, fungi are particularly amenable to laboratory investigations involving the use of isotopically labeled substrates, which first became available in the middle 1950's.

The genesis of the major structural features of fungal metabolites may be briefly summarized:

(a) The majority of phenolic rings are derived from acetic acid, although a minority have shikimic acid and its metabolic associates as precursor.

(b) Various "extra" carbon atoms such as C-methyl, O-methyl, and N-methyl groups, which are additional to the major structural precursors,

†Manuscript submitted March 1, 1965.

are frequently derived from formate or its biological equivalent from the C_1 metabolic pool. In certain cases, however, additional C-methyl groups are derived from C3 of propionic acid.

(c) Terpenes, steroids and terpenoid residues attached to phenolic system have mevalonic lactone as their immediate precursor and hence are derived indirectly from acetate.

(d) Other structural fragments have amino acids and hence glucose as their source.

Examples of these various possibilities are described and discussed in the following pages.

BIOSYNTHESIS FROM ACETIC ACID

The acetate theory of biosynthesis which postulates that the "head-to-tail" union of acetic acid molecules is involved in the biogenesis of many phenols was originally formulated in a simple manner by Collie in 1893. [48] An independent statement of the same concept was advanced by Birch in 1953 [16] and was first subjected to the test in 1955. [24] The organism, *Penicillium griseofulvum* Dierckx, produces 2-hydroxy-6-methylbenzoic acid (I), and when grown upon a medium containing $CH_3C^{14}OOH$,† the benzoic acid has the predicted labeling shown in (I).

$$4 \times CH_3\overset{x}{C}OOH \longrightarrow$$

I

Similar experiments with [carboxy-C^{14}] acetic acid clearly show that griseofulvin (III), which is also elaborated by *P. griseofulvum* Dierckx, is derived biosynthetically by the head-to-tail union of seven acetic acid [25] residues as in (II):

II   III Griseofulvin

† [1-C^{14}] Acetic acid is used more frequently than [2-C^{14}] acetic acid to avoid the mixing of the label which occurs with methyl-labeled acetic acid on passage through the tricarboxylic acid cycle.

Considerable circumstantial evidence indicates that the penultimate stage in the biogenesis of griseofulvin is the one-electron oxidative coupling of the benzophenone (IV) to the spiran, dehydrogriseofulvin (VI) by way of the diradical (V). The ultimate stage is then the hydrogenation of dehydrogriseofulvin (VI) to griseofulvin (III). This view of the final steps in the biosynthesis of griseofulvin is strongly supported by the chemical synthesis[94] of ($\pm$) dehydrogriseofulvin (VI) from the benzophenone (IV) and by the isolation from the metabolites of *P. patulum* of the benzophenone (IV) and of dehydrogriseofulvin (VI) in addition to griseofulvin.[83] In addition to geodoxin (VIII)[73] and asterric acid (IX)[52] the fungus *Aspergillus terreus* furnishes the metabolites geodin (VII, R = CH$_3$)[5] and erdin (VII, R = H)[5] which have obvious structural affinities with griseofulvin.

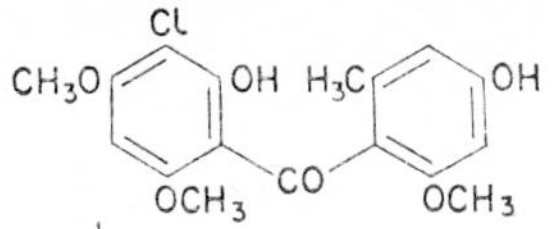

IV

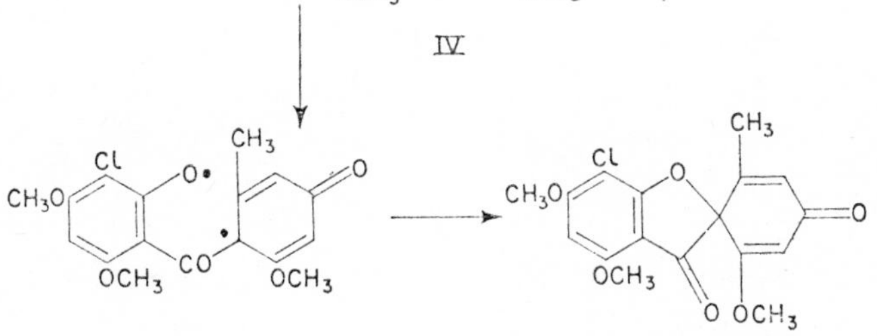

V

VI dehydrogriseofulvin

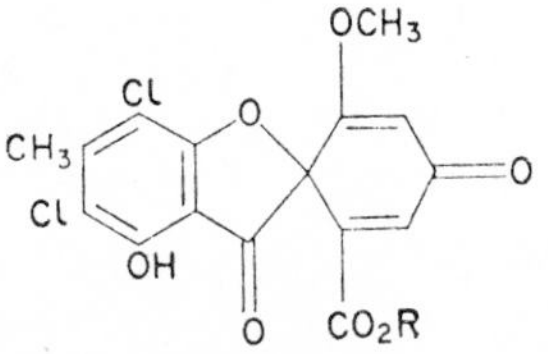

VII R = H : erdin
R = CH$_3$: geodin

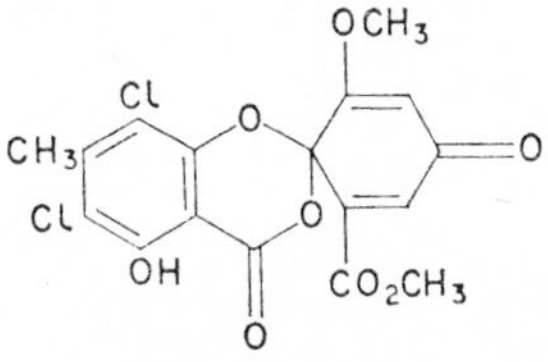

VIII geodoxin

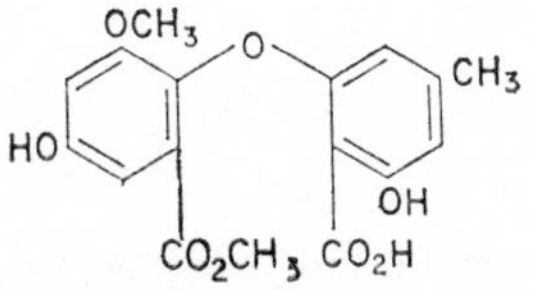

IX asterric acid

The methyl ether (XII) of (±) geodin has been synthesized [94] by the oxidative coupling of the benzophenone (X) by way of the di-radical (XI). Hence, although no direct evidence is available it may be inferred that the biogenesis of geodin and erdin proceeds similarly to that of griseofulvin.

Geodoxin (VIII) may be formed phytochemically from geodin by a Baeyer-Villiger type oxidation (cf. Hassall) [73] or from geodin hydrate (XIII) followed by an oxidative coupling. [73] The co-occurrence, among the metabolites of *A. terreus* of geodin, erdin, geodoxin and asterric acid together with the laboratory conversion [52] of sulochrin (XIV), a metabolite of *Oospora sulphurea-ochracea*, into asterric acid (IX) by way of the spiran ester (XV)

provides very strong circumstantial evidence for the suggestion that in the natural process sulochrin (XIV), geodin (VII, R=CH₃), asterric acid (IX) and geodoxin (VIII) are produced from one another in turn.

Another straightforward example of biosynthesis from acetate, again involving seven acetate units, is the formation of alternariol (XVI) by *Alternaria tenius* as follows: [100]

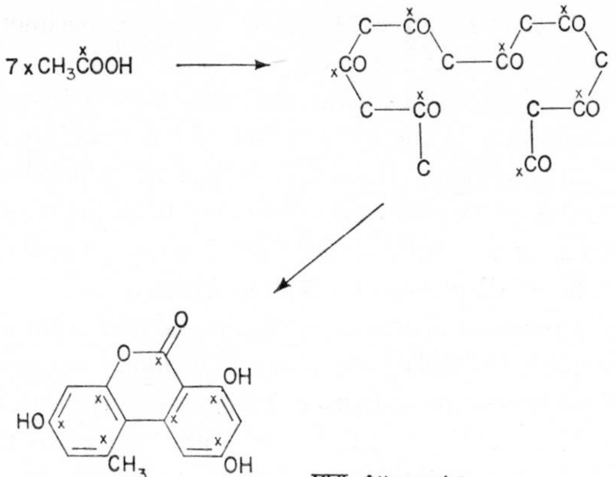

XVI Alternariol

The study of the biosynthetic pathways in the fungus *Daldinia concentrica* (Bolt) Ces. and de Not has revealed several points of considerable interest. [1] The dark color of this organism is due to the presence of 4,9-dihydroxyperylene-3,10-quinone (XVII) and the polymeric quinone (XVIII) which are

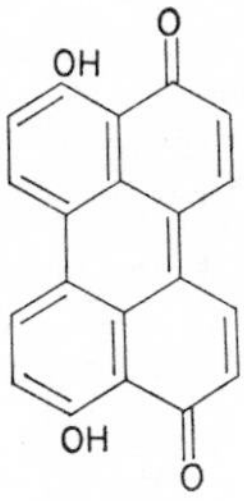

XVII

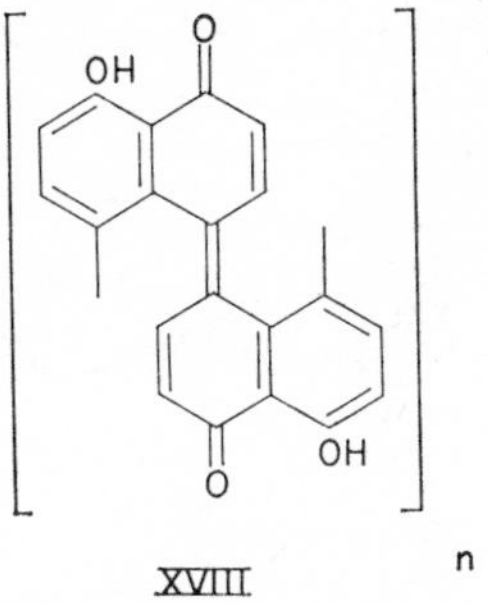

XVIII

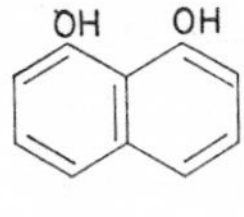

XIX

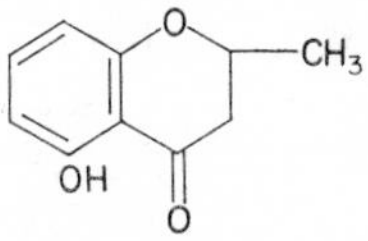

XX

derived from one of the primary metabolites, 1,8-dihydroxynaphthalene (XIX). This naphthol and the associated chromanone (XX) are both acetate derived and from a study of various strains of *D. concentrica* it seems that these $C_{\cdot 0}$ benzenoid compounds are alternative metabolites of a common acetate derived precursor. *D. concentrica* is notable as one of the very few fungi in which both partial and complete aromatization of an "acetate-derived" structure has been observed.

Although the assertion can seldom be tested experimentally, it has frequently been objected that the wide variety of substances isolable from laboratory cultures of microorganisms are pathological by-products which have little if any relevance to the metabolism of the same organism growing in its "natural" environment. However, it has been possible to study a whole range of strains of *D. concentrica*, ranging from highly defective vegetative and conidial strains to fully sexual "wild" strains. In all cases the same metabolic processes are displayed in varying degrees.

A more highly condensed aromatic system is the perinaphthenone nucleus (XXII) of atrovenetin (XXIII) [4, 86] from *Penicillium atrovenetum* and of herqueinone and norherqueinone from *P. herquei*. Incorporation experiments with sodium [1-C^{14}] acetate and [2-C^{14}] mevalonic lactone are consistent with the derivation of the perinaphthenone nucleus from acetate units and the C$_5$ side chain from acetate or mevalonate as in the sequence (XXI)→(XXII)→(XXIII). [101]

XXIII Atrovenetin

Another biogenetically interesting metabolite is curvularin (XXIV), a metabolite of a *Curvularia* species. [27] This compound is derived from eight acetate units and is the first example of a naturally occurring macrolide lactone having a methyl group as the only alkyl substituent. Curvularin constitutes an interesting structural, and possibly biosynthetic link, between the macrolide antibiotics (p. 1042) and acetate derived phenols. The ease of

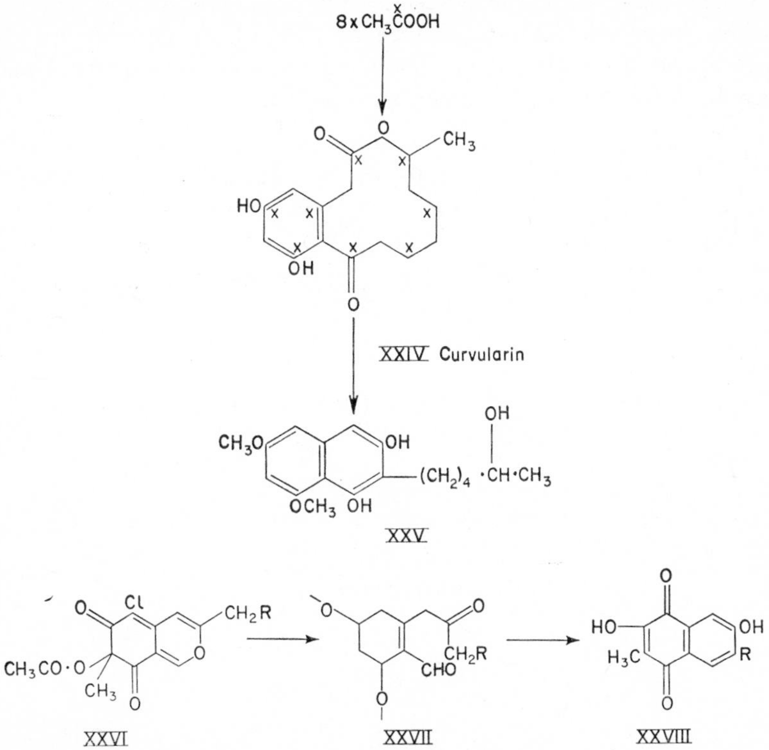

$8 \times CH_3\overset{x}{C}OOH$

XXIV Curvularin

XXV

XXVI   XXVII   XXVIII

conversion of di-O-methyl curvularin into the naphthol (XXV), together with the similar, facile conversion of various hydrosclerotiorin derivatives, type (XXVI), into naphthoquinones, type (XXVIII), by way, *inter alia*, of the intermediate, type (XXVII), [66] provides an acceptable laboratory analogy for the validity of the postulated mechanism [10] for the derivation of polycyclic aromatic systems from poly-β-keto methylene chains.

Preliminary investigations [96] indicated that the linear tetracyclic system of oxytetracycline (XXX) is derived biogenetically from seven molecules of acetic acid together with one molecule of glutamic acid and three C_1 units as in (XXIX). However, more recent work [82] has established that 6-methyl-1,3,10,11,12-pentahydroxynaphthacene-2-carboxamide (XXXI) is the normal biological precursor of the tetracyclines.† It would thus appear probable that the nucleus of these metabolites is derived entirely from acetate

† (*Added in proof—January 1967*)—Since the submission of this manuscript in March 1965, extensive and elegant investigations concerning the biosynthesis of the tetracyclines have been reported by J. R. D. McCormick and his associates.

units and that the initial conclusions involving glutamic acid may be invalid. Rutilantinone [88] (p. 1043) and its congeners are similarly derived from nine acetate units and one propionate unit (p. 1043). It is interesting to speculate that these linear polycyclic systems occupy an intermediate structural and possibly biogenetic position between an open chain precursor (or closed chain of the macrolide type, p. 1041), and the fully aromatized polynuclear phenols of, for example, the anthraquinone type.

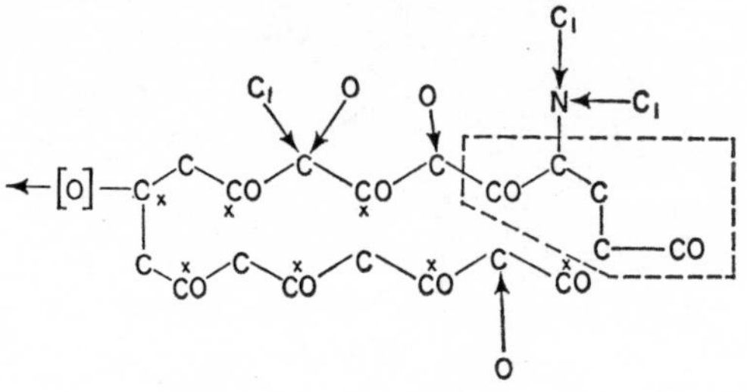

XXIX

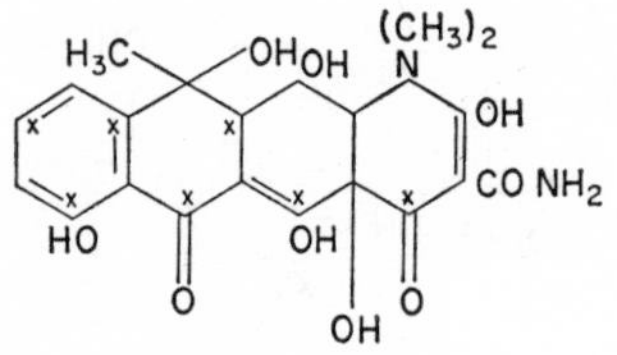

XXX oxytetracycline

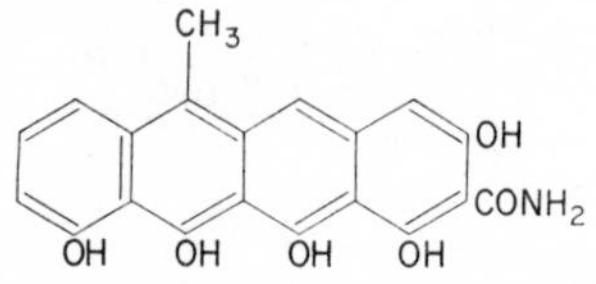

XXXI

A necessary consequence of the validity of the concept that phenolic compounds are generally derived from acetic acid, is that those phenolic oxygen atoms which correspond to the oxygen functions of the parent poly-β-ketomethylene chain must be derived directly from the carbonyl group of this chain. Thus, for example, the oxygen atoms attached to C4, C6 and C7 of orsellinic acid (XXXIII) should be those which occur at C4. C6 and C8 in the precursor (XXXII).

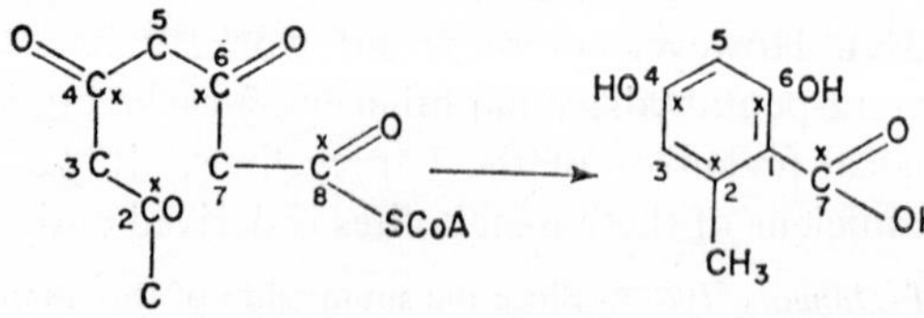

XXXII   XXXIII Orsellinic acid

Experiments upon the biosynthesis of orsellinic acid (XXXIII), which should arise from the cyclization of a precursor, type (XXXII), show that this theoretical requirement is realized. [63] Orsellinic acid is a metabolite of *Chaetomium cochliodes* Pall. When grown upon a medium containing $CH_3C^{14}O^{18}$ ONa, this organism furnishes orsellinic acid (XXXIII) having the requisite distribution of C^{14} labeling, whilst the phenolic hydroxyls and the carboxyl groups contain incorporated O^{18}. Further, the C^{14}/O^{18} ratio at C4 and C6 in (XXXIII) are equal and the same as that in the parent acetic acid.

It is now generally recognized that the "head-to-tail" union of acetic acid, involves not the free acid but acetyl-CoA, and thus the resultant product (e.g. XXXII) is a chain terminated by the thiolester group. Hence, hydrolysis of this thiol ester, with H_2O^{16}, must precede the production of free orsellinic acid. The correctness of this view is substantiated by the fact that the atom % excess of O^{18} in the carbonyl group is only half that of the atom % excess of O^{18} in the phenolic hydroxyl groups. [63]

A further extension and definition of the biosynthetic route involving acetic acid has been demonstrated. Thus, the utilization of acetic acid for fatty acid biosynthesis involves the carboxylation of acetyl-CoA to yield malonyl-CoA units which then condense with the release of the fixed carbon dioxide. [98]

XXXIV

An analogous sequence of reactions has been demonstrated in the bio-synthesis of penicillic acid (XLVII) and, hence, of the orsellinic acid precursor. In an extensive and briefly reported investigation utilizing a variety of labeled precursors Bentley and Kiel [8] have shown that the methoxyl group of penicillic acid arises from [CH_3-C^{14}] methionine, in accord with accepted concepts (cf. p. 1037). It was further demonstrated that the orsellinic acid precursor is formed by the condensation of one molecule of acetyl-CoA and three molecules of malonyl-CoA (derived from acetyl-CoA by carboxylation) as in scheme (XXXIV). Thus, the early stages of orsellinic acid biosynthesis are analogous to fatty acid biosynthesis. In agreement with the formation of malonyl-CoA from acetyl-CoA and carbon dioxide which is later released, Bentley and Kiel[8] showed that $NaHC^{14}O_3$ is not incorporated into penicillic acid.

Although the conversion of malonyl-CoA into acetyl-CoA has been reported with certain microorganisms[75] this reaction apparently does not occur to any extent in *P. cyclopium*, and thus the reaction acetyl-CoA → malonyl-CoA is irreversible[8] in this case and may be compared with the irreversible sequence, acetate → mevalonate.[18, 29]

A necessary consequence of this modification of biosyntheses involving acetate is that the first (or "starter") unit in any polyketomethylene system must be a monobasic acid (e.g. acetic acid) and that subsequent units are derived from malonate or less frequently from methyl malonate (cf.the biosynthesis of macrolides, p. 1041). Evidence for this is available. Thus *P. urticae* furnishes 6-methyl salicylic acid as a metabolite. Mycelium from shaken cultures of *P. urticae* were resuspended in a glucose-free Czapek-Dox medium containing sodium (1-C^{14}) acetate and diethyl malonate. The isotope content of C6 of the resultant 6-methylsalicylic acid was always 12–15 per cent higher than that of the carboxyl group, thereby demonstrating that unlabeled malonate is utilized in preference to labeled acetate for *extension* of a carbon chain, the terminal methyl of which is preferentially derived from acetate.[15, 41]

XXXV   XXXVI Citrinin

In addition to completely aromatic ring systems many fungal metabolites include heterocyclic residues, particularly those containing oxygen. The derivation of several oxygen heterocyclic fungal metabolites from acetate has been confirmed.[20, 14]

Thus, citrinin (XXXVI),[45] a metabolite of numerous organisms including *P. citrinum* Thom and *A. terreus*, is biosynthesized from five molecules of acetic acid with the insertion of three C_1 units as shown in (XXXV).[20] One of the introduced C_1 fragments is oxidized to the carboxyl group. The structurally cognate metabolite palitantin (XXXVII) [34] from *P. palitans* and *P. frequentans* is similarly derived from acetate. [23, 47]

Further development of the palitantin type molecule (cf. p. 1036) gives rise to sclerotiorin (XXXVIII), [55] a metabolite of *P. sclerotiorum* van Beyma and *P. multicolor*. This halogen-containing compound has an acetate derived nucleus into which are inserted one acetyl residue, a halogen atom and three C_1-methyl groups as in (XXXIX). [20] Rotiorin (XLI), [80] a co-pigment with sclerotiorin, has an analogous labeling pattern [14] and is presumably biosynthesized by the sequence (XXXIX) → (XL) → (XLI). Preliminary experiments [14] with rubropunctatin [74] (XLII, R = $C_5H_{11}n$) from *Monascus rubropunctatus* Sâto and monascin (XLIII) [59] from *M. rubropunctatus* Sâto and *M. purpureus* Wentii, indicate a similar mode of biogenesis.

A more detailed investigation [77] of the biosynthesis of sclerotiorin (XXXVIII) and of rotiorin (XLI) by *P. sclerotiorum* van Beyma shows that the main poly-β-ketide chain of these metabolites is assembled from a terminal two-carbon unit derived from acetate with chain-building units provided by malonate. Partial decarboxylation of introduced labeled malonate clearly establishes (at least in this system) the reversibility (cf. ref. 75) of the acetate-to-malonate conversion. The outstanding observation from the experiments with rotiorin is that the acetoacetyl unit of the β-oxo-lactone system in this metabolite is derived from acetate without participation of malonate. Further, sodium (1-C^{14}) butyrate is incorporated intact into this β-oxo-lactone system. This provides additional evidence for the view that the butyrate is oxidized to acetoacetate which is then incorporated into the β-oxo-lactone system of rotiorin as an intact unit as previously adumbrated. [105] In citrinin (XXXVI), sclerotiorin (XXXVIII), rotiorin (XLI) and rubropunctatin (XLII, R = $C_5H_{11}n$), the masked aldehyde groups marked * are derived by reduction of a carboxyl group of an acetic acid residue. In palitantin (XXXVII), frequentin (CXXXI) and monascin (XLIII) this biological reduction has proceeded to the primary alcohol stage.

In the above compounds the oxygen heterocyclic rings are derived (presumably) directly. In other fungal metabolites the hetero rings arise indirectly from benzenoid systems, which are in turn acetate derived.

Thus, penicillic acid (XLVII), a metabolite of *P. cyclopium* Westling incorporates insignificant amounts of [2-C^{14}] mevalonic lactone, but [1-C^{14}] acetic acid is readily incorporated to give penicillic acid with the labeling pattern (XLVII). [12] Birch et al., [12] suggested the sequence, acetate → orsellinic acid (XLIV) → (XLV) → (XLVI) → penicillic acid (XLVII), and this has been confined by Mosbach [84] using *P. baarnense*. Further the formation of orsellinic acid by *P. cyclopium* has been established. [8] The fission of orsellinic acid as in (XLV) is analogous to the "Woodward" oxidation of phenols which has been invoked in connection with the biogenesis of the strychnos

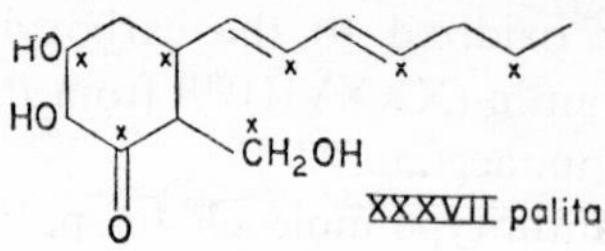

XXXVII palitantin

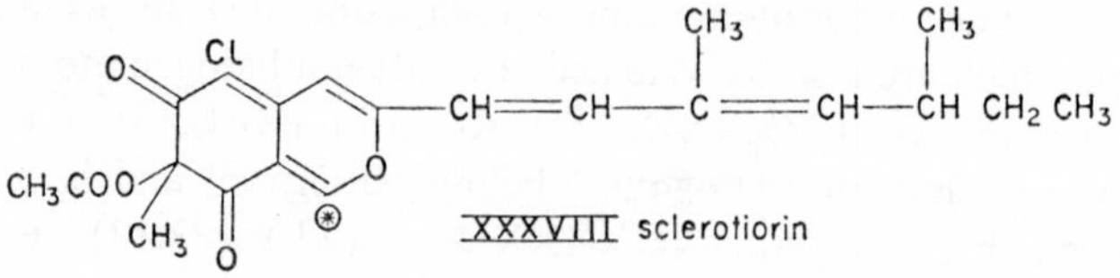

XXXVIII sclerotiorin

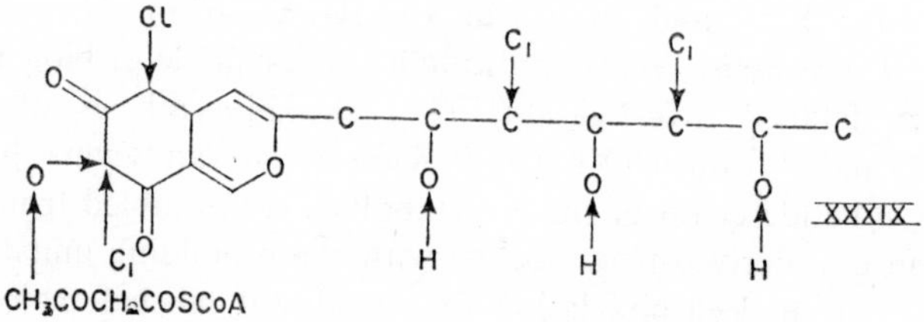

XXXIX

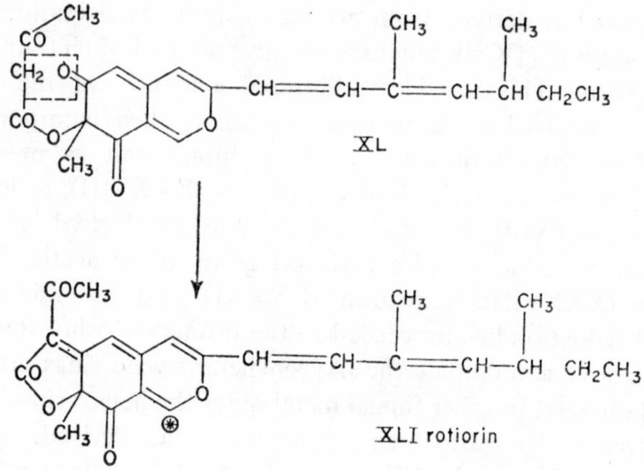

$CH_3COCH_2COSCoA$

XL

XLI rotiorin

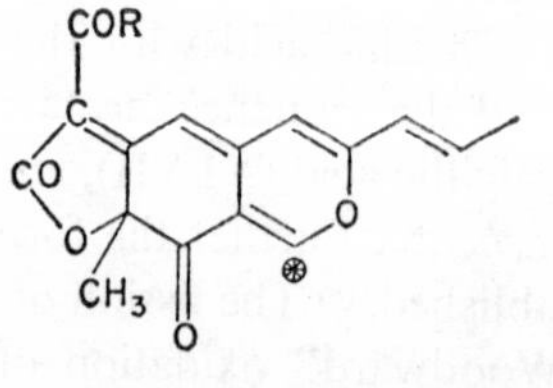

XLII R = n -C$_5$H$_{11}$: rubropunctatin
R = n -C$_7$H$_{15}$: monascorubrin

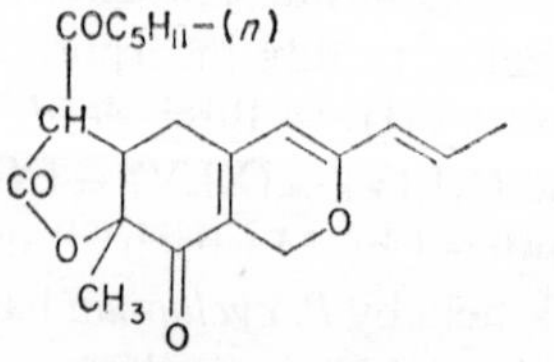

XLIII monascin

and associated alkaloids. Penicillic acid is an important example of a route to a substance which contains an "isoprene" unit which does not involve mevalonic acid or valine.

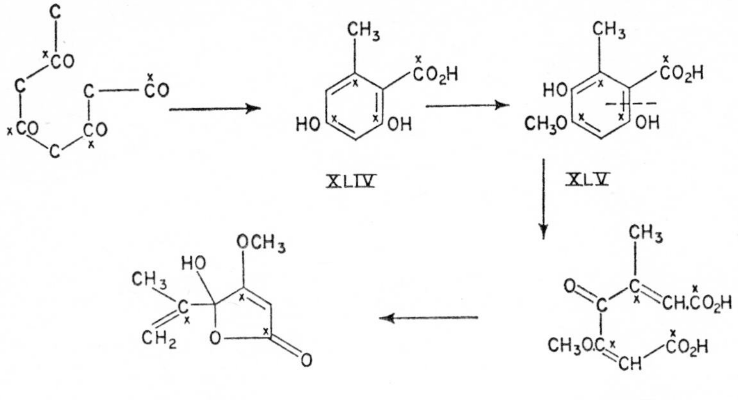

XLIV

XLV

XLVII penicillic acid

XLVI

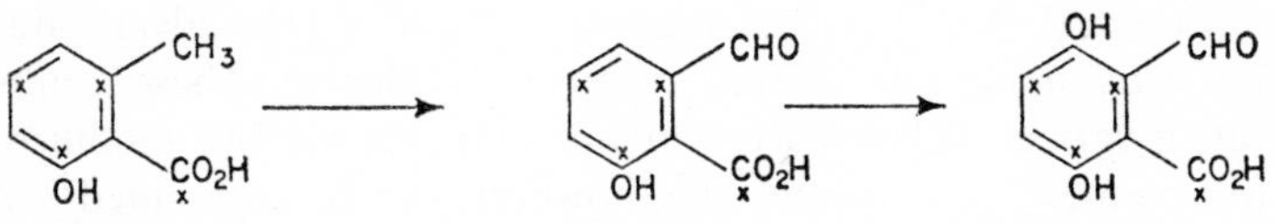

XLVIII

X LIX

L

An unequivocal demonstration of the oxidative fission of a benzene ring has also been afforded [40] in the biosynthesis of patulin (LIII), a metabolite of *P. patulum*. The growth of this organism upon a glucose solution containing specifically labeled 6-methylsalicylic acid (XLVIII) furnishes patulin with the labeling pattern (LIII). This result is only compatible with the biosynthetic sequence (XLVIII) → (XLIX) → (L) → (LI) → (LII), which does not appear to involve the formation of an intermediate catechol as in the "Woodward" fission.

Citromycetin (LIV) [92] is a metabolite of various penicillia including *P. frequentans*. Experiments with [1-C^{14}] acetic acid and $HC^{14}OOH$ have shown [20] that the carbon skeleton is derived entirely from acetic acid with the labeling pattern (LIV). This is not immediately reconcilable with the derivation of citromycetin by a "head-to-tail" junction of acetic acid units and could be interpreted either as an additional case of biosynthesis involving the fission of aromatic (or pre-aromatic) rings [105] or alternately an example of biosynthesis involving a carbon-carbon linkage of two chains as in (CXL). Recent evidence [22, 64] does indeed provide minimal evidence that two chains are involved.

The definition of the biosynthetic pathways to the simple tropolones, e.g

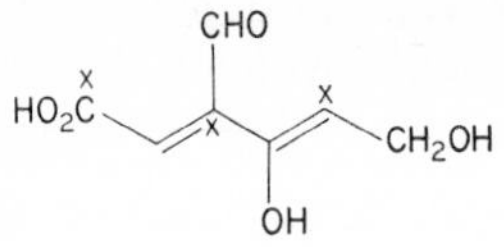

L II

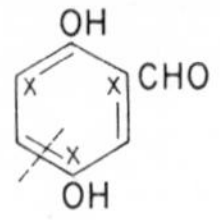

L I

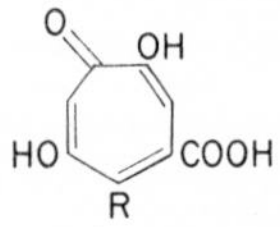

L V

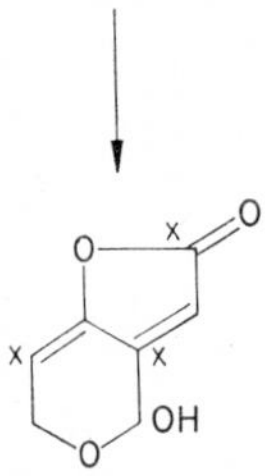

L III Patulin

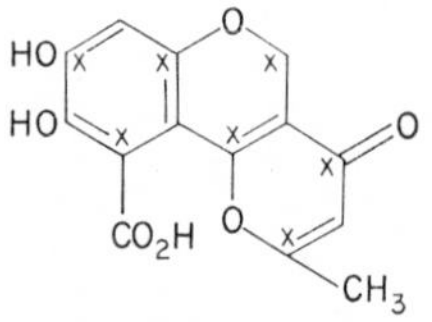

L IV Citromycetin

stipitatonic (LV; R = CO_2H) and stipitatic (LV; R = H) acids, produced by *Penicillium stipitatum*, has proved particularly elusive. These compounds incorporate a variety of labeled precursors, and thus various modified paths appear to operate. The principal one, however, can be repesented[7] as

$$1 \text{ Acetyl-CoA} + 3\text{-malonyl-CoA} + 1C_1\text{-unit} \rightarrow C_9 \text{ precursor} + 3CO_2$$

Tropolones

THE ORIGIN OF "EXTRA" CARBON ATOMS

Inspection of the structural features of natural products in general and of microbial metabolites in particular frequently reveals the presence of C_1 carbon residues which are additional or "extra" to those which stem from the major precursor units.

Thus, for example, citrinin (XXXVI) is biosynthesized[10] from five molecules of acetic acid together with three "introduced" C_1 residues as in (XXXV). Sclerotiorin (XXXVIII), rotiorin (XLI) and aurantiogliocladin (LXXII, R = CH_3),[21] to quote three further examples, contain "extra" C_1 units. In all these compounds the "extra" C_1 residues are attached to carbon. Mycophenolic acid (LXIII)[17] possesses an O-methyl group (as a methoxyl) and a nuclear, "extra" C-methyl group. Aurantiogliocladin (LXXII, R = CH_3) and griseofulvin (III) likewise contain methoxyl groups. Incorporation experiments[17] with $HC^{14}OOH$ and $CH_3C^{14}OOH$ have conclusively shown that the "extra" carbon atoms in the foregoing examples are derived from formate, or its biological equivalent. Formate is also the precursor of the methoxyl groups in spirilloxanthin (LVI), a carotenoid metabolite of the photosynthetic bacterium, *Rhodospirillum rubrum*. [36]

Cumulative evidence shows that the genesis of "extra" carbon atoms attached to oxygen and nitrogen, and many of those attached to carbon, is the C_1 metabolic pool and that these "extra" carbon atoms are attached to the appropriate receptor centres through transmethylation from C_1 donor systems (e.g. choline, methionine and tetrahydrofolic acid). In those molecules which are acetate derived it is most probable that the C-methyl groups are introduced by transmethylation into the poly-β-keto system arising from the "head-to-tail" union of acetic acid residues. [10]

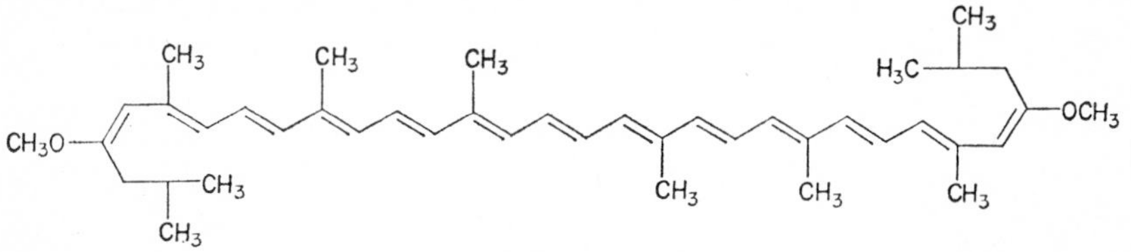

LVI Spirilloxanthin

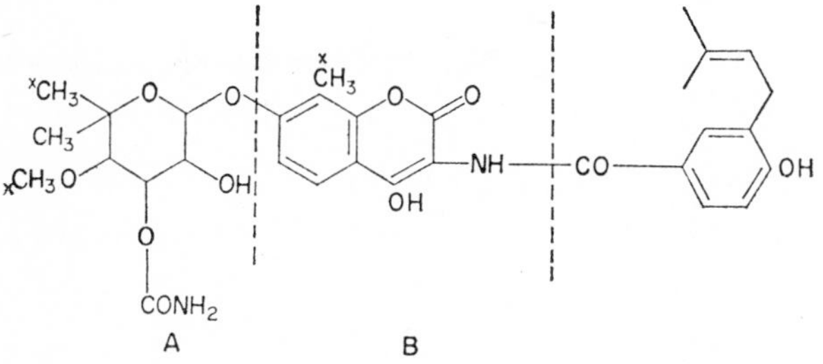

LVII Novobiocin

Incorporation experiments with [$C^{14}H_3$]-methionine show that the methoxyl and C-methyl group attached to the benzene ring of mycophenolic acid (LXIII) are derived from methyl methionine. [17] The two methyl groups attached to the nitrogen atom of oxytetracycline (XXX) arise from the same precursor. [96]

Fermentation experiments [24] with *Streptomyces niveus* in the presence of [$C^{14}H_3$]-methionine yield novobiocin (LVII), in which the labeling is distributed between the C-methyl residue of the coumarin system (B, in LVII) (35 per cent), the O-methyl group of the noviose moiety (A; in LVII) (35 per cent), and the *gem*-dimethyl group of the sugar residue (A; in LVII). Probably only one C-methyl in the sugar residue of novobiose is labeled.

$[C^{14}H_3]$-Methionine is also incorporated into the two nuclear C-methyl groups in actinomycin (LVIII).

It is shown[46] (p. 1053) that the coumarin ring of novobiocin (LVII) arises from tyrosine, and hence from shikimic acid.[53] Similarly the nucleus of actinomycin (LVIII) is probably biosynthesized by the oxidative condensation of two molecules of the appropriate anthranilic acid,[51] which in turn arises from shikimic acid. These experiments, particularly those on the C-

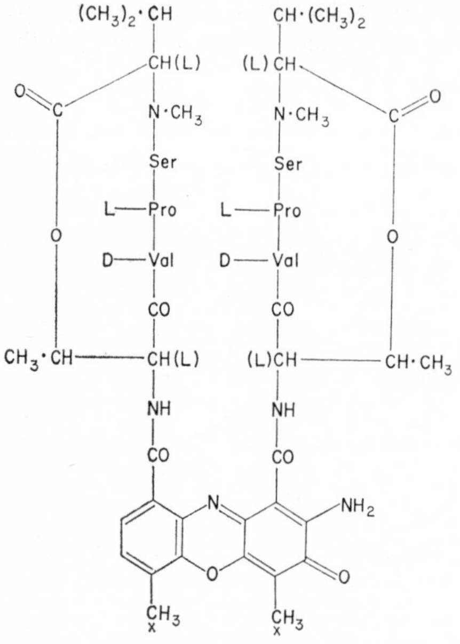

LVIII Actinomycin

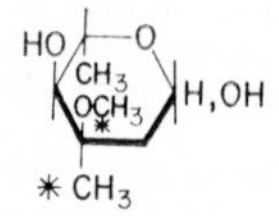

LIX Cladinose

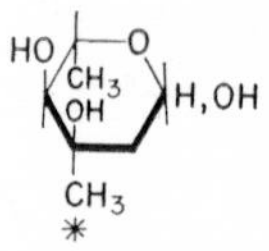

LX Mycarose

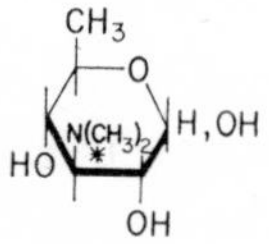

LXI Mycaminose

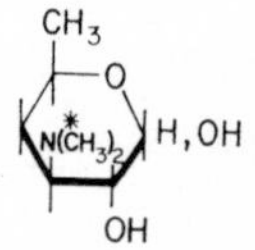

LXII Desosamine

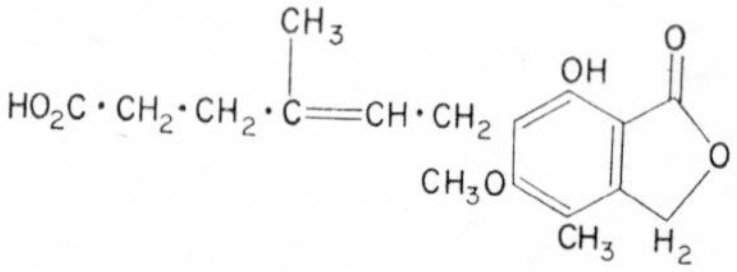

LXIII Mycophenolic acid

methylation of novobiocin, provide the first unequivocal demonstration of the transfer of methyl groups from methionine (probably as the S-adenosyl derivative)[89] to carbon in an aromatic ring derived from shikimic acid.

Similar experiments with the same methyl cation donor have demonstrated the important role of C_1 units in the biosynthesis of the unusual, branched-chain sugars which occur in numerous fungal metabolites. Thus, investigations[13] with novobiocin demonstrate that the O-methyl and probably one of the C-methyl groups of the novobiose residue (A in LVII) are derived from $[C^{14}H_3]$-methionine. Particularly informative results have accrued from studies on the biosynthesis of the macrolide antibiotics where it has been shown that the methyl residues marked (*) in the sugars cladinose

(LIX), from erythromycin A and B, and mycarose (LX) from *inter alia*, erythromycin C and magnamycin A and B, are derived from $[C^{14}H_3]$-methionine. [50] In the dimethylamino sugars, mycaminose (LXI), from *inter alia*, magnamycin A and B, and desosamine (LXII) from various macrolides, including erythromycin A, B and C, the N-methyl residues are similarly derived. [81, 68] It has further been shown [43, 67] that these sugars are derived from D-glucose without cleavage of the chain. The alternative suggestion that these branched-chain sugars arise from smaller carbohydrate units by ketol [78] and Claisen [107] type condensations are thus untenable.

The lactone rings of the macrolide antibiotics, for example, erythromycin (LXIV, R_1 = LIX, R_2 = LXII) and methymycin (LXVI), which are produced by various species of *Streptomyces*, possess several "extra" carbon atoms sited on alternate carbon atoms. These "extra" carbon atoms could be derived from the C_1 pool [23] as in the examples just discussed, but as an alternative Woodward suggested [80] the intervention of propionate residues as in (LXV). Studies [28] on the biosynthesis of methymycin (LXVI) by *Streptomyces Venezuelae* have confirmed its derivation from five propionate units and one acetate residue as in (LXV). Hence the "extra" C-methyl groups in the alternate positions in the linear chain are the terminal methyls of the propionic acid residues. Bently [6] has pointed out that the data from these labeling experiments are also consistent with the incorporation of six propionate units and the subsequent loss of the additional C-methyl at C-8. The indifferent incorporation of acetate into methymycin would be in accord with this suggestion. Similar work [69] has confirmed that the lactone ring of erythromycin (LXIV; R_1 = LIX, R_2 = LXII) is derived from seven propionate units. Thus, for example, incorporation experiments with $[1-C^{14}, 3-T]$ propionic acid show that the whole of the tritium is localized in the C-methyl groups, whilst the C^{14} activity is confined to the carbon atoms 1, 3, 5, etc., of the macrolide ring.

In erythromycin the asymmetric centres between C-1 and C-8 are mainly, if not exclusively, of the opposite configuration to those between C-10 and C-13. [56] A similar situation obtains in the case of neo-methymycin and of picromycin. It was suggested [56] that these and possibly other macrolide rings arise from the union, at a late stage in the biosynthesis, of two "prefabricated" chains (cf. citromycetin, p. 1037) rather than by successive condensation of C_2 or C_3 units. However, the absence of two "starter molecules" of propionic acid together with incorporation experiments using methylmalonic acid [70] clearly make this attractive hypothesis untenable, at least for erythromycin.

In contrast to the other macrolides the lactone ring of the antibiotic, magnamycin (LXVII) contains only one C-methyl group. The results of biosynthetic experiments upon this metabolite are complicated, but it seems

LXIV   R₁ = Cladinose LIX
       R₂ = Desosamine LXII } Erythromycin

LXV   LXVI Methymycin

LXVII Magnamycin

LXVIII ε–Pyrromycinone (Rutilantinone)

LXIX   LXX

certain that only part of the lactone ring is formed from acetate and propionate residues.

Further variants of the acetate-propionate theme are known. Thus, 2-methylbutyric acid, a metabolite of the intestinal helminth, *Ascaris lumbricoides*, is biosynthesized from one molecule each of acetic and propionic acid. [93] ϵ-Pyrromycinone [88] (rutilantinone) (LXVIII) is the aglucone of various antibiotics, including pyrromycin, cinerubin A and B, and the rutilantins, which are produced by numerous *Actinomyces* species. Incorporation experiments[88] with $CH_3C^{14}OOH$ and $CH_3CH_2C^{14}OOH$ have clearly shown that ϵ-pyrromycinone is biosynthesized from nine acetate units and one propionate unit, as in (LXX), rather than by the alternative involving ten acetate units and one C_1 unit as in (LXIX), It is interesting to note that *P. baarnense*, which produces orsellinic acid as a major metabolite, also gives rise to smaller amounts of homo-orsellinic (4,6-dihydroxy-2-ethylbenzoic) acid, the "starter unit" of which is propionic acid. [85]

It seems highly probable that further investigation will demonstrate the derivation of natural products from acetic and propionic acids in varying proportions.

QUINONES

There is only limited information available concerning the biosynthesis of quinones from either plant or animal sources, but tracer experiments with fungal quinones indicate that these compounds are derived from acetate in the usual manner.

Thus helminthosporin [30] (LXXI), an anthraquinonoid pigment of *Helminthosporium graminium* Rabenhorst, and emodin (LXXVII) [62] from *P. islandicum* have the labeling pattern shown when produced on a medium containing [carboxy-C^{14}]-acetic acid. Investigations [95] with rugulosin (LXXVIII), a metabolite from *Penicillium brunneum* Udagawa, clearly show this anthraquinone to be similarly derived and that the C-Me residue corresponds to the "starter unit" of the original chain since incorporation experiments with [2-C^{14}] malonate furnish labeled rugulosin-C which is devoid of activity in this residue.

Gliocladium roseum Bainier furnishes the *p*-benzoquinone, aurantiogliocladin (LXXII, R = CH_3) the corresponding quinol, rubriogliocladin and gliorosein (LXXIII) or (LXXIV). Tracer experiments [21] with $CH_3C^{14}OOH$ and $HC^{14}OOH$ support the derivation of these compounds as in (LXXV) where the C-methyl group and the methoxyl groups are derived from formate or its equivalent in the C_1 pool. These labeling patterns are, thus, in accord with the biosynthesis of *p*-benzoquinones from an orsellinic acid type precursor (LXXVI) to the accompaniment of oxidation and decarboxylation, rather than from glucose. [76]

The results with aurantiogliocladin also indicate that the various

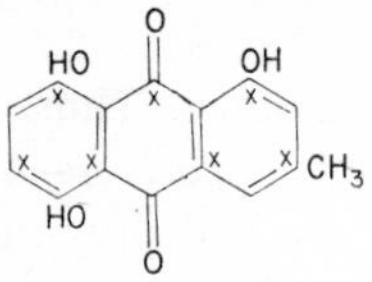

LXXI Helminthosporin

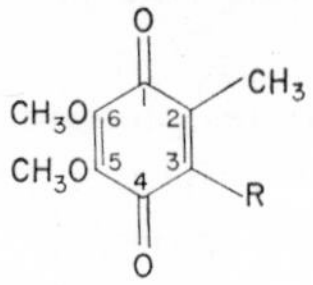

LXXII $\begin{cases} R = CH_3: \text{ Aurantiogliocladin} \\ R = (—CH_2CH=C—CH_2—)n: \text{ Ubiquinones} \\ \qquad\qquad\quad | \\ \qquad\qquad\; CH_3 \end{cases}$

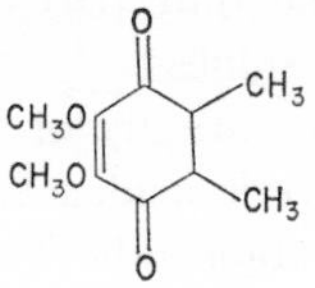

LXXIII

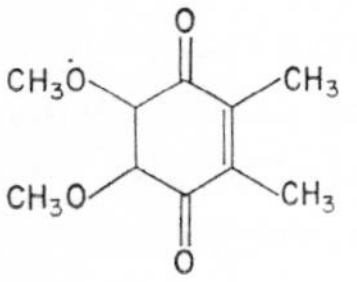

LXXIV

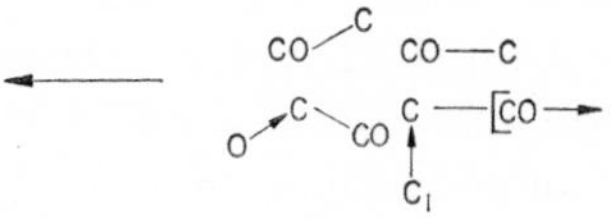

LXXV

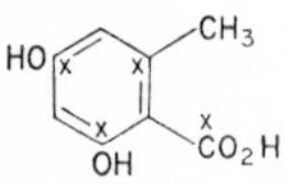

LXXVI

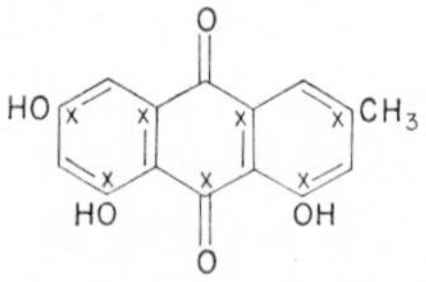

LXXVII

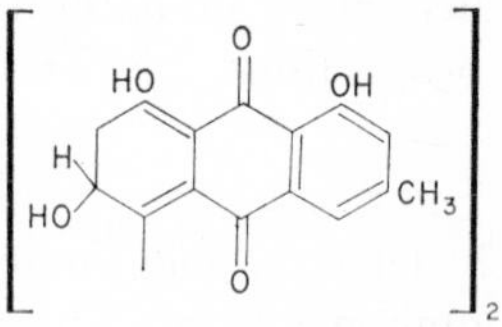

LXXVIII Rugulosin

ubiquinones {LXXII, R = [—CH₂CH=C(CH₃)CH₂—]n} are formed in a similar manner, by the introduction (as the pyrophosphate) of the appropriate isoprenoid substituent at C5 instead of a C-methyl unit. [105]

The biosynthesis of emodin and helminthosporin in conjunction with the occurrence of emodin in higher plants and the structures of other plant and fungal metabolites provides strong presumptive evidence for the production of the large number of naturally occurring quinones, particularly anthraquinones, by a similar process from acetate units.

Whilst no information appears to be currently available concerning the mode of biosynthesis of xanthones, several possibly significant examples have been recorded of the co-occurrence of structurally, closely related anthraquinones and xanthones (or derivatives of xanthones). Thus, *Aspergillus versicolor* (Viull) Tiraboschi gives rise [39, 90] to the anthraquinones, averufin (LXXIX) and aversin (LXXX) or (LXXXI), together with the xanthones, sterigmatocystin (LXXXII; R = H) and 6-methoxysterigmatocystin (LXXXII; R = OMe), whilst the pigments from certain types of ergot contain the anthraquinone, endocrocin (LXXXIII) together with the complex xanthone derivatives, ergoflavin (LXXXIV) [3] and ergochrysin A (LXXXV). [2] Although there is evidence in certain cases of fungal metabolism

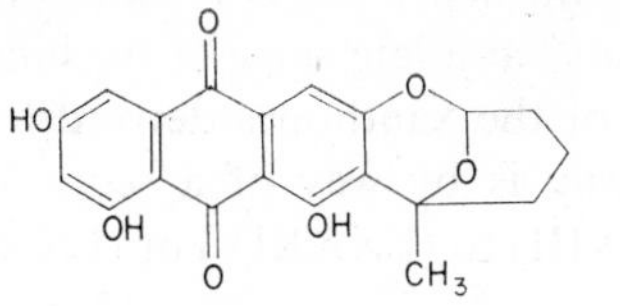

LXXIX Averufin

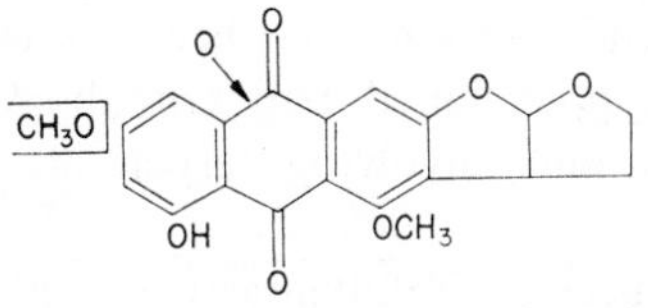

LXXX Aversin

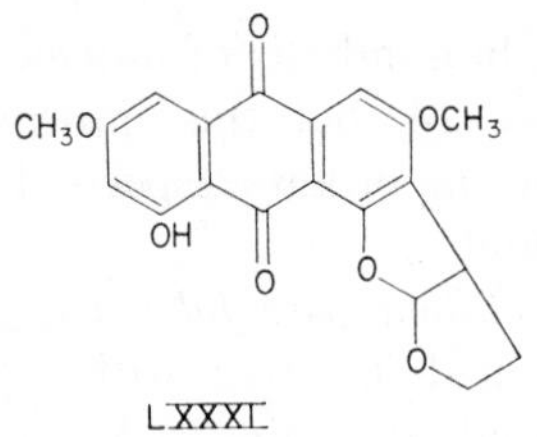

LXXXI

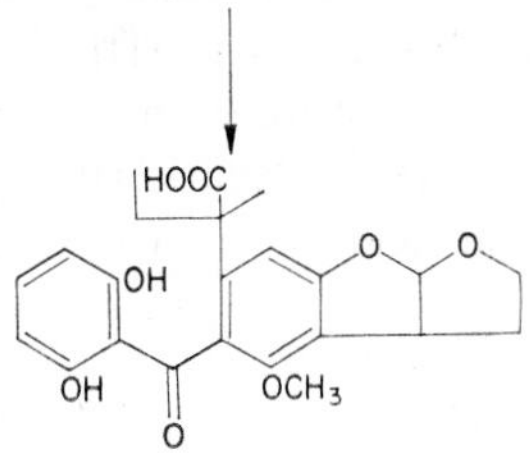

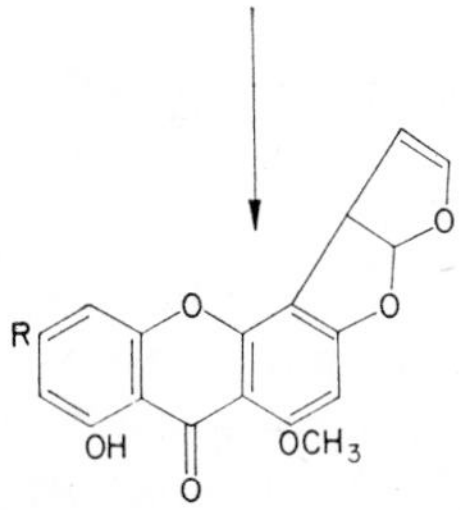

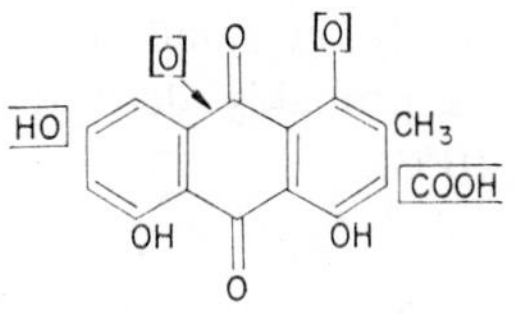

LXXXIII Endocrocin

LXXXII
R = H, Sterigmatocystin
R = OMe, 6 - Methoxysterigmatocystin

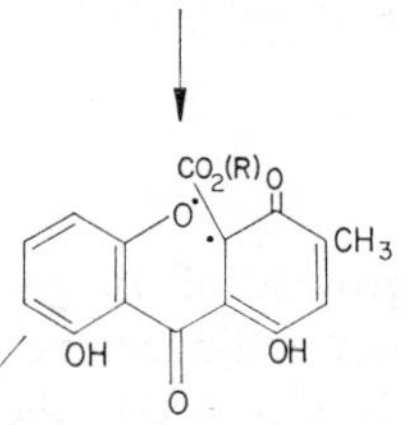

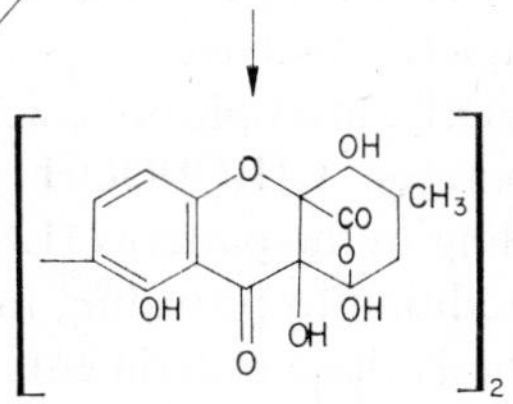

LXXXIV Ergoflavin

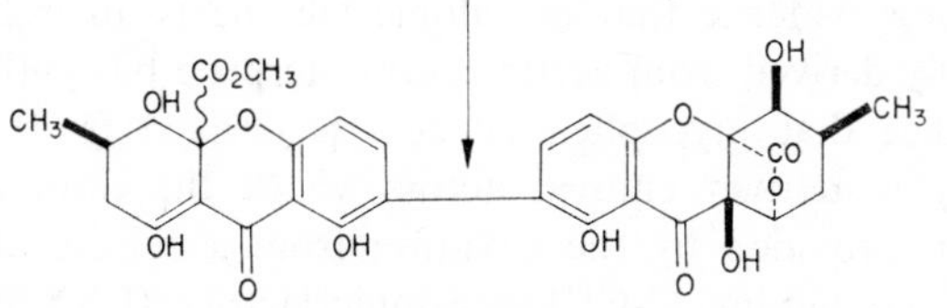

LXXXV Ergochrysin A

L

that benzophenones (and hence possibly xanthones) arise from the junction of two pre-formed units† at a late stage of the biosynthetic sequence, it seems probable in the case of the xanthones derived from *A. versicolor* and from ergot, that the pathway is by way of a sequence of the type (LXXX) to (LXXXII) and (LXXXIII) to (LXXXIV) or (LXXXV).

TERPENES

The biosynthesis of terpenes and terpenoid residues has been discussed in Chapter 14, but this information is supplemented and corroborated in certain important respects by investigations involving terpenoid, fungal metabolites.

Penicillium griseofulvum Dierckx produces griseofulvin (III) directly from acetic acid, together with mycelianamide (LXXXVI) in which there is a terpenoid side chain. [18] Addition of $CH_3C^{14}OOH$ to the culture medium gives griseofulvin and mycelianamide which are labeled as in (III) (p. 1026) and (LXXXVI), respectively. The efficiency of incorporation of acetic acid is substantially the same in both compounds. The aromatic ring of mycelianamide is probably derived from shikimic acid or a biogenetic associate (cf. p. 1053).

L XXXVI mycelianamide

The growth of *P. griseofulvum* Dierckx upon a substrate containing [2-C^{14}]-mevalonic lactone (LXXXVII) furnishes mycelianamide in which the labeling is restricted to the side chain as in (LXXXVI), whilst the griseofulvin is completely inactive.

Similarly, mycophenolic acid, a metabolite of *P. brevi-compactum* Dierckx, incorporates $CH_3C^{14}OOH$ and [2-C^{14}]-mevalonic lactone (LXXXVII) according to the patterns (LXXXVIII) and (LXXXIX), respectively.

In addition to providing further evidence for the validity of the "acetate" hypothesis these experiments confirm the terpenoid nature of the respective side chains in mycelianamide and mycophenolic acid. They also furnish compelling evidence that mevalonic lactone is an irreversible intermediate (originally derived from acetic acid) in terpene biosynthesis.

Evidence that mycophenolic acid is derived from a precursor of type (XC) by oxidative removal across *ab* of the terminal isopropyl residue has been provided by the isolation from a culture of *P. brevi-compactum* Dierckx, containing [2-C^{14}]-mevalonic lactone (LXXXVII), of acetone and

† Personal communication from Professor C. H. Hassall.

mycophenolic acid in approximately equimolecular quantities and of approximately equal, molar, specific activities.†

This result provides very strong circumstantial evidence that the biosynthesis of the benzofuran ring system, which is such a characteristic feature of many higher plant products, proceeds by a similar oxidative cleavage of an isopentenyl fragment.

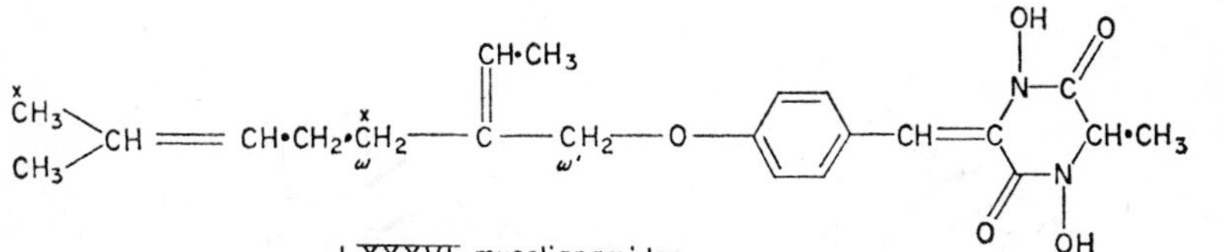

LXXXVI mycelianamide

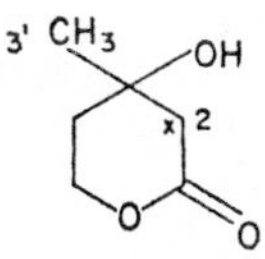

mevalonic
LXXXVII lactone

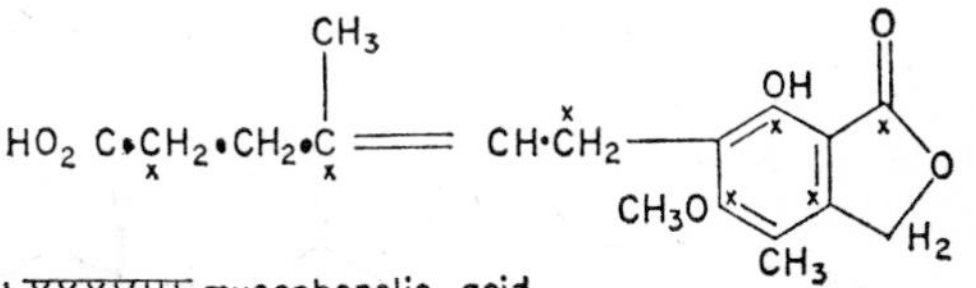

LXXXVIII mycophenolic acid

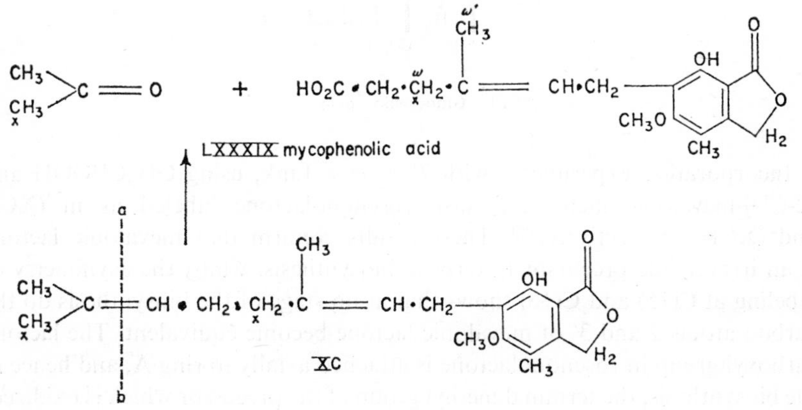

LXXXIX mycophenolic acid

XC

In the biosynthesis of mycelianamide and of mycophenolic acid from [2-C^{14}]-mevalonic lactone, it is particularly to be noted that the labeled carbon atom at the ω position in the side chain is not interchanged with that at the ω' position. This is in agreement with the results of other investigators[51] for squalene and carotenoid biosynthesis. This asymmetry of labeling persists in the terminal methyl groups of terpene chains, but is difficult to investigate experimentally in open chain terpenes such as squalene

† Personal communication from Professor A. J. Birch and Dr. R. W. Rickards.

and the side chain of mycelianamide. The asymmetry of labeling has, however, been defined by examining cyclic, terpenoid, fungal metabolites in which the relevant carbon atoms are chemically distinguishable.

The metabolites employed were rosenonolactone [72] (XCI), which is produced by *Trichothecium roseum* Link, and gibberellic acid [37] (XCIII) from *Gibberella fujikuroi*.

XCI Rosenonolactone   XCII Rosenonolactone

XCIII Gibberellic acid

Incorporation experiments with *T. roseum* Link, using $CH_3C^{14}OOH$ and [2-C^{14}]-mevalonic lactone, furnish rosenonolactone labeled as in (XCI) and (XCII), respectively. [29] These results confirm that mevalonic lactone is an irreversible precursor in terpene biosynthesis, whilst the asymmetry of labeling at C(15) and C(16) shows that at no stage of the biosynthesis do the carbon atoms 2 and 3′ of mevalonic lactone become equivalent. The lactone carboxyl group in rosenonolactone is attached axially to ring A, and hence in the biosynthesis, the terminal methyl group of the precursor which is oxidized, is that which finally occupies the axial position. Furthermore, since rosenonolactone has the absolute configuration (XCI), [72] it is the β-methyl group at C(1) which is oxidized. Similar stereospecificity is associated with the incorporation of [2-C^{14}]-mevalonic lactone into gibberellic acid as in (XCI). [15]

Under appropriate conditions of growth *T. roseum* Link furnishes the antifungal metabolite, trichothecin (XCIV), which is the crotonic ester of a sesquiterpene. Biogenetic experiments with [2-C^{14}]-mevalonic lactone indicate the derivation of trichothecin as shown. [60]

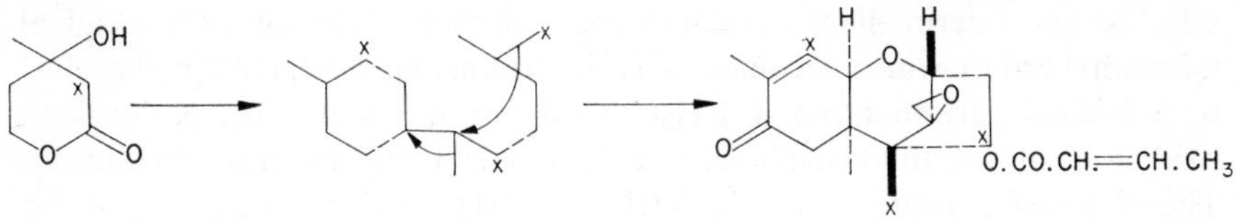

XCIV   Trichothecin

The close structural affinity between trichothecin and a number of other fungal metabolites, e.g. diacetoxyscirpenol (XCV), [54, 61] isolated from the culture filtrates of *Fusarium diversisporum, F. sambucinum, F. scirpi, F. equiseti* and *Gibberella intricans*, trichodermin (XCVI), [65] a metabolite of a *Trichoderma* species, and verrucarol (XCVII), [99] the sesquiterpenoid moiety of the metabolite, verrucarin A, from *Myrothecium verrucaria*, strongly suggests that the biosynthesis of these metabolites and their congeners follows a similar pathway.

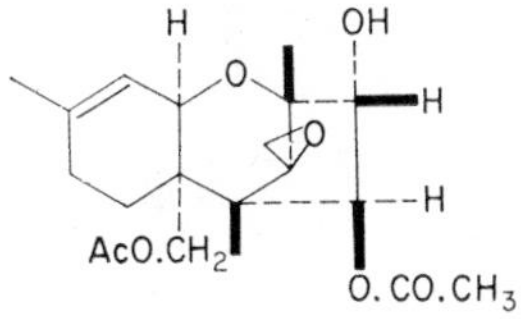

XCV   Diacetoxyscirpenol

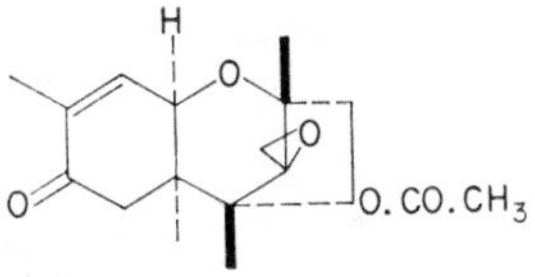

XCVI   Trichodermin

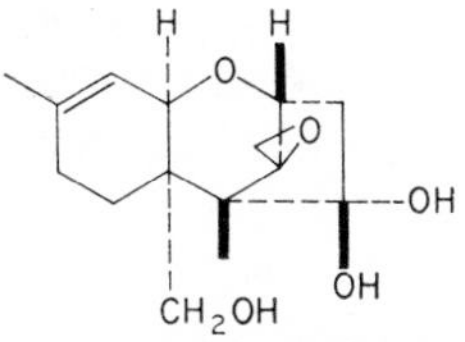

XCVII   Verrucarol

Biosynthetic experiments with gibberellic acid have also served to illuminate the mechanism of the phytochemical formation of the D/E bridged ring system. This problem has been discussed by Wenkert [103] from a theoretical standpoint in the case of the analogous phyllocladene system (CII). The conversion of a pimaradiene precursor of type (XCVIII) into the tetracyclic system (CII) may proceed as in the sequence (XCVIII) → (XCIX) → (C) →

(CI) → (CII) where the overall result involves migration of C6 from C7 to C18, by the intermediary of a non-classical carbonium ion. The original C7 methyl group, which becomes=CH₂ in the final product, remains attached to a labeled carbon atom if CH₃C¹⁴OOH be the precursor. Kuhn-Roth oxidation of tetrahydrogibberellic acid (CIII) confirms this attachment. The alternative route from (XCVIII) to (CII) involves migration of the methyl group from C7 to C18, which is an unlabeled carbon atom, as in the sequence (XCIX) → (CIV) → (CV) → CII). This is excluded by the experimental evidence.

An elegant confirmation of the participation of a precursor of type (LXXXVIII) in the biosynthesis of gibberellic acid, by *Gibberella fujikuroi*, has been provided by the demonstration[71] that (−)-kaurene labeled in the

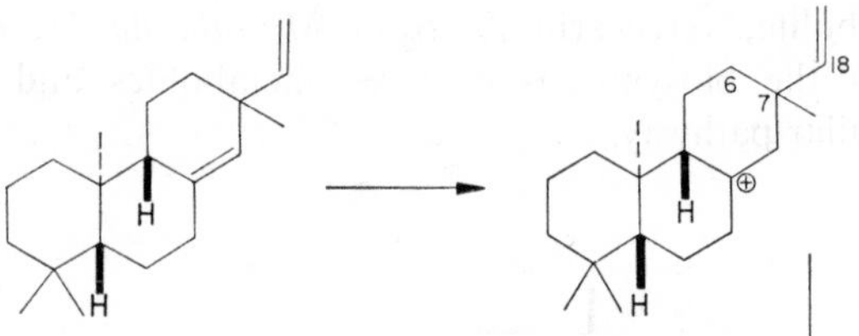

XCVIII   XCIX

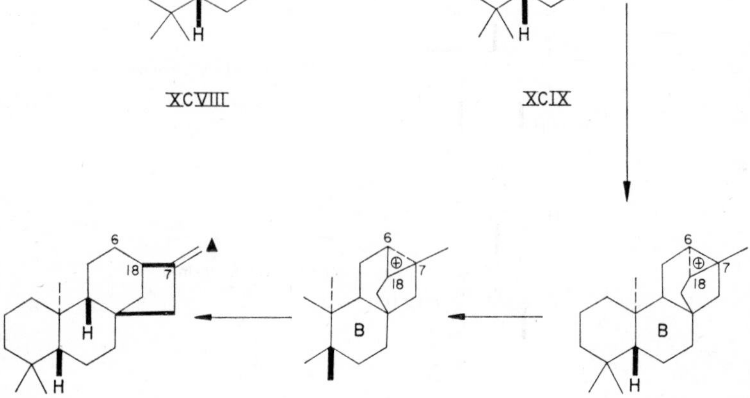

CII   CI   C

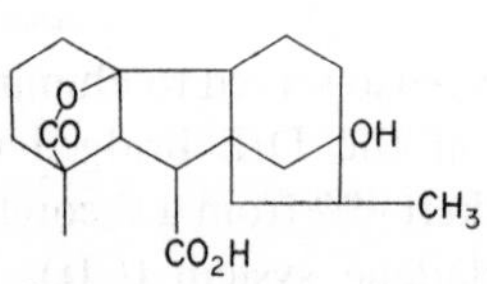

CIII 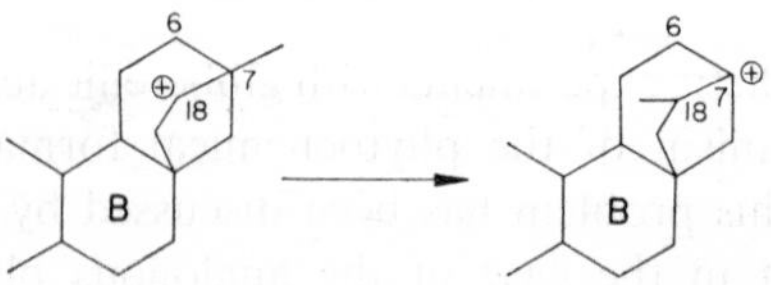   CIV   CV

terminal methylene residue with [C¹⁴] as in (CII) is incorporated intact into gibberellic acid: the total label is retained in the exocyclic methylene residue as in (XCIII). The production [71] *inter alia*, of (—)-kaurene and gibberellic acid by *G. fujikuroi* is of obvious biogenetic significance. (—)-Kaurene has previously been obtained only from a number of Australian shrubs: its production by a microorganism provides an interesting link between the biogenetic processes of higher plants and fungi.

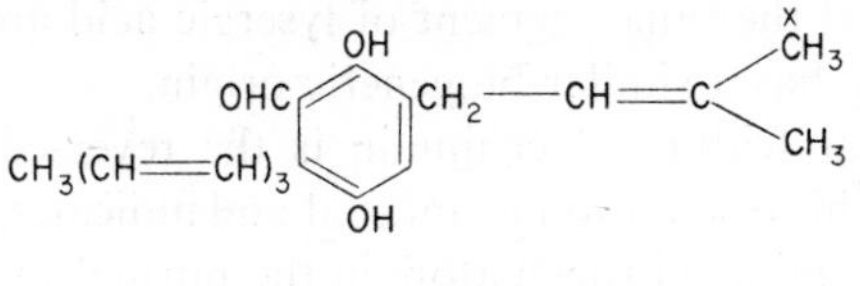

CVI a   Auroglaucin

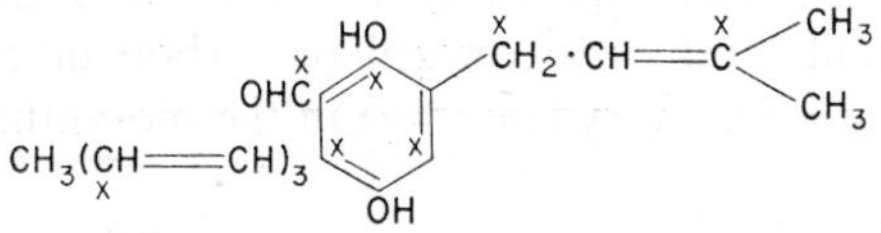

CVI b   Auroglaucin

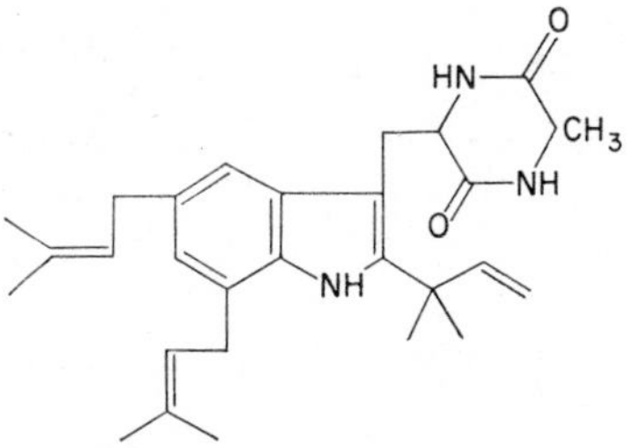

CVII   Echinulin

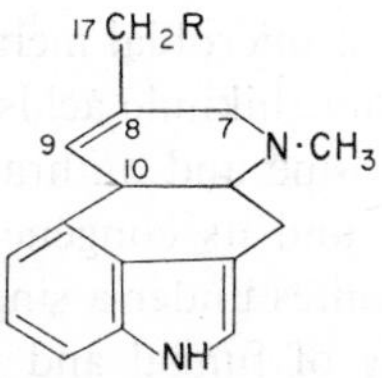

CVIII { R= H, Agroclavin
       { R= OH, Elmoclavin

The irreversible derivation of a single isopentenyl unit from [2-C¹⁴]-mevalonic lactone is illustrated by an investigation using auroglaucin (CVI), a metabolite of *Aspergillus novus* (*A. pseudoglaucus* Blochwitz, NRRL 46). [31] Biosynthesis of this phenol on a medium containing $CH_3C^{14}OOH$ gives the labeling pattern (CVIb) whilst [2-C^{14}]-mevalonic lactone yields the pattern (CVIa). Auroglaucin furnishes another interesting example of the reduction of a carboxyl to an aldehyde group.

The three pendant isopentenyl residues of the fungal alkaloid echinulin (CVII) are similarly derived[11] from mevalonic lactone, which has been established[9] as the precursor of carbon atoms 7, 8, 9, 10 and 17 in the ergot alkaloids, agroclavin (CVIII; R = H) and elmoclavine (CVIII; R = OH). It may thus be deduced that the same segment of lysergic acid and hence of the various ergot alkaloids, has a similar biogenetic origin.

An interesting structural feature of echinulin is the reversed terpenoid residue in the 2-position. This orientation is unusual and indicates that alkylation initially occurs at the indole nitrogen atom in the normal manner to be followed by a cyclic rearrangement to C-2.

The introduction of terpenoid residues into aromatic rings most probably occurs by way of the appropriate pyrophosphate which O- or C-alkylates the aromatic ring as in (CX) and (CIX) respectively. It is implicit in this concept that attachment of terpenoid residues to oxygen or carbon takes place at the aromatic ring stage, that is at a very late stage in the biosynthesis.[105]

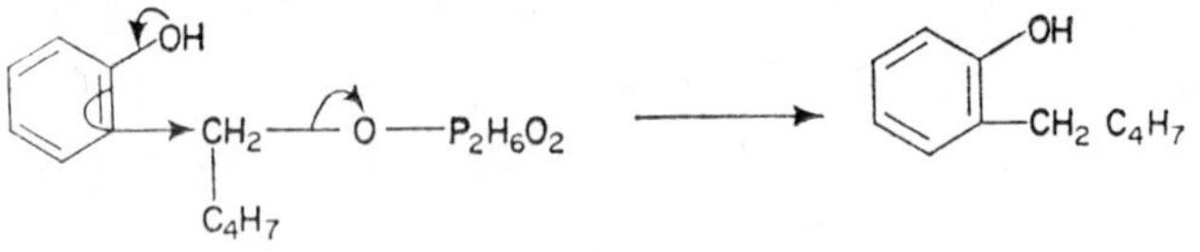

CIX

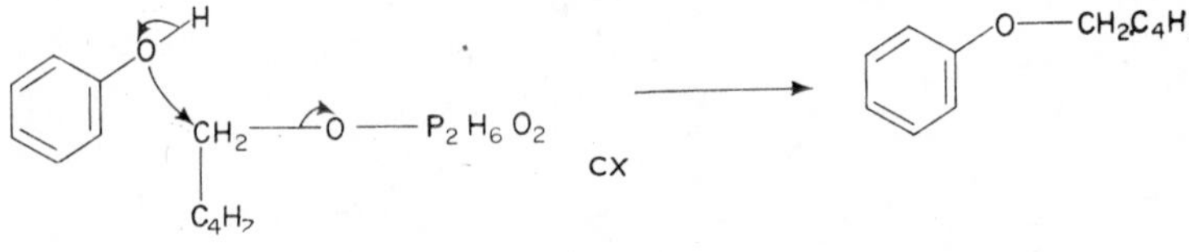

CX

STRUCTURAL UNITS DERIVED FROM AMINO ACIDS AND SHIKIMIC ACID

In addition to the peptides a number of microbial metabolites are derived wholly or in part from amino acids, from shikimic acids or from both, and since aromatic amino acids such as tyrosine and anthranilic acids are biosynthesized by way of shikimic acid[53] and its congeners, it seems logical to discuss the biogenesis of these metabolites under a single heading.

Whilst aromatic rings in the majority of fungal and microbial products are derived from acetic acid, a minority has shikimic acid and its biogenetic associates as precursor.

Thus, the usual aminocoumarin ring system of the antibiotic, novobiocin (CXII),[76] is derived from tyrosine (CXI), the entire carbon skeleton of

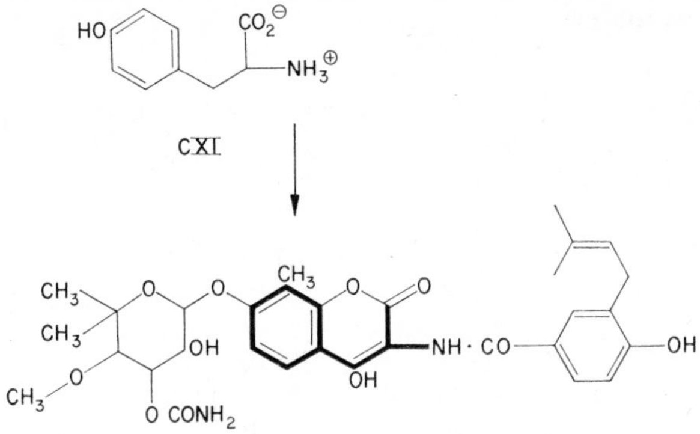

CXI

CXII   Novobiocin

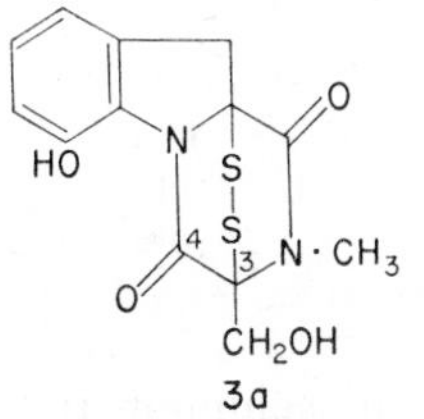

CXIII   Gliotoxin

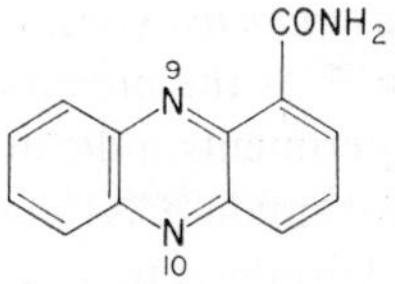

CXIV

which is incorporated into the coumarin nucleus. [46] Additional work shows that the pendant aromatic ring is also derived from tyrosine whilst the use of tyrosine labeled with [O^{18}] in the carboxyl residue clearly indicates that the heterocyclic ring of the coumarin moiety is formed by an oxidative cyclization. [42] Similarly, fermentation experiments [106] with [1-C^{14}]-phenylalanine and with phenylalanine-H^3 show that this amino acid is incorporated *en bloc* into the indole ring of gliotoxin, (CXIII), the characteristic sulfur containing metabolite of *Trichoderma virida*. Carbon atoms 3, 3a and 4 appear to be derived from serine, whilst the N-methyl residue stems from methionine.

The non-incorporation [18] of acetate or mevalonate into the benzenoid ring of mycelianamide furnishes strong presumptive evidence for the derivation of the benzenoid and heterocyclic rings from tyrosine (and hence shikimic acid), and alanine as follows:

LXXXVI

Similarly the dioxopiperazine ring of echinulin (CVII), a metabolite of various *Aspergillus glaucus* types, is derived from two molecules of alanine, [9] whilst tryptophan [19] is the precursor of the indole nucleus.

Preliminary experiments indicate that at least one of the aromatic rings of phenazine-1-carboxamide (CXIV) which occurs as a 3 : 1 molecular complex with the 9,10-dihydroderivative and constitutes the pigment, chlororaphin, in *Pseudomonas chlororaphis* NRRL B-977, is derived from anthranilic acid. The various microbial phenazine pigments, thus, probably arise biosynthetically by oxidative coupling of two molecules of anthranilic acid and represent additional cases of aromatic biosynthesis proceeding by way of the shikimic acid pathway.

Although only limited experimental evidence is available it is very probable that, in addition to the polypeptide fungal products, a number of simpler compounds are derived directly from amino acids. [105]

Flavacol, (CXV), [57] a metabolite of *Aspergillus flavus*, and pulcherriminic acid, (CXVI), [49] from the yeast *Candida pulcherrima* (Lindner) Windisch, are undoubtedly derived from two molecules of leucine. Similarly, aspergillic acid (CXVII) [87] and deoxyaspergillic acid (CXVIII), [87] metabolites of *A. flavus*, probably arise from one molecule of leucine and one of isoleucine. In agreement with this probability the biosynthesis of tenuazonic acid (CXIX), [97] a metabolite of *Alternaria tenuis*, has been shown to proceed

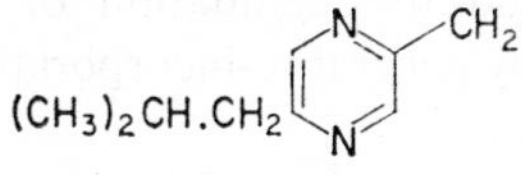

$(CH_3)_2CH.CH_2$ — [pyrazine ring] — $CH_2CH(CH_3)_2$

CXV flavacol

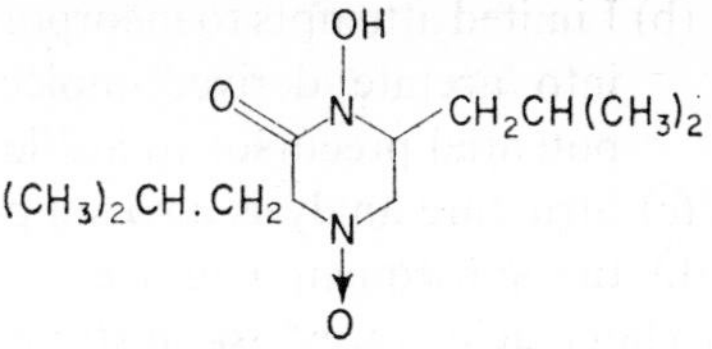

$(CH_3)_2CH.CH_2$ — [ring, OH, O] — $CH_2CH(CH_3)_2$

CXVI pulcherriminic acid

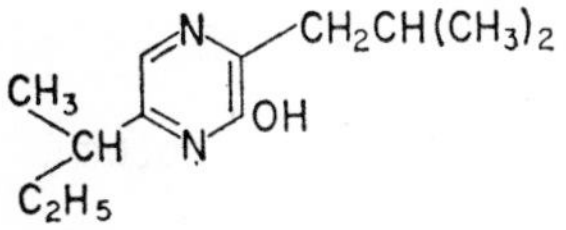

CH_3 $>CH$ — [pyrazine ring, OH] — $CH_2CH(CH_3)_2$
C_2H_5

CXVII aspergillic acid

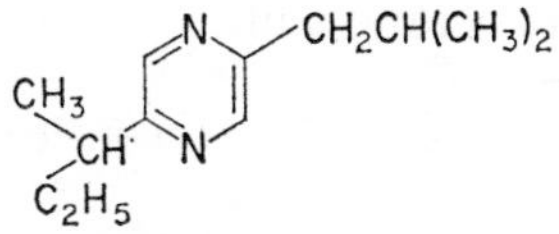

CH_3 $>CH$ — [pyrazine ring] — $CH_2CH(CH_3)_2$
C_2H_5

CXVIII deoxyaspergillic acid

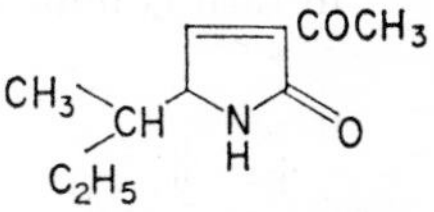

CH_3 $>CH$ — [ring, N—H, O] — $COCH_3$
C_2H_5

CXIX tenuazonic acid

from one molecule of isoleucine and two molecules of acetic acid and that the

$$>N-CH(CO)\overset{|}{\underset{|}{C}}(CH_3)_2$$

fragment in penicillin is derived from valine.

It has been suggested [33] that oxidation of the amino groups in amino acids is probably involved in the biosynthesis from amino acids of O-diazoacetylserine, 6-diazo-5-oxo-L-norleucine and β-nitropropionic acid: this also applies to the biosynthesis of pulcherriminic acid (CXVI), aspergillic acid (CXVII) and mycelianamide (LXXXVI). Tracer experiments using *Penicillium atrovenetum* G. Smith, which furnishes β-nitropropionic acid in high yield, supports this view and strongly suggests that aspartic acid is the precursor of β-nitropropionic acid. [26]

STRUCTURAL CORRELATIONS

Finally, it is of interest to consider some of the possible relationships between fungal metabolites.

With the establishment of the general validity of the concept that the biosynthesis of many fungal metabolites proceeds from acetic acid, it has been suggested that "the initial biogenetic steps proceed to produce a common, large intermediate (or its various biological equivalents) and that secondary modifications of this intermediate yield a series of closely inter-related end products". [104] "Evidence on this point . . . is scanty but on balance favors [this] type of process." [32]

Circumstantial support for this hypothesis comes from a number of sources:

(a) In the restricted number of cases where information is available the labeling, except for a terminal methyl group, appears to be uniform within limits of experimental error.

(b) Limited attempts to incorporate specifically labeled potential precursors into acetate derived molecules usually lead to degradation of the potential precursor to acetic acid followed by general re-incorporation.

(c) Structure analysis also supports this view.

In the subsequent pages an analysis of metabolites possibly related to orsellinic acid is used to illustrate this thesis.

Penicillium brevi-compactum Dierckx yields the metabolites (CXX), (CXXI), (CXXII) and (CXXIII). [91] These may arise sequentially from (CXX) which in turn is built from five acetate units.

P. brevicompactum also furnishes mycophenolic acid (LXIII) (p. 1040), which exhibits more extensive peripheral modifications of the orsellinic acid nucleus. *P. griseofulvum* and *P. patulum* yield 6-methylsalicylic acid, an acetate derived metabolite of the orsellinic acid type, which has undergone de-oxygenation at C-4. These organisms also convert 6-methylsalicylic acid into gentisyl alcohol and gentisic acid by way of (CXXIV) and (CXXV) which is the precursor of patulin (CXXVI). [35, 40] Ustic acid (CXXVII), a metabolite of *A. ustus* may similarly be derived by *para*-oxidation of (CXXI).

A. melleus and *A. ochraceus* furnish mellein (CXXVIII) possibly from (CXX) by 4-deoxygenation, as in the formation of 6-methyl-salicylic acid. [105]

Extension of the methyl residue in an orsellinic acid type precursor by a linear chain of four acetate units could furnish palitantin (CXIII), [34] a metabolite of *P. palitans* and *P. frequentans*, and frequentin (CXXXI), a metabolite of *P. frequentans*, by way of (CXXIX). These metabolites almost certainly exemplify non-aromatic stages preceding a fully aromatic nucleus. Auroglaucin (CVI) [31] and flavoglaucin (CXXXIII) [31] may be derived from palitantin type precursor by more extensive peripheral modifications of (CXXIX) as in (CXXXII).

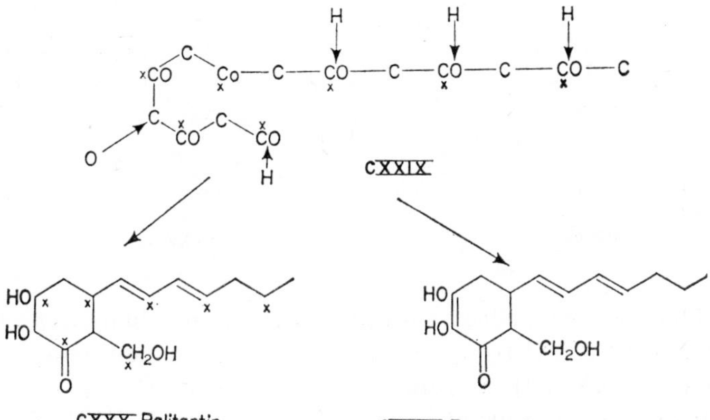

CXXIX

CXXX Palitantin

CXXXI Frequentin

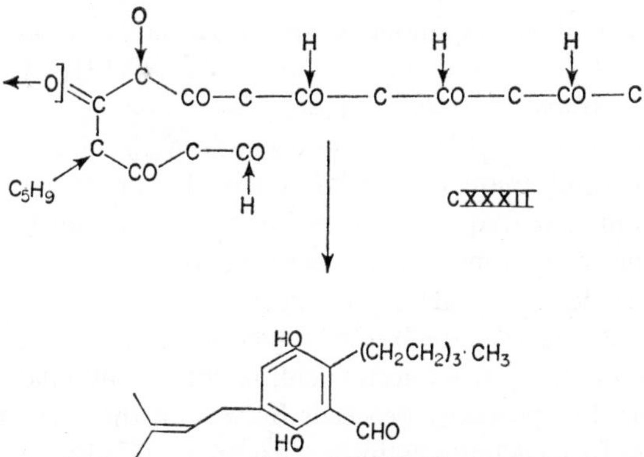

CXXXII

CXXXIII Flavoglaucin

More profound modification of the orsellinic acid type nucleus (or precursor) may furnish metabolites which, at first sight, appear to be quite unrelated to their precursors and to each other. Thus cyclization of (CXXXIV) as in (a) may yield a six-membered oxygen heterocyclic system type (CXXXV) or a naphthalene derivative (CXXXVI) as in (b).

Citrinin (XXXVI) a metabolite of many fungi, including *P. citrinum* and *A. terreus*, and a dihydroderivative of the pyronoquinone (CXXXV), arises biosynthetically from five acetate units and three C_1 units by way (presumably) of the orsellinic system (CXXXIV). Substitution of R in (CXXXIV) by a

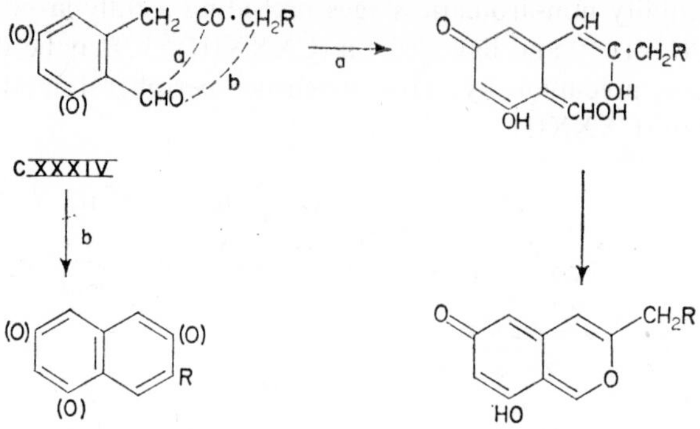

$$(O)\text{—}CH_2\ CO\cdot CH_2R \xrightarrow{\ a\ } \text{(quinone)}$$

(CXXXIV)

(CXXXVI) (CXXXV)

chain of four acetate residues followed by cyclization as in route a will furnish the quinone (CXXXVII) from which peripheral modification can yield sclerotiorin (XXXVIII), a characteristic metabolite of *P. sclerotiorum* and *P. multicolor*.[41] Introduction of a C_1 unit into (CXXXVII) followed by oxidation and acylation with $CH_3COCH_2COSCoA$ gives (XXXIX) which on aldolization forms rotiorin (XLI), a co-pigment of sclerotiorin (cf. p. 1035).

Similarly, the analogous quinone (CXXXVIII) may give rubropunctatin[74] (XLII, $R = n\text{—}C_5H_{11}$) and monascorubrin[58] (XLII, $R_1 = n\text{—}C_7H_{15}$), metabolites of *Monascus rubropunctatus* Sâto and *M. purpureus* Wentii respectively. Monascin (XLIII) a non-aromatic molecule analogous to palitantin (CXXX) and frequentin (CXXXI) is also produced by these fungi. Whilst palitantin and frequentin probably represent stages of biosynthesis *preceding* aromatization, monascin is more likely derived from the aromatic precursor (XLII, $R = n\text{—}C_5H_{11}$) by reduction.

As already indicated (p. 1037), the biogenesis of citromycetin (CXXXIX), which is derived entirely from acetic acid, is not readily related to a straight chain precursor, but probably proceeds by way of the carbon–carbon junction of two pre-formed units as in, for example, (CXL). The intermediate (CXLI) is equivalent to (CXLII) which may be regarded as the precursor of fulvic acid (CXLIII), a metabolite of *P. griseofulvum* Dierckx.

This brief survey, which is expounded more fully elsewhere,[105] indicates the possibility of a close structural and biogenetic affinity between many fungal metabolites, and is compatible with the derivation of these metabolites by secondary modifications of relatively few, similarly constituted, primary progenitors.

The establishment of a chemical correlation between fungal metabolites as adumbrated in these pages may find application in the taxonomy of fungi. In particular, taxonomic subdivisions, based upon the chemical relationships of appropriate metabolites, might enable further subdivisions of extensive

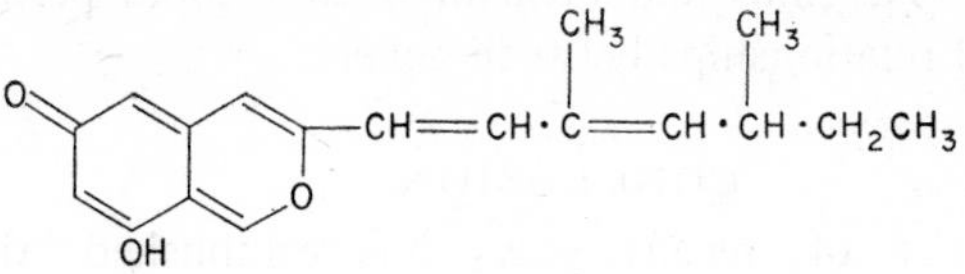

C XXXVII

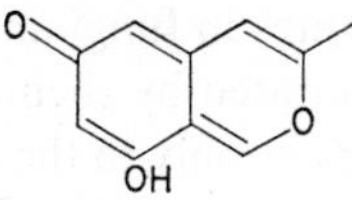

C XXXVIII

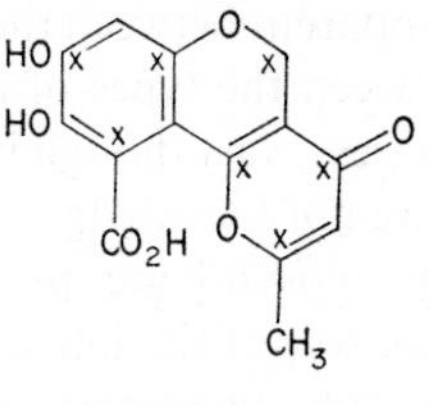

C XXXIX Citromycetin

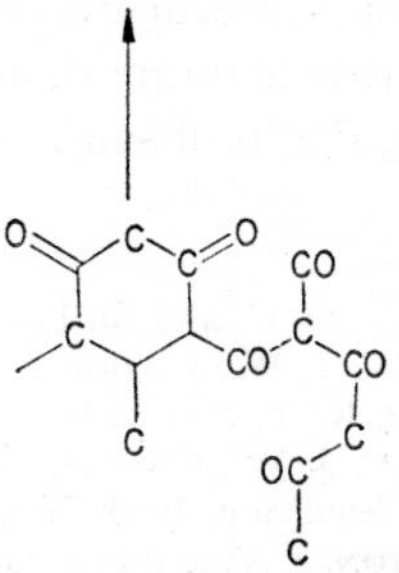

CXL

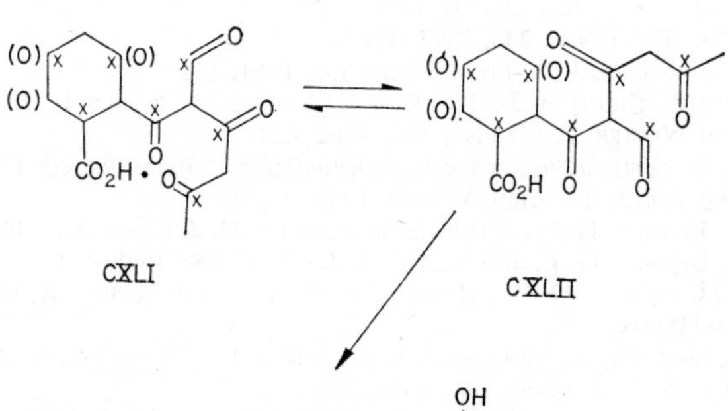

CXLI   CXLII

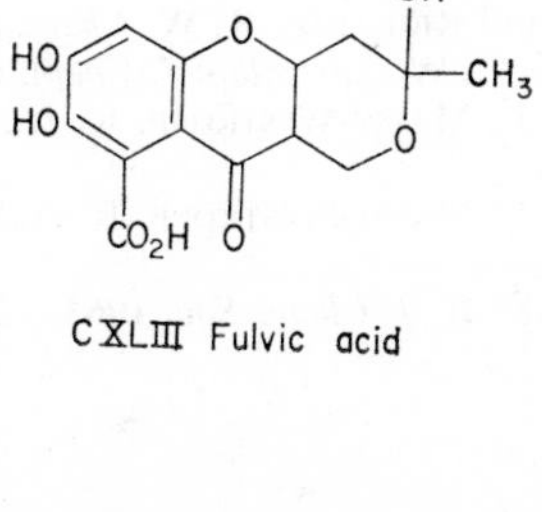

CXLIII Fulvic acid

genera such as the *Aspergillus* and *Penicillium* and could perhaps indicate hitherto unsuspected relationships between genera.

CONCLUSION

The rapid progress of recent years has established the principa pathways by which fungal and microbial products are biosynthesized. It has become evident that a limited number of ubiquitous, biosynthetic reactions operate in fungal metabolism. Further, an increasing degree of correspondence is apparent between the biosynthetic routes in fungi and the higher plants and between the types of metabolites elaborated by them.

But this progress, vast though it has been, brings us only to the threshold of a fascinating area of knowledge. The next advances must surely consist in the exploration of biosynthetic processes by cell-free, enzymic extracts, the definition of the role of the unusual metabolites in the economy of the microorganisms and the elucidation of the sequence of the various reactions by which primary precursors are converted into the ultimate metabolites.

The immediate future should provide at least a partial solution to these and other intriguing problems.

REFERENCES

1. ALLPORT, D. C. and BU'LOCK, J. D. *J. Chem. Soc.* **1960**, 654.
2. APSIMON, J. W., CORRAN, A. J., CREASEY, N. G., MARLOW, W., WHALLEY, W. B. and SIM, K. Y. *Proc. Chem. Soc.* **1963**, 313.
3. APSIMON, J. W., CORRAN, A. J., CREASEY, N. G., SIM, K. Y. and WHALLEY, W. B. *Proc. Chem. Soc.* **1963**, 209; ASHER, J. D. M., McPHAIL, A. T., ROBERTSON, J. M., SILVERTON, J. V. and SIM, G. A. *Proc. Chem. Soc.* **1963**, 210.
4. BARTON, D. H. R., DE MAYO, P., MORRISON, G. A. and RAISTRICK, H. *Tetrahedron* **6**, 48 (1959).
5. BARTON, D. H. R. and SCOTT, A. I. *J. Chem. Soc.* **1958**, 1767, and references cited therein.
6. BENTLEY, R. *Ann. Rev. Biochem.* **31**, 606 (1962).
7. BENTLEY, R. *J. Biol. Chem.* **238**, 1895 (1963).
8. BENTLEY, R. and KEIL, J. G. *Proc. Chem. Soc.* **1961**, 111.
9. BHATTACHARJI, S., BIRCH, A. J., BRACK, A., HOFMANN, A., KOBEL, H., SMITH, D. C. C., SMITH, H. and WINTER, J. *J. Chem. Soc.* **1962**, 421.
10. BIRCH, A. J. In *Fortschritte der Chemie Organischer Naturstoffe*, ed. L. Zechmeister, vol. 14, p. 186. Springer-Verlag, Vienna, 1957.
11. BIRCH, A. J., BLANCE, G. E., DAVID, S. and SMITH, H. *J. Chem. Soc.* **1961**, 3128.
12. BIRCH, A. J., BLANCE, G. E. and SMITH, H. *J. Chem. Soc.* **1958**, 4582.
13. BIRCH, A. J., CAMERON, D. W., HOLLOWAY, P. W. and RICKARDS, R. W. *Tetrahedron Letters* **25**, 26 (1960).
14. BIRCH, A. J., CASSERA, A., HOLKER, J. S. E., SMITH, H., THOMPSON, G. A., FITTON, P. and WHALLEY, W. B. *J. Chem. Soc.* **1962**, 3583.
15. BIRCH, A. J., CASSERA, A. and RICKARDS, R. W. *Chem. and Ind., London* **1961**, 792.
16. BIRCH, A. J. and DONOVAN, F. W. *Australian J. Chem.* **6**, 360 (1953).
17. BIRCH, A. J., ENGLISH, R. J., MASSY-WESTROPP, R. A., SLAYTOR, M. and SMITH, H. *J. Chem. Soc.* **1958**, 365.
18. BIRCH, A. J., ENGLISH, R. J., MASSY-WESTROPP, R. A. and SMITH, H. *J. Chem. Soc.* **1958**, 369.
19. BIRCH, A. J. and FARRAR, K. R. *J. Chem. Soc.* **1963**, 4277.

20. BIRCH, A. J., FITTON, P., PRIDE, E., RYAN, A. J., SMITH, H. and WHALLEY, W. B. *J. Chem. Soc.* **1958**, 4576.
21. BIRCH, A. J., FRYER, R. I. and SMITH, H. *Proc. Chem. Soc.* **1958**, 343.
22. BIRCH, A. J., HUSSAIN, S. F. and RICKARDS, R. W. *J. Chem. Soc.* **1964**, 3494.
23. BIRCH, A. J. and KOCOR, M. *J. Chem. Soc.* **1960**, 866.
24. BIRCH, A. J., MASSY-WESTROPP, R. A. and MOYE, C. J. *Australian J. Chem.* **8**, 539 (1955).
25. BIRCH, A. J., MASSY-WESTROPP, R. A., RICKARDS, R. W. and SMITH, H. *J. Chem. Soc.* **1958**, 360.
26. BIRCH, A. J., MCLOUGHLIN, B. J., SMITH, H. and WINTER, J. *Chem. and Ind., London* **1960**, 840.
27. BIRCH, A. J., MUSGRAVE, O. C., RICKARDS, R. W. and SMITH, H. *J. Chem. Soc.* **1959**, 3146.
28. BIRCH, A. J., PRIDE, E., RICKARDS, R. W., THOMSON, P. J., DUTCHER, J. D., PERLMAN, D. and DJERASSI, C. *Chem. and Ind., London* **1960**, 1245; *idem, J. Chem. Soc.* **1964**, 5274.
29. BIRCH, A. J., RICKARDS, R. W., SMITH, H., HARRIS, A. and WHALLEY, W. B. *Tetrahedron* **7**, 241 (1959).
30. BIRCH, A. J., RYAN, A. J. and SMITH, H. *J. Chem. Soc.* **1958**, 4773.
31. BIRCH, A. J., SCHOFIELD, J. and SMITH, H. *Chem. and Ind., London* **1958**, 1321.
32. BIRCH, A. J. and SMITH, H. *Chem. Soc., London, Special Publ.* **12**, 1 (1958).
33. For a review *see* BIRCH, A. J. and SMITH, H. In *Ciba Foundation Symposium on Amino Acids and Peptides with Antimetabolic Activity*, eds. G. E. W. Wolstenholme and C. M. O'Connor, p. 247. Churchill, London, 1958.
34. BOWDEN, K., LYTHGOE, B. and MARSDEN, D. J. S. *J. Chem. Soc.* **1959**, 1662.
35. BRACK, A. *Helv. Chim. Acta* **30**, 1 (1947).
36. BRAITHWAITE, G. D. and GOODWIN, T. W. *Nature* **182**, 1304 (1958).
37. For a review *see* BRIAN, P. W., GROVE, J. F. and MACMILLAN, J. In *Fortschritte der Chemie Organischer Naturstoffe*, ed. L. Zechmeister, vol. 18, p. 350. Springer-Verlag, Vienna, 1960.
38. BROCKMANN, H. and LACKNER, H. *Naturwiss.* **47**, 230 (1960).
39. BULLOCK, E., KIRKALDY, D., ROBERTS, J. C. and UNDERWOOD, J. G. *J. Chem. Soc.* **1963**, 829.
40. BU'LOCK, J. D. and RYAN, A. J. *Proc. Chem. Soc.* **1958**, 222.
41. BU'LOCK, J. D. and SMALLEY, H. M. *Proc. Chem. Soc.* **1961**, 209.
42. BUNTON, C. A., KENNER, G. W., ROBINSON, M. J. T. and WEBSTER, R. B. *Tetrahedron* **1963**, 1001.
43. BUTTE, J. C. and CORCORAN, J. W. *Fed. Proc.* **21**, 89 (1962).
44. CARTER, R. E. and RICHARDS, J. H. *J. Am. Chem. Soc.* **83**, 495 (1961).
45. CARTWRIGHT, N. J., ROBERTSON, A. and WHALLEY, W. B. *J. Chem. Soc.* **1949**, 1563.
46. CHAMBERS, K., KENNER, G. W., ROBINSON, M. J. T. and WEBSTER, B. R. *Proc. Chem. Soc.* **1960**, 291.
47. CHAPLEN, P. and THOMAS, R. *Biochem. J.* **77**, 91 (1960).
48. COLLIE, J. N. *J. Chem. Soc.* **63**, 329 (1893).
49. COOK, A. H. and SLATER, C. A. *J. Chem. Soc.* **1956**, 4133.
50. CORCORAN, J. W. *J. Biol. Chem.* **236**, P. C. 27 (1961); GRISEBACH, H., ACHENBACH, H., and HOFHEINZ, W. *Tetrahedron Letters* **1961**, 234; MAJER, J., PUZA, M., DOLEZILOVA, L. and VANEK, Z. *Chem. and Ind.* **1961**, 669.
51. See, for example, CORNFORTH, J. W., CORNFORTH, R. H., POPJÁK, G. and YOUHOTSKY-GORE, I. *Biochem. J.* **66**, 10P (1957); **69**, 146 (1958); AMDUR, B. H., RILLING, H. and BLOCH, K. *J. Am. Chem. Soc.* **79**, 2647 (1957); BRAITHWAITE, G. D. and GOODWIN, T. W. *Biochem. J.* **67**, 13P (1957).
52. CURTIS, R. F., HASSALL, C. H., JONES, D. W. and WILLIAMS, T. W. *J. Chem. Soc.* **1960**, 4838.
53. DAVIES, B. D. *Advances in Enzymol.* **16**, 287 (1955).
54. DAWKINS, A. W., GROVE, J. F. and TIDD, B. K. *Chem. Comm.* **1965**, 27.
55. DEAN, F. M., STAUNTON, J. and WHALLEY, W. B. *J. Chem. Soc.* **1959**, 3004.

56. DJERASSI, C., HALPERN, O., WILKINSON, D. I. and EISENBRAUN, J. *Tetrahedron* **4**, 376 (1958).
57. DUNN, G., NEWBOLD, G. T. and SPRING, F. S. *J. Chem. Soc.* **1949**, 2586.
58. FIELDING, B. C., HAWS, E. J., HOLKER, J. S. E., POWELL, A. D. G., ROBERTSON, A., STANWAY, D. N. and WHALLEY, W. B. *Tetrahedron Letters* **5**, 24 (1960).
59. FIELDING, B. C., HOLKER, J. S. E., JONES, D. F., POWELL, A. D. G., RICHMOND, K. W., ROBERTSON, A. and WHALLEY, W. B. *J. Chem. Soc.* **1961**, 4579.
60. FISHMAN, J., JONES, E. R. H., LOWE, G. and WHITING, M. C. *Proc. Chem. Soc.* **1959**, 127.
61. FLURY, E., MAULI, R. and SIGG, H. P. *Chem. Comm.* **1965**, 26.
62. GATENBECK, S. *Acta Chem. Scand.* **12**, 1211 (1958).
63. GATENBECK, S. and MOSBACH, K. *Acta Chem. Scand.* **13**, 1561 (1959).
64. GATENBECK, S. and MOSBACH, K. *Biochem. Biophys. Res. Comm.* **11**, 166 (1963).
65. GODTFREDSEN, W. O. and VANGEDAL, S. *Proc. Chem. Soc.* **1964**, 188; ABRAHAMSSON, S. and NILSSON, B. *Proc. Chem. Soc.* **1964**, 188.
66. GRAHAM, N. B., PAGE, H., ROBERTSON, A., TRAVERS, R. B., TURNER, R. and WHALLEY, W. B. *J. Chem. Soc.* **1957**, 4924.
67. GRISEBACH, H. and ACHENBACH, H. *Z. Naturforsch* **17b**, 6 (1962).
68. GRISEBACH, H. and ACHENBACH, H. *Z. Naturforsch* **19b**, 561 (1964); GRISEBACH, H. and ACHENBACH, H. *Tetrahedron Letters* **1962**, 569.
69. GRISEBACH, H., ACHENBACH, H. and GRISEBACH, U. C. *Naturwiss.* **47**, 206 (1960); CORCORAN, J. W., KANEDA, T. and BÜTTE, J. C. *J. Biol. Chem.* **235**, PC 29 (1960); GRISEBACH, H., HOFHEINZ, N. and ACHENBACH, H. *Naturwiss.* **48**, 101 (1961).
70. GRISEBACH, H., HOFHEINZ, W. and ACHENBACH, H. *Z. Naturforsch.* **17b**, 64 (1962); VANEK, Z., PUZA, M., MEJER, J. and DOLEZILOVA, L. *Folia Microbiol.* **6**, 408 (1961); CORCORAN, J. W. *Lloydia* **27**, 5 (1964).
71. GROSS, B. E., GALT, R. H. B. and HANSON, J. R. *J. Chem. Soc.* **1964**, 295.
72. HARRIS, A., ROBERTSON, A. and WHALLEY, W. B. *J. Chem. Soc.* **1958**, 1799; GREEN, B., HARRIS, A., SMITH, H. and WHALLEY, W. B. *Chem. and Ind., London* **1958**, 1369; WHALLEY, W. B., GREEN, B., ARIGONI, D., BRITT, J. J. and DJERASSI, C. *J. Am. Chem. Soc.* **81**, 5520 (1959).
73. HASSALL, C. H. and McMORRIS, T. C. *J. Chem. Soc.* **1959**, 2831.
74. HAWS, E. J., HOLKER, J. S. E., KELLY, A., POWELL, A. D. G. and ROBERTSON, A. *J. Chem. Soc.* **1959**, 3598.
75. HAYAISHI, O. *J. Biol. Chem.* **215**, 125 (1955).
76. HINMAN, J. W., CARON, E. L. and HOCKSEMA, H. *J. Am. Chem. Soc.* **78**, 2019 (1956); **79**, 3789 (1957); SHUNK, C. H., STAMMER, C. H., KACZKA, E. A., WALTON, E., SPENCER, C. F., WILSON, A. N., RICHTER, J. W., HOLLY, F. W. and FOLKERS, K. *J. Am. Chem. Soc.* **78**, 1770 (1956).
77. HOLKER, J. S. E., STAUNTON, J. and WHALLEY, W. B. *J. Chem. Soc.* **1964**, 16.
78. HOUGH, L. and JONES, J. K. N. *Nature* **167**, 180 (1951).
79. See, for example, HUENNEKENS, F. M. and OSBORN, M. J. *Advances in Enzymol.* **21**, 369 (1958).
80. JACKMAN, G. B., ROBERTSON, A., TRAVERS, R. B. and WHALLEY, W. B. *J. Chem. Soc.* **1958**, 1825.
81. MAJER, J., PUZA, M., DOLEZILOVA, L. and VANEK, Z. *Chem. and Ind., London* **1961**, 669.
82. McCORMICK, J. R. D., JOHNSON, S. and SJOLANDER, N. O. *J. Amer. Chem. Soc.* **85**, 1692 (1963).
83. McMASTER, W. J., SCOTT, A. I. and TRIPPETT, S. *J. Chem. Soc.* **1960**, 4628.
84. MOSBACH, K. *Acta Chem. Scand.* **14**, 457 (1960).
85. MOSBACH, K. *Acta Chem. Scand.* **18**, 1591 (1964).
86. NEILL, K. G. and RAISTRICK, H. *Chem. and Ind., London* **1956**, 551.
87. NEWBOLD, G. T., SHARP, W. and SPRING, F. S. *J. Chem. Soc.* **1951**, 2679.
88. OLLIS, W. D., SUTHERLAND, I. O., CODNER, R. C., GORDON, J. J. and MILLER, G. A. *Proc. Chem. Soc.* **1960**, 347.
89. PARKS, L. W. *J. Am. Chem. Soc.* **80**, 2023 (1958).

90. PUSEY, D. F. G. and ROBERTS, J. C. *J. Chem. Soc.* **1963**, 3542.
91. RAISTRICK, H. *Proc. Roy. Soc. London* **136** B, 481 (1949–50).
92. ROBERTSON, A., WHALLEY, W. B. and YATES, J. *J. Chem. Soc.* **1951**, 2013.
93. SAZ, H. J. and WEIL, A. *J. Biol. Chem.* **235**, 914 (1960).
94. SCOTT, A. I. *Proc. Chem. Soc.* **1958**, 195; DAY, A. C., NABNEY, J. and SCOTT, A. I. *Proc. Chem. Soc.* **1960**, 284.
95. SHIBATA, S. and IKEHAWA, T. *Chem. Pharm. Bull. Japan* **11**, 368 (1963).
96. SNELL, J. F., BIRCH, A. J. and THOMSON, P. L. *J. Am. Chem. Soc.* **82**, 2402 (1960); *idem, J. Chem. Soc.* **1962**, 425.
97. STICKINGS, C. E. and TOWNSEND, R. J. *Biochem. J.* **74**, 36P (1960).
98. STUMPF, P. K. *Ann. Rev. Biochem.* **29**, 261 (1960).
99. TAMM, CH. and GUTZWILLER, J. *Helv. Chim. Acta* **45**, 1726 (1962).
100. THOMAS, R. *Proc. Chem. Soc.* **1959**, 88; THOMAS, R. *Biochem. J.* **78**, 748 (1961).
101. THOMAS, R. *Biochem. J.* **78**, 807 (1961).
102. VISCHER, E. B. J. *J. Chem. Soc.* **1953**, 815.
103. WENKERT, E. *Chem. and Ind., London* **1955**, 282.
104. WHALLEY, W. B. *Chem. and Ind., London* **1958**, 131.
105. WHALLEY, W. B. In *Recent Developments in the Chemistry of Natural Phenolic Compounds*, ed. W. D. Ollis, p. 20. Pergamon, London, 1961.
106. WINSTEAD, J. A. and SUHADOLNIK, R. J. *J. Am. Chem. Soc.* **82**, 1644 (1960).
107. WOODWARD, R. B. *Angew. Chem.* **69**, 50 (1957).

CHAPTER 19

FORMATION OF CARCINOGENIC POLYNUCLEAR HYDROCARBONS

ELIAHU BOGER

Bio-Research Institute, Cambridge, Massachusetts

CONTENTS

I. INTRODUCTION   1065
II. OCCURRENCE AND ORIGINS   1066
III. MODE OF FORMATION   1069
IV. PRECURSORS OF CARCINOGENS IN TOBACCO   1074
   A Case Study in Carcinogenesis   1074
V. SUMMARY   1076
   REFERENCES   1077

I. INTRODUCTION

Polycyclic aromatic hydrocarbons (PAH) are commonly found in nature. They have been detected in polluted airs and urban soils as well as in rural soils distant from major highways and industries. They are among the pyrolytic products of wood, and might also be formed in soil by related low-temperature processes, as they occur in the transformation of plant organic matter to peat and lignite. [11a]

Polycyclic hydrocarbons bear structural similarities to steroids and bile acids from which they can be made chemically. In addition, there are striking similarities between the postulated mode of their formation from simpler molecules during pyrolysis, and the routes by which condensed rings in phenolic products (see Chapter 12) or some polynuclear alkaloids (see Chapter 17) are produced in plants.

Volkman in 1875 recognized and reported a causative relationship between coal tar and the high incidence of skin tumors in tar-industry workers. Forty years later, Yamagiwa and Ichikawa [54] experimentally demonstrated his finding by producing skin carcinomas with prolonged application of coal tar distillate to rabbit-ear epithelium.

Since then, researchers have succeeded in synthesizing and elucidating the structures of over 500 carcinogenically active compounds. Cook and his co-workers [18] isolated the generally-occurring and highly active 3,4-benzpyrene (benzo-[a]-pyrene) (I) from the high-boiling fractions of coal tar distillates. This carcinogen was synthesized [19] by several methods and shown to be equally as active as the compound isolated from tar.

Chemical syntheses have been developed for other carcinogenic hydrocarbons, i.e. 1,2,5,6-dibenzanthracene (dibenzo-[a,h]-anthracene) (II), and 20-methylcholanthrene (III).

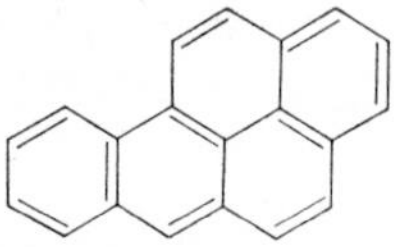

I

Benzo-[α]-pyrene

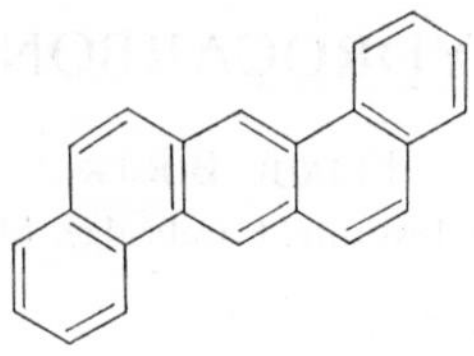

II

Dibenzo-[α,h]-anthracene

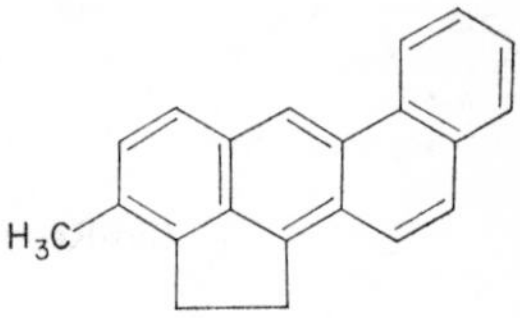

III

20-Methylcholanthrene

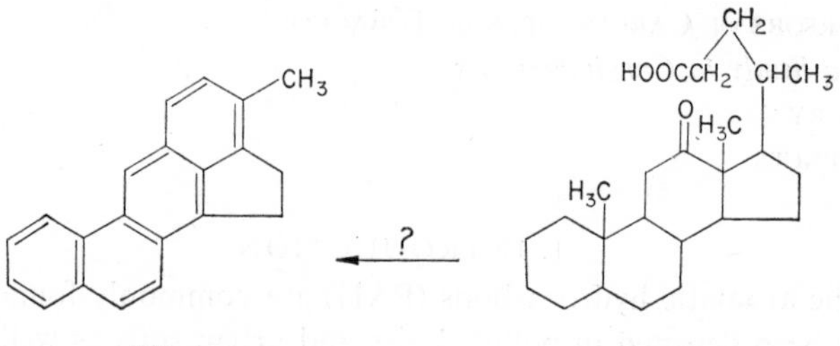

III

IV

Desoxycholic acid

Wieland and Dane's synthesis of (III) from desoxycholic acid (IV) in 1933 [52] led to the hypothesis that carcinogenic agents are produced *in vivo* by abnormal metabolism of steroids.

However, all attempts to isolate carcinogenic derivatives of naturally occurring compounds (steroids, etc.) from tumor tissues or body fluids of cancerous subjects have been unsuccessful. Present evidence strongly supports an external source as the only origin of carcinogenic agents affecting man. [13a]

This same evidence demonstrates that polycyclic hydrocarbons are products resulting from chemical transformations of reacting materials essential to human life. The objective of this article is to review the evidence in the literature for the occurrence, origin and mode of formation of these carcinogens and to note those relevant theories creating recent interest.

II. OCCURRENCE AND ORIGINS

Carcinogenic polycyclic hydrocarbons occur in a great many materials finding widespread usage. Although quite generally they are products of pyrolysis in processes initiated by man, natural phenomena such as forest fires are also important contributors to their formation. Combustion of fossil fuels yields the most significant amount of these carcinogens and thus their presence (in the atmosphere) is largely proportional to the degree of industrialization. [45] The pyrolysis of plants leads to a secondary source on which attention has recently been focused because of the established etiologic correlation between smoking (tobacco) and lung cancer. [44] (Other apparent sources of carcinogenic polycyclic hydrocarbons usually lead back to one of the just mentioned ones.) The hydrocarbons isolated most frequently are: (I); (II); benzo[a]anthracene (V); benzo[c]phenanthrene (VI); chrysene (VII); benzo[e]pyrene (VIII); benzo[rst]pentaphene (IX); benzo[j]fluoranthene (X); and benzo[b]fluoranthene (XI).

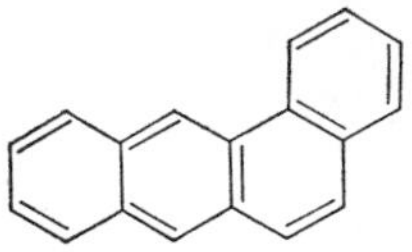

V

Benzo [α] anthracene

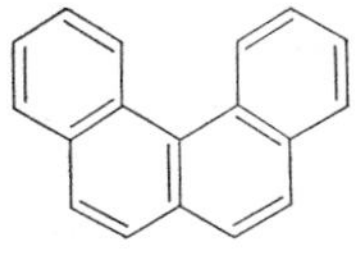

VI

Benzo [c] phenanthrene

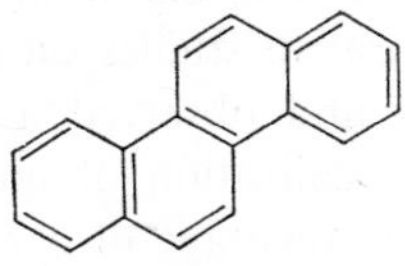

VII

Chrysene

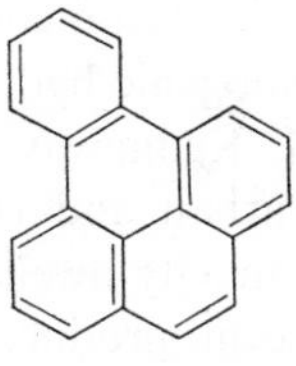

VIII

Benzo [e] pyrene

Various carcinogenic polycyclic hydrocarbons are present in most of the diverse forms of pyrolyzed fossil fuels. Gasoline and diesel fuel soot, coal tar, coal gas, petroleum tars and waxes, as well as many other materials are at the origin of carcinogens. For example, C. R. Begeman estimated that 1·8 per cent of the benzo[a]pyrene content of the atmosphere over urban areas resulted from the gas combustion products of automobiles. [9] Similarly, G. E. Moore and M. Katz investigated diesel exhausts in railway tunnels in an attempt to find the percentage of polycyclic aromatic hydrocarbons contributed by the different modes of transportation. Their findings indicate that the majority of polycyclic aromatic hydrocarbons arise from the combustion of fuels in general urban activities [39] rather than from that of transport vehicles.

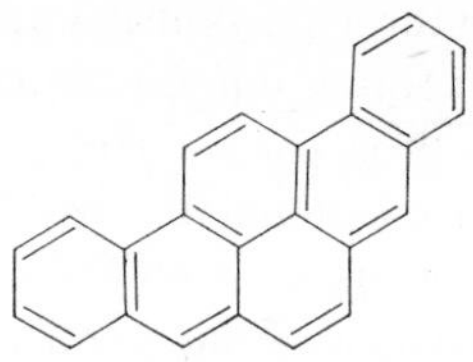

IX

Benzo [rst] pentaphene

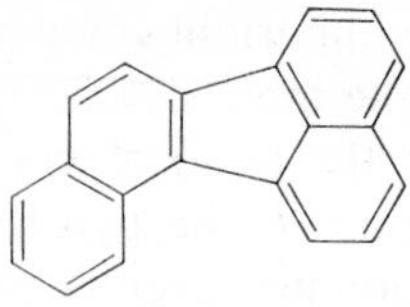

X

Benzo [j] fluoranthene

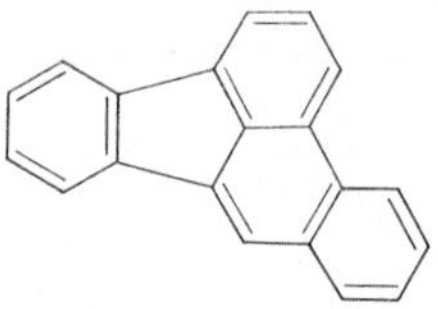

XI

Benzo [b] Fluoranthene

Industrial and domestic combustion of fossil fuels are responsible for the majority of carcinogenic hydrocarbons contaminating urban atmospheres. [5] E. L. and N. M. Kennaway made comparative studies on the incidence of lung cancer in urban and rural dwellers and observed a significant lung cancer increase in city-dwellers. [35] The localization of industry in urban areas, it would seem, produces the higher percentage of carcinogenic atmospheric contamination. Various samplings reflect the degree of such contamination. Los Angeles, famous for its "smog", had in the winter of 1959 an average of 5·2 μg benzo[a]pyrene per 10^3 m^3 of air, while Youngstown had, during the same interval, an average of 27·8 μg/10^3 m^3 of air. [45] That Youngstown, a significantly smaller city, has an average of over five times the amount of benzpyrene than Los Angeles is explained by the high density of industrialization in Youngstown. In areas lacking concentrated industrilization, domestic use remains as a source for carcinogenic hydrocarbons. It has been suggested by R. E. Waller that "a large part (of benzpyrene) seems to come from domestic fires". [51] "The ubiquity of atmospheric pollution is well demonstrated by an analysis made in March 1952 upon a kilogram of freshly fallen snow at Ashridge, Hertfordshire. This contained 1 to 2 micrograms of pyrene and traces of 3,4-benzpyrene and anthanthrene." [20]

Derivatives of pyrolyzed fossil fuels find a variety of uses and are frequently carcinogenic hazards. Tars are common derivatives which contain large amounts of polycyclic hydrocarbons—up to 3 per cent at room temperature, and the vapor at 300°C, up to 4·4 per cent. [13] Tar-industry workers may inhale as much as 2·98 μg of benzpyrene per hour. Studies by Hueper have shown that, in addition to tars, the following substances are skin-carcinoma hazards: anthracene oil, coal tar, coke, creosote oil, high-boiling petroleum oils, petroleum asphalt, paraffin oil, pitch, shale oil and soot, all being fuel derivatives. [30] Polycyclic hydrocarbons are at the origin of most of the biologically active compounds in these materials. [13, 10, 31, 12, 46] The concentration of benzpyrene in shale oil, for example, was shown to be 0·01 per cent. [10] Shubik et al. isolated a large variety of carcinogenic hydrocarbons from petroleum waxes including benzpyrene, chrysene, benzanthracene and fluoranthene.

Pyrolysis of some plants also yields carcinogenic polycyclic hydrocarbons. Smoke condensate from cigarettes contains the compounds (I), (II), (VI) and (IX). [44] The plant derivatives, however, are less carcinogenically active than those from the fossil fuels. D. Hoffman and E. L. Wynder found that exhaust condensate from a V-8 engine had twice the tumor potency of cigarette-smoke condensate. Burning a total of 500 cigarettes, J. A. S. Gilbert and A. J. Lindsey could isolate 4·0 μg of benzpyrene from their smoke, 10·0 μg from the stubs and 0·3 μg from the ash. [26]

J. M. Campbell and R. L. Cooper observed an extraordinarily high incidence of cancer of the nasal sinuses in the Transvaal Bantu. They traced the occurrence to the use of an indigenous snuff containing 3,4-benzpyrene. On investigation, they found that the snuff was made from burned tobacco and plants. [14, 16] Even the soot derived from coffee contains carcinogenic polycyclic hydrocarbons. [36]

The widespread occurrence of polycyclic hydrocarbons poses a major problem in identifying their origins. Usually (but not always, note the case of smoked meats [48]) they are derived directly from the pyrolysis of either fossil fuel or a select group of plants.

III. MODE OF FORMATION

Carcinogenic hydrocarbons are formed during incomplete combustion of many natural substances at high temperatures. The mechanism of this pyrosynthesis most probably involves the formation of radicals. Various experiments have demonstrated a strong temperature dependence of the formation of polycyclic aromatic hydrocarbons and have yielded a narrow band (660–740°C) of permissible temperatures for best results. This temperature dependence is probably correlated to the ease of formation of the radicals and to their statistical recombination.

As early as 1866, Berthelot demonstrated the synthesis of certain aromatic hydrocarbons, including benzene, from pyrolyzed acetylene. [11] Van Duuren reported the pyrosynthesis of pyrene and the carcinogenically active benzo[α]-pyrene from stigmasterol. [50]

XII   I   XIII

Stigmasterol   Benzo [a] pyrene   Pyrene

A. J. Lindsey [38] in a study of polycyclic aromatic hydrocarbon formation has suggested a mechanism involving CH radicals. He has spectroscopically discovered their presence in flaming methane, ethane, propane and other fuels, while noting that the combustion residues contained polycyclic aromatic hydrocarbons. Hurd et al. [32] have proposed a mechanism involving the polymerization of radicals formed during the pyrolysis of low molecular compounds. They have stressed the significance of C_3 fragments, specifically the propadienyl–propargyl resonance hybrid, $\cdot CH=C=CH_2 \longleftrightarrow CH \equiv C—CH_2 \cdot$, and the isomeric trimethine fragment, $\cdot CH=CH—CH:$, in the formation of arenes. In addition, they have pointed out that simple aromatics may serve as a source for higher arenes.

The major work on the proposed mechanism of radical formation during the synthesis of carcinogenic polycyclic hydrocarbons has been carried out by G. M. Badger and his co-workers at the University of Adelaide, South Australia. Badger has systematically subjected various compounds to pyrolytic conditions similar to those in cigarettes or industrial fuel processes and analyzed the products formed for carcinogenic polycyclic hydrocarbons. [1-8] He has developed a scheme involving radical formation, chain propagation and chain termination for the general mechanism of formation of polycyclic hydrocarbons, which serves as a working hypothesis for general application. Comparison of bond dissociation energies reveals that, for example, at high temperatures the initial decomposition of toluene would give a majority of benzyl radicals: $C_6H_5—CH_3 \rightarrow C_6H_5—CH_2 \cdot + H$. Similar theoretical treatment indicates that decomposition of ethylbenzene, propyl benzene and butyl benzene yields mostly benzyl radicals and some phenyl radicals. Analysis of product residues demonstrates that both benzyl and phenyl radicals must be intermediates resulting from the pyrolytic dissociation of the above materials. The possible starting materials which would lead to polycyclic hydrocarbons are numerous and are usually found together. Therefore, in addition to benzyl and phenyl radicals, napthyl, phenylbutenyl, phenylbutadienyl and many others are formed during pyrolysis. They may either polymerize or combine with each other and polymerize subsequently. These radicals result from the fission of carbon–carbon single bonds and carbon–hydrogen bonds which are weaker than unsaturated or aromatic bonds.

A table of relevant bond dissociation energies of various compounds is given.

TABLE 1. BOND DISSOCIATION ENERGIES OF VARIOUS COMPOUNDS

(From *The Strength of Chemical Bonds*, T. L. Cottrell, Ed., Academic Press, 1954)

Bond	Bond dissociation energies (kcal/mole)
CH_3-CH_3	83
$C_2H_5-C_2H_5$	78
$C_6H_5-CH_3$	89
$C_6H_5CH_2-CH_2C_6H_5$	47
C_2H_5-H	98
C_6H_5-H	102
$C_6H_5CH_2-H$	77·5
$CH_2=CH_2$	125–140
$CH\equiv CH$	<187

Because of their relative strength, olefinic and acetylenic linkages, as well as benzoid rings, are not as likely to break down under similar pyrolytic conditions as are the single bond linkages.

The starting materials dissociate to form radicals which recombine in diverse patterns to yield less hydrogenated and more condensed products. The degree of hydrogenation of the intermediate compounds is not important, for both hydrogenation and dehydrogenation occur readily at high temperatures. A great variety of products result from the initial materials. Badger and his co-workers have pyrolyzed n-butyl benzene and have isolated and identified seventeen cyclic hydrocarbons from the residue.[7] Under similar conditions, they obtained forty cyclic hydrocarbons from the pyrolysis of n-decane.[6] That carcinogenic polycyclic hydrocarbons are formed, at least in part, by the pyrolysis of single-ring and aliphatic compounds is thus certain.

In further work, Badger and his colleagues have postulated and carefully investigated a mechanism for the formation of 3,4-benzpyrene from aliphatic reactants. Their proposed scheme can be diagrammatically represented as:

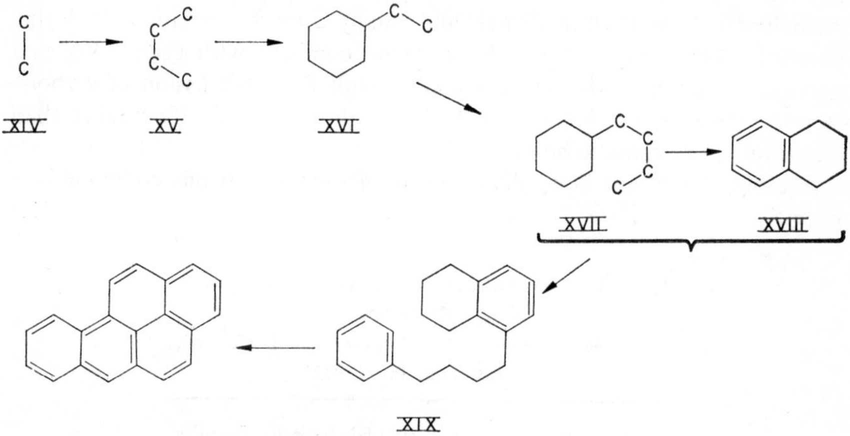

This scheme is a working hypothesis representative of individual mechanisms for specific hydrocarbons and serves as a detailed model.

The first step is the formation of a two-carbon unit (C_2), such as acetylene or ethylene (for **XIV**). Acetylene has been identified in the combustion products of organic compounds [41] and in tobacco smoke. [22]

This is followed by the formation of four-carbon compounds (C_4), such as 1,3-butadiene, $CH_2=CH—CH=CH_2$ (for **XV**). Both acetylene and butadiene have been shown to yield benzpyrene upon pyrolysis.

The following step is a dimerization to 4-vinyl cyclohexene (for **XVI**).

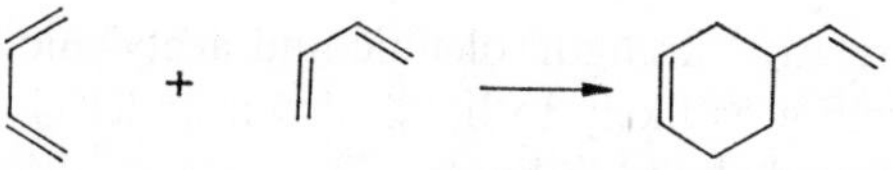

This Diels–Alder reaction was first reported by Hague and Wheeler in 1929 [29] and studied kinetically by Rowley and Steiner. [43] Hague and Wheeler have also postulated a scheme for the aromatization of vinyl cyclohexene:

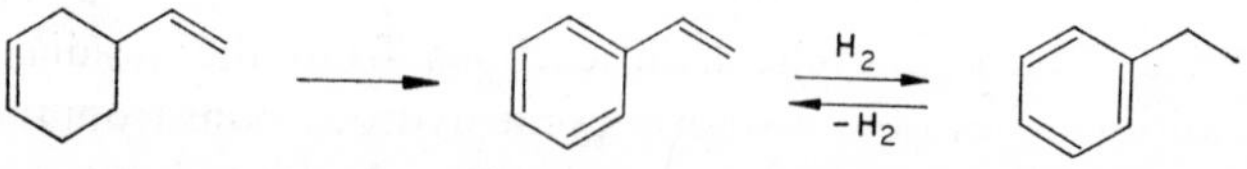

In their scheme, both styrene and ethyl benzene appear as intermediates. Gil-Av and his co-workers, however, maintain that a shift of the double bond from the vinyl group to the six-membered ring occurs prior to dehydrogenation. [23]

Gil-Av's proposed mechanism seems the more probable, since researchers have not been able to establish direct dehydrogenation of cyclohexenes to aromatics under thermal conditions.

Most probably, the C_6-C_4 units (butyl benzene, phenylbutadiene, etc., for XVII) are formed from the C_6-C_2 units by the following radical mechanisms: [1, 2]

(8) $Ph—CH=CH \cdot + PhCH=CH_2 \rightarrow Ph—CH=CH—CH=CH_2 + Ph \cdot$

(2) $Ph—CH_2—CH_2 \cdot + CH_2=CH_2 \rightarrow Ph—CH_2—CH_2—CH_2—CH_2 \cdot$

(3) $Ph \cdot + CH_2=CH—CH=CH_2 \rightarrow Ph—CH_2—CH=CH—CH_2 \cdot$

Condensation of the C_6-C_4 units yields XVIII which can then add to another C_6-C_4 unit to form XIX. The cyclization of XIX followed by its aromatization (occurring readily at high temperatures) gives benzo[a]pyrene (I).

In order to confirm his hypothesis, Badger has carried out the pyrolysis of the various intermediate compounds found in his proposed mechanism. The yields of benzo[a]pyrene formed at 700°C are given in Table 2.

TABLE 2. YIELDS OF BENZO [a] PYRENE UPON COM-
BUSTION AT 700°C

Compound	% Benzpyrene in tar
Acetylene	2·00
1,3-Butadiene	0·34
Ethyl benzene	0·065
Styrene	0·02
n-Butyl benzene	0·92
Phenyl butadiene	0·12
Tetralin	0·17

To give additional support for his hypothesis, Badger pyrolyzed C[14] labeled tetralin [5] and n-butyl benzene. [6] The resulting tars contained benzo-[α]pyrene with a degree of radioactivity in good agreement with the proposed mechanism.

Badger's postulated mechanism for the formation of benzo[α]pyrene serves as a model around which mechanisms for other specific polycyclic hydrocarbons may be developed. As both Hurd and Badger suggest, they are, at least in part, based on the formation, polymerization and combination of radicals at pyrolysis temperatures.

IV. PRECURSORS OF CARCINOGENS IN TOBACCO
A Case Study in Carcinogenesis

The correlation of incidence of lung cancer to smoking has stimulated a thorough investigation of tobacco smoke for polycyclic carcinogens. This recent work with tobacco serves as an illustrative example of present research in chemical carcinogenesis.

Tobacco contains a great number and variety of organic substances. The many possibilities have made the search for precursors of cancer inducers difficult. It has gradually been recognized that the tobacco leaf itself does not contain the active agents, but that the carcinogens are formed during the smoking process. [53]

Cooper and Lindsey have suggested the cigarette paper, consisting primarily of cellulose, as a possible source of benzpyrene. [21] Cardon and his co-workers carefully pyrolyzed cigarette paper to substantiate its toxicity on pyrolysis. [17] They found that 0·04 g of the paper (the amount in the average cigarette) yielded 0·042 γ of 3,4-benzpyrene. However, the pyrolyzed tobacco of one cigarette (0·96 g) yielded 0·122 γ of 3,4-benzpyrene. It therefore seems that the contribution of the paper to the carcinogenic effect of the smoke is minor. This has been confirmed by Stenhagen. [47]

Research in tobacco focused on the combustion of the components of the tobacco leaf. Gilbert and Lindsey [25] pyrolyzed ten of the major constituents of the leaf and isolated varying amounts of eleven polycyclic hydrocarbons (see Table 3).

Several plausible groups of precursors of tobacco smoke carcinogens have been suggested and studied. The tobacco paraffins were first proposed as possible precursors. Both Lam [37] and Wynder [53] have investigated the paraffins which they define as n- and iso-hydrocarbons from C_{12} to C_{35}. Wynder has screened the pyrolysis tar of these paraffins and found that it contained many polycyclic aromatic hydrocarbons. Injection of the pyrolyzate into mice yielded a 77 per cent carcinoma incidence. Rayburn, however, objected to the paraffins as being important precursors and maintained that Wynder's data were not sufficiently analytical. [42] The more recent studies of

TABLE 3. FORMATION OF POLYCYCLIC HYDROCARBONS DURING PYROLYSIS OF TEN OF THE MAJOR CONSTITUENTS OF THE TOBACCO LEAF, ACCORDING TO GILBERT AND LINDSEY (in micrograms per 100 g at 650°C)

	Cellulose	Lignin	Pectin	Starch	Sucrose	Glucose	Fructose	Malic Acid	Citric Acid	Oxalic Acid
Acenaphthylene	160	80	20	56	24	27	104	16	50	15
Fluorene	584	8000	287	32	12	7	118	632	173	3
Anthracene	337	544	539	104	70	36	139	70	98	30
Pyrene	219	33	133	35	24	66	35	166	24	2
Fluoranthene	164	58	152	94	35	45	106	136	6	—
3-Methylpyrene	131	—	29	94	15	1	11	119	89	1
1:2 Benzanthracene	186	44	273	116	41	43	120	130	5	—
1:2 Benzpyrene	65	22	34	4	2	11	2	8	37	—
3:4 Benzpyrene	78	47	45	17	10	29	33	35	17	1
Anthanthrene	10	—	9	1	—	5	5	1	2	0·3
Coronene	44	—	15	3	3	1	5	6	11	2

Badger *et al.* also indicate that, although tobacco paraffins may lead in part to polycyclic carcinogens, they are not the major contributors. [2]

Next, researchers centered their attention on the role of terpenes as precursors. Solanesol, borneol, linalool and other terpenes have been isolated from the tobacco leaf. [33] When these compounds are pyrolyzed at temperatures ranging from 500 to 800°C, they produce large amounts of isoprene. Isoprene also constitutes 50 to 80 per cent of the total unsaturated gaseous hydrocarbons present in tobacco smoke (0·87 to 4·2 mg/cigarette). [47]

Kennaway has found that the pyrolyzate of isoprene formed a strongly carcinogenic tar. [34] Gil-Av and Shabtai [24] have isolated benzo[a]pyrene from this tar in 0·1 per cent amounts.

The latter authors have proposed a mechanism for the formation of polycyclic aromatic hydrocarbons from terpenes during tobacco pyrolysis: [24]

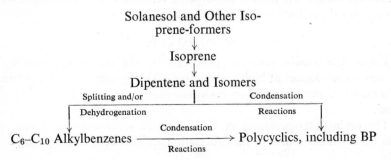

Grossman *et al.* have lent support to this scheme by confirming that derivatives of solanesol are specific precursors to the cyclohexene ring. [27] In addition, Grossman and his co-workers have found that aromatization occurs above 550°C, and they have successfully isolated alkylbenzenes and napthalenes. [28] It is noteworthy that Gil-Av and Shabtai's suggested mechanism, supported by Grossman's work, is in accordance with the general theory of formation proposed by Badger.

The investigation of tobacco smoke pyrolyzate led to the identification of several heterocyclic polynuclear carcinogens, i.e. dibenz[a,j]acridine (XX) and dibenz[a,h]acridine (XXI).

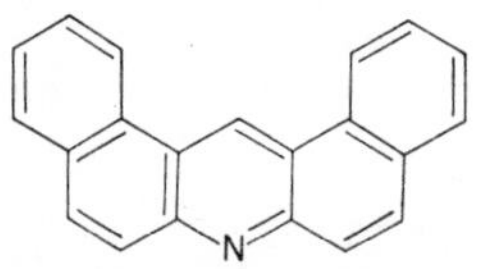

XX

Dibenz [a,j] acridine

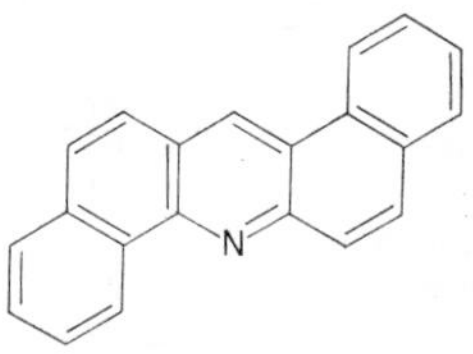

XXI

Dibenz [a,h] acridine

Van Duuren *et al.* [49] have shown that the basic constituents of the tobacco leaf are the precursors of these heterocyclic carcinogens. These workers pyrolyzed one of these alkaloids, namely nicotine, at 750°C and have identified both carcinogens in the tar residue.

Tobacco research has led to the identification of several active carcinogens and many of their possible precursors. It has shown that aliphatic and aromatic compounds can, on pyrolysis, lead to both polycyclic aromatic hydrocarbons and heterocyclic polynuclear substances, several each of which are carcinogenically active.

Furthermore, tobacco research has initiated and spurred on work in discovering the mechanisms of formation of these carcinogens.

This line of research might lead to the elimination of some of the factors responsible for the production of toxic materials in cigarette smoke and, therefore, reduce the hazard of smoking (compare the Neukomm–Bonnet process for the reduction of PAH in tobacco smoke [40]).

V. SUMMARY

Polynuclear carcinogens are produced by the incomplete combustion of various substances at high temperatures. This production is a continuous process which occurs in human environment, thus creating a hazard to mankind.

The optimal temperatures of PAH formation range between 660° and 740°C. The main source of their formation are industrial outfits, automobile engines and, to a lesser degree, cigarettes. Studies on pyrolysis of several precursors of PAH have shown that the nature of the pyrolyzed compound affects the yield of the carcinogens formed. In the case of tobacco components, for example, isoprenoid compounds appear to be the major contributors to the formation of benzpyrenes.

A working hypothesis for the mechanism of the pyrosynthesis of PAH has been proposed. According to this hypothesis, benzpyrene is formed from simple units by a step-wise synthesis. The reactions involved are predominantly radical in nature: radicals are formed by bond fission in the pyrolyzed compounds. Other reactions such as diene synthesis, isomerization, condensation, cyclization and dehydrogenation also occur. This working hypothesis has been supported by a series of experiments which included the pyrolysis of the postulated intermediates and the use of isotopically-labeled compounds.

An analogy exists between these reactions involving free radicals and many pathways for the formation of natural compounds, presumably involving enzymes.

REFERENCES

1. BADGER, G. M., BUTTERY, R. G., KIMBER, R. W. L., LEWIS, G. E., MORITZ, A. G. and NAPIER, I. M. *J. Chem. Soc.* **1958**, 2459.
2. BADGER, G. M. and SPOTSWOOD, T. M. *J. Chem. Soc.* **1960**, 4423.
3. BADGER, G. M., KIMBER, R. W. L. and SPOTSWOOD, T. M. *Nature* **187**, 663 (1960).
4. BADGER, G. M., KIMBER, R. W. L. and NOVOTNY, J. *Austral. J. Chem.* **15**, 605 (1962).
5. BADGER, G. M., KIMBER, R. W. L. and NOVOTNY, J. *Austral. J. Chem.* **15**, 616 (1962).
6. BADGER, G. M. and NOVOTNY, J. *Austral. J. Chem.* **16**, 623 (1963).
7. BADGER, G. M., KIMBER, R. W. L. and NOVOTNY, J. *Austral. J. Chem.* **17**, 771 (1964).
8. BADGER, G. M., KIMBER, R. W. L. and NOVOTNY, J. *Austral. J. Chem.* **17**, 778 (1964).
9. BEGEMAN, C. R. *Soc. Auto. Engineers* **1962**, 440c.
10. BERENBLUM, I. and SCHOENTAL, R. *Brit. J. Exptl. Pathol.* **24**, 232 (1943).
11. BERTHELOT, M. *Ann. Chim. Phys.* **9**(4), 453 (1866).
11a. BLUMER, M. *Science* **134**, 474 (1961).
12. BOGOVSKI, P. *Acta Unis Intern Contra Cancrum* **18**, 37 (1962).
13. BONNET, J. *Natl. Cancer Inst. Monographs* **9**, 221 (1962).
13a. BUU HOI, N. P. *Cancer Res.* **24**, 1520 (1964).
14. CAMPBELL, J. M. and COOPER, R. L. *Chem. & Ind. (London)* **1955**, 64.
15. CAMPBELL, J. M. and LINDSEY, A. J. *Brit. J. Cancer* **10**, 649 (1956).
16. CAMPBELL, J. M. and LINDSEY, A. J. *Chem. & Ind. (London)* **1957**, 951.
17. CARDON, S. Z., ALVORD, E. T., RAND, H. J. and HITCHCOCK, R. *Brit. J. Cancer* **10**, 485 (1956).
18. COOK, J. W., HEWETT, C. L. and HIEGER, I. *J. Chem. Soc.* **1933**, 395.
19. COOK, J. W. and HEWETT, C. L. *J. Chem. Soc.* **1933**, 398.
20. COOPER, R. L. and LINDSEY, A. J. *Chem. & Ind. (London)* **1953**, 1205.
21. COOPER, R. L. and LINDSEY, A. J. *Chem. & Ind. (London)* **1954**, 1260.
22. FISHEL, J. B. and HASKINS, J. F. *Ind. Eng. Chem.* **41**, 1374 (1949).
23. GIL-AV, E., SHABTAI, J. and STECKEL, F. *J. Chem. & Eng. Data* **5**, 103 (1960).
24. GIL-AV, E. and SHABTAI, J. *Nature* **197**, 1065 (1963).
25. GILBERT, J. A. S. and LINDSEY, A. J. *Brit. J. Cancer* **11**, 398 (1957).
26. GILBERT, J. A. S. and LINDSEY, A. J. *Brit. J. Cancer* **10**, 646 (1956).
27. GROSSMAN, J. D., IKEDA, R. M., DESZYCK, E. J. and BAVLEY, A. *Nature* **199**, 661 (1963).

M

28. GROSSMAN, J. D., IKEDA, R. M., DESZYCK, E. J. and BAVLEY, A. *17th Tob. Chem. Res. Conf.*, Montreal, 1963, p. 9.
29. HAGUE, E. N. and WHEELER, R. V. *J. Chem. Soc.* **1929**, 378.
30. HUEPER, W. C. In *Cancer*, ed. R. W. Raven, p. 404. Butterworth Pub., London, vol. I, part I, 1957.
31. HUEPER, W. C. and PAYNE, W. W. *Arch. Pathol.* **70**, 372 (1960).
32. HURD, C. D., MACON, A. R., SIMON, J. I. and LEVETAN, R. V. *J. Am. Chem. Soc.* **84**, 4509 (1962).
33. JOHNSTONE, R. A. W. and PLIMMER, J. R. *Chem. Revs.* **59**, 885 (1959).
34. KENNAWAY, E. L. *Brit. Med. J.* **2**, 1 (1925).
35. KENNAWAY, E. L. and KENNAWAY, N. M. *Brit. J. Cancer* **1**, 260 (1947).
36. KURATSEINE, M. and HUEPER, W. C. *J. Natl. Cancer Inst.* **20**, 37 (1958).
37. LAM, J. *Acta Pathol. Microbiol. Scand.* **37**, 421 (1955).
38. LINDSEY, A. J. In *Tobacco and Health*, p. 21, eds. G. James and T. Rosenthal. C. C. Thomas Publ. Co., Springfield, Ill., 1962.
39. MOORE, G. E. and KATZ, M. *Internatl. J. Air Pollution* **2**, 221 (1960).
40. NEUKOMM, S. and BONNET, J. U.S. Patents 3 039 475, *Chemical Abstracts* **57**, 12919b (1961).
41. NIEUWLAND, J. A. and VOGT, R. R. *The Chemistry of Acetylene*. Reinhold Pub. Corp., New York, 1945.
42. RAYBURN, C. H., WARTMANN, W. B., JR. and PEDERSEN, P. M. *Science* **128**, 1344 (1958).
43. ROWLEY, D. and STEINER, H. *Discussions Faraday Soc.* **10**, 198 (1951).
44. SMOKING AND HEALTH, *Report of the Advisory Committee to the Surgeon General of the USPHS*, USPHS Publ. 1103 (1964).
45. SAWICKI, E. *Natl. Cancer Inst. Monograph* **9**, 209 (1962).
46. SHUBIK, P., SAFFIOTTI, U., LYINSKY, W., PIETRA, G., RAPPAPORT, H., TOTH, B., RAHA, C. R., TOMATIS, L., FELDMAN, R. and RAMAHI, H. *Toxicology and Appl. Pharmacol.* Suppl. 4 (1962).
47. STENHAGEN, E. *Acta Soc. Med. Upsalensis* **64**, 322 (1959).
48. TILGNER, D. J. *Fleischwirtschaft* **10**, 649 (1958).
49. VAN DUUREN, B. L., BILBAO, J. A. and JOSEPH, C. A. *J. Natl. Cancer Inst.* **25**, 53 (1960).
50. VAN DUUREN, B. L. In *Tobacco and Health*, p. 33, eds. G. James and T. Rosenthal. C. C. Thomas Publ. Co., Springfield, Ill., 1962.
51. WALLER, R. E. *Brit. J. Cancer* **6**, 8 (1952).
52. WIELAND, H. and DANE, E. *Z. Physiol. Chem., Hoppe-Seyler's* **219**, 240 (1933).
53. WYNDER, E. L., WRIGHT, G. F. and LAN, J. *Cancer* **12**, 1073 (1959).
54. YAMAGIWA, K. and ICHIKAWA, K. *J. Cancer Res.* **3**, 1 (1918).

AUTHOR INDEX

Page numbers in italic figures indicate references at the end of articles.

AACH, H. G. 504, *526*
AARONSON, S. 721, *732*
ABBOT, L. D., Jr. 273, *306*
ABBOTT, M. T. 567, 568, *585*
ABDULLAH, M. 334, 381, 410, *454*
ABE, M. 1004, 1006, *1015*
ABEGG, F. A. 839, *895*
ABELES, R. H. 718, *732*
ABELSON, P. H. 11, 23, *37*, 43
ABERCROMBIE, M. J. 334, 373, 381, 424, *454*
ÅBERG, B. 728, *732*
ABRAHAM, E. P. 27, 28, *43*
ABRAHAM, S. 116, *198*
ABRAHAMSSON, S. 1049, *1062*
ABRAMS, R. 57, 58, 67, *96*, 560, 562, 563, 565, 572, *583*, 584, *586*
ABRAMSKY, T. 253, 261, *312*, 711, *741*
ACERBO, S. N. 919, 920, 922, 927, 929, *937*, 939
ACHENBACH, H. 766, *798*, 1041, *1061*, *1062*
ACKERMAN, W. W. 61, *101*, 696, *732*
ACKLIN, W. 1006, *1017*
ACS, G. 495, *535*
ADAMS, E. 15, 29, 31, 34, *37*, 40, *42*, 749, 797
ADAMS, J. B. 334, 381, 441, 443, *454*, *455*
ADAMS, M. H. 334, 381, 433, *455*
ADAMS, M. R. 387, *467*
ADAMS, R. 971, 980, *1015*
ADELBERG, E. A. 23, *37*, *41*, *43*
ADITYACHAUDHURY, N. 968, *1019*
ADLER, E. 123, *204*, 692, *741*, 917, 927, *937*
ADLER, J. 546, 547, 548, 550, 551, 570, 571, *580*, *586*
AFANAS'ER, P. V. 496, 504, *533*
AGHORAMURTHY, K. 768, *798*
AGRANOFF, B. W. 89, *96*, 137, 159, 160, *188*, 210, *241*, 648, *672*, 845, *896*, 948, *951*, 952
AGRANOFF, W. 725, *735*
AGURELL, S. 955, 1006, *1015*, *1021*
AHLGRIMM, E. D. 842, *895*
AHMAD, A. 955, 989, 1001, *1019*
AHMAD, B. 728, *732*
AILHAUD, G. 124, 129, 130, *188*

AIRTH, R. L. 290, *306*
AJL, S. 446, *475*
AKAZAWA, T. 334, 358, 371, 381, 390, 403, 405, *455*, *468*, 862, *897*
AKAZAWA, Y. 862, *897*
AKOYUNOGLOV, G. 321, 334, *455*
ALAUPOVIC, P. 179, *195*
ALBERS, M. 502, *528*
ALBERT, A. 706, *733*
ALBERTS, A. W. 112, 114, 115, *188*, *189*, *194*, *199*
ALBERTSON, J. N. 688, *733*
ALBON, N. 376, 396, *455*
ALBRECHT, A. M. 11, *43*
ALBRECHT, H. 803, *823*
ALBRECHT, M. 127, 158, *199*
ALDRICH, F. L. 618, *636*
ALDRICH, P. E. 647, *678*, 843, *896*
ALDRICH, R. A. 261, *310*, *311*, *312*
ALEXA, G. 821, 822, 823
ALEXANDER, G. J. 215, 219, *242*
ALEXANDER, J. A. 880, *899*
ALEXANDER, M. 561, *583*
ALFIN-SLATER, R. B. 132, *200*
ALGRANATI, I. D. 372, 405, 416, *455*
AL-KHALIDI, U. 701, *733*
ALLEN, E. H. 481, 483, 495, *533*
ALLEN, F. W. 543, *578*
ALLEN, M. B. 269, 289, 290, *306*, *308*, 658, 661, *672*
ALLEN, P. J. 376, *455*
ALLENDE, J. E. 15, *38*, 512, 520, *526*, *528*, *532*
ALLFREY, V. G. 483, 508, 522, *526*
ALLISON, A. C. 482, 484, *526*
ALLISON, J. B. 481, *526*
ALLISON, M. J. 23, *37*, 959, *1015*
ALLPORT, D. C. 756, *798*, 1029, *1060*
ALONSO DE LAMA, J. M. 813, *824*
ALONZO, N. 135, *201*
ALPERN, R. J. 148, *204*
ALTENBERN, R. A. 697, *733*
ALTERMATT, H. A. 364, 414, 420, *455*
ALTMAN, K. I. 486, *529*
ALVORD, E. T. 1074, *1077*
ALWORTH, W. L. 966, 1015
AMDUR, B. 946, *951*

AMDUR, B. H.　214, *242*, 1040, 1047, *1061*
AMES, B. N.　24, 29, 30, 31, 32, *37*, *42*, 505, 506, *526*, 685, *733*
AMES, S.　669, 670, *672*
AMIARD, G.　240, *245*
AMINOFF, D.　375, 438, *455*
ANAN, F. K.　284, *307*
ANDERS, M.　499, *530*, 563, 567, 568, 572, 573, *584*, *585*, *586*, *587*
ANDERS, N.　567, 568, 569, 571
ANDERSON, C. E.　156, *193*
ANDERSON, D. G.　647, 649, 654, 658, *673*, 676, 858, 879, 891, *897*, *899*
ANDERSON, E. I.　140, *203*
ANDERSON, E. P.　92, *99*, 356, 360, *455*, *464*
ANDERSON, J. M.　329, *456*, 664, 665, *673*
ANDERSON, J. S.　358, 374, 430, 432, *455*, 467, *469*
ANDERSON, L.　123, 160, *195*, *203*, 725, *736*, 955, *1015*
ANDERSON, M. L.　708, 709, *742*
ANDERSON, R. C.　629, *636*, 961
ANDERSON, R. F.　658, *673*
ANDERSON, R. L.　344, *455*
ANDO, O.　701, *736*
ANDO, T.　379, 410, 412, *469*
ANDRADE, F.　164, 184, 185, *189*
ANDREEVA, N. A.　704, *733*
ANDREOLI, A. J.　690, *733*
ANDREWS, E. H.　950, *951*
ANDREWS, P.　424, *455*
ANEJI, R.　784, 787, *799*
ANET, F. A. L.　971, *1015*
ANFINSEN, C. B.　486, 488, 514, 518, 519, 528, *529*, *534*
ANFINSEN, C. B., Jr.　178, *189*, 235, *244*
ANITA, M.　26, *37*
ANKEL, H.　364, 424, *455*
ANKER, H. S.　106, *189*, 208, 224, *241*, *243*
ANSELL, G. B.　105, 131, 135, 139, 140, 143, 149, 154, 155, 165, *189*
ANTHONY, D. D.　561, *583*
APELLA, E.　*38*
APGAR, J.　497, 498, 499, *528*, *530*, 543, *578*
APOSHIAN, H. V.　545, 548, 549, 550, *579*, *580*
APPEL, H.　1010, *1017*
APPELMAN, M. M.　406, *455*
APSIMON, J. W.　1044, *1060*
ARAI, K.　618, *636*, 1014, *1023*
ARCA, M.　498, *527*
ARCAMONE, F.　*311*
ARCHER, B.　947, *952*
ARCHER, B. L.　650, *673*, 948, *951*
ARCHER, D. A.　*1015*
ARCOS, J. C.　*527*

ARCUS, A. C.　450, *455*
ARDIZIO, P.　841, *895*
AREND, P.　405, *463*
ARIAS, I. M.　288, *307*
ARIGONI, D.　214, 225, *242*, *243*, 860, 868, 875, 876, 879, 880, 882, 884, 888, *897*, *898*, *899*, *900*, 1000, 1003, 1006, *1017*, *1018*, *1020*, 1048, *1062*
ARION, W. J.　342, 345, *469*
ARISON, B. H.　331, *474*
ARLINGHAUS, R.　509, 510, 511, 512, 513, 514, 516, *527*, *529*, *533*
ARLINGHAUS, R. B.　15, *41*
ARMITAGE, J. B.　711, *733*
ARMSTRONG, F. B.　23, *37*
ARMSTRONG, H.　836, *895*
ARMSTRONG, R.　832, *894*
ARNAKI, M.　645, *673*
ARNOLD, M.　658, *673*
ARNOLD, M. L.　387, *471*
ARNOLD, W.　745, *797*
ARNOLD, Z.　858, *897*
ARNOLDT, R. I.　612, 618, *636*
ARNON, D. I.　323, 329, 330, 332, 336, *455*, *462*, *472*, *473*, *474*, *475*
ARNSTEIN, H. R. V.　4, 6, 19, 21, 28, *37*, 140, 141, *189*, 502, *528*, 543, *578*
ARONOFF, S.　690, *733*, 866, *898*, 962, *1015*
ARONSON, M.　377, *455*
ARREGUIN, B.　943, 946, *951*
ARSOVE, S.　174, *193*
ARTMAN, M.　28, *37*, 504, 518, *527*
ARTOM, C.　140, 148, 149, 158, *189*, *192*
ASAHINA, Y.　769, *798*, *951*
ASAI, M.　700, 701, 702, 703, *733*, *737*, *738*
ASCHAN, O.　834, *894*
ASCHNER, M.　377, 378, 417, *463*
ASHANOW, H.　975, *1021*
ASHER, J. D. M.　1044, *1060*
ASHWELL, G.　91, 94, *97*, *101*, 368, 445, 446, 447, 449, *455*, *460*, *472*, *475*, 728, 737
ASKONAS, B. A.　486, 520, *527*
ASPEN, A. J.　28, *37*
ASSELINEAU, J.　121, 122, *189*
ASTENGO, R.　834, *894*
ASTRACHAN, L.　501, 503, *535*, 542, *578*
ATHINOES, E.　436, *455*
ATKIN, L.　680, *741*
ATKINSON, D. E.　10, 11, *40*, 344, *471*
ATKINSON, M. R.　381, 382, *455*
AUDA, B. M.　131, *198*
AUDA, H.　1010, *1017*
AUDLEY, B. G.　948, *951*
AUDLEY, B. J.　699, *733*
AUERBACH, V. H.　686, *737*
AUGUST, J. T.　563, 566, 567, 568, *584*, *585*

AULIN-ERDTMAN, G. 933, *937*
AUSTIN, D. J. 788, *799*
AUSTIN, F. L. 631, *637*
AUSTRIAN, R. 92, *101*, 363, 422, 433, *472, 473*
AVI-DOR, Y. 337, *456*
AVIGAD, G. 357, 371, 377, 378, 394, 396, 418, *455, 460, 463, 464, 467*
AVIGAN, J. 217, 220, 222, *242, 243*
AVINERI-SHAPIRO, S. 377, 378, 417, *463*
AVIZONIS, P. V. 832, *894*
AXELROD, A. E. 501, 502, 504, *534*
AXELROD, B. 160, *201*, 325, 337, 348, 364, 402, 446, *455, 472*, 521, *529*
AXELROD, J. 8, *37*, 92, *101*, 288, *311*, 356, 363, 375, 435, *455, 473*, 592, 596, 620, 622, 623, 624, 625, *635, 636, 638*
AXELROD, L. R. 133, *244*
AYENGAR, P. 79, *97*
AYER, W. A. 971, *1015*
AYRES, P. J. 228, *244*
AYREY, G. 948, *951*

BABAD, H. 372, 393, *455*
BABBAR, I. 728, *732*
BABOR, K. 971, *1015*
BACH, M. 26, *38*
BACH, M. K. 553, *581*
BACHHAWAT, B. K. 426, *469*, 646, *673*, 945, 946, *951*, 961, *1021*
BACHMANN, R. 810, *825*
BACON, D. F. 11, 14, *43*
BACON, J. S. D. 376, 395, 396, *455, 459*
BADDILEY, J. 89, 90, 93, 94, *96, 100*, 158, *189*, 357, 361, 362, 366, 427, 430, 431, *455, 456, 457, 470*, 694, *733*
BADENHUIZEN, N. P. 403, 412, *455*
BADER, G. 290, *310*
BADER, S. 882, *899*
BADGER, G. M. 1068, 1070, 1071, 1072, 1073, 1074, 1075, 1076, *1077*
BADIEI, S. E. 962, *1018*
BAER, E. 135, *189*
BAGATELL, F. K. 59, *96*
BAGDASARIAN, M. 257, *307*
BAGGETT, B. 230, *244*
BAICH, A. 11, 12, 14, *38, 43*
BAILEY, J. M. 384, 411, *455, 470, 475*
BAILEY, R. W. 412, 413
BAINE, J. O. 619, 624, *636*
BAISTED, D. J. 225, *243*, 879, *899*
BAKER, D. R. 979, *1021*
BAKER, H. 718, *739*
BAKER, W. 818, *823*
BALDESTEN, A. 57, *100*

BALDWIN, B. C. 597, 599, 608, 609, 615, *635*
BALDWIN, E. 609, *635*
BALDWIN, R. L. 550, 568, *580, 585*
BALFOUR, Y. M. 176, *191*
BALINSKY, D. 804, *823*
BALL, C. D. 936, *937*, 955, 964, *1017*
BALLIO, A. 83, 91, 92, 93, *96, 101*
BALLOU, C. E. 136, 137, 138, 162, 163, *189, 191, 194, 201, 203*
BALLOU, J. E. 482, *534*
BALTIMORE, D. 566, 568, *584, 585*
BAN, Y. 223, *243*, 886, *900*
BANDURSKI, R. S. 11, *43*, 336, 337, 438, 439, 440, *455, 475*, 566, *587*, 614, *635, 639*, 944, *951*
BANERJEE, E. 488, *535*
BANK, A. 497, *527*
BANKS, J. 139, 145, *204*
BANNUSCHER, H. 724, *737*
BANTZ, A. C. 694, *741*
BARANOWSKI, T. 123, *189*, 398, 401, *455, 469*
BARBER, G. 92, *97*
BARBER, G. A. 357, 362, 371, 374, 415, 435, *455, 456, 459*
BARBER, M. J. 667, *673*
BARBER, M. S. 662, *673*
BARBIER, M. 882, *900*
BARBIERI, P. 715, *733*
BARCHIELLI, R. 715, 716, *733*
BARCLAY, R. K. 541, *578*
BARGER, G. 990, *1015*
BARKER, H. A. 22, *44*, 58, *97*, 106, 107, 124, *189*, 202, 370, 376, 390, *459*, 476, 717, *733, 736, 742*
BARKER, S. A. 376, 377, 383, 392, 396, 408, 411, *456*
BARKER, W. F. 233, *244*
BARKULIS, S. S. 373, 432, *476*
BARLOW, G. B. 843, *896*
BARLTROP, J. A. 868, *898*
BARNABEI, D. 521, *534*
BARNABEI, O. 507, *527*
BARNARD, D. 650, *673*, 947, *952*
BARNES, F. W. 71, *97*
BARNES, M. F. 962, *1022*
BARNES, M. M. 606, *635*
BARNETT, L. 492, *528*
BARONDES, S. H. 503, 509, *527*
BARRATT, R. W. 23, *37*
BARRETT, J. 270, 271, *307*
BARRETT, J. M. 715, *739*
BARRON, E. J. 106, 109, 112, 116, 134, 146, *189, 195*
BARRY, G. T. 438, *456*
BARRY, J. M. 485, 514, *531, 533*

BARRY, R. D. 570, *586*
BARRY, V. C. 416
BAR-TANA, J. *189*
BARTLETT, M. F. 832, *894*
BARTLEY, W. 337, *456*
BARTLEY, W. C. 592, 629, *637*
BARTON, D. H. R. 815, 818, *823*, 832, 858, 859, 863, 871, 872, 879, 884, *894*, *897*, *898*, *899*, *900*, 955, 979, 981, 982, 985, 986, 988, 989, 1003, *1015*, *1018*, 1027, 1030, *1060*
BARTRAM, K. 641, *675*
BARTTER, F. C. 228, *244*
BASS, S. T. 357, 358, *474*
BASSETT, E. W. 755, 797, 832, *894*, 909, *937*
BASSETT, H. L. 476, *797*
BASSHAM, J. A. 92, 97, 320, 321, 322, 326, 327, 332, 333, 334, 335, *456*, *457*, 485, *527*
BATE-SMITH, E. C. 807, 818, *823*, 926, *937*
BATTAILE, J. 854, *896*
BATTERSBY, A. R. 882, *900*, 955, 957, 977, 978, 979, 980, 981, 982, 983, 985, 986, 1000, 1001, 1003, *1015*, *1016*
BAUER, L. 807, *823*
BAUGH, C. M. 705, *733*, *738*
BAUMAN, N. A. 150, *189*
BAUMANN, E. 601, 611, *635*
BAUMGARTEL, J. 289, *307*
BAUNI, G. 813, *825*
BAUTZ, E. K. F. 502, 503, *527*
BAVETTA, L. A. 15, *38*
BAVLEY, A. 1076, *1077*, *1078*
BAXTER, J. H. 625, *635*
BAXTER, R. M. 955, 1004, 1006, *1016*
BAYERLE, H. 745, *797*
BAYLIS, P. E. T. 933, *937*
BAYLISS, B. J. 131, *189*
BAZZANO, G. 882, 887, 899
BDOLAH, A. 520, *533*
BEAK, P. 871, *898*
BEAL, J. L. 885, *900*, 981, *1016*
BEAN, R. C. 371, 448, *456*
BEARDEN, J. H. 129, *196*
BEAUCAMP, K. 682, *736*
BEBBINGTON, A. 379, 411, *456*
BECHET, J. 11, *38*
BECK, L. W. 146, *199*
BECKER, Y. 501, 502, 503, *527*, 566, *585*
BEELER, D. A. 649, 654, *673*, 879, 891, *899*
BEER, M. 415, *458*
BEERS, R. F., Jr. 539, 542, 577, *583*
BEERS, R. J., Jr. 556, 557, 558, *582*
BEETS, M. G. J. 836, *895*
BEEVERS, H. 339, 340, 364, *462*, *465*, *468*, *472*, *473*
BEGEMAN, C. R. 1067, *1077*

BÉGIN, N. 485, *527*
BEHKI, R. M. 552, 553, *581*
BEHRMANN, E. J. 487, *530*
BEINERT, H. 107, *202*, 944, *951*
BEKHOR, I. J. 15, *38*
BELAVADI, B. 409, *461*
BELFRAGE, P. 156, *189*
BELIC, I. 641, *676*
BELJANSKI, M. 484, 485, *527*
BELL, D. 553, *581*
BELL, D. J. 376, 396, *455*
BELL, E. 504, 508, *533*
BELL, T. T. *741*
BELLAMY, W. D. 723, *735*
BELLER, B. *532*
BELMAN, S. 631, *638*
BELOCOPITOW, E. 406, *455*
BELTZ, R. E. 552, *581*
BENEDICT, J. H. 146, *199*
BENESCH, R. 438, 439, *459*
BENESCH, R. E. 438, 439, *459*
BENITEZ, A. 268, *312*
BENN, M. H. 972, 1012, *1016*, *1017*
BENNET, J. R. 132, *189*
BENNET, P. 121, 122, *189*
BENNETT, C. J. 35, 36, 37, *38*
BENNETT, J. C. 492, 493, 494, *527*
BENNETT, M. J. 680, *734*
BENNETT, R. 330, *456*
BENNETT, R. D. 226, *243*, 881, 882, 883, 886, 893, *899*, *900*, *1016*
BENNETT, T. P. *527*
BENSCH, K. G. 484, *530*
BENSON, A. A. 92, *97*, 130, 136, 158, *189*, *190*, 320, 321, 325, 335, *456*, *467*, *470*
BENT, K. J. 485, *527*
BENTLEY, M. 67, *96*
BENTLEY, R. 1033, 1034, 1035, 1038, 1041, *1060*
BENVENISTE, M. P. 879, *899*
BENVENISTE, P. 887, *900*, *901*
BENZER, S. 494, 496, 498, *527*, *528*, *535*
BENZIMAN, M. 414, *456*
BERDAHL, J. M. 871, *898*
BERENBLUM, I. 1069, *1077*
BERG, B. N. 233, *244*
BERG, P. 125, *190*, 337, *456*, 494, 495, 496, 497, 498, 502, 508, 518, *527*, *532*, *535*, 539, 546, 561, 563, 564, 567, 568, 569, 570, 574, *577*, *580*, *583*, *584*, *585*, *587*
BERGER, C. R. A. 5, 15, *44*, 519, *535*
BERGER, L. 143, *190*, 342, 343, *456*
BERGERET, B. 618, *636*
BERGKVIST, R. 91, 92, *97*
BERGMANN, E. 208, *241*
BERGMANN, F. 208, *241*
BERGMANN, F. H. 495, 496, 508, *527*

BERGQUIST, A. 23, *43*
BERGSTRÖM, S. 128, 146, *190*, 233, 234, 235, 238, 239, *244, 245*
BERKELEY, B. J. 360, *456*
BERLIN, C. M. 507, *533*
BERMAN, M. 485, *533*
BERNAERTS, M. J. 447, *456*
BERNARD, E. 295, *307*
BERNARD, M. 879, 882, 890, *899*
BERNARD-DAGAN, C. 882, *900*
BERNAUE, K. 810, *826*
BERNFELD, H. C. 360, *456*
BERNFELD, M. R. 493, *527*
BERNFELD, P. 340, 341, 360, 386, 392, 397, *456, 467*
BERNHARD, K. 117, *190*, 627, 628, *635*, 803, *823*
BERNHAUER, K. 301, *307*, 713, 717, *733*
BERNHEIMER, H. P. 92, *101*, 363, 422, 433, *472, 473*
BERNLOHR, R. W. 487, 495, *527*
BERNS, D. S. 291, 292, 296, *307*
BERNSTEIN, I. A. 56, 59
BERNSTEIN, R. L. 357, *456*
BERNSTEIN, S. 438, 439
BERQUIST, P. L. 574, *587*
BERRY, J. F. 126, 127, 140, 142, 143, 144, 145, 159, 168, *190, 199, 200, 202*
BERTANI, L. E. 58, *97*, 548, *580*
BERTHELOT, M. 1069, *1077*
BERTHET, L. 402, *470*
BERTHOLET, M. P. E. 833, *894*
BERTSCH, L. L. 551, *580*
BESHOW, G. 495, *530*
BESSMAN, M. J. 546, 547, 548, 550, *579, 580*
BESSMAN, S. P. 274, *309, 637*
BESSON, G. 643, 659, *677*
BETTENDORF, G. *742*
BETTHEIL, J. J. 692, *737*
BETTS, J. J. *635*
BETZ, R. F. 70, *100*
BEUMER, H. 208, 241
BEVAN, C. W. 968, *1016*
BEVILL, R. D. 360, *456*
BEYER, K. F. 228, *243*
BHAKUNI, D. S. 981, *1015, 1018*
BHARGAVA, P. M. 76, *98*
BHATTACHARJI, S. 1006, *1016*, 1052, 1054, *1060*
BHEEMESWAR, B. 495, *529*
BICKELHAUPT, F. 832, *894*
BICKING, J. B. 682, *737*
BIEBER, R. E. 360, *456*
BIEHL, J. P. 629, *636*
BIEMANN, K. 968, *1016*
BIGGS, M. W. 222, *243*

BIGLEY, D. B. 868, *898*
BILBAO, J. A. 1076, *1078*
BILL, M. C. 807, *826*
BILLEK, G. 452, *472*, 780, *798*, 926, 927, 929, *937, 938*
BILLEN, D. 545, *579*, 696, *733*
BILLETER, A. 566, 567, *585*
BILLETER, M. A. 566, *585*
BINKS, R. 955, 957, 978, 983, 985, 1000, 1003, *1015, 1016*
BINNS, F. 688, *736*
BIRBECK, M. S. C. *527*
BIRCH, A. J. 700, *733*, 748, 751, 755, 757, 758, 760, 768, 770, 784, *797, 798*, 805, 807, 808, *823*, 842, 846, 850, 852, 868, 869, 872, 873, *895, 896, 898*, 1006, *1016*, 1026, 1030, 1031, 1034, 1035, 1037, 1038, 1039, 1040, 1041, 1043, 1046, 1047, 1048, 1051, 1052, 1053, 1054, 1055, 1057, *1060, 1061, 1063*
BIRECKA, H. 975, *1016*
BIRKICHT, E. 333, *475*
BIRKINSHAW, J. H. 448, *458*, 909, *937*
BIRNSTIEL, M. L. 573, *586*
BISHOP, J. 486, 514, *527*
BISHOP, J. O. 509, *527*
BISWAS, B. B. 565, 572, *584, 586*
BITTNER, F. 931, *938*
BJÖRN, L. O. 295, *307*
BLACK, A. L. 485, *527*
BLACK, C. C. 331, 332, 334, *456, 474*
BLACK, S. 11, 16, 25, *38*, 944, *952*
BLACKFAN, K. D. 208, *241*
BLACKLOW, R. S. 177, *196*, 437, *456, 475*
BLACKLOW, S. 91, *101, 102*
BLACKWOOD, U. B. 716, *733*
BLAKLEY, R. L. 58, *97*, 141, *190*
BLANCE, G. E. 1052, *1060*
BLANCHARD, P. H. 376, 396, *455*
BLASS, U. 664, 665, *673*
BLIGH, E. G. 226, *243*
BLINC, M. 392, 397, *471*
BLINKS, L. R. 289, 290, 292, *306, 309*
BLIX, G. 172, 173, *190*
BLOCH, K. 23, *38*, 105, 106, 112, 114, 115, 117, 118, 119, 120, *190, 193, 196, 198, 200, 201, 202*, 205, 208, 209, 211, 213, 214, 215, 218, 219, 220, 221, 224, 227, 233, *241, 242, 243, 244*, 496, *532*, 648, 655, *673*, 835, 844, 845, 873, 880, *895, 896, 898, 899*, 943, 944, 946, 948, *951, 952*, 1000, *1018*, 1040, 1047, *1061*
BLOCK, K. 647, *673*
BLOMSTRAND, R. 146, *195*
BLONDIN, G. A. 240, *245*, 879, 880, 881, 890, 892, *899*
BLOOM, E. S. 708, *740*

BLOOM, W. 657, *675*
BLOOMFIELD, D. K. 117, *190*
BLOOR, W. R. 104, 105, *190*
BLUM, S. W. 971, *1020*
BLUMENTHAL, H. J. 352, *456, 459*
BLUMER, M. 1065, *1077*
BLUMSON, N. L. 94, *96*, 362, 366, *456, 457*
BLUNDELL, M. J. 917, *939*
BO, W. J. 399, *456*
BOARDMAN, N. K. 268, *307*, 329, *456*
BOBBITT, J. M. 832, *894*
BOCK, K. W. 350, *457*
BOCK, R. 510, *531*
BOCK, R. M. 599, 612, *637*
BODMER, W. 548, 549, 550, *580*
BOECK, L. H. 885, *900*
BOECKH-BEHRENS, G. *1021*
BOERI, E. 687, *736*
BOESENBERG, H. 931, 936, *938*
BOGARD, L. 711, *733*
BOGERT, M. T. 745, *797*
BOGOCH, S. 174, *190, 193*
BOGORAD, L. 248, 249, 252, 254, 257, 258, 259, 261, 264, 268, 269, 271, 273, 289, 291, 294, 295, 297, 298, 299, 301, 303, 304, *307, 308, 310, 311, 312*, 806, 807, *823*
BOGOROCH, R. 507, *532*
BOGOVSKI, P. 1069, *1077*
BOHLMAN, F. 641, *675*
BOHLMANN, F. 975, *1021*
BOITER, T. A. 132, *203*
BOJARSKI, T. B. 520, *530*, 553, *581*
BOKMAN, A. H. 687, *740*
BOLDEN, A. H. 160, *193*, 453, *459*, 726, 735
BOLINDER, A. E. 710, *733*
BOLLETER, A. 782, *799*
BOLLIGER, A. 597, *636*
BOLLUM, F. J. 552, 553, 554, 555, *581, 582*
BOLOGNA, I. 553, *581*
BOLTON, E. T. 11, *43*
BOLTRALIK, J. J. 373, 432, *476*
BOMAN, H. G. 544, 572, 573, *579, 586*
BONNER, D. M. 12, 36, *42, 43*, 687, 737, 739
BONNER, J. 503, 508, *527, 531*, 567, *585*, 647, 652, 659, *673, 676*, 681, *733*, 834, 842, 843, 881, 883, 886, *894, 895, 896, 899, 900*, 941, 942, 943, 944, 945, 946, 947, 948, 949, 950, 951, *952*
BONNET, J. 1069, 1076, *1077, 1078*
BONNETT, R. 299, 301, *307*, 667, *673*, 711, 733
BONSIGNORE, A. 324, *457*
BOOIJ, H. L. 258, *307, 311*
BOOTH, A. N. 624, 625, *635*

BOOTH, V. H. 668, *673*
BOPP, M. 806, *824*
BORCHGREVINK, C. F. 182, *195*
BOREK, E. 208, *241*, 499, *527*, 572, 573, 574, *586*
BORETTI, B. 715, 733
BORETTI, G. 715, 716, *733*
BORGSTRÖM, B. 128, 146, 182, 186, *190*
BORIKHINA, M. G. 1012, *1018*
BORISOVA, A. I. 716, *741*
BORKENHAGEN, L. F. 4, 5, *38*, 142, 143, 144, 155, 156, 157, *190, 197*
BORNSTEIN, B. T. 106, *189*
BORSOOK, H. 481, 482, 483, 484, 485, 486, 487, *527*
BORST, P. 566, 567, *584, 585*
BORTHWICK, H. A. 289, *309*
BOSCH, L. 506, *535*
BOSCHETTI, A. 650, *675*
BOSTRÖM, H. 352, 438, 439, 443, *457, 464*, 612, *635, 639*
BOSWELL, G. A. 219, *242*, 887, *900*
BOTHNER-BY, A. A. 959, *1016*
BOTTOMLEY, W. 807, *824, 825*, 971, *1016*
BOUCHILLOUX, S. 615, *635*
BOULCY-URISON, M. *635*
BOULTER, D. 850, *896*
BOURGEOIS, S. 569, *586*
BOURNE, E. J. 376, 377, 379, 383, 392, 396, 408, 411, *456, 462*
BOUTWELL, R. K. 402, *463*
BOVARD, F. 481, 483, *533*
BOWDEN, K. 958, *1016*, 1035, 1056, *1061*
BOXER, G. E. 571, *586*
BOYER, F. 627, *635*
BOYER, P. D. 372, 392, *460*
BOYLAND, E. 605, 606, 612, 630, 631, *635*
BRACHET, J. 488, *527, 532*
BRACK, A. 957, 1004, *1016, 1017*, 1052, 1054, 1056, *1060, 1061*
BRADBEER, C. 127, *190*, 340, *457*
BRADBURY, F. R. 608, *635*
BRADFIELD, A. E. 856, *897*
BRADLEY, D. F. 92, *97*
BRADLEY, R. M. 89, *96*, 111, 112, 113, 115, 137, 159, 160, *188, 190, 201*
BRADLOW, H. L. 235, *244*
BRADY, R. O. 89, *96*, 107, 109, 111, 112, 113, 115, 137, 159, 160, 166, 167, 170, 171, 172, 177, *188, 190, 191, 196, 201*, 208, *241*, 435, *457*, 717, *733*
BRAGANCA, B. 92, *98*, 355, 356, *464*
BRAGDON, J. H. 180, 182, *190, 201*
BRAITHWAITE, G. D. 645, 647, 663, *673*, 843, *896*, 1039, 1040, 1047, *1061*
BRAND, F. C. 132, *202*
BRANDT, I. K. 601, *635*

BRANTE, G. 155, *190*
BRATEK, M. D. 975, *1020*
BRAUNS, D. A. 904, 906, 916, *937*
BRAUNS, F. E. 904, 905, 906, 916, 926, *937*
BRAUNSTEIN, A. E. 36, *38*
BRAWERMAN, G. 503, 523, *527*, 542, *578*
BRAY, H. G. 592, 604, 605, 607, 629, *635*
BRAY, R. 712, 713, *733*
BRAY, R. C. 299, *307*, 712, 713, *733*
BRECCIA, A. 958, *1017*
BREGOFF, H. M. 142, *192*, 696, *740*
BREMER, J. 141, 148, 154, *190*, 238, *245*, 599, *635*
BRENAN, J. P. M. 819, *824*
BRENNER, J. 542, *578*
BRENNER, S. 492, 501, 503, *527*, *528*, 542, 543, *579*
BRESLER, A. E. 565, *584*
BRESLOW, E. 728, *738*
BRESLOW, R. 682, *733*
BRESSLER, R. 112, 113, 121, *191*
BRETTHAUER, R. 510, *531*
BRETTHAUER, R. K. 416, *457*
BREUER, C. B. 508, 510, 511, *527*, *529*
BREUER, H. 233, *244*
BREUER, S. W. 955, 957, 985, *1015*
BREUSCH, F. L. 117, *191*, 208, *241*
BREWER, H. W. 976, *1017*
BRIAN, P. W. 1048, *1061*
BRIDGES, J. W. 593, *635*
BRIESKORN, C. 860, 889, *897, 901*
BRIGGS, L. H. 868, 871, 872, *898*
BRIGGS, T. 237, 239, *245*
BRILL, W. J. 330, *474*
BRINER, M. 889, *901*
BRINGI, N. V. 997, *1022*
BRINK, N. G. 448, *457*
BRITT, J. J. 1048, *1062*
BRITTEN, R. J. 508, 509, 518, 521, *531*, *533*
BRITTON, B. B. 352, *476*
BROBERG, P. L. 84, *100*
BROCHMANN-HANSSEN, E. 979, *1017*
BROCK, T. D. 516, *527*
BROCKERHOFF, H. 106, 135, 137, 138, 146, 162, 163, *191, 195*
BROCKHAUS, R. 807, *824*
BROCKMANN, H. *1061*
BRODIE, B. B. 597, 615, *635, 637*
BRODY, M. 292, *307*
BROHERG, P. L. 703, *740*
BRONSTEIN, S. B. 488, *535*
BROOKS, C. J. W. 860, *897*
BROQUIST, H. P. 28, *38*, 40, *42, 43*, 709, *733*

BROSSARD, M. 150, *199*
BROT, N. 22, *38, 44*, 718, *733*
BROTMAN, M. 492, *527*
BROWN, A. M. 415, *457*
BROWN, B. 9, 23, 24, *43*, 486, *529*, 810, *827*
BROWN, B. M. 708, *739*
BROWN, B. R. 813, *824*
BROWN, D. D. 622, *635, 710*, 733
BROWN, D. H. 91, 92, *98, 101*, 342, 343, 344, 351, 352, 373, 379, 387, 399, 401, 404, 405, 410, 424, 425, *455, 461, 462, 463, 465*
BROWN, E. G. *733*
BROWN, F. B. 714, *733*
BROWN, G. B. 720, *739*
BROWN, G. L. 498, *534*, 539, 541, 543, *577, 578*
BROWN, G. M. 22, *38*, 86, 97, 679, 681, 682, 684, 688, 694, 695, 698, 699, 705, 706, 707, 708, 727, 729, *733, 734, 735, 737, 739, 740, 742*, 962, *1021*
BROWN, H. 486, *527*
BROWN, J. 129, 130, *191*, 486, *527*
BROWN, J. B. 153, *197*
BROWN, J. G. 364, 365, *467*
BROWN, J. R. *201*
BROWN, J. S. 269, 289, *308*
BROWN, J. W. 484, *529*
BROWN, R. 230, *244*, 508, *528*
BROWN, R. R. 687, *734*
BROWN, R. T. 1003, *1016*
BROWN, R. W. 106, *204*
BROWN, S. A. 749, 750, 788, 791, 796, 797, 799, 918, 928, 929, *937*, 955, *1017*
BROWN, T. E. 335, 336, *474*
BROWN, T. H. 980, *1016*
BRÜCKER, W. 803, 804, 805, *824, 827*
BRÜGGEMANN, J. 9, *38, 42*
BRUMM, A. F. 79, *98*, 156, *197*
BRUMMOND, D. O. 321, 371, 415, *457, 464*, 556, *582*
BRUNETTI, P. 436, *457*
BRUNS, G. P. 274, *307*
BRYANT, M. P. 23, *37*
BUBLITZ, C. 123, *191*, 728
BUCHANAN, B. B. 330, *466*
BUCHANAN, D. L. 485, *527, 534*
BUCHANAN, J. G. 89, 90, 92, *96, 97*, 158, *189*, 371, 389, *457*
BUCHANAN, J. M. 19, 20, 21, 22, *39, 40, 42, 43*, 59, 61, 62, 63, 64, 65, 66, *97, 98, 99, 101, 102*, 544, *579*, 718, *738*
BUCHER, N. L. R. 213, *242*
BÜCHER, T. 123, *191*
BÜCHI, G. 968, *1016*
BUCHMAN, E. R. 681, *733*

BUCKLEY, S. D. 12, *41*
BUDZ, D. M. 180, *196, 202*
BUEDING, E. 344, 351, 399, *457, 469,* 595, *637*
BUELL, G. C. 122, 123, 129, *191*
BUETTNER-JANUSCH, V. 89, *100,* 544, *579*
BULL, A. T. 377, 416, *458*
BULLOCK, E. 261, 299, *307,* 1044, *1061*
BULMAN, N. 483, *527*
BULOCK, J. D. 122, *202,* 756, *798,* 1029, 1034, 1037, 1056, 1058, *1060, 1061*
BUMILLER, S. 726, *734*
BUNTON, C. A. 1053, *1061*
BURCHENAL, J. H. 709, *733*
BURDON, R. H. 564, 565, 566, 567, *584, 585*
BURGER, M. 13, 14, *39,* 374, 435, *457*
BURGER, M. M. 374, 431, *457, 461*
BURGER-RACHAMIMOV, H. 414, *456*
BURGHELEA, G. 821, 822, *823*
BURGSTAHLER, A. W. 848, *896*
BURGUS, R. C. 303, *309,* 717, *736*
BURK, D. 334, *475*
BURKA, E. R. 510, 514, 516, 517, *527, 531,* 543, *578*
BURMA, D. P. 92, *97,* 344, 345, 346, 371, 389, *457,* 556, 561, 565, 567, 568, *582, 583, 585*
BURNELL, R. H. 971, *1015*
BURNETT, J. H. 642, *673*
BURNETT, J. R. 486, *527*
BURNHAM, B. F. 255, 257, *307*
BURNS, J. J. 450, *457,* 727, 728, 729, 730, 731, *734, 735, 737*
BURNS, R. O. 24, 27, *38, 39,* 704, *735*
BURNY, A. 502, *531*
BURR, G. O. 917, *938*
BURSTEIN, S. 860, *897*
BURTON, A. 541, *578*
BURTON, D. 803, *824*
BURTON, K. 381, 382, *457*
BURTON, R. M. 92, *99,* 170, 171, 176, *191,* 360, 374, 435, *457, 467*
BUSCH, H. 521, *534*
BUSS, C. D. 658, *676*
BUTENANDT, A. 687, *734,* 832, 883, *894, 900*
BUTLER, F. P. 704, *734*
BUTLER, G. C. 595, *637*
BUTLER, J. A. V. 520, *528, 529,* 541, 542, *578*
BUTLER, R. 643, *675*
BUTLER, W. L. *312*
BUTTE, J. C. 1041, *1061, 1062*
BUTTERY, R. G. 1070, 1073, *1077*
BUU-HOI, NG. PH. *527,* 1066, *1077*

BYERRUM, R. U. 690, *736,* 936, *937,* 955, 962, 964, 971, 975, 1004, *1017, 1018, 1019, 1021, 1023*
BYKHORSKII, Y. Y. 711, *734*
BYRD, C. 571, *586*
BYRNE, W. L. 4, 5, *41,* 142, 156, 157, *200*
BYRON, J. E. 132, *191*

CABIB, C. E. 91, 92, 93, *97, 100*
CABIB, E. 344, 349, 355, 357, 372, 382, 391, 399, 402, 405, 416, 419, 424, 445, *455, 457, 466*
CAGLIOTI, L. 860, *897*
CAHN, R. S. 650, *673*
CAIN, B. F. 871, 872, *898*
CAIN, C. K. 448, *471*
CAIRNS, J. 541, 550, *578, 580*
CAIS, M. 860, 867, 868, *897, 989*
CALBORI, C. 498, *527*
CALDWELL, M. L. 341, *470*
CALKINS, D. G. 708, *740*
CALLIDE-SIEUZAC, C. 882, *900*
CALVIN, M. 92, *97,* 320, 321, 322, 325, 326, 327, 328, 332, 333, 334, 335, *455, 456, 457, 467, 468, 470, 475,* 664, 665, 666, *673, 674, 677,* 921, *937, 938*
CALVO, J. M. 24, *38*
CAMA, H. R. 671, *675*
CAMBIE, R. C. 868, 871, 872, *898*
CAMERON, D. W. 872, 873, *898,* 1040, *1060*
CAMIENER, G. W. 681, *734*
CAMMARANO, P. 511, *528*
CAMPAGNARI, F. 125, 126, *191*
CAMPBELL, A. N. 855, *897*
CAMPBELL, D. H. 483, *527*
CAMPBELL, J. M. 1069, *1077*
CAMPBELL, L. L. 697, *734*
CAMPBELL, M. 289, *312*
CAMPBELL, P. L. 507, *534*
CAMPBELL, P. N. 486, 516, 520, *527, 528, 533, 534, 535*
CAMPILLO-CAMPBELL, A. DEL 646, *673*
CAMPO, R. D. 444, *457*
CANALE-PAROLA, E. 371, 415, *457*
CANDY, D. J. 362, 366, 372, 373, 391, 425, *457*
CANELLAKIS, E. S. 76, *97,* 544, 545, 552, 553, 555, 560, 561, 562, 563, *579, 581, 582, 583, 584, 587*
CANELLAKIS, Z. N. 561, 562, 563, *583, 584*
CANELLOS, G. P. 180, *195*
CANFIELD, R. E. 514, *528*
CANN, M. C. 226, *243*
CANNING, L. C. 521, *529*
CANNON, J. R. 299, 301, *307,* 711, *733*

CANNON, M. 512, 517, *528*
CANTAROW, A. 76, *100*
CANTONI, G. L. 7, 8, *38*, *41*, 498, *528*, *534*, 543, 558, *578*, *583*, *635*, *636*
CAPSTACK, E., Jr. 225, *243*, 879, 890, 892, *899*
CAPUTTO, R. 92, *97*, 344, 353, 354, 355, *457*, *474*
CARA, M. P. 868, *898*
CARBON, J. A. 556, *582*
CARBONNE, J. U. 288, *308*
CARDINAL, R. 289, *310*
CARDINI, C. E. 91, 92, *97*, 344, 349, 351, 352, 353, 354, 355, 361, 371, 372, 374, 375, 382, 389, 390, 399, 402, 403, 404, 405, 406, 411, 419, 434, 445, *457*, *458*, *460*, *466*, *471*, *474*, *639*
CARDINI, E. E. 598, *636*
CARDON, S. Z. 1074, *1077*
CAREY, F. G. 91, 92, *97*
CAREY, J. B., Jr. 238, *245*
CARLE, A. 812, 818, 819, 820, 821, 822, *825*
CARLSEN, E. N. 518, 519, *528*
CARLSON, A. S. 376, 379, 407, 411, *462*
CARLSON, D. M. 93, *97*, 357, 362, 375, 438, *458*, *464*
CARLSON, G. L. 22, *38*, 682, *734*
CARLTON, B. 37, *38*
CARLTON, B. C. 491, *535*
CARMINATTI, H. 371, 372, 402, 404, 405, 406, 416, *455*, *466*
CARNAHAN, J. E. 329, 330, *468*, *474*
CARO, L. G. 520, *528*
CARON, E. L. 1043, 1052, *1062*
CARPENTER, A. T. 259, 261, *307*
CARR, H. G. 153, *191*
CARR, S. 172, 182, 183, *193*, *198*
CARRINGTON, T. R. 376, 396, *456*
CARROLL, D. M. 290, 291, *311*
CARROLL, E. 57, *100*, 544, *579*
CARSIOTIS, M. 36, *38*
CARSS, B. 89, 90, *96*, 158, *189*
CARTER, A. C. 230, *244*
CARTER, C. E. 66, *97*
CARTER, H. E. 130, 136, 155, 165, 169, 170, *191*, *204*
CARTER, R. E. 1061
CARTWRIGHT, G. E. 265, *312*
CARTWRIGHT, N. J. 1034, *1061*
CASINOVI, C. 91, 92, 93, *96*
CASINOVI, G. C. 847, *896*, 1010, *1017*
CASPERSSON, T. 488, *528*
CASPI, E. 893, *900*
CASSERA, A. 1034, 1035, 1048, *1060*
CASTANERA, E. C. 717, *733*
CASTLE, M. 880, 881, *899*
CATHOU, R. E. 19, 20, 21, *39*, *40*

CATLIN, B. W. 548, *580*
CATTORETTI, E. 207, *241*
CAVALIERI, L. F. 541, 551, *578*, *580*
CAVALLINI, D. 9, *41*
CAVE, A. 883, *900*
CAVILL, G. W. K. 845, 847, *896*, 1010, *1017*
CECI, L. N. 24, 27, *43*
CEPURE, A. 94, *100*, 358, 361, 373, 378, 394, *469*
CERWINSKY, E. W. 483, *534*
CHAGOYA, V. 453, *581*
CHAIKOFF, I. L. 116, 124, 131, 132, 139, *191*, *195*, *198*, *202*, *205*, 211, 224, 233, 234, 235, *242*, *243*, *244*
CHAKRABARTI, J. 997, *1017*
CHAKRAVORTY, M. 446, *458*
CHAMBERLAIN, J. W. 868, 871, *898*
CHAMBERLAIN, M. 563, 564, 567, 568, 569, 570, *580*, *584*, *585*
CHAMBERLIN, M. 546
CHAMBERS, K. 1040, 1053, *1061*
CHAMBERS, R. W. 556, *577*
CHAN, E. 37, *44*
CHAN, F. L. 821, *825*
CHAN, P. C. 707, *737*
CHAN, W. R. 868, *898*
CHANDLER, B. 541, 569, *578*
CHANDLER, B. L. 542, *578*
CHANDLER, B. V. 647, *676*
CHANDLER, J. P. 140, *193*
CHANDORKAR, K. R. 403, 412, *455*
CHANDRA, G. R. 507, *535*
CHANDRASEKHR, B. 566, *587*
CHANG, V. M. 569, *586*, 597, *639*
CHANNON, H. J. 208, 211, *241*
CHANTRENNE, H. 488, *527*, *528*
CHAO, F. C. 36, *39*
CHAPEVILLE, F. 498, *528*
CHAPLEN, P. 1035, *1061*
CHAPMAN, G. M. 981, *1015*
CHAPMAN, J. A. 520, *531*
CHARALAMPOUS, F. C. 160, *191*, 453, *458*, 726, *734*
CHARGAFF, E. 153, 173, 174, 178, *191*, *201*, 521, *529*, 539, 540, 542, *577*
CHATAGNER, F. 618, *636*
CHATTERJEE, A. N. 374, 430, *458*
CHATTERJEE, S. K. 522, *528*
CHAUDHURI, A. C. 228, *243*
CHAVCHANIDZE, V. V. 492, *528*
CHAYKIN, S. 209, *241*, 647, *673*, 844, *896*, 948, *951*, 962, *1022*
CHEFURKA, W. 123, *191*
CHELDELIN, V. H. 446, 450, *458*, *464*, 680, 693, 694, 698, 714, 724, *734*, *737*, *740*
CHEN, C. 885, *900*

CHEN, D. 788, 791, *799*
CHEN, I.-W. 160, *191*, 453, *458*, 726, *734*
CHEN, K. K. 629, *636*
CHEN, P. S. 228, *244*
CHEN, R. W. 235, *244*
CHEN, Y. T. 728, *736, 737, 738*
CHENG, T. 326, *463*
CHENG, T. Y. 551, *581*
CHENOWETH, R. G. 955, *1022*
CHERKOVA, M. 495, *533*
CHESTERS, C. G. C. 377, 416, *458*
CHIANG, C. 449, *458*
CHIANG-HSIA, S. 486, *531*
CHICHESTER, C. O. 641, 645, 646, 647, 648,
  649, 654, 658, 659, 663, 665, 669, *673,
  676, 677, 678, 855, 897*
CHIDESTER, J. L. 566, *587*
CHIRIBOGA, J. 371, 382, 389, *457*
CHIRITĂ, A. 821, 822, *823*
CHISHOLM, M. D. 796, *799*, 958, *1023*
CHIU, T. H. 345, *458*
CHOJNACKI, T. 144, 149, 154, *189, 191*
CHOLNOKY, L. 663, 665, 666, *673*
CHOPARD-DIT-JEAN, L. H. 331, *465*
CHOW, T. C. 944, *951*
CHRIST, E. J. 116, *191*
CHRISTENSEN, H. N. 485, 486, *528, 533*
CHRISTIAN, W. 51, *101*
CHRISTMAN, D. R. 961, 962, 963, *1017,
  1022*
CHUNG, A. E. 122, *191*
CHUNG, C. W. 565, *584*
CIEGLER, A. J. 658, *673*
CIFONELLI, J. A. 91, 92, *97, 99*, 373, 425,
  443, *458, 466, 471*
CIOTTI, M. N. 693, *737, 742*
CLAES, H. Z. 661, 662, 670, *673*
CLAIRE, F. M. 796, *799*
CLAPP, J. W. 593, *636*
CLARE, N. T. 630, *636*
CLARK, B. 124, 128, 129, 130, 150, 157,
  191, 196
CLARK, C. 976, *1017*
CLARK, J. M. 498, *528*
CLARK, L. C. 208, *241*
CLARK, M. F. 510, *528*
CLARK-LEWIS, J. W. 807, *825*
CLARKE, D. D. *939*
CLARKE, E. A. 1008, *1017*
CLARKE, I. D. 822, *824, 827*
CLAYTON, R. B. 215, 220, 221, *242, 243*,
  845, 873, *896, 899*
CLEGG, J. S. 372, 391, *458*
CLELAND, W. W. 171, *191*
CLEMEDSON, C. J. 618, *636*
CLEMENT, J. H. 985, *1016*
CLEMENTS, J. H. 1003, *1016*

CLEMO, G. R. 846, 848, *896*
CLEZY, P. S. 270, 271, *307*
CLICK, E. M. 10, 11, *42*
CLICK, R. E. *528*
COCHRAN, D. W. 566, *587*
COCKBAIN, E. G. 650, *673*, 948, *951*
COCKBAIN, F. G. 948, *951*
CODNER, R. C. 1032, 1043, *1062*
COHAN, M. S. 6, *43*
COHEN, A. 424, *458*
COHEN, A. E. 552, *581*
COHEN, E. 485, 520, *530*
COHEN, G. N. 17, 18, 25, 27, *38, 41, 42*
COHEN, L. H. 66, *97*
COHEN, P. P. *38, 39, 40*, 72, *99*, 178, *191*,
  592, 608, *636, 637*
COHEN, S. 482, 484, *528, 739*
COHEN, S. S. 446, *458, 461*, 501, *528*, 539,
  542, 560, *577, 583*
COHEN, T. 815, 818, *823*, 981, 989, *1015*
COHEN-BAZIRE, G. 273, *307*, 462, 657,
  660, 664, *675*
COHN, D. V. 183, 185, *196*, 521, *530*
COHN, M. 140, *193*, 342, 383, *458*, 488,
  528
COHN, R. 625, *636*
COHN, W. E. 543, 556, *578, 582*
COLBURN, R. W. 32, 34, *38*
COLEMAN, M. H. 106, *191*
COLEMAN, R. 128, 129, *191*
COLLIE, J. N. 745, 751, 797, 1026, *1061*
COLLINS, F. D. 146, 147, 164, 165, *191,
  192*
COLODZIN, M. 163, *192*
COLOWICK, S. P. 78, *97*, 342, 343, 353,
  456, 458, 692, 693, *737, 742*
COLVIN, J. R. 354, 415, *458, 464*
COMB, D. G. 91, *97*, 173, *192, 201*, 350,
  352, 361, 436, 437, *458*, 508, *528*
COMFORT, A. 251, *307*
COMLY, L. T. 511, *530*
COMTE, P. 805, *824*
CONN, E. E. 788, *799*, 804, *824*, 957, *1019*
CONNEY, A. H. *527*
CONROY, H. 968, 997, *1017*
CONSTANTIN, J. M. 146, *192*
CONSTANTOPOULOS, G. 227, 228, *243*
CONWAY, E. 657, *675*
CONWAY, T. 512, *532*
CONWAY, T. W. 512, *528*
COOK, A. H. 1054, *1061*
COOK, J. W. 1065, 1066, *1077*
COOK, W. H. 178, *192*
COOKSON, G. H. 257, 261, *307*
COOKSON, R. C. 871, *898*
COOLEY, S. L. 618, *639*
COOMBER, J. 268, *312*

COOMBS, H. I.   615, *636*
COON, M. J.   208, *241,* 646, *673, 674,* 697, *738, 740,* 945, 946, *951,* 961, *1021*
COON, M. S.   646, *673*
COOPER, C.   520, *528*
COOPER, J. R.   345, *473,* 921, *939*
COOPER, R. L.   1068, 1069, 1074, *1077*
COOPER, S.   566, 567, *584*
CORCORAN, J. W.   299, 307, 711, *734, 741,* 1041, *1061, 1062*
COREY, E. J.   876, 877, 878, 879, 884, *899, 900*
CORI, C. F.   342, 343, 352, 353, 370, 379, 384, 385, 587, 397, 398, 399, 400, 401, 402, 410, 411, *455, 456, 457, 458, 459, 462, 463, 464, 465, 472*
CORI, G. T.   342, 343, 352, 353, 370, 379, 384, 385, 397, 398, 399, 400, 402, 411, *458, 461, 462, 463, 464, 465, 472*
CORI, O.   52, 97, 347, *458*
CORMAN, J.   341, *458*
CORNFORTH, J.   949, *951*
CORNFORTH, J. W.   125, 173, *192,* 209, 210, 214, 218, *241, 242,* 647, 648, 650, *673, 674, 676,* 844, *896,* 1040, 1047, *1061*
CORNFORTH, R. H.   209, 214, *241, 242,* 647, 648, 650, *673, 674, 676,* 844, *896,* 1040, 1047, *1061*
CORNTHWAITE, D.   804, *824*
CORONADO, A.   15, *38,* 520, *528*
CORRAN, A. J.   1044, *1060*
CORRIVAUX, D.   18, *38*
CORTIS-JONES, B.   277, 278, 280, *310*
CORWIN, A. H.   261, 262, *310*
COSBY, E. L.   324, *473*
COSCIA, C. J.   905, 929, 930, *937*
COSTES, C.   866, *898*
COTTRELL, M.   237, *245*
COUCH, J. R.   710, *734*
COUGHLIN, C. A.   23, *37*
COULON, A.   166, *202*
COULSON, C. B.   916, *937*
COULTHARD, C. E.   448, *458*
COUSIN, H.   930, *937*
COUTSOGEORGOPOULOS, C.   555, 562, *582*
COWARD, K. H.   727, 728, *740*
COWIE, D. B.   485, *530*
COX, R. A.   502, *528*
COYLE, T.   944, *951*
COYNE, B. A.   485, *528*
CRABBÉ, P.   835, 846, 848, 860, 863, 879, *895, 896*
CRADDOCK, V. M.   486, 487, *528*
CRAIG, J.   407, *465*
CRAIG, J. A.   694, 698, *734*
CRAIG, J. W.   407, *458*
CRAINE, E. M.   92, *98*

CRAMER, F.   493, 512, *528*
CRAMER, J. W.   593, *636*
CRANE, F. L.   331, *458*
CRANE, R. K.   343, *473*
CRATHORN, A. R.   520, *528*
CRAVEN, G. R.   519, *528*
CRAVIOTO, J.   481, 487, *535*
CRAWFORD, I. P.   36, *38,* 685, *734, 742*
CRAWFORD, M. A.   609, *637*
CREASER, E. H.   488, *528*
CREASEY, N. G.   1044, *1060*
CREASEY, W. A.   124, *192*
CRESPI, A. M.   958, *1017*
CRESPI, H. L.   291, 292, *307, 309*
CRESSON, E. L.   719, 721, *742, 952*
CREVELING, C. R.   360, *459*
CRICK, F. H. C.   492, *528,* 541, 547, 550, *577*
CRITTENDEN, E. R. S.   400, *460*
CROCCO, R. M.   507, *529*
CROCKEN, B. J.   149, *192*
CROCKER, T. T.   488, *529*
CROMWELL, B. T.   142, *192,* 968, *1017*
CRONYN, M.   935, *938*
CROSBIE, G. W.   544, *579*
CROSS, B. E.   868, 869, 870, *898*
CROSSLEY, M. L.   619, *639*
CROUT, D. H. G.   972, *1017*
CROWDER, M.   148, *192*
CROWLEY, M. P.   855, *897*
CRUICKSHANK, E. M.   *738*
CRUICKSHANK, J. G.   570, *586*
CUBILES, R.   693, *740*
CUMMINGS, W.   813, *824*
CUMMINS, J. T.   450, *458,* 698, *734*
CUNNINGHAM, L.   548, *580*
CURRAN, G. L.   208, *241*
CURTIS, R. F.   1027, 1028, *1061*
CUTOLO, E.   92, *99,* 355, *468, 636*
CYNKIN, M. A.   446, *459*

D'ABRAMO, F.   441, *458*
D'ADAMO, A. F.   963, *1017*
DAHL, J. L.   363, *461*
DALGLEISH, C. E.   487, 488, *528,* 686, 687, 688, *734*
DALTON, L. K.   762, *798*
DALY, J.   624, *638*
DALY, J. W.   622, *636*
DANCEWICZ, A. M.   257, *309*
DANCHEVA, K. I.   495, *533*
DANE, E.   1066, *1078*
DANFORTH, W. H.   401, 406, 407, *458, 459*
DANGSCHAT, G.   802, 803, *824*
DANIEL, H.   130, *189*
DANIEL, V.   561, *583*

DANIELSSON, H.   238, 239, *245*
DANKERT, M.   358, 407, *459, 469, 471*
DANON, D.   415, *469*
D'ARI, L.   374, 432, *469*
DARK, F. A.   427, *473*
DARLING, S.   28, *38*
DARMSTADT, R. A.   544, 545, *579*
DARNELL, J. E.   566, *584, 585*
DARROW, R. A.   360, *459*
DAS, H. K.   522, *528*
DAUBEN, W. G.   211, 218, 219, 223, 233,
   235, *242, 243, 244,* 863, 886, 887, *897,*
   900
DAUGHADAY, W. H.   160, *192,* 725, *734*
DAUS, L. L.   92, *97*
DAVENPORT, J. B.   858, *897*
DAVID, R.   882, *900*
DAVID, S.   1052, *1060*
DAVIDOFF, D.   121, *192*
DAVIDOFF, F. F.   121, *192*
DAVIDSON, A. G.   216, 222, *242, 243*
DAVIDSON, D. W.   507, *534*
DAVIDSON, E. A.   92, *98,* 352, 361, 363,
   401, 441, *459, 464, 469*
DAVIDSON, J. N.   539, 542, 552, 553, *577,*
   581
DAVIDSON, P. F.   542, *578*
DAVIE, E. W.   521, *534*
DAVIES, B. D.   1040, 1052, *1061*
DAVIES, D. D.   804, *823*
DAVIES, D. R.   551, *580*
DAVIES, J. E.   760, *798*
DAVIES, M. C.   510, 511, *527*
DAVIS, B. D.   25, 32, 34, *38, 41,* 684, 706,
   734, 748, 749, 797, 804, 808, *824, 826,*
   905, 907, 910, 911, 912, 920, 921, 922,
   923, 926, *937, 938, 939*
DAVIS, B. R.   871, 872, *898*
DAVIS, E. M.   230, *244*
DAVIS, F. F.   543, *578*
DAVIS, J. B.   655, 656, *674*
DAVIS, P.   641, *676*
DAVISON, A. N.   184, 188, *192*
DAVISON, P. F.   541, *578*
DAWKINS, A. W.   1049, *1061*
DAWSON, A. M.   124, *202*
DAWSON, R. F.   959, 961, 962, 963, 964,
   1016, 1017, 1022
DAWSON, R. M. C.   105, 127, 136, 137,
   139, 140, 142, 153, 154, 160, 162, 163, 185,
   189, 192, 193, 203, 725, *735*
DAY, A. C.   *1063*
DAY, H. G.   385, *463*
DAYTON, P. G.   730, *735*
DEAN, F. M.   771, *798,* 1035, *1061*
DEARDEN, M. J.   858, *897*
DEASY, C. L.   482, 483, 485, *527*

DEBUCH, H.   119, 135, 139, 166, 174, 176,
   192, 197
DE CASTRO, F. T.   687, *734*
DECHAVASSINE, M.   627, *635*
DECKER, K.   107, *199*
DECKER, R. H.   687, *734*
DECKERS, W.   832, 889, *894*
DEDEKEN, R. H.   11, 12, *38*
DEDONDER, R.   371, 382, 417, 418, 419,
   459, 470
DEDONDER, R. A.   416, *459, 471*
DEEDS, E.   624, 625, *635*
DE FEKETE, M. A. R.   403, 404, 406, *460,*
   466, 471
DEFFNER, G.   807, 818, *824*
DE FLORA, A.   324, *457*
DEFRANCHESCHI, A.   629, *636*
DE GARILHE, M. P.   548, *580*
DEGIER, J.   148, *200*
DE GIOVANNI, R.   548, *580*
DEHAAS, G. H.   192
DEICHMILLER, M. P.   482, *528*
DEKKER, C. A.   539, *577*
DEKKER, E. E.   646, 654, *673, 674*
DEKKER, K.   *674*
DEKONING, A. J.   165, *192*
DE LA HABA, G.   8, *38,* 54, *100,* 324, *470*
DE LA HABA, G. L.   516, *535*
DELALLA, O. F.   178, *192*
DELAUMENY, J.-M.   122, *194*
DELAVIER-KLUTCHKO, C.   9, 10, 19, *38,*
   39
DELBRÜCK, A.   *194,* 440, 441, *461, 462*
DELBRUCK, M.   541, *577*
DELEY, J.   447, 448, *456, 459*
DELLUVA, A. M.   59, *97, 101*
DELUCA, H. F.   163, *194*
DELWICHE, C. C.   142, *192*
DELWICHE, E. A.   722, *734*
DEMAIN, A. L.   28, 29, *42*
DE MATTEIS, F.   273, *307*
DEMAYO, P.   858, 862, *897,* 1030, *1060*
DE MEIO, R. H.   440, *459,* 597, 612, 618,
   636
DEMMLER, K.   *826*
DE MONTELLANO, P. R. O.   879, *899*
DEMOSS, J. A.   35, *38*
DE MOSS, R. D.   446, *459*
DEMPSEY, M. E.   216, 223, *242*
DEMPSEY, W. B.   724, *734*
DENAMUR, R.   91, 92, 93, *97*
DENNIS, D. T.   870, *898*
DEROBICHON-SZULMAJSTER, H.   17, 18, 25,
   38, 40, *42,* 92, *99,* 360, *467*
DERRIEN, E.   289, *307*
DESLONGCHAMPS, P.   971, *1015*
DESNUELLE, P.   124, 129, 130, 146, *188, 192*

DE STEVENS, G. 904, 917, 920, 926, 933, 936, *937*, *938*
DESZYCK, E. J. 1076, *1077*, *1078*
DEUEL, H. J. 670, *674*
DEUEL, H. R., Jr. 104, 105, 106, 132, 133, 135, 138, 139, 140, *192*, *200*
DEUTSCH, J. F. 541, *578*
DEVI, A. 553, *581*
DE WAARD, A. 108, *198*, *204*, 647, *676*
DEWEY, D. L. 25, *38*, *44*
DEWEY, L. J. 936, *937*, 955, 964, *1017*, *1019*
DEWEY, V. C. 704, *734*
DEYKIN, D. 132, *194*
DEZANI, S. 207, *241*
DHALIWAL, A. S. 566, *587*
DIAMOND, I. 288, *311*
DICKENS, F. 97, 345, *459*
DICKENSON, P. B. 950, *951*
DICKERMAN, H. 22, *44*
DICKERSON, A. G. 419, *459*
DICKHART, W. 875, *899*
DICKINSON, B. 395, 396, *455*
DICKMAN, S. R. 24, 27, *42*, 520, *528*
DIECKMANN, M. 495, 496, 497, 498, 508, 527, *532*, 561, *583*
DIETZEL, E. 307
DIGIROLOMO, A. 94, *96*, 501, 503, *528*
DIGIROLOMO, M. 94, *96*
DILLER, E. R. 131, *198*
DILS, R. R. 112, 116, 141, 150, 157, *192*, *193*, *196*, *202*
DIMARCO, A. 711, 715, 716, *733*, *734*
DIMILIA, A. 496, *533*
DINGMAN, C. W. 503, *527*
DINNING, J. S. 718, *734*, *741*
DINTZIS, H. M. 514, 515, *532*
DI PRISCO, G. 687, *741*
DISRAELY, M. N. 707, *741*
DITTMER, J. C. 137, *192*, *193*
DITTMER, K. 719, 720, *734*, *735*, *739*
DITURI, F. 209, *241*, 647, *674*, 946, *951*
DIXON, F. J. 482, *528*
DJAO, E. H. 884, *900*
DJERASSI, C. 216, *242*, 832, 856, 860, 867, 868, 871, 877, 878, *894*, *897*, *898*, *899*, 976, *1017*, 1041, 1048, *1061*, *1062*
DOBBING, J. 188, *192*
DÖBEREINER, U. 366, *462*
DOBROGOSZ, W. J. 446, *459*
DOBSON, T. A. 979, *1015*
DOCTOR, B. P. 496, 497, *528*
DOCTOR, V. M. 709, *734*
DODGE, L. W. 620, *637*
DODYK, F. 375, 438, *455*
DOERFLER, W. 502, *528*
DOERING, W. VON E. 228, *244*

DOERR, N. 777, *798*
DOERSCHUK, A. P. 595, *636*, 728, *736*
DOETCH, R. N. 23, *37*
DOI, A. 403, *459*
DOI, K. 403, 412, *459*
DOI, R. H. 507, *528*, 566, *584*
DOISY, E. A. 448, *471*
DOLBY, L. J. 996, *1022*
DOLEZILOVA, L. 1041, *1061*, *1062*
DOLIN, M. I. 557, *583*
DOMAGK, G. F. 350, *459*
DONALDSON, K. O. 19, 20, 21, *38*
DONATI, G. J. 709, *741*
DONDON, J. 556, *582*
DONDON, L. 556, *582*
DONISCH, V. 145, 149, 152, 153, 154, *193*, *201*
DONNIGER, C. 650, *674*
DONOVAN, F. W. 748, 751, 758, 760, 770, 797, *798*, 805, 807, 808, *823*, 1026, *1060*
DORFMAN, A. 91, 92, *97*, *99*, 373, 425, 426, 441, 443, 444, *458*, *459*, *466*, *470*, *471*, *472*
DORFMAN, R. I. 228, 230, 233, *243*, *244*
DOROUGH, G. D. 665, 666, *674*
DOTY, P. 541, *578*
DOUDOROFF, M. 362, 370, 376, 377, 383, 389, 390, 391, 414, 446, 448, *459*, *460*, *462*, *469*, *475*, *476*, 944, *952*
DOUGHERTY, E. C. 290, *306*
DOUGLAS, H. C. 8, *41*, 660, *674*
DOUNCE, A. L. 488, *528*
DOW, D. S. 116, *196*
DOWNIE, E. D. 521, *532*
DOY, C. H. 34, 35, *38*, *39*, *41*, 684, 685, *735*
DRABKIN, D. L. 286, *307*, *313*, 487, 504, *531*
DRAPER, P. 438, 439, *459*
DRESEL, E. I. B. 249, 254, 261, 264, *307*, *308*, 711, *735*
DREWES, S. E. 820, *824*
DREYER, W. J. 35, 36, 37, *38*, 492, 493, 494, *527*
DREYFUS, J.-C. 484, 485, 486, 502, *531*, *533*
DREYFUSS, J. 10, 11, *39*
DRISCOLL, C. A. 719, 721, *742*
DROZ, B. 520, *535*
DRUMMEY, G. D. 180, *202*
DRUMMOND, G. I. 400, *459*
DUBECK, M. 955, *1017*
DUCAY, E. D. 486, *531*
DUCHOW, E. 660, *674*
DUCK-CHONG, C. 483, *528*
DUER, I. 946, *951*
DULANEY, E. L. 571, *586*

DULBECCO, R. 542, *578*
DULIT, E. 216, 222, *242, 243*
DUNCAN, A. M. 592, 598, *636*
DUNN, D. B. *528*, 548, 571, 572, *580, 586*
DUNN, G. 1054, *1062*
DUPERON, R. 883, *900*
DURAISWAMI, D. 58, *96*
DURBIN, R. 447, *460, 461*
DURELL, J. 7, *38*
DURHAM, L. J. 976, *1017*
DURR, A. 879, *899*
DURR, F. 646, *674*
DURR, I. F. 209, *241*
DUTCHER, J. D. 1041, *1061*
DUTTON, G. J. 92, 97, *101*, 355, 375, 435, *459, 473*, 592, 595, 596, 597, 598, *636, 638*
DUTTON, H. J. 120, *193*
DUVIGNEAUD, V. 140, *193*, 719, 720, *734, 735, 739*
DVORKIN, B. 508, *532*
DZIEWIATKOWSKI, D. O. 438, 439, 444, *457, 459*, 595, *636*

EADE, R. A. 771, *798*
EAGLE, H. 76, *101*, 485, *528*, 725, *735*
EAKIN, E. A. 719, *735*
EAKIN, R. E. 58, 61, *101*, 680, 719, *735*, 742
EASTHAM, J. F. 235, *244*
EBERHARDT, G. 910, 911, 924, 927, 929, *937*
EBERHARDT, K. H. 889, *901*
EBERT, K. H. 413, *459*
EBNÖTHER, A. 758, *798*
ECKERT, R. 810, *826*
EDELMAN, G. M. 519, *528*
EDELMAN, I. S. 507, *532*
EDELMAN, J. 377, 396, 409, 419, *459*
EDER, H. A. 181, *195*
EDMONDS, M. 57, *96*, 560, 562, 563, 565, 572, *583, 584, 586*
EDMUNDOWICZ, J. M. 450, *459*
EDSON, N. L. 450, *455, 467*
EDSTROM, R. D. 375, 432, 433, *459*
EDWARDS, J. A. 832, *894*
EDWARDS, P. N. 832, *894*, 998, 999, 1000, 1003, *1017, 1019*
EDWARDS, S. 452, *470*
EFIMOCHKINA, E. F. 686, *735*
EGAMI, F. 10, *44*
EGGE, H. 175, *198*
EGGERER, H. 209, 210, *241*, 647, 648, *672, 676*, 722, *741*, 833, 835, 844, 845, 857, *894, 896*, 948, *951, 952*
EGGERS, H. J. 566, 568, *584*
EGI, N. 593, *636*

EHRENSTEIN, M. 233, *244*
EHRENSVARD, G. 71, *99*, 706, *741*, 907, 908, *939*
EHRET, A. 10, 11, *40*
EHRHARDT, M. 989, *1020*
EICHHORN, J. 228, *243*
EICHHORN, M. M. 446, *459*
EIGNER, E. A. 487, 496, *531*
EIKENBERRY, E. K. 509, 512, *528*
EIL, J. D. 556, *582*
EILER, J. J. 153, *191*
EINARSSON, K. 238, *245*
EISEN, H. N. 520, *530*
EISENBERG, F., Jr. 160, *193*, 413, 418, 453, *459*, 726, 730, *735*
EISENBERG, M. A. 719, *735*
EISENBRAUN, E. J. 871, *898*, 1010, *1017*
EISENBRAUN, J. 1041, *1062*
EISENSTADT, J. M. 523, *527*, 542, *578*
EISNER, T. 846, *896*
EL-BASYOUNI, S. Z. 791, *799*
ELBEIN, A. D. 93, *98*, 364, 365, 371, 415, 432, *456, 459, 462*
ELBERFELD, H. 36, *39*
ELDER, J. A. 839, *895*
ELFORD, H. L. 21, 22, *40*, 719, 720, *735*
ELLINGBOE, J. 156, *193*
ELLIOTT, R. F. 269, 289, *308*
ELLIOTT, W. H. 238, *245*
ELLIS, R. B. 137, 162, *193, 195*
ELLS, V. R. 631, *637*
ELSON, D. 543, *579*
ELVEHJEM, C. A. 682, *738*
ELWYN, D. 140, 141, 151, 154, 156, *193*, 200, 204, 485, *531*
EMDE, H. 836, 857, *895*
EMERSON, O. H. 624, 625, *635*
EMERSON, R. 289, 292, *307, 308*, 334, *459*
ENDRES, H. 807, 818, *824*
ENER, M. 221, *243*
ENGEL, L. L. 228, 230, *244*
ENGELBERG, H. 504, 518, *527*
ENGELBRECHT, L. 1006, *1022*
ENGLANDER, J. J. 498, *528*
ENGLANDER, S. W. 498, *528*
ENGLARD, S. 703, *737*
ENGLISH, R. J. 768, 784, *798*, 842, 846, 852, *895*, 1034, 1038, 1039, 1046, 1053, *1060*
ENNIS, H. L. 514, *531*
ENRIONE, J. 565, *584*
ENSIGN, J. C. 690, *735*
ENTENMAN, C. 124, 142, *205*, 544, *579*
ENTNER, N. 556, *582*
EPHRUSSI-TAYLOR, H. 541, *578*
EPSTEIN, C. J. 518, 519, *529*
EPSTEIN, R. 507, *529*

EPSTEIN, S. S. 716, *735*
ERBLAND, J. 127, 135, 147, 150, 158, *199*
ERDTMAN, H. 793, *799*, 930, 933, *937*
ERGE, D. 1006, *1018*
ERICKSON, R. E. 331, *474*
ERICKSON, R. L. 566, *585*
ERICSON, K. B. 573, *586*
ERIKSSON, K. G. 544, 572, *579*, *586*
ERIKSSON-QUENSEL, I. B. 290, 291, *308*
ERRARA, M. 510, 511, *535*
ERWIN, J. 117, 118, 119, 120, *193*, *196*
ERWIN, M. J. 66, *97*
ESCHENMOSER, A. 213, 214, *242*, 858, 860, 875, 876, *897*, *899*
ESPADA, J. 90, *97*, 358, *460*
ESPOSITO, R. G. 704, *735*
ESSERY, J. M. 958, 962, *1017*
ESTABROOK, R. W. 123, *193*
ETINGOF, R. N. 696, *738*
EUGSTER, C. H. 641, 656, *674*, *675*
EUW, J. V. 885
EVANS, A. 507, *534*, 567, 568, 569, 571, *585*
EVANS, C. 728, *734*
EVANS, G. W. 979, *1016*
EVANS, T. H. 412, *460*
EVANS, W. C. 803, *824*, 916, *937*, 961, *1017*
EVELYN, S. R. 815, 818, 819, 820, *824*, *826*
EVERETT, G. A. 497, 498, 499, *530*, 543, *578*
EYKMAN, J. F. 908, *937*
EYLAR, E. H. 412, 436, *460*
EYRING, E. J. 23, *43*
EYRING, H. 666, *676*
EYSTER, C. 335, 336, *474*
EYZAGUIRRE, J. P. 489, *528*

FAHIEN, L. A. *39*
FAIGLE, H. 920, *938*
FAILEY, R. B. 629, *636*
FAIRBAIRN, J. W. 968, 979, *1017*
FALASCHI, A. 570, 571, *586*
FALES, H. M. 955, 957, 985, 986, 1006, *1015*, *1016*, *1017*
FALK, J. E. 249, 254, 261, 264, *307*, *308*, *311*, 711, *735*
FALK, K. 745, *797*
FANCHER, H. 546, *580*
FANSHIER, D. 92, *100*
FANTES, K. H. 715, 716, *735*
FARBER, E. 504, *535*
FARKAS, W. 26, *39*
FARRAR, K. R. 1054, *1060*
FARRELL, D. G. 424, *455*
FARRELL, G. L. 228, *244*
FAUCONNEAU, G. 91, 92, 93, *97*

FAULKNER, P. 344, 351, *460*, 495, *529*
FAULKNER, R. 508, 522, *526*
FAURE, M. 136, *193*, *200*
FAVORSKY, A. E. *894*
FAVRE-BONVIN, J. 805, *824*
FAZAKERLEY, S. 671, *674*
FEELEY, J. 507, *531*
FEFFERMAN, R. 544, 572, *579*
FEHR, T. 1006, *1017*
FEIGE, A. 962, *1018*
FEIGELSON, P. 487, 488, *529*, 686, *735*
FEINGOLD, D. S. 92, *97*, *100*, 345, 354, 355, 356, 363, 364, 371, 372, 377, 378, 394, 416, 417, 418, 420, 421, 422, 423, 424, 447, *455*, *458*, *460*, *461*, *463*, *464*, *468*, *473*
FELDBRUEGGE, D. H. 880, *899*
FELDMAN, R. 1069, *1078*
FELIX, D. 858, 860, *897*
FELLIG, J. 172, *203*
FELSENFELD, H. 174, *204*, 437, *475*
FENTON, J. L. B. 273, *308*
FENWICK, M. L. 566, *585*
FERGER, M. F. 483, 512, *530*
FERGUSON, J. 946, *951*
FERGUSON, J. J. 209, *241*, 646, 647, *674*, *677*
FERNÁNDEZ-MORGAN, H. 136, 178, *193*
FERRARI, R. A. 130, *190*
FERRIER, R. J. 326, 450, *468*
FESSENDEN, J. M. 514, *534*
FESSENDEN, M. 512, *529*
FESTENSTEIN, G. N. 240, *245*
FIEDLER, H. *639*
FIELD, H., Jr. 132, *203*
FIELDING, B. C. 1035, 1058, *1062*
FIELDING, L. 155, 157, *190*
FIESER, L. F. 233, *244*
FIESER, M. 233, *244*
FIGARD, P. H. 140, 141, 148, *190*, *194*
FIGDOR, S. K. 832, *894*
FIGGE, F. H. 273, *312*
FILMER, D. B. 630, *636*
FINCH, A. C. M. 818, *823*
FINCHAM, J. R. S. 13, *39*
FINDLAY, M. 162, 185, *193*
FINDLAY, W. P. K. 909, *937*
FINEAN, J. B. 136, 178, 182, *193*
FINEBERG, R. A. 519, *529*
FINELLI, V. N. 160, *195*, 726, *736*
FINK, K. 697, *735*
FINK, R. M. 697, *735*
FINKELSTEIN, J. 694, *741*
FIRTH, M. E. 173, *192*
FISCHER, A. G. 957, 985, *1022*
FISCHER, E. 593, *636*
FISCHER, E. H. 400, 401, 402, *460*, *464*, *465*, *467*, *476*, 484, *527*

FISCHER, E. N.   400, *461*
FISCHER, G. A.   19, *39*
FISCHER, H.   269, 270, *308*
FISCHER, H. O. L.   725, *735*, 802, 803, *824*
FISCHER, R.   1004, 1006, *1021*
FISCHER, W.   361, *460*
FISH, C. A.   219, *242*
FISH, W. A.   216, 222, *242, 243*
FISHEL, J. B.   1072, *1077*
FISHER, F. G.   866, *898*
FISHER, H.   251
FISHER, J. M.   516, *532*
FISHER, L. R.   672, *675*
FISHLER, M. C.   142, *205*, 544, *579*
FISHMAN, J.   861, *897*, 1048, *1062*
FISOS, H. G.   789, *799*
FITCH, W. M.   494, *529*
FITELSON, J.   875, *899*
FITT, P. S.   557, *583*
FITTING, C.   370, 377, 391, 414, *460*
FITTON, P.   1034, 1035, 1037, *1060, 1061*
FLAKS, J. G.   66, *97*
FLAVIN, M.   9, 16, 19, *39*, 109, *193*
FLEEKER, J.   962, *1017*
FLEISCHER, S.   178, *194*, 484, *529*
FLEISNER, E.   572, 573, *586*
FLES, D. A.   641, *676*
FLETCHER, A. M.   704, *735*
FLETCHER, M. J.   483, *529*
FLING, M.   18, *39, 43*
FLOKSTRA, J. M.   936, *937*
FLORINI, J. R.   508, 510, 511, *527, 529*
FLORKIN, M.   *636*
FLOSS, H.-G.   1004, 1006, *1017, 1021, 1022, 1023*
FLOYD, K. W.   718, *735*
FLURY, E.   1049, *1062*
FLYNN, K.   944, *952*
FODOR, G.   959, *1021*
FOLCH, J.   135, 136, 137, 138, 166, 172, 174, 182, 183, 185, *193, 198, 204*
FOLCH-PI, J.   182, 183, *193*
FOLIN, O.   481, *529*
FOLKBERG, K.   571, *586*
FOLKERS, K.   331, *474*, 647, *678*, 694, 721, *741, 742*, 843, *896, 952*, 1043, 1052, *1062*
FOLKES, J. P.   484, *529*
FOLTZ, R. L.   974, *1022*
FONKEN, G. J.   219, *242*, 887, *900*
FONTAINE, M.   289, *308*
FORCHIELLI, E.   230, *244*
FORD, J. E.   714, 715, *735*
FORK, D. C.   285, 290, *309*
FORMICA, J. V.   166, 167, *190*
FORREST, H. S.   23, *43*, 688, 701, 708, *735, 739, 741*

FORSYTH, W. G. C.   807, 815, 818, *824*
FOSTER, D. O.   338, *472*
FOSTER, D. W.   93, *97*, 361, *460*
FOSTER, E. M.   153, *204*
FOSTER, J. W.   26, *41*
FOSTER, M. A.   20, *39*
FOULKES, D. M.   978, *1016*
FOULKES, E. C.   277, 279, 280, 281, *308*
FOWDEN, L.   *39*
FOWLER, L. R.   832, *894*
FOX, C. F.   565, 567, 568, 569, 570, *584, 585*
FOX, C. L.   61, *101*
FOX, D. L.   *674*
FOX, F. C.   568, 570, *585*
FOX, G.   484, *529*
FRAENKEL, D.   432, *460*
FRAENKEL-CONRAT, H.   488, 494, 504, *526, 529, 534*
FRANCESCONI, L.   834, 838, *894*
FRANCIS, D. M.   507, *534*
FRANCIS, R. J.   977, 978, 981, 1003, *1015, 1016*
FRANK, O.   718, *739*
FRANKLIN, M.   566, *584*
FRANKLIN, R. E.   540, *577*
FRANKLIN, R. M.   566, 567, 568, *584, 585*
FRANKLIN, T. J.   592, 604, 605, 607, 629, *635*
FRANTZ, I. D., Jr.   216, 221, 222, 223, 240, *242, 243*
FRANZL, R. E.   135, *201*
FRASER, P. E.   618, *637*
FRECH, M. E.   693, *737*
FREDERICKSON, D. S.   132, 178, 179, 181, 182, *193, 201*, 235, 236, *244*
FREEDLAND, R. A.   91, 92, *98*
FREEMAN, N. K.   178, *198*
FREEMAN, T.   482, 484, *528*
FREINKEL, N.   160, *193*, 725, *735*
FRENCH, C. S.   268, 269, 289, *308, 312*
FRENCH, D.   379, 380, 384, 389, 392, 396, 409, *460, 469*
FRENCH, J. E.   182, *201*
FRESCO, J. R.   556, *582*
FREUDENBERG, K.   793, *799*, 807, 813, 814, 815, *824, 827*, 926, 931, 932, 933, 934, 936, *937, 938*
FREUNDLICH, M.   18, 24, *39*, 704, *735*
FREY, C. N.   680, *741*
FREY, M. J.   883, *900*
FREY-WYSSLING, A.   808, *824*, 834, *895*
FRIED, V. A.   509, *529*
FRIEDKIN, M.   19, *39, 43*, 140, *193*, 560, *583*
FRIEDLER, L.   601, *636*
FRIEDMAN, A. R.   955, 962, 989, *1017, 1019*

FRIEDMAN, D. 407, *465*
FRIEDMAN, D. L. 22, *42*, 405, 406, *460*
FRIEDMAN, E. 631, *636*
FRIEDMAN, H. C. 713, *735*
FRIEDMAN, M. 934, *938*
FRIEDMAN, S. M. 521, *529*
FRIEDRICH, W. 301, *308*
FRIEFELDER, D. 541, *578*
FRIEND, J. 668, *674*
FRITSCH, A. 419, *459*
FRITZSON, P. 697, *740*
FROMAGEOT, C. 618, *636*, 659, *674*
FRONTALI, L. 498, *527*
FRONTICELLI, C. 496, *533*
FROSOLONO, M. F. 156, *193*
FRUTON, J. S. 487, *529*
FRYDMAN, R. B. 358, 371, 375, 403, 405,
    411, 434, *460*
FRYER, R. I. 850, *896*, 1038, 1043, *1061*
FUCHS, E. 502, *528*
FUCHS, H. 687, *742*
FUJII, S. 362, *460*
FUJIMOTO, A. 353, 354, *460*
FUJIMOTO, M. *309*
FUJINO, Y. 165, 169, 170, *191*
FUJIOKI, T. 237, *245*
FUJITA, Y. 290, 291, 293, 294, *308*, *309*, 835,
    836, 837, 838, 840, 841, 865, *895*, *897*
FUJIWARA, T. 292, *308*
FUKUHARA, H. 502, 520, *532*, *535*
FUKUI, S. 447, *460*
FUKUI, T. 521, *529*
FUKUMOTO, K. 1003, *1018*
FUKUSHIMA, D. 777, *798*
FUKUSHIMA, D. K. 224, *243*
FUKUYAMA, T. 438, 439, *471*
FUKUZUMI, T. 865, *897*
FULCO, A. J. 118, *193*
FULD, M. 397, *467*
FULLER, R. C. 321, 330, *456*, *470*
FULLER, W. 498, *534*
FUNATSU, G. 504, *526*
FUOCO, L. 715, *733*
FURLONG, N. B. 552, *581*
FURMAN, R. H. 179, *195*
FURTH, J. J. 561, 563, 567, 568, 569, 571,
    583, *584*, *585*
FURUKAYA, Y. 435, *463*
FURUYA, T. 979, *1017*
FUTTERMAN, S. *735*

GABRIEL, O. 91, *97*, 368, *460*
GABY, W. L. 448, *471*, 521, *529*
GAFFRON, H. 334, *460*
GAISER, P. 712, 717, *733*
GAITONDE, M. K. 183, 184, 185, *193*, *194*

GAL, E. M. 140, *201*
GALANOS, D. S. 165, 170, *191*, *194*
GALE, E. F. 484, *529*
GALKOWSKII, T. T. 377, 396, *476*
GALLAGHER, C. H. *204*
GALLAGHER, T. F. 224, *243*, 620, *637*
GALLAI-HATCHARD, J. 148, *194*
GALLIARD, T. 159, 163, *194*
GALLOWAY, B. 92, *101*, 355, *472*
GALSTON, A. W. 834, 842, *894*, 941, 942,
    951
GALT, R. H. B. 869, 870, *898*, 1050, 1051,
    1062
GAMBAL, D. 152, *194*
GAMBLE, J. L. 208, *241*
GANAPARTI, K. 836, *895*
GANDER, J. E. 372, 392, *460*
GANGULI, N. C. 92, *97*, 355, *460*
GANGULY, J. 110, 112, 131, *200*, *204*,
    760, *798*
GANGULY, S. 715, *735*
GANT, D. E. 714, *735*
GANZ, A. 884, *900*
GAPONENKO, V. I. 269, *312*
GARBUS, J. 163, *194*
GARCIA-BUNUEL, L. 176, *191*
GARDIKAS, C. 277, 278, 295, *309*
GARDINER, R. C. 710, *733*
GARDNER, T. S. 745, *797*
GARFINKEL, D. 485, *529*
GARIBALDI, J. A. 379, *472*
GARNJOBST, L. 706, *741*, 907, 908, *939*
GARREN, L. D. 507, *529*
GARRICK, M. O. 36, *39*
GARRY, B. J. 29, *37*
GARTON, G. A. 659, 667, *674*
GASCOIGNE, J. A. 415, *457*, 835, 843, *895*,
    896
GASCOIGNE, R. M. 848, 876, *896*
GASSMAN, M. 257, 273, *308*
GAST, J. H. 618, *636*
GASTAMBIDE-ODIER, M. 122, *194*
GATENBECK, S. 1033, 1037, 1043, *1062*
GATT, S. 168, *194*
GAUHE, A. 615, *638*
GAUTSCHI, F. 215, *242*
GAZZINELLI, G. 520, *528*
GEAR, J. R. 977, 981, 982, 1000, *1017*,
    1018, *1019*, *1022*
GEARIEN, J. E. 959, *1022*
GEE, S. 497, *527*
GEHATIA, M. 417, *460*
GEHRING, L. B. 67, *99*
GEHRMANN, G. 486, *529*
GEIDUSCHEK, E. P. 567, 568, 569, *585*, *586*
GEIGER, E. 485, *529*
GEILING, E. M. K. 884, *900*

GEISSMAN, T. A. 746, 750, 772, 775, 776, 777, 778, 788, *797, 798,* 805, 806, 807, *824,* 971, 972, *1016, 1017*
GELBOIN, H. V. 508, *529*
GEMERSHAUSEN, J. *38*
GEORGE, P. 284, *308*
GEORGIEV, G. P. 501, 518, *529*
GERVAG, J. E. 989, *1018*
GESCHWIND, I. I. 686, *735*
GESSNER, T. 608, 622, *636*
GETTLER, A. O. 619, 624, *636*
GETZ, G. 146, *195*
GETZENDANER, M. E. 61, *101*
GHALAMBOR, M. A. 91, *97,* 344, 350, 432, 433, *460, 462*
GHOLSON, R. K. 690, *735,* 962, *1018, 1022, 1023*
GHOSAL, S. 832, *894,* 998, 999, 1000, *1019*
GHOSH, H. P. 403, *460, 472*
GHOSH, J. J. 749, *797*
GHOSH, S. 344, 346, 437, *461*
GIACOMONI, D. 567, *585*
GIANTURCO, M. 971, 980, *1015*
GIBBONS, A. P. 371, 415, *457*
GIBBS, M. 323, 332, 334, *456, 461, 474,* 955, *1015*
GIBBS, M. H. 209, *241,* 647, *677,* 843, *896,* 946, *952*
GIBSON, D. B. 722, *742*
GIBSON, D. M. 79, *97,* 109, *194, 201,* 204
GIBSON, F. 19, 32, 34, 35, *38, 39, 41,* 684, *735,* 907, 908, *938*
GIBSON, K. D. 140, 141, 148, 154, *194,* 204, 254, 255, 257, 266, *308, 312,* 696, 711, *735*
GIBSON, M. I. 32, 34, *39*
GIELEN, W. 175, 176, *197*
GIERER, A. 510, *529, 579*
GIGG, R. H. 165, *191*
GIL-AV, E. 1073, 1075, *1077*
GILBERT, G. A. 379, 411, *461*
GILBERT, J. A. S. 1069, 1074, *1077*
GILBERT, J. M. 364, 365, *461, 467*
GILBERT, W. 501, 503, 509, 512, 513, 517, *528, 529,* 542, 574, *578, 587*
GILBERTSON, T. J. 962, 964, *1019*
GILCHRIST, B. M. 667, *674*
GILDEN, R. V. 508, *527*
GILDER, H. *308*
GILFILLAN, J. L. 843, *896*
GILGAN, M. W. 400, *459*
GILLESPIE, R. 393, *476*
GILVARG, C. 25, 26, 32, 34, *38, 39,* 40, 41, *44,* 1000, *1018*
GIMENEZ, W. T. 143, *190*
GINOZA, H. S. 697, *733*

GINSBURG, V. 90, 92, 93, 94, *97, 100,* 355, 356, 358, 361, 364, 365, 367, 369, 372, 397, 411, 420, 421, 422, *460, 461, 462, 465, 466*
GIOVANNOZZI-SERMANNI, G. 1010, *1017*
GIRI, K. V. 409, *461*
GITTERMAN, C. O. 571, *586*
GLADSTONE, L. 567, *585*
GLASER, L. 91, 93, 94, *97, 98, 99,* 352, 357, 358, 361, 362, 363, 371, 373, 374, 414, 422, 424, 425, 430, 431, 435, *457, 461,* 465, 467
GLASSMAN, E. 481, 483, *533*
GLEASON, J. R. 387, *467*
GLOCK, G. E. 51, *98*
GLOMSET, J. A. 132, *194*
GLOOR, U. 890, *901*
GLOVER, J. 240, *245,* 664, 665, 670, 671, *674, 677*
GLOVER, M. 240, *245*
GNAMM, H. 822, *824*
GODIN, P. J. 855, 857, *897*
GODINAUX, E. 557, *583*
GODMAN, G. C. 444, *461*
GODNER, T. N. 267, *308*
GODNEV, T. N. 866, *897*
GODSON, G. N. 520, *529*
GODTFREDSEN, W. O. 1049, *1062*
GOEBEL, W. F. 334, 381, 433, *455, 463,* 471
GOEDDER, H. W. 682, *736*
GOEGGEL, A. 1003, *1020*
GOEGGEL, H. 1000, *1018*
GOFFINET, B. 240, *245*
GOFMAN, J. W. 178, *192, 198*
GOGGEL, K. H. 682, *736*
GOLD, A. M. 219, *242,* 880, *899*
GOLD, E. 553, *581*
GOLD, M. 499, *530,* 553, 572, 573, 574, *581, 586, 587*
GOLDBERG, A. 273, *308*
GOLDBERG, I. H. 172, *194,* 404, 440, *461,* 470, 501, 504, 507, 519, 520, *529, 533,* 565, 567, *584*
GOLDBERG, L. 356, 421, *472*
GOLDBERG, M. L. 351, *461*
GOLDBERG, N. D. 363, *461*
GOLDBERGER, R. F. 518, 519, *529*
GOLDEMBERG, S. H. 370, 371, 393, 402, 404, 405, 406, 416, *461, 466*
GOLDEN, M. 176, *191*
GOLDFABER, L. 443, *472*
GOLDFINE, H. 122, 150, *189, 205*
GOLDIN, A. 693, *737*
GOLDMAN, D. S. 372, 391, *461, 466*
GOLDMAN, P. 112, 114, *188, 194*
GOLDSCHMID, O. 818, *825,* 933, *938*

GOLDSCHMIDT, M. E. 304, *313*
GOLDSMITH, T. H. 671, *674*
GOLDSTEIN, A. 486, 487, 495, 509, 514, *529*
GOLDSTEIN, D. B. 487, 495, 509, 514, *529*
GOLDSTEIN, G. W. 288, *308*
GOLDSTEIN, J. *527*
GOLDSTEIN, L. 488, *529*
GOLDSTEIN, M. 230, *244*, 338, *463*
GOLDSTEIN, N. P. 131, *205*
GOLDSWORTHY, P. H. 484, *529*
GOLDTHWAIT, D. A. 62, 63, *98*, 561, *583*
GOLDWASSER, E. 543, 560, 565, *579, 583, 584*
GOMATOS, A. J. 566, *585*
GOMATOS, P. J. 566, 567, 570, *585, 586*
GOMPERTZ, S. M. 355, 356, 360, *461*
GONANO, F. 494, *535*
GONATAS, J. 176, *198*
GONCALVES, I. R. J. 407, 434, *459, 461*
GONON, W. F. 340, *467*
GONZALES, N. S. 91, 92, *98*, 372, 419, *461*
GONZALEZ, C. 556, *582*
GOODALL, McC. 622, *637*
GOODEVE, A. M. 959, *1018*
GOODMAN, D. S. 217, 220, *242*, 648, *676*
GOODMAN, D. W. 210, *241*
GOODMAN, H. M. 510, *533*, 567, *585*
GOODMAN, M. 92, *97*
GOODMAN, S. D. 131, 132, 179, 180, *194, 197, 204*
GOODSALL, R. A. 521, *530*
GOODWIN, R. H. 267, *308*
GOODWIN, T. W. 641, 643, 645, 647, 650, 651, 652, 654, 655, 657, 658, 659, 661, 663, 667, 670, *672, 673, 674, 675*, 681, 699, 700, 701, 702, *733, 735*, 843, 866, 882, 891, 892, *896, 898, 899, 900*, 1039, 1040, 1047, *1061*
GOODYEAR, G. H. 694, *742*
GØRANSSON, G. 151, *194*
GORDON, C. N. 571, *586*
GORDON, J. 544, 572, *579*
GORDON, J. J. 1032, 1043, *1062*
GORDON, M. 61, *101*
GORDON, R. S., Jr. 178, 179, 181, 182, *190, 193*
GORDON, S. A. 334, *456*
GORE, I. Y. 209, 218, *241, 242*, 647, *676*
GORINI, L. 13, 14, *39*
GORMAN, J. 507, *529*
GORSKI, J. 402, *463*
GOSLING, L. G. 540, *577*
GOSS, M. J. 918, *939*
GOSSELIN, L. 647, *676*
GOTO, K. *309*
GOTT, C. L. 304, *313*
GOTTESMAN, M. E. 561, 562, 563, *583*

GOTTLIEB, A. 15, *39*
GOTTSCHALK, A. 173, *190, 192, 194*, 340, 390, *461*
GOULD, B. S. 15, *40*, 510, 511, 520, *531*
GOULD, H. 502, *528*
GOULD, M. F. 394, *461*
GOULD, R. G. 180, *194*
GOUT, P. W. 506, *535*
GOUTAREL, R. 883, *900*, 993, *1018*
GOUTIER, R. 553, *581*
GOWER, B. G. 958, *1018*
GRABNER, M. 29, 30, 31, *40*
GRADO, C. 137, 138, *194*
GRAFF, M. 224, *243*
GRAHAM, H. 834, *895*
GRAHAM, N. B. 1031, *1062*
GRAHAM, S. 726, *734*
GRAHLE, A. 842, *895*
GRANGAUD, R. 641, 671, *675*
GRANGER, R. 855, *897*
GRANICK, S. 249, 252, 254, 256, 257, 258, 261, 262, 263, 264, 266, 267, 270, 271, 272, 273, 274, *307, 308, 310, 312*, 711, *733*
GRANT, J. K. 615, *636*
GRANT, P. K. 872, *898*
GRASSL, M. 209, *241*
GRASSMAN, W. 341, *461*, 807, 818, *824*
GRAVES, D. J. 400, 401, *460, 461, 465, 475*
GRAY, C. H. 264, 273, 276, 287, 288, *308, 311*
GRAY, E. 18, *41*
GRAY, E. D. 521, *529*, 553, *581*
GRAY, G. M. 127, 135, 136, *194, 199*
GRAZI, E. 326, *463*
GREATHOUSE, G. A. 414, *467*
GREBNER, E. E. 447, *460, 461*
GREEN, A. A. 398, 399, 400, *458, 461*
GREEN, B. 1048, *1062*
GREEN, D. E. 106, 107, 123, 125, 178, *194, 196*, 944, *951*
GREEN, J. 667, *674*
GREEN, J. P. 172, *194*
GREEN, M. 446, *461*, 553, *581*
GREEN, N. M. 520, *531*
GREENBERG, D. M. 4, 5, 6, 9, 12, 16, 19, *39, 40, 41, 42, 43*, 78, *98*, 140, 141, 148, 154, 156, 157, *190, 194, 196, 201, 204*, 519, *529*, 601, 630, *638*, 710, *739*
GREENBERG, E. 403, *461, 472*
GREENBERG, G. R. 60, 61, 63, 66, 89, *96, 98*, 548, *580*
GREENCARD, O. 487, 488, *529*, 686, *735*
GREENSHIELDS, R. N. 394, *461*
GREENSPAN, C. M. 569, *585*
GREENWOOD, F. L. 170, *191*
GREGORY, H. 885, *900*
GREGORY, J. D. 21, *39*, 614, *636*

GREINER, C. M. 336, *455*
GRENBY, T. H. 606, *636*
GRENSON, M. 11, *38*
GREULL, G. 108, *202*, 682, *737*
GREVILLE, G. D. *194*
GRIBOFF, G. 548, *580*
GRIEG, C. G. 597, *636*
GRIESE, A. 51, *101*
GRIFFIN, A. C. 521, *529*
GRIFFIN, B. E. 556, *582*
GRIFFIN, N. J. 707, *735*
GRIFFIN, W. J. 335, *470*, 961, *1017*
GRIFFITH, G. D. 962, *1018*
GRIFFITH, M. 147, *199*
GRIFFITH, T. 690, *736*, 962, *1018*
GRIFFITH, W. H. 142, *194*
GRIFFITHS, M. 642, 660, 664, *675*
GRILL, P. 233, *244*
GRILLO, T. A. I. 403, *462*
GRIMSHAW, J. 690, *735*, 808, *824*, 962, *1018*
GRINSTEIN, M. 252, *308*
GRISBACH, H. 366, *462*
GRISEBACH, H. 766, 772, 774, 776, 777, 798, 805, 806, *824*, *827*, 1004, 1013, *1021*, 1041, *1061*, *1062*
GRISEBACH, N. 791, *799*
GRISEBACH, U. C. 766, *798*, 1041, *1062*
GRISOLIA, S. 76, *99*, 688, *739*
GROB, E. C. 643, 647, 648, 650, 659, *675*, *677*
GRODSKY, G. M. 288, *308*
GROENIGER, E. 555, *582*
GRÖGER, D. 989, 1000, 1004, 1006, 1008, *1017*, *1018*, *1021*, *1022*, *1023*
GROLLMAN, A. P. 372, 397, 446, 449, *462*
GROMET-ELHANAN, Z. 520, *529*
GROOM, V. 169, *194*
GROS, E. G. 885, *900*, 962, 964, *1019*
GROS, F. 501, 503, 509, 517, *529*, *533*, 542, 569, *578*, *586*
GROSS, B. E. 1050, 1051, *1062*
GROSS, D. 376, 396, *455*, 959, 960, 962, *1018*, *1020*
GROSS, J. 483, 508, *531*
GROSS, P. R. 501, 502, *532*
GROSS, S. R. 10, 14, 24, 27, *38*, *39*, *40*, 706, *741*, 803, *825*, 907, 908, *939*
GROSSMAN, J. D. 1076, *1077*, *1078*
GROSSMAN, L. 58, *98*
GROVE, J. F. 1048, 1049, *1061*
GROVER, P. L. 605, *636*
GRUELL, G. *738*
GRUENSTEIN, M. *472*
GRUNDON, M. F. 1008, *1017*
GRUNEBERG-MANAGO, M. 555, 556, 557, 558, 559, 560, *582*, *583*

GRÜNEWALD, H. 140, *201*
GRYDER, R. M. 352, *470*
GUAL, C. 233, *244*
GUARINO, A. J. 68, *98*, 354, *462*
GUEST, J. R. 20, 22, 37, *39*, 491, *535*
GUEX, W. 668, *677*
GUGLIELMETTI, L. 882, 889, *899*, *901*
GUIDICE, G. 511, *528*
GUILD, W. R. 569, *585*
GUILLORY, R. J. 399, *467*
GUIRARD, B. M. 694, *738*
GULLAND, J. M. 691, *735*, 978, *1018*
GUNDENON, C. 288, *311*
GUNDERSON, W. 13, 14, *39*
GUNJA, Z. H. *462*
GUNSALUS, I. C. 36, *43*, 340, *473*, 538, *577*, *723*, *735*
GUNSTONE, F. D. 106, *195*
GÜNTHER, G. 123, *204*
GÜNTHER, H. 1004, *1017*
GUNTHER, J. K. 498, *528*
GUNTZ, G. 91, 92, 93, *97*
GUPTA, R. M. 955, 968, 982, *1018*
GURD, F. R. N. 178, *195*
GURIN, S. 107, 125, *190*, *204*, 208, 209, 227, 233, 236, 237, 238, *241*, *243*, *244*, *245*, 647, *674*, *677*, 945, 946, *951*, *952*
GUROFF, G. 485, *530*
GURR, M. I. 145, *196*
GUSEVA, A. R. 1012, 1013, *1018*
GUSS, J. K. 557, 558, *582*, *583*
GUSTAFSON, A. 179, *195*
GUSTAFSON, B. E. 289, *308*
GUT, M. 228, 230, 233, *243*, *244*, 858, 860, *897*
GUTZWILLER, J. 1049, *1063*
GYORGY, P. 377, *476*
GYORGYFY, C. 663, 665, *673*

HAAGEN-SMIT, A. J. 482, 483, 485, *527*, 830, 833, 834, 835, 836, 837, 838, 840, 857, 860, *894*, *895*, *897*, 948, 949, *952*
HAARSTAD, V. B. 995, *1022*
HABER, R. G. *798*
HABERLAND, E. 419, *472*
HACKETT, D. P. *528*
HAEGER-ARONSON, B. 273, *309*
HAERLE, H. 153, *191*
HAESSLER, H. A. 124, *195*
HAFT, D. E. 181, *195*
HAGEN, A. 113, 115, *199*
HAGEN, P. O. 150, *189*
HAGERMAN, D. D. 451, *462*
HAGERMAN, R. H. 323, *462*
HÄGGMARK, A. 58, *97*, 548, *580*
HAGOPIN, L. M. 180, *195*

HAGUE, E. 719, *735*
HAGUE, E. N. 1072, *1078*
HAGY, J. A. 626, 627, 629, *637*
HAHN, G. 990, 1003, *1018*
HAHN, O. 931, *939*
HAIGH, W. G. 340, *462*
HAIGHT, R. D. 27, 28, *41*
HAJRA, A. K. 117, *195*
HAKALA, M. T. 708, *735*
HAKIM, A. A. 556, *582*
HALKERSTON, I. D. K. 228, *243*
HALL, B. D. 542, 566, 567, 569, *578*, *585*
HALL, C. W. 90, 93, *97*, 130, *200*, 358, 367, 372, 397, *461*, *462*
HALL, E. S. 1003, *1018*
HALL, J. A. 745, 797, 836, *895*
HALL, L. M. 72, *99*
HALL, M. O. 142, 149, *195*
HALL, P. D. 503, *529*
HALLDAL, P. 292, *309*
HALLIDAY, J. W. 160, *195*, 725, *736*
HALPERN, A. 838, *895*
HALPERN, O. 1041, *1062*
HALPERN, Y. S. 23, *39*
HALVORSON, H. 507, 510, *529*, *531*
HALVORSON, H. O. 487, *535*
HAMADA, K. 716, *736*
HAMILTON, D. M. 376, 380, 407, 413, 414, *462*
HAMILTON, J. G. 882, 887, *899*
HAMILTON, L. D. 541, *578*
HAMILTON, T. H. 507, *529*
HAMMAKER, L. 288, *311*
HAMMEL, C. L. 274, *309*
HAMNER, K. C. 681, *736*
HAMPEL, B. 940
HANAHAN, D. J. 104, 105, 106, 133, 135, 136, 137, 138, 142, 144, 146, 155, *191*, *195*, *201*, 219, *242*
HANAOKA, C. 281, 284, *309*
HANAWALT, P. C. 542, *578*
HANCOCK, J. E. H. 228, *244*
HANCOCK, R. L. *535*
HANDA, S. 172, *204*
HANDLER, P. 81, 82, *99*, *100*, 690, 692, 693, *736*, *740*, 760, *798*
HANES, C. S. 324, 385, 392, 398, *462*
HANESSIAN, S. 367, *462*
HANKE, P. 379, 410, *475*
HANKES, L. V. 688, *736*
HANN, R. M. 450, *462*
HANSEN, J. H. 882, 887, *899*
HANSEN, R. G. 91, 92, 93, *97*, *98*, *100*, 357, 358, 360, 362, 372, 393, 416, *457*, *458*, *462*, *471*, *474*, *476*
HANSHOFF, G. 73, *100*

HANSON, J. R. 868, 869, 870, *898*, 1003, *1018*, 1050, 1051, *1062*
HANSSON, E. 482, *529*
HAPER, B. J. T. 978, *1015*
HAQ, M. Z. 971, *1015*
HARADA, T. 614, 615, *638*
HARARY, I. 208, *241*, 337, *462*
HARBERS, E. 76, *98*, 545, 561, *579*, *583*
HARBORNE, J. B. 746, *797*
HARDENBROOK, H. 393, *476*
HARDESTY, B. 509, 510, 517, *529*
HARDMAN, J. K. 36, 37, *39*
HARDWIGER, L. A. 962, *1018*, *1022*
HARFORD, C. G. 553, *581*
HARLAN, W. R., Jr. 116, 117, *195*
HARLEY-MASON, J. 609, *636*, 996, *1018*
HARODA, Y. 228, *243*
HAROLD, F. M. 234, *244*
HARPER, B. J. T. 955, 977, 979, *1016*
HARPER, E. M. 91, 92, *101*, 355, 433, *473*
HARPUR, R. P. 344, 351, *462*
HARRINGTON, H. *42*
HARRIS, A. 487, *531*, 1034, 1048, *1061*, *1062*
HARRIS, A. Z. 320, *456*
HARRIS, D. L. 681, 713, *735*, *736*
HARRIS, H. 507, *529*
HARRIS, J. O. 688, *736*
HARRIS, M. 414, *467*
HARRIS, P. M. 146, *195*
HARRIS, R. V. 120, *195*
HARRIS, S. A. 694, *741*
HARRISON, J. S. 398, *474*
HART, P. 126, 146, 147, 154, *198*
HÄRTEL, O. 930, *939*
HARTIALA, K. J. V. 597, 615, *636*
HARTMAN, P. E. 29, 30, 31, *40*, 506, *526*
HARTMAN, S. C. 62, *98*
HARTMAN, Z. 29, 30, 31, *40*
HARTNETT, C. 160, *192*, 725, *734*
HARTREE, E. F. 153, *195*, 448, *464*
HARTT, C. E. 917, *938*
HARUNA, I. 566, *584*
HARVEY, P. 407, *459*
HARVEY, R. A. 702, 703, *742*
HASEGAWA, E. 441, *462*
HASEGAWA, M. 806, 807, *825*, 923, *938*
HASEGAWA, S. 520, *532*
HASELKORN, R. 509, *529*, 565, 569, 570, *584*
HASHEM, M. 804, *824*
HASKELL, T. H. 367, *462*
HASKIN, M. A. 374, 430, *455*
HASKINS, J. F. 1072, *1077*
HASLAM, E. 803, 804, *824*, *825*
HASLEWOOD, G. A. D. 238, 239, *245*, 615, *636*

HASSALL, C. H. 1027, 1028, 1046, *1061*, *1062*
HASSAN, M. UL 446, 449, *462*
HASSELSTROM, T. 851, 867, *896*
HASSID, W. Z. 91, 92, 93, 94, *97*, *100*, *101*, 345, 354, 355, 356, 357, 358, 361, 362, 364, 369, 370, 371, 372, 373, 376, 377, 379, 382, 383, 384, 385, 389, 390, 393, 394, 398, 407, 411, 415, 416, 417, 420, 421, 422, 423, 424, 448, *455*, *456*, *459*, *460*, *461*, *462*, *464*, *466*, *468*, *469*, *473*, *475*, *476*
HATA, K. *939*, *940*
HATCH, F. T. 19, 20, *39*, *43*, 180, *195*
HATEFI, Y. 6, *40*, 141, *196*, 710, *737*
HATHAWAY, J. A. 344, *471*
HATHWAY, D. E. 802, 804, 805, 807, 808, 813, 815, 816, 817, 818, 819, 820, 821, 822, *825*
HATTON, A. 293, *309*
HATTORI, A. 290, 291, 293, 294, *308*, *309*
HAUGE, S. M. 668, *678*
HAUK, R. 404, *462*
HAUN, J. R. 226, *243*, 881, 883, 886, *899*
HAUROWITZ, F. 484, 486, *527*, *529*
HAUSER, G. 160, 173, 183, 184, 185, *195*, *198*, 435, *462*, 521, *531*, 726, *736*
HAUSMANN, R. 573, 574, *586*
HAVEL, R. J. 181, 182, *193*, *195*
HAWKE, J. C. 146, *195*
HAWKINS, G. R. 58, *98*
HAWKINS, W. B. 276, 277, *309*
HAWORTH, R. D. 803, 804, 808, 818, *824*, *825*
HAWORTH, W. N. 379, 394, 397, 411, 417, *462*
HAWS, E. J. 1035, 1058, *1062*
HAWTHORNE, J. N. 105, 135, 137, 138, 139, 140, 143, 150, 159, 162, 163, 165, 182, *189*, *193*, *194*, *195*, *196*
HAWTREY, A. O. 513, *529*
HAXO, F. 657, 660, 668, *675*, *677*
HAXO, F. T. 285, 289, 290, *309*
HAYAISHI, O. 23, *39*, 83, *100*, 686, 687, 688, 690, 691, 693, 731, *733*, *737*, *739*, *740*, 1034, 1035, *1062*
HAYANO, M. 228, 233, *243*, *244*
HAYASHI, M. 501, 502, 503, *534*, 541, 542, 567, 569, *578*, *585*, *586*
HAYASHI, M. N. 541, 569, *578*, *585*, *586*
HAYASIDA, A. 448, *462*
HAYATSU, R. 971, *1015*
HAYES, P. M. 92, *97*
HAYES, T. L. 178, *198*
HAYNES, L. J. 981, *1018*
HAYWOOD, A. M. 521, *529*, 566, *584*
HEARD, R. D. H. 226, *243*

HEARN, W. R. 303, *309*
HEATH, E. C. 91, 93, *97*, *98*, 344, 346, 350, 365, 375, 422, 432, 433, 446, *459*, *460*, *462*, 682, *736*
HEATH, H. 258, 263, 264, 304, *309*
HEBER, V. 332, *462*
HECHT, L. 496, *531*, 693, *740*
HECHT, L. I. 552, 553, 560, 561, *581*, *583*
HECHTER, O. 226, 227, 228, 230, *243*, *244*
HEDE, R. 541, *578*
HEDING, L. 502, 503, *527*
HEDRICK, J. L. 4, 5, *39*
HEETER, M. 566, *584*
HEFTMAN, E. 870, *898*
HEFTMANN, E. 225, 226, *243*, 879, 881, 882, 883, 885, 886, 893, *899*, *900*, *1016*
HEGBOM, L. 933, *937*
HEGGE, E. 661, *675*
HEGNAUER, R. 840, *895*
HEHRE, E. J. 376, 379, 380, 384, 399, 407, 411, 412, 413, 414, *462*
HEIDELBERGER, C. 76, *98*, 544, 545, 561, *579*, *583*
HEIDELBERGER, M. 483, *530*
HEILBRON, I. M. 211, *241*, 873, *898*
HEIMBERG, M. 485, *530*
HEIMBERGER, W. 931, 936, *938*
HEIMER, R. 436, *462*
HEINRICH, H. E. 301, *309*
HEINRICH, M. R. 71, *98*
HEINRICH, R. 350, *459*
HEINRIKSON, R. L. 543, *579*
HEINTZELER, M. 808, *826*
HEINZ, E. 485, *530*, *532*
HEISLER, C. R. 709, *736*
HELE, P. 106, 107, 108, 135, *195*, 944, *951*
HELE, T. S. 615, *636*
HELINSKI, D. R. 36, *39*, 491, *535*
HELLE, K. B. 450, *462*
HELLEINER, C. W. 21, *39*, 553, *581*
HELLMAN, K. P. 962, *1018*
HELLMAN, L. 224, *243*
HELLMAN, N. N. 413, *465*
HELMKAMP, G. 883, *900*
HELMREICH, E. 399, 400, 401, 402, *459*, *462*, *464*, 520, *530*
HEMERLINE, A. 352, *456*
HEMMING, F. W. 890, *901*
HEMMINGSEN, D. 295, *309*
HEMS, R. 337, *465*
HENDERSON, F. G. 629, *636*
HENDERSON, J. F. 544, *579*
HENDERSON, L. M. 687, 688, 690, *734*, *735*, *736*, 742, 961, 962, *1018*, *1022*
HENDERSON, R. B. 697, *735*
HENDLER, R. W. 485, 520, 521, *530*
HENDLEY, D. D. 556, *582*

HENDRICKS, S. B. 289, *309, 312,* 839, *895,* 943, *952*

HENDRICKSON, J. B. 845, 854, 856, 859, 862, 863, 873, 875, *896, 897,* 998, *1018*

HENDRY, R. A. 130, *191*

HENNEY, H. R. 510, *530*

HENNING, U. 36, *39,* 209, 210, *241,* 491, *535,* 833, 835, 844, 845, 857, *894, 896,* 948, *951, 952*

HENNING, V. 647, 648, *672, 675, 676*

HENRICK, C. A. 870, *898*

HENRY, J. 567, *585*

HENRY, S. S. 140, *193*

HENSHAW, E. C. 501, 503, 520, *528, 530*

HEPPEL, L. A. 144, *203,* 555, 556, 557, 558, 559, 560, *582, 583,* 691, *736*

HERBERT, E. 144, *195,* 552, 553, 560, 561, *581, 583*

HERBERT, E. J. 882, 887, *900,* 955, 1011, *1018*

HERBERT, R. B. 985, *1016*

HERGERT, H. L. 814, 815, 818, 820, *825,* 933, *938*

HÉRISSÉY, H. 930, *937*

HERMAN, C. 15, *42*

HERMAN, E. C. 708, 709, *742*

HERMAN, R. 238, *245*

HERMANN, S. 448, *463*

HERNANDEZ, H. H. 131, *195*

HEROK, J. 802, 808, *826*

HERS, H. G. 349, 410, 449, 450, *463*

HERSHEY, A. D. 541, *578*

HESS, G. 707, *740*

HESSE, R. H. 955, 981, 982, *1015*

HESTRIN, S. 377, 378, 394, 399, 413, 414, 415, 417, 418, *455, 459, 460, 463, 469*

HEUSLER, R. 802, 808, *826*

HEUSSER, 213, 214, *242*

HEVESY, G. 139, *195*

HEWETT, C. L. 1065, 1066, *1077*

HEWITT, J. 15, *42*

HEYDEMAN, M. T. 340, *463*

HEYMANN, H. 373, 432, *476*

HIAI, S. 550, *580*

HIATT, H. 501, 503, *529,* 542, *578*

HIATT, H. H. 56, *98,* 338, *463,* 501, 503, 520, *528, 530,* 543, 553, *578, 581*

HIBBERT, H. 412, *460*

HICKEY, F. C. 216, 222, *242, 243*

HICKMAN, J. 445, 446, 449, *455*

HICKMAN, J. W. 449, *475*

HICKS, M. 520, *528*

HIDY, P. H. 385, *463*

HIEGER, I. 1065, *1077*

HIFT, H. 944, *951*

HIGA, A. 504, *531,* 542, *578*

HIGASHI, T. 483, 520, 523, *530*

HIGGINS, G. 947, *952*

HIGHET, R. J. 955, 957, 985, 988, *1015, 1018*

HIGUCHI, M. 309

HIGUCHI, T. 791, *799,* 923, 934, 936, *938*

HILDITCH, T. P. 105, 106, *195*

HILL, M. 510, 511, *535*

HILL, R. B. 484, *530*

HILL, R. C. 265, *312*

HILL, R. D. 985, *1019*

HILL, R. J. 141, *197*

HILLARY, E. P. 340, *471*

HILLIS, W. E. 806, 807, 812, 815, 817, 818, 819, 820, 821, 822, *823,* 825

HILMOE, R. J. 556, 557, 558, 559, *582, 583,* 691, *736*

HILPERT, H. 520, *534*

HILZ, H. 405, 438, 439, 440, *463*

HIMES, R. H. 710, *736*

HIMWICH, W. A. 616, 619, *636*

HIND, G. 332, *463*

HINDORF, H. 975, *1021, 1022*

HINDS, H. A. 544, 545, *579*

HINDS, L. DEC. 442, *467*

HINKS, N. T. 597, *636*

HINMAN, J. W. 1043, 1052, *1062*

HINREINER, E. H. 797

HIRATA, M. 23, *39*

HIRD, H. J. 523, *530*

HIROKAWA, R. 511, 516, 520, *530, 531*

HIRS, C. H. W. 610, *638*

HIRSCH, U. 34, *41*

HIRST, E. L. 394, 397, 417, 418, *462, 463*

HIRST, M. 955, 981, 982, *1016*

HIRTH, L. 879, 887, *899, 900, 901*

HIS, W. 619, *636*

HITCHCOCK, M. 632, *636*

HITCHCOCK, R. 1074, *1077*

HIZUKURI, S. 405, 406, *463*

HOAGLAND, A. N. 27, *44*

HOAGLAND, M. B. 86, *98,* 483, 494, 495, 496, 508, 509, 511, 512, *530,* 699, *736*

HOARE, D. S. 26, *37,* 258, 263, 264, 304, *309,* 724, *736*

HOBSON, P. N. 379, 411, *463*

HOCHBERG, R. B. 883, *900*

HOCHESTER, R. M. 569, *586*

HOCHSTEIN, F. A. 1004, *1023*

HOCHSTER, R. M. 446, 447, *460, 463*

HOCKSEMA, H. 1043, 1052, *1062*

HOCQUARD, E. 519, *533*

HODGE, J. E. 35, *39,* 684, *736*

HODGES, R. 872, *898*

HODGKIN, D. C. 299, *309,* 717, *738*

HOFERT, J. 402, *463*

HOFFMAN, C. A. 413, *465*

HOFFMAN, C. H. 647, *678,* 843, *896, 952*

HOFFMAN, P. 380, 426, *463*
HOFFMAN-OSTENHOF, O. 160, *197,* 452, *472,* 726, *737, 739*
HOFHEINZ, W. 1041, *1061, 1062*
HOFMANN, A. 957, 1006, *1016, 1017,* 1052, 1054, *1060*
HOFMANN, K. 122, *195, 198,* 721, *736*
HOGAN, R. 718, *734*
HOGENKAMP, H. P. C. 717, *736*
HOGNESS, D. S. 360, *475*
HOKIN, L. E. 126, 127, 128, 137, 145, 162, 163, 185, *195, 196, 197, 200,* 520, *530*
HOKIN, M. R. 126, 127, 128, 137, 145, 163, 185, *195, 196,* 520, *530*
HOLADAY, D. 694, *742*
HOLDEN, K. G. 301, *311*
HOLDEN, M. 268, *309*
HOLDSWORTH, E. S. 25, *39,* 714, 715, *735*
HOLKER, J. S. E. 1034, 1035, 1058, *1060, 1062*
HOLL, J. 162, *204*
HOLLAND, B. H. 521, *529*
HOLLEY, R. W. 495, 497, 498, 499, *528, 530, 533,* 543, *578*
HOLLMAN, S. 450, *463*
HOLLMANN, S. 363, *463*
HOLLOWAY, C. F. 143, *204*
HOLLOWAY, P. W. 117, 118, 120, *196,* 1040, *1060*
HOLLY, F. W. *952,* 1043, 1052, *1062*
HOLMAN, D. M. 448, *471*
HOLMES, D. W. 483, *534*
HOLMES, W. L. 222, *243*
HOLMSEN, J. 615, *638*
HOLT, A. S. 270, *309*
HOLT, L. B. 264, *308*
HOLTZER, R. L. 520, *528*
HOLZAPFEL, C. W. 872, 873, *898*
HOLZEL, A. 356, 421, *472*
HOLZER, H. 350, *457, 470,* 682, 730, *736*
HOMERECK, E. 812, *826*
HONEL, H. 866, *898*
HONJO, M. 435, *463*
HOOGENDARN, B. W. 506, *535*
HOOPER, N. K. 122, *196*
HOPKINS, J. N. 502, *534*
HOPP, H. 822, *824*
HOPPER, I. 113, 115, *199*
HORECKER, B. A. 337
HORECKER, B. L. 29, *37,* 51, 54, *98,* 320, 321, 324, 325, 326, 338, 344, 345, 346, 347, 432, 445, 446, *457, 460, 462, 463, 469, 471, 475, 476,* 682, *736*
HÖRHAMMER, L. 137, 162, *196, 204*
HORIUCHI, Y. 836, *895*
HORNING, M. G. 112, 121, *196, 199,* 214, 235, *242, 244,* 844, *896*

HOROWITZ, H. H. 728, *736*
HOROWITZ, N. H. 13, 18, *39, 42, 43*
HOROWITZ, S. T. 352, *456*
HORTON, A. A. 700, 702, *735*
HORTON, H. R. 353, *476*
HORWITT, M. K. 682, *736*
HORWITZ, S. B. 450, 451, *463, 466*
HOSHI, R. 486, *534*
HÖSS, H. G. 962, 968, *1021*
HOTCHKISS, R. D. 433, 450, *463, 466,* 708, *742*
HOTTA, K. 701, *736*
HOTTA, S. 235, *244*
HOUGH, L. 424, *455,* 1041, *1062*
HOUGHLAND, G. V. C. 226, *243,* 881, *899*
HOULAHAN, M. B. 27, *41*
HOUSE, H. O. 777, *798*
HOWE, C. 173, *201*
HOWELL, J. McC. 671, *677*
HOWELL, R. R. 507, *529*
HOWELLS, D. J. 699, 700, *736*
HOWES, F. N. 821, *825*
HOYER, B. H. 507, *531*
HSU, W. T. 567, 568, *585*
HUANG, R. C. 508, *527,* 567, *585*
HUANG, R. L. 218, *242*
HUBBARD, N. 264, 265, *310*
HUBBARD, R. 303, *309*
HUBBARD, R. W. 360, *456*
HÜBNER, G. 962, 975, *1018, 1021*
HÜBSCHER, G. 124, 127, 128, 129, 130, 141, 145, 150, 157, *191, 192, 193, 196*
HUDSON, C. S. 379, 389, 450, *462, 474, 475*
HUDSON, P. B. 544, 545, *579*
HUELIN, F. E. 858, *897*
HUENNEKENS, F. M. 6, *40,* 125, 141, *196, 203,* 709, 710, 718, *736, 737, 739, 741, 1062*
HUEPER, W. C. 1069, *1078*
HUFF, J. B. 946, *952*
HUFF, J. W. 58, 71, *102,* 209, *241,* 647, *677,* 724, *736,* 843, *896*
HUFHAM, J. B. 717, *736*
HUGGINS, C. G. 164, 183, 184, 185, *189, 196,* 521, *530*
HUGHES, C. A. 971, *1019*
HUGHES, D. E. 86, *100,* 691, *736*
HUGHES, D. W. 270, *309*
HUGHES, E. F. X. 367, *472*
HUGHES, H. B. 621, 627, 629, *636*
HULANICKA, D. 120, *196*
HULLIN, R. 946, *951*
HÜLSMANN, W. C. 116, *191, 196*
HULTIN, E. 386, *463*
HULTIN, T. 483, 495, 509, 512, *530, 535*
HULTMAN, H. I. 618, *636*
HUMPHREY, J. H. 483, 520, *527, 530*

HUMPHREYS, G. K. 19, *39*, 78, *98*
HUMPHREYS, S. R. 693, *737*
HUNT, R. 616, *636*
HUNTER, G. D. 218, *242*, 520, 521, *528*, 530
HURD, C. D. 1070, *1078*
HURD, S. S. 400, *460*
HURLBERT, B. S. 832, *894*
HURLBERT, R. B. 57, 79, 91, 92, *98*, 544, 560, *579, 583*
HURWITZ, J. 320, 325, 345, 445, *463, 475*, 499, *530*, 561, 562, 563, 565, 566, 567, 568, 569, 571, 572, 573, *583, 584, 585, 586, 587*, 682, 723, *736*
HUSEMANN, E. 416, *463*
HUSSAIN, S. F. 1037, *1061*
HUTCHESON, R. M. 446, 450, *474*
HUTCHISON, D. J. 709, *733, 741*
HUTT, H. H. 104, *196*
HUTTON, T. W. 219, *242*
HUTTRER, C. 289, *310*
HUXLEY, H. E. 509, 510, *531*
HUZITA, Y. 834, *894*
HYLIN, J. W. 971, 1004, *1019*

IACCARINO, M. 687, *736*
IACOBUCCI, G. A. 1004, *1023*
IBRAHAM, R. K. 779, 791, *798, 799*
ICHIHARA, A. 4, 5, 6, *40*, 141, 156, 157, *196*
ICHIKAWA, K. 1065, *1078*
ICHIYAMA, A. 690, *736*
IDLER, D. R. 159, *203*, 597, *639*
IGARSKI, R. T. 507, *528*
IGAVE, I. *463*
IKAWA, M. 486, *530*, 724, *736, 740*
IKEDA, K. 299, *312*, 520, *532*, 712, *741*
IKEDA, M. 690, 691, *733, 736, 739*
IKEDA, R. M. 1076, *1077, 1078*
IKEHAWA, Y. 1043, *1063*
IKUTA, A. 990, *1023*
ILLINGWORTH, B. 343, 379, 387, 397, 399, 401, 402, 404, 410, 411, *455, 457, 458, 463*, 465, 467
ILVES, S. M. 345, 354, *468*
IMAI, K. 701, 702, 703, *737*
IMAI, M. 37, *40*
IMAI, Y. 160, *196*, 726, *736*
IMAICHI, K. 179, *204*
IMASEKI, H. 778, 788, *798*
IMASEKI, I. 955, 956, 957, 981, *1017, 1019*, *1022*
IMSANDE, J. 693, *736*
INAGAKI, A. 23, *39*
INAGAMI, K. 687, *738*
INGELMAN, B. 386, *463*

INGLIS, H. S. 855, 857, *897*
INGOLD, C. K. 650, *673*
INGRAHAM, L. L. 125, *196*, 682, *739*
INGRAM, P. 353, *460*
INHOFFEN, H. H. 641, *675*
INMAN, R. B. 549, *580*
INSOCOE, J. K. 375, 435, *455*
IODICE, A. A. 257, *309*
IRVINE, D. H. 284, *308*
ISBELL, H. S. 390, *463*
ISHERWOOD, F. A. 397, *462*, 728, *736*, 737, 738
ISHIDATE, M. 593, *636*
ISHII, K. J. 645, *675*
ISHII, Y. 351, *463*
ISHIKAWA, H. 934, *938*
ISHIKAWA, K. 502, 503, *532*, 728, *742*
ISHIKAWA, S. 728
ISHIKURA, H. 498, *528*
ISHIMOTO, N. *471*
ISLER, O. 331, *465*, 641, 668, 669, 671, *675, 677*
ISSELBACHER, K. J. 92, *98*, 124, 125, 129, 180, *195, 196, 202*, 356, 360, *455, 464*
ISSELBACHER, K. Z. 355, 356, *463*
ITO, E. 90, 91, *98*, 368, 429, *464, 471*
ITO, H. 520, *532*
ITO, J. 36, *38*
ITO, T. 485, *530*
IVERACH, G. G. 971, 1003, *1015, 1016*
IVES, D. R. 570, *586*
IWAHARA, S. 719, *737*

JACKAM, L. M. 661, 667, *675*
JACKANICZ, T. M. 962, *1019*
JACKEL, S. S. 728, *737*
JACKMAN, G. B. 1035, 1041, *1062*
JACKMAN, L. M. 655, 656, 662, *673, 674*, 907, 908, *938*
JACKSON, A. H. 261, *309*
JACKSON, C. P. 414, *471*
JACKSON, D. S. 15, *40*, 520, *530*
JACKSON, E. M. 691, *735*
JACKSON, J. F. 551, *580*
JACKSON, R. J. 502, *532*
JACKSON, R. W. 413, *465*
JACOB, A. 117, *196*
JACOB, F. 500, 501, 503, 505, *527, 530*, 542, 543, *578*
JACOB, J. 572, *586*
JACOB, M. 504, *532*
JACOB, M. I. 109, *201*
JACOB, T. M. *586*
JACOBELLI, G. 598, *637*
JACOBI, H. 883, *900*
JACOBS, W. A. 51, *99*

JACOBSEN, R. P. 227, *243*
JACOBSON, B. 92, *98*, 352, 361, 363, 372, 393, *462, 464*
JACOBSON, G. M. 883, *900*
JACOBSON, K. B. 496, *530*
JACOBSON, S. 360, *456*
JACOBY, W. B. 687, *737*
JAENICKE, L. 19, 22, *40*, 66, *98*, 350, *457*, 707, *737*
JAFFE, H. 252, 264, 271, *308*
JAFFE, J. 552, 553, *581*
JAFFÉ, M. 592, 601, 608, 631, *637*
JAGANNATHAN, V. 353, *464*
JAGENDORF, A. T. 332, *463*
JAGER, O. 884, *900*
JAIN, A. C. 781, 782, *799*
JAKOBY, W. B. 321, *464*, 686, 737
JAMES, A. L. 93, *100*, 357, 361, *470*
JAMES, A. T. 116, 117, 120, *195, 196, 199, 203*, 891, *901*
JAMES, M. E. 944, *952*
JAMES, R. 989, *1015*
JAMES, S. P. 592, 604, 605, 606, 607, 629, *635, 637*
JAMIKORN, M. 652, 657, 658, *674*
JANG, R. 325, 364, 373, 421, 423, *455, 472*, 729, *738*
JANOT, M.-M. 993, *1018*
JARRIGE-GUNTZ, G. 93, *97*
JAWORSKI, E. 373, 425, *464*
JAYKO, M. E. 233, 234, *244*
JEANES, A. 412, 416, 424, *464, 465*
JEANLOZ, R. W. 227, *243*
JEDEIKIN, L. A. 124, 126, *196*
JEFFREY, D. J. 604, 607, *637*
JEFFRIES, P. R. 808, *825*, 870, *898*
JEFFS, P. W. 986, *1019*
JEGER, O. 214, *242*, 860, 875, 876, *897, 899*
JELLINEK, P. H. 226, *243*
JENCKS, W. P. 125, *196*
JENKINS, J. A. 653, 669, *676*
JENKINS, J. K. 971, *1015*
JENKINS, T. W. 7, *42*
JENKINS, W. T. 724, *737*
JENSEN, A. 667, *675*
JENSEN, S. L. 657, 658, 660, 661, 662, 663, *675*
JEPSON, J. B. 611, *637*
JESAITS, M. A. 577
JETSCHMANN, K. 333, *475*
JEŽO, I. 971, *1015*
JOFFE, S. 393, *476*
JOHNE, S. 1008, *1018*
JOHNS, S. R. 962, 1009, *1019*
JOHNSON, A. B. 12, *40*
JOHNSON, A. W. 261, 299, 301, *307*, 711, 717, *733, 737*

JOHNSON, B. C. 625, *637*, 718, *739*
JOHNSON, B. L. 746, 775, 776, *797, 798*
JOHNSON, D. F. 226, *243*, 881, 882, 883, *899, 900*
JOHNSON, G. A. 175, *196*
JOHNSON, J. M. 129, 130, *196*
JOHNSON, M. J. 27, *43*
JOHNSON, M. K. 637
JOHNSON, S. 1031, *1062*
JOHNSTON, J. A. 944, 945, 946, *952*
JOHNSTON, J. D. 215, 219, *242*
JOHNSTON, J. M. 129, 130, *191, 196*
JOHNSTONE, R. A. W. 1075, *1078*
JOKLIK, W. K. 337, *456*, 501, 502, 503, *527*
JOKURA, K. 90, *100*, 365, *469*
JOLLOW, D. J. 117, *197*
JONDORF, W. R. 597, 615, *635, 637*
JONES, A. P. 629, *636*
JONES, C. A. 93, *99*
JONES, D. F. 1035, *1062*
JONES, D. W. 1027, 1028, *1061*
JONES, E. E. 28, *40, 42*
JONES, E. J. 943, *952*
JONES, E. R. H. 861, *897*, 1048, *1062*
JONES, F. T. 624, 625, *635*
JONES, G. 379, *470*
JONES, J. K. N. 334, 367, 373, 381, 424, 444, 450, *454, 464*, 1041, *1062*
JONES, K. M. 22, *39*
JONES, L. R. 448, *471*
JONES, M. E. 72, *98*
JONES, O. N. 155, *191*
JONES, O. T. G. 265, 266, 267, *309, 311*, 699, *733, 735*
JONES, P. 843, *896*
JONES, R. F. 292, *309*
JONES, T. H. D. 707, *737*
JORDAN, D. O. 539, 541, *577*
JORDAN, E. 92, *102*
JORDON, E. 36, *43*
JORGENSEN, E. 780, *798*
JORGENSEN, E. C. 746, 775, 776, *797, 798*
JORGENSEN, O. B. 410, 412, *464*
JOSEPH, C. A. 1076, *1078*
JOSHI, S. 693, *737*
JOSSE, J. 547, 550, 551, *580*
JOURDIAN, G. W. 91, *98*, 174, *201*, 375, 436, 437, 438, *457, 464, 471*
JOYEUX, Y. 419, *459*
JOZON, E. 419, *459*
JUBY, P. F. 962, *1017, 1019*
JUCKER, E. 643, 662, 667, 668, 669, *675*
JULITA, P. 716, *733*
JUNEJA, H. R. 1010, *1017*
JUNG, A. 681, *741*
JUNGALWALA, F. B. 670, 671, *675*
JUNGBLUT, P. W. 483, 486, 516, 520, *530*

JUNGWIRTH, C. 10, 14, 24, *39, 40*
JUNI, E. 422, 424, *474*
JURKOWITZ, L. *535*
JÜTTING, G. 722, *738*
JUVA, K. 15, *41*

KACZKA, E. A. 571, *586*, 1043, 1052, *1062*
KACZKOWSKI, J. 959, *1019*
KAGI, J. 498, *531*
KAHAN, F. M. 568, 571, *585*
KAHNT, F. W. 228, *244*
KAIHARA, M. 592, 630, *637*
KAISER, A. D. 547, *580*
KAJI, A. 511, 523, *530*, 605, 614, 615, *637*
KAJI, H. 511, 523, *530*
KALÁČ, V. 971, *1015*
KALAN, E. B. 748, *797*
KALBERER, F. 957, *1017*
KALCKAR, H. M. 69, 78, 92, *97, 98, 99, 101*, 124, *196*, 337, 355, 356, 360, 363, 370, 382, 432, *455, 464, 467, 468, 473*, 596, *638*
KALER, V. L. 269, *312*
KALETTA-GMÜNDER, U. 349, *464*
KALF, G. F. 522, *530*
KALINA, M. 357, *464*
KALITZKI, M. 841, *895*
KALYANPUR, M. G. 24, *38*
KAMEN, A. 124, *203*
KAMEN, M. D. 106, *189*, 252, *308*, 337, *474*
KAMEYAMA, T. 344, *464*, 502, 510, *530*
KAMM, E. D. 211, *241*, 873, *898*
KAMMEN, H. O. 544, 562, 565, *579, 584*
KANAI, Y. 435, *463*
KANAMORI, M. 23, *40*
KANDA, M. 446, *474*
KANDEL, S. I. 955, 1004, 1006, *1016*
KANDLER, O. 90, *98*
KANDUTSCH, A. A. 216, 220, 221, 225, *242, 243*, 878, 883, *899*
KANE, M. R. 552, *581*
KANEDA, T. 1041, *1062*
KANEKO, K. 28, *43*
KANESHIRO, T. 141, 150, *196, 198*
KANFER, J. 450, *457*, 728, *737*
KANFER, J. N. 155, 157, 158, 177, *196, 197*
KANG, H. H. 687, *734*
KANO, H. 90, *98*
KANYAN, A. 542, *578*
KAPIL, R. S. 1003, *1016*
KAPLAN, A. 15, *40, 41*
KAPLAN, N. 370, *459*
KAPLAN, N. O. 83, *101*, 450, 451, *463, 466, 476*, 692, 693, 694, *737, 738, 742, 952*
KARA, J. 556, *582*
KARASEK, M. 566, *587*

KARASEK, M. A. 16, *40*
KARASSEVITCH, Y. 18, *40*
KARGL, T. E. 652, *677*
KARIBIAN, D. 29, *40*
KARMEN, A. 121, 131, 180, *196, 197, 204*
KARNOVSKY, M. L. 146, 156, 170, 171, 176, *193, 197, 199, 200*, 435, *462*
KARPATKIN, S. 402, *464*
KARRER, P. 641, 643, 656, 658, 662, 667, 668, 669, *674, 675*
KARVAŠ, M. 971, *1015*
KASE, N. 239, *244*
KASHIDO, Y. 766, *798*
KASIDA, Y. 1008, *1020*
KASLANDER, J. 593, *637*
KASS, D. J. 592, *638*
KATAGIRI, H. 701, 702, 703, *737*
KATAGIRI, M. 32, 34, *40, 42*, 922, *938*
KATCHMAN, B. 692, *737*
KATES, M. 130, 186, 188, *197, 202*
KATSURAI, T. J. 290, *312*
KATTERMAN, R. 350, *470*
KATUNUMA, N. 707, 708, *737*
KATZ, E. 15, *40*
KATZ, J. 291, 292, *307, 309*
KATZ, M. 1067, *1078*
KATZEN, H. M. 20, 21, 22, *40*
KATZMAN, P. A. 448, *471*
KAUFMAN, S. 709, *737*
KAUFMANN, H. P. 887, *901*
KAUFMANN-BOETSCH, B. 452, *470*
KAUSS, H. 355, *464*
KAWAI, F. 702, 703, *739*
KAWAMATA, J. 566, *584*
KAWAMURA, I. 934, *938*
KAWAMURA, T. 934, *938*
KAWANO, N. 792, *799*
KAWASAKI, T. 681, *739*
KAY, L. D. 6, *40*, 141, *196*, 320, *456*, 710, *737*
KAYE, A. M. 563, *584*
KAZENKO, A. 413, *465*
KAZIRO, K. 281, 284, *309, 312*
KAZIRO, Y. 681, *737*
KAZUNO, T. 239, *245*
KEARNEY, E. B. 703, *737*
KEARNEY, P. C. 6, *42*
KEECH, D. B. 337, *464, 474*, 722, *741*
KEENAN, R. W. 153, 162, *197*
KEGLEVIC, D. 4, *37*, 140, 141, *189*
KEIGHLEY, G. 482, 485, *527*
KEIGHLEY, G. C. 481, *527*
KEIGHLEY, G. L. 483, 484, *527*
KEIL, J. G. 1033, 1034, 1035, *1060*
KEILICH, G. *1021*
KEILIN, D. 448, *464*
KEIR, H. M. 552, 553, 555, *581, 582*

KEITH, J. 400, *459*
KEKWICK, R. G. 947, *952*
KELLER, E. B. 481, 483, 487, 508, 512, *530, 531, 536*
KELLER, P. J. 400, *464*, 485, 520, *530*
KELLER, V. 643, 659, *677*
KELLER, W. 598, 599, *637*
KELLERMAN, G. M. 117, *197, 637*
KELLING, K. L. 964, *1021*
KELLY, A. 1035, 1058, *1062*
KELLY, M. 273, *308*
KELLY, R. B. 566, *585*
KELLY, S. 160, *198*, 422, 423, *466*, 726, 738
KELSEY, F. E. 884, *900*
KELSEY, M. I. 265, 266, *310*
KEMP, J. D. 10, 11, *40*
KEMP, P. 137, 138, 139, 162, 163, *195*
KEMPF, E. 91, 92, 93, *98*
KEMPNER, E. S. 485, *530*
KENCH, J. E. 277, 278, 295, *309*
KENDAL, L. P. 353, *464*
KENNAWAY, E. L. 1068, 1075, *1078*
KENNAWAY, N. M. 1068, *1078*
KENNEDY, E. P. 4, 5, *38*, 88, 89, *98*, 122, 123, 124, 126, 127, 128, 139, 140, 142, 143, 144, 146, 152, 154, 155, 156, 157, 158, 159, 161, 163, 168, 169, 170, 171, *190, 191, 192, 196, 197, 200, 202, 204*, 726, *739*
KENNER, G. W. 1040, 1053, *1061*
KENNEY, F. T. 488, *530*
KENT, A. B. 400, 401, *464, 465*
KENT, P. W. 438, 439, *459*
KEOGH, M. F. 1004, *1021*
KEPPLER, H. H. *825*
KERB, E. 837, *895*
KERESZTESY, J. C. 19, 20, 21, *38*, 694, *741*
KERN, M. 520, *530*
KERR, D. S. 561, *583*
KESSEL, I. 209, 210, *241*, 647, *675, 676*, 833, 835, 844, 857, *894*, 948, *952*
KESSLER, G. 345, 354, *468*
KESSLER, G. K. 422, 423, *464*
KESTON, A. S. 153, *191*
KEYNAN, A. 504, *531*
KHAN, A. W. 354, 415, *464*
KHAN, N. H. 971, *1015*
KHARASCH, M. 657, *675*
KHARCHENKO, M. F. 402, 403, *464*
KHORANA, H. G. 498, *532*, 551, 570, 571, *580, 586*, 698, *739*
KIBBY, M. R. 593, *635*
KIDDER, G. W. 704, *734*
KIDSON, C. 501, *530*
KIELLEY, R. K. 552, 553, *581*
KIESSLING, W. 370, 398, *464*
KIHARA, H. 486, *530*

KIHARA, H. K. 487, *535*
KIHO, Y. 516, *530*
KIKUCHI, G. 255, 273, 281, 284, *309, 310, 312*
KILBY, B. A. 372, 373, 391, 425, *457*
KIM, Y. T. 566, *587*
KIMBER, R. W. L. 1068, 1070, 1071, 1073, 1074, *1077*
KIMMEL, J. R. 288, 292, *309*
KINDL, H. 160, *197*, 726, *737, 739*
KINDLER, S. H. 26, *40*
KING, C. G. 728, *736, 737*
KING, D. W. 484, *530*
KING, F. E. 760, 778, *798*, 807, *825*
KING, H. G. C. 812, 818, 819, 820, *825*
KING, J. 405, 407, *473*
KING, T. E. 446, 450, *458, 464*, 694, 698, 714, *734, 737*
KING, T. J. 778, *798*
KINSELL, L. 179, *204*
KINSLEY, B. M. 543, *579*
KIRBY, A. J. 979, *1015*
KIRBY, G. W. 882, 887, *900*, 955, 978, 979, 981, 982, 985, 986, 988, 989, 1003, 1011, *1015, 1018, 1019*
KIRBY, K. S. 501, *530*
KIRK, M. 321, 335, *456*, 485, *527*
KIRKALDY, D. 1044, *1061*
KIRKMAN, H. N. 93, *97, 461*
KIRKWOOD, S. 360, 361, *456*, 955, 1008, *1017, 1019, 1020, 1022*
KIRSCHNER, K. 113, 115, *199*, 648, *675*
KIRSCHNER, N. 622, *637*
KISAKI, T. 966, *1019*
KISHI, T. 700, 701, 702, 703, *737, 738*
KISLIUK, R. L. 20, 21, 22, *40*
KISO, N. 172, *204*
KISSELER, N. A. 509, *534*
KISTLER, J. P. 185, *189*, 521, *531*
KITAY, E. 58, *101*
KITTENGER, G. W. 393, *464*
KITTLER, M. 440, *463*
KIYASU, J. Y. 122, 128, 144, 146, 152, 155, 158, *197, 205*
KIZEN, M. 659, *675*
KJAER, A. 28, *40*
KJELDGAARD, N. O. 543, *579*
KJELLIN, K. 544, 572, 573, *579, 586*
KJÖLBERG, O. 397, 412, *465*
KLAEMBT, H. D. 791, *799*
KLASON, P. 918, 930, *938*
KLATSKIN, G. 288, 292, *309*
KLEIHER, M. 485, *527*
KLEIN, H. P. 109, *197*
KLEIN, J. 27, *44*
KLEIN, J. R. 692, *736*
KLEIN, W. 132, *197*

KLEINSCHMIDT, A. K. 541, *578*, 978, *1019*
KLEMPERER, H. G. 562, 564, 565, *584*
KLENK, E. 119, 135, 139, 166, 173, 174, 175, 176, *190, 197*
KLENOW, H. 324, 345, 354, *463, 465*
KLEPPE, K. 94, *100*, 358, 448, *469*
KLETHI, J. 91, 92, *98, 99*
KLOENOW, H. 552, *581*
KLOPTOWSKI, T. 29, 31, *40*
KLOSTERMANN, H. J. 944, *952*
KLOTZSCH, H. 332, *475*
KLUNGSØYR, L. 450, *462*
KLYBAS, V. 345, *473*, 921, *939*
KLYNE, W. 871, *898*
KNAPE, G. 440, *463*
KNAPP, J. 722, *738*
KNAUSS, H. J. 209, *241*
KNIGHT, E., Jr. 557, *583*
KNIGHT, J. A. 1003, *1016*
KNIGHT, J. C. 216, *242*
KNIGHT, R. H. 605, 606, *637*
KNIGHT, S. G. 449, *458*
KNÖFEL, D. 964, *1021*
KNOPF, A. 510, *535*
KNOPF, P. M. 517, *531*
KNOWLES, J. 179, *204*
KNOWLES, P. F. 803, 804, *825*
KNOX, K. W. 377, 394, *465*
KNOX, W. E. 487, *530*, 686, 687, 692, *734, 737, 739, 741*
KNUTSON, C. A. 424, *465*
KO, S. 883, 893, *900*
KOBATA, A. 92, *98*, 368, *465*
KOBAYASHI, H. 486, *534*
KOBAYASHI, T. 386, *465*
KOBEL, H. 957, 1006, *1016, 1017*, 1052, 1054, *1060*
KOCH, A. L. 484, *530*
KOCH, K. 745, *797*
KOCHEN, J. 127, *199*
KOCOR, M. 1035, 1041, *1061*
KODAMA, K. 450, *476*
KOENIGK, E. 712, *737*
KOEPPE, R. E. 141, *197*
KOEPSELL, H. J. 413, *465*
KOERNER, J. F. 548, *580*
KOFLER, M. 331, *465*
KOHLER, A. R. 709, *733*
KOHN, P. 344, *465*
KOIKE, K. 487, *530*
KOLACHOV, P. 410, *469*
KOLACHOV, P. J. 377, 396, *469*
KOMPIS, I. 989, 1001, *1019*
KOMROWER, G. M. 356, 421, *472*
KON, S. K. 672, *675*, 714, 715, *735, 737*
KONDO, M. 718, 730, *741*
KONISHI, S. 16, *44*

KONO, M. 593, *639*
KONOGI, H. 556, *582*
KONOVA, I. V. 716, *741*
KONSTANECKI, ST. V. 817, *825*
KOPAC, M. J. 12, *43*
KOPACZYK, K. C. 168, 173, *197*
KOREY, S. R. 152, 176, *198, 462*
KORI, J. 690, *735*
KORKES, S. 448, *473*
KORN, E. D. 121, 182, *192, 198*, 438, 439, 441, 442, *465*
KORNBERG, A. 74, 75, 80, 82, 83, 85, *98, 99, 100, 101*, 124, 126, 127, 142, 143, 154, *198, 204*, 337, 368, *465, 469*, 544, 545, 546, 547, 548, 549, 550, 551, 552, 553, 556, 557, 559, *579, 580, 581, 582*, 688, 690, 691, 692, 704, *737, 739, 740, 741*
KORNBERG, H. A. 680, *734*
KORNBERG, H. L. 337, 340, *465*
KORNER, A. 483, 501, 502, 503, 507, *531, 532*
KORNFELD, R. 358, 361, 404, 405, 438, 439, *457, 465*
KORNFELD, S. 93, 94, *98, 99*, 352, 357, 358, 361, 362, 422, 435, 438, 439, *461, 465*
KORTE, F. 705, 724, *737*
KORZENOVSKY, M. 131, *198*
KORZYBSKI, T. 144, 149, *191*
KOSHLAND, D. E. 488, *531*
KOSHLAND, D. E., Jr. 353, 360, 384, *465, 476*
KOSOBUTSKAYA, L. M. 268, *309*
KOSUGE, T. 788, *799*
KOTAKE, Y. 686, *737*
KOUKOL, J. 957, *1019*
KOUPALAS, V. M. 165, *194*
KOVACS, H. P. 975, *1022*
KOVAL, G. J. 166, 167, *190*
KOWALSKI, E. 257, *309*
KOWALSKY, A. 360, *465*
KOWANKO, N. 955, 989, 995, *1019*
KOZINSKI, A. W. 552, *581*
KOZINSKI, P. B. 552, *581*
KRAFT, R. 931, 936, *938*
KRAICER, J. 508, *531*
KRAKOW, J. 555, 562, *582*
KRAKOW, J. S. 552, 553, 562, 565, 567, 568, 569, 570, *581, 584, 585*
KRAKOWER, G. W. 877, *899*
KRAMPITZ, L. O. 682, *737, 738*
KRASNA, A. J. 712, 713, *738*
KRASNOUSKY, A. A. 268, *309*
KRATZ, W. A. 289, *310*
KRATZL, K. 920, 922, 926, 927, *938*
KRAUS, F. 810, *825*
KRAUSS, R. W. 295, *307*
KRAYCHY, S. 620, *637*

KREBS, E. G. 400, 401, 402, *461, 464, 465, 476*

KREBS, H. A. 337, 340, 382, *457, 460, 465, 467,* 592, 629, *637,* 727, 728, *740*

KREHL, W. A. 682, *738*

KREISER, T. H. 27, 28, 29, *40, 41*

KREMER, G. 119, *197, 198*

KREMERS, E. 830, 834, 836, 840, *894*

KREMERS, R. E. 926, 933, *938*

KRETSINGER, R. H. 15, *40,* 510, 511, *531*

KRIMSKY, I. 1000, 1009

KRINIKHIDZE, K. S. 493, *528*

KRINSKY, N. 664, 665, *675*

KRIPPAHL, G. 332, 333, 335, *475*

KRISHNA, G. 880, *899*

KRISMAN, C. R. 411, *465, 468*

KRITCHEVSKY, D. 222, *243*

KROGER, H. 556, 567, 568, *582, 585*

KROGMANN, D. W. 334, *456*

KRONE, W. 497, *536,* 543, *578*

KROON, A. M. 522, *531*

KRUG, R. 512, 517, *528,* 561, *583*

KRUG, R. M. 566, 567, 570, *585*

KRUGMA, S. 807, *825*

KRUH, J. 484, 485, 486, 502, *531, 533*

KRUMDIECK, C. L. 705, *738*

KRZEMINSKI, L. F. 647, *675*

KUENTZEL, H. 493, 512, *528*

KUHN, R. 175, *198,* 694, *738*

KUKRAL, J. C. 436, *455*

KULKARNI, B. D. 240, *245*

KUMAR, A. 255, *309*

KUMIN, S. 253, *312,* 711, *741*

KUNITAKE, G. 132, *200*

KUNITZ, M. 342, 343, *465*

KUNO, S. 731, *736*

KUO, M. M. 28, *40*

KUPIECKI, F. P. 697, *738*

KUPKE, D. W. 268, *312*

KURAHASHI, K. 79, 92, *99,* 337, 356, 360, *464, 465, 474*

KURATSEINE, M. 1069, *1078*

KURIKI, Y. 94, *100*

KURLAND, C. 501, 503, *529*

KURLAND, C. G. 542, 543, *578, 579*

KURSANOV, A. L. 805, *825*

KÜRSCHNER, K. 904, *938*

KURTH, E. F. 821, *825*

KURZ, W. G. 710, *733*

KUSAKE, T. 349, *463*

KUSHIDA, H. 362, *460*

KUWADA, S. 700, 701, 702, 703, *733, 737, 738*

KUZIN, A. 834, *894*

LABBE, R. F. 261, 264, 265, 273, *309, 310, 311, 312*

LABERGE, M. 507, *529*

LACHANCE, J. P. 108, *198*

LACK, L. 711, *742*

LACKNER, H. *1061*

LACY, P. E. 520, *531*

LADD, J. N. 22, *44,* 717, *736*

LAGERKVIST, U. 67, 71, *99, 100,* 498, *527*

LAI, C. Y. 326, *463*

LAINE, T. 696, *741*

LAIRD, A. H. 609, *636*

LAJTHA, A. 485, *529*

LAKSHMANAN, M. R. 671, *675*

LAM, J. 1074, *1078*

LAMBERTON, J. A. 762, 763, *798,* 1009, *1019*

LAMBERTS, B. L. 964, *1019*

LAMBORG, M. R. 481, 483, 498, 502, 503, *531*

LAMBRECHT, R. 270, *308*

LAMFROM, H. 517, *531*

LAMPE, V. 817, *825*

LAMPEN, J. O. 446, *467*

LAMPORT, D. T. A. 15, *40*

LAN, J. 1074, *1078*

LANDRIDGE, R. 566, *585*

LANDS, W. E. M. 126, 146, 147, 148, 154, *198, 200, 201*

LANE, M. D. 336, *466*

LANG, A. 870, *898*

LANG, A. L. 227, *243*

LANG, K. 616, 617, *637*

LANG, N. 504, *533*

LANG, S. 616, *637*

LANGDON, R. G. 108, *198,* 211, *242,* 860, 873, *897, 898*

LANGE, C. F. 344, *465*

LANGEMANN, A. 331, *465*

LANGLYKKE, A. F. 341, *458*

LANGRIDGE, R. 570, *586*

LANKE, L. S. 289, *308*

LANNON, T. J. 592, *638*

LARDY, H. A. 91, 92, *99,* 123, 160, *198, 203,* 338, 349, 356, *466, 470, 472*

LAREAU, J. 56, *98,* 338, *463*

LARNER, J. 92, *101,* 160, *192, 200,* 341, 355, 371, 379, 388, 397, 399, 402, 405, 406, 407, 410, 411, *458, 460, 463, 465, 471, 474, 725, 734*

LARRABEE, A. R. 19, 20, 21, *39, 40,* 718, *738*

LARSEN, B. 345, 354, *465*

LARSEN, H. 270, *310,* 333, *465*

LARSEN, J. 502, *531*

LARSEN, P. O. 28, *38, 40*

LARSON, R. L. 28, *38, 40*

LASCELLES, J. 254, 255, 257, 264, 273, *307, 310*

LASTER, L. 287, 288, *312*
LATHE, G. H. 288, *310*
LAUENSTEIN, K. 486, *529*
LAURIE, W. 955, 1000, 1003, *1016*
LAURYSSENS, M. 108, *195*
LAVER, W. G. 255, 304, *308, 310*
LAVES, F. 213, *242*
LAVINTMAN, N. 411, *465*
LAW, J. 209, *241*, 647, *673*, 844, *896*, 948, *951*
LAW, J. H. 122, 137, 165, *191, 196, 198, 205*
LAW, J. N. 141, 150, *196*
LAW, M. D. 132, *203*
LAWRENCE, M. 568, *585*
LAWRENCE, W. J. C. 746, *797*
LAWRENCE, W. S. 619, *637*
LAWRIE, W. 983, *1016*
LAWTON, R. G. 996, *1022*
LAYTON, L. L. 438, 439, *465*
LAZAROW, A. *465*
LAZDUNSKI, M. 129, 130, *188*
LAZZARINI, R. A. 10, 11, *40*
LEA, C. H. 135, 146, *201*
LEACH, F. R. 687, *734*
LEAHY, J. 486, 514, *527*
LEARNER, A. 417, *462*
LEAVITT, R. I. 23, *40*
LEBARON, F. 521, *531*
LEBARON, F. N. 135, 136, 137, 138, 166, 174, 183, 184, 185, *193, 198*
LEBEDEVA, A. I. *894*
LEBLOND, C. P. 482, 520, *531, 535*
LEBOEUF, M. 883, *900*
LEBRAS, G. 17, 25, *41, 42*
LEDER, I. G. 54, 81, *99, 100*, 324, *470*
LEDERBERG, J. 362, 377, 383, *459*, 548, 549, 550, *580*
LEDERER, E. 121, 122, 138, *189, 194, 198*, 289, *310*, 863, 882, *897, 900*
LEE, H. A. 718, *732*
LEE, M. 566, *587*
LEE-HUANG, S. 551, *580*
LEEMAN, A. 834, *894*
LEE PENG, C. H. 125, *198*
LEES, M. 172, 182, 183, *193, 198*
LEETE, E. 690, *738*, 832, 885, *894, 900*, 955, 956, 958, 959, 960, 961, 962, 963, 964, 965, 968, 978, 981, 985, 989, 995, 998, 999, 1000, 1001, 1003, *1017, 1018, 1019, 1020, 1021, 1023*
LEGGE, J. W. 275, 276, 278, 279, 281, 287, *310*
LEHFELDT, J. 975, *1021, 1022*
LEHMAN, G. 745, *797*
LEHMAN, I. R. 546, 547, 548, 549, 550, 551, *579, 580*
LEHMANN, A. 333, *475*
LEHMANN, B. 934, *938*
LEHMANN, F. 208, *241*
LEHNINGER, A. L. 140, *193*, 446, 449, *462*, 560, *583*, 728, 730, *734, 741*
LEIBMAN, K. C. 544, 545, 561, *579, 583*
LEINWEBER, F. 11, *40*
LEITZ, F. H. B. 961, *1020*
LELOIR, L. F. 91, 92, 93, *97, 99, 100*, 337, 344, 345, 349, 351, 352, 353, 354, 355, 357, 358, 359, 360, 361, 371, 372, 374, 382, 389, 390, 391, 399, 402, 403, 404, 405, 406, 411, 419, 424, 434, 445, *457, 459, 465, 466, 468, 471, 474*, 598, *636*
LEMBERG, R. 275, 276, 277, 278, 279, 280, 281, 282, 286, 287, 290, *308, 310*
LEMIN, A. J. 877, *899*
LEMMON, R. M. 222, *243*
LENGYEL, P. 493, *531*, 556, *577*
LENHERT, P. G. 717, *738*
LENNARZ, W. J. 112, 114, 115, 118, 124, *198, 199*
LENTZ, C. P. 337, *471*
LEONARD, N. J. 971, *1020*
LEONIAN, L. H. 720, 725, *738*
LEONOWICZ, A. *940*
LEPAGE, G. A. 544, *579*
LERMAN, M. I. 501, 518, *529*
LERNER, B. 135, *201*
LERNER, N. H. 807, 818, *823*
LEROSEN, A. L. 669, *678*
LEROY, G. V. 230, *244*
LESTER, R. 288, *308, 310*
LETCHER, R. 971, *1019*
LEUPOLD, F. 119, *198*
LEUTHARD, F. 349, *464, 466*
LEVENBERG, B. 63, 64, *99*
LEVEQUE, P. *738*
LEVERE, R. D. 274, *310*
LEVETAN, R. V. 1070, *1078*
LEVIN, J. G. 32, 34, *40*, 930, *938*
LEVINE, M. 140, *198*
LEVINE, M. L. 379, 380, 389, *460*
LEVINE, P. A. 51, *99*
LEVINSON, H. S. 341, 386, *471*
LEVINTHAL, C. 504, *531*, 541, 542, *578*
LEVINTOW, L. 516, *533*, 698, *738*
LEVIS, G. 158, *200*
LEVVY, G. A. 598, *637*
LEVY, H. 227, *243*, 631, *637*
LEVY, M. 485, *528*
LEW, F. 870, *898*
LEWALLEN, L. L. 858, *897*
LEWIN, L. M. 136, *198, 204*
LEWIS, C. M. 289, *308*
LEWIS, D. O. 893, *900*
LEWIS, G. E. 1070, 1073, *1077*

LEWIS, H. B.   595, *636*
LEWIS, J. C.   725, *738*
LEWIS, K.   27, *44*
LEZIUS, A.   720, *738*
LI, C. H.   686, *735*
LI, T.   498, *531*
LIAAEN, S.   667, *675*
LIAO, S.   *535*
LIBENSON, L.   57, *96*, 560, *583*
LICHSTEIN, H. C.   696, 722, *733, 739*
LICHTER, E.   552, *581*
LIEBERMAN, I.   74, 75, 80, *98, 99*, 368, *465*, 710, *738*
LIEBERMAN, S.   227, 230, *243, 244*
LIEBISCH, H. W.   959, 975, *1020, 1022*
LIEBMAN, A. A.   966, *1015, 1020*
LIEBMAN, K. C.   76, *98*
LIEDE, V.   1004, 1006, *1021*
LIEDTKE, U.   176, *197*
LIETZE, A.   484, *529*
LIFSCHUTZ, J.   233, *244*
LIGHT, R. J.   112, 114, 115, 118, *198*
LIJINSKY, W.   645, 659, 667, *674*
LILIENWEISS, G.   885, *900*
LILLY, V. G.   720, 725, *738*
LIMBACH, D.   331, *456*
LIN, E. C. C.   450, *466*
LIN, P. H.   625, *637*
LIN, T.-Y.   373, 424, *466*
LINCOLN, R. E.   652, 653, *676*
LINDAHL, V.   444, *466*
LINDBERG, M.   215, *242*
LINDBERG, M. C.   228, *244*
LINDBERG, O.   692, *737*
LINDGREN, F. T.   178, 179, *198*
LINDLAR, H.   671, *675*
LINDSEY, A. J.   1068, 1069, 1070, 1074, *1077, 1078*
LINDSTEDT, S.   235, 239, *244, 245*
LINKER, A.   380, 426, *463*
LINN, B. O.   843, *896*
LINNER, E.   656, *674*
LIPINSKI, B.   257, *309*
LIPMAN, F.   542, 543, *578*
LIPMANN, F.   51, 52, 72, 87, *97, 98, 99, 100*, 124, 125, *189, 196*, 337, 347, 371, 382, 399, 402, 405, 438, 439, 440, 441, *455, 458, 462, 463, 466*, 471, 474, 487, 495, 498, 503, 504, 510, 511, 512, 517, 519, *526, 527, 528, 531, 532, 535*, 559, *583*, 614, 626, *636, 637*, 694, *738*, 944, *951, 952*
LIPSCHITZ, W. L.   595, *637*
LIRO, J. I.   268, *310*
LISS, M.   450, 451, *466*
LISSAU, A.   162, *204*
LITCHFIELD, J. T.   629, *637*
LITMAN, R. M.   550, *580*

LITTAUER, U. Z.   556, 557, 559, 561, 574, *582, 583, 587*
LITTLE, H. N.   218, *242*, 265, 266, *310*, 880, *899*
LITTLEFIELD, J. W.   483, 508, *531*, 571, *586*
LITTLEJOHN, W. R.   835, 836, 840, 842, 852, *895*
LIU, L. H.   877, *899*
LIU, T.-Y.   122, *195, 198*
LLOYD, A. G.   441, *466*
LOCHHEAD, A. C.   92, *99*, 433, *467*
LOCK, M. V.   334, 373, 381, 424, *454*
LOCKE, L. A.   23, 24, *43*
LOCKWOOD, L. B.   448, *466*
LOCKWOOD, W. H.   279, 281, *310*
LOEFFLER, J. E.   267, *310*
LOERCHER, R.   368, 430, *466*
LOEW, P.   1003, *1020*
LOEWUS, A.   726, *735*
LOEWUS, F. A.   160, *193, 198*, 422, 423, *459, 466*, 726, 729, *735, 738*
LOFLAND, H. B.   148, 149, *189*
LOFTFIELD, R. B.   487, 496, *530, 531*
LOGAN, M. A.   15, *41*
LONDON, I. M.   252, 274, 277, 288, *307, 310*
LONG, B.   719, *735*
LONG, C.   135, *198*
LONGCHAMPT, J. E.   233, *244*
LOOMANS, M. E.   163, *194*
LOOMIS, W. B.   854, *896*
LOPER, J. C.   29, 30, 31, *40*
LORAH, C. L.   216, 221, *242*, 878, *899*
LORCH, E.   113, 115, 116, *198, 199, 738*
LORNITZO, F. A.   372, 391, *461, 466*
LOSEV, A. P.   664, *676*
LOSSOW, W. J.   131, 132, *202*
LOUDEN, M. C. L.   959, *1020*
LOUDEN, M. L.   959, *1020*
LOUDEN, M. T. L.   959, 960, *1020*
LOUDON, J. D.   *825*
LOUGHLIN, R. E.   21, 22, *40*
LOUGHMAN, B. C.   791, *799*
LOVENBERG, W.   330, *466*
LOVERN, J. A.   105, 106, 133, *198*
LOVINY, T.   27, *41*
LOWDEN, J. A.   175, *204*
LOWE, G.   861, *897*, 1048, *1062*
LOWE, G. L.   557, *582, 583*
LOWENSTEIN, J. M.   337, 340, *465*
LOWRY, O. H.   344, 400, *466, 469*
LOWRY, P. T.   289, *310, 312*
LOWTHER, D. A.   520, *531*
LOWY, P. H.   482, 483, 485, *527*
LUBIMENKO, M. V.   268, *310*
LUBIMENKO, W.   268, *310*

LUBIN, M. 514, *531*
LUBORSKY, S. 558, *583*
LUCK, D. N. 514, *531*
LUCK, J. M. 353, *464*
LUCKNER, M. 1006, *1020*
LUDEWIG, H. 990, 1003, *1018*
LUDOWIEG, J. 443, *472*
LUKENS, L. N. 15, *40*, 64, 65, *99*
LUKTON, A. 645, 646, 647, *673, 676*
LUMRY, R. 666, *676*
LUZZATI, M. 29, 31, *40*
LYINSKY, W. 1069, *1078*
LYMAN, C. M. 694, *742*
LYNCH, V. H. 92, *97*
LYNE, R. R. 417, *462*
LYNEN, F. 9, *40, 42*, 107, 108, 111, 112, 113, 116, *198, 199, 202*, 209, 210, *241, 637*, 647, 648, *672, 675, 676*, 720, 722, *738, 741*, 833, 835, 844, 845, 857, *894, 896*, 944, 947, 948, *951, 952*
LYNEN, F. J. 646, *676*
LYNN, W. S., Jr. 227, 230, 238, *243, 244, 245*
LYRAS, C. 726, *734*
LYTHGOE, B. 239, *245*, 1035, 1056, *1061*

MAAS, W. K. 11, 12, 13, 14, *40, 43*, 694, 695, 696, 697, 731, *738*
MAAS, W. S. G. 766, *798*
McBEE, R. H. 370, 392, *472*
McCALDIN, D. J. 958, 978, *1015, 1016, 1017*
McCALLA, D. R. 749, 750, 797, 806, *826*
McCANN, M. P. 707, *741*
McCAPRA, F. 989, 1000, 1003, *1018, 1020*
McCARTHY, B. J. 507, 508, 509, 518, 521, *531, 533*
McCLUER, R. H. 175, *196*
McCOLLESTER, D. L. 181, *193*
McCONNELL, W. B. 411, 467
McCORKINDALE, J. 450, *467*
McCORKINDALE, N. J. 981, *1020*
McCORMICK, D. B. 446, 449, 450, *467, 474*, 723, *738*
McCORMICK, J. R. D. 34, *41*, 1031, *1062*
McCREADY, R. M. 364, 398, *462, 472*
McCULLOGH, W. G. 688, *738*
McDONALD, E. 985, *1016*
McDONALD, M. 342, 343, *465*
MacDONALD, S. F. 258, 261, *309*
McELROY, W. D. 605, 614, 615, *637*
McEVOY, D. 699, *735*
McFARLANE, A. S. 482, 483, 484, *528, 530, 531*
McFARLANE, E. S. 502, *535*
MacFARLANE, M. G. 127, 135, 136, 159, *194, 199*

McGARRAHAN, K. 213, *242*
McGEACHIN, R. L. 387, *467*
McGILL, D. B. 492, *527*
McGILVERY, R. W. 438, 439, *456*, 592, 608, *636, 637*
MACHEBOEUF, M. 178, *199*
McILWAIN, H. 692, *738*
McINTOSH, B. J. 884, *900*
McINTOSH, E. N. 696, *739*
McISAAC, W. M. 610, 627, *637*
McKENNIS, H. 626, 627, 629, *637*
McKEON, J. F. 301, 303, 304, *312*
McKIBBON, J. M. 136, *199*
MACKINNEY, G. 641, 645, 646, 647, 653, 654, 655, 658, 659, 669, *673, 676, 677, 678*
MACKINNON, J. 344, 351, *457*
MACLAGAN, N. F. 620, *637*
McLAIN, L. W. *204*
MacLAREN, J. 699, 700, *738*
MacLAREN, J. A. 84, *99*
McLAUGHLIN, J. J. A. 290, *306*
McLEAD, I. M. 139, 145, 168, *202*
McLEAN, E. J. T. 523, *530*
McLOUGHLIN, B. J. 1055, *1061*
McMAHAN, J. R. 680, *742*
McMAHON, V. 120, *203*
McMANUS, T. T. 116, *200*
McMASTER, W. J. 1027, *1062*
McMENAMY, R. H. 485, *531*
MacMILLAN, J. 1048, *1061*
McMORRIS, T. C. 1027, 1028, *1062*
McMULLEN, A. I. 950, *952*
McMURRAY, W. C. 126, 127, 139, 140, 142, 143, 144, 145, 152, 154, 155, 156, 159, 168, *190, 199, 200, 202*
McNICKLE, C. M. 341, *465*
MacNUTT, W. S. 58, 84, *99, 101*, 688, 699, 701, *735, 739*
MACON, A. R. 1070, *1078*
MACOW, J. 696, *741*
McPHAIL, A. T. 1044, *1060*
McPHERSON, C. 143, *190*
McQUILLEN, K. *531*
McQUISTAN, M. 653, 661, *676, 677*
MacRAE, E. K. 251
MACRAE, G. D. *952*
McRORIE, R. A. 446, *469*
McSHAN, W. H. 112, *205*
McSWAIN, B. D. 329, *455*
McSWEENEY, G. P. 947, 948, *951, 952*
McSWINNEY, R. R. 263, *310*
MADISON, J. T. 497, 498, 499, *530*, 543, *578*
MADSEN, A. 268, 273, *310*
MADSEN, N. B. 337, 402, 403, *465, 466*
MAGALDI, A. 6, *42*

MAGASANIK, B. 25, 29, 40, 41, 42, 43, 67, 99
MAGEE, W. L. 148, 194
MAGRILL, D. S. 981, 1020
MAHADEVAN, S. 131, 200
MAHER, J. 376, 396, 475
MAHESHWARI, N. 567, 585
MAHESHWARI, S. C. 566, 587
MAHLER, H. R. 563, 565, 584, 599, 612, 637
MAICKEL, R. P. 597, 615, 635, 637
MAIER, B. 1004, 1022
MAIER, J. 832, 889, 894
MAIER, W. 959, 1020
MAIHS, E. A. 815, 819, 824, 826
MAIN, R. K. 553, 581
MAITLAND, P. 813, 815, 824
MAITRA, U. 573, 574, 586
MAJER, J. 1041, 1061, 1062
MAJERUS, P. W. 112, 114, 115, 189, 199
MAJNO, G. 156, 199
MAJOR, R. T. 694, 742
MAJUMDAR, C. 561, 565, 583
MAKINO, K. 687, 738
MAKITA, A. 172, 204, 312
MALEY, F. 91, 92, 99, 356, 361, 466
MALEY, F. G. 361, 466
MALEY, G. F. 91, 92, 99, 692, 702, 738, 740
MALKIN, T. 136, 199
MALOGNE, L. A. 614, 638
MAMOON, A. M. 107, 190
MANDEL, H. G. 566, 585
MANDEL, L. R. 572, 586
MANDEL, P. 91, 92, 93, 98, 99, 504, 532, 544, 579
MANDELES, S. 486, 531
MANDELSTAM, J. 484, 531
MANDELSTAM, P. 368, 430, 466
MANGIAROTTI, G. 324, 457
MANGIAROTTI, M. 324, 457
MANGUM, J. H. 22, 40
MANIS, J. G. 609, 638
MANN, J. 985, 1017
MANN, J. D. 955, 1020
MANN, P. F. E. 398, 474
MANN, P. J. G. 738
MANN, T. 450, 464, 691, 738
MANN, W., Jr. 364, 373, 421, 423, 472
MANNER, G. 15, 40, 510, 511, 520, 531
MANNER, P. 184, 200
MANNERS, D. J. 370, 393, 397, 462, 465, 466
MANNERS, D. L. 412, 465
MANNICK, M. 519, 531
MANSON, D. 612, 630, 631, 635
MANSON, H. S. 284, 307
MANSON, L. A. 718, 738

MANSON, W. 91, 92, 99
MANSOUR, T. E. 344, 466
MÅNSSON, B. 438, 439, 443, 457
MANTROVA, G. V. 711, 734
MANTSAVINOS, R. 552, 553, 554, 581, 587
MANTZOS, J. 158, 200
MAPSON, L. W. 92, 101, 363, 473, 596, 638, 727, 728, 736, 737, 738, 740
MARAGOUDAKIS, M. E. 27, 43
MARBAIX, G. 502, 531
MARCO, G. 373, 425, 464
MARCUS, A. 507, 531
MARCUS, L. 510, 531
MARDESHEV, S. R. 696, 738
MARDONES, E. 15, 38, 520, 528
MARÉCHAL, L. R. 370, 371, 393, 416, 461, 466
MARGOLIN, P. 14, 24, 40
MARGOLIS, M. 124, 203
MARIEQ, J. 671, 677
MARINETTI, G. V. 127, 135, 147, 150, 158, 168, 199, 202
MARINI-BETTOLO, G. B. 847, 896, 1010, 1017
MARION, L. 690, 735, 738, 955, 958, 959, 962, 975, 1008, 1016, 1017, 1018, 1019, 1020, 1021, 1022, 1023
MARKER, R. E. 745, 797
MARKHAM, E. 299, 307
MARKL, G. 866, 898
MARKLEY, F. X. 832, 856, 894, 897
MARKLEY, K. S. 889, 901
MARKOVITZ, A. 92, 93, 99, 362, 466
MARKOWITZ, A. 373, 425, 426, 466
MARKS, B. H. 153, 197
MARKS, G. S. 261, 299, 301, 303, 304, 307, 310, 312
MARKS, P. 543, 578
MARKS, P. A. 510, 514, 516, 517, 527, 531
MARLOW, W. 1044, 1060
MARMUR, J. 450, 466, 569, 585
MARNATI, M. P. 715, 733, 734
MARQUISEE, M. 497, 498, 499, 530, 543, 578
MARSDEN, D. J. S. 1035, 1056, 1061
MARSH, C. A. 598, 637
MARSH, J. B. 117, 181, 199, 487, 504, 531
MARSHAK, A. 539, 577
MARSHALL, A. C. 131, 198
MARSHALL, E. K., Jr. 628, 637
MARSHALL, M. 40, 72, 99
MARTEN, A. 832, 894
MARTIN, D. B. 112, 121, 196, 199
MARTIN, F. B. 201
MARTIN, J. A. 1003, 1016
MARTIN, J. B. 146, 199
MARTIN, R. G. 24, 29, 30, 31, 37, 41, 44, 505, 506, 526

MARTIN, R. O. 979, *1016, 1020*
MARTIN, W. G. 178, *192*
MARTIN-SMITH, M. 981, *1020*
MARTIUS, C. 890, *901*
MARTZ, D. C. 485, *532*
MARUO, B. 136, 158, *189*
MARUSHIGE, K. 37, *40*, 503, *531*
MARUYAMA, H. 336, *466*
MARVIN, D. A. 541, *578*
MARX, W. 441, 442, *473*
MARX-FIGINI, M. 416, *467*
MASAYAMA, T. 686, *737*
MASE, Y. 655, *676*
MASIAR, P. 486, *531, 532*
MASON, H. H. *467*
MASON, H. S. 717, *736*, 935, *938*
MASON, J. W. 777, *798*
MASON, M. 6, 7, *42*
MASON, M. F. 625, *635*
MASRI, A. S. 624, *635*
MASSARO, E. J. 124, *199*
MASSENGALE, O. N. 659, *676*
MASSICOT, J. 955, *1020*
MASSONET, R. 641, 671, 675, *676*
MASSY-WESTROPP, R. A. 755, 757, 768, 784, *797, 798*, 842, 846, 852, *895*, 1026, 1034, 1038, 1039, 1046, 1053, *1060, 1061*
MASUDA, T. 700, 701, 702, 703, *733, 737, 738*
MASUI, T. 239, *245*
MATCHETT, J. 955, 1008, *1020*
MATHES, H. 807, 818, *824*
MATHEWS, M. B. 442, 443, *467, 471, 472*
MATHEWSON, J. A. 261, 262, *310*
MATHIAS, A. P. 89, 90, *96*, 158, *189*, 509, 510, *531*
MATIOLI, G. T. 412, 436, *460*
MATKOVICS, B. 239, *245*
MATRONE, G. 681, *736*
MATSUHASHI, M. 94, *99*, 364, 365, 366, 374, 430, *455, 461, 467*
MATSUHASHI, S. 364, 365, *467*
MATSUMOTO, K. 659, *675*
MATSUMURA, S. 114, 115, 118, *200*
MATSUO, M. 766, *798*, 1014, *1020, 1023*
MATSUO, Y. 9, 19, *41*
MATTHAEI, J. H. 493, 503, *532, 542, 578*
MATTHAEI, J. M. 493, 512, *528*
MATTHEW, M. 257, *308*
MATTHEWS, R. E. F. 510, *528*, 566, 574, *585, 587*
MATTOON, J. R. 27, 28, *41*
MATTSON, F. H. 146, *199*
MATUS, A. 566, *585*
MAUDGAL, R. K. 214, *242*
MAULI, R. 1049, *1062*
MAUNG, K. *462*

MAUZERALL, D. 249, 258, 262, 263, *310*
MAXWELL, E. S. 92, *99, 101*, 144, *203*, 356, 360, 363, *464, 467, 473*, 596, *638*
MAY, E. L. 688, *739*
MAY, J. 1012, *1016*
MAYAUDON, J. 320, 325, *467*
MAYBERRY, R. H. 446, 449, 450, *474*
MAYER, H. 269, *310*, 432, *467*
MAYER, P. 837, 855, *895*
MAYER, R. M. 365, 411, *467*
MAYER, W. 802, 808, 810, 812, 813, *825, 826*
MAZUR, Y. 877, *899*
MEAD, G. C. 552, *581*
MEAD, J. F. 117, 119, 120, 166, *200, 205*
MEADOW, P. M. 374, 430, *467*
MEANEY, M. F. 334, 381, 441, *455*
MEATH, J. A. 174, *193*
MECHERY, J. 707, *740*
MEDVEDEV, ZH. A. 486, *531*
MEHLER, A. 497, *527*
MEHLER, A. H. *98*, 337, *469*, 686, 687, 688, 692, *737, 739*
MEHLER, R. A. 627, 628, *638*
MEHTA, R. 718, *739*
MEIDELL, G. E. 355, 356, 360, *470*
MEIER, J. 858, 860, *897*
MEIER, J. R. 235, *244*
MEIGER, TH. M. 758, *798*
MEISTER, A. 4, 12, 13, 25, 27, 28, 37, *41*, 592, 610, 618, *637*
MEJER, J. 1041, *1062*
MELO, A. 357, *467*
MELOCHE, H. P. 350, *467*
MELVILLE, D. B. 720, 721, *734, 739*
MELVILLE, R. 819, *824*
MENDELSOHN, B. 930, *939*
MENDELSOHN, D. 238, *245*
MENDELSOHN, L. 238, *245*
MENDICINO, J. 405, *467*
MENTZER, C. 805, *824*
MERALLA, S. 930, *939*
MERCER, E. H. *527*
MERCER, E. I. 866, 882, 891, *898, 900*
MERGER, F. 813, *825, 826*
MERKENSCHLAGER, M. 9, *38*
MERKILL, S. H. 543, *578*
MERKL, I. 147, 148, 154, *198, 200*
MERKLE, K. 807, *824*
MERRIFIELD, R. B. 525, *531*
MERRILL, S. H. 497, 498, 499, *530*
MERVYN, L. 716, *741*
MESELSON, M. 501, 503, *527*, 542, 543, *578*
METCALFE, C. R. 807, *823*
METZENBERG, R. L. *40*, 72, *99*
METZGER, H. 519, *530*
METZLER, D. E. 22, *41*

METZNER, P.   270, *310*
MEYER, A. S.   230, 233, *244*
MEYER, C. M.   335, *467*
MEYER, K.   380, 426, 436, *462, 463*
MEYER, K. H.   340, 386, 397, 412, 414, *467*
MEYER, W. L.   400, *467*
MEYERHOF, O.   349, *467*
MEYERS, J. W.   23, *41*
MEYERS, M. B.   788, *799*
MICHAELIS, R.   448, *458*
MICHAELS, G.   179, *204*
MICHEL-DURAND, E.   808, *826*
MICHELSON, A. M.   94, *100*, 362, *469*, 539, 542, 556, *577, 582*
MICOU, J.   488, *529*
MIDGEY, J. E. M.   543, *579*
MIGLIACCI, A.   715, 716, *733, 734, 739*
MII, S.   555, 556, 557, 558, 560, *582, 583*
MIKATA, M.   714, 715, *740*
MIKUTA, E. T.   686, *741*
MILAS, N. A.   641, *676*
MILCH, S.   224, *243*
MILES, P. A.   263, *311*
MILLER, A.   521, *532*
MILLER, C. S.   682, *737*
MILLER, E. C.   593, 620, *636, 637*
MILLER, G. A.   1032, 1043, *1062*
MILLER, I. M.   299, *312*, 711, 712, *741*
MILLER, J. A.   130, *190*, 593, 620, *636, 637*
MILLER, L. P.   598, *637*
MILLER, O. N.   882, 887, *899*
MILLER, R.   509, 517, *529*
MILLER, R. M.   335, *467*
MILLER, R. W.   65, *99*
MILLER, S. C.   71, *102*
MILLER, W. L.   402, *467*
MILLERD, A.   944, *952*
MILLS, G. C.   93, *99*
MILLS, G. T.   91, 92, *99, 101*, 355, 356, 363, 422, 427, 433, *467, 472, 473*
MILLS, J. S.   877, *899*
MILNER, Y.   371, *467*
MINAMIKAWA, T.   358, 371, 390, 403, *468*
MINGHETTI, A.   715, 716, *733*
MINGIOLI, E. S.   32, *44*, 684, *734*
MINOR, F. W.   414, *467*
MINTHORN, M. L., Jr.   141, *197*
MIRAS, C. J.   158, *200*
MIROV, N. T.   839, *895*
MIRSKY, A. E.   508, 522, *526*
MITCHELL, D.   290, *311*
MITCHELL, H. K.   27, *41*, 685, 708, *733, 735*
MITCHISON, J. M.   501, 502, *532*
MITRA, A. K.   411, *467*
MITSCHER, L. A.   860, 867, 868, *897, 898*
MITSUDA, H.   702, 703, *739*

MITSUHASHI, S.   34, *41*, 446, *467*, 804, *826*, 923, *938*
MITTELMAN, N.   344, 354, *474*
MITTENZWEI, H.   270, *308*
MIURA, Y.   520, *532*
MIYAKOSHI, T.   273, *310*
MIZUMO, K.   703, *733*
MIZUSAKI, S.   966, *1019*
MLEVISA, V.   858, *897*
MOAT, A. G.   688, *733*
MOATTI, J. P.   641, 671, *765*
MOATTI, M. P.   641, 671, *675, 676*
MOBBERLEY, M. L.   216, 221, *242, 243*
MOEKSI, H.   125, *204*
MOFFAT, J. G.   698, *739*
MOHRHAUER, H.   119, *197*
MOKRASCH, L. C.   76, *99*, 184, *200*
MOLDAVE, K.   495, 512, 514, *529, 534, 535*, 592, 610, *637*
MÖLLER, E. F.   85, *102*, 694, *742*
MOLNAR, D. A.   706, 707, *734*
MOLNAR, G.   858, *897*
MOLNAR, J.   436, *467, 471*
MOLTZ, A.   728, 730, *734*
MOMMAERTS, W. F. H. M.   399, *467*
MONDON, A.   989, *1020*
MONDOVI, B.   9, *41*
MONEY, T.   989, 1000, 1003, *1018, 1020*
MONKOVIC, I.   977, 983, 1008, *1020*
MONOD, J.   377, 383, 408, *468, 474*, 500, 501, 505, *530*, 542, *578*
MONOZ, J. M.   337, *466*
MONRO, R.   503, 504, 511, *526, 532*, 543, *578*
MONTAGNIER, L.   566, *585*
MONTAVON, M.   668, 671, *675, 677*
MONTERMOSO, J. C.   943, 944, *952*
MONTEVERDE, N. A.   268, *310*
MONTGOMERY, J. A.   714, *739*
MONTGOMERY, J. P.   597, *636*
MONTJAR, M.   501, 502, 504, *534*
MONTY, K.   152, *194*
MONTY, K. J.   10, 11, *39, 40, 42*
MOOHR, J. W.   567, 568, *585*
MOON, M. W.   571, *586*
MOORE, C.   947, *952*
MOORE, C. U.   252, *308*
MOORE, E. C.   57, *98*, 560, *583*
MOORE, G. E.   1067, *1078*
MOORE, S.   479, 482, *534*, 610, *638*
MOORE, T.   670, *676*
MOOTOO, B. S.   1003, *1018*
MORALES, D. R.   544, *579*
MORATO, T.   233, *244*
MORAWIECKA, B.   485, *527*
MORDOH, J.   411, *468*
MORELEC-COULON, M. J.   136, *193, 200*

MORETTI, A. 426, *468*
MORGAN, A. 958, *1020*
MORGAN, H. E. 402, *468*
MORGAN, K. 370, 392
MORGAN, R. S. 188, *192*
MORGAN, W. S. 552, *581*
MORIARTY, S. 880, *899*
MORIMOTO, I. 934, *938*
MORITA, T. 502, 503, *532*
MORITAKA, S. 702, *739*
MORITZ, A. G. 1070, 1073, *1077*
MORIYAMA, Y. 520, *532*
MORRIS, D. 28, *37*
MORRIS, H. P. 554
MORRIS, J. G. 723, *739*
MORRISON, F. R. 838, *895*
MORRISON, G. A. 1030, *1060*
MORRISON, R. A. 558, *583*
MORSINGH, F. 966, *1020*
MORTENSON, L. E. 329, 330, *468, 474*
MORTIMER, D. C. 92, *97*, 371, 389, *457*
MORTIMER, P. I. 778, *798*
MORTON, R. A. 240, *245*, 890, *901*
MORTON, R. K. 381, 382, *455*
MOSBACH, E. H. 224, *243*, 728, *734, 737*
MOSBACH, K. 766, *798*, 1033, 1035, 1037, 1043, *1062*
MOSCATELLI, E. A. 160, *200*
MOSER, H. W. 170, 171, 176, *200*
MOSES, V. 273, *308*, 320, 321, 326, 450, *468*, 921, *938*
MOSETTIG, E. 222, *243*, 870, *898*
MOSHIER, T. A. 27, 28, *41*
MOSLEIN, E. M. 210, *241*, 844, *896*, 948, *952*
MOSOLOV, V. V. 496, 504, *533*
MOSS, G. P. 879, *899*
MOTHES, E. 962, *1020*
MOTHES, K. 954, 955, 959, 962, 964, 965, 975, 978, 989, 1000, 1004, 1006, 1008, *1018, 1019, 1020, 1021, 1022, 1023*
MOTHES, U. 789, *799*, 1004, 1006, *1017, 1021, 1023*
MOTOZAKI, S. 720, *739*
MOUBASHIER, R. A. 771, *798*
MOUNTS, T. L. 120, *193*
MOUSTA, F. E. 296, *532*
MOYE, C. J. 700, *733*, 755, *797*, 1026, 1039, *1061*
MOYED, H. S. 29, *41*, 67, *99*
MOYER, A. N. 507, *535*
MOYER, A. W. 140, *193*
MUDD, J. A. 496, *528*
MUDD, J. B. 116, *200*
MUDD, S. H. 7, 8, *41*, 955, 958, 985, *1017, 1020, 1021*
MUELLER, G. 791, *799*

MUELLER, G. C. 402, *463*
MUELLER, J. H. 719, *739*
MUENCH, K. 574, *587*
MUIR, H. 107, 124, *201*
MUIR, H. M. 252, *310*, 711, *739*
MUIR, R. D. 448, *471*
MUKERJEE, S. K. 784, 787, *799*
MUKHERJEE, S. 132, *200*
MULDER, E. 148, *200*
MULDER, L. *192*
MÜLLER, A. 330, *468, 475*
MÜLLER, D. 448, *468*
MÜLLER, G. 716, *739*
MULLER, O. 301, *307*, 712, 716, 717, *733, 739*
MUNCH-PETERSEN, A. 91, 92, 93, *98, 99, 101*, 355, 356, 357, *464, 468, 473*
MUNRO, A. 501, 502, 503, *532*
MUNRO, H. N. 523, 521, *530, 532*
MUNSCHE, D. 955, 1006, *1021*
MURALT, A. V. 643, *675*
MURAR, J. 486, *531, 532*
MURATA, T. 334, 358, 371, 381, 390, 403, 405, *455, 468*
MURPHY, C. F. 986, *1021*
MURPHY, T. A. 372, 391, *468*
MURRAY, A. W. 885, *900*
MURRAY, K. E. 858, *897*
MURRILL, J. B. 961, 978, 981, *1020*
MURTHY, S. K. 131, *200*
MUSCULUS, O. 592, *637*
MUSGRAVE, O. C. 757, *798*, 1030, *1061*
MYERS, C. M. 598, 629, *637*
MYERS, J. 289, *310*
MYERS, J. W. 23, *41*
MYERS, M. 817, *826*
MYERS, T. C. 556, *582*
MYRBÄCK, K. 389, 392, *468*

NABNEY, J. *1063*
NAEF, H. 860, *897*
NAGABHUSHANAM, A. 409, *461*
NAGASAWA, M. 865, *897*
NAGATA, T. P. 550, *580*
NAGY, E. 663, 665, *673*
NAIMARK, A. 182, *195*
NAJJAR, V. A. 353, *468, 470, 472*
NAKADA, H. I. 352, *476*
NAKAGAWA, T. 923, *938*
NAKAJIMA, H. 284, 285, 286, 295, *310, 311, 313*
NAKAJIMA, O. 284, 285, 295, *311*
NAKAMOTO, T. 512, *532*, 565, 567, 568, 569, 570, *584, 585*
NAKAMURA, M. 371, *468*
NAKAMURA, S. 690, 691, *736, 739*

NAKAMURA, T. 11, *41*
NAKAMURA, Y. 378, 394, *473*
NAKAO, A. 19, *41*
NAKAO, N. 485, *527, 534*
NAKATA, A. 566, *584*
NAKATA, Y. 446, *474*
NAKAYAMA, H. 681, *739*
NAKAYAMA, T. 645, 658, *673, 676*
NAKAYAMA, T. O. M. 645, 646, 647, 648, 649, 656, 657, 659, 660, 663, 665, 669, 670, *673, 675, 676, 677, 678*
NAKAYAWA, T. 165, *191*
NAMIKO, O. *309*
NAPIER, I. M. 1070, 1073, *1077*
NASH, C. P. 682, *739*
NATAKE, M. 446, *468*
NATH, R. 19, *39*
NATHAN, H. A. 718, *739*
NATHANS, D. 503, 504, 511, 517, *532*
NATHANS, D. G. 543, *578*
NATHENSON, S. G. 374, 430, 431, *468, 471*
NAUGHTON, M. A. 514, 515, *532*
NAVES, Y. 838, 841, *895*
NAYA, Y. 813, *827*
NAYUDAMMA, Y. 812, *826*
NEAL, G. E. 339, *468, 473*
NEDATE, S. 659, *675*
NEEDHAM, J. 724, *739*
NEELY, W. B. 413, *468*
NEHER, R. 228, *244*
NEIDLE, A. 29, *41*
NEILL, J. M. 379, 411, *462*
NEILL, K. G. 1030, *1062*
NEISH, A. C. 364, 414, 420, *455, 468*, 749, 750, 766, 772, 773, 790, 791, 796, 797, 798, *799*, 802, 805, 806, 807, 817, *826, 827*, 907, 909, 921, 923, 927, 928, 929, *937, 938*, 957, 958, *1021, 1023*
NELSON, G. E. N. 448, *466*, 658, *673*
NELSON, N. 631, *638*
NELSON, N. M. 370, 392, *472*
NELSON, O. E. 403, *468*, 653, *677*
NELSON, W. O. 696, *740*
NEMER, M. J. 141, 154, 156, *200*
NEMETH, A. M. 257, 299, *311*
NÉMETH, P. E. 955, 985, *1020*
NERY, R. *635*
NES, W. R. 225, 240, *243, 245*, 879, 880, 881, 890, 892, *899*
NEUBACHER, J. 726, *739*
NEUBAUER, D. 979, *1021*
NEUBERG, C. 837, 855, *895*
NEUBERGER, A. 6, 19, *37*, 252, 254, 255, 256, 257, 265, 304, *308, 310, 311*, 686, 696, 711, *734, 735, 739*
NEUFELD, E. F. 92, 94, *97, 100*, 130, *200*, 345, 354, 355, 356, 358, 361, 363, 364, 369,

NEUFELD, E. F.—(*cont.*)
371, 372, 374, 375, 416, 420, 421, 422, 423, 434, 435, 438, 439, *456, 460, 461, 464, 465, 466, 468*, 693, *737*
NEUHAUS, F. C. 4, 5, *41*, 142, 156, 157, *200*, 374, 430, *473*
NEUKOMM, S. 1076, *1078*
NEUMANN, D. 959, 964, *1021*
NEUPREZ, R. *636*
NEURATH, H. 485, 520, *530*
NEUSCHUL, P. 448, *463*
NEVE, R. A. 261, *311*
NEVRAJEVA, N. 834, *894*
NEWBOLD, G. T. 1054, *1062*
NEWBURGH, R. W. 693, *737*
NEWSCHWANDER, W. W. 879, *899*
NICHOL, C. A. 708, 709, *742*
NICHOLANS, R. A. *311*
NICHOLAS, H. J. 225, *243*, 855, 873, 880, 882, 889, 891, 892, *897, 898, 899, 900, 901*
NICHOLAS, R. E. H. 263, *310*
NICHOLS, A. V. 178, 179, *198*
NICHOLS, K. E. 294, *311*
NICHOLSON, D. C. 276, 287, *308, 311*
NICHOLSON, L. W. 377, 396, 410, *469*
NICOLAIDES, N. 213, *242*
NICOLAUS, R. A. 287, *308*
NICOLLETTI, R. *311*
NIEFT, M. L. 132, *200*
NIELANDS, J. B. *312*
NIELSEN, B. 979, *1017*
NIEUWLAND, J. A. 1072, *1078*
NIGAM, V. N. 409, *461*
NIKAIDO, H. 90, 92, *100*, 365, 432, *469*
NIKLAS, A. 482, *532*
NIKUNI, J. 759, *798*
NIKUNI, Z. 403, 412, *459*
NILSSON, B. 1049, *1062*
NILSSON, J. 295, *307*
NILSSON, M. 782, *799*
NIMMO, C. 948, 949, *952*
NIMURA, T. 720, *739*
NIRENBERG, M. W. 493, 503, 504, 509, *526, 527, 532*, 542, *578*
NISHIDO, G. 264, *311*
NISHIMURA, S. 496, 499, *530, 532, 586*
NISHIZUKA, Y. 83, *100*, 690, 691, 693, 731, 733, 736, *739*
NISIDA, M. 728, *741*
NISMAN, B. 502, 520, *532, 535*
NIYOGI, S. K. 570, *586*
NOBLESSE, C. 418, *459*
NODA, H. 707, 708, *737*
NOLL, H. 494, 504, 511, 518, *532, 534, 535*
NOMURA, M. 542, *578*
NOONER, D. W. 866, *898*
NORBERG, E. 379, 380, 389, *460, 469*

NORD, F. F. 904, 905, 906, 909, 910, 911, 912, 913, 914, 915, 916, 917, 918, 919, 920, 922, 924, 926, 927, 929, 930, 933, 934, 936, *937, 938, 939, 940*
NORDIN, J. H. 360, *456*
NORDLIE, R. C. 338, 342, 345, *469, 472*
NORDSTRÖM, L. 386, *463*
NORGARD, D. W. 647, 658, *673*
NORRIE, M. 277, 278, 280, *310*
NORRIS, A. T. 114, 115, 118, *200*, 496, *532*
NORRIS, G. 331, *456*
NORRIS, L. T. 92, *97*
NORRIS, P. *309*
NORTH, B. 653, *677*
NORTH, R. J. 483, *528*
NOSE, Y. 614, *637,* 681, *739*
NOTATION, A. D. 971, *1021*
NOTT, J. 413, *468*
NOVELLI, G. D. 86, *98,* 499, 502, 510, 511, 523, *528, 530, 532,* 694, 697, 698, 699, *736, 738, 739*
NOVOA, W. B. 400, *460*
NOVOTNY, J. 1068, 1070, 1071, 1074, *1077*
NOWACKI, E. 971, 974, 975, 1004, *1021, 1022*
NOZU, K. 566, *584*
NUGTEREN, D. H. 120, *200*
NUNHEIMER, T. D. 28, 29, *42*
NURSTEN, H. E. 803, *824*
NUSBAUM-CASSUTO, E. 650, *676*
NUSSENBAUM, S. 379, 411, *469*
NUTTER, W. E. 485, *532*
NYC, J. 4, *41*
NYC, J. F. 142, 149, *192, 194, 195, 204*

O'BRIEN, B. M. 556, *582*
O'BRIEN, J. R. P. 727, 728, *740*
O'BRIEN, P. J. 90, 92, 93, *97, 100,* 356, 358, 367, 438, 439, *461, 465, 469*
O'CALLAGHAN, C. H. 715, 716, *735*
O'CARRA, P. 290, 291, *311*
OCHOA, S. 107, 109, *193, 199,* 321, 337, 342, 343, *458, 462, 464, 469, 475,* 484, 485, 493, 496, *527, 531, 532, 533,* 555, 556, 557, 558, 559, 560, 565, 566, 567, 568, 569, 570, *582, 584, 585,* 688, *739*
OCKNER, R. K. 273, *311*
O'DELL, B. L. 708, *740*
O'DONNELL, V. J. 226, *243*
O'DONOVAN, D. 958, *1021*
OECHLER, F. 745, *797*
OEHLERT, W. 482, *532*
OESTERLING, M. J. 481, *533*
O'FARRELL, A. F. 858, *897*
OFENGAND, E. J. 495, 496, 497, 508, *527, 532*

OFNER, A. 671, *677*
OGAN, A. U. 968, *1016*
OGASAWARA, N. 690, *735*
OGATA, K. 502, 503, 511, 516, 520, *530, 532,* 719, 737
OGAWA, T. 284, *309*
OGILVIE, J. W. 860, *897*
OGLE, J. D. 15, *41*
OGUR, M. 29, *41*
OGUR, S. 29, *41*
OHAD, I. 415, *469*
O'HEOCHA, C. 290, 291, 292, *309, 311*
OHLSSON, E. 392, *469*
OHTAKA, Y. 506, *532,* 566, *584*
OHTSUKA, E. 571, *586*
OKADA, S. 553, *581*
OKAMOTO, K. 446, 450, *469, 476*
OKAMOTO, T. 483, 510, *532, 534*
OKAMURA, N. 521, *534*
OKANY, A. 955, 1004, 1006, *1016*
OKAY, S. 289, *311*
OKAZAKI, R. 94, *100, 101,* 362, 365, *469*
OKAZAKI, T. 94, *100, 101,* 362, 365, *469,* 546, 548, 549, *580*
OKUDA, K. 239, *245*
OKUDA, S. 366, *469*
OKUI, S. 487, *530*
OKUMURA, S. 720, *739*
OLAVARRIA, J. M. 344, 351, 354, 371, 402, 404, 405, 406, *466*
OLAVESEN, A. H. 401, *469*
OLCAY, A. 905, 906, *939*
OLIVEIRA, M. M. 148, *200*
OLIVER, I. T. 92, *100,* 363, 404, *470, 471*
OLLEY, J. N. 136, *195*
OLLIS, W. D. 806, 818, *823, 824,* 1032, 1043, *1062*
OLMSTEAD, P. S. 557, *582, 583*
OLSEN, C. W. 682, *739*
OLSON, J. A. 215, *242,* 670, *676*
OLSON, M. E. 484, *532*
OLSON, R. E. 178, 179, 181, 182, *200*
OLSZEWSKA, M. J. 488, *532*
OMORI, S. 511, 520, *530, 532*
ONCLEY, J. L. 178, 179, 181, *200*
ONDARZA, R. 91, 92, *99*
ONEYAMA, R. 981, *1019*
ONISHI, I. 865, *897*
ONO, K. 179, 181, *193,* 235, 236, *244*
OOYAMA, J. 28, *41*
ORATZ, M. 487, *533*
ORCHEN, M. 152, *198*
O'REILLY, K. T. 296, *307*
ORLOWSKI, S. 724, *737*
ORO, J. 866, *898*
ORR, S. F. D. 612, *635*
ORRELL, S. A., Jr. 399, *469*

2 O

ORTEGA, M. V.   688, *739*
ORTEGA, M. W.   962, *1021*
ORTH, H.   251, 269, *308*
ORTH, H. D.   *1021*
ORTIGOZA-FERADO, J. A.   *40*
ORTIZ, P. J.   555, 556, 557, 558, 559, 563, *582, 584*
OSAWA, T.   556, *582*
OSBORN, M. J.   373, 374, 432, 433, *460, 469, 471, 473, 476,* 709, 710, *736, 737, 739, 1062*
OSMAN, H. G.   645, 657, *674*
OSTENDORF, P.   334, *475*
OSTROW, J. D.   288, *311*
OSUCH, M. V.   885, *900*
OTAGAKI, M.   237, *245*
OTSUKA, H.   502, 503, *532*
OTTKE, R. C.   943, *952*
OURA, H.   494, 510, 518, *534*
OURISSON, G.   835, 862, 879, 887, *895, 897, 899, 900, 901*
OVE, P.   710, *738*
OVERATH, P.   115, *200,* 722, *741*
OVEREND, W. G.   835, *895*
OVERTON, K. H.   860, *897*
OWEN, J. N.   832, 852, *894, 896*
OWEN, L. N.   848, *896*
OWENS, O. H.   267, *308*
OWENS, W. M.   211, *241,* 873, *898*
OYAMA, H.   265, *311*
OZONE, K.   403, *462*

PAABO, K.   235, *244*
PACE, N.   123, *205*
PACKHAM, M. A.   595, *637*
PACLT, J.   914, *939*
PADBERG, G.   176, *197*
PAGE, H.   1031, *1062*
PAGE, I. H.   610, 627, *637*
PAGE, S.   509, 510, *531*
PAI, C. H.   722, *739*
PAINE, C. M.   485, *532*
PALADE, G. E.   520, *528*
PALADINI, A. C.   92, *97,* 353, 355, 355, *457,* 610, *638*
PALLERONI, N. J.   446, 448, *469*
PALMER, F. B.   163, *200, 202*
PAN, S. C.   377, 396, 410, *469*
PANCZEL, M.   663, 665, *673*
PANEK, A.   372, 391, *469*
PANGBORN, M. C.   136, *200*
PAPPENHEIMER, A. M., Jr.   264, *311*
PARDEE, A. B.   18, *44,* 693, 699, 704, *736, 742*
PARK, J. T.   91, *100,* 356, 374, 430, *458, 469, 473*

PARK, R. B.   321, *469,* 843, *896,* 943, 944, 946, 947, *952*
PARKE, D. V.   *637*
PARKER, F.   132, *194*
PARKER, L. F. J.   711, 714, *733, 735*
PARKS, L. W.   8, *41,* 1040, *1062*
PARKS, R. E., Jr.   363, *461*
PARMEGGIANI, A.   402, *468*
PARNAS, J. K.   398, *469*
PARRY, G. V.   882, *900,* 955, 983, 1000, 1001, 1003, *1016*
PARSONS, L. G.   727, 728, *740*
PARTHIER, B.   523, *532*
PARTRIDGE, C. W. H.   687, *739*
PARTRIDGE, M.   358, *470*
PARTRIDGE, R.   619, *639*
PASCHKIS, K. E.   76, *100*
PASESHNICHENKO, V. A.   1012, 1013, *1018*
PASSERON, S.   358, *459, 469*
PASSET, J.   855, *897*
PASSONNEAU, J. V.   344, 400, *466, 469*
PASTERNAK, C. A.   *464*
PATAT, F.   413, *459*
PATEL, R. Z.   609, *637*
PATLAK, C. S.   485, *530*
PATO, M. L.   708, *739*
PATRICK, A. D.   379, 411, *461,* 843, *896*
PATSCHKE, L.   776, *798*
PATTABIRAMAN, T. N.   426, *469*
PATTE, J.   *41*
PATTE, J. C.   18, 27, *38, 41*
PATTERSON, A.   979, *1017*
PATTERSON, D. S. P.   *311*
PATTERSON, J. D. E.   182, *193*
PAUCKNER, W.   807, 818, *824*
PAUL, A. G.   1004, *1021*
PAUL, H. E.   631, *637*
PAUL, M. F.   631, *637*
PAULING, L.   669, *678*
PAULUS, E.   818, 819, 820, *826*
PAULUS, H.   18, *41,* 152, 158, 159, 161, 170. *197, 200,* 726, *739*
PAYLING WRIGHT, G.   188, *192*
PAYNE, W. J.   446, *469*
PAYNE, W. W.   1069, *1078*
PAYSANT-DIAMENT, M.   139, 140, *200*
PAZUR, J. H.   92, 94, *100,* 355, 356, 357, 358, 360, 361, 362, 373, 377, 378, 379, 380, 389, 392, 394, 396, 409, 410, 412, 422. 432, 448, *460, 469, 470*
PEABODY, R. A.   63, *98*
PEANASKY, R. J.   349, *470*
PEARLMAN, R.   496, *532*
PEARSON, C. M.   399, *467*
PEARSON, J. R.   485, *532*
PEAT, S.   379, 383, 384, 388, 389, 410, 411. *455, 456, 462, 463, 470*

PÉAUD-LEONOËL, C. 382, 418, *470*
PECK, H. D., Jr. 440, *470*
PEDERSEN, P. M. 1074, *1078*
PEETERS, G. J. 372, 393, *462*
PEISACH, J. 12, *41*
PELTER, A. 214, *242*, 844, *896*
PELUFFO, R. O. 117, 120, *196*
PEÑA, R. 508, *532*
PENDLINGTON, S. 699, *733*
PENFOLD, A. R. 838, 850, 856, *895, 896,
  897*
PENNINGTON, D. 660, *678*
PENNINGTON, R. J. 79, *99*, 337, *465*
PENNY, I. F. 135, *198*
PENSWICK, J. R. 497, 498, 499, *530*, 543,
  578
PEPPER, J. M. 926, *939*
PERAINO, C. 13, *41*
PERKINS, H. R. 427, 429, 430, 431, *470, 471*
PERLIN, A. S. 411, *467*
PERLMAN, D. 715, *739*, 1041, *1061*
PERLMAN, R. L. 373, 441, 443, *470*
PERLZWEIG, W. A. 724, *736*
PERRY, J. J. 26, *41*
PERRY, M. B. 334, 367, 373, 381, 424, *454,
  464*
PERRY, R. P. 518, *532*
PERUTZ, M. F. *532*
PETERKOFSKY, A. 497, 500, 519, *527*, 717,
  739, 742
PETERKOFSKY, B. 15, 26, *41, 532*
PETERS, H. 688, *742*
PETERS, J. M. 19, *41*, 710, *739*
PETERS, R. A. 727, 728, *740*
PETERS, T. 483, 487, 516, 520, 523, *530,
  532, 535*
PETERS, V. J. *740*
PETERSEN, W. E. 372, 392, *460*
PETERSON, W. H. 694, *741*
PETIX, J. 147, *199*
PETRACEK, F. J. 671, *678*
PETROVA, A. N 410, *470*
PETRYKA, Z. *311*
PETZOLD, E. N. 661, *676*
PEYSER, P. 728, 730, *734*
PFEFFERKORN, L. C. 512, *530*
PFIFFNER, J. J. 708, 717, *736, 740*
PFLÜGER, H. 119, *197*
PHAGPOLNGARM, S. 658, 661, *672*
PHILLIPS, A. 948, *951*
PHILLIPS, A. H. 209, *241*, 647, *673*, 844, *896*
PHILLIPS, B. P. 224, *243*
PHILLIPS, G. R. 517, *532*
PHILLIPS, G. T. 1003, *1018*
PHILLIPS, L. L. 341, *470*
PHILLIPS, M. 918, *939*
PHILP, J. 822, *826*

PIANTADOSI, C. 156, *193*
PIATAK, D. M. 893, *900*
PICKEN, J. M. 424, *455*
PICKWORTH, J. 299, *309*
PIERARD, A. 14, *42*
PIERCE, F. T., Jr. 222, *243*
PIERINGER, R. A. 126, 158, *197, 200*
PIERPONT, W. S. 86, *100*
PIETRA, G. 1069, *1078*
PIEZ, K. A. 485, *528*
PIGMAN, W. 341, *470*
PIGMAN, W. W. 390, *463*
PIHL, A. 697, *740*
PIJEWSKA, L. 985, *1016*
PILGERAM, L. O. 140, *201*
PILOTY, O. 593, *636*
PINA, M. 553, *581*
PINCUS, G. 227, *243*
PINDRED, H. K. 808, *824, 825*
PINJANI, M. 405, *467*
PIRIE, A. 337, *474*
PIRIE, N. W. 440, *470*
PITOT, H. C. 13, *41*
PITT, G. A. J. 671, *677*
PITTARD, A. J. 34, *41*
PIZER, F. L. 137, *189, 201*
PIZER, L. I. 6, *41*, 142, *201*
PLATT, B. S. 727, 728, *740*
PLAUT, G. W. E. 84, *100*, 692, 699, 700,
  702, 703, 721, *736, 738, 740, 742*
PLENTL, A. A. 76, *100*
PLIENINGER, H. 936, *939*, 1004, 1006, *1021*
PLIMMER, J. R. 1075, *1078*
PLOTZ, 230, *244*
PLUNKETT, A. O. 1003, *1016*
PLUSCEC, J. 257, 258
POGELL, B. M. 344, 352, *470, 474*, 722,
  723, *740*
POLAK, E. H. 836, *895*
POLGAR, A. 658, 669, *676, 678*
POLHAMUS, L. 943, 944, *952*
POLLAK, J. K. 483, *528*
POLLARD, C. 948, 949, *952*
POMMER, H. 641, *675*
PON, N. G. 321, *469, 470*
PONCHON, F. 556, *582*
PONTECORVO, G. 688, *740*
PONTIS, H. G. 91, 92, 93, *98, 100*, 356, 357,
  361, 372, 419, *461, 470*
PONTIS, S. M. E. 357, *470*
PONTREMOLI, S. 324, *457*
POOLE, A. G. 136, *199*
POPJÁK, G. 107, 108, 112, 116, 124, 135,
  193, 195, 198, 201, 204, 209, 210, 214, 218,
  241, 242, 647, 648, 650, *673, 674, 676*, 833,
  834, 844, 847, 858, *894, 896*, 949, *951, 952*,
  1040, 1047, *1061*

PORCELLATI, G. 154, *201*
PORETTI, C. G. 643, *675*
PORRA, R. J. 264, 265, *311*
PORTER, G. A. 507, *532*
PORTER, J. 813, *824, 952*
PORTER, J. N. 109, *201*
PORTER, J. W. 109, 112, *201, 202, 204,* 209, *241,* 647, 648, 649, 652, 653, 654, 658, 670, *673, 675, 676, 678,* 833, 858, 879, 880, 891, *894, 897, 899*
PORTER, J. W. G. 714, *735*
PORTER, K. R. 444, *461,* 520, *532*
PORTER, R. R. 486, *532*
POSSMAYER, F. 158, 161, 162, *201*
POSTERNAK, T. 345, 354, 452, *470*
POTTER, A. L. 362, 377, 383, *459*
POTTER, R. L. 89, *100,* 544, *579*
POTTER, V. R. 79, 91, 92, *98,* 144, *195,* 544, 552, 553, 560, 561, *579, 581, 583*
POTTINGER, P. K. 404, *470*
POULIK, J. A. 519, *528*
POUYET, J. 541, *578*
POVER, W. F. R. 141, 150, 157, *196*
POWELL, A. D. G. 1035, 1058, *1062*
POWELL, J. F. 26, *41,* 427, *473*
POWELL, R. G. 791, *799*
POWER, F. W. 609, *637*
PRABHU, K. A. 370, 398, *472*
PRAGER, R. H. 955, 1003, *1015*
PRATT, E. A. 548, 549, *580*
PREISS, J. 81, 82, 93, *100,* 357, 358, 363, 364, 403, 424, *460, 461, 470, 472,* 561, *583,* 690, 693, *740*
PRELOG, V. 650, *673,* 993, *1018*
PRESTON, W. H., Jr. 226, *243,* 881, 883, 886, *899*
PREUSSE, C. 601, *635*
PRICE, J. M. 592, 620, 630, *637,* 687, 724, *734, 740*
PRICE, L. 267, 287, *313*
PRICE, T. D. 208, *241,* 544, 545, *579*
PRICER, W. E., Jr. 124, 126, 127, 142, *198,* 548, *580,* 692, 710, *737, 740*
PRICKETT, P. S. 659, *676*
PRIDE, E. 1034, 1035, 1037, 1041, *1061*
PRIDE, H. S. 450, *472*
PRIDHAM, J. B. *637*
PRIEST, R. E. 687, *740*
PRIOR, B. E. 273, *307*
PRITCHARD, E. T. 137, 141, 145, 146, 156, *201, 203*
PRITCHARD, G. G. 335, *470, 475*
PROCHOROFF, N. N. 350, *470*
PROCKOP, D. J. 15, *40, 41*
PROKOFIEV, A. A. 834, 844, *894*
PROSEN, R. J. 299, *309*
PROVOST, P. *38*

PRUNTY, F. T. G. 263, *310*
PUGH, E. L. 112, 114, 115, 118, *204*
PULLMAN, M. E. 353, *468, 470*
PURCELL, A. E. 647, 652, *676,* 881, *899,* 946, 950, *952*
PURDOM, P. 277, 279, 280, 281, *308*
PURKO, M. 696, *739, 740*
PUSEY, D. F. G. 1044, *1063*
PUTMAN, E. W. 92, *100,* 362, 376, 377, 383, 390, *459, 476*
PUZA, M. 1041, *1061, 1062*

QUACKENBUSH, F. W. 647, 652, 653, 655, 661, 669, *675, 676, 677*
QUASTEL, J. H. 344, 351, *460, 462, 738*
QUAYLE, J. R. 321, *470*
QUIRIN, C. 504, *532*
QURESHI, A. A. 728, *732*

RABIN, B. R. 321, *470*
RABINOWITCH, E. I. 334, *470*
RABINOWITZ, J. 946, *951*
RABINOWITZ, J. C. 330, *466,* 710, 718, *736, 740, 741*
RABINOWITZ, J. L. 208, 209, 230, 238, *241,* 244, 245, 450, *470,* 647, 674, 945, *952*
RABINOWITZ, M. 404, *470,* 484, 507, 510, 516, 519, *532, 533*
RABOURN, W. J. 655, 669, *676*
RABSON, R. 6, *42*
RACHELE, J. R. 140, *201*
RACHMELER, M. 36, *44,* 685, *742*
RACKER, E. 51, 54, 57, *100,* 321, 324, 325, 345, 350, 351, *461, 470, 473, 474,* 921, *939*
RACUSEN, D. W. 944, 945, 946, *952*
RADDING, C. M. 180, *201,* 550, 551, *580*
RADHAKRISHNAN, A. N. 6, 12, 23, *41, 42, 43*
RADIN, N. S. 117, 168, 173, *195, 197, 201,* 252, *311,* 711, *740*
RADOVICH, J. 486, *523*
RAFELSON, M. E., Jr. 23, *42*
RAFFY, A. 289, *308*
RAFTER, G. W. 342, *470*
RAFTERY, M. 290, 292, *311*
RAHA, C. R. 1069, *1078*
RAISTRICK, H. 448, *458,* 1030, 1056, *1060, 1062, 1063*
RAJALAKSHMI, S. 693, *740*
RALL, T. W. 400, 402, *470, 473*
RALPH, R. K. 498, 501, 510, *528, 530, 532,* 566, *585, 586*
RAMAGE, R. 985, *1016*
RAMAHI, H. 1069, *1078*
RAMAIAH, A. 344, *471*

RAMAKRISHNAN, C. V. 337, *471*, 944, *951*
RAMAMURTI, K. 414, *471*
RAMASARMA, T. 143, 156, *201*
RAMIN, H. 959, *1020*
RAMIREZ, M. I. 930, *937*
RAMOS, F. 14, *42*
RAMPERSAND, O. *532*
RAMSTAD, E. 885, *900*, 955, 959, 981, 1004, 1006, *1015, 1016, 1018, 1021, 1022*
RAMUZ, H. 978, 979, *1015*
RAND, H. J. 1074, *1077*
RAO, B. G. 226, *243*
RAO, D. R. 690, *736*, 962, *1018*
RAO, J. B. 812, *826*
RAO, M. V. 971, *1015*
RAO, S. 341, *475*
RAPER, R. 208, *241*
RAPIN, A. M. C. 432, *467*
RAPOPORT, G. 419, *459, 471*
RAPOPORT, H. 301, *311*, 965, 966, 979, *1015, 1016, 1020, 1021, 1022*, 1069, *1078*
RAPPORT, M. M. 135, *201*
RASENACK, D. 931, 936, *938*
RASSOW, B. 918, *939*
RATNER, S. 481, 482, 483, *530, 533*
RAUDA, V. 405, 406, 407, *473*
RAUEN, H. M. 707, *740*
RAVEL, J. M. 58, *101*, 696, *740*
RAY, D. S. 542, *578*
RAY, S. N. 727, *740*
RAY, W. J. 498, *528*
RAYBURN, C. H. 1074, *1078*
RAYROUD, A. 331, *465*
READ, J. 834, 836, *894, 895*
REALE, M. J. *939*
RECALDIN, D. A. C. L. 377, 409, 419, *459*
RECONDO, E. 358, 375, 403, 407, 434, *459, 469, 471, 474*
REDDI, K. K. 565, *584*
REDDY, S. K. 724, *740*
REDFEARN, E. R. 664, 665, 671, *674, 677*
REDFIELD, B. 22, *44*, 717, *739, 742*
REDUZZI, F. *636*
REES, W. R. 379, 389, 410, *470*
REESE, E. T. 341, 386, *471*
REEVE, E. B. 482, 485, *532, 534*
REEVES, R. E. 334, 381, 433, *455, 471*
REICH, E. 501, 507, *529, 533*, 565, 566, 567, *584, 585*
REICHARD, P. 57, 58, 71, 73, 77, 78, *97, 99, 100, 101*, 544, 548, 560, *579, 580, 583*
REICHART, E. *637*, 944, *952*
REICHEL, L. 645, *677*
REICHENTHAL, J. 34, *41*
REICHERT, E. *637*
REICHMAN, M. E. 541, *578*
REICHSTEIN, T. 450, *471*, 885

REID, B. L. 710, *734*
REID, E. 488, *533*
REID, W. W. 806, *826*, 879, 882, 890, *899, 901*
REINER, B. 548, *580*
REINOUTS, P. VAN HAGA 959, *1021*
REINWEIN, D. 107, *199*
REIS, J. 691, *740*
REISER, R. 122, 123, 129, *191*
REISS, O. 23, *38*
REISSIG, J. L. 345, 354, *471*
REIT, D. J. 777, *798*
REITHEL, F. J. 393, 448, *464, 471*
REITSMA, R. H. 839, 850, 855, 868, *895, 897*
REMY, C. N. 8, *42*, 572, *586*
RENDI, R. 496, 522, *533*
RENDINA, G. 697, *740*
RENNIE, S. D. 142, *192*
RESNICK, P. R. 863, *897*
RETTIG, A. *1017*
REUSCHE, W. 975, *1021*
REVEL, M. 543, *578*
REX, R. W. 818, *826*
REYNOLDS, J. J. 684, 705, 707, *733, 737, 740*, 955, 985, *1015*
REYNOLDS, M. S. 724, *740*
REZNIK, H. 931, 936, *938*
RHIZA 858, *897*
RHODES, D. N. 105, 135, 146, *192, 201*
RICE, L. 446, 450 *474,*
RICE, L. I. 442, *473, 474*
RICE, S. A. 541, *578*
RICH, A. 15, *40*, 509, 510, 511, 512, 514, 516, *528, 530, 531, 533, 535*, 551, 556, 567, *580, 582, 585*
RICH, C. E. 510, *535*
RICH, K. 548, *580*
RICHARDS, H. H. 498, *528*
RICHARDS, J. 553, *581*
RICHARDS, J. H. 223, *243*, 845, 854, 862, 873, 875, 886, *896, 900, 1061*
RICHARDSON, C. C. 545, 548, 549, 550, *579, 580*
RICHARDSON, K. E. 160, *201*
RICHERT, D. A. 255, 257, *309, 311*
RICHMOND, J. E. 485, *531*
RICHMOND, K. W. 1035, *1062*
RICHMOND, M. H. 429, *471*
RICHTER, G. 137, *196*
RICHTER, J. W. 1043, 1052, *1062*
RICK, C. M. 653, *676*
RICKARDS, R. W. 757, *798*, 808, *826*, 872, 873, *898*, 1026, 1030, 1034, 1037, 1040, 1041, 1047, 1048, *1060, 1061*
RIESS, W. 971, *1015*
RIFKIND, R. A. 510, 517, *531*

RIGGS, T. R. 485, *528, 533*
RILEY, J. G. 441, *459*
RILEY, R. F. 142, *201*
RILLING, H. 835, *895*, 946, *951*, 1040, 1047, *1061*
RILLING, H. C. 211, 214, *241, 242*, 658, 659, *677*
RIMINGTON, C. 257, 258, 261, 263, 264, 273, 303, *307, 308, 311*, 711, *735*
RINES, H. W. 403, *468*
RINGELMANN, E. 720, 722, *738*
RINGLER, R. L. 123, *201*
RIS, H. 542, *578*
RISEBROUGH, R. W. 501, 503, 509, *529, 533*, 542, *578*
RITTENBERG, D. 106, 112, *201*, 208, 224, 233, *241, 243, 244*, 252, 276, 277, *310, 311, 312*, 481, 482, 483, *530, 533*, 711, *740*
RITTENBERG, S. C. 690, *735*
RITTER, C. 1006, *1020*
RIVERA, A. 35, *39*
RIZKI, M. T. M. 304, *311*
ROBBINS, D. J. 624, *635*
ROBBINS, P. W. 21, *39*, 87, *100*, 357, 371, 399, 402, 438, 439, 440, *456, 471, 472*, 543, 559, *579, 583*, 614, *637*
ROBERTS, E. 696, *740*
ROBERTS, E. A. H. 817, 818, *826*
ROBERTS, E. C. 448, *471*
ROBERTS, J. B. 807, 815, 818, *824*
ROBERTS, J. C. 760, *798*, 1044, *1061, 1063*
ROBERTS, J. J. *637*
ROBERTS, M. F. 968, *1017*
ROBERTS, P. J. P. 340, *475*
ROBERTS, R. B. 509, 518, *531*
ROBERTS, R. R. 508, 509, 518, 521, *533*
ROBERTSON, A. 771, *798*, 1031, 1034, 1035, 1037, 1041, 1048, 1058, *1061, 1062, 1063*
ROBERTSON, A. F. 148, *201*
ROBERTSON, A. V. 807, *826*, 955, 958, *1021*
ROBERTSON, J. D. 178, *193*
ROBERTSON, J. H. 299, *309*
ROBERTSON, J. M. 831, *894*, 1044, *1060*
ROBERTSON, W. 15, *42*
ROBINSON, D. 597, 599, 608, 609, 615, 632, *635, 638*
ROBINSON, D. S. 113, 115, 146, 181, 182, *195, 201*
ROBINSON, F. M. 843, *896*
ROBINSON, G. B. 436, *467, 471*
ROBINSON, G. M. 807, *826*
ROBINSON, J. D., Jr. 172, *194, 201*
ROBINSON, J. R. 862, *897*
ROBINSON, K. W. 818, *823*
ROBINSON, M. 569, *585*
ROBINSON, M. J. T. 1040, 1053, *1061*

ROBINSON, R. 211, 213, *242*, 261, *311*, 745, 769, *797*, 807, *826*, 832, *894*, 955, 975, 978, 983, 990, 992, 1004, *1018, 1021*
ROBINSON, W. G. 646, *673*, 945, 946, *951*, 961, *1021*
ROBINSON, W. S. 565, 567, 568, 569, 570, *584, 585*
ROCHE, J. 615, *635*
ROCKENBACH, J. 573, *586*
ROCKWITH, R. 948, 952
RODBELL, M. 142, 144, 179, *201*
RODÉN, L. 443, 444, *466, 471*
RODGMAN, A. 865, *897*
RODIONOVA, M. A. 523, *534*
RODNIGHT, R. 692, *738*
RODWELL, V. W. 724, *736, 740*
ROGERS, J. *636*
ROGERS, J. S. 822, *824*
ROHEIM, P. S. 181, *195*
ROHRMANN, E. 694, *742*
ROLL, P. M. 57, *100*, 544, *579*
ROMEIKE, A. 959, *1021*
ROOD, R. 174, *201*, 437, *471*
ROODYN, D. B. 522, *533*
ROSE, C. S. 377, *476*
ROSE, I. A. 57, *100*, 337, *474*, 544, *579*
ROSE, W. L. 481, *533*
ROSELL-PEREZ, M. 405, 406, 407, *465, 471*
ROSEMAN, S. 91, *97, 98, 100*, 173, 174, 177, *192, 201*, 344, 346, 350, 352, 361, 375, 422, 436, 437, 438, *455, 456, 458, 459, 461, 462, 464, 471*
ROSEN, S. M. 432, *469, 471, 476*
ROSENBERG, A. 173, 174, *201*
ROSENBERG, B. H. 541, *578*
ROSENBERG, L. E. 485, *533*
ROSENBLUM, C. 711, 712, 713, *738, 741*
ROSENFELD, G. 228, *244*
ROSENFELD, R. S. 224, *243*
ROSENTHAL, S. 8, 20, 21, 22, *40, 42, 43*
ROSHANMANESH, A. 29, *41*
ROSIEK, O. 257, *309*
ROSIN, N. L. 879, 890, *899*
ROSS, B. D. 265, *311*
ROSS, W. C. J. 832, *894*
ROSSELET, J. P. 345, 354, *470*
ROSSITER, R. J. 126, 127, 134, 137, 139, 140, 142, 143, 144, 145, 146, 149, 152, 153, 154, 156, 159, 160, 161, 162, 163, 168, 180, 185, *190, 193, 199, 200, 201, 202, 203*
ROTFARB, R. M. 267, *308*
ROTHBERG, S. 687, 688, *740*
ROTHERHAM, J. 143, *202*
ROTHFIELD, L. *469*
ROTHLEDER, E. E. 183, *198*
ROTHSCHILD, J. *42*
ROTHSCHILD, M. A. 487, *533*

ROTHSTEIN, M. 28, *42*, 601, 630, *638*
ROUSER, G. 168, *199, 202*
ROUSH, A. H. 70, *100*
ROUSSOS, G. G. 548, 549, *580*
ROUX, D. G. 807, 815, 818, 819, 820, *824, 826*
ROUX, J. 451, *462*
ROVESTI, P. 838, *895*
ROVTH, A. G. 840, *895*
ROWAN, T. 702, *740*
ROWBURY, R. J. 19, *42*
ROWE, C. E. 147, *202*
ROWE, J. R. 777, *798*
ROWE, J. W. 876, *899*
ROWEN, J. W. 83, *100*, 690, 691, *740*
ROWLAND, R. L. 865, *897*
ROWLEY, D. 1072, *1078*
ROWLEY, P. 326, *463*
ROY, A. B. 592, 615, *638*
ROY, S. C. 522, *528*, 715, *735*
RUBENSTEIN, I. 541, *578*
RUBENSTEIN, J. J. 180, *195*
RUDDAT, M. 870, *898*
RUDIGER, W. 866, *898*
RUDNEY, H. 208, *241*, 646, 647, *674, 677*, 945, 946, *951, 952*
RUDOLPH, S. G. 273, *306*
RUEFF, L. *637*, 944, *952*
RÜEGG, R. 331, *465*, 668, 669, 671, 675, *677*
RUELIUS, H. W. 615, *638*
RUELL, D. A. 394, *462*
RUIZ, E. E. 183, 184, 185, *198*
RUMBERG, B. 330, 331, *468, 471, 475*
RUMMERT, G. 641, *675*
RUMPF, J. A. 235, *244*
RUNDELL, J. T. 376, 396, *455*
RUPPENDER, H. 344, 351, *457*
RUSANIWSKYJ, W. 858, *897*
RUSCHMANN, J. 957, *1017*
RUSCONI, A. 715, *734, 739*
RUSSEL, C. S. 253, 254, 257, 261, 299, *311, 312*
RUSSELL, A. E. 216, 220, 221, *242, 243*, 878, 883, *899*
RUSSELL, C. S. 711, *741*
RUSSEY, W. E. 879, *899*
RUST, A. C. 131, *198*
RUTBERG, L. 57, *100*, 560, *583*
RUTLEDGE, P. S. 868, *898*
RUTMAN, R. J. 76, *100*
RUTTER, W. J. 92, *100*, 360, 387, *471*
RUVEDA, E. A. 981, *1016*
RUZICKA, L. 213, 214, *242*, 843, 848, 849, 850, 858, 859, 863, 865, 866, 875, 877, 879, 845, 875, 876, *895, 896, 899*
RYAN, A. 573, *586*

RYAN, A. J. 1034, 1037, 1043, 1056, *1061*
RYAN, K. J. 230, *244*
RYCHLIK, I. 486, 495, *533*
RYHAGE, R. 648, *676*
RYSER, G. 669, *677*

SABA, N. 227, 228, *243, 244*
SABATANI, D. 520, *533*
SABATH, L. D. 507, *529*
SABESIN, S. M. 180, *202*
SABLE, H. Z. 59, 68, *96, 98*, 354, *462*, 552, *581*
SACHS, P. 257, *311*
SACKTOR, B. 123, *193, 202*
SADDI, R. 487, *533*
SADRON, C. 541, *578*
SAFFIOTTI, U. 1069, *1078*
SAFFRAN, E. M. 28, *42*
SAGARDIA, F. 400, *471*
SAGER, R. 661, *677*
SAGERS, R. D. 330, *474*
SAGISAKA, S. 28, *42*
SAHASHI, Y. 714, 715, 720, 723, *739, 740*
SAITO, M. *471*
SAITO, Y. 687, 688, *740*
SAKAKIBARA, A. 934, *938*
SAKAMI, W. 19, *42*
SAKAO, H. 714, 715, *740*
SALAS, M. 341, *474*
SALITIS, G. 363, *471*
SALAS, M. 341, *474*
SALL, T. 450, *470*
SALLACH, H. J. 4, 5, 6, *39, 42, 44*, 141, 142, *202, 204*
SALTMARSH, M. J. *637*
SALTMARSH-ANDREW, M. 432, *476*
SALTON, M. R. J. 427, *471*
SALZMAN, N. P. 76, *101*
SAMAUNA, U. P. 501, 518, *529*
SAMEC, M. 392, 397, *471*
SAMUEL, D. 124, 129, 130, *188*
SAMUELS, H. H. 567, 568, *585*
SAMUELS, L. D. 507, *533*
SAMUELS, L. T. 228, 230, *243, 244*
SAMUELSSON, B. 238, 239, *245*
SANADI, D. R. 79, *97, 483, 529*, 692, *737*
SANCHEZ, Q. E. 487, *534*
SANDER, H. 1013, *1021*
SANDERMANN, W. 225, *243*, 832, 845, 850, 851, 852, 853, 854, 863, 866, 867, 870, 871, 872, *894, 896, 898*
SANDERS, F. 711, *740*
SANDERS, F. K. 566, *585*
SANDERSON, A. R. 89, 90, *96*, 158, *189*, 430, *471*
SANDINE, W. E. 28, *38, 40*

SANDKE, G. 975, 1022
SANDO, C. E. 889, 901
SANDOVAL, A. 659, 673
SANGER, F. 478, 533
SANGER, R. 519, 533
SANGHVI, A. T. 216, 223, 240, 242
SAN GUPTA, A. K. 887, 901
SANKAWA, U. 975, 1022
SANO, S. 264, 272, 308, 311
SAN PIETRO, A. 330, 331, 456, 474
SANSOM, B. F. 485, 533
SANTAVY, F. 985, 1016
SANTER, U. V. 301, 303, 304, 312
SAPERSTEIN, S. 645, 659, 677
SARCIONE, E. J. 519, 533, 620, 638
SARETT, H. P. 680, 694, 740
SARGENT, J. R. 486, 533
SARKAR, N. K. 553, 581
SARMA, D. S. R. 693, 740
SARMA, P. S. 682, 687, 693, 738, 740, 741
SARNAT, M. T. 569, 586
SASAKI, M. 716, 736
SASAKI, T. 631, 638
SASSENRATH, E. N. 140, 201
SASTRY, K. N. S. 812, 826
SASTRY, P. S. 130, 131, 188, 197, 200, 202
SATANI, E. 703, 739
SATO, J. 486, 534
SATO, K. 723, 740
SATO, M. 90, 98
SATO, R. 11, 32, 40, 41, 922, 938
SATO, T. 438, 439, 471
SATOH, K. 687, 738
SATOH, P. S. 228, 243
SAUER, F. 112, 114, 115, 118, 204
SAUNDERS, D. R. 124, 202
SAUNDERS, J. P. 616, 619, 636
SAUNDERS, P. P. 28, 40, 42
SAVARD, K. 230, 244
SAVEY, G. 668, 677
SAVIARD, M. 627, 635
SAWADA, H. 350, 446, 471, 474
SAWHNEY, P. C. 728, 732
SAWICKI, E. 1067, 1068, 1078
SAZ, H. J. 340, 471, 1043, 1063
SCARDI, V. 687, 736
SCHACHMAN, H. K. 550, 551, 580
SCHACHTER, D. 592, 599, 609, 618, 638
SCHACHTSCHABEL, D. 497, 536, 543, 578
SCHAECTER, M. 510, 533
SCHAEFFER, J. 509, 510, 511, 512, 513, 514, 516, 527, 529, 533
SCHAEFFER, P. 264, 311
SCHAFER, CH. 974, 975, 1021, 1022
SCHAPIRO, F. 485, 533
SCHAPIRO, G. 484, 485, 486, 502, 531, 533

SCHARFF, M. D. 516, 533
SCHAYER, R. W. 631, 638
SCHEDL, H. P. 228, 244
SCHEER, B. T. 403, 475
SCHEIBLE, W. J. 648, 678
SCHENK, E. 880, 899
SCHENKER, V. 227, 243
SCHEPARTZ, A. I. 692, 737
SCHER, W. I. 12, 42
SCHEUERBRANDT, G. 119, 202
SCHICKE, H. G. 705, 737
SCHIEDT, U. 962, 968, 1021
SCHILDKRAUT, C. L. 545, 548, 549, 550, 579, 580
SCHILLER, S. 373, 426, 443, 471, 472
SCHILLING, J. A. 426, 475
SCHIMKE, R. T. 507, 533
SCHIMMEL & CO. 919, 924, 939
SCHIRCH, L. G. 6, 7, 42
SCHJEIDE, O. A. 518, 519, 528
SCHLESINGER, M. J. 646 674,
SCHLESINGER, S. 89, 100, 544, 579
SCHLESSINGER, D. 509, 512, 514, 517, 520, 531, 533
SCHLESSINGER, M. J. 543, 578,
SCHLOSSBERGER, H. G. 687, 734
SCHLOSSMANN, K. 9, 38, 40, 42
SCHLUBACH, H. H. 380, 418, 419, 472
SCHLUMPRECHT, L. 889, 901
SCHLYK, A. A. 866, 897, 898
SCHMID, C. 109, 202
SCHMID, G. 172, 203
SCHMID, H. 758, 782, 797, 798, 799, 1000, 1023
SCHMID, R. 254, 257, 273, 288, 295, 310, 311, 312, 399, 402, 472, 711, 740
SCHMIDT, D. M. 802, 808, 826
SCHMIDT, G. 370, 398, 458, 496, 497, 507, 511, 518, 533, 693, 740
SCHMIDT, H. 746, 747, 797
SCHMIDT, L. H. 629, 636
SCHMIDT, O. T. 802, 808, 810, 812, 813, 826
SCHMIDT-NIELSON, S. 615, 638
SCHMITZ, H. 79, 98
SCHNEIDER, W. C. 143, 202, 553, 581
SCHOCH, T. J. 379, 389, 475
SCHÖENHEIMER, R. 71, 76, 97, 100, 188, 202, 208, 224, 241, 243, 481, 482, 483, 530, 533
SCHOENTAL, R. 1069, 1077
SCHOFIELD, J. 1051, 1057, 1061
SCHÖFINIUS, I. 959, 1020
SCHOLDA, R. 452, 472
SCHOLEFIELD, P. G. 485, 527
SCHOLZ, C. 990, 1015
SCHÖPF, C. 745, 797

SCHOPFER, W. H. 452, *470*, 643, 659, *675, 677*, 681, *741*
SCHRAMM, G. 566, *579, 587*
SCHRAMM, I. M. 520, *533*
SCHRAMM, M. 142, 157, *202*, 399, 414, *463, 472*
SCHRECKER, A. W. 85, *101*, 704, *741*
SCHREIBER, K. 1012, *1022*
SCHREIBER, S. S. 487, *533*
SCHRIEBMAN, I. 612, *636*
SCHRÖDER, W. 322, *475*
SCHROEDER, E. A. R. 324, 325, *470*
SCHROEDER, W. A. 669, *678*
SCHROEPFER, G. J., Jr. 216, 223, 240, *242*
SCHRÖTER, H.-B. 959, 964, 965, 1006, *1020, 1021, 1022*
SCHUBERT, W. J. 904, 905, 906, 910, 911, 912, 917, 918, 919, 920, 922, 924, 926, 927, 929, 930, 934, *937, 938, 939*
SCHUDEL, P. 641, 669, *675, 677*
SCHULMAN, M. P. 61, *101*, 255, 257, *309, 311*
SCHULTZ, A. S. 680, *741*
SCHULZ, D. W. 400, *466*
SCHULZE, E. 805, *827*
SCHUSTER, E. 807, 818, *824*
SCHÜTTE, H. R. 955, 959, 960, 962, 964, 974, 975, 1004, *1018, 1019, 1020, 1021, 1022*
SCHUTTE, M. R. 962, *1018*
SCHUTZ, R. S. 959, *1016*
SCHWARTZ, A. K. 36, *42*
SCHWARTZ, A. M. 414, *467*
SCHWARTZ, H. C. 265, *312*
SCHWARTZ, S. 273, 299, *311*, 712, *741*
SCHWARZ, V. 356, 421, *472*
SCHWEERS, W. 853, 863, *896*
SCHWEET, R. 481, 483, 486, 509, 510, 511, 512, 513, 514, 517, *527, 529, 533*
SCHWEET, R. S. 495, 509, 511, 512, 513, 516, *533*
SCHWEIGERT, B. S. 57, *100*, 544, *579*, 687, 709, *736, 740*
SCHWEIZER, E. 113, 115, *199*
SCHWENK, E. 214, 215, 219, *242*
SCHWERDT, R. F. 448, *476*
SCHWIETER, A. 668, *677*
SCHWIETER, U. 669, *677*
SCHWIMMER, S. 379, *472*
SCHWINK, I. 34, *42*
SCIOSCIA-SANTORO, A. 9, *41*
SCORNIK, O. A. 512, *530*
SCOTT, A. I. 989, 1000, 1003, 1004, *1018, 1020, 1022*, 1027, 1028, *1060, 1062, 1063*
SCOTT, E. 296, *307*
SCOTT, H. M. 91, 92, *98*
SCOTT, J. F. 561, *583*

SCOTT, J. J. 254, 255, 257, 259, 261, 304, *307, 308, 310*, 696, 711, *735, 739*
SCOTT R. B. 504, 508, *533*
SCOTT, S. S. 94, *101*, 430, *473*
SCOTT, W. M. 717, *736*
SCRIMGEOUR, K. G. 22, *40*
SEAKINS, A. 181, *201*
SEAKINS, J. W. T. 807, 813, 816, 817, 819, *825*
SEAMAN, G. R. 711, *740*
SEATON, J. D. 216, 223, *242*
SEBRING, E. E. 76, *101*
SEBYLA, T. 975, *1016*
SEED, R. W. 504, 519, 520, *533*
SEEGMILLER, C. G. 364, 373, 421, 423, *472*, 729, *738*
SEGAL, A. 9, 19, *39*
SEGAL, H. L. 438, 439, 440, *472*, 599, 610, 614, *638*
SEGAL, S. 485, *533*
SEGAL, S. J. 507, *534*
SEGUIN, A. 801, *826*
SEITZ, I. F. 402, 403, *464*
SÉJOURNÉ, T. 618, *636*
SEKERIS, C. E. 504, *533*
SEKHARA VARMA, T. N. 426, *469*
SEKIGUCHI, M. 560, 566, *583, 584*
SELIM, A. S. M. 9, 19, *42*
SELINGER, Z. 399, *472*
SELLIN, H. G. 519, 520, *533*
SENIOR, J. R. 124, 125, 128, 130, *202*
SENOH, S. 624, *638*
SERAIDARIAN, K. 693, *740*
SERAIDARIAN, M. 693, *740*
SERAYDARIAN, K. 399, *467*
SERENI, F. 507, *527*
SERLUPPI-CRESCENZI, G. 83, 91, 92, 93, 96, *101*
SESHADRI, T. R. 768, 779, 781, 782, 784, 787, *798, 799*, 806, *826*
SETLOW, R. B. *534*
SEUBERT, W. 108, *202*
SEVERTZOV, A. N. 501, 518, *529*
SHABTAI, T. 1073, 1075, *1077*
SHADAKSHARASWAMY, M. 92, *100*, 355, 356, 360, 361, 373, 378, 394, *469, 470*
SHAFIZADEH, F. 414, *476*
SHAH, R. C. 745, *797*
SHAH, S. N. 131, 132, *202*
SHANNON, P. 552, *581*
SHAPIRO, B. 126, 128, *189, 202, 203*
SHAPIRO, L. 566, *584*
SHAPIRO, S. K. 8, *42*
SHAPOSHNIKOV, V. N. 716, *741*
SHARLAT, I. V. 496, 504, *533*
SHARMA, G. M. 989, *1018*
SHARP, M. 27, *43*

SHARP, W. 1054, *1062*
SHARPE, E. S. 413, *465*
SHATKIN, A. J. 516, *533*, 567, *585*
SHATKIN, J. 566, *584*
SHATTON, J. B. 23, *43*, 44, *472*
SHAW, D. R. D. 90, *101*, 430, 431, 450, *472*
SHAW, E. 705, *733, 741*
SHAW, E. N. 705, *738*
SHAW, K. B. 299, *307*
SHAW, N. 717, *737*
SHAY, H. *472*
SHEDLOVSKY, A. E. 29, *42*
SHEFER, S. 224, *243*
SHEMIN, D. 252, 253, 254, 255, 257, 261, 276, 277, 299, *307, 308, 310, 311, 312, 313*, 711, 712, 713, *733, 734, 740, 741, 742*
SHEN, L. 358, 403, *470, 472*
SHENCK, C. H. *952*
SHEPPARD, H. 211, *242*
SHERRATT, H. S. A. 130, *196*
SHERRY, S. P. 822, *826*
SHERWIN, C. P. 609, 610, 611, *638*
SHETLAR, M. R. 426, *475*
SHIBATA, K. 268, *312*
SHIBATA, S. 766, 769, *798*, 805, *827*, 955, 956, 957, 975, *1019, 1022*, 1043, *1063*
SHIGEURA, H. T. 571, *586*, 748, 797, 912, 920, 921, 922, 923, *939*
SHIMAZONO, H. 911, 912, 913, 914, 915, 916, 920, *939*
SHIMAZONO, N. 344, *464*, 681, 728, *737, 742*
SHIMIZU, F. 91, *97, 98*, 437, *458*
SHIMIZU, K. 228, 237, *243, 245*,
SHIMIZU, S. 268, *312*
SHIMOMURA, T. 378, 394, *473*
SHIMURA, K. 16, 28, *42, 44*, 486, *534*
SHIN, M. 330, *472*
SHIOTA, T. 707, *741*
SHIRATORI, T. 132, 179, *194*
SHIRK, H. G. 414, *467*
SHIVE, W. 59, 61, *101*, 696, *732, 740, 741*
SHLYK, A. A. 267, 269, *308, 312*, 664, *676*
SHNEOUR, E. A. 647, 665, 667, *677*
SHOCKLEY, T. E. 450, *472*
SHODA, T. 707, 708, *737*
SHOEMAKER, W. C. 485, *531*
SHOPPEE, C. W. 871, *898*
SHORB, M. S. 716, *733*
SHORT, W. F. 448, *458*
SHOTLANDER, V. L. 164, 165, *192*
SHRAGO, E. 338, *472*
SHRIMPTON, D. M. 304, *312*
SHUBIK, P. 1069, *1078*
SHUEY, E. W. 94, *100*, 357, 362, 422, *470*

SHUKLA, J. P. 370, 389, *472*
SHUNK, C. H. 331, *474*, 843, *896*, 1043, 1052, *1062*
SHURLEY, H. M. 426, *475*
SIBATANI, A. 550, *580*
SIDBURY, J. B., Jr. 353, *472*
SIDDONS, P. T. 655, 656, *674*
SIEGEL, L. M. 10, 11, *42*
SIEGEL, S. M. 936, *939*
SIEGELMAN, H. W. 289, *312*, 775, *798*
SIEGFRIED, K. J. 964, 1003, *1020*
SIEKEVITZ, P. 483, *534*
SIEVERS, A. F. 822, *824, 827*
SIGG, H. P. 1049, *1062*
SIH, C. J. 370, 392, 449, *458, 472*
SILBERMAN, R. 521, *529*
SILBERT, J. E. 92, *101*, 367, 373, 443, *472*
SILVA, L. B. 808, *824, 825*
SILVA, O. L. 710, *733*
SILVERMAN, B. E. 27, *43*
SILVERMAN, D. A. *535*
SILVERMAN, M. 66, *98*, 710, *733*
SILVERTON, J. V. 1044, *1060*
SIM, G. A. 1044, *1060*
SIM, K. Y. 1044, *1060*
SIMMER, H. 688, *742*
SIMMONDS, N. W. 807, *827*
SIMMONDS, S. 140, *193*
SIMMONS, N. S. 541, *578*
SIMMS, E. S. 75, 80, *98, 99*, 368, *465*, 546, 547, 548, 550, *579, 580*
SIMON, H. 989, 1004, 1006, *1018, 1020*
SIMON, J. I. 1070, *1078*
SIMON, L. 566, *584*
SIMON, L. N. 556, *582*
SIMONSEN, J. 858, 863, 872, *894, 897*
SIMONSEN, J. L. 832, 852, 856, *894, 897*
SIMPSON, F. J. 344, 345, *472, 476*
SIMPSON, K. 649, *678*
SIMPSON, K. L. 659, 669, *677*
SIMPSON, M. V. 485, 522, *530, 534*
SIMPSON, S. A. 228, *244*
SIMS, P. 605, 606, *635, 636*
SINEX, M. 519, *534*
SINGER, M. F. 498, *534*, 543, 556, 557, 558, 559, *578, 582, 583*
SINGER, T. P. 123, *201*
SINGHAL, R. L. 507, *535*
SINGLETON, F. 836, 849, *895*
SINGLETON, J. W. 287, 288, *312*
SINOHARA, H. 436, *472*
SINSHEIMER, R. L. 541, 548, 566, 568, *577, 578, 580, 584, 585*
SIPERSTEIN, M. D. 233, 235, 238, *244, 245*, 885, *900*
SIRETEANU, L. 821, 822, *823*
SIRLIN, J. L. 572, *586*

SIROTNAK, F. M. 709, *741*
SISTROM, W. R. 273, *307*, 642, 664, *675*
SIU, P. M. L. 6, *43*, 336, *472*
SIU, R. 895
SIZER, J. W. 724, *737*
SJOLANDER, N. O. 34, *41*, 1031, *1062*
SJÖSTRAND, T. 280, *312*
SJÖVALL 239, *245*
SKARZYNSKI, B. 883, *900*
SKEGGS, H. R. 58, 71, *102*, 647, *678*, 682, 737, 843, *896*, *952*
SKELTON, D. C. 485, *532*
SKODA, J. 556, *582*
SKÖLD, O. 77, *100*
SKRIMSHIRE, G. E. H. 448, *458*
SKY-PECK, H. H. 436, *472*
SLAPIKOFF, S. 514, *534*
SLATER, C. A. 1054, *1061*
SLATER, W. G. 364, *472*
SLAUGHTER, C. 16, 19, *39*
SLAUNWHITE, W. R., Jr. 230, *244*
SLAYTOR, M. 768, 784, *798*, 1038, 1039, *1060*
SLEIN, M. W. 342, 343, 346, 446, *456*, *458*, *472*
SLIZEWICZ, P. 417, *459*
SLOANE STANLEY, G. H. *198*
SLONIMSKI, P. P. 29, 31, *40*
SLOVER, G. A. 373, 426, *472*
SMALLEY, H. M. 1034, 1058, *1061*
SMART, C. L. 412, 417, 423, *475*
SMEDLEY, I. 836, *895*
SMELLIE, R. M. S. 552, 553, 556, 564, 565, *581*, *582*, *584*
SMILEY, J. D. 447, *472*
SMIRNOV, B. P. 523, *534*
SMIRNOV, M. V. 501, 518, *529*
SMITH, A. D. 13, *42*
SMITH, A. H. 485, *527*
SMITH, B. 28, *43*
SMITH, C. 373, 432, *476*
SMITH, D. B. 155, 165, *191*
SMITH, D. C. C. 1006, *1016*, 1052, 1054, *1060*
SMITH, D. W. E. 29, 30, *42*, *44*
SMITH, E. E. B. 91, 92, *99*, *101*, 355, 356, 363, 422, 427, 433, *467*, *468*, *472*, *473*
SMITH, E. J. 91, *101*
SMITH, E. L. 288, 292, 299, 301, *307*, *309*, 494, *534*, 711, 714, 716, *733*, *735*, *741*, 760, *798*
SMITH, F. 360, *456*, 944, *952*
SMITH, G. F. 983, *1022*
SMITH, G. N. 122, *202*
SMITH, H. 757, 768, 784, *798*, 842, 846, 852, 868, 869, *895*, *896*, *898*, 1006, *1016*, 1026, 1030, 1034, 1035, 1037, 1038, 1039,

SMITH, H.—*cont.*
1043, 1046, 1048, 1051, 1052, 1053, 1054, 1055, 1057, *1060*, *1061*, *1062*
SMITH, I. 499, *530*
SMITH, J. D. 516, *528*, *534*, 548, 571, *580*, *586*
SMITH, J. H. C. 266, 267, 268, 269, 270, *312*, 658, *677*
SMITH, J. N. 596, 597, 598, 601, 608, 609, 612, 615, 620, 622, 629, 632, *636*, *637*, *638*
SMITH, L. C. 21, *42*
SMITH, L. H., Jr. 73, *100*, *101*
SMITH, M. 551, *581*
SMITH, M. E. 12, *42*, 145, *196*
SMITH, M. J., Sr. 553, *581*
SMITH, M. S. 91, *101*, 399, *456*
SMITH, O. H. 35, *42*, 684, *741*
SMITH, O. W. 230, *244*
SMITH, R. A. 340, 353, 354, *460*, *473*
SMITH, R. H. 852, *896*
SMITH, S. 116, *202*
SMITH, S. J. 981, *1020*
SMITH, S. M. 432, *460*, *482*
SMITH, S. M. J. 555, *582*
SMITH, S. W. 127, 143, 144, 146, *197*, *202*
SMITH, T. 147, *199*
SMITHE, P. N. 377, *476*
SMYRNIOTIS, P. Z. 54, *98*, 321, 324, 325, 346, 446, *462*, *463*, *475*
SMYTH, D. G. 479, *534*
SMYTH, R. D. 22, *44*
SMYTHE, R. D. 717, *733*
SMYTHIES, J. R. 609, *636*
SNAREY, M. 855, 857, *897*
SNATZKE, G. 884, *900*
SNELL, E. E. 6, 23, *42*, *43*, 58, 86, *97*, *101*, 486, *530*, 690, 694, 698, 723, 724, 725, *733*, *734*, *735*, *736*, *738*, *740*, *741*, 742
SNELL, J. F. 1031, *1039*
SNYDER, A. L. 295, *312*
SO, S. G. 521, *534*
SOBERÓN, G. 487, *534*
SODD, M. A. 170, 171, *191*, 435, *457*
SOKAL, J. E. 620, *638*
SOKATCH, J. R. 344, *473*
SOKOLOFF, L. 507, 508, *529*, *534*
SOLMS, J. 91, 92, *101*, 356, 423, *473*
SOLMSSEN, U. 658, *675*
SOLOMON, H. M. 273, *312*
SOLOMON, J. B. 605, *635*
SOLOMON, S. 227, 230, *243*, *244*
SOLS, A. 341, 343, *473*, *474*
SOLT, M. L. 959, 961, 963, *1016*, *1017*, *1022*
SOMERFIELD, G. A. 813, *824*
SOMEROSKI, J. F. 690, *736*, 962, *1018*
SOMERS, G. F. 324, *473*

SOMERSON, N. L.   28, 29, *42*
SOMERVILLE, R. L.   548, *580*
SONDERHOFF, R.   208, 219, *241*
SONDHEIMER, F.   877, *899*
SONNE, J. C.   59, *97, 101*
SOODAK, M.   48, *101*
SÖRBO, B.   598, 610, 612, 618, *636, 638*
SÖRBO, B. H.   617, 618, *638*
SORENSON, N. A.   667, *675, 677*
SORM, F.   486, *533,* 556, *582,* 858, *897*
SORMOVA, Z.   556, *582*
SOUCEK, M.   974, *1022*
SPACKMAN, D. H.   482, *534*
SPAHR, P. F.   *528,* 571, 574, *586, 587*
SPALLA, C.   711, 715, 716, *733, 734*
SPANNER, S.   154, 155, *189*
SPARK, A. A.   667, *673*
SPEARING, C. W.   437, *475*
SPECTOR, L.   72, *98*
SPECTOR, W. S.   616, *638*
SPELL, W. H.   718, *741*
SPENCE, J. C.   727, 728, *740*
SPENCER, B.   614, 615, *638*
SPENCER, C. F.   1043, 1052, *1062*
SPENCER, D.   523, *534*
SPENCER, E. Y.   862, *897*
SPENCER, M.   498, *534*
SPENSER, I. D.   690, *738,* 955, 958, 959,
   962, 968, 971, 977, 978, 981, 982, 983, 990,
   1008, *1017, 1018, 1020, 1021, 1022*
SPERBER, I.   614, 633, *638*
SPERRY, W. M.   132, *202*
SPEYER, J. F.   24, 27, *42,* 493, *531*
SPIEGELMAN, S.   501, 502, 503, 506, 518,
   529, 532, 534, 535, 541, 542, 566, 567, 569,
   578, 584, 585, 586
SPIKES, J. D.   666, *676*
SPIRIN, A. S.   509, *534,* 543, *578*
SPIRO, M. J.   519, *534*
SPIRO, R. G.   519, *534*
SPITELLER, G.   968, *1022*
SPITELLER-FRIEDMAN, M.   968, *1022*
SPOLTER, L.   441, 442, *473*
SPORN, M. B.   503, *527*
SPOTSWOOD, T. M.   1070, 1073, 1075, *1077*
SPRAGUE, J. M.   682, *737*
SPRECHER, M.   748, *797,* 912, 920, 921, 922,
   923, *939*
SPRING, F. S.   1054, *1062*
SPRINSON, D. B.   32, 33, 34, *40, 42,* 140,
   166, *193, 202, 204,* 712, 713, *739,* 748, *797,*
   804, *827,* 907, 912, 920, 921, 922, 923, 930,
   938, 939, 1000, *1022*
SPYRIDES, G.   512, *532*
SQUIRES, C.   109, 112, 116, *189, 202*
SQUIRES, C. L.   438, 439, *455,* 614, *635*
SRB, A. M.   13, *42*

SRERE, P. A.   235, *244,* 345, *473,* 921, *939*
SRIBNEY, M.   167, 168, 169, *194, 202,* 955,
   1022
SRINIVASAN, P. R.   33, 34, 35, *39, 42,* 573,
   574, *586,* 748, *797,* 912, 920, 921, 922, 923,
   930, *939*
SRIVASTA, S. K.   507, *535*
STABURSKIV, A.   883, *900*
STACEY, M.   377, 392, *456*
STADLER, P.   858, 860, *897*
STADLER, R.   341, *461*
STADTMAN, E. R.   17, 18, 25, *42,* 107,
   190, 202, 627, 628, *638,* 694, 697, 722, *741,*
   944, *952*
STAEHELIN, T.   494, 504, 510, 518, *532, 534,*
   535
STAEHLIN, M.   544, 545, *579*
STAFFORD, H. A.   6, *42,* 933, *939*
STAFFORD, W. H.   711, *733*
STAHL, R. C.   29, 30, 31, *40*
STAINIER, R. Y.   686, *736*
STALL, A.   268, *313*
STALON, V.   14, *42*
STAMMER, C. H.   1043, 1052, *1062*
STANACEV, N. Z.   130, *191*
STANDEN, H.   608, *635*
STANDFAST, A. F. B.   448, *458*
STANIER, R. Y.   267, 270, 273, *307, 312,*
   538, *577,* 641, 642, 657, 660, 664, *675, 677,*
   687, *736*
STANISHEVSKAYA, E. M.   866, *898*
STANLEY, R. G.   851, *896,* 946, *952*
STANSLY, P. G.   107, 126, *202*
STANWAY, D. N.   1058, *1062*
STANY, Z.   645, *673*
STAPLE, E.   227, 233, 236, 237, 238, 239,
   243, 244, 245
STARR, J. L.   544, 561, 572, 574, *579, 583,*
   587
STARR, M. P.   645, 659, *677*
STAUB, A.   342, 343, *473*
STAUNTON, J.   981, *1016,* 1035, *1061, 1062*
STEBERL, E. A.   112, *202*
STECHER, R.   962, *1018*
STECKEL, F.   1073, *1077*
STEDMAN, R. L.   858, *897*
STEEL, R.   337, *471*
STEELE, W. J.   521, *534,* 647, *677*
STEGLICH, W.   979, *1015*
STEIN, A.   176, *198*
STEIN, G.   858, *897*
STEIN, R. P.   868, *898*
STEIN, W. H.   479, 482, *534,* 610, *638*
STEIN, Y.   128, *202*
STEINBERG, D.   124, 180, *201, 203,* 217,
   220, 222, *242, 243,* 484, 486, 488, 516, *534,*
   535

STEINER, D. F. 405, 406, 407, *473*
STEINER, H. 1072, *1078*
STEINER, R. F. 519, *534*, 539, 542, *577*
STEKOL, J. A. 140, *203*, 615, *638*
STENHAGEN, E. 1074, 1075, *1078*
STENLAKE, J. B. 981, *1020*
STENT, G. S. 505, 506, *534*, 541, *577*
STEPHAN, P. 802, 808, *826*
STEPHEN, J. M. L. 481, 487, *535*
STEPHENSON, M. 497, *534*
STEPHENSON, M. L. 561, *583*
STERMITZ, F. R. 979, *1021*, *1022*
STERN, J. R. 22, *42*
STETTEN, D., Jr. 140, *203*, 355, *473*
STETTEN, DE W. 760, *798*
STETTEN, M. J. 342, *473*
STETTEN, M. R. 15, *42*, 61, *101*, 342, 355, 410, *473*
STEUER, H. 745, *797*
STEVENS, A. 19, *42*, 567, 570, *585*, *586*
STEVENS, B. M. 488, *533*
STEVENS, C. M. 24, *38*
STEVENSON, F. J. 890, *901*
STEVENSON, I. H. 375, 435, *459*, *638*
STEWART, A. W. 834, *895*
STEWART, D. N. 485, *527*
STEWART, H. B. 123, *194*, *203*
STEWART, W. S. 681, *736*
STICKINGS, C. E. 1054, *1063*
STICKLAND, L. H. 353, *464*
STILLER, E. T. 694, *741*
STILLER, M. 322, 339, *473*
STOCK, A. 858, *897*
STOCKER, J. H. 813, *824*
STOCKMANN, H. 832, 852, 866, 872, *894*
STOECKENIUS, W. 542, *578*
STOFFEL, W. 120, 121, *203*, 890, *901*
STOFFYN, A. 172, *203*
STOFFYN, P. 172, *203*
STOKER, J. R. 789, *799*
STOKES, A. R. 540, *577*
STOKES, W. M. 216, 222, *242*, *243*
STOKKE, K. 667, *677*
STOLLE, K. 989, 1000, *1018*, *1022*
STOLZENBACH, F. E. 693, *737*, *742*
STONE, D. 227, *243*
STONE, J. E. 917, 918, *937*, *939*
STOODLEY, R. J. 334, 367, 373, 381, 424, *454*, *464*
STORCH, R. 510, *530*
STOREY, I. D. E. 92, *97*, *101*, 355, 375, 435, *473*, 592, 595, 597, *636*, *638*
STORK, G. 848, *896*
STOTZ, E. 127, 135, 147, 158, 168, *199*, *202*
STOUDT, T. H. 219, *242*
STRAEHLIN, M. 556, *582*
STRAIN, H. H. 662, *677*

STRANGE, R. E. 26, *41*, 427, *473*
STRASSMAN, M. 22, 23, 24, 27, *43*, *44*
STRAUB, F. B. 518, 519, *534*, *535*
STRAUSS, D. B. 565, *584*
STRECKER, H. J. 12, 13, *40*, *41*, *42*, *43*, 448, *473*
STRICKLAND, E. H. 136, *189*
STRICKLAND, K. P. 123, 126, 127, 137, 139, 140, 142, 143, 144, 145, 146, 152, 154, 157, 158, 159, 160, 161, 162, 168, 180, 185, *193*, *200*, *201*, *202*, *203*
STRICKLER, N. 693, *740*
STROHMAN, R. C. 483, *534*
STROMINGER, J. L. 90, 91, 92, 93, 94, *98*, *99*, *100*, *101*, 144, *203*, 355, 356, 357, 362, 363, 364, 365, 366, 368, 374, 427, 428, 429, 430, 431, 440, 441, 442, *455*, *461*, *464*, *466*, *467*, *468*, *469*, *471*, *473*, 596, *638*
STRONG, F. M. 163, *194*, 694, *737*
STRUVE, W. G. 374, 430, *473*
STUART, K. L. 981, *1018*
STUMPF, P. K. 92, *97*, 107, 109, 112, 115, 116, 120, 127, *189*, *190*, *200*, *202*, *203*, 323, 355, 364, 372, 420, 421, 449, *461*, *473*, *474*, 891, *901*, 1033, *1063*
SU, D. 556, *582*
SU, J. C. 92, 93, *101*, 372, 417, *473*
SUBRAHMANYAM, D. 137, 145, 146, 157, 161, *203*
SUDYINA, E. G. 269, *312*
SUEOKA, N. 494, 497, *534*, 550, 551, *580*, *581*
SUGANO, H. 502, 503, *532*
SUGAWARA, S. 378, 394, *473*
SUGG, J. Y. 376, 412, *462*
SUGIMURA, A. 92, *99*
SUGINO, Y. 89, *101*, 143, *203*
SUGITA, Y. 265, *311*
SUGIYAMA, T. 358, 371, 390, 403, 405, *468*
SUHADOLNIK, R. J. 955, 957, 985, *1022*, *1023*, 1053, *1063*
SUKHOV, G. V. 851, 872, *896*
SULD, H. M. 238, *245*
SUMMERS, L. A. *825*
SUNAGA, K. 520, *532*
SUNDARAM, T. E. 687, *741*
SUNDVIK, E. 593, *638*
SURMATIS, J. D. 671, *677*
SUSKIND, S. R. 36, *38*, *39*, *43*
SUSSMAN, M. 373, 433, *473*
SUTHERLAND, E. W. 353, 400, 402, *458*, *470*, *473*, *476*
SUTHERLAND, I. 299, *307*, 711, *733*
SUTHERLAND, I. O. 1032, 1043, *1062*
SUWAL, P. N. 968, *1017*
SUYTER, M. 124, *204*
SUZUBEI, Y. 295, *307*

SUZUKI, I. *738*
SUZUKI, K. 176, *203*
SUZUKI, N. 366, *469*
SUZUKI, S. 91, 94, *100*, *101*, 365, 366, 368, 441, 442, *469*, *473*, *474*
SUZUKI, T. 438, 439, *471*, 720, 723, *739*, *740*
SUZUKI, Y. 703, *739*
SVEDBERG, T. 290, *312*
SVENNERHOLM, L. 155, 175, 176, *203*
SVENSON, I. 544, 572, 573, *579*, *586*
SVENSON, P. A. *534*
SWAIN, A. P. 858, *897*
SWAIN, T. 750, 772, 777, *797*, *798*, 802, 804, 805, 806, 807, 810, 814, 818, 822, *823*, *824*, *825*, *827*
SWANSON, A. L. 437, *464*
SWANSON, M. A. 379, 384, 385, 398, 411, *458*
SWARTZ, M. N. 547, 551, *580*, 693, *737*
SWEENEY, E. W. 507, *533*
SWEET, D. 59, *97*
SWELL, L. 131, 132, *203*
SWICK, R. W. 485, *534*, 722, *741*
SYKES, G. 448, *458*
SYKES, W. O. 592, 629, *637*
SYNGE, R. L. M. 485, *534*
SZABOLCS, J. 663, 666, *673*
SZANTIVANYI, A. 486, *532*
SZOT, Z. 257, *309*
SZULMAJSTER, J. 22, *43*
SZYBALSKI, W. 550, *580*

TABECHIAN, H. 688, *734*
TABONE, D. 598, *637*
TABONE, M. J. 598, *637*
TABOR, C. W. 8, *43*
TABOR, H. 8, *43*, 627, 628, *638*, *741*
TABOR, W. A. 1004, *1022*
TADOKORO, T. 728, *741*
TAFT, H. L. 342, *473*
TAGAWA, K. 329, 330, 332, *473*, *475*
TAGAWA, T. 330, *472*, *474*
TAGGART, J. V. 599, 609, 618, *638*
TAIT, G. H. 257, 265, 266, *308*, *311*, *312*
TAIT, J. F. 228, *244*
TAJIMA, M. 981, *1019*
TAKAGI, V. 561, *583*
TAKAGI, Y. 346, 350, 446, 449, 462, *471*, *474*
TAKAHASHI, H. 687, *738*
TAKAHASHI, N. 368, *474*
TAKAHASHI, T. 511, *530*
TAKANAMI, M. 483, 510, 516, *532*, *534*, 561, *583*

TAKEDA, I. 701, 702, 703, *737*
TAKEDA, Y. 482, *534*
TAKEMURA, K. H. 218, *242*
TAKEMURA, T. 284, 285, 295, *311*
TAKESHITA, M. 731, *736*
TAKETA, K. 344, *474*
TAKEYAMA, S. 19, 20, 22, *39*, *43*
TALAMO, B. 112, 114, 115, *189*
TALBERT, P. T. 125, *203*
TALMADGE, D. W. 486, *532*
TALMADGE, P. 255, *309*
TALMAN, E. L. *312*
TALWAR, G. P. 507, *534*
TAM, K. L. 1006, *1016*
TAMAKI, E. 268, *312*, 966, *1019*
TAMBOR, J. 817, *825*
TAMM, CH. 1049, *1063*
TAMM, I. 566, 567, 568, 570, *584*, *585*, *586*
TAMURA, G. 10, 11, *43*, 946, *952*
TANAKA, K. 498, *538*
TANAKA, S. 450, *476*
TANAKA, T. 686, *741*
TANDLER, C. J. 572, *586*
TANENBAUM, S. W. 28, *43*, 755, 797, 832, *894*, 909, *937*
TANG, Y. W. 659, *673*
TANI, J. 520, *530*
TANNER, H. A. 335, 336, *467*, *474*
TANNER, K. G. 917, 918, *937*, *939*
TARNOWSKI, W. 405, *463*
TARTTER, A. *312*
TARVER, H. 140, *198*, 481, *483*, *534*
TASHIRO, Y. 520, *533*
TATA, J. R. 399, *474*, 507, *534*
TATIBANA, M. 731, *736*
TATSUM, K. 593, *638*
TATTRIE, N. H. 135, *203*
TATUM, E. L. 32, 34, 36, *38*, *43*, 566, 567, *584*, *585*, 706, 720, *741*, 907, 908, *939*, 943, *952*
TAURO, P. 507, *529*
TAVORMINA, P. A. 209, *241*, 647, 677, 843, *896*, 946, *952*
TAYLOR, D. C. 370, 393, *466*
TAYLOR, E. H. 1004, *1022*
TAYLOR, J. B. 955, 985, 986, 988, *1015*, *1016*
TAYLOR, J. H. 541, *577*
TAYLOR, W. E. 136, *199*
TAYLOR, W. H. 422, 424, *474*
TAYLOR, W. I. 993, 999, *1018*, *1022*
TCHEN, T. T. 209, 214, 227, 228, *241*, *242*, *243*, 647, 650, *673*, *677*, 835, 844, *895*, *896*, 948, *951*, *952*
TCHOLA, O. 326, *463*
TEAS, H. J. 18, *43*, 943, 944, *952*
TECCE, G. 498, *527*

TEE, J. L. 667, *673*
TEJERINA, G. 20, *39*
TEKMAN, S. 687, *734*
TELSER, A. 373, 441, 443, *470*
TEMIN, H. M. 570, *586*
TEMPLE, K. 135, *199*
TEMPLE, R. J. 25, *43*
TEPLY, L. J. 682, *738*
TERAYAMA, H. 502, 503, *532*
TERNBAH, M. 971, *1015*
TESTA, E. 349, *466*
TETSUO, Y. 494, 497, *534*
TEWFIC, S. 323, 449, *474*
THAIN, E. M. 694, *733*, 855, 857, *897*
THANNHAUSER, S. J. 172, *203*, 693, *740*
THEIL, E. C. 572, 574, *586, 587*
THIERFELDER, H. 609, 610, 611, *638*
THIERFELDER, K. 745, *797*
THIES, W. 840, 841, *895*
THIESSEN, W. E. 863, *897*
THIMANN, K. V. 893, *900*
THOMAS, A. F. 955, *1020*
THOMAS, A. J. 22, 23, 24, *43*
THOMAS, C. A. 541, *578*
THOMAS, C. A., Jr. 541, *578*
THOMAS, E. W. 791, *799*
THOMAS, G. M. 955, 979, 985, 986, 988, *1015*
THOMAS, H. 208, 219, *241*
THOMAS, H. J. 714, *739*
THOMAS, P. R. 962, *1022*
THOMAS, R. 997, *1022*, 1029, 1030, 1035, *1061, 1063*
THOMPSON, A. 377, 396, *476*
THOMPSON, A. E. R. 607, *638*
THOMPSON, G. A. 1034, 1035, *1060*
THOMPSON, G. A., Jr. 153, 156, *203*, 647, 652, *676*, 946, 950, *952*
THOMPSON, J. F. 686, *741*
THOMPSON, J. H. 671, *677*
THOMPSON, L. 89, *100*, 544, *579*
THOMPSON, M. J. 222, *243*
THOMPSON, P. J. 850, *896*
THOMPSON, R. C. 482, *534*
THOMPSON, R. E. 430, *473*
THOMPSON, R. H. S. 148, *194*
THOMPSON, W. 137, 145, 146, 159, 160, 161, 162, 163, *192, 202, 203*
THOMSON, P. J. 1041, *1061*
THOMSON, P. L. 1031, 1039, 1041, *1063*
THORELL, B. 488, *534*
THORIN, H. 155, *203*
THORPE, W. V. *635*
THRENN, R. H. 430, *473*
TICE, S. V. 618, *637*
TIDD, B. K. 1049, *1061*
TIEMANN, F. 930, *939*

TIETZ, A. 107, 109, 128, *201, 202, 203*
TILDEN, E. B. 379, 389, 450, *462, 474*
TILGNER, D. J. 1069, *1078*
TINELLI, R. 94, *101*
TISCHER, J. 667, *677*
TISELIUS, A. 384, *475*
TISSIERES, A. 502, 509, *533, 534*, 569, *586*
TITCHENER, E. B. 109, *194, 204*, 722, *742*
TITUS, E. O. 885, *900*
TIWARI, H. P. 971, 985, *1019, 1022*
TJADEN, M. 132, *194*
TKACZ, L. 597, 612, *636*
TOBITA, T. 486, *535*
TOCCHINI-VALENTINI, E. P. 569, *586*
TOCHKIURA, T. 719, *737*
TODD, A. 556, *582*
TODD, A. R. 299, 301, *307*, 711, *733*
TODD, G. 831, *894*
TOENNIES, G. 7, *43*
TOKUSHIGE, M. 23, *39*
TOLBERT, N. E. 6, *42, 43*, 335, *474*
TOMATIS, L. 1069, *1078*
TOMCHICK, R. 8, *37*, 622, 625, *635*
TOMES, M. L. 652, 653, *677*
TOMIMURA, T. 284, *309*
TOMINAGA, H. 502, 503, *532*
TOMITA, H. 865, *897*
TOMKINS, G. 211, *242*
TOMKINS, G. M. 235, *244*, 375, 435, *455*, 507, *529*
TOMLINSON, R. 138, *203*
TOMS, E. J. 28, *37*
TOOHEY, J. 717, *742*
TOOHEY, J. I. 264, 301, *312*
TOOMEY, R. E. 112, 114, 115, *203*
TOPPER, Y. J. 346, *474*
TORIBIO, F. 813, *827*
TORII, K. 11, *43*
TORRES, H. N. 406, *455*
TORRIANI, A. M. 377, 383, 408, *468, 474*
TORTO, F. G. 667, *677*
TOTH, B. 1069, *1078*
TOTH, G. 341, *461*
TOUSTER, O. 363, 446, 449, 450, *463, 467, 474, 740*
TOWERS, G. H. N. 766, 779, 788, 791, *798, 799*
TOWNSEND, R. 1054, *1063*
TOWNSLEY, P. M. *312*
TRAKATELLIS, A. C. 501, 502, 504, *534*
TRAMS, E. G. 111, 112, *190*
TRAUT, R. R. 371, 399, 402, 405, *471, 472, 474*
TRAUTNER, T. A. 547, 551, *580*
TRAVERS, R. B. 1031, 1035, 1041, *1062*
TRAVIS, R. H. 228, *244*

TREADWELL, C. R. 131, 132, *191, 203, 204, 205*
TREBLE, D. H. 700, 701, *735*
TREFFERS, H. P. 483, *530*
TREHARNE, K. J. 866, *898*
TREHARNE, R. W. 335, 336, *474*
TRELLE, C. J. 518, 519, *528*
TRENNER, N. R. 331, *474*
TREVELYAN, W. E. 398, *474*
TRIA, E. 521, *534*
TRIER, G. 976, *1023*
TRIPPETT, S. 1027, *1062*
TRISTRAM, G. R. 208, 211, *241*
TRIVEDI, A. H. 656, *674*
TRIVELLONI, J. C. 375, 434, *474*, 598, *638*
TROCKMAN, R. W. 216, 223, *242*
TROJANOWSKI, J. *940*
TROLL, W. 631, *638*
TROWN, P. W. 27, 28, *43*
TROXLER, R. F. 295, 297, 298, *312*
TRUCCO, R. E. 344, 353, 354, *457, 474*
TRUEBLOOD, K. N. 299, *309*
TRUESDAIL, J. H. 694, *742*
TRUMAN, D. E. S. 522, *534*
TRUMBULL 962, *1017*
TRUNNELL, J. B. 709, *734*
TRUSOV, V. I. 139, *203*
TSAI, C. Y. 403, *468*
TSCHANG, J. L. 659, *674*
TSCHESCHE, R. 884, 885, *900*
TS'O, P. O. P. 543, *579*
TSUBOI, K. K. 545, *579*
TSUCHIYA, H. M. 413, *465*
TSUGAWA, R. 720, *739*
TSUGITA, A. 494, *534*
TSUJI, H. 690, 691, *736, 739*
TSUJIMOTO, H. Y. 329, 330, *455, 474*
TSUKAMOTO, H. 593, *638*
TSUNODA, T. 720, *739*
TSUNOO, S. 631, *638*
TSUSHIMA, K. 281, *309, 312*
TSUYUKI, H. 159, *203*, 597, *639*
TUNG, T.-C. 123, *203*
TURBA, F. 504, 520, *534, 536*
TURBERT, H. 597, *638*
TURCHINI, J. 289, *307*
TURIAN, G. 657, 659, *677*
TURNER, A. F. *586*
TURNER, D. H. 92, *101*, 355, *474*
TURNER, D. W. 989, *1015*
TURNER, F. A. 959, *1022*
TURNER, J. F. 92, *101*, 332, 334, 355, 371, 389, *456, 474*
TURNER, J. M. 257, *311*
TURNER, M. E. *467*
TURNER, R. 1031, *1062*
TURNEY, J. R. 379, *470*

TUTTLE, L. C. 694, *738*
TUTTLE, L. P. 360, *456*
TYCHAK, E. 858, *897*
TYLER, V. E. *1022*

UCHIMURA, F. 281, *309, 312*
UCHINO, H. 718, 730, *741*
UDENFRIEND, S. 15, *39*, 40, 41, 140, 141, 148, 154, *194, 204*, 485, *530, 532, 637*
UEDA, I. 690, *735*
UEDA, K. 681, *739*
UEDA, S. 1003, *1020*
UEHLEKE, H. 654, *674*
UL HASSAN, M. 728, 730, *741*
ULLAL, V. V. 745, *797*
ULRICH, B. 682, *736*
UMBARGER, E. 10, 14, 24, *39, 40*
UMBARGER, H. E. 6, 9, 23, 24, 25, 27, *38, 39, 40, 43*, 142, *203*, 704, *735*, 810, *827*
UMBARGER, M. A. 6, *43*, 142, *203*
UMBREIT, W. W. 36, *43*, 723, *735, 741*
UNDERHILL, E. W. 772, 773, *798*, 805, 806, 807, 817, *827*, 959, *1022*
UNDERKOFLER, L. A. 694, *741*
UNDERWOOD, J. G. 1044, *1061*
UNO, T. 593, *639*
UNRAU, A. M. 985, *1019*
UPPER, C. D. 870, *898*
URATA, G. 256, 273, *308, 312*
URBACH, G. 807, 815, 817, *825*
URITANI, I. 862, *897*
URSPRUNG, J. J. 876, 877, 878, *899*
UTTER, M. F. 79, *99*, 337, *464, 465, 474*, 722, *741*

VAGELOS, P. R. 109, 110, 111, 112, 114, 115, 117, 119, 121, *188, 189, 194, 196, 199, 203*
VALENTA, Z. 832, *894*, 971, 1011, *1015, 1022*
VALENTINE, C. 879, 882, 890, *899*
VALENTINE, R. C. 329, 330, *468, 474*
VALIANT, J. 721, *742*
VALLEE, B. L. 498, *531*
VALVERDE-LOPEZ, S. 971, *1015*
VAN BAALEN, C. 708, *741*
VAN BRUGGEN, J. T. 448, *471*
VANDEENEN, L. L. M. 136, 148, 186, *192, 200, 204*
VANDER WENDE, C. 402, *467*
VANDE WEILE, R. 227, *243*
VAN DUIN, J. 506, *535*
VAN DUUREN, B. L. 1070, 1076, *1078*
VANEK, Z. 1041, *1061, 1062*
VANGEDAL, S. 1049, *1062*
VAN HEYNINGEN, R. 337, *474*

VANHOUNY, G. V. 131, *204*
VAN NIEL, C. B. 327, *474*, 658, 667, *676, 677*
VAN SLYKE, D. D. 519, *534*
VAN TAMELEN, E. E. 974, 995, 996, *1022*
VARDANIS, A. 405, *474*
VARMA, T. N. R. 648, 658, *677*
VARNA, T. N. R. 855, *897*
VARNER, J. E. 507, *535*
VASSEL, B. 619, *639*
VAUGHAN, M. 124, 148, *200, 203*, 486, 488, 516, *534, 535*
VAUGHAN, S. T. 28, *43*
VAUGHN, M. H. 291, *312*
VAVRA, J. J. 27, *43*
VELICK, S. F. 485, *530, 534*
VELLUZ, L. 240, *245*
VENETIANER, P. 519, *535*
VENKATARAMAN, P. R. 563, *584*
VENKATARAMAN, R. 19, *43*, 140, *204*, 325, *474*
VENNESLAND, B. 6, *42*
VERACHTERT, H. 357, 358, *474*
VERDIER, R. 855, *897*
VERNON, L. P. 337, *474*
VESCIA, A. 687, *741*
VESTER, J. W. 178, 179, 181, 182, *200*
VESTERMARK, A. 612, *635, 639*
VESTLING, C. S. 342, 343, *473*
VIERA, E. 705, *741*
VIGNAIS, P. 641, 671, *675*
VIGNAIS, P. M. *204*
VIGNAIS, P. V. *204*
VIGNOS, P. J. *636*
VIGROS, P. J., Jr. 8, *38*
VILKAS, E. 138, *189*
VILLANEUVA, V. R. 882, *900*
VILLAR-PALASI, C. 92, *101*, 355, 371, 399, 402, 405, *465, 471, 474*
VILLA-TREVINO, S. 504, *535*
VILLE, A. 805, *824*
VILLEE, C. A. 451, *462*
VILLOTTI, R. 877, *899*
VILLOUTREIX, J. 650, *676*
VINING, L. C. 1004, *1022*
VIÑUELA, E. 341, *474*
VIRGIN, H. 267, *312*
VIRTANEN, A. I. 696, *741*
VISCHER, E. B. J. *1063*
VISHIN, M. L. 1006, *1022*
VISHINIAC, W. 337, *475*
VITOLS, E. 718, *741*
VITUCCI, J. C. 904, 906, 909, 916, 918, 920, *939*
VIZSOLYI, J. P. *586*
VLASENOK, L. I. 269, *312*
VOGEL, H. 304, *311*

VOGEL, H. J. 11, 12, 14, 23, 25, 27, 28, *38, 40, 42, 43, 44*, 694, *738*
VOGEL, R. H. 12, *43*
VOGEL, W. 821, *827*
VOGT, M. 542, *578*
VOGT, R. R. 1072, *1078*
VOLCANI, B. E. 22, *44*, 690, 724, *740, 741*
VOLK, W. A. 94, *101*, 660, *678*
VOLKIN, E. 501, 503, *535*, 542, 552, *577, 578, 581*
VOLLMER, K. 791, *799*
VOLWILER, W. 484, *529*
VONBULOW-KOSTER, J. 117, *190*
VON DER DECKEN, A. 483, 487, 504, 512, 516, *533, 535*
VON EHRENSTEIN, G. 494, 498, 503, 504, 511, *528, 532, 535*, 543, *578*
VONEULER, H. 123, *204*, 692, *741*
VON KORFF, R. W. 944, *951*
VON MERING, J. 592, *637*
VON RUDLOFF, E. 780, *798*
VON WACEK, A. 930, *939*
VOORMA, H. O. 506, *535*
VYAS, S. 11, 12, 13, 14, *43*

WACHSMAN, J. T. 520, *535*
WACKER, H. 702, 703, *742*
WADDELL, J. G. 723, *741*
WAELSCH, H. 29, *41*
WAGENKNECHT, A. C. 136, *198, 204*
WAGLE, S. R. 718, *739*
WAGNER, A. F. *952*
WAGNER, F. 301, *307*
WAGNER, H. 117, 137, 162, *190, 196, 204*
WAGNER, R. P. 6, 23, *37, 42, 43*
WAGNER-JAUREGG, T. 745, *797*
WAHBA, A. J. 19, *43*, 445, 446, 449, *455, 475*
WAINER, A. 158, *189*, 440, *475*
WAINWRIGHT, S. D. 37, *44*, 502, *535*
WAINWRIGHT, T. 10, 11, *43*
WAITE, M. 110, 112, 114, 115, *203, 204*
WAJDA, M. 188, *192*
WAKIL, S. J. 106, 107, 109, 112, 113, 114, 115, 116, 117, 118, 119, 120, 121, 125, *191, 194, 195, 196, 201, 203, 204*, 219, *242*, 599, 612, *637, 722, 742*, 760, *798*
WAKISAKA, G. 718, 730, *741*
WALBRIDGE, C. T. 291, *312*
WALDSCHMITT, M. 9, *38, 44*, 705, *742*
WALKER, B. H. 968, *1016*
WALKER, D. G. 341, *475*
WALKER, G. 718, *741*
WALKER, G. J. 379, 410, *475*
WALKER, J. 836, *895*
WALKER, L. M. 485, *533*

WALKER, M. 288, *310*
WALLACE, J. M. 543, *579*
WALLACH, O. 830, 833, *894*
WALLER, G. R. 961, 962, 1010, *1017, 1018, 1022, 1023*
WALLER, R. E. 1068, *1078*
WALLIS, M. 645, *677*
WALSH, K. A. 668, *678*
WALTER, H. 484, 486, *529, 535*
WALTON, E. *952,* 1043, 1052, *1062*
WALWICK, E. R. 553, *581*
WANG, D.-H. 403, *475*
WANG, J. H. 400, *475*
WANG, L. 373, 425, *464*
WANG, T. P. 83, *101,* 692, 693, *742*
WARAWA, E. J. 871, *898*
WARBURG, O. 51, *101,* 332, 333, 334, 335, *475*
WARD, C. 373, 433, *475*
WARD, G. B. 698, *742*
WARD, V. 521, *529*
WARDROP, A. B. 916, 917, *939*
WARNER, J. R. 510, 514, *533, 535*
WARNER, R. C. 567, 568, *585*
WARREN, C. K. 667, *673*
WARREN, F. L. 971, 974, *1019, 1022*
WARREN, L. 91, *101, 102,* 174, 177, *196, 204,* 437, *456, 475*
WARREN, M. E. 979, *1016, 1020*
WARREN, W. A. 516, *535*
WARSHAW, J. B. *204*
WARSHAWSKY, H. 520, *535*
WARTMANN, W. B., Jr. 1074, *1078*
WARWICK, A. J. 778, *798*
WARWICK, G. P. *637*
WASSEL, G. 979, *1017*
WASSERMAN, H. H. 301, 303, 304, *312*
WASSON, G. W. 112, *202,* 209, *241*
WASSON, R. L. 777, *798*
WATANABE, I. 502, 503, *532*
WATANABE, M. 563, *584*
WATANABE, Y. 16, *44*
WATERFIELD, W. R. 996, *1018*
WATERHOUSE, D. F. 632, *639*
WATERLOW, J. C. 481, 487, *535*
WATJEN, A. 140, *203*
WATKIN, J. E. 750, 772, 773, *797, 798,* 805, 806, 807, 817, *827*
WATKINS, D. 15, *40,* 520, *530*
WATKINS, W. M. 355, 356, 360, 372, 393, 394, *461, 475*
WATSON, C. J. 289, 299, *310, 312,* 712, *741*
WATSON, D. 174, *201,* 437, *464, 471*
WATSON, D. P. 1004, *1019*
WATSON, J. D. 501, 503, 509, 510, *529, 533, 535,* 541, 542, 547, *577, 578*
WATSON, P. R. 416, 424, *464, 465*

WATSON, R. W. 446, *463*
WATTS, R. 155, *195*
WATTS-TOBIN, R. J. 492, *528*
WEATHERBY, J. H. 626, 627, 629, *637*
WEBB, J. L. 226, *243*
WEBB, M. E. 130, *196*
WEBBER, J. M. 414, *476*
WEBER, E. J. 165, *191*
WEBER, G. 488, 507, *535*
WEBER, M. A. 27, *44*
WEBSTER, B. R. 955, 983, 1000, 1003, *1015,* 1040, 1053, *1061*
WEBSTER, G. C. 487, 495, *527, 535*
WEBSTER, G. R. 148, 183, *193, 194, 204*
WEBSTER, L. T., Jr. 125, 126, *191*
WEED, L. L. 71, *102*
WEEDON, B. C. L. 641, 655, 656, 662, 667, *673, 674, 677, 678*
WEERSING, S. 131, *204*
WEGNER, G. H. 153, *204*
WEHMER, C. 840, 841, *895*
WEIBULL, C. 384, *475*
WEIDEL, W. 687, *734*
WEIDEMANN, G. 361, *460*
WEIL, A. 1043, *1063*
WEILAND, H. *312*
WEILL, C. E. 379, 410, *475*
WEILL, J. D. 567, 568, *585*
WEIMBERG, R. 446, 448, 450, *475*
WEINFELD, H. 57, *100,* 544, *579*
WEINGES, K. 807, 813, 814, 815, *824, 827*
WEINHOUSE, S. 22, 23, 24, 27, *43,* 124, 126, *196, 472*
WEINSTEIN, I. B. 521, *529*
WEINSTOCK, C. H. 702, 703, *742*
WEISBLUM, B. 494, 496, 498, *527, 535*
WEISBLUM, P. 498, *528*
WEISMAN, R. A. 706, 707, *734, 742*
WEISS, A. 140, *203*
WEISS, B. *204*
WEISS, S. 140, *203*
WEISS, S. B. 88, *98,* 122, 127, 128, 142, 143, 144, 146, 154, 1o7, *197, 202, 204,* 495, *535,* 565, 567, 568, 569, 570, *584, 585*
WEISS, U. 32, 34, *44*
WEISSBACH, A. 140, *193, 204,* 320, 321, 325, 445, *463, 475,* 548, *580*
WEISSBACH, H. 22, *38, 44,* 620, 622, 623, 635, 717, 718, *733, 739, 742*
WEISSMAN, C. 566, 567, *584, 585*
WEISSMAN, S. M. 553, *581*
WEITKAMP, H. 705, *737*
WEIZMANN, A. 877, *899*
WELCH, A. D. 708, *735*
WELIKY, I. 228, *244*
WELKIE, G. W. 566, *587*
WELLS, L. W. 648, *678*

WELLES, W. W.   216, 221, *242*, 878, *899*
WEMPLE, J. N.   1003, *1020*
WENDT, H. J.   *1018*
WENGER, E.   860, *897*
WENKERT, E.   808, 810, *827*, 832, 867, 868, 871, *894*, *898*, 958, 989, 997, 1004, *1022*, 1049, *1063*
WENT, F. W.   845, *896*
WERBIN, H.   224, 230, *243*, *244*
WERKMAN, C. H.   106, *204*
WERNER, R.   416, *463*
WERTHEIM, M.   397, *467*
WERTHESSEN, N. T.   214, *242*
WESSELY, L.   944, *952*
WEST, C. A.   870, *898*
WEST, R.   252, 277, *310*
WESTALL, R. G.   257, *313*
WETTER, L. R.   143, 156, *201*
WETTSTEIN, A.   228, *244*
WETTSTEIN, F. O.   **494**, 504, 510, 518, *532*, *534*, *535*
WEYGAND, F.   705, *742*, 805, *827*, 1004, 1006, *1018*, *1020*, *1021*, *1022*, *1023*
WHALLEY, W. B.   771, *798*, 1031, 1034, 1035, 1037, 1041, 1044, 1048, 1052, 1054, 1055, 1056, 1058, *1060*, *1061*, *1062*, *1063*
WHATLEY, F. R.   330, 332, *475*
WHEAT, R. W.   91, 92, *101*
WHEELDON, L. W.   127, 136, *199*
WHEELER, M.   379, 410, *475*
WHEELER, R.   778, 788, *798*
WHEELER, R. V.   1072, *1078*
WHEELER, T. S.   745, *797*
WHELAN, W. J.   334, 340, 370, 379, 381, 384, 389, 392, 410, 411, *454*, *455*, *463*, *468*, *470*, *475*
WHELDALE, M.   746, *797*
WHEREAT, A. F.   181, *199*
WHIPPLE, G. H.   276, 277, *309*
WHISTLER, R. L.   412, 417, 423, *475*
WHITE, A.   181, *195*, 508, *532*, 760, *798*
WHITE, A. M.   140, *201*
WHITE, B. N.   426, *475*
WHITE, F. G.   682, *739*
WHITE, J. G.   299, *309*
WHITE, J. W., Jr.   376, 396, *475*
WHITE, R. W.   862, *897*
WHITE, T.   805, 812, 818, 819, 820, *825*, *827*
WHITEHEAD, R. W.   718, *735*
WHITEHOUSE, M.   125, *204*
WHITEHOUSE, M. W.   236, 237, 238, 239, *244*, *245*
WHITELEY, H. R.   330, *475*
WHITFIELD, H. J., Jr.   29, 30, *44*
WHITING, M. C.   861, *897*, 1048, *1062*
WHITTEN, L. K.   630, *636*
WHITTINGHAM, C. P.   335, *470*, *475*

WHYTE, M.   131, 180, *197*, *204*
WIAME, J. M.   11, 14, *38*, *42*
WICKLIFF, J. L.   866, *898*
WIDDOWSON, D. A.   989, *1015*
WIECHERS, A.   981, *1015*
WIEGANDT, H.   175, *198*
WIEHLER, G.   958, *1023*
WIELAND, H.   1066, *1078*
WIELAND, O.   107, 124, *199*, *204*, 944, *952*
WIELAND, T.   85, *102*, 694, *738*, *742*
WIESMEERY, H.   92, *102*
WIESNER, K.   832, *894*, 971, 1011, *1015*, *1022*
WIEWIOROWSKI, M.   975, *1020*
WIGHTMAN, F.   958, *1023*
WILBER, P. B.   552, *581*
WILD, G. M.   384, *460*
WILDMAN, S. G.   *534*, 566, *587*, 839, *895*, 943, *952*
WILDMAN, W. C.   955, 985, 986, 1006, *1015*, *1016*, *1017*, *1021*
WILGRAM, G. F.   143, *204*
WILKEN, D. R.   416, *457*
WILKEN, J.   372, 393, *462*
WILKINS, M. H. F.   498, *534*, 540, 541, 577, *578*
WILKINSON, D. I.   216, *242*, 1041, *1062*
WILKINSON, I. A.   379, 383, 411, *456*
WILKINSON, J. F.   277, 278, 295, *309*
WILKINSON, J. H.   620, *637*
WILLENBRINK, J.   332, *462*
WILLIAMS, C. O.   822, *827*
WILLIAMS, K.   606, *635*
WILLIAMS, P. N.   105, 106, *195*
WILLIAMS, R. H.   132, *194*, 405, 406, 407, *473*
WILLIAMS, R. J.   680, 694, 724, *734*, *742*
WILLIAMS, R. J. H.   641, 650, 655, *674*, *675*
WILLIAMS, R. P.   303, 304, *309*, *313*
WILLIAMS, R. T.   593, 597, 599, 608, 609, 612, 614, 632, 634, *635*, *638*, *639*
WILLIAMS, T. W.   1027, 1028, *1061*
WILLIAMS, W. L.   *740*
WILLIAMS-ASHMAN, H. G.   139, 145, *204*, *535*
WILLIAMSON, A.   509, 511, 512, 513, 516, *533*
WILLIAMSON, A. R.   367, *475*
WILLIAMSON, D. H.   345, *459*, 691, *736*
WILLIAMSON, I. P.   112, 114, 115, *203*, 948, *952*
WILLIAMSON, R.   509, 510, *531*
WILLIS, C.   868, *898*
WILLIS, J. E.   5, 6, *44*, 142, *204*
WILLIS, J. L.   850, *896*
WILLMER, J. S.   657, 658, *674*
WILLSTAEDT, E.   389, *468*

WILLSTÄTTER, R. 268, *313*
WILSMHURST, J. K. 871, 872, *898*
WILSON, A. C. 699, 704, *742*
WILSON, A. N. *952*, 1043, 1052, *1062*
WILSON, A. T. 92, *97*, 320, 335, *456*, *475*
WILSON, D. B. 360, *475*
WILSON, D. M. 446, *475*
WILSON, D. W. 71, *98*, *102*
WILSON, E. J. 379, 389, *475*
WILSON, E. M. 955, 1003, *1015*
WILSON, H. P. 540, *577*
WILSON, H. R. 541, *578*
WILSON, J. D. 140, 141, 148, 154, *194*, *204*
WILSON, L. G. 438, 439, 440, *455*, *475*, 614, *635*, *639*
WILSON, R. G. 688, *742*
WIMER, E. 487, *533*
WINCKELM US, D. 510, 511, *535*
WINDSOR, E. 27, *44*
WINKLER, A. 15, *40*, 520, *530*
WINKLER, K. 1006, *1021*
WINNICK, R. E. 483, *535*
WINNICK, T. 481, 483, 487, 520, *529*, *535*, 721, *736*
WINSTEAD, J. A. 1053, *1063*
WINTER, A. 893, *900*
WINTER, J. 1006, *1016*, 1052, 1054, 1055, *1060*, *1061*
WINTERSBERGER, E. 522, *535*
WINTERSTEIN, E. 976, *1023*
WINTROBE, M. M. 265, *312*
WINZLER, R. J. 436, *455*, *467*, *471*, 519, *535*
WISE, C. D. 286, *307*, *313*
WISE, E. M., Jr. 151, *204*
WISER, R. 130, *189*, *190*
WISLICENUS, H. 918, *939*
WISS, O. 687, 688, *742*, 890, *901*
WITCOFF, H. 135, 138, 139, *204*
WITKOP, B. 15, *40*, 622, 624, *636*, *638*
WITT, H. T. 330, *468*, *475*
WITTENBERG, J. 143, 154, *204*, 252, 261, *312*, *313*, 711, *741*, *742*
WITTER, R. F. 147, *199*
WITTING, L. *952*
WITTING, L. A. 648, *678*, 833, *894*
WITTREICH, P. E. 843, *896*
WIXOM, R. L. 23, *40*, *44*
WIZERKANIUK, M. 440, *459*, 612, *636*
WOESE, C. R. 518, *535*
WOLF, A. P. 961, 963, *1017*
WOLF, B. 142, *204*, 708, *742*
WOLF, D. E. 331, *474*, 647, *678*, 721, *742*, 843, *896*, *952*
WOLF, G. 5, 15, *44*, 426, *468*, 519, *535*
WOLF, H. P. 349, *464*, *466*
WOLFE, J. B. 352, *476*

WOLFE, L. S. 175, *204*
WOLFE, R. S. 330, 371, 415, *457*, *474*
WOLFF, D. *146*, *197*
WOLFF, J. B. 267, 287, *313*, 450
WOLFROM, M. L. 377, 396, 414, *476*
WOLIN, M. J. 345, *476*
WOLKEN, J. J. 670, *678*
WOLOCHOW, H. E. 376, 390, *476*
WOMACK, M. 481, *533*
WONG, E. 778, *798*
WONG, K. G. 495, *535*
WONG, P. S. 654, 658, 659, *673*, *676*
WOOD, B. J. 943, 946, *951*
WOOD, B. J. B. 120, *195*
WOOD, E. 357, 358, *470*
WOOD, H. C. S. 702, *740*
WOOD, H. G. 106, *204*, 336, 372, 393, *462*, *472*, *476*, 722, *741*
WOOD, J. L. 618, *639*
WOOD, P. 179, *204*
WOOD, P. B. 606, *635*
WOOD, W. A. 36, *43*, 132, *191*, 344, 345, 350, 448, *455*, *467*, *472*, *476*, 696, *739*, *740*
WOOD, W. B. 502, *535*
WOODRUFF, H. B. 571, *586*
WOODS, D. D. 19, 20, 21, 22, *39*, *43*, 723, *739*
WOODWARD, R. B. 213, *242*, 992, 995, 1004, *1023*, 1041, *1062*
WOOL, I. G. 507, *532*, *535*
WOOLEY, J. G. 961, *1017*
WOOLF, L. I. *639*
WOOLFOLK, C. A. 330, *475*
WOOLLEY, D. W. 694, *742*
WORK, E. 25, 26, *37*, *38*, *44*
WORK, T. S. 486, *527*
WORMSER, E. H. 18, *44*
WORTHINGTON, R. E. 303, *309*
WORTMAN, B. 441, *476*
WOSILAIT, W. D. 400, 402, *470*, *473*, *476*
WREN, J. J. 521, *535*
WRIGHT, B. E. 226, *243*, 373, 433, *475*, 708, 709, *742*, 882, *900*
WRIGHT, D. 788, *799*, 928, 929, *937*
WRIGHT, E. W. 59, *96*
WRIGHT, G. F. 1074, *1078*
WRIGHT, I. G. 1000, *1020*
WRIGHT, L. D. 58, 71, *102*, 647, *678*, 719, 720, 721, *735*, *742*, 843, *896*, *952*
WRIGHT, N. G. 16, 25, *38*
WRISTON, J. C. 832, *894*
WRISTON, J. C., Jr. 450, *459*, 711, *742*
WU, C. 487, *535*
WU, P.-H. L. 690, *736*, 962, 964, *1018*, *1023*
WUHRMANN, J. J. 645, *678*

WURSCH, J. 218, *242*
WYATT, G. R. 91, 92, *97*, 372, 391, *468*, 539, 571, *577*
WYNDER, E. L. 1074, *1078*
WYNDHAM, R. A. 287, *310*

YAGI, K. 556, *582*
YAGIRI, Y. 718, 730, *741*
YAMADA, H. 450, *476*
YAMADA, K. 728, *742*
YAMADA, M. 284, *309*, 792, *799*
YAMADA, T. 598, *639*
YAMAGIWA, K. 1065, *1078*
YAMAGUCHI, M. 285, *313*, 661, *678*
YAMAHA, T. 374, 434, *458*
YAMAKAWA, T. 172, *204*
YAMAMOTO, H. 649, *678*
YAMAMOTO, H. Y. 663, 665, *678*
YAMANOTO, R. S. 131, *205*
YAMAOKA, K. 285, *313*
YAMASAKI, K. Y. 237, *245*
YAMAZAKI, M. 766, *798*, 805, *827*, 955, 957, 989, 990, 1014, *1019, 1020, 1022, 1023*
YANG, K. S. 962, *1022, 1023*
YANIV, H. 34, *44*
YANKEELOV, J. A., Jr. 353, *476*
YANKOFSKY, S. A. 567, *585*
YANOFSKY, C. 35, 36, 37, *38, 39, 42, 44*, 491, 494, *535*, 684, 685, 687, 688, *734, 739, 741, 742*
YANOFSKY, S. A. 518, *535*
YARD, A. S. 626, 627, 629, *637*
YARMOLINSKY, M. B. 516, *535*
YATES, J. 1037, *1063*
YENGOYAN, L. S. 188, *197*
YEOWELL, D. A. 955, 985, 1000, *1015, 1016, 1023*
YOGI, K. *798*
YOKOYAMA, H. 645, 646, 647, 648, 649, *673, 678*
YOKOYAMA, S. 172, *204*
YONEDA, M. 555, *582*
YONEYAMA, Y. 265, *311*
YOSHIDA, A. 486, *535*
YOSHIDA, H. 10, *44*
YOSHIDA, S. 923, *938*
YOSHIKAWA, H. 438, 439, *471*, 550, *580*
YOSHIKAYA, H. 265, *311*
YOSHIMURA, H. 593, *638*
YOSHIMURA, S. 446, *468*
YOSHINO, T. 718, 730, *741*
YOUHOTSKY-GORE, I. 647, *673*, 1040, 1047, *1061*
YOUNG, H. L. 123, *205*
YOUNG, L. 605, 606, 607, *636, 637, 638, 639*

YOUNG, R. J. 487, 498, *532, 535*
YOUNG, V. K. 289, *308*
YOUNGER, L. 405, *473*
YOUNGKEN, A. H. W., Jr. 884, *900*
YOUNGKEN, H. W. 959, *1022*
YUAN, C. 119, *205*
YUGARI, Y. 25, *39, 44*
YUNIS, A. A. 401, *476*
YURA, T. 12, 37, *40, 44*

ZABIN, F. 4, *41*
ZABIN, I. 106, 117, 165, 166, 169, 170, 174, *204, 205*, 208, 233, *241, 244*, 647, *677*, 943, *952*
ZACHAU, H. G. 495, *535*
ZAFFARONI, A. 227, *243*
ZAITSEVA, N. I. 711, *734*
ZAK, R. *532*
ZAKRZEWSKI, S. F. 708, 709, *742*
ZALKIN, H. 122, *198, 205*
ZALKOW, L. H. 856, *897*
ZALOKAR, M. 487, 518, *536*, 659, 661, 668, *677, 678*
ZAMBONI, V. 629, *636*
ZAMECNIK, P. C. 481, 483, 487, 497, 498, 502, 503, 508, 512, *530, 531, 534, 536*, 561, *583*
ZAMENHOF, S. 367, *475*, 540, 544, 548, 572, 574, *577, 579, 580, 586, 587*
ZAMIR, A. 497, 498, 499, *530*, 543, *578*
ZAPROMETOV, M. N. 804, 805, *825, 827*
ZASKE, M. R. 265, *310*
ZATMAN, L. J. 692, *742*
ZAUNER, J. 922, *938*
ZBARSKY, S. H. *639*
ZEBE, E. C. 112, *205*
ZECHMEISTER, L. 341, *461*, 658, 659, 669, 671, *673, 676, 678*
ZEIGLER, N. R. 289, *310*
ZEIJLEMAKER, F. C. J. 822, *827*
ZELEZNICK, L. D. 373, 432, *476*
ZELLER, P. 671, *675*
ZENK, M. H. 791, *799*, 804, *827*
ZEVENHUIZEN, L. P. T. M. 412, *476*
ZIEGLER, W. 780, *798*
ZILL, L. P. 335, *474*
ZILLIG, W. 497, 502, *528, 536*
ZILLIG, W. D. 543, *578*
ZILLIKEN, F. 92, *100*, 356, 377, *469, 476*
ZILVERSMIT, D. B. 124, 139, 142, 182, *191, 205*
ZILVERSMITH, D. B. 544, *579*
ZIMMERMAN, E. 504, *536*
ZIMMERMAN, E. F. 566, *584*
ZIMMERMAN, S. B. 547, 548, *580*
ZINCKE, T. 931, *939*

ZINDER, N. D.   566, 567, *584*
ZIPPER, H.   486, *535*
ZIPSER, D.   516, *536*
ZODROW, H.   716, *742*
ZODROW, K.   716, *742*
ZOELLNER, N.   693, *740*

ZSCHENDERLEIN, A.   918, *939*
ZUBAY, G.   510, *534, 536,* 561, *583*
ZULALIAN, J.   957, 985, 1022, *1023*
ZURECK, A.   962, *1018*
ZWINGELSTEIN, G.   805, *824*

SUBJECT INDEX

* An asterisk after the page number indicates that the structural formula is given on this page, with or without additional information.

† A dagger after the page number indicates that the biosynthesis is treated on this page; additional information may also be given.

→ An arrow indicates that the first-named substance is mentioned as a precursor of the second substance, or as an intermediate, a by-product, a coenzyme, or any other cofactor of the reaction leading to the biological formation of the substance named after the arrow.

AAA →lysine, 27*†, 28, 29
AAA-semialdehyde →lysine, 28†, 29
Abbreviations of nucleosides, and mono- and polynucleotides, 538
Abequose, 427
Abietadiene, 871, 872
Abietane, 893
Abietane type of resin acids, 871
Abietic acid, 863, 864*, 872
Acceptor RNA, nucleotide sequence in, 498
Acceptors, glucosyl, 404
Acceptors, glycosyl, 384, 385
Acenaphthylene, 1075
Acetaldehyde, 56, 57*
   active form of, 682
   →acetyl CoA, 107
   →cholesterol, 208
   →D-deoxyribose-5-phosphate, 349, 350
   →threonine, 16
Acetamide dideoxysugars, 365*†
Acetamide →cholesterol, 208
Acetamidobenzoic acid, 626*†
   secretion of, 633
Acetate, 3
   addition to precursor, 751
   condensation of, 751
   linear condensation of, 752*
   →alkaloids, 997, 998, 999, 1000, 1001
   →carotenoids, 643, 644
   →cholesterol, 208
   →flavone, 773*
   →heme, 253*
   →phenolic plant products, 776
   →piperidine and pyridine alkaloids, 967*, 968†
   →porphobilinogen, 254
   →porphyrin, 252
   →rubber, 943, 944*
   →succinate, via glyoxalate cycle, 340
Acetate hypothesis, 751
   in alkaloid biogenesis, 997, 998, 999, 1000

Acetate-malonate pathway, 766
Acetate theory of biosynthesis of phenolic substances, 1026
Acetic acid, head-to-tail union of, 1026, 1033, 1037, 1039
   in aromatic biosynthesis, 751
   →alkaloids, 1012, 1013
   →flavonoids, 747
   →fungal metabolites, 1025, 1026, 1029, 1030, 1031, 1032, 1033, 1034, 1035, 1037, 1038, 1039, 1041, 1043, 1044, 1046, 1048, 1051, 1052, 1055, 1056, 1057
Acetic thiokinase, 109, 125
Acetoacetate →cholesterol, 208, 209*
Acetoacetic acid, product of fungal metabolism, 910
   →alkaloids, 1009
   →hygrine, 958*, 959
Acetoacetyl CoA, 107†, 646
   →cholesterol, 208
   →long-chain fatty acids, 113
   →mevalonic acid, 843
   →rubber, 944*†, 945
   →squalene, 210*, 211
Acetoin, 682†
   →riboflavin, 701
Acetohydrazide, acetylation, 627
α-Aceto-α-hydroxy acid, 21*
Acetohydroxyacid synthetase, 23
α-Aceto-α-hydroxybutyrate, 23
Acetoisovanillone, 624
Acetolactate, 23
Acetone →cholesterol, 208
Acetone cyanohydrin, 617*
Acetonitrile, 616, 617*, 618
Acetophenone, 790†, 791*†
Acetovanillone, 624
Acetyl adenylate →acetyl CoA, 125
Acetylase, in mercapturic acid formation, 605

1139

Acetylases, 626
Acetylation, 626
  coenzyme of, 694
  as detoxication reaction, 591, 592
  enzymic mechanism of, 628
  types of compound undergoing, 626
  zoological distribution of, 628
N-Acetylation of sugar phosphates, 351
Acetyl CoA, 256, 626†, 628
  in aromatic biosynthesis, 751
  in detoxication reactions, 592
  in head-to-tail union of acetate, 1033, 1034
  role in acetylation, 626
  →butyryl CoA, 107
  →carotene, 646
  →cholesterol, 208, 209
  →fatty acids, 110
  →fungal metabolites, 1033, 1034, 1038
  →glucose-6-phosphate, 341
  →malonyl-CoA, 760, 761*
  →mevalonic acid, 843
  →orsellinic acid, 1033*, 1034
  →palmitic acid, 112
  →rubber, 944*†, 945
  →squalene, 210*, 211
Acetyl CoA-synthetase, 125
Acetyl carboxylase, 110
Acetylcholine, 626†
N-Acetylcyclohexylalanine, 628
N-Acetyl-L-cysteine, derivatives of, 601*†
N-Acetyl-S(1, 2-dihydro-2-hydroxyaryl) cysteine, 606*
Acetylene, 1072, 1073
N-Acetyl-D-galactosamine, in bacterial cell wall polysaccharides, 426
  nonenzymatic epimerization of, 362
  phosphorylation of, 344, 368
N-Acetylgalactosamine-1-phosphate, 354†
N-Acetyl-D-galactosamine-6-O-[35S]-sulfate, 441
N-Acetyl glucosamine, 173
  in bacterial cell wall polysaccharides, 426, 427
  inhibition of hexokinase by, 342
  phosphorylation of, 344
  →N-acetyllactose, 372
Acetylglucosamine lactyl-amino acid derivatives, 368
N-Acetyl-D-glucosamine-1-phosphate, 352†, 354†
N-Acetyl-D-glucosamine-6-phosphate, 437, 438
  from glucosamine-6-phosphate 352†
  →1-phosphate, 345
  →sialic acids, 346

β-N-Acetylglucosaminidase, action on bacterial cell wall, 428
N-Acetylglutamate, 13, 14
  →carbamyl phosphate, 72
Acetyl glutamate synthetase, 14
N-Acetyl-glutamic-γ-semialdehyde, 12
N-Acetyl-γ-glutamyl phosphate, 12, 13
N-Acetyl-S-2-hydroxybutylcysteine, 607
1-Acetyl-2-isonicotinyl hydrazine, 627
N-Acetyl-lactose, 372†
N-Acetyl-D-mannosamine, phosphorylation of, 344
  →N-acetylneuraminic acid, 173, 174, 350, 437, 438
N-Acetyl-D-mannosamine-6-phosphate → NAN, 437†, 438
  →sialic acids, 346
N-Acetyl-7-methoxytryptamine, 620†, 623*†
N-Acetyl muramic acid, 429†
  in bacterial cell wall polysaccharides, 426
N-Acetyl neuraminic acid, 173, 174†, 350†, 437†, 438†
  →N-acetyl-D-mannosamine, 436
  →glycoproteins, 437, 438
N-Acetylneuraminic acid aldolase, 436
N-Acetylneuraminic acid-9-P, 174
N-Acetylneuraminyl-(2→3)-β-D-galacto-pyranosyl-(1→4)-D-glucose, 438†
Nα-Acetylornithine, 11, 13
Acetyl phosphate, 330, 351*†, 682
4-Acetyl quinoline, 995†
N-Acetylserotonin →melatonin, 623*†
N-Acetyl sphingosine, 173
N-Acetyl-D-talosamine, 362
2-Acetyl-thiamine pyrophosphate, 682
Acetyl transacylase, 114
Acetyl transfer, 682
α1-Acid glycoprotein, 436†
Acid mucopolysaccharides, 443†
Aconitase, 24
Aconitine, 1011*†
Acridone alkaloids, 1006†
Acrifoline, 970*†, 971†
2-Acroleyl-3-aminofumarate, 688*†
Acrylic acid synthesis, 631
Acrylonitrile, 617*
Acrylyl CoA, 697
Actinidine, 971, 1009*†
Actinomycin, 522, 523, 1040*†
Actinomycin D, 507, 567, 573
  effect on porphyrin biosynthesis, 273
  effect on replication of viruses, 566
  inhibition of RNA synthesis by, 565, 569, 570
Active acetaldehyde, 21, 22, 23*, 350, 682
Active formaldehyde, 6*

Active glycolic aldehyde, 350*†
Acyl carrier protein, 114
Acyl CoA, α,β-unsaturated →fatty acids, 108
Acyl CoA →fatty acids, by elongation mechanism, 117
Acyl dehydrogenase, 107, 108
Acyl derivatives, high energy, 682
Acylglycines, 599
N-Acyl-D-mannosamine-6-P →N-acyl neuraminic acid-9-P, 174
N-Acyl neuraminic acid-9-P, 174†
Acyloin, 23
N-Acyl sphingosine, 166†
    in gangliosides, 176
Acyl transferases, 146, 147
β-Acyl transferase, 148
Adaptor RNA, 488, 489, 494, 496, 498, 499, 500, 517, 521, 522
    pCpCpA terminus of, 506
Adenine, 46*, 47*, 49, 50, 539*
    in pseudovitamin B12, 714, 715
    →adenylic acid, 69
    →folic acid, 705
    →pteridine, 705
    →riboflavin, 699, 700
Adenine deaminase, 699
Adenine oligonucleotides, 570
Adenocarpine, 964*†
Adenosine, 49
Adenosine-2′,5′-diphosphate, 692
Adenosine-diphosphate derivatives of sugars, 90
Adenosine diphosphate glucose, coenzyme function of, 88
Adenosine diphospho glycosides, see ADP-glycosides
Adenosine-5′-monophosphate, 539, 540*
Adenosine, 5′-mono-, di- and triphosphates of, 544
Adenosine-5′-phosphate, 49, 545
    activation of phosphorylase by, 399, 400
Adenosine-3′,5′-phosphate, cyclic, effect on, phosphofructokinase, 344
    UDP-glucose transglycosylase, 406, 407
Adenosine 5′-phosphobenzoate →hippuric acid, 599†
Adenosine-5′-phosphosulfate, 10*†, 87*†, 439, 440, 559, 612
Adenosine triphosphate, see ATP
Adenosine triphosphate, in photosynthesis, 329
S-Adenosyl ethionine, 148
S-Adenosylhomocysteine, 122, 573, 622, 623†
    →cysteine, 8*†

S-Adenosylmethionine, 7, 8, 122, 572, 573, 621, 622*†
    as a source of C-methyl groups, 783, 784
    as a methyl donor, 22
    in detoxication reactions, 592
    in methylation of RNA, 499
    →S-adenosylhomocysteine, 623
    →alkaloids, 955
    →chlorophyll, 266
    →choline, 140
    →cysteine, 8*†
    →lecithin, 148, 149
S-Adenosylmethionine hydrolase, 574
Adenylcobamide coenzyme, 22
Adenylic acid, 49, 66†, 67*†, 539, 540*
    in CoA, 85
    from adenine, 69*†
Adenylic acid-containing coenzymes, 81
Adenylic and sulfuric acids, mixed anhydrides of, 87†
Adenylosuccinase, 65, 67
Adenylosuccinate, 65, 66†*
Adenylosuccinic acid, 30*†
Adenylphosphoryl CO2, 946
Adenyl 5′-methylene diphosphonate, inhibitor of polynucleotide phosphorylase, 556
Adonitol, 450
ADP, 49, 79†, 80†, 371, 373, 375
    phosphate exchange, 559
    polymerization of, 556, 557
    regeneration of ATP from, 382
ADP-D-galactose, 358†
ADP-glucose, 90, 358†
    phosphorolysis of, 407
    →bacterial polysaccharides, 373
    →glucosides, 375, 434
    →saccharides, 371
    →starch, 403, 404
    →sucrose, 390
ADP-glucose:glucan transglucosylase, 411
ADP-glucose pyrophosphorylase, 358
ADP-glucose:glycogen transglucosylase, 403
ADP-glucose:starch transglucosylase, 405
ADP-hexoses, 358†
ADP-D-mannose, 358†
ADP sulfurylase, 559
Adrenaline, 620†, 621*, 622
    metabolism of, 619
    methylation of, 622, 624
Adrenalone, methylation of, 624
Adrenocortical steroid hormones, 226†, 229*†
Adrenocorticotropin, 508
Aegeline, 956*†, 957
Agar, 439

Agathic acid, 864*
Aglycon, 318, 434, 598
    →glucuronosides, 375
    →glycoside, 374, 375
Aglycon-glycosides, 368†
Agnosterol, 215
    →cholesterol, 221*†
Agroclavin, 1004, 1005*†, 1006†, 1051*, 1052†
AICAR →histidine, 29†, 30*†
Ajaconine, 1010*, 1011
Ajmalicine, 1001*
Ajmaline, 955, 989, 992*, 999, 1000, 1001, 1003
Akuammicine, 995*
D-Ala-D-ala →bacterial cell wall, 429†
L-Alanine, 3, 4
    in nicotinic acid synthesis, 687
    →alkaloids, 1004
    →bacterial cell wall, 429
    →fungal metabolites, 1054*
D-Alanine,
    in bacterial cell wall, 427
    →bacterial cell wall, 429
β-Alanine,
    transamination to pyruvic acid, 731
    →pantothenic acid, 85, 694, 695*†, 696, 697, 698
L-Alanine-hydroxypyruvate transaminase, 5, 6
Alanine transfer RNA, 497
Alanyl-methionine, 496
Alanyl-RNA synthetase, 495
β-Alanyl CoA, 697
Albaspidin, 783*
Albumin, 481, 482, 483, 485, 486, 487, 502, 504, 511, 516
    association with cell membranes, 520
    secondary structure, 519
Aldimine derivative, of amino-acrylic acid
    →cysteine, 9*†
Aldolases, 323, 324, 339, 349, 350, 367
Aldol condensation, 348, 349
Aldose-1-phosphate, 352, 368, 369, 384, 385, 386, 387
    →saccharide, 370
Aldose oxidases, 445
Aldose-polyol reactions, 451
Aldoses, 450
    oxidation or dehydrogenation of, 448
    transformations to ketoses, 446
    →ketoses, 451
Aldosterone, 228†, 229*†, 507
Aldouronic acids, 445
Alginic acid, 373†, 422†, 424
Alizarin, 770*

Alkaloids,
    acridine, 1006†
    amaryllidaceae, 985†
    aporphine, 979, 983*
    atypical, 954*
    benzophenanthridine, 981†
    berberine, 982
    biogenetically related to pregnenolone, 1012*†
    bis-benzylisoquinoline, 980*, 981
    β-carboline, 990†, 991*†
    cinchona, 993*†
    clavine, 1004
    colchicine and related substances, 984*†
    definition, 953
    derived from norlaudanosoline, 978*†
    deriving their O- and N-methyl groups from methionine or formate, 955
    ergoline, 1004†, 1005*†
    ergot, 1004†, 1005*†, 1052
    erythrina, 988*†
    fungal, 1052
    furoquinoline, 1008†
    garrya, 1010*†
    indole, 984, 989*†, 990*†, 992*†, 1001*†, 1002*†, 1003, 1004
    indole, biogenesis according to Wenkert, 997†, 998*†
    indolenine, 990†
    isoquinoline, 975†, 976*†, 983, 985
    lycorme and related substances, 986*†
    lycopodium, 968†, 970*†
    miscellaneous, 1014*
    nonheterocyclic amines and related compounds, 955†
    oxindole, 994, 996
    phthalide-isoquinoline, 982*
    protoberberines, 982*†
    pyridine and piperidine, 961†, 967*†
    pyrrolidine, 958*†
    pyrrolizidine, 971†, 972*†
    quinazoline, 1006†
    quinazolino-β-carboline, 990, 991*†
    quinoline, 745, 1006†
    quinolizidine, 972†, 973*†, 974*†
    related to anthranilic acid, 1007*†
    related to phenylalanine, 955†, 956*
    solanum, 1013*†
    steroidal, 832, 893†, 1009†, 1012*†, 1013*†
    terpenoid, 1009*†
    tropane, 959†, 960*†, 961*†
    veratrum, 1013*†
    vinca, 1001*
C-Alkaloid H, 995*
Alkanethiosulfonates, 618
Alkylation, carbon-alkylation, 781

Alkylbezenes, 604, 1075, 1076
Alkyl cyanides, 617*
2-Alkyl-4-hydroxyquinolines, 1006†, 1007*†
Allo-isoleucine, 496
Allophycocyanins, 289, 290, 291, 293†, 294
Allopregnane, 883
Allose, phosphorylation of, 344
D-Allose-6-phosphate, activation of UDP-
glucose transglycosylase by, 406
Allylisopropylacetimide,
stimulation of δ-amino-levulinic acid
synthesis by, 273
stimulation of porphyrin synthesis by, 273
Allylisopropylacetylcarbamide, stimulation
of porphyrin synthesis by, 273
Aloe-emodin, 770*
Alternariol, 1029*†
D-Altronate, 445, 446, 449†
D-Altronic acid, 447*
D-Altrose, 446
phosphorylation of, 344
Amaryllidaceae alkaloids, 985†
Amber, 493
Ambrein, 876*†
Amidotransferase, 31
Amination of sugar phosphates, 351
Aminoacetone, 256
ω-Aminoacetophenone →ephedrine, 956*†,
957
Amino acid-activating enzymes, 86
Amino acid activation, 489
Amino acid adenylates, 86†
Amino acid-AMP compounds, 494, 495
Amino acid biosynthesis, techniques used
in the study of, 2
Amino acid incorporation, recurring sequence of reactions in, 513
Amino acid sequence in proteins, genetic
code for, 491, 492
Amino acid synthesis, source of amino
nitrogen, 4
Amino acids,
N-acetylation, 627
activation of, 86, 494
acyl activation of, 489
amino donors, 4
aromatic, 33*†
in bacteria, 907†, 908*†
in fungi, 908
binding of activated, 560
branched-chain, 21*†, 22†, 24
carboxyl activation of, 488
families of, 3†, 4
free, intracellular pools of →protein, 485
→fungal metabolites, 1026, 1052
general biosynthetic pathways, 3, 4
glucuronides of, 593

Amino acids—(cont.)
identification with codons, 493
incorporation into proteins, 484
in proteins, 478, 479
the α-ketoglutarate family, 3†, 4
lineal sequential incorporation into the
two different chains of rabbit hemoglobin, 515
the pentose family, 3†, 4
phenyl-substituted, acetylation of, 629
the pyruvate family, 3†, 4
synthesis of the aromatic ring, 32, 33
transport across the cell membrane, 485
the triose family, 3†, 4†
Aminoacrylate →cysteine, 9*†
Amino acyl-adenosine esters, 495
Amino acyl adenylates, 86†
Amino acyl-RNA, 489†, 491, 493, 495, 496,
500, 511, 512, 513, 522
bound to mRNA-ribosomes, 511
→sRNA, 489
Amino acyl-RNA-mRNA-ribosome complex, 511
Amino acyl-RNA synthetases, 489, 491,
495, 496
L-α-Aminoadipate →lysine, 27*†, 28
4-Aminoazobenzene, methylation of, 620
o-Aminobenzaldehyde →alkaloids, 1002*,
1004
p-Aminobenzoic acid, 32, 688, 706†
arginine conjugation, 632
in folic acid, 704, 705*
in pantothenic acid synthesis, 696
→pteroic acid, 707
p-Amino-benzoyl-glutamate, 707, 708*†
α-Aminobutyrolactone, 8†
1-Amino-3,4-dimethyl-6-ribityl-amino-
benzene →vitamin B 12, 714
4-Aminodiphenyl, 612
Amino ethanol, phosphorylation of, 143
3-Aminoethyloxindole, 997
1-Amino-4-formyl buta-1,3-diene-1,2-
dicarboxylic acid, 688*†
Aminoglycolipid, 169†
→Tay-Sachs ganglioside, 177
2-Amino-4-hexahydrophenylbutyric acid,
N-acetylation, 627
2-Amino-4-hydroxyl-6-(1',2'-dihydroxy-
propyl)-pteridine, 708
2-Amino-4-hydroxyl-6,7-dimethyl, 5,6,7,8-
tetrahydropteridine, 709
2-Amino-4-hydroxyl-6-hydroxymethyl dihydropterin, 707
2-Amino-4-hydroxyl-6-hydroxymethyl
pteridine →folic acid, 707
2-Amino-4-hydroxy pteridine, 708

2-Amino-4-hydroxypteridine-6-carboxalde-
hyde →folic acid, 706, 707
4-Amino-5-imidazole carboxamide, 61*
5-Aminoimidazole-4-carboxamide, 699
reaction with PRPP, 69
5-Amino-4-imidazolecarboxamide ribonucleotide, 65*†, 67
5-Amino-4-imidazole carboxylic acid
ribonucleotide, 64*†, 65
5-Aminoimidazole ribonucleotide, 64*†
5-Aminoimidazole ribonucleotide carboxylase, 64
5-Amino-4-imidazole-N-succinocarbox-
amide ribonucleotide, 65*†
α-Amino-β-ketoadipate-pyridoxal phosphate-enzyme complex, 255, 256*†
α-Amino-β-ketoadipic acid →δ-aminolevu-
linic acid, 254†, 255†, 256*†
α-Aminoketone, 256
Aminoketone synthetase, 255, 256
7-Amino 8-ketopelargonic acid→biotin, 720
2-Amino-6-ketopimelate, cyclized (dehydrated) form of→lysine, 25*, 26*†
δ-Aminolevulinate→bile pigment, 296, 297,
298, 299
δ-Aminolevulinic acid, 254†, 255, 256†, 257,
272, 273
control of globin and hemoglobin synthesis by, 274
→porphobilinogen, 253*, 254, 257
stimulators of biosynthesis, 273
→uroporphyrinogen III, 253*
→vitamin B_{12}, 299, 711, 712, 713
δ-Aminolevulinic acid dehydrase, 253, 257
δ-Aminolevulinic acid synthetase, 254, 255,
257, 273
δ-Aminolevulinic acid transaminase, 254,
257
3-Aminomethylindole →gramine, 957*†,
958
α-Aminomethyl muconic acid, 688*†
2-Amino-1-naphthol, 631
Aminopterin →riboflavin, 699
m-Aminophenol, sulfation of, 439
2-Amino-4-phenylbutyric acid, N-acetylation, 627
5-Amino-1-ribosyl-4-imidazole-carbox-
amide-5′-phosphate →histidine, 29†,
30*†
Amino sugars, acetylation, 627
Aminotransferase, 352
AMP, 49, 540*
effect on fructose-1,6-diphosphate formation and decomposition, 344
incorporation into RNA, 561
Amurensin, 785, 786*
Amygdalin, 434†

Amylase, 486
association with cell membranes, 520
α-Amylase, 340, 392
inhibition of amylosucrase by, 407, 408
role in polysaccharide synthesis, 386, 387
secondary structure, 519
β-Amylase, 392, 397
Amylodextrins, 376†, 377†, 379†, 409†
as glycosyl donor, 379
→dextran, 380
Amylo-1,6-glucosidase, 397, 410
Amyloheptaose →dextran, 380, 414
Amylomaltase, 377, 408, 409, 410
Amylopectin, 379†, 385†, 386*, 387*, 397†,
398*, 407†
as glycosyl donor, 379
from amylose, 411†
structure of, 397
→maltose, 392
Amylose, 370†, 371†, 385†, 387†, 397†,
398†, 399†, 402†, 308†
as glycosyl donor, 379
structure of, 397
→amylopectin, 411
→maltose, 392
Amylosucrase, 376, 407, 409
Amylose 1,4→1,6-transglucosidase, 411
Amyrin, α-, and β-, 875†, 876, 877
β-Amyrin, 879†, 890†, 891, 892
→friedelin, 877, 878*
Anabasine, 961†, 962†, 963*†, 964*†
Anacardic acid, 754*†, 762*†, 767
Anagyrine, 973*†, 975†
Androcymbine, 984*†, 985†
Androgens, 230, 231*†
→estrogens, 233, 234*†
Andrographolide, 868
$Δ^4$-Androstene-3, 17-dione, 230, 231*†,
232*†
→estrone, 233, 234*†
Androstenedione-19-oic acid, 233
Androsterone →sulfate, 614
Anethole, 744*
Aneurin, 680*†
Angelic acid, origin in terpenes, 834*
Angolensin, 778, 779*
Angustifoline, 973*†, 975†
Angustifolionol, 781*, 783
Angustione, 783*, 830, 831*
Anhalamine, 976*†
Anhalonidine, 976*†
Anhydrides of sulfuric and adenylic acid,
mixed, 87†
N^5, N^{10}-Anhydroformyl tetrahydrofolic
acid, 63
1,5-Anhydroglucitol-6-phosphate, inhibi-
tion of hexokinase by, 342

Anhydro-rhodovibrin, 664†
Aniline,
 acetylation of, 626
 →glucuronide, 594*
 →mercapturic acid, 603*
 →sulfamate, 612, 613*, 615
Anisaldehyde, 915
Anisic acid, 914, 915
Anisyl alcohol, 915
Annofoline, 970*†, 971*
Annotinine, 968†, 970*†
Anthanthrene, 1075
Antheraxanthin, 665, 666†
Anthocyanidin, 777, 806, 807, 814†, 815
 in tannins, 805
Anthocyanins, 746, 776*†
 positions of hydroxylation in, 746
Anthracene, 1075
 →mercapturic acid, 604
 →premercapturic acid, 605
Anthranilate cycle, 683, 687
Anthranilic acid, 687, 908
 →actinomycin, 1040
 →alkaloids, 990, 991*†, 1000, 1004*,
  1006, 1007*, 1008*, 1009
 →fungal metabolites, 1054
 →nicotinic acid, 682, 683*†, 684
 →tryptophan, 34†, 35*†
Anthranilic-1-deoxy-ribonucleotide
 →tryptophan, 35*†
Anthranilic ribonucleotide →tryptophan,
 35*†
Anthraquinones, 769†, 1032, 1044†
Anthraquinonoid pigments, 1043
Anthrones, 769†
Antibiotics, influence on bacterial cell wall
 synthesis, 430, 431
Antibodies,
 association with cell membranes, 520
 secondary structure, 519
Anti-codons, 498
Anziaic acid, 765*
ApA, 558, 570
ApApA, 558
ApApApU, 558
Apiin, 366
Apiose, 366†, 367*†
 origin in terpenes, 834*
Apocarotenoids, 668
Apoproteins, 519
APS, 10*†, 87*†, 439, 440, 612, 613, 614†
APS-kinase, 10, 440
APS-phosphokinase, 613, 614
APS-sulfokinase, 88
ApU, 558
ApUp, 558

Araban, 364†, 372†, 385†, 419†, 420†, 421†,
 422†, 445
D-Arabinose, 446
 →disaccharide, 378
 oxidation of, 448
L-Arabinose, 346*†, 364†, 420*, 445†, 446
 free, occurrence, 444
 oxidation of, 448
L-Arabinose isomerase, 346
D-Arabinose-5-phosphate →KDO, 433
1-β-D-Arabinosyl-uracil 5'-diphosphate, in-
 hibitor of polynucleotide phosphoryl-
 ase, 556
Arabitol, 451
D-Arabitol, 450
D-Arabonolactone, 448†
L-Arabonolactone, 448†
Arachidonic acid, 119†, 120†, 121†, 761*†
 in lecithin, 147
Arachidyl CoA, 117†
Arbutin, 375†, 434†
Argemonine, 978*†, 979
Arginine, 3, 12, 13†, 59, 60*
 in riboflavin synthesis, 699
Arginine biosynthesis, repression of, 14
Arginine conjugation, 632
Argininosuccinase, 14
Argininosuccinate synthetase, 14
Argininosuccinic acid →arginine, 13
Aromatic amines, acetylation of, 628, 629
Aromatic compounds, polyketomethylene
 intermediates in the biosynthesis of, 751
Aromatic rings, hydroxylation of, 791
Aroyl-CoA, in detoxication reactions, 592
N²-Aroyl-L-arginines, 632
Aroyl-glutamic acids, 632
Aroyl glutamines, 632
Artemesia ketone, 846, 847*, 848*†, 855
Arterenone, methylation of, 624
Arylacetic acids, glutamine conjugation, 609
Arylalkyl cyanides, 617*
Arylamine sulfokinase, 615
2-Arylchromones, 782
S-Arylcysteine →mercapturic acid, 604,
 605*
Arylcysteines, acetylation of, 629
S-Arylcysteinylglycine →mercapturic acids,
 604, 605*
Ascaridole, 838
L-Ascorbate, cyclic production and reuse
 of, 729, 730
Ascorbic acid, 449†, 727†, 728†, 729*†
 stimulation of proline hydroxylation by,
 15
Aspartate, 3
 →arginine, 13
 →carbamyl aspartate, 73*

Aspartate—(*cont.*)
→histidine, 29, 30
→lysine, 26
Aspartic acid, 4
→adenylic acid, 66
→nicotinic acid, 962, 963*
→β-nitropropionic acid, 1055
→pantothenic acid, 695*, 696
→purine, 64, 65
→pyrimidine ring, 71
→threonine, 16, 17*
Aspartic carbamyl transferase, 73
Aspartic-β-semialdehyde, 25†, 26†, 28
→lysine, 17
→threonine, 17*†
Aspartic semialdehyde dehydrogenase, 16, 25
Aspartokinases, 16, 18, 25
holorepressor of, 18
multivalent repression of, 18
repression or inhibition of, 17, 18
β-Aspartylphosphate,
→lysine, 25†, 26†
→threonine, 17*†
Aspergillic acid, 1054†, 1055*
Astaxanthin, 667, 671
Asterric acid, 1027*, 1028
Atabrine, inhbition of RNA synthesis by, 569
Atisine, 1010*†, 1011†
ATP, 49, 94
enzymic hydrolysis, 692
in glycosidic bond formation, 395
in photosynthesis, 329
in protein synthesis, 487
regeneration from ADP, 382
role in glycoside synthesis, 382
transphosphorylation with, 79, 80
→ADP-glucose, 358
→poly A, 562, 653, 564
→RNA, 561, 565
ATP-Imidazole cycle, 29, 30
ATP-PRPP pyrophosphorylase, 31
ATP-sulfurylase, 10, 87, 439, 612, 614
Atranorin, 766†
Atrovenetin, 1030*†
Aurantiogliocladin, 1038, 1043†, 1044*
Aureomycin, effect on d-urobilin excretion, 276
Aureusidin, 776
Auroglaucin, 1051*†, 1052, 1057†
Aurones, 746, 776*†, 777†
Auxotroph, 2
Aversin, 1044, 1045*
Averufin, 1044, 1045*

Avidin,
inhibition of carboxylation of propionyl CoA by, 722
inhibition of fatty acid synthesis, 109
inhibitor of acetyl carboxylase, 110
Avidin-combinable materials, 721
Avidin-sensitive fatty acid synthetase, 116
Axerophthol, 863
Azafrin, 668
8-Azaguanine, 488
8-Azaguanosine 5'-diphosphate, polymerization of, 556
6-Azaguanosine triphosphate, in RNA synthesis, 568
Azaserine, inhibitor of purine synthesis, 64*
6-Azauracil analogue of UDP-glucose, 363
6-Azauridine 5'-diphosphate, inhibitor of polynucleotide phosphorylase, 556
Azauridine triphosphate, 568
Azelaic acid →biotin, 719

Bacillus macerans enzyme, 379, 389
Bacitracin, influence on bacterial cell wall synthesis, 430
Bacterial cell wall, structure, 427, 428
Bacterial cell wall components, 374†
Bacterial cell wall polysaccharides, 426†
Bacterial chlorophyll, 269*, 270, 271
Bacterial polysaccharides, 373†, 422
Bacteriochlorophyll, 251, 264, 267, 273, 327
hydrolysis of, 268
Bacteriophage, T2, DNA from, 541
Bac′erioverdin, 270
Baicalein, 775*†
Balfourodine, 1007*†, 1008†
Barbital, effect on dehydrogenase, 362
Base pairing (genetic code), 492
Batyl alcohol, 135
B₁₂ coenzymes, 682
Behenyl CoA →lignoceryl CoA, 117
Belladine, 956*†, 957
Benzamide, excretion as ornithuric acid, 608
1:2 Benzanthracene, 1075
Benzene,
detoxication of, 633, 634
→mercapturic acid, 602*, 604
→premercapturic acid, 605
Benzene hexachloride, 608
Benzilic acid rearrangement, in tannin biosynthesis, 810
Benzimidazole,
in vitamin B₁₂, 711, 714
→B₁₂ vitamers, 715
Benzimidazole cobamide coenzyme, 717
Benzo[a]anthracene, 1067*, 1069
Benzo[b]fluoranthene, 1067, 1068*

Benzo[j]fluoranthene, 1067, 1068*
Benzofuran ring system, 1047†
Benzoic acid,
    arginine conjugation, 632
    excretion as ornithuric acid, 608
    ortho-hydroxylation of, 791
    →glucuronide, 594*
    →hippuric acid, 598, 599, 600*
    →piperidine alkaloids, 968, 969*
    →tropic acid, 960, 961*†
Benzonitrile, 616, 617*
Benzo[rst]pentaphene, 1067, 1068*
Benzo[c]phenanthrene, 1067*
Benzophenanthridine alkaloids, 975
3,4-Benzopyrene, does not form a mercap-
    turic acid, 604
Benzo-[a]-pyrene, 1065, 1066*, 1068, 1069,
    1073, 1074, 1075
    pyrosynthesis of, 1070*
Benzo[e]pyrene, 1067*
p-Benzoquinones, 1043†, 1046†
Benzoyl-adenylate →hippuric acid, 599†
N^2-Benzoylarginine, 632*
Benzoyl-CoA →hippuric acid, 599†
Benzoylglucuronide, 608
1:2 Benzpyrene, 1075
3,4-Benzpyrene, 1065, 1066*, 1068, 1069,
    1073, 1074, 1075
    formation from aliphatic reactants, 1072*
Benztriazole →B_{12} vitamers, 715
Benzyl chloride →mercapturic acid, 602*
Benzyl cyanide, 617*
Benzylisoquinoline →cularine, 981*
1-Benzylisoquinoline alkaloids, 976, 977,
    978
Benzyl viologen →fatty acids, 107
Berbamine, 980*
Berberastine, 982*†
Berberine, 955, 981†, 982*†
Berberine alkaloids, 982
Betulic acid, 889
Betulin, 889
Bicarbonate →fatty acids, 109
Bicyclofarnesol skeleton, 860†
Biflavonyls, 818
Bilanes, 275*, 276
Bile acids, 233†, 236*†, 883
Bilene, 291
Bile pigments, 274, 275*, 279†, 298†
    absorption maxima, 275, 276
    biogenesis of, 276, 277
    biosynthetic relationship between chloro-
        phyll and, 298
    structural relationships, 274
Bile pigment formation, numbering system,
    278*
Bile salts, and cholesterol esterase, 131

Bilidienes, 275*, 276, 290, 291, 297
Biliene, 275*, 276
Biliproteins, 292, 293†, 294†, 295†, 296†,
    297†
    distribution and composition, 289, 290
Bilirubin, 275*, 277, 287, 288†, 289
    excretion of, 295
    indirect reaction with diazotized sulfanilic
        acid, 288
    →urobilin, 287†
Bilirubin glucuronide, 288†, 289
    direct reaction with van den Bergh's re-
        agent, 288
    →urobilin, 287†
Bilitrienes, 275*, 276, 297
Biliverdin, 275*, 277†, 278†, 279†, 280†,
    281†, 282†, 283†, 284†, 285†, 286,
    295†, 296†, 297
    structural relationship with porphyrins,
        274*
    →urobilin, 287
Biliverdin diethyl ester, 287
Biliverdin-Fe, 280*†
Biliverdin-Fe-globin, 282, 283*†
Biliverdin-like bile pigments, 296
Biliverdin precursors, 295†
Biliverdin-protein complex, 295, 296
Biliverdin reductase, 287
Biliviolins, 297
"Binding" enzyme, 512
Biochanin-A, 777†
Biochemical genetics, 35, 36, 37
Biocytin, 721
Biopterin, 704
Biotin, 718†, 719†, 720†
    chemical structure, 718, 719*
    complex with CO_2, 722
    effect on polyene formation, 659
    →fatty acid synthesis, 109
    functions of, 722
    possible precursors of, 719*
    prosthetic group, 110
Biotin-like materials, 721
Biotin sulfoxide, 720, 721
Biotin sulfur, sources of, 720
Biotin synthesis, control of, 722
Biotin vitamers, 719
N-Biotyl-L-lysine, 721
Bisabolene, 893
γ-Bisabolene, 856*, 857, 858*†, 859*†
Bis(2-amino-1-naphthyl) phosphate, 631
Bis-benzylisoquinoline alkaloids, 980*, 981
2,4-Bis (2-carboxycyclopropyl) deuteropor-
    phyrin, 265
Bis-dehydrolycopene, 651
Bisdehydropinoresinol, 933
Bisflavones, 792

Bixin, 668
BMC, see β-methylcrotonic acid
BMC-CoA, see β-methylcrotonyl CoA
BOG, see β-methyl-β-hydroxyglutaryl
BOG-CoA, see β-hydroxy-β-methylglutaryl
    CoA
Bond dissociation energies, 1071
Borneol, 837*, 841, 849*†
    pyrolysis of, 1075
L-Bornesitol, 423*†
α-Boswellic acid, 874*
Branched-chain fatty acids →plasmalogens,
    153
Branching enzyme, 369, 379, 383, 385,
    386, 387, 388, 389, 410, 411
Brayleyanin, 785*
Brevifolin carboxylic acid, 810*, 812
Brevilagins, 810, 811*, 812
Bromobenzene,
    detoxication of, 601
    →premercapturic acid, 605
1-Bromobutane →mercapturic acid, 607
5-Bromo-CTP, in RNA synthesis, 568
5-Bromodeoxyuridine 5′-triphosphate, 547,
    548
5-Bromodeoxyuridine triphosphate kinase,
    548
5-Bromocytosine, 548
5-Bromoindoxylsulfate, 615
4-Bromo-6-methoxybenzimidazole   →B$_{12}$
    vitamers, 715
Bromo-paraffins, epoxidation of, 607
Bromopropane →mercapturic acid, 602*,
    606
Bromouracil, 551
    incorporation into DNA, 548
5-Bromouridine 5′-diphosphate, polymeri-
    zation of, 556
5-Bromo-UTP, in RNA synthesis, 568
Brucine, 989*
Bufadienolide, 885†
Bufotenine, 954*
1,3-Butadiene, 1072, 1073
Butadienolides, 874
Butan-2-ol →glucuronide, 594*
Butein, 791
tert-Butyl alcohol →glucuronide, 594
Butyl benzene, 1073, 1074
1,2-Butyleneoxide, 607
Butylmercapturic acid, 607
Butyrate, 107†, 108†
    →cholesterol, 208
    →fungal metabolites, 1035
Butyryl adenylate, 125
Butyryl-CoA, 107†, 256
    →fatty acids, 110
Butyryl CoA-synthetase, 125

Cadaverine
    →adenocarpine, 964*
    →Δ′-piperideine, anabasine, 963, 964*
    →quinolizidine alkaloids, 973, 974, 975
Cadinene, 856*, 893
Cafestol, 864*, 867, 868*†
Caffeic acid, 746
    →lignin, 750†, 751†
    →quercetin, 772, 806
Caffeine, 955
Calciferol, 240*†
Callose, 371†, 416
Calycanthine, 1003*†, 1004
Calycotamine, 976*†
Campesterol, 883
Camphene, 841
Camphor, 837*, 841, 844†
Camphospermonol, 762*†
Canadine, 981†, 982*†
Canthin-6-one, 990†, 991*†
Capsorubin, 666
Caracurine V, 995*
Caracurine-VII, 994*†, 996
Carane, 846*
Carbamate kinase, 14
Carbamic acid, 14
Carbamyl-β-alanine ribonucleotide →pyri-
    midine ring, 76*
Carbamyl aspartate, 73*†, 74*†
    →polynucleotides, 71
Carbamyl phosphate, 72*†
    from citruline, 73†
    →arginine, 13*†, 14
    →biotin, 720
    →carbamyl aspartate, 73*
    →citrulline, 72, 73*
    →pyrimidines, 72, 73
Carbamyl phosphate synthetase, 14
Carbohydrate biogenesis, general patterns
    of, 319
Carbohydrate-containing glyceride com-
    pounds, 166
Carbohydrates, 745
β-Carboline alkaloids, 990†, 991*†
Carbon-carbon linkages, formation of, 781
Carbon dioxide fixation, pathways of, 336
Carbon-methylation, 781, 782
Carbon-reduction cycle, in photosynthesis,
    322
Carboxamide, 61*
Carboxyamides →glucuronides, 594
Carboxydismutase, 321, 322
3-O-Carboxyethyl-N-acetylglucosamine, in
    bacterial cell wall polysaccharides, 426
2-Carboxy-4-ketopenitol, 321
2-Carboxy-3-ketopenitol, in photosynthesis,
    320*

Carboxylase, 682
Carboxylic ester glucuronides, 593
1-(o-Carboxyphenylamino)-1-deoxyribu-
lose-5-phosphate
→nicotinic acid, 683*†, 684
→tryptophan, 35*†
N-o-Carboxyphenyl-D-ribosylamine, 684
N-o-Carboxyphenyl-D-ribosylamine-5-
phosphate
→nicotinic acid, 683*†, 684
→tryptophan, 35*†
Carcinogenic polycyclic hydrocarbons,
1066*, 1067*
mode of formation, 1069
occurrence and origins, 1066, 1069
pyrosynthesis of, 1070*
Carcinogens, 508
heterocyclic polynuclear, 1076
Carcinogens in tobacco, precursors of, 1074
Cardanol, 762*†
Cardenolides, 885†
Cardiac aglycones, 884†
Cardiac glycosides, 884†
Cardiolipin, 135, 136*, 159†
Cardol, 762*†, 763
Δ³-Carene→artemesia ketone, 846, 847*
Δ⁴-Carene, 849*†, 851
Carene (Δ³-, Δ⁴-), 841
α-Carotene, 652†, 653†, 656†, 661, 663, 666
structure, 642*
β-Carotene, 643†, 649†, 650, 652†, 653†,
654, 655, 656†, 657, 658, 659, 660, 661,
663, 664, 665, 666, 669, 671, 672, 866
acetate labeled, degradation by $KMnO_4$
and CrO_3, 644
all-trans, 669
chemical synthesis, 641
formation from leucine, 645, 646
position of the 2 carbon of mevalonic
acid in, 647*
positions of carboxyl and methyl carbons after synthesis from acetate, 644*
structure, 642
→vitamin A, 670
γ-Carotene, 652†, 653†, 654, 655, 656†, 659,
660
structure, 642*
→torularhodin, 668*, 669
δ-Carotene, 656†
ε-Carotene, 656†
η-Carotene, 656†
ξ-Carotene, 651, 652, 653†, 655, 656†, 657,
660, 661, 664†
all trans form, 670
Carotene X, 661, 663

Carotene biosynthesis,
from mevalonic acid, 647, 648
separation from xanthophyll synthesis,
662
Carotenes, 866, 891†, 946, 950
aliphatic series of, 651
cyclization of, 655, 656*
epoxides of, 664, 665
sequential formation from a saturated
C_{40} precursor, 653
unifying theory of biogenesis, 652, 655,
656
Carotenogenesis
diphenylamine upon, 657, 658
stimulating effect of light on, 659
Carotenoid biosynthesis
from acetate, 643, 644
in Chlorella X-ray mutants, 661
in photosynthetic bacteria, 663, 664
photoinduction in, 659
three steps in, 654
two opposing theories of, 660
varying degrees of inhibition in mutants,
660
Carotenoid dehydrogenase, 658
Carotenoid diepoxide, 666
Carotenoids, 293, 294, 647†, 648†, 650, 890
aliphatic and alicyclic, 656
all-cis configuration, 669
allene groupings in, 667
all-trans configuration, 669
alterations of the 40 carbon chain, 651
aromatic, 661
as antioxidants, 664
bacterial, 661
cis-trans isomerization, 669, 670
conversion of one to another, 667
formation of the 40 carbon chain, 643
from yeast, 668*†, 669
functions of, 641, 642
hydroxylated, 665
β-ionylidene ring in, 670
modification of, 662
numbering system, 642*
oxygenation of, 662
peroxide formation in, 666
protective action on photosynthesis, 665
provitamin A activity of, 670
steric modifications, 669
structure, 642
with carbonyl groups, 666
Carotol, 856, 857*
Carpaine, 967*†, 968†
Carrageenan, 439
Carvacrol, 837*, 838, 841
Carvone, 837*, 839*†, 840, 841, 854†
Carvotan-acetone, 837*, 842

Caryophyllene, 831*, 833, 842
  perspective view of the molecule, 831
β-Caryophyllene, 856*, 859
Cassaine, 867
Catalase, 248, 263†, 277, 483, 488, 523
  migration to another cell after synthesis, 520
Catechin, 801, 805†, 806*, 819
  dimerization, 813
  enzymic oxidation of, 817
  polymerization, 814*, 816*, 817
Catechins, 774*, 812, 813, 814, 815
  in tannins, 807
  →tannins, 805
Catechol-O-methyl transferase, 8, 622, 624
Catechols, 763†
  4-alkyl (or alkenyl), 763*†
  methylation of, 619, 625
  4-substituted, methylation, 623*
Catharanthine, 1001*
CDP, 49, 79†, 375
  →dCDP, 58
  phosphate exchange, 559
  polymerization of, 556
CDP-Abequose, 90, 365
CDP-Ascarylose, 364, 365
CDP-Choline, 88*†, 89, 90
  effect on phospholipid biogenesis, 88
CDP-3,6-Dideoxy-D-arabino-hexose, 90
CDP-3,6-Dideoxy-D-galactose, 365
CDP-3,6-Dideoxy-D-glucose, 365
CDP-3,6-Dideoxy-D-mannose, 365*†
CDP-3,6-Dideoxy-L-mannose, 365
CDP-3,6-Dideoxy-D-xylo-hexose, 90
CDP-Diglyceride, 726
CDP-Ethanolamine, 88†, 89†, 90
  effect on phospholipid biogenesis, 88
CDP-D-Glucose, 90
  →dideoxyhexose, 364
  →glucosides, 375, 434
CDP-D-Glucose oxidoreductase, 365
CDP-Glycerol, 89†, 90
  →teichoic acids, 431
CDP-4-Keto-6-deoxy-D-glucose, 364†
  →CDP-tyvelose, 365*
CDP-Paratose, 364, 365
CDP-Ribitol, 90
  →teichoic acids, 430†, 431
CDP-Tyvelose, 90, 364, 365*†
Cedrene, 856*, 859*†
Cellobiose, 370†, 414†
  as glycosyl donor, 377, 394
  oxidation of, 447
  phosphorolysis of, 392
  →saccharides, 377, 416
Cellobiose phosphorylase, 370
Cellotetraose, 414†

Cellotriose, 414†
cx-Cellulase, role in polysaccharide synthesis, 386
Cellulases, 341, 416
Cellulose, 371†, 385†, 414†, 415†, 416†
  hydrolysis of, 341
Cellulose primer, 371
Cell wall glycopeptide, 429†
Central dogma, in protein synthesis, 500
Cephaeline, 955, 983*†, 984
Cephalosporin C, 27, 28
Ceramide, 166†, 167†, 168, 169†, 171, 172
  →sphingomyelin, 168
Ceramide-glucose-galactose-N-acetylgalactosamine, 177†
Cerebron, 170
Cerebronic acid, 170
N-Cerebronyl-O'-galactosyl sphingosine, 171†
Cerebroside →sulfatide, 173
Cerebrosides, 166, 168, 169†, 170*†, 171†, 172†, 176, 183
Cerebroside sulfate, 169†, 172*, 173†
Cerin, 876, 877*
Cernuine, 970*†, 971†
Ceroptene, 782*
Cevine, 1013*†, 1014
Chain elongation, of monoenoic acids, 119
Chaksine, 1009*
Chalcone epoxides, 777, 778*
Chalcone oxides →isoflavones, 777, 778*
Chalcones
  →aurones, 777
  →flavonoids, 774*, 776
Chanoclavine, 1005*, 1006
Chebulagic acid, 802, 804, 808, 809*, 810
Chebulic acid, 792*, 804, 808, 809*, 810, 812
Chebulinic acid, 802, 804, 808, 809*, 812
Chelidonine, 981†, 982*†
Chenodesoxycholic acid →cholic acid, 235, 236*†, 237†
Chimonanthine, 1003*†, 1004
Chimyl alcohol, 135, 153
Chitin, 373†, 424†, 425†
Chitin synthetase, 373, 425
Chloral hydrate, detoxication of, 592, 633, 634
Chloramphenicol
  effect on porphyrin biosynthesis, 273
  effect on protein synthesis, 516
Chloretone
  effect on dehydrogenase, 363
  stimulation of ascorbic synthesis by, 728
Chloride, requirement in photosynthesis, 335
Chlorin, 251
Chloroatranorin, 766†

Chlorobactene, 661
Chlorobenzene
    detoxication of, 601
    →mercapturic acid, 602*
    →premercapturic acid, 605
Chlorobenzenes, tetra-, penta- and hexa-,
    do not form mercapturic acids, 604
4-Chloro-1,2-benztriazole →B$_{12}$ vitamers,
    715
p-Chlorobenzyl cyanide, 617*
Chlorobium chlorophylls, 268, 270, 271
Chlorocruorin, 271
2-Chloroethyl-β-D-glucoside, 598†
Chlorogenic acid, 801
p-Chloromercuribenzoate, effect on uro-
    porphyrinogen I formation, 259
S-(Chlorophenyl) cysteine, 608
Chlorophyll, 266†, 268, 272, 298†, 299, 330,
    331
    biosynthetic relationship between bile
        pigments and, 298
    control of the stereo configuration of
        carotenoids, 670
    relation between occurrence of caro-
        tenoids and, 662
    role in photosynthesis, 327
    synthesis of, 661
Chlorophyll a, 248, 250*, 251, 263, 267†,
    268†, 269, 270, 293, 294, 297, 298,
    328*, 329
Chlorophyll a$_I$, 330, 331
Chlorophyll b, 269*†, 270, 329
Chlorophyll c, 270
Chlorophyll d, 269*, 270, 271
Chlorophyll e, 270
Chlorophyll biosynthesis, connection to
    phytol biosynthesis, 866
Chlorophyll a holochrome, 263†
Chlorophyllase, 268
Chlorophyll-types, 271
Chlorophyllide, esterification with phytol,
    268
Chlorophyllide a, 267
Chlorophyllide holochrome, 268
Chlorophyllide a holochrome, 263†
Chlorophylls, 891†
    hydrolysis of, 268
Chloroplast reaction, 665
Chlororaphin, 1054
Chloroxanthin, 664†
Choleglobin, 279†, 280, 283*†, 284†
Choleglobin mixture, 280, 281, 283, 284
Choleheme, 279*, 282, 284
Cholehemochromogen, 280
Cholemyoglobin, 284
$\Delta^{5, 7}$-Cholestadienol, 223*
    →cholesterol, 217*†

Cholestanol, 224, 225*
$\Delta^{5, 7, 20}$-Cholestatriene-3β-ol →vitamin D,
    239
Cholesten-3β-ol, 235
Δ^4-Cholesten-7α-ol-3-one, 238†
Cholestenone, 225
Δ^4-Cholesten-3-one, 234
Δ^5-Cholesten-3-one, 234
Δ^5-Cholesten-3β, 7α, 26-triol, 238†
Δ^7-Cholestenol, 222†, 223*
    →cholesterol, 216, 217*†
Cholesterol, 180†, 182†, 207†, 208†, 211†,
    213, 214†, 215*†, 217*†, 646†, 873,
    877, 878, 880, 946
    distribution of acetate carbon in, 218*
    distribution of acetate carbon atoms in
        side chain of, 218*
    in plants, 883†
    isoöctyl side chain of, 235
    →adrenocortical steroid hormones, 229*,
        230
    →alkaloids, 1012
    →cholic acid, 233, 236*
    →diosgenin, 886
    →pregnanediol, 227†
    →pregnenolone, 227* 231*
    →progesterone, 227, 229*, 231*
    →steroidal alkaloids, 893
Cholesterol esterase, 131
Cholesterol esters, 131†, 132
Cholesteryl chloride, 208
Cholic acid, 233†, 235†, 236*†, 237*†
    →conjugation with glycine, 599, 600
Choline, 19†, 140†, 620†, 621*
    as methyl donor, 1039
    →phosphorylcholine, 142, 143
Choline phosphatides, 142†
Choline phosphokinase, 143
Choline plasmalogen, 145†, 152†
Choline sulfate, 614, 615
Choline sulfokinase, 614
Cholyl CoA, 237*†, 238
Chondroitin, sulfation of, 441
Chondroitin sulfate, 439, 441†
    complexes with protein, 444
    →hybrid oligosaccharides, 380
Chondroitin sulfate A, 442†
Chondroitin sulfates, 11
    A, B and C, 443†
    A and C, 373†
Chorismic acid, 3
    →aromatic amino acids, 907*†, 908
    →phenylalanine, tyrosine, 33*†, 34†
    →tryptophan, 34, 35*
Chromanones, 1029*
Chromatin, 508
Chromones, C-methylated, 781

Chrysanthemum carboxylic acid, 855†
Chrysene, 1067*, 1069
Chrysin glucuronide, 598
Chylomicrons, 178, 179, 180, 182
Chymotrypsinogen, association with cell membranes, 520
Cinchona alkaloids, 993*†
Cinchonamine, 989, 993*†
Cinchonidine, 993*†
Cinchonine, 993*†
Cineole, 337*, 838, 841, 851*†
Cinerubin A and B, 1043
Cinnamic acid, 766, 774
  glycine conjugation, 600*
  →catechin, 805
  →coumarin, 789
  →lignin, 749, 750†
  →quercetin, 772
  →substituted coumarins, 788, 791
trans-Cinnamic acid, 789, 986*
  microbiological degradation of, 916
  →trans-p-coumaric acid, 788
Cinnamic acid-cis-trans-isomerase, 789
Cinnamic acids, 745, 747, 751†, 776†, 806†
  →lignin, 926
Cinnamic alcohols →lignin, 926
Cinnamoyl-tetrahydroanabasine, 964*†
Cistrons, 30, 31, 32, 506
Citral, 837*, 838, 839*†, 840, 841
  →geraniol, 855
  →terpenes, 836, 838, 840
Citral a, 838
Citric acid cycle, 2
Citrinin, 1034*†, 1035, 1038
Citromycetin, 770, 771*†, 1037†, 1038*, 1042, 1058†, 1059*†
Citronellal, 837*, 838, 841, 851*†
  →terpenes, 836
Citronellol, 841
Citrostadienol, 877, 878*
Citrovorum factor, 709
Citrulline, 72†, 73*†
  →arginine, 13
  →carbamyl phosphate, 73
Cladinose, 1040*†, 1041†
Clavine alkaloids, 1004, 1006
Clavolonine, 970*†, 971†
CMP, 49, 375
  →dCMP, 57
  incorporation into RNA, 561, 565
CMP-N-Acetyl neuraminic acid, 91
CMP-3-Deoxyoctulosonic acid, 91
CMP-N-Glycolyl neuraminic acid, 91
CMP-KDO
  in KDO transfer, 438
  →lipopolysaccharide, 432†, 433†
  →KDO-lipopolysaccharides, 375

CMP-NAN, 177†, 437†, 438†
  in feedback control of glycoprotein biosynthesis, 439
  in NAN transfer, 438
  →colominic acid, 375, 438
  →glycoproteins, 374, 438
  →sialyllactose, 375
  →sialyloligosaccharides, 375
  →Tay-Sachs ganglioside, 177
CMP-NGN, 437†
CMP sequences, formation of, 564
CoA, 682, 694, 695†, 697†, 698†
CoASH, 85†, 86*†
Cobalt, insertion into the corrin ring, 301
Cobalt hydride, from Vitamin B₁₂, 716, 717
Cobamide, 59
Cobanamide, 712
Cobinamide, 300*
Cobinic acid, 300*
Cobryic acid, 300*
Cobrynic acid, 300*, 301
Cocaine, 959†, 960*†
Cocarboxylase, 681
(+)-Coclaurine, 979*, 981
Codeine, 955, 977*†, 979†
Codon, modulating, 517
Codons, 492, 493, 494, 498, 511, 514
  assignment to amino acids, 493
Coenzyme A, 85†, 86*†, 694, 695†, 697†, 698†
Coenzyme A derivatives →fatty acids, 761
Coenzyme Q, 331
Coenzymes, 48
  containing adenylic acid, 81
Coffeasterone, 887
Colchicine, 953, 954*, 955, 984*†, 985†
  and related alkaloids, 984*†
Colitose, 427, 432
Collagen, 478, 482, 486, 511
  association with cell membranes, 520
  low in hydroxyproline, 519
Colominic acid, 375†, 438†
Complex carbohydrates, 434†
Complex lipids, 177†, 178
Conalbumin, 486
Condensed tannins, different classes of, 805
Connessine, 1012*
Conhydrine, 966*†, 967*, 968†
Ψ-Conhydrine, 968
γ-Coniceine, 967*†, 968†
Conidendrin, 793*
Coniferaldehyde, 934, 935*
Coniferin, 926, 927*, 930
D-Coniferin →lignin, 931, 933
Coniferyl alcohol, 793*, 795, 796, 926, 927*, 930, 933, 935*, 936

Coniferyl alcohol—(cont.)
dehydrogenation product of, (DHP), 931, 932, 933, 936
→lignin, 749, 917, 930, 931, 932
structural relationship with products of fungal metabolism, 916
Coniferyl aldehyde, 930
Coniine, 966*†, 967*, 968†
Conjugates, physiological properties of, 632
Conjugation
definition of, 590
relationship to oxidation, reduction and hydrolysis, 633, 634
Conjugation reactions
mechanistic classification of, 590, 591, 592
miscellaneous, 629
occurring in liver or kidney, 591, 592
occurring throughout the body, 591, 592
Copolymers of polydeoxyribonucleotides, 550†, 551
Copper-8-hydroxyquinolate, 704
Coproporphyrin, 265, 272
four isomers of, 251
Coproporphyrin I, 250*, 251, 253
Coproporphyrin III, 250*, 251, 258, 264
Coproporphyrinogen, 262†, 264
Coproporphyrinogen I, 253†, 264
Coproporphyrinogen III, 253†, 263*†, 264
Coproporphyrinogen oxidase, 264
Coproporphyrinogen III oxidase, 263
Coproporphyrinogens, 261†
Coprostanol, 224*†
Cordycepin, 571
Corilagin, 802, 808, 809*
Coronene, 1075
Correllogenin, 226, 886
Corrin, 299†, 300*, 301†, 712
resemblance to uroporphyrin III, 299, 300
structural relationship to porphyrins, 299
Corrin-aminopropanol-phosphoribose, 301
Corrinoids, 300*, 716
Corrin ring formation, 302*†
Corticosterone, 228*†
Cortisol, 229*†, 508
influence on glycogen-synthetase activity, 405
Cortisone, 229*†
Corydine, 978*†, 980†
Corynantheidine, 992*
p-Coumaric acid, 746, 986*
→coumarins, 788*
→lignin, 750†
→quercetin, 806
trans-p-Coumaric acid, 789

Coumarin, 789†
precursors of, 790*†
Coumarins, 788†, 791†
7-hydroxylated, 788†
Coumarin system, in novobiocin, 1039
p-Coumaryl alcohol →lignin, 917
Co-uroporphyrin, 301
Crab-dAT, 551
Creatine, 8†, 620†, 621*, 622
Crinamine, 986†, 987*†, 988
Crocetin, 668
Crotonase, 108
Crotonisine, 979*†, 981†
Crotonyl CoA
→butyrate, 108
→long-chain fatty acids, 113
Crotonyl fragment, incorporation into phenolic plant products, 763, 764
Cryptolepine, 1002*†, 1004†
Cryptopleurine, 974*†, 975†
Cryptowoline, 978*†, 979†
α-Cryptoxanthin, 666†
β-Cryptoxanthin, 666†
α-Crystallin, 508
CTP, 49, 79†, 89, 90, 94
effect on phospholipid biogenesis, 88
in CoA synthesis, 698
transphosphorylation with, 79
→CDP-choline, 88
→RNA, 561, 565
Cularine, 981*†
Cuppressene, 871
Curare alkaloids, 996
C-Curarine-I, 995*
γ-Curcumene, 856*
Curvularin, 757, 758*†, 1030†, 1031*†
Cuscohygrine, 958*†, 959†
Cutscum, 177
Cyanacetic acid, 616, 617*, 618
Cyanide
detoxication of, 615
→thiocyanate, enzymic conversion, 616
Cyanides, organic →thiocyanate, 616, 617
Cyanide-thiocyanate detoxication, 591
Cyanidin, 773†, 805†, 806*, 807
precursors of, 806
Cyanobenzoic acid, 617*
Cyanocobalamins, 711†, 712†, 713†, 714†, 715†
Cyanogen, 617*
chloride, 617*
halides, 617*
iodide, 617*
Cyanohydrin glycosides, 617*
Cyanohydrins, 617*
Cyclase, 31

Cyclic adenosine-3′,5′-phosphoric acid, action on phosphorylase, 401, 402
Cyclic dextrins, 389†
Cyclic phosphodiester oligoribonucleotides, 558
Cyclic photophosphorylation, 330, 336
Cyclitols, 452*†
  interconversions of, 452
Cycloartanol, 887*
Cyclo dextrinase, 379
Cyclodextrin transglucosylase, 410
Cyclohexanecarboxylic acid, excretion as ornithuric acid, 608
Cyclohexanecarboxylic acids, 802
Cyclohexylalanine, acetylation of, 628
Cyclohexylpropane-type derivatives, from lignin, 905
Cyclopentanoperhydrophenanthrene nucleus, in adrenocortical steroids and cholesterol, 226, 227
Cyclopropane, 122†
Cyclopropane acid, 122†
Cyclopropane fatty acids, 122†
Cyclopropane fatty acid synthetase, 122
Cyclopropene acid, 122†
Cyclopropyl ethers, 634
p-Cymene, 838, 841, 855
Cyprinol sulfate, 615
Cystamine, 698
Cystathionase, 9, 36
Cystathionine, 9†
  →cysteine, 8*†
  →methionine, 18, 19, 20*†
Cystathionine synthetase, 9, 36
Cysteic acid, 696
Cysteine, 3, 7†, 8*†
  acetylation of its derivatives, 627
  effect on UDP-glucose transglycosylase, 406
  →biotin, 720
  →methionine, 18, 20*
  →sulfite, 618, 619*†
  →sulfopolysaccharides, 440
  →tryptophan, 36
Cysteine biosynthesis, utilization of sulfate for, 9, 10
Cysteine conjugation, 607, 608
Cysteine desulfhydrase, 9
Cysteine sulfhydrase, 9, 11
Cysteine sulfinate, 618, 619*†
Cysteine sulfinic acid, 11, 440
Cystine, 3, 7†, 8*†
Cytidine, 49
  5′-mono, -di, and -triphosphates of, 544
Cytidine deoxyribonucleotides, from cytidine nucleotides, 58†

Cytidine diphosphate choline, 88*†, 143*†
  →lecithin, 144
  →monophosphoinositide, 160
Cytidine-diphosphate derivatives of sugars, 90
Cytidine diphosphate diglyceride, 89*†
  →monophosphoinositide, 160
  →phosphatidyl glycerophosphate, 158
  →phosphatidyl serine, 157
Cytidine diphosphate ethanolamine, 88†, 89†
  →phosphatidyl ethanolamine, 154
Cytidine diphosphate glycerol, 89†, 158
Cytidine diphosphate pantothenic acid, 699
Cytidine monophosphate derivatives of sugars, 91
Cytidine-5′-monophospho-N-acetylneuraminic acid, in N-acetylneuraminic acid transfer, 438
Cytidine nucleotides, 57, 58
  concerned with phospholipid synthesis, 90
  specific function of, 88
Cytidine 3′-phosphate, 545
Cytidine-5′-phosphate, 49, 545
Cytidine triphosphate, 76*†
Cytidylic acid, 49, 75†
Cytisine, 973*†
Cytochrome, 329, 330, 331
Cytochrome c, 272, 478, 481
Cytochrome f, 273
Cytochrome oxidase, cyanide-inhibited, 618
Cytochromes, 258, 263†, 266
Cytochromes a and c, 265
Cytochromes a, a₁ and a₃, prosthetic group of, 270
Cytosine, 46*, 47*, 49, 50, 539*

dADP, 50
dAdT, 555
dAdT Copolymer, 551
dAdU, 551
DAHP →phenylalanine, tyrosine, 33*†
DAHP Synthetase, 33
Damascenine, 955, 1006†, 1007*†
Dammarenediol, 876*†
Dammarenolic acid, 874*
dAMP, 50
DAP, 25†, 26*†
L-DAP →lysine, 26†
meso-DAP →lysine, 26*†
DAP Decarboxylase, 26, 27
DAP Racemase, 26
Darutigenol, 868
dAT, from crab, 551
dAT Copolymer, 550, 551, 554

dATP, 50, 544
→copolymers, 550
polymerization of, 555
dATP-Glucose →phytoglycogen, 403
dCDP, 50, 57, 58†
dCDP-D-Glucose, 358†
dCMP, 50, 57†
dCTP, 50
→CDP-glucose, 358
→copolymers, 550
Deacylase, Co⁺⁺ activated, 26
Decarboxylases, 92, 95
Decarboxylation
of nucleoside diphosphate sugars, 364
of 6-phospho-aldohexonic acids, 347
of UDP-hexuronic acids, 359
Decarboxylation reactions, 95
Decenoates, α,β- and β,γ, 118†
Dehydroangustione, 783*
Dehydro-L-ascorbic acid →ascorbic acid, 730
3,4,3′,4′-Dehydro-β-carotene, 671
Dehydro-γ-carotene, 669
7-Dehydrocholesterol, 223*, 225
→cholesterol, 216, 217*†
→vitamin D, 239, 240†, 241
7-Dehydrocholesterol, 5,8-peroxide of →
vitamin D₃, 241
Dehydrodiconiferyl alcohol, 931, 932*, 933
Dehydrodigallic acid, 810*, 812
Dehydrodiisoeugenol, 930
Dehydrodivanillin, 935*
Dehydroepiandrosterone, 230, 232*†
→sulfate, 613, 614
Dehydrogenases, 5, 92, 93, 95, 445
TPN-linked, 51
Dehydrogenation
of nucleoside diphosphate sugars, 363
of UDP-sugars, 359
progressive, during lignin formation, 933
Dehydrogriseofulvin, 1027*†
Dehydrohexahydroxydiphenic acid, 812
6,7-Dehydrohyoscyamine →hyoscine, 959†, 960*†
Dehydrolycopene, 651
2,3-Dehydro-norlaudanosoline, 978*†, 979
Dehydroquinase, 34, 804
5-Dehydroquinate synthetase, 33
5-Dehydroquinic acid, 804
→phenylalanine, tyrosine, 33*†, 34
→shikimic acid, 748*†
Dehydroretinal, 671
3,4-Dehydro-rhodopin, 664†
5-Dehydroshikimic acid, 802, 803*, 804
→phenylalanine, tyrosine, 33*†, 34
→precursor of hexahydroxydiphenic acid, 808, 810

5-Dehydroshikimic acid—(cont.)
→shikimic acid, 748*†
Dehydroshikimic reductase, 34, 804
7-Dehydro "β"-sitosterol, 239
Dehydrosqualene, 210, 212*†
7-Dehydrostigmasterol, 239
Delpheline, 955, 1011*†, 1012†
Delphinidin, 807
Demecolcine, 955, 984*, 985
Demethoxymatteucinol, 782*
Demethylase, 624
Dendrobine, 1014*
D-Enzyme, 379, 388, 389, 410
3′-Deoxyadenine, 571
Deoxyadenosine, 50
Deoxyadenosine-5′-phosphate, 50, 571
Deoxyadenylate, 550, 551, 555
Deoxyadenylic acid, 50
3-Deoxy-D-arabino-heptulosonic acid-7-
phosphate →phenylalanine, tyrosine, 33*†
Deoxyaspergillic acid, 1054†, 1055*
DeoxyCDP-choline, 89
Deoxycholic acid, 239†
glycine conjugation, 600
Deoxycorticosterone, 228*†, 229*†
DeoxyCTP, 90
Deoxycytidine, 50
5′-mono-, di-, and triphosphates of, 544
Deoxycytidine diphosphate choline, 89, 143
Deoxycytidine diphosphate derivatives, 89
Deoxycytidine diphosphate ethanolamine, 89
Deoxycytidine diphosphate glycosides, see dCDP-glycosides
Deoxycytidine nucleotides, 58†
Deoxycytidine-5′-phosphate, 50
Deoxycytidine triphosphate, see dCTP
Deoxycytidylate, 550, 551
Deoxycytidylic acid, 50, 78†
6-Deoxy-6-fluoro-D-glucose →maltose ana-
logues, 392
2-Deoxy-D-galactose →2-deoxy-D-glucose, 361
Deoxy-D-gluconolactone, 448†
2-Deoxy-D-glucose, 361*, 446
oxidation of, 448
phosphorylation of, 344
2-Deoxyglucose-6-phosphate, effect on
UDP-glucose transglycosylase, 406
Deoxyguanosine, 50
Deoxyguanosine-5′-phosphate, 50
Deoxyguanylate, 550, 551
Deoxyguanylic acid, 50
Deoxyhexoses, formation of, 95
2-Deoxy-3-ketogluconic acid, 446†
Deoxylutein, 671

Deoxynucleoside 5'-triphosphates, 545, 548
  polymerization of, 546
Deoxynucleoside 5'-triphosphate phospho-
  kinases, 552, 553
Deoxynucleotides, in DNA, 546
Deoxynucleotide "X", linear 3'-5' polymer
  of, 538
DeoxyPRPP, 70
Deoxyribonucleic acid, 540
  incorporation of ribonucleotides into, 562
Deoxyribonucleic acid nucleotidyltransferases, 545, 553
Deoxyribonucleoside 3'-phosphates, 544
Deoxyribonucleoside 5'-triphosphates →
  DNA, 546
Deoxyribonucleosides, 57†, 70
  nomenclature of, 50
Deoxyribonucleotides, 58†, 59†, 539
  nomenclature of, 50
  of purine, 70†
  pyrimidine, 77†
2-Deoxy-D-ribose, 47, 48*, 51†, 56†
  from ribonucleosides or ribonucleotides,
    57†
  →glycosides, 434
Deoxyribose-1-phosphate, 70†
  →purine deoxyribonucleosides, 70
Deoxyribose-5-phosphate, 56, 57*†, 350†
  aldolase pathway, 56†
  →deoxyribose-1-phosphate, 70
Deoxysugars, 363†
6-Deoxy-D-talose, 363†
Deoxythymidylate, 550, 551
Deoxyuridine, 50
  →DNA pyrimidines, 78
Deoxyuridine-5'-phosphate, 50
Deoxyuridine triphosphatase, 548
Deoxyuridine-5'-triphosphate, 547
Deoxyuridylic acid, 50
  →thymidylic acid, 78
Dephospho CoA, 699
Dephospho CoA kinase, 86
Dephospho CoA pyrophosphorylase, 86
Dephospho coenzyme A →CoA, 86
Depsides, 764, 766*, 768
Depsidones, 764, 768
De-repression, 505, 507
Derived lipids, 177†
Desamido DPN, 82*†, 693
  →DPN, 82*
Desamido NMN, 81, 82*†
  amination of, 82
  →desamido DPN, 82
Desaturation, of long-chain fatty acyl
  esters of CoA, 118
3-Desmethyl, 3-formyl chlorophyll a, 269*†

14-Desmethyl-lanosterol →cholesterol,
  215*†
Desmosterol →cholesterol, 215*†, 216,
  222*†
Desosamine, 1040*, 1041†
Desoxycholic acid → carcinogenic agents,
  1066*
Desthiobiotin →biotin, 719*†, 720†
2-Desvinyl, 2-acetyl, 3,4-dihydrochloro-
  phyll a, 269*, 270
2-Desvinyl, 2-formyl chlorophyll a, 269*,
  270
2-Desvinyl, 2-formyl protoporphyrin IX,
  271
2:4-Desvinyl, 2-4-hydroxyethyl protoporphyrin IX, 271
2-Desvinyl,   2-α-hydroxyethylpyrropheo-
  phorbide a, 269*, 270
Detoxication, definition of, 590
Deuteroporphyrin, 265
Dextran, 376†, 380†, 385†, 412†, 413†
  energy of hydrolysis, 382
  structure, 412
Dextranase, role in polysaccharide synthesis, 386
Dextran dextrinase, 414
Dextran sucrase, 376, 412, 413, 417, 418
Dextrin dextranase, 380
Dextrin primer, 371
Dextrins, 379†
  as primer, 384
  cyclic, 379†, 389†
  linear, as glycosyl donor, 379
  transglycosylation from, 409
  →amylose, 370
  →amylose, amylopectin, glycogen, 398
  →dextran, 413
Dextroinositol →galactoside, 434
Dextropimaric acid, 864*, 865*†, 867*, 871,
  872
Dextropimaric type of resin acids, 871
dGdC Copolymer, 550, 551
dGDP, 50
dGDP-Mannose, 358†
  dehydrogenation of, 364
dGDP-Mannuronic acid, 364†
dGMP, 50, 58†
dGTP, 50
  →copolymers, 550
DHFA, 709†
DHP = dehydrogenation product of
  coniferyl alcohol, 931, 932, 933, 936
Diaboline, 994*†, 996†, 997
Diacetoxyscirpenol, 1049*
2,4-Diacetyldeuteroporphyrin, 265
Diacetyldeuteroporphyrinogen, 264
1,2-Diacetylhydrazine, 627*†

Diacetyl sulfanilamide, 627†, 627*
Diacrylicdeuteroporphyrinogen, 264
Diacylglycerophosphatides →plasmalogens, 153
2,6-Diamino-4-hydroxypteridine, 708
Diaminopimelate, 3
α,ε-Diaminopimelic acid, 25†, 26*†
mesoDiaminopimelic acid, in bacterial cell wall, 430
Diaminopimelic decarboxylase, 724
2,6-Diaminopurine →B₁₂ vitamers, 715
4,5-Diamino uracil, in riboflavin synthesis, 700, 701
Diaphorase, 11, 21
Diarylbutanes, 793
O-Diazoacetylserine, 1055
6-Diazo-5-oxo-L-norleucine, 1055
    inhibitor of purine synthesis, 64*
Dibenz[a, h]acridine, 1076*
Dibenz[a, j]acridine, 1076*
1,2,5,6-Dibenzanthracene, 1066*
    does not form a mercapturic acid, 604
Dibenzo-[a, h]-anthracene, 1066*
N:N′-Dibenzoylornithine, 608
2,4-Dibromodeuteroporphyrin, 265
3,5-Dicarbethoxy-1,4-dihydrocollidine, stimulation of porphyrin synthesis by, 273
Dicarboxylate shuttle, 930
Dicentrine, 978*†, 980†
2,8-Dichloroadenine →B₁₂ vitamers, 715
Dichlorobenzenes, o-, m- and p-, mercapturic acids of, 604
5,6-Dichlorobenzimidazole →B₁₂ vitamers, 715
3,4-Dichloronitrobenzene →mercapturic acid, 606
Dicrotalic acid, 972*†
Dicrotaline, 972*†
Dictamnine, 787*, 1008
Dicyanide hemochromogens, 282
Dicyano α,5-dihydroxyheme, 282*
Dicyanoferric α,5-dihydroxyheme, 281
Dicyano-ferroprotoporphyrin, 279
Dicyano-ferropseudoheme, 280
Dicyano α-keto, 5-hydroxyheme, 282*†
Dicyanoverdoheme, 281
dIdC, 555
3,6-Dideoxy-L-galactose, 432
Dideoxyhexoses
    in bacterial cell wall, 427
    nucleoside diphosphates of, 364
3,6-Dideoxy-D-mannose, 432
Dieldrin, 634
1-p-(β-Diethylaminoethoxyl) phenyl-1-(p-tolyl)-2-(p-chlorophenyl) ethanol, 222

N,N-Diethyldithio-carbamic acid → glucuronide, 595*
Digitanol, 884
Digitonin, 434†
    in separation of chlorophylls a and b, 329
Digitoxigenin, 874*, 885†, 886*
Digitoxin, 884
α,α′-Diglyceride →triglyceride, 129
D-α,β-Diglyceride, 127†
    →L-α-lecithin, 144
    →phosphatidyl ethanolamine, 154
    →triglyceride, 127, 128
Diglyceride kinase, 126
    in Na, K-transport, 127
Diglycerides, 106*
α,β-Diglycerides →phosphatidic acid, 126
Diglyceride transacylase, 129
Digoxigenin, 885
O-Dihydric phenols, 34
Dihydrobilirubin →urobilin, 287†
3,4-Dihydro-β-carboline, 990
Dihydrocarvone, 837*, 839*†
Dihydrochalcones, 776
Dihydrocholesterol, 224, 225*
Dihydrocumic alcohol, 841
2,3-Dihydrodipicolinic acid →lysine, 25†, 26*†
Dihydroflavonols, C-methylated, 782
Dihydrofolic acid, 19, 707†, 709†
trans-2,3-Dihydro-3-hydroxy-anthranilic acid, 34
S-(1,2-Dihydro-2-hydroxy-1-naphthyl) glutathione →premercapturic acid, 606*†
Dihydroiresin, 860*
Dihydroiresone, 860*
Dihydroisocoumarin, 779†, 808
Dihydroisocoumarins, 779†
Dihydrolanosterol, 887
24,25-Dihydrolanosterol →cholesterol, 216, 217*†, 220†, 221*
Dihydrolipoate, 59
Dihydrolycopene, 656, 664†
Dihydromesobilirubin →urobilin, 287†
1,2-Dihydronaphthalene-1,2-epoxide →premercapturic acid, 606*†
1,6-Dihydronicotinic acid →anabasine, 964†
Dihydroorotase, 74
Dihydroorotate, 74*†
    →orotate, 74*
Dihydroorotic dehydrogenase, 74
3,4-Dihydro-4-oxoquinazoline →B₁₂ vitamers, 715
Dihydrophytoene, 650
Dihydropteroic acid, 707
Dihydrosphingosine, 165, 166†, 167†, 169†
    →sphingosine, 167

5,6-DihydroUMP, 497
Dihydrouracil, 697
Dihydroxyacetone, in transaldolase-catalyzed reaction, 325, 326
Dihydroxyacetone phosphate,
changes in free energy during photosynthetic formation, 334
in aldol condensations, 349
in photosynthesis, 323*†
→glucose-6-phosphate, 339
→sedoheptulose-1,7-diphosphate, 324
→triglyceride, 123, 129
3,4-Dihydroxyacetophenone, methylation
of, 624
Dihydroxy-acid dehydrase, 23
α,β-Dihydroxy acids →branched chain
amino acids, 21*†, 23
dl-3,4-Dihydroxyamphetamine, methylation of, 622
3,4-Dihydroxybenzoic acid, methylation of,
621
Dihydroxy-benzoic acids, 768
3,4-Dihydroxybenzoylacetic acid →alka-
loids, 974, 975
3,3'-Dihydroxy-β-carotene, 662
3α,12-Dihydroxy-Δ⁶-cholenic acid, 239
20α-22ξ-Dihydroxycholesterol →pregneno-
lone, 227*†, 228
3α,7α-Dihydroxycoprostane →cholic acid,
235, 236*, 238
3α,12α-Dihydroxycoprostane, 238
3α,7α-Dihydroxycoprostanic acid, 236*
3α,12α-Dihydroxycoprostanic acid, 235
α,γ-Dihydroxy-β,β-dimethyl butyric acid,
694
4,6-Dihydroxy-2-ethylbenzoic acid, 1043
2-(1,2-Dihydroxyethyl)-thiaminepyrophos-
phate, 350*†
3',4'-Dihydroxyflavan, 817
3',4'-Dihydroxy flavones, 776
α,5-Dihydroxyheme, 277, 279*†, 280, 281,
284
α,5-Dihydroxyheme-globin, 281
3,4-Dihydroxy-5-methoxyphenylacetic acid,
glutamine conjugation, 609
3,5-Dihydroxy-3-methylpentanoic acid,
843*
β,δ Dihydroxy-β-methylvaleric acid →
cholesterol, 209
1,8-Dihydroxynaphthalene →fungal metabolites, 1029*
Dihydroxyperylene quinone, 757*†, 1029*
3,4-Dihydroxyphenylacetaldehyde, 999
→alkaloids, 976, 977, 992*, 995
3,4-Dihydroxyphenylethylamine →alka-
loids, 976, 977*

3,4-Dihydroxyphenylethyl methylamine,
methylation of, 622
3,4-Dihydroxyphenylmethyl carbinol,
methylation of, 624
2,3-Dihydroxyphenylpropionic acid, 916
3,4-Dihydroxyphenylpyruvic acid →alka-
loids, 977*, 978
4,8-Dihydroxyquinoline-2-carboxylic acid,
629
3,5-Dihydroxystilbenes, 807
24,25-Dihydrozymosterol→cholesterol, 220
Diisoprenoid-alcohol-pyrophosphate, 948
3,3'-Diketo-β-carotene, 667
Diketo-L-gulonic acid →ascorbic acid, 730
7,8-Diketopelargonic acid →biotin, 720
Dimethylacrylate→cholesterol, 208, 209*
β,β-Dimethylacrylic acid, 786
β,β-Dimethylacrylyl-CoA, 646
N⁶-Dimethyladenine, 571*, 572
Dimethyl allyl alcohol, 843*, 845
Dimethylallyl pyrophosphate, 649*†, 650
→carotenoids, 648
→rubber, 945*†, 948, 949
→squalene, 210†, 211*†
→terpenes, 844*†, 845
4-Dimethylallyltryptophan →alkaloids,
1005*†, 1006†
p-Dimethylaminobenzaldehyde, reaction
with pyrroles and polypyrroles, 257, 259
Dimethylaminoethanol
phosphorylation of, 143
→choline, 620, 621
5,6-Dimethylbenzimidazole →vitamin B₁₂,
713, 714, 715, 716, 717
5,6-Dimethylbenzimidazole cobamide coenzymes, 58
5.6-Dimethylbenzimidazole-5'-phosphate →
vitamin B₁₂, 713
Dimethylbenzoglyoxaline riboside →
vitamin B₁₂, 716
5,7-Di-O-methylcatechin, 817
Δ⁸,²⁴ 4,4-Dimethylcholestadiene-3β-ol, 215
Dimethylcitraconate, 24
Di-O-methyl curvularin →naphthol derivative, 1031*
Dimethyl-ethanolamine, 142
incorporation into lecithin, 148, 149
N²-DimethylGMP, 497
N²-Dimethylguanine, 572*
2,4-Dimethyl-3-hydroxy-5-hydroxymethyl
pyridine, a pyridoxal antagonist, 723
4,5-Dimethyl-o-phenylenediamine →vita-
min B₁₂, 714
2,4-Dimethylpyrrole, 304
5,6-Dimethyl-9-(D-1'-ribityl)-isoalloxazine,
703

6,7-Dimethyl-9-(D-1'-ribityl)isoaloxazine, 701*†
6,7-Dimethyl-8-ribityllumazine, from guanine, 731*
→riboflavin, 701*†, 702, 703
N,N-Dimethyltryptamine, 957*†
D-α,β-Dimyristin→phosphatidic acid, 126
Dinitriles, 617*
Dinucleoside monophosphates, 558
Dinucleotides, 558, 564
D-α,β-Diolein, diunsaturated→lecithin, 144
Dioscorine, 968†, 969*†
Diosgenin, 226, 885, 886*†
Diosphenol, 839*†
Diosphenolene, 839*†
Dipalmitoyl-α-cephalin, 148
Dipentene, 837*, 838, 841, 1075
Diphenyl-propenes, tautomeric, 813
Diphosphatidylglycerol, 136*, 159
1,3-Diphosphoglycerate
  in photosynthesis, 322*†
  in regeneration of ATP, 382
  →glucose-6-phosphate, 338, 339
Diphosphoinositide, 136, 137, 159†, 162†, 163†, 184
Diphosphonucleotides, 78†
Diphosphopyridine nucleotides, 81†
Diphosphoribulose carboxylase, 321
Diphosphothiamine, 681
Dipicolinic acid, 26*†, 28
Dipyridine hemochromogens, 282
Dipyrrole, produced by a mutant of S. marcescens, 303*, 304
Dipyrrylmethane, 258
Disaccharides, 368†, 369†, 371†, 377†, 384†, 389†, 393†
  as glycosyl donors, 376, 387
  oxidation of, 448
Disialogangliosides, 175, 176
Diterpene alcohol pyrophosphate, 949
Diterpene family, prominent members of, 864*
Diterpenes, 830, 832, 842, 863†
  acyclic, 1011
  cyclic, 866†, 873
  ionic mechanisms in the biogenesis of, 865*
  monocyclic, 863
Dithiol-disulfide system, protein containing a, 11
Divaricatic acid, 764*†, 765
Divinyl pheoporphyrin, 267
DNA, 545†, 546†, 552†
  as a template in synthesis of DNA, 457
  average molecular weight, 541
  double helix, 541, 547
  double-stranded, 542, 568, 569

helical structure of, 541
  hydrogen bonding in, 541, 547
  in chloroplasts, 523
  in mitochondria, 522
  methylated bases in, 572*
  molecular models of, 541
  primary chemical structure, 539*, 540
  replication of, 541, 547
  ribosomal, 518
  RNA as a complementary copy of, 492
  single-stranded, 568, 569
  structure of, 541
  template for RNA synthesis, 568, 569
DNAase, 502, 523, 554, 563
  in ribosomes, 509
DNA Methylase, 572, 573
DNA Nucleotidyltransferase, "terminal", 555
DNA Phosphatase-exonuclease, 549
DNA Polymerase, 545, 546, 547, 548, 549, 550, 551, 553, 554, 555, 562
  of calf thymus, 554, 555
T2 DNA Polymerase, 548
DNA Primers, 548, 549, 554, 555
  in nucleic acid synthesis, 546
DNA Replication, 547, 548, 549
  template mechanism, 547
DNA-RNA Hybrids, 568
DNA Synthesis
  mechanisms of, 550†
  "nearest-neighbor" sequences, 547
DNA Template, 567
Dodecahydrolycopene, 653†
Dopamine
  methylation of, 622, 624
  →alkaloids, 976, 977*, 981, 983, 985, 989
DPN, 81†, 82*†, 83†, 689†, 691†
  3-acetyl pyridine analog of, 693
  effect on polyol conversions, 451
  interconversions of TPN and, 689, 692
  requirement in sterol and carotenoid biogenesis, 648
DPNase, 689, 692
DPNH, 691†
  effect on DPN kinase, 693
DPN Kinase, 689, 692
DPN Pyrophosphorylase, 82, 689, 691
DPN Synthetase, 82
DR-Aldolase, 57
Drimenol, 860*
dTDP, 373, 374, 375
dTDP-2-Acetamido-2-deoxy-D-galactose, 93
dTDP-2-Acetamido-2-deoxy-D-glucose, 93
dTDP-Acetamidodideoxy sugars, 94
dTDP-N-Acetylgalactosamine, 361†
dTDP-N-Acetylglucosamine, 358†

DPN—(cont.)
  epimerization of, 361
dTDP-2-Amino-2-deoxy-D-glucose, 94
dTDP-6-Deoxy hexoses, 94
dTDP-Galactose, 94, 358†
  →dTDP-glucose, 361
dTDP-Galactose pyrophosphorylase, 358
dTDP-Glucosamine, 358†
dTDP-D-Glucose, 94, 357†, 361†
  →acetamide dideoxysugars, 365
  →dTDP-L-rhamnose, 362, 366*
  →dTDP-streptose, 366*
  →glucosides, 375, 434
dTDP-Glucose pyrophosphorylase, 357, 358
dTDP-4-Keto-6-deoxy-D-glucose, 365†
dTDP-D-Mannose, 94
dTDP-L-Rhamnose, 94, 357, 362†, 366*†
  →bacterial cell wall polysaccharides, 373
  →cell wall polysaccharides, 432
  →rhamnolipids, 374, 435
  →rutin, 374, 435
dTDP-D-Ribose, 94
dTDP-Streptose, 366*†
dTMP, 540*
dTMP Kinase, 552, 553
dTTP
  →copolymers, 550
  →dTDP-galactose, 358
  →dTDP-glucosamine, 358
  →dTDP-glucose, 357
dUDP, 50
Dulcitol, 450
dUMP, 50
dUTP, 50

Eburicoic acid, 223†, 224*, 887*†
Ecgonine, 959†, 960†
Echimidinic acid, 972
Echinulin, 1051*, 1052†, 1054†
Effectors, 506
Ehrlich's reagent, for pyrroles and poly-
  pyrroles, 257, 259
$\Delta^{11, 14}$-Eicosadienoic acid, 120†, 121†
Eicosahydrolycopene, 653†
$\Delta^{4, 7, 10, 13}$-Eicosatetraenoic acid, 119
$\Delta^{5, 8, 11, 14}$-Eicosatetraenoic acid, 119, 121†
$\Delta^{5, 8, 11}$-Eicosatrienoic acid, 119
$\Delta^{7, 10, 13}$-Eicosatrienoic acid, 119
$\Delta^{8, 11, 14}$-Eicosatrienoic acid, 120, 121
Δ^{13}-Eicosenoic acid, 119
Eleagnine, 990†, 991*†
Eleutherin, 758, 759*†
Eleutherinol, 758*
Eleutherol, 758, 759*†

Ellagic acid, 792*, 802, 804, 808, 809*, 812
Ellagitannins, 808
Ellipticine, 1002*†, 1004†
Elmoclavine, 1051*, 1052†
Elymoclavine, 1004, 1005*†, 1006†
Emetine, 983*†, 984
Emodin, 744*, 769*, 770, 1043†, 1044*
Endocrocin, 769*†, 770, 1044, 1045*
Endonuclease, 548, 549
Enolase, 339
Enolic glucuronides, 593, 594
3-Enolpyruvyl shikimate-5-phosphate
  →aromatic amino acids, 907*
  →phenylalanine, tyrosine, 33*†, 34†
3-Enolpyruvyl shikimate synthetase, 34
Enol hydrase, 107, 108
  specific for acyl-ACP thioesters, 114
Enoyl reductase, 108, 109, 117
Enzyme repression, multivalent, 18, 25
Enzymes, hydrolytic, role in polysaccharide
  synthesis, 386, 387
Eosome, 518
Eperuic acid, 868
Ephedrine, 955, 956*†
Epiandrosterone, 213, 230
  →sulfate, 614
Epi-catechin, 815
Epi-gallocatechin, 818
Epi-gallocatechin gallate, 818
DL-Epiinosose-2, 161
Epimerases, 91, 92, 93, 94, 345, 359
  DPN-dependent, 361
Epimerization
  of nucleoside diphosphate sugars, 358
  of sugar phosphates, 345
  of UDP-sugars, 359
Epimerization reactions, 95
Epinephrine
  action on phosphorylase, 401, 402
  effect on UDP-glucose transglycosylase,
  406, 407
Epinine, methylation of, 622
Epistephanine, 981†
Epoxidation, in premercapturic acid forma-
  tion, 606*
Epoxy pigments, 665, 666†
1,2-Epoxy-1,2,3,4-tetrahydronaphthalene,
  606
Erdin, 1027*, 1028
Eremophilone, 856, 857*†
Ergochrysin A, 1044†, 1045*†
Ergoflavin, 1044†, 1045*†
Ergoline alkaloids, 955, 1004†, 1005*†
Ergosomes, 510
Ergosterol, 219*†, 648, 874*, 880
  effect on polyene formation, 659
  introduction of the C-28 methyl into, 8

Ergosterol—(*cont.*)
→vitamin D₂, 239, 240*†
Ergot alkaloids, 1004†, 1005*†, 1052
Ergotamine, 1004, 1005*†
Erysopine, 988*†, 989†
Erythrina alkaloids, 988*†
Erythritol, occurrence in lichens, 769
D-Erythro-1,3-dihydroxy-2-amino-4-trans-octadecene, 166*†
α-Erythroidine, 988*†, 989†
D-Erythro imidazole glycerol phosphate → histidine, 32*†
Erythrol, 450
Erythromycin, 767*†, 954*, 1041†, 1042*
Erythromycin A, B and C, 1041†
Erythronic acid-4-phosphate, 351†
D-Erythrose →D-sedoheptulose-1-phosphate, 349
D-Erythrose-4-phosphate, 53*†, 54*†, 324*†
    changes in free energy during photosynthetic formation, 334
    in pentose phosphate cycle, 348
    in photosynthesis, 323*
    in transaldolase-catalyzed reaction, 325, 326*
    from fructose-6-phosphate, 351†
    →aromatic amino acids, 907, 908*
    →lignin, 921, 922
    →phenylalanine, tyrosine, 32, 33*†
    →D-sedoheptulose-1,7-diphosphate, 324, 349
    →shikimic acid, 748*, 921, 922
Erythro-sphingomyelin, 169
Erythrulose, in transaldolase-catalyzed reaction, 325
Eserine, 989*, 1003*†, 1004*
Ester glucuronides, 593
Esters, of higher alcohols, 133†
Estradiol-17β, 230†, 231*†
Estriol, in plants, 883
Estrogens, 230†, 231†
    from androgens, 233†, 234*†
Estrone, 230†
    from testosterone, 233, 234*†
    in plants, 883
    →sulfate, 613
Ethanethiosulfonate, sodium, 618
Ethanol
    →butyrate, 107
    →cholesterol, 208
    →sulfate, 613
Ethanolamine, 140†, 141†, 154†
    →alkaloids, 1011
Ethanolamine plasmalogen, 145†, 155†
Ethanolamine phosphatides, 153†
N-Ether glucuronides, 593

Ethereal sulfates, 611†, 613*, 632
    secretion of, 633
    synthesis of, 591, 592, 612
α-Ethoxypropioguaiacone, from lignin, 904
Ethyl benzene, 1072, 1073*
Ethylene chlorohydrin →glucoside, 598
Ethyleneglycol →acetaldehyde, effect of vitamin B₁₂ on, 718
2-Ethylhexoic acid →glucuronide, 594*
Ethyl malonate →lichen, 766
Ethylmercapturic acid sulfoxide, 607*
Ethyl methanesulphonate →mercapturic acid, 603*
Eucalyptus genus, four principal types of, 838, 839
Eudesmol, 856*, 893
Eudolesmol, 857
Eugenin, 781*
Eugenitin, 781*, 782†
Eugenol, 933
Euphol, 874*, 879, 884
Evodiamine, 991*
Evoxanthine, 1008*†, 1009†
Evoxine, 788*
Exonuclease, 548, 549

Factor B (vitamin B₁₂), 714, 715, 716
    →vitamin B₁₂, 716
FAD, 704†
FAD Reductase, 21
Farnesene, 856*, 858
Farnesic acid, toxicity of, 832
Farnesic acids, 858, 860
Farnesiferol A, 860
Farnesol, 833, 845, 856*, 857, 858, 859
    trans, trans- and *cis,trans-*, 858
    →longifolene, 863*
    →sesquiterpenes, 859*
Farnesyl pyrophosphate, 648, 649†, 857, 858, 949, 950
    cis-, 862
    trans-trans, 949
    →squalene, 210†, 211*†, 212*
    →terpenes, 844*†, 845
Farnesyl pyrophosphate synthetase, 648
Fatty acid activation, 129
Fatty acid oxidation, 108
Fatty acids, 106†, 108†, 760*†, 761*†
    activation of, 125
    branched-chain, 121, 122
    cyclic, 121, 122
    desaturation of, 117
    elongation mechanism, 117†
    →glucose-6-phosphate, 341
    in lecithin, 147
    long-chain, 107†, 108†, 109†

Fatty acids—(cont.)
    dehydrogenation, 117
    unsaturated, elongation of, 121
    monounsaturated, 117†, 119†
    odd-numbered, 121
    polyunsaturated, 119†, 120†
    short-chain, 107†, 108†
    synthesis associated with particulate
        fractions, 116
    synthesis in the soluble portion of the
        cell, 109
Fatty acid spiral, 107
Fatty acid synthetase, 108, 111, 112, 114,
    115, 119
Fatty acid transferase, 132
Fatty acyl CoA, 124†, 125†
    →α,β-diglycerides, 129
    →triglyceride, 128
Fatty acyl CoA-cholesterol acyltransferase,
    132
Fatty acyl CoA synthetase, 124
Fawcettiine, 970*†, 971†
Felinin, 831*, 832
Fenchene, 841
Fenchol, 846*, 849*†
Fenchone, 841
Fenchyl alcohol, 841
Fe-protoporphyrin IX, 250*, 277
Ferredoxin, 329, 330
Ferredoxin-TPN reductase, 330
Ferrihemoglobin, 278
Ferritin, 487, 519
Ferrochelatase, 265
Ferrous sulfate, effect on polyene forma-
    tion, 659
Ferruginol, 871
Ferryl complexes, 284
Ferulic acid, 746, 791†, 933, 934, 935*
    →lignin, 750†
    →quercetin, 772
Festuclavine, 1005*†, 1006†
Fe-uroporphyrin, 301
Fibrin, 481
Fibrinogen, 478, 486
Fibroin, 486
    of silk, association with cell membranes,
        520
(−)Fisetinidol, 820
Flavacol, 1054†, 1055*
Flavan-2,3-diols, 807
Flavan-3,4-diols, 807, 812, 813, 814, 815,
    820
    in tannins, 805
Flavan-3-ols, 812, 813
    in tannins, 805
Flavanonol, 776*†, 777
Flavans, 813

Flavan-2,3,4-triols, 807, 814
Flavaspidic acid, 783*
Flavin adenine dinucleotide, 84*†, 85*†,
    703†, 704†
    enzymic hydrolysis, 692
Flavin mononucleotide, 85*†, 703†, 704
Flavin nucleotides, 703†, 704†
Flaviolin, 759, 760*, 770
Flavoglaucin, 1057*†
Flavone biosynthesis, glycosylation in, 775,
    776
Flavones, 745, 746, 750†, 773*†, 776*†
    carbon methylation in, 782
    hydroxylation patterns of, 746
Flavanones, 746
Flavonoid biosynthesis
    common precursor in, 746
    coupling of a C_6-C_3 unit to a C_6 unit, 246,
        247*
    genetic control of hydroxylation in, 775,
        776
Flavonoid compounds, 772†, 773†, 774†,
    776†, 791†
Flavonoid precursors, of tannins, 818
Flavonoids, 806, 808, 820
    in tannins, 805
Flavonols, 774*, 776
Flavopereirine, 1002*†, 1004†
Flindersine, 787*, 1007*, 1008
Fluoranthene, 1069, 1075
Fluorene, 1075
N-2-Fluorenylacetamide, 554
C-Fluorocurarine, 995*
5-Fluorocytosine, 548
p-Fluoronitrobenzene →mercapturic acid,
    602*
Fluorophenylalanine, 496
5-Fluorouracil, 548
    analogue of UDP-glucose, 363
5-Fluorouridine 5′-diphosphate, polymeri-
    zation of, 556
5-Fluoro-UTP, in RNA synthesis, 568
FMN, 703†, 704
Folic acid, 63, 704†, 705*†, 706†, 707†
    conjugated forms of, 708
    containing three to seven glutamic acid
        residues, 708, 709
    in pantothenic acid synthesis, 696
    interrelationship between vitamin B_{12}
        and, 718
    proposed pathway for the biosynthesis of,
        706*
Folic acid biosynthesis, intermediates active
    in, 708
Folic acid coenzymes, 682
Folic acid derivatives, as methyl donors, 19
Folic acid precursor, from guanine, 731*

Formaldehyde
  active, 6*
  →choline, 140
  in transaldolase-catalyzed reaction, 325
Formamide →thiazole, 681
5-Formamido-4-imidazolecarboxamide
    ribonucleotide, 65*†, 66†
2-Formamido-1-naphthyl hydrogen sulfate,
    630*†
Formate
  →ajmaline, 1003
  →alkaloids, 955, 957
  →choline, 140
  →eburicoic acid, 887
  →fungal metabolites, 1026, 1039, 1043
  →leucopterin, 705
  →riboflavin, 700
  →β-sitosterol, 880
  →thymine, effect of vitamin B₁₂ on, 718
Formimido glutamic acid, 710
Formiminoglycine →N¹⁰-formyl THFA,
    710
5-Formimino-THFA →N¹⁰-formyl THFA,
    710
Formononetin, 777†, 778, 791
Formyl acetic acid→pantothenic acid, 695*,
    697
Formyl anthranilic acid, 687
Formylase, 686
Formylation, 630
1-Formylfolic acid, 707
Formylglycinamide ribonucleotide, 63*†
Formylglycinamidine ribonucleotide, 63*†
  inhibitors of formation, 64
Formylkynurenine →nicotinic acid, 683*†,
    686, 962*†
3-Formylpropionic acid →alkaloids, 990
Formyl tetrahydrofolic acid →histidine, 29
N¹⁰-Formyl tetrahydrofolic acid →purine,
    65
N⁵-Formyl THFA, 709†, 710†
N¹⁰-Formyl THFA, 710†
Formyl transfer, 682
Free energy changes during glycoside bond
    formation, 369, 381
Frequentin, 1035, 1056†, 1057*†, 1058
Friedelan-3β-ol, 876, 877*
Friedelin, 876, 877*†, 878*†
β-D-Fructofuranose, 390
β-D-Fructofuranosyl-α-D-ribohexo-
    pyranosyl-3-ulose, 447†
Fructokinase, 342, 343
β-D-Fructopyranose, 390
Fructans, 372†, 417†, 418†, 419†
D-Fructose, 376, 446†
  free, 445†
    occurrence, 444

D-Fructose—(cont.)
  from D-glucose, 452†
  from D-mannitol, 450†
  from sorbitol, 450†
  from sorbose, 452†
  incorporation of C¹⁴O₂ during photo-
    synthesis into, 326
  phosphorylation of, 344
  →ascorbic acid, 728
  →D-glucose, 452
  →rhamnose, 435
  →sorbose, 452
  →sucrose, 370, 371, 377, 389
Fructose diphosphatase, 323, 324, 338,
    339, 344
D-Fructose-1,6-diphosphate, 344†, 349†
  activator of ADP-glucose synthesis, 358
  changes in free energy during photo-
    synthetic formation, 334
  in photosynthesis, 323*†
  →glucose-6-phosphate, 338, 339
  →triglyceride, 129
D-Fructose-1-phosphate, 344†, 349†
  →glucose-6-phosphate, 354
  phosphorylation of, 368
D-Fructose-6-phosphate, 53*, 54*, 344†
  as an intermediate in the mannitol-
    sorbitol phosphate conversion, 451
  changes in free energy during photo-
    synthetic formation, 334
  from mannitol-1-phosphate, 450†
  from mannitol-6-phosphate, 450†
  from sorbitol-6-phosphate, 450†
  in pentose phosphate cycle, 348
  in photosynthesis, 321, 323*†
  in transaldolase-catalyzed reaction, 325,
    326*
  phosphorylation of, 344
  →erythrose-4-phosphate, 324, 351
  →GDP-mannose, 361
  →glucosamine-6-phosphate, 352
  →D-glucose-6-phosphate, 338, 339, 346
  →D-mannose-6-phosphate, 346, 347
  →sucrose, 390
  →sucrose phosphate, 372
N-Fructosyl anthranilic acid, 35
Fructosyl exchange, 419
Fructosyl fructosyl glucoside, 380†
Fructosyl-glucosyl-fructoside, 376†
Fructosyl residue, transfer of, 418
Fructosyl sucrose, 396†
Fructosyl sucrose: sucrose transfructo-
    sylase, 419
D-Fructuronate, 445†, 446†
  hydrogenation of, 449
D-Fructuronic acid, 447*
  →ascorbic acid, 729

Fucan sulfate, 439
L-Fucosamine, in bacterial cell wall poly-
    saccharides, 426
L-Fucose, 363†, 446
    phosphorylation of, 344
L-Fucose containing polysaccharide, 361,
    422†
Fucosterol, 882†
Fucosyl lactose, 372†, 397†
Fucoxanthin, 667
L-Fuculose, 446†
    phosphorylation of, 344
L-Fuculose-1-phosphate, 344†, 450
Fulvic acid, 770, 771*†, 1058†, 1059*†
Fumarase, 339
Fumaric acid →arginine, 13
Fungal alkaloids, 1052
Fungal metabolites
    biosynthesis from acetic acid, 1026
    major structural features, 1025
    origin of "extra" carbon atoms, 1025,
        1038, 1039
    quinones, 1043†
    structural correlations between, 1055
    structural units derived from amino
        acids and shikimic acid, 1052
    terpenes, 1046†
Funtamafrine B, 1012*
Funtumine, 1012*
Furano compounds, 787
Furanoterpenoids, 861
Furan ring, origin of, 787
Furfural, detoxication of, 631*
Furocoumarins, 789†
Furoic acid, 631
    excretion as ornithuric acid, 608
Furomycin, action on phosphorylase, 402
Furoquinoline alkaloids, 1008†
Furoquinoline systems, 832
Furoylacetic acid, 631, 632*
α-Furoylglycine, 631
Furylacrylic acid, 631*†, 632*†
    glycine conjugation, 600*
Furylacryloylglycine, 631*†
Furylacryluric acid, 631*†
Furylpropionic acid, 631, 632*
Fusarubin, 770, 771*†
    sulfate of, 615

D,L-Galactan, 372†
Galactans, 416†, 417†, 420†, 421†, 422†
Galactan sulfate, 439
L-Galactonate, 728
L-Galactonic acid →ascorbic acid, 728
D-Galactono-γ-lactone, 448†

L-Galactonolactone →ascorbic acid, 729*†,
    730
O-β-D-Galactopyranosyl-(1 →4)-D-N-
    acetylglucosamine, 394†
3-β-D-Galactopyranosyl-D-arabinose, 394†
5-β-D-Galactopyranosyl-D-arabinose, 394†
3-β-D-Galactopyranosyl-D-galactose, 394†
6-β-D-Galactopyranosyl-D-galactose, 394†
D-Galactosamine
    acetylation of, 627
    phosphorylation of, 344, 368
D-Galactosamine-1-phosphate, 354†
D-Galactose, 420*
    in bacterial cell wall polysaccharides, 426,
        427
    in cerebrosides, 170
    oxidation of, 448
    phosphorylation of, 344, 368
    →ascorbic acid, 728, 729*
    →bacterial cell wall polysaccharides, 432
    →disaccharide, 378
    →glycosides, 434
    →inositol, 726
    →trisaccharide, 377
L-Galactose, 446
Galactose-deficient lipopolysaccharide, 432
Galactosemia, enzyme defect in, 356
Galactose-4-epimerase, 361
D-Galactose-1-phosphate, 94, 344†, 354†
    derivative of UDP-N-acetylglucosamine,
        368
    →dTDP-galactose, 358
    →glucose derivatives, 359, 360
    →glucose-1-phosphate, 171
    →UDP-galactose, 356
D-Galactose-6-phosphate
    activation of UDP-glucose transglycosy-
        lase by, 405, 406
    →1-phosphate, 345
Galactose-1-phosphate uridyl transferase,
    356
    lack of, in galactosemia, 356
Galactophosphatidyl choline, 165
Galactophosphatidyl ethanolamine, 165
Galactophosphatidyl serine, 165
β-Galactosidase, 168, 488, 502, 510, 516
    secondary structure of, 519
Galacto-sphingomyelins, 165
Galactosylarabinose, 378†
Galactosyl-containing glycerides, 130*†
α-Galactosyl diglyceride, 130*†
Galactosyl fructoside, 378†
Galactosylgalactose, 378†
Galactosyl glucose, 418†
    →raffinose, 377
Galactosyl glucosyl fructoside, 377†
    →levan, 418

Galactosyl inositol, 375†, 434†
Galactosyl lactose, 396†
Galactosyl-mannosyl-rhamnose in bacterial cell wall polysaccharides, 432
Galactosyl sphingosine, 169†, 171
Galactosyl sucrose, 377†, 394†, 396†
→trisaccharides, 378
Galacto-waldenase, 360
Galacturonan, 422†
D-Galacturonate, 446
D-Galacturonic acid, 420*, 447*
→ascorbic acid, 729*†
in bacterial cell wall polysaccharides, 426
phosphorylation of, 345
Galacturonic acid kinase, 354
D-Galacturonic acid-1-phosphate, 345†, 356†
D-Galacturonolactone→ascorbic acid, 728, 729*†
Galathamine, 987*†, 988†
Gallates, aerobic oxidation of, 808
Gallic acid, 801, 802, 803*†, 804, 808, 810, 812
metabolism of the 3-methyl ether, 625*
methylation, 624*, 625
mono-methyl ethers of, 624*†, 625*†
Gallocatechin, 816*, 817
Gallotannins, 803, 804, 808
Galsucrose, 378†
Ganglioside B, 175*
Ganglioside G_{MI}, 175*
Gangliosides, 166, 169†, 173†, 174, 176†, 177†, 438†
of brain, 175
from brain of patients with Tay-Sachs disease, 176
from horse erythrocytes, 176
Garbanzol, 778
Garrya alkaloids, 1010*†
Garryine, 1010*†, 1011†
GDP, 49, 79†, 80†, 371, 372, 373
phosphate exchange, 559
polymerization of, 556
GDP-Arabinose, 93
GDP-Colitose, 93, 365
GDP-6-Deoxy-D-mannose, 93
GDP-6-Deoxy-D-talose, 93
GDP-3,6-Dideoxy-L-galactose, 365
GDP-3,6-Dideoxy-L-xylo-hexose, 93
GDP-Fructose, 93, 357, 362†
GDP-L-Fucose, 93, 95, 357, 361†, 362†, 397†, 422
→fucosyl lactose, 397
→saccharides, 372
GDP-Galactose, 93
GDP-L-Galactose, 93
→saccharides, 372

GDP-D-Glucose, 93, 357†, 362†
→bacterial polysaccharides, 373
→cellulose, 415
→glucosides, 434
→saccharides, 371
GDP-D-Glycero-D-manno-heptose, 93, 367*†
GDP-L-Guluronic acid →alginic acid, 373, 424
GDP-4-Keto-D-rhamnose, 362
GDP-Lactose, 93
GDP-Mannose, 93, 95, 357†, 361†, 362†
dehydrogenation of, 363
reductive epimerization of, 362
→alginic acid, 424
→extracellular polysaccharides, 373
→GDP-L-fucose, 361
→mannan, 416
→saccharides, 372
GDP-Mannose dehydrase, 362
GDP-Mannose pyrophosphorylase, 357
GDP-D-Mannuronic acid, 93, 363†
→alginic acid, 373, 424
GDP-D-Rhamnose, 362†
GDP-Talomethylose, 362†
Gelsemine, 989*, 996*†, 997†
Genes, operator, regulator and structural, 505
Genetic code, 542
for amino acid sequence in proteins, 491, 492, 493
Gentiobiose, 434
→saccharides, 377, 416
Gentiobiosides, 375†, 434†
Gentisic acid, 1056
Gentisyl alcohol, 1056
Gentrogenin, 226, 886
Geodin, 1027*, 1028
Geodin hydrate, 1028
Geodin methyl ether, 1028*
Geodoxin, 1027*, 1028†
Geranic acid, toxicity of, 832
Geraniol, 833, 837*, 838, 839, 841, 846*, 847, 855†, 857
cis-, 846
→cyclic monoterpenes, 848, 849*
→indole alkaloids, 1003
→terpenes, 836, 840
→α-terpineol, 848*, 849*
Geraniol pyrophosphate, 945*†, 949
trans-, 949
→rubber, 949
Geranylgeranic acid, toxicity of, 832
Geranylgeraniol, 863, 866
→deterpenes, 865*
→phytol, 866

Geranylgeraniol pyrophosphate →gibberellic acid, 869, 870*
Geranylgeranyl pyrophosphate, 648, 651*
Geranyl linalool, 863, 866
Geranylmyrcene, 863
Geranyl pyrophosphate, 648, 649†
  →squalene, 210†, 211*†
  →terpenes, 844*†
Germanicol, 875
Gibberellic acid, 507, 869, 870*†, 1048*†, 1049, 1050†, 1051†
Gibberellins, 866, 870*†
Ginkgetin, 818
Gitoxigenin, 885
Glabra lactone, C-acylated, 786*
Gliorosein, 1043†, 1044*
Gliotoxin, 954*, 955, 1053*†
Globin synthesis, control by δ-aminolevulinic acid and by hemin, 274
γ-Globulin, 480, 486
Glucagon
  action on phosphorylase, 401, 402
  effect on glycogen synthetase, 407
Glucamylase, 341
α-Glucan, 403†
β-1,2-Glucan, 371†
β-1,3-Glucan, 371†, 416†
α-Glucan branching glucosyl-transferase, 411
α-1,4-Glucan: α-1,4-glucan-6-glucosyl transferase, 411
α-1,4-Glucan oligosaccharides, as glycosyl donor, 379
Glucans, 397†, 416†
α-1,4-Glucans, 379†
α-Glucan synthetase, 403
Gluco-cerebroside in gangliosides, 176
Glucokinase, 341, 342
Glucomanno-sphingomyelins, 165
D-Gluconate, phosphorylation of, 344
Gluconic acid, 446
D-Gluconolactone, 448†
Glucono γ-lactone, 446†
Glucono δ-lactone, 446†
D-Gluconolactone-6-phosphate→D-ribose-5-phosphate, 348*†
D-Glucopyranose-6-phosphate →D-ribose-5-phosphate, 348*†
β-D-Glucopyranuronosides, 592, 593*
Glucopyranosyl-(1 →6)-D-galactose, 377†, 394†
β-D-Glucopyranosyl-(1 →6)-β-D-glucopyranose, 434
D-Glucosamine
  acetylation, 627
  →glycoproteins, 435, 436
  phosphorylation of, 344

α-D-Glucosamine-1-phosphate
  acetylation of, 352
  →dTDP-glucosamine, 358
D-Glucosamine-6-phosphate, 352†
  →N-acetyl glucosamine-6-phosphate, 352
  activation of UDP-glucose transglycosylase by, 405, 406
Glucosamine-6-phosphate N-acetylase, 352
Glucosaminuronic acid-containing polysaccharides, 367
D-Glucose, 376, 446
  free, 445†
    occurrence, 444
  from D-fructose, 452†
  from sorbitol, 450†
  in bacterial cell wall polysaccharides, 426, 427
  inhibitor of amylomaltase reaction, 408
  oxidation of, 447, 448
  phosphorylation of, 344
  product of fungal metabolism, 910
  reduction of, 449
  →ascorbic acid, 728, 729*, 730
  →fructose, 452
  →fungal metabolites, 1026
  →inositol, 453, 725, 726
  →lactose, 372, 393
  →lignin, 918, 919
  →maltose, 377
  →melibiose, 394
  →methyl p-methoxycinnamate, 910
  →phenylalanine, tyrosine, 32, 33
  →saccharides, 370
  →shikimic acid, 923, 924
α Glucose, structural analogy with myoinositol, 725*
β-D-Glucose, oxidation of, 448
Glucose dehydrogenase, 446
α-D-Glucose-1,6-diphosphate
  coenzyme of phosphoglucomutase, 353*
  requirement for phosphoglucomutase, 345
Glucose-6-nitrate, 726
D-Glucose oxidase, 445
  action on amylomaltase reaction, 408
Glucose-6-phosphatase, 342
Glucose-1-phosphate, 94, 352
  activation of glycogen synthetase by, 405
  energy of hydrolysis, 382
  →ADP-glucose, 358
  →amylopectin, glycogen, 398
  →amylose, 387, 398
  →dCDP-glucose, 358
  →dTDP-glucose, 357
  →GDP-glucose, 357
  →glucose-6-phosphate, 353*, 354
  →lactose, 392, 393

Glucose-1-phosphate—(*cont.*)
→lactose phosphate, 372
→sucrose, 389
α-D-Glucose-1-phosphate, 392
→amylose, 398
→saccharide, 370
β-D-Glucose-1-phosphate, 377†, 391, 392, 414†
→saccharide, 370
Glucose-6-phosphate, 51, 336†, 354†
activation of UDP-glucose transglycosylase by, 405
by phosphorylation with pyrophosphate, 342†
by reversed glycolysis, 339†
changes in free energy during photosynthetic formation, 334
from fatty acids, 341†
from glucose 340†
from glucose-1-phosphate, 343†, 352†
in photosynthesis, 321, 323*†
key position in the biosynthesis of carbohydrates, 319
→D-fructose-6-phosphate, 346, 347
→GDP-mannose, 361
→glucose-1-phosphate, 353*
→inositol, 453, 725, 726
→lactose, 392
→6-phosphogluconolactone, 52*
→D-ribose-5-phosphate, 347
→trehalose, 391
→trehalose phosphate, 372
Glucose-6-phosphate dehydrogenase, 52, 53, 347, 348
Glucose-6-phosphates, inhibition of hexokinase by, 342
D-Glucose-1-sorboside, 376†
Glucose-1-phosphate transferase, 353, 354
D-Glucose-1-xyloketoside →sucrose, 377
α-Glucosidase, 340, 412
α-1,6-Glucosidase, 340
β-Glucosidase, 341, 507, 931
Glucoside conjugation, 591, 592, 598
Glucosides, 375†, 594, 595
α-1,4-Glucosidic bonds
energy of, 383
hydrolysis of, 383
α-1,6-Glucosidic bonds, 383†
energy of hydrolysis of, 383
Glucosiduronic acids, 435†
Glucosyl-fructosido-fructoside, 419†
→levan, 418
Glucosyl-fructosyl fructosides, 376†
Glucosyl-fructosyl-glucoside, 376†
Glucosyl maltose, 377†, 396†
Glucosyl mannose, 378†
3-O-α-D-Glucosyl mannose, 394†

6-O-α-D-Glucosyl mannose, 394†
Glucosyl sucrose, 396†
α-D-Glucosyl-D-xylose, 370†
Glucuronan, 420
D-Glucuronate, 446
hydrogenation of, 449
→pentose, 449
reduction of, 449
Glucuronate pathway, 730
D-Glucuronic acid, 447*, 449*
in bacterial cell wall polysaccharides, 426
phosphorylation of, 344, 345, 368
role in detoxication, 590
→ascorbic acid, 729, 730
→D-glucurono lactone, 728, 729*†
Glucuronic acid conjugation, 591, 592
α-D-Glucuronic acid-1-phosphate, 344†, 345†, 354†
β-Glucuronidase, 288
Glucuronide formation, enzymic mechanism of, 593
Glucuronides, 593*, 594, 595†
β configuration of, 597
pK values, 632
conjugated, precursors of, 595, 596
secretion of, 633
types of, 592, 593
types of compounds forming, 594, 595
N-Glucuronides, 593
Glucuronide synthesis, zoological distribution, 597
Glucuronidogenic substances, 596
Glucuronolactone
→ascorbic acid, 728, 729*†, 730
→xylan, 420
Glucuronosides, 375†
Glucuronyl acceptors, 596
Glucuronyl residue, acceptors of, 596
Glucuronyl transfer in plant tissues, 598
Glucuronyl transferase, 596, 597
Glutamate, 3
→lysine, 28
→ornithine, 11, 12*, 13
→pantothenic acid, 697
Glutamate-phosphohydroxy-pyruvate transaminase, 5
Glutamic acid, 4
→folic acid, 707
in folic acid, 704, 705*, 707
→oxytetracycline, 1031, 1032
→pyrrolidine ring of nicotine, 964, 965*
D-Glutamic acid →bacterial cell wall, 429
L-Glutamic acid →ornithine, 12*
Glutamic-DAP transaminase, 26
Glutamic dehydrogenase, 4
Glutamic semialdehyde, 28
→ornithine, 11, 12*†, 13

Glutamine, 62*
  →cytidylic acid, 75
  →DPN, 82, 83
  →guanylic acid, 67
  →histidine, 29, 30
  in amination of sugar-6-phosphates, 352
Glutamine conjugation, 591, 592, 609*, 632
γ-Glutamyl-S-cysteine derivatives, 605
Glutarylcoenzyme A, 27
ε-N-(L-Glutaryl-2)-L-lysine →lysine, 28†
Glutathione
  effect on UDP-glucose transglycosylase,
    406
  role in formation of mercapturic acid,
    604*
Glutathione S-aryltransferase, 605, 606
Glutathione S-epoxidetransferase, 606
Glutathione reductase, 11
D-glyceraldehyde →D-fructose-1-
    phosphate, 349
Glyceraldehyde-3-phosphate, 322*†
  activator of ADP-glucose synthesis, 358
  changes in free energy during photo-
    synthetic formation, 334
  from xylulose-5-phosphate, 351†
  in photosynthesis, 323*
  in transaldolase-catalyzed reaction, 325,
    326*†
  →D-fructose-1,6-diphosphate, 349
  →nicotinic acid, 962, 963*
  →xylulose-5-phosphate, 324*†
D-Glyceraldehyde-3-phosphate, 56, 57*
  →glucose-6-phosphate, 339
L-Glyceraldehyde-3-phosphate, in trans-
    aldolase-catalyzed reaction, 325
Glyceraldehyde-3-phosphate dehydro-
    genase, 322, 339
Glycerate →serine, 5*, 142
D-Glycerate dehydrogenase, 5
Glyceric acid kinase, 6
Glycerides, carbohydrate-containing, 130*†
Glycerol, 450
  effect on polyene formation, 659
  →nicotinic acid, 962, 963*
  →rhamnose, 435
Glycerol-1-alkoxyl-2-acyl-3-phosphoryl-
    ethanolamine, 155*
Glycerol esters, 106*
Glycerol moiety, of triglyceride, 122†
Glycerol phosphatides, 158†
L-Glycero-3-phosphate
  →CDP-glycerol, 89
  in bacterial cell wall, 427
Glycerokinase, 123, 124
D-Glycero-O-mannoheptose-7-phosphate→
    heptose nucleotide, 367

L-α-Glycerophosphate, 123†
  →inositol monophosphatide, 726
  →teichoic acids, 431
  →triglyceride, 122
Glycerophosphate cycle, 123
L-α-Glycerophosphate dehydrogenase, 123,
    124
Glycerophosphatides, 133*
Glyceryl ether phospholipids, 155*†
Glyceryl ethers, 133†, 135
Glycerylphosphoryl choline, 142†
Glycerylphosphoryl ethanolamine, 153†
Glycinamide ribonucleotide, 62†, 63*†
Glycinamide ribonucleotide kinosynthase,
    63
Glycinamide ribonucleotide transformylase,
    63
Glycine, 3, 5*†, 6†
  hippuric acid synthesis, 591
  →δ-aminolevulinic acid, 254, 255, 256*
  →heme, 253*
  →leucopterin, 705
  →porphobilinogen, 254
  →porphyrin, 252
  →pyridoxal, 723
  →riboflavin, 700
  →serine, 141
  →threonine, 16
  →vitamin B₁₂, 711, 712
Glycine N-acylase, 599
Glycine conjugates
  pK values, 632
  secretion of, 633
  types of acids forming, 599, 600
Glycine conjugation, 609, 610
Glycocholic acid, 599†
Glycocyamine →creatine, 620, 621
Glycogen, 371†, 379†, 385†, 387†, 391,
    397†, 402†, 403†, 407†, 411†
  as glucosyl acceptor, 404
  as glucosyl donor, 379
Glycogen
  energy of hydrolysis, 382
  particulate, 399
  phosphorylation of, 352
  structure of, 397
Glycogen accumulation in tissues of
    patients with Pompe's disease, 410
Glycogen-storage disease, cardiomegalic,
    410
Glycogen synthetase, 402, 403, 405
Glycolaldehyde
  →pyridoxal, 723
  →D-xylulose-1-phosphate, 349
Glycolaldehyde phosphate →D-xylulose-
    1,5-diphosphate, 349

Glycolate
  formation during photosynthesis, 336
  →serine, 6
Glycolic acid, accumulation during photosynthesis, 335
Glycolic aldehyde →acetyl phosphate, 351*
Glycolipids, 166, 171†, 435†
  of brain, 170
N-Glycolyl neuraminic acid, 176, 437
N-Glycolyl neuraminic acid-9-phosphate, 174
Glycolysis, reversal of, 338, 339
Glycolytic cycle, 337
Glycolytic pathway, 2, 32
Glycopeptide, 428
  cell wall, 374†, 429†
Glycophospholipids, 165
Glycoproteins, 435†, 436†, 519
  sialic acid-containing, 375†
Glycoprotein synthesis, feedback controls of, 439
Glycoside bonds, 320†, 368†
  de novo synthesis of, 320
Glycoside donor, 384
Glycoside groups, 383*
Glycosides, 374†, 384†, 434†
  cardiac, 884†
Glycoside synthesis, role of ATP in, 382
Glycoside transglycosylases, 371
Glycosyl acceptors, 369–380, 384
Glycosyl donors, 90, 368–380, 384, 385
  for amylose, 398
  standard free energy of hydrolysis of, 382
Glycosyl groups, 383*
Glycosyl transfer, intramolecular, 388
Glycylglycine, activation of enzymes by, 360
Glycyl-methionine, 496
Glycyl-RNA-synthetase, 495
Glycyltaurine conjugation, 630
Glycyl-tryptophan, 496
Glyoxal, in chemical synthesis of pteridine, 706
Glyoxalate
  formation during photosynthesis, 336
  from isocitrate, 340†
  →glycine, 7
  →serine, 6
Glyoxalate cycle, 7, 28, 340, 341
Glyoxylate, see glycoxalate
GMP, 49
  →dGMP, 58
  in sRNA, 498
  incorporation into RNA, 561
Gossypitrin, 775
Gramine, 955, 957*†, 958
Griseofulvin, 757*†, 1026*†, 1027†, 1028, 1038, 1046

Growth hormone, 507
  effect on mucopolysaccharide formation, 443, 444
GTP, 49, 79†, 94, 357
  requirement for peptide bond formation, 512, 513, 514
  transphosphorylation with, 79, 80
  →GDP-glucose, 357
  →GDP-mannose, 357
  →RNA, 565
GTP: α-D-glucose-1-phosphate-guanylyl transferase, 362
Guaiacyl glycerol, 934, 935*
Guaiacyl glycerol-β-coniferyl ether, 932*, 933, 934, 935*
Guaiacylglycerol-β-coniferyl ether units of softwood lignin,
  enzymic degradation, 935*
Guaiacyl glycerol-β-pinoresinol, 933
Guaiacyl lignin, 934
Guaiacyl propane units →lignin, 930
Guaiacyl residues, formation during lignin biosynthesis, 916, 918
Guaiaretic acid, 793*
Guaiol, 856*
Guanidino acetic acid
  methylation of, 8
  →creatine, 620, 621, 622
Guanidoacetate-N-methyl transferase, 622
Guanine, 46*, 47*, 49, 50, 539*
  →B12 intermediate, 731
  →folic acid, 705
  →folic acid precursor, 731*
  →guanosine, 69
  →guanylic acid, 69
  →riboflavin, 699, 700, 701
  →riboflavin precursor, 731*
Guanosine, 49, 69†
  →dihydrofolate, 705
  →folic acid, 705
  5′-mono-, di-, and triphosphates of, 544
Guanosine diphosphate cobinamide, 715
Guanosine-diphosphate derivatives of sugars, 93
Guanosine diphosphate glycosides, see GDP-glycosides
Guanosine-5′-diphosphate-4-keto-6-deoxy-D-mannose, 361
Guanosine nucleotides →folic acid, 705
Guanosine-5′-phosphate, 49
Guanosine triphosphate, see GTP
  requirement for oxalacetate-synthesizing enzyme, 337
  →vitamin B12, 716
Guanylic acid, 49, 66†, 67*

L-Gulonate, 449†
    dehydrogenation of, 446
    →L-xylulose, 447
L-Gulonic acid, 449*
    →ascorbic acid, 728, 729*†, 730
    →L-gulonolactone, 728, 729*†, 730
L-Gulonolactone
    →ascorbic acid, 728, 729*†, 730
    →L-galactonolactone, 728, 729*†
    →L-xylulose, 450
Gulose, phosphorylation of, 344
L-Guluronic acid, in alginic acid, 424
Gutta, 942, 949
Gyrophoric acid, 765*, 766†

Haemanthamine, 955, 987*, 988
Haemanthidine, 986†, 987*†
Halfordine, 1014*
Haptoglobin, 285
Harmaline, 990†, 991*†
Harman, 990†, 991*†
Harmine, 989*
Head-to-tail union of acetate, 106, 757,
    758*, 774, 806, 1026, 1033, 1037, 1039
Head-to-tail union of isopentane, 846, 856
Heliotridine, 971, 972*
Helminthosporal, 862*†
Helminthosporin, 1043†, 1044*
Hematin, 278, 285
    →biliverdin, 295
Hematoporphyrin, 265
Hematoporphyrin IX, 264, 271
Hematoporphyrin dimethyl ester, absorp-
    tion spectrum of, 251, 252
Hematoporphyrinogen, 264
Heme, 250*, 251, 253*†, 263, 264†, 266, 278
    →biroprotein, 295, 296, 298
    →biliverdin, 277
    comparison to vitamin B_{12} porphyrin,
    711*
Heme a, 271*
Hemicelluloses, 422†, 423
Hemichromogens, 285
Hemin, control of globin and hemoglobin
    synthesis by, 274
m-Hemipinic acid, 817
Hemiterpenes, 830
    biologically active, 843*
Hemochromogens, 282, 285
Hemoglobin, 248, 263†, 266, 278, 279, 285,
    478, 480, 484, 486, 487, 494, 499, 502,
    503, 504, 511, 514, 515, 517, 519
    →bile pigments, 276, 277, 278, 281
    →biliprotein, 295
    →biliverdin, 281, 282, 283*, 284

Hemoglobin-haptoglobin →biliverdin, 285,
    295
Hemoglobin synthesis, control by δ-
    aminolevulinic acid and by hemin, 274
Hemoproteins, 266, 277, 278
    →bile pigments, 279, 282, 283*, 295,
    296, 297, 298
Heparin, 439, 441†, 442†
    complexes with protein, 444
Heparitin, 373†, 443
Heptadeconic acid, 121†
Heptose nucleotide, 367*†
Heptoses, in bacterial cell wall poly-
    saccharides, 427
Herqueinone, 1030
Heteropolymers of adenylic, guanylic,
    uridylic and cytidylic acids, 538
Heteropolysaccharides, N-free, 424†
Hexachlorobenzene, 634
    stimulation of porphyrin synthesis by,
    273
Hexadecahydrolycopene, 653†
Δ^9-Hexadecenoic acid, 119
Hexahydrocadalene, 859*†
L-Hexahydrophenylalanine, N-acetylation,
    627
Hexahydroxydiphenic acid, 804, 808, 809*,
    810, 812
Hexanoate →cholesterol, 208
Hexapeptide from bacterial cell wall, 430
Hexitols, 450†
Hexokinase, 341, 342, 343, 344
Hexokinases, 368
    specificity towards monosaccharides, 343,
    344
Hexonic acids, 447
    →ketopentoses, 450
Hexosemonophosphate shunt, 51
Hexose phosphates, 338†, 339†
Hexose-6-phosphates, 344†
    activation of UDP-glucose transglyco-
    sylase by, 405
Hexoses, 359†
Hexuronic acids, 359†
Hibbert ketones, 927, 931
Hibbert's monomers, from lignin, 904
High density lipoprotein, 178, 179, 180, 181
Hill reaction, 665
Himbacine, 968†, 969*†
Hiochic acid, 946
Hippeastrine, 985†, 986*†
Hippuric acid, 599†
Hippuric acid synthesis, 591, 592, 598*, 599,
    609
    enzymic mechanism of, 599
    zoological distribution of, 599

Histamine
  acetylation of, 626, 627
  →imidazole-4-acetic acid →riboside, 631
  methylation of, 620, 621, 622
Histidine, 3, 29†, 30†, 32*†, 59, 60*, 685
Histidine biosynthesis, enzymes of, 31
Histidine synthetase, 506
L-Histidinal →histidine, 31, 32*†
L-Histidinol →histidine, 31, 32*†
Histidinol dehydrogenase, 31
L-Histidinol phosphate →histidine, 32*†
Histidinol phosphate phosphatase, 31
Histones, linked to DNA, 542
Holaphyllamine, 1012*†
Holaphylline, 883, 884*, 1012*†
Holarrhimine, 1012*
Homoaconitase, 27
Homoaconitate, 27
Homocitrate →lysine, 27*†
Homocysteine
  acetylation of its derivatives, 627
  →cysteine, 8*†
  →methionine, 19†, 20*†, 21
  S-methylation of, 8
Homoisocitrate →lysine, 27*†
Homo-orsellinic acid, 1043
Homoserine, 3, 25†, 26†, 574
  →methionine, 17, 18, 19†, 20*
  →threonine, 16, 17*
Homoserine dehydrase, 9
Homoserine dehydrogenase, 16
  repression and inhibition of, 18
Homoserine kinase, 16
Hordenine, 955, 956*†
Hormones, adrenocortical and sex steroid, 226†
Hortiacine, 991*
Hortiamine, 991*
HP Phosphatase, 31
Hyaluronate, 373†
Hyaluronic acid, 425†, 426†, 441, 443†
  →hybrid oligosaccharides, 380
Hyaluronic acid synthetase, 426
Hyaluronidase, 426
  as transglycosylase, 380
Hydracrylonitrile, 617*
Hydrangenol, 779*†, 780†
  precursors of, 779, 780
Hydrastine, 955, 982*
Hydratropic acid, glycine conjugation, 600*
Hydrazides, acetylation of, 627, 629
Hydrazine, acetylation of, 626, 627, 629
β-L-Hydroacid dehydrogenase, 447
Hydrocarbons, 133†
  aliphatic, aromatic, halogenated, nitro, detoxication of, 601
  carcinogenic, 1066*

Hydrocarbons—(cont.)
  polycyclic aromatic, 1065, 1066*, 1067*, 1074, 1075
Hydrogen cyanide, 632
Hydrolysis, standard free energy of, 382
Hydrolytic enzymes, 340
  role in polysaccharide synthesis, 386, 387
Hydroquinone, 744*
Hydroquinone gentiobioside, 434†
Hydroquinone β-glucoside, 434
Hydrosclerotiorin derivatives →naphthoquinones, 1031*
p-Hydroxyacetophenone, 744*
N-Hydroxy-2-acetylaminofluorene →glucuronide, 594*
β-Hydroxyacyl dehydrogenase, 108
19-Hydroxy androstenedione →estrone, 233, 234*†
3-Hydroxyanthranilate, from anthranilate, 688
3-Hydroxyanthranilate oxidase, 683, 687
3-Hydroxy anthranilic acid, 690
  →alkaloids, 1006†, 1007*†
  →nicotinic acid, 683*†, 687, 962*†
5-Hydroxy-anthranilic acid, 687
Hydroxyaspartic acid, 696
p-Hydroxybenzaldehyde, 916, 933
  from lignin, 904
  in lignin biosynthesis, 917
p-Hydroxybenzoic acid, 791†, 908, 916
  →protocatechuic acid, 803
o-Hydroxybenzyl alcohol β-glycoside, 434
β-Hydroxybutyryl CoA →long-chain fatty acids, 113
2-Hydroxy-4-carboxyadipic acid, 810
α-Hydroxy, β-carboxy-isocaproate →L-leucine, 24*†
β-Hydroxy, β-carboxy-isocaproate →L-leucine, 24*†
2'-Hydroxychalcone epoxide, 778
Hydroxy chlorobactene, 661
Δ⁵-3β-Hydroxycholenic acid, 234, 235, 236*, 885
7-α-Hydroxycholesterol →cholic acid, 236*, 238†
20α-Hydroxycholesterol →pregnenolone, 227*†, 228
22ξ-Hydroxycholesterol, 228
22-Hydroxycholesterol, 883
25-Hydroxycholesterol, 235
26-Hydroxycholesterol, 235
p-Hydroxycinnamaldehyde, 934
p-Hydroxycinnamic acid, 934
  precursors of, 911
  →lignin, 750
  →quercetin, 772

p-Hydroxycinnamyl alcohol, 910, 928
  structural relationship with products of fungal metabolism, 916
β-Hydroxyconiferyl alcohol, 935*
3β-Hydroxycoprostane, 235
17-α-Hydroxycorticosterone, 229*†
18-Hydroxycorticosterone, 228
3-Hydroxycoumarin →sulfate, 613
4-Hydroxycoumarin →glucuronide, 594*
7-Hydroxycoumarin, 788*†
β-Hydroxydecanoyl CoA dehydrase, 118
β-Hydroxydecanoyl CoA
  dehydration of, 118
  →rhamnolipids, 374, 435
3-Hydroxy-3-dehydro-β-carotene, 671
17-α-Hydroxy-11-dehydrocorticosterone, 229*†
3β-Hydroxydehydrogenase, 228, 229
17-α-Hydroxy-11-desoxycorticosterone, 229*†
Hydroxydihydroeremophilone, 856
4-Hydroxy-3,5-di-iodobenzoic acid, methylation of, 620, 621
3-Hydroxy-4,5-dimethoxybenzoic acid, 625*†
4-Hydroxy-3,5-dimethoxybenzoic acid, 625*†
7-Hydroxy-3,6-ditigloyloxytropane →tropane alkaloids, 961*
Hydroxyeremophilone, 856
Hydroxyethyl group, donor of, 682
Hydroxyethyl thiamine, 682
Hydroxyethyl thiamine pyrophosphate, 21, 22, 23*, 680*, 682
3-Hydroxyflavanone, 778
α-Hydroxyheme, 277, 282
α-Hydroxyheme-globin, 283*†
α-Hydroxyhemochromogen, 280*†, 281
Hydroxyhopanone, 876*†
6-Hydroxyhyoscyamine →hyoscine, 959†, 960*†
Hydroxyindole-O-methyl transferase, 622, 623
β-Hydroxyisovaleraldehyde
  →carotene, 645
  origin in terpenes, 834*
Hydroxyisovalerate →cholesterol, 208, 209*†
β-Hydroxyisovaleric acid →carotene, 645
β-Hydroxyisovaleryl-CoA, 646
α-Hydroxy-β-ketoacid reductoisomerase, 23
3-Hydroxykynurenine →nicotinic acid, 683*†, 687
β-Hydroxylacyl dehydrogenase, 107
Hydroxylamine
  effect on uroporphyrinogen I formation, 259

Hydroxylamine—(cont.)
  reduction of, 11
Hydroxylamines →glucuronides, 593, 594
Hydroxylase, hydroxylating proline residues in the peptide, 15
13-Hydroxylupanine, 973*†, 975†
Hydroxylycopene, 658
Hydroxylysine, 29†
4-Hydroxy-3-methoxy phenylpyruvic acid, 935*
α-Hydroxymethyl-α-(N-acetylaminomethylene)-succinic acid, 724
Hydroxymethylation, in pantothenic acid synthesis, 696
2-Hydroxy-6-methylbenzoic acid, 1026*†
Hydroxymethylcytosine, 47*, 548, 551
Hydroxymethyldihydropteridine, 707
Hydroxymethylglutarate
  →carotene, 646
  →cholesterol, 208
  →squalene, 210*†, 211
β-Hydroxy-β-methyl glutaric acid, 843*
  →carotene, 645
β-Hydroxy-β-methylglutaryl-CoA, 646, 647
  →cholesterol, 208, 209
  →mevalonic acid, 843
  →rubber, 944*†, 945*, 946
  significance in terpenoid biogenesis, 890
Hydroxymethyl group, transfer of, 6
Hydroxymethylpyrimidine →thiamine, 681
1-Hydroxymethyltetrahydro-β-carboline, 990†, 991*†
Hydroxymethyltetrahydrofolic acid, 6*
  →serine, 141
Hydroxymethyl THFA dehydrogenase, 718
Hydroxyneurosporene, 660
2-Hydroxyphenazine →B₁₂ vitamers, 715
4-Hydroxyphenoxyacetic acid, 791†
p-Hydroxyphenylacetic acid, 611
p-Hydroxyphenylacetyl-CoA, 611
p-Hydroxyphenyllactic acid
  →lignin, 750, 928*†, 929
  →tyrosine, 749*†
p-Hydroxyphenylpropane compounds → lignin, 930
o-Hydroxyphenylpropionic acid, 916
p-Hydroxyphenylpyruvic acid
  →alkaloids, 974, 975, 981
  →aromatic amino acids, 907†, 908*†
  →lignin, 750, 928*†, 929
  →tyrosine, 33*†, 34†
  product of fungal metabolism, 910*
17-Hydroxypregnenolone, 228*†, 232*†
17-α-Hydroxyprogesterone, 229*†, 230, 231*†
Hydroxyproline, 3, 14†, 15†
  absence in pre-collagen peptides, 15

2-Hydroxy purine, in chemical synthesis of pteridine, 706
Hydroxypyruvate, 5*†
→active glycolic aldehyde, 350
→serine, 141, 142
Hydroxyresveratrol, 779, 780*
Hydroxy-spheroidene, 664†
Hydroxy-spheroidenone, 664†
Hydroxy steroids, 3-α and 3-β- →sulfates, 614
Hydroxystilbene aglycones, 818
Hydroxystilbenes, 807
in tannins, 805
p-Hydroxystyrene, 793*
Hydroxytropanes, tiglic acid esters of, 960
4-Hydroxytryptamine derivatives, 957*
5-Hydroxytryptophan →alkaloids, 957
Hydroxo benzimidazole cobamide, 717
Hygrine, 958*†, 959†
→cuscohygrine, 958*, 959
Hyoscine, 959†, 960*†
Hyoscyamine, 955, 959†, 960*†
→hyoscine, 959, 960*
Hypericin, 744*, 792
Hypothyroidism, 444
Hypoxanthine, 46*, 47*, 49, 60†, 61†, 548, 551
in sRNA, 497
→inosine, 69
→inosinic acid, 69

IAP →histidine, 32*†
IAP transaminase, 31
Ibogaine, 989
L-Iditol, 450
L-Idonic acid, 449†
IDP, 49
polymerization of, 556
IDP-glucose, 357
IDP-mannose, 357, 358
L-Iduronic acid, 362†, 363†
IGP →nicotinic acid, 683*†, 684
IGP hydrolase, 683
Imidazole-4-acetic acid
methylation of, 620
→N-riboside, 631*
Imidazole acetol phosphate→histidine, 32*†
Imidazole acetol phosphate transaminase, 31
Imidazole glycerol phosphate →histidine, 29†, 30†, 685
Imidazole-N-methyl transferase, 622
Imidazole ring, 64†
ImGP →histidine, 29†, 30†, 32*†
ImGP Dehydrase, 31

IMP, 49, 497
in histidine synthesis, 30*†
Indican, 611*
Indole, 36†
→alkaloids, 1002*, 1004
→nicotinic acid, 683*†, 685
Indoleacetic acid, 507
Indole alkaloids, 984, 989*†, 990*†, 992*†, 1001*†, 1002*†, 1003, 1004
biogenesis according to Wenkert, 997†, 998*†
Indole-3-glycero phosphate, 3
→nicotinic acid, 683*†, 684, 685
→tryptophan, 35*†
Indolenine, 1003*, 1004
Indolenine alkaloids, 990†
Indolyl-3-acetic acid, 611
glutamine conjugation, 609
Indolylacetyl-CoA, 611
Indolylacetylglutamine, 611
Indoxylsulfate, 615
Indoxylsulfate, potassium, 611*
Initiators of deoxynucleotidyl residue transfer, 555
Inorganic pyrophosphatase, 342
Inosine, 49, 69†, 690
→erythronic acid-4-phosphate, 351
Inosine diphosphate glycosides, see IDP-glycosides
Inosine-5′-phosphate, 49
Inosine triphosphate
see ITP
in RNA synthesis, 568
requirement for oxalacetate-synthesizing enzyme, 337
Inosinic acid, 49, 59†, 61†, 66*†
→adenylic acid, 66
→guanylic acid, 67
Inosinicase, 66
Inosinic dehydrogenase, 67
Inositol, 160†, 453†, 724†, 725
cleavage to D-glucuronic acid, 726
function of, 726
→galactosylinositol, 375
D-Inositol, 452*†
Inositol diphosphate, 183
Inositol galactosides, 434†
Inositol metadiphosphate, 137
Inositol monophosphate, 137
Inositol monophosphatides, 726†
Inositol-1-phosphate, 726
Inositol phosphatides, 136, 159†, 160†, 161†
Inositol phosphokinase, 159
Inositol phospholipid, 159†
Inositol triphosphate, 138*
Insularine, 980*, 981†

Insulin, 478, 480, 486
  action on glucokinase, 342
  association with cell membranes, 520
  effect on mucopolysaccharide formation, 443
  effect on UDP-glucose transglycosylase, 406, 407
  secondary structure, 519
Inulin, 417†
  as fructosyl donor, 380, 396
Invertases, 376, 396, 445
Iodobenzene →premercapturic acid, 605, 666
β-Ionone, 830, 831*
  effect on carotenoid synthesis, 658, 659
  effect on sterol synthesis, 659
β-Ionone groups, in carotenes, 642
Ipomeamarone, 861*†
IpPP-Isomerase, 948
Iresin, 860*, 893
Iresin family of sesquiterpenes, 860*†
Iridodial, 1009*, 1010
Iron-porphyrin-protein, 248
Iron protoporphyrin, 278
Iron-protoporphyrin IX, 248, 250*, 251
Iron protoporphyrin pyridine hemochromogen, 280
Ismine, 986†, 987*†, 988†
Isoalloxazine ring, of riboflavin, 699, 700
Isoamyl alcohol, 836, 837, 838
  origin in terpenes, 834*
Isoamylene, origin in terpenes, 834*
Isobalfourodine, 1007*†
Isobutyrate →plasmalogens, 153
Isobutyric acid →fatty acids, 121
Isocapraldehyde, from cholesterol side chain, 227*†, 228
Isocaproic acid
  →fatty acids, 121
  from cholesterol side chain, 227*†
Isocitrate →succinate, 340
Isoeugenitin, 781*, 782†
Isoeugenitol, 781*
Isoeugenol, dimerization of, 930
Isoeuphol, 214*
Isoflavones, 777*†
Isohexahydroxydiphenic acid, 812
Isoiresin, 860*
Isoleucine, 3, 17†, 21*†, 22†, 24†, 25
  →fungal metabolites, 1054, 1055
  →tiglic acid, 961*
Isoleucyl-RNA synthetase, 496
Isolysergic acid, 1004
Isomaltose, 392†, 409†, 410†
Isomaltotriose, 377†, 396†
Isomerases, 445, 446
Isomerization, ketose-aldose, 346

Isomiropinic acid, 871
Isoniazid, inhibitor of pyridoxal kinase, 724
Isonicotinic acid hydrazide, inhibitor of pyridoxal kinase, 724
Isonicotinic hydrazide, acetylation, 627
Isonicotinylhydrazide
  acetylation of, 626
  stimulation of glycolate formation during photosynthesis by, 335
Isopelletierine, 966*†
Isopentane units, head-to-tail combinations of, 846, 856
Δ³-Isopentenol, 845
Δ³-Isopentenol pyrophosphate, 647, 648, 649
  →β-carotene, 648
  →lycopene, 648, 651*
Isopentenol isomerase, 648
Isopentenyl pyrophosphate
  →alkaloids, 1005*, 1006†, 1008
  in transfer of isoprenoid residue, 785*†
  →rubber, 945*†, 948, 949
  →squalene, 210*†, 211*
  →terpenes, 844*†, 845
Δ³-Isopentol, 843*
Isopentyl pyrophosphate, in terpene biosynthesis, 835
Isophyllocladene, 864*, 867*, 871, 872
Isopimaric acid, 871
Isopimpinellin, 789, 790*
Isopiperitenone, 837*
Isoporphobilinogen, 259
Isoprene, 867
  active, 843
    →terpenes, 835, 847
  in terpenes, 830
  origin in terpenes, 834*
  pyrolysis of, 1075
  →terpenes, 745
Isoprene-formers, 1075
Isoprene rule, biogenetic, 833, 843, 848, 858
Isoprenoid monomer of rubber, 943*†
Isoprenoid polymerization, 949
Isoprenoid residue, introduction by alkylation or acylation, 784
Isoprenoids, 946
  C₄₀, 643
Isopropanolamine →vitamin B₁₂, 712
4-Isopropylcyclohex-1-ene-carboxylic acid, glycine conjugation, 600*
Isopulegol, 837*
Isopyridoxal, 724
Isoquinoline, N-methylation of, 620
Isoquinoline alkaloids, 932, 975†, 976*†, 985
Isorenieratene, 661
Isoreserpinine, 1000†, 1001*†

Isoriboflavin, 703
(+)-Isothebaine, 979*†, 980†, 981
Isotrilobine, 980*
Isovaleraldehyde, 836, 837, 838
   origin in terpenes, 834*
   →terpenes, 836
Isovalerate →cholesterol, 208
Isovaleric acid, 838
   →fatty acid, 121
   origin in terpenes, 834*
Isoxanthopterin, 708
ITP, 49, 357
   transphosphorylation with, 79

Javanicin, 770, 771*†
Jervine, 971, 1013*†, 1014

Kahweol, 864*, 868*†
(−)-Kaurene, 868, 870*†, 871
   →gibberellic acid, 1050, 1051
Kawain, 747*
   precursor of, 747*
KDO, 427, 432, 433*†
KDO-Lipopolysaccharides, 375†
KDO-Nucleotide, 432
Kephalin B, 134, 153, 155*†, 156†
Kerasin, 170
Keratin sulfate, 439
Keratosulfate, 441
Kestose, 396†
β-Ketoacyl-ACP reductase, 114
α-Ketoadipate →lysine, 27*†, 28
α-Ketoadipic acid →vitamin B$_{12}$, 712
α-Keto- ε-aminocaproic acid →anabasine,
   963, 964*†
2-Keto-5-amino-3,5-dideoxynononic acid,
   436*
7-Keto-8-aminopelargonic acid →biotin,
   720
α-Keto-δ-aminovaleric acid, 965*†, 966
α-Ketobutyrate, 3
   formation during cysteine synthesis, 8*†
α-Ketobutyric acid →branched chain amino
   acids, 21*†, 23
Keto-carotenoids, 664†
2-Keto-3-deoxygluconate, 445†, 446†
2-Keto-3-deoxy-gluconate-6-phosphate, 350
2-Keto-3-deoxy-D-gluconic acid, 447*
4-Keto-6-deoxyhexose intermediates, in epimerization reactions, 362
2-Keto-3-deoxyoctonate, 427, 432, 433*†
2-Keto-3-deoxyoctonate-8-phosphate   →
   KDO, 433
α-Keto-β,β-dimethylbutyric acid →panto-
   thic acid, 694

2-Keto-3,6-diphospho-L-gulonic acid, in
   photosynthesis, 326
4-O-β-3-Keto-D-galactosido-D-gluconate,
   447†
4-O-β-3-Keto-D-galactosido-D-glucose,
   447†
5-Ketogluconate reductase, 446
5-Keto-D-gluconic acid, 446†
   reduction of, 449
5-Ketoglucono-idono-reductase, 449
5-Keto-glucose →inositol, 726
Ketoglutaraldehyde, 254*
α-Ketoglutarate, 3, 254*
   →fatty acids, 107
   →lysine, 27
α-Ketoglutarate family, 11†
α-Ketoglutaric acid, 254*
   product of fungal metabolism, 910
3-Ketoglycosides, 447†
3-Ketogulonate, 446†
3-Ketogulonic acid, 449*
2-Keto-L-gulano-lactone →ascorbic acid,
   729*†
α-Keto-β-hydroxy acids, reduction of, 23
α-Keto, 5-hydroxy heme (α-keto, 5-OH
   heme), 277, 281
α-Keto, 5-hydroxyheme-globin, 283*†
α-Keto-β-hydroxy-isovaleric acid, 23
α-Keto-β-hydroxy-β-methylvaleric acid, 23
α-Ketoisocaproate →L-leucine, 21*†, 24*†
α-Keto-isovalerate →branched chain amino
   acids, 21*†, 24*
α-Ketoisovaleric acid →pantothenic acid,
   694, 695*†
Ketol acceptor, 54
Ketol donor, 54
Ketol group, 54*
Ketopantoic acid →pantothenic acid, 694,
   695*†, 696†
Ketopantoic lactone →pantothenic acid,
   694, 696
4-Ketopentanol →thiazole, 681
Ketopentose phosphates, 682
   epimerization of, 345
Ketopentoses, 450†
3-Keto-6-phosphogluconate, 347
   →D-ribose-5-phosphate, 348*†
4-Ketoproline, 15
2-Keto-rhodovibrin, 664†
Ketose-1-phosphates, 349
Ketoses, 446†, 450
   →aldoses, 451
   →sucrose analogues, 370
Ketosides, 419†
2,2′-Keto-spirilloxanthin, 664†
Ketosyl transfer, 419
β-Ketothiolase, 107, 108

24-Ketotrihydroxycoprostane, 237
D-Ketouronic acids, 445†
　reduction of, 449
Ketovaline →pantothenic acid, 694, 695*†
Ketsucrose, 447†
Kinase reactions, 79
Kinases, 69
Khellin, 789, 790*
Klason lignin, 923, 924, 926
Krebs cycle, 252
Kryptogenin, 886
Kynurenic acid, 630
Kynureninase, 683, 687
Kynurenine →nicotinic acid, 683*†, 686
Kynurenine formamidase, 683, 686
Kynurenine hydroxylase, 683, 687

Laccase, 935, 936
L-Lactaldehyde, 350
3-O-D-Lactic acid ether of N-acetylglucos-
　amine, in bacterial cell wall polysacch-
　arides, 426, 427
Lactic dehydrogenase, 338
Lactobacillic acid, 122†
Lactobionate, oxidation of, 447
Lactonase, 52
　(aldono), 728
Lactone, of 6-phosphogluconic acid, 347
Lactones, 448†
　of onic acids, 448†
Lactose, 372†, 392†, 445†
　as glycosyl donor, 377, 383
　energy of hydrolysis, 382
　oxidation of, 447
　→sialyllactose, 375
　→trisaccharide, 377
Lactose-1-phosphate, 372†, 392†, 393†
　→lactose, 392, 393
Lactosyl fructoside, 396†
Laminaran, 371†, 416
Laminarinases, 377, 416
Laminaribiose, 370†, 393†
　→saccharides, 377, 416
Lanatoside A, 885†
Lanceol, 856*
Lanosterol, 655, 877, 879, 880, 887, 891
　→cholesterol, 213, 214, 215*†, 216,
　217*†, 220*†
Lapachenol, 785, 786*
Latex, 942
Lathosterol, 222†, 223*
Lavandulol, 846, 847*
Lecanoric acid, 764*, 766†
Lecithin, 88†, 127*, 134, 142†, 143†, 144†,
　145†, 149†, 183
　alternative pathways, 147†, 148†, 150†
　from liver, 135

Lecithin—(cont.)
　mono- and polyunsaturated fatty acids
　　in two fractions (A and B) of, 146, 147
　→phosphatidic acid, 126
　positional asymmetry of fatty acids in,
　　146
　selective incorporation of fatty acids
　　into, 148
Leprotene, 661
Leptospermone, 783*, 786, 787†
Leucine, 3, 21*†, 22†, 23†
　→alkaloids, 976
　→carotene, 645, 646
　→cholesterol, 208
　→fungal metabolites, 1054
Leucoanthocyanidins, 813, 814, 817, 819,
　820, 822
　in tannins, 807
　→tannins, 805
Leucocyanidin, polymerization of mono-
　meric, 814
Leucodelphinidin (XXV), 816*, 817
Leucofisetinidin (XXVII), 816*, 819
Leucofisetinidin tannins, 819, 820
Leucopterin, 705†
Leucorobinetinidin, (XXVIII), 816*, 819
　polymeric, 820
Levan, 377†, 378†, 385†, 417†
　energy of hydrolysis, 382
Levan sucrase, 377, 378, 394, 396, 417, 418,
　419
Levo-inositol →galactoside, 434
Levopimaric acid, 864*, 865*†, 871, 872
Levulinic acid, formation by ozonolysis of
　rubber, 947*
Lichen biosynthesis, 766
Lichen compounds, 764†
Light energy, in photosynthesis, 333, 334
Light quantum, in photosynthesis, 333,
　334, 335
Lignans, 792, 793*†, 794*
Lignification, 904, 905, 907
　aromatization during, 905, 907
　in higher plants, 916
Lignin, 749†, 750†, 796, 917†, 918†, 922†,
　923†, 930†, 931†, 933†
　biosynthesis from glucose as seen by
　　C14-labeling of vanillin, 919, 920
　building stones of, 905, 909, 910†, 912,
　　916, 926*
　coniferyl, 791
　definition, 904
　formation from carbon dioxide, 917
　formation from D-glucose, 918, 919, 922
　from aromatic amino acids, 928*†, 929†
　high polymer nature of, 905, 906
　hydrogenation of, 905

Lignin—(cont.)
p-hydroxyphenylmethyl building unit of, 926*
origin of guaiacyl and syringyl building stones, 916
phenylpropane building stones of, 926*
phenylpropane skeleton, 905, 917
polymerization of monomers into, 930
primary building stones in the biogenesis of, 906, 907, 917, 925, 931
problems of the biogenesis of, 906
reactions leading to the formation of, 928*†
secondary building stones of, 906, 907, 931, 932*
separation from carbohydrates, 904, 905
sinapyl, 791
structure of, 905
synthetic, 795
syringyl building unit of, 926*
vanillyl building unit of, 926*
Lignin biosynthesis
aromatization process in microorganisms, 907
carbohydrate precursors, 918
formation of tetramers, 933
the enzymes involved, 934, 936
the shikimic acid pathway, 922, 923
Lignin building stones
conversions of, 930
genesis of, 925
structural relationship with products of fungal metabolism, 916
Lignin formation, dimeric intermediates, 932
Lignins, 791†
Klason, 923, 924, 926
Lignoceric acid, 170
Lignoceryl CoA, 117†
Limit dextrin, 411
Limonene, 837*, 841, 846*, 849*†, 850*†, 854*†
→carvone, 854
→terpenes, 836, 838
Limonin, 874*, 884
Linalool, 837*, 838, 841, 846*, 847, 857
→cyclic monoterpenes, 848
pyrolysis of, 1075
→terpenes, 836, 838, 840
Linamarin, 617*
Linoleic acid, 119†, 121†
from oleic acid, 120†
in lecithin, 147
→linolenic acid, 120
α-Linolenate pathway, of desaturation of oleate, 119, 120

γ-Linolenate pathway, of desaturation of oleate, 119
α-Linolenic acid, 119†
γ-Linolenic acid →arachidonic acid, 120, 761*
Lipases, 146, 521
Lipid acceptor, 170
→cerebroside, 171
Lipid, complex, 177†, 178†
Lipid-muramyl pentapeptide, 374†, 430†
Lipids
derived, 177†
methylation of, 149, 150
Lipid transport, 179
Lipoamino acids, 159
Lipoamino esters of phosphatidyl glycerol, 159
Lipoic acid
action of, 327*
coenzyme for rhodanese, 618
in photosynthesis, 329
→biotin, 720
→vitamin B_{12} coenzyme, 718
Lipopeptides, 521
Lipopolysaccharides, 433†
bacterial, 374†, 427, 431†, 432†, 438
galactose-deficient, 432
incorporation of KDO into, 433
structure of, 429
Lipoprotein lipase, 182
Lipoproteins, 178†, 179–182, 522
high density, 178, 179, 180, 181
low-density, 178, 179, 180, 181, 182
plasma, 178, 179
α-Lipoproteins, 178, 180, 181
β-Lipoproteins, 178, 181, 182
Lipositol, 136
Lipovitellenin, 178
Lipovitellin, 178
Lipoxidase, 668
Lipoyl dehydrogenase, 11
Lobelanine, 968†, 969*†
Lofoline, 970*†, 971†
Longifolene, 863*†
Lophenol, 877, 878*, 879
Lophocerine, 976*†
→pilocereine, 976*
Lotaustralin, 617*
Low-density lipoproteins, 178, 179, 180, 181, 182
Lumazine, 702, 703
Lumichrome, 701
Lumiflavin, 701
Lumisterol, 240*†
Lunacrine, 1007*†
Lupanine, 973*†, 975†
Lupeol, 839, 874*, 876, 877, 878*, 889

Lupin alkaloids, 973*†
Lupinine, 973*†, 974
Lutein, 663, 664, 666†
  relation to rhodoxanthin, 667
Lutein diepoxide, 666†
Lutein epoxide, 664, 666†
Lycoctonine, 1011*†, 1012
Lycodine, 970*†, 971†
Lyconnotine, 970*†, 971†
Lycopene, 642, 650, 651, 652†, 653†, 654, 655, 656†, 659, 663, 664†
  incorporation of mevalonic acid into, 647
  poly-*cis* form, 670
cis-Lycopene, 653†
Lycopene synthesis, genes affecting, 653, 654
Lycopersene, 650
Lycopodine, 970*†, 971†
Lycopodium alkaloids, 968†, 970*†
Lycorine, 955, 985†, 986*†
Lysergic acid, 1004, 1005*†, 1052
Lysine, 3, 17†, 25†, 26*†
  alternative pathway, 27
  α-aminoadipate pathway, 27*†
  →anabasine, 962, 963, 964*
  →bacterial cell wall, 429
  →quinolizidine alkaloids, 973, 975
Lysine decarboxylase, 724
Lysine-diaminopimelate quota, 25
Lysolecithin, 135, 150
  →lecithin, 147
L-α-Lysophosphatides, 133*
Lysophosphatidic acid, 126†
  acylation of, 126
  →phosphatidic acid, 126
Lysophosphatidyl ethanolamine, 154, 155
Lysophosphatidyl inositol →phosphatidyl inositol, 162
Lysozyme, 478, 514
  action on bacterial cell wall, 428
  secondary structure, 519
L-Lyxonic acid →ascorbic acid, 730
D-Lyxose, 446
L-Lyxose →ascorbic acid, 730

Macdougallin, 216*
Macrolide antibiotics, 1031, 1040, 1041
Macrolide lactone, 1030, 1031
Macrolides, 1032, 1034, 1041
Maculosidine, 787*
Magnamycin, 1041, 1042*
  A and B, 1041†
Magnesium divinylpheoporphyrin a_5, 263†, 267
Magnesium incorporating enzyme, 298
Magnesium pheoporphyrin, 270

Magnesium protoporphyrin
  →chlorophyll, 266
  monoester →chlorophyll, 266
Magnesium protoporphyrin IX, 263†, 266†
  →chlorophyll, 266
  esterification of, 266
  monomethyl ester, 263†
  →protochlorophyllide *a*, 267
Magnesium-vinyl pheoporphyrin a_5, 263*†, 267
Magnoline, 980*
Malate
  from glyoxalate, 340†
  from pyruvate, 337†, 338†
  →phosphoenolpyruvate, 340
Malic acid, in carotenoid synthesis, 666
Malic dehydrogenase, 338
Malic enzyme, 337, 338
Malonate
  →fatty acids, 108
  →fungal metabolites, 1034, 1035
Malonic acid →alkaloids, 998
Malonic semialdehyde →pantothenic acid, 695*, 697
Malononitrile, 617*
Malonyl CoA, 256
  condensation with acetyl CoA, 111
  →fatty acids, 110, 121
  →fungal metabolites, 1033, 1034, 1038
  →long-chain fatty acids, 109, 760†, 761*†
  →orsellinic acid, 1033*, 1034
  →palmitic acid, 112
Malonyl CoA decarboxylase, 111
Malonyl CoA pathway for fatty acid synthesis, 116
Malonyl transacylase, 114
Maltase, 340
Maltobionate, oxidation of, 447
Maltodextrins
  as glucosyl acceptors, 404, 410
  as glucosyl donors, 410
  as glycosyl donors, 409
Maltose, 370†, 377†, 391†, 445†
  analogues of, 370†, 392†
  as glucosyl acceptor, 404, 410
  as glycosyl acceptor, 408
  as glycosyl donor, 377, 383, 385
  energy of hydrolysis, 382
  oxidation of, 447
  transglucosylation from, 409
  →amylopectin, glycogen, 398
  →amylose, 398, 408
  →β-D-glucose-1-phosphate, 414
  →panose, 377
  →trisaccharide, 377
Maltose phosphorylase, 370, 377, 392, 414

Maltoside oligosaccharides, as glucosyl acceptors, 404
Maltosyl fructoside, 376†, 396†
Maltotetraose, 409†
as primer, 384
Maltotriose, 409†, 410†
as glucosyl acceptor, 404
as glucosyl donor, 409
as primer, 384
Malvalic acid, 122†
Mandelonitrile, 617*
D-Mandelonitrile β-gentiobioside, 434
Manganese, requirement in photosynthesis, 335, 336
Mannan, 346, 372†, 416†
D-Mannitol, 450
D-Mannitol-1-phosphate, 450
→D-sorbitol-6-phosphate, 451
D-Mannitol-6-phosphate, 450
Mannoheptulose, free, occurrence, 444
D-Mannonate, 445, 446, 449†
D-Mannonic acid, 447*
D-Mannose, 346, 446
free, 445†
occurrence, 444
in bacterial cell wall polysaccharides, 426, 427
phosphorylation of, 344, 345
→ascorbic acid, 728
→bacterial cell wall polysaccharides, 432
→disaccharide, 378
→glycosides, 434
D-Mannose-1-phosphate, 354†
→GDP-mannose, 357, 361
D-Mannose-6-phosphate, 345†, 346†, 347†
→GDP-mannose, 361
→D-mannose-1-phosphate, 345
Mannosides, 346
D-Mannuronic acid
in alginic acid, 424
polysaccharide containing, 364†
Manool, 864*, 865*†
Margaric acid, 121
Marrubium, 892
Matrine, 973*†
Matteucinol, 782*
C-Mavacurine chloride, 992*
Melatonin, 620†, 623*†
Melezitose, 376†, 395†
Melibiose, 394†, 418†
oxidation of, 447
→raffinose, 377
Melibiosyl-fructoside →levan, 378
Melilotic acid, 916
Mellein, 1056*†
Membranes of the endoplasmic reticulum, role in protein synthesis, 520

Menadione, 21
Δ³-Menthene, 846*
Menthofuran, 839*†, 855, 868
Menthol, 839*†, 840, 841, 842, 846*, 855
Menthol types of monoterpenes, 849
Menthone, 837*, 839*†, 841, 842, 846*, 855
Meprobamate →glucuronide, 594*
"MER-29", 222
2-Mercaptobenzothiazole →glucuronide, 595*
β-Mercaptoethanol amine
→CoA, 695
in CoA, 85, 86
β-Mercaptopyruvate, 618, 619*†
Mercapturic acid formation
mechanism of, 604*, 605*
zoological distribution of, 607
Mercapturic acids
pK values, 632
types of compounds forming, 602*, 603*
Mercapturic acid synthesis, 591, 601*
Mescaline, 609, 955, 956*†
Mesobilierhythrin, 275*
Mesobilirhodin, 275*, 276
Mesobilirubin, 275*, 288†
→urobilin, 287†
Mesobilirubinogen, 275*, 276, 288†, 289
→urobilins, 287†
Mesobiliverdin, 286, 287
diethyl ester, 287
Mesobiliviolin, 275*, 276
Meso-inositol
→other cyclitols, 452*
→scyllitol, 452*
Mesoporphyrin, 265
Mesoporphyrin IX, structural relationship with bile pigments, 274*, 276
Messenger RNA, 488, 489, 490, 494, 500, 511, 517, 521, 522, 538, 542
measurement of the half-life of, 15
polycistronic, 32
Messenger RNA production, stimulus for, 504
Metalloporphyrins, absorption spectrum, 252
Metals, detoxication as sulfides, 632
Metanephrine, 624
Metatabilactone, 1009*†
Meteloidine, 961*†
Methanol, 623
Methemoglobin, 285
N⁵,N¹⁰-Methenyl THFA, 710†
Methionine, 3, 17†, 18†, 19†, 20*†, 25
active, 7
as methyl donor, 1039
as the source of thiol sulfur, 7
in biological methylation, 620, 621, 622

Methionine—(cont.)
  in detoxication, 591
  in C-methylation, 784
  in methylation of bases in RNA, 572, 573
  →actinomycin, 1040
  →ajmaline, 1003
  →alkaloids, 955, 1012
  →biotin, 720
  →branched-chain sugars, 1040, 1041
  →choline, 140
  →cysteine, 8*†
  →fungal metabolites, 1053
  →methyl p-methoxycinnamate, 913, 914
  →novobiocin, novobiose, 1040
  →penicillic acid, 1034
  →phenolic plant products, 768
  →β-sitosterol, 880
  →stigmasterol, 882
  →vitamin B₁₂, 712, 713
Methionine biosynthesis, requirement of
    vitamin B₁₂ coenzymes, 718
Methionine sulfoxide, 11
  →biotin, 720
Methionine transadenosylase, 7
Methostenol, 878
  →cholesterol, 216, 217*†, 221†, 222*
m-Methoxycinnamic acid →quercetin, 772
2-Methoxyestrone, 620
3-Methoxy-4-hydroxy phenylpyruvic acid,
    934
6-Methoxysterigmatocystin, 1044†, 1045*†
5-Methoxytryptamine, 623, 957*†
2-Methyl adenine, 571*, 572*
  in sRNA, 497
  in vitamin B₁₂, 714
N'-Methyl adenine, 571*, 572*
N⁶-Methyl adenine, 571*, 572*
4-Methylaminobutanal →nicotine, 966
Methylaminocytidine, in sRNA, 497
2-Methyl-4-amino-5-hydroxymethyl pyrimi-
    dine, in thiamine, 680
3-Methylaminomethylindole   →gramine,
    957*†, 958
Methylamylpyrrole, 303, 304
N-Methyl anhalonidine, 975, 976
Methyl anisate, 909*
    demethylation and hydroxylation, 914,
    915
Methylation, 619
    as detoxication reaction, 591, 592
    biological, types of compounds under-
    going, 620, 621*
    enzymic mechanism of, 620
    zoological distribution of, 625
C-Methylation, 8
N-Methylation, 8
S-Methylation, 8

5-Methylbenzimidazole →B₁₂ vitamers, 715
3-Methylbut-2-enal,   origin   in   terpenes,
    834*
3-Methyl-Δ²-butenol, 843*
3-Methyl-Δ³-1-butenol, 843*
3-Methyl-2-butenyl fragment, in transfer
    of isoprenoid residue, 785
α-Methylbutyric acid
  →fatty acids, 121
  →tropane alkaloids, tiglic acid, 961*†
2-Methylbutyric acid, 1043†
Methyl caffeate, 914, 915*
Methylcholanthrene, 508, 1066*
14α-Methyl-Δ⁸-cholesten-3β-6α diol, 216*
4α-Methyl-Δ⁷-cholestenol, 216
  →cholesterol, 216, 217*†, 221†, 222*
4α-Methyl-Δ⁸-cholestenol, 216
  →cholesterol, 216, 217*†, 221†, 222*
4α-Methyl-Δ⁷-cholestenol, 878
2-Methylchromone, precursors of, 790*†
Methyl cinnamate, 909*
β-Methylcinnamic acid, glycine conjuga-
    tion, 600*
Methyl p-coumarate, 912*, 913, 915*, 916
  →methyl p-methoxycinnamate, 913, 914,
    915*
β-Methylcrotonaldehyde
    isoprenoid unit building block in caro-
    tenoid synthesis, 645
    origin in terpenes, 834*
β-Methylcrotonic acid, 946, 948
  →carotene, 645
    in terpene biosynthesis, 835
    origin in terpenes, 834*
  →phytol, 866, 872
  →pulegone, 852*
  →resin acids, 872
  →rubber, 842†
β-Methylcrotonyl-CoA, 646, 946
β-Methylcrotonyl CoA carboxylase, effect
    of biotin on, 722
3-Methylcyclohexanone,   formation   by
    chemical degradation of pulegone, 852
5-Methylcytosine, 548, 571*, 572*
N-Methylcytisine, 975
2-O-Methyl-deoxyaldose, 366
Methyldeoxycytidylic acid, deamination of,
    77
5-Methyldeoxyuridine, 78
Methyl donor, 8
24-Methylene-cycloartanol, 887*
3-Methylene-indolenine →gramine, 957*†,
    958
1-Methylenepyrrolizidine, 971, 972*
Methylenetetrahydrofolic acid →serine, 141
N⁵,N¹⁰-methylene THFA, 6*
  →methionine methyl, 19, 20

3-Methylene-7,11,15-trimethyl-1-hexa-
decene, 865*
Methyl-D-galacturonate, 728
Methylgeraniolene side chain in mycelianamide, 852
Methyl-α-D-glucopyranoside, oxidation of,
447
2-O-Methyl-D-glucose→maltose analogues,
392
6-O-Methyl-D-glucose→maltose analogues,
392
3-O-Methyl-β-D-glucose-1-phosphate →
maltose analogues, 392
Methylglucoside, 384
trans-β-Methylglutaconate →cholesterol,
208, 209*†
β-Methylglutaconyl-CoA, 646
α-N-Methylglutamic-γ-aldehyde →tropane
alkaloids, 959†, 960*†
MethylGMP, 497
Methyl group donors, 1039
for methionine, 19
C-Methyl groups in fungal metabolites,
origin of, 1025, 1038
N-Methyl groups in fungal metabolites,
origin of, 1025
O-Methyl groups in fungal metabolites,
origin of, 1025, 1038
Methyl group, transfer of, 7
Methyl groups, reversible formation of, 6
Methylguanine, in sRNA, 497
7-Methylguanine, 572*
N'-Methylguanine, 571*, 572*
N²-Methylguanine, 572*
2-Methyl-heptanedione-3,6, 853
Methylheptenol, 841
Methylheptenone, 838, 841
effect on carotene synthesis, 658
1-Methylhistamine, 621*, 622
S-Methyl homocysteine →methionine, 18,
20*†
2-Methyl-3-hydroxy-4-carboxy-5-hydroxy-
methyl-pyridine, 724
4-Methyl-5(2-hydroxyethyl)-thiazole, in
thiamine, 680
β-Methyl-β-hydroxyglutaric acid, in carotenoid synthesis, 645
6-Methyl-7-hydroxy-8-ribityllumazine, 703
2-Methylhypoxanthine →vitamin B₁₂,
714
1-Methyl IMP, 497
Methyl isoferulate, 913*, 914†, 915*, 916
Methylisopropylbenzoic acid derivatives,
832
Methylmalonyl CoA, 22, 109†
→succinyl CoA, effect of biotin on,
722

Methyl p-methoxycinnamate, 909*†, 910†,
911†, 912†, 913†, 914†, 915*, 916,
920†, 929
C¹⁴-labeling, 920*
distributions of activity after formation
from D-glucose-1-C¹⁴ and D-glucose-6-
C¹⁴, 911*
metabolism in Lentinus lepideus, 909
metabolism of, 912
Methyl p-methoxycinnamate formation,
connection with aromatic amino acids
biogenesis, 911, 912
N-Methylnicotinamide, secretion of, 633
O-Methylnorbelladine, 985†, 986*, 987*,
988
α-N-Methylornithine
→hygrine, 959
→hyoscyamine, 959, 960*†
→N-methylpyrrolidine ring of nicotine,
964, 965*†
6-Methyl-1,3,10,11,12-pentahydroxy-
naphthacene-2-carboxamide →tetra-
cyclines, 1031, 1032*
Methylpentose-containing polysaccharide,
422†
Methylpherases, 7
Methylphloroacetophenone →usnic acid,
783*
Methyl-n-propylmaleimide, 270
2-Methyl-2-propyl-1,3-propanediol dicarba-
mate →glucuronide, 594*
3-Methylpyrene, 1075
N-Methyl-pyridinium, 619*†, 621*
N-Methyl-Δ'-pyrrolinium salt
→hygrine, 958*, 959
→nicotine, 965*†
Methylsalicylate →sulfate, 614
6-Methylsalicylic acid, 755*†, 756, 764,
909, 1034†, 1056
→patulin, 1037*, 1038
4α-Methyl sterols, 879
5-Methyl tetrahydrofolate-homocysteine
transferase, 718
Methyl-THFA, 20, 22
N⁵-Methyl-THFA→methionine, 19, 20, 21,
22
Methyl-THFA oxidase, 21
5'-Methylthioadenosine, 8†
2-Methyl thiouracil, 620†, 621*
Methyl transfer, 682
Methyltransferases, 622, 624
N-Methyltryptamine, 1003*, 1004
→alkaloids, 955, 956*†
2-Methyltryptophan →alkaloids, 995
5-Methyluracil, 571*, 572*
5-Methyluridine, 78
5-O-Methyl (+) vibo-inosose, 452*†

Methymycin, 1041†, 1042*
Methysticin, 747*
Metmyoglobin, 284
Mevaldic acid, 214
Mevalonate
→fungal metabolites, 1030
→β-sitosterol, 882
→squalene, 210*†, 211
→sterol sapogenins, 226
→stigmasterol, 226
Mevalonic acid, 649, 650, 751*†, 843*, 845, 854, 855
→alkaloids, 976, 997, 999*, 1000, 1001*, 1004, 1006, 1010, 1012, 1013
→carotenes, 647, 648, 650, 655
→cholesterol, 209, 843†, 883
→chrysanthemum carboxylic acid, 855
→digitoxigenin, 884, 885
→gibberellic acid, 869, 870*
→helminthosporal, 862*
→ipomeamarone, 861, 862
→phenolic plant products, 768
→phytol, 866
→pleuromutilin, 872*†, 873
→rubber, 945*†, 946, 947*, 948
significance in terpenoid biogenesis, 890, 891, 892
source of isoprenoid units, 784, 785*
→soyasapogenol A, 888
→squalene, 214, 650, 879
→stigmasterol, 881, 882
→terpenes, 843†, 844*†
→thujone, α-pinene, 853
Mevalonic kinase, 209
Mevalonic acid lactone
→fungal metabolites, 1026, 1035, 1046, 1047*, 1048, 1051, 1052
→monoterpenes, 850, 851
→rosenonolactone, 868, 869*
→tricothecin, 861*
Mevalonic acid-5-phosphate →rubber, 948
Mevalonic acid pyrophosphate →rubber, 945*†, 948
Microsomes, 522
Milk proteins, association with cell membranes, 520
Mimosine, 966*, 971†
Mirene, 867*, 871
Miropinic acid, 871
Mitomycin, 548
Mitraphylline, 994*†, 996†
Modulating triplets, 506
(+) Mollisacacidin, 819
Monascin, 1035†, 1036*, 1058
Monascorubrin, 1036*, 1058†
Monoacetylhydrazine, acetylation, 627*†
Monoazahemochromogen, 281

Monobenzoyl-L ornithine, N^{2-} or N^{5-}, 608
3,4-Monodehydro-carotene, 671
Monoenoic acids, 118†
β-Monoglyceride →α,β-diglyceride, 129
Monoglycerides, 106*
α-Monoglycerides →triglycerides, 129
Monoglyceride transacylase, 129
Monomethylaminoethanol, phosphorylation of, 143
Monomethylethanolamine, 142
α-Monopalmitin →triglyceride, 129
Monophosphoinositides, 134*, 136, 137, 159†, 160†, 161†, 184
alternative pathway, 161†, 162†
Mono-phosphonucleotide sugars, in sugar transfer, 437, 438
Monophosphoramidate, in phosphate transfer, 354
Monophosphorylhistidine, in phosphate transfer, 354
Monosaccharides, 359†
→disaccharides, 371
hydrogenation of, 449
phosphorylation of, 343
reducing, 444†, 445†
occurrence, 444
Monosialoganglioside, 175, 176
Monovinyl-monohydroxyethyl deuteroporphyrin IX, 264
Monoterpenes, 830, 832, 842, 844†, 845†, 850†, 851, 852
acyclic, 835, 839†, 840, 846*
bicyclic, 846*, 849*†
cyclic, 847, 848†
cyclopentanoid, 845
frequency of occurrence of, 841
in the mint species, 839*†
ionic mechanisms in the biogenesis of, 849
irregular, 847*
monocyclic, 833, 846*, 849*†
of the Labiatae family, 837*, 838
peppermint types, 839†
radical mechanisms in the biogenesis of, 850
spearmint types, 839†
tricyclic, 846*
Monoterpene hypothesis, of alkaloid biogenesis, 999, 1000, 1001, 1003
Montanine, 987*, 988
Moreacol, 763
Morindadiol, 770*
Morphine, 955, 977*†, 978†, 979†
Mucins, 173, 436†
Mucoitin sulfate, 439
Mucolipids, 169†, 173†, 174, 175
Mucopeptides, muramic acid containing, 429†

Mucopolysaccharides, S-free, 424†
Mucoproteins, 173
Multicistronic operons, 506
Multiflorine, 973*†, 975†
Muramic acid, 427*
Muramic acid-amino acid derivatives, 368
Muramic acid-containing mucopeptides, 429†
Muscarine, 1014*
Muscopyridine, 967*†, 968†
Mutant, microbial, 2
Mutarotation, of maltose, 392
Mutases, 345, 368
MVA-kinase, 948
MVA-5-phosphate, 948
Mycaminose, 1040*, 1041†
Mycarose, 1040*, 1041†
Mycelianamide, 852, 853*†, 1046*†, 1047*†, 1053, 1055
Mycocerosic acid, 122
Mycolic acid, 122
Mycophenolic acid, 767*, 768†, 784, 787, 852, 853*†, 1038, 1039†, 1040*, 1046†, 1047*†, 1056
Myelin lipids, 182
Myoglobin, 263†, 277, 279, 281, 284, 285
  →biliverdin, 278, 281
  ferryl complex of, 284
  three-dimensional model of, 480
Myo-inositol, 725*
  →galactoside, 434
  →hemicellulose, 422
  →monophosphoinositide, 160, 161
  →pectin, 423
Myo-inositol-1-phosphate, 137
Myo-inositol-2-phosphate, 137
Myo-inosose-2, 161
Myokinase, 79
Myosin, 511
Myrcene, 841, 846*, 850*†
  →cyclic monoterpenes, 848
Myristoleic acid, 117†
Myrobalans, 802

NAD, 690†
NAN, 173, 174†, 437†, 438†
  in gangliosides, 176, 177
NAN aldolase, 174
NAN-9-phosphate →NAN, 437†, 438†
Napharamine, 1009*, 1010
Naphthalene
  derivatives of, 770†
  →mercapturic acid, 604, 605
  →premercapturic acid, 605, 606
  premercapturic acid of, 606*†, 607*†

Naphthoquinones, 770†
  in fungi, 1031*†
Naphthylamine
  detoxication of, 630
  →sulfamate, 612, 615
2-Naphthylamine metabolism, phosphate conjugation in, 631
Naphthyl-mercapturic acid, 606*, 607*
2-Naphthylsulfamate, 612†
Narcotine, 955, 982*
Narwedine, 987*†, 988†
Necic acids, 971, 972
Neoabietic acid, 865*†
Neo-methymycin, 1041
Neophytadiene, 865*
Neoxanthin, 664
Nepetalactone, 845
Nerol, 846
  →terpenes, 836, 840
Nerolidol, 210†, 833, 856*, 857, 848
  →alkaloids, 1010*, 1011
  →bisabolene, 858*
Nerolidyl pyrophosphate, 858
Nerolidyl-X →squalene, 210, 212*†
Nerol pyrophosphate, 945*†, 949
  cis, 949
  →rubber, 949
Nervon, 170
Nervonic acid, 170
Neuraminic acid, 173, 436*
Neurokeratin, 183
Neurosporaxanthin, 659
Neurosporene, 651, 652, 653†, 655, 656†, 659, 660, 664†
  all-trans form, 670
  cis form, 653†
  poly-cis form, 670
NGN, 437
Niacin, 682†, 683*†, 684
  →pyridine nucleotides, 689*, 690
  relationship to tryptophan, 730
Nicotinamide
  interconversion of nicotinic acid and, 693
  methylation of, 8
  role in DPN synthesis, 83
  →NMN, 81*
  →pyrimidine alkaloids, 962
  →pyridine nucleotides, 689*, 690
Nicotinamide-containing coenzymes, 81†
Nicotinamide mononucleotide, 81*†, 83, 689*†, 690†, 714
Nicotinamide mononucleotide pyrophosphorylase, 689, 690
Nicotinamide ribonucleoside, 83†
Nicotinamide riboside, 689*†, 690
Nicotinamide riboside kinase, 689, 691

Nicotinamide riboside phosphorylase, 689, 690

Nicotinamide ribotide, 689*†, 690†

Nicotine, 955, 961†, 962†, 963*†
→nornicotine, 966
pyrrolidine ring of, 964, 965*†

Nicotinic acid, 682†, 683*†, 684, 690
biosynthesis in animals and some microorganisms, 962*†
biosynthesis in higher plants, 962†, 963*†
excretion as ornithuric acid, 608
glycine conjugation, 600*
methylation of, 625
→DPN, 81
→glucuronide, 594*
→nicotinamide, 693
→pyridine alkaloids, 961, 963*

Nicotinic acid mononucleotide, 81, 82*†
relationship to vitamin B₁₂, 731
→vitamin B₁₂, 713, 714

Nitrite, reduction of, 11

Nitrobenzaldehyde, m- and p-→acetamidobenzoic acids, 626*

5-Nitrobenzimidazole →B₁₂ vitamers, 715

p-Nitrobenzoic acid, arginine conjugation, 632

o-Nitrobenzyl glucuronide, 592

Nitrobutane →mercapturic acid, 603*

Nitroparaffin →mercapturic acid, 603*

o-Nitrophenyl-β-D-galactoside, as glycosyl donor, 378

p-Nitrophenyl sulfate, as sulfate donor, 614

β-Nitropropionic acid, 1055

o-Nitrotoluene, detoxication of, 592

NMN, 81*†

N⁺MN, 689*†, 690†

N⁺MN pyrophosphorylase, 689, 690

Non-cyclic photophosphorylation, 330, 336
→adrenaline, 620, 621, 622
→alkaloids, 982*, 983
methylation of, 622, 624

Noradrenaline N-methyl transferase, 622

19-Norandrostenedione, 233

Norbelladine, 957, 985†, 986*†

d-Nor-Ψ-ephedrine, 956*†

Norherqueinone, 1030

Norlaudanosoline, 977*†, 978*, 979, 981

Nornicotine, 966

Norpinic acid, 853

Norpluviine, 985†, 986*†

Norprodigiosin, 303*

Notatin, 445, 448

Noviose moiety, in novobiocin, 1039

Novobiocin, 1039*†, 1040†
aminocoumarin ring system of, 1052†, 1053*†

Novobiocin—(cont.)
influence on bacterial cell wall synthesis, 431

Novobiose, in novobiocin, 1039

N⁺RP, 689*†, 690†, 692

NRPH →DPNH, 691

N⁺R Pyrophosphorylase, 689, 690

Nucleic acids
enzymic methylation of, 571, 572, 573
general properties, 540
primary chemical structure, 539
secondary structure, 540
synthesis of mixed polymers, 546

Nucleohistones, 541

Nucleoprotamines, 541

Nucleoproteins, 542

Nucleoside diphosphate, phosphate exchange, 559

Nucleoside diphosphate aldose, 358†

Nucleoside diphosphate analogs, polymerization of, 556

Nucleoside diphosphate derivatives of sugars, epimerization of, 359

Nucleoside diphosphate glucose →amylose, amylopectin, glycogen, 398

Nucleoside-diphosphate-glucose transglycosylase, 402

Nucleoside diphosphate glycosides, 369, 386, 387

Nucleoside diphosphate glycoside transglycosylase, 386, 387

Nucleoside diphosphate hexosamine sulfate →sulfopolysaccharides, 441

Nucleoside diphosphate monosaccharide, 384, 385

Nucleoside diphosphate oligosaccharides, 368

Nucleoside diphosphates, 356, 544

Nucleoside diphosphate sugars, 355†
decarboxylation of, 364
dehydrogenation of, 363
epimerization of, 358

Nucleoside diphosphate transferases, 369

Nucleoside diphosphate transglycosylases, 369

Nucleoside diphosphokinase, 337

Nucleoside kinases, 70

Nucleoside 5′-monophosphates, 544

Nucleoside-5′-phosphate, 69*†

Nucleoside phosphorylases, 68, 70, 77, 83, 370

Nucleosides, 370†
chemical structure, 539
configuration of carbon 1, 68*
di- and triphosphate derivatives of, 78†
from purines, 68†
→nucleotides, 69

Nucleoside triphosphates, 544
   as phosphoryl donors, 79, 80
   →nucleoside diphosphate aldose, 358
5′-Nucleotidase, 689, 691
Nucleotide bases in sRNA, unusual, 497
Nucleotide codewords, assignment to amino
   acids, 493
Nucleotide glycosides, 368
Nucleotide heteropolymers, 556†
Nucleotide homopolymers, 556†
5′-Nucleotide precursors of RNA, 545
Nucleotide pyrophosphatase, 689, 691
Nucleotide pyrophosphorylases, 69, 70, 77
Nucleotides, 48†, 61†, 69*†, 80†
   as precursors for nucleic synthesis, 544
   chemical structure, 539
   dephosphorylation of, 544
   →deoxyribonucleotides, 58
5′-Nucleotides, role in nucleic acid syn-
   thesis, 544
Nucleotide sequences in RNA, complementary to those of DNA template, 567
Nucleotide sugars, 51†, 94†
Nucleotide "X", linear 3′-5′ polymer of,
   538
Nupharidine, 975, 1009*, 1010

Obscurines, α- and β-, 970*†, 971†
Ochre, 493
Ocimene, 841, 848, 850*†
Δ⁸, ¹¹-Octadecadienoic acid, 119
α⁹, ¹²-Octadecadienoic acid, 119
6,9-Octadecadienoyl-CoA, 120†
Δ⁹-Octadecenoic acid, 119
Δ¹¹-Octadecenoic acid, 119
11,12-Octadecenoic acid, 114†
Octahydrolycopene, 653†
Octanoate
   →cholesterol, 208
   →long-chain fatty acids, 109
Octanoic thiokinase, 599
Octanoyl CoA →fatty acids, 110
D-Octulose-1,8-diphosphate, 349†
Octulose-8-phosphate, in transaldolase-
   catalyzed reaction, 325, 326
OESTR, see also ESTR
Okenone, 663, 664
Olean-13(18)-ene, 876, 877*
Oleanolic acid, 874*, 889
Oleic acid, 117†, 119†
   desaturation of, 119
   →biotin, 720
   →linoleic acid, 120
Oleoresin, 863
Oleyl CoA, 120
Oleyl methyl ketone, 762*†

Oligodeoxynucleotides, 571
Oligodeoxyribonucleotide transferase, 552
Oligo-1,4 →1,4-glucan transferase, 379,
   410
Oligo-isoprenoids, 949
Oligoribonucleotide primers, 564
Oligoribonucleotides, 538, 558
   phosphorolysis of, 558, 559
Oligosaccharides, 368†, 369†, 392†, 396†
   as glucosyl acceptors, 404
   as glycosyl donors, 379
   hybrid, 380†
   →sialyloligosaccharides, 375
Olivacine, 1002*†, 1004†
Olivetoric acid, 765*†, 766
Olivil, 793*
"One gene-one enzyme" hypothesis, 36
Onic acids, 445, 449†
α-Onocerin, 876*†
Operator genes, 505
Operon, 506
Operon hypothesis, 30, 31, 32
Opium, and related alkaloids, 977*†
Opsopyrrole dicarboxylic acid, 259
(+)-Orientaline. 979*, 980
Ornithine, 3, 11†, 12*†
   activation of enzymes by, 360
   in riboflavin synthesis, 699
   →citrulline, 72, 73*
   →hygrine, 959
   →nicotine, 962, 965
   →pyrrolidine ring of nicotine, 964, 965*†
   →pyrrolizidine alkaloids, 971, 972*
   →stachydrine, 958
   →tropane alkaloids, 959, 960*
Ornithine-arginine interconversion, 13
Ornithine conjugation, enzymic mechanism
   of, 608*
Ornithine cycle, 13
Ornithine-δ-transaminase, 12, 13
Ornithine transcarbamylase, 14
Ornithuric acid,
   pK value, 632
   secretion of, 633
Ornithuric acid synthesis, 591, 592, 608*,
   609, 610
   zoological distribution of, 608
Orotate, 74*†
Orotic acid, 47*, 49, 71*
   →nucleic acid pyrimidines, 74
   →pyrimidines, 71
Orotidine, 49
Orotidine-5′-phosphate, 49, 75*†
Orotidine-5′-phosphate decarboxylase, 75
Orotidine-5′-phosphate pyrophosphorylase,
   75
Orotidylic acid, 49

Orsellinic acid, 764*†, 766, 768, 769*†,
    779, 1032*†, 1033†, 1034†, 1035,
    1037*†, 1043, 1056, 1057
Osthol, 830, 831*
Ovalbumin, 486
Oxalacetate, 3
    from phosphoenolpyruvate, 336†
    from pyruvate, 337†, 338†
    →alkaloids, 1008
    →fatty acids, 107
    →phosphoenolpyruvate, 340
Oxalacetate-synthesizing   enzyme,   337,
    338
Oxalacetic acid, product of fungal meta-
    bolism, 910
Oxalacetic acid decarboxylase, effect of
    biotin on, 722
Oxidation reactions, 95
Oxidation-reduction reactions, 450
Oxidative metabolism, 792
α,β-Oxidoketones, 777
Oxidoreductase, 934
Oxido-reductions, involving polyols, 451
19-Oxoandrostenedione →estrone, 233,
    234*†
α-Oxoglutarate, 257
1-Oxo-1,2,3,4-tetrahydro-β-carboline,   990,
    991*
Oxybiotin, 720, 721*
Oxyheme, 277
Oxyhemochromogen, 280*†
Oxynervon, 170
Oxynervonic acid, 170
Oxypeucedanin, 788*
Oxypseudoheme, 277, 282*†
Oxytetracycline, 1031†, 1032*†, 1039†

PABA, 706†, 707
    CoA derivative of, 707, 708*†
    in folic acid, 704, 707
PABA-Glutamate, 705, 706, 707
    proposed pathway for the synthesis of,
    708*†
Palade granules, 508
Palitantin, 1035†, 1036*, 1056†, 1057*†,
    1058
Palmitate, 110†, 111†, 114†
    →cholesterol, 208
Palmitic acid, 109†, 110†, 112†, 115†
    in lecithin, 147
    →palmitoleic acid, 117, 118
    →triglyceride, 128
    →cis-vaccenic acid, 118
Palmitic aldehyde, 166†, 169†
    →sphingosine, 166, 167
Palmitoleic acid, 117†, 119, 121†

Palmityl CoA
    →ceramide, 167
    →sphingosine, 166, 167
    →stearyl CoA, 117
Panose, 377†, 396†, 409†, 410†
Pantetheine, 86, 694, 695*†, 698
    in fatty acid synthesis, 116
Pantetheine-4′-PO₄, 694, 695*†
Pantoic acid, 694†, 695*†, 696, 697
    →pantothenic acid, 85
Pantonine →pantothenic acid, 695*, 696
Pantothenate →δ-aminolevulinic acid, 255
Pantothenic acid, 694†, 695*†, 696, 697†,
    698, 731†
    in CoA, 85, 86
    origin of, 695*†
    structure of, 694, 695*
    →CoA, 695*
Pantothenic   acid-cysteine   decarboxylase,
    698
Pantothenic acid-4′-PO₄, 694, 695*†
Pantothenyl cysteine, 694, 695*†, 698
Pantoyladenylate, 697
Pantoyl lactone →pantothenic acid, 694, 696
PAP, 10*†, 11
pApA, 558, 559, 570
pApApA, 558
pApApApU, 559
Papaverine, 977*†
PAPS, 10*†, 87*†, 439*†, 440*†, 612, 613*†,
    614†, 615
    in detoxication reactions, 592
    reduction of, 11
    →sulfatide, 173
Palmitoleyl CoA →cis-vaccenic acid, 118
Paracotoin, 747*
    precursor of, 747
Paramylon, 416†
Paranephrine, 624
Patulin, 756*†, 768, 1037†, 1038*†, 1056*†
pCpCpA sequence, in sRNA, 498
Pectic substances, 364†, 420†, 421†, 422†
Pectin, 373†
Pectinic acids, 423†
Pectins, 420, 421, 422†, 423†
Peganine, 1008*†, 1009†
ψ-Pelletierine, 966*†
Pellotine, 975
Penicillic acid, 1033†, 1034†, 1035, 1037*†
Penicillin, 1055
    influence on bacterial cell wall synthesis,
    430
Penicillin N, 28, 29
Penicillinase, 507
Penniclavine, 1005*
Pentachloronitrobenzene →mercapturic
    acid, 602*

Pentacyclic triterpenes, 888*†
5,7,3′,4′,5′-Pentahydroxy-flavan-3,4-diol, 816*, 817
Pentalysine, 516
Pentapeptide, from bacterial cell wall, 430
Pentitols, 450†
Pentonic acids, 447, 448†
Pentosans, 364†, 419†
Pentose cycle, 51
Pentose family of amino acids, 29†
Pentose phosphate
  nonoxidative pathway, 52, 53, 56
  oxidative pathway, 51, 56
Pentose phosphate cycle, 321, 348, 351
Pentose phosphate isomerase, 53
Pentose phosphate pathway, 2, 29, 32
Pentose phosphates, 51†, 344†
  equilibrium between, 324, 325
Pentoses, 359†, 449†
  free, occurrence, 444
Pentosuria, 444, 446, 449, 450
Pepsinogen, secondary structure, 519
Peptidases, in mercapturic acid formation, 605
Peptide bond formation, 489, 512, 513, 514
  acquisition of secondary and tertiary structure, 517, 518
  events subsequent to, 516
  fate of the ribosome, 517, 518
  fate of sRNA and mRNA, 517, 518
  possible mechanism for, 513*
  release of the peptide chain, 517
Peptide chains, nascent, 514, 516
Peptide conjugation, 630
Peptide synthetase, 491, 512, 514
Peptidyl-RNA complexes, 511, 517
Perillaldehyde, 837*, 838, 841
Perinaphthenone, 1030*
Perlatolic acid, 765*
Permeases, 505
Pernicious anema, 277
Peroxidase-oxidase, 683, 686
Peroxidases, 248, 263†, 277, 934, 936
Perseitol, 450
Perylene quinone, 792
Petaline, 981*
Peucenin, 785*
Phellandrene, 837*, 838, 841
Phellandric acid, glycine conjugation, 600*
Phenanthrene → premercapturic acid, 606
Phenazine → B₁₂ vitamers, 715
Phenazine-1-carboxamide, 1053*, 1054†
Phenazine methosulfate, 167
Phenazine pigments, microbial, 1054
Phenol
  detoxication of, 590
  detoxication in insects, 598

Phenol—(cont.)
  →glucuronide, 594*
  →potassium phenyl sulfate, 611
Phenolase, 913, 914
Phenol-dehydrogenase, 931
Phenol β-glucoside, 598†
Phenolic biosynthesis, acetate hypothesis, 758, 761, 764, 769, 770, 771
Phenolic plant products
  1-arylpropane-derived, 753*†
  biosynthesis of particular groups of compounds, 755
  chemical-genetical approach to biosynthesis, 745
  cyclization, 752*†
  earlier studies on biosynthesis, 745
  extension of acyl residues by C₂ units, 760†
  phenylpropane-derived, 752*†
Phenolic rings in fungal metabolites, origin of, 1025
Phenol oxidase, 934, 936
Phenols, 755†
  methylation of, 619
  polyhydric, orientation of methylation, 623
  sulfate conjugation of, 611, 612, 613
Phenol sulfokinase, 614, 615
Phenothiazine, peptide conjugate of, 630
Phenoxyacetic acid, hydroxylation of, 791
Phenylacetate → phenylacetylglutamine, 610, 611
Phenylacetic acid
  excretion as ornithuric acid, 608
  glycine conjugation, 600*
  →glucuronide, 594*
  glutamine conjugation, 609
  →tropic acid, 959, 967*
Phenylacetyl-AMP → phenylacetyl-glutamine, 610
Phenylacetyl-CoA
  in detoxication reactions, 592
  →phenylacetylglutamine, 610, 611
Phenylacetylglutamine, 609*†, 610†
Phenylacetylglycine, 611
Phenylalanine, 3, 32†, 33*†, 748†, 749*†, 907†, 908*†
  a pteridine cofactor for the oxidation to tyrosine, 709
  →alkaloids, 955, 956*, 984*, 985, 986*, 1004
  →cocaine, 960
  →cyanidin, 806
  →gliotoxin, 1053
  →lignin, 749, 750, 928*, 929
  →quercetin, 772, 773
  →tropic acid, 959

Phenylalanine hydroxylase, 485
γ-Phenyl-α-amino-butyric acid, acetylation of, 626
Phenylbutadiene, 1073
Phenylcoumarane derivatives, 930
S-Phenylcysteine, acetylation of, 626
α-Phenylenediamine →B₁₂ vitamers, 715, 716
1-Phenylethyltetrahydroisoquinoline, hydroxylated, 984*†, 985†
Phenyl-α-glucoside, as glycosyl donor, 378
Phenylglucuronide, 590
Phenylglycine, N-acetylation, 627
Phenyl hydrogen sulphate, 611*, 613*
Phenyllactic acid →cinnamic acid, 750
1-Phenylpropane precursors, compounds derived from, 772*
Phenylpropane unit in flavonoids, 247*
Phenylpropanoid precursors →flavonoid compounds, 772, 773*
Phenyl pyruvate →phenylalanine, 33*†, 34†
Phenylpyruvic acid
  →aromatic amino acids, 907†, 908*†
  →cinnamic acid, 750
  →flavonols, 806
  →tropic acid, 959, 961*
Phenylpyruvic oligophrenia, 610
Phenylsulfamic acid, 612†, 613*
Phenyl sulfate, potassium, 611†
α-Phenyltetralins, 793
Pheophytins, 269
Phlean, 417†
Phlobaphene, 815
Phlobatannins, 817, 818, 820
Phloretin β-glucoside, 434
Phlorizin, 434, 776†
  effect on UDP-glucose transglycosylase, 406
Phloroacetophenones, C-methylated, 783
Phloroglucinol derivatives, C-dimethylation of, 782
Phosphatase, 5, 6, 391, 392, 445
  in formation of L-arabinose, 346
  prostatic, 693
  two different kinds from spinach, 324
Phosphate conjugation, 631
Phosphate-diester lipids, 133*, 142†
Phosphate-monoester lipid, 133, 142
Phosphate transfer, intramolecular, 345
Phosphate-triester lipids, 134, 135*, 164, 165
Phosphatidal compounds, 134*
Phosphatidase A, 135, 136, 146, 147, 148
Phosphatidase C, 136, 150, 161
Phosphatidase D, 136, 152, 167
Phosphatides, 183
  involvement of inositol in the synthesis of, 726

Phosphatidic acid, 123†, 124*†, 126†, 128†, 133, 142, 726
  occurrence in tissue, 127
  two pathways of biosynthesis, 127
  →CMP-Pdig, 161
  →α,β-diglycerides, 128
  →monophosphoinositide, 160
  →phosphoglycerides, 140
Phosphatidic acid cycle, 128
Phosphatidic acid-inositol transferase, 161
Phosphatidic acid phosphatase, 127, 128, 145
Phosphatidopeptides, 164, 178, 182, 183, 184†, 185
Phosphatidyl choline, 127*, 134, 141†, 149†, 150†, 151†
Phosphatidyl compounds, alternative pathways of biosynthesis, 151
Phosphatidyl ethanolamine, 89†, 127*, 134, 141†, 145†, 151†, 153†, 154†, 155†, 156, 183
  from egg, 135
  stepwise methylation of, 149
  →lecithin, 148, 149
  →phosphatidyl serine, 157
Phosphatidyl ethanolamine N-methyltransferase, 141, 150
Phosphatidyl glycerols, 134*, 136, 158†, 159†
Phosphatidyl glycerophosphate, 158†
Phosphatidyl inositol, 136, 137, 138, 159†, 160†
1-Phosphatidyl-L-myo-inositol, 138
1-Phosphatidyl-L-myo-inositol-4,5-diphosphate, 138
1-Phosphatidyl-L-myo-inositol-4-phosphate, 138
Phosphatidyl myo-inositol mannosides, 138, 139*
Phosphatidyl serine, 133*, 134, 141†, 151†, 154, 155, 156†, 157†, 158†, 183
Phosphatidyl serine synthetase, 157
3′-Phosphoadenosine-5′-phosphate, 10*†, 11, 613†, 614
3′-Phosphoadenosine-5′-phosphosulfate, 10*†, 87*†, 439*†, 440*†, 612, 613*†, 614†
  in detoxication reactions, 592
  →sulfatide, 173
Phosphoaldose-1-pyrophosphates, 368†
5-Phosphodeoxyribosylpyrophosphate, 57
Phosphodiesterases, 48, 402
3′,5′-Phosphodiester bonds, 539*, 540*
  in DNA, 546, 572
Phosphodihydroxyacetone, in photosynthesis, 323*
Phosphodoxin, 331

Phosphoenolpyruvate
   activator of ADP-glucose synthesis, 358
   from fatty acids, 341†
   from pyruvate, 337†, 338†
   in protein synthesis, 487
   in regeneration of ATP, 382
   role in lignin biosynthesis, 930
   →N-acyl neuraminic acid-9-P, 174
   →alkaloids, 1000
   →aromatic amino acids, 907, 908*
   →glucose-6-phosphate, 339†
   →KDO, 433
   →lignin, 921, 922
   →muramic acid, 429
   →NAN, 437
   →oxalacetate, 336
   →phenylalanine, 32, 33*†, 34
   →shikimic acid, 748*, 921, 922
   →tyrosine, 32, 33*†, 34
Phosphoenolpyruvate carboxykinase, 337
Phosphoenolpyruvate carboxytransphos-
      phorylase, 336
Phosphoenzyme form of phosphogluco-
      mutase, 353
Phosphoenzyme intermediate of a triple
      enzyme, 342
Phosphoethanolamine, 154†
   →ethanolamine, 141
1-Phosphofructoaldolase, 349
Phosphofructokinase, 344, 402
Phosphoglucoisomerase, 346, 347
Phosphoglucomutase, 345, 353, 368
   phosphoenzyme form of, 343
6-Phosphogluconate, 51, 52*†
   δ-lactone of, 52*†, 347
   →ribose-5-phosphate, 347, 348*
   →ribulose-5-phosphate, 52
6-Phosphogluconate dehydrogenase, 52, 53,
      56, 347, 348
6-Phosphogluconic dehydrase, 350
6-Phosphogluconolactonase, 53, 347, 348
6-Phosphogluconolactone, 52*†, 347
   hydrolysis of the lactone, 52
3-Phosphoglyceraldehyde, 53*, 54*†, 55*
   incorporation of $C^{14}O_2$ during photosyn-
      thesis into, 326, 327
2-Phospho-D-glycerate →glucose-6-phos-
      phate, 339
3-Phosphoglycerate, 321
   changes in free energy during photo-
      synthetic formation, 334
   incorporation of $C^{14}O_2$ during photosyn-
      thesis into, 326, 327
   in photosynthesis, 320*
   variations during light-dark changes of
      photosynthesis 332
   →glucose-6-phosphate, 339

3-Phosphoglycerate—(cont.)
   →glyceraldehyde-3-phosphate, 322*†
   →phosphoserine, 157
   →serine, 4, 5*
3-Phosphoglycerate dehydrogenase, 5
Phosphoglycerides, 127*, 133*, 139†, 140†,
      145†
Phosphoglyceryl kinase, 339
Phosphoglyceryl mutase, 339
Phosphoglycolic acid, 335
Phosphohexokinase, 338
6-Phosphohexonic acids, decarboxylation
      of, 449
Phosphohexose isomerase, 323, 324, 339
Phosphohomoserine, 19
   →threonine, 16*, 17*†
Phosphohomoserine mutaphosphatase, 16
Phosphohydroxypyruvate, 141
   →phosphoserine, 157
   →serine, 5*
Phosphoinositide complex, 164
Phosphoinositide-protein complexes, 184
Phosphoinositides, 183, 184
Phosphoketolase, 351
Phosphoketopentose epimerase, 53, 55, 324,
      325
Phospholipids, 151†, 180†, 182†
Phosphomannan, 416†
Phosphomannoisomerase, 346, 347
5-Phosphomevalonate, 209†, 647
   →squalene, 210*†, 211
   →terpenes, 844*†
Phospho-MVA-kinase, 948
4′-Phospho-pantetheine
   prosthetic group, 115
   →CoA, 86, 695*†, 698
4′-Phosphopantothenic acid →CoA, 695*†,
      698
4′-Phosphopantothenylcysteine →CoA,
      695*†
Phosphoproteins, 519
Phosphopyruvate →hexose phosphates, 338
Phosphopyruvate carboxylase, 336
Phosphoramidic hexose transphosphoryl-
      ase, 354
Phosphoribomutase, 68
Phosphoribose isomerase, 324, 325, 347, 348
5-Phosphoribose pyrophosphokinase, 61
Phosphoribosylamine, 62*†, 63*, 68
Phosphoribosyl-AMP→histidine, 30†, 32*†
N-1(5′-Phosphoribosyl)-ATP→histidine,
      30†, 32*†
Phosphoribosyl-ATP pyrophosphohydro-
      lase, 31
Phosphoribosyl-formimino-AICAR →histi-
      dine, 30†, 32*†
N-(5-Phosphoribosyl) glutamine, 62

5-Phosphoribosyl-1-pyrophosphate, 57, 61, 62*, 68, 69, 368
→histidine, 29†, 30†
→nicotinic acid, 683
→pyridine nucleotides, 689*, 690
→tryptophan, 35
5-Phosphoribosyl pyrophosphate amido-transferase, 62
Phosphoribulosyl-formimino-AICAR → histidine, 30†, 32*†
Phosphorolysis of polyribonucleotides and oligoribonucleotides, 558, 559
Phosphorylase, 369, 370, 383, 384, 385, 386, 387, 390, 393, 397, 404, 411
Phosphorylase a, 387, 399, 400, 401, 406
Phosphorylase b, 399, 400, 401, 406
Phosphorylase b-kinase, 400
Phosphorylase phosphatase, 400
Phosphorylase reactions, 370, 398, 399
Phosphorylases, 369, 383
Phosphorylases "a" and "b", interconversion between, 401
Phosphorylation
of aldohexoses, 344
of monosaccharides, 343
of sugars, 368
Phosphorylcholine, 88, 143†
→CDP-choline, 88
→lecithin, 142
stimulation by CTP, 88
Phosphorylcholine-ceramide transferase, 168, 169
Phosphorylcholine-cytidyl transferase, 88, 144, 145
Phosphorylcholine-glyceride transferase, 144, 145
Phosphorylethanolamine, 153, 154†, 156
→cytidine diphosphate ethanolamine, 88, 89
Phosphorylethanolamine-cytidyl transferase, 88
N-Phosphorylglycine, in phosphate transfer, 354
Phosphoserine, 5*†, 141, 142, 156†, 157†
Phosphoserine phosphatase, 5, 141, 157
Phosphoserine-RNA, 519
5-Phosphoshikimic acid
→aromatic amino acids, 907†, 908*†
product of fungal metabolism, 910*
Phosvitin, 518
Photolysis of CO₂, in photosynthesis, 333
Photolysis of water, in photosynthesis, 333
Photophosphorylation, 330
cyclic and noncyclic, 330, 336
Photoreception, 670
Photoreceptive pigments, 293, 294, 295

Photosynthesis, 320, 329
alternate pathway for, 335, 336
carbon reduction cycle, 322
cycle of 321
electron transport system of, 330
energy changes during, 333, 334
light and dark stages of, 332
redistribution of carbon in photosynthetic carbohydrate, 326, 327
Phrenosine, 170
Phthienoic acid, 122
Phycobilin-protein-complex, 295, 296
Phycobilins, 290, 291, 296†, 297†, 298†
Phycobiliproteins, 289, 290, 291, 292†, 293, 294, 296†, 297†, 298
influence of light on biosynthesis, 293, 294, 295
physical properties, 290
C-Phycocyanin, 290, 291, 296
R-Phycocyanin, 290, 291
Phycocyanins, 289, 290, 291, 292, 293, 294, 295, 296, 296†, 298
"H" and "D", 292
"protio"- and "deuterio"-, 292
Phycocyanobilins, 290, 296, 297
B-Phycoerythrin, 290
C-Phycoerythrin, 290, 291
R-Phycoerythrin, 291
Phycoerythrins, 289, 290, 291, 292†, 293, 294
Phycoerythrobilin, 291
Phycourobilin, 291
Phyllocladane, 893
Phyllocladene, 864*, 871, 1049†, 1050*†
γ-Phytadiene, 865
Phytadienes, 865
Phytin, 137
Phytochrome, 289
Phytoene, 650, 651*†, 652, 653†, 654, 655, 656, 657, 658, 659, 660, 661, 664, 668, 669
cis form, 670
common C₄₀ precursor of carotenoids, 651
structure of, 651
synthesis, genes affecting, 654
Phytofluene, 651, 652, 653†, 654, 655, 656†, 657, 659, 660, 661, 664†, 669
cis form, 670
Phytoglycogen, 403†, 411†
Phytol, 270, 863, 864*, 865†, 866†, 891†
→chlorophyll a, 268
Phytosphingosine, 165
Phytosterols, 225†, 226†, 872, 882, 887, 890
PICE, 264, 265
β-Picoline, 693
Picolinic acid, 688

Picolinic carboxylase, 690
Picraphylline, 989*
Picromycin, 1041
Pilocereine, 976*†
Pimaradiene →phyllocladene, 1049, 1050*
Pimaradienes, 867*, 871
Pimarane, 893
Pimarane type of resin acids, 871
Pimelic acid →biotin, 719*, 720
Pimelyl CoA →biotin, 720
α-Pinene, 837*, 838, 841, 846*, 849*†, 850*†, 851, 853†, 854*†
β-Pinene, 841, 850*†
Pinidine, 967*†, 968†
D-Pinitol, 452*†
Pinocamphone, 837*
Pinomyricetin, 782
Pinoquercetin, 782
D, L-Pinoresinol, 932*
Pinosylvin, 779, 780*
Pipecolate, 27*†, 28, 29
Δ′-Piperideine
  →anabasine, 963, 964*†
  →adenocarpine, 964*
  →alkaloids, 966*, 968, 974, 975, 1009
  →piperidine alkaloids, 966*
Δ′-Piperideine-2-carboxylate →anabasine, 963, 964*†
Δ′-Piperideine-6-carboxylate →lysine, 27*†, 28
Δ′-Piperideine-2,6-dicarboxylate →lysine, 25†, 26*†
Piperidine alkaloids, 961†, 966*†, 967*†, 968†, 969*†
Piperidone carboxylate, 28
Piperitenone, 837*, 838, 839*†, 841, 855
Piperitol, 841
Piperitone, 837*, 838, 839*†, 841, 846*, 855
Plant phenols
  biosynthesis of
    nine-carbon atom arylpropane unit, 747
    extension of three-carbon side chain, 748
  biosynthesis of the C₆-C₃ unit, 748
Plasma lipoproteins, 178, 179
Plasmalogen cholesterol, 183
Plasmalogen diglyceride
  →choline plasmalogen, 152
  →ethanolamine plasmalogen, 155
Plasmalogen ethanolamine, 134*
Plasmalogens, 133, 135, 145†
Plastoquinone, 331*, 890, 891†
Plastoquinone II, 330, 331
Platynecine, 971, 972*
Pleuromutilin, 872*†, 873
Pleurospermine, 974*†, 975
Plumieride, 1000†, 1001*†

PNase, 689, 692
Poly A, 538, 556, 557, 558, 561, 562†, 563†, 564†, 570, 571
Poly A + poly U complex, 569, 570
Polyadenylate residues, polyribonucleotides terminating in, 565
Polyadenylic acid, 538, 556
Poly AG, 493
Poly AGUC, 538, 556, 557, 561
Polyamines, effect on RNA synthesis, 567, 568
Poly AU, 493, 538, 556, 561
Poly C, 538, 561, 571
Polycations, activation of enzymes by, 360
Polycistronic messenger, 506
Polycyclic aromatic hydrocarbons, pyrosynthesis of, 1070*
Polycyclic aromatic systems, in fungi, 1031†
Polycyclic hydrocarbons, 1065, 1066, 1074, 1075
  do not form mercapturic acids, 604
Polycytidylic acid, 538
Polydeoxyadenylate, 571
Polydeoxyadenylate copolymer, 555
Polydeoxycytidylates, 571
Polydeoxyribonucleotide copolymers, 550*, 551†
Polydeoxyribonucleotide-primers, 569
Polydeoxyribonucleotides, 545†
Polydeoxythymidylic acid, 538, 571
Poly dT, 538
Poly d "X", 538
Polyene dearrangement, three categories of, 660
Polyenes
  C₄₀, 642
  effects of various compounds on the formation of, 659
Poly G, 538, 571
Polyganglioside, 174
Polyglucans, 385†
Polyglycerol phosphate, 427
  →teichoic acids, 374
Polyglycerophosphatide, 158
Polyglycine, 428
Polyguanylic acid, 538
Polyheptose, 431
Polyheptose phosphate, 427
Polyisoprenoid production, cessation of chain growth, 950
Polyisoprenoids, 890
Poly-β-ketoacids
  branched →Lycopodium alkaloids, 968, 969*
  →piperidine alkaloids, 967*†, 968, 969*
  →pyridine alkaloids, 967*†, 968
Poly-β-ketomethylene acid, 769*

Poly-β-ketomethylene chains, 752*†, 754
→polycyclic aromatic systems, 1031*
Polyleucoanthocyanidins, 815, 818, 819†, 820†
Polymethionine, 497
Polynucleotide phosphorylase, 555, 556, 558, 559, 560
  effects of primers on polymerization catalyzed by, 557
  inhibitors of, 556
  in vito function, 559, 560
Polynucleotide phosphorylases, 557
Polynucleotides
  methylation of, 572
  synthetic, affinity for ribosomes, 510
Polyol-aldose reactions, 451
Polyols, 450†
Polyoma virus, DNA from, 542
Polyoxyethylene sorbitan monoöleate, as replacement for biotin, 721
Polyphenoloxidases, 817, 818, 820, 935, 936
Polyphenols, 801, 802, 804, 820, 821, 822
Polyphenylalanine, 493
Polyphosphoinositides, 159†, 162†, 163†
Polyporenic acid A, 830, 831*
Polyporic acid, 766
Polyprenols, 858†
Polypyrroles
  linear, 261
  reaction with Ehrlich's reagent, 257
  →vitamin B$_{12}$, 301
Polypyrrolic precursor, of vitamin B$_{12}$, 299
Polyribitol phosphate, 427
  →teichoic acids, 374
Polyribonucleotide-primers, 569
Polyribonucleotides, 539*, 540*, 555†
  homopolymeric, 570†, 571†
  phosphorolysis of, 558
  synthesis from ribonucleoside 5′-triphosphates, 560
  synthetic, inhibitors of RNA synthesis, 569
  templates for synthesis of, 569
Polyribosomes, 491, 508, 510, 511, 517, 520
  electron micrograph of, 510
  in reticulocytes, 510
Polysaccharidases, role in polysaccharide synthesis, 386, 387
Polysaccharide-hydrolyzing enzymes, 340
Polysaccharides, 368†, 369†, 370†, 384†, 385†
  as glycosyl donors, 379
  bacterial, 373†, 422, 433†
  bacterial cell wall, 373†, 426†
  branched, 384†, 386†, 387†, 397
  capsular, 433†
  extracellular, 373†

Polysaccharides—(*cont.*)
  methylpentose containing, 422†
  N-free, 416
  of connective tissue, 443†
  phosphorylation of, 354, 355
  sulfate-containing, 439†
  unbranched, 386†
Polysomes, 491, 510
Polyterpenes, 830, 890†
Poly U, 493, 538, 557, 564†, 565†, 570, 571
Poly UG, 499
Polyunsaturated fatty acids, 119†, 120†, 121†
Poly U-ribosome complex, 510
Polyuridylate residues, polyribonucleotides terminating in, 565
Polyuridylic acid, 538
Polyuronosides, 422†
Poly "X", 538
Pompe's disease, 410
Porphobilin, 257
Porphobilinogen, 257†, 261†, 297
  stimulators of biosynthesis, 273
  →corrin, 299, 301
  →porphyrins, 253*†, 254†
  →uroporphyrinogens, 257, 258, 260, 261, 262
  →vitamin B$_{12}$, 299, 712
Porphobilinogen deaminase, 258
Porphyria, 261
  acute, 257, 273
  congenital, 277
Porphyrin a, 265
Porphyrin c, 265, 272
Porphyrin biosynthesis, control of, 272
Porphyrin-protein, 248
Porphyrinogen, 249*
Porphyrins, 249, 250*, 252†, 254, 263, 297†, 298†
  absorption spectrum, 252
  distribution in nature, 249
  incorporation of Co^{2+} into, 265
  side chains of, 271, 272*†
  stimulators of biosynthesis, 273
  structural relationships, 249
  substituents of β-pyrrolic carbon atom 2, 271
  with hydroxyl and carbonyl substituents, 270
Porphyropsin, 671
Precalciferol, 240*†
Precondylocarpine, 1002*, 1004
Prednisolone, effect on glycogen synthetase, 407
Pregna-4-en-20α-ol-3-one, 883, 884*
Pregnane, 883
Pregnanediol, 227†

5α-Pregnane-3β-ol-20-one, 884*
21-C¹⁴-Δ⁵-Pregnene-3β-ol-20-one glucoside 885
Pregnenolone, 227*†, 228, 231*†
  alkaloids related biogenetically to, 1012*
  →progesterone, 228, 229*, 231*, 893
  →sulfate, 614
  →testosterone, 232*
Premercapturic acids, 604, 605, 606*†
  compounds which form, 605
Prenyl residue, 785, 786, 787
C-Prenylation, 785*
PR-Enzyme, 400
Prephenic acid, 3, 803*, 804
  →aromatic amino acids, 907†, 908*†
  →indole alkaloids, 997, 999
  →lignin, 750
  →phenylalanine, 32, 33*†, 749*†
  →tyrosine, 32, 33*†, 749*†
Prephenic acid pathway, 804
Primary-hydroxyl phosphates, 343†
Primer, 384, 385
  in phosphorylase a reaction, 399
  polysaccharide biosynthesis in the absence of, 387
  polysaccharide biosynthesis with, 386, 387
Primer DNA, 545
Pristane, 866
Proanthocyanidins, 807, 813
Procaine, detoxication of, 634
Prodigiosin, 301†, 303*†, 304†
Proflavin, 573
Progesterone, 227, 228, 229*†, 230, 231*†, 883, 884*, 893†
Proline, 3, 11†, 12*†
  →alkaloids, 1004, 1008
  →pyrrolidine ring of nicotine, 964, 965*
  →stachydrine, 958
Proline hydroxylase, 519
Prolycopene, 653†, 661
1,2-Propanediol →propionaldehyde, effect of vitamin B₁₂ on, 718
4-Propenylphenol, oxidation of, 793
Propionic acid
  →fatty acids, 121
  →fungal metabolites, 1026, 1032, 1041, 1042*, 1043
  →pantothenic acid, 697
Propionic acid units →phenolic plant products, 767
Propionyl CoA, 256, 697
  →methylmalonyl CoA, 109
2-Propionyl porphyrin, 271
Prosthetic-group-removing enzyme, 400
Protamines, associated with DNA, 542
Protein biosynthesis, 86†, 87†

Protein biosynthesis—(cont.)
  attachment of non-amino acid constituents, 519
  biosynthetic reaction, 511, 512
  by non-ribosomal systems, 521, 522
  dynamic state and nature of turnover, 482, 483, 484
  energy for, 486, 487
  general mechanism of, 484, 485, 486, 487 488
  inadequacies of the general mechanism, 521
  involvement of RNA in, 488
  irreversibility of, 484
  mechanism of, 489
  methods employed in the study of, 481
  overall scheme of, 489, 490
  primary protein structure, 518
  regulation of, 504
  response to conditions, 487, 488
  role of free peptides as intermediates in, 485, 486
  role of lipids and membranes, 517, 520
  secondary protein structure, 518, 519
  site of, 508
  template mechanism of, 488, 518
  tertiary protein structure, 518, 519
  time required for, 487
  trinucleotide code in, 492
Protein-lipopolysaccharide conjugates, 431
Proteins
  amino acids of, 478, 479
  formation in chloroplasts, 523
  formation in mitochondria, 522
  half-life of, 482, 483
  primary structure, 478
  produced for secretion from the cell, 520
  secondary structure, 478, 479
  tertiary structure, 478, 480
  unique features of, 480
Protein-sulfomucopolysaccharide complexes, 444
Protetrahydrolycopene, 653†, 661
Proteolipids, 178, 182†, 183†, 184†
Protoberberine, 983*, 984
Protocatechuic acid, 803*†
Protocatechuic aldehyde→alkaloids, 985, 986*†
Protochlorophyll, 272
Protochlorophyll a, 263*†, 267
  lacking the phytol group, 267
Protochlorophyll holochrome, 268
Protochlorophyll a holochrome, 263†
Protochlorophyllide, 272, 273, 299
Protochlorophyllide a, 263*†, 267†, 268
  phytol ester of, 267
Protochlorophyllide holochrome, 268

Protochlorophyllide *a* holochrome, 263†
Protoheme, 280
  pyridine hemochromogen of, →biliverdin, 278, 280
Protohemochromogen, 281, 282
Protopine, 955, 981†, 982*†
Protoporphyrin, 272, 278
  fifteen isomers of, 251
  incorporation of zinc into, 265
  monomethyl ester, 266
Protoporphyrin IX, 251, 254†, 258, 261†, 263†, 264†, 270, 271, 278, 285
  →biliprotein, 295, 298
  incorporation of iron into, 265
  incorporation of magnesium and zinc into, 266
  structural relationship with bile pigments, 274*, 276
Protoporphyrin-iron chelating enzyme, 264, 265
Protoporphyrin monomethyl ester → chlorophyll, 266
Protoporphyrinogen IX, 263*†, 264†, 272
Protoporphyrin IX-types, 271
Provitamin A, 671
PRPP, 61, 62*, 70, 81
  →histidine, 29, 30
  →nicotinic acid, 683, 684
  →orotidine-5′-phosphate, 75
  →pyridine nucleotides, 689*, 690
  →tryptophan, 35
Pseudoheme, 277, 279*†, 280, 282*, 284, 285
PseudoUMP, 497
Pseudouridine, 543*
  in sRNA, 497
Pseudouridine 5′-diphosphate, polymerization of, 556
Pseudouridine diphosphate glucose→glycogen, 403
Pseudouridine-5′-glucuronic acid, 435
Pseudovitamin B₁₂, 714, 717
Psilocybine, 957*†
Psoralene, 787*
Psychosine, 169†, 171†, 172
  →cerebroside, 171
Pteridine, 705*†, 707
  chemical synthesis, 706
  from guanine, 731*
Pteridine (2-amino-4-hydroxy-6-hydroxymethyl dihydropteridine, reduced →pteroic acid, 707
Pteridine diphosphate, 707
Pteridine ring, 704†
Pteroic acid, 705*, 706†, 707†
  → folic acid, 707
Pulcherriminic acid, 1054, 1055*

Pulegenic acid, 852, 853*
Pulegone, 837*, 839*†, 841, 852*†, 855, 868
Pulvinic acid, 766†
Pungenin aglycon, 750†, 790
Purine and pyrimidine analogs
  incorporation into DNA, 548
  in DNA synthesis, 547
Purine and pyrimidine base pairs in DNA, 541
Purine deoxyribonucleotides, 70†
Purine nucleoside monophosphates, 59†
Purine nucleotide, 46*
Purine nucleotides, glycosidic bond in, 46
Purine ring, 60†, 61
Purines, 46*, 47*, 49, 50, 539*
  in vitamin B₁₂, 711, 714
  methylated, 46
  N-methylation of, 8
  → nucleosides, 68
Puromycin, 180, 181
  effect of porphyrin biosynthesis, 273
  effect on protein synthesis, 436, 516
Purpurogenone, 770, 771*
Putrescine
  →alkaloids, 1008
  →pyrrolidine ring of nicotine, 964, 965*
  →pyrrolizidine alkaloids, 971, 972*
  →spermidine, 8
  →tropine, 959, 960*
Pyocyanine, 954*
Pyrene, 1075
  pyrosynthesis of, 1070*
Pyrethric acid, 855
Pyrethrin, 855
Pyridine, methylation of, 620, 621, 625, 632
Pyridine acetate, methylation of, 619
Pyridine-3-aldehyde, 693
Pyridine alkaloids, 961†, 967*†
Pyridine-3-carbinol, 693
Pyridine α, 5-dihydroxyhemochromogen, 281
Pyridine hemochromogen →biliverdin, 295
Pyridine hemochromogens, 278, 279, 280*, 281
Pyridine α-hydroxy hemochromogen, 281
Pyridine nucleotidase, 689, 692
Pyridine nucleotides, 81†, 689*†, 690†
Pyridine nucleotide transhydrogenase, 693
Pyridine protohemichromogen, 284
  →biliverdin, 285
Pyridine protohemochromogen, 281, 287
Pyridine verdohemochromogen, 281
Pyrido-quinazolinone, 1008*, 1009
Pyridoxal, 722*†, 723†, 724
  →δ-aminolevulinic acid, 255
  antagonist of, 723
  breakdown products of, 724

Pyridoxal—(*cont.*)
  coenzyme for decarboxylation, 723
  cofactor for transamination, 723
  stimulation of production by carboxylic
    acids in the Krebs' cycle, 723
Pyridoxal kinase
  activation of, 724
  competitive inhibitors of, 723
  inhibitors of, 724
Pyridoxal phosphate, 7, 723†, 724
  in cystathione synthetase, 9
  in nicotinic acid synthesis, 687
  in phosphorylase b, 401
  in threonine synthetase, 16
  in tryptophan biosynthesis, 685
  in tryptophan synthetase, 36
Pyridoxal phosphate-enzyme complex, 255,
    256*
Pyridoxal phosphate-enzyme-glycine com-
    plex, 255, 256*
Pyridoxamine, 722
  →pyridoxal, 723
Pyridoxamine-5-phosphate, 7
  →pyridoxal, 723
  →pyridoxal-5-phosphate, 723
4-Pyridoxic acid, 724
5-Pyridoxic acid, 724
Pyridoxine, 722*, 724
Pyridoxine biosynthesis, control of, 724
4-Pyridoxine lactone, 724
Pyrimidine, 59, 60*, 71†, 72†, 76†
Pyrimidine deoxyribonucleotides, 77†
Pyrimidine nucleoside monophosphates,
    71†
Pyrimidine nucleotide, 46*
Pyrimidine nucleotides, glycosidic bond in,
    47
Pyrimidine pyrophosphate→thiamine, 681
Pyrimidine ring, precursors of the, 71, 72
Pyrimidines, 46*, 47*, 49, 50, 539*
  →nucleotides, 76
Pyroclavine, 1005*†, 1006†
Pyrogallol, derivatives of, methylation, 623,
    624*
Pyrogallol phenols→tannins, 820
Pyronoquinone, dihydroderivative of,
    1057†, 1058*†
Pyrophosphates, 356
Pyrophosphate, hydrolysis of, 393
Pyrophosphate-glucose phosphotransferase,
    342
5-Pyrophosphomevalonate, 647
  →squalene, 210*†, 211
  →terpenes, 844*†
Pyrophosphorylases, 62, 90–95
1-Pyrophosphorylribose-5'-phosphate →
    vitamin B₁₂, 713

Pyrrole, 249*
Pyrrole ring, in tryptophan, 34†, 35†
Pyrroles, reaction with Ehrlich's reagent, 257
Pyrrolidine alkaloids, 958†
Δ'-Pyrroline
  →alkaloids, 975, 1008*, 1009
  →nicotine, 965*†, 966
Δ'-Pyrroline-5-carboxylate reductase, 12
Δ'-Pyrroline-5-carboxylic acid→proline,
    12*†
Pyrrolizidine alkaloids, 971†, 972*†
Pyrromycin, 1043
ε-Pyrromycinone, 1042*†, 1043†
Pyruvate, 3
  incorporation into carbohydrate, 338, 339
  product of fungal metabolism, 910
  role in lignin biosynthesis, 930
  →N-acetyl neuraminic acid, 350
  →branched-chain amino acids, 21*, 22, 23
  →cholesterol, 208
  →glucose-6-phosphate, 337
  →lysine, 25, 26
Pyruvate carboxylase, 337
Pyruvate family, 16†
Pyruvate kinase, 337, 338, 487
Pyruvate oxidase, 682
Pyruvate phosphoroclastic reaction, 330

Quantum yield of photosynthesis, 333, 334,
    335
Quaternary bases, as detoxication products,
    632
Q-Enzyme, 379, 383, 385, 387, 388, 389, 411
Quercetin, 772†, 773*†, 805†, 806*
  cleavage of, 773*
  precursors of, 806
Quercetin glucoside→rutin, 374, 435
Quercetin glucuronide, 598
Quercetin rhamnosyl-(1→6)-glucoside,
    374†, 434†, 435†
Quercimeritrin, 775
Quinaldic acid, detoxication, 630
Quinaldylglycine, 630†
Quinaldylglycyltaurine, 630*†
Quinamine, 993*†, 994†
Quinazoline alkaloids, 1006†
Quinazolino-β-carboline alkaloids, 990,
    991*†
Quinazolone alkaloids, 990, 991*†
Quinic acid, 802, 803, 804
Quinic dehydrogenase, 804
Quinidine, 993*†
Quinine, 955, 993*†, 995†
Quinoline
  →alkaloids, 1009
  methylation of, 620, 632

Quinoline alkaloids, 1006†
Quinoline-2-carboxylic acid, detoxication, 630
Quinolinic acid, 683*†, 688†
→desamido NMN, 83*†
→nicotine, 962, 963*†
→nicotinic acid, 962, 963*†
Quinolinic acid ribonucleotide →desamido NMN, 83*†
Quinolizidine alkaloids, 972†, 973*†, 974*†
Quinone, polymeric, 1029*
Quinone methides, polymerization of, 931
Quinone-methide radicals, during lignin formation, 931*, 933
Quinone polymerization, of tannins, 815, 816, 817, 818
Quinovose, nucleoside diphosphosulfo derivatives of, 130
Quinoxaline→B₁₂ vitamers, 715
Quinuclidine ring, in alkaloids, 993†

Raffinose, 377†, 394†
oxidation of, 447
→levan, 418
→melibiose, 394
→trisaccharides, 378
Reduction of sulfate to sulfide, 10*
Regulator genes, 505
Renierapurpurin, 661
Renieratene, 661
Repressor molecules, 505
Repressor-operon concept, 505
Reserpic acid, 1000
Reserpine, 989, 992*, 997, 1000
Reserpinine, 1000
Resin acids, 863, 871, 872
rate of turnover, 873
transformations of, 867*
Resorcinol derivatives, 755†
Resorcinols, 763†
Resveratrol, 752*†, 779, 780*
Reticuline, (+) and (−), 977*†, 978†, 979, 981, 982
Retinene, 671
Retinene reductase, 671
Retinoic acid, 671
Retronecic acid, 971†, 972*†
Retronecine, 971, 972*
Retrosine, 971†, 972*†
Rhamnolipids, 374†, 435†
Rhamnose, 435†
→bacterial cell wall polysaccharides, 432
D-Rhamnose, 363†, 446
polysaccharide containing, 362
L-Rhamnose, 363†, 366*†, 422, 446
→glycosides, 434

L-Rhamnose—(cont.)
in bacterial cell wall polysaccharides, 426, 427
L-Rhamnosyl-(1→3)-L-rhamnosyl-β-hydroxydecanoyl-β-hydroxydecanoic acid, 435†
D-Rhamnulose, 446†
L-Rhamnulose, 446†
phosphorylation of, 345
L-Rhamnulokinase, 345
L-Rhamnulose-1-phosphate, 345†, 350
L-Rhamnulose-1-phosphate aldolase, 350
Rhein, 770*
Rhetsinine, 991*
Rhodanese, 616, 617, 618, 619
Rhodopin, 664†
Rhodopsin, 671
Rhodovibrin, 664†
Rhodoviolascin, 658
Rhodoxanthin, 667
Rhombifoline, 973*†, 975†
Rhynocophylline, 994*†, 996
Ribitol, 450, 451
Ribitol-5-phosphate,
in bacterial cell wall, 427
→teichoic acids, 430
Ribityl alcohol, 84
6-Ribitylamino-5-aminouracil, 703
4-Ribitylamino-5-aminouracil→riboflavin, 701*†
4-(1'-D-Ribitylamino)-5-amino-2,6-dihydroxylpyrimidine, 703
8-Ribityllumazine, 703
Riboflavin, 84*†, 699†, 701*†, 702, 703†
incorporation of C¹⁴ compounds into, 700
phosphorylation of, 85
precursor from guanine, 731*
proposed scheme for synthesis, 701*
synthesis of the ribityl side chain, 703
→vitamin B₁₂, 714
Riboflavin-phosphate, 703†
Ribonuclease, 478, 480, 486, 487, 492, 495, 522
association with cell membranes, 520
complete sequence of amino acid residues in, 479
secondary structure of, 519
Ribonucleic acid, 542, 565†
involvement in protein synthesis, 488
Ribonucleic acid nucleotidyltransferase, 567
Ribonucleoprotein particles, 508
Ribonucleoside→deoxyribonucleoside, 57
Ribonucleoside 5'-diphosphates
polymerization of, 556
→polyribonucleotides, 555
Ribonucleoside 2'- and 3'-phosphates, 544

Ribonucleosides, nomenclature of, 49
Ribonucleoside 5′-triphosphates
  analogs of incorporation into RNA, 568
  enzyme systems requiring all four, 565
  incorporation into DNA, 562
Ribonucleotide residue, formation of sequences containing a certain, 562
Ribonucleotides, 539, 545
  2′, 3′ cyclic phosphodiesters of, 48
  incorporation into DNA, 562
  incorporation into terminal positions of ribonucleic acid, 560
  nomenclature of, 48, 49
  phosphate ester position in, 47, 48
Ribonucleotidyl-DNA, 562
Ribonucleotidyl DNA primer, 563
D-Ribose, 47, 48*, 51†
  oxidation of, 448
  product of fungal metabolism, 910
  →deoxyribose, effect of vitamin B_{12} on, 718
  →glycosides, 434
  →RNA, effect of vitamin B_{12} on, 718
Ribose conjugation, 631
Ribose phosphate, 51†
D-Ribose-1-phosphate, 68*†, 354†
  from ribose-6-phosphate, 348†
  →nucleoside, 370
  →pyridine nucleotides, 689*, 690
D-Ribose-5-phosphate, 53*†, 55*†, 62,* 325*
  activation of UDP-glucose transglycosylase by, 406
  changes in free energy during photosynthetic formation, 334
  from D-glucose-6-phosphate, 347†, 348*†
  in equilibrium with ribulose-5-phosphate, 324, 325
  in pentose phosphate cycle, 348
  in transaldolase-catalyzed reaction, 325, 326
  →D-octulose-1, 8-diphosphate, 349
  →5-phosphoribosyl-1-pyrophosphate, 61, 62
  →ribose-1-phosphate, 68*, 345
  →D-ribulose-5-phosphate, 347
  →sedoheptulose-7-phosphate, 324*, 350
Ribosomal RNA, 488, 538
Ribosomes, 508, 509, 511, 512, 513, 514, 516, 517, 518, 520, 521, 522, 523
  complexing between mRNA and, 509, 510
  hypothetical model of the function in protein synthesis, 510
  RNA in, 543
Ribosome-mRNA complex, 511
Ribosylthymine diphosphate, 559
  polymerization of, 556

Ribosylthymine triphosphate, in RNA synthesis, 568
5-Ribosyluracil, 543*
  in sRNA, 497
5-Ribosyl uridylic acid, 403
RiboTMP, 497
D-Ribulokinase, 344
D-Ribulose, 446†, 450†
  incorporation of $C^{14}O_2$ during photosynthesis into, 326, 327
  phosphorylation of, 344
L-Ribulose, 446†, 450†
  →L-arabinose, 346*
  phosphorylation of, 344
D-Ribulose-1, 5-diphosphate, 53, 320*, 321
  changes in free energy during photosynthetic formation, 334
  enol form of, 320*
  regeneration of, 321
  variations during light-dark changes of photosynthesis, 332
  →3-phosphoglycerate, 322
  →ribulose-5-phosphate, 325*
Ribulose-5-phosphate, 52*†, 55*†
  changes in free energy during photosynthetic formation, 334
  from glucose-6-phosphate, 347†
  in equilibrium with xylulose-5-phosphate and ribose-5-phosphate, 324, 325
  →ribose-5-phosphate, 53
  →teichoic acids, 430
D-Ribulose-5-phosphate, 325*
  epimerization of, 345*
  in photosynthesis, 321
  →D-ribose-5-phosphate, 347, 348*†
  →ribulose-1, 5-diphosphate, 325*
L-Ribulose-5-phosphate, 344†
  →L-arabinose, 346*
  epimerization of, 345*
D-Ribulose-5-phosphate kinase, 325
Ricinine, 953, 954*, 955, 961†, 963*†
Rimuene, 867*, 871, 872
RNA, 567†
  acceptor, 561
  adaptor, 488
  amino acid acceptor, 543
  as a primer, 570
  as template, 566, 567
  complementary, 567
  complementary base pairs, 542
  DNA-dependent, 500
  DNA-directed, 567†
  double-stranded, 566
  enhancement of, 568†
  helical conformation, 542
  informational, 500
  inhibition by actinomycin D, 565†

RNA—(*cont.*)
  inhibition of synthesis, 569
  intrachain hydrogen-bonding, 542
  involvement in protein synthesis, 488
  messenger, 488
  methylated bases in, 572*
  polycistronic, 517
  phosphorolysis of, 48, 558
  primary chemical structure, 539*, 540*, 542
  replicative form, 566
  ribosomal, 488
  RNA- primed, 565†
  secondary structure, 542
  single stranded structure, 542, 566
  synthesis from ribonucleoside 5'-triphosphates, 560
D-RNA, 500
mRNA, 489, 490, 491, 492, 494, 500, 507, 508, 511, 512, 514, 516, 517, 518, 521, 522, 538, 542, 567
  binding of ribosomes, 503
  complementarity to DNA, 503
  complexing between ribosomes and, 509, 510
  functional characteristics of, 500, 501, 502, 503, 504
  metabolic instability of, 501
  origination from DNA, 501, 502
  in polyribosomes, 510
  regulation of protein formation by, 504, 505
  size of, 502
  stimulation of protein synthesis by, 503
rRNA, 538, 542, 543, 564, 567
sRNA, 489†, 490, 491, 493, 494, 495, 496, 497, 511, 512, 513, 514, 516, 517, 518
  amino acid binding or recognition site, 498
  attachment to ribosomes, 511
  denaturation of, 498
  double-stranded helix, 498
  methylation of, 499, 500
  pCpCpA terminal sequence in, 499, 511, 512
  secondary structure of, 498
  unusual nucleotide bases in, 497
sRNA_{ala}
  complete nucleotide sequence of, 497
  two possible conformations for, 498, 499*
sRNA_{cySH}, coding and recognition sites, 498, 499
sRNA_{met}, 497
sRNA_{ser}, 518
sRNA_{val}, 497
tRNA, 496, 538, 542, 543, 567

RNAse, 499, 513, 514, 517, 518, 522, 523, 563
RNAase, in ribosomes, 509, 510, 512
RNA methylase, 572, 573
RNA, nucleotidyltransferase, 563, 565
RNA Polymerase, 502, 507, 555, 562, 567, 568, 569, 570, 571
RNA Primer, 565
mRNA-Ribosomes, attachment of amino acyl-RNA to, 511
RNA Synthetase, 566, 567
RNA Synthesis, DNA-dependent, 522
RNA-Synthesizing enzymes, induction by infecting virus, 566
RNA Template, in protein synthesis, 488
RNA Viruses, replication of, 565
mRNA Templates, 496, 509
(−) Robinetinidol, 819
Roemerine, 981
Rosenonolactone, 868†, 869†, 1048*†
Rosmarinecine, 971, 972*
Rotiorin, 1035†, 1036*†, 1038
Rubber, 839†, 840†, 842, 947*†, 949, 950
  acetate as the precursor of, 943
  biosynthesis
    further problems, 949
    growth of the polyisoprene chain, 949
    nature and genesis of the isoprenoid monomer, 943
    polymerization enzymes, 949
    regulation of, 951
    steric considerations, 949
  degradation by ozonolysis, 947*
  distribution of, 941, 942
  polymerization of the isoprenoid monomer, 948†
  structure of, 942
Rubiadin, 770*
Rubrioglocladin, 1043†, 1044*
Rubropunctatin, 1035†, 1036*, 1058†
Rugulosin, 1043†, 1044*
Rugulosin-C, 1043
Rutaecarpine, 991*
Rutilantinone, 1032†, 1042*†, 1043†
Rutilantins, 1043
Rutin, 374†, 434†, 435†

Sabinene, 841
Saccharides, 369–380†, 389†
Saccharopine →lysine, 27*†, 28†
Saccharopine dehydrogenase, 28
Safranin T, 167
Salicin, 384, 434
Salicylic acid, 791†
Salicylic acid derivatives, 755†
Saligenin β-glucoside, 384

Salutaridine, 977*†, 978†, 979
Salutaridinol, 978†
Salutaridinol-I, 977*†, 978†
Samidin, O-acylated, 786*
α-Santalene, 856*, 859*†
Sapogenins, 226, 874, 883, 885†
  steroid, 745
Sarpagine, 992*
Schardinger dextrins, 379†
Sclareol, 864*, 873, 891†
Sclerotiorin, 1035, 1036*, 1038, 1058†
Scillaren A, 874*
Scyllitol →meso inositol, 452*
Scyllo-inositol →galactoside, 434
Scyllo-meso-inosose →meso inositol and
  scyllitol, 452*
Scymnol sulfate, 615
Securinine, 1014*
Sedamine, 968†, 969*†
Sedinine, 968†, 969*†
Sedormid, stimulation of porphyrin syn-
  thesis by, 273
Sedridine, 966*†
D-Sedoheptulose
  free, occurrence, 444
  incorporation of $C^{14}O_2$ during photo-
    synthesis into, 326
  phosphorylation of, 354
  product of fungal metabolism, 910*
D-Sedoheptulose-1,7-diphosphate,   324†,
  344, 349†
  changes in free energy during photo-
    synthetic formation, 334
  phosphatase which splits, 324
D-Sedoheptulose-1-phosphate, 349†
  phosphorylation of, 344
D-Sedoheptulose-7-phosphate,   54*†,   55*,
  324*†, 350†
  activation of UDP-glucose transglyco-
    sylase by, 406
  changes in free energy during photo-
    synthetic formation, 334
  in photosynthesis, 321, 323*†
  in transaldolase-catalyzed reaction, 325,
    326*†
  →D-glycero-D-manno heptose, 367
Sedoheptulose phosphates, in pentose
  phosphate cycle, 348
Selagine, 970*†
Semiporphyrinogens, 249
Senecioic acid, 946
  as an acylating agent, 687
Senecioyl CoA, 786*
Senecioyl residue, 786
Seneciphyllic acid, 972
Separating acid, see chorismic acid
Sequoytol, 452*†

Serine, 3, 4†, 5†, 141†, 142†
  aldimine derivative of →cysteine, 9*†
  →alkaloids, 1011
  →cysteine, 8*
  →dihydrosphingosine, 166, 167
  →ethanolamine, 141
  →fungal metabolites, 1053
  →lecithin, 148, 149
  →methionine, 19, 20
  →nicotinic acid, 683, 685
  →phosphatidyl serine, 157
  →pyridoxal, 723
  →riboflavin, 699
  →tryptophan, 36
Serine biosynthesis, alternative pathways of,
  4, 5, 6
Serine conjugation, 629
Serine deaminase, 9
Serine dehydrase, 36
Serine hydroxymethylase, 141
Serine phosphatides, 156†
Serine plasmalogen, 156†, 158
Serine transhydroxymethylase, 6, 7
Serotonin, 957*†
  acetylation, 627
  methylation of, 620
  →melatonin, 623
Serpentine, 989, 992*
Sesquiterpene alcohol pyrophosphate, 949
Sesquiterpenes, 830, 844†, 855†, 856*, 1010
  ionic mechanisms in the biogenesis of,
    859*
  of the iresin family, 860*†
  stereochemic configuration, 860, 861
Sex hormones, 226†, 230†
  male and female, from cholesterol, 231*†
Shikimic acid, 748*†, 749*, 802, 803*, 804†,
  909, 921†, 923†, 924†
  →actinomycin, 1040
  →alkaloids, 1000, 1006
  →aromatic amino acids, 908*
  →caffeic acid, 751
  C^{14}-labeling, 924
  distribution in higher plants, 923
  from glucose, 920†, 921†
  →fungal metabolites, 1025, 1046, 1052,
    1054
  →hydrangenol, 780
  →indole alkaloids, 997
  →lignin, 749, 750, 923, 924
  →methyl p-methoxycinnamate, 912
  →nicotinic acid, 682
  →novobiocin, 1040
  →PABA, 706
  →phenolic plant products, 776
  →phenylalanine, 33*†, 34†, 749*
  →phenylpropanoid compounds, 748*

Shikimic acid—(cont.)
  →quercetin, 772, 806
  →stilbenes, 780
  →tyrosine, 33*†, 34†, 749*
Shikimic acid pathway, 780, 804, 808
Shikimic acid-phenylalanine pathway, 766
  →cinnamic acid, 788
Shikimate-5-phosphate →phenylalanine,
    tyrosine, 32, 33*†, 34†
Sialic acid-containing substances, 436†
Sialic acid-9-phosphatase, 437, 438
Sialic acids, 173, 346†, 435, 436*
Sialyllactose, 375†, 438†
Sialyloligosaccharides, 375†, 438†
Sinapic acid
  →ferulic acid, 791
  →lignins, 750†, 791
  →quercetin, 772
Sinapyl alcohol, 926, 927*, 928
  →lignin, 917
  structural relationship with products of
    fungal metabolism, 916
Sinoacutine, 977*†, 979†
Sinomenine, 977*†, 979†
β-Sitosterol, 225*†, 226†, 873, 874*, 877,
    878*, 879, 880*†, 882†, 883, 887,
    888, 889, 890, 891, 892, 1001
  origin of the ethyl group in, 881*
  →stigmasterol, 881
Skimmianine, 1008
Skimmin →umbelliferone, 789*†
Skytanthine, 971
Slippage, in amino acid incorporation into
    proteins, 516
Solanesol, 890*†
  pyrolysis of, 1075, 1076
Solanidine, 1013*†
Solorinic acid, 770*†
Soluble RNA, 496, 543, 561
Soluble RNA-hydroxyproline, 15
D-1,5-Sorbitan-6-phosphate, activation of
    UDP-glucose transglycosylase by, 406
D-Sorbitol, 449†, 450
  oxidation of, 452
D-Sorbitol-6-phosphate, 450
  →D-mannitol-1-phosphate, 451
L-Sorbose, 450†
  from fructose, 452†
  →fructose, 452
  →D-glucose-1-sorboside, 376
L-Sorbose-6-phosphate, in transaldolase-
    catalyzed reaction, 325
Sorigenin, 759*†, 770
Sotetsuflavone, 792*
Soyasapogenol A, 888*†
Soyasapogenol D, 888
Sparteine, 973*†, 975

Spermine, activation of enzymes by, 360
Spermidine, 8†
  effect on RNA synthesis, 568
Spermostrychnine, 994*†, 997†
Sphaeropherin, 765*
Spheroidene, 664†
  demethylated, 664†
Spheroidenone, 660, 664†
Sphingolipids, 165, 166, 170, 172, 173
Sphingomyelin, 135, 166, 168*†, 169†,
    183
Sphingosine, 165, 166*†, 167†, 168, 169†,
    170, 172, 173, 183
  in gangliosides, 176
  →ceramide, 167
  →psychosine, 171
Sphingosine-containing lipids, 169†
Sphingosine sulfate, 168
Spinasterol, 882†
Spiran, 1027
Spiran ester, 1028*
Spirographis heme, 271
Spirographis porphyrin, 271
Spirolactone, 788
Spirilloxanthin, 658, 663, 664†, 1039*†
  demethylated, 658
  monodemethylated, 664†
25α-Δ5-Spirosten-3β-ol, 226
25β-Δ5-Spirosten-3β-ol, 226
25α-Δ5-Spirosten-3β-ol-12-one, 226
25β-Δ5-Spirosten-3β-ol-12-one, 226
Squalene, 209, 210†, 211*†, 212*†, 214,
    648, 649, 650, 651, 655, 842, 843†,
    844†, 845, 857, 873, 875, 879†, 887,
    891, 892, 946
  all trans-configuration, 213, 879
  cyclization of, 879, 880, 882, 885, 887,
    888, 889, 892
  role in β-sitosterol and triterpene bio-
    synthesis, 882
  →β-amyrin, 879, 890
  →cholesterol, 211, 213*, 214, 215*, 879
  →eburicoic acid, 887
  →ergosterol, 219
  →hydrocarbons, 133
  →sapogenin, 885
  →β-sitosterol, 880*, 882
  →soyasapogenol A, 888*
  →sterols, 843, 875*, 876*
  →tetracyclic triterpene, 886
  →triterpenes, 843, 875*, 876*
  →zymosterol, 219
Starch, 403†, 404†
  as glucosyl acceptor, 404
  digestion of, 340
Starch granule, 412†
Starch synthetase, 403

Stearic acid, 114†
  in lecithin, 147
  →oleic acid, 117
Stearyl alcohol →plasmalogens, 153
Stearyl CoA, 117†, 172
  →arachidyl CoA, 117
Stearyl CoA synthetase, 113
Stercobilin, 275*, 276, 277, 286, 289†
1-Stercobilin, 289
Stercobilinogen, 275*, 276, 289†
1-Stercobilinogen, 289
Sterculic acid, 122†
Sterigmatocystin, 1044†, 1045*†
Steroidal alkaloids, 893†, 1009†, 1012*†, 1013*†
Steroid hormones, in plants, 883†
Steroid sulfokinase, 614
Sterol biogenesis
  control of, 890
  effect of β-ionone on, 659
Sterols, 646†, 647†, 648†, 650, 891*, 892
  formation of -methyl and -ethyl groups in the side chains, 880
  of plants, 873†, 874*, 878
  →vitamin D, 239
Steviol, 870
7-Stigmasten-3β-ol, 877, 878*
Stigmasterol, 225†, 226*†, 873, 874*, 880, 881†, 882†, 883, 887
  →carcinogenic polycyclic hydrocarbons, 1070*
Stachydrine, 955, 958*, 959†
Stilbenes, 752, 779†, 780*†, 808
  precursors of, 780*
Stipitatic acid, 1038*†
Stipitatonic acid, 1038*†
Strandin, 173†, 174, 175, 176
Streptomycin
  biosynthesis of streptose in, 366
  effect on polyene formation, 659
  effect on protein synthesis, 516
Streptose, 366*†
Structural genes, 505
Strychnine, 994*†, 995†, 996†, 997
Ψ-Strychnine, 994*†, 997†
Strychnos alkaloids, 1035, 1037
Strychnospermine, 994*†, 997†
(−)—Stylopine, 981†, 982*†
Styrene, 1072, 1073*
6-Styryl-α-pyrones, 747*
Suberic acid →biotin, 719
Suberosin, 785*
Succinate
  from acetate via glyoxalate cycle, 340†
  from fatty acids, 341†
  from isocitrate, 340†
  →heme, 253

Succinate—(cont.)
  →porphyrin, 254
  →propionate, effect of biotin on, 722
  →vitamin B12, 711, 712
Succinate-glycine cycle, 254
Succinic acid →nicotinic acid, 962, 963*
Succinic acid decarboxylation, effect of biotin on, 722
N-Succinyl-2-amino-6-ketopimelate →lysine, 26*†
Succinylation, 26
Succinyl-CoA
  in regeneration of ATP, 382
  →δ-aminolevulinic acid, 255, 256*
  →heme, 253
  →porphyrin, 254
  →vitamin B12, 712
N-Succinyl-L-DAP →lysine, 26*†
O-Succinylhomoserine →methionine, 19
Sucrose, 370†, 371†, 377†, 389†, 445†
  as glycosyl acceptor, 376
  as glycosyl donor, 376, 377, 382, 385
  energy of hydrolysis, 382
  oxidation of, 447
  →amylose, amylopectin, 398
  →dextran, 412, 413
  →fructosyl fructosyl glucoside, 380
  →glucose, 445
  →glycogen, 398, 407
  →levan, 417
  →raffinose, 394
Sucrose analogues, 370†, 390†
Sucrose phosphate, 372†, 390†
  →sucrose, 390
Sucrose phosphorylase, 370, 384, 390
  transglucosylase activity of, 376, 377
Sugar alcohols, 449†, 450†
Sugars
  branched-chain, 1040*†
  nonphosphorylated
    decarboxylations, 449
    dehydrogenations, 449
    hydrogenations, 445
    isomerizations, 445
    oxidations, 445
Sugiol, 871
Sulfadimethoxine →glucuronide, 594*
Sulfamates, 612, 615
Sulfanilamide, 607, 629
  N-acetyl, 627, 628*
  S-acetyl, 627, 628*
  acetylation of, 626
  N-acetylation, 627
  S-acetylation, 627
Sulfate
  activation of, 10
  reduction to sulfide, 10*

Sulfate—(*cont.*)
  role in detoxication, 591
  types of compounds conjugating with, 611, 613
N-Sulfate, 612
S-Sulfate, 612
Sulfate conjugation, 611
  zoological distribution of, 615
Sulfate donor, 87
Sulfate esters, 612, 613
Sulfatides, 166, 169†, 172*†, 173†
Sulfation
  of monomeric sugar derivatives, 440, 441
  of polysaccharides, 441, 442
Sulfide
  formation from sulfate, 10*
  formation from sulfite, 11
Sulfinate, 618
Sulfisoxazole →glucuronide, 593, 595*
Sulfite, 11†
  protein-bound, 10†, 11
  reduction to sulfide, 11
S-Sulfocysteine, 11
α-(6-Sulfogalactosyl) diglyceride, 130*†
Sulfokinase, 441, 613, 614
Sulfomucopolysaccharides, 443†
  complexes with proteins, 444
Sulfonamides
  →glucuronides, 594
  inhibitors of folic acid synthesis, 708
Sulfopolysaccharides, 11, 439†, 442†
  mechanisms for sulfation of, 440, 441, 442
Sulfotransferase, 442, 612, 614
Sulfoxides, 607
Sulfuric and adenylic acids, mixed anhydrides of, 87†
Sulfuryl adenylate, 87†, 614
Sulochrin, 1028*
Syringaldehyde
  from lignin, 749, 904
  in lignin biosynthesis, 917, 918
Syringin, 926, 927*
Syringyl residues, formation during lignin biosynthesis, 916, 918

Tachysterol, 240*†
D-Tagatose, 446†, 450†
D-Tagaturonate, 445†, 446†, 447*
  hydrogenation of, 449
Takamaltase, 378, 394
D-Talomethylose, 363†
  polysaccharide containing, 362
Talose, phosphorylation of, 344
Tannin
  crystalline, 810
  definition, 801

Tannin—(*cont.*)
  factors influencing the formation of, 821†
  formation from precursors, 808, 812
  precursors of, 814*†
Tannins
  biogenesis of precursors of, 802
  condensed, 802, 804†, 812†, 813†
    acid catalyzed polymerizations, 812†, 813†
    polyleucoanthocyanidins of unknown structure, 819†
    quinone type polymerizations, 815†
  hydrolyzable, 802†, 804, 808†
  possible mode of origin, 820†
Taspine, 983*†
Taurocholic acid, 238
Tay-Sachs disease, brain ganglioside from patients with, 176
Tay-Sachs ganglioside, 177*†
  →monosialoganglioside, 177
Tazzetine, 986†, 987*†
TDP, 50
TDP-Glucose, 422
TDP-D-Glucose oxidoreductase, 365
TDP-Rhamnose, 422†
TDR, 5′- mono-, di-, and triphosphates of, 544
Teichoic acids, 374†, 427, 428, 430†, 431†
Teloidine, 961*†
Template mechanism, of protein synthesis, 488
Tenuazonic acid, 1054†, 1055*†
Terchebin, 810, 811*, 812
Teresantalol, 846*
Terminal DNA nucleotidyltransferase, 555
Terpene-alcohol-pyrophosphates, 949
Terpene biogenesis, 1046
  current broad concept of, 842
  cyclization mechanism, 893
  early suggested precursors and mechanisms, 836
  in plants, future studies, 892
  nature of a basic five-carbon units, 833, 834*
Terpenes, 844†, 946
  acyclic, 839
  cyclopentanoid, 847
  definition of, 830
  early speculations on the biogenesis of, 833, 835
  genetic control of, 838
  isoprene-like nature of, 830
  monocyclic, 848†
  occurrence frequency of, 840
  pyrolysis of, 1075

Terpenes—(cont.)
  which do not contain multiples of five carbon atoms, 830, 831*
  with masked or incomplete isoprenoid structures, 830, 831*
Terpenoid alkaloids, 1009*†
Terpenol pyrophosphates, 879
α-Terpinene, 837*, 838, 841, 846*
γ-Terpinene, 837*, 838, 841, 855
Terpinene types of monoterpenes, 849
Terpinenol-(4), 841
α-Terpineol, 837*, 838, 841, 848*†, 849*†
Terpinolene, 841
Terramycin, effect on d-urobilin excretion, 276
Testosterone, 230, 231*†, 232*†, 507
  alternate scheme for biogenesis of, 232*†
  →estrone, 233, 234*
Tetracyclines, 1031†
Tetrahydrofolic acid, 6, 709†
  as methyl donor, 1039
  in pantothenic acid synthesis, 696
  →thymidylic acid, 78
Tetrahydrofurans, 793
Tetrahydrogibberellic acid, 1050*
1,2,3,4-Tetrahydroisoquinoline alkaloids, 975†, 976*†
Tetrahydrolycopene, 652, 653†, 656
Tetrahydrophytoene, 652, 653
Tetrahydropteroyl coenzyme, 20
Tetrahydropteroylmonoglutamate, methyl derivatives of, 20, 22
Tetrahydropteroyltriglutamate, methyl derivatives of, 20, 22
2′, 4′, 6′, 4-Tetrahydroxychalcone-2′-glycoside →phloridzin, 776
3α,7α,12α,24-Tetrahydroxycoprostane →cholic acid, 237†
3α,7α,12α,26-Tetrahydroxycoprostane, 237*†, 238†
5,7,3′,4′-Tetrahydroxyflavan, 817
5,7,3′,4′-Tetrahydroxyflavan-3,4-diol, 814
7,3′,4′,5′-Tetrahydroxyflavan-3,4-diol, 816*, 819
(−)7,3′,4′,5′-Tetrahydroxyflavan-3-ol, 819
Tetralin, 1073, 1074
Tetralysine, 516
Tetranucleotide, phosphorolysis of, 559
Tetranucleotide primers, 564
Tetranucleotide triphosphates, 558
Tetrapyrrole, cyclization of, 261
Tetrapyrrole ring, two modes of closure of, 301
Tetrapyrroles, open-chain, 277, 278
Tetrapyrrylmethanes, linear, 261
Tetrasaccharides, 377†, 392†
Tetraterpenes, 830

Tetronic acids, 447
Thalassemia, glycoprotein biosynthesis in, 436
Thebaine, 955, 977*†, 979†
THFA, 6, 709†
  as methylation agent, 19, 22
  formyl derivatives of, 709†
Thiamine, 680*†
  effect on polyene formation, 659
  pyrimidine moiety, 680
  thiazole moiety, 680
Thiamine chloride hydrochloride, 680*
Thiamine monophosphate, 682
  →thiamine, 681
Thiamine pyrophosphate, 54, 681†
  →active glycolic aldehyde, 350
Thiaminokinase, 681, 682
Thiazole, 681†
  →thiamine, 681
2-Thiazole alanine, 31
Thiazole monophosphate→thiamine, 681
Thiazolidinedicarboxylic acid, 681
Thiochrome assay, measurement of thiamine activity, 681
Thiocyanic acid, 632
Thiocyanate synthesis, 615
Thioesters, β-hydroxy decanoyl, 118
6-Thioinosine 5′-diphosphate, inhibitor of polynucleotide phosphorylase, 556
Thiols, methylation of, 619
Thiomethyladenosine, 574
Thiophenol, 612
Thioredoxin, 58
Thiosulfate, 612, 618, 619†
  in the sulfate-sulfide reactions, 11
  in thiocyanate synthesis, 617, 618
  role in detoxication, 591
Thiosulfonates, 618
Thiouracil, S-methylation of, 620, 621
2-Thiouridine 5′-diphosphate, polymerization of, 556
Thitsiol, 763
Threo-1,3-dihydroxy-2-amino-4-*trans* octadecene, 169
Threo-D₈-α-hydroxy-β-carboxyisocaproic acid, 24
Threonine, 3, 16†, 17*†, 18†, 25
  →isoleucine, 17
  →vitamin B₁₂, 712, 713
Threonine aldolase, 16
Threonine deaminase, 23
Threonine dehydrase, 23
Threonine-sRNA, 18
Threonine synthesis, alternative pathway for, 16
Threonine synthetase, 16
Threo-sphinogomyelin, 169

γ-Thujaplicin, 831*, 832
Thujone, 841, 846*, 849*†, 853†
Thujyl alcohol, 841
Thymidine, 50
in synthesis of folic acid, 710
Thymidine 3′-diphosphate, 544
Thymidine diphosphate-4-acetamido-
dideoxyhexoses, 365*†
Thymidine-diphosphate derivatives of
sugars, 93, 94
Thymidine diphosphate glycosides, see
dTDP-glycosides
Thymidine diphosphate glycosides, epi-
merization of, 361
Thymidine-5′-phosphate, 50, 77†, 539, 540*
Thymidine-5′-phosphate, 571
Thymidine polynucleotides, 571
Thymidine-3′-triphosphate, 544
Thymidine triphosphate, see also dTTP
Thymidylate kinase, 552, 553
Thymidylic acid, 19†, 50, 77, 78*†, 539, 540*
Thymine, 46*, 47*, 50, 539*, 571*, 572*
in sRNA, 497
→riboflavin, 699
Thymohydroquinone, 837*
Thymol, 837*, 838, 841
Thyroglobulins, 519
association with cell membranes, 520
Thyroxine, 507
effect on mucopolysaccharide formation,
443, 444
Tiglic acid, 960, 961*†
origin in terpenes, 834*
Tigogenin, 874*
TMP, 50
Tocopherols, 891†
Toluene, does not form a mercapturic acid,
604
Tolunitrile, 617*
β-o-Tolylpropionic acid, glycine conjuga-
tion, 600*
Tomatidine, 1013*†
Torularhodin, 668*†, 669†
Torulene, 660
Torulin, 668*†, 669†
Toxiferine I, 995*
TPNase, 689, 692
TPN, 81†, 83†, 84*†, 689†, 692†
effect on polyol conversions, 451
enzymic hydrolysis, 692
TPNH, in photosynthesis, 329
TPNH-Diaphorase, 330
TPNH-DPN Transhydrogenase, 330
Transacetylases, 628
Transacetylation, 11
Transaldolase, 53, 54, 325, 367, 921
mechanism of action of, 326
Transaminases, 5, 34

Transamination, 4, 907
with alanine, 23
with glutamate, 23
Transcription (genetic code), 492, 500
Trans-N-deoxyribosylases, 70
Transethylation reactions, 8
Transferases, 92, 94, 95, 369, 373
Transfer RNA, 496, 538, 543
Transformylase, 66
Transformylase reactions, 63
Transfructosylases, 380, 396
Transfructosylation, 418, 419
Transgalactosylase, 378
Transglucosidases, 369, 384, 419
Transglucosylases, 377, 410
Transglycosylases, 369, 371, 376, 379, 382,
384, 389, 391, 392, 394, 396
Transglycosylation, 320, 368, 369, 384, 386
from dextrins, 409
Transketolase, 53, 54, 55, 324, 325, 350,
367, 921
Translation (genetic code), 492, 500
Transmethylases, 7, 21, 22
Transmethylation, 8, 1039
Transpeptidation, 604, 605
Transphosphorylation
between ATP and nucleoside diphos-
phates, 79, 80
between nucleotides, 78, 79, 80
Trehalose, 391†, 445†
oxidation of, 447
→saccharides, 377, 416
Trehalose phosphate, 372†, 391†
→trehalose, 391
2,4,5-Triamino-6-hydroxypyrimidine, 704
in folate synthesis, 705
Tricarboxylic acid cycle, 254, 337
Trichlorobenzenes, mercapturic acids of,
604
Trichloroethanol →glucuronide, 594*
Trichloroethyl glucuronide, 592
1,1,1,-Trichloro-2-methyl-2-propanol,
stimulation of ascorbic synthesis by, 728
Trichodermin, 1049*
Trichothecin, 861*†, 1048†, 1049*†
Trienoic acids, 119†
5-Trifluoromethylbenzimidazole →B₁₂
vitamers, 715
Triglycerides, 106*, 123†, 128†, 129†, 180†
Trigonelline, 690
3,4,5-Trihydroxybenzoic acid, methylation
of, 621
Trihydroxybenzylisoquinoline →alkaloids,
980*, 981
3,4,5-Trihydroxycinnamic acid, 804
3α,7α,12α-Trihydroxycoprostane →cholic
acid, 235, 236*, 237*, 238

3α,7α,12α-Trihydroxycoprostanic acid → cholic acid, 236*†, 237*†, 238†
(−)7,3′,4′-Trihydroxyflavan-3,4-diol, 816*, 819
(+)7,3′,4′-Trihydroxyflavan-3,4-diol, 819
(−)7,3′,4′-Trihydroxyflavan 3-ol, 819, 820
3,4′,7-Trihydroxyflavanone, 778
3α,7α,12α-Trihydroxy-24-oxo-coprostane, 237
β-(3,4,5-Trihydroxyphenyl)propion-aldehyde →alkaloids, 985
3,5,4′-Trihydroxystilbenes, 807
Trihydroxytoluic acid, depsides containing, 767*
Trimethoxybenzoic acid, 1000
Trinucleotide code, in protein synthesis, 492
Trinucleotide codon, 496
Trinucleotide diphosphates, 558
Trinucleotide primers, 564
Triose phosphate isomerase, 323, 339
Triose phosphates
  in photosynthesis, 323*
  in tryptophan biosynthesis, 685
Triparanol, 222
Triphosphoinositide, 137, 138*, 159†, 162†, 163†, 183, 184
Triphosphonucleotides, 78†
Triphosphopyridine nucleotide, 83†, 84*†
Trisaccharides, 369, 377†, 384†, 392†, 394†, 396†
  as glycosyl donors, 376
Trisialoganglioside, 175, 176
Triterpenes, 830, 839†, 842, 844†, 873†, 874*, 891†
  control of biogenesis, 890
  pentacyclic, 873, 875*†, 876*†, 886†, 889†
  tetracyclic, 879†, 886†, 887
Tropane alkaloids, 959†, 960*†, 961*†
Tropane bases, 832
Tropanone carboxylic acid →tropane alka-loids, 959†, 960*†
Tropic acid, 959†, 961*†
Tropine, 959†, 960†
Tropolone ring, of colchicine, 985†
Tropolones, 832, 1037†, 1038†
Tryptamine
  →alkaloids, 957*†
  →indole alkaloids, 989, 990, 991*, 992, 995, 997, 1002*, 1004
Trypsin inhibitor, secondary structure, 519
Trypsinogen, association with cell mem-branes, 520
Tryptophan, 3, 34†, 35*†, 690
  relationship to niacin, 730
  →alkaloids, 957*, 1000, 1004, 1006, 1008
  →DPN, 83
  →fungal metabolites, 0154

Tryptophan—(cont.)
  →indole alkaloids, 989, 993*, 994
  →nicotinic acid, 682, 683*†, 685, 686, 962*
Tryptophan biosynthesis, terminal steps in, 685
Tryptophan pyrrolase, 487, 488, 507, 683, 686
Tryptophan synthetase, 491, 494, 683, 685
  components A and B, 36
  three reactions catalyzed by, 36
Tryptophyl-RNA synthetase, 495, 496
TTP, 50, 94
Tubercolostearic acid, 122†
Tuberostemonine, 1014*
d-Tubocurarine, 980*
Turpentine, 872
Tween 80, as replacement for biotin, 721
Tylophorine, 974*, 975
Tylophorinine, 974*, 975
Tyramine →alkaloids, 955, 956*†, 985, 986*†
Tyrosinase, 803, 913, 935, 936
Tyrosine, 3, 32†, 33*†, 748, 479*†, 750, 907†, 908*†
  ethyl or methyl ester →sulfate, 614
  →alkaloids, 955, 956*, 976, 977*, 983, 984*, 985, 986*, 999
  →fungal metabolites, 1054
  →lignin, 928*, 929
  →novobiocin, 1040, 1052, 1053*
  →quercetin, 772
Tyrosine decarboxylase, 723
Tyrosine-α-ketoglutarate transaminase, 488, 507
Tyrosine-O-sulfate, 614
Tyrosyl-RNA synthetase, 495
Tyvelose, 427, 432

Ubiquinones, 890, 1044*†
UDP, 49, 79†, 80†, 371, 372, 373, 374, 375
  phosphate exchange, 559
  polymerization of, 556, 557
UDP-2-Acetamido-2-deoxy-D-galactose, 91
UDP-2-Acetamido-2-deoxy-D-glucose, 91
UDP-2-Acetamido-2-deoxy-D-glucose-6-(D-galactopyranosyl phosphate), 91
UDP-2-Acetamido-2-deoxy-D-glucose-6-sulfate, 91
UDP-N-Acetyl-D-galactosamine, 356, 361†
  →heparitin, 373
  →mucopolysaccharides, 443
UDP-N-Acetyl-D-galactosamine sulfate, 356, 441
UDP-N-Acetyl-D-glucosamine, 355, 356
  →bacterial cell wall glycopeptide, 374

UDP-N-Acetyl-D-glucosamine—(*cont.*)
→bacterial cell wall lipopolysaccharides, 374
→chitin, 373, 425
→chondroitin sulfates, 373
epimerization of, 361
→hyaluronic acid, 373, 425, 426
in feedback control of glycoprotein synthesis, 439
→mucopolysaccharides, 443
→teichoic acids, 374
UDP-N-Acetylglucosamine-6-fucose, 368
UDP-N-Acetyl-D-glucosamine-6-phosphate, 355
UDP-N-Acetyl-D-glucosamine pyruvic acid, 429†
UDP-N-Acetylglucosamine pyrophosphorylase, 425
UDP-N-Acetyllactosamine, 368
UDP-N-Acetyllactosamine fucoside, 368
UDP-Acetylmannosamine, 361†
UDP-N-Acetylmuramic acid, 429†
UDP-N-Acetylmuramic acid-peptides, 91
UDP-N-Acetylmuramyl pentapeptide, 430†
→bacterial cell wall, 374
UDP-N-Acetylneuraminic acid →D-galactopyranosyl-(1 →4)-2-acetamido-2-deoxy-D-glucose, 91
UDP-2-Amino-2-deoxy-D-galactose, 92
UDP-2-Amino-2-deoxy-D-glucose, 92
UDP-Apiose, 367*†
UDP-L-Arabinose, 92, 320, 355, 356, 361†, 364†
→araban, 421†, 423†
→hemicellulose, 421†, 423†
→saccharides, 372
UDP-Colominic acid, 92
UDP-Dihydroxyacetone, 92
UDP-1,3-Dihydroxy-2-propanone, 92
UDP-D-Fructose, 92
→fructosan, 419
→saccharides, 372
UDP-L-Fucosyl-(1 → ?)-D-galacto-pyranosyl-(1 →4)-2-acetamido-2-deoxy-D-glucose, 92
UDP-Galactose, 92, 94†, 95, 171†, 172, 320, 355, 359†
from UDP-glucose, 356†
inhibitor of UDP-glucose dehydrogenase, 363
→bacterial cell wall lipopolysaccharides, 374
→bacterial polysaccharides, 373
→cerebroside, 171
→fucosyl lactose, 397
→galactosyl inositol, 375
→glycolipids, 435

UDP-Galactose—(*cont.*)
→inositol galactosides, 434
→lactose, 392, 393
→pectic substances, 421
→psychosine, 171
→saccharides, 372
UDP-Galactose-4-epimerase, 171, 360
deficiency in bacteria, 432
UDP-Galactose: inositol galactosyl transferase, 434
UDP-Galactose-polysaccharide transferase. 433
UDP-Galactose pyrophosphorylase, 358
UDP-Galacturonic acid, 92, 320, 355, 356, 361†, 363
decarboxylation of, 364
→araban, hemicellulose, 421†, 423†
→pectins, 373, 421†, 423†
UDP-Glucosamine, dehydrogenation of, 367
UDP-Glucosaminuronic acid, 367†
UDP-Glucose, 92, 94†, 95, 172, 320, 355*†, 357, 358, 363*
as glycosyl donor, 382, 395
dehydrogenation of, 363
energy of hydrolysis, 382
in detoxication reactions, 592, 598
in tumor cells, 403
→amylose, 402
→bacterial cell wall lipopolysaccharides, 374
→bacterial polysaccharides, 373
→cellulose, 415
→glucan, 416
→glucosides, 375, 434
→lactose, 392
→saccharides, 371, 372
→starch, 403, 404
→sucrose, 389, 390
→teichoic acids, 374
→trehalose, 391
→UDP-apiose, 367*
→UDP-galactose, 171, 359
→UDP-glucuronic acid, 593, 596
→UDP-L-rhamnose, 362
UDP-Glucose dehydrogenase, 363, 367, 596
UDP-Glucose:D-fructose-glucosyl transferase, 390
UDP-Glucose:α-glucan transferase, 403
UDP-Glucose:α-glucan transglucosidase, 403
UDP-Glucose:α-glucan transglucosylase, 406, 411
activation of, 406
inhibition of, 406
UDP-Glucose:glycogen transferase, 403

UDP-Glucose:glycogen transglucosidase, 403

UDP-Glucose:glycogen transglucosylase, 371, 399, 403, 404

UD- and I-forms, 405, 406

UDP-Glucose pyrophosphorylase, 357, 402

UDP-Glucose:starch transferase, 403

UDP-Glucose:starch transglucosidase, 403

UDP-Glucose synthetase, deficiency in bacteria, 432

UDP-Glucose transglycosylase, 405

UDP-Glucuronic acid, 92, 95, 320, 355, 356, 363*†, 597

  α-configuration of, 597

  decarboxylation of, 364

  in detoxication reactions, 592

  →araban, 420†, 421†, 423†

  →chondroitin sulfates, 373

  →conjugated glucuronic acids, 595*, 596†

  →extracellular polysaccharides, 373

  →glucosiduronic acids, 375, 435

  →hemicellulose, 420†, 421†, 423†

  →heparitin, 373

  →hyaluronic acid, 373, 425, 426

  →mucopolysaccharides, 443

  →pectins, 420†, 421†, 423†

  →UDP-apiose, 367*

  →UDP-galacturonic acid, 361

  →xylan, 420†, 421†, 423†

UDP-Glucuronic acid carboxylase, 364

UDP-Glucuronic acid transglycosylase, 596

UDP-Glucuronolactone, 420

UDP-Glycosides, 356†

  →glycosides, 374

UDP-Glycosyl transglycosylases, 394

UDP-GNAc-Lactyl-L-ala, 429†

UDP-GNAc-Lactyl-L-ala-D-glu, 429†

UDP-GNAc-Lactyl-L-ala-D-gly-L-lys, 429†

UDP-GNAc-Lactyl-L-ala-D-glu-L-lys-L-ala-D-ala, 430†

UDP-4-Ketohexose, 360

UDP-L-Idose, 362†, 363†

UDP-L-Iduronic acid, 92

UDP-Muramic acid, 356

UDP-Polyacetylneuraminic acid, 356

UDP-L-Rhamnose, 92, 355, 362†

  →rhamnolipids, 374, 435

  →rutin, 374, 435

UDP-Sugars, transformations of, 349

UDP-Sugar-synthesizing enzymes, 356

UDP-Transglucuronylase, 596

UDP-D-Xylose, 92, 95, 320, 355, 356, 364†, 420†

  epimerization of, 361

  →extracellular polysaccharides, 373

  →hemicellulose, 420, 423

UDP-D-Xylose—(cont).

  →saccharides, 372

  →xylan, 420, 423

Uleine, 1002*†, 1004†

Umbellic acid diglucoside →umbelliferone, 789*†

Umbelliferone, 789*†

Umbelliferose, 418

UMP, 49, 75*†

  formation of sequences, 564

  incorporation into RNA, 561, 564, 565

  →pantothenic acid, 695, 697

  repression of arginine biosynthesis by, 14

  →uridylic acid, 77*

Urea, 59, 60*

  in riboflavin synthesis, 699

β-Ureidopropionate →pantothenic acid, 695*, 697

Ureotelic animals, 14

Urethane →mercapturic acid, 603*

Uric acid, 46, 59, 60*†

  →folic acid, 706*

Uricotelic metabolism, glycine and ornithine conjugation, 609, 610

Uridine, 49

  from uracil, 77*†

  5'-mono-, di-, and triphosphates of, 544

  →deoxyuridine, effect of vitamin B_{12} on, 718

Uridine diphosphate, *see also* UDP

Uridine diphosphate derivatives of sugars, 91, 92

Uridine diphosphate galactose →cerebroside, 170

Uridine diphosphate glucose, 355

  in detoxication reactions, 592

Uridine diphosphate glucuronic acid

  →conjugated glucuronic acids, 595*, 596†

  in detoxication reactions, 592

Uridine diphosphate glycosides, 355, 356

Uridine diphosphate sugars, *see* UDP-Sugars

Uridine diphospho, *see also* UDP

Uridine diphosphoacetylmuramulpentapeptide, 430†

Uridine diphosphogalactose-4-epimerase, 360

Uridine diphosphoglucose pyrophosphorylase, 355, 356

Uridine nucleotides, by glycoside transfer, 356†

Uridine-5'-phosphate, 49, 75*†

Uridine phosphate, *see also* UMP

Uridine-5'-phosphate pyrophosphorylase, 77

Uridine phosphorylase, 77

Uridine-5'-phosphosulfate, 559

Uridine triphosphate, amination of, 76*
Uridine triphosphate, *see also* UTP
Uridylic acid, 13, 14, 49, 71†
  amination of, 75
  from uracil, 77*†
  from uridine, 77*†
  →thymidylic acid, 77, 78*
Urobilin, 276, 277, 287†, 291
d-Urobilin, 276, 286, 291
L-Urobilin, 275*, 276
i-Urobilin, 275*, 276, 289. 291
Urobilinogens
  l-, d-, and i-, 289†
  →urobilin, 287†
Urobilinoid pigments →urobilin. 287†
Uronic acids
  hydrogenation of, 449
  reduction of, 449
  transformations of, 447
Uroporphyrin, 257, 259, 265
  four isomers of, 251
Uroporphyrin I, 250*, 251, 253, 258
Uroporphyrin III, 250*, 251, 258, 261
  resemblance to corrin, 299, 300
Uroporphyrin III-metal complexes →
  corrin, 301
Uroporphyrinogen, decarboxylation of, 261,
  263
Uroporphyrinogen I, 253†, 258†, 259, 260,
  261†, 262†
Uroporphyrinogen III, 253*†, 258†, 259†,
  260†, 261†, 262†, 263
  →corrin, 299, 301
Uroporpyrinogen III cosynthetase, 253,
  259, 260, 261
Uroporphyrinogen decarboxylase, 253, 262,
  263
Uroporphyrinogens, 257†
Uroporphyrinogen I synthetase, 253, 258,
  259, 260, 261
UTP, 49, 79†, 80†, 393†
  transphosphorylation with, 79
  →UDP-glucose, 355
  →RNA, 564, 565
Urochloralic acid, 592
Ursolic acid, 874*, 889†
Urushiol, 762*†, 767
Usnic acid, 783*†
Ustic acid, 1056*
Uteroverdin, 286
Uzarigenin, 884*

cis-Vaccenic acid, 114†, 118†
  →cyclic fatty acid, 122
  desaturation of, 121†

Valerate
  →cholesterol, 208
  →plasmalogens, 153
Valine, 3, 21*†, 22†, 24†
  in pantothenic acid synthesis, 694, 695*
  →carotene, 645
  →penicillin, 1055
Valonic acid, 810*, 812
Valyl-RNA synthetase, 496
Vancomycin, influence on bacterial cell
  wall synthesis, 430, 431
Van den Bergh reaction, 288
Vanillic acid, 935*
Vanillin, 935*
  C14-labeling, 920*, 924
  degradation of, 919, 921*, 925*
  from lignin, 749, 904, 905
  in lignin biosynthesis, 917, 919
Vanilloyl methyl ketone, from lignin, 904
Vanillyl alcohol, 935*
Veatchine, 1010*†, 1011†
Veratramine, 971, 1013*†, 1014
Veratric acid, 773
Verdoglobin, 281
Verdoheme, 280†, 281, 282, 285
Verdoheme-globin, 283*†
Verdohemochrome, 284, 286*
Verdohemochromogen, 280*†, 281, 285
Verrucarin A, 1049
Verrucarol, 1049*
Vetivone, 856*
(+) Vibo-inosose, 452*†
Vinca alkaloids, 1001*
Vincamedine, 1000
Vincamine, 1001*, 1003
Vindoline, 989, 1000†, 1001*†, 1003
Vinylacrylic acid, 867
4-Vinyl cyclohexene, 1072*
Violaxanthin, 664, 665, 666†
Visamminol, 785, 786*
B12 Vitamers, 714, 715, 716
Vitamin A, 669, 670†
Vitamin A1, 671
Vitamin A2, 671
Vitamin A acid, 671
Vitamin A aldehyde, 671
  5,6- mono-epoxide, 671
Vitamin B1, 680*†
Vitamin B2, 699†, 701*†
Vitamin B6, 722*†
  →δ-aminolevulinic acid, 255
Vitamin B12, 58, 299†, 300*, 711†, 712,
  713†, 714†, 716†
  coenzyme form of 717†, 718†
  derivative of, in transmethylases, 21,
  22
  in protein biosynthesis, 718

Vitamin B₁₂—(*cont.*)
interrelationship between folic acid and, 718
labeling pattern in, 713*
relationship to nicotinic acid mononucleotide, 731
structural relationship to porphyrins, 299
Vitamin B₁₂ coenzymes, requirement in various reactions, 718
Vitamin B₁₂ intermediate, from guanine, 731
Vitamin B₁₂ porphyrin, 711*
Vitamin C, 727†, 728†, 729*†
dietary requirement for species, 727
Vitamin D, 239†
Vitamin D₂, 240*†
Vitamin D₃, 240†
from 7-dehydrocholesterol, 223
Vitamin K₁, 891†
Vitamin-nucleotide combinations, 697
Vitamins, 48
B₁₂-like, interrelationships in, 714
interconversions among, 730
involved in the biosynthesis of their own precursors, 731
relationship to purines, 731
Voacangarine, 989*
Vomicine, 994*†, 997†
Vulpinic acid, 766†

Wagonin, 775*†
Walden inversion, 392
in glucuronide conjugation, 597
Warmingone, 663, 664†
Wax esters, 133†
Wieland-Gumlich aldehyde, 994*†, 995†, 996†
alkaloids biogenitically related to, 995*†, 997

Xanthine, 46*, 47*, 49
→riboflavin, 699, 701*
→xanthylic acid, 69
Xanthones, 1044†, 1046†
Xanthophylls, 652, 660, 661†, 662†, 663†, 664, 665, 666†
acidic, 668
carbonyl-like pigments, 667
epoxides of, 665, 666
hydroxylated, 668
leaf, interrelationships of, 666
methoxylated, 668
neutral, 668
oxygenation by molecular oxygen, 665
Xanthopterin →folic acid, 705
Xanthosine, 49
Xanthosine-5′-phosphate, 49
Xanthosine triphosphate, 568

Xanthurenic acid
4,8-diglucuronide, 629*, 630†
metabolites of, 629*
8-methyl ether, 620
8-monoglucuronide, 629*, 630†
Xanthurenic acid excretion, in B₆-deficiency, 630
Xanthyletin, 785, 786*
Xanthylic acid, 49, 67*†, 76
→guanylic acid, 67
XMP, 49
Xylan, 364†, 385†, 419†, 420†
oligosaccharides, 372†
Xylitol, 449†, 450
→lignin, 922
→D- or L-xylulose, 451*
D-Xylose, 364†, 446
oxidation of, 448
reduction of, 449
→glycosides, 434
→maltose analogues, 392
→saccharides, 370
→trisaccharide, 378
D-Xylose-1-phosphate →UDP-xylose, 420
Xylosucrose, 378†
Xylosyl fructoside, 378†
D-Xylulose, 377, 446†, 450†
phosphorylation of, 344
→xylitol, 451
→L-xylulose, 452
L-Xylulose, 446†, 447†, 449*, 450†
free, occurrence, 444
→xylitol, 451*
D-Xylulose-phosphate, epimerization of, 345*
D-Xylulose-1,5-diphosphate, 349†
D-Xylulose-1-phosphate, 349†
Xylulose-5-phosphate, 53*†, 54†, 55*†, 325*, 344†
changes in free energy during photosynthetic formation, 334
in equilibrium with ribulose-5-phosphate, 324, 325
in pentose phosphate cycle, 348
→glyceraldehyde-3-phosphate, 324*†, 351
Xysmalogenin, 884*, 885

Yamogenin, 226, 886
Yohimbine, 992*†, 997
Yohimbine alkaloids, 999*†

β-Zeacarotene, 661
Zeaxanthin, 662, 663, 664, 665, 666†
Zeorin, 876*†
Zingiberene, 856*
Zwischenferment, 347
Zymosterol, 219†, 220*
→cholesterol, 215*†, 219